SYMBOLS MOST FREQUENTLY USED IN THE NATIONAL UNION CATALOG

GEORGIA *continued*

GAU	Atlanta University, Atlanta.
GAuA	Augusta College, Augusta.
GColuC	Columbus College, Columbus.
GCuA	Andrews College, Cuthbert.
GDC	Columbia Theological Seminary, Decatur.
GDS	Agnes Scott College, Decatur.
GDecA*	Agnes Scott College, Decatur.
GDecCT*	Columbia Theological Seminary, Decatur.
GDoS	South Georgia College, Douglas.
GEU	Emory University, Atlanta.
GHi	Georgia Historical Society, Savannah.
GMM	Mercer University, Macon.
GMW	Wesleyan College, Macon.
GMiW	Woman's College of Georgia, Milledgeville.
GMilvC*	Woman's College of Georgia, Milledgeville.
GOgU	Oglethorpe University, Oglethorpe University.
GSDe*	University of Georgia, DeRenne Library.
GU	University of Georgia, Athens.
GU-De	— DeRenne Georgia Library.
GU-Ex	— Georgia State College of Business Administration Library, Atlanta.

HAWAII

HU	University of Hawaii, Honolulu.
HU-EWC	Center for Cultural and Technical Interchange between East and West, Honolulu.

ILLINOIS

I	Illinois State Library, Springfield.
IC	Chicago Public Library.
ICA	Art Institute of Chicago, Chicago.
ICF	Chicago Natural History Museum, Chicago.
ICF-A	— Edward E. Ayer Ornithological Library.
ICHi	Chicago Historical Society, Chicago.
ICIP	Institute for Psychoanalysis, Chicago.
ICJ	John Crerar Library, Chicago.
ICMILC*	Center for Research Libraries, Chicago.
ICMcC	McCormick Theological Seminary, Chicago.
ICN	Newberry Library, Chicago.
ICRL	Center for Research Libraries, Chicago.
ICU	University of Chicago, Chicago.
ICarbS	Southern Illinois University, Carbondale.
IEG	Garrett Theological Seminary, Evanston.
IEN	Northwestern University, Evanston.
IEdS	Southern Illinois University, Edwardsville.
IGK	Knox College, Galesburg.
IHi	Illinois State Historical Library, Springfield.
ILS	St. Procopius College, Lisle.
IMunS	Saint Mary of the Lake Seminary, Mundelein.
INS	Illinois State University, Normal.
IRA	Augustana College Library, Rock Island.
IRivfR	Rosary College, River Forest.
IU	University of Illinois, Urbana.
IU-M	— Medical Sciences Library, Chicago.
IU-U	— Chicago Undergraduate Division, Chicago.

IOWA

IaAS	Iowa State University of Science and Technology, Ames.
IaDL	Luther College, Decorah.
IaDuC	Loras College, Dubuque.
IaDuU	University of Dubuque, Dubuque.
IaDuU-S	— Theological Seminary Library.
IaDuW	Wartburg Theological Seminary, Dubuque.
IaU	University of Iowa, Iowa City.

IDAHO

IdB	Boise Public Library.
IdPI	Idaho State University, Pocatello.
IdPS*	Idaho State University, Pocatello.
IdU	University of Idaho, Moscow.

INDIANA

In	Indiana State Library, Indianapolis.
InAndC	Anderson College, Anderson.
InCollS*	St. Joseph's College, Rensselaer.
InGo	Goshen College Biblical Seminary Library, Goshen.
InHi	Indiana Historical Society, Indianapolis.
InIB	Butler University, Indianapolis.

INDIANA *continued*

InLP	Purdue University, Lafayette.
InNd	University of Notre Dame, Notre Dame.
InOlH*	St. Leonard College Library, Dayton, Ohio.
InRE	Earlham College, Richmond.
InRenS	St. Joseph's College, Rensselaer.
InStme	St. Meinrad's College & Seminary, St. Meinrad.
InU	Indiana University, Bloomington.

KANSAS

K	Kansas State Library, Topeka.
KAS	St. Benedict's College, Atchison.
KAStB*	St. Benedict's College, Atchison.
KKcB	Central Baptist Theological Seminary, Kansas City.
KHi	Kansas State Historical Society, Topeka.
KMK	Kansas State University, Manhattan.
KStMC*	St. Louis University, School of Divinity Library, St. Louis, Mo.
KU	University of Kansas, Lawrence.
KU-M	— Medical Center Library, Kansas City.
KWiU	Wichita State University, Wichita.

KENTUCKY

Ky-LE	Library Extension Division, Frankfort.
KyBgW	Western Kentucky State College, Bowling Green
KyHi	Kentucky Historical Society, Frankfort.
KyLo	Louisville Free Public Library.
KyLoS	Southern Baptist Theological Seminary, Louisville.
KyLoU	University of Louisville, Louisville.
KyLx	Lexington Public Library.
KyLxCB	Lexington Theological Seminary, Lexington. (Formerly College of the Bible)
KyLxT	Transylvania College, Lexington.
KyMoreT	Morehead State College, Morehead.
KyU	University of Kentucky, Lexington.
KyWA	Asbury College Library, Wilmore.
KyWAT	Asbury Theological Seminary, Wilmore.

LOUISIANA

L	Louisiana State Library, Baton Rouge.
L-M	Louisiana State Museum Library, New Orleans.
LCA	Not a library symbol.
LCS	Not a library symbol.
LHi	Louisiana History Society, New Orleans.
LNHT	Tulane University Library, New Orleans.
LNT-MA	Tulane University, Latin American Library, New Orleans.
LU	Louisiana State University, Baton Rouge.
LU-M	— Medical Center Library, New Orleans.
LU-NO	— Louisiana State University in New Orleans.

MASSACHUSETTS

M	Massachusetts State Library, Boston.
MA	Amherst College, Amherst.
MB	Boston Public Library.
MBAt	Boston Athenaeum, Boston.
MBBC*	Boston College, Chestnut Hill.
MBCo	Countway Library of Medicine. (Harvard-Boston Medical Libraries)
MBH	Massachusetts Horticultural Society, Boston.
MBHo*	Massachusetts Horticultural Society, Boston.
MBM*	Countway Library of Medicine (Harvard-Boston Medical Libraries).
MBMu	Museum of Fine Arts, Boston.
MBU	Boston University.
MBdAF	U.S. Air Force Cambridge Research Center, Bedford.
MBrZ	Zion Research Library, Brookline.
MBrigStJ*	St. John's Seminary, Brighton.
MBtS	St. John's Seminary Library, Brighton.
MCM	Massachusetts Institute of Technology, Cambridge.
MCR	Radcliffe College, Cambridge.
MCSA	Smithsonian Institution, Astrophysical Observatory, Cambridge.
MChB	Boston College, Chestnut Hill.
MH	Harvard University, Cambridge.
MH-A	— Arnold Arboretum.
MH-AH	— Andover-Harvard Theological Library.
MH-BA	— Graduate School of Business Administration Library.
MH-FA	— Fine Arts Library. (Formerly Fogg Art Museum)
MH-G	— Gray Herbarium Library.
MH-HY	— Harvard-Yenching Institute. (Chinese-Japanese Library)

MASSACHUSETTS *continued*

MH-L	— Law School Library.
MH-P	— Peabody Museum Library.
MH-PR	— Physics Research Library.
MHi	Massachusetts Historical Society, Boston.
MMeT	Tufts University, Medford.
MNF	Forbes Library, Northampton.
MNS	Smith College, Northampton.
MNoeS	Stonehill College Library, North Easton.
MNtcA	Andover Newton Theological School, Newton Center.
MSaE	Essex Institute, Salem.
MShM	Mount Holyoke College, South Hadley.
MU	University of Massachusetts, Amherst.
MWA	American Antiquarian Society, Worcester.
MWAC	Assumption College, Worcester.
MWC	Clark University, Worcester.
MWH	College of the Holy Cross, Worcester.
MWalB	Brandeis University, Waltham.
MWelC	Wellesley College, Wellesley.
MWhB	Marine Biological Laboratory, Woods Hole.
MWiW	Williams College, Williamstown.
MWiW-C	— Chapin Library.

MARYLAND

MdAN	U.S. Naval Academy, Annapolis.
MdBE	Enoch Pratt Free Library, Baltimore.
MdBG	Goucher College, Baltimore.
MdBJ	Johns Hopkins University, Baltimore.
MdBJ-G	—John Work Garrett Library.
MdBP	Peabody Institute, Baltimore.
MdBWA	Walters Art Gallery, Baltimore.
MdU	University of Maryland, College Park.
MdW	Woodstock College, Woodstock.

MAINE

MeB	Bowdoin College, Brunswick.
MeBa	Bangor Public Library.
MeU	University of Maine, Orono.
MeWC	Colby College, Waterville.
MeWaC*	Colby College, Waterville.

MICHIGAN

Mi	Michigan State Library, Lansing.
MiAC	Alma College, Alma.
MiD	Detroit Public Library.
MiD-B	— Burton Historical Collection.
MiDA	Detroit Institute of Arts, Detroit.
MiDU	University of Detroit, Detroit.
MiDW	Wayne State University, Detroit.
MiEM	Michigan State University, East Lansing.
MiEalC*	Michigan State University, East Lansing.
MiGr	Grand Rapids Public Library.
MiH*	Michigan College of Mining and Technology, Houghton.
MiHM	Michigan College of Mining and Technology, Houghton.
MiU	University of Michigan, Ann Arbor.
MiU-C	— William L. Clements Library.

MINNESOTA

MnCS	St. John's University, Collegeville.
MnH*	Minnesota Historical Society, St. Paul.
MnHi	Minnesota Historical Society, St. Paul.
MnRM	Mayo Clinic and Foundation Library, Rochester.
MnSJ	James Jerome Hill Reference Library, St. Paul.
MnSSC	College of St. Catherine, St. Paul.
MnU	University of Minnesota, Minneapolis.

MISSOURI

MoHi	Missouri State Historical Society, Columbia
MoK	Kansas City Public Library.
MoKL	Linda Hall Library, Kansas City
MoKU	University of Missouri at Kansas City, Kansas City.
MoS	St. Louis Public Library.
MoSB	Missouri Botanical Garden, St. Louis.
MoSC*	Concordia Seminary Library, St. Louis.
MoSCS	Concordia Seminary Library, St. Louis.
MoSM	Mercantile Library Association, St. Louis.
MoSU	St. Louis University, St. Louis.
MoSU-D	— School of Divinity Library, St. Louis.
MoSW	Washington University, St. Louis.
MoU	University of Missouri, Columbia.

The National Union Catalog

Pre-1956 Imprints

The National Union Catalog

Pre-1956 Imprints

A cumulative author list representing Library of Congress printed cards and titles reported by other American libraries. Compiled and edited with the cooperation of the Library of Congress and the National Union Catalog Subcommittee of the Resources Committee of the Resources and Technical Services Division, American Library Association

Volume 334

LINCOLN LODGE - LINNÉ, CARL VON (EU)

Mansell 1974

Mansell Information/Publishing Limited
3 Bloomsbury Place, London WC1

The American Library Association
50 East Huron Street, Chicago, Illinois 60611

The paper on which this catalog has been printed is supplied by
P. F. Bingham Limited and has been specially manufactured by the
Guard Bridge Paper Company Limited of Fife, Scotland.
Based on requirements established by the late William J. Barrow
for a permanent/durable book paper it is laboratory certified
to meet or exceed the following values:

Substance 89 gsm
pH cold extract 9.4
Fold endurance (MIT ½kg. tension) 1200
Tear resistance (Elmendorf) 73 (or 67 × 3)
Opacity 90.3%

Library of Congress Card Number : 67–30001
ISBN: 0 7201 0413 0

Printed by Balding & Mansell Limited, London and Wisbech, England
Bound by Bemrose & Sons Limited, Derby, England

American Library Association

Resources and Technical Services Division

Publisher's Note

Because of the large number of sources from which the information in the National Union Catalog has been collected over a long period of time an understanding of its scope and an acquaintance with its methods is necessary for the best use to be made of it. Users are therefore earnestly advised to make themselves familiar with the introductory matter in Volume 1. This fully defines the scope of the Catalog and sets out the basis on which the material reported to the National Union Catalog has been edited for publication in book form.

National Union Catalog Designation

Each main entry in the Catalog has been ascribed a unique identifying designation. This alphanumeric combination appears uniformly after the last line of the entry itself and consists of:
1 The letter N, signifying National Union Catalog.
2 The initial letter under which the entry is filed.
3 A number representing the position of the entry within the sequence under its initial letter.
This National Union Catalog designator is sufficient both to identify any main entry in the Catalog and to establish its position within the sequence of volumes. It is, however, recommended that when referring to titles by the National Union Catalog designation a checking element, such as the key word or initials of the title, be added.

Reported Locations

Alphabetic symbols which represent libraries in the United States and Canada follow the National Union Catalog designation. These groups of letters signify which libraries have reported holding copies of the work. The first library so represented usually is the one that provided the catalog information.

Printed on the end sheets of each volume is a list of most frequently used symbols, each followed by the full name of the library. *List of Symbols*, containing a comprehensive list of symbols used, is published as a separate volume with the Catalog. The Library of Congress has also issued *Symbols Used in the National Union Catalog of the Library of Congress*. In cases where a symbol is not identified in these lists the National Union Catalog Division of the Library of Congress will, on enquiry, attempt to identify the library concerned.

Other Developments

Under the terms of their agreement with the American Library Association, the publishers have undertaken to apply, as far as is practicable, new developments in library science and techniques which may have the effect of further enhancing the value of the Catalog. To this end, the publishers will be pleased to receive suggestions and enquiries relating to technical and production aspects of the Catalog and will be glad to consider proposals calculated to improve its utility and amenity. Mansell Information/Publishing Limited will be pleased also to advise libraries on possible applications of the methods and techniques developed for this and similar projects to their own requirements.

J.C.
London, *August 1968*

VOLUME 334

Lincoln Lodge Seminar on Educational Television,
University of Wisconsin, 1953.
　Proceedings

　　see under

National Association of Educational Broadcasters.
　Lincoln Lodge seminar on educational television.

The Lincoln log. v. 1-　Mar. 1920-　Cleveland. O., Lincoln High school.

　Succeeded by the Log.

NL　0375595　OC1 OC1WHi

The Lincoln log cabin almanac ...
　　see under　McMurty, Robert Gerald, 1906-

636.33　Lincoln Longwool Sheep Breeders' Association.
L63b　　Brief history of the Lincoln longwool sheep
　　from the year 1750　　Lincoln, 1950.
　　18p. illus. 19cm.

　Cover title.

　1. Sheep.

NL　0375597　IU DNAL

Lincoln long-wool sheep breeders' association.
　Flock book. v. 1-45. 1892-1936.
　Lincoln, Eng.
　　v.

NL　0375598　OU ICJ

Lincoln lore. no. 1-
　Apr. 15, 1929-
　Fort Wayne, Ind., Lincoln National Life Insurance Co.
　　no. in　　v. 29 cm. weekly.
　Issued by the Lincoln Historical Research Foundation, 1929-32.
　Editor: Apr. 1929-　　　　　L. A. Warren.
　Indexes:
　No. 1-500, Apr. 1929-Nov. 7, 1938. 1 v.
　No. 501-1000, Nov. 14, 1938-June 7, 1948. 1 v.

　1. Lincoln, Abraham, Pres. U. S., 1809-1865.　I. Warren, Louis
Austin, 1885-　　ed. II. Lincoln National Life Insurance Company,
Fort Wayne, Ind. III. Lincoln Historical Research Foundation, Fort
Wayne, Ind.

　E457.L74　　　　　　　　　　29-22564 rev 2*

　　NdU MsSM CoD WHi ICRL KyU NbHi NN
　　NcD MWA OFH OC1WHi PHi OOxM WaT NcU GEU KyHi WaS
NL　0375599　DLC OrU CtN1C AzTeS DSI MB MiU-C PP KT

Lincoln lore. Fort Wayne

Lincoln national life foundation.
　Lincoln bibliography, cumulative, Check list. Alphabetical
index of authors compiled from the chronological bibliography
appearing quarterly in Lincoln lore, 1930/39-　　　　Fort
Wayne, Ind., Lincoln national life foundation, 1942-

Lincoln lore; a magazine of literature and art.
　v.

New York [19　　　　　　　　　　　　　27cm.
　v. illus.
　Issued by the pupils of the Lincoln school of Teachers college, New York city.

────── Alumni issue.

　1. Schools—Student publications—
university. Teachers college. Lincoln　　　　U. S.—Lincoln. I. Columbia
N. Y. P. L.　　　　　　　　　　　　　school.
　　　　　　　　　　　　　　　　　　　January 31, 1939

NL　0375601　NN DLC

Lincoln lore; a magazine of literature and art.
　Lincoln verse, story, and essay (First series);
selections
　　see under　Mearns, Hughes, 1875-　ed.

Lincoln Lunatic Asylum
　　see　Lawn Hospital for the Insane,
Lincoln, Eng.

Lincoln-McClellan campaign pamphlets. [v. p.] 1864.
　49 pamphlets in 1 v. 23 cm.
　Title from spine.
　Includes material by McClellan.

　1. Campaign literature, 1864—Democratic. 2. U. S.—Pol. & govt.—
Civil War.　I. McClellan, George Brinton, 1826-1885.

　E458.4.L765　　　　　　　　　　57-55715

NL　0375604　DLC

Lincoln McKeever (Motion picture script)
　LINCOLN McKEEVER. [n. p.] 1955.　150 l. 28cm.

　Shooting script.
　On cover: Maxwell Shane, July 5, 1955.

　1. Moving picture plays--Texts and outlines.

NL　0375605　NN

The Lincoln magazine. A home journal of social and civic
freedom. v. 1-2; June 1905-Sept. 1906. Dansville, N. Y.
[New York anti-saloon league] 1905-06.
　2 v. in 1. illus. 32cm. monthly.
　H. H. Russell, editor.
　Merged into the American issue, New York ed.

　1. Temperance—Period.　I. Russell, Howard Hyde, 1855-　ed.
II. New York anti-saloon league.
　　　　　　　　　　　　　　　11-32586

　Library of Congress　　　　HV5285.L6

NL　0375606　DLC

The Lincoln marriage temple, a shelter for
cabin in which Mr. Lincoln's parent's
were married
　　see under　[Hutton, Daniel Mac-Hir]
1871-1951.

---

q973.7　Lincoln material, chiefly manuscripts, selected
L63Mℓino　by J. G. Randall from various collections.
facsim.　　7v.

　　Photographic reproductions.
　　Vol.1, 3, 4, are octavo size; v.5 folio.

NL　0375608　IU

Micro-
film　　[Lincoln material in the McCormick historical
E　　　　association,Chicago]
120
　　Positive.
　　Includes a facsimile of Lincoln's speech on
sectionalism,and letters from C.H.McCormick and
J.D.Davidson.

NL　0375609　ICU

---

q973.7　Lincoln material selected by J. G. Randall from
L63Mℓinn　the Division of manuscripts in the Library of
facsim.　　Congress. 1860-1866.
　　v.

　　Photographic reproductions of manuscripts,
among which is included some typewritten and
some printed material.
　　Vol.2, 6-9, 13, 15,　　　　　　are octavo
size.

NL　0375610　IU

LINCOLN medals.　Boston,1875.

　By H.W.H.

NL　0375611　MH

Lincoln Medical College of Cotner University,
Lincoln, Neb. Annual announcements for the
sessions of 1890-91 to 1892-3 (1.-3.); 1897-8 (6.);
1903-4 (14.). 8° & 12°. Lincoln, 1890-1903.
　Organized in 1890 as the Medical Department of Nebraska Christian University. In 1891 became the Medical
Department of Cotner University.

NL　0375612　DNLM

The Lincoln memorial: a record of the life,
assassination, and obsequies of the martyred
president
　　see under　Shea, John Dawson Gilmary,
1824-1892.

The Lincoln memorial: album immortelles
　　see under　Oldroyd, Osborn Hamiline,
1842-1903.

Lincoln memorial association.
　The life of Abraham Lincoln, drawn from
original sources and containing many speeches,
letters and telegrams hitherto unpublished
　　see under　Tarbell, Ida Minerva, 1857-

VOLUME 334

Lincoln memorial center association
   Our priceless heritage. ₍Springfield, Ill., 1955₎
   folder, ₍3₎p. 1 illus. 28cm.

NL 0375616   IHi

The Lincoln memorial collection. Relics of the war of
the rebellion. Autographs of soldiers and sailors and
government officials. Collected by Julius E. Francis,
Property of the Lincoln birthday association. In the
rooms of the Buffalo historical society, Young men's library building, Buffalo, N. Y. ₍Buffalo, Art-printing
works of Matthews, Northrup & co., 1887₎

55 p. 24 x 19ᶜᵐ.

1. Lincoln, Abraham, pres. U. S.—Relics. I. Francis, Julius E. II. Lincoln birthday association, Buffalo.

Library of Congress   E457.65.L74   5–11415

NL 0375617   DLC MB MH Nh NIC IU OClWHi

Lincoln memorial collection of Chicago.
   Catalogue of articles owned and used by Abraham Lincoln.
Now owned by the Lincoln memorial collection of Chicago ...
₍Chicago, 1887₎
   ₍16₎ p. 22½ᶜᵐ.

1. Lincoln, Abraham, pres. U. S., 1809–1865—Museums, relics, etc.
                                                        6–861
Library of Congress   E457.65.L746

NL 0375618   DLC

E457   LINCOLN MEMORIAL COLLECTION OF CHICAGO.
.1   Lincoln memorial collection;letters and documents
.Z9   etc.,written by Abraham Lincoln;law books and fur-
v.2   niture...
₍Lincoln   ₍In Henkels,S.V. The collection of autographs
          formed by the Hon.James T.Mitchell...and the entire
          Lincoln memorial collection of Chicago,Ill. ₍Philadelphia,1894₎ 27cm. p.99-110. plates,fold.facsim₎
             Detached copy.
             ₍Booksellers' and auction catalogs of Lincolniana. v.2,no.1₎

NL 0375619   ICU

Lincoln memorial collection of Chicago.
   Sketch of the life of Abraham Lincoln and a catalogue
of articles once owned and used by him, now owned by
the Lincoln memorial collection of Chicago. ₍Milwaukee,
188–?₎
   30 p., 1 l. illus. 22ᶜᵐ.
   Cover-title: Sketch of the life of Abraham Lincoln and a catalogue of
articles ... now owned by the Lincoln memorial collection, on exhibition
at the Exposition building.
   Advertising matter interspersed.

1. Lincoln, Abraham, pres. U. S., 1809–1865.

Library of Congress   6–860

NL 0375620   DLC

Lincoln memorial collection of Chicago.

Z999   Mitchell, James Tyndale, 1834–1915.
.H505   ... The valuable collection of autographs and historical
no.731   papers collected by the Hon. Jas. T. Mitchell ... Also the entire
          Lincoln memorial collection of Chicago ... Catalogue compiled
          and sale conducted by Stan. V. Henkels at the book auction
          rooms of Thos. Birch's sons ... Philada., Pa. ₍Philadelphia,
          1894₎

Lincoln memorial commission
      see   U.S. Lincoln memorial commission.

Lincoln memorial company.
   The birthplace of Abraham Lincoln
      see   ₍Burgers, D   M   ₎
   Lincoln memorial; the birthplace of
Abraham Lincoln.

Lincoln Memorial, Hodgenville, Kentucky, the birthplace
of Lincoln. Hodgenville, Herald-news ₍1933₎
   ₍15₎ p. illus. 21 cm.

1. Lincoln, Abraham, Pres. U. S.—Birthplace. 2. Hodgenville, Ky.
Lincoln Memorial Building.   I. Herald-news, Hodgenville, Ky.

E457.32.LA2   54–54358

NL 0375624   DLC RPB

Lincoln memorial library, Brookings, S.D.
      see
South Dakota. State college of agriculture and
      mechanic arts, Brookings. Lincoln memorial
      library.

Lincoln memorial park, Lincoln City, Indiana
      see under   ₍Lindsey, U.S.₎

₍Lincoln memorial publishing co., Decatur, Ill.₎
   Trails and shrines of Abraham Lincoln. ₍Decatur, Ill., The
Lincoln memorial publishing co., ᶜ1934₎
   cover-title, 27, ₍5₎ p. illus. 21ᶜᵐ.

1. Lincoln, Abraham, pres. U. S., 1809–1865. 2. Lincoln national
memorial highway. 3. Illinois—Descr. & trav.—Guide-books.   I.
Title.
                                                   35–6414
Library of Congress   E457.64.L56
——— Copy 3.
Copyright A 74484   ₍3₎   923.173

NL 0375627   DLC NIC OClWHi MiU-C WHi

Lincoln Memorial Shrine, Redlands, Calif.
   The Lincoln Shrine, Redlands, California;
an account of its conception, execution, and the
works of art which it contains
      see under title

Lincoln memorial society of New England.
   Official Souvenir Program issued by the Lincoln
Memorial Society of New England in its Celebration
of the Fiftieth Anniversary of the Issuance of
the Emancipation Proclamation by President
Abraham Lincoln. ... Held in the Grand Hall,
Mechanics Building, ... January 1 and 2, 1913.
(Caption title).   [Boston, The Chapple
Press, 1913]
   1 p.l., 41 p. illus. 4to. In brown paper
covers. Bound in green cloth.

NL 0375629   CSmH

Lincoln Memorial; the birthplace of Abraham
   Lincoln. Official papers establishing the
   marriage of his parents
      see under   ₍Burgers, D   M   ₎

Lincoln memorial university, Cumberland Gap, Tenn.
      see
Lincoln memorial university, Harrogate, Tenn.

Lincoln memorial university, Harrogate, Tenn.
   The annual commemoration of the birthday of Abraham
Lincoln by the Lincoln memorial university, Mayflower hotel,
Washington, D. C., February 12 ... 1931 ... Cumberland
Gap, Tenn., Lincoln memorial university, 1931.
   3–81 p. 21ᶜᵐ.
   On cover: Tributes and testimony to Abraham Lincoln and his living
memorial ...

1. Lincoln, Abraham, pres. U. S.—Addresses, sermons, etc. 2. Lincoln,
Abraham, pres. U. S.—Anniversaries, etc.
                                            32–23028 Revised
Library of Congress   E457.7.L738
                             ₍r43c2₎   123.173

NL 0375632   DLC ICU RPB OClWHi

Lincoln Memorial University, Harrogate, Tenn.
   The Blue and gray
      see under title

Lincoln Memorial University, Harrogate, Tenn.
   Booklet of information, October, 1906. Lincoln Memorial
University, near Cumberland Gap, Tenn. ₍Cumberland
Gap? 1906₎
   16 p. illus. 15 cm.
   Cover title.

LD3071.L7A53   57–55811

NL 0375634   DLC

Lincoln memorial university, Harrogate, Tenn.
   Booklet of information, October, 1907. Lincoln memorial
university, Cumberland Gap, Tenn. ₍Cumberland Gap? 1907₎
   cover-title, 16 p. illus. 14½ᶜᵐ.

                                            E 15–1436 Revised
U. S. Off. of educ. Library   LD3071.L72
   for Library of Congress   ₍r43b2₎

NL 0375635   DHEW

Lincoln memorial university, Harrogate, Tenn.
   Catalog.
   Cumberland Gap, Tenn.,
      v. illus., pl. 22½ᶜᵐ.
   At head of title: Lincoln memorial university.

Library of Congress   LD3071.L7   ca 10—5615 Unrev'd

NL 0375636   DLC NN NjP

VOLUME 334

Lincoln memorial university, *Harrogate, Tenn.*
Celebration of Lincoln's birthday and of the twentieth anniversary of the founding of Lincoln memorial university, Cumberland Gap, Tennessee, February 10, 11, 12, 1917. ₍Cumberland Gap, 1917₎
cover-title, 37, ₍1₎ p., 1 l. 23ᶜᵐ.

1. Lincoln, Abraham, pres. U. S.—Anniversaries, etc.
18–845 Revised
Library of Congress   E457.7.L74

NL 0375637   DLC OC1WHi MB NN

Lincoln memorial university, *Harrogate, Tenn.*
... Frederick Hill Meserve tribute. Addresses of Frederick Hill Meserve and Carl W. Schaefer on the occasion of the presentation of the photographs of Abraham Lincoln to Lincoln memorial university, October 4, 1941. ₍Harrogate, Dept. of Lincolniana, Lincoln memorial university, 1941₎
cover-title, 16 p. 25½ᶜᵐ.
At head of title: Supplement to Lincoln herald, October, 1941.
Portrait on cover.
"Limited to 500 copies."
1. Lincoln, Abraham, pres. U. S.—Portraits. I. Meserve, Frederick Hill, 1865– II. Schaefer, Carl Walter Scott, 1884– III. Lincoln herald. Supplement.
42–19151 Revised
Library of Congress   E457.6.M584
₍r43c2₎   923.173

NL 0375638   DLC

Lincoln Memorial University, Harrogate, Tenn.
From my window at Lincoln Memorial University
see under   Kincaid, Robert Lee, 1893–

E457   Lincoln Memorial University, Harrogate, Tenn.
.M887
Lincoln herald.
₍Harrogate, Tenn., Lincoln Memorial University₎

308
Z
Box 699 Lincoln memorial university, Harrogate, Tenn.
Lincoln memorial university ... ₍Harrogate, Tenn., 1927?₎
₍19₎ p. illus. 10x22ᶜᵐ.

NL 0375641   NNC

Lincoln Memorial University, *Harrogate, Tenn.*
Lincoln Memorial University. Compiled and edited by John L. Dickson. Harrogate ₍ᶜ1928₎
40 p. illus., ports., map. 22 cm.
Facsim. of letter from Calvin Coolidge to Dr. John Wesley Hill, chancellor, Lincoln Memorial University (1 leaf) inserted.

I. Dickson, John L., ed.
LD3071.L72A5   54–47788

NL 0375642   DLC MB RPB NNC

308
Z
Box 699 Lincoln memorial university, Harrogate, Tenn.
Lincoln memorial university ... why it is, it should be, it must be, it is America's hope. Harrogate, Tenn., Lincoln memorial university ₍19——₎
₍27₎ p. illus.

On cover: The why and wherefore.

NL 0375643   NNC

Lincoln memorial university, Harrogate, Tenn.
A little book about Lincoln Memorial University 1916–1917, Cumberland Gap, Tennessee. [Cumberland Gap, Tennessee, Lincoln Memorial University, 1917]
28 p. illus. 16mo.   In cream paper covers. Bound in green cloth.

NL 0375644   CSmH

Lincoln Memorial University, *Harrogate, Tenn.*
The living memorial to Lincoln. Cumberland Gap, Tenn. ₍191–?₎
63 p. incl. illus., ports. 22 cm.

I. Title.
LD3071.L73A58   57–55806

NL 0375645   DLC ICU OC1WHi NNC CSmH

LD3071
.L73A58 Lincoln Memorial University, Harrogate, Tenn.
1917   The living memorial to Lincoln. By Richard Lloyd Jones.   Cumberland Gap, Tenn. ₍1917?₎
64 p. illus.,ports. 21 cm.
"Reprinted by the University."
On cover: A souvenir issued in commemoration of the twentieth anniversary of Lincoln Memorial University, celebrated on Lincoln's birthday, February 10th, 11th, 12th, 1917.
I. Jones, Richard Lloyd. II. Title.

NL 0375646   T RPB MH

Lincoln memorial university, Harrogate, Tenn.

Meserve, Frederick Hill, 1865–
The photographic portraits of Abraham Lincoln; a descriptive list of the portraits in the Meserve collection, copies of which were presented to Lincoln memorial university by Carl W. Schaefer, a trustee of the university. By Frederick H. Meserve ... ₍New York₎ Priv. print. ₍Charles J. Amm co., inc.₎ 1941.

LINCOLN Memorial University, Harrogate, Tenn.
Preliminary report on the use of radio receiving sets allocated to Lincoln Memorial Univeristy. Harrogate, Tenn., 1931.

NL 0375648   NNC

Lincoln memorial university, *Harrogate, Tenn.*
... Program, Frederick Hill Meserve tribute, October 4, 1941, Hall of citizenship, Lincoln memorial university, Harrogate, Tennessee. ₍Harrogate, 1941₎
cover-title, ₍4₎ p. illus. (ports.) 24ᶜᵐ.
At head of title: Supplement to Lincoln herald, October, 1941.

1. Meserve, Frederick Hill, 1865– 2. Lincoln, Abraham, pres. U. S.—Portraits. I. Lincoln herald. Supplement.
42–19150 Revised
Library of Congress   E457.6.M585
₍r43c2₎   923.173

NL 0375649   DLC

Lincoln memorial university, Harrogate, Tenn.
Program of the celebration of Lincoln birthday and 20th anniversary of Lincoln memorial university to be held Feb. 10, 11, 12, 1917. Cumberland Gap. Tenn. ₍Bost. The Chapple press₎ n. d. ₍1917?₎
₍11₎ p.

NL 0375650   OC1WHi

₍Lincoln memorial university, *Harrogate, Tenn.₎*
Said Abraham Lincoln: —— ₍Cumberland Gap, Tenn., Lincoln memorial university, 1931₎
cover-title, ₍40₎ p. illus., plates (part double) 21½ x 28ᶜᵐ.
Descriptive of the Lincoln memorial university.

I. Title.   31–6689 Revised
Library of Congress   LD3071.L723A5 1931
₍r44c2₎   378.768

NL 0375651   DLC

Lincoln memorial university, Harrogate, Tenn.
This is Lincoln. ₍Harrogate, ᶜ1941₎ 19 p. illus. 22cm.
Includes the outstanding Meserve Lincoln photographs reproduced in poster stamps. — cf. Letter from Lincoln memorial university inserted.

1. Lincoln, Abraham, 16th pres.   U. S.—Portraits, statues, etc.
I. Meserve, Frederick Hill, 1865–
N. Y. P. L.   February 16, 1944

NL 0375652   NN ICN

Lincoln memorial university, Harrogate, Tenn. Class of 1941.
The ... Railsplitter; published by the senior class of Lincoln memorial university, Harrogate, Tenn., 1941.
1 v. illus. 27 cm.
Wooden covers with painted illustration.
Photograph of Lincoln by A. Gardner (Nov. 15, 1863) in pocket.

NL 0375653   RPB

E457   **Lincoln memorial university,** Harrogate, **Tenn.**
.2   Dept. of Lincolniana.
.H73   **Holden, Walter Simpson,** 1865–
Abraham Lincoln, man of inner conflict, by Walter S. Holden. Harrogate, Tenn., Dept. of Lincolniana, Lincoln memorial university, 1944.

Z8505   **Lincoln memorial university,** Harrogate, **Tenn.**
.L55   Dept. of Lincolniana.
Lindstrom, Ralph Godfrey, 1891–
A Californian's collection of Lincolniana, by Ralph G. Lindstrom ... Harrogate, Tenn., Dept. of Lincolniana, Lincoln memorial university, 1944.

Lincoln memorial university, *Harrogate, Tenn. Dept. of Lincolniana.*
The Department of Lincolniana of Lincoln memorial university, Harrogate, Tennessee; R. Gerald McMurtry, director. ₍Harrogate, ᶜ1939₎
20 p. illus. (incl. ports., facsims.) 25½ᶜᵐ.
Caption title.

1. Lincoln, Abraham, pres. U. S.—Museums, relics, etc.   I. McMurtry, Robert Gerald, 1906–
41–3352 Revised
Library of Congress   E457.65.L748
₍r43d2₎   923.173

NL 0375656   DLC TU

VOLUME 334

E475
.55
.B8
Lincoln memorial university, Harrogate, Tenn. Dept. of Lincolniana.

Bullard, Frederic Lauriston, 1866-1952.
"A few appropriate remarks," Lincoln's Gettysburg address, by F. Lauriston Bullard ... Harrogate, Tenn., Dept. of Lincolniana, Lincoln memorial university, 1944.

E457
.3
.S69K5
Lincoln memorial university, Harrogate, Tenn. Dept. of Lincolniana.

Kincaid, Robert Lee, 1893-
Joshua Fry Speed, Lincoln's most intimate friend, by Robert L. Kincaid. Harrogate, Tenn., Dept. of Lincolniana, Lincoln memorial university, 1943.

Lincoln memorial university, Harrogate, Tenn. Dept. of Lincolniana.
The Lincoln log cabin almanac ...
see under   McMurty, Robert Gerald, 1906-

Lincoln memorial university, Harrogate, Tenn. Dept. of Lincolniana
The Lincolns of Tennessee
see under   Williams, Samuel Cole, 1864-

784.7
L638l
[LINCOLN MEMORIAL UNIVERSITY, Harrogate, Tenn. Dept. of Lincolniana]
Lincoln's Thanksgiving hymn. [19--?]
[8]p. illus.(incl. ports, facsims.(incl. music))
Caption title.
Includes The president's hymn: Give thanks all y people, by Rev. Dr. Muhlenberg and facsim. of cover of Harper's Weekly, journal of civilization v.7, no.362, in which the hymn appeared.
Signed at end: Compliments of Department of Lincolniana, Stewart W. McClelland, R. Gerald McMurtry, Robert   L. Kincaid.

NL 0375661   TxU WHi

E457
.98
.L556
Lincoln Memorial University, Harrogate, Tenn. Dept. of Lincolniana.

Lincoln, Abraham, Pres. U. S., 1809-1865.
Lincoln's Thanksgiving proclamation named the last Thursday in November as a day of national thanksgiving and praise. Harrogate, Tenn., Dept. of Lincolniana, Lincoln Memorial Univ.,1945.

[Lincoln memorial university, Harrogate, Tenn. Dept. of Lincolniana]
This is Abraham Lincoln
see under   Meserve, Frederick Hill, 1865-

R747
.L47
Lincoln Memorial University, Harrogate, Tenn. Medical Department, Knoxville, Tenn.
Announcement and catalogue, 1st-22d, 18 -1910/11. Knoxville, 18 -1910.
v. in   illus., tables. 20 cm.
Formerly Tennessee Medical College, Knoxville.
Title varies slightly.

1. Medical colleges.

NL 0375664   TU DNLM DLC TKL

The Lincoln Memorial, Washington, D. C. Alexandria, Va., Action Publication, °1950.
30 p. illus., ports. 23 cm.

1. Washington, D. C. Lincoln Memorial.

F203.4.L73L5   975.3   56-32596

NL   0375665   DLC NIC IU

Lincoln memorials
see under   [Indiana Lincoln union]

LINCOLN-MERCURY times.   -41, no. 5,   May, 1949; [new ser.] v.1-9, no.1, July/Aug.1949-Jan./ Feb.1957
Dearborn, Mich.   v.   illus.(part col.)
18+28cm.

Monthly, 1948-May, 1949, bimonthly, July/Aug.1949-Jan./Feb.1957.
Absorbed Fine cars (not in the library), July/Aug.1956.

Title varies: July/Aug.1956-Jan./Feb.1957, Lincoln and Mercury times combined with Fine cars.
Published by the Ford motor company.
Ceased publication with Mar./Apr.1957.

1. House organs. I. Ford motor company. II. Fine cars.

NL   0375668   NN MH MiD

TX715
.F697
Lincoln-Mercury times.

The Ford treasury of favorite recipes from famous eating places. (Compiled by Nancy Kennedy) New York, Simon and Schuster (1950)

TX715
.K355
Lincoln-Mercury times.

Kennedy, Nancy, comp.
The second Ford treasury of favorite recipes from famous eating places. Art director: Arthur Lougee. New York, Simon and Schuster (195

...LINCOLN MIGRATION CENTENNIAL,1830-1930. Vincennes,Indiana,March 6,1930. Vincennes,Indiana,Western sun & General advertiser,1930. 8p. Illus. Ports. Map

Covers are facsim.of Western sun & General advertiser,Vincennes,(Ind.),Sat. Mar.6,1930,v.xxi,no.4.

NL   0375671   InU

Lincoln mining district, Colo.
see   Lincoln district, Colo.

Lincoln Minster
see   Lincoln Cathedral.

LINCOLN minster. [Architectural and historical notes of Lincoln cathedral./ Lincoln,188-?]
pp.4. Plan.

NL   0375674   MH

Lincoln Minster. [Architectural & historical notes. Ground plan.]
No title-page. [Lincoln. Williamson. 189-?] (3) pp. 8°.
Cover title.

NL   0375675   MB NjP

Lincoln minster. (Lincoln: W. K. Morton, 19---) 2l, 1 double plan. 8°.
Cover-title.

1. Cathedrals, Gt. Br.: Eng.: Lincoln.
N. Y. P. L.

February 9, 1917.

NL   0375676   NN MH OO

Lincoln monument association
see
National Lincoln monument association.

The Lincoln Monument, in memory of Scottish-American soldiers, unveiled in Edinburgh, August 21, 1893
see under   [Scottish-American Soldiers' Monument Committee]

F869
S3
.9
P64L5
Lincoln Monument League.
Grand athletic and military tournament, under the auspices of the Lincoln Monument League, by the United States troops stationed at San Francisco and vicinity, at the Presidio, Sept. 9th, Admission Day, 1897. [San Francisco?] 1897.
16 p. illus., ports. 24cm.

Cover title.
"The Lincoln Monument League was organized March 20th, 1897, for the purpose of promoting the erection of a Monument to the memory of Abraham Lincoln ..."

1. San Francisco. Presidio. 2. Lincoln, Abraham, Pres. U. S., 1809-1865. Monuments, etc. 3. Tournaments. 4. Admission Day. I. Title.

NL   0375679   CU-B CSmH

Lincoln monument league.
Lincoln Day, February 12th, 1900. It is the desire of the Lincoln Monument League that Lincoln Day services be held in every schoolhouse in the State of California ... [caption title].
[San Francisco, 1900]
2 leaves. Octavo.   In 3/4 green morocco and marbled boards; gilt top; padded with blank leaves.
The annual address of the League is printed vertically on p. [3] & [4]; and signed W. W. Stone, President ...

NL   0375680   CSmH

VOLUME 334

F856
L5
1900
Lincoln Monument League.
Proceedings of the State Convention of the Lincoln Monument League held in San Francisco, June 16th, 1900. San Francisco, C. W. Gordon, Printer, 1900.
7 p. 22cm.

Cover title.

1. Lincoln, Abraham, Pres. U. S., 1809-1865 - Monuments, etc.

NL 0375681　CU-B RPB CSmH

KB
H1
77
As55t
1887
Lincoln Mortgage and Trust Co., Ashland, Kan.
First mortgage bonds secured upon improved farms, negotiated and guaranteed both principal and interest by the Lincoln Mortgage and Trust Co., Ashland, Kansas. Capital $100,000 Kansas City, Mo., Pearl printing co., 1887.
39p. 22cm.

1. Mortgages. Kansas.

NL 0375682　KU

Lincoln Motor Company.
Book of instruction, Lincoln motor cars. Jan. 1st, 1932. 1st ed. Detroit [1932]
84 p. illus. 23 cm.
Cover title: Book of instruction, Lincoln twelve cylinder motor cars.

1. Lincoln automobile.
TL215.L5A5 1932　　　50-52591

NL 0375683　DLC

Lincoln Motor Company.
Book of instruction, Lincoln motor cars. Jan. 1st, 1932. 11th ed. Detroit [1932]
86 p. illus. 23 cm.
Cover title: Book of instruction, Lincoln eight cylinder motor cars.

1. Lincoln automobile.
TL215.L5A5 1932k　　　50-52592

NL 0375684　DLC

Lincoln Motor Company, Detroit.
The Lincoln.

Detroit: The Brotherton Co., 19　　　f°.
v. illus. (part col'd.)

Monthly (no issue June, 1924).

1. House organs. 2. Automobiles—　Per. and soc. publ.
N. Y. P. L.　　　September 16, 1926

NL 0375685　NN

Lincoln Motor Company.
The Lincolnian
see under title

Lincoln Motor Company.

Milestones. Detroit, Mich. [1924]
51 p. col. illus. 15cm.

1. Automobiles. 2. Transportation—History. I. Title.

NL 0375687　ViU

Lincoln Motor Company.
A pledge made good by deeds
see under　Detroit free press.

Lincoln motor company, Detroit
Reference book, Lincoln V-12. [The Author]
v.
Includes Book of instruction and Reference books for various models.

NL 0375689　MiD WaS

Lincoln Motor Company
see also　Ford Motor Company. *Lincoln-Mercury Division.*

Lincoln Motor Works Company
see
Reliance Electric and Engineering Company.

Lincoln mounts the Anglo-American stage
see under　[Parker, Henry Taylor] 1867-

Lincoln musical college.
University extension method, elementary harmony
see under　[Williams, Guy Bevier]

Lincoln National Bank and Trust company, Fort Wayne, Ind.
Lincoln National Bank and Trust company, Fort Wayne, Indiana; 40th anniversary, 1905-1945. [Fort Wayne, Ind., Wayne Paper Box & Printing Corp., 1945]
[20]p. illus. 22x29cm.

NL 0375694　OrU

Lincoln National Bank of the City of New York.
The inspiration of Abraham Lincoln's Gettysburg address
see under title

Lincoln national bank of the city of New York.
... Lincoln national bank of the city of New York, and Lincoln safe deposit company. [History and origin] [New York, South pub. co., printers, 1898]
[32] p. illus. 20½ x 17½[cm]

1. Lincoln safe deposit company, New York.
　　　　　CA 8—960 Unrev'd
Library of Congress　　HG2013.N54L5

NL 0375696　DLC

Lincoln National Bank of the City of New York.
The Lincoln National Bank of the City of New York. [Its history and origin.] The Lincoln Safe Deposit Company. [New York, South Pub. Press, 1905?]
32 p. illus. 8°.

NL 0375697　NN

THE LINCOLN NATIONAL BANK OF THE CITY OF NEW YORK.
[Officers, directors, statements, January 21, 1903.] [New York, 1903.]

nar.24°. pp.(4). Port.
Cover serves as title-page.

NL 0375698　MH

Lincoln national life foundation.
Abraham Lincoln: the Hoosier youth; Paul Manship's heroic bronze statue, presented by the Lincoln national life foundation, sponsored by the Lincoln national life insurance company. Fort Wayne, Ind., 1932.
19 p. incl. front., illus. 27½[cm].
"The sculptor": p. 9-11.

1. Fort Wayne. Lincoln statue. 2. Manship, Paul, 1886-　I. Lincoln national life insurance co., Fort Wayne. II. Title.
　　　　　　32-29640
Library of Congress　　E457.6.L76
——— Copy 2.　　　F534.F7L6
Copyright A 55187　[3]　　923.173

NL 0375699　DLC OC1 IHi

Lincoln national life foundation.
Addresses delivered at the dedication of the heroic bronze statue, "Abraham Lincoln-the Hoosier youth", September 16, 1932. Entrance plaza of The Lincoln National Life insurance company, Fort Wayne, Indiana. [Fort Wayne, Ind., Lincoln National Life insurance co., 1932]
1 p.l., 12, [2] p. illus. 23 cm.

NL 0375700　MiU-C CStbS CU MB OC1WHi

Lincoln national life foundation.
Lincoln bibliography, cumulative, Check list. Alphabetical index of authors compiled from the chronological bibliography appearing quarterly in Lincoln lore, 1930/39— Fort Wayne, Ind., Lincoln national life foundation, 1942-
v. 16½[cm].

1. Lincoln, Abraham, pres. U. S.—Bibl.　I. Lincoln lore.
　　　　　　42-19599
Library of Congress　　Z8505.L5
　　　[5]　　012

NL 0375701　DLC OC1WHi

VOLUME 334

Lincoln national life foundation, Fort Wayne, Ind.
...Lincoln paintings.　Fort Wayne, Ind.: The Lincoln nat'l
life ins. co., c1934-38.　1 v.　plates.　32½cm.

Reproductions of paintings made for the Lincoln national life foundation; mounted
and bound by The New York public library.

1. Lincoln, Abraham, 16th pres.　　U. S.—Portraits.
N. Y. P. L.　　　　　　　　　　　　　January 26, 1939

NL 0375702　NN

ML128
.L28W3　Warren, Louis Austin, 1885-
　　　　Lincoln sheet music; check list [by] Louis A. Warren, director, Lincoln national life foundation.　Fort Wayne, Ind., Lincolniana publishers, 1940.

Lincoln national life foundation.
　'Lincoln's beard
　　　see under　Lincoln, Abraham, pres. U. S.
1809-1865.

Lincoln national life insurance co., Fort Wayne.

Lincoln national life foundation.
　　Abraham Lincoln: the Hoosier youth; Paul Manship's
heroic bronze statue, presented by the Lincoln national life
foundation, sponsored by the Lincoln national life insurance
company.　Fort Wayne, Ind., 1932.

Lincoln National Life Insurance Company,
　Fort Wayne, Ind.
　　Addresses delivered at the dedication of
the heroic bronze statue "Abraham Lincoln—The
Hoosier Youth"
　　see under　Lincoln national life foundation.

LINCOLN NATIONAL LIFE INSURANCE COMPANY, Fort
　　Wayne, Ind.
　　...Annual statement...
19

Fort Wayne, Ind. [, 19　　　　　　　　　f°.
　no.

NL 0375707　NN

E457
.L74　Lincoln National Life Insurance Company, Fort
　　　Wayne, Ind.
　　　Lincoln lore.　no. 1–
　　　　Apr. 15, 1929–
　　Fort Wayne, Ind., Lincoln National Life Insurance Co.

Lincoln National Life Insurance Company,
　Fort Wayne, Ind.
　　Little known Lincoln episodes
　　　see under　[Warren, Louis Austin] 1885-

Lincoln national life insurance co., Fort Wayne.
　Non-forfeiture values American experience
table, Lincoln national life insurance co.,
Fort Wayne, Indiana.　Ann Arbor, Mich., Edwards
brothers, inc. [1933?]
　1 ℓ., 17 tab. on 30 ℓ.　27cm.
"Photo-lithoprint reproduction of author's manuscript."

　1. Insurance, Life—Rates and tables.

NL 0375710　MiU

　The Lincoln national life insurance company
　　pays honor to a great name.　The news [of
　　the General fireproofing company, Youngstown,
　　Ohio] April, 1931, p. 5-7.　106

NL 0375711　MiKW

LINCOLN NATIONAL MONUMENT ASSOCIATION, Atlanta,
　　Ga.
　　Appeal to the loyal and patriotic people of
the U.S.　[Atlanta, Ga., 1867].

　4°.　pp. (3).

NL 0375712　MH

LINCOLN NATIONAL MONUMENT ASSOCIATION, Spring-
　　field, Ill.
　[Resolutions.　Springfield, Ill. 1865.]

　4°.　1 page.

NL 0375713　MH

LINCOLN NATIONAL MONUMENT ASSOCIATION,
　　Springfield, Ill.
　　To the associated press of the United States.
[A circular.　Springfield, Ill.]1865.

　4°.　pp. (2).

NL 0375714　MH

Lincoln, Nebraska, directory ... 1907–
　including Bethany, Burnham, College View, Havelock, Normal, University Place, West Lincoln and Yankee Hill ...
Lincoln, Neb., J. North & company [°1906]–
　v. plate, fold. map.　24-24½cm.
Title varies slightly.

　1. Lincoln, Neb.—Direct. 2. Bethany, Neb.—Direct. 3. College View,
Neb.—Direct. 4. Havelock, Neb.—Direct. 5. Normal, Neb.—Direct. 6.
University Place, Neb.—Direct. 7. West Lincoln, Neb.—Direct. 8. Burn-
ham, Neb.—Direct. 9. Yankee Hill, Neb.—Direct.

　Library of Congress　F674.L7A18
　　　　　　　　　　　　　　　　　　　　7-7163

NL 0375715　DLC

Lincoln, Nebraska industries.　[Lincoln, Neb.]

NL 0375716　MiD

Lincoln, Nebraska's capital city, 1867–1923 ... over 50
years of Lincoln's progress shown by word and picture ... [Lincoln, Neb., Woodruff printing company,
°1923]
　2 p. L., [3]-191, [2] p.　illus. (incl. maps)　20 x 28cm.
Contains advertising matter.
"Published by authority of the Lincoln Chamber of commerce."

　I. Lincoln, Neb.　I. Woodruff printing company, Lincoln, Neb.

　Library of Congress　F674.L7L6
　　　　　　　　　　　　　　　　　　23-6905

NL 0375717　DLC MWA WaS OU OCl KU

Lincoln news.　Oct. 1925–
　Lincoln University, Pa. [Lincoln University]
　　　　illus.　31cm.　5 no. a year,
Oct.-May.

NL 0375718　CtY

Lincoln news.　v. 1–
　　Oct. 1930–
　[Lincoln University, Pa., Lincoln University]
　　　31cm.

NL 0375719　CtY

Lincoln Normal University for Colored Students, *Marion,
Ala.*
see
Alabama.　State College for Negroes, *Montgomery.*

Lincoln number of the Kentucky School journal
　　see under　Kentucky school
journal.　[Supplement]

... Lincoln number, 29 ...　Tarrytown, N. Y., Reprinted,
W. Abbatt, 1926.
　56 p.　20cm.　(The Magazine of history, with notes and queries. Extra number.　no. 125 (v. 32, no. 1))
　CONTENTS.—With Lincoln at Gettysburg, by J. B. Remensnyder.—
Lincoln at Gettysburg, by Nicolay and Hay.—Lincoln as an example
to young men, by A. J. Beveridge.—How Lincoln won New England,
from the Chicago tribune.—The vision of Calhoun, from the Chicago
tribune.—The mint of Lincoln's wit, from the Chicago tribune.—Lincoln and wounded officer, by T. L. Livermore.—What his nurse knew,
from the Watchman and reflector. — Lincoln to George Robertson,
1855.—Memories of war days, Anon. (Chicago tribune, 1909)

　1. Lincoln, Abraham, pres. U. S., 1809-1865.

　Library of Congress　E173.M24 no. 125
　　　　　　　　　　　　　　　　　　27-3223

NL 0375722　DLC MiU OCl

... [Lincoln number, 31 ...　Tarrytown, N. Y., Reprinted, W.
Abbatt, 1927.
　68 p.　front.　26½cm.　(The Magazine of history with notes and queries.
Extra number.　no. 133 (v. 34, no. 1))
　CONTENTS.—Donn Piatt's criticism, from the Chicago tribune.—What
Tom Pendel saw, from the Chicago tribune.—Homely or handsome, from
the Chicago tribune.—An ex-slave's tribute to Lincoln (Booker T. Wash-
ington) from the Chicago tribune.—Lincoln and the children, from the
Chicago tribune.—Reminiscences of one of Kearny's staff (J. C. Jack-
son) from the Evening post, New York.—The religion of Lincoln (F.
Lauriston Bullard) from the Congregationalist.—Robert Todd Lincoln,
from the New York tribune.

　1. Lincoln, Abraham, pres. U. S., 1809-1865.

　Library of Congress　E173.M24 no. 133
　　　　　　　　　　　　　　　　　　27-25113

NL 0375723　DLC MiU OCl

VOLUME 334

E457
•5
•L74
[Lincoln obsequies, etc. Scrap book of mounted newspapers clippings relating to the assassination and obsequies of Abraham Lincoln]
227 p.

NL 0375724   DLC

... Lincoln oder McClellan? An die Deutschen in Amerika
   see under   [Lieber, Francis] 1800-1872.

The Lincoln of Carl Sandburg; some reviews of "Abraham Lincoln: the war years"
   see under   Harcourt, Brace and company.

---

ar W
13291
Lincoln pamphlets 1-2.   [v. p., 1865-1909]
   2 v. illus. 24cm.

   1. Lincoln, Abraham, Pres. U.S., 1809-1865.

NL 0375727   NIC

La
711.33
L93Li
Lincoln parish, La. *Development Board*
   Lincoln parish resources and facilities, survey by Lincoln parish planning board. Published in cooperation with state of Louisiana, Department of public works, Planning division...   [Baton Rouge, 1943]
   80p., 1 l. illus., map (fold.) 28cm.

   1. Natural resources--Louisiana.. 2. Lincoln parish, La.--Econ. cond. I. Title. II. Louisiana. Department of public works. Planning division.

NL 0375728   LU

Lincoln Parish, *La. Development Board.*
   Lincoln Parish resources and facilities; [second] survey. Published in cooperation with State of Louisiana Dept. of Public Works, Planning Division. [Baton Rouge, 1953]
   128 p. illus., maps (part fold., part col.) 28 cm.

   1. Lincoln Parish, La.   I. Title.

F377.L5A5   917.6391   55-62167

NL 0375729   DLC LU MsU

Lincoln Parish, *La. Planning Board*
see
Lincoln Parish, *La. Development Board.*

Lincoln Parish Training School, *Grambling, La.*
see **Louisiana.** Grambling College, *Grambling.*

NL 0375732   MiD

L362.11
P1
Lincoln Park Sanitarium Company.
   Lincoln Park sanitarium. Its location, surroundings, interior furnishings and resources for the treatment of patients, with sketches of Lincoln Park and the chief features of the sanitarium building. [Chicago, 189-]
   [10], 9-47 p. front, plates. 20x27½ᶜᵐ.
   Half-title.
   Verso of each leaf is blank.

NL 0375733   ICJ ICHi

C13
3
Lincoln party, resolutions, etc., leading to formation. Col. Goddard's letter of acceptance. Addresses delivered at a meeting to ratify the candidacy of Robert H.I. Goddard for the office of United States senator, held in Infantry hall, Providence, Saturday, September 29, 1906 ... Providence [1906]

NL 0375734   CtY MH

Lincoln patriotic army
   ... Volunteer private's regular equipment, Lincoln patriotic army New York, [or 1918].   HS 2330
   [32]p. port., facsim. 12 x 16 cm.   •L53

NL 0375735   DLC

JS13
L698
Lincoln Plantation, Me.
   Annual report of the municipal officers...
Norway, Me., 1931. 1v. 8°

NL 0375736   DLC

The Lincoln plot. Samuel B. Arnold's long-delayed revelation ... [Clippings from New York Sun, Dec. 8, 9, 10, 11, 12, 13, 14, 15, 16, 17, 18, 19, 20, 1902 mounted on sheets making] 34 l. f°.

NL 0375737   NN

The Lincoln postage stamp catalogue
see
The Lincoln illustrated, priced and descriptive catalogue of British, colonial & foreign postage stamps.

Lincoln preparatory school, Boston
   see Northeastern university, Boston. Lincoln preparatory school.

Lincoln printing company, *Chicago.*
   ... Form A-2 under the Securities act of 1933 as amended, including Supplement S-T relating to securities being registered which are to be issued under an indenture to be qualified under the Trust indenture act of 1939. Chicago, Lincoln printing company [1941]
   cover-title, 1 p. l., 45 p. incl. forms. 25½ᵐ.
   At head of title: Revised edition, February, 1941.

   1. Securities—U. S.   I. Title.
                                        42-16983
   Library of Congress   HG4556.U6L5 1941

NL 0375740   DLC.

Lincoln Printing Company, Chicago.
Lincoln review; news and information about business and securities.
   [Chicago, 19

Lincoln publishing company, *Chicago.*
   The 1915 pilot from coast to coast on the Lincoln highway; contains accurate maps of the roads ... maps of cities and towns ... principal and historical points of interest, side trips, population, altitude, resources and all data of use to motorists. Comp. and pub. by the Lincoln publishing company incorporated. Chicago, Ill., [1914-
   v. illus. (incl. port., maps, plans) 26ᶜᵐ.

   1. Automobiles—Road guides.   I. Title.   II. Title: Lincoln highway.
   Library of Congress   HE356.L7L5   15-1900

NL 0375742   DLC MB

Lincoln readers
   see under   Davidson, Isobel, 1869-

Lincoln Record Society, *Lincoln, Eng.*
   Publications. v. 1–
   1910/11–
   Lincoln, Eng.
   v. illus. 24-34 cm.
   Two or 3 vols. a year, 1910/11-1914/15; annual, 1915/16-
   Publication year for 1911- ends Sept. 30; for 19   Aug. 31

   1. Lincolnshire, Eng.—Hist.—Sources.

   DA670.L69R5   56-17919

Vi MoSW-L OU MdBP MiD-B NIC IU CaOTU TxLT
NL 0375744   DLC TxU NbHi NBuU CU KU IaAS GU OrU CSt

Lincoln Record Society, *Lincoln, Eng.*
   The publications of the Lincoln Record Society (for the ancient diocese and the county of Lincoln), founded in the year 1910. Parish register section.
   v. 1-9
   [Horncastle: W. K. Morton & Sons, 1914-25] 9 v. plates. 26cm.
   Vol. 1 published in Lincoln.
   Suspended publication.

   I. Parish registers—Gt. Br.—Eng.—
   N. Y. P. L.   Lincolnshire.   December 17, 1935

NL 0375745   NN Vi MiU OCl PHC MB

Lincoln record society, *Lincoln, Eng.*
   ... Report and list of subscribers. 1910–
   [Lincoln, Printed for the Lincoln record society, 1910–
   v. 24½ᵐ.
                                        13-12651
   Library of Congress   DA670.L69L73

NL 0375746   DLC CU MB NcGU GU OCl MiU

Lincoln red cattle society
   see its earlier name   Lincolnshire red shorthorn association.

... Lincoln red herd book
   see under   Lincolnshire red shorthorn association.

VOLUME 334

Lincoln red shorthorn society
     see its earlier name   Lincolnshire red
shorthorn association.

Lincoln regnant
     see under   [Cowgill, Frank Brooks] 1856-

E   Lincoln relics. Remarkable collec-
5   tion of Maine historical society, now
L 6399 exhibited at library; includes several
       autograph letters.   n.p.,n.d.
v.1
     Binder's title: Abraham Lincoln.
     Pamphlets, v.1.
     Caption title.
     Newspaper clipping, mounted.

   NL 0375751   ICN

Lincoln Reproductions, inc., *Fort Wayne.*
     City of Fort Wayne, Allen County, Indiana. **Fort Wayne,**
1954.
     map 188 x 88 cm.
     Scale ca. 1: 14,500.
     Blue line print.
     Indexed.

     1. Fort Wayne—Maps.

     G4094.F7 1954.L5   Map 54-455

   NL 0375752   DLC

A **Lincoln Republican.**
     The **new regime;** a true epic, by a **Lincoln Republican.**
[n. p., 1915?]

   NL 0375753   ?

Lincoln Republican club, Detroit, Mich.
     ... Twentieth annual banquet, Wednesday
evening, February tenth, 1909, Opera house.
n.p., 1909.
     8 p. por. 26 cm.
     Contains program and menu.

   NL 0375754   RPB

Lincoln Republican club, Grand Rapids, Mich.
     Annual banquet of Lincoln Republican club
and Young Men's Republican club of Grand
Rapids, Michigan... [Grand Rapids, 19
     v.   illus.(port.)   22.5-23 cm.

     1907 has "Kent county, Mich."

   NL 0375755   MiU-C

Lincoln Republican club, *Grand Rapids.*
     Annual banquet of Lincoln Republican club and Young
men's Republican club of Grand Rapids. Friday evening,
February 27 [1903] in commemoration of Lincoln's birthday. Auditorium, Grand Rapids, Michigan. [Grand
Rapids, Dickinson brothers, printers, 1903]
     [16] p. illus. (incl. port., music) 24½[cm].

     1. Lincoln, Abraham, pres. U. S.—Anniversaries, etc.   I. Young men's
Republican club, Grand Rapids.

                                  17–28127

     Library of Congress   E457.7.L75

   NL 0375756   DLC

LINCOLN REPUBLICAN CLUB OF BOSTON.
     Annual banquet, 1st.
—   [Boston. Litchfield & B. 1895.]   v. Portr. on
Sq. 8°.

   NL 0375757   MB

Lincoln Republican League.
     Empire or republic? [Minneapolis? 1900]
     31 p. port. (on cover) 17 cm. (Lincoln Republican booklet,
no. 2)
     Caption title: The imperial policy and our Philippine colonies.

     1. Campaign literature, 1900. 2. Philippine Islands — Hist. — In-
surrection, 1899–1901. 3. U. S.—Colonial question. 4. Lincoln, Abraham, Pres. U. S., 1809–1865. I. Title. II. Title: The imperial policy
and our Philippine colonies.

     E738.L5   58–51502

   NL 0375758   DLC MH

Lincoln Republican League.
     Lincoln, McKinley, Bryan. [Minneapolis? 1900]
     48 p. ports. 18 cm. (Lincoln Republican booklet, no. 3)
     Includes extracts from speeches of Lincoln, McKinley, and Bryan.

     1. Lincoln, Abraham, Pres. U. S., 1809–1865. 2. McKinley, William,
Pres. U. S., 1843–1901. 3. Bryan, William Jennings, 1860–1925. 4.
Campaign literature, 1900.

     E738.L53   58–50420

   NL 0375759   DLC

---

xE738   Lincoln Republican League
L5   Lincoln Republican booklets. Campaign of
     1900.   [Minneapolis, 1900]
     4v.in 1. ports. 18cm.

     Cover title.
     Edited by Elwood S.Corser.
     Originally issued as four campaign pamphlets
     Contents.- v.1. To the soldiers of our Civil
War.- v.2. Empire or republic?- v.3. Lincoln,
McKinley, Bryan.- v.4. A prayer, a poem, a plat-
form.

   NL 0375760   IaU MB

Lincoln Republican League.
     To the soldiers of our Civil War. [Minneapolis? 1900]
     15 p. port. (on cover) 18 cm. (Lincoln Republican booklet,
no. 1)
     Cover title.
     Caption title: Lincoln Republicans to the soldiers of the Civil War.

     1. Campaign literature, 1900. 2. Philippine Islands—Hist.—Insur-
rection, 1899–1901. 3. U. S.—Colonial question. 4. Lincoln, Abraham,
Pres. U. S., 1809–1865. I. Title. II. Title: Lincoln Republicans to
the soldiers of the Civil War.

     E738.L55   58–51501

   NL 0375761   DLC

Lincoln review, Boston
     see   Lincoln house review.

The **Lincoln review;** made by Lincoln children.
Lakewood, O., Lincoln elementary school. '19 -
     v. 27 1/2 x 21 cm.

     Mimeographed.

   NL 0375763   OClWHi

Lincoln review; news and information about business and
securities.
     [Chicago, 19
     v. tables, diagrs. 33½[cm]. monthly.
     Caption title.
     Issued by Lincoln printing company, Chicago, and Lincoln engraving
& printing corporation, New York.

     1. U. S.—Econ. condit.—Period. 2. Securities—Period. I. Lincoln
printing company, Chicago. II. Lincoln engraving and printing corporation, New York.

     Library of Congress   HC101.L5   43–36497
                                  [3]   330.5

   NL 0375764   DLC

Lincoln Rochester Trust Company. Discretionary
     Common Trust Fund 1.
     Report. 1st-   1950/51-
Rochester, N.Y.
     Annual.
     Report year ends January 31.

   NL 0375765   ICU

Lincoln safe deposit company, New York.
     ... Lincoln national bank of the city of New York
and Lincoln safe deposit company [History and
origin]
     see under   Lincoln national bank of the
city of New York.

Lincoln Safe Deposit Company, New York.
     ...Report on audit of accounts for the year 1913.
New York, 1913.   v   4°.

     . New York City.—Safety deposit   companies.
N. Y. P. L.   May 24, 1922.

   NL 0375767   NN

Lincoln Safe Deposit Company, *New York.*
     The tax on your income. [Synopsis of that part of the
federal income tax law affecting individuals, with data from the
rules and regulations of the Treasury Department.]   New York
[1913].   16 p.   8°.

     Title from cover.

     1. Income tax, U. S., 1913.
N. Y. P. L.   April 23, 1914.

   NL 0375768   NN

Lincoln school, *New York*
     see
Columbia university. *Teachers college. Lincoln school.*

Lincoln school, *Wauwatosa, Wis.*
     see
Wauwatosa, Wis. Lincoln school.

VOLUME 334

Lincoln school curriculum studies.

See

Columbia university. Teachers college. Lincoln school.
...Lincoln school curriculum studies.

379.782
L838*l*

Lincoln School District. Board of Education.
Lincoln looks ahead; general report of
the co-operative study of the Lincoln
schools, [by] Clyde M. Hill and S.M. Brownell. [Lincoln, cl947]
viii, 102p. illus. 28cm.
"The Report of the co-operative study of
the Lincoln schools ... is summarized in
Lincoln looks ahead."—p.iv.
"This summary of the Report [...] was prepared by Francis H. Horn."—p.[vi]
1. Lincoln, Neb. - Public schools. I.
Hill, Clyde Milton, 1886-   II. Brownell,
Samuel Miller, 1900-   III. Horn,
Francis H. IV.   Title. V. Title: A
cooperative   study of the Lincoln
schools.

NL 0375772   TxU NcU IaU CU TU

Lincoln School District. *Board of Education.*
Report of the co-operative study of the Lincoln schools,
1945-1946 [by] Clyde M. Hill and S. M. Brownell, directors of
the study. [Lincoln, 1947]
xiv, 867 p. fold. maps, diagrs. 24 cm.
On cover: A cooperative study of the public schools, Lincoln, Nebraska.
1. Lincoln, Neb.—Public schools.   I. Hill, Clyde Milton, 1886-
II. Brownell, Samuel Miller, 1900-   III. Title: A cooperative study of
the public schools, Lincoln, Nebraska.
LA324.L5L5   379.782   47-6337*

NL 0375773   DLC MiD WaTC OrSaW OrU ICU PPPL NBuC NIC N

Hist.
WY   Lincoln School for Nurses, New York
19   Lincoln School for Nurses; on the occasion
L739S   of its 100th anniversary invites the public
1939   to review the growth in spirit and accom-
        plishment, which has brought "The Society
        for the Relief of Worthy, Aged, Indigent
        Colored Persons" of 1839 to its present-
        day organization and public service.
        [New York, 1939?]
        [12] p. illus. 20 1/2 cm.
        1. Schools, Nursing - hist. - New York
        City.

NL 0375774   WU-M

Lincoln school of commerce, Lincoln, Neb.
Marti, David Benjamin, 1877-   comp.
Dictionary of money and market terms, issued by the Lin-
coln school of commerce, Lincoln, Nebraska. Compiled by
D. B. Marti ... [Lincoln, Neb.] *1934.
102p.

Lincoln school of Teachers college, N.Y.
see Columbia university. Teachers college,
Lincoln School.

Lincoln school supply company
see Stephenson School Supply Co.,
Lincoln, Neb.

E457
.L75   [Lincoln scrap book. Mounted newspaper clippings
        relating to Lincoln].

NL 0375778   DLC

... The Lincoln series of self-teaching readers, on the
German reproductive system, as practised in the best
Prussian schools. No. 1–   ... By a teacher.
Philadelphia, Merrihew & son, 1865
v. illus. 18¼ᶜᵐ.
At head of title: Lincoln series, no. 1.
Also issued under title: The Philadelphia series of self-teaching read-
ers ...

1. Readers and speakers—1800-1870.   I. Merrihew & son, Philadelphia.
                                                12-6776
Library of Congress   PE1119.A1L65

NL 0375779   DLC

Lincoln settlement association.   The Lincoln
settlement.   [B'klyn]1915. 8p.

NL 0375780   NBLiHi

Lincoln sheet music check list.   [Box 1110]
Fort Wayne, Ind., Lincolniana publishers cl940.
[12] p.

NL 0375781   Or

The Lincoln shrine, Redlands: California: an
account of its conception, execution, and the
works of art which it contains.   Dedicated
February 12, 1952. [Los Angeles, Calif. Printed
by Bruce Mc Callister, February, 1952]
2 p. 1., 15, [1] p. 26 1|2 cm.
"The Shrine was presented to the city of Redlands by Mr. and Mrs. Robert Watchorn, who built
it to honor Lincoln and ...also in memory of
their son Emory Ewart Watchorn." cf. p. 1.

NL 0375782   CSmH ICU RPB WHi NNC

Lincoln shrine stands at Hodgenville, Ky. Illinois
central magazine, February, 1922, p. 13-16.

NL 0375783   MiKW

Lincoln society of Peekskill, N. Y.
Lincoln in Peekskill; the Lincoln exedra, the Lincoln memorial in books, exercises at the dedication of the Lincoln
memorial in Peekskill, October 6, 1925, in commemoration of
the visit of Abraham Lincoln to Peekskill, February 19, 1861.
[Peekskill; The Lincoln society in Peekskill [1926]
cover-title, 22 p. illus. (incl. ports.) 23ᶜᵐ.

1. Peekskill, N. Y. Lincoln memorial. 2. Lincoln, Abraham, pres.
U. S.—Anniversaries, etc.
Library of Congress   F129.P37L5
                                                27-1137

NL 0375784   DLC

Lincoln society of Peekskill, N. Y.
... Proceedings at the
annual dinner
[Peekskill] Highland Democrat co., print, *1911–
v. illus. 22½ᶜᵐ. (Publication of the Lincoln society of Peekskill,
N. Y., no.   )
Cover-title.

Library of Congress   11-7856

NL 0375785   DLC MB

Lincoln society of Peekskill, N. Y.

Anderson, Homer.
Where I saw Lincoln. Address at the sixth annual Lincoln
banquet, February 12, 1909. By Homer Anderson, first vice
president of Lincoln society, Peekskill, N. Y. (Corporal, Co.
I, 90 Reg. O. V. I.) [Peekskill, N. Y., 1909]

1.96   Lincoln Soil Conservation District, S. D.
Ad6Ze   Zephyrette. v. 1-   Canton, S. D.
          Ceased in 1944. - cf. letter 10-6-47.

NL 0375787   DNAL

A Lincoln souvenir. [Lake Geneva? Wis., The Herald?
1904]
1 l. 30½ᶜᵐ.
Caption title.
No. 2 of a volume of pamphlets lettered: Gerritt Smith to his neighbors
[etc.]

1. Lincoln, Abraham, pres. U. S.—Relics.
                                                17-12291
Library of Congress   E458.8.S65

NL 0375788   DLC

Lincoln souvenir book. One hundredth anniversary
see under [Bancroft, T.D.]

A Lincoln souvenir, compliments of the Leland
Hotel, Springfield, Illinois
see under   Lincoln, Abraham, pres. U.S.
1809-1865.

Lincoln speaks Spanish
see under [Henry, Frank E   ]

The Lincoln spelling-book
see under American tract society, Boston.

The Lincoln stabilizer.
[Cleveland, Lincoln Electric Co.]
v. in   illus., diagrs. 29 cm. 4 or 5 no. a year (irregular)
Title varies: 1932-June/July 1939, The Welder's
stabilizer.—Aug./Sept. 1939-May/July 1958, The Stabilizer.

1. Welding—Period.   I. Lincoln Electric Company.
TS227.A24   671.5205   43-21975 rev*

NL 0375793   DLC TxU IU NN

LINCOLN standard aircraft co., Lincoln, Neb.
Flight.
Author. 1926. 29p. illus. diagrs.

Cover-title.
"Aeronautical terms": p.24-25.

NL 0375794   WaS

VOLUME 334

Lincoln Standard Aircraft Corporation,
Lincoln, Nebraska

 1924 L-S-5 commercial plane, $3950.00.
Author, 1924.
 [4] p. illus.

1.Airplanes - Catalogs 2.Transport planes I.Title

NL 0375795   OrP

Lincoln State School and Colony, *Lincoln, Ill.*
see
Illinois. State School, *Lincoln.*

The Lincoln Statue at the University of Wisconsin,
erected 1909. Addresses at ceremonies of
acceptance
 see under   Lincoln Fellowship of Wisconsin.

The Lincoln story-annual 1809, 1909 [port. of
Lincoln] One Hundredth Anniversary. [cover
title].   Philadelphia, The Biddle press,
copyright 1908.
 63 leaves printed on rectos only.   illus.
4to.   In 3/4 green morocco and marbled boards
with orig. brown paper front cover bound in.
 Another issue of the Lincoln story-calendar
with quotation printed in red at foot of nearly
every leaf.
 I. Whipple, Wayne, 1856-   ed.

NL 0375798   CSmH

The Lincoln story-calendar. 1809. 1909; one hundredth
anniversary. Philadelphia, The Biddle press, '1908.
 cover-title, 64 l. illus. 27ᶜᵐ.
 "With a short story for every week ... mainly rewritten by Wayne
Whipple from his 'Story-life of Lincoln.' "

 I. Whipple, Wayne, 1856-

 8-36381

NL 0375799   DLC IU OClWHi

The Lincoln story-calendar, 1910. Philadelphia, Franklin
Print. Co. ['1909]
 [55] l. illus. 26 cm.
 Cover title.
 Includes anecdotes from W. Whipple's Heart of Abraham Lincoln,
The little life of Lincoln, and Why Lincoln loved the South.

 1. Lincoln, Abraham, Pres. U. S.—Anecdotes.   I. Whipple,
Wayne, 1856-1942, comp.
 E457.99.L472   54-49280

NL 0375800   DLC

The Lincoln story-calendar, 1911. [New York, E. P. Dutton & company, '1910]
 cover-title, 55 l. illus. 28ᶜᵐ. $1.25
 Compiled by Wayne Whipple.

 1. Lincoln, Abraham, pres. U. S., 1809-1865.   I. Whipple, Wayne,
1856-   comp.
 10-26929
 Library of Congress

NL 0375801   DLC CSmH

Lincoln studies in structural arc welding
 see under   Lincoln Electric Company.

Lincoln study club, Detroit.
 [Year book]
 v.

NL 0375803   MiD-B OClWHi

Lincoln Sunday
 see under   American missionary association.

Lincoln telephone and telegraph co., *Lincoln, Neb.*
 Practical telephony ... by the Lincoln tel. and tel. co.
Lincoln, Neb., Telephone engineering school, 1920
 v. illus., maps, diagrs. 28½ᶜᵐ.

 1. Telephone—Operators' manuals.   I. Title.
 Library of Congress   TK6163.L5   22-9063

NL 0375805   DLC

Lincoln tetralogy
 see under   Snider, Denton, Jacques, 1841-

Lincoln, the capital city of Nebraska. Lincoln, Kelley &
Philleo, 1887.
 1 sheet, fold. in 13 l. 9 x 11½ᶜᵐ.

 1. Lincoln, Neb.—Descr.—Views.
 Library of Congress   F674.L71.7   Rc-56 rev.

NL 0375807   DLC

Lincoln the friend of man. Lincoln day in the
Sunday school
 see under   American missionary association.

Lincoln the Hoosier
 see under   Indiana Lincoln Union.

Lincoln: the man ... "Navdy"
 see under   [Vanderbilt, John]

Lincoln the rebel candidate.   n. p. [1864.]   5-8 p.   8°.

 Caption-title.
 Repr.: Richmond enquirer, Sept. 5, 1864; Richmond examiner, Oct. 17, 1864.
 Bound with: Pendleton, G. H. Hear Hon. Geo. H. Pendleton.

 I. Lincoln, Abraham, 16th president   of the U. S. 2. McClellan, George
Brinton, 1826-85. 3. U. S.—Politics,   1864.
N. Y. P. L.   February 20, 1917.

NL 0375811   NN

1886   Lincoln. The tribute of a grateful race. [anon.]
 Washington Evening Star, 1886.
 13 p. 16°.   [Evening Star, April 1876]
 [Toner Excerpts]

NL 0375812   DLC

Lincoln; the youth, the man, the statesman and
the student.   n. p., n. d.
 31 p.   por.   16 cm.
 The first 6 pages contain a short life of
Lincoln, the remainder advertise the Lincoln
library, pub. by Frontier press company,
Buffalo, N. Y.

NL 0375813   RPB

LINCOLN trade review, Lincoln, Neb.
 Annual review edition, Saturday Jan.
3, 1914. The author. 1914. 48p.

NL 0375814   WaS

Lincoln Trust Company, *New York.*
 Cumulative trust estates: what they are, how
they are made, what they can do ...   New York,
The Company, [1905]
 8 p.   12°.
 Title from cover.

NL 0375815   NN

Lincoln trust company, *St. Louis.*
 United States bankruptcy law of 1898. Uniform system. Together with the general orders and forms adopted
and established by the Supreme court of the United States,
and the special rules in bankruptcy, adopted by the U. S.
district court for the eastern district of Missouri. St
Louis, Lincoln trust co. [1899]
 1 p. l., 173 p. 8°.   Mar. 23, 99-59

NL 0375816   DLC

Lincoln University, Chester co., Pa.
 Annual report of pres. 1872-

NL 0375817   NjP

Lincoln University, Chester Co., Pa.
 Biographical catalogue. 1912-
Lancaster, Pa., New Era Printing Company.
 23cm.

 "Up to and including the year 1907-08 it
was customary to print a list of the graduates
of the College and of the Theological Seminary
in the annual issues of the University catalogue."
 Title varies: 1912, Statistical catalogue
of the students of the Collegiate and Theological Depart-   ments of Lincoln University.

NL 0375818   CtY

Lincoln University, Chester Co., Pa.
 Bulletin. Published for the friends and
alumni of Lincoln everywhere.

 [Lincoln University, Pa.]
 illus. 28cm. quarterly.

NL 0375819   CtY

VOLUME 334

Lincoln university, *Chester Co., Pa.*
Catalogue of Lincoln university, Chester County, Penna. ...

Philadelphia, 18
v. plates. 21½-23½ᶜᵐ.
On cover: Lincoln university, college and Theological
seminary ...

Library of Congress   LD2851.L7   CA 10—232 Unrev'd

NL 0375820   DLC Nh CtY NjP PHi PPL

Lincoln university, Chester co.,Pa.
The Charter of Lincoln university. Original
act, April 29th, 1854, supplements, April 4th,
1866 and February 18th, 1871. ₍Pennsylvania, 1871₎
₍4₎ p.

NL 0375821   PSt

Lincoln university, Chester county, Pa.
... Class-day exercises at Lincoln university.
Class of '73. Monday, June 16th, 1873 ...
Oxford, Pa., "Press," book and job printer, 1873.
40 p. 22 cm. Orig. blue paper covers.
At head of title: Hodie mihi, cras tibi.

NL 0375822   CSmH

Lincoln university, *Chester Co., Pa.*
Four Lincoln university poets. Waring
Cuney, William Allyn Hill; Edward Silvera,
Langston Hughes. Foreword by President
William Hallock Johnson.
[Lincoln University Herald, V. 33, no. 3,
March, 1930]
16 p.

NL 0375823   TNF

Lincoln university, Chester co., Pa.
General statement. n.p., n.d.

NL 0375824   Nh

Lincoln university, Chester,co., Pa.

Van Rensselaer, Cortlandt, 1808–1860.
God glorified by Africa. An address delivered on December 31, 1856, at the opening of the Ashmun institute, near
Oxford, Pennsylvania. By C. Van Rensselaer ... Philadelphia, J. M. Wilson, 1859.

Lincoln university, Chester Co., Pa.
... Inauguration of professors! December 15th, 1874.
Oxford, Chester Co., Pa., I. T. Massey, printer, 1874.
2 p. l, 10, ₍4₎ p. 21½ᶜᵐ.
At head of title: Lincoln university.

1. Lincoln university, Chester Co., Pa. Theological dept.
E 12–732
Library, U. S. Bur. of   Education LC2851.L72A2

NL 0375826   DHEW MB

Lincoln university, *Chester Co., Pa.*
Laws of Lincoln university. ₍n. p., 1867?₎
cover-title, 7 p. 22ᶜᵐ.

CA 9–3995 Unrev'd
Library of Congress   LC2851.L675A2

NL 0375827   DLC

Lincoln University, Chester co., Pa.
Lincoln news
see under title

Lincoln university, *Chester Co., Pa.*
Lincoln university; college and theological seminary
Biographical catalogue 1918. Lancaster, Pa., Press of
the New era printing company, 1918.
2 p. l, 157 p. 23½ᶜᵐ.

1. ₍Lincoln university—Registers₎
E 18–946
Library, U. S. Bur. of   Education LC2851.L72A3

NL 0375829   DHEW

Lincoln university, *Chester Co., Pa.*
Lincoln university, Pennsylvania. Its history and
work. ₍Philadelphia, Printed by Allen, Lane & Scott,
189–?₎
32 p. 16½ᶜᵐ.

1. Lincoln university, Chester Co., Pa.
E 15–1437
Library, U. S. Bur. of   Education LC2851.L72

NL 0375830   DHEW

Lincoln University, Chester co., Pa.
The Lincolnian
see under title

Lincoln university, Chester Co., Pa.
Negro problem ... letters of Rev. James
McCosh [and others] n.p., 1879.

NL 0375832   NjP

Lincoln University, Chester co., Pa.
The revival of 1884... Lincoln
University, 1884.
4 p. O.

NL 0375833   OO

Lincoln university, Chester co., Pa.
Solution of the Negro problem; statements showing work and wants of Lincoln university. n.p.
1883.

NL 0375834   Nh

Lincoln university, Chester co., Pa.
Solution of the Negro problem; statements
showing work and wants of Lincoln university.
Cinc.,1885.

NL 0375835   Nh

Lincoln University, Chester co., Pa.
Statistical catalog of the students of
the Collegiate and Theological departments
see its Biographical catalogue.

Lincoln university, *Jefferson City, Mo.*
Annual catalogue
Jefferson City, Mo.,
v. illus., plates. 20½-22½ᶜᵐ.

Library of Congress   LC2851.L64   CA 10–5516 Unrev'd

NL 0375837   DLC MB Or PPL

Lincoln University, Jefferson City, Mo.
Archives. 1949–
[Jefferson City?]
illus. 28cm. annual.

NL 0375838   CtY

LC2851   Lincoln University, Jefferson City, Mo
L6k   A bibliography of faculty members, 1951; comp. by A. P.
1951   Marshall. [Jefferson City, Mo.] Lincoln University, Inman E.
Page Library [1951]
13 p. (Lincoln University, Jefferson City, Mo. Library.
Occasional publications, no. 5)

Cover title.

1. Lincoln University, Jefferson City, Mo. - Bibl. I. Marshall,
A   P   comp.

NL 0375839   CU

Lincoln university, *Jefferson City, Mo.*
Biennial report of Board of regents ... to the
General assembly of the state of Missouri.
Jefferson City ₍19
v. 23ᶜᵐ.

CA 20–111 Unrev'd
Library of Congress   LC2851.L638

NL 0375840   DLC Or

Lincoln university, Jefferson City, Mo.

Missouri.
Biennial reports of the Missouri normal schools and Lincoln
institute, for 1877 and 1878. Thirtieth General assembly.
Jefferson City, Carter & Regan, state printers and binders,
1879.

E. W. Johnson   Lincoln University, Jefferson City, Mo.
Collection   Bulletin.
E.
L6394   Jefferson City.
23cm.

NL 0375842   CtY

VOLUME 334

Lincoln University, Jefferson City, Mo.
Historical sketch of Lincoln Institute
see under   Foster, Richard Baxter, 1826–

E185
.5
.M62

Lincoln University, Jefferson City, Mo.
The Midwest journal. v. 1–
winter 1948–
Jefferson City, Mo., Lincoln University.

Lincoln University, *Jefferson City, Mo.*
Report and recommendations of the president of the university on the state of affairs in the institution.
₁Jefferson City₎
v.   29 cm.   annual.
Report year ends Aug. 31.

LC2851.L643   378.778   55–31835 ‡

NL   0375845   DLC

Z881
.L742

Lincoln University, Jefferson City, Mo. Library.
Lincoln's page. v. 1–   Sept. 1950–
₁Jefferson City₎ Mo., Inman E. Page Library, Lincoln University.

Lincoln University, *Jefferson City, Mo. Library.*
Occasional publication. no. ₁1₎–
Jefferson City, Mo., 1944–
no. in   v.   29 cm.

No. 1 issued without title.

Z881.J4   027.7778   57–44787

NL   0375847   DLC MoS AAP TxU NN

Lincoln University, *Jefferson City, Mo. Library.*
Report of the University librarian.
₁Jefferson City₎
v.   28 cm.   annual.
Report year ends June 30.

Z733.J4L54   027.7778   51–61814 ‡

NL   0375848   DLC LU

027.7
L63s

Lincoln University, Jefferson City,
Missouri. Library.
Staff manual, compiled by the Library Staff. Editors: Dudley Randall, Chairman, Catharine Long ₁and others₎
1st ed.   Jefferson City, Mo., 1953.
80 p. 29cm.

1. Libraries, University and college. 2. Libraries--Staff manuals.

NL   0375849   LU MiU NNC IU TxU DCU

Lincoln University, *Jefferson City, Mo. School of Journalism.*
Bibliography of the Negro press.   Jefferson City ₁194–₎
11 p.   28 cm.
Caption title.

1. Negro press—Bibl.

Z6951.L5   016.325260973   48–33181*

NL   0375850   DLC

Lincoln University, Jefferson City, Mo. School of Journalism.
Journalism series.

NL   0375851   MdBJ NN

Lincoln university, Lincoln, Ill.
see
Lincoln college, Lincoln, Ill.

Lincoln university, Lincoln university, Pa.
see
Lincoln University, Chester co., Pa.

Lincoln university, Oxford, Pa.
see
Lincoln university, Chester Co., Pa.

Lincoln University, St. Louis, Mo. School of
Law.
Announcements.

St. Louis, Mo.
In   v.

At head of title: Lincoln University bulletin

NL   0375855   NNC-L ViU-L

Lincoln University, San Francisco, Calif.
Law School.
₁Announcements₎

San Francisco, Calif.
In   v.

called College of Law.

NL   0375856   NNC-L

Lincoln verse, story and essay ...
see under   Mearns, Hughes, 1875–

LINCOLN versus Lenin; the conflict of our age. (IN:
°Jacob Boehme society. Quarterly. Woodside, N.Y. 28cm. v. 1,
no. 2 (winter, 1952-53) p. [23]-32. ports.)

1. Lincoln, Abraham, 16 pres.   U.S.   2. Lenin, Vladimir,
Il'ich. 1870-1924.

NL   0375858   NN

Lincoln voters' league.
First annual meeting of the Lincoln voters' league held Kalamazoo, Mich., May 16-18, 1910 in commemoration of the fiftieth anniversary of the nomination of Abraham Lincoln to the presidency of the United States.   ₁n.p.,
1910?₎
23 p.   23.5 cm.

NL   0375859   MiU-C

The Lincoln way; a guide for those who have the will to self-improvement. . Two thousand thought-stimulating questions selected from about three hundred thousand which are answered by the Lincoln library of essential information. Buffalo, N. Y., The Frontier Press Company, ₁°1928₎.
96 p.   24ᶜᵐ.

NL   0375860   ICJ OO ICRL

Lincoln Woman's Club.
Lincoln, Illinois, 1903; views of streets, residences, State institutions, public buildings, Chautauqua grounds ₁and₎ portraits of citizens. ₁Lincoln, 1903?₎
1 v.   (illus., ports.)   15 x 24 cm.

1. Lincoln, Ill.—Descr.—Views.

F549.L7L5   54–49289

NL   0375861   DLC IEdS

The Lincoln year of the Atlantic monthly, a "scrap" book. ₁Boston₎ 1929.
facsim.: ₁46₎ p.   illus.   27½ x 23½ᶜᵐ.

A facsimile of mounted newspapers clippings and ms. t.-p.
Criticism of a serial entitled "Lincoln the lover" by Wilma Frances Minor, purporting to contain hitherto unpublished letters of Lincoln to Ann Rutledge and other friends, and from Ann to Lincoln. Three installments of this serial appeared in the Atlantic monthly, Dec. 1928-Feb. 1929.
One of 6 photostat copies issued by the Massachusetts historical society.

1. Minor, Wilma Frances. Lincoln the lover. 2. Lincoln, Abraham, pres. U. S., 1809-1865. 3. The Atlantic monthly.   I. Massachusetts historical society.

Library of Congress   E457.35.M687   29–18814

NL   0375862   DLC NN

Lincolne, Abraham.
The Australasian farmer's guide. By Abraham Lincolne...
Melbourne: Walker, May and Co., 1869.   viii, 10–184 p.   12°.

1. Agriculture, Australasia.
N. Y. P. L.   April 1, 1924.

NL   0375863   NN CSt

Lincolne, William, of Halesworth, Sussex.
COLLECTIONS and recollections of the late Mr. William Lincolne, etc. By one of their sons. London, 1848.

sm. 8°.

NL   0375864   MH

A Lincolne Shire gentleman.
The Copy of a Letter From a Lincolne Shire Gentleman
see under title

VOLUME 334

The Lincolnian. v. 1, no. 1-10,
Nov. 1918-Dec. 1919. Detroit, Lincoln
Motor Company, 1918-19.
1 v. photostat (positive)

Monthly.

1. Detroit - Periodicals and newspapers
I. Lincoln Motor Company

NL 0375866   MiD

The Lincolnian.

J W. Johnson
Collection
AA
L6388

Lincoln University,Pa.
illus. 45cm.

Published by the students of Lincoln
University.

NL 0375867   CtY

The Lincolnian; published by the students of the
Lincoln high school, Tacoma, Wash. Sept. 1917-
June 1922. v. 1-5; v. 1 (1923) -date.
Published monthly throughout the school
year until 1922, afterwards one issue a year,
in June.
No volume numbers assigned after 1927.
1923-24 both assigned v. 1; 1925-27, v. 3-5.
Title varies slightly with new ser.

NL 0375868   WaT

Lincolniana book plates and collections
see under   Fowler, Alfred, 1889-   ed.

Lincolniana. Containing Bancrofts memorial
address, letters, newspaper cuttings,etc.
T921   n.p.   4°
.1736   Portraits and plates.

NL 0375870   PBL

Lincolniana. In memoriam. Boston, W. V. **Spencer.**
1865.
vi p. 1 l, 346 p. 24½ x 19ᶜᵐ.
"Only 250 copies printed." This copy not numbered.
₍"Bibliographical list of books and pamphlets; containing sermons, ora-
dions, eulogies, poems, or other papers relating to the assassination, death,
and funeral obequies of Abraham Lincoln": p. ₍334₎-346.
CONTENTS.—Sermons.—Eulogies, speeches, and letters.—Appendix.

1. Lincoln, Abraham, pres. U. S.—Addresses, sermons etc. 2. Lincoln,
Abraham, pres. U. S.—Bibl.   I. Spencer, William V., Boston, pub.

16-9236

Library of Congress   E457.8.A15

NjP ViU MiU-C NN MB PBL
NL 0375871   DLC CaBVaU NIC DI N CtY PHi PPPrHi OClWHi

Lincolniana Publishers, Fort Wayne, Indiana.
Lincoln sheet music check list
see under title

Lincolniana Publishers, Fort Wayne, Indiana.   *"20th".50.525.310
Manuscript reproduction series. No. 1.
— *Photostat facsimile.* Fort Wayne, Ind. [1933.] 1 v. 11 × 8½ inches.

D3876 — T r. — Manuscripts. Facsimiles. English.

NL 0375873   MB

Lincolniensis, Robertus
see   Grosseteste, Robert, bp. of Lincoln,
1175?-1253.

Lincoln's abolitionism.

See *under*

₍Hill, John₎ of Petersburg, Ill.

... Lincoln's birthday a holiday in the District
of Columbia
see under   U.S. Congress. House. Committee on the District of Columbia.

Lincoln's birthday; exercises for the schoolroom
see under   Educational publishing company.

Lincoln's earliest home
see under   ₍Cutler, John C

Lincoln's Emancipation proclamation. Original
manuscript copy of the first draft of the
Emancipation proclamation presented to
New York avenue Presbyterian church,
Washington, D.C.
see   Lincoln, Abraham, pres. U.S., 1809-
1865.
Emancipation proclamation ... 1951.

Lincoln's failures. Evanston, Ill., C. H. McIntire ₍n. d.₎
broadside. 28 x 18 cm.

1. Lincoln, Abraham, Pres. U. S., 1809-1865.   I. McIntire, Christian Harry.

E457.2.L84   57-54528

NL 0375880   DLC

Lincoln's favorite hymn; Oh, why should the
spirit of mortal be proud
see   [Knox, William] 1789-1825.
Oh, why should the spirit of mortal be proud?
1924.

Lincoln 's Home Cycle Co., Springfield,Ill.
Lincoln's Home Cycle company. H.W.
Rokker, proprietor. Springfield, Ill, 1897.
16 p. illus. 19 1/2cm.

Catalog.

NL 0375882   OClWHi

Lincoln's home village rebuilt in memoriam.
₍New York Times book review and magazine,
Feb. 6, 1921.

NL 0375883   OClWHi

Lincoln's Industrial-commercial reference
see   Lincoln, Edwin Stoddard, 1885-
Industrial-commercial electrical reference.

Lincoln's Inn, London.
A guide to Lincoln's Inn. ₍London,
Wildy, 1953.
24 p. illus. 12 x 17 cm.

Lw 1. Inns of court, London. I. & Lw I.
Title.

NL 0375885   N-L

Lincoln's Inn,London.
The honourable society of Lincoln's Inn
Quincentenary celebration,MDCCCCXXII.
₍London, H.& K.,ltd., 1922₎
51 p.incl.plates.   27½ᶜᵈ.
Half-title: 1422 to 1922. Record of the
celebrations commemorating the growth and
prosperity of the society during five hundred years in one abode.

NL 0375886   MiU-L CtY MiU

TREASURE
ROOM

Lincoln's Inn, London
Notes from a Catalogue of the paintings,
framed drawings, prints and photographs in
the possession of the Hon. Society of
Lincoln's Inn. ₍London? 18--₎

42 l. 33cm.

Manuscript.

NL 0375887   MH-L

Lincoln's Inn, *London.*
The records of the honorable society of Lincoln's Inn ...
Admissions from A. D. 1420 to ₍A. D. 1893, and chapel registers₎
... ₍London₎ Lincoln's Inn ₍Printed by H. S. Cartwright₎
1896.
2 v. 26ᶜᵐ.
Edited by W. Paley Baildon. *cf.* Pref.
CONTENTS.—v. 1. 1420-1799.—v. 2. 1800-1893, and chapel registers

1. Lawyers—Gt. Brit. 2. Registers of births, etc.—London.   I. Baildon, William Paley, 1859-1924, ed. II. Title.

31-16311

NL 0375888   DLC WaU OU CSt-L MB IaU PU NN NcD CtY

VOLUME 334

Lincoln's Inn, *London.*
The records of the honorable society of Lincoln's Inn. The Black books ... ₁London₁ Lincoln's Inn ₁Printed by H. S. Cartwright₁ 1897–1902.
4 v. fold. fronts., illus., plates, plans. 26ᶜᵐ.
Edited by W. P. Baildon. *cf.* Prefaces signed : James Douglas Walker.
CONTENTS.—v. 1. 1422–1586.—v. 2. 1586–1660.—v. 3. 1660–1775.—v. 4. 1776–1845. Calls to the bar, 1776 to 1845. The site of Lincoln's Inn, by W. P. Baildon. Maps and plans. A catalogue of portraits. List of painters, and engravers. Catalogue of plate. The heraldry of Lincoln's Inn. Appendix.
1. Lawyers—Gt. Brit. ₁1. Attorneys—Gt. Brit.₁ 2. London—Hist.—Sources. I. Baildon, William Paley, 1859–1924, ed. II. Walker, James Douglas, 1841–1920. III. Title. IV. Title: Black books.
1–4143 Revised
Library of Congress   DA687.L7L7
——— Copy 2.   ₁r31e2₁

NcD PP CtY
NL 0375889   DLC CaBVaU WaU-L PU-L NN CSt-L WaU MiEM

Lincoln's Inn, London.
The study and practice of the law, considered in their various relations to society, in a series of letters
see under   [Raithby, John] 1766–1826.

Lincoln's Inn, *London. Library.*
Catalogue of books on foreign law, founded on the collection presented by Charles Purton Cooper, esq., to the Society of Lincoln's Inn. Laws and jurisprudence of France. ₁Ancient part₁ London, Printed by C. Roworth and sons, 1849.
xv, 435, ₁1₁ p. 26½ᶜᵐ.
Preface signed : F. W. H. ₁i. e. Frederick William Halfpenny₁
"Ancient part extending from the year 400 to the year 1789."
No more published.
1. Law—France—Bibl.—Catalogs. I. Cooper, Charles Purton, 1793–1873. II. Halfpenny, Frederick William.
18–10930
Library of Congress   Z6458.F8L6

NL 0375891   DLC WaU-L KU MH CtY PPB

Lincoln's Inn, *London. Library.*
A catalogue of pamphlets, tracts, proclamations, speeches, sermons, trials, petitions from 1506 to 1700 in the library of the honourable society of Lincoln's Inn. London, Printed at the Chiswick press for the honourable society of Lincoln's Inn, 1908.
xii, 481, ₁1₁ p. 26½ᶜᵐ.
Compiled by W. P. Baildon.
Titles arranged chronologically, with index of persons and places, and index of subjects.
1. Gt. Brit.—Hist.—Tudors, 1485–1603—Bibl. 2. Gt. Brit.—Hist.—Stuarts, 1603–1714—Bibl. 3. Gt. Brit.—Pol. & govt. —1485–1603—Bibl. 4. Gt. Brit.—Pol. & govt.—1603–1714—Bibl. 5. Law—Gt. Brit.—Bibl. 6. Pamphlets—Bibl.   I. Baildon, William Paley.
9–7317
Library of Congress   Z2018.L54

NL 0375892   DLC WaU-L MWA DFo NjR CtY ICJ

Lincoln's inn, *London. Library.*
A catalogue of the manuscripts in the library of the honourable society of Lincoln's inn. By the Rev. Joseph Hunter, F. S. A. London ₁Printed by Eyre and Spottiswoode₁ 1838.
xviii, 157, ₁1₁ p. 26½ x 16ᶜᵐ.
"Prepared under the direction of the honourable Board of commissioners on the public records ... The catalogue has been already printed in the appendix to the report which the commissioners on records made to His late Majesty at the beginning of the last year."—Pref.
1. Manuscripts. Gt. Brit.—Catalogs. 2. Law—Gt. Brit.—Manuscripts. 3. Gt. Brit.—Hist.—Sources—Bibl.   I. Hunter, Joseph, 1783–1861. II. Gt. Brit. Record commission.
15–10124
Library of Congress   Z6621.L83

NL 0375893   DLC NNGr MH PPL

Lincoln's Inn, *London. Library.*
A catalogue of the printed books, to which is prefixed a short account of the manuscripts, in the library of Lincoln's Inn. London, Printed by G. Davidson, 1835.
3 p. l., 215, ₁1₁ p. 26½ᶜᵐ.
Interleaved.

1. Law—Bibl.—Catalogs. 2. Gt. Brit.—Hist.—Bibl.—Catalogs.
36–1530
Library of Congress   Z6459.L85
          ₁2₁   018.1

NL 0375894   DLC MH PBm PPL

Lincoln's Inn, *London. Library.*
Catalogue of the printed books in the library of the Hon. society of Lincoln's Inn. By William H. Spilsbury, librarian ... London, Printed for the Society by C. Roworth & sons, 1859.
viii, 970 p., 1 l. 24ᶜᵐ.
——— ... Supplementary volume, containing the additions from 1859–1890. By John Nicholson, librarian. London, Printed for the Society, by C. F. Roworth, 1890.
2 p. l., 467, ₁1₁ p. 25ᶜᵐ.
1. Law—Bibl.—Catalogs. 2. Gt. Brit.—Hist.—Bibl.—Catalogs.   I. Spilsbury, William Holden, 1803–1877. II. Nicholson, John, 1829 or 30–1894.
18–10940-1
Library of Congress   Z6459.L85

NL 0375895   DLC PPB NIC WaU-L PU-L CU CtY NcD MH IEN

Lincoln's Inn, London. Library.
Catalogue of the printed books in the library of the Hon. society of Lincoln's Inn. By William H. Spilsbury, librarian ... Supplement ₁no. 1– April 1859–[May 1881. London, C. F. Roworth, 1862–81]
pts. in   v.   25 cm.

NL 0375896   NIC MH-L

Lincoln's inn, *London. Library.*
Specimen of a catalogue of the books on foreign law lately presented by Charles Purton Cooper, esq., to the Society of Lincoln's inn. London, C. Roworth and sons, 1847.
1 p. l., vi, 80 p. 25ᶜᵐ.
A selection of Spanish titles, including desiderata, submitted by the compiler, F. W. Halfpenny, for approval or modification.
1. Law—Spain—Bibl.   I. Cooper, Charles Purton, 1793–1873. II. Halfpenny, F. W.
3–19498
Library of Congress   Z6458.S7L7

NL 0375897   DLC MB NjP CtY MeB NN

Lincoln's Inn, London. Library.
Z6620   Hunter, Joseph, 1783–1861, *comp.*
.G7H8   Three catalogues; describing the contents of the Red book of the Exchequer, of the Dodsworth manuscripts in the Bodleian library, and of the manuscripts in the library of the honourable society of Lincoln's Inn. By the Rev. Joseph Hunter, F. S. A. London, Pickering, 1838.

Lincoln's Inn Fields theatre.
TS   At the theatre in Lincolns-Inn-Fields.
1690   Tuesday, June[!] the fifth, 1716. A comedy
120   call'd, Old batchelor. For the benefit of
           Lovelace and White, box-keepers. Box.
           [London, 1716]
broadside. 13.9x16.8cm., in folder 15.5cm.
Printed within ornamental border.
A ticket to the performance of the Congreve play.
Unbound, as issued; in half morocco folder.

NL 0375899   MH

Wk   The LINCOLN'S-INN 'squire; or The Protestant
A100   turn'd papist. A new ballad. To the tune of,
+736l   The king and the abbot of Canterbury.
          London₁Printed for James Moore,and sold by
          the Booksellers and Pamphletsellers of London
          and Westminster.[1736?] 7p. 32cm.
          Attributed to Lord Hervey in the Wrenn catalogue, where it is dated 1736.

NL 0375900   TxU OCU

Lincoln's last journey; hitherto unpublished pictures which have just come to light. ₁n. p., 19—₁
1 v.   29 cm.
A scrapbook containing 9 photos, reproduced by courtesy of Historical Pictures, Springfield, Ill., accompanied by title and captions clipped from an unidentified publication of 1937. Includes also, a photostat copy (positive) of "Obsequies of President Lincoln; order of funeral procession."
1. Lincoln, Abraham, Pres. U. S.—Funeral journey to Springfield.
E457.52.L77   54–1592

NL 0375901   DLC

Lincoln's last official letter found by Attorney General Daugherty....
₁Typescript copy of newspaper article, for "release", Feb. 18, 1923₁

NL 0375902   OC1WHi

Lincoln's page. v. 1–   Sept. 1950–
₁Jefferson City₁ Mo., Inman E. Page Library, Lincoln University.
v. in   illus. 29–32 cm.
Frequency varies.
Numbering irregular : v. 1, no. 3 repeated.

I. Lincoln University, Jefferson City, Mo.   Library.
Z881.L742   027.7778551   60–41449

NL 0375903   DLC

f973.7   Lincoln's re-election. Photographic reproduc-
L63Mℓinr   tions of pages, selected by J. G. Randall,
fascim.   from Albany, Baltimore, Boston, Buffalo,
           Philadelphia and Washington newspapers, in
           the Library of Congress.
           36ℓ.
The reproductions, arranged in chronological order (July 16–Sept.29,1864) show usually the first page, sometimes another page, and, occasionally, two pages from the Albany journal, Aug.12, Sept.15; Albany evening journal, Aug.
13, Sept.15; Baltimore daily gazette, Aug.23, 26, 27; Boston daily advertiser, Aug.27 (p.₁1₁-₁2₁) 31, Sept.14, 16, 29(two pages); Commercial advertiser, Buffalo, Aug.30, Sept.15; Daily constitutional union, Washington, July 16, Aug.10, 13, 15(p.₁1₁-₁2₁), 16, 20; Morning express, Buffalo, July 27, Aug.2, 24, 26, 29, Sept.15; The Press, Philadelphia, Aug.17, 19; The Sun, Baltimore, Aug.20, 30, 31, Sept.14, 16.

NL 0375905   IU

Lincoln's royal reception. (In, War lyrics and songs of the South. London, 1866, p. 165–167)

NL 0375906   RPB

Lincoln's Soldiers' and Sailors' Monumental Association.
Lincoln monument association. An appeal to the soldiers and sailors of the United States. [Springfield?Ill., 1865]
folder, [2] L.   26cm.
Caption title.
The second leaf is blank for names of subscribers.
Signed by the Executive Committee, Geo. H. Hand, chairman [and others].

NL 0375907   IHi

VOLUME 334

Lincoln's spirituality.
   (In Magazine of history, with notes and
queries. Tarrytown, N.Y., 1922. 26.5 cm.
Extra number, no. 85 (v. 22, no. 1) p. 51-52)

NL   0375908   RPB

Lincoln's Thanksgiving hymn
   see under   [Lincoln Memorial University,
Harrogate, Tenn. Dept. of Lincolniana]

... Lincoln's treatment of Gen. Grant. [New York, 1864]
   8 p.   23⁻.
   At head of title: Document no. 12. Sold at 13 Park row, and at all
Democratic newspaper offices.
   Democratic campaign document. Contains also: Mr. Lincoln's treat-
ment of Gen. McClellan.—The taint of disunion.

Library of Congress   CA 7-1514 Unrev'd

NL   0375910   DLC TxU NIC CtY MB MBC NNC OCIWHi

Lincoln's triplet epigram; three witnesses
who heard it used by it's author ...
   n.p., n.d.
      19, [1] p.   16mo.

NL   0375911   RPB

Lincoln's views; the political opinions in the
United States, in 1860 and 1790. ...
September, 1882.
      88 p.   8vo.

NL   0375912   RPB

Lincolnshire, Charles Robert Wynn-Carrington, marquis
   of, 1843-1928.
   see
   Carrington, Charles Robert Wynn-Carrington, 1st
   earl, 1843-1928.

Case
G   Lincolnshire, Eng.
4531
.24   A breefe relation by the commoners in Lincolnshire, of their legall interest, and that
   nothing of interest the undertakers have in law.
   [London, 1651?]   p.17-20.

      Binder's title: Draining of the fens.
      Caption title.
      A fragment.

NL   0375914   ICN

---

*pEB65   Lincolnshire, Eng.
16385   A copy of the petition delivered to the King
642hb   at Newark, in His Majesties passage to York, by
   divers of the inhabitants of the county of
   Lincoln.
      London, Printed for John Franke, 1641[1642].

      broadside. 33.5x23.5cm.
      Steele 2050 (England).
      Petition presented 17 March 1642; first
   printed at York with title: The humble petition
   of His Majesties loyall subjects ...

NL   0375915   MH

Lincolnshire, Eng.
   The declaration and protestation of divers
the knights, gentry, freeholders, and others of
the foresaid county, whose names are
subscribed. To the Right Honorable Francis,
lord Willoughby, lord lievtenant of the county of
Lincolne, and of the city of the county of
Lincolne
   see under title

---

*pEB65   Lincolnshire, Eng.
16385   The declaration of the gentry, ministers,
660d   free-holders of the county and citty of
   Lincolne.
      [London] Printed for H.M. at the Princes Armes
   in Chancery-lane, 1659[1660]

      broadside. 34x25.5cm.
      Proposing the assembling of a full and free
   Parliament.

NL   0375917   MH CtY

Case
G   Lincolnshire, Eng.
4531
.24   ...Here is abbreviated the cause now depending
   in the Parliament betwixt the vndertakers, and
   the owners, and commoners in the fenns in Lin-
   colnshire/wherein the late Earle of Lindsey was
   vndertaker...   [London? 1650?]   10p.

      Binder's title: Draining of the fens.
      Caption title.

NL   0375918   ICN

---

*EO65   Lincolnshire, Eng.
16385   The hvmble petition of divers baronets,
642h2b   knights, esqviers, gentlemen, clergy, and free-
   holders of the covnty of Lincolne: to the Right
   Honorable the House of commons, now in the high
   court of Parliament assembled. With a letter
   sent to Master Speaker, from the knights,
   esquiers, gentry, and freeholders of the same
   county. For the presenting of their petition to
   the Honourable House of commons, now in Parliament assembled.
      [London] First printed at Yorke, and now re-
   printed for Iohn   Thomas, 1642. August 1.

      8p. 18.5cm.
      A pro-royalist petition, originally printed
   as a broadside (Steele 2225, England).

NL   0375920   MH CtY

Lincolnshire, Eng.
   Lincolnshire parish registers. Marriages
      see under   Phillimore, William Phillimore
   Watts, 1853-1913, ed.

Lincolnshire, *Eng.*
   Lincolnshire records. Abstracts of final concords, temp.
Richard I., John, and Henry III ...
London, Spottiswoode & co., printers, 1896
      v. 22¹⁻.
   Privately printed.
   "This, the first volume of Lincolnshire records preserved at the Public
record office ever printed, is published with the ... help of the Lincoln-
shire architectural and archaeological society ... the whole merit of the
work belongs to Mr. W. Boyd ... I am responsible ... for the index ..."—
Pref., signed: W. O. Massingberd.
   I. Lincolnshire, Eng.—Antiq.   I. Gt. Brit. Public record office.
II. Architectural and archaeological society of the counties of Lincoln and
Nottingham. III. Boyd, W. IV. Massingberd, William Oswald.

                         CA 10-5485 Unrev'd
Library of Congress   DA670.L7L715

NL   0375922   DLC FU CtY PU-L

Lincolnshire, Eng.
   Poll for the election of the shire for the county
of Lincoln taken June 25, 26, & 27, 1818. With the
speeches delivered from the hustings on the occasion; and an alphabetical list of all the towns in the
county ... with the population of each ... also a
summary of the returns of that act, as far as relates
to the county of Lincoln.   Lincoln, Brooke, 1818.
      179 p.   O.

NL   0375923   NcD

Lincolnshire, Eng.
   Post office directory of Lincolnshire
      see under title

---

*EO65   Lincolnshire, Eng.
16385   The protestation and declaration of divers
643p   knights, gentlemen, esquires, and free-holders
   of the counties of Lincolne and Nottingham:
   against the unjust oppressions and inhumane
   proceedings of William earle of New-castle and
   his Cavaleers: wherein they doe declare themselves enemies to all such violent courses,
   and protest to hazzard their lives and estates
   in defense of his Majesty, the common-wealth,
   and the high court of Parliament.
      The true copy, sent to be printed at London,
   anno Dom. 1643.
      8p.   18.5cm.
      Title vignette.

NL   0375925   MH

Lincolnshire, England.
   Records of some sessions of the peace in
   Lincolnshire, 1381-1396

   see under

   Gt. Brit. Court of Quarter Sessions of the
   Peace (Lincolnshire)

Case
G   Lincolnshire, Eng.
4531
.24   A relation of the proceedings & causes of complaint, between the vndertakers with the Earle of
   Lindsey, in the levell of fenns in Lincolnshire
   betwixt Bourne and Kime Eae, and the owners and
   commoners there.   [London? 1649?]   16p.

      Binder's title: Draining of the fens.
      Caption title.

NL   0375927   ICN

942.062   Lincolnshire, Eng.
C499   To the Kings Most Excellent Majestie. The hum-
v.2   ble petition of His Majesties loving subjects in
   the countie of Lincolne: presented to him at
   Shrewsbury, October 2. Together with His Majesties answer to the said petition.   London,
   Printed for Joseph Horton, Octob. 14, 1642.
      1 p.l., 6p.   19cm.
      [Civil war declarations, ordinances, petitions,
   etc., 1641-49. v.2, no.42]

      1. Great Britain--Hist.--Civil war, 1642-1649--
   Sources.

NL   0375928   IU CtY

---

*pEB65   Lincolnshire, Eng.
16385   To the Right Honourable, Francis lord
642t   VVilloughby, lord lievtenant of the county of
   Lincolne, and Lincolneshiere. The declaration
   and protestation of divers of the knights,
   gentry, freeholders and others of the foresaid
   counties /...
      July 19. London, Printed for Joseph Hunscott,
   1642.

      broadside. 33x24cm.

NL   0375929   MH

VOLUME 334

Lincolnshire, Eng.
*EB65   To the Right Honourable, the Lords and Commons
L6385   assembled in Parliament: the humble petition of
644t   the inhabitants in the county of Lincoln.
[London,1644]

broadside. 26x15.5cm.
Imperfect: left edge cropped.

NL 0375930   MH

Broadside
G   Lincolnshire, Eng.
4548   To the supream authority of the nation, in
.51   Parliament assembled. The humble petition of
divers freemen of England...inhabitants in the
county of Lincoln, in the behalf of themselves
and others, the lords, owners, and commoners of,
and in the fennes...in the said county lying between Bourn and Kyme. [London?1650?]   36x
26cm.

Broadside.

NL 0375931   ICN

Lincolnshire, Eng.
Two petitions presented to the supreme
authority of the nation
see under   [Lilburne, John] 1614?-1657.

Lincolnshire, Eng.
see also its   Administrative division,
Holland, Parts of, Eng.

DA670   Lincolnshire, Eng. Archives Committee.
L89A2   Archivists' report. 1948/49-

[Lincoln?]
v. in

1955/56 also numbered 7-

NL 0375934   CU ICN CLU IEG

281.359
L63   Lincolnshire, Eng. Chamber of agriculture.
...Wheat act, 1932. Record. [London,
W.J.Lloyd & co., ltd., printers, 1939]
19 p.   22cm.

At head of title: Lincolnshire Chamber of
agriculture.

NL 0375935   DNAL

Lincolnshire, Eng. Committee for the militia.
*pEB65   The copy of a letter sent from the Committee
L6385   at Lincoln, to the House of commons, directed to
642c   the speaker of the said House, and subscribed
with the names of the said Committee.
June 6. London,Printed for Joseph Hunscott.
1642.

broadside. 34x24cm.
Steele 2167 (England).

NL 0375936   MH

Lincolnshire, England - County council.
Lincolnshire ... official handbook.
2d. ed. Cheltenham, Ed.J.Burrow,n.d.
55p.illus.map,O.

NL 0375937   CaBViP

Lincolnshire; a county of infinite charm
see under   [Mee, Arthur] 1875-1943.

Lincolnshire and Nottinghamshire architectural and
archæological society
see
Architectural and archæological society of the county of
Lincoln.

Lincolnshire and Nottinghamshire Church Union.
Proceedings of a General Meeting, held ...
Jan. 15th, 1852.   Retford, 1852.
8 p. 8°. [In v. 795, College Pamphlets]

NL 0375940   CtY

Lincolnshire architectural and archæological society
see
Architectural and archæological society of the county of
Lincoln.

Lincolnshire architectural society
see
Architectural and archæological society of the county of
Lincoln.

463.38
L63   Lincolnshire Beekeepers' Association.
The relationship of honeybees and seed
production. [Heckington, Lincolnshire
Co., Eng.] Lincolnshire Seed Growers'
Association [1951?]
[8] p.

1. Fertilization of plants by insects.
I. Lincolnshire Seed Growers' Association.

NL 0375943   DNAL

424.9
L63   Lincolnshire Beekeepers' Association.
Year book.
[Leadenham (Lincs.) Eng.,

1. Apiculture. Societies.

NL 0375944   DNAL

Lincolnshire churches. An account of the churches
in the division of Holland
see under   [Lewin, Stephen]

Lincolnshire curly-coated pig breeders' association, Inc.
The herd book of Lincolnshire curly-
coated pigs ... v. 1-   1907-   Sleaford,
F. Sewards, [1907-   ]
v.

NL 0375946   OU

Lincolnshire curly-coated pigs breeders' association.
The Lincolnshire curly coated pig. [1909?]

NL 0375947   DNAL

Lincolnshire gentry in 1635. n. imp.
5 p.

NL 0375948   MiD-B

A Lincolnshire grasier.
The grasier's complaint and petition for redress
1726.
see under title.

A Lincolnshire grazier.
The complete grazier
see under   Horne, Thomas Hartwell, 1780-1862.

The LINCOLNSHIRE historian. v. [1]-2; 1947-65.
Lincoln.   2v. illus., plates. maps(part fold.). 22cm.

Lacking: v.2, no.1, 1954.
Irregular.
Supersedes the Local historian.
Organ of the Lincolnshire local historical society.
Ceased publication with v.2. no.12. 1965.

1. Lincolnshire, Eng. --Hist. --   Per. and soc. publ. I. Lincolnshire local history society, Lin-   coln, Eng.

NL 0375951   NN IU MiU CU CLU MdBJ MH NIC CtY OCl

Lincolnshire in 1836: displayed in a series of nearly
one hundred engravings, on steel and wood; with accompanying descriptions, statistical and other important information, maps, &c. Lincoln, J. Saunders, jun., 1836.
xvi, 170, [1] p. illus., pl., fold. map. 21¾ᵐ.
Attributed to Mary Saunders, of Lincoln, by
the British Museum.

Subject entries: Lincolnshire.

Library of Congress, no.   DA670.L7L7.

NL 0375952   DLC

Lincolnshire Local History Society.
Local history, its interest and value. Pub.
and issued by the Lindsey local history society
affiliated to the Lindsey rural community
council.
Lincoln,Lincolnshire chronicle and leader,
[1930?] 31,[1]pp. 18cm.
"A list of books", pp.21-28.

NL 0375953   CtY NN MH

VOLUME 334

806
LIN

Lincolnshire Local **History** Society.
Report and statement of accounts.   Lincoln,
Eng.
v. 25-34cm. annual.

Title varies: -1952/53, Report.
*Name changed from Lindsey local history
society in 1947.*

NL 0375954   IU NN

---

*Lincolnshire Lunatic Asylum
at Bracebridge, near Lincoln.* Annual reports of
the committee of visitors and medical superintendent to the four local authorities, parties to
the union. 1., 1862-3; 2., 1854; 4.-8., 1856-60
47., 1899. 8°. Lincoln, 1854-1900.

Opened August 9, 1852. First report from opening to Dec.
21, 1853. The parties to the contract of union are: For
the parts of Lindsey, for the parts of Holland, for the city
of Lincoln, for the county borough of Grimsby.

NL 0375955   DNLM

Lincolnshire magazine.
Official organ of the Lindsey
local history society. Subscription beginning v. 1, Sept./Oct.,
1932. St. Peters Chambers, Silver
St., Lincoln, The Society.

NL 0375956   MiU ICN CU

Lincolnshire Medical Benevolent Society.
——. Annual statements of the officers. 86.,
1888-9; 87., 1889-90. 2 l.; 2 l. 4°. Lincoln.

NL 0375957   DNLM

Lincolnshire Medical Benevolent Society.
Rules, with a list of the officers and subscribers,
1886. 23 pp. 16°. Lincoln, J. Williamson. 1886.
Instituted Sept. 21, 1854.

NL 0375958   DNLM

Lincolnshire Naturalists' Union.
Transactions.
Lincoln, Eng.
v. illus.
Annual; semiannual, 1967-
Began 1905.

NL 0375959   ICRL DSI

Lincolnshire notes & queries. A quarterly journal ... devoted to the antiquities, parochial records, family history,
folk-lore, quaint customs &c. of the county. v. 1-24 (no.
1-192); Jan. 1888-Oct. 1936. Horncastle, W. K. Morton
[etc.], 1888-[1936].
24 v. plates, maps, facsims., geneal. tables (part fold.) 28ᶜᵐ.
No numbers issued in 1899.
Title varies slightly.
Editors: Jan. 1888-Oct. 1898, J. C. Hudson (with E. L. Grange, 1888-91;
E. M. Sympson, 1892-98).—Jan. 1900-July 1921, E. M. Sympson (with
W. O. Massingberd, 1900-July 1910; A. R. Madison, 1900-Apr. 1912).—
Oct. 1921-Jan. 1923, C. W. Foster.—Apr. 1923-Oct. 1936, R. C. Dudding.

ᵇ"A list of existing sepulchral brasses in Lincolnshire", by G. E. Jeans,
was issued as a supplement, July 1889-Oct. 1892, and Jan. 1895. (Sepa-
rately bound)
"Lincolnshire folk names for plants", by E. A. Woodruffe-Peacock,
was issued as a supplement, Apr. 1894-Apr. 1897. [With v. 4]
"The natural history of Lincolnshire", edited by E. A. Woodruffe-
Peacock, was issued as a supplement, Jan. 1896-Oct. 1897. (Separately
bound)
"Abstracts of Lincolnshire wills proved in the Prerogative court of
Canterbury", edited by C. W. Foster, was issued as a supplement,
Jan./July 1922-Apr. 1934. 352 p. (concluded in July 1934, p. 55-56)
[With v. 17-28]

Continued in next column

Continued from preceding column

"A list of the high sheriffs of Lincolnshire, 1154-1935 [i. e. 1938,"
W. King-Fane, was issued as a supplement, Jan.-Oct. 1936. [With v. 24]
No more published.

1. Lincolnshire, Eng.—Antiq.—Period. 2. Lincolnshire, Eng.—Hist.—
Period. 3. Lincolnshire, Eng.—Geneal.—Period. I. Hudson, John
Clare, ed. II. Grange, Ernest L., ed. III. Sympson, Edward Mansel,
1860-1921, ed. IV. Massingberd, William Oswald, 1848-1910, ed. V.
Maddison, Arthur Roland, 1843-1912, ed. VI. Foster, Charles Wilmer,
1866-1935, ed. VII. Dudding, Reginald Charles, d. 1937, ed.

9-2909 Revised
Library of Congress   DA670.L69N5

NL 0375962   DLC MH OC1 MB

Lincolnshire notes and queries.

[Jeans, George Edward] 1848-
A list of the existing sepulchral brasses in Lincolnshire.
[Horncastle, 1892-95]

BR763
.L5L54

Lincolnshire Old Churches Trust.
Report. 1st-
1953-
[Lincoln]
[v. illus. 22 cm. annual.

1. Church finance—Lincolnshire, Eng. 2. Church maintenance and
repair.
BR763.L5L54   55-28053

NL 0375964   DLC NN

Lincolnshire pedigrees
see under Maddison, Arthur Roland, ed.

BR 670
.L69
R3

Lincolnshire record society.
The publications of the Lincolnshire record
society.
Horncastle [Printed for the Lincolnshire record
society by] W. K. Morton, 1891-

analyzed.

NL 0375966   DLC OC1

Lincolnshire Record Society.
Rules 1889
(Circular)

NL 0375967   MWA

Lincolnshire red shorthorn association.
... Lincoln red herd book. v. 1-
Lincoln [etc.] 1895-
plates. 8°.
Cover-title: Lincolnshire red shorthorn association
herd register (On spine: Lincolnshire herd register)
Issuing office varies: v. 47-58, Lincoln Red Short-
horn Society. v. 60-   Lincoln Red Cattle Society.
Title varies: v. 1-41 (1895-1935) Register of Lin-
colnshire red shorthorn herds. v. 42-   [1942]-
Lincoln red herd book.
Not published 1936-1941; for pedigrees during those
years (bulls 28285-32615) see in Coates herd book,
v. 82-87.

NL 0375968   DNAL

Lincolnshire red shorthorn association.
Register of Lincolnshire red shorthorn herds ... Pub.
by the Lincolnshire red shorthorn association ...

Lincoln,
v. illus., pl. 22ᶜᵐ.

1. Shorthorn cattle. 2. Cattle—Herd-books.
ᴄᴀ 13-259 Unrev'd
Library of Congress   SF193.S5L5

NL 0375969   DLC OU

Lincolnshire Regiment
see
Gt. Brit. *Army. Royal Lincolnshire Regiment.*

The Lincolnshire survey, temp. Henry I. Ed. by James
Greenstreet ... London, Priv. print. by Wyman & sons,
1884.
iv p., 1 l., 27 numb. l., 29-37, [1] p. facsim. (27 p.) 38 x 28ᶜᵐ.
Each page of facsim. accompanied by page of translation.

1. Lincolnshire, Eng. 2. Real property—Lincolnshire. I. Greenstreet,
James, ed.
9-1662
Library of Congress   DA670.L7L8

NL 0375971   DLC NcD ICN CtY OC1 MdBP

Lincolnshire topographical society, Lincoln, Eng.
An account of the religious houses, formerly
situated on the eastern side of the river Witham
see under Oliver, George, 1782-1867.

Lincolnshire topographical society, *Lincoln, Eng.*
A selection of papers relative to the county of Lincoln,
read before the Lincolnshire topographical society, 1841,
1842. Lincoln, Printed by W. & B. Brooke, 1843.
2 p. l., 114 p. 10 pl. (partly col.) incl. plans. fold. map. 21½ x 17ᶜᵐ.
Contents.—Willson, E. J. Opening address.—Bedford, W. Geology of
Lincoln.—Cookson, W. D. The Malandry hospital for lepers; Leprosy of the
middle ages.—Oliver, G. Temple Bruer and its knights.—Nicholson, W. A.
Advantage of recording the discovery of local antiquities; Tattershall castle.

Subject entries: Lincolnshire.
2-21789
Library of Congress, no.   DA670.L7L7.

NL 0375973   DLC MnHi

Lincolnshire wills
see under Maddison, Arthur Roland,
1843-1912.

PR
975
.L583

The Lincolnshire wonder; or, A comical dialogue, which lately happened between an old
woman of fourscore and ten, and a youth
about twenty, with whom the lately married.
London, Printed and sold in Aldermary Church
Yard [1800?]
8p. 18cm.

Illustration on front cover.
Paper covers.

1. Chap-books,   English.

NL 0375975   ScU

VOLUME 334

Lincolnton, N.C. Presbyterian church.
Memorial tributes, Rev. Robert Zenas Johnston, 1834-1908. Durham, 1908.

NL 0375976   NcU Nc

Lincolnton, N.C. Presbyterian Church.
Reports and directory. Lincolnton, 190-
illus. D.
Report year ends April.
Annual.

NL 0375977   NcU

Cp283.09
L74s   Lincolnton, N.C. St. Luke's Episcopal Church.
Order of service at the consecration of St.
Luke's Church, Lincolnton, N.C., August 12,
1886. ₁Lincolnton, 1886₎
₁3₎p. 28cm.
"Ordination services ... August 13th, 1886,"
p.₍3₎

NL 0375978   NcU

Lincolnville, *Me.*
Annual report of the town officers ...

Camden, Me.
v. tables. 22½-23½ᶜᵐ.

has title: Annual report of the selectmen, treasurer and supt. of schools of the town ...

CA 34-2196 Unrev'd

Library of Congress   JS13.L699   352.07415

NL 0375979   DLC

H1
.A19   Lincombe Lodge Research Library, Oxford.

Scienza nuova; international journal of reviews and studies in psychosociological and humanistic sciences. v. 1, no. 1-3/4; 1954-₁55₎, Oxford, Lincombe Lodge Research Library.

Linco's travels
see under   ₍Arne, Thomas Augustine₎
1710-1778. [Supplement]

Lincrusta-Walton...   New York: Trow's prtg. and bookbinding co., 1881. 2 pams. 23cm.

NL 0375982   NN MB

---

*NK3505 Lincrusta-Walton française. ₁Paris, 1900?₎
L5   137 plates. 29 1/2cm.

Cover-title.

1. Linorusta-Walton.

NL 0375983   NBuG

Lincrusta-Walton, the Sunbury wall decoration. A new linoleum product. London, Waterlow and sons, limited, printers, 1880.
14 p. 22ᶜᵐ.
Invented by Frederick Walton, but there is no indication that this book was written by him.

1. Lincrusta-Walton.

9-2321†

Library of Congress   TH8471.L6

NL 0375984   DLC

Lincy, Antoine Jean Victor le Roux de

see

Le Roux de Lincy, Antoine Jean Victor, 1806-1869.

₍Lind,   ₎
The truth about the stage
see under   Corin, psued.

Lind, *Dr., pseud.*

see

Cherenzi-Lind, Omar, 1902–

Lind, Aage
Guldkareten. Paris, Presses de la Cité [1947]

69 p.
Poems

NL 0375988   MH

Lind, Aage.
... Mosejord; skuespil i fire akter. København, A. F. Høst & søn, 1913.
158 p. 23½ᶜᵐ.   kr. 3

I. Title.

13-25746

NL 0375989   DLC NN

FILM
9217
PL   Lind, Abraham A
A manual of the Mardia language; containing grammatical rules ... Kedgaon, India, The author, 1913.
v,150 p. On film (Negative)

Microfilm. Original in British Museum.

1. Mardia language.

NL 0375990   CU

Lind, Abram.
A chapter of the Chinese Penal code ... Leiden, E. J. Brill, 1887.
4 p. l., 79, xxv p., 2 l., ₍3₎ p. 23ᶜᵐ.
Proefschrift—Leiden.
Includes text and translation of sections 152-156 of the Penal code of the Manchu dynasty.
"List of law terms": p. ₍75₎-79.
"Stellingen": ₍3₎ p. at end.
Bibliography: p. 2-3.

17-9094

NL 0375991   DLC WaU IaU CaBVaU PU-L NN

Lind, Aïda M.
'Round the world in rhyme, by Aïda M. Lind. Boston, Chapple publishing company, ltd., 1929.
2 p. l., 43 p. front. 18½ᶜᵐ.

1. Voyages around the world.   I. Title.

Library of Congress   PS3523.I 5R6 1929   29-13169

NL 0375992   DLC

Lind (Albert) ₍1844- ₎. *Ueber Zwillingsschwangerschaft und deren Verlauf. 32 pp. 8°.
Berlin. G. Lange ₍1864₎

NL 0375993   DNLM

Lind, Albin, joint author.
Priser och löner

see under

Eronn, Lars.

PT
9875   Lind, Albin
L63S6   Skogen brinner, roman. Stockholm, Folket
   i bild [c1943]
239 p. port. 19cm.

NL 0375995   CLU

Lind, Alfred, 1862-
Zur chirurgischen behandlung von ulcus ventriculi ... Berlin, Vogt ₁894₎
34, ₍2₎ p.

Inaug.-diss., Berlin, 1894.
Lebenslauf.
"Litteratur": p. ₍35₎

1. Stomach - Ulcers.

NL 0375996   NNC DNLM

Lind, Alfred August.
Om vocalljudens sammansaettning.
Inaug. diss. Upsala, 1869.

NL 0375997   ICRL

Lind, Andrew William, 1901-
Cultural beliefs and practices of the childbearing period and their implication for nursing practice ...
see under   Hawaii (Ter.) Board of Health. Public Health Nursing.

HC
687   Lind, Andrew William, 1901-
H3L6e   Economic succession and racial invasion in
1931a   Hawaii. Chicago, University of Chicago, 1931.
viii,434 ℓ.

Thesis (Ph.D.) - University of Chicago, 1931.
Photocopy.
Includes bibliography.

1. Hawaii - Econ. condit. 2. Hawaii - Population. I. Title.

NL 0376002   CLU

VOLUME 334

Lind, Andrew William, 1901–
... Economic succession and racial invasion in Hawaii ... by Andrew William Lind ... Chicago, Ill., 1936.

1 p. l., 24, 390–411 p. diagr. 24ᶜᵐ.

Part of thesis (PH. D.)—University of Chicago, 1931. Photolithographed.
"Private edition, distributed by the University of Chicago libraries."

1. Hawaiian islands—Econ. condit. 2. Hawaiian islands—Population.

Library of Congress	HC687.H3L5 1931	36–36487
Univ. of Chicago Libr.		
———— Copy 2.	₍2₎	309.1969

NL 0376003   ICU DLC NIC NcD NcU PBm MiU OU OCU

Lind, Andrew William, 1901–
Hawaii's Japanese, an experiment in democracy. By Andrew W. Lind ... Princeton, N. J., Princeton university press, 1946.

vii, 264 p. plates. 22½ᶜᵐ.

1. World war, 1939–1945—Hawaiian islands. 2. Japanese in the Hawaiian islands. I. Title.

| D767.92.L5 | 940.53969 | A 47–16 |

Princeton univ. Library
for Library of Congress   ₍25₎†

CaBViP OrPS CaBVaU OrP OrSaW OrU–Or
CaBVa NjP NcGU OClW DI MB TxU ICU ViU PPT DLC–MH PP
NL 0376004   NjP MiU OrU WaT MeB NIC WaS Or OrCS Wa

Lind, Andrew William, 1901–
Hawaii's people ₍by₎ Andrew W. Lind with the technical assistance of Robert Schmitt. Honolulu, University of Hawaii Press, 1955.

xii, 116 p. maps, diagrs., tables. 24 cm.
Bibliographical footnotes.

1. Hawaiian Islands—Population. 2. Hawaiian Islands—Soc. condit. I. Title.

| HB3693.H3L5 | 309.1969 | 54–8402 |

OrP PPT PP NcD OO OCl NcRS MsSM OrMonO WaSp WaT WaS
OOxM MH CU DI NN IU CaBVa KEmT CaBViPA NIC OrSaW Wa
NL 0376005   DLC CaBVaU OrU KMK PU PSt TxU CU–B OCU

Lind, Andrew William, 1901–
An island community; ecological succession in Hawaii ₍by₎ Andrew W. Lind ... Chicago, Ill., The University of Chicago press ₍1938₎

xxii, 337 p. incl. tables. maps (part fold.) diagrs. (2 fold.) 23½ᶜᵐ.
Bibliography at end of each chapter.

1. Hawaiian islands—Econ. condit. 2. Hawaiian islands—Population. 3. Agriculture—Hawaiian islands. I. Title.

		38–9748
Library of Congress	HC687.H3L47	
———— Copy 2.		
Copyright A 116122	₍5₎	330.9969

PBm NcD OClW OU OO WaU ViU
NL 0376006   DLC CaBVaU WaWW OrP OrU MiU FMU KEmT

Lind, Andrew William, 1901–
The Japanese in Hawaii under war conditions, by Andrew W. Lind ... This study is submitted by the American council as a document of the eighth conference of the IPR to be held in December, 1942 ... New York, American council, Institute of Pacific relations ₍1942₎

2 p. l., 16, 16a–b, 17–30 numb. l. 28 x 21½ᶜᵐ. (American council paper no. 5)

Errata slip inserted.
Reproduced from type-written copy.

1. Japanese in the Hawaiian islands. 2. World war, 1939–1945—Hawaiian islands. I. Institute of Pacific relations. 8th conference, Mont Tremblant, Que., 1942.

		43–17556
Library of Congress	DU627.5.L5	
	₍4₎	325.25209969

NL 0376007   DLC WaSpG ViU CSt–H CSt CaBVaU

Lind, Andrew William, 1901–
The Japanese in Hawaii under war conditions, by Andrew W. Lind ... Honolulu, New York, American council, Institute of Pacific relations ₍1943₎

3 p. l., 41 p. 23ᶜᵐ. (American council paper no. 5)

"Submitted by the American council as a document of the eighth conference of the Institute of Pacific relations held in Mont Tremblant, Quebec, Canada, in December, 1942."

1. Japanese in the Hawaiian islands. 2. World war, 1939–1945—Hawaiian islands. I. Institute of Pacific relations. 8th conference, Mont Tremblant, Que., 1942.

		A 45–5454
Harvard univ. Library		
for Library of Congress	[DU627.5.L]	
	₍2₎	325.25209969

NL 0376008   MH RPB NcD NN CaBVaU

Lind, Andrew William, 1901–
Modifications of Hawaiian character,
(In Reuter, E.B. Race & culture contacts. 1934. p. 228–245)

NL 0376009   OU

Lind, Andrew William, 1901–
... A study of mobility of population in Seattle, by Andrew W. Lind. Seattle, University of Washington press ₍1925₎

63 p. illus. (maps) 25½ᶜᵐ. (University of Washington publications in the social sciences. v. 3, no. 1)
Bibliography: p. 63.

1. Seattle—Population. I. Title: Mobility of population in Seattle.

| Library of Congress | HB1987.S6L5 | 26–27089 |

WaTC OrU DLC NN WaU–L NIC WaWW PBm CU WaU OU
NL 0376010   DLC MiU MB OCU DL OCl ViU ICJ OrP WaS

Lind, Anton.

Wiener sängerbund.
Fünfundsiebzig jahre Wiener sängerbund, eine rückschau im auftrage der vereinsleitung verfasst von regierungsrat Anton Lind ... Statistischer anhang von post-oberinspektor Rudolf Ehrenböck ... Entwurf des umschlages vom vereins-mitgliede arch. Herbert Mair. Wien ₍"Mollard" buch- u. kunstdruckerei₎ 1931.

Lind, Anton, ed.
Penal battalion, by Roy Baker...
see under   Baker, Roy, pseud.

Lind, Astrid.
Margareta Smedsdotter, av Astrid Lind. Stockholm, A.-b. Lindqvists förlag ₍1943₎

325, ₍1₎ p. 1 l. 21½ cm.

I. Title.

| PT9875.L58M3 | 47–41440 |

NL 0376013   DLC

Lind, Benno.
... Über das letzte Fermatsche theorem, von Benno Lind ... Leipzig and Berlin, B. G. Teubner, 1910.

1 p. l., ₍23₎–65 p. 24ᶜᵐ. (Abhandlungen zur geschichte der mathematischen wissenschaften mit einschluss ihrer anwendungen ... hft. XXVI. 2)
"Literaturverzeichnis": p. ₍52₎–60.

1. Congruences and residues. 2. Fermat's theorem.

| | | 10–8722 |
| Library of Congress | QA21.A2 hft. 26. 2 | |

NL 0376014   DLC CU OCU MiU ICJ NjP NN

Lind, Bredo.
Med MTB i øygarden. Oslo, J.G. Tanum, 1950.

52 p. illus. 26cm.

1. World War, 1939–1945. Naval operations, Norwegian.

NL 0376015   MnU NN

Lind, Bror Christer
see   Lind, Christer, 1912–

Lind, C
Cheese rennet and its action ... London, Chr. Hansen's laboratory, ltd. ₍n.d.₎
12 p. illus., tables, diagrs. 22 cm.

1. Rennet. 2. Cheese. I. Title.

NL 0376017   IaAS

Lind, C.
Driftsstatistiske Undersøgelser over Viktualiehandelen i København og Frederiksberg, af C. Lind... København: Nielsen & Lydiche, 1935. 298–327 p. incl. tables. 25cm.

"Særtryk af Nationaløkonomisk Tidsskrift."
"Et Led i de Undersøgelser...som foretages af Institutet for Historie og Samfundsøkonomi."

1. Groceries—Trade and stat.— Denmark. I. Institutet for Historie og Samfundsøkonomi, Copenhagen.
N. Y. P. L.   December 9, 1937

NL 0376018   NN

Lind, C
The effect of rennet on the contraction of the curd, by C. Lind and M. Jensen. London, Chr. Hansen's laboratory, ltd. ₍n.d.₎
12 p. tables. 22 cm.

Bibliographical foot-notes.

1. Rennet. 2. Cheese. I. Jensen, M. joint author.   II. Title.

NL 0376019   IaU

286.2
L64   **Lind, C.**
The provision trade, by C. Lind... ₍Copenhagen₎ Gyldendalske boghandel, nordisk forlag, 1935.
52 p. 25 1/2cm. (Statistical investigations into the economy of retailing. Bulletin no.2. Institute of economics and history, Copenhagen)

NL 0376020   DNAL

Lind, C.
Statshusmandsbrug i Fyns Stift
see under   Institutet for Historie og Samfundsøkonomi.

VOLUME 334

Lind, Carl.
Carl xii i Turkiet ... af Carl Lind ... Carlstad, C. Kjellin & c:o, 1875.
99 p. 20ᵐ.
Akademisk afhandling—Uppsala.

1. Karl XII, king of Sweden, 1682–1718. 2. Northern war, 1700–1721. 3. Sweden—For. rel.—Turkey. 4. Turkey—For. rel.—Sweden. 1. Title.
36–32018
Library of Congress　　　DL739.L5 1875
₍2₎　　　　　　948.5

NL 0376022　　DLC NIC

Lind, Carl.
Geology of iron deposits at Princeton, Montana, and economic aspects of iron ore in Montana, by Carl Lind ... Butte, Montana school of mines, 1942.
33p. map, charts, tables.
Senior thesis.

NL 0376023　　MtBuM

Lind, Carl Erik.
Untersuchungen über die rationalen Punkte der ebenen kubischen Kurven vom Geschlecht eins. Uppsala, 1940.
96 p. 25 cm.
Inaug.-Diss.—Uppsala.
Extra t. p. with thesis statement inserted.
Bibliography: p. ₍94₎–96.

1. Curves, Cubic. 1. Title.
QA567.L6　　　　　57–52439

NL 0376024　　DLC MiU NNC CLU LU MH

Lind, Charles: Untersuchungen über m-Jodchinolin und seine Derivate. Freiburg i. B.: Speyer & Kaerner 1909. 39 S. 8°
Freiburg i. B., Phil. Diss. v. 1909, Ref. Gattermann
₍Geb. 3. Juli 81 Hamburg; Wohnort: Hamburg; Staatsangeh.: Hamburg; Vorbildung: Oberrealsch. Karlsruhe Reife Juli 03; Studium: Tübingen 1, Straßburg 3, Freiburg i. B. 6 S.; Rig. 29. Okt. 09.₎　　[U 10. 1067]

NL 0376025　　ICRL PU NN MH

Lind, Christer, 1912–1942, *ed.*
Stigen och regnbågen, med efterskrift av Yrjö Hirn. Helsingfors, Söderström ₍1943₎
248 p. illus., port. 21 cm.
Poems from various countries.

1. Literature, Primitive. 2. Swedish poetry—Translations from foreign literature. 1. Title.
PN1347.L5　　　　50–49774

NL 0376026　　DLC

Lind, Christer, 1912–1942.
Vindarnas bröllop. Helsingfors, Söderström ₍1940₎
78 p. 21 cm.
Poems.

1. Title.　　　　　**Full name: Bror Christer Lind.**
PT9875.L59V5　　　　48–39162*

NL 0376027　　DLC

Lind, Christian, 1876–
... Ueber geschwülste des limbus corneae ...
Berlin, Ebering ₍1915₎
31, ₍1₎ p.
Inaug.-diss., Berlin, 1915.
Lebenslauf.
"Literatur": p. ₍29₎–31.

1. Cornea – Diseases.

NL 0376028　　NNC CtY DNLM

461.4
L64　　Lind, E　　M
Plankton algae from north-western Ireland. Dublin, Hodges, Figgis, 1945.
311–320 p.　(Proceedings of the Royal Irish Academy, v. 50, sect. B, no. 18)

NL 0376029　　DNAL

Lind, Earl, *pseud.*
Autobiography of an androgyne, by Earl Lind ... Ed., with introduction, by Alfred W. Herzog ... New York, The Medico-legal journal, 1918.
3 p. l., xiii, 265 p. 5 port. (incl. front.) fold. form. 19½ᵐᵐ.
"First edition, 1,000 copies ..." no. 447.

1. Sexual perversion. 1. Herzog, Alfred Waldemar, 1866–　*ed.* 11. Title.
Library of Congress　　HQ76.L7　　19–2787

NL 0376030　　DLC PPC ViU NN

Lind, Edmund George, 1829–1909.
Music of color. Baltimore, ₍1894₎
12 p. 26 col. plates. 24 x 32 cm.
Cover title.
In portfolio.
Typewritten text.
1. Music and color.

NL 0376031　　MdBP

Lind, Edmund LeRoy, 1900–
... A thermodynamic study of aqueous cadmium chloride solutions ... by Edmund LeRoy Lind ... ₍Chicago₎ 1936.
1 p. l., 35 p. illus., diagrs. 24ᵐᵐ.
Thesis (PH. D.)—University of Chicago, 1931.
Lithoprinted.
"Private edition, distributed by the University of Chicago libraries, Chicago, Illinois."

1. Cadmium chloride. 2. Thermodynamics. 3. Electrolysis. 4. Solution (Chemistry)
36–37568
Library of Congress　　QD501.L765 1931
Univ. of Chicago Libr.
—— Copy 2.　　　　₍3₎　　541.39

NL 0376032　　ICU DLC NIC CU NcD OCU MiU

Lind, Egmont, joint author.

Nørlund, Poul, 1888–
Danmarks romanske Kalkmalerier, af Poul Nørlund og Egmont Lind. Avec un résumé en français ₍tr. par Hélène Laurent-Lund₎ København, Selskabet til Udgivelse af Danske Mindesmærker, A. F. Høst, 1944.

Lind, Einar, *pseud.*
see Hydén, Nils, 1870–

Lind, Elena Marchant, joint ed.

₍Martínez Zuviría, Gustavo Adolfo₎ 1883–
Pata de Zorra, by Hugo Wast ₍pseud.₎ edited by P. G. Evans ... and Elena Marchant Lind ... Garden City, N. Y., Doubleday, Doran & company, inc. ₍*1937₎

Lind, Emil
Arabismus-Zionismus. Lpz.: J. Kranzbühler & Cie., 1931.
249p.

NL 0376036　　OCH OU

Lind, Emil, 1890–
Albert Schweitzer; aus seinem Leben und Werk. Bern, P. Haupt, 1948.
216 p. illus., ports. 24 cm.
"Das literarische Werk ₍Albert Schweitzers₎": p. 196–199. "Schrifttum über Albert Schweitzer in deutscher Sprache": p. 199–205.

1. Schweitzer, Albert, 1875–　2. Schweitzer, Albert, 1875– — Bibl.
A 48–7062*
Harvard Univ. Library
for Library of Congress　　₍1₎

NL 0376037　　MH CU MB MiU OU OCl IU NcD MiD

Lind, Emil, 1890–
Albert Schweitzer; aus seinem Leben und Werk. Autorisierte Jubiläumsausg. zum 80. Geburtstage Dr. Schweitzers. Wiesbaden, Necessitas-Verlag, 1955 ₍*1954₎
388 p. illus., ports. 20 cm. (Die Weissen Hefte, 5)
"Das Schrifttum Albert Schweitzers": p. 347–354. Bibliography: p. 355–371.

1. Schweitzer, Albert, 1875–
CT1098.S45L5　　　　56–34336

NL 0376038　　DLC PPC NN PU DNLM NjPT

Lind, Emil, 1890–
...Albert Schweitzer zum 75. Geburtstage. Speyer, O. Dobbeck, 1950. 84 p. illus. 19 cm. (Schriftenreihe: Albert Schweitzer. Heft 1)

586823B. 1. Schweitzer, Albert,　　1875–
N. Y. P. L.　　　　November 27, 1951

NL 0376039　　NN MH-AH MB CtY PU NjPT

Lind, Emil, 1890–
Ein Meister der Menschheit: Albert Schweitzer; der Beitrag des Philosophen und Menschenfreundes Albert Schweitzer zur Lösung der Kulturkrise der Gegenwart. Bühl-Baden, Verlag Konkordia, 1954.
95 p. port. 21 cm. (Grosse Erzieher der Menschheit, Bd. 4)
Includes bibliographical references.

1. Schweitzer, Albert, 1875–　1. Title. (Series)
A 55–7875
Harvard Univ. Library
for Library of Congress　　₍2₎

NL 0376040　　MH CU NcD

4BX
1396　　Lind, Emil, 1890–
Speyer und der Protestantismus; ein Buch vom Kämpfen, Leiden, Siegen und Schaffen des Protestantismus in der Stadt der Protestation. Heidelberg, Evangelischer Verlag, 1929.
144 p.

NL 0376041　　DLC-P4 MH CtY

VOLUME 334

941.47
L742sp
1929
LIND, Emil, 1890-
Speyer und die Protestantismus. Heidelberg, Evangelischer Verlag, 1929-1930.
v. plates 21.5cm.
V.2. is 2. Aufl.
Contents.--v.1.
--v.2. Die zweite Protestation von Speyer; ein Sammelbericht.

NL 0376042   MH-AH

Lind, Emma.
Overtro [four one act plays]. København: Nordisk Forlag, 1902. 4 p.l., 111 p. 12°.

Suppe, Steg og Kage. Det gode Selskab. Aabent Hus. Stavnsbunden.

1. Drama (Danish). 2. Titles.
N.Y.P.L.   January 6, 1915.

NL 0376043   NN

Law
Lind, Erik, 1888-   ed.

Sweden. *Laws, statutes, etc.*
Den nya arvslagen jämte dithörande författningar, med förklaringar utg. av Arthur Lindhagen och Erik Lind. Stockholm, Norstedt [1929]

Lind, Erik Henrik, 1849-1931.
Fornnordiska dopnamn i urval lämpat för nutida bruk; med förklaringar, av E. H. Lind. Uppsala: Almqvist & Wiksell [1917]. viii, 32 p. 16°.

i. Names (Forenames) Norse.
N.Y.P.L.   May 22, 1918.

NL 0376045   NN MnU

Lind, Erik Henrik, 1849-1931.

Benzelstierna, Gustaf, 1687-1746.
... G. Benzelstjernas Censorsjournal, 1737-1746, utgifven af L. Bygdén och E. Lewenhaupt. Med inledning af L. Bygdén och register af E. H. Lind. [Stockholm, Kongl. boktryckeriet, 1884-85]

Lind, Erik Henrik. Namnhistoriska bidrag till frågan om de gamla norska konungaättens härstamning. Extr. fr. Historisk tidskrift. XVI. Årg. Stockholm, 1896. 8°. pp. 237-254.   IcF52A715

NL 0376047   NIC

PD2362
.L69
Lind, Erik Henrik, 1849-1931.
Norsk-isländska dopnamn ock fingerade namn från medeltiden. Samlade ock utgivna av E. H. Lind, med understöd af det Svenska ecklesiastikdepartementet, den Norska Nansenfonden ock det Isländska bokmentafelaget. Uppsala, Lundequist [1905-15]
x p., 1306 columns.
Issued in 9 parts.

NL 0376048   ICU NIC IU CSt ICN NcU

Lind, Erik Henrik, 1849-
Norsk-isländska dopnamn ock fingerade namn från medeltiden, samlade ock utg. af E. H. Lind ... Uppsala, A.-B. Lundequist; [etc., etc., 1915]
x p., 1306 col. 25½cm.
Issued in 9 parts, 1905-15.

1. Names, Personal—Norwegian. 2. Names, Personal—Icelandic.

13-24993 Revised

Library of Congress   CS2375.N6L5

NL 0376049   DLC WaU CU CtY

Lind, Erik Henrik, 1849-
Norsk-Isländska dopnamn ock fingerade namn från medeltiden. Supplementvand. Utgitt av det Norske Videnskaps-Akademi i Oslo. Oslo, J. Dybwad, 1931.
920p. 26cm.

1. Names, Personal - Norwegian. 2. Names, Personal - Icelandic. I. Title.

NL 0376050   NcU NIC ICU

CS2593
L56
Stack
Lind, Erik Henrik, 1849-
Norsk-isländska personbinamn från medeltiden. Samlade ock utgivna med förklaringar av E.H. Lind. Uppsala, Lundequistska bokhandeln [1920-21]
vii p., 416 columns. 26s.

1.Names, Personal - Norwegian. 2.Names, Personal - Icelandic and Old Norse. 3.Norwegian language - Etymology - Names. 4.Icelandic and Old Norse languages - Etymology - Names. I.Title.

MdBJ
NL 0376051   CSt CU CtY NcU NIC MnU ICU IU ICN TxU

Lind, Erik Henrik, 1849-1931.
... Om rättstafningen. Dess uppgift och dess öden i vårt land, af E. H. Lind ... (4. tusendet.) Stockholm, A. Bonnier [1891]
32 p. 19 cm. (Studentföreningen Verdandis småskrifter [4. bd.] 36)

1. Swedish language—Orthography and spelling.   i. Title.

AC50.U73 nr. 36   24-25041

NL 0376052   DLC

AS284
S74
no.36
Lind, Erik Henrik, 1849-
Om rättstavningen dess uppgift och dess öden i vårt land. 2. översedda uppl. Stockholm, A. Bonnier [1917]
40 p. (Studentföreningen Verdandis småskrifter, 36)

1. Swedish language - Orthography and spelling. I. Title.

NL 0376053   CU

PD5775
L5
Scandinavian
Dept.
Lind, Erik Henrik, 1849-
Om rim och verslemningar i de svenska landskapslagarne; iaktttagelser. Upsala, E. Edquist, 1881.
91 p. (Upsala Universitets Årsskrift 1881. Filosofi, språkvetenskap och historiska vetenskaper. 3)

Has bound in his Versifikation i Gulatingslagen. (141-151 p.
Extract from an unidentified periodical)

1. Swedish language - Old Swedish - Versification. 2. Law - Sweden.

NL 0376054   CU MH-L ICU MH

Lind, Erik Henrik.
— Svenska personnamn i den norsk-isländska medeltidslitteraturen samlade av E. H. Lind. *In* Svenska personnamn och medeltiden antecknade och ordnade av Magnus Lundgren, Erik Brate, E. H. Lind. Uppsala, 1892-1934, pp. 323-58, 365-67.
400S10
"Nyare bidrag till kännedom om de svenska landsmålen ock svenskt folkliv. X. 6-7."

NL 0376055   NIC

Lind, Erik Henrik, 1849-1931.
Värmländska ordspråk, ordstäv ock talesätt. Stockholm: P. A. Norstedt & Söner, 1896. 48 p. 8°. (Nyare bidrag till kännedom om de svenska landsmålen och svenskt folklif. [v.] 11, [no.] 2.)

1. Swedish language.—Dialects: Värmland. 2. Proverbs (Swedish).
N.Y.P.L.   June 25, 1912.

NL 0376056   NN CU NIC

Lind, Erik Theodor
see Lind, Theodor, 1908-

Lind, Ernst.
Fågelliv vid Hovran. [Stockholm, Natur och kultur, 1955]
122 p. illus. 23 cm.

1. Birds—Sweden—Hovran.   i. Title.

A 56-1294
Purdue Univ. Library
for Library of Congress   [8]

NL 0376058   InLP

Lind, Ernst, 1850-
Die fontanellen und maasse des schaedels...
Inaug. Diss. Berlin, 1876

NL 0376059   ICRL DNLM PPC

Lind, *Mrs.* Ethel Vera (Everett) 1900-
... The effect of a strong magnetic field on the electrode potentials of iron and nickel ... by Ethel Everett Lind ... [Chicago] 1934.
1 p. l., 39 p. incl. illus., tables, diagrs. 24cm.
Thesis (PH. D.)—University of Chicago, 1931.
Lithoprinted.
"Private edition, distributed by the University of Chicago libraries, Chicago, Illinois."

1. Electromotive force. 2. Iron. 3. Nickel.

Library of Congress   QD561.L47 1931   34-10255
Univ. of Chicago Libr.
Copy 2.   [2]   537.5

NL 0376060   ICU DLC CU OU NcD MiU OCU

Lind, Francis Thomas, 1879-1916.
The letters of Mayo Lind, with an introduction by J. Alex. Robinson... St. John's, N. F: Robinson & Co., Ltd., 1919. 175 p. front., illus. 12°.

88766A. 1. European war, 1914-18.   —Personal narratives (Canadian).
2. Robinson, John Alexander,   1862-
N.Y.P.L.   July 3, 1923.

NL 0376061   NN CaNfSM

VOLUME 334

[Lind, Frank]
Art of modern conjuring, magic and illusions, a practical treatise on the art of parlour and stage magic, illusings, spiritualism, vantriloguism. . Lond, Ward, 1886
351 p
By Henri Garenne [pseud.]

NL 0376062   PU

[Lind, Frank]
The art of modern conjuring, magic and illusions. A practical treatise on the art of parlour and stage magic, illusions, spiritualism ... etc., etc., by Professor Henri Garenne [pseud.] With 162 illustrations. London, New York, Ward, Lock and co. [1886]

xii, 351 p. illus. 18½ᶜᵐ.

1. Conjuring.   I. Title. II. Title: Modern conjuring.

Library of Congress   GV1547.L87   34—15577

[a45c1]   798.8

NL 0376063   DLC TxU CU MH NN

Lind, Frank.
My occult case book.   London, New York, Rider [1953] ix, 214 p. illus. 20cm.

1. Occult sciences.

NL 0376064   NN

Lind, Fred A.
The rigid constitution, by Fred A. Lind. [1920]
152–159 p.   (In Papers in jurisprudence)
With folios.

NL 0376065   WaU-L

Lind, Friedrich-Karl, Zahnarzt a. Husum: Die angeblich zahnsteinlösende Wirkung der Zahnpasten Solvolith und Litholyst. [In Maschinenschrift] 23 S., 2 Bl. Tab. 4°(2°). — Auszug: (Kiel 1921: Schmidt & Klaunig). 2 Bl. 8°
Kiel, Med. Diss. v. 17. Okt. 1921, Ref. Hentze
[Geb. 8. Febr. 84 Klein-Glienicke; Wohnort: Kiel; Staatsangeh.: Preußen; Vorbildung: G. Birkenfeld bis Prima 06; Studium: Bonn 2, Berlin 2, Kiel 2 S.; Coll. 17. Okt. 21; Zahnärztl. Approb. 20. Nov. 13.]   [U 21. 4371]

NL 0376066   ICRL

Lind, Fritz, 1907–
Die schlüsselgewalt der ehefrau. ... Erlangen, 1935. 134 p.
Inaug. Diss. – Würzburg, 1935.
Lebenslauf.
Schrifttum.

NL 0376067   ICRL CtY

Lind, G.
... Lijst van werken over tandheelkunde in nederlandsche bibliotheken, samengesteld door G.Lind,F.Duijvensz en G.H.Bisseling.
's-Gravenhage, 1918.
vi p.,1 l.,48 p. 21½ᶜᵐ.

At head of title: Nederlandsche maatschappij tot bevordering der tandheelkunst.
"Voorbericht" signed: De bibliotheek-en museum-commissie: Lind.Duijvensz.Bisseling.
1.Dentistry—Bibliography. [1.Nederlandsche maatschappij tot bevordering der tandheelkunst,Amsterdam. Bibliotheek-en museum-commissie.

NL 0376068   MiU DNLM PU-D

Lind, Georg
Die Lehre von der Rückwirkung der erfüllten Resolutivbedingung mit Rücksicht auf das Bürgerliche Gesetzbuch ... von ... Georg Lind ... Hamburg, M. Baumann, 1898.

25 p. 21cm.

Inaug.-Diss. - Erlangen.
Bibliographical footnotes.

NL 0376069   MH-L ICRL

PQ6613
.U5C38   **Lind, Georg Rudolf.**
Jorge Guilléns Cántico; eine Motivstudie. Frankfurt a. Main, V. Klostermann [1955]
152 p. 26 cm. (Analecta Romanica ; Beihefte zu den Romanischen Forschungen, Heft 1)
Bibliography : p. 152.

1. Guillén, Jorge, 1893-   Cántico.   (Series)

Harvard Univ. Library   A 56—3349
for Library of Congress   [67c1]

NIC CtY CU ScU ViU MeB TxU NN IaU PSt KU FU GU
NL 0376070   MH PU LU FU CSt OrU CU-S DLC OU ICU ICN

Lind, George Dallas, 1847–
Best methods of teaching in country schools, by G. Dallas Lind. Rev. and enl. by the author of Preston papers [Lucy A. Yendes] New York, Hinds & Noble, [1899.

vi, 249 p. 19¼ᶜᵐ.
First edition, 1880, has title: Methods of teaching in country schools.

1. Teaching. 2. Rural schools.   I. Yendes, Lucy A., 1851-   ed. II. Title.

Library of Congress   LB1555.L7   0—1033

NL 0376071   DLC DHEW MB NN KEmT KU PWcT NcD ODW

Lind, George Dallas.
Easy experiments in chemistry and natural philosophy. For educational institutions of all grades and for private students. By G. Dallas Lind. Danville, Ind., The "Normal teacher" publishing house, 1880.

iv, 5–102 p. 20ᶜᵐ.

1. Science—Study and teaching.

Library of Congress   Q181.L74   9–10414†

NL 0376072   DLC OCl OO

EDUC-T   **Lind, George Dallas.**
Q   Easy experiments in chemistry and natural
181   philosophy. For educational institutions
.L74   of all grades and for private students. By
1885   G. Dallas Lind. Danville, Ind., The "Normal
         teacher" publishing house, 1885.
         102 p.

NL 0376073   MoU

Lind, George Dallas.
Lessons in physiology for beginners including brief and plain descriptions of the most important parts of the human body and the action of alcohol and other stimulants by George D. Lind ... Danville, Ind., Indiana publishing company, 1897.
vi, 157 p. illus. 21 cm.
1. Physiology. 2. Hygiene - Juvenile literature.

NL 0376074   CU

Lind, George Dallas, 1847–
Lessons in physiology. For use in schools. Including anatomy, physiology, and hygiene and the effects of alcohol and other stimulants on the human body and mind. By George D. Lind ... Danville, Ind., Indiana publishing company, 1892.
viii, 301 p. incl. illus., pl., tables. 21ᶜᵐ.

1. Physiology (Elements) 2. Hygiene.

Library of Congress   QP36.L75   6—46741

NL 0376075   DLC

Lind, George Dallas, 1847–   supposed author.
Love, wedlock and parentage; or philosophy of the sexes
see under [Jewett, M   ]

Lind, G[eorge] Dallas.
Man: embracing his origin, antiquity, primitive condition, races, languages, religions, superstitions, customs, peculiarities, civilization, nature and constitution, physical structure, the care and preservation of the body, the mental and moral faculties, etc., etc., by G. Dallas Lind ... Chicago, T. S. Denison, 1884.
xii, 13–750 p. illus. (incl. ports.) 23ᶜᵐ.

1. Anthropology—Juvenile and popular literature. 2. Ethnology—Juvenile and popular literature.

Library of Congress   GN31.L74   5–29762†

NL 0376077   DLC PU DNLM CU ODW

Lind, George Dallas
The marvelous story of man. London, Sieley, n.d.
311p.

NL 0376078   PBa

Lind, George Dallas.
Methods of teaching in country schools. By G. Dallas Lind. Danville, Ind., "Normal teacher" publishing house, J. E. Sherrill, 1880.
viii, 9–243 p. illus. (plan) 20ᶜᵐ. (On cover: Normal teacher publications)

1. Teaching.

Library of Congress   LB1555.L68   6—28196

NL 0376079   DLC KEmT

[Lind, George Dallas]
The mother's guide and daughter's friend. A compendium of valuable information for women ... By an old practitioner. Indianapolis, Webster publishing company, 1886.
555 p. 20ᶜᵐ.

1. Woman—Health and hygiene.

Library of Congress   RG121.L74   8-913†

NL 0376080   DLC DNLM

VOLUME 334

Lind, George Dallas, 1847–
Normal outlines of the common school branches; designed as an aid to teachers and pupils in the method of teaching and studying by topics ... By G. Dallas Lind ... Danville, Ind., "Normal teacher" publishing house, J. E. Sherrill, 1880.
vii, 10–200 p. 19½ᵐ. *(On cover: Normal teacher publications)*

1. Teaching—Outlines, syllabi, etc.   I. Title.

Library of Congress   LB1555.L72   6—28195

NL 0376081   DLC PU KAS

Lind, George Dallas, 1847–
The races of men and languages. By G. D. Lind ... Chicago, T. S. Denison [1884]
1 p. l., p. 119–522. illus. 22ᵐ. *(Lettered on cover: Standard library)*
Label mounted on cover: The races of man in all ages.
Separate issue of the author's "Man", book II, chap. I–III, p. 119–522.

1. Anthropology. 2. Ethnology.   I. Title. II. Title: The races of man in all ages.

[GN31.L74]   A 30–924
Title from American   Univ. Printed by L. C.

NL 0376082   DAU

4HQ [Lind, George Dallas, 1847–
644   The secret sins of society, by an old practitioner. Chicago, Lakeview Pub. Co., 1881.
399 p.

NL 0376083   DLC-P4

Lind, George Dallas.
The teachers' and students' library; a compendium of knowledge necessary to teachers, students, and the general reader, embracing reading, penmanship, arithmetic ... By G. Dallas Lind ... Chicago, T. S. Denison, 1882.
v, [6]–532 p. illus. 23½ᵐ.

1. Education—Addresses, lectures, etc. 2. Teaching.

E 10–1076
Library, U. S. Bur. of   Education LB17.L64

NL 0376084   DHEW OC1JC

Lind, George Dallas, 1847–
Teachers and students' library, a compendium of knowledge necessary to teachers-students and the general reader. Chicago, Denison, 1883.
532 p.

NL 0376085   PU

Lind, George Dallas, 1847–
200 lessons outlined in U. S. history, geography, English grammar, arithmetic, and physiology, by G. Dallas Lind ... New York city, Hinds & Noble, [1899].
2 p. l., [9]–200 p. 19ᵐ.

1. U. S.—Hist.—Outlines, syllabi, etc. 2. Geography—Outlines, syllabi, etc. 3. English language—Outlines, syllabi, etc. 4. Arithmetic—Outlines, syllabi, etc. 5. Physiology—Outlines, syllabi, etc.   I. Title.

0–1136 Revised
Library of Congress   LT305.L5

NL 0376086   DLC PU

Lindau, Albert, 1904–
Tatsächlicher und gemessener Feinheitgrad geschliffener Flächen, von Dr.-Ing. Albert Lindau. Braunschweig: F. Vieweg & Sohn Akt.-Ges., 1934. 42 p. incl. diagrs., tables. illus. (incl. charts.) 25cm. (Technische Hochschule Carolo-Wilhelmina, Brunswick, Germany. Versuchsfeld für Schleif- und Poliertechnik. Forschungsarbeiten. Heft 2.)

"Schrifttum," p. 41–42.

1. Grinding and polishing. I. Ser.

NL 0376087   NN IU

Lindau, Albert, 1904–
Zusammenhang zwischen tatsächlichem und gemessenem feinheitgrad geschliffener stahlflächen bei anwendung eines tastverfahrens. ...Braunschweig, 1934. 42 p.
Inaug. Diss. –Techn. Hochsch. Braunschweig, 1934.
Lebenslauf.

NL 0376088   ICRL

Lindau, Alfred Milton, 1898–
... Civil procedure at common law. [Cambridge, Mass., 192–?]
288 p. 26cm.

Title from label mounted on cover.
Manuscript; notes taken at Harvard law school.
Pages 281–288 left blank.

NL 0376089   MH-L

PT2623   Lindau, Anna (Kalisch) 1855–
.L4682   Märchen ... Mit illustrationen von Woldemar
Rare bk Friedrich, Arthur Langhammer, Fanny Römer [u. a.]
room   Berlin, G. Grote, 1865.
144 p. illus.

NL 0376090   ICU

*Lindau, Arvid, 1892–   ed.

... Liber gratulatorius in honorem Einar Sjövall quo die annos LXV complevit 7. iunii 1944 ab amicis et collegis dedicatus. Lund, H. Ohlssons boktryckeri, 1944.

Lindau, Arvid, 1892–
... Studien über kleinhirncysten; bau, pathogenese und beziehungen zur angiomatosis retinæ, von Arvid Lindau. Lund, H. Ohlssons buchdruckerei, 1926.
128, [2] p. plates. 24½ᵐ. *(On cover: Acta pathologica et microbiologica scandinavica ... Supplementum I)*
At head of title: Aus dem Pathologisch-anatomischen Institut der Kgl. universität zu Lund.
The author's thesis, Lund.
Imprint on cover: København, Levin & Munksgaard, 1926.
"Literaturverzeichnis": p. [120]–128.

1. Cerebellum—Diseases. 2. Cysts.

[Full name: Arvid Vilhelm Lindau]
A C 37–2487
John Crerar library
for Library of Congress   [4]

NL 0376092   ICJ ICRL WaU CU DNLM PU ViU OC1W-H

Lindau, August, b. 1850
Haftet der Verkäufer eines Grundstücks, auf welchem Realservituten lasten, für Eviktion, wenn er dem Käufer von jenen keine Anzeige gemacht hat? ... [von] August Lindau ... Opponenten: ... Petzsch ... Rohde ... Krey ... Greifswald, F.W. Kunike, 1875.
2 p. l., 35 p. 21cm.
Inaug.-Diss. - Greifswald.
"Lebenslauf": p. 34.

NL 0376093   MH-L PU

Lindau, August Ferdinand.
Kritische bemerkungen zu den poesien des Horaz. Oels, 1845.

NL 0376094   NjP

LINDAU, August Ferdinand.
De Usu et Praestantia Artium et Literarum Graecorum. Vratislav, 1815.
sm.8°. f.(1), pp.37.

NL 0376095   MH

LINDAU, August Ferdinand.
Novum in Platonis Timaeum et Critiam Conjecturarum atque Emendationum Specimen. Vratislaviae, 1816.
f.(1), pp.vii, 70. Table.

NL 0376096   MH

Lindau, August Ferdinand, ed.
Quae feruntur Odaria
see under   Anacreon. Greek.

Lindau, August Ferdinand
Zu Platon's Timaus u. a. kritik & philosophie. Hildesheim, 1830.

NL 0376098   PBm

Lindau, Baruch, 1759–1849.
ראשית למודים ... בהכמת לימודיות ומדעיות. נדפס פעם
שלישית בהוספות ושנוים. קראקא, בבית וכדפוס ר. נ. ה. וּן א.
ש. כהנא שפירא.   W Krakówie, 1821.
unpaged. 22 cm.

1. Science—Early works to 1800.
Title transliterated: Reshit limudim.

Q157.L5 1821   54–47528 ‡

NL 0376099   DLC

Lindau, Baruch, 1759–1849.
ראשית למודים.
[Lemberg] Landesdruckerei des M. F. Poremba [1869]
2 v. in 1. 22 cm.

1. Science—Early works to 1800.
Title transliterated: Reshit limudim.

Q157.L5 1869   54–47527 ‡

NL 0376100   DLC

Lindau, Carl.
Der beste ton. Regeln des anstandes, und anleitung, durch ein anständiges und gesittetes benehmen sich im gesellschaftlichen leben angenehm und beliebt zu machen. Ein sitten- und höflichkeitsspiegel für junge leute. Hrsg. von Carl Lindau. 7.verbesserte aufl. Erfurt, F. Bartholomäus [1882]
2 p. l., 134 p., 1 l. 19ᵐ.

1. Etiquette—Germany. I. Title.

BJ1903.L74 1882

NL 0376101   MiU

VOLUME 334

PT1101
L5
v. 16   Lindau, Carl   ed.
     Im Coupe für Nichtraucher. Humoresken. Erfurt, F.
Bartholomäus [1882?]
     74 p.   (Lindau's Reisebibliothek, Bd. 16)

NL   0376102   CU

PT1101
L5
v. 14   Lindau, Carl   ed.
     Im Coupe zweiter Classe. Humoresken. Erfurt, F.
Bartholomäus [1882?]
     73 p.   (Lindau's Reisebibliothek, Bd. 14)

NL   0376103   CU

PT1101
L5
v. 18   Lindau, Carl   ed.
     Im Damen-Coupé. Novelletten und Miscellen. Erfurt,
F. Bartholomäus [1882?]
     75 p.   (Lindau's Reisebibliothek, Bd. 18)

NL   0376104   CU

PT1101
L5
v. 17   Lindau, Carl   ed.
     Im Rauch-Coupé. Humoresken. Erfurt, F. Bartholomäus
[1882?]
     74 p.   (Lindau's Reisebibliothek, Bd. 17)

NL   0376105   CU

PT1101
L5
v. 11   [Lindau, Carl]   ed.
     Novellen und Novelletten.   Bd. I.   Erfurt, F. Bartholomäus
[1882?]
     60 p.   (Lindau's Reisebibliothek, Bd. 11)

NL   0376106   CU

Lindau, Carl, 1853–1924.
     Die drei Engel, Operette in 3 Akten
       see under   Hellmesberger, Joseph,
1855–1907.

M1503
Z66F8
1943   Lindau, Carl, 1853–1934. Der Fremdenführer.

     Ziehrer, Carl Michael, 1843–1922.
      [Der Fremdenführer. Piano-vocal score. German]

     Der Fremdenführer, Operette in einem Vorspiel und drei
Akten von L. Krenn und C. Lindau; Neubearbeitung: Walter
Hauttmann. Musik von C. M. Ziehrer; Neubearbeitung:
Erik Jaksch. Klavierauszug zum Dirigieren eingerichtet
von Fritz Zwerenz. Wien, L. Doblinger, °1943.

Lindau, Carl, 1853–1934.
     Frühling am Rhein
       see under   Eysler, Edmund, 1874–1949.

Lindau, Carl, 1853–1934, joint author.
     [Rosenstein, Leo] 1862–
     Johann der Zweite. Operette in drei akten, von Leo
Stein [pseud.] und Carl Lindau. Musik von Edmund
Eysler ... Leipzig [etc.] J. Weinberger, °1908.

Lindau, Carl, 1853–1934, tr.

Knoblock, Edward, 1874–
     ... Kismet, groteskes traumspiel aus "Tausend und eine
nacht". Englisches original von Eduard Knoblauch. Nach
der uebersetzung von Carl Lindau für das Künstlertheater neu
bearbeitet in 8 bildern. Musik von Josef Gustav Mraczek.
München, Drei masken-verlag, g. m. b. h., °1912.

M33
Z54L3   Lindau, Carl, 1853–1934. Die Landstreicher.

     Ziehrer, Carl Michael, 1843–1922.
     [Die Landstreicher; arr.]

     Die Landstreicher; Operette in 2 Acten u. einem Vorspiele
von L. Krenn und C. Lindau. Zweihändiger Clavierauszug
mit unterlegtem Text. [Arrangement von Gustav Blasser]
Wien, L. Doblinger [n. d.] Pl. no. D. 2488.

ML50
.E376L5
1917   Lindau, Carl, 1853–1934. Liebessport.

     Eibenschütz, Albert.
     [Liebessport. Libretto. German]

     Liebessport; Operette in drei Akten von August Neidhart
und Karl Lindau. Textbuch der Gesänge. München, O.
Halbreiter, °1917.

Lindau, Carl, 1853–1934.
     "Mona Vanna", oder Einquartierung in Pisa.
Ein nacktes Seelengemälde in einem Mantel ohne
Aufzug. Von Carl Lindau und Julius Wilhelm.
Wien, J. Eisenstein & Co., 1903.
     20p.

     Microcard edition.

NL   0376114   ICRL

Lindau, Carl, 1853–1934.
     "Monte Carlo;" Operette in 3 Akten von C. Lindau und F.
Antony (nach einem Stoffe von H. Hülgerth). Musik von L. R.
Chmel. Wien: J. Chmel, cop. 1907. 80 p. 8°.

     1. Drama (German). 2. Antony, F.   jt. au. 3. Huelgerth, Heribert.
4. Chmel, Ludwig Roman, composer.   5. Title.
N. Y. P. L.   February 7, 1913.

NL   0376115   NN

Lindau, Carl, 1853–1934, and B. Jenbach.
     La mujer romántica; opereta en tres actos basada en la come-
dia de Ernt Wicherts, original de Carl Lindau y Béla Jenbach;
música del maestro Carl Weinberger, adaptada á la escena
española por Pedro Muñoz Seca, Pedro Perez Fernandez y Rafael
Calleja, traducida al castellano por Hector Kummer... Madrid:
R. Velasco, 1912. 76 p. 12°.

     Without music.

     1. Drama (German). 2. Jenbach,   Bela, jt. au. 3. Muñoz Seca, Pedro.
4. Pérez Fernández, Pedro. 5. Cal-   leja, Rafael, 1874– . 6. Wichert,
Ernst, 1831–1902. 7. Kummer, Hec-   tor, translator. 8. Title.
N. Y. P. L.   December 8, 1919.

NL   0376116   NN CtY

Lindau, Carl, 1853–1934.
     La mujer romántica, opereta en tres actos,
basada en la comedia de Ernt Wicherts.
Original de Carl Lindau y Béla Jenbach. Música
del maestro Carl Weinberger. Adaptada á la
escena española por Pedro Muñoz Seca, Pedro
Pérez Fernández y Rafael Calleja. Traducida al
castellano por Hector Kummer... Madrid, R.
Velasco, 1912.
     76p.

     Microcard edition.

NL   0376117   ICRL

Lindau, Carl, 1853–1934.
     Die romantische Frau. Operette in drei Akten (nach einem
Lustspiele E. Wicherts) von C. Lindau und B. Jenbach. Musik
von C. Weinberger. Leipzig: L. Doblinger, cop. 1911. 165 p.
8°.

     1. Drama (German). 2. Jenbach,   Béla, jt. au. 3. Weinberger, Carl,
composer. 4. Wichert, Ernst. 5. Title.
N. Y. P. L.   February 3, 1913.

NL   0376118   NN

---

*ML50
.T66L4
1914   Lindau, Carl, 1853–1934.
     [Teresita. Libretto. German]
     Teresita, die weisse Sklavin; Operette in
3 Akten. Musik nach Motiven von Emil Waldteu-
fel, arrangiert von Bela von Ujj. Braunschweig,
Henry Litolff [c1914]
     68 p. illus. 20cm.

     1. Operas—Librettos.   I. Waldteufel, Emil,
1837–1915.

NL   0376119   MB

Lind, George Dallas, 1847–   3598.206
     200 lessons outlined in U. S. history, geography, English gram-
mar, arithmetic and physiology.
     New York. Hinds & Noble. [1900?] 200 pp. 12°.

     *D5609 —.T.r. — Courses of study.   May 4,   1900

NL   0376120   MB

Lind, Gustaf Herman, 1869–1945.
     Egnahemsträdgården. Handledning vid den
mindre trädgårdens skötsel. Stockholm,
Aftonbladets tryckeri, 1909.
     96 p. 8°. (Aftonbladets och Dagens
populärabibliotek 1.)

NL   0376121   NN

Lind, Gustaf Herman, 1869–1945.
     Småbrukarens trädgårdsbok; handledning
vid skotseln av trädgårdar vid mindre lantbruk
och egna hem.   1914.
     (Siléns praktiska bibliotek)

NL   0376122   RP

SB466
S82S8
L5   Lind, Gustaf Herman, 1869–1945.
Landscape   Stockholmsträdgårdar under gångna tider; en kort redogörelse
Arch.   för äldre trädgårdar i Stockholmstrakten och deras mästare.
Library   Stockholm, Saxon & Lindström [1941]
     222 p. illus., ports.

     1. Gardens - Sweden - Stockholm.   2. Gardening - Biog.

NL   0376123   CU

Lind, Gustaf Herman, 1869–
     Svensk frukt; färglagda avbildningar jämte beskrivningar
över i sverige odlade frukt- och bärsorter, av Gustaf Lind ...
Stockholm, A.-B. M. Bergvalls förlag [pref. 1924]
     3 p.-l., [96] p. 48 col. pl. 31ᵐ.

     Consists of colored plates with descriptive letterpress.
"Litteratur" for each fruit.

     1. Fruit—Pictorial works. [1. Pomology—Pictorial works]
2. Fruit—Sweden. [2. Sweden—Pomology]

                                      Agr 30-224

     Library, U. S. Dept. of   Agriculture 93L642

NL   0376124   DNAL

VOLUME 334

Lind, Gustaf Herman, 1869-1945.
Våra frukter och bär; kortfattad beskrifning öfver på fritt land i Sverige odlade viktigare frukt- och bärsorter. Stockholm, Wahlström & Widstrand [1912]
158 p. 19 cm.

1. Fruit-culture - Sweden. 2. Berries - Sweden. i.t.

NL 0376125   NNBG

Lind, Gustaf Herman, 1869-
Våra medicinalvaxter, ...Stockholm, M. Bergvalls forlag 1917.
48 p. 48 col. plates.

NL 0376126   PU-A

Lind, Gustaf Herman, 1869-1945.
Våra prydnadsträd och buskar; kort beskrivning över i Sverige planterade viktigare träartade prydnadsväxter. På uppdrag av Kungl. Lantbruksstyrelsen utarbetad. 2. uppl. Stockholm, Wahlström & Widstrand [1926]
254 p. illus. 20 cm.
Bibliography: p. [232]

1. Trees - Sweden. 2. Shrubs - Sweden.
3. Plants, Ornamental - Sweden. i.t.

NL 0376127   NNBG

Lind, H. W.
Katechismus der Nähmaschinenkunde. Bielefeld: E. Gundlach A.-G. [1912.]   152 p.   12°.

1. Sewing machines.
N.Y.P.L.   June 10, 1913.

NL 0376128   NN

PT9076   Lind, Hans
L5N6   Nordlandsviser. Ny utg. ved Hallfrid Christiansen.   Oslo.
1936   O. Norli. 1936.
          93 p.

This collection first published in 1910.

NL 0376129   CU

948.04   Lind, Hans Daniel, 1847- 1924.
F873bℓ   Fra kong Frederik den Andens tid; bidrag til den dansk-norske sømagts historie, 1559-1588.   København, Gyldendal, 1902.

334 p.   24cm.
1. Frederik II, King of Denmark, 1534-1588. 2. Denmark. History, Naval. 3. Norway. History, Naval.

NL 0376130   MnU InU

Lind, Hans Daniel, 1847-
Kong Kristian den Fjerde og hans Mænd paa Bremerholm. Af H. D. Lind... København: Gyldendal, 1889.   4 p.l., 449 p. 8°.
Med Understøttelse af Marineministeriet og den Hjelmstjerne-Rosencroneske Stiftelse.

161357A. 1. Christian IV., king of   Denmark and Norway, 1577-1648.
2. Navy, Danish-Hist.-Biog.
N.Y.P.L.   March 16, 1925

NL 0376131   NN MH

Lind, Hans Daniel, 1847-
Nyboder og dets beboere, især i ældre tid; efter trykte og utrykte kilder. Med et titelbillede, efter tegning af Carl Thomsen, og et litograferet kort. Udgives med offentlig understøttelse.   København, Klewing-Evers, 1882.
Front. and plan.

NL 0376132   MH

Lind, Hans Daniel, 1847-
Om nogle af søetatens kongelige tjenere under Frederik den Tredje og deres økonomiske vilkaar. Ved sogneprest H. D. Lind ...   Kjøbenhavn, Hoffensbergske etabl., 1896.
16 p. 23ᶜᵐ.
Særtryk af Personalhistorisk tidsskrift, 3. række, v. bind.

1. Denmark—Navy—Hist.

                                        14-9728
Library of Congress   VA493.L6

NL 0376133   DLC

---

84   Lind, Harald
Aø8   Observations on the quaternary geology of
9   Andørja - Rolla - Gratangen (Troms, Northern Norway). Tromsø, Norway, Tromsø Museum, 1955.
          21, [3]p. illus., maps. 23cm. (Acta borealia. A. Scientia, no. 9)
          Bibliography: p.[23-24]

1. Geology, Stratigraphic - Quaternary. 2. Geology - Norway.

NL 0376134   CtY

Lind, Helge, *pseud.*
    see
Borgen, Johan, 1902-

Lind, Helmut: Das Sarkom des Kiefers. [Maschinenschrift] 30 S. m. Tab. 4°. — Auszug: (Kiel 1922: Schmidt & Klaunig). 1 Bl. 8°
Kiel, Med. Diss. v. 10. März 1922   [U ss. 6660]

NL 0376136   ICRL

Lind, Henrik, *pseud.*
En doktor kom og skrev ...   København, Schultz, 1952.
160 p. 21 cm.

I. Title.

PT8175.L513D6   A 53-2905
Minnesota. Univ. Libr.
for Library of Congress   [8]†

NL 0376137   MnU OCl MH OrP WaT DLC

PT8175   Lind, Henrik, *pseud.*
L513E3   Efter konsultationstid. København, J. H. Schultz, 1955.
          151 p. 20 cm.

I. Title.

Minnesota. Univ. Libr.   A 56-740
for Library of Congress   [8]

NL 0376138   MnU MH DLC

Lind, Henry C
Rhode Island annotations to the Restatement of the law of security, as adopted and promulgated by the American Law Institute; prepared under the auspices of the Rhode Island Bar Association. St. Paul, American Law Institute Publishers, 1953.
74 p. 24 cm.

1. Security (Law)—Rhode Island. 2. Annotations and citations (Law)—Rhode Island. I. American Law Institute. Restatement of the law of security. II. Title.

                347.3   54-18834

NL 0376139   DLC NBuU-L GU-L ViU-L CU NNC NcD

Lind, Henry C
Rhode Island annotations to the Restatement of the law of security, as adopted and promulgated by the American Law Institute; prepared by Henry C. Lind under the auspices of the Rhode Island Bar Association. St. Paul, 1953.
209 p. 24 cm.
Cover title: Restatement of the law of security, Rhode Island annotations.
1. Security (Law) Rhode Island. Lw 1. Security. U.S.   Lw 2. Pledge. Lw 3. Liens.Lw 4.Surety   ship and guaranty. Lw 5. Citations.Rhode Island.Lw 6.Rhode Island.

NL 0376140   N-L

Lind, Hertha, 1908-
... Höhenklimabehandlung der Augentuberkulose ...   [n.p., n.d.]
Inaug.-Diss. - Freiburg.
Lebenslauf.
"Literatur": p. [16]

NL 0376141   CtY

PZ33   Lind, Hiltrud.
.L477   Ein Riese namens Emil; eine Bilderbuchgeschichte. Mit Illustrationen von Gerhard Lahr. [1. Aufl.] Berlin, Kinderbuchverlag [n. d.]
          [32] p. col. illus. 28 cm.

I. Lahr, Gerhard, illus. II. Title.

PZ33.L477   68-94187

NL 0376142   DLC

Lind, Ida May, joint ed.

Condon, Randall Judson, 1862-1932, *ed.*
    ... High and far, edited by Randall J. Condon ... and Ida May Lind ... Boston, Little, Brown, and company, 1936.

PE1117   Lind, Ida May, joint ed.
.C64
1936   Condon, Randall Judson, 1862-1931, *ed.*
          The new Atlantic readers ... edited by Randall J. Condon ... and Ida May Lind ... Boston, Little, Brown, and company, 1936.

Lind, Ida May, joint ed.

Condon, Randall Judson, 1862-1932, *ed.*
    ... The understanding prince, edited by Randall J. Condon ... and Ida May Lind ... Boston, Little, Brown, and company, 1936.

VOLUME 334

Lind, Ida May, joint ed.

Condon, Randall Judson, 1862–1932, *ed.*
  ... The wonderful tune, edited by Randall J. Condon ... and Ida May Lind ... Boston, Little, Brown, and company, 1936.

---

*
PS3511
.A86Z99 Lind, Ilse (Dusoir) 1917–
.L55D4
1955   The design and meaning of Absalom, Absalom! ₍n. p.₎ 1955.
    p. 887–912. 28cm. ₍Faulkner miscellaneous material₎
    Reproduced from PMLA, vol. LXX, no. 5 (Dec. 1955)

    1. Faulkner, William, 1897–   Absalom, Absalom!

NL 0376147   ViU

Lind, Ilse (Dusoir) 1917–
  Richard Jago: a study in eighteenth century localism. Philadelphia, 1945.
    ₍5₎ l, 3–118 p. 23 cm.
    Thesis—Univ. of Pennsylvania.
    Bibliography: p. ₍115₎–118.

    1. Jago, Richard, 1715–1781.

PR3519.J14Z8   928.2   A 47–6008*
Pennsylvania. Univ.   Library
for Library of Congress   ₍a51c₎†

NL 0376148   PU NcD DLC MB ICU OC1W OU NcU NN OrU

---

*
PS3511
.A86Z99 Lind, Ilse (Dusoir) 1917–
.L55T4
1955   The teachable Faulkner. ₍n. p.₎ 1955.
    p. 284–287. 22cm. ₍Faulkner miscellaneous material₎
    Reproduced from College English, Feb. 1955.

    1. Faulkner, William, 1897–   —Study and teaching.

NL 0376149   ViU

Lind, Ivan, 1890–
  Ekonomisk geografi; en skildring av jordens näringsliv. 3. uppl. Uppsala, A. Lindblad ₍1943–47₎
    2 v. maps. 20 cm. (Göteborgs handelsinstituts läroboksserie, 7–8)
    Imprint of v. 1 covered by label: Göteborg, Gumpert; v. 2 has imprint: Göteborg, Gumpert.

    1. Geography, Economic. I. Title. (Series: Gothenburg, Sweden. Handelsinstitutet. Göteborgs handelsinstituts läroboksserie, 7–8)

HF1025.L5   49–16297*

NL 0376150   DLC

HF3680 Lind, Ivan, 1890–
.G6L74   Göteborgs handel och sjöfart, 1637–1920. Historisk-statistisk översikt. Göteborg, W. Zachrissons boktryckeri, 1923.
    260 p. tables. (Skrifter utg. till Göteborgs stads trehundraårsjubileum genom jubileumsutställningens publikationskommitte, 10)

    1. Gothenburg, Sweden—Comm. 2. Shipping—Gothenburg, Sweden. I. Title. Series: Gothenburg, Sweden. Jubileumsutställningen, 1923. Publikationskom-   mitte. Skrifter, 10.

NL 0376151   ICU NN CtY NNC PPAmSwM

Lind, Ivan, 1890–
  Mexiko; natur och folk. Stockholm, Natur och kultur ₍1951₎
    170 p. illus., maps. 18 cm. (Natur och kultur, 161)

    1. Mexico. I. Title.

F1208.L72   54–36758

NL 0376152   DLC NN TxU

278
L64   **Lind, Ivan,** 1890–
Bd.4   Näringsgeografi med varukännedom för handelsskolor, praktiska mellanskolor, högre folkskolor och liknande läroanstalter. 4. uppl.   Uppsala, Lindblad ₍1953₎
    220 p.

    1. Geography, Economic. I. Västhagen, Nils, joint author.

NL 0376153   DNAL

Lind, Ivan, 1890–
  Studier i västkusthamnarnas ekonomiska geografi ... Göteborg, Elanders boktryckeri, 1920.
    xii, 337 p., 1 l. incl. tables. illus., maps. 20½ᶜᵐ.
    Akademisk avhandling—Upsala.
    "Källor och litteratur": p. ₍vii₎–ix.

    1. Harbors—Sweden. 2. Sweden—Econ. condit.

    21–15781
Library of Congress   HC375.L6

NL 0376154   DLC ICJ PU CtY

N5278
.L5   **Lind, J.**
    Catalogue d'une collection d'anciens tableaux de diverses écoles faisant partie du cabinet de J. Lind; la vente à Stockholm ... le 27 octobre 1897. Stockholm R. Bukowski, 1897.
    20 p. 25 cm.

NL 0376155   DLC

WZ
260   **Lind, James,** 1716–1794
L742tG   ... Abhandlung vom Scharbock. Nach der 2. Ausg. aus dem Englischen übersetzt, von D. Johann Nathanael Pezold. Riga und Leipzig, Johann Friedrich Hartknoch, 1775.
    [16], 717, [10] p. 18 cm.
    "Bibliotheca scorbutica: oder, Chronologisches Verzeichniss aller derjenigen Schriften die bisher über den Scharbock herausgekommen sind": p. 460–[726]

    I. Pezold, Johann Nathanael, 1739–1813, tr.

NL 0376156   DNLM CtY-M NNNAM

WZ
100   **LIND, James,** 1716–1794
qL742
    A collection of miscellaneous biobibliographical material on this person, together with abstracts, résumés, etc. of his works, may be found on the shelves under the above call number.

NL 0376157   DNAL DNLM

W 4   **LIND, James,** 1716–1794
E23   ... De morbis venereis localibus
1748   ... Edinburgi, 1748.
L 2   17 p. 21 cm.
    Diss. - Edinburgh.

NL 0376158   DNLM

RBS.   **Lind, James,** 1716–1794.
Bd.Pam.   *De morbis venereis localibus.
v.618   Edbg.: 1748.
    (Thesaurus medicus Edinburgensis novus. Edbg. & Lond.: 1785, v.1, p. 381–407)

NL 0376159   NNNAM PPL DNLM

LIND, James. 1716–1794.
         De morbis venereis localibus.
1748.   (Smellie's Thes. med., vol. 1, pp. 381–407. Edin. 1788.)

NL 0376160   MB

Lind, James, 1716–1794.
    A description of rifled ordnance
      see   Lind, James, 1736–1812.

Lind, James, 1716–1794.
    Dissertatio medica, inauguralis, de febre remittente putride paludum ...
      see
    Lind, James, 1736–1812.

WZ
260   **Lind, James,** 1716–1794
L742esF   Essai sur les maladies des Européens dans
1785   les pays chauds, et les moyens d'en prévenir les suites; suivi d'un appendice sur les fièvres intermittentes, & d'un mémoire qui fait connoître une méthode simple pour dessaler l'eau de mer, & prévenir la disette des comestibles dans les navigations de long cours ... Traduit de l'anglois sur la dernière éd., publiée en 1777, & augm. de notes; par M. Thion de La Chaume ... Paris,

    Théophile Barrois le jeune, 1785.
    2 v. 18 cm.
    Imperfect: p. [i]–[ii] of v. 1 (half-title?) wanting.

    I. Thion de La Chaume, Claude Esprit, 1750–1786, ed. and tr.

NL 0376164   DNLM CaBVaU OC1W-H ICJ

Lind, James, 1716–1794.
    Essai sur les moyens les plus propres a conserver la santé des gens de mer ... Paris, A. Boudet, 1758.
    92p., 1l. 17cm.

    1. Seamen. 2. Naval hygiene.

NL 0376165   CtY-M

VOLUME 334

RC
961
.L74

Lind, James, 1716-1794.
An essay on diseases incidental to Europeans
in hot climates. With the method of preventing
their fatal consequences. By James Lind ... To
which is added, an Appendix concerning intermittent fevers. To the whole is annexed, a simple
and easy way to render salt water fresh, and to
prevent a scarcity of provisions in long voyages at sea ... London, Printed for T.Becket
and P.A.De Hondt, 1768.
6 p.l.,348,[8] p. 20½cm.

1.Tropics--Diseases and hygiene.

     MiU NcD PPC
NL 0376166   MiU CaBVa CU-M DNLM MBCo NcD-MC CaBVaU

WZ
260
L742es
1771

Lind, James, 1716-1794
An essay on diseases incidental to Europeans
in hot climates. With the method of preventing their fatal consequences ... To which is
added, an appendix concerning intermittent
fevers. To the whole is annexed, a simple and
easy way to render salt water fresh, and to
prevent a scarcity of provisions in long voyages at sea. The 2d ed., enl. and improved ...
London, T. Becket and P. A. De Hondt, 1771.
xv, 375, [9] p. 21 cm.
Imperfect: p. [i-ii] (half-title?) wanting.

NL 0376167   DNLM PPC PPL ViU MBCo

Lind, James, 1716-1794.
An essay on diseases incidental to
Europeans in hot climates. With the
method of preventing their fatal consequences. 3d ed. London, printed for
T. Becket, 1777.
xvi,379,[9]p. (8vo) 21½cm.

     MWA
NL 0376168   KU-M NNNAM MBCo PPC MH DNLM PPAmP ICRL

Lind, James, 1716-1794.
An essay on diseases incidental to hot
climates...4th ed. Lond. 1783.
357 p.

NL 0376169   PPPH

Lind, James, 1716-1794.
An essay on diseases incidental to Europeans in hot
climates. With the method of preventing their fatal consequences. By James Lind ... 4th ed. ... London, Printed for J. Murray, 1788.
xvi, 358, [9] p. 21½ᶜᵐ.

1. Tropics—Diseases and hygiene.

7—32414

Library of Congress   RC961.L74

     ICJ PPL PPC
NL 0376170   DLC DNLM MBCo NcD-MC NcD CtY OClW-H

WZ
260
L742es
1792

Lind, James, 1716-1794
An essay on diseases incidental to Europeans
in hot climates. With the method of preventing their fatal consequences ... To which is
added, an appendix concerning intermittent
fevers. And a simple and easy way to render
sea water fresh, and to prevent a scarcity of
provisions in long voyages at sea. The 5th
ed. ... London, J. Murray, 1792.
xvi, 357, [8] p. 21 cm.

NL 0376171   DNLM CtY PP PPC MBCo N LU

RC961
L64
1808

Lind, James, 1716-1794.
An essay on diseases incidental to Europeans
in hot climates, with the method of preventing
their fatal consequences, by James Lind ...
To which is added, an appendix, concerning
intermittent fevers; and a simple and easy
way to render sea water fresh, and to prevent
a scarcity of provisions in long voyages
at sea. 6th ed. ... London, Richardson,
1808.
xiv, 402 p. 21½cm.

NL 0376172   NNC PPC MB NcU-H DNLM MBCo CtY

Lind, James, 1716-1794.
An essay on diseases incidental to Europeans, in hot
climates, with the method of preventing their fatal consequences. By James Lind ... To which is added, an appendix, concerning intermittent fevers, and a simple and
easy way to render sea water fresh, and to prevent a scarcity of provisions in long voyages at sea. 1st American,
from the 6th London ed. ... Philadelphia, Printed by
W. Duane, 1811.
viii, 268 p. 21¼ᶜᵐ.

1. Tropics—Diseases and hygiene. 2. Malarial fever.

7—32413

Library of Congress   RC961.L76

     ViU NcD OU PPL
NL 0376173   DLC NcD-MC KyU MBCo NcU NNNAM DNLM

WZ
260
L742e
1757

Lind, James, 1716-1794
An essay, on the most effectual means, of
preserving the health of seamen, in the Royal
Navy. Containing, cautions necessary for
those who reside in, or visit, unhealthy
situations; with directions, proper for the
security of all such, as attend sick persons
in fevers. And an appendix of observations,
on the treatment of diseases in hot climates ... London, A. Millar [etc., etc.] 1757.
xxiv, 119 p. 16 cm.
Imperfect: p. [i-ii] (half-title?) wanting.

NL 0376174   DNLM

WZ
260
L742e
1762

Lind, James, 1716-1794
An essay on the most effectual means of
preserving the health of seamen, in the Royal
Navy. Containing directions proper for all
those who undertake long voyages at sea, or
reside in unhealthy situations. With cautions
necessary for the preservation of such persons
as attend the sick in fevers ... The 2d ed.,
improved and enl. ... London, D. Wilson,
1762.
xxiii, [1], 143, 6, [1] p. 22 cm.

NL 0376175   DNLM KU-M NNNAM OClW-H ICN PPPH

---

*EC75
A1442
771o

Lind, James, 1716-1794.
An essay on the most effectual means of
preserving the health of seamen in the royal
navy. And a dissertation on fevers and infection.
Together with observations on the jail distemper,
and the proper methods of preventing and stopping
its infection. By James Lind ... A new edition,
much enlarged and improved.
London, Printed for D.Wilson and G.Nicol, in the
Strand.MDCCLXXIV.
8°. xx,363,[1]p. 21cm.
No.4 in a   volume of medical tracts.

NL 0376176   MH NcD PPC KyU NN NNNAM RPJCB

Lind, James, 1716-1794.
An essay on the most effectual means of
preserving the health of seamen in the
Royal Navy...
London: D. Wilson and G. Nicol, 1778.

NL 0376177   NNNAM MWA

WZ
260
L742e
1779

Lind, James, 1716-1794
An essay on the most effectual means of
preserving the health of seamen in the Royal
Navy. [3d ed.] And A dissertation on fevers
and infection. [2d ed. enl.] Together with
observations on the jail distemper, and the
proper methods of preventing and stopping
its infection ... A new ed., much enl. and
improved. London, J. Murray, 1779.
xx, 363, [1] p. 22 cm.
A dissertation on fevers and infection was

first published in 1763 under title: Two
papers on fevers and infection.

NL 0376179   DNLM PPC

Lind, James, 1716-1794, supposed author.
Essays on several subjects, viz. I. On the late
act to prevent clandestine marriages ...
     see under title

WZ
260
L742twF
1780

Lind, James, 1716-1794
Mémoires sur les fièvres et sur la contagion, lus à la Société de médecine & de philosophie d'Edimbourg ... Ouvrage traduit de
l'anglois, & augm. de plusieurs notes, par M.
Henri Fouquét ... Montpellier, Jean-François
Picot, 1780.
xxiv, 303, [1] p. 18 cm.
Translation of Two papers on fevers and
infection.

I. Fouquet, Henri, 1727-1806, ed. and tr.

NL 0376181   DNLM NNNAM

WZ 260
L515
1798

Lind, James, 1716-1794.
Mémoires sur les fièvres et sur la contagion, lus à la Société de médecine et de
philosophie d'Edimbourg, par Jacques Lind.
Ouvrage traduit de l'anglois ... par Henri
Fouquét. A Lausanne, Chez les Libraires
associés, 1798.
xx, 294 p.
(1. Fever. 2. Communicable diseases.)
[3. Fever - Early works to 1800. 4.
Communicable   diseases - Early works
to 1800.   I. Fouquet, Henri, 1727
-1806, tr.   II. Title.

NL 0376182   CaBVaU CtY-M DNLM

Lind, James, 1716-1794.
Middelen ter bewaaring der gezondheid op
d'oorlog's schepen ... Uit get Engelsch vertaald.
Volgens den 2. druk. Met aanmerkingen en een
verhandeling der voornaamst ziektens op de Oost-
Indische schepen der Vereenigde Nederlanden verm.
door Paulus de Wind ... 2. druk. Middelburg,
[1764]
19.5 cm.
t.-p. defaced.

NL 0376183   CtY

WZ
260
L742eDu
1760

Lind, James, 1716-1794
Middelen ter gezondheid op 's Konings Schepen ... Uit het Engelsch vertaald. Met aanmerkingen en eene verhandeling der voornaamste
ziektens op de Oost-Indische schepen der vereenigde Nederlanden verm. door Paulus de
Wind ... Middelburg, Louis Taillefert [op-
dracht 1760]
[10], 180, [1] p. 21 cm.
Translation of An essay on the most effectual means of preserving the health of seamen
in the Royal Navy.

NL 0376184   DNLM CtY

VOLUME 334

WZ
260
L742esDu
1781
Lind, James, 1716-1794
Proeve over de ziekten der Europeers in heete gewesten; en de middelen tot voorkooming van haare doodlijke gevolgen. Waar achter gevoegd is een aanhangsel, behelzende: eene verhandeling over de tusschenpoozende koortsen; eenvouwdig en gemakkelijk middel, om het zeewater zoet te maaken; en hulpmiddel tegen gebrek aan eetwaaren op zee ... Uit het Engelsch. Amsterdam, Martinus de Bruyn, 1781.
xii, 352 p. 23 cm.

NL 0376185   DNLM

Lind, James, 1716-1794.
Three letters relating to the navy
see under title

Lind, James, 1716-1794.
Three letters to Dr. Price ...

see

Lind, John, 1737-1781

18th
cent.
Lind, James, 1716-1794.
Traité du scorbut, contenant des recherches sur la nature, les causes & la curation de cette maladie ... traduit de l'Anglois ... auquel on a joint la traduction du Traité du scorbut de Boerhaave, commenté par Van Swieten. Paris, Ganeau, 1756.
2v. 18cm.
Sec. entries made.

NL 0376188   CtY-M PPJ DNLM CaBVaU PPC

616.39 Lind, James, 1716-1794.
L742tF2 Traité du scorbut, divisé en trois parties; contenant des recherches sur la nature, les causes & la curation de cette maladie; avec un table chronologique & critique de tout ce qui a paru sur ce sujet: traduit de l'Anglois de Lind. Auquel on a joint la traduction du Traité du scorbut de Boerhaave, commenté par Van Swieten. Nouv. éd.   Paris, Ganeau, 1771.
v. 17cm.

"Bibliotheque scorbutique": v.2, p.31-250.

NL 0376189   IU-M MH CtY-M

Lind, James, 1716-1794.
Traité du scorbut, divisé en trois parties, contenant des recherches sur la nature, les causes & la curation de cette maladie; avec un tableau chronologique & critique de tout ce qui a paru sur ce sujet: traduit de l'anglois de m.Lind ... Auquel on a joint la traduction du Traité du scorbut du Boerhaave, commenté par Van Swieten. Nouvelle éd. ... Paris, Méquignon aîné, 1783.
2 v. 16½cm.

"Bibliothèque scorbutique,ou tableau chronologique de tout ce qui a été publié jusqu'ici sur le scorbut": v.2,p.31-250.

"Traité du scorbut,traduit des Aphorismes de Boerhaave, commentés par m.Van Swieten": v.2,p.,251,-441.

1.Scurvy. I.Boerhaave,Hermann,1668-1738. II.Swieten, Gerard,freiherr van,1700-1772.

NL 0376191   MiU PPC NjP DNLM NNNAM CaBVaU

WZ
260
L742tF
1788
Lind, James, 1716-1794
Traité du scorbut ... contenant des recherches sur la nature, les causes & la curation de cette maladie; avec un tableau chronologique & critique de tout ce qui a paru sur ce sujet: traduit de l'anglois ... Auquel on a joint la traduction du traité du scorbut [des Aphorismes] de Boerhaave, commenté par Van-Swieten. Nouv. éd. ... Paris, Méquignon l'aîné, 1788.
2 v. 18 cm.

NL 0376192   DNLM CtY-M MWA

18th
Cent.
Lind, James, 1716-1794.
Trattato dello scorbuto diviso in tre parti, con un catalogo cronologico, di quanto è finora comparso sopra questo soggetto. Opera del cel. sig. Lind ... tradotta in lingua toscana dal sig. dot. Luca Martini ... Si aggiungono li due egregi trattati sopra la stessa materia del cel. sig. Boerhaave, e del sig. Addington. Venezia, Niccolò Pezzana, 1766.
xxxii, 535p. 18cm.
Boerhaave's treatise on scurvy is taken from his Aphorisms, with com   mentary by Van Swieten.

NL 0376193   CtY-M DNLM

LIND, JAMES, 1716-1794
A treatise of the scurvy. In three parts. Containing an inquiry into the nature, causes, and cure, of that disease. Together with a critical and chronological view of what has been published on the subject. By James Lind ... Edinburgh, Printed by Sands, Murray and Cochran for A. Millar, 1753.
xv, 456 p.   8vo

First edition. Garrison-Morton: 3713. Lind is considered as the founder of naval hygiene in England.
Bound in half calf over marbled boards; in cloth case. With stamp of Newcastle Infirmary Medical Library on title-page. From the library of J. K. Lilly, Jr.

DNLM CtNowaB
NL 0376195   InU ICJ NN PPC NIC NcU-H NNNAM CaBVaU

Lind, James, 1716-1794.
A treatise on the scurvy. In three parts. Containing an inquiry into the nature, causes, and cure, of that disease. Together with a critical and chronological view of what has been published on the subject. By James Lind ... 2d ed. cor., with additions and improvements. London, A. Millar, 1757.
xvi, (2) p., 1 l., 476 p. 20½cm.

1. Scurvy.
7-37787†
Library of Congress   RC663.L74

NL 0376196   DLC CaBVaU MnU DNLM PPHa PPC MiU CSmH

Mann
Microfilm
RJ
396
G56
Lind, James, 1716-1794.
A treatise on the scurvy. In three parts. Containing an inquiry into the nature, causes, and cure of that disease. Together with a critical and chronological view of what has been published on the subject. 2d ed. corr. with additions and improvements. London, A. Millar, 1757.

On film with Gli   sson, Francis. De rachitide. Londini   1650.

Continued in next column

Continued from preceding column

Microfilm copy made of the original by Medicofilm Service, Army Medical Library, Washington. Negative.
Collation of the original: xvi, 476 p.

1. Scurvy.

NL 0376198   NIC KyU IaU DNLM

Lind, James, 1716-1794.
A treatise on the scurvy. In three parts. Containing an inquiry into the nature, causes, and cure, of that disease. Together with a critical and chronological view of what has been published on the subject. By James Lind ... The 3d ed., enl. and improved. London, S. Crowder [etc.] MDCCLXXII.
xiv, 2, 559, [1] p. 21¼ʷ.

1. Scurvy. 2. Scurvy—Bibl.
35-36245
Library of Congress   RC663.L74 1772

KU-M CtNowaB
NL 0376199   DLC DNLM MWA NcD-MC PPC PU ViRA CaBVaU

Lind, James, 1716-1794.
Treatise on scurvy; a bicentenary volume containing a reprint of the first edition of A treatise of the scurvy by James Lind, with additional notes. Edited by C. P. Stewart and Douglas Guthrie. Edinburgh, University Press, 1953.
440 p. port., facsim., geneal. table. 23 cm.

1. Scurvy.
[RC663.L   ]
A 54-1623
William H. Welch Med.   Library
for Library of Congress   [1]

NNNAM OrU-M
CaBVaU NcU OU NcD NNC-M PPC NIC CtY-M DNLM NcD-MC
NL 0376200   MdBJ-W OrCS OkU-M ViU TU CLSU MU FU-HC

Lind, James, 1716-1794.
Two papers on fevers and infection. Which were read before the Philosophical and medical society, in Edinburgh. By James Lind ... London, D. Wilson, MDCCLXIII.
2 p. l., 119 p. 21ᶜᵐ.

1. Fever. 2. Contagion and contagious diseases.
35-36249
Library of Congress   RC106.L5

NL 0376201   DLC CaBVaU MnU-B PPC CU-M DNLM CtY PPL

WZ
260
L742esG
1773
Lind, James, 1716-1794
... Versuch über die Krankheiten denen Europäer in heissen Climaten unterworfen sind. Nebst der Methode ihre gefährlichen Folgen zu verhüten ... Aus dem Englischen übersetzt. Riga und Leipzig, Johann Friedrich Hartknoch, 1773.
[12], 328, [8] p. 18 cm.
Translated by Johann Nathanael Pezold.
"Die kalten Fieber betreffend": p. 256-303;
"Vorschläge, den Mangel an süssem Wasser und

Lebensmitteln auf der See zu verhüten": p. 304-323.

I. Pezold, Johann Nathanael, 1739-1813, tr.

NL 0376203   DNLM MBCo ICJ

VOLUME 334

Lind, James, 1716–1794.
.... Versuch über die Krankheiten der Europäer in warmen Ländern, und die Mittel gegen die Folgen derselben nebst einem Anhange über die Wechselfieber, und einer Abhandlung von einer einfachen Methode das Seewasser trinkbar zu machen. Mit vielen Anmerkungen von Thion de la Chaume, ... Aus dem Englischen und Französischen. .... Riga, J. F. Hartknoch, 1792.
470 p. 20ᶜᵐ.
At head of title: Jacob Lind, ...

NL 0376204   ICJ

British   Lind, James, 1736–1812
Tracts   A description of rifled ordnance; fitted
1776   with sectors, telescopes, &c. In which is con-
L64   tained, an account of the nature and proper-
           ties of rifles in general. Edinburgh,
           W. Creech and T. Cadell, 1776.
           vii, 31p. plates. 23cm.

NL 0376205   CtY

Lind, James, 1736–1812.
Dissertatio medica, inauguralis, de febre remittente putrida paludum quae grassabatur in Bengalia A. D. 1762. Quam ... ex auctoritate ... Gulielmi Robertson ... Academiæ edinburgenæ præfecti ... pro gradu doctoris ... eruditorum examini subjicit Jacobus Lind, Britannus. Prid. id. septemb. ₁768₎ ... Edinburgi, apud Balfour, Auld, et Smellie, academiæ typographos, M,DCC,LXVIII.
3 p. l., 44 p. front. (fold. map) 19ᶜᵐ.
1. Malarial fever. 2. Malarial fever—Bengal.
                                          36–36682
Library of Congress   RC164.I 3L5

NL 0376206   DLC PPC MB DNLM

B616.936
L64dE   LIND, James, 1736–1812.
         A treatise on the putrid and remitting
         fen fever, which raged at Bengal in the
         year 1762. Tr. from the Latin, of a
         dissertation on that subject, by James
         Lind... London, E. and C. Dilly, 1772.
         ₍iii₎–vii, 61 p.   19cm.

         Translation of: De febre remittente
         putrida paludum quae grassabatur in
         Bengalia A.D.   1762.
         1.Malarial   fever in Bengal, 1762.

NL 0376207   MnU

Lind, James, 1736–1812.
A treatise on the putrid & remitting marsh fever which raged at Bengal in the year 1762 ... Edinburgh, Elliot, 1776.
70 p.

NL 0376208   PPPH MH

Lind, Jenny
see
Lind-Goldschmidt, Jenny Maria, 1820–1887.

WMA   Lind, Jens Georg, b. 1794.
L742D   De delirio tremente sic dicto; commentatio
1822   medica quam pro licentia summos in medicina
        honores rite obtinendi publice defendere
        studebit auctor... Respondente ornatissimo
        Nicolao Christiano Möhl... die Martii. h.
        l. q. s. Hauniae, Leteris Boae Brünnichii,
        1822.
        (6), 106, (6) p. 19 cm.
        "Conspectus literaturae hujus morbi, quatenus
        nobis cognitae": p. (1–4) (3d group).
        1. Psychoses, Alcoholic. ₍I. Möhl, Nicolai
        Christian, 1798–   1830. II. Title.

NL 0376210   WU-M DNLM

Lind, Jens Vilhlem August, 1874–
... Ascomycetes and Fungi imperfecti ...
Kristiania, A.W. Brøgger, 1924.
28 p.   II pl.   27 cm.   (Report of the scientific results of the Norwegian expedition to Novaya Zemlya 1921. No. 19)
"Literature cited": p. 27.

NL 0376211   CtY

Lind, Jens Vilhelm August, 1874–
The barberry bush & its law; being a translation from Berberisbusken og berberisloven, af J.Lind. Kobenhaven, Trykt hos Nielsen & Lydiche (A.Simmelkiaer) 1915.
cover-title, 28 numb.ℓ.   28 x 21½ cm.
Typewritten copy.

NL 0376212   MiU

Lind, Jens Vilhelm August, 1874–
Danish fungi as represented in the herbarium of E. Rostrup; rev. by J. Lind; printed at the expence ₍!₎ of the Carlsberg-fund. Copenhagen, Gyldendalske boghandel, 1913.
3 p. l., 648, ₍2₎ p. illus. (incl. ports.) ix pl. 25ᶜᵐ.
1. Fungi—Denmark.   I. *Rostrup, Emil, 1831–1907.
                                          Agr 13–1672 Revised
U. S. Dept. of agr. Library   462L642D
for Library of Congress   ₍r38b2₎

         ICJ CaBVaU
NL 0376213   DNAL WaU NcU NcRS NIC CU OU NcU MiU

Lind, Jens Vilhelm August, 1874–
Danmarks havebrug og gartneri til aaret 1919; udviklingen gennem tiderne. Ved Svend Bruun og Axel Lange. Med c. 300 illustrationer. Kjøbenhavn og Kristiania, Gyldendal, Nordisk forlag, 1920.

AS281   Lind, Jens Vilhelm August, 1874–   joint
.D223   author.
rækkke 8, **Jessen, Knud,** 1884–
vol. 3,   Det danske markukrudts historie, af Knud Jessen og Jens
           Lind. Med 1 oversigtsskema ... København, A. F. Høst &
           søn, 1922–23.

Lind, Jens Vilhelm August, 1874–
... Fungi collected on the north-coast of Greenland by the late Dr. Th. Wulff, by J. Lind. (With 1 plate) 1924.
(*In* Meddelelser om Grønland. København, 1927. 28ᶜᵐ. bd. LXIV, p. ₍289₎–₍304₎ pl.)
Den II. Thule ekspedition til Grønlands nordkyst 1916–18, nr. 12.
"List of literature" : p. 302.
1. Fungi—Greenland.   I. Wulff, Thorild, 1877–1917.
                                          A 42–2070
John Crerar library
for Library of Congress   [Q115.D39 vol. 64]
                           ₍2₎   (506)

NL 0376216   ICJ TxU

Lind, J₍ens Vilhelm August₎ 1874–
Fungi (micromycetes) collected in Arctic North America (King William Land, King Point, and Herschell Isl.) by the Gjöa expedition under Captain Roald Amundsen 1904–1906, determined by J. Lind. Christiania: J. Dybwad, 1910. 25 p., 1 pl. 4°. (Videnskabs-Selskabet i Christiania. Skrifter. I. Mathematisk-naturvidenskabelig Klasse. 1909. no. 9.)
Bibliography, p. 22–24.

1. Fungi, Arctic regions.
N. Y. P. L.   November 20, 1911.

NL 0376217   NN

Lind, Jens Vilhelm August, 1874–
... The geographical distributior of some Arctic micromycetes, by J. Lind. København, Andr. Fred. Høst & søn, Bianco Lunos bogtrykkeri, 1927.
45 p. incl. tables. 24ᶜᵐ. (Kgl. danske videnskabernes selskab. Biologiske meddelelser. VI, 5)
Bibliography : p. ₍39₎–45.

1. Fungi—Arctic regions. 2. Botany—Geographical distribution.
                                          A C 35–446
Title from Stanford Univ.
Library of Congress   [AS281.D212 VI, 5]

NL 0376218   CSt NNBG MoU TU PPAmP MiU NN

Lind, Jens Vilhelm August, 1874–
... Micromycetes, by J. Lind. København, C. A. Reitzel, 1933.
5 p. 27½ᶜᵐ. (Meddelelser om Grønland udgivne af Kommissionen for videnskabelige undersøgelser i Grønland, bd. 104, nr. 6)
At head of title: ... The Scoresby sound committee's 2nd east Greenland expedition in 1932 to King Christian IX's Land. Leader: Einar Mikkelsen.

1. Fungi—Greenland.   I. Scoresbysund komitéens Østgrønlandsekspedition til Kong Christian IX's Land. 2d, 1932. II. Title.
                                          A 45–304
Yale univ. Library
for Library of Congress   Q115.D39 bd. 104, nr. 6
——— Copy 2.   QK615.L5
                         ₍3₎†

NL 0376219   CtY DLC TxU NIC ViU OCU

Lind, Jens Vilhelm August, 1874–
... Micromycetes from north-western Greenland found on plants collected during the Jubilee expedition 1920–23, by J. Lind. 1926.
(*In* Meddelelser om Grønland. København, 1929. 23ᶜᵐ. bd. LXXI, p. ₍159₎–179)
Jubilæumsekspeditionen nord om Grønland, 1920–23. Nr. 4.
"List of literature" : p. 177–179.
1. Fungi—Greenland.
                                          A 42–2086
John Crerar library
for Library of Congress   [Q115.D39 vol. 71]
                          ₍2₎   (506)

NL 0376220   ICJ MB CtY NN TxU CU

Q115   Lind, Jens Vilhelm August, 1874–
O 84   The micromycetes of Svalbard. Oslo, I
no.13   kommisjon hos J. Dybwad, 1928.
        61 p. illus., fold. map. 27cm. (Norges
        Svalbard- og Ishavs-undersøkelser. Skrifter
        om Svalbard og Ishavet, Nr.13)

        At head of title: Det Kongelige Departement
        for Handel, Sjøfart, Industri, Håndverk og
        Fiskeri.

        1. Fungi - Svalbard.   I. Title.

NL 0376221   GU KMK

Lind, Jens Vilhelm August, 1874–   615.32 R800
.... Om lægeplanter i danske klosterhaver og klosterbøger. København, H. Koppel, 1918.
115, [2] p. 21ᶜᵐ.
At head of title: J. Lind.
"Udgivet af Dansk medicinsk-historisk selskab."
"Litteratur," p. [106]–111.
Contents. — Kilder til kundskab om middelalderens medicinske anvendelse af planterne. — Lægeplanteavl i klosterhaverne. — Urterne i Hendrik Harpestrengs Lægebog. — Naturstudier. — Monografier af nogle faa lægeplanter.

NL 0376222   ICJ

VOLUME 334

Lind, Jens Vilhelm August, 1874–
Skadelige svampe i vore haver af Jens Lind under medvirkning af prof. dr. F. Kølpin Ravn ... København, C. J. Cato, 1910.
1 p. l., ₍9₎–104 p. illus. 23ᶜᵐ.
Særtryk af de Samvirkende danske haveselskabers tidsskrift "Haven." p. 97–104, advertising matter.

1. Fungi. 2. Vegetable pathology.   ɪ. Ravn, Frederik Kølpin.

Agr 10–1021

Library, U. S. Dept. of   Agriculture   462L642

NL 0376223   DNAL

Lind, Jens Vilhelm August, 1874–
... Studies on the geographical distribution of Arctic circumpolar micromycetes, by J. Lind. København, Levin & Munksgaard, 1934.
152 p. 24½ᶜᵐ. (K. Danske videnskabernes selskab. **Biologiske meddelelser.** xɪ, 2)
"List of literature": p. 148–152.

1. Fungi. 2. Botany—Arctic regions.

A C 34–3559

Columbia univ. Library
for Library of Congress   [AS281.D212 xi, 2]

NL 0376224   NNC MoU NcU PPAmP PU TU MiU

Lind, Jens Vilhelm August, 1874–
... Systematic list of fungi (*Micromycetes*) from north-east Greenland (N. of 76° N. lat.) collected by the "Danmark-expedition" 1906–1908, determined by J. Lind. With plate x. 1910.
(*In* Meddelelser om Grønland. København, 1917. 28ᶜᵐ. **bd. xLIII,** p. ₍147₎–162. pl. x)
Danmark-ekspeditionen til Grønlands nordøstkyst, 1906–1908. bd. III, nr. vɪ.
"List of papers dealing with fungi of northern east Greenland": p. ₍149₎–150.

1. Fungi—Greenland.

A C 39–2460 Revised

John Crerar library
for Library of Congress   [Q115.D39 vol. 43]
                             ₍r40e2₎   (508)

NL 0376225   ICJ CtY DLC NN MB

Lind, Johanna Maria
        see
Lind-Goldschmidt, Jenny Maria, 1820–1887.

Lind, Johannes Jacobus
... Ad titulum Digestorum, qui est de aleatoribus ... defendet Johannes Jacobus Lind ... Lugduni Batavorum, apud viduam M. Cyfveer, j. fil., 1816.
4 p. l., 40 p. 24cm.
Diss.- Leiden.

NL 0376227   MH-L

Lind, John
The value of the Scriptures, and duty of distributing them ... Chambersburgh, Pa. The Soc., 1815.

NL 0376228   PPPrHi

1885   Lind, John, M.D.
A case of a penetrating wound by a bayonet passing through the heart, in which the patient survived the accident upwards of nine hours.
[In Medical records and researches. [Editor anon.] 8°. London, for T. Cox, 1798. p. 59–69]

NL 0376229   DLC

Lind, John, writer on heart problems in children.
Angiocardiographic studies in children by John Lind and Carl Wegelius. Chicago, Ill., Yearbook publisher, 1954.

NL 0376230   OrU-M

Lind, John, writer on heart problems in children
Heart volume in normal infants, a roentgenological study. ₍Translated by Ulla Schott₎ Stockholm, Bonniers boktr., 1950.
126, ₍1₎ p. diagrs. 25 cm. (Acta radiologica. **Supplementum 82)**
At head of title: From the Paediatric Clinic of Karolinska institutet at the Norrtull's Hospital, Stockholm, Sweden. **Head: Professor Arvid Wallgren.**
Bibliography: p. 120–₍127₎

1. Heart. 2. Infants. 3. Diagnosis, Radioscopic.   ɪ. Title. (Series)

A 51–2584

Michigan. Univ. Libr.
for Library of Congress   ₍2₎

NL 0376231   MiU MoU ViU

Lind, John, 1737–1781.
Works by this author printed in America before 1801 are available in this library in the Readex Microprint edition of **Early American Imprints** published by the American Antiquarian Society. This collection is arranged according to the numbers in Charles Evans' American Bibliography.

NL 0376232   DLC

₍Lind, John₎ 1737–1781.
Anmerkungen über die vornehmsten acten des Dreyzehnten Parlaments von Grossbritannien, von dem verfasser der Briefe über den jetzigen zustand von Polen, nebst einem aussöhnungsplan. Nach der ersten ausgabe von 1775 aus dem engl. übersetzt ... Braunschweig, Fürstl. waisenhaus-buchhandlung, 1778.
12 p. l., 334 p., 1 l. 21ᶜᵐ. (*Added t.-p.:* Amerikanisches archiv, hrsg. von Julius August Remer ... 3. bd.)
The original English edition has subtitle "Vol. 1. Containing remarks on the acts relating to the colonies ..." Vol. 1 only published.
1. Gt. Brit. Parliament, 1768–1774. 2. U. S.—Pol. & govt.—Revolution. 3. Gt. Brit—Pol. & govt.—1760–1820.

8–29238

Library of Congress   E211.R38 vol. 3

NL 0376233   DLC MiU-C MB OCl

₍Lind, John₎ 1737–1781.
An answer to the Declaration of the American Congress ... London, Printed for T. Cadell ₍etc.₎ 1776.
132 p. 20ᶜᵐ.

1. U. S. Declaration of independence. 2. U. S.—Pol. & govt.—Revolution.   ɪ. Title.

3–24747

Library of Congress   E221.L74

NIC IEN NcD ICN MiU-C OWoC NjP MiU ViU PMA
NL 0376234   DLC RPB N NcU CtY ViW IaU NNC IU NN PPL

Microfilm
E
133
₍Lind, John₎ 1737–1781.
An answer to the Declaration of the American Congress ... London, Printed for T. Cadell ₍etc.₎ 1776.
132 p. 20ᶜᵐ.
Microfilm copy.
Negative; original in University of Chicago Library.

NL 0376235   ICU

Microfiche
J4   [Lind, John] 1737–1781.
An answer to the Declaration of the American Congress ... London, Printed for T. Cadell [etc.] 1776.
Jeffersonian Americana ES 99–101.
Sabin 41281.

NL 0376236   ViU ICRL PSt OU CaBVaU

₍Lind, John₎ 1737–1781.
An answer to the Declaration of the American Congress ... 2d ed. London, Printed for T. Cadell ₍etc.₎ 1776.
132 p. 20¼ᶜᵐ.

NL 0376237   CtY PPL CLU-C

₍Lind, John₎ 1737–1781.
An answer to the Declaration of the American Congress ... 3d ed. London, Printed for T. Cadell ₍etc.₎ 1776.
132 p. 20¼ᶜᵐ.

1. U. S. Declaration of independence. 2. U. S.—Pol. & govt.—Revolution.   ɪ. Title.

17–28117

Library of Congress   E221.L743

NL 0376238   DLC PPL MiU-C RPJCB

₍Lind, John₎ 1737–1781.
An answer to the Declaration of the American Congress ... The 4th ed. London, Printed for T. Cadell ₍etc.₎ 1776.
132 p. 20¼ᶜᵐ.
₍Miscellaneous pamphlets, v. 225, no. 8₎

1. U. S. Declaration of independence. 2. U. S.—Pol. & govt.—Revolution.   ɪ. Title.

3–24746

Library of Congress   AC901.M5 vol. 225

NL 0376239   DLC NNC NWA NcGU MH MiU-C RPJCB

₍Lind, John₎ 1737–1781.
An answer to the Declaration of the American Congress ... 5th ed. London, Printed for T. Cadell ₍etc.₎ 1776.
132 p. 21½ᶜᵐ.

1. U. S. Declaration of independence. 2. U. S.—Pol. & govt.—Revolution.   ɪ. Title.

17–13763

Library of Congress   E221.L744

MiU-C OClWHi GMW KU FTaSU RPJCB MShM
NL 0376240   DLC CLU-C PPL N IU IaU PHi OFH PV MnHi

₍Lind, John₎ 1737–1781.
An answer to the Declaration of the American Congress ... The 6th ed. Aberdeen, Printed for J. Boyle, 1777.
₍3₎–132 p. 19ᶜᵐ.
Published anonymously.

Subject entries: 1. U. S. Declaration of independence. 2. U. S.—Pol. & govt.—Revolution.

3–24746

Library of Congress, no.   E221.L745.

NL 0376241   DLC NN ViU RPJCB MB

VOLUME 334

₍Lind, John₎ 1737–1781.
An answer to the Declaration of the American Congress ... 4th ed. Dublin, Printed by P. Higly, 1777.
viii, 88 p. 21ᶜᵐ.

1. U. S. Declaration of independence. 2. U. S.—Pol. & govt.—Revolution. I. Title.

17–28118

Library of Congress   E221.L7432

NL 0376242   DLC MdBJ-G

₍Lind, John₎ 1737–1781.
The Declaration of independence of the American Congress; to which is added the Answer to the Declaration, with notes, by an eminent person. Dublin, Printed by P. Higly, 1782.
2 p. l., ₍iii₎–vii, ₍1₎–88 p. 19½ᶜᵐ.

1. U. S. Declaration of independence. I. Title. II. Title: Answer to the Declaration of the American Congress.

S D 32–24

Library, U. S. Dept. of   State JK128.L5

NL 0376243   DS

₍Lind, John₎ 1737–1781, *supposed author.*
Defence of Lord Pigot. London, 1777.
328, 72, ₍1₎ p. 26 cm.
"Ascribed also to Alexander Dalrymple."—Halkett & Laing.
Manuscript notes inserted.
"Errata et addenda" : page at end.

1. Pigot, George Pigot, baron, 1719–1777. 2. India—Pol. & govt.—1765–1947. I. Dalrymple, Alexander, 1737–1808, supposed author. II. Title.

DS470.P5L5   58–51082

NL 0376244   DLC WU NcD MiU ICU MnU

₍Lind, John₎ 1737–1781.
An Englishman's answer, to the address, from the delegates to the people of Great-Britain, in a letter to the several colonies, which were represented in the late Continental congress. New-York: Printed by James Rivington, 1775.
26 p. 20½ᶜᵐ.
₍Hazard pamphlets, v. 38, no. 1₎
Signed: An Englishman.
1. U. S.—Pol. & govt.—Revolution. 2. U. S. Continental congress. 1775. I. The twelve United Colonies ... To the inhabitants of Great Britain. I. Title.

Library of Congress   AC901.H3 vol. 38   20–13496

NL 0376245   DLC NIC RPJCB ICN MH PPL CtY MiU-C

₍Lind, John₎ 1737–1781.
A letter to the Right Honourable Willoughby Bertie, by descent earl of Abingdon ... In which His Lordships candid and liberal treatment of the now Earl of Mansfield, is fully vindicated ... London, Printed for T. Payne & son ₍etc.₎ 1778.
xii, 86 p. 20½ᶜᵐ.
Published anonymously.
An answer to certain passages, reflecting on the Earl of Mansfield, in the Earl of Abingdon's Thoughts on Mr. Burke's Letter to the sheriffs of Bristol.

1. Abingdon, Willoughby Bertie, 4th earl of, 1740–1799. Thoughts on Mr. Burke's Letter to the sheriffs of Bristol. 2. Mansfield, William Murray, 1st earl of, 1705–1793. 3. Gt. Brit.—Pol. & govt.—1760–1789. 4. U. S.—Pol. & govt.—Revolution. I. Title.

Library of Congress   E211.L74   5–2952 Revised
—— Copy 2. ₍With   Burke, Edmund. A letter from Edmund Burke ... to John   mund Burke ... to John
iffs. London, 1777₎   Farr and John Harris, esqrs. sheriffs. London, 1777₎   E211.B942   ₍r42d2₎

PPAmP MiU-C ViU
NL 0376246   DLC MH ICRL NIC NN KyU NcD CtY N ICN

Micro 3
[Lind, John] 1737–1781.
A letter to the Right Honourable Willoughby Bertie, by descent Earl of Abingdon ... In which His Lordships candid and liberal treatment of the now Earl of Mansfield, is fully vindicated ... London, Printed for T. Payne & Son [etc.] 1778.
Microcard edition (3 cards).   (Jeffersonian Americana)
Published anonymously.
An answer to certain passages, reflecting on the Earl of Mansfield, in the Earl of Abingdon's Thoughts on Mr. Burke's Letter to the sheriffs of Bristol.
Sabin 41283.

NL 0376247   ViU PSt TxU CaBVaU

₍Lind, John₎ 1737–1781.
Letters concerning the present state of Poland. Together with the manifesto of the courts of Vienna, Petersburgh, and Berlin. And the letters patent of the King of Prussia. London, Printed for T. Payne, 1773.
2 p. l., ₍360₎ p. 21ᶜᵐ.
"Manifesto" and each of the four letters paged separately. Letters II–IV each have special t.-p.

1. Poland—Hist.—Partition period, 1763–1796. I. Title.

19–2298

Library of Congress   DK434.L5

NL 0376248   DLC NIC IU OCl MoU MU CtY InU MdBP

₍Lind, John₎ 1737–1781.
Letters concerning the present state of Poland. Letter IV. London, Printed for T. Payne, 1773.
140 p. 20cm.

1. Poland—Hist.—Partition period, 1763–1796. I. Title.

NL 0376249   NIC

DLL34 L5 1773   ₍Lind, John₎ 1737–1781.
Letters concerning the present state of Poland. With an Appendix, containing the Manifestoes of the Courts of Vienna, Petersburg, and Berlin and other authentic papers. 2. ed.   London, Printed for T. Payne, 1773.
393p. 22cm.

Letters each have special t.p.

1. Poland — Hist. — Partition period, 1763–1796. I. Title.

NL 0376250   IaU CaBVaU MdBJ KyU MB NN MA

₍Lind, John₎ 1737–1781.
Remarks on the principal acts of the Thirteenth Parliament of Great Britain. By the author of Letters concerning the present state of Poland ... Vol. I. Containing remarks on the acts relating to the colonies. With a plan of reconciliation. London, Printed for T. Payne, 1775.
xvi, ₍4₎, 500 p. 22ᶜᵐ.
No more published.

1. Gt. Brit. Parliament, 1768–1774. 2. U. S.—Pol. & govt.—Revolution. 3. Gt. Brit.—Pol. & govt.—1760–1820. I. Title.

Library of Congress   E211.L75   8–33567

NcD CtY ViU MiU-C MB
NL 0376251   DLC NN CaOTP MWiW-C ICRL UU LNHT ICN

Microfiche J4
[Lind, John] 1737–1781.
Remarks on the principal acts of the Thirteenth Parliament of Great Britain. By the author of Letters concerning the present state of Poland ... Vol. I. Containing remarks on the acts relating to the colonies. With a plan of reconciliation. London, Printed for T. Payne, 1775.
Jeffersonian Americana ES 1502–13
No more published.
Sabin 41284.

OU
NL 0376252   ViU CaBVaU PPAmP MWA PSt OU RPJCB TxU

Lind, John, 1737–1781.
Réponse à la Declaration du Congrès américain ... Par M. Linde. Traduit de l'anglois par M. Freville. A La Haye: Chez P. F. Gosse, 1777.   2 p.l., 205(1) p.   22cm. (8°.)

Sabin 41282.   Knuttel 19145.
First leaf blank.

972079A. 1. Declaration of Independence. 2. United States—Hist.—Revolution—Constitutional aspects.   pendence. 2. United States—Hist.— 1749–1832, tr.   I. Fréville, Anne François Joachim,
N. Y. P. L.   June 22, 1939

NL 0376253   NN PHi MiU-C MH MB CSmH NNC RPJCB

₍Lind, John₎ 1737–1781.
Three letters to Dr. Price containing remarks on his Observations on the nature of civil liberty, the principles of government, and the justice and policy of the war with America ... By a member of Lincoln's Inn, F. R. S., F. S. A. London, Printed for T. Payne ₍etc.₎ 1776.
1 p. l., xxii, 163 p. 20ᶜᵐ.

1. Price, Richard, 1723–1791. Observations on the nature of civil liberty ... 2. U. S.—Pol. & govt.—Revolution. 3. U. S.—Hist.—Revolution—Causes. I. Title.

Library of Congress   E211.P9685   11–3988

NNC NN RPJCN NBuU ICRL
NL 0376254   DLC MH MH-BA CtY NcD ICN MiU-C MBAt NNC

Microfiche J4
[Lind, John] 1737–1781.
Three letters to Dr. Price containing remarks on his Observations on the nature of civil liberty, the principles of government, and the justice and policy of the war with America ... By a member of Lincoln's Inn, F. R. S., F. S. A. London, Printed for T. Payne [etc.] 1776.
Jeffersonian Americana ES 128–32
Sabin 41286.

NL 0376255   ViU CaBVaU OU PSt

Lind, John, 1854–
La gente de México, por John Lind, ex-representante personal del presidente Wilson en México. Tr. por la Secretaría de instrucción publica y bellas artes. Veracruz, Tip. de la Sria. de i. p. y b. a., 1915.
34 p. 18ᶜᵐ.
Signed: Tradujo, J. M. Coéllar.

1. Mexico. I. Coéllar, J. M., tr. II. Title.

17–14437

Library of Congress   F1208.L74

NL 0376256   DLC TxU

JX2318 .L65 1900   Lind, John, 1854–
Gov. Lind's speech accepting re-nomination for governor, delivered at St. Paul auditorium, September 6, 1900. ₍St.Paul, Allied printing trades council, 1900?₎
48 p.   illus.(port.)   15x7cm.

Caption title.
On cover: Acceptance speech of Governor John Lind.
Portrait on cover.

NL 0376257   MnHi

809.72 L64m   Lind, John, 1854–
The Mexican people.   Minneapolis [1914?]
31p.

Reprinted from the Bellman, Minneapolis, Minn.

NL 0376258   IU MWelC

VOLUME 334

Lind, John, 1854–
...Tariff revision and Canadian reciprocity. Speeches of Hon. John Lind of Minnesota, and Hon. John A. Sullivan of Massachusetts. In the House of representatives. Washington, D. C., 1904.
15 p.

I. Sullivan, John Andrew, 1868–1927.

NL 0376259   MiD-B MH

RC435   Lind, John Edward, 1888–
.L5   [Collected papers, reprints, etc. in psychopathology]
5 pam.
[1] Combined psychoses. (Repr. Jour. of nerv. & ment. dis. v. 42, Apr. 1915, p. 217–34. [2] The mental examination of negroes. 14 p. (Repr. Internat. clinics. v. 3, ser. 26, c1916) [3] Constitutional psychopathy and its conflict with social conditions. 16 p. (Ibid., v. 3, ser. 27. [4] Phylogenetic elements in the psychoses of the negro. (Repr. Psychoanal. rev. v. 4, 1917. p. 303–332) [5] The situation psychosis. 33 p. (Repr. Med. rec. July 5, 1919)

NL 0376260   DLC

Lind, John Edward, 1888–
... Diagnostic pitfalls in the mental examination of negroes. By John E. Lind ... [n. p.] ʿ1914.
5, [1] p. 20ᶜᵐ.
Caption title.
"Reprinted from the New York medical journal for June 27, 1914."

1. Negroes. 2. Insanity—Diagnosis and semeiology. I. Title.

Library of Congress   RC602.L5   14-13972

NL 0376261   DLC

Lind, John Edward, 1888–   joint tr.

Adler, Alfred, 1870–1937.
The neurotic constitution; outlines of a comparative individualistic psychology and psychotherapy, by Dr. Alfred Adler ... Authorized English translation by Bernard Glueck ... and John E. Lind ... New York, Moffat, Yard and company, 1917.

Lind, John Edward, 1888–   tr.

Stekel, Wilhelm, 1868–
... The technique of dream interpretation, by Dr. Wilhelm Stekel, tr. by John Edward Lind ... [New York, 1917]

Lind, John Gustav(e), a. Ogden, Utah: Geologische Untersuchungen der Beziehungen zwischen den Gesteinsspalten, der Tektonik und dem hydrographischen Netz des Gebirges bei Heidelberg. Mit 1 Kt. Heidelberg: Winter 1910. 40 S. 8° ¶(Aus: Verhandlungen d. Naturhist.-Med. Vereins zu Heidelberg. N. F. Bd 11.)
Heidelberg, Naturw.-math. Diss. v. 18. Juli 1910, Ref. Salomon
[Geb. 26. Jan. 67 Stockholm; Wohnort: Heidelberg; Staatsangeh.: Vereinigte Staaten; Vorbildung: Univ. Utah B. S. Juni 95; Studium: Chicago 2, Jena 1, Heidelberg 4 S.; Rig. 20. Juni 10.]   [U 10. 2200]

NL 0376264   ICRL NNC MH PU CtY

Lind, John W.
England and the New York press; history and criticism, by J. W. Lind. [Chillicothe, Mo., Hatcher printing co., ʿ1915]
22 p. 17ᶜᵐ. $0.25

I. Title.

Library of Congress   D632.L5   15-17215

NL 0376265   DLC

Lind, John Wilhelm, 1861–
Handbook for carpet measurers, cutters and salesmen, including topics of general interest to the trade, with illustrations and diagrams, by John W. Lind. New York, G. Lyndoe, The American carpet and upholstery journal, 1905.
ix, 137 p. illus., diagrs. 19¼ᶜᵐ.

1. Carpets.

Library of Congress   TS1775.L7   5–26779

NL 0376266   DLC ICJ OrP NN MB

Lind, Jonas, tr.

Weiss, André, 1858–1928.
... Tysklands krænkelse af Belgiens og Luxemburgs neutralitet, ved André Weiss ... oversættelse ved Jonas Lind. Paris, A. Colin, 1915.

Lind, Jonathan

see

Lind, John, 1737–1781.

Lind, Joseph
De dialecto Pindarica. I. Prolegomena et de vocalismo Pindarico ex proximis sonis non apto... publice defendet Josephus Lind... Lundae, Apud Hjalmar Möller bibliopolam universitatis, 1893.
1., [2], 48 p. 26cm.

Thesis (Ph.D.) Lund university, 1893.

NL 0376269   NcD NjP NN CtY MiU ICRL

Lind, Justin Timotheus Balthasar
see   Linde, Justin Timotheus Balthasar, Freiherr von, 1797–1870.

Lind, Karl, 1831–1901, ed.
Ein Antiphonarium mit Bilderschmuck aus der Zeit des XI. und XII. Jahrhunderts im Stifte St. Peter zu Salzburg befindlich

see under   Catholic Church. Liturgy and ritual. Antiphonary.   [supplement]

Lind, Karl, 1831–1901
Blaetter für ältere Sphragistik. Hrsg. von der k.k. Central-Commission zur Erforschung und Erhaltung der Kunst- und historischen Denkmale. Wien, Gerold, 1878
xix p. ½plates

1. Seals (Numismatics)

NL 0376271   MH

Lind, Karl, 1831- 1901
Meisterwerke der kirchlichen glasmalerei. Hrsg. unter der artistischen leitung von prof. Rud. Geyling und Alois Löw; text von dr. Karl Lind. Wien, S. Czeiger [1894–97]
text: 1 l., 7 p. 50 x 33ᶜᵐ. and 50 col. pl. 85 x 55ᶜᵐ.
Published in parts.

I. Title.   2—21160

Library of Congress   NK5848.A2L5

NL 0376272   DLC OCl OO MB

Lind, Karl, 1831–1901.
Austria. *Zentral-kommission für denkmalpflege in Wien.*
Mittheilungen der Kaiserl. königl. central-commission zur erforschung und erhaltung der baudenkmale ... I.–xix. jahrg., 1856–1874. Wien, K. K. Hof- und staatsdruckerei [etc.] 1856–74.

Lind, Karl, 1831–1901.
Städte-wappen von Österreich-Ungarn nebst den landeswappen und landesfarben. Text von Dr. Karl Lind ... Wien, A. Schroll & co., 1885.
1 p. l., 14, [1] p. 26 col. pl. (2 fold.) 30ᶜᵐ.   3-27765

NL 0376274   DLC

Lind, Karl, 1831–1901.
Ueber den krummstab; eine archäologische skizze ... Wien, Prandel, 1863.
55 p. illus. 25.5 cm.
1. Crozier.

NL 0376275   NjP

Lind, Karl, 1831–1901.
Das Wappen der Stadt Wien. Ein Versuch zur Festellung der Geschichte dieses Wappens. Wien, Druck der kais. kön. Hof- und Staatsdruckerei, 1866.
36 p. illus., coats of arms (part col.) 25 cm.
Bibliographical footnotes.

1.Heraldry in Austria. Vienna. I.Title.

NL 0376276   MnU

Lind, Karl 1869–
Ueber das eindringen von pilzen in kalkgesteine... Inaug. Diss. Leipzig, 1898

NL 0376277   ICRL CtY

VOLUME 334

W 4
M96
1940
Lind, Karl August, 1916–
   Ein Beitrag zum Serumeisen und zur Eisenmangel-Krankheit. Wiesbaden, Ritter, 1940.
   47 p.

   Inaug.-Diss. - Munich.
   Bibliography: p. 45–46.

NL 0376278   DNLM MnU

Lind, Knud Peter, 1844–
   Frederik Anton Monrad Krabbe, født 16. decb. 1808, † 8. juni 1881. I. Ligprædiken af K. P. Lind ... II. Slægtsoptegnelser af A. Thiset ... Kjøbenhavn, Hoffensberg & Traps etabl., 1882.
   46 p. fold. geneal. tab. 22½ᶜᵐ.
   Trykt som manuskript.
   "Optegnelser om de ældre led af den paa Damsgaard hjemmehørende adelsslægt Krabbe med en stamtavle til nutiden. Ved A. Thiset": p. 7–46.

   1. Krabbe, Frederik Anton Monrad, 1808–1881. 2. Krabbe family. I. Thiset, Anders, 1850–

16–824
   Library of Congress   CS909.K8

NL 0376279   DLC

Lind, Kristina Ehrenström-
   see
   Ehrenström-Lind, Kristina.

Lind, L.
   Det Danske bibliothek. Kjøbenhavn, 1725.
   8vo.

NL 0376281   NN

Lind, L.
   Paa alle de Danske skrifter in det Danske bibliothek. Kjøbenhavn, 1725.
   8vo.

NL 0376282   NN

Lind, L   J
   Escape from Crete, being the personal narrative of a prisoner of war on the island of Crete and his escape by submarine to Alexandria ... By L. J. Lind. Sydney, N. S. W., Australasian publishing co. pty. ltd. ₁1944₎
   100 p. illus. (map) plates. 19ᶜᵐ.

   1. World war, 1939– —Prisoners and prisons, German. 2. World war, 1939– —Personal narratives, Australian. 3. World war, 1939– —Crete. I. Title.

45–6502
   Library of Congress   D805.G3L5
   ₁4₎   940.547243

NL 0376283   DLC

Lind, Lars Fredrik, 1750–1805.
   Domarens pröfning efter Sveriges lag; eller, Sättet at utröna lagens rätta förstånd mening och grund. Stockholm, Tryckt hos C. F. Marquard, 1799.
   200 p. 22 cm.
   With this are bound: Selling, Magnus. Kort anwisning till kam-kammar-werket. Hernösand, 1802 and Edman, Johan. Samling af skattläggnings-methoder. 1. delen. Upsala, 1773.

   1. Law—Sweden—Interpretation and construction. I. Title.

48–30672*

NL 0376284   DLC

Lind, Lars Fredrik, 1750–1805.
   Domarens pröfning efter Sveriges lag; eller, Sättet att utröna lagens rätta förstånd, mening och grund. Ny uppl, utg. med anmärkningar och register af A. Philipsson. Stockholm, A. Bonnier, 1848.
   183 p. 18 cm.

   1. Law—Sweden—Interpretation and construction. I. Philipsson, Aron, 1826–1881, ed. II. Title.

48–30517*

NL 0376285   DLC

Lind, Léon, 1903–
   ... Megalérythème épidémique (cinquième maladie) ... Paris, 1932.
   Thèse - Univ. de Paris.
   "Bibliographie": p. ₍57₎–66.

NL 0376286   CtY DNLM

875.1
R263vY1
Lind, Levi Robert, 1906–
   A collation of the six known manuscripts of the metrical version of the Vita sancti Malchi by Reginald of Canterbury. ₍Urbana₎ 1935.
   2v.
   Manuscript.
   Reginald's metrical version is based on St. Jerome's Vita sancti Malchi.

   1. Reginald of Canterbury, fl.1112. Vita sancti Malchi. 2. Hieronymus Sophronius, Eusebius, Saint. Vita sancti Malchi.

NL 0376287   IU

PA3612
.N6
1940
Lind, Levi Robert, 1906–
   Nonnus Panopolitanus.
   ... Dionysiaca, with an English translation by W. H. D. Rouse ... Mythological introduction and notes by H. J. Rose ... and notes on text criticism by L. R. Lind ... Cambridge, Mass., Harvard university press; London, W. Heinemann, ltd., 1940–42.

QM21
.V426
Lind, Levi Robert, 1906–   tr.
   Vesalius, Andreas, 1514–1564.
   The Epitome of Andreas Vesalius, tr. from the Latin with pref. and introd. by L. R. Lind; with anatomical notes by C. W. Asling and a foreword by Logan Clendening. New York, Macmillan Co., 1949.

Lind, Levi Robert, 1906–   ed.
   Lyric poetry of the Italian Renaissance; an anthology with verse translations. With an introd. by Thomas G. Bergin. New Haven, Yale University Press, 1954.
   xxvii, 384 p. 23 cm.

   1. Italian poetry (Collections) 2. Italian poetry—Translations into English. 3. English poetry—Translations from Italian. I. Title.

   PQ4208.L5   851.04   53–7770

WaSpG CaBVaU MtU WaS WaSp CaBVa OrCS
MiU OC1JC NcD WaU Or OrMonO OrPR OrU WaT IdU
NjN OOxM OC1 OC1W NN ViU CtY OCU PSC PU PPT
MB MsU MsSM NcRS PLF PBm PSt TxU OU OO KyLE TU
NL 0376290   DLC OrP PIm NjR IdPI NSyU GAT Wa NIC

Lind, Levi Robert, 1906–
   Medieval Latin studies: their nature and possibilities, by L. R. Lind ... Lawrence ₍University of Kansas press₎ 1941.
   4 p. l., 48 p. 23ᶜᵐ. (Half-title: Humanistic studies, no. 26)
   University of Kansas publications.
   Bibliographies: p. 30–44.

   1. Latin philology, Medieval and modern. 2. Latin philology, Medieval and modern—Bibl. I. Title.

41–52747
   Library of Congress   PA2807.L5
   ₍7₎   479

PSt MoU ViU OrU KU-M OrPR CaBVaU WaWW OrU
NL 0376291   DLC TxU OU OCU ODW OO PU PHC MB PSC

881
A8e.Yli
Lind, Levi Robert, 1906–
   The modernity of Aristotle's Ethics _ ₍Chicago₎ 1935.
   cover-title, p.418–423.

   Reprinted from the Classical journal, vol.XXX. no.7, April 1935.

NL 0376292   IU

Lind, Levi Robert, 1906–
   The Vita sancti Malchi of Reginald of Canterbury; a critical edition with introduction, apparatus criticus, notes and indices, by Levi Robert Lind ... Urbana, Ill., 1936.
   ₍4₎ p. 24ᶜᵐ.
   Abstract of thesis (PH. D.)—University of Illinois, 1936.
   Vita.
   Contains only a description of the manuscript.

   1. Reginald of Canterbury, fl. 1112. Vita sancti Malchi.

36–37539
   Library of Congress   PA8420.R2L5 1936
   Univ. of Illinois Libr.
   ——— Copy 2.   ₍2₎   879.1

NL 0376293   IU DLC

Lind, Levi Robert, 1906–   ed.
   Reginald of Canterbury, fl. 1112.
   The Vita sancti Malchi of Reginald of Canterbury; a critical edition with introduction, apparatus criticus, notes, and indices by Levi Robert Lind. Urbana, The University of Illinois press, 1942.

Lind, Levi Robert, 1906–
   What Rome has left us, by L. Robert Lind ... Williamsport, Pa., The Bayard press ₍*1935₎
   2 p. l., 7–34 p. 21ᶜᵐ. ₍Historical studies. Ser. I. Modern European history₎
   Bibliographical foot-notes.

   1. Rome—Civilization. I. Title.

A 38–1199
   Minnesota. Univ. Library
   for Library of Congress   ₍2₎

NL 0376295   MnU OCU

Lind, Lilo.   *6890.1.1912.2
   Ihr Russe.
   (In Deutsche Roman-Zeitung. Jahrgang 1912. Band 2, pp. 212–215. Berlin. 1912.)

NL 0376296   MB

Lind, Lizzy, af Hageby.
   see
   Lind af Hageby, Lizzy, 1878–

VOLUME 334

LIND, LUCILE SNOW.
There's just one song. Words and music by Lucile Snow Lind.
Philadelphia, Theodore Presser co. [c1935]

With piano accompaniment.

1. Songs, U. S. 2. Songs, Secular—1870-

NL 0376298   NN

Lind, Mary Viola.
Mountain hearts, by Mary Viola Lind. Los Angeles, Calif.,
The Times-mirror press [*1933]
2 p. l., [7]-144 p. 23½ cm.

I. Title.
Library of Congress   PZ3.L639Mo   33-8629

NL 0376299   DLC

Lind, Mayo.
See
Lind, Francis Thomas, 1879-1916.

Lind, Mélanie, tr.   FOR OTHER EDITIONS
SEE MAIN ENTRY

La Grange, Clémentine (de Chaumont-Quitry) *baronne de.*
Open house in Flanders, 1914-1918: Château de la Motte au
Bois, by Baroness Ernest de La Grange ... translated from the
unpublished French by Mélanie Lind; with an introduction
by Field-Marshal the Viscount Allenby ... New York, Frederick A. Stokes company, 1930.

Lind, Melva.
Modern language learning: the intensive
course as sponsored by the United States army
and implications for the undergraduate course
of study. Department of French language and
literature, Mount Holyike college.   Provincetown, Mass., The Journal press, 1947.
81 p.   25 cm.
Published also in Genetic psychology monographs, 1948, 38.
"References": p. 75-81.

NL 0376302   PU-Penn

Lind, Melva.
Modern language learning, the intensive course as sponsored by the United States Army, and implications for the
undergraduate course of study, by Melva Lind. Conflict, a
study of some interactions between appetite and aversion in
the white rat, by Martin Arnold Tolcott. Provincetown,
Mass., Journal Press, *1948.
142 p.   diagrs. (Genetic psychology monographs, v. 38, 1st half)
The second article is Tolcott's thesis, Columbia Univ.
"References": p. 75-81, 141-142.

1. Languages, Modern—Study and teaching. 2. Desire. I. Tolcott, Martin Arnold. Conflict, a study of some interactions between
appetite and aversion in the white rat. II. Title. III. Title: Conflict,
a study of some interactions between appetite and aversion in the
white rat.   (Series)

LB1101.G4 vol.   38, no. 1   407   49-99*
——— Copy 2.   PB38.U6L5

NL 0376304   DLC ViU TxU OU OCU PPPL PU PPT

---

848   Lind, Melva.
B4573ZL   Un parnassien universitaire: Emmanuel
Des Essarts.   Paris, Les Presses universi-
taires de France, 1928.
239 p. illus. 23 cm.

Bibliography: p. 223-234.

1. Des Essarts, Emmanuel, b. 1839.

NL 0376305   LU NIC CSt IEN NcD NcU InU MiU CtY MH

Lind, Millard, 1918-
Answer to war; illustrated by Allan Eitzen. Scottdale,
Pa., Mennonite Pub. House, 1952.
143 p. 20 cm.

1. Pacifism. I. Title.

BR115.P4L5   289.7   52-30259 ‡

NL 0376306   DLC PSC NjPT ViHarEM OB1C-M

Lind, Miriam Sieber.
Such thoughts of Thee, and other poems. Scottdale, Pa.,
Herald Press, 1952.
81 p. 21 cm.

I. Title.

PS3523.I 513S9   811.5   52-9168 ‡

NL 0376307   DLC OB1C-M

Lind, Mogens, 1898-   *ed.*
Aarets gang i Danmarks land. København, Berlingske
forlag, 1939.
unpaged (chiefly illus.) 33 cm.

1. Denmark—Descr. & trav.—Views. I. Title.

DL113.L5   63-56281 ‡

NL 0376308   DLC

Lind, Mogens, 1898-
Neiiendam, Tavs.
... Grønne vagabonder. København, Eget forlag, 1920.

Lind, Mogens, 1898-
Haandbog for diplomater og statsmænd. Illustreret af
Hans Bendix. København, R. Naver, 1948.
61 p. illus. 20 cm.

1. Diplomatic and consular service. I. Title.

JX1662.L5   49-20852*

NL 0376310   DLC

Lind, Mogens, 1898-
Haandbog i bueskydning, af Mogens Lind ... København,
Gyldendal, Nordisk forlag, 1928.
32 p. incl. front., illus. 20½ cm.
"Det danske spejderkorps benytter til sine instruktionskursus i bueskydning de principper og regler, der er angivet i denne haandbog, der
desuden er anerkendt af Dansk bueskytte klub."

1. Archery. 2. Bow and arrow.
Library of Congress   GV1185.L5   29-3556

NL 0376311   DLC

Lind, Mogens, 1898-   *ed.*
Pengene eller livremmen, en humørfyldt alvorsbog. Bid-
drag af Jørgen Bast [et al.] Privatøkonomens betragtninger
ved Otto Bjerrum. København, Westermann [*1951]
195 p. illus. 16 cm.

1. Saving and thrift. I. Title.

HG7933.L5   52-37420 ‡

NL 0376312   DLC NN

GT   Lind, Mogens, 1898-
3020   Tabacgrinos, hvad de sagde, digtede, tegnede
L64t   og fortalte om tobak. København, P. Haase,
1941.
79 p. illus. 20cm.

1. Smoking. 2. Tobacco. I. Title.

NL 0376313   CLU OC1

Lind, Mogens, 1898-
Til Elise. København, R. Naver, 1952.
86 p. port. 18 cm.

I. Title.

Minnesota. Univ. Libr.   A 52-10239
for Library of Congress   [2]

NL 0376314   MnU

Lind, Mogens, 1898-
We Danes—and you. Illus. by Herluf Jensenius. [Copen-
hagen] National Travel Assn. of Denmark, 1948.
29 p. illus. 20 cm.

1. Denmark—Soc. life & cust.

DL131.L5   914.89   48-25649*

NL 0376315   DLC TxU CtY NN OrCS IdPI

Scan 889.50
Lind, Mogens, 1898-
We Danes and you. Illus. by H.Jensenius. [Copen-
hagen] National Travel Assn. of Denmark, 1950
29 p. illus.

NL 0376316   MH

EducT 60.16.2850
LIND,Murray F.
Handbook of solutions to problems in
differential and integral calculus. Pt.1-6.
[New York,1928?].

Manifold copy.

NL 0376317   MH

Lind, N. P., ed.
Nykterhets-basunen; temperans-och
prohibitions-sånger ... Minneapolis, Minn.,
[1889]
31+[1] p.

NL 0376318   RPB

VOLUME 334

372
N21
1942
[Lind, Nellie Victoria, 1891-]   ed.
In-service growth of school personnel...
[Washington, D.C.] National education association,
c1942.
pp.229-576. front. illus., plates. 23cm.
(National education association of the United States.
Department of elementary school principals. 21st year-
book, 1942)

1. Teachers. 2. Teaching. I. Jacob, Walter, jr.,
jt. ed. II. Bear, Mata Virginia, jt. ed. III. Title.

NL 0376319   LU

Lind, Nellie Victoria, 1891-
Music appreciation—its contribution to leisure-time interest
[by] Nellie V. Lind.
(*In* National education association of the United States. *Addresses
and proceedings, 1935.* p. 369-370)

1. Music—Analysis, interpretation, appreciation. 2. Leisure.
I. Title.
E 36-326
Library, U. S. Office of   Education L13.N212 1935
Library of Congress   [L13.N4 1935]

NL 0376320   DHEW

TC540
L7
Lind, Nils E.
The dams of Al Taif, Saudi Arabia. [Jidda,
Saudi Arabia, American Legation, 1945.]
11 p. plates, fold. map. 27 cm.
Cover title
At head of title on p. 1.: This is a State
Department dispatch ... no. 9.

1. Dams. 2. Saudi Arabia. 3. Al Taif dams.
4. Water supply – Saudi Arabia. II. Title.

NL 0376321   DI

Lind, Ole.
...Det ene med det andre som Amanda sier; roman.   Oslo:
Cammermeyer, 1937.   243 p.   21cm.

953044A. 1. Fiction, Norwegian.   I. Title.
N.Y.P.L.   August 15, 1938

NL 0376322   NN

HF1160
.S3H3
Lind, Ole.
Sandefjord, Norway. Handelsgymnasiet.
Sandefjord kommunale handelsgymnasium og Handels-
skole, 1904-1954. Jubileumsberetning utarb. av Ole Lind.
[Sandefjord, 1954]

Lind, Olof, 1701-1765.
Deutsch Schwedisches und Schwedisch
Deutsches Lexicon...Stockholm, 1749.

NL 0376324   PPL

Bonaparte
Collection LIND, OLOF, 1701-1765
No.8841   Teutsch-schwedisches und schwedisch-teutsches
lexicon oder wörter-buch. Orda-bok på tyska och
swänska, så ock på swänska och tyska...   Stockholm, I.F.Lochner, 1740-49.
2v. in 1.   21x17½cm.

Engraved t.-p.
Vol.2 has special t.-p.: Swänsk och tysk
orda-bok. Schwedisch-teutsches wörter-buch.

NL 0376325   ICN CU

Lind, Omar Cherenzi-
see
Cherenzi-Lind, Omar, 1902-

831.91
L742a1
S9
Lind, Oskar von.
Gedichte von Oskar von Lind. Eutin,
W. Struve, 1909.
112p.   19cm.

NL 0376327   TNJ

Lind, Otto, 1909-
... Untersuchungen über die bakteriziden Eigen-
schaften der Milchsäure, Essigsäure und Salzsäure
und ihre Verwendung als Konservierungsmittel für
Fleisch ...   Giessen, 1937.
Diss. - Giessen.

NL 0376328   CtY

Lind, Ove.
Brassa för fyllning; historisk roman från ett äventyrsmättat tidsskede.   Stockholm, Ljus [1950]
340 p.   22 cm.

I. Title.
A 51-4625
Minnesota. Univ. Libr.
for Library of Congress   [3]

NL 0376329   MnU

TR650
.F66
Lind, Ove, ed.
Fotografiska föreningen, *Stockholm.*
Min bästa bild, svensk fotografi under 60 år. Redigerad
av Ove Lind. [Stockholm] Ljus [1948]

Lind, Ove.
Den tysta sanden; historisk roman från ett äventyrsmättat
tidsskede.   Stockholm, Ljus [1949]
363 p.   illus.   21 cm.

I. Title.
A 50-2680
Minnesota. Univ. Libr.
for Library of Congress   [3]

NL 0376331   MnU

Lind, P   Pedersen.
"Klintebakken;" Folkeskuespil i 3 Akter, af P. Pedersen Lind.
Særlig egnet for Dilettantkomedie og Fælleslæsning.   Ribe:
Ribe Bogtrykkeris Forlag, 1932.   56 p.   21½cm.

757917A. 1. Drama, Danish. I. Title.
N.Y.P.L.   August 15, 1935

NL 0376332   NN

Lind, Patricia E
Nature of mumps virus action on red cells.
Aust. j. exp. biol. 26:93-106, Jan. 1948.

NL 0376333   PU-D

B1297
L5
Lind, Paul, 1878-
Abhandlung über das Verhältnis Lockes zu
Newton.   [Berlin, R. Lantzsch, 1915]
86 p.   25ᶜᵐ.
Inaug. Diss. - Berlin.
Vita.
Bibliography: p. [83]-84.

1. Locke, John, 1632-1704.   2. Newton, Sir
Isaac, 1642-1727. I. Title.

NL 0376334   CSt CtY MH MoSU MiU

Lind, Paul von, 1858-
Immanuel Kant und Alexander von Humboldt. Eine
rechtfertigung Kants und eine historische richtigstellung.
Erlangen, Buchdr. von F. Junge (Junge & sohn) 1897.
44 p., 1 l.   22ᶜᵐ.
Inaug.-diss.—Erlangen.
Curriculum vitae.

1. Kant, Immanuel, 1724-1804. 2. Humboldt, Alexander, freiherr von,
1769-1859.
1-13228
Library of Congress   B2799.C8L7

NL 0376335   DLC NNUT PU CtY NjP TxU NIC

---

arW
35397
Lind, Paul von, 1858-
"Kant's mystische Weltanschauung," ein
Wahn der modernen Mystik; eine Widerlegung
der Dr. C. du Prel'schen Einleitung zu
Kant's Psychologie.   München, M. Poessl,
[1892]
viii, 144 p.   23cm.

1. Kant, Immanuel, 1724-1804.

NL 0376336   NIC IEN

Lind, Paul von.
Moderner geschmack und moderne musik; eine gegen-
wartsstudie, von P. von Lind.   Leipzig und Zürich, Gebrüder Hug, 1891.
56 p.   15½ x 11½ᶜᵐ.

1. Music—Addresses, essays, lectures.
11-72
Library of Congress   ML197.L5

NL 0376337   DLC

VOLUME 334

LIND, Paul von, 1858–
Eine unsterbliche entdeckung ,Kants, oder Die vermeintliche "lücke" in Kants system. Eine historische rechtfertigung Kants. Leipzig, H. Haacke, 1898.

pp.ix, 62.   Phil 3493.9

NL 0376338   MH

Lind, Peter Engel, bp., 1814–1903.
Eet bidrag til svar paa det spørgsmaal: hvorledes kan arbeiderklassens kaar forbedres?   Kjøbenhavn, I commission i Schubothes boghandling, 1848.   8 p.   17cm.

1. Labor—Denmark.

NL 0376339   NN

Lind, P₁eter₎ E₁ngel₎, 1814–1903.   C 1968.52.13
Christendommens indflydelse paa de occidentalske folkeslags sociale forhold fra aar 500 til 814. Kjøbenhavn, T. Lind, 1858.
pp. (iv), 129+.

NL 0376340   MH

Lind, P₁eter₎ E₁ngel₎, 1814–1903.
Christendommens indflydelse paa den sociale forfatning fra dens stiftelse til Justinian. Kjøbenhavn, T. Lind, 1852.
pp. vi, 180.

NL 0376341   MH

Lind, P₁eter₎ E₁ngel₎ 1814–1903.
Fortegnelse over skrifter passende for sognebibliotheker. 1844–1862. Fortsættelse af Marckmanns. Med tillæg. Ved P. E. Lind ... Udgiven af det Kgl. Landhuusholdningsselskab. Kjøbenhavn, G. S. Wibes bogtrykkeri, 1864.

vi p., 1 l., 71 p. 19ᶜᵐ.
A supplement, covering 1863–1872, appeared in 1873. A new ed., by various contributors, was issued by the society in 1889.

1. Bibliography—Best books.   I. K. Danske landhusholdningsselskab.

Library of Congress   Z1035.L74   6-46407

NL 0376342   DLC

Lind, Peter Engel, 1814–1903.
Johan Gordon. En fortaelling. Kjobenhavn, Schubothe, 1836.
180 p.   18 cm.

NL 0376343   VtU

Lind, Poul.
Renset Tuberkulin, dets Fremstilling og Egenskaber ... Kjøbenhavn, Munksgaard, 1945.

284 p. illus. 24 cm.
Afhandling—Danmarks farmaceutiske Højskole, Copenhagen.
Summaries in Danish and English.

1. Tuberculin₁—Preparation₎

                            Med 48-542

U. S. Army Medical Libr.   [W4C78 1944]
for Library of Congress   ₁1₎

NL 0376344   DNLM

56.7
L64   Lind, R   C
Formerly run-down farm pays own improvement cost.   [n.p., 1949]
2 l.

1. Soil conservation. Kansas.

NL 0376345   DNAL

D790
.A535   Lind, Ragnar G., ed.
79th   U. S. *Army Air Forces. 79th Fighter Group.*
The Falcon; combat history of the 79th Fighter Group, United States Army Air Forces, 1942–1945. ₁Edited by Ragnar G. Lind. Munich? 1946₎

LIND, Ralph A.
The future of labor relations; excerpts from an address at a meeting of the Wirebound Box Manufacturers Assn.in New Orleans,La.,February 23,1940. [New Orleans?,1940.]

pp.14.

NL 0376347   MH

Lind, Ralph A.
... The practical nature of collective cooperation, by Ralph A. Lind ... Albert S. Regula ... ₁and₎ A. L. Kress ...   New York, N. Y., American management association, °1938.

44 p. incl. forms. 23ᶜᵐ. (₁American management association₎ Personnel series, no. 34)
"Papers ... presented at the Personnel conference of the American management association held at ... Chicago, February 15–16–17, 1938."—p. ₁2₎

1. Trade-unions—U. S. 2. Employment management.   I. Title.
                                        38-20905
Library of Congress   HF5549.L48
——— Copy 2.
Copyright AA 265135   ₁3₎   331.880973

NL 0376348   DLC OrU MU PPT OU

Lind, Richard, 1912–
Luthers Stellung zum Kreuz- und Türkenkrieg. Giessen, 1940.

71 p. 21 cm.
Diss. (Lic.)—Giessen.
Vita.
Bibliography : p. 68–69.

1. Luther, Martin, 1483–1546. 2. War and religion.   I. Title.

BR333.L48   51-50906

NL 0376349   DLC NIC

Lind, Robert V. C., *pseud.*
see Crimi, Vincent.

Lind, Robert Wilhelm, Referendar: Die ₁Freiheitsberaubung des § 239 des Strafgesetzbuches unter ₁besonderer Berücksichtigung ihrer Mittel. Berlin [1915]: Petzold. 39 S. 8° Rostock, Jur. Diss. v. 15. Nov. 1915, Ref. Wachenfeld
[Geb. 13. Febr. 89 Hamburg; Wohnort: Hamburg; Staatsangeh.: Hamburg; Vorbildung: Wilhelm-G. Hamburg Reife 08; Studium: Heidelberg 1, Kiel 1, Berlin 1, Rostock 3, Kiel 3 S.; Rig. 26. Juli 15.]   [U 15. 584

NL 0376351   ICRL MH-L MiU

Lind, Rudolf
Das kracken von kohlenwasserstoffen unter atmosphärischem druck
Inaug. Diss. Darmstadt, 1930.

NL 0376352   ICRL

Lind, Samuel Colville₁, 1879–   **joint author.**
Moore, Richard Bishop, 1871–
... Analytical methods for certain metals including cerium, thorium, molybdenum, tungsten, radium, uranium, vanadium, titanium and zirconium, by R. B. Moore and S. C. Lind, J. W. Marden, J. P. Bonardi, C. W. Davis, and J. E. Conley. Washington, Govt. print. off., 1923.

Lind, Samuel Colville, 1879–
... Biographical memoir of Ross Aiken Gortner, 1885–1942, by Samuel Colville Lind. Presented to the academy at the autumn meeting, 1943.

(*In* National academy of sciences, Washington, D. C. *Biographical memoirs.* City of Washington, 1945. 23ᶜᵐ. Vol. XXIII, 6th memoir, 1 p. l., p. 149–180. front. (port.))
"Bibliography of Ross Aiken Gortner": p. 161–180.

1. Gortner, Ross Aiken, 1885–1942.
                                        46-16350
Library of Congress   Q141.N2 vol. 23, 6th memoir

NL 0376354   DLC CU IU

Lind, Samuel Colville, 1879–
The chemical effects of alpha particles and electrons, by Samuel C. Lind ... New York, The Chemical catalog company, inc., 1921.

182 p. incl. illus., tables, diagrs. 23ᶜᵐ. (American chemical society. Monograph series)
Bibliographical foot-notes.

1. Radioactivity. 2. Electrons.   21-9220 Revised
Library of Congress   QC721.L7 1921
                    ₁r46t3₎   539.7

NL 0376355   OCU OC1 NcD NcRS CU MtU OrPR OrP IdU MtBC CaBVaU DLC TU PPT PPUG ViU MB ICJ DNLM ODW OU

Lind, Samuel Colville, 1879–
The chemical effects of alpha particles and electrons, by Samuel C. Lind ... 2d (rev. and enl.) ed. ... New York, The Chemical catalog company, inc., 1928.

252 p. illus., diagrs. 23½ᶜᵐ. (American chemical society. Monograph series ₁no. 2₎)

1. Radioactivity. 2. Electrons.
                                        28-9312 Revised
Library of Congress   QC721.L7 1928

NL 0376356   NcD NcRS PPAtR CU NcD WaTC WaS NmU IdU OrPR OrPS DLC TU PPTU ViU MiU OCU OC1W ICJ OOxM

QD181
.R6T7   Lind, Samuel Colville, 1879–
Truesdale, Edward Cushman, 1901–
Chemical effects produced by radon on the system : hydrogensulfur–hydrogen-sulfide ... by Edward Cushman Truesdale ... ₁Minneapolis? 1932₎

Lind, Samuel Colville₁ 1879–   joint author.

Lanning, Francis Chowning, 1908–
Chemical reactions produced by the radiation of aqueous solutions with alpha particles from radon ... by Francis Chowning Lanning ... ₁Baltimore, 1938₎

VOLUME 334

Lind, Samuel Colville, 1879–   joint author.

Rosenblum, Charles, 1905–
The effect of radon on the carbon monoxide oxidation.
The catalytic effect of carbon dioxide formed ... By Charles
Rosenblum ... ₍Washington, D. C., 1932₎

Lind, Samuel Colville, 1879–   joint author.

Glockler, George, 1890–
The electrochemistry of gases and other dielectrics, by G.
Glockler ... and S. C. Lind ... New York, J. Wiley & sons,
inc.; London, Chapman & Hall, limited, 1939.

Lind, Samuel Colville, 1879–   joint author.

Parsons, Charles Lathrop, 1867–
... Extraction and recovery of radium, uranium and vanadium from carnotite, by Charles L. Parsons, R. B. Moore,
S. C. Lind and O. C. Schaefer. National radium institute
cooperative agreement ... Washington, Govt. print. off., 1915.

QD1
.J95

Lind, Samuel Colville, 1879–   ed₊

The Journal of physical chemistry. v. 1–
Oct. 1896–
Easton, Pa., Mack Print. Co.

Lind, Samuel Colville, 1879–   joint author.

Copeland, Charles Sallaz, 1908–
Neutrons by alpha ray bombardment of light elements ... by
Charles Sallaz Copeland ... ₍Baltimore, 1938₎

Lind, Samuel Colville, 1879–
Ozonisierung des Sauerstoffes
durch α-Strahlen. 16 pp., 1 pl. 8°. Wien,
A. Hölder, 1911.
Forms No. 11 of Mitt. a. d. Inst. Radiumforsch.

NL 0376364   DNLM

Lind, Samuel Colville, 1879–
Progress of chemistry in the first
quarter of the 20th century. n. p.
1927.
J. chem. Educ., 4, 1927, p.1104.

NL 0376365   PU–S

Lind, Samuel Colville, 1879–
... The radium-uranium ratio in carnotites, by S. C. Lind and
C. F. Whittemore. Washington, Govt. print. off., 1915.
29 p. illus., pl. 23ᶜᵐ. (₍U. S.₎ Bureau of mines. Technical paper
88. Mineral technology 6)
At head of title: ... Department of the interior. Bureau of mines.
Joseph A. Holmes, director.
First edition, 1915.
"Publications on mineral technology": p. 29.

1. Carnotite. 2. Radium. 3. Uranium.   I. Whittemore, Charles F.,
joint author.   15–26363 Revised
Library of Congress   TN1.U6 no. 88
—— Copy 2.   TN948.R3L7

OrU OrCS
NL 0376366   DLC TxU PP NN OU OO OCl MiU ICJ WaU

Chem.
540.81
L742S

Lind, Samuel Colville, 1879–
Scientific publications. [n. p., n. d.]
3 v. illus. 23 cm.
Binder's title.
Includes monographs and articles reprinted
or detached from various journals and originally issued 1903–27.

1. Chemistry. Collected works.

NL 0376367   NcD

Lind, Samuel Colville, 1879– joint author.

Marks, Barnard Mitchell, 1905–
Some gaseous reactions under the influence of ionizing agents
... by Barnard Mitchell Marks ... ₍Minneapolis, 1931₎

Lind, Samuel Colville, 1879–   joint author.
Shiflett, Chester Hines, 1897–
The temperature coefficient of the combination of hydrogen
and oxygen under alpha radiation ... by Chester Hines Shiflett
... ₍Baltimore, 1933₎

LIND, Samuel Colville, 1879–
Über die bildung des bromwasserstoffgases
aus den elementen. Inaug.-diss. Leipzig,
1906.

NL 0376370   MH-C PU CtY OCU

LD3907
.G7
1949
.L5

Lind, Sidney Edmund, 1914–
The supernatural tales of Henry
James; conflict and fantasy. New
York, 1948.
vi,435 typewritten leaves. 29cm.
Thesis (Ph.D.) – New York Universi-
ty, Graduate School, 1949.
Bibliography: p.₍430₎-435.

NL 0376371   NNU-W

4PT-
Den.-
83

Lind, Søren.
Flygtige sange; illustreret af Carlo Wognsen.
Aalborg, Frede og L. C. Lauritzen, 1948.
45 p.

NL 0376372   DLC-P4

---

*Lind, Sven Ivar, 1902–   joint ed.

... Mureri. Stockholm, Lindfors ₍1936₎

Lind, Sven Ivar, 1902–   joint ed.

... Träbyggnadskonst. Stockholm, Lindfors ₍1938₎

Lind, Sven Ivar Harald
see Lind, Sven Ivar, 1902–

DL291
.S85L5

Lind, Th
Svaneke bys historie. Udg. af Foreningen Svanekes ven-
ner. Svaneke, I kommission hos T. Platou, 1955.
208 p. illus., ports., maps. 27 cm.
Includes bibliographical references.

1. Svaneke, Denmark—Hist.

Minnesota. Univ. Libr.   A 56–741
for Library of Congress   ₍8₎

NL 0376376   MnU DLC

Lind, Theodor, 1908–
Poesiens mission. København, Gyldendal, 1947.
259 p. 24 cm.
Thesis—Københavns universitet.
Bibliography: p. ₍248₎–250.

1. Poetry. I. Title.   Full name: Erik Theodor Lind.

PN1031.L5   49–15455 rev*

NL 0376377   DLC CtY ICU NjP NN MH IU

Lind, Theodor Christian, 1885–
Bornholms Rundkirker
see under Høst, Oluf, 1884–   illus.

Lind, Theodor Christian, 1885–
Gyldendals forfatter-lexikon, ved Th. Lind. København
og Kristiania, Gyldendal, 1915.
148, ₍4₎ p. illus. 18½ cm.

1. Bio-bibliography. I. Title.

Z1010.L56   15–22769 rev

NL 0376379   DLC ICJ NB Or

PT7978
L5

Lind, Theodor Christian, 1885–   ed.
Krydsede klinger; digternes fejde 1877–80, med et forord af
Otto Borchsenius. København, Gyldendal, 1918.
x, 92, [3] p.

"Trykt i 500 salgseksemplarer."
"Naervaerende udgave følger teksten, som den findes i de
første tryk i 'Ude og hjemme' og 'Naer og fjern'.– Note at
end signed: Th. Lind.

1. Danish poetry – 19th cent. I. Title.

NL 0376380   CU MiU IU

Lind, V. N., tr.

Fouillée, Alfred Jules Émile, 1838–1912.
... Темпераментъ и характеръ. Переводъ В. Н.
Линда. Москва, Изд. магазина "Книжное дѣло",
1896.

Lind, Volmer, 1871–   comp.
Kongeriget Danmarks praktiserende sagførere. København, Berlingske tidende, 1929.
327 p. ports., facsims. 27 cm.

1. Lawyers—Denmark—Biog. I. Title.

52–55820

NL 0376382   DLC

VOLUME 334

Lind, W
   Die insel Föhr. Kirchen und denkmaeler.
Nach original aufnahmen, von W. Lind. [n. p.,
O. C. Nerong, 18--?]
   cover-title, 12 phot. 17 cm.
   Twelve mounted photos. on folded strip.
   1. Sylt (Island) - Descr. & trav. - Views.

NL 0376383   CU

Lind, W. Murdoch.   No. 14 in **M.450.172
   Happy times in Georgia. Song and dance. [With accompaniment
   for the pianoforte.]
= Boston. Oliver Ditson Co. 1892. 5 pp. 36 cm.

D8736 — T.r. — Negro minstrels.

NL 0376384   MB

Lind, W   Murdoch.
   Punch and Judy; a tragico-comical drama ...
New York, c1906.
   32 p. illus. 19 cm.
   The "Crest" version.

NL 0376385   RPB

Lind, Wallace Ludwig, 1887–
   Internal-combustion engines; their principles and application to automobile, aircraft, and marine purposes, by Wallace
L. Lind ... Boston, New York [etc.] Ginn and company
[*1920]
   v, 225 p. illus., diagrs. 21½ᶜᵐ.

   1. Gas and oil engines.   I. Title.   20—6497

   Library of Congress   TJ755.L795

NL 0376386   DLC MtBC Or IdU ViU NcRS CU

Lind, Wallace Ludwig, 1887–

[U. S. *Naval academy, Annapolis*] *Dept. of engineering and
   aeronautics.*
   Internal-combustion engines: their principles and application to automobile, aircraft, and marine purposes, by officers
of the Department of engineering and aeronautics. Annapolis, Md., The United States naval institute, 1931.

Lind, Walter, 1884–
   Zur Lehre von den Voraussetzungen der
Aufrechnung nach dem Rechte des Bürger-
lichen Gesetzbuches unter Berücksichti-
gung des gemeinen Rechts ... von Walter
Lind .... Heidelberg, K. Rössler, 1905.
   41, [1] p. 22cm.
   Inaug.-Diss. - Heidelberg.
   "Lebenslauf": p.[42]
   "Benutzte Literatur": p.[7]-8.

NL 0376388   MH-L ICRL

Lind, Wilhelm.
   Buromaschinen. 2., vollkommen neu bearb. Aufl. des 1940
erschienenen Werkes Lind-Berger, Büromaschinen. Füssen,
C. F. Winter [1954–
   v. illus. 22 cm. (Lehrbücher der Feinwerktechnik, Bd. 5)
   Includes bibliography.

   1. Office equipment and supplies.   I. Title.

   HF5520.L5   58–36990 ‡

NL 0376389   DLC

M1045   Lind, William, arr.
.H98P7
       Hylin, Einar.

       Primavera, arrangemang för salongs-orkester av **William
       Lind.** Stockholm, C. Gehrman [1946]

M1353   Lind, William, arr.
.G
       Gäfvert, Hans Åke.

       Rapsodie miniature; arr. William Lind. Pianosolo med
       salongorkester. [Stockholm] Nordiska musikförlaget [1944]

M1145   Lind, William, arr.
.H9R9
       Hylin, Einar.

       Rythm in F, arrangemang för salongs-orkester av **William
       Lind.** Stockholm, C. Gehrman [1946]

DS   Lind af Hageby, Axel Reinhold Ferdinand.
478   Minnen från ett tre-årigt vistande i Engelsk
.L74   Örlogstjenst, 1857-1859; anteckningar.
       Stockholm, A. Bonnier [1860]
          468 p. illus., maps.

          1.India--Hist.--Sepoy Rebellion,1857-1858.
          2.India--Descr.& trav. I.Title.

NL 0376393   MiU

4DS   Lind af Hageby, Axel Reinhold Ferdinand.
Ind.   Reisebilder und Skizzen aus Indien
523   und dem letzten indischen Kriege, 1857
       -1859. Leipzig, H. Mendelssohn, 1861.
          424 p.

NL 0376394   DLC-P4

       Lind af Hageby, Emilie Augusta Louise
                   see
       Lind af Hageby, Lizzy, 1878–

LIND-AF-HAGEBY,   Lizzy,1878–
   Address of Miss Lind-af-Hageby at the public meeting of the American anti-vivisection
society. Feb.5,1909. Philadelphia,1909.

NL 0376396   MH PPHa

Lind-Af-Hageby, Lizzy, 1878–
   ... The animals' cause. A selection of papers
contributed to the International Anti-Vivisection and
Animal Protection Congress
          see under   International Anti-Vivisection and
Animal Protection Congress, London, 1909.

Lind-af-Hageby, Lizzy, 1878–
   August Strindberg; a study by L. Lind-af-Hageby...intro-
ductory note by Robert Loraine. London: The A. K. Press[,
1928?] 87 p. port. 12°.

390533A. 1. Strindberg, August,   1849–1912.   January 2, 1929
N. Y. P. L.

NL 0376398   NN CU MH CSt ICarbS NcU IEN

PT9815   Lind af Hageby, Lizzy, 1878–
.L52   August Strindberg; the spirit of revolt.
1913   Studies and impressions. London, S. Paul
        [1913]
           370p. illus.

           1 Strindberg, August, 1849-1912.

NL 0376399   NcU GU NIC LU CU FU MH ICN NN CtY

Lind af Hageby, Lizzy, 1878–
   August Strindberg, the spirit of revolt; studies and impressions by L. Lind-af-Hageby. New York, D. Appleton and
company, 1913.
   370 p. front., plates, ports. 19½ᶜᵐ.
   Printed in Great Britain.
   "List of Strindberg's chief writings": p. 356–362.

   1. *Strindberg, August, 1849-1912.
      [*Real name:* Emilie Augusta Louise Lind af Hageby]
                                           13–35826 Revised

   Library of Congress   PT9815.L5
                             [r42b2]

                  TU MU ICU LU OrP WaS WaSp WaSpG
NL 0376400   DLC MiU OU OCl OClW NN NdU PU MB NjP

Lind-af-Hageby, Lizzy, 1878–
   Be peacemakers; an appeal to women of the twentieth century
to remove the causes of war. By L. Lind-af-Hageby...   London: The A. K. Press[, 1924]. 54 p. 12°.
   Cover-title.

   1. War and peace.   January 14, 1926
   N. Y. P. L.

NL 0376401   NN

Lind-af-Hageby, Lizzy   , 1878–
   The constructive side of the anti-vivisection
movement. 1913.
   8 p.

   "Read before the International anti-vivisection and animal protection congress, Washington,
D.C., Dec. 9, 1913."

   1. Vivisection.

NL 0376402   NNC-M

HV   LIND AF HAGEBY, Lizzy, 1878–
4915   "Ecrasez l'infâme!" An exposure of
L742e   the mind, methods, pretences and failure
1929   of the modern inquisition. London,
        Animal Defence and Anti-Vivisection
        Society [1929]
           vi, 113 p.
           1. Vivisection

NL 0376403   DNLM

VOLUME 334

Lind af Hageby, Lizzy *i. e.* **Emilie Augusta Louise, 1878–**
... Evidence by Miss Lind-af-Hageby. Given on May 1st and June 5th, 1907. London, Miss Lind-af-Hageby's anti-vivisection council [1907]

1 p. l., 237 p. 21½cm.

At head of title: The Royal commission on vivisection.
With mounted clippings on the subject of vivisection and cruelty to animals.

1. Vivisection.

22–11477

Library of Congress   HV4943.G5A4 1907 b

NL 0376404   DLC

Lind-af-Hageby, Lizzy, 1878–
...La fonction de la femme dans l'évolution sociale ... Conflans-Honorine, 1922. 16 p. 14cm.
(L'Idée libre. Brochure. no. 32)

"Traduit de l'anglais par Manuel Devaldès."

1. Woman—Social position. I. Ser.

NL 0376405   NN

Lind af Hageby, Lizzy   1878–
Mountain meditations and some subjects of the day and the war, by L. Lind-af-Hageby ... London, G. Allen & Unwin ltd. [1918]

216, [1] p. 19ᶜᵐ.

"First published in 1917."

CONTENTS.—Mountain-tops. — The borderland.—Reformers.— Nationality.—Religion in transition.

I. Title.

18–14085

Library of Congress   AC8.L6

NL 0376406   DLC WaS

Lind-af-Hageby, Lizzie, 1878–
On immortality, a letter to a dog, by L. Lind-af-Hageby. London: The writer [19—] 42 p. illus. 18cm.

NL 0376407   NN

Lind af Hageby, Lizzy, 1878–
The shambles of science; extracts from the diary of two students of physiology, by Lizzy Lind of Hageby and Leisa K. Schartau. London, E. Bell, 1903.

xvi, 206 p. 20½ᶜᵐ.

"First edition, July 1903 ... Reprinted, August 1903."

1. Vivisection.   I. Schartau, Leisa Katherina, joint author. II. Title.
[Real name: Emilie Augusta Louise Lind af Hageby]
10–6

Library of Congress   HV4943.G6L7

NL 0376408   DLC DCU CtY NN

Lind af Hageby, Lizzy, 1878–
The shambles of science; extracts from the diary of two students of physiology, by L. Lind af Hageby and L. K. Schartau. 4th and rev. ed. London, The author [pref. 1904]
xxxii, 216 p. 18½cm.

1. Vivisection. I. Schartau, Leisa Katherina, (jt. au.) II. Title.

NL 0376409   NNC

Lind af Hageby, Lizzy, 1878–
What is vivisection? n.p.,n.d.

NL 0376410   MH

Lind-Gapp, Otto, ed.

Law   **Austria.** *Laws, statutes, etc.*
Das Abgabenrechtsmittelgesetz, mit Erläuterungen von Otto Lind-Gapp. 2., verb. Aufl. Wien, Brüder Hollinek, 1955.

Lind-Gapp, Otto, ed.

Law   **Austria.** *Laws, statutes, etc.*
Die Einbringung der öffentlichen Abgaben, Abgabeneinhebungsgesetz und Abgabenexekuutionsordnung mit Erläuterungen von Otto Lind-Gapp. Wien, Brüder Hollinek, 1950.

Lind-Gapp, Otto.
Die österreichische gemeindegesetzgebung und das abgabenrecht der länder und gemeinden ... Wien, Staatsdruckerei, 1925–27.

Lind-Goldschmidt, Jenny Marie, 1820–1887.
Album of music containing Jenny Lind songs
see under title [Supplement]

Lind-Goldschmidt, Jenny Maria, 1820–1887.
Autograph letter signed, Hamburg, July 1, 1852.. ..a few months before she married Otto Goldschmidt, her accompanist in America.

NL 0376415   PPAmSwM

Lind-Goldschmidt, Jenny Maria, 1820–1887.
Autograph letter signed Jenny L. Goldschmidt, written to "Liebe Mme. Joachim", Montag Morgen, Streis Hotel, n. d.
4 p.

NL 0376416   PPAmSwM

Lind-Goldschmidt, Jenny Maria, 1820–1887.
Autograph letter signed Jenny Lind Goldschmidt, written to "Theuerste Frau Joachim" from Hotel de Russie, Berlin, 3. Marz, 1875.
4 p.

NL 0376417   PPAmSwM

Lind-Goldschmidt, Jenny Maria, 1820–1887.
Autograph verse signed, Phila...Dec. 1850. ....signed with her maiden name.

NL 0376418   PPAmSwM

Lind-Goldschmidt, Jenny Maria, 1820–1887, defendant.
Bunn, Alfred, 1796?–1860, *plaintiff.*
The case of Bunn *versus* Lind, tried at the Court of Queen's bench, Guildhall, City, before Mr. Justice Erle and a special jury, on Tuesday, February 22nd, 1848, given in full, from short-hand notes taken at the time, with a series of letters from plaintiff and defendant, produced thereat, with others from both, now for the first time published. To which are added, notes explanatory and critical. By Alfred Bunn ... London, W. S. Johnson, 1848.

Lind-Goldschmidt, Jenny Maria, 1820–1887.
[A collection of magazine articles and newspaper clippings relating to Jenny Lind]
see under title [supplement]

Lind-Goldschmidt, Jenny Maria, 1820–1887.
Herd sang
see under   Lindblad, Adolf Fredrik, 1801–1878.

Lind-Goldschmidt, Jenny Maria, 1820–1887.
Incidents in the life of Jenny Lind, the noble-hearted Swede...
see under title

Lind-Goldschmidt, Jenny Maria, 1820–1887.
The Jenny Lind glee book: consisting of the most popular songs, sung by Mad'lle Jenny Lind...
see under   Paine, David, 1820–1887.

Lind-Goldschmidt, Jenny Maria, 1820–1887.
The Jenny Lind melodist
see under title

Lind-Goldschmidt, Jenny Maria, 1820–1887.
Jenny Lind utom scenen; förtroliga brev till hennes förmyndare H. M. Munthe, i urval och med kommentarier utgivna av Lotten Dahlgren. Stockholm, Wahlström & Widstrand [1928]

415 p. incl. front. (port.) illus., facsim. 22½ᶜᵐ.

1. Musicians—Correspondence, reminiscences, etc. I. Munthe, Henrik Mathias, 1798–1880. II. *Dahlgren, Lotten, 1851– ed.

Library of Congress   ML420.L7D2

29–30961

NL 0376425   DLC NN MiD PPAmSwM

Lind-Goldschmidt, Jenny Maria, 1820–1887.
Programme of Mademoiselle Jenny Lind's concert
see under title

Lind-Goldschmidt, Jenny Maria, 1820–1887.
Programme of Mademoiselle Jenny Lind's grand concert ...
see under title

VOLUME 334

Lind van Wijngaarden, Cornelis de, 1892–
De betrouwbaarheid van physiologische ijkingen uitgewerkt voor digitalis, benevens een onderzoek over het drogen en bewaren van digitalisbladeren ... door Cornelis de **Lind van Wijngaarden** ... Utrecht, Drukkerij firma **Schotanus & Jens,** 1925.

167, ₁1₁ p. pl., tables (1 fold.) diagrs. 23½ᶜᵐ.

Proefschrift—Utrecht.
Erratum slip laid in.
"Stellingen": 1 leaf laid in.

1. Digitalis. I. Title.

                        33–37092

Library of Congress   RS165.D5L5 1925   615.32381

NL 0376428   DLC ICU CtY

LIND van WIJNGAARDEN, Jan Daniël de
Antonius Walaeus...proefschrift...
Rijksuniversiteit te Leiden...1891.
Leiden, Los, 1891.
xiv229p. front. 22cm.

NL 0376429   MH-AH ICN

889
L753be
1907

LIND VAN WIJNGAARDEN, Jan Daniël de, 1862–1939.
Bethlehems bornput. Twaalf leerredenen.
Utrecht, Ruys, 1907.
260p. 23cm.

NL 0376430   MH-AH

943
Ref.346
L753do
.1905

LIND VAN WIJNGAARDEN, Jan Daniël de, 1862–1939.
De Dordtsche leerregels of de vijf artikelen tegen de Remonstranten. Opnieuw uitgegeven en van historische toelichtingen voorzien. Utrecht, Ruys, 1905.
143p. 19cm.

Tweede druk.

NL 0376431   MH-AH

889
L753st
1908

LIND VAN WIJNGAARDEN, Jan Daniël de, 1862–1939.
De staf van Aäron. Twaalf leerredenen.
Utrecht, Ruys, 1908.
270p. 24cm.

NL 0376432   MH-AH

Lind von Hageby, Axel
    see   Lind af Hageby, Axel Reinhold Ferdinand.

LIND BROTHERS, New York.
All the world is listening. Created and produced in the interests of more effective business communication. New York ₁1953₎ 32 p. illus., ports. 29cm.

NL 0376434   NN NBuG ViU

Lind university, *Lake Forest, Ill.*
    see
Lake Forest university, *Lake Forest, Ill.*

Linda, Josef, 1789–1834, joint author.

PG5022
.A2
1879

₁Hanka, Václav₎ 1791–1861.
Die altböhmischen gedichte der Grünberger und Königinhofer handschrift im urtexte und in deutscher uebersetzung, herausgegeben von Josef Jireček. Prag, F. Řivnáč, 1879.

891.86
L64
0j1926

Linda, Josef, 1789–1834.
Jaroslav Šternberg v boji proti tatarům; divadelní hra od Jozefa Lindy. V Praze ₁Karel Janský₎ 1926.
209p. illus. 19cm. (Stožár, sv. 7)

"Ve 100 prodejných a 15 neprodejných výtiscích se 6 kresbami Jana Konůpka. Text zrevidoval a doslovem opatřil Dr. Frant. Krčma, typografickou úpravu navrhl K. Dyrynk a na holandu vytiskla Státní tiskárna. Do kůže svázal Antonín Tvrdý podle návrhu Cyrila Boudy." No.84.
Red morocco with gilt vignettes on boards.

I. Title. II. Krčma, František, ed.

NL 0376438   IU CaOTP NcU CU

Linda, Josef, 1789–1834.
Jaroslav Šternberg v boji proti tatarům; divadelní hra.
V Praze, Nakl. České akademie věd a umění, 1930.
xv, 163 p. 19 cm. (Novočeská knihovna, čís. 10)

1. Jaroslav ze Šternberka, d. ca. 1290—Drama. I. Title.

PG5038.L55J3   55–48117 ‡

NL 0376439   DLC TxU CSt CtY InU MB MH PSt

PG5022
.A2
1829

Linda, Josef, 1789–1834, joint author.
Hanka, Václav, 1791–1861.
Kralodworsky rukopis. Zbjrka staročeskych zpiewoprawnych basnj, s niekolika ginymi staročeskymi zpiewy. Nalezen a wydan od Waclawa Hanky ... s diegopisnym uwodem od Waclawa Aloysia Swobody ... Praze, J. G. Calve, 1829.

PG5022
.A2E5
1852

Linda, Josef, 1789–1834, joint author.
Hanka, Václav, 1791–1861.
Manuscript of the Queen's Court. A collection of old Bohemian lyrico-epic songs, with other ancient Bohemian poems. Translated by A. H. Wratislaw ... Prague, V. Hanka, 1852.

PG5022
.A3
1875

Linda, Josef, 1789–1834, joint author.
₁Hanka, Václav₎ 1791–1861.
Rukopis Zelenohorský a Královédvorský. 3. opravené vyd. V Praze, I. L. Kober, 1875.

PG3300
.S6
1823

Linda, Joseph, 1789–1834, joint author.
                FOR OTHER EDITIONS
                SEE MAIN ENTRY
₁Hanka, Václav₎ 1791–1861.
Судъ Любуши; древнее чешское стихотворение. Москва, Въ Тип. С. Селивановскаго, 1823.

Linda, Josef, 1789–1834.
Záře nad pohanstvem; nebo Václav a Boleslav. Vyobrazení z české dávnověkosti. Po stu letech 2. vyd. upravil a moderním jazykem přepsal Vilém Bitnar, 1818–1918. Praha, Nakl. Veraikonu, 1919.
140 p. 21 cm.

1. Boleslav I, Duke of Bohemia, 906 or 7–967—Fiction. 2. Wenceslaus, Saint, Duke of Bohemia, 907?–935?—Fiction. I. Title.

PG5038.L55Z2 1919   68–48122

NL 0376444   DLC

Linda, Josef, 1789–1934.
Záře nad pohanstvem; nebo, Václav a Boleslav. Vydal Jan Máchal. V Praze, Nakl. České akademie věd a umění, 1924.
xii, 158 p. illus. 19 cm. (Novočeská knihovna, č. 8)

1. Boleslav I, Duke of Bohemia, 906 or 7–967—Fiction. 2. Wenceslaus, Saint, Duke of Bohemia, 907?–935?—Fiction. I. Title. (Series)

PG5038.L55Z2 1924   68–44065

NL 0376445   DLC NcU IU CSt CtY MB MH NN PSt

Linda, Josef, 1789–1834.
Záře nad pohanstvem; nebo, Vaclav a Boleslav. Vyobrazení z dávnověkosti vlastenské od Josefa Lindy. ₁K vyd. připravil Václav Stejskal. Doslov napsal Karel Krejčí₎ V Praze, Nakl. ELK, 1949.
191 p. 22 cm. (Národní klenotnice, sv. 38)

1. Boleslav I, Duke of Bohemia, 906 or 7–967—Fiction. 2. Wenceslaus, Saint, Duke of Bohemia, 907?–935?—Fiction. I. Title.

PG5038.L55Z2 1949   69–49550

             MiU InU MB IU
NL 0376446   DLC WaU CoU NNC CU ICU PSt NjP TxU CLU

Linda, Lucas de, 1625–1660, comp.
Lucæ de Linda Descriptio orbis & omnium ejus rerumpublicarum. In qua præcipua omnium regnorum & rerumpublicarum. Ordine & methodice pertractantur quorum seriem versa ostendit pagina. Amstelodami: Apud Jacobum de Zetter, 1665.
8 p.l., 1156 p., 6 l. 19cm. (8°.)

Sabin 41288.
Title vignette.
Added engraved t.-p., signed: I. v Meurs sculp.
Many pages wrongly numbered.
Taken partly from Pierre d'Avity's "Les estats, empires, et principautes du monde" and Joannes de Laet's "Nieuwe wereldt."—cf. p. 239 and ₁1115₎

9911. I. Geography. 2. Manners and customs. I. Avity, Pierre d', sieur de Montmartin, 1573–1635. Les estats, empires, et principautes du monde. II. Laet, Joannes de, 1582–1649. Nieuwe wereldt. N.Y.P.L.   *Revised* May 19, 1937

NL 0376447   NN RPJCB IU MH ICN FU NjP MnU PU CtY

Linda, Lucas de, 1625–1660, *comp.*
Lucæ de Linda Descriptio orbis et omnium ejus rerumpublicarum. Nunc primum in Germania edita, & innumeris locis emendata, plurimis suppleta, ac à multis, iisque gravissimis erroribus purgata. Jenae, impensis M. Birckneri, 1670.
8 p. l., 1448, ₁14₎ p. 16½ᵐ.

First published at Leyden in 1655.
A compilation, taken largely from "Les empires, royaumes, estats ... et principautes du monde" of Pierre d'Avity. Book XII is from the "Nieuwe wereldt" of Johannes de Laet.

1. Geography—17th-18th cent. I. Avity, Pierre d', sieur de Montmartin, 1573–1635. II. Laet, Johannes de, 1593–1649. III. Title.

                       5–38265

Library of Congress   G114.L7

NL 0376448   DLC ICN PCC

F660
L742d

Linda, Lucas de, 1625–1660.
Le Descrittioni Vniversali Et Particolari del Mondo, & delle Republiche. Di Lvca Di Linda. ... Tradotte, Osseruate, & Accresciute, Dal Marchese Maiolino Bisaccioni. All' Altezza Serenissima dell' Arciduca Ferdinando Carlo D'Avstria, Etc.
In Venetia, Per Combi, & La Noù. MDCLX. Con Licenza de' Superiori, & Priuilegio.
11 p.ℓ., 887 p. port. 23cm. 4°

Continued in next column

VOLUME 334

Continued from preceding column

Added t.-p., engraved: Le Descrittione Vniuersali et Particolari del Mondo et delle Repvbliche Di Luca di Linda. Picini sculpsit.
Transl. from: Lucæ De Linda Descriptio Orbis ... Lugduni Batavorum, 1655, which is a compilation, taken largely from "Les empires ..." of Pierre d'Avity, first pub. St. Omer, 1614, Book XII is from the "Nieuwe wereldt"

of Johannes de Laet, first pub. Leyden, 1625.
"Licentia" (5th p.ℓ.) Signed: 10. Giugno 1659. Nicolò Sagredo.
Title vignette.
Bound in contemporary vellum.

NL 0376451   RPJCB ICN ViU CU NN ICU CSt

₍Linda, Lucas de₎ 1625–1660, comp.
Orbis lumen et Atlantis ivga tecta retecta: das ist: Newe aussführliche entdeck- vnd beschreibung der gantzen welt, aller darinn enthaltener keyserthumb, königreichen ... länder vnd republicqen, &c. deren inwohner sitten, religion ... &c. Ingleichem der päbste, käyser, könige vnd fürsten succession vnd ordnung, &c. Vnd endtlichen dess Röm. reichs freyer ritterschafft, vnd dess löblichen Hansee-bunds, &c. Auss vnuerwerfflichen gründen vnd zeugnüssen verschiedener glaubhaffter authorum mit höchstem fleiss zusammen getragen. Franckfurt am Mayn, W. Serlin vnd G. Fickwirth, 1656.

Added t.-p., engr.
Translation of the "Descriptio orbis et omnium ejus rerum publicarum," Leyden, 1655, compiled by Linda. Taken largely from "Les empires, royaumes, estats ... et principautez du monde" of Pierre d'Avity; book XII is from the "Nieuwe wereldt" of Johannes de Laet.

1. Geography.   I. Avity, Pierre d', sieur de Montmartin, 1573–1635. II. Laet, Johannes de, 1593–1649.

Library of Congress   G113.L75   5-37236†

NL 0376453   DLC PCC FU ICU

G   LINDA, LUCAS DE, 1625–1660.
11   ₍Le₎ relationi, et descrittioni universali et
.505   particolari del mondo, di Lucca di Linda et dal
       marchese Maiolino Bisaccioni. Tradotte, osseruate, & nouuamente molto accresciute.   Venetia, Per Combi, & La Nou,1664.
       ₍12₎,100₍9₎ p. port. 22cm.

Imperfect copy: trimmed, with loss of first word of title and some headings.

NL 0376454   ICN MiU-C NNH

Linda, Lucas de, 1625–1660.
Le relationi et descrittioni vniversali et particolari del mondo. Di Lvca di Linda, et dal marchese Maiolino Bisaccioni tradotte, osseruate, & nuouamente molto accresciute, e corrette ...   Venetia, Presso Combi, & La Noù, 1672.
10 p. l., 932 p. 22½ x 17cm.
Title vignette.
Added t.-p., engr., with title: Le descrittioni vniversali et particolari del mondo delle republiche. Di Luca di Linda.
Preface signed by the editor: Giacomo Rossi.
1. Geography.   I. Bisaccioni, Majolino, conte, 1582–1663, tr.   II. Rossi, Giacomo, ed.

Library of Congress   G114.L8   7-6303

NL 0376455   DLC CtY FU NN

Linda, Lucas de, 1625–1660.
Le relationi, et descrittioni vniversali, et particolari del mondo. Di Lvca di Linda, et dal marchese Maiolino Bisaccioni tradotte, osseruate, & nuouamente molto accresciute, e corrette...   Bologna, Per Gioseffo Longhi, 1674.   8 p.l., 954 ₍i. e. 956₎ p. 22cm. (4°.)

See: Grässe, IV, 213.
Pages 695–696 wrongly numbered 595–596 and followed by p. 695–696.

Dedication signed: Gioseffo Longhi.
Taken partly from Pierre d'Avity's "Les estats, empires, et principautez du monde."
Book 12 is from the "Nieuwe wereldt" of Joannes de Laet.
With inscription: di franc Baldacchini(?).

541326A. 1. Geography. I. Avity, Pierre d', sieur de Montmartin, 1573–1635. Les estats, empires et principe, 1582–1649. Nieuwe wereldt. II. Laet, Joannes de, 1582–1663, tr. III. Bisaccioni, Majolino, conte.

NL 0376457   NN WU RPJCB CaBViPA

Linda, William.
"David Copperfield", a dramatization of Charles Dickens' favorite novel. In three acts, by William Linda ... Minneapolis, Minn., The Northwestern press, ᶜ1935.
128 p. plates, diagr. 19cm.

I. Dickens, Charles. David Copperfield. II. Title.

Library of Congress   PR4558.A37L5   CA 35-108 Unrev'd
———— Copy 2.
Copyright D pub. 33991   [823.83] 812.5

NL 0376458   DLC

Linda, William.
"Oliver Twist" a dramatization of Charles Dickens' immortal novel in three acts ... Minneapolis, Minn. , Northwestern press, c.1936.
119, [6] p. 19 cm.

NL 0376459   RPB MiD DLC

PN6111B
.L5R6   Linda, William.
           "Robinson Crusoe", a comedy in three acts, a dramatization of Daniel Defoe's immortal novel of adventure. Minneapolis, The Northwestern Press, 1935.
           107 p. diagr. 19cm.

I. Defoe, Daniel, 1661?–1731. Robinson Crusoe. II. Title.

NL 0376460   ViU OCl DLC

Linda Hall Library, *Kansas City, Mo.*
Bibliographic bulletin. no.1–
Kansas City, 1950–
no. 28 cm.
Title varies: no. 2, Bibliographical bulletin.

1. Bibliography—Period.

Z1007.L74   52-38395

NL 0376461   DLC TxU MiU NN

Z733
.K3L5   Linda Hall Library. Kansas City, Missouri.
           The book collection and services of the Linda Hall Library: an outline guide.
           43 p. illus. 23cm.

1. Kansas City, Mo. Linda Hall Library.

NL 0376462   AAP

Z881
.K1685   **Linda Hall Library,** *Kansas City, Mo.*
            Bulletin.
            Kansas City, 19
            v. 29 cm.

Z881.K1685   51-32768

NL 0376463   DLC

Linda Hall Library, *Kansas City, Mo.*
Firearms. A list of books on rifles, shotguns, pistols, revolvers, machine guns, cartridges, gunsmithing and a few selected titles on ballistics. Mostly published after 1940. Kansas City, 1953.
₍10₎ p. 28 cm. (*Its* Bibliographic bulletin no. 5)
At head of title: Linda Hall Library, Science and Technology.

1. Firearms—Bibl.   (Series)

Z1007.L74 no. 5   016.6234   54-32004

NL 0376464   DLC MB MiU PPF MiD PPT

Linda Hall Library, Kansas City, Mo.
Firearms. A list of books on rifles, shotguns, pistols, revolvers, machine guns, cartridges, gunsmithing, ballistics, and a few titles on ordnance. Rev. and enl. Kansas City, 1954.
[12] l. 28 cm. (Its Bibliographic bulletin no. 5)

NL 0376465   NIC

Linda Hall Library, *Kansas City, Mo.*
Floods. A list of references on methods for handling emergencies resulting from floods and on rehabilitation techniques which follow. Kansas City, 1953.
₍11₎ p. 28 cm. (*Its* Bibliographic bulletin no. 4)
At head of title: Linda Hall Library, Science and Technology.

1. Floods—Bibl.   (Series)

Z1007.L74 no. 4   016.36152   54-30519

NL 0376466   DLC MiU

Z   Linda Hall Library, Kansas City, Mo.
6004   Floods. A list of references on methods
P5   for handling emergencies resulting from
L74   floods and on rehabilitation techniques
         which follow. Kansas City, 1954.
         8 l. 28 cm. (Its Bibliographic bulletin no. 10)

Revision of Bibliographic bulletin no. 4.

1. Floods   Bibl. I. Title. II. Series.

NL 0376467   NIC KMK MiU PPF

Linda Hall Library, Kansas City, Mo.
Geology and related subjects (excluding mining, metallurgy and economic geology).
A list of books, periodicals and documents in the Linda Hall Library. Kansas City, Mo.,1954.
[3] 90 l. 28 cm. (Its Bibliographic bulletin no. 9)
Compiled by E. H. Mueller.

1. Geology - Bibl. I. Mueller, E. H., comp.

NL 0376468   DI NNC NcU PPF MiU KMK NIC CaBVaU

VOLUME 334

026
L74z8
Linda Hall Library, Kansas City, Mo.
Linda Hall Library; science and technology,
outline of book collection and services.
Kansas City, Mo. ₍1951₎.
41 ℓ. 29 cm.

Cover title.

1. Technical libraries. 2. Scientific libraries. 3. Libraries, Special

NL 0376469   DAS IU NNC

Linda Hall Library, *Kansas City, Mo.*
A list of books on statistical quality control. Kansas City,
1951.
6 p. 28 cm. (*Its* Bibliographical bulletin no. 2)

1. Quality control—Bibl.   I. Title: Statistical quality control.
(Series: Linda Hall Library, Kansas City, Mo. Bibliographic bulletin
no. 2)
Z1007.L74 no. 2   52-38536
                      *016.3112 016.658562

NL 0376470   DLC

Linda Hall Library, *Kansas City, Mo.*
A list of books on statistical quality control available in
Linda Hall Library. Kansas City, 1954.
12 ℓ. 29 cm. (*Its* Bibliographic bulletin no. 8)
At head of title: Linda Hall Library. Science and technology.
"A revision of Bibliographic bulletin no. 2."

1. Quality control—Bibl.   I. Title: Statistical quality control.
(Series)
Z1007.L74 no. 8   54-44548
                      *016.3112 016.658562

NL 0376471   DLC NIC PPF MiU

Z
1007
.L74
no. 3
Linda Hall Library, Kansas City, Mo.
A list of items on cybernetics. Kansas City,
1951.
4 p. 28 cm. (Its Bibliographic bulletin,
no. 3)
Caption title.

1. Cybernetics--   Bibl.

NL 0376472   MiU

Linda Hall Library, *Kansas City, Mo.*
A list of serial holdings in the collections of **Linda Hall**
Library. Kansas City, 1951₁
1 v. (loose-leaf) 29 cm. (*Its* Bulletin no. 3)

1. Periodicals—Bibl.—Catalogs.   (Series)

Z881.K1685 no. 3   016.505   51-34069

NL 0376473   DLC DNAL TxU WyU

Linda Hall Library, Kansas City, Mo.
Mathematical programming and mangerial
planning; a selected bibliography. Kansas
City, Missouri, Linda Hall Library ₍1955₎
14 ℓ. (Its Bibliographical bulletin # 12)

NL 0376474   PPF

Linda Hall Library, *Kansas City, Mo.*
Meteorology and climate and related subjects; a list of
books, periodicals and documents in the Linda Hall Library.
Kansas City, 1954.
48 ℓ. 28 cm. (*Its* Bibliographic bulletin no. 7)
At head of title: Linda Hall Library, Science and Technology.
"Prepared and edited : E. H. Mueller."

1. Meteorology—Bibl. 2. Climatology—Bibl.   I. Mueller, E. H.
II. Title.   (Series)
Z1007.L74 no. 7   016.5515   55-27352

NL 0376475   DLC PPF LU MiU NNC IdPI

Linda Hall Library, *Kansas City, Mo.*
Mining and metallurgy; a list of books, periodicals and
documents in the Linda Hall Library. ₍Compiled by E. H.
Mueller₎ Kansas City, 1955.
64 ℓ. 29 cm. (*Its* Bibliographic bulletin no. 11)

1. Mining engineering—Bibl. 2. Metallurgy—Bibl.   I. Title.

Z1007.L74 no. 11   016.622   55-57287 ‡

NL 0376476   DLC MiD NNC PPF MiU LU

Linda Hall Library, Kansas City, Mo.

Outline of book collection and services.
Kansas City, Mo. [1951]

41 ℓ. 29 cm.

NL 0376477   CaBVaU

Linda Hall Library, *Kansas City, Mo.*
Pharmacy, pharmacology and related subjects; a list of
titles in the Linda Hall Library. Kansas City, 1954.
32 ℓ. 28 cm. (*Its* Bibliographic bulletin no. 6)

1. Pharmacy—Bibl.   I. Title.   (Series)

Z1007.L74 no. 6   55-18981

NL 0376478   DLC PPF MiU DNLM IdPI CaBVaU

ZQ 157
L45
1956
Linda Hall Library, Kansas City, Mo.
Some milestones in the history of science,
to 1800; based upon selections of printed
books in the collection of the Linda Hall
Library. Kansas City, Mo., 1956.
52 p. illus. 23 cm.

1. Science - Early works to 1800 - Bibl.
2. Science - Hist. I. Title.

NL 0376479   CaBVaU

Linda ₍Incidents in the Life of a Slave-Girl
see Jacobs, Harriet (Brent) 1818-1896.
Incidents in the life of a slave child.

La linda Magalona
see under Pierre de Provence et Maguelonne.

M1
.S444
v.99,
no.11
Linda mia. Arranged from traditional
Pyrenean melodies by M. H. Sturgis and
W. P. Blake. 35 ₍cts₎, Boston, Carl
Prüfer, 34 West St. ₍°1882₎ Pl. no. C. P.
339.
20-22 p. 35cm. ₍Songs of the Pyrenees, with
Spanish, French and English words, no. 9₎.
₍Sheet music collection, v. 99, no. 11₎
Stamp of Henry McCaffrey, Music, Baltimore on
cover.

1. Songs with piano. I. Sturgis, M
H   arr.   II. Blake, W
P   jt. arr.

NL 0376482   ViU

Linda Vista vineyards, mission San José, Alameda co.₎
Cal. . . . C. C. McIver, proprietor. ₍San Francisco,
H. S. Crocker co.,₎ 1894₎
[60] pp. illus. obl. 12°.

F869.L6L6   1-Re-2782

NL 0376483   DLC

Lindaal Jacobs, Henri Louis
see Jacobs, Henri Louis Lindaal.

Lindaas, Annäeus, comp.
Forhandlinger

see under

Drammens medicinske selskap.

WB
1
GN6
D7L
1955
LINDAAS, Annäeus
Trekk av medisinens historie i
Drammen, fra 1827-1908. Drammen,
Handelstrykkeriet, 1955.
26 p. ports.
On cover: Collegium medicorum
Drafniense.
1. Drammens medicinske selskap

NL 0376486   DNLM

Lindabury, Richard Vliet, 1850-
Argument of Richard V. Lindabury on behalf of the
Prudential insurance company of America, before the
Committee on the judiciary of the Senate of the United
States, in support of Senate bill no. 3026, for the regula-
tion of the business of insurance. ₍Newark, N. J., 1906₎
cover-title, 59 p. 23ᶜᵐ.

1. Insurance, Life—U. S.—State supervision.   I. The Prudential insurance company of America.

                                              20-76
Library of Congress   HG8535.L5

NL 0376487   DLC

Lindabury, Richard Vliet, 1850-
Between Miriam Berger, complainant-respondent, and United
States Steel Corporation, et al., defendants-appellants. On appeal
from order in chancery allowing a preliminary injunction. Brief
of R. V. Lindabury for appellants.   Newark: Baker Prtg. Co.,
1902. 23 p. pap. 4°.

1. Corporations.—Jurisprudence, U. S..   N. J., 1902. 2. United States Steel
Corporation. 3. Berger, Miriam.   4. Lindabury, R. V.
N. Y. P. L.   January 12, 1915.

NL 0376488   NN

VOLUME 334

Lindabury, Richard Vliet, 1850–
... In the matter of consolidation of the railway properties of the United States into a limited number of systems. Statement of the Birmingham southern railroad company. Richard V. Lindabury, Charles MacVeagh, Charles S. Belsterling, A. Benners, of counsel. Dated June 25, 1923. New York, N. Y., The Evening post job printing office, inc. ₁1923₎
cover-title, 7 numb. l. fold. map. 30½ᶜᵐ.
At head of title: Interstate commerce commission, Washington, D. C. No. 12,964. Consolidation of railroads.
1. Railroads—Consolidation.   1. MacVeagh, Charles, joint author.
11. Belsterling, Charles Stearne, 1874–   joint author.   11. Benners, A.,
joint author.   1v. Bir-   mingham southern railroad company.
Title from Bureau of   Railway Economics.   A 23-2150

NL 0376489   DBRE DIC

LINDABURY, Richard Vliet, 1850–
In the Supreme court of the United States October term, 1916. No. 481. United States of America, appellant, vs. United States steel corporation et al., appellees. Appeal from the District court of the United States for the district of New Jersey.   Statement of the case [1916?]

NL 0376490   MH-BA

Lindabury, Richard Vliet, 1900–
Study of patriotism in the Elizabethan drama.   Lond. Milford, n.d.

218 p.

NL 0376491   PU

Lindabury, Richard Vliet, 1900–
A study of patriotism in the Elizabethan drama ... by Richard Vliet Lindabury. ₁Princeton, N. J., 1931₎
2 p. l., ₁vii₎-viii p., 2 l., ₁3₎-218 p. 23ᶜᵐ.
Thesis (PH. D.)—Princeton university, 1930.
Bibliography: p. ₁203₎-212.

1. English drama—Early modern and Elizabethan—Hist. & crit.
2. Gt. Brit.—Nationality. 3. Patriotism.
Library of Congress   PR658.P3L5 1930   31-32748
Princeton Univ. Libr.
——— Copy 2.   ₁3₎   822.309

OU AAP MoU LU FTaSU MsSM IdU OrCS KEmT NSyU DLC
NL 0376492   NJP NcGU ViU NcD PBm MH OCIW OCU MiU

Lindabury, Richard Vliet, 1900–
A study of patriotism in the Elizabethan drama, by Richard Vliet Lindabury ... Princeton, Princeton university press, 1931.
viii p., 2 l., ₁3₎-218 p. 23½ᶜᵐ. (₁Princeton university₎ Princeton studies in English. no. 5)
Issued also as thesis (PH. D.) Princeton university.
Bibliography: p. ₁203₎-212.

1. English drama—Early modern and Elizabethan—Hist. & crit.
2. Gt. Brit.—Nationality. 3. Patriotism.
Library of Congress   PR658.P3L5 1931   33-8115
₁5₎   822.309

OrU
NL 0376493   DLC PSC NcU ViU MB KMK AU DAU WaTC

Lindabury, Depue & Faulks.
... Between United States of America, petitioner, and United States steel corporation and others, defendants. Argument ...   New York (1914)
cover-title, vii, 248 p.   23.5 cm.

NL 0376494   DL

Lindabury, Depue & Faulks,
... Between the United States of America petitioner, and United States steel corporation and others, defendan⁺s.   Statement of the case.   New York (1914?)
cover-title, viii, 560 p.   fold. tables.
23.5 cm.

NL 0376495   DL

Lindach, Hans, pseud.
see Weller, Hermann, 1878–

Lindacher, E
Die Conservirung der Früchte u. Gemüse in Flacons und Dosen der Fruchtsäfte, Gelées und Confituren. (Schwefeln, Glaciren, Candiren und Carmeliren der Dickfrüchte.) Eine praktische Anleitung, dieselben haltbar nach den neuesten Methoden zu conserviren. Bearbeitet von E. Lindacher, ... Mit 50 Abbildungen. ..... 2. bedeutend verbesserte und vermehrte Auflage. Metz, im Selbstverlage des Verfassers; E. Seifert, 1897.
68 p. illus., 1 fold. pl. 21½ᶜᵐ.
Slip pasted over imprint reads: Metz, K. Lupus, 1902.

NL 0376497   ICJ

TP
577   Lindacker, Gustav.
L554   Der Bierwürzekontrollmessapparat Erhard-
1890   Schau, seine Zerlegung und Montierung. ₁Linz,
Verein der Beamten der k.k. technischen Finanz-
kontrolle in Österreich, 1890?₎
40, xiv p.   illus.

1. Beer.   2. Brewing industry—Austria.

NL 0376498   NSyU

PT8137   Lindälv, Elof, joint ed.
H22
Hänninger, Nils, ed.
Skolproblem hemma och ute. Festskrift till L. Gottfrid Sjöholm 4. april 1952. ₁Redigerad av Nils Hänninger och Elof Lindälv₎ Stockholm, Svenska bokförlaget ₁1952₎

W.C.L.   Lindahl, Albert
M780.88
A512CX   Midnight chimes; composed by Albert Lin-
no.6   dahl. Boston, Oliver Ditson [185-]
7 p.   33 cm.   (Chimes and rhymes, morceau
[sic] de salon]
For piano.
[No. 6] in a vol. with binder's title:
Music [collected by] C. E. Barton.

1. Piano music.   I. Title.

NL 0376500   NcD

M35   Lindahl, Albert, arr.
.P
Partant pour la Syrie; arr. for the piano forte by Albert Lindahl. London, Chappell ₁18—₎ Pl. no. 9119.

M1642   Lindahl, Albert.
.L5586
1860   The soldier's adieu ₁by Albert₎ Lindahl. Augusta, Ga., Blackmar & Bro.; Richmond, Va., J. W. Randolph, P. H. Taylor ₁etc., etc.₎ Duncan & Co., Lith., Columbia, S. C. ₁186–?₎
4 p.   30cm.   (Blackmar & Bro's collection of standard music, vocal and instrumental, arranged for the piano-forte.)

NL 0376502   ViU

Lindahl, Alex.
Stockholm.   Stockholm, Göteborg, A. Lindahl, ₁n.d.₎
₁8₎ plates (1 fold. double) 11x17cm.
Portfolio of photographic views of Stockholm, Sweden.

NL 0376503   OrCS

Lindahl (Alfred): Symptomerne Smerte og Myopathi i Thorax' Musculatur ved Hjærtesygdomme og beslægtede Tilstande. København 1935. 300 pages. 8°.
Copenhague. — Th. méd.

NL 0376504   ICRL

Lindahl (Ambrosius Ludow[icus]) and Peterson (S. E.)
*Expositio curvarum, intra quas, post geminam reflexionem, ad punctum radians revertitur lumen. [Parts I-II.]
Upsaliae, 1810. 2 pts. 4°.

NL 0376505   NN

Lindahl, August Rikard
see Lindahl, Rikard, 1897–

₁Lindahl, C   J   ₎
Svenska millionärer; minnen och anteckningar af Lazarus ₁pseud.₎. Stockholm, P.A. Huldberg, 1897-1905.
10 v. in 5. ports.

v.5 published by Köersnors Boktryckori-Aktiebolag; v.6 by Iduns Kungl. Hofboktr. Filial; v.7-10, by Aktieb. Varias Boktryckori.
v.5-10 marked Ny följd, ₁I₎-VI.

NL 0376507   MH-BA NN

4PE   Lindahl, Carl Eric
116   A new English reader; för fyraåriga och treåriga realskolans första klass samt folkskolans avslutningsklasser [av] Carl-Eric Lindahl [och] Stanley Carpenter. Stockholm, Svenska Bokförlaget [1954]
146 p.

NL 0376508   DLC-P4

Lindahl, Carl Fredrik.
Über den verschluss der fotalen augenbecherspalte, die entwicklung der dehnerveninsertion und die anlage des pecten bei vogeln. Von C. Lindahl und A. Jokl. (In Festskrift tillägnad prof. J. Aug. Hammar på hans 60-årsdag den 21 augusti 1921. 1921. no. XIX, 20p. II el.)

NL 0376509   OU

Lindahl, Edward.
Landet under havet, en bok för Holland ₁av₎ Edward Lindahl, under medverkan av Ivar Harrie och Åke Lindström. Stockholm, Sällskapet Bokvännerna ₁1953₎
unpaged. illus. 22 cm.

1. Netherlands—Descr. & trav.   I. Title.
DJ39.L5   54-30255 ‡

NL 0376510   DLC

VOLUME 334

948.504
Ox2bℓ Lindahl, Edward.
Rikskansleren Axel Oxenstjernas
fredsunderhandlingar i Tyskland, 1634-
1636. Historisk afhandling, som jämte
theser i modersmålet, med tillstånd
af högvördiga domkapitlet i Växjö,
kommer att offentligen försvaras af
Edward Lindahl, torsdagen den 29 sept.
1870... Lund, Tryckt uti Berlingska
boktr., 1870.

90 p.   22cm.
1.Oxenstierna, Axel Gustafsson,
grefve,1583- 1654. 2.Germany.
History.1618- 1648.

NL 0376511   MnU

TJ840   Lindahl, Eric Jean, joint author.
.B45   FOR OTHER EDITIONS
1953   SEE MAIN ENTRY
Beitler, Samuel Reid, 1899-
Hydraulic machinery, by Samuel R. Beitler ¡and¿ Eric J.
Lindahl. New York, Ronald Press Co. ¡1953, *1947¿

Lindahl, Erik.
Lexicon lapponicum, cum interpretatione vocabulorum
sveco-latina, et indice svecano lapponico; in usum tam illorum,
quibus cura ecclesiarum in Lapponia committenda, aut jam
commissa est, quam aliorum curiosorum et linguarum studiosorum, indigenarum et exterorum: illustratum praefatione la-
tino-svecana ... Johannis Ihre; nec non auctum grammatica
lapponica. A dom. Erico Lindahl ... et Johanne Öhrling ...
confectum. In lucem editum, cura et impensis illustriss. r: æ in

3 p. l., ¡iii¿-lxxx, 716 p.   27 x 20½ᵐ.

1. Lappish language—Dictionaries — Latin. 2. Lappish language—
Dictionaries—Swedish. 3. Swedish language—Dictionaries — Lappish.
I. Öhrling, Johan, b. 1718, joint author. II. Ihre, Johan, 1707-1780. III.
Title.
Library of Congress   PH725.L5
                                      43-49786
                                      ¡2¿

NL 0376514   DLC OC1 ICN CtY MH NN ViU PPAmP

4HD   Lindahl, Erik Robert, 1891-
2610   Arbetsdagens förkortning några nationalekonomiska synpunkter. Malmö,
Förlagsaktiebolagets i Malmö boktryckeri, 1925.
35 p.

(Skrifter utgivna av Fahlbeckska stiftelsen, 5)

NL 0376515   DLC-P4 MH NN ICU DL

LINDAHL, ERIK ROBERT, 1891-
The consumption price index of the Bank of Sweden, by
Erik Lindahl... [Gothenburg?] 1933. iii, 46, 7, 12 f.
incl. tables. 28½cm.

Reproduced from typewritten copy.

832960A. 1. Prices—Index numbers—Sweden, 1931-1932.

NL 0376516   NN OC1

Lindahl, Erik Robert, 1891-
...Études sur la théorie de la monnaie et du capital; conception
dynamique de la théorie économique... Traduit de l'anglais par
M. Th. Génin. Paris, Librairie de Médicis ¡1939¿ 143 p.
23cm.

1. Capital. 2. Interest—Rates.   3. Money, 1933-

NL 0376517   NN

Lindahl, Erik Robert, 1891-
Die gerechtigkeit der besteuerung; eine analyse der
steuerprinzipien auf grundlage der grenznutzentheorie,
von Erik Lindahl. Lund, Gleerup ¡1919¿

3 p. l., ¡v¿-ix, 226 p., 1 l. 25ᶜᵐ.
Added t.-p., with note: Inaug. diss.—Lund.

1. Taxation.   I. Title.
                                                  24-25066
Library of Congress   HJ2309.L5

NL 0376518   DLC KU MB NN ICU CtY

Lindahl, Erik Robert, 1891-
Jämförande undersökning av industriens beskattning i Sverige och utlandet, av Erik Lindahl ... [Stockholm], Sveriges
industriförbund, [1927].
57 p. incl. tables. 24½ᶜᵐ. (*In* [Publikationer] utgivna av Sveriges industriförbund, Avd.: Diverse publikationer n:o 22.)

NL 0376519   ICJ NN

Lindahl, Erik Robert, 1891-
... Jordbruksbefolkningens levnadskostnader, utredning
verkställd på uppdrag av 1942 års jordbrukskommitté, av Erik
Lindahl och Lars Lemne. Stockholm, I. Marcus boktryckeri-
aktiebolag, 1944.
71 p. tables, diagrs. 24ᶜᵐ. (¡Sweden¿ Statens offentliga utredningar
1944 : 1)
At head of title: ... Jordbruksdepartementet.

1. Cost and standard of living—Sweden. 2. Peasantry—Sweden. I.
Lemne, Lars Gunnar, 1916- joint author. II. Sweden. Jordbruks-
kommittén, 1942. III. Sweden. Jordbruksdepartementet.

J406.R15 1944:1   47-22633

NL 0376520   DLC DNAL

[LINDAHL, Erik Robert, 1891-
National income of Sweden,1861-1930. Pt.I-II.
[By Erik Lindahl,Einar Dahlgren,Karin Kock].
London,P.S.King & Son,Ltd.,[cop.1937].

22 cm.
Forms vol.III of Wages,cost of living and
national income in Sweden,1860-1930,by the
staff of the Institute for Social Sciences,Uni-
versity of Stockholm.

NL 0376521   MH

Lindahl, Erik Robert, 1891-
Penning- och kreditväsendet, av Erik Lindahl och Ulrich
Herz. Revid. uppl. av Erik Lindahl: Penning- och bank-
väsendet. Uppsala, Distribueras genom Nationalekonomiska institutionen vid Uppsala universitet, 1948.
56 l. 30 cm.

1. Money. 2. Credit.   I. Herz, Ulrich, joint author. II. Title.

HG221.L546 1948a   59-21179*

NL 0376522   DLC

Ng440   Lindahl, Erik Robert, 1891-
+955L   Penning- och kreditväsendet; grundlinjer
till förelläsningar. Rev. uppl. Uppsala,
Distribueras genom Nationalekonomiska
Institutionen vid Uppsala Universitet, 1955.
58 ℓ. 30 cm.

1. Money (Works pub. 1939-   )
2. Credit.

NL 0376523   CtY

4HC   Lindahl, Erik Robert, 1891-
630   Penningpolitikens mål. Malmö, Förlagsaktiebolagets i Malmö boktryckeri,
1929.
98 p.

(Skrifter utgivna av Fahlbeckska stiftelsen, 14)

NL 0376524   DLC-P4 ICU NN

Lindahl,Erik Robert,1891-
Penningpolitikens medel,av Erik Lindahl.
Malmö, Förlagsaktiebolagets i Malmö boktryckeri, 1930.
180,¡2¿ p. 25½ᶜᵐ. (Half-title: Skrifter utgivna
av Fahlbeckska stiftelsen, XVI)
Imprint on cover: Lund, C.W.K.Gleerup.
"Ansluter sig til det i denna skriftserie förut
publicerade arbetet 'Penningpolitikens mål'."—Förord.

1.Currency question. I.Title.
                          HB236.S85 L7

NL 0376525   MiU NN MH ICU

Lindahl, Erik Robert, 1891-
... Promemoria angående förutsättningarna för och verk-
ningarna av en engångsskatt å förmögenhet i Sverige, utarbetad av Erik Lindahl. Stockholm, I. Marcus boktryckeri-aktiebolag, 1942.
82 p. 24ᶜᵐ. (¡Sweden¿ Statens offentliga utredningar 1942:52)
At head of title: ... Finansdepartementet.
On cover: Distribueras av Nordiska bokhandeln.

1. Property tax—Sweden.   I. Sweden. Finansdepartementet.
                                                  46-31281
Library of Congress   J406.R15 1942:52

NL 0376526   DLC

Lindahl, Erik Robert, 1891-
Studies in the theory of money and capital, by Erik Lindahl
... London, G. Allen & Unwin ltd. ¡1939¿
2 p. l., 9-391 p. diagrs. 22ᶜᵐ. (Half-title: The library of economics ...
P. N. Rosenstein-Rodan, general editor ... Section 2: New works, 1)
The greater part of the book has been translated by Tor Fernholm.
cf. Pref.
"First published in 1939."
CONTENTS.—The dynamic approach to economic theory.—The rate of
interest and the price level (1930)—The place of capital in the theory
of price (1929)—Appendix: The problem of balancing the budget (1935)
1. Economics. 2. Money. 3. Interest and usury. 4. Prices. 5. Capital.
I. Fernholm, Tor, 1904-   tr. II. Title.
Library of Congress   HB501.L5   40-12682
                              ¡12¿   330.1

OrU WaTC CLSU
MH-BA ViU IU OC1 ICJ CU OrPR WaWW CaBVaU WaS IdPI
NL 0376527   DLC MH NN NcD OU PBm PU TU PHC OCU OO

Lindahl, Erik Robert, 1891-
Studies in the theory of money and capital,
by Erik Lindahl. New York, Farrar & Rinehart,
1939.
391 p. 22 cm. (The Library of economics.
Section 2: New works, 1)

NL 0376528   DCU NcRS CoU AU FU MtU IdU OrCS ICJ MiU

Lindahl, Ernst Emanuel.
Med blommande gräs; dikter. Lund, P. Lindstedts universitetsbokhandel ¡1951¿
76 p. 23 cm.

I. Title.
                                                  A 52-4715
Minnesota. Univ. Libr.
for Library of Congress   ¡3¿

NL 0376529   MnU

VOLUME 334

Lindahl, Ernst Emanuel.
Siktförbättring; dikter. Lund, P. Lindstedts universitetsbokhandel ₁1952₎
77 p.   24 cm.

I. Title.

A 53-3957

Minnesota. Univ. Libr.
for Library of Congress   ₁₃₎

NL 0376530   MnU

Lindahl, George Raymond.
Butikshandelen med fødevarer i Danmark; en undersøgelse af dansk butikshandels praksis med forskellige rationaliseringsforslag. Udg. ved Udenrigsministeriets foranstaltning. København, 1952.
62 p. illus., port. 29 cm.
Issued also in English.
Bibliography: p. 61.

1. Self-service stores. 2. Grocery trade—Denmark. I. Title.
HF6201.G7L48   A 53-7380
New York Univ.   Libraries
for Library of Congress   ₁₃₎†

NL 0376531   NN DLC DNAL

Lindahl, George Raymond.
Retail food distribution; an examination of Danish food retailing practices and suggestions for improvement. ₁Copenhagen? 1952₎
46 l. illus. 27 cm.

1. Food industry and trade—Denmark. 2. Retail trade—Denmark. 3. Self-service stores. I. Title.
HD9015.D42L5   *664 658.9414   53-26098 ‡
U. S. Dept. of Agr. Libr.
for Library of Congress

NL 0376532   DLC DNAL

Lindahl, Göran.
Högkyrkligt, lågkyrkligt, frikyrkligt i svensk arkitektur, 1800–1950. Stockholm, Svenska kyrkans diakonistyrelses bokförlag ₁1955₎
175 p. illus. 24 cm.

1. Church architecture—Sweden. 2. Churches—Sweden. I. Title.
NA5784.L5   56-28007 ‡

NL 0376533   DLC KU MnU NNC ICLT

Lindahl, Göran.
Möte på torsdag, ett sociologiskt reportage, av Göran Lindahl och Allan Lundberg. Stockholm, O. Eklund, 1947.
208 p. illus. 24 cm.

1. Dalecarlia, Sweden—Soc. condit. I. Title.
HN580.D3L5   53-34950 ‡

NL 0376534   DLC MnU

Lindahl, Gösta.
Zigenarväckelse; intryck från zigenarkonferensen i Rennes den 1–5 juni 1955. Fotografierna är tagna av författaren. Stockholm, Förlaget Filadelfia ₁1955₎
45 p. illus. 19 cm.

1. Missions—Gipsies. 2. Revivals—France. I. Title.
BV3697.L5   63-41480 ‡

NL 0376535   DLC ICN

Lindahl, Hans Jakob. Historisk Sang.
Extr. fr. Minerva. Kiøbenhavn, 1790. 8°.
pp. 278–280.   IcC63T971
A satirical poem, dated at end: Reikevig i Island den 12te Septbr. 1789, on corruption and nepotism prevalent in Iceland.

NL 0376536   NIC

Lindahl, Hans Jakob.

—— Den islandske Almues offentlige aarlige Udgifter og Pligter. Kiøbenhavn, 1788. 8°. pp. 36.   IcG4L742

NL 0376537   NIC MH

Z
630.7   **Lindahl, Harry A.**
L64h   How to teach elementary agriculture in
Thesis   the seventh and eighth grades. 1923. 83p.

NL 0376538   WaPS

Lindahl, Ivan Leroy, 1919–
Feeding qualities for livestock of distiller's corn by-products from fungal amylase-converted mashes, compared with those from malt amylase-converted mashes, by Ivan L. Lindahl ₁and others₎ Washington ₁U. S. Govt. Print. Off.₎ 1952.
31 p. 24 cm. (U. S. Dept. of Agriculture. Technical bulletin no. 1053)
Caption title.
"Literature cited": p. 29–31.
1. Feeding and feeding stuffs. ₁1. Distillers' by-products as feeding stuff₎ 2. Distilling industries—By-products.   (Series)
S21.A72 no. 1053   636.08557   Agr 52-295
U. S. Dept. of Agr. Libr.   1Ag84Te no. 1053
for Library of Congress   ₁5*₎†

NL 0376539   DNAL DLC

635.9   **Lindahl, J   C**
L64t   Trees of Hot Springs National Park and vicinity ... Hot Springs, Ark., Hot Springs Natural History Association, 1938.
52p. illus. 29cm. (Hot Springs natural history journal, no.4)

1. Trees--Arkansas. 2. Hot Springs National Park. I. Title.

NL 0376540   LU DNAL

Lindahl, Johan Harald Josua, ₁1844–1912
...Description of a devonian ichthyodorulite, heteracanthus uddeni, n. sp., fr. Buffalo, Iowa.   Cincinn., 1897)

NL 0376541   OO

Q
11   **Lindahl, Johan Harald Josua,** 1844–1912.
P53T7++   Description of a skull of Megalonyx Leidy,
n.s.   n. sp. Read before the American Philosophical Society, January 2, 1891.   ₁Philadelphia, Published by the Society, 1893₎
v.17
pt.1   10 p. plates. 30cm. (American Philosophical Society, Philadelphia. Transactions, new ser., v. 17, pt. 1)

1. Megalonyx. 2. Sloths.

NL 0376542   NIC PPAmP Md

Lindahl, Johan Harald Josua, 1844–1912, ed.

Cincinnati society of natural history.
Journal. v. 1–22, no. 2; Apr. 1878–Nov. 1917. Cincinnati ₁1878–1917₎

Lindahl, Johan Harold Joshua, 1844–
Om pennatulid-slagtet Umbellula cuv. I text... af Josua Lindahl.. Stockholm, P.A. Norstedt & Soner, 1874.
15 p.   31 cm.
Akademisk Afhandling (Ph.D.) Lund.

NL 0376544   DNLM DI-GS NN OU PU-Z

Lindahl, Johan Harald Josua, 1844–1912, tr.

Yhlen, Gerhard von.
Report of the sea-fisheries of the Län of Göteborgand Bohus in the year 1877. By Gerhard von Yhlen. Tr. by Josua Lindahl.
(*In* Report of the commissioner ₁of fish and fisheries₎ for 1877. Washington, 1879. 22ᶜᵐ. p. ₁741₎-750)

Lindahl, Jonas, respondent.
... Dissertatio mathematica de longitudine loci, ex tempore invenienda, quam ...
see under   Liedbeck, Lars, praeses.

Lindahl, Jonas, respondent.
... Dissertatio mathematica de trigonometria plana, qvam ...
see under   Liedbeck, Lars, 1707–1762, praeses.

Lindahl, Josephus E., respondent.
... Dissertatio geographica de Smolandia...
see under   Arrhenius, Laurentius, 1680–1730. praeses.

Lindahl, Josua, 1844–1912.

see

Lindahl, Johan Harald Josua, 1844–1912.

Lindahl, Kai Curry-
see Curry-Lindahl, Kai.

Lindahl, Lawrence Gaylerd, 1901–
Movement analysis as an industrial training method ... by Lawrence Gaylerd Lindahl ... ₁Lancaster, Pa.₎, Lancaster press, inc.,₁1945₎
cover-title, ₁1₎, 420–436 p. 1 illus., diagrs. 23ᶜᵐ.
Based on thesis (PH. D.)—Purdue university.
"Reprinted from Journal of applied psychology, vol. 29, no. 6, December, 1945."
Vita: p. ₁3₎ of cover.
"References": p. 436.

1. Motion study. 2. Employees, Training of.
T58.L52   47-23257

NL 0376551   DLC

VOLUME 334

Lindahl, Lilly Esther Junia.
An introduction to German, by L. E. J. Lindahl ... New York, Farrar & Rinehart, incorporated, 1936.
xx, 300 p. front., plates, 2 port. on 1 pl. 19½ᶜᵐ.

Maps on lining-papers.
Includes songs with music.
"The German section of each lesson ... in connected prose form ... is a ... narrative describing a trip through Germany."—Pref.

1. German language—Chrestomathies and readers. 2. German language—Grammar—1870– 3. Germany—Descr. & trav.

Library of Congress   PF3111.L48   36-10136
——— Copy 2.
Copyright A 94237   ₍₃₎   438.242

NL 0376552   DLC NcD PPT OCl ViU

Lindahl, Martin Leroy, 1903–
Cooperation between the Interstate commerce commission and the state commissions in railroad regulation, by Martin L. Lindahl ... ₍Ann Arbor, Mich.₎ 1935₎
₍1₎ 338–397 p. 25½ᶜᵐ.

Thesis (PH. D.)—University of Michigan, 1933.
"Reprinted from the Michigan law review, vol. 33, no. 3, January, 1935."

1. Railroads and state—U. S. 2. U. S. Interstate commerce commission. I. Title.

Library of Congress   HE2757.1933.L5   35-5480
Univ. of Michigan Libr.   ₍2₎   385.016822

NL 0376553   MiU DLC OrU MsU PU-L OU OO OCU

Lindahl, Martin Leroy, 1903–   joint author.

Purdy, Harry Leslie, 1901–
Corporate concentration and public policy, by Harry L. Purdy, Martin L. Lindahl ₍and₎ William A. Carter ... New York, Prentice-Hall, inc., 1942.

Lindahl, Nils Robert.
Vollständiges glossar zu Notkers Boethius De consolatione philosophiae buch I ... Uppsala, Almqvist & Wiksells buchdruckerei-a.-g., 1916.
viii, 110 p., 1 l. 25½ᶜᵐ.

Akademisk afhandling—Upsala.
"Litteraturverzeichnis" : p. ₍vii₎–viii.

1. Notker Labeo, ca. 950–1022—Glossaries, vocabularies, etc. 2. German language—Old High German—Glossaries, vocabularies, etc.

20-8160

Library of Congress   PF3988.Z5L5

NL 0376555   DLC PU PBm CtY ICU OU CU WU

Lindahl, Olavus Eric   respondent.
... Primae scientiae educationis lineae...
see under   Boëthius, Daniel, 1751–1810, praeses.

S£5da   **Lindahl, Per Eric**
131   Über die Determination der Richtung der
9   ersten Furche im Seeigelei, von Per Eric
Lindahl und Åke Stordål ... Berlin,1937.
1p.ℓ.,₍286₎-293,₍1₎p. 24cm. (₍Arbeten
från Zootomiska institutet vid Stockholms
högskola. Bd.IX, no.9₎)
"Sonderabdruck aus Wilhelm Roux' Archiv
für Entwicklungsmechanik der Organismen.
136.Bd."
"Angeführte Literatur": p.292-293.

NL 0376557   CtY

S£5da   **Lindahl, Per Eric**
131   Über eineiige Zwillinge aus Doppeleiern ...
9   Leipzig₍1937₎
cover-title,₍389₎-393p. illus. 24cm.
(₍Arbeten från Zootomiska institutet vid
Stockholms högskola. Bd.IX, no.8₎)
"Sonderdruck aus dem 'Biologischen
Zentralblatt', 57.Bd., Juli/August,1937."
"Literaturverzeichnis": p.393.

NL 0376558   CtY

Lindahl, Per Eric
Zur kenntnis der physiologischen grundlagen der determination im seeigelkeim. ... Stockholm, 1936.
Inaug. Diss. - Stockholm, 1936.
Literatur.

NL 0376559   ICRL

Z8850   Lindahl, Per Erik, joint author.
.9
.K3   **Kärnell, Karl Åke.**
August Strindberg, 1849-1949. ₍Katalogen utarb. av Karl-Åke Kärnell och Per-Erik Lindahl. Malmö, Sydsvenska dagbladets aktiebolag, 1949₎

Lindahl (Petrus)
*Circa eloquentiam ecclesiasticam. Upsaliae. 1794.
1 p.l., 10 pp. 4°.

NL 0376561   NN

540.82   Lindahl, Ralf G
S958   Cadalene investigations: on the hydroxycadalenes, and
Ser.A.II.48   a naphtholic compound, $C_{15}H_{18}O$, from cadalene. Helsinki,
Suomalainen Tiedeakatemia, 1953.
60 p. illus. 26 cm. (Suomalaisen tiedeakatemian
toimituksia. Series A. II, Chemica, 48)

Thesis - Finland Institute of Technology.
Bibliography: p. ₍58₎-60.

I. Hydrocarbon research. 2. Suomalainen Tiedeakatemia,
Helsingfors. II. Title. (Series:Suomalainen Tiedeakatemia,
Helsingfors. Suomal-   aisen tiedeakatemian toimituksia.
Series A. II.: Chemica   48)

NL 0376562   N

Lindahl, Rikard, 1897–
Inlärningsprocessen, en kritisk översikt och psykologisk analys, av Rikard Lindahl. Göteborg, Elanders boktryckeri aktiebolag, 1946.
301 p., 1 l. illus., diagrs. 24½ cm.

"Citerad litteratur" : p. ₍295₎–301.

1. Educational psychology. I. Title.
₍Full name: August Rikard Lindahl₎

LB1051.L66   370.15   48–13732
₍1₎

NL 0376563   DLC MiU CtY OU NNC OrU

LD   **Lindahl, Roland Eugene.**
2668   Vocational rehabilitation of the
R4   disabled civilian in Kansas.
1950   34 l. (K.S.U. Master's Report, 1950)
L742

NL 0376564   KMK

Lindahl, Sven Peter August, 1843-1908, tr.
August Herman Franke... en lifsbild fran tyska pietismens tid...
see under   [Nietschmann, Hermann Otto] 1840-1929.

PT   **Lindahl, Sven Peter August,** 1848-1908.
9995   Blommor vid vägen; samlade af S. P. A. L.
.L48B3   Rock Island, Ill., Lutheran Augustana Book
Concern
v. 16 cm.

NL 0376566   MnHi

Lindahl, Sven Peter August, 1848-1903.
Bersell, Anders Olof, 1853-1903.
Församlingsskolans läsebok. Utarb. af A. O. Bersell under medverkan af S. P. A. Lindahl och W. Ljung. Rock Island, Ill., The Lutheran Augustana book concern ₍1890₎

4PT   **Lindal, Hans,** 1903–
Nor.-   Blankt stål; fortellinger. Bergen, Sambåndets
134   forlag, 1950.
203 p.

NL 0376568   DLC-P4

Lindal, Hans, 1903–
Nye plogjern, med forord av Einar Gerhardsen. Oslo, Ansgar forlag, 1948.
167 p. 20 cm.

1. Christian life. I. Title.

BV4505.L52   60-32632*

NL 0376569   DLC

DL991   **Lindal, Harald,** ed.
.M17L5   Boken om Maglarp; en sockenkrönika. ₍Malmö, 1954₎
334 p. illus., ports., maps. 23 cm.

1. Maglarp, Sweden—Hist.

A 55-4315
Minnesota. Univ. Libr.
for Library of Congress   ₍2₎

NL 0376570   MnU DLC NN

Lindal, Harald.
Skånes historia fram till 1719, av Harald Lindal... Lund: C. W. K. Gleerups förlag₍, 1930₎. 163 p. incl. table. illus. (incl. map, ports.) 12°.

NL 0376571   NN

LÍNDAL, Jakob H.
Bendingar vestan um haf. Akureyri, Prentað í Prentsmiðju B.Jónssonar, 1904.
Scan 3651.404.10
pp.56.
"Prentað á kostnað höfundarins."

NL 0376572   MH

VOLUME 334

Lindal, Jakob H
—— Hið góða og illa innræti í mann-
inum. Hugleiðingar alþýðumannsins.

Winnipeg, Prentsmiðja Ólafs S. Porgeirs-
sonar, 1920. 8°. pp. 26.   IcH31V512

NL 0376573   NIC

Lindal, Jakob H Íslendíngar í Vatnabygð-
um. Frumbúar bygðarinnar. Manntal
Íslendínga í austurparti Saskatchewan-
fylkis árið 1919. Samið hefir J. H.
Lindal. Winnipeg, Prentsmiðja Ólafs S.
Thorgeirssonar, 1920. 8°. pp. 14 + (2),
map in text.   IcC71L561

NL 0376574   NIC

Lindal, Jakob H
Misskilningur, tilfelli úr daglega lífinu;
saga. Winnipeg, Viking press ltd., 1919.
195 p. ‹With: Fridjorsson, Gudmundur.
Sólhvörf. 1921›

NL 0376575   WaU NIC

Lindal, Jakob H. Stríðið við þúfurnar
eftir Jakob H. Lindal. Sjerprentun úr
Ársriti Rœktunarfjelags Norðurlands.
Akureyri, 1915. 8°. pp. 66.   IcN1P188
Covertitle.

NL 0376576   NIC

Lindal, Jakob H.
—— Um trjárœkt. Eftir Jakob H.
Lindal. Sérprentun úr Ársriti R[œktun-
arfélags] N[orður]l[and]s, XIII. árg.
(Akureyri, 1916.) 8°. pp. 51, *illustr.*
IcN1L561
With the author's autograph. Covertitle.

NL 0376577   NIC

Lindal, P. J.
see Lindal, Petter Johan, 1844–1890.

Lindal, Petter Johan, 1844–1890.
Återfunnen runsten vid Árby. In Uppl. Fmför.
Tskr. II. bd. 1879–80. p. xl–xli.

NL 0376579   NIC

QK31
.L5
L5 Lindal, Petter Johan
Carl von Linné i Smalands nation. Anteckningar
af P. J. Lindal. Upsala, J. Thimgrens boktr.,
1878.
29 p. 19 cm.
"Särtryck i 100 exemplar ur tidningen Upsala-
Posten 1878, n. 4–8."
Copy 1 inscribed: Ryttmästaren och Riddaren
m. m. Välborne Hr. C. A. Klingspor vördsamt fr.
förf.
1. Linné, Carl von, 1707–1778. a. b. Klingspor, C   A

NL 0376580   NNBG

Lindal, Petter Johan, 1844–1890, comp.
Hammer, Christian, 1818–1905.
Catalogue de la Bibliothèque Hammer à Stockholm. Divi-
sion étrangère ... Stockholm, Impr. S. Stål, 1886–88.

Lindal, Petter Johan
Granskade runinskrifter. Anteckningar. I. Verna-
mo-stenen. In Sv. Fmför. Tskr. I. bd.
1871–72. p. 179–183, figs., 1 pl. - II. Frövi-
stenen B. Ibid. II. bd. 1873–74. p. 84–88, figs.

NL 0376582   NIC

Lindal, Petter Johan
Nyfunnen runsten i Uppsala. Extr. fr. Kgl.
Akad. Månadsbl. IV. årg. 1875. 8°. p. 124–125.

NL 0376583   NIC

Lindal, Petter Johan
Nyfunnen runsten vid Steninge. In Uppl.
Fmför. Tskr. II. bd. 1877. p. ix–x, fig.

NL 0376584   NIC

Lindal, Petter Johan
Runstenarne i Upsala, beskrifna och tolkade.
Fotografierna af A. Löfström. Upsala, 1881.
11 p. 8 pls. sm. 4°.

NL 0376585   NIC CtY

Lindal, Petter Johan
Tillämnad samling af runstenar i Upsala.
In Uppl. Fmför. Tskr. II. bd. 1883. p. cxliii–cxlv.

NL 0376586   NIC

Lindal, Petter Johan, 1844–1890.
Utförsel af runstenar. In Uppl. Fmför. Tskr.
II. bd. 1881–82. p. lxxix–lxxxii.

NL 0376587   NIC

Lindal, Valdimar Jacobson.
See
Lindal, Walter Jacobson, 1887–

JL187
L5 Lindal, Walter Jacobson, 1887–
Canadian citizenship and our wider loyalties. Foreword
by Solomon Frank. Winnipeg, Canada Press Club ¡1946¡
xiv, 157 p. 18 cm.

1. Citizenship—Canada. 2. Canada—For. rel.—Gt. Brit.
A 48–8196*
Harvard Univ. Library
for Library of Congress   ¡1¡

NL 0376589   MH CaOTU NcD CaBVa CaBVaU CaBViP DLC

G8235
.L742 Lindal, Walter Jacobson, 1887–
The Saskatchewan Icelanders, a strand
of the Canadian fabric. Foreword by George
Wilfred Simpson. Winnipeg, Man., Columbia
Press, ¡c1955¡
363 p. illus., ports. 23 cm.

1. Icelanders in Saskatchewan.

WaU CaBViPA CaBVa CaBVaU
NL 0376590   WHi C NN IEN NIC CaOTU InU CtY CLU

Lindal, Walter Jacobson, 1887–
Two ways of life; freedom or tyranny, by W. J. Lindal,
foreword by William Creighton Graham. Toronto, The Ryerson press ¡1940¡
xv p., 1 l., 154 p. 20½ᶜᵐ.
Bibliography: p. 151–154.

1. Democracy. 2. Totalitarianism. 3. World politics. 4. Nationalism
and religion. I. Title.
Library of Congress   JC423.L54   41–11623
¡3¡   321.6

NL 0376591   DLC MH PBm NcD CaBVa CaBVaU

Lindamira.
The lover's secretary; or, The adventures of
Lindamira
see The adventures of Lindamira.

PN6120
.C5L48 Lindamood, Mona Card.
A wonderful Christmas.
[Santa Ana?] c1931.
1 pam. 16°

NL 0376593   DLC RPB

Lindamood, Mason M.
Speed control of induction motors by means
of saturable transformers, by Mason M. Lindamood
and William J. Frede, Jr. [Cincinnati, 1951]
48 l. plates, diagrs. 29 cm.
Thesis (Electrical Engineer) - Univ. of
Cincinnati, 1951.
Bibliography: l. 48.

NL 0376594   OCU

Lindamour, *pseud.*
see
Gildon, Charles, 1665–1724.

BF
1725
L5 Lindanger, Alfa.
Your sun's return; the technique of computing a solar revolution chart. With
thirteen chart illustrations, together with
the noon date method of finding an unknown
birth-time, and an accurate method of rec-
tification by arcs of events. [Oceanside,
Calif., Langford Press] c1950.
47p. illus.

"The material in this book appeared as
a part of a series of student's lessons in
The American astrology magazine from December 1946 to April 1949."

1. Astrology. I. Title.

NL 0376597   UU

VOLUME 334

Lindanus, Guilielmus Damasus
see Lindt, Willem van der, bp., 1525–1588.

Lindanus, Wilhelmus
see Lindt, Willem van der, bp., 1525–1588.

Lindanus, William Damasus, 1525–1588
see Lindt, Willem van der, bp., 1525–1588.

Lindars, Frederick William, 1879–
New York *(State) Transit commission.*
₁...₁ Valuation as of June 30th, 1921, of the physical property of rapid transit and street surface railroads in the city of New York together with financial and statistical data pertinent thereto. Report by John H. Madden, valuation engineer ₁and₁ Fred W. Lindars, chief accountant. February 15th, 1922. ₁New York, M. B. Brown printing & binding co., 1922₁

Barrie,
masken-verlag.

M1500
.I145W5
Case
Lindau, Carl, 1853–1934. Wien bei Nacht.

Hellmesberger, Joseph, 1855–1907.
₁Wien bei Nacht₁
Wien bei Nacht. ₁ca. 1904₁

Lindau, Carolus Otto
see Lindau, Otto, 1839–

Lindau, Erich
Der Freimaurerspiegel ₁von₁ Satura ₁pseud.₁ I: Weltanschauung oder Kulturschande? München, Fortschrittliche Buchhandlung ₁c1929₁

48 p.
No more published?

1. Freemasons – Germany.

NL 0376606 MH

---

b
Hitler
coll.
₁Lindau, Erich₁
Der Freimaurerspiegel, III: Wohltätigkeitsverein oder Geheimbündelei gemäss Paragraph 128 RStGB? Leipzig ₁c1932₁

48 p.

Dedication by author (1932).

NL 0376607 DLC NNC

[Lindau, Friedrich]
Kriegsfahrten von Jena bis Belle-Alliance. Erinnerungen eines soldaten der english-deutschen legion in Deutschland, England, Portugal, Spanien, Frankreich und den Niederlanden. Hrsg. von H. Lüders ... Leipzig, R. Voigtländer, 1898.
234 p., 1 l. illus. 19 cm. (Biographische volksbücher. Nr. 36–43)
1. Peninsular war, 1807–1814 – Personal narratives. 2. Europe – Hist. – 1789–1815. I. Luders, Hermann, ed. II. Title.

NL 0376608 CU

833
S3342w
Lindau, G
Ich und meine Frau; drey Erzählungen. Wien, F. Haas, 1815.
156 p. front.(illus.) 17 cm.

Bound with: Schilling, G. Wallmann der Schütze.

NL 0376609 NcU

Lindau, Georg Hermann Leonhardt, 1888–
see Lindau, Hermann, 1888–

Lindau, Gerhard, tr.

G.
₁...₁urg am Wittenbergplatz, roman. Detmold, Meyer-₁...₁chhandlung, 1931.

₁...₁ndau, Gero, 1906–
Ueber die einwirkung von eiweisstoffen auf ₁...₁eisenhydroxydsol. Inaug. diss. Berlin, 1929
Bibl.

NL 0376612 ICRL CtY OU

Lindau, G₁ustav₁ 1866–1923.
Acanthaceae, von G. Lindau. Mit 336 einzelbildern in 38 fig. (*In* Die natürlichen pflanzenfamilien, begr. von A. Engler und K. Prantl. Leipzig, 1887– 25ᶜᵐ. IV. teil, 3. abt. B (1895) p. 274–354)
"Gedruckt im januar 1895."
Supplement, in Nachträge z. II.–IV. t. (1897) p. 304–309, and in Ergänzungsheft I (1900) p. 71–72.
Classed under ₁haupt₁abt. IV, Embryophyta siphonogama.

Subject entries: Acanthaceae.

Library of Congress, no. QK97.E6.

NL 0376613 DLC MH-A PPTU OU

Lindau, Gustav, 1866–1923.
Die algen ... Von prof. dr. Gustav Lindau ... Berlin, J. Springer, 1914–16.
3 v. illus. 21ᶜᵐ. (*Added t.-p.:* Kryptogamenflora für anfänger ... Hrsg. von prof. dr. Gustav Lindau ... 4. bd.)
Vol. 3, cover-title has date 1917.
CONTENTS.–1.–2. abt. ₁Grünalgen₁ Von prof. dr. Gustav Lindau.– 3. abt. Die meeresalgen. Von prof. dr. Robert Pilger.

1. Algne. I. Pilger, Robert Knuds Friedrich, 1876–

Agr 14–1158

U. S. Dept. of agr. Library 461.4L641A
for Library of Congress ₁a37r20e1₁

NL 0376614 DNAL FMU NcD MiU

Lindau, Gustav, 1866–1923.
Die Algen. 2., umgearb. und verm. Aufl. von Hans Melchior. Berlin, J. Springer, 1930.
2 v. illus. 21 cm. (Kryptogamenflora für Anfänger. 4. Bd.)

1. Algae. (Series)

NL 0376615 CaBVaU OCU OO CU

Lindau, Gustav, 1866–1923.
Die als fossile pilze beschriebenen abdrücke und versteinerungen, von G. Lindau.
(*In* Die natürlichen pflanzenfamilien, begr. von A. Engler und K. Prantl. Leipzig, 1887– 25ᶜᵐ. I. teil, abt. 1** (1900) p. 518–523)
Published July 31, 1900.
Classed under ₁haupt₁abt. II, Euthallophyta.

1. Fungi, Fossil.

Library of Congress QK97.E6 3–29958

NL 0376616 DLC PPTU OU

Lindau, Gustav, 1866–1923.
Schröter, Joseph, 1837–1894.
Ancylistineae, von J. Schröter. Mit 20 einzelbildern in 4 fig.
(*In* Die natürlichen pflanzenfamilien, begr. von A. Engler und K. Prantl. Leipzig, 1887–1909. 25ᶜᵐ. I. teil, 1. abt. (1897) p. 88–92)

NL 0376618 DLC PPTU OU

Lindau, Gustav, 1866–1923.
Auriculariales, von G. Lindau. Mit 21 einzelbildern in 2 fig.
(*In* Die natürlichen pflanzenfamilien, begr. von A. Engler und K. Prantl. Leipzig, 1887– 25ᶜᵐ. I. teil, abt. 1** (1900) p. 82–88; 553)
Pages 82–88: "Gedruckt im october 1897"; p. 553: "Gedruckt im februar 1900".
Classed under ₁haupt₁abt. II, Euthallophyta.

1. Auriculariales.

Library of Congress QK97.E6 3–29944

NL 0376618 DLC PPTU OU

Lindau, G₁ustav₁ 1866–1923.
Bemerkungen über die heutige systematik der pilze. Von Dr. G. Lindau ... Cassel, Druck von Gebr. Gotthelft, 1897.
cover-title, 11, ₁1₁ p. 23½ᶜᵐ.
Separat-abdruck aus "Botanisches centralblatt," bd. LXX, 1897.

1. Fungi. 2. Botany—Classification.

Library of Congress QK604.L74 5–24818†

NL 0376619 DLC

VOLUME 334

Lindau, Gustav, 1866–1923, joint author.
Haselhoff, Emil.
Die beschädigung der vegetation durch rauch; handbuch zur erkennung und beurteilung von rauchschäden, von dr. E. Haselhoff ... und dr. G. Lindau ... Mit 27 abbildungen im text. Leipzig, Gebrüder Borntraeger, 1903.

Lindau, Gustav, 1866–1923.
Schröter, Joseph, 1837–1894.
Chytridineae, von J. Schröter. Mit 83 einzelbildern in 28 fig.
(*In* Die natürlichen pflanzenfamilien, begr. von A. Engler und K. Prantl. Leipzig, 1887–1909. 25ᶜᵐ. I. teil, 1. abt. (1897) p. 64–87)

Lindau, Gustav, 1866–1923.
Dothideales, von G. Lindau. Mit 44 einzelbildern in 4 fig.
(*In* Die natürlichen pflanzenfamilien, begr. von A. Engler und K. Prantl. Leipzig, 1887–─25ᶜᵐ. I. teil, 1. abt. (1897) p. 373–383)
"Gedruckt im februar 1897."
Nachträge (bis 31. december 1899) in I. teil, abt. 1** (1900) p. 541–542.
Classed under (haupt)abt. II, *Euthallophyta.*

1. Dothideales.

Library of Congress   QK97.E6   3—29939

NL 0376622   DLC PPTU OU

Lindau, Gustav, 1866–1926.
Saccardo, P(ier) A(ndrea) 1845–
... Elenchus fungorum novorum qui anno 1896 innotuerunt, adjectis additamentis. Congesserunt P. A. Saccardo et G. Lindau. (Dresden) 1897.

Lindau, Gustav, 1866–1923.
Schröter, Joseph, 1837–1894.
Entomophthorineae, von J. Schröter. Mit 36 einzelbildern in 7 fig.
(*In* Die natürlichen pflanzenfamilien, begr. von A. Engler und K. Prantl. Leipzig, 1887─25ᶜᵐ. I. teil, 1. abt. (1897) p. 134–141)

Lindau, Gustav, 1866–1923.
Die flechten. Von prof. dr. Gustav Lindau ... Berlin, J. Springer, 1913.
vi p., 1 l., 36, 250 p. illus. 21ᶜᵐ. (*Added t.-p.:* Kryptogamenflora für anfänger ... Hrsg. von ... Gustav Lindau ... 3. bd.)
Bibliography: p. (23)–(25)

1. Lichens.

Library, U. S. Dept. of   Agr 14–65 Revised
Agriculture 461.5L642

NL 0376625   DNAL

Lindau, Gustav, 1866–1923.
Die flechten, von dr. Gustav Lindau ... Zweite, durchgearbeitete auflage ... Berlin, J. Springer, 1923.
vi p., 1 l., (36), 252 p. Illus. 21ᶜᵐ. (*Added t.-p.:* Kryptogamenflora für anfänger ... Hrsg. von dr. Gustav Lindau ... 3. bd.)
Bibliography: p. (23)–(24)

1. Lichens.

Library, U. S. Dept. of   Agr 34–738
Agriculture 461.5L642
[QK583   ]

NL 0376626   DNAL OOxM CtY PU-B DI TU OCU

Lindau, Gustav, 1866–1923.
... Die flechten; eine übersicht unserer kenntnisse, von prof. dr. G. Lindau ... mit 54 figuren. Berlin und Leipzig, G. J. Göschen, 1913.
123 p. illus. 16ᶜᵐ. (Sammlung Göschen. (683))
"Literatur": p. (5)–6.

1. Lichens.

Library of Congress   QK581.L5   13–17682

NL 0376627   DLC MB OOxM CtY CU

Lindau, Gustav, 1866–1923.
Fungi imperfecti, von G. Lindau.
(*In* Die natürlichen pflanzenfamilien, begr. von A. Engler und K. Prantl. Leipzig, 1887─25ᶜᵐ. I. teil, abt. 1** (1900) p. 347–349; 558)
Pages 347–349: issued Feb. 7, 1900; p. 558: "Gedruckt im februar 1900".
General natural history of entire group.
Classed under (haupt)abt. II, *Euthallophyta.*

1. Fungi imperfecti.

Library of Congress   QK97.E6   3—29954

NL 0376628   DLC PPAN CtY OU

Lindau, Gustav, 1866–1923, joint ed.
SB731 .S547
Sorauer, Paul, 1839–1916.
Handbuch der pflanzenkrankheiten, begründet von Paul Sorauer. 4., vollständig neubearb. aufl. hrsg. von prof. dr. Paul Graebner ... prof. dr. G. Lindau ... und prof. dr. L. Reh ... Berlin, P. Parey, 1921–

Lindau, Gustav, 1866–1923.
Schröter, Joseph, 1837–1894.
Helvellineae, von J. Schröter. Mit 39 einzelbildern in 7 fig.
(*In* Die natürlichen pflanzenfamilien, begr. von A. Engler und K. Prantl. Leipzig, 1887–1909. 25ᶜᵐ. I. teil, 1. abt. (1897) p. 163–172)

Lindau, Gustav, 1866–1923.
Schröter, Joseph, 1837–1894.
Hemiascineae, von J. Schröter. Mit 20 einzelbildern in 5 fig.
(*In* Die natürlichen pflanzenfamilien, begr. von A. Engler und K. Prantl. Leipzig, 1887─25ᶜᵐ. I. teil, 1. abt. (1897) p. 143–149)

Lindau, Gustav, 1866–1923.
Hilfsbuch für das sammeln der ascomyceten mit berücksichtigung der nährpflanzen Deutschlands, Österreich-Ungarns, Belgiens, der Schweiz und der Niederlande, von professor Dr. Gustav Lindau ... Berlin, Gebrüder Borntraeger, 1903.
iv, (2), 139 p. 16¼ᶜᵐ. (*On cover:* Hilfsbuch II)

1. Ascomycetes.

Library, U. S. Dept. of   Agr 4–400
Agriculture 462L641

NL 0376632   DNAL ICJ NIC CU

Lindau, Gustav, 1866–1923.
Hilfsbuch für das sammeln parasitischer pilze mit berücksichtigung der nährpflanzen Deutschlands, Österreich-Ungarns, Belgiens, der Schweiz und der Niederlande nebst einem anhang über die thierparasiten, von Dr. Gustav Lindau ... Berlin, Gebrüder Borntraeger, 1901.
vi, 90 p. 18½ x 11ᶜᵐ.

1. Food plants. 2. Fungi.

Library, U. S. Dept. of   Agr 6–176
Agriculture 462L641Hp

NL 0376633   DNAL MH NIC MH-A CU

LINDAU, Gustav, 1866–1923.
Hilfbuch für das sammeln parasitscher pilze mit berücksichtigung der einheimischen nährpflanzen...2e aufl. Berlin, Gebrüder Borntraeger, 1922.

NL 0376634   MH

Lindau, Gustav, 1866–1923.
Hilfsbuch für das sammeln und präparieren der niederen kryptogamen mit besonderer berücksichtigung der verhältnisse in den tropen, von prof. dr. Gustav Lindau ... Berlin, Gebrüder Borntraeger, 1904.
iv p., 1 l., 78 p. 18½ x 11ᶜᵐ. (*On cover:* Hilfsbuch III)

1. Plants—Collection and preservation. 2. Cryptogams.

Library of Congress   QK61.L74   5–31028

NL 0376635   DLC ICJ NIC OU

Lindau, Gustav, 1866–1923.
Hilfsbuch für das sammeln und präparieren der niederen kryptogamen, von prof. dr. Gustav Lindau. 2. neubearb. aufl., von prof. dr. O. C. Schmidt. Berlin, Gebrüder Borntraeger, 1938.
vi p., 1 l., 98 p. 19½ x 11½ᶜᵐ. (*On cover:* Hilfsbuch III)
"Schriftenverzeichnis": p. 86–91.

1. Plants—Collection and preservation. 2. Cryptogams.   I. Schmidt, Otto Christian, 1900–

Library of Congress   QK61.L74 1938   42–1283
(2)   578

NL 0376636   DLC ICU NNC MnU

Lindau, Gustav, 1866–1923.
Die höheren pilze. (*Basidiomycetes.*) Von prof. dr. Gustav Lindau ... Berlin, J. Springer, 1911.
vi p., 1 l. 232 p. illus. 21ᶜᵐ. (*Added t.-p.:* Kryptogamenflora für anfänger ... Hrsg. von prof. dr. ... I. bd.)

1. Basidiomycetes.

Library, U. S. Dept. of   Agr 12–1044
Agriculture 462L641H

NL 0376637   DNAL

Lindau, Gustav, 1866–1923.
Die höheren pilze. (Basidiomycetes.) Berlin, J. Springer, 1917.
vi, 234 p. illus. 21 cm. (Added t.-p.: Kryptogamenflora für anfänger. Hrsg. von prof. dr. Gustav Lindau. I. bd.)

1. Basidiomycetes.   I. Series.

NL 0376638   TU CU OrCS PSt

VOLUME 334

Lindau, Gustav, 1866–1923.
Die höheren pilze, *Basidiomycetes*, mit ausschluss der brand- und rostpilze, von prof. dr. Gustav Lindau. In 3. aufl. völlig neu bearb. von prof. dr. Eberhard Ulbrich ... Berlin, J. Springer, 1928.
xii, 497, [1] p. illus., xiv pl. in pocket, port. 21cm. (*Added t.-p.:* Kryptogamenflora für anfänger ... begründet von prof. dr. Gustav Lindau, fortgesetzt von prof. dr. R. Pilger. 1. bd.)
"Wichtigste literatur": p. 49–53.
1. Basidiomycetes. I. Ulbrich, Eberhard, 1879– ed.
Agr 29-575
Library, U. S. Dept. of Agriculture 462L641H

NL 0376639 DNAL WaU NIC CtY CU MH-A PU-B OCU MiU

Lindau, Gustav, 1866–1923.
Hyphomycetes, von G. Lindau. Mit vielen textfiguren.
(*In* Die natürlichen pflanzenfamilien, begr. von A. Engler und K. Prantl. Leipzig, 1887– 25cm. I. teil, abt. 1** (1900) p. 415–517; 508–559)
Pages 415–517, 508–559: Gedruckt im februar 1900.
Classed under [haupt]abt. II, *Euthallophyta.*
1. Hyphomycetes.
3-29957 Revised
Library of Congress QK97.E6

NL 0376640 DLC PPT OU OO

Lindau, Gustav, 1866–1923.
Hypocreales, von G. Lindau. Mit 129 einzelbildern in 13 fig.
(*In* Die natürlichen pflanzenfamilien, begr. von A. Engler und K. Prantl. Leipzig, 1887– 25cm. I. teil, 1. abt. (1897) p. 343–372)
"Gedruckt im februar 1897."
Nachträge [bis 31. december 1897] in I. teil, abt. 1** (1900) p. 540–541.
Classed under [haupt]abt. II, Euthallophyta.
1. Hypocreales.
3—29938
Library of Congress QK97.E6

NL 0376641 DLC PPT

Lindau, Gustav, 1866–1923.
Hysteriineae, von G. Lindau. Mit 46 einzelbildern in 8 fig.
(*In* Die natürlichen pflanzenfamilien, begr. von A. Engler und K. Prantl. Leipzig, 1887– 25cm. I. teil, 1. abt. (1897) p. 265–278)
"Gedruckt im mai 1896."
Nachträge [bis 31. december 1899] in I. teil, abt. 1** (1900) p. 534–535.
Classed under [haupt]abt. II, *Euthallophyta.*
1. Hysteriineae.
3—29918
Library of Congress QK97.E6

NL 0376642 DLC PPT OU

QK 3 Z991 no. 15
Lindau, Gustav, 1866-1923.
Index nominum omnium receptorum atque synonymorum nec non iconum quae Nylanderi synopsis lichenum. Berlin, 1907.
37 p.
1. Lichens. 2. Title.

NL 0376643 NIC NcD NcU NN

Lindau, Gustav, 1866-1923, ed.
Kryptogamenflora fuer anfaenger...
see under title

Lindau, Gustav, 1866–1923.
Laboulbeniineae, von G. Lindau. Mit 52 einzelbildern in 5 fig.
(*In* Die natürlichen pflanzenfamilien, begr. von A. Engler und K. Prantl. Leipzig, 1887– 25cm. I. teil, 1. abt. (1897) p. 491–505)
"Gedruckt im april 1897."
Revised by R. Thaxter.
Nachträge [bis 31. december 1899] von G. Lindau, in I. teil, abt. 1** (1900) p. 544.
Classed under [haupt]abt. II, *Euthallophyta.*
1. Laboulbeniineae. I. Thaxter, Roland, 1858–
3—29941
Library of Congress QK97.E6

NL 0376645 DLC PPTU OU

Lindau, Gustav, 1866–1923.
Lichenologische Untersuchungen. Von Dr. Gustav Lindau, ... Heft I. Ueber Wachsthum und Anheftungsweise der Rindenflechten. Mit 3 lithographirten Tafeln. Dresden, C. Heinrich, 1895.
v, [1], 66 p. III pl. (partly col., 1 fold.) 30 x 24cm.
No more published.

NL 0376646 ICJ PPAN

Lindau, Gustav, 1866-1923.
Sorauer, Paul, 1839–1916.
Manual of plant diseases, by Prof. Dr. Paul Sorauer. 3d ed. Prof. Dr. Sorauer in collaboration with Prof. Dr. G. Lindau ... and Dr. L. Reh ... Translated by Frances Dorrance. Volume I: Non-parasitic diseases, by Prof. Dr. Paul Sorauer ... With 208 illustrations in the text. [Wilkes-Barré, Pa., The Record press, °1914–22]

Lindau, G[ustav] 1866–1923.
Melanconiales, von G. Lindau. Mit 97 einzelbildern in 11 fig. (*In* Die natürlichen pflanzenfamilien, begr. von A. Engler und K. Prantl. Leipzig, 1887– 25cm. I. teil, abt. 1** (1900) p. 398–415; 558)
p. 398–415: "Gedruckt im januar 1900;" p. 558: "Gedruckt im februar, 1900."
Classed under [haupt]abt. II, Euthallophyta.
Subject entries: Melanconiales.
3-29936
Library of Congress, no. QK97.E6.

NL 0376648 DLC PPT OU

Lindau, Gustav, 1866–1923.
Die mikroskopischen pilze. Von prof. dr. Gustav Lindau ... Mit 558 figuren im text. Berlin, J. Springer, 1912.
vi p., 1 l., 276 p. illus. 22cm. (*Added t.-p.:* Kryptogamenflora für anfänger ... Hrsg. von prof. dr. Gustav Lindau ... 2. bd.)
1. Fungi. I. [Title]
Agr 12-1364
Library, U. S. Dept. of Agriculture 462L641M
Library of Congress QK603.L48
[a37b1] 589.2

NL 0376649 DNAL PU-B PPAB DLC

Lindau, Gustav, 1866–1923.
Die mikroskopischen pilze ... Von dr. Gustav Lindau ... 2., durchgesehene aufl. ... Berlin, J. Springer, 1922.
2 v. illus. 21½cm. (*Added t.-p.:* Kryptogamenflora für anfänger ... Hrsg. von dr. Gustav Lindau ... 2. bd., 1.–2. abt.)
CONTENTS.—1. abt. Myxomyceten, phycomyceten und ascomyceten.—2. abt. Ustilagineen, uredineen, *Fungi imperfecti.*
1. Fungi.
Agr 25-563
Library, U. S. Dept. of Agriculture 462L641M

NL 0376650 DNAL CU MH-A OCU OrCS CaBVaU

Lindau, Gustav, 1866-1923.
Schröter, Joseph, 1837–1894.
Monoblepharidineae, von J. Schröter. Mit 5 einzelbildern in 2 fig.
(*In* Die natürlichen pflanzenfamilien, begr. von A. Engler und K. Prantl. Leipzig, 1887– 25cm. I. teil, 1. abt. (1897) p. 106–107)

Lindau, Gustav, 1866-1923.
Schröter, Joseph, 1837–1894.
Mucorineae, von J. Schröter. Mit 56 einzelbildern in 14 fig.
(*In* Die natürlichen pflanzenfamilien, begr. von A. Engler und K. Prantl. Leipzig, 1887–1909. 25cm. I. teil, 1. abt. (1897) p. 119–134)

Lindau, Gustav, 1866-1923.
Nylanderi Synopsis Lichenum. Index nominum ...
see Nylander, William, 1822-1899.
Synopsis methodica lichenum

Lindau, G[ustav] 1866–1923.
Perisporiales, von G. Lindau. Mit 54 einzelbildern in 7 fig. (*In* Die natürlichen pflanzenfamilien, begr. von A. Engler und K. Prantl. Leipzig, 1887– 25cm. I. teil, I. abt. (1897) p. 325–343)
"Gedruckt im januar 1897."
Nachträge [bis 31. december 1899] *in* I. teil, abt. 1** (1900) p. 539–540.
Classed under [haupt]abt. II, Euthallophyta.
Subject entries: Perisporiales.
3-29937
Library of Congress, no. QK97.E6.

NL 0376654 DLC OU PPTU

Lindau, Gustav, 1866-1923.
Schröter, Joseph, 1837–1894.
Peronosporineae, von J. Schröter. Mit 41 einzelbildern in 11 fig.
(*In* Die natürlichen pflanzenfamilien, begr. von A. Engler und K. Prantl. Leipzig, 1887–1909. 25cm. I. teil, 1. abt. (1897) p. 108–119)

Lindau, Gustav, 1866-1923.
Schröter, Joseph, 1837–1894.
Pezizineae, von J. Schröter. Mit 70 einzelbildern in 30 fig.
(*In* Die natürlichen pflanzenfamilien, begr. von A. Engler und K. Prantl. Leipzig, 1887– 25cm. I. teil, 1. abt. (1897) p. 173–243)

Lindau, Gustav, 1866-1923.
Die pflanzlichen parasiten sorauer's handbuch der pflanzenkrankheiten. II. 1908.

NL 0376657 PPAN

SB 731 L74 4th ed.
Lindau, Gustav, 1866-1923.
Die pflanzlichen Parasiten, hrsg. von G. Lindau. [4., vollständig neubearbeitete Aufl.] Berlin, P. Parey [c1921-23]
2 v. illus., tables. 25 cm. (Handbuch der Pflanzenkrankheiten, begrundet von Paul Sorauer. 4. Aufl., 2.-3. Bd.)
Includes bibliographical foot-notes.

NL 0376658 NIC

VOLUME 334

Lindau, Gustav, 1866–1923
Phacidiineae, von G. Lindau. Mit 93 einzelbildern in 12 fig.
(*In* Die natürlichen pflanzenfamilien, begr. von A. Engler und K. Prantl. Leipzig, 1887–   25ᶜᵐ. I. teil, 1. abt. (1897) p. 243–265)
"Gedruckt im april 1896."
Nachträge ⟨bis 31. december 1899⟩ in I. teil, abt. 1** (1900) p. 533–534.
Classed under ⟨haupt⟩abt. II, *Euthallophyta.*

1. Phacidiineae.

Library of Congress   QK97.E6   3–29917

NL 0376659   D̲L̲C̲ PPT OU

Lindau, Gustav, 1866–1923.
Schröter, Joseph, 1837–1894.
Phytomyxinae, von J. Schröter. Mit 6 einzelbildern in 1 fig.
(*In* Die natürlichen pflanzenfamilien, begr. von A. Engler und K. Prantl. Leipzig, 1887–   25ᶜᵐ. I. teil, 1. abt. (1897) p. 5–8)

Lindau, Gustav, 1866–1923.
Die Pilze Deutschlands, Oesterreichs und der Schweiz … Leipzig, E. Kummer, 1884–1910; Leipzig, Akademische verlagsgesellschaft m. b. h., 1920–

Lindau, Gustav, 1866–1923.
… Die pilze, eine einführung in die kenntnis ihrer formenreihen, von prof. dr. G. Lindau … mit 10 figurengruppen im text. Leipzig, G. J. Göschen, 1912.
128 p. illus. 16ᶜᵐ. (Sammlung Göschen. ⟨574⟩)

1. Fungi.

                                12–13224
Library of Congress   QK604.L76

NL 0376662   DLC CU MH MB NjNbR

Lindau, Gustav, 1866–1923
Durand, Théophile, 1855–1912.
Primitiae florae costaricensis, par Th. Durand … et H. Pittier … t. ⟨1⟩–3, fasc. 1. Bruxelles, Jardin botanique de l'état, 1891–1901.

Lindau, Gustav, 1866–1923.
Schröter, Joseph, 1837–1894.
Protoascineae, von J. Schröter. Mit 11 einzelbildern in 3 fig.
(*In* Die natürlichen pflanzenfamilien, begr. von A. Engler und K. Prantl. Leipzig, 1887–   25ᶜᵐ. I. teil, 1. abt. (1897) p. 150–156)

Lindau, Gustav, 1866–1923.
Pyrenomycetineae, von G. Lindau.
(*In* Die natürlichen pflanzenfamilien, begr. von A. Engler und K. Prantl. Leipzig, 1887–1909.   25ᶜᵐ. I. teil, I. abt. (1897–325))
~Natural history of entire order, with general systematic outline.
"Gedruckt im januar 1897."
"Nachträge ⟨bis 31. december 1899⟩ in I. teil, abt. 1** (1900) p. 539–544.
Classed under ⟨haupt⟩abt. II, *Euthallophyta.*

1. Pyrenomycetineae.

                                3–29986 Revised
Library of Congress   QK97.E6

NL 0376665   DLC PPT OU OO

Lindau, Gustav, 1866–1923.
Schröter, Joseph, 1837–1894.
Saprolegniineae, von J. Schröter. Mit 48 einzelbildern in 15 fig.
(*In* Die natürlichen pflanzenfamilien, begr. von A. Engler und K. Prantl. Leipzig, 1887–   25ᶜᵐ. I. teil, 1. abt. (1897) p. 93–105)

Lindau, Gustav, 1866–1923.
… Spalt- und schleimpilze; eine einführung in ihre kenntnis, von prof. dr. Gustav Lindau … mit 11 abbildungen. Berlin und Leipzig, G. J. Göschen, 1912.
116 p. illus. 16ᶜᵐ. (Sammlung Göschen. ⟨642⟩)
"Literatur": p. ⟨4⟩

1. Schizomycetes. 2. Bacteria. 3. Myxomycetes.

                                13–5014
Library of Congress   QK604.L78

NL 0376667   DLC FMU MtBC

Lindau, G⟨ustav⟩ 1866–1923
Sphaeriales, von G. Lindau. Mit 364 einzelbildern in 37 fig. (*In* Die natürlichen pflanzenfamilien, begr. von A. Engler und K. Prantl. Leipzig, 1887–   25ᶜᵐ. I. teil, I. abt. (1897) p. 384–491)
"Gedruckt im februar 1897."
Nachträge ⟨bis 31. december 1899⟩ in I. teil, abt. 1** (1900) p. 543–544.
Classed under ⟨haupt⟩abt. II, Euthallophyta.

Subject entries: Sphaeriales.

                                3–29940
Library of Congress, no.   QK97.E6.

NL 0376668   DLC PPT

Lindau, Gustav, 1866–1923.
Sphaeropsidales, von G. Lindau. Mit 293 einzelbildern in 23 fig.
(*In* Die natürlichen pflanzenfamilien, begr. von A. Engler und K. Prantl. Leipzig, 1887–   25ᶜᵐ. I. teil, abt. 1** (1900) p. 349–398; 558)
Pages 349–398: "Gedruckt im december 1899"; p. 558: "Gedruckt im februar 1900".
Classed under ⟨haupt⟩abt. II, *Euthallophyta.*

1. Sphaeropsidales.

                                3–29955
Library of Congress   QK97.E6

NL 0376669   DLC OU

Lindau, Gustav, 1866–1923.
Thesaurus litteraturae mycologicae et lichenologicae ratione habita praecipue omnium quae adhuc scripta sunt de mycologia applicata quem congesserunt G. Lindau et P. Sydow. Lipsiis, Fratres Borntraeger, 1908–17.
5 v.   25 cm.
Vol. 1, pub. in 2 pt., 1907–08; v. 2, in 2 pt., 1908–09; v. 3, in 2 pt., 1912–13.
Contents.—v. 1. Complectens enumerationem autorum A–L.—v. 2. Complectens enumerationem alphabeticam autorum M–Z.—v. 3. Complectens corrigenda, supplementum, enumerationem alphabeticam titulorum annorum 1907–1910.
1. Mycology—Bibl. 2. Lichens⟨—Bibl.⟩   I. Sydow, Paul, 1851–1925, joint author.

Z5356.F97L5   Agr 11–802 rev 4

U. S. Dept. of Agr. Libr.   241.75L63
for Library of Congress   ⟨r57cß⟩†

        NNBG OOxM OU IaU WaU CU ICJ TU NcU
NL 0376670   DNAL OrCS IdU PPAN DLC KU FTaSU InU NIC

Z5356   Lindau, Gustav, 1866–1923, comp.
.F97L7   Thesaurus litteraturae mycologicae et lichenologicae ratione habita praecipue omnium quae
(B)   adhuc scripta sunt de mycologia applicata quem congesserunt G. Lindau et P. Sydow. Lipsiis, Fratres Borntraeger, 1908–17 ⟨New York, Johnson Reprint Corp., 194–?⟩
         5 v.
         "Reprinted with the permission of the original publishers."
         Contents.—v.1. Complectens enumerationem alphabeticam auto-   rum A–L.—v.2. Com-
         plectens enume-   rationem alphabeticam

Continued in next column

Continued from preceding column

autorum M–Z.—v.3. Complectens corrigenda, supplementum, enumerationem alphabeticam titulorum annorum 1907–1910.—v.4. Capitula I–VI respiciuntur non primae litterae titulorum, sed argumenta.—v.5. Capitula VII–VIII respiciuntur non primae litterae titulorum, sed argumenta.

    1. Fungi—Bibl.   2. Lichens—Bibl.   I. Sydow, Paul, joint   comp.

NL 0376672   ICU AAP LU NcD CLU NcRS N TxU MiU

Lindau, Gustav, 1866–1923.
Tremellineae, von G. Lindau. Mit 27 einzelbildern in 5 fig.
(*In* Die natürlichen pflanzenfamilien, begr. von A. Engler und K. Prantl. Leipzig, 1887–   25ᶜᵐ. I. teil, abt. 1** (1900) p. 88–96; 553)
Pages 88–96: "Gedruckt im october 1897"; p. 553: "Gedruckt im februar 1900."
Classed under ⟨haupt⟩abt. II, *Euthallophyta.*

1. Tremellineae.

Library of Congress   QK97.E6   3–29945

NL 0376673   DLC PPT OU

Lindau, Gustav, 1866–1923.
Über die anlage und entwicklung einiger flechtenapothecien … von Gustav Lindau … Regensburg, Druck der F. H. Neubauer'schen buchdr. (F. Huber) 1888.
44, ⟨2⟩ p. double col. pl. 22½ᶜᵐ.
Inaug.-diss.—Berlin.
Lebenslauf.
"Separat-abdruck aus 'Flora', jahrg. 1888."

1. Apothecium. 2. Lichens.

                                Agr 13–136
U. S. Dept. of agr. Library
for Library of Congress   ⟨a39b1⟩

NL 0376674   DNAL ICRL

Lindau, H. G. Paul.
    See
Lindau, Paul, 1839–1919.

Lindau, Hans Rudolf David, 1875–
Gustav Freytag, von Hans Lindau. Mit einem bildnis Freytags nach Karl Stauffer und einem faksimiledruck. Leipzig, S. Hirzel, 1907.
viii, 482 p. front. (port.) fold. facsim. 23½ᶜᵐ.

1. Freytag, Gustav, 1816–1895.

Library of Congress   PT1873.Z5L5   8–22105 Revised

        MH PPT NjP
NL 0376676   DLC CtY PBm OU OCU MiU MB GU CSt CU

Lindau, Hans Rudolf David, 1875–
Gustav Freytag und Heinrich von Sybel. (In: Prussia. Koenigliche Bibliothek, Berlin. Fuenfzehn Jahre Königliche und Staatsbibliothek. Berlin, 1930. sq. 4°. p. 175–180.)

1. Freytag, Gustav, 1816–1895.   2. Sybel, Heinrich, 1817–1895.
N. Y. P. L.   June 6, 1931

NL 0376677   NN

VOLUME 334

Lindau, Hans.
Ein Heiliger von Port-Royal und Kardinal Richelieu. (Festschrift für Alois Riehl von Freunden und Schülern zu seinem siebzigsten Geburtstage dargebracht. Halle a. S., 1914. 8°. p. 43-103.)

1. Duvergier, Jean, abbot of St. Cyran   2. Richelieu, Louis François Armand du Plessis de, duc.
N. Y. P. L.   August 5, 1914.

NL 0376678   NN

193
F44Zt.j   Lindau, Hans Rudolf David, 1875-
Johann Gottlieb Fichte und der neuere Socialismus. Berlin, Fontane, 1900.
107p. 22cm.

Cover title.
Bibliographical references: p. [94]-107.

1. Fichte, Johann Gottlieb, 1762-1814.
2. Socialism.   I. Title.

NL 0376679   IEN MH CU

Lindau, Hans [Rudolf David] 1875-
Johann Gottlieb Fichtes lehren von staat und gesellschaft in ihrem verhältnis zum neueren sozialismus. [n. p.] 1899.
1 p. l., 107, [2] p. 8°.
Inaug.-diss.—Leipzig.
Vita.

1-G-2003

NL 0376680   DLC NjP CtY PU IEN

Lindau, Hans Rudolf David, 1875-

Wundt, Wilhelm Max, 1832-1920.
Logik. Eine untersuchung der principien der erkenntniss und der methoden wissenschaftlicher forschung, von Wilhelm Wundt ... 2. umbearb. aufl. Stuttgart, F. Enke, 1893-95.

Lindau, Hans Rudolf David, 1875-   ed.
Die Schriften zu J. G. Fichte's Atheismus-Streit. München, G. Müller, 1912.
xxix, 387 p. 23 cm. (Bibliothek der Philosophen, 4. Bd.)
Bibliography: p. 387.

1. Fichte, Johann Gottlieb, 1762-1814. 2. Atheism.   (Series)

B2849.A8L5   58-53597

NN MH ICU NBC CLSU OCH CaBVaU
NL 0376682   DLC TxU NcD CSt ICN NIC NNC ICN MoSU

Lindau, Hans Rudolf David, 1875-

Wundt, Wilhelm Max, 1832-1920.
System der philosophie, von Wilhelm Wundt. 3. umgearb. aufl. ... Leipzig, W. Engelmann, 1907.

Lindau, Hans Rudolf David, 1875-
Die theodicee im 18. jahrhundert; entwicklungsstufen des problems vom theoretischen dogma zum praktischen idealismus, von Hans Lindau. Leipzig, W. Engelmann, 1911.
xvi, 306 p. 23 cm.

1. Theodicy. 2. Philosophy and religion. 3. Idealism.   I. Title.
                                                             12—4820
Library of Congress   BT160.L7

NL 0376684   DLC NN CU CaBVaU NcD

PT107
.L56   Lindau, Hans Rudolf David, 1875-
Unkritische Gänge. Berlin, E. Fleischel, 1904.
192p.

1. German literature - Addresses, essays, lectures. I. Title.

NL 0376685   NcU MH TNJ

PN2640
.D48   Lindau, Heinrich.
v.30   Nur einen orden! Schwank in 1 akt, von Heinrich Lindau...
33p. 15cm. (In Deutscher bühnen-almanach. 1865. v.30)

NL 0376686   NNU-W PU

Lindau, Heinrich, 1879-
Der Kinderkrieg, Harzer Dorfkomödie in zwei Aufzügen. Leipzig, A. Strauch [1943]
67 p. 16 cm. (Das Volksspiel, 19. Heft)

I. Title.   (Series)
PT2623.I 564K5   49-39236*

NL 0376687   DLC

Lindau, Heinrich, 1879-
Der rote Faden. Posse mit Gesang in 1 Aufzug, von Heinrich Lindau. Musik von K. Fensterbusch.   Mühlhausen i. Thür.: G. Danner[, 1927]. 40 p. 12°. (Danner's Thalia. Nr. 188.)
Without music.

391471A. 1. Drama, German.   2. Title.
N. Y. P. L.   January 2, 1929

NL 0376688   NN

Lindau, Heinrich, 1879-
Weihnacht in der Pecherhütte, nach einer Erzählung Peter Roseggers. [2. Aufl.] Rotenburg an der Fulda, Deutscher Laienspiel-Verlag [1952] 19 p. 22cm. (Die Volksbühne. Heft 16)

1. Christmas plays, German. I. Series.
II. Rosegger, Peter, 1843-1918. Der liebe Gott geht durch den Wald. III. Title.

NL 0376689   NN

Lindau, Heinrich Gustav Paul, 1839-1919.
see Lindau, Paul, 1839-1919.

Lindau, Hermann, 1888-
... Ein Beitrag zur Kenntnis seltenerer Nabeltumoren ... Jena, 1916.
38 p., 1 l. 22 cm.
Inaug. - Diss. - Jena.
Lebenslauf.
Full name: Georg Hermann Leonhardt Lindau.

NL 0376691   CtY DNLM

Lindau, J.   W
Scientific methods in warp sizing. n. t. p. [Boston, 1909]
6 p. 8°. (Nat. Assoc. of Cotton Manufacturers)

NL 0376692   NN

Lindau, Johann. 15 cent. Geschichte des dreizehnjaehrigen krieges. 186 pp. (Script. rer. Prussc. v. 4, p. 490.)

NL 0376693   MdBP

Lindau, Johann Gottfried, respondent.
... De poena pvrgatorii non praestiti in processv criminali ...
see under Breuning, Christian Heinrich, b. 1729, praeses.

Lindau, Johann Karl Franz Bruno Ludwig, 1921-
Das Medaillenkabinett des Postmeisters Johann Schorndorff zu Basel; seine Geschichte bis zur Erwerbung durch das Historische Museum Basel. Basel, Helbing & Lichtenhahn, 1947.
247 p. 24 cm.
Inaug.-Diss.—Basel.
"Erscheint gleichzeitig als Band 28 der Basler Beiträge zur Geschichtswissenschaft."

1. Schorndorff, Johann, 1705-1769. 2. Medals. 3. Coins.   I. Title.

CJ6321.L5   48-25596*

NL 0376695   DLC NcU

Lindau, Johann Karl Franz Bruno Ludwig, 1921-
Das Medaillenkabinett des Postmeisters Johann Schorndorff zu Basel, seine Geschichte bis zur Erwerbung durch das Historische Museum Basel. Basel, Helbing & Lichtenhahn, 1947.
246 p. 25 cm. (Basler Beiträge zur Geschichtswissenschaft, Bd. 28)
Issued also as diss., Basel.
Includes bibliographies.

1. Schorndorff, Johann, 1705-1769. 2. Basel. Universität. Historisches Museum. 3. Medals. 4. Coins.   I. Title.   (Series)

CJ6321.L5 1947a   49-20826*

NL 0376696   DLC NNC CtY IU NcD CoU OU WU MoU

Lindau, K   J   ed.
Universal-Register der homöopathischen Journalistik...
see under Hirsch, J, physician.

Lindau, Karl.

See

Lindau, Carl, 1853-1934.

VOLUME 334

Lindau, M. B., of Dresden
    see Lindau, Martin Bernhard, b. 1818.

Lindau, Marcus von.

    See

Marcus von Lindau.

Lindau, Martin Bernhard, b. 1818.
    Geschichte der haupt- und residenzstadt Dresden. Dresden, R. Kuntze, 1859–63.
    2 vol. Plates.

NL 0376701   MH NN

DD901 **Lindau, Martin Bernhard,** b. 1818.
.D75L7   Geschichte der königlichen haupt- und residenzstadt Dresden von den ältesten zeiten bis zur gegenwart. Von M. B. Lindau. 2. verb. aufl. ... Dresden, R. von Grumbkow, 1885.
    vi, ₍1₎, 1050 p. plates (part col., part fold.) ports., plans (part fold.) 23ᶜᵐ.

    1. Dresden—Hist.

NL 0376702   ICU MH MU ICU

Lindau, Martin Bernhard, b. 1818, ed.

Gregg, Josiah, 1806–1850?   FOR OTHER EDITIONS
                 SEE MAIN ENTRY
    Karawenzüge durch die westlichen prairieen und wanderungen in Nord-Mejico. Nach dem tagebuche des Amerikaners Josias Gregg, bearbeitet von M. B. Lindau ... Mit einem titelkupfer und einer karte. Dresden und Leipzig, Arnoldische buchhandlung, 1845–

Lindau, Martin Bernhard, b. 1818.

    Lucas Cranach. Ein Lebensbild aus dem Zeitalter der Reformation. Von M.B. Lindau... Leipzig, Veit & Comp., 1883.
    x, 402 p. front.(port.) 23 cm.

    1. Cranach, Lucus, 1472–1553. 2. Reformation. Germany. Biography.

NL 0376704   NNUT PPLT ICU

Lindau, Martin Bernhard, b. 1818, tr.

F1213
.M40
    Mason, R   H
    Mexikanische bilder, von R. G. ₍1₎ Mason. Aus dem englischen von M.B. Lindau. Dresden, R. Kuntze, 1853.

Lindau, Martin Bernhard, b. 1818, tr.

Cottrell, Charles Herbert.
    Sibirien. Nach seiner naturbeschaffenheit, seinen gesellschaftlichen und politischen verhältnissen und als strafcolonie geschildert, von Charles Herbert Cottrell. Aus dem englischen übers. und mit anmerkungen begleitet von M. B. Lindau. Dresden und Leipzig, Arnold, 1846.

Lindau, Martin Bernhard, b. 1818, tr.

Byam, George.
    Wanderungen durch südamerikanische republiken. Von Georg Byam ... Aus dem englischen von M. B. Lindau. Dresden, A. Kuntze, 1851.

Lindau, Mose S
    South Dakota annotations to the Restatement of the law of conflict of laws, as adopted and promulgated by the American Law Institute, prepared by Mose S. Lindau under the auspices of the junior bar section of the State Bar of South Dakota. St. Paul, American Law Institute, 1940.
    118 p. 24 cm.

    1. Conflict of laws—South Dakota. 2. Annotations and citations (Law)—South Dakota. I. American Law Institute. Restatement of the law of conflict of laws. II. Title.

                   41–4035 rev*

NL 0376708   DLC NBuU-L NcD-L ViU-L PPT GU-L WaU-L

Lindau, Norman C.
    Cooks and cardinals; comedy in one act, by Norman C. Lindau. (In: Harvard University. 47 Workshop. Plays... New York, 1920. 12°. Series 2, p. ₍57–91.₎)

10972A. 1. Drama (American).   2. Title.
N.Y.P.L.
                                  July 5, 1921.

NL 0376709   NN MB

Lindau, Norman C
    A little act of justice. ₍1920?₎
    24 l. 27 cm.
    Typescript (carbon copy)

    I. Title.

    PS3523.I 514L5   66–59838

NL 0376710   DLC

Lindau, Norman C.

47 workshop.
    Plays of the 47 workshop. Second series. Torches, by Kenneth Raisbeck; Cooks and cardinals, by Norman C. Lindau; A flitch of bacon, by Eleanor Holmes Hinkley; The playroom, by Doris F. Halman. New York, Brentano's, 1920.

Lindau .... Otto) [1839-] * De leucaemia infantium. - 31 pp. 8°. *Berolini, G. Schade, [1862]*

    Full name: Carolus Otto Lindau.

NL 0376712   DNLM

Lindau, Otto Brandt von
    see Brandt von Lindau, Otto.

4PT Lindau, Paul, 1839–1919.
Ger   Der Abend; Schauspiel in vier
6491 Aufzügen. Leipzig, Reclam [   ]
    72 p.

    (Universal-Bibliothek, 5032)

NL 0376714   DLC-P4 MB

Lindau, Paul, 1839–1919.
    Der Abend. Schauspiel in vier Aufzügen. Leipzig, Reclam ₍n.d.₎
    72p.

    Microcard edition.

NL 0376715   ICRL

Lindau, Paul, 1839–1919.
    Der agent. Roman. 3. tausend. Breslau, S. Schottlaender ₍etc.₎ New York, G. E. Stechert, 1899.
    337 p. 8°.   1–19899—M 4

NL 0376716   DLC NIC WU OCl MtBC

Lindau, Paul, 1839–1919
    Die ahnen, ein roman von Gustav Freytag. Breslau, Schottlaender, 1831. 69p.

NL 0376717   OClW

PQ   Lindau, Paul, 1839–1919.
2370   Alfred de Musset von Paul Lindau.
.L55x   Berlin, A. Hofmann & company, 1877.
    xiv, 302 p. 21 cm.

    1. Musset, Alfred de, 1810–1857.
    I. Title

NL 0376718   OKentU IU

Lindau, Paul, 1839–1919.
    Alfred de Musset. 2ᵉ verbesserte und ergänzte aufl. Berlin, A. Hofmann & comp. 1877.
    pp. xiv, ₍1₎, 312. (Allgemeiner verein für deutsche literatur.)

NL 0376719   MH PP PPL CtW OClW CtY IaU NIC WaU NjP

PQ2370 Lindau, Paul, 1839–1919.
I56   Alfred de Musset. 3. unveränderte Ausg.
1879   Berlin, A. Hofmann, 1879.
    xvi, 312 p.

    1. Musset, Alfred de, 1810–1857.

NL 0376720   CU NcU

Lindau, Paul, 1839–1919.
    Altes und neues aus der Neuen welt. Eine reise durch die Vereinigten Staaten und Mexico. Von Paul Lindau ... Berlin, C. Duncker, 1893.
    2 v. 21½ᶜᵐ.

    Subject entries: 1. U. S.—Descr. & trav. 2. Mexico—Descr. & trav.

                            3–22107

    Library of Congress, no.   E168.L75.

NL 0376721   DLC MB ICJ NN NcD MoU CtY TNJ

VOLUME 334

Lindau, Paul, 1839– *1919.*
　　Altes und neues aus der Neuen welt. Eine reise durch die
Vereinigten Staaten und Mexico. Von Paul Lindau ... Berlin, C. Duncker, 1893.
　　2 v. 21½ᵐ.

　　Micro-opaque.　Louisville, Ky., Lost Cause
Press, 1965.　9 cards.　7.5 x 9.5cm.　(Clark,
T. D.　Travels in the New South, I, 391)

　NL 0376722　　　FMU CSt MsU TxU UU

Lindau, Paul, 1839–1919.
　　Paul Lindau's Amerika-reisen. Volksausg. ... Berlin, C.
Duncker's verlag, 1899.
　　2 v. in 1. 21ᵐ.

　　1. U. S.—Description and travel.　2. Mexico—Description and travel.
I. Title: Amerika-reisen.

Minn. hist. society. Libr.　　　　　　　　　A 28—1090
　for Library of Congress　　　［a40b1］

　NL 0376723　　　MnHi WU CaBViPA

Lindau, Paul, 1839–
　　An der westküste Klein-Asiens. Eine sommerfahrt
auf dem Ägäischen meere, von Paul Lindau. 2. aufl. Berlin, Allgemeiner verein für deutsche litteratur, 1900.
　　3 p. l., ［3］-330 p. front. (port.) plates. 22ᵐ.

　　1. Asia Minor—Descr. & trav.

　　　　　　　　　　　　　　　　　　　1-18585

　Library of Congress　　　DS52.L7

　NL 0376724　　　DLC MB MoU CtY

Lindau, Paul, 1839–1919.
　　De andere. Een fantastisch spel in vier bedrijven, door Paul
Lindau, vertaald door H. W. van Rijswijk.　Zaandijk: J. Heijnis
Tsz. ［191–?］　136 p. incl. plan.　12°.

　　1. Drama (German).　2. Rijswijk,　H. W. van, translator.　3. Title.
N. Y. P. L.　　　　　　　　　　　　　　　　　May 14, 1921.

　NL 0376725　　　NN

832.08　Lindau, Paul, 1839-1919.
D763　　Der Andere; Schauspiel in vier Aufzügen.
v.29　　Dresden, B.G.Teubner, 1893.
　　　　88p. 19cm.

　　　　Bound with Die Söhne des Geistes, von
　　　　C.W. Geissler.

　NL 0376726　　　CLSU

Lindau, Paul, 1839– *1919.*
　　Der andere. Schauspiel in vier aufzügen, von Paul
Lindau ... New York, Druck von I. Goldmann, 1893.
　　83 p. 20½ᵐ.

　　I. Title.

　Library of Congress　　　PT2423.L7A7 1893

　　　　　　　　　　　　　　　　　18-1204

　NL 0376727　　　DLC

Lindau, Paul, 1839-1919.
　　Der Andere; Schauspiel in vier Aufzügen.
New York, Druck I. Goldmann, 1893.
　　83p.

　　Microcard edition.

　NL 0376728　　　ICRL MoU

Lindau,　　　　　Paul. 1839– *1919*
　　Der Andere. Schauspiel in vier Aufzügen.
— Leipzig. Reclam. ［1906.］ 87 pp. ［Universal Bibliothek. 4817.］
16°.

　NL 0376729　　　MB MH

　　　　Lindau, Paul, 1839-1919
Hkn　　Der Andere; Schauspiel in 4 Aufzügen. Bearb.
y055　von Fred Bruno.　Bad Kissingen Vertriebsstelle
　　　& Verlag deutscher Bühnenschriftsteller und
　　　Bühnenkomponisten［1946］
　　　2p.ℓ.,3-71p.　29cm.

　NL 0376730　　　CtY CU

Lindau, Paul, 1839– *1919*
　　Angerathene Kinder; Lustspiel in vier Aufzügen, von Paul
Lindau.　Berlin: ［R. Boll,］ 1894.　127 p., 1 pl.　8°.

　　At head of title: Als Manuscript vervielfältigt.

　　1. Drama (German).　2. Title.
N. Y. P. L.　　　　　　　　　　　　　　　January 6, 1917.

　NL 0376731　　　NN

ar V　Lindau, Paul, 1839-1919.
10972　Arme Mädchen; Roman.　Berlin, W.
　　　Spemann ［18–?］
　　　399 p. 20cm.　(His Romane, 2)

　NL 0376732　　　NIC

PT2423 Lindau, Paul, 1839-1919.
.L7A76　Arme mädchen; roman von Paul Lindau.　Stuttgart und
19—　Berlin, Cotta ［19—］
　　　258 ℓ. 17½ᵐ.

　NL 0376733　　　ICU

LINDAU,Paul,1839– *1919.*
　　Arme mädchen; roman.　6ᵉ aufl. Stuttgart,
Union deutsche-verlagsgesellschaft,［189–?］

　　Added title-page reads: Berlin: romane,2.
　　　　　　　　　　　50514.59.10

　NL 0376734　　　MH

Lindau, Paul, 1839– *1919.*
　　Arme mädchen, roman von Paul Lindau.
7.auflage.　Stuttgart, Union deutsche
verlagsgesellschaft ［n.d.］
　　2 p.ℓ.,399 p.　(Half-title:Berlin,
romane von Paul Indau. 11.)

　NL 0376735　　　MtBC

Lindau, Paul, 1839-1919.
　　Arme mädchen; roman ... 8. aufl.
Stuttgart, 1901.

　NL 0376736　　　NjP

Lindau, Paul, *1839– 1919.*　　　　　　　3
　　Arme Mädchen.　Stuttgart: J. G. Cotta'sche Bhdlg. Nachf.,
1909.　394 p.　10. ed.　12°.

　NL 0376737　　　NN

PT　Lindau, Paul, 1839-1919
2423　Arme Mädchen; Roman.　Stuttgart, J. G. Cotta
L7　［1914］
A85　258p.　18cm.　(Cotta'sche Handbibliothek, 190)

　NL 0376738　　　WU

Lindau, Paul, 1839-1919.
　　Aus dem literarischen Frankreich.　Breslau,
Schottlaender, 1882.
　　383 p.

　NL 0376739　　　NNC MH PPL

Lindau, Paul, 1839-1919
　　Aus dem literarischen Frankreich. 2.Aufl.　Breslau,
Schottlaender, 1882.

　　383 p.
　　Microfilm, positive, of Harvard College Library copy

　NL 0376740　　　MH

Lindau, Paul, 1839-1919.
　　Aus dem Orient.　Flüchtige Aufzeichnungen.　Von Paul
Lindau.　Breslau: S. Schottlaender, 1890.　296 p.　12°.

237327A.　1. Balkan states—Descr.　　　and trav. to 1900.
N. Y. P. L.　　　　　　　　　　　　　　October 15, 1926

　NL 0376741　　　NN MnU WU PPG MH

830　Lindau, Paul, 1839-1919.
L742　Aus der Hauptstadt; Berliner Plau-
tAU　dereien.　5.Aufl.　Dresden, F.W.
　　　Steffens ［n.d.］
　　　409p. 19cm.

　　　CONTENTS.— Lebende und Todte.— Planlose
　　　Wanderungen: A.Durch die Theater. B.Durch
　　　die Kunstausstellungen. C.Durch den Gerichtssaal.

　　　√1.Germany – Biog. √2.Berlin – Intellectual
　　／life. √3.　　　　　　　Berlin – Descr.√I.Title.

　NL 0376742　　　CLSU

Lindau, Paul, 1839-1919.
　　Aus der Neuen welt.　Briefe aus dem osten und westen der
Vereinigten Staaten, von Paul Lindau.　Berlin, F. Salomon,
1885.
　　viii, 385, ［1］ p.　22½ᵐ.

　　1. U. S.—Descr. & trav.　I. Title.

　　　　　　　　　　　　　　　　　2—4425

　Library of Congress　　　E168.L74

　NL 0376743　　　DLC PPG CtY

VOLUME 334

ar V
10968
Lindau, Paul, 1839–1919.
  Aus Venetien; eine Sommerreise.
Düsseldorf, Schaub, 1864.
  158 p. 17cm.

NL 0376744   NIC

Lindau, Paul, 1839– 1919.
  ... Ausflüge ins kriminalistische. München, A. Langen
[1909]
  272 p. front. (port.) 19½ᵐᵐ.
  CONTENTS.—Mörder.—Indizien.—Grete Beier.—Das drama von Allenstein.—Der hauptmann von Köpenick.

Library of Congress   9–28794

NL 0376745   DLC PU-L

[Lindau, Paul,] 1839–1919.
  "Bayreuther Briefe. Augenblicksbilder aus den Tagen der Patronatsaufführungen des "Parsifal." Leipzig: E. Schloemp, 1882. iv, 54 p. 2. ed. 12°.
  With this is bound: Lindau, P. Nüchterne Briefe aus Bayreuth. Breslau, 1880.

1. Wagner, Richard, 1813–83: Parsi-   fal. 2. Title.
N. Y. P. L.   August 28, 1918.

NL 0376746   NN

Lindau, Paul, 1839–1919.
  Bayreuther briefe vom Reinen thoren. "Parsifal" von Richard Wagner. Von Paul Lindau ... Breslau, S. Schottlaender, 1883.
  2 p. l., 60 p. 20ᵐ.
  Sonderabdruck aus der "Kölnischen zeitung."

1. Wagner, Richard. Parsifal.   I. Title.

Library of Congress   ML410.W17L6
                                          10—18820

NL 0376747   DLC NIC MH

Lindau, Paul, 1839–1919.
  Die beiden Leonoren. Lustspiel in vier Aufzügen.
— Leipzig. Reclam. [1904.] 88 pp. [Universal-Bibliothek. 4590.]
16°.

NL 0376748   MB MH

Lindau, Paul, 1839– 1919.
  Berlin; romane, von Paul Lindau ... Stuttgart, Cotta
[1890]–1901.
  3 v. in 5. 20ᵐ.
                    CONTENTS.
  I. Der zug nach dem westen. 9. aufl. 1898.
  II. Arme mädchen. 8. aufl. 1901.
  III. Spitzen. [1890] 3 v.

I. Title. II. Title: Der zug nach westen. III. Title: Arme mädchen.
IV. Title: Spitzen.
                                          2–4280 Revised

NL 0376749   DLC NN

Lindau,   Paul, 1839–1919.
  Berlin. Romane von Paul Lindau. [Band] I.   6897-436
— Stuttgart. Cotta. 1912. I v. 19.5 cm., in 8s.
  Contents. — I. Der Zug nach dem Westen. 2.
  Each part is catalogued separately.   3.

NL 0376750   MB

Lindau, Paul, 1839–1919.
  Die blaue Laterne. Berliner Roman.
Stuttgart, Cotta, 1907.
  2 v. in 1.

NL 0376751   MBU PPG

LINDAU, Paul, 1839–1919.
  Die blaue laterne; Berliner roman. 5.und
6.aufl. Stuttgart,etc.,J.G.Cotta'sche buchhandlung nachfolger,1908.

  2 vol.   50514.59.8

NL 0376752   MH RPB

PT
2423
L7
B5
Lindau, Paul, 1839–1919
  Die blaue Laterne; Berliner Roman.
Stuttgart, J. G. Cotta, 1925.
  2v. in 1. 20cm.

NL 0376753   WU ViFreM

Lindau, Paul, 1839–1919.
  Die Brüder, Roman. Dresden, C. Reissner, 1896.
  271 p. 20 cm.

I. Title.

PT2423.L7B7   65–72693 ‡

NL 0376754   DLC NIC NN

Lindau, Paul, 1839–1919.
  Die Brueder: Roman.   Dresden, Reissner,
1897.

NL 0376755   MA

Lindau,   Paul. 1839–1919.
  Die Brüder. Schauspiel in vier Aufzügen.
— Leipzig. Reclam. [1908.] 86 pp. Plans. [Universal-Bibliothek. 4972.] 16°.

NL 0376756   MB OCI

Lindau, Paul, 1839–1919.
  Die Brüder. Schauspiel in vier Aufzügen.
Leipzig, Reclam [n.d.]
  86p.

  Microcard edition.

NL 0376757   ICRL

Lindau, Paul, 1839–1919.
  ...Diana. Schauspiel in fünf Acten, von Paul Lindau. Zum erstenmal aufgeführt: im Laube'schen Stadttheater zu Wien am 25. October 1873, im Königl. Schauspielhause zu Berlin am 12. November 1873.   Leipzig, Metzger & Wittig, 1873.   122 p. 21cm.
  At head of title Bühnenmanuscript.

279319B. 1. Drama, German.   I. Title.
N. Y. P. L.   March 30, 1945

NL 0376758   NN

Lindau, Paul, 1839–1919.
  Dramaturgische Blätter. Beiträge zur Kenntniss des modernen Theaters in Deutschland und Frankreich. Stuttgart, C. F. Simon, 1874–75.
  2 v. in 1. 17½ cm.
— —— Neue Folge, 1875–1878. Breslau, S. Schottlaender, 1879.
  v. 21 cm.
                        PT652.L5 Suppl.
  1. German drama—19th cent.—Hist. & crit. 2. French drama—19th cent.—Hist. & crit. 3. Theater—Germany. 4. Theater—France. I. Title.
PT652.L5   832.804   34–38206 rev*

NL 0376759   DLC CSt MH NN CLSU

PT
652
L74
1877
Lindau, Paul, 1839–1919.
  Dramaturgische Blätter; Beiträge zur Kenntnis des modernen Theaters in Deutschland und Frankreich. 2. Aufl. Stuttgart, C. F. Simon, 1877.
  2 v. in 1. 18cm.

  1. German drama--19th cent.--Hist. & crit.
  2. French drama--19th cent.--Hist. & crit.
  3. Theater--Ger   many. 4. Theater--
France. I.   Title.

NL 0376760   NIC MiU RPB MdBP InU MB

Lindau, Paul, 1839–1919.
  Dramaturgische Blätter. Neue Folge, 1875–1878, von Paul Lindau... Breslau: S. Schottlaender, 1879. 2 v. in 1. 20½cm.

218587B. 1. Drama—Hist. and   crit. 2. Drama, German—Hist.
and crit.
N. Y. P. L.   March 3, 1943

NL 0376761   NN CU TNJ IU MH RPB ICU

Lindau, Paul, 1839–1919.
  ...Ein Erfolg. Lustspiel in vier Acten, von Paul Lindau... Leipzig, B. G. Teubner [1874] 119 p. 21cm.
  At head of title: Bühnen-Manuscript

279319B. 1. Drama, German.   I. Title.
N. Y. P. L.   March 30, 1945

NL 0376762   NN

838
L742e
1900
Lindau, Paul, 1839–1919
  Ein erfolg, lustspiel in vier
akten. 2.aufl.   Berlin, Bloch
[1900]
  95p. D.

NL 0376763   IaU

Lindau, Paul, 1839–1919.
  Die ermordung des advocaten Bernays. Breslau, S. Schottlaender [1883]
  45, [1] p. 8°. (Deutsche bücherei, hft. 30)

                                          1–6443

NL 0376764   DLC

Lindau,   Paul. 1839–
  Die Erste. Schauspiel in vier Aufzügen.
— Leipzig. Reclam. [1907.] 64 pp. [Universal-Bibliothek. 4924.]
16°.

NL 0376765   MB

VOLUME 334

Lindau, Paul, 1839–1919.
Ferdinand Lassalle's letzte rede. Breslau, S. Schottlaender, 1882.
23 p. 24ᶜᵐ. (Deutsche bücherei. ₍IV₎)

1. Lassalle, Ferdinand Johann Gottlieb, 1825–1864.

Library of Congress   HX273.L3L5   1–6424

NL 0376766   DLC NN

Lindau, Paul, 1839–1919, ed.
Ferdinand Lassalles Tagebuch
see under Lassalle, Ferdinand Johann
Gottlieb, 1825–1864.

PT
2423
L7F38
1899
Lindau, Paul, 1839–1919.
Ferien im Morgenlande; Tagebuchblätter aus
Griechenland, der europäischen Türkei und Klein-
Asien. 2. Aufl. Berlin, Fontane, 1899.
282 p.

NL 0376768   CLU

832.8
L742pXS
Lindau, Paul, 1839–1919.
Franz Hallers, comedia dramática de Lindau,
Gorsse, y Forest. Traducida por Sinibaldo
Gutierrez. Madrid, R. Velasco, 1916.
84p. 20cm.

Translation of Le procureur Halleurs.

I. Gorsse, Henry Joseph Augeste de. II.
Forest, Louis, 1872. III. Gutierrez, Sinibaldo, tr. IV. Title.

NL 0376769   IEN

PQ6217
N937
no.100
Lindau, Paul, 1839–1919.
Franz Hallers; comedia dramática en
cuatro actos, original de Lindau, Gorsse
y Forest, traducida por Sinibaldo Gutierrez.

(In La Novela teatral, año 3, 1918,
no.100)

I. Forest, ᴸᵒᵘⁱˢ II. Gutierrez, Sinibaldo,
tr. III. Title.

NL 0376770   PPiU

4PT
Ger.
6389
Lindau, Paul, 1839–1919
Frau Susanne, Schauspiel in fünf
Aufzügen von Paul Lindau und Hugo
Lubliner. Leipzig, Druck von B. G.
Teubner, 1884.
95 p.

NL 0376771   DLC-P4

Lindau, Paul, 1839–1919, ed.
Die Gegenwart. Wochenschrift für literatur, kunst und
öffentliches leben ... 1.– bd.; jan. 1872–

Berlin, G. Stilke ₍etc.₎, 1872₎–19

Lindau, Paul, 1839–1919.
Die Gehilfin; Berliner Roman in drei Büchern, von Paul Lindau... Breslau: S. Schottlaender, 1895. 2 v. 8°.

1. Fiction (German). 2. Title.
N.Y.P.L.   July 8, 1918.

NL 0376773   NN PPL

Lindau, Paul, 1839–1919.
Die Gehilfin. Berliner Roman in drei Büchern. Breslau,
Schlesische Buchdruckerei, Kunst- und Verlags-Anstalt.
New York, G. E. Stechert, 1895.
2 v. 21 cm.

I. Title.

PT2423.L7G4   60–59736 ‡

NL 0376774   DLC NIC

PT343
L5₇
Lindau, Paul, 1839–1919.
Gesammelte Aufsätze. Beiträge zur Literaturgeschichte der
Gegenwart. Berlin, G. Stilke, 1875.
vi, 453 p.

1. German literature - 19th cent. - Hist. & crit.

NL 0376775   CU CtY RPB PPG MiU OCI NN MH GU

809
L742
Lindau, Paul, 1839–1919.
Gesammelte Aufsätze; Beiträge zur Liter-
aturgeschichte der Gegenwart. 2. Aufl.
Berlin, Freund & Jeckel, 1880.
vi, 453 p. 20 cm.

NL 0376776   N NcU OU PBm

PT2423
L7G8
1880
Lindau, Paul, 1839–1919.
Gräfin Lea. Schauspiel in fünf aufzügen, von Paul Lindau. Berlin, Freund & Jeckel, 1880.
₍5₎, 112 p. 18½ᶜᵐ.

NL 0376777   ICU NN OCU OCIW PU PSC

Lindau, Paul, 1839–1919.
Gräfin Lea. 2. Aufl. Berlin, Freund, 1880.
112p. 18cm.

NL 0376778   IEN

Lindau, Paul, 1839–1919.   FOR OTHER EDITIONS
    SEE MAIN ENTRY
The Great streets of the world, by Richard Harding Davis,
Andrew Lang ... ₍and others₎ Illustrated by A. B. Frost,
W. Douglas Almond ... ₍and others₎ New York, C. Scrib-
ner's sons, 1892.

Lindau, Paul, 1839–1919.
Hängendes moos. Roman, von Paul Lindau. Breslau,
Schlesische verlags-anstalt, vorm. S. Schottlaender; New-
York, G. E. Stechert; ₍etc., etc.₎ 1893.
286 p. 20ᶜᵐ.

1. Title.

18–1206

Library of Congress   PT2423.L7H3   1893

NL 0376780   DLC MB

Lindau, Paul, 1839–1919.
Hängendes moos. Roman, von Paul Lindau. Breslau,
Schlesische verlags-anstalt, vorm. S. Schottlaender; New-
York, G. E. Stechert, 1897.
286 p. 20ᶜᵐ.

NL 0376781   NIC

LINDAU, Paul, 1839–1919
Hängendes moos; roman. 4ᵉˢ tausend.
Breslau, S. Schottlaender, etc., etc., 1897.

NL 0376782   MH

Lindau, Paul, 1839–1919.
Hanging moss, by Paul Lindau ... tr. from the German
by Winchester Ayer and Helen Folger. New York, D.
Appleton and company, 1892.
300 p. 18½ᶜᵐ. (On cover: Appletons' town and country library. no.
107)

1. Ayer, Winchester, tr. II. Folger, Helen, tr. III. Title.

Library of Congress   PZ3.L64H   7–19022
Copyright 1892: 45476   ₍a22f1₎

NL 0376783   DLC MB PPL OCIW

₍LINDAU, PAUL₎ 1839–1919.
Harmlose Briefe eines deutschen Kleinstädters.
Leipzig, A. H. Payne, 1871. 168 p. 19cm.

1. Wit and humor, German. I. Title. II. Eines deutschen kleinstädters.

NL 0376784   NN PU OCIW

Lindau, Paul, 1839–1919.
Harmlose Briefe eines deutschen Kleinstädters.
2. Aufl... Breslau, S. Schottlaender, 1879.
2 v. in 1.

NL 0376785   MiD

Lindau, Paul, 1839–1919.
... Der held des tages. Berlin, Concordia deutsche verlagsanstalt, H. Ehbock ₍1909₎
275, ₍3₎ p. 18½ᶜᵐ.
CONTENTS.— Der held des tages.— Lenzes gebot.— Ihre lieblingseigen-
schaft am manne.—Wie ich spiritist wurde.—Lisas brautfahrt.—Betty.—
Eine auferstandene.—Die weisse boa.

9–14224

NL 0376786   DLC OCI OO

Lindau, Paul, 1839–1919.
Helen Young, a story, by Paul Lindau. Tr. from the
German by P. J. McFadden. Chicago and New York,
Rand, McNally & company, 1892.
2 p. l., 7–183 p. 19½ᶜᵐ. (On cover: Globe library. v. 1, no. 168)

1. McFadden, P. J., tr.

Library of Congress   PZ3.L64He   7–19021†
    (Copyright 1892: 13532)

NL 0376787   DLC

VOLUME 334

ar V
10960　Lindau, Paul, 1839-1919.
　　　　Helen Young; Erzählung.　Stuttgart, J.
　　Engelhorn, 1885.
　　　　142 p.　18cm.　(Engelhorn's allgemeine
　　Romanbibliothek, Bd. 3)

NL　0376788　　NIC MH

Lindau, Paul, 1839-1919.
　... Helene Jung.　Erzählung von Paul Lindau.　Stuttgart,
J. Engelhorn, 1885.
　142 p.　18cm.　(Engelhorn's allgemeine romanbibliothek ... 2. jahrg.,
bd. 3)

　　ɪ. Title.
Library of Congress　　PT2423.L7H38　　　44-46667

NL　0376789　　DLC CLSU MH DCU-IA NN PPG MeB

Lindau,　　　　Paul, 1839-1919.
Der Herr im Hause.　Lustspiel in vier Aufzügen.
Leipzig.　Reclam.　[1909.]　80 pp.　Plan.　[Universal-Bibliothek.
5102.]　14 cm., in 8s.

NL　0376790　　MB AAP OU

Lindau, Paul, 1839-1919.
　　Der Herr im Hause.　Lustspiel in vier Aufzügen.
Leipzig, Reclam ⟨n.d.⟩
80p.

Microcard edition.

NL　0376791　　ICRL

Lindau, Paul, 1839-1919.
Herr und Frau Bewer; Novelle.
Breslau, Schottlaender, 1882.

247 p.

NL　0376792　　PPG

Lindau,　　　　Paul, 1839-1919
Herr und Frau Bewer.　137 pp.
(In Novellen und Humoresken. Chicago. [1885.])

NL　0376793　　MB PPG

Lindau, Paul, 1839-1919.
　... "Herr und frau Bewer."　Novelle von Paul Lindau
... New-York, G. Munro ₁1885₎
　25 p.　32cm.　(Die deutsche library. bd. 9, no. 176)

　　ɪ. Title.
Library of Congress　　PT1332.D4　　　17-9794

NL　0376794　　DLC

Lindau, Paul, 1839-1919.
　　Herr und frau Bewer.　Novelle, von Paul Lindau. 10. aufl.
Mit einem briefe von Emil Augier an den verfasser.　Breslau,
S. Schottlaender; New York, G. E. Stechert; ₍etc., etc.₎ 1899.
　3 p. l., viii p., 1 l., 247 p.　19cm.

　　ɪ. *Augier, Émile, 1820-1889.　ɪɪ. Title.
　　　　　　　　　　　　　　　　　　　　1-9960
Library of Congress　　(❉)　(PT2423.L7H4 1899)

NL　0376795　　OCl

PT2423 Lindau, Paul, 1839-1919.
.L7H6　　Herr und Frau Bewer; novelle von Paul Lindau.　Mit
1909　illustrationen von Paul Telemann.　11. aufl.　Berlin, S.
　　　　Schottlaenders schlesische verlagsanstalt ₍°1909₎
　　　　313, ₍1₎ p.　illus.　19½cm.
　　　　Contents.—Herr und Frau Bewer.—In einer droschke zweiter klasse.—Kollege
Schnabel.

NL　0376796　　ICU

Lindau,　　　　　Paul, 1839-1919.
　I de rikas stadsdel.　Roman.　Öfversättning från tyska originalet.
⊨ Stockholm.　Bonnier.　[1887.]　291 pp.　[Berlin i våra dagar. ɪ.]
16°.

D9915 — T.r. — S.r. — Sweden. Lang. Works in.

NL　0376797　　MB

Lindau, Paul, 1839-
　... Illustrierte romane und novellen ...
Berlin, S. Schottlaender ₍°1909₎
　v. illus. 20cm.　　　　　　　　　10-2839

NL　0376798　　DLC PBm

Lindau, Paul, 1839-1919.
　　Im fieber.　Novelle von Paul Lindau.　2. aufl.
Breslau, S. Schottlaender, 1890.
　248 p.　18½cm.

NL　0376799　　ViU PPL

PT2423 Lindau, Paul, 1839-1919.
.L7I3　　Im Fieber; Novelle.　3.Aufl.　Breslau, S.
1890　Schottlaender, 1890.
　　　　248 p.

NL　0376800　　ICU NN

Lindau, Paul, 1839-1919.
　In folge einer wette.　In Neuer
deutscher novellenschatz.　1884-87
v.16, pp. 197-253.

NL　0376801　　OClW OU

ar V
10964　Lindau, Paul, 1839-1919.
　　　　Interessante Fälle; Criminalprocesse
　　aus neuester Zeit.　Breslau, S. Schott-
　　laender, 1888.
　　　　298 p.　19cm.

　　　　　1. Trials.　I. Title.

NL　0376802　　NIC MH-L

Y
952　LINDAU, PAUL, 1839-1919.
.L 64　　Johannistrieb.　Schauspiel in vier aufzügen.
　　　　Berlin, G.Stilke, 1878.
　　　　140p.

Six pages of music following text.

NL　0376803　　ICN PU OCU

Lindau, Paul, 1839-1919.
　Jungbrunnen.　Lustspiel in vier Acten.
Berlin, F. Bloch, 1882.
　75 p.　8°.

NL　0376804　　NN

Lindau, Paul, 1839-1919.
　... Klaus Bewer's wife, from the German of Paul Lindau,
by Clara S. Fleishman.　New York, H. Holt and company,
1886.
　2 p. l., 253 p.　17cm.　(Leisure season series. ₍no. 5₎)

　　ɪ. Fleishman, Clara S., tr.　ɪɪ. Title.

Library of Congress　　PZ3.L64K　　　7-19020

NL　0376805　　DLC MB MH

Lindau, Paul, 1839-1919.
　　Kleine Geschichten, von Paul Lindau...　Leipzig: F.
Fleischer, 1872.　2 v. in 1.　12°.
　Contents: Bd. 1. Stecknadeln. Josephine — Nini — Ninon. Geschichte einer
jungen Französin. Bd. 2. Ein aufgefangener Brief. In Folge einer Wette. Der
Tod der Frau Baronin.

48502A.　1. Fiction (German).　　　2. Title.
N. Y. P. L.　　　　　　　　　　　　　　　August 7, 1922.

NL　0376806　　NN PPG CtY DLC-P4

Lindau, Paul, 1839-1919
Der König von Sidon.　Erzählung.　Breslau.
Schottlaender, 1898.
249p.　19cm.

NL　0376807　　TNJ

Lindau, Paul, 1839-1919.
　Der könig von Sidon.　Erzählung von Paul Lindau ...
Breslau, Kunst- und verlagsanstalt v. S. Schottlaender;
New York, G. E. Stechert; ₍etc., etc.₎ 1898.
　3 p. l., 249 p.　19cm.
　　　　　　　　　　　　　　　　　9-2944

NL　0376808　　DLC PPL

Hkn
y509　Lindau, Paul, 1839-1919.
　　　　Der König von Sidon ...　Bremen[etc.]Verlag
　　der Wiking-Bücher[1914]
　　　　300p., 1ℓ.　15½cm.　(Wiking-Bücher)
　　"Toggenburg": p.[193]-300.

NL　0376809　　CtY

PT
2423　Lindau, Paul, 1839-1919.
L7　　　Der Komödiant.　Schauspiel in drei Ab-
K8　theilungen und fünf Aufzügen.　Berlin, A.
　　　　Entsch, 1892.
　　　　64+ p.　22cm.

　　　　At head of title:　Bühnen-Manuscript.
　　　　CUL copy imperfect: all after p. 64
　　lacking.

NL　0376810　　NIC WU

Lindau,　　　　　Paul, 1839-1919.
Der Komödiant. Schauspiel in drei Abteilungen und fünf Aufzügen.
Leipzig.　Reclam.　[1906.]　103 pp.　Music.　[Universal-Biblio-
thek.　4787.]　16°.

NL　0376811　　MB

VOLUME 334

Lindau, Paul, 1839-1919
Die kranke köchin. Die liebe im dativ.
Zwei ernsthafte geschichten, ... Mit
15 illus. von Julius Ehrentraut; 2. aufl.
Stuttgart und Lpz., E. Hallberger, 1881. 105p.
illus.

NL 0376812   OU

Lindau, Paul, 1839-1919.
Lace; a Berlin romance, by Paul Lindau. New York,
D. Appleton and company, 1889.
324 p. 19ᶜᵐ. (*On cover:* Appletons' town and country library. no. 30)

ɪ. Title.

Library of Congress   PZ3.L64L   7-19019

NL 0376813   DLC WaTC PPL NN ViU MB PU

Lindau, Paul, 1839-1919.
Literarische rücksichtslosigkeiten. Feuilletonistische und polemische aufsätze von Paul
Lindau ... Leipzig, J. A. Barth, 1871.
4 p.l., 302 p.   18ᶜᵐ.
CONTENTS.--Feuilletonistische aufsätze vermischten
inhalts.--Kritisch-polemische aufsätze.

1.Literature--Addresses,essays,lectures.   I.Title.

NL 0376814   MiU IaU NIC PU CLSU

Lindau, Paul, 1839-1919.
Literarische rücksichtslosigkeiten. Feuille-
tonistische und polemische aufsätze, von Paul
Lindau ... 2. unveränderte aufl. Leipzig,
J. A. Barth, 1871.
4 p. l., 312 p. 19ᶜᵐ.

NL 0376815   NNC PU MiU MH CtY

Lindau, Paul, 1839-1919.
Literarische Rücksichtslosigkeiten.
Feuilletonistische und polemische Aufsätze.
3. unveränderte Aufl. Leipzig, J.A. Barth,
1871.
302 p. 19cm.

NL 0376816   GU CU OCU MH NcU

Lindau, Paul, 1839-1919.
...Maria und Magdalena. Schauspiel in vier Acten, von Paul
Lindau. Zum erstenmal aufgeführt auf dem Laube'schen Stadt-
theater zu Wien am 19. October 1872. Leipzig, Metzger &
Wittig, 1872.   123 p.   21cm.
At head of title: Bühnenmanuscript.
With autograph of author.

279319B. 1. Drama, German.   I. Title.
N. Y. P. L.   March 27, 1945

NL 0376817   NN OC1W

Lindau, Paul, 1839-1919.
... Maria and Magdalena. A play, in four acts. Adapted
for the American stage from the German original of Paul
Lindau, by L. J. Hollenius ... New York, R. M. De Witt
[1874]
44 p. 19¼ᶜᵐ. (*On cover:* De Witt's acting plays. no. 154)
Title-page mounted on p. [1]

ɪ. Hollenius, L. J., tr.   ɪɪ. Title.

                                                    18—1208
Library of Congress   PT2423.L7M31

NL 0376818   DLC MB MiU RPB MH NcD OU IU PU

Lindau, Paul, 1839-1919.
Mayo; erzaehlung. Breslau, Schottlaender, 1884.
262 p.

NL 0376819   PU PPG

Lindau, Paul, 1839-1919.
... "Mayo." Erzählung von Paul Lindau ... New-
York, G. Munro [1884]
19 p. 32ᶜᵐ. (Die deutsche library, bd. 9, no. 166)

ɪ. Title.

Library of Congress   PT1332.D4   17-9783

NL 0376820   DLC

PT2423 Lindau, Paul, 1839-1919.
.L7H6   Mayo; erzählung von Paul Lindau.   Mit illustrationen
1909   von Paul Telemann.   Berlin, S. Schottlaenders schlesische
          verlags-anstalt [1909]
          318 p. illus.   19½ᶜᵐ. (*Added t.-p.:* Paul Lindau.   Illustrierte romane und
          novellen.   2. bd.)
          With his Herr und Frau Bewer.   Berlin [1909]
          CONTENTS.--Mayo.--Mein freund Hilarius.--Die kleine Madonna.

NL 0376821   ICU

Lindau, Paul, 1839-1919.
Mr. and Mrs. Bewer; from the 8th German ed. of Paul
Lindau ... tr. by Mrs. D. M. Lowrey.   Chicago and New
York, Rand, McNally & company, 1892.
1 p. l., 5-230 p. 19¼ᶜᵐ. (*On cover:* Globe library. v. 1, no. 172)

ɪ. Lowrey, Mrs. D. M., tr.   CA 9-2268 Unrev'd

Library of Congress   PZ3.L64M

NL 0376822   DLC

4K   Lindau, Paul, 1839-1919
Ger   Der Mörder der Frau Marie Ziethen.
1741   Ziethen oder Wilhelm? Nachwort von
         Max Neuda. Mit einem Situationsplan
         der Elberfelder Oertlichkeiten und
         einem Grundriss des Ziethen'schen
         Hauses. Breslau, Schlesische Buch-
         druckerei, Kunst- und Verlags-Anstalt
         vormals S. Schottlaender; New York,
         G. E. Stechert, 1892.
             152 p.

NL 0376823   DLC-P4 NIC MH-L

Lindau, Paul, 1839-
Molière ... Leipzig, Druck von Metzger & Wittig,
1871.
1 p. l., 102 p. 21¼ᶜᵐ.
Promotionsschrift--Rostock.

1. Molière, Jean Baptiste Poquelin, 1622-1673.   ɪ. Title.

                                                    12-11665
Library of Congress   PQ1852.L5

NL 0376824   DLC NcU

Lindau, Paul, 1839-1919.
Molière;eine ergänzung der biographie
des dichters, aus seinen werken.. Leipzig,
Barth, 1872.
viii,102 p. mounted front.(port.)
24 ᶜᵐ.

1.Molière,Jean Baptiste Poquelin,
1622-1673.

NL 0376825   NjP NRU MB OC1W PU NN

Lindau, Paul, 1839-1919.   (Hungarian)
Molière; tr. by Banfi Zsigmond. Budapest,
Franklin, 1879.

NL 0376826   OC1

LINDAU, Paul, 1839-1919
Molière in Deutschland. Wien,1867.

pp.(2),24.
"Separatabdruck aus der Internationalen revue,nr.4."
Also contained in his "Literarische rücksichtslosigkeiten".3e aufl.,1871,pp.158-178.

NL 0376827   MH InU

LINDAU, Paul, 1839-1919.
Molière und die beiden Béjart. [Breslau,
1886].

pp.(16).
Nord und sud,1886,xxxvii.391-406.

NL 0376828   MH

LINDAU, Paul, 1839-1919.
Molière's "Tartüffe" und Gutzkow's "Urbild
des Tartüffe." Berlin,[186-?]

pp.32.
"Separat-abdruck aus dem feuilleton des
Berliner fremden-und anzwigeblatts."

NL 0376829   MH

Lindau,   Paul. 1839-
Nacht und Morgen. Schauspiel in vier Aufzügen. Von Paul Lindau.
Leipzig. Reclam. [1909] 79 pp. [Universal-Bibliothek. 5087.]
16°.

NL 0376830   MB

Lindau, Paul, 1839-1919, ed.
Nord und süd. Eine deutsche monatsschrift. bd. 1-
apr. 1877-
Berlin, G. Stilke; [etc., etc.] 1877-

VOLUME 334

Lindau, Paul, 1839–1919.
... Novellen und humoresken von Paul Lindau und Ernst Eckstein ... Chicago, L. Schick [1885]
137 p., 1 l., [5]–15 p. 19ᶜᵐ. (Collection Schick, no. 8)
CONTENTS.—Herr und Frau Bewer, von Paul Lindau.—Eine abendwanderung, von Ernst Eckstein.

I. Eckstein, Ernst, 1845–1900. II. Title. III. Title: Herr und Frau Bewer.
IV. Title: Eine abendwanderung.

Library of Congress   PT1337.S4   17-20444

NL 0376832   DLC CU OO

ML 410   LINDAU, PAUL, 1839–1919
.W15 L6   Nüchterne Briefe aus Bayreuth.   Breslau,
S. Schottlaender, 1876.
51 p.

Reprinted from Schlesische Presse.

1. Wagner, Richard—Der Ring des Nibelungen.

NL 0376833   InU MH PPG CtY

LINDAU, Paul, 1839–1919.
Nüchterne Briefe aus Bayreuth. 8e durch eine vorrede vermehrte aufl. Breslau, 1877.
pp. xi, 89.
"Separat-abdruck aus der Schlesischen presse."
The same. 9e aufl. Breslau, 1879.   Mus 864.1.974
sm. 8°.   Mus 864.1.975

NL 0376834   MH

Lindau, Paul, 1839–1919.
Nüchterne briefe aus Bayreuth, von Paul Lindau ... Separat-abdruck aus der "Schlesischen presse." 10. aufl. Breslau, S. Schottlaender [1881]
xi, [2], [4]–89, [1] p. 19ᶜᵐ.

Subject entries: Wagner, Richard. Der ring des Nibelungen.
3-21247

Library of Congress, no.   ML3860.W13.

NL 0376835   DLC NN IaU

PT2423   Lindau, Paul, 1839–1919.
.L7Z75   Nur Erinnerungen.   Stuttgart und
Berlin, J.G. Cotta'sche, 1917.
2 v. port. 24 cm.

Vol. 1, 3. u. 4. Aufl.; v. 2, 2. u. 3. Aufl.

NL 0376836   TU CU RPB MH CLSU ICU OrU

PT
2423   Lindau, Paul, 1839–1919
.L7   Nur Erinnerungen. Stuttgart, Cotta, 1919
N9   [v. 2: 1918]
2 v. front (port.) 23cm.

Vol. 1: 5. and 6. ed.; vol. 2: 4. ed.

NL 0376837   MH NN
TNJ OC1W IU PBm NcU CaBVaU WU NjP MiU

Lindau, Paul, 1839–1919.
Proben modernster übersetzungskunst. II. Othello, der Mohr von Venedig von William Shakespeare, übersetzt von Friedrich Bodenstedt ... [Leipzig, J. A. Barth, 1871]
p. [279]–302. 21cm.

Detached from the author's Literarische rücksichtlosigkeiten.

NL 0376838   PU-F

Lindau, Paul, 1839–1919.
Le procureur Hallers; pièce en quatre actes, adaptée d'après Paul Lindau par Henry de Gorsse et Louis Forest ... [Paris, Impr. de L'Illustration, 1914]
34, [2] p. illus. (incl. ports.) 30ᶜᵐ. (On cover: La petite illustration, no. 46, série-théâtre, no. 26)
Adapted from the author's "Der andere."
"Revue de la critique": 2 p. at end.

I. Gorsse, Henry Joseph Auguste de. II. Forest, Louis, 1872–
III. Title.

Library of Congress   PQ1223.I 62 no. 26   18-1205
— Copy 2.   PT2423.L7A74

NL 0376839   DLC NN MB ICN ViU PSt

Lindau, Paul, 1839–1919.
Le procureur Hallers; pièce en quatre actes, adaptée d'après Paul Lindau par Henry de Gorsse et Louis Forest. [Paris, Impr. de l'Illustration, 1914]
34p. illus. (On cover: La Petite illustration, no. 46. Série théâtre, no. 26)

Microcard edition.

NL 0376840   ICRL

LINDAU, Paul, 1839–1919.
Le procureur Hallers; pièce en quatre actes, adaptée d'après Paul Lindau, par Henry de Gorsse & Louis Forest. Paris, Librairie théatrale, 1922, cop. 1914.
1. 8°. pp. 44.
"Réprésentée pour la 1re fois le 16 octobre 1913, au théâtre Antoine."
50514.59.11

NL 0376841   MH PBm

Lindau, Paul, 1839–1919.
Rachel Felix. Von Paul Lindau. Düsseldorf, Stahl, 1863.
66 p. 18½ᶜᵐ.

1. Félix, Elisa Rachel, 1821?–1858.

Library of Congress   PN2638.R3L5   13-18273

NL 0376842   DLC

Lindau, Paul, 1839–1919.
Richard Wagner; avec le portrait de Richard Wagner. Traduit en Français par Johannès Weber. Paris, Hinrichsen, 1885.
xvi, 289 p. 19 cm.
PARTIAL CONTENTS.—Tannhäuser à Paris.—L'anneau du Nibelung à Bayreuth.—L'anneau du Nibelung à Berlin.—Parsifal à Bayreuth.

1. Wagner, Richard, 1813–1883.

ML410.W1L543   53-51224

NL 0376843   DLC

ML
410
.W1
L744
1887
Lindau, Paul, 1839–1919.
Richard Wagner. Tannhaeuser à Paris, L'anneau du Nibelung à Bayreuth et à Berlin, Parsifal à Bayreuth, La mort de R. Wagner. Traduit en français par Johannès Weber. Nouv. éd. Paris, L. Westhausser, 1887.
239 p. port.
"Les articles réunis dans ce volume ont paru d'abord dans divers journaux."

1. Wagner, Richard, 1813–1883.

NL 0376844   MiU MH

Lindau, Paul, 1839–
Der Schatten. Schauspiel in vier Aufzügen.
— Leipzig. Reclam. [1904] 87 pp. [Universal-Bibliothek. 4637.] 16°.

NL 0376845   MB

Lindau, Paul, 1839–
Schau- und lustspiele. Breslau, 1888.
348 p.

NL 0376846   PHC

Lindau, Paul, 1839–1919.
"... So ich dir!" Schauspiel in vier aufzügen von Paul Lindau. (Nach der aufführung im "Deutschen schauspielhause" zu Hamburg eingerichtetes regiebuch) ... Berlin, 1903.
128 p. 18ᶜᵐ.
At head of title: Bühnen-manuskript.

I. Title.

Library of Congress   PT2423.L7S6 1903   18-1207

NL 0376847   DLC

Lindau, Paul, 1839–1919.
Die Sonne. Schauspiel.
— Leipzig. Reclam. [1906] 79 pp. [Universal Bibliothek. 4754.] 16°.

NL 0376848   MB

Lindau, Paul, 1839–1919.
Spitzen; roman. 4ᵉ aufl. Berlin, etc. W. Spemann, [1888].
2 vol. (paged contin.) pp. (4) (3), 530. (His Berlin; romane. 3.)

NL 0376849   MH

ar V
10971
Lindau, Paul, 1839–1919.
Spitzen; Roman. 5. Aufl. Stuttgart, Union Deutsche Verlagsgesellschaft [18—?]
2 v. 19cm. (His Romane, 3)

NL 0376850   NIC

Lindau, Paul, 1839–1919.
Spitzen; roman ... 8. aufl. Stuttgart, 1904.

NL 0376851   NjP

VOLUME 334

PT2423 **Lindau, Paul,** 1839–1919.
.L7S8   Spitzen. Roman von Paul Lindau. 13.–15. aufl. Stutt-
1920   gart und Berlin, J. G. Cotta, 1920.
          [7], 530 p. 18^{cm}. (*Added t.-p.:* Berlin, romane von Paul Lindau. III)

NL 0376852   ICU PPG

832.8
L74t   **Lindau, Paul,** 1839–1919
          Theater. Berlin, G. Stilke, 1873.
          257p. 19cm.
          CONTENTS.– Marion.– In diplomatischer
          Sendung.– Maria und Magdalena.

NL 0376853   TNJ PU

LINDAU, Paul, 1839–1919.
     Theater. Berlin, G. Stilke, etc., 1873–81.

     4 vol.
     Vol.1 and 3 are "2e aufl."
                    50514.59.5

NL 0376854   MH OCU CtY

838   **Lindau, Paul,** 1839–1919
L742th   Theater... 2.aufl.   Berlin,
1873   Freund, 1879–   [1873–   ]
          v. D.
          Imprint of Bloch stamped on t.-p.
          Contents: 1.bd. Marion. In diplomatischer
          sendung. Maria und Magdalena.–

NL 0376855   IaU RPB NjP

          Lindau, Paul, 1839–1919.
          Theater. Berlin, Freund & Jeckel, 1879–1881.
             4 v. in 2. Bd. 1–4. 12°.
             2. ed.

NL 0376856   NN CU

          Lindau, Paul, 1839–1919.
          Der Tod der Frau Baronin (Erzählung,
          Stecknadeln (Novelle), Infolge einer
          Wette (Novelle) Mit Illustrationen von
          Julie Werkenthin.   Berlin, Schlesische
          Verlags-Anstalt [1912]
          357p. illus. 19cm.   (*His* Illus-
          trierte Romane und Novellen, 9.Bd.)

NL 0376857   IEN

          Lindau, Paul, 1839–1919.
          Toggenburg u. a. Geschichten..
          Breslau, Schottlaeneder, 1883.

          217 s.

NL 0376858   PPG

          Lindau, Paul, 1839–1919.
          Tragische Geschichten; illustriert von René Reinicke. Stutt-
          gart: Carl Krabbe[, 19—?]. 157 p. illus., pl. 8°.
              Contents: Schnuck; eine Hundegeschichte. Vater Adrian; eine Jugenderin-
          nerung. Französische Stunde; eine junge Mädchen Geschichte. Weihnachten hinter
          Schloss und Riegel; eine tragische Geschichte.

NL 0376859   NN WU NjP

          Lindau, Paul, 1839–1919.
          Ueberflüssige Briefe an eine Freundin; gesam-
          melte Feuilletons.   Breslau, S.Schottlaender,
          1877.

          313 p.

NL 0376860   MH NcU OC1W

          Lindau, Paul, 1839–1919.
          Ueberflüssige Briefe an eine Freundin; gesam-
          melte Feuilletons. 3. unveränderte Aufl. Bres-
          lau, S. Schottlaender, 1878.
          313 p.

NL 0376861   MiD

          Lindau, Paul, 1839–1919.
          Underligt folk; noveller. Öfversättning
          från tyskan. Stockholm, Bonnier [1889]
          299 p.

NL 0376862   WaU

          Lindau, Paul, 1839–1919.
          Ungerathene Kinder. Lustspiel in vier Aufzügen, von Paul
          Lindau. Berlin: [R. Boll,] 1894. 127 p., 1 pl. 8°.
             At head of title: Als Manuscript vervielfältigt.
          In: NGB p. v. 169, no. 6.

          1. Drama (German). 2. Title.
          N. Y. P. L.   July 24, 1918.

NL 0376863   NN

          Lindau,   Paul. 1839–1919.
          Ungeratene Kinder. Lustspiel in vier Aufzügen.
          Leipzig. Reclam. [1907.] 88 pp. Diagrams. [Universal-Bi-
          bliothek. 4893.] 16°.

NL 0376864   MB OU

          Lindau, Paul, 1839–1919.
          Unter den linden.   In
          The great streets of the world, by ....
          Richard Harding Davis, Andrew Lang... [& others]
          illus. by A.B. Frost, W.Douglas Almond...
          & others   N.Y., C.Scribner's sons, 1892.
          p. 175–210.

NL 0376865   OC1

832.08 **Lindau, Paul,** 1839–1919.
D763   Die Venus von Milo; Schauspiel in einem
v.39   Aufzuge.   Leipzig, B.G.Teubner, 1895.
          52p. 20cm.

          Bound with Der Herr Director, von M.
          Schacht.

          1.Praxiteles, 4th cent.B.C. – Drama.

NL 0376866   CLSU

          Lindau, Paul, 1839–1919.
          Die Venus von Milo. Schauspiel in einem auf-
          zuge. Von Paul Lindau. Breslau, Schlesische
          buchdruckerei, kunst- und verlags-anatalt v. S.
          Schottlaender; New York, Gustav E. Stechert
          [etc., etc.] 1897.
             115 p.   20 x 10^{cm}

          1. Venus of Melos—Drama.

NL 0376867   ViU

          Lindau,   Paul. 1839–1919.
          Die Venus von Milo. Schauspiel in einem Aufzug.
          — Leipzig. Reclam. [1910.] 44 pp. [Universal-Bibliothek. 5205.]
          14½ cm., in 8s.

NL 0376868   MB

ar V   **Lindau, Paul,** 1839–1919.
10962   Vergnügungsreisen; gelegentliche Auf-
          zeichnungen.   Stuttgart, C. F. Simon,
          1875.
             228 p. 15cm.

NL 0376869   NIC PPG

          Lindau, Paul, 1839–1919.
          Verschamte arbeit; schauspiel in drei
          aufzugen.   Berlin, Freund, 1881.
          109p.

NL 0376870   OC1W PU

          LINDAU, PAUL, 1839–1919.
          Vorspiele auf dem Theater. Dramaturgische Skizzen von
          Paul Lindau. Dresden: A. Hauschild, 1895. 210 p. 8°.

          569921A. 1. Stage.

NL 0376871   NN

PN2641 **Lindau, Paul,** 1839–1919.
.L55   Vorspiele auf dem Theater; dramaturgische
          Skizzen. Dresden, Verlag des Universum,
          1895.
          210p. 19cm.

          1.Theater – Germany. 2.Theater – France.

NL 0376872   NcU CLSU InU

          Lindau, Paul, 1839–1919
          Vorspiele auf dem Theater; dramaturgische Skizzen.
          Leipzig, Reclam [1895?]

          210 p.

NL 0376873   MH

          Lindau, Paul, 1839–1919.
          Wie ein lustspiel entsteht und vergeht.
          Berlin, Grote, 1876. 76p., illus.

NL 0376874   OC1W

          Lindau, Paul, 1839–1919.
          Wunderliche leute. Kleine erzählungen.
          Breslau. 1888. D.

NL 0376875   CU PPL

VOLUME 334

Lindau, Paul, 1839–1919.
　Der zug nach den westen, roman ...
7. aufl.　Berlin, W.Spemann [n.d.]

　　396p.　20cm.　(Berlin. I)

NL 0376876　ScU CLSU

872
L741
s
　Lindau, Paul, 1839–1919.
　　Der zug nach dem westen; roman, von Paul
Lindau.　Berlin und Stuttgart, W. Spemann
[1886]
　　4 p.l., 396 p.　20cm (Added t.-p.: Berlin,
romane von Paul Lindau, I)

NL 0376877　CU CtY

---

ar V
10970
　Lindau, Paul, 1839–1919.
　　Der Zug nach Westen; Roman. 9. Aufl.
Stuttgart, J. G. Cotta Nachfolger, 1898.
　　396 p. 19cm.　(His Romane, 1)

NL 0376878　NIC

　Lindau, Paul, 1839–1919.
　　Der zug nach dem westen; roman ... 10. aufl.
Stuttgart, 1903.

NL 0376879　NjP

Lindau, Paul, 1839–1919.
　Der Zug nach dem Westen; Roman. Stuttgart: J. G. Cotta'sche Bhdlg. Nachf., 1908. 2 p.l., 396 p. 11. ed. 12°.

NL 0376880　NN PSC OU IdU

　Lindau, Paul, 1839–1919.
　Der Zug nach dem Westen. Roman von Paul Lindau. 12. Auflage.
＝ Stuttgart. Cotta. 1912. (4), 396 pp. [Berlin. Romane. I.]
19.5 cm., in 8s.

NL 0376881　MB

PT2423 Lindau, Paul, 1839–1919.
.L7Z74 Der zug nach dem westen; roman von Paul Lindau.
1919 13.–15. aufl. Stuttgart und Berlin, Cotta, 1919.
　[3], 396 p. 19cm. (Added t.-p.: Berlin, romane von Paul Lindau, I)

NL 0376882　ICU

Lindau, Paul, 1839–1919.
　Der Zug nach dem Westen.　Stuttgart: J. G. Cotta'sche
Buchhandlung Nachfolger, 1921.　396 p.　12°.　(Berlin, 1.)

NL 0376883　NN WU MB MH

Lindau, Rodolphe, 1829–1900.
　　see Lindau, Rudolf, 1829–1900.

Lindau, Rudolf.
　Franz Mehring zu seinem 100. Geburtstag am 27. Februar
1946. Berlin, Einheit [1946]
　14 p. 21 cm.

1. Mehring, Franz, 1846–1919.

HX273.L65　　　　　　　　　　　　　A F 48–2272*

Wisconsin. Univ. Libr.
for Library of Congress　　[1]†

NL 0376885　WU DLC NN

Lindau, Rudolf.
　Probleme der Geschichte der deutschen Arbeiterbewe-
gung. Berlin, Dietz [1947]
　62 p. 21 cm.

　"Die überarbeitete Niederschrift eines Vortrages, den der verfasser vor leitenden Funktionären der Sozialistischen Einheitspartei
Deutschlands in Chemnitz und Schwerin gehalten hat."

1. Socialism in Germany. 2. Trade-unions—Germany—Hist.
I. Title.

HX273.L653　　　　　　　　　　　　49–15076*

NL 0376886　DLC CSt-H

Lindau, Rudolf.
　Zwei Parteien, zwei Wege, zwei Welten. Zum 40. Jahres-
tag der Formierung der Bolschewiki zu einer selbständigen
Partei. Berlin, Verlag Kultur und Fortschritt, 1952.
　22 p. 21 cm. (Vorträge im Haus der Kultur der Sowjetunion,
Berlin)

1. Rossiĭskaia sot͡sial-demokraticheskaia rabochaia partii͡a.
2. Kommunisticheskai͡a partii͡a Sovetskogo Soi͡uza. I. Title.

JN6598.R6L49　　　　　　　　　　56–42385 ‡

NL 0376887　DLC WU MH NIC

[Lindau, Rudolph,] of Dresden, and W. A. Lindau.
　Merkwürdigkeiten Dresdens und der Umgegend. Ein
Taschenbuch für Fremde und Einheimische, nach W. A. Lindau's
topographischen Werken bearbeitet, mit einer neuen Beschreibung der Sammlungen für Wissenschaft und Kunst. Zweite...
verbesserte und viel vermehrte Auflage...　Dresden: in der
Arnoldischen Buchhandlung. 1829.　viii p., 1 l., 216 p.　front.
(fold. map)　24°.

　First edition appeared in 1826.

1. Dresden.—Description. 2. Lin-　　dau, Wilhelm Adolf, 1779–1849.
jt. au. 3. Title.
N. Y. P. L.　　　　　　　　　　　December 3, 1915.

NL 0376888　NN MH

Lindau, Rudolph, of Dresden, and W. A. Lindau.
　Merkwürdigkeiten Dresdens und der Umgegend, mit einer
neuen Beschreibung aller Sammlungen für Wissenschaft und
Kunst. Ein Taschenbuch für Fremde und Einheimische, von
Rudolph und Wilhelm Adolph Lindau. Vierte, sehr verbesserte
Auflage besorgt von J. G. Wiemann...　Dresden: In der Arnol-
dischen Buchhandlung, 1835.　viii p., 1 l., 407(1) p.　fold. front.,
2 fold. maps.　24°.

　First edition appeared in 1826.

1. Dresden.—Description. 2. Lindau,　Wilhelm Adolf, 1779–1849, jt. au.
3. Wiemann, J. G., editor. 4. Title.
N. Y. P. L.　　　　　　　　　　　December 2, 1915.

NL 0376889　NN CtY

Lindau, Rudolf, of Dresden.
　Die walachei und moldau.
Dresden u. Leipzig, 1849.
　12mo.

NL 0376890　NN

Lindau, Rudolf, 1829–1910.
　Alte Geschichten.
— Berlin. Fleischel & Co. 1904. (5), 288 pp. 16°.
　Contents. — Ein Wiedersehen. — Hans der Träumer. — Yadest. — Nelly
Delano. — Der Kapitän der 'Santa Junta.' — Der Abend. — Die Geschichte
des Negerfürsten Mioko Koango.

NL 0376891　MB

Lindau, Rudolf, 1829–1910.
　Auf der Fahrt. Kurze Erzählungen von Rudolph Lindau.
Berlin: F. & P. Lehmann, 1886.　254 p.　12°.

　Contents: Einleitung: Die Reisegefährten. Nelly Delano. Der Kapitän der
Santa Junta. Des Kapitäns Brautfahrt. Der Geächtete. John Bridges' Braut. Ver-
lorenes Mühen. Mutter Careys Küchlein. Fred. Sedschi. Der Hafenmeister. Erste
Liebe.

277368A. 1. Fiction, German. 2. Title.
N. Y. P. L.　　　　　　　　　　　February 1, 1927.

NL 0376892　NN

---

ar V
10956
　Lindau, Rudolf, 1829–1910.
　　Auf der Fahrt; kurze Erzählungen.
Berlin, F. Fontane, 1892.
　　254 p. 19cm.

　　Imprint from label mounted on t. p.

NL 0376893　NIC

D87
I5
　Lindau, Rudolf, 1829–1910.
　　Aus China und Japan; Reise-Erinnerungen.
Berlin, F. Fontane, 1896.
　　402+ p.

　　Imperfect: all after p.402 wanting.

1. Asia - Descr. & trav.

NL 0376894　CU NIC CtY

PT
2424
L2
A15
1926
　Lindau, Rudolf, 1829–1910
　　Ausgewählte Erzählungen. [Vorwort von Hans
Lindau] Berlin, Volksverband der Bücher-
freunde [1926]
　　467p. illus. 19cm.

NL 0376895　WU

[Lindau, Rudolf] 1829–1900.
　Le chemin de fer du Pacifique.　N.p.,n.pub.,
[1869]
　2v.,26cm.

　Caption title
　Rev.des deux mondes.

NL 0376896　CaBViPA CaBViP

PT
2424
L2
E6
　Lindau, Rudolf, 1829–1900
　　Erzählungen aus dem Osten. Berlin,
Buchverlag fürs Deutsche Haus, 1909.
　　285p. 18cm. (Die Bücher des Deutschen
Hauses, 4 Reihe, Bd. 98)

NL 0376897　WU MoSW

Lindau, Rudolf, 1829–1910.
　Erzählungen eines effendi. Ber.,
Fontane, 1896.
　　184 p.

NL 0376898　PBm

VOLUME 334

Lindau, Rudolf, 1829–1910.
... Erzählungen und novellen von Rudolf Lindau ... I.
Chicago, L. Schick ₁1885₎
2 p. l., 79 p., 1 l., ₁5₎–36 p., 1 l., ₁5₎–9 p. 19ᶜᵐ. (Collection Schick, no. 1)
CONTENTS.—Hans der träumer.—Verlorenes mühen.—Erste liebe.
No more published?

Library of Congress   PT1337.S4   17–10015

NL 0376899   DLC PU MiU

Lindau, Rudolf, 1829–1910.
Der Fanar und Mayfair. Roman, von Dudolf Lindau.
Berlin, F. Fontane & co., 1898.
2 p. l., 396 p. 18½ᶜᵐ.

I. Title.
1–19378
Library of Congress   PT2424.L2F3 1898

NL 0376900   DLC

---

ar V   **Lindau, Rudol** , 1829–1910.
10957   Der Gast. Breslau, S. Schottlaender,
1883.
256 p. 19cm.

NL 0376901   NIC PPG

LINDAU, Rudolf, 1829–1910.
Gesammelte Romane und Novellen. Berlin,
F. Fontane & Co., ₁1893₎.

19 cm. Port.
Half-title: Gesammelte Schriften, 6.
Contents: Zwei Seelen. Der Gast.

NL 0376902   MH

Lindau, Rudolf, 1829–1910
Gesammelte romane und novellen. Ber. 1904.
6v. 1 front. (por. v. 6) 20cm.
Contents.
v. 1. Im park von Villers.—Gordon Baldwin.—Das rote
tuch.—Verkehrtes leben.
v. 2. Gute gesellschaft.—Souvenir.—Tödliche fehde.
v. 3. Robert Ashton.—Das glückspendel.
v. 4. Die kleine welt.—Lebensmüde.—Liquidirt.—Der
seher.—Treu bis in den tod.
v. 5. Reisegefährten.
v. 6. Zwei seelen.—Der gast.

NL 0376903   CU OOxM OrP OC1W

PT   **Lindau, Rudolf,** 1829–1910
2424   Das Glückspendel; und, Der Gast. Novellen.
L2   Berlin, Buchverlag fürs Deutsche Haus, 1909.
G55   270p. 18cm. (Die Bücher des Deutschen
Hauses, 5. Reihe, Bd. 103)

NL 0376904   WU

Lindau, Rudolf, 1829–1910.
Gordon Baldwin; Novelle. Berlin, Gebrüder
Paetel, 1878.

NL 0376905   MH NIC

Lindau, Rudolf, 1829–1910.
... Gordon Baldwin, and The Philosopher's pendulum. By
Rudolph Lindau. New York, D. Appleton and company,
1878.
163 p. 16½ᶜᵐ. (Appletons' new handy-volume series ₁v. 4₎)

I. Title. II. Title: The philosopher's pendulum.

Library of Congress   PZ3.L642G   7–19016

NL 0376906   DLC PPL

Lindau, Rudolf, 1829–1910
Gute Gesellschaft.   Roman

2 vols. in 1. B. Breslad. 1579

NL 0376907   OC1W

---

arV   **Lindau, Rudolf,** 1829–1910.
10953   Gute Gesellschaft. 2. Aufl. Breslau,
S. Schottlaender, 1883.
303 p. 19cm.

NL 0376908   NIC

Lindau, Rudolf, 1829–1910.
Japan. Eene reisbeschrijving door Rodolphe Lindau. Leyden, Breuk & Smits, 1865.
vii, 264 p. 23ᶜᵐ.
Engr. t.-p.

1. Japan—Descr. & trav.   I. Title.
4–29660
Library of Congress   DS809.L74

NL 0376909   DLC

Lindau, Rudolf, 1829–1910.
Die kleine welt; drei novellen von Rudolph Lindau. Die kleine
welt. Ein verkehrtes leben. Der seher. Berlin, gebrüder Paetel,
1880.
pp. 316.

NL 0376910   MH PPG

Lindau, Rudolf, 1829–1910
Die kleine welt. (in Heyse, Paul,
ed. Neuere deutscher novellenschatz.
1884–1887. v. 7, p. ₁161₎–252.)

NL 0376911   OU OC1W

Lindau, Rudolf, 1829–1910.
Der lange Holländer.

(Gartenlaube, 1887)

NL 0376912   PPG

Lindau, Rudolf, 1829–1910.
Der lange Holländer [and other stories]. Von Rudolph Lindau.
Berlin, F. & P. Lehmann, 1889.
pp. (7), 227.

NL 0376913   MH PPL

Lindau, Rudolf, 1829–
Liebesheiraten, roman. Berlin, F.
Fontane & co., 1894.

2 p. l., 201 p. 20cm.

NL 0376914   FU CtY

Lindau, Rudolf, 1829–1910.
... Liquidated, and The seer. By Rudolph Lindau ...
New York, D. Appleton and company, 1878.
179 p. 16½ᶜᵐ. (Appletons' new handy-volume series ₁v. 15₎)

Library of Congress   PZ3.L642L   7–19018†

NL 0376915   DLC PPL MB

Lindau, Rudolf, 1829–1910.
Liquidirt. Novelle von Rudolph Lindau. Stuttgart
und Leipzig, E. Hallberger, 1877.
2 p. l., 206 p. 19ᶜᵐ.

9–408

NL 0376916   DLC NIC OC1W

Lindau, Rudolf, 1829–1910.
Liquidirt. Novelle von Rudolph Lindau. Stuttgart:
Deutsche Verlags-Anstalt₁, 1880₎. 2. ed. 206 p. 12°.

236261A. 1. Fiction, German.   2. Title.
N. Y. P. L.   June 28, 1926

NL 0376917   NN

Lindau, Rudolf, 1829–1910.
Martha. Roman af Rudolf Lindau ... Christiania,
R. Hviids enkes bogtrykkeri, 1892.
332 p. 16ᶜᵐ. ₁With Dickens, Mary A. Selma Malet. Christiania, 1891₎
"'Morgenbladets' føljeton."

I. Title.
17–11950
Library of Congress   PT8961.D5S4

NL 0376918   DLC

Lindau, Rudolf, 1829–1910.

Masterpieces of German fiction. Chicago, L. Schick ₁*1890₎

Lindau, Rudolf, 1829–1910.

Masterpieces of German fiction. ₁Golden-rod ed.₎ From
the German of Rudolph Lindau, Fanny Lewald, Ernst
Eckstein, Adolph Wilbrandt, Paul Heyse and Hans
Hopfen. Chicago, Laird & Lee ₁*1895₎

PT   **Lindau, Rudolf,** 1829–1910
2424   Morgenland und Abendland. Mit einer Einlei-
L2   tung von Wilhelm Rath. Hamburg, Verlag der
M6   Deutschen Dichter-Gedächtnis-Stiftung ₁1917₎
133p. illus. 19cm. (Hausbücherei der
Deutschen Dichter-Gedächtnis-Stiftung, Bd. 59)

NL 0376921   WU

VOLUME 334

Lindau, Rudolf, 1829–1910.
Eine Nachlese, eigenes und fremdes.
Berlin, E. Fleischel, 1910.
290 p. 19 cm.

NL 0376922 CoU

Lindau, Rudolf, 1829–1910.
... Novellen und humoresken ... 1885
see under Wichert, Ernst, 1831–1902.

Lindau, Rudolph, 1829–1910. FOR OTHER EDITIONS
Auerbach, Berthold, 1812–1882. SEE MAIN ENTRY
... Novellen und humoresken von Berthold Auerbach,
J. J. Cremer, Rudolph Lindau und Ludwig Anzengruber
... Chicago, L. Schick [1886]

Lindau, Rudolf, 1829–1910.
... Novellen und skizzen von R. Lindau, A. Wilbrandt,
H. Lorm [pseud.], und H. Seidel ... Chicago, L. Schick [1886]
77 p., 1 l., [5]–41 p., 1 l., [5]–24 p., 1 l., [5]–12 p. 19ᶜᵐ. (Collection
Schick, no. 11)
CONTENTS.—Im park von Villers von Rudolph Lindau.—Am heiligen
damm von Adolph Wilbrandt.—Die philosophie eines kusses, von Hie-
ronymus Lorm [pseud.]—Der gute alte onkel, von Heinrich Seidel.

I. Wilbrandt, Adolph von, 1837–1911. II. Landesmann, Heinrich, 1821–
1902. III. Seidel, Heinrich, 1842–1906. IV. Title. V. Title: Im park von
Villers. VI. Title: Am heiligen damm. VII. Title: Die philosophie eines
kusses. VIII. Title: Der gute alte onkel. 17–20447 Revised

Library of Congress PT1337.S4 no. 11

NL 0376925 DLC CU OO

Lindau, Rudolf, 1829–1910.
Our little world. Tr. from the German of Rudolph Lindau, by Cornelia Day Wilder. St. Paul, Price, McGill
& co., 1889.
1 p. l., 149 p. 17½ᶜᵐ.

I. Wilder, Cornelia Day, tr.

Library of Congress PZ3.L642O 7–19017†

NL 0376926 DLC MnHi

Lindau, Rudolf, 1829–1910
Peines Perdues. Une liquidation.
Fred. Le Pendule Philosphique. Le Vision-
naire.
341 p. D. Paris. 1880.

NL 0376927 OC1W

Lindau, Rudolf, 1829–1910.
The philosopher's pendulum. A tale from Germany.
(In Tales from Blackwood. No. 19, pp. 160–204. Edinburgh.
[1879.]) 87.31

NL 0376928 MB OOxM

PT2424 Lindau, Rudolf, 1829–1910.
L2Z3 The philosopher's pendulum, and other stories. Edinburgh.
1883 W. Blackwood, 1883.
322 p.

CONTENTS. – The philosopher's pendulum: a tale from Germany. –
Gordon Baldwin. – Weariness: a tale from France. – The seer: a
tale. – "Fred": a tale from Japan.

NL 0376929 CU

4DC Lindau, Rudolph.
.933 Die preussische Garde im Feldzuge 1870–71.
Berlin, E. S. Mittler, 1872.
147 p.

NL 0376930 DLC-P4 TNJ NIC

LINDAU, Rudolf, 1829–1910.
Reisegefährten; novellen. Neue ausgabe.
Berlin, F. Fontane & co., 1894.

NL 0376931 MH

---

ar V Lindau, Rudolf, 1829–1910.
10951 Robert Ashton; Roman. 2. Aufl. Stuttgart, E. Hallberger, 1879.
2 v. in 1. 18cm.

NL 0376932 NIC

Lindau, Rudolf,
Schiffbruch; Novellen Stuttg.
Lpz., Hallberger, 1877.

231 s.

NL 0376933 PPG

---

ar V Lindau, Rudolf, 1829–1910.
10950 Schiffbruch; Novellen-Cyklus. 2. Aufl.
Stuttgart, E. Hallberger, 1880.
231 p. 19cm.

NL 0376934 NIC

PT2424 Lindau, Rudolf, 1829–1910.
.L2S4 Schweigen; neue novellen von Rudolf Lindau. 2. aufl.
1895 Berlin, F. Fontane & co., 1895.
[5], 128 p. 19½ᶜᵐ.
CONTENTS.—Schweigen.—Der hamal.—Ein ganzes leben.

NL 0376935 ICU

Lindau, Rudolf, 1829–1910. The Seer. 24 pp.
(Blackwood's Mag. v. 129, 1881, p. 78.)

NL 0376936 MdBP

Lindau, Rudolf, 1829–1910.
... Stories and novels, from the German of Rudolf Lindau ... Chicago, L. Schick [1885]
94 p., 1 l., [5]–42 p., 1 l., [5]–10, [2] p. 19ᶜᵐ. (Overland library. no. 1)
CONTENTS.—Hans, the dreamer.—All in vain.—First love.

Library of Congress PZ3.L642S 7–19015†

NL 0376937 DLC NN

Lindau, Rudolf, 1829–1910.
Toedtliche Fehde. 23 pp.
(In Novellen und Humoresken. Chicago. [1885.])

NL 0376938 MB PPG

Lindau, Rudolf, 1829–1910.
Türkische geschichten. Berlin, F. Fontane & co., 1897.
3 p. l., 488 p. 12°.

CONTENTS.—Der grüne schleier.—Der klageschrei.—Die weisse hand.—
Die schöne Dschanfeda.—Gülmes wesir.—Der Sebildschi.—Der verlorene
freund. — Tiffli Külchan bey. — Der Hüledschi. — Die prinzessin Djevherli
Hanum.—Der kluge Toros Agha.—Der goldene reif.

1–19379

NL 0376939 DLC PPL MB

Lindau, Rudolf, 1829–1910.
Ein unglückliches Volk. Roman. Berlin,
F. Fontane, 1903.
2v. 19cm.

NL 0376940 TNJ MH InU

Lindau, Rudolf, 1829–1910
Verlorenes Mühen, und andere Novellen. Chicago,
Laird [191–?]
1 v. illus. 18 cm.

NL 0376941 NjP

PT Lindau, Rudolf, 1829–1910
2424 Vier Novellen und Erzählungen. Berlin,
.L2 Paetel, 1878.
Z7 242p. 19cm.
1878
Contents.– Das rothe Tuch.– Tödtliche Fehde.–
Nach der Niederlage.– Robert E. Cooper jun.

NL 0376942 TNJ OC1W

Lindau, Rudolf, 1829–1910.
Un voyage autour du Japon par Rodolphe Lindau. Pa-
ris, Hachette et cie., 1864.
2 p. l., 315 p. 19ᶜᵐ.
"Récits publiés une première fois dans la Revue des deux mondes."—
Introd.

1. Japan—Descr. & trav.

1–F–3646
Library of Congress DS809.L75

NL 0376943 DLC DCU-H CU FTaSU

---

ar V Lindau, Rudolf, 1829–1910.
10948 Wintertage; drei Erzählungen aus Frankreich. Breslau, S. Schottlaender, 1883.
324 p. 19cm.

NL 0376944 NIC NN

DR Lindau, Rudolf, 1829–1910
427 Zwei Reisen in der Türkei. Berlin, F.
L5 Fontane, 1899.
146p. 21cm.

1. Turkey – Descr. & trav. I. Title

NL 0376945 WU

VOLUME 334

PT
2423
.L3V3
Lindau, Rudolf, 1829-1910.
Zwei Seelen.   Stuttgart, Deutsche Verl.
Anst. [n.d.]
237-423 p.
Bound with Lewald-Stahr, Fanny, 1811-1889.
Vater und Sohn. Stuttgart, Deutsche Verl.
Anst., n.d.

NL 0376946   NBuU

4PT
Ger
6420
Lindau, Rudolf, 1829- 1910.
Zwei Seelen; Roman. Stuttgart,
Deutsche Verlags-Anstalt, 1888.
268 p.

NL 0376947   DLC-P4 NIC

Lindau, Rudolf, 1829-1910.
Zwei Seelen ...   New York, George Munro,
1889.
25 p.   [Die deutsche library, no. 216]

NL 0376948   DLC

Lindau, Rudolph, 1829-1910
see   Lindau, Rudolf, 1829-1910.

PT
2424
.L3
A58
Lindau, Wilhelm Adolf, 1774-1849
Adolar. Von dem Verfasser des Romans:
Heliodora. Freyburg, Craz, 1802.
2v. 18cm.

NL 0376950   TNJ

Soc
DC
236.7
D8
L56
Lindau, Wilhelm Adolf, 1774-1849.
Darstellung der Ereignisse in Dresden,
im Jahr 1813. Von einem Augenzeugen.
Dresden, Arnold, 1816.
272p.

Half-title: Napoleons Feldzug in
Sachsen im Jahr 1813; Ergänzungsband.
Attributed to Wilhelm Adolf Lindau.-
cf. Brit. Mus.

NL 0376951   FTaSU

PT 2424 LINDAU,WILHELM ADOLF,1774-1849
.L3 E3   Eduard; ein romantisches Gemählde, nach
Walter Scott's Waverley bearb. von W.A. Lindau.
Dresden, In der Arnoldischen Buchhandlung, 1821-
1822.
3 v.

I. Scott, Sir Walter, bart.,1771-1832.

NL 0376952   InU

PT 2424 LINDAU,WILHELM ADOLF,1774-1849
.L3 E7   Erminia, die Einsiedlerin unter Roma's
Ruinen, von dem Verfasser der Heliodora. Meissen, K. F. W. Erbstein, 1800.
235 p.

NL 0376953   InU

Lindau, Wilhelm Adolf, 1774-1849, tr.

Hunter, John Dunn, 1798?-1827.
Der gefangene unter den wilden in Nord-Amerika; nach
J. D. Hunter's Denkwürdikeiten seines aufenthalts unter den-
selben und seiner schilderung des charakters und der sitten der
westlich vom Mississippi wohnenden stämme, hrsg. von W. A.
Lindau ... Dresden, P. G. Hilscher ¡Meissen gedruckt¡ 1824.

Lindau, Wilhelm Adolf, 1774-1849.
Гелиодора; или, Гречанка, играющая на лютнѣ. Переводъ съ нѣмецкаго. Москва, Въ Тип. Лазаревыхъ ин-та
восточныхъ языковъ, 18
v. 18cm.

ɪ. Title.   *Title transliterated: Geliodora.*

PT2424.L3G48   56-50183

NL 0376955   DLC

Lindau, Wilhelm Adolf, 1774-1849, tr.

Morier, James Justinian, 1780?-1849.
Hadschi Baba's abenteuer. Herausgegeben von Jakob Mo-
rier. Aus dem englischen übersetzt von Rudolf Wald ¡pseud.¡
... Leipzig, Rein, 1824.

Lindau, W[ilhelm] A[dolf] 1774-1849.
Heldengemählde aus der Vorzeit der
europäischen Völker.   Leipzig, C. Cnobloch,
1817.
2 p.l., 242 p. 16°.

NL 0376957   NN

S833.6
L74h
v.1-3
Lindau, Wilhelm Adolf, 1774-1849
Heliodora, oder die Lautenspielerin aus
Griechenland. Meissen, bey K. A. W.
Erbstein, 1800.
3v. in 1. fronts. 17cm.

NL 0376958   TNJ

Lindau, Wilhelm Adolf, tr.
Leben und sitte in Persien
see under Malcolm, Sir John, 1769-1833.

[Lindau, Wilhelm Adolf, 1774-1849]
Mährchen, hrsg. von dem Verfassers des Romans Heliodora.
Görlitz, 1805.

NL 0376960   MH

Lindau, Wilhelm Adolf, 1774-1849, ed. & tr.
Napoleon auf dem Bellerophon
see under Maitland, Sir Frederick Lewis,
1777-1839.

DD
901
.D76
L56
1824
Lindau, Wilhelm Adolf, 1774-1849
Neues Gemählde von Dresden, in Hinsicht
auf Geschichte, Oertlichkeit, Kultur, Kunst
und Gewerbe, von W. A. Lindau. 3. Aufl.
Dresden, Arnold, 1824.
xx, 364p. map. 18cm. (His Dresden und
die Umgegend, 1)

1. Dresden - History. I. Title.

NL 0376962   TNJ

Lindau, Wilhelm Adolf, 1774-1849, tr.

Cunningham, Allan, 1784-1842.
Paul Jones. Historischer roman von Allan Cunningham. Aus dem englischen übersetzt von Wilhelm Adolf
Lindau ... Dresden und Leipzig, Arnoldische buchhandlung, 1842.

PT 2424
.L3 P6
Lindau, Wilhelm Adolf, 1774-1849
Die Pilgerinnen; ein Roman von dem Verfasser
der Heliodora. Meissen, F. W. Goedsche, 1812.
238 p.

NL 0376964   InU

¡Lindau, Wilhelm Adolf¡ 1774-1849.
Portugiesische sprachlehre; eine vollständige und fassliche
anweisung zur erlernung der portugiesischen sprache, für schulen und zum selbstunterricht bearb. von Joseph Aldoni ¡pseud.¡
Leipzig, J. C. Hinrichs, 1813.
iv. ¡vii¡-x, 186, ¡2¡ p. 22¼ᵐ.

1. Portuguese language—Grammar. ɪ. Title.

34-4802

Library of Congress   PC5067.L5   469.5

NL 0376965   DLC MBAt ICU

PT2424
.L3R7
1889
¡Lindau¡ Wilhelm Adolf¡ 1774-1849.
Romantische Geschichten. Vom Verfasser des
Romans: Heliodora. Leipzig, C. E. Kollmann,
1819.
262 p.

NL 0376966   ICU

BR333 ¡Lindau, Wilhelm Adolph¡ 1774-1849, *comp.*
.L74   Stimmen aus drei jahrhunderten über Luther und sein
werk ... Dresden, Arnold, 1817.
xii, 180 p. front. (port.) 1 illus. 20¼ᵐ.
Introductory remarks signed: W. A. Lindau.

1. Luther, Martin, 1483-1546.

NL 0376967   ICU OClW

Lindau, Ger. Evangelisch-Lutherische Kirche
see   Evangelisch-Lutherische Kirche in
Lindau.

Lindau, Ger. (Bavaria) Sankt-Marien
(Reichsstift)
see   Lindau (Reichsstift)

VOLUME 334

Lindau, Ger. (Bavaria) (City) Psychotherapiewoche
see
Lindauer Psychotherapiewoche.

Lindau, Ger. (Bavaria)(City) Stadtmuseum.
Kostbarkeiten aus dem Stadtmuseum zu Lindau [bearb. von W.Ricklinger] Lindau im Bodensee, 1951

[32] p. illus.

NL 0376971   MH

Lindau, Ger. (Bavaria)(City) Stadtmuseum.
Das Lindauer Heimatmuseum, von Hans Jordan und Karl Gröber. Augsburg: Dr. B. Filser Verlag G.m.b.H. [1932] 54 p. facsims., illus. (incl. plans), plates, ports. 23cm. (Führer durch die bayerischen Orts- und Heimatmuseen. Bd. 2.)

1. Museums, Historical—Germany industries and trade—Germany— Hans, curator. II. Gröber, Karl, N.Y.P.L. —Lindau am Bodensee. 2. Art Lindau am Bodensee. I. Jordan, 1885-   . III. Ser. November 15, 1937

NL 0376972   NN DDO DLC-P4

Lindau, Ger.(Bavaria)(City) Stadtmuseum.
Möbel und Edles Gerät aus dem Stadtmuseum zu Lindau. [Bearb. von W.Ricklinger] Lindau im Bodensee, 1951

[32] p. illus.

NL 0376973   MH

Lindau (Reichsstift)
Extorquierte apologia eines befürsten frey-weltlich-adelichen IX hundert jahr allbereith in der insul Lindau stehenden reichs-stifft gleichen names...
see under title

Lindau im Bodensee
see   Lindau, Ger. (Bavaria)

Lindauer, Gottfried, 1839-1926.

Cowan, James, 1870-
Maori biographies. Sketches of old New Zealand. Compiled by James Cowan. Descriptive catalogue of Maori portraits painted by Herr G. Lindauer. Auckland, Printed for H. E. Partridge by the Brett printing and publishing company, limited, 1901.

DU423 .C74

Lindauer, Gottfried, 1839-1926.

Cowan, James, 1870-1943.
Pictures of old New Zealand; the Partridge collection of Maori paintings by Gottfried Lindauer. Described by James Cowan. Auckland, London [etc.] Whitcombe & Tombs limited [1930]

TN 665 L5

Lindauer, Gustav
Compendium der Hütten-Chemie mit besonderer Anwendung auf die Metallurgie des Eisens. Zunächst für Hüttenmänner zum Selbststudium, wie auch zur Benützung an montanistischen Lehranstalten. Prag, K. André, 1861.
488p. 23cm.

1. Metallurgy 2. Chemistry, Physical and theoretical 3. Iron - Metallurgy I. Title

NL 0376978   WU NN CtY

[LINDAUER, Jos.]
Unterstützung des breviers welches Louis Carson Dechent de la paroisse de Lünemonde 1779 herausgegeben hat, mit einem anhange von minderung oder gänzlicher aufhebung mehrerer kirchengesetze. [München, Crätz], 1782.

NL 0376979   MH

017.4 L64

Lindauer, Joseph.
Bücher-verzeichniss der Joseph Lindauer'schen leihbibliothek... München, 1825.

616 p.   19cm.

1.Catalogs, Booksellers' of Germany. I. Title.

NL 0376980   MnU

LINDAUER, JOSEPH, fl. 1889.
De Polybii vocabulis militaribus. Monachii, 1889.

54 p.
Inaug.-Diss. - Erlangen.

NL 0376981   DDO ICRL IU MH NjP CU

Lindauer, Louis, 1896-
Forms & procedure in matrimonial cases, a desk book for lawyers, law clerks & law students. [Brooklyn? 1948]
145 p. 2 fold. tables (in pocket) 24 cm.

1. Divorce—New York (City)—Forms.

48-20802*

NL 0376982   DLC FU-L ICU

LINDAUER, MICHAEL, printer, Munich.
Druck- und Schrift-Proben der Buchdruckerei von Michael Lindauer in München. [München] 1825.
[37]l. 26cm.

NL 0376983   ICN

Lindauer Psychotherapiewoche.
Vorlesungen und Vorträge. [1.]- 1950-
Stuttgart, Hippokrates-Verlag.
v. 24 cm.

1. Psychotherapy—Addresses, essays, lectures.

RC480.L5   52-40099

NL 0376984   DLC DNLM

Linday, George N
The application of the law of virtual work to trusses and beams. Author [1925?].
59 p. diagrs.

Blueprint.

1.Girders. 2.Strains & stresses. 3.Trusses. I.Title.

NL 0376985   OrP

Linday, George N.
... Some points in bridge design. Effect on trusses and plate girders due to imperfect roller-support. [By] Geo. N. Linday ... [Chicago, Western society of engineers, °1904]
11 p. diagrs. 23ᵐᵐ.
Caption title.
Advance copy—subject to revision.
"Railway bridge calculation by end shear table, by Josiah Gibson": p. [7]-11.

1. Bridges—Design.   i. Gibson, Josiah.

Library of Congress   TG300.L74   6-42062†

NL 0376986   DLC

439.73 L64

Lindbäck, Erland.
Främmande ord i svenskan. Ordlista, texter, övningar för skolor och självstudier [av] Erland Lindbäck och Karl Johan Ulander.   Stockholm, Norstedt [1952]

vi, 147 p.   20cm.

1. Swedish language. Foreign words and phrases. I. Ulander, Karl Johan, jt. author.   II. Title.

NL 0376987   MnU

Lindbäck-Larsen, Odd, 1897-
6. divisjon, av oberst Odd Lindbäck-Larsen ... Oslo, Gyldendal, 1946.
180, [6] p. front., illus. (incl. ports.) maps. 24 x 18¼ᵐᵐ.

1. Norway. Hæren. 6. divisjon. 2. World war, 1939-1945—Regimental histories—Norway—6. divisjon. 3. World war, 1939-1945—Campaigns—Norway.

D763.N61 6th.L5   47-23496

NL 0376988   DLC NN MnU

Lindbäck-Larsen, Odd, 1897-
Skandinavias sikkerhet; bidrag til problemets belysning. Utarbeidet for Norges forsvarsforening av premierløitnant O. Lindbäck-Larsen... Oslo: B. Bentzens boktrykkeri, 1932.
56 p. illus. (charts.)   22½cm.
Cover-title.
CONTENTS.—Løste det danske forsvar sin opgave under verdenskrigen.—Omkring Danmarks forsvarsproblem.—Russland og Skandinavia.—Opbygningen av den finske hær.—Den militærpolitiske innstilling i Sverige.—Norges sikkerhet.—Sammenfatning.

691948A. I. Defence—Scandinavia.   I. Norges forsvarsforening. N.Y.P.L.   February 23, 1934

NL 0376989   NN

Lindbæk, Elise Aubert
see
Lindbæk, Lise, 1905-

VOLUME 334

LINDBAEK, Jannik.
   Dansk laesebog for folkehøjskolen. Udgivet af Foreningen for højskoler og
landbrugsskoler. V. udgave.   Odense, I
kommission hos Andelsbogtrykkeriet i
Odense, 1922.

   viii, 483 p.   23cm.

   1. Danish language. Chrestomathies and
readers. I. Foreningen for højskoler og
landbrugsskoler.

NL 0376991   MnU

Lindbaek, Johannes Peter, 1872–1919.

Catholic church. *Pope.*
   Acta pontificum danica; pavelige aktstykker vedrørende
Danmark 1316–1536 ... København, I kommission hos G. E. C.
Gad, 1904–15.

Lindbaek, Johannes Peter, 1872–1919, ed.

Selskabet for udgivelse af kilder til dansk historie, *Copen-*
hagen.
   Aktstykker og oplysninger til Statskollegiets historie
1660–1676. Udg. ved J. Lindbæk af Selskabet for udgivelse af kilder til dansk historie ...   Med understøttelse af Ministeriet for kirke- og undervisningsvæsenet.
København, I kommission hos G. E. C. Gad, 1903–

Lindbæk, Johannes Peter, 1872–1919.
   De danske Franciskanerklostre, udgivet med Understøttelse
af Carlsbergfondet. København: G. E. C. Gad, 1914.   2 p.l.,
311(1) p.   illus.   4°.

   Author's name at head of title.

1. Architecture (Ecclesiastical), Den-   mark. 2. Franciscans, Denmark.
3. Monasteries, Denmark. 4. Title.   March 30, 1915.
N. Y. P. L.

NL 0376994   NN MH CtY DHN

Lindbaek, Johannes Peter, 1872-1919.
   De danske helligaandsklostre; fremstilling og aktstykker, ved J. Lindbaek og G. Stemann. Udgivet med understøttelse af Carlsbergfondet. København, i komm. hos
G. E. C. Gad, 1906.

   221, xxxvi p.   illus.

   1. Monasteries – Denmark.
   1. Ospedalieri — Danimarca. — 2. Cavalieri dello Spirito Santo — 3.
Ospedali — Danimarca.   1. Stemann, Gustav Carl Vilhelm Heinrich,
1845–

NL 0376995   CtY MH

Lindbaek, Johannes Peter, 1872-1919.
   Forspillet til verdenskrigen; stormagtspolitik 1871–1914, af
Johs. Lindbæk. ｢København｣ H. Aschehoug & co., Kjøben-
havnskontoret, 1917.

   2 p. l., 237, ｢2｣ p.   22½ᶜᵐ.

   "Litteraturfortegnelse over de vigtigste af de benyttede værker":
｢2｣ p. at end.

   1. European war, 1914–1918—Causes. 2. Europe—Politics—1871–
1. Title.
   Library of Congress   D511.L45 1917   20—14357
                                ｢a35b1｣   940.3112

NL 0376996   DLC NN

Lindbæk, Johannes Peter, 1872–1919.
   Forspillet til verdenskrigen; stormagtspolitik 1871–1914, af
Johs. Lindbæk. ｢Kjøbenhavn｣ H. Aschehoug & co., Kjøben-
havnskontoret, 1917.

   2 p. l., 237, ｢10｣ p.   22½ᶜᵐ.

   "Andet oplag—2.–3. tusinde."
   "Litteraturfortegnelse over de vigtigste af de benyttede værker":
p. ｢239｣–｢240｣

   1. European war, 1914–1918—Causes. 2. Europe—Politics—1871–
1. Title.
                                                            36–31590
   Library of Congress   D511.L45   1917 a
                                ｢2｣   940.3112

NL 0376997   DLC

282
L64   Lindbaek, Johannes Peter, 1872–1919.
         Pavernes forhold til Danmark under
       kongerne Kristiern I og Hans.   København,
       I kommission hos G.E.C. Gad, 1907.

         308 p.   24cm.

         Thesis - Copenhagen.
         1. Papacy. Hist. 2. Catholic Church. Re-
       lations (Diplomatic) Denmark. 3. Christian
       I, king of Den-   mark, 1426–1481.
       4. Hans, king of   Denmark, 1455–1513.

NL 0376998   MnU ICRL

Lindbaek, Johannes Peter, 1872–1919.
   Statskollegiet og de danske Købstaeder.   (Dansk historisk
Forening.   Historisk Tidsskrift.   Kjøbenhavn, 1913.   8°.
Række 8, Bind 4. p. 132–146.)

   Til Edvard Holm paa hans 80-aarige Fødselsdag.

1. Cities—History, Denmark, 1661–75.
N. Y. P. L.   April 3, 1913.

NL 0376999   NN

Z
1014   Lindbaek, Johannes Peter, 1872–1919.
L74+   To bogfortegnelser fra det 16.
         aarhundredes begyndelse. Meddelte af
       Johs. Linbaek med oplysninger af Ellen
       Jørgensen.   Kjøbenhavn, I kommission
       hos Gyldendal, 1913.
         ｢307｣–334 p.   27cm.

         Detached from Danske magazin. 6.
       raekke, 1. bd., 4. hft.

         1. Bibliogr   aphy--Early printed
       books--16th   century--Catalogs.

NL 0377000   NIC

WM   **LINDBAEK, Lise, 1905–**
274   Alkoholisme kan helbredes;
L742a   Antabus hjælper til.   København,
1951   Nyt Nordisk Forlag, 1951.
            141 p.
            1. Alcoholism - Treatment
            2. Antabuse

NL 0377001   DNLM

Lindbæk, Lise, 1905–
   ...Bataljon Thälmann.   Oslo: Tiden norsk forlag ｢etc., etc.｣
1938.   224 p.   charts, facsims., plates.   24cm.

974066A.   1. Spain—Hist.—Civil   war, 1936–1939.
N. Y. P. L.   August 16, 1939

NL 0377002   NN

Lindbæk, Lise, 1905–
   F. N.; inntrykk og opplevelser fra Lake Success og Paris.
Oslo, Gyldendal, 1949.

   188 p.   22 cm.

   1. United Nations.
                                    Full name: Elise Aubert Lindbæk

   JX1977.L5   50–28637

NL 0377003   DLC NN OU NNC

Lindbæk, Lise, 1905–
   Jødene vender hjem, av Lise Lindbæk og Max Hodann.
Oslo, H. Aschehoug & co., 1935.

   213, ｢3｣ p. illus. (maps) plates (incl. port.) 23ᶜᵐ.

   1. Palestine—Descr. & trav. 2. Jews in Palestine. 3. Jews—Restora-
tion. 4. Jewish question.   i. Hodann, Max, 1894–   joint author. ii.
Title.
   Library of Congress   DS126.L5   35–38327

NL 0377004   DLC MH

Lindbæk, Lise, 1905–
   Spania og vi, med tegninger av Willy Midelfart. ｢Oslo｣
Dreyer ｢1946｣

   149 p. illus. 22 cm.

   1. Spain—Hist.—Civil War, 1936–1939—Personal narratives, Norwegian. 2. Norway—For. rel.—Spain. 3. Spain—For. rel.—Norway.
4. Spain—Hist.—Civil War, 1936–1939—Foreign participation—Norwegian.   i. Title.
                                    Full name: Elise Aubert Lindbæk.

   DP269.9.L55   49–13004*
                                    ｢1｣

NL 0377005   DLC NN

Lindbæk, Lise, 1905–
   Tisíc norských lodí; hrst příběhů o činnosti norského
námořnictva v druhé světové válce. ｢Z norského originálu
Tusend ｢sic｣ norske skip přeložila Nina Neklanová. 1. auto-
risované vyd.｣ Praha, Svoboda, 1948.

   213 p. 22 cm. (Knihovna Svoboda, sv. 37)

   1. World War, 1939–1945—Norway. 2. Merchant marine—Norway.
i. Title.
                                    Full name: Elise Aubert Lindbæk.

   D763.N6L512   50–56320

NL 0377006   DLC

Lindbæk, Lise, 1905–
   Tusen norska fartyg, en antologi över norska sjömäns insats
i det andra världskriget, av Lise Lindbæk; översättning av
Lisbeth och Louis Renner. Stockholm, A. Bonnier ｢1944｣

   206 p., 1 l. 22½ᶜᵐ.

   "Originalets title: Tusen norske skip."

   1. World war, 1939–1945—Norway. 2. Merchant marine—Norway.
i. Renner, Louis, tr. ii. Renner, Lisbeth, joint tr. iii. Title.
                                    ｢Full name: Elise Aubert Lindbæk｣
                                                         45–19610
   Library of Congress   D763.N6L52
                                ｢3｣   940.53481

NL 0377007   DLC

Lindbæk, Lise, 1905–
   Tusen norske skip, en antologi over norske sjøfolks innsats i
den annen verdenskrig, ved Lise Lindbæk. ｢New York, Norwegian shipping and trade mission, 1943｣

   263 p. 22½ᶜᵐ.

   "Første utgave."

   1. World war, 1939-   —Norway. 2. Merchant marine—Norway.
i. Norway. Norwegian shipping and trade mission. ii. Title.
                                    ｢Full name: Elise Aubert Lindbæk｣
                                                         44–45813
   Library of Congress   D763.N6L5

NL 0377008   DLC MiD OCl WaT OrU WaS

VOLUME 334

Lindbæk, Lise, 1905–

Tusen Norske skip, en antologi over Norske sjøfolks innsats I den annen verdenskrig. Arnesen pr. [1943]

NL 0377009 OrP

Lindbæk, Lise, 1905–
Tusen norske skip, en antologi over norske sjøfolks innsats i den annen verdenskrig, ved Lise Lindbæk. Oslo, Gyldendal norsk forlag, 1945.
213 p., 1 l. 24ᶜᵐ.
"I denne annenutgave ... er et par avsnitt tatt ut. Ellers er den i alt vesentlig et uforandret opptrykk av første."—Forord.
1. World war, 1939–1945—Norway. 2. Merchant marine—Norway. I. Title.
[Full name: Elise Aubert Lindbæk]
D763.N6L5 1945   47–18287

NL 0377010 DLC

Lindbæk, Lise, 1905–
Tusen norske skip; en antologi over norske sjøfolks innsats i den annen verdenskrig. Ny øket utg. Oslo, Gyldendal, 1948.
266 p. 24 cm.
1. World War, 1939–1945—Norway. 2. Merchant marine—Norway. I. Title.
Full name: Elise Aubert Lindbæk.
D763.N6L5 1948   49–14154*

NL 0377011 DLC

Lindbæk, Lise, 1905–
Vi var i Sovjet. Oslo, Falken forlag, 1951.
251 p. 19 cm.
1. Russia—Descr. & trav.—1945— I. Title.
DK28.L46   52–29406 ‡

NL 0377012 DLC NN NNC

Lindbæk, Sofie (Aubert) 1875–
Årgang 1875. Oslo, Tiden norsk forlag [1948]
188 p. illus., ports. 24 cm.
I. Title.
PT8950.L63A65   49–25309*

NL 0377013 DLC OC1

[Lindbaek, Sofie (Aubert)] 1875–
Fanny Ramm; fortaelling. Kristiania, H. Aschehoug & co., 1900.
210 p. 18cm.
Author's pseudonym, Sossen Aubert, at head of title.

NL 0377014 MnU

Lindbæk, *Fru* **Sofie (Aubert)** 1875–
... Fra det Norske selskabs kreds, et utvalg vers og breve. Kristiania, H. Aschehoug & co. (W. Nygaard) 1913.
3 p. l., 168 p. illus. 22½ᶜᵐ.   kr. 2.85

I. Title.

14 707

NL 0377015 DLC CU

Lindbæk, Fru Sofie (Aubert) 1875– ed.
Aubert, *Fru* **Elise Sofie (Aars)** 1837–1909.
Fra krinoline-tiden; Elise Auberts ungdomsbreve og dagbøker, ved Sofie Aubert Lindbæk. Kristiania, H. Aschehoug & co., 1921.

Lindbaek, Sofie (Aubert), 1875–
...Hjemmet pa Akershus. Aubertske papirer. Oslo, H. Aschehoug & co. (W. Nygaard), 1939.
345p. illus., ports., facsim.

NL 0377017 OC1

Lindbæk, Sophie (Aubert) 1875–
Hjemmet paa fæstningen. 1912.

NL 0377018 NdU

Lindbaek, Fru Sofie (Aubert) 1875–
Karl Johans Breutill Rikstathallaren Mören, 1816–1818.
Stockholm (Historiska Handlingar) Stockholm, 1935.

NL 0377019 IEN

LINDBÆK, Fru Sofie (Aubert), 1875–
Landflygtige; af Aubert'ske papirer. Kristiania, H. Aschehoug & Co., 1910.

Ports. and other illustr. Scan 2330.5

NL 0377020 MH

Lindbæk, Sofie (Aubert) 1875–
Nye tomter. Oslo, Tiden norsk forlag [1950]
167 p. ports. 24 cm.
"'Nye tomter' slutter seg på et vis til første bind av mine erindringer, 'Årgang 1875'—for så vidt som jeg er det nødvendige gjennomgangsledd."—Forord.
I. Title.
A 51–3853
Minnesota. Univ. Libr. for Library of Congress   [2]

NL 0377021 MnU OC1 NN

Lindbaek, Fru Sofie (Aubert) 1875– tr.
Heerfordt, Christian Frederik, 1871–
Om betydningen af et nordisk erhvervspolitisk samarbejde efter verdenskrigens ophør, af dr. C. F. Heerfordt. [København, 1918]

Lindbæk, Fru Sofie (Aubert) 1875– ed.

Aubert, Ludvig Mariboe Benjamin, 1838–1896.
En suss fra femti-aarene, L. M. B. Auberts dagbøker i utdrag ved Sofie Aubert Lindbæk. Kristiania, H. Aschehoug & co., 1922.

Lindbæk, Fru Sofie (Aubert) 1875– ed.

Mörner, Carl Carlsson, *greve,* 1755–1821.
... Stattholder Carl Mörners brev til Carl Johan, 1816–1818; utgitt av Sofie Aubert Lindbæk og Reidar Omang. Oslo, I kommisjon hos J. Dybwad, 1938.

Lindbæk, *Fru* **Sofie (Aubert)** 1875–
... Student. Kristiania, H. Aschehoug & co. (W. Nygaard) 1907.
2 p. l., 262 p. 19ᶜᵐ.

8–3662

NL 0377025 DLC

Lindbaeková, Lise
see **Lindbæk, Lise,** 1905–

Lindballe, Julius Emil.
Alvor og skæmt. Original. Faste og löse rim. Af Julius Emil Lindballe ... Ridgefield Park, N. J., Forfatterens forlag, 1905.
108 p., 1 l. front. (port.) 18ᶜᵐ.

5–32538

NL 0377027 DLC

S371.394
L64   **Lindbeck, Carl.**
Individualisering och koncentration i folkskolans undervisning inom klassens ram. Principiella spörsmal och metodiska linjer, av Carl Lindbeck... [Stockholm? Author, 1931]
32p. 19cm.
1. Teaching - Sweden. 2. Teaching - Elementary schools. 3. Individual instruction. I. Title.

NL 0377028 NNC-T

S370.1
L64   **Lindbeck, Carl.**
Växande liv och tynande, några ord till föräldrar, lärare och andra målsmän för ungdomen och dess fostran, av Carl Lindbeck. [Borlänge, Dalarnes tidnings- och boktryckeri, 1952]
92, [1]p. plates. 22cm.
1. Education - Theories and principles.

NL 0377029 NNC-T

VOLUME 334

Lindbeck, Clas.
Visro.   n. p. , n. d.
72 p.
"Tryckt i 300 exemplar. No. 241."

NL 0377030 MH

Lindbeck, H   T
How to care for brushes and get the most out of
them, by H.T. Lindbeck and Geo. Boardman Perry
... St. Louis, Mo., American painter and
decorator, c1938.
11 p.   illus.   (American painter and decorator. Reprint no. 106)
Wooster brush service manual, ed. by F. N.
Vanderwalker, bound in between p. 6 and 7.
1. Brooms and brushes. I. Title. II. Perry,
George Boardman.

NL 0377031 WaPS

Lindbeck, John M   H
Communist China and American Far Eastern policy;
₍based on an address made at Ohio State University on July
21, 1955. Washington₎ Dept. of State ₍1955₎
21 p. 22 x 10 cm. (₍U. S.₎ Dept. of State. Publication 6198. Far
Eastern series, 70)

1. East (Far East)—Politics. 2. U. S.—For. rel.—1945—
8. China—For. rel.—1949—   I. Title.

DS518.1.L5   *951.05   56-60247 ‡

NL 0377032 DLC NjP PPT PPD NIC DS WaU-L

Lindberg, A   F
... Nicaragua, the Central American
republic with a future, by A. F. Lindberg
... Boston, New York ₍etc.₎ The Bankers
publishing company ₍1920₎
cover-title,₍11₎ p. illus.(ports.)
24cm.
"Reprinted from the Bankers magazine,
New York, February, 1920."
1. Nicaragua-Econ. condit. I. Title.

NL 0377033 DS TxU

BX
6225   **Lindberg, Alfred E   1869-1941.**
.L5B5   Bibel-nyckeln. Utg. av Alfr. E. Lindberg.
2. uppl. ₍Worcester, Mass., 191-?₎
40 p. 15 cm.

1. Questions and answers--Theology. 2.
Bible--Text-books. I. Title.

NL 0377034 MnHi

BX
6225   **Lindberg, Alfred E   1869-1941.**
.L5K7   Kristendomsskolan. Utg. av Alfr. E.
Lindberg. Boston ₍1910₎
29 p. 21 cm.

1. Questions and answers--Theology. 2.
Bible--Text-books. I. Title.

NL 0377035 MnHi

Lindberg, Arne Olof, 1912-
Some recent changes in the vocabulary of the
Swedish language.   1951.
408 l.
Thesis - Ohio State University.

NL 0377036 OU

Lindberg, Arthur E
Education in the Virgin Islands.
Wash., 1932.

4 p.

NL 0377037 PP

LINDBERG, August, 1846-1916.
Barndoms- och ungdomsminnen. Stockholm, A.
Bonnier,₍1915₎.

24°. Front.(col.) and other illustr.
Scan 8547.120

NL 0377038 MH

927.92   Lindberg,   August , 1846-1916.
L742   Barndoms- och ungdomsminnen ₍av₎ August
Lindberg. 2. uppl. Stockholm, A. Bonnier
₍1915₎
194 p. illus. (1 col.) ports. 16 cm.

Bound with his De första teaterminnena.
Stockholm ₍1916₎

1. Lindberg, Johan August, 1846-1916.

NL 0377039 NcD

Lindberg, August, 1846-1916.
De första teaterminnena.   Stockholm: A. Bonnier ₍1916₎
4 p.l., 503(1) p., 1 l., front. illus. (incl. port.) 24°.

Author's name at head of title.

1. Stage (Swedish). 2. Actors and   acting.—Biography. 3. Title.
N.Y.P.L.   May 7, 1917.

NL 0377040 NN

927.92   Lindberg,   August, 1846-1916.
L742   De första teaterminnena ₍av₎ August
Lindberg. 2. uppl. Stockholm, A. Bonnier
₍1916₎
503 p. illus., facsims., ports. 16 cm.

Bound with his Barndoms- och ungdomsminnen.
Stockholm ₍1915₎

1. Lindberg, Johan August, 1846-1916.

NL 0377041 NcD MH

Lindberg, August, 1885-

Vad Finland försvarar. ₍Stockholm, I. Hæggströms lito.,
1940₎

Lindberg, Axel Valdemar, 1860-   *ed.*
Samling författningar rörande Finlands sjöfart, utgivna av
A. V. Lindberg ... ₍Helsingfors₎ Eget förlag, säljes och distribueras å Sjöfartsstyrelsens sjökartverk ₍1922₎
xxii, 385 p. 20ᵐ.

1. Maritime law—Finland. I. Finland. Laws, statutes, etc.
II. Title.   35-32825

Library of Congress   HE587.F5L5
                                           ₍347.709471₎ 349.471077

NL 0377043 DLC

Lindberg, Ben A   *ed.*
Cases in personnel administration. New York, Prentice-
Hall, 1954.
586 p. illus. 24 cm. (Prentice-Hall industrial relations and personnel series)

1. Personnel management—Case studies. I. Title.

HF5549.L49   658.3   54—11902 †

OrCS CaBVaU
        OCl TxU NcD NN MB IU ViU IaU MiU NcU Wa WaS WaSpG
NL 0377044   DLC CoU KEmT DS OO NcRS OU OCU PU-W PSt

Lindberg, Bengt
Studies on glycosides, especially the α/β
transformation. Stockholm,1950.
Akademisk avhandling - Stockholm.

NL 0377045 CtY

Lindberg, Bengt Jacob, 1904–
... Experimental studies of colour and non-colour attitude in
school children and adults, especially with regards to its condition in different types according to the individual psychology
of Sjöbring and the anthropometric index of Strömgren, together with two psychological tests, by Bengt J. Lindberg ...
Copenhagen, Levin & Munksgaard, E. Munksgaard, 1938.
170 p. 2 col. pl., diagrs. 25ᶜᵐ. (On cover: Acta psychiatrica et neurologica. Supplementum xvi)
At head of title: From the Psychiatric department of Malmö general
hospital, chief: Dr. R. Holmström; and the Psychiatric university clinic
at Lund, Sweden, chief: Prof. dr. H. Sjöbring.

"The translation of the work has been carried out for the most part
by Mr. O. Morton ... but Mr. A. King ... has translated two of the chapters."—Pref.
"References" : p. ₍166₎–170.

1. Color—Psychology. 2. Psychology, Pathological. I. Morton, O.,
tr. II. King, Arthur Henry, 1910–   tr. III. Title: Colour and non-
colour attitude in school children and adults.
                                                              39–13503
Library of Congress   BF789.C7L5
                                           ₍3₎   [159.961331] 152.1331

NL 0377047   DLC NjP MoU PPT ViU OrU CaBVaU ICRL

Lindberg, Bengt Jacob, 1904–
Psycho-infantilism. ₍From the Swedish by Helen Frey₎
Copenhagen, E. Munksgaard, 1950.
126 p. 26 cm. (Acta psychiatrica et neurologica. Supplementum
61)
Bibliography : p. ₍125₎–126.

1. Infantilism. 2. Psychiatry—Cases, clinical reports, statistics.
(Series)

RJ135.L513   616.89   50–54910

NL 0377048   DLC MoU ViU CtY-M

VOLUME 334

Lindberg, Bernhard Waldemar, 1866–
Electronism; diagnosis and treatment, by B. W. Lindberg
... Kansas City, Mo., La Rue printing company, 1929–
v. front. (port.) illus. 29½ᶜᵐ.
Errata slip inserted before p. ₍iii₎, v. 1.

1. Electrodiagnosis. 2. Electrotherapeutics. I. Title.

Library of Congress   RM872.L6   29-21526

NL 0377049   DLC DNLM

Lindberg, Börje
Hur läser folk annonser? En utredning av
Börje Lindberg och Bertil Neuman. Stockholm, Nordisk rotogravyr, 1945.
143 p. illus., diagrs., tables.

1. Advertising research. 2. Advertising –
Sweden. I. Neuman, Bertil
jt. auth.

NL 0377050   NNC NN

PF3628 **Lindberg, C   H.**
.L7   Tysk-engelsk-svensk minnesbok, af C. H. Lindberg.
Stockholm, P. A. Norstedt & söners förlag ₍1880₎
₍4₎, 84 p. 21½ᶜᵐ.

NL 0377051   ICU

Lindberg, Carl.
Terrängordet köl (käl, kielas); en betydelsehistorisk och
-geografisk undersökning. Uppsala, Almqvist & Wiksells
boktr., 1941.
xv, 320 p. illus., maps (1 fold.) 25 cm.
Akademisk avhandling—Uppsala.
Bibliography in "Viktigare förkortningar" (p. ₍xi₎-xv) Bibliographical footnotes.

1. Köl (The word) 2. Names, Geographical. I. Title.

PD1819.K6L5   54-50959

NL 0377052   DLC TxU CtY CU PU ICU MH

Lindberg, Carl Carlsson, 1883–
... Världskriget till sjöss i europeiska farvatten ... av
C. C: son Lindberg ...
Stockholm, Marinlitteraturföreningen, 1916–
v. illus. (incl. ports.) maps. 22½ᶜᵐ. (Marinlitteraturföreningen
n: r 19)
On cover: ... Världskriget III ...

1. European war, 1914—   —Naval operations. I. Title.

Library of Congress   D580.L5   21-15689

NL 0377053   DLC ICJ NjP

Lindberg, Carl Frederick, 1894–
Dominant factors in the development of public education in
Kansas, by Carl Frederick Lindberg ... ₍Lawrence? Kan.,
1934₎
8 p. 23ᶜᵐ.
Thesis (PH. D.)—University of Kansas, 1933.
"Reprinted from University of Kansas Bulletin of education."

1. Education—Kansas—Hist. 2. Public schools—Kansas.

Library of Congress   LA289.L5 1933   35-1247
₍2₎   370.9781

NL 0377054   DLC PU MiU OU

Lindberg, Carl Fredrik, illus.
Antiquitées suédoises. 1873–75
see under   Montelius, Oscar, 1843–1921.

Lindberg, Carl Fredrik.
Från jernåldern ...
see under   Montelius, Oscar, 1843–1921.

786.5   **Lindberg, Carl Ludv**
L64h   Handbok om orgverket, dess historia,
1861   konstruktion, och rätta vård, uppgift om
bruliga orgstämmor, dispositioner till
större och mindre orgverk, kostnadsförslag
och kontrakt i och för orgbyggnader, pröfning
af nya orgverk m.m., jemte tre plancher öfver
orgverkets mekaniska delar. Till ledning
för organister, orgbyggare, musikdirektörer,
kyrkoherdar, m. fl. 2., tillökta och för-
bättrade, uppl.   Strengnäs, A. Berglund
₍1861₎
106p. illus.   20cm.

NL 0377057   IU

Lindberg, Carl Olov, ed.
Flygboken, allt i popular form om civil-, militar-, segel-
och modellflyg, under redaktion av Carl-Olov Lindberg
₍och₎ K. G. Molin, företal av K. J. A. Silfverberg. Stockholm, Saxon & Lindström ₍1945₎
246 p. illus. 19 cm.
Includes bibliography.

1. Aeronautics. I. Molin, K. G., joint ed. II. Title.

TL546.7.L53   63-48880 ‡

NL 0377058   DLC

Lindberg, Carl Olov.
Jordhusbygge; arbetsbeskrivningar och ritningar. Mate-
rialet samlat och bearbetat av Carl-Olov Lindberg och K. G.
Molin. Ritningarna till de moderna husen utförda av Folke
Hederus. Stockholm, Hem i Sverige, 1950.
64 p. illus., plans. 24 cm.
Bibliography: p. 54–59.

1. Building, Adobe. 2. Architecture, Domestic—Sweden.
I. Molin, K. G., joint author. II. Title.

A 51–1640

Illinois. Univ. Library
for Library of Congress   ₍1₎

NL 0377059   IU DNAL

4DK-   **Lindberg, Carolus,** 1889–
213   Aunuksen asunnoilla; Itä-Karjalan
kansanomaista rakennuskulttuuria. Porvoo,
W. Söderström [1943]
172 p.
At head of title: Carolus Lindberg, Jouko
Hautala.

NL 0377060   DLC-P4

Lindberg, Carolus, 1889–

Wennervirta, Ludvig, 1882–
... Finlands konst, fran förhistorisk tid till våra dagar.
Medarbetare: Aarne Europaeus, U. T. Sirelius, K. K. Mein-
ander ₍o. a.₎ ... Stockholm, Bokförlaget Natur och kultur,
1926.

Lindberg, Carolus, 1889–
... Finlands kyrkor. Helsingfors, Förlag
bildkonst [1935]
407 p. illus. (incl. maps, plans) 31 cm.
" Litteraturförteckning": p. 384–390.

NL 0377062   00

DK465 **Lindberg, Carolus,** 1889–
H5L742 ...Helsingfors, Nordens vita stad. Borgå &
Helsingfors, W. Söderström osakeyhtiö ₍1931₎
60 p., 68 pl. on 34 l. illus. (incl.maps,
plans) 29½x23½ᶜᵐ.
Plates printed on both sides.
At head of title: Carolus Lindberg.
Text in Swedish, German, English and French.

1. Helsingfors. I. Title.

NL 0377063   CSt-H CtY

Lindberg, Carolus, 1889–
Helsinki, pohjolan valkea kaupunki.
Helsinki, Werner Söderström Osakeyhtiö ₍1931₎
60 p. illus., maps. 30cm.

Finnish, German, English, and French.

NL 0377064   NIC MnU

Lindberg, Carolus, 1889–
Om teglets anvendning i finska medeltida gråstenskyr-
kor ₍af₎ Carolus Lindberg ... Helsingfors ₍H. Schildts
tryckeri₎ 1919.
1 p. l., 5–146 p., 1 l. front., illus., plates. 33ᶜᵐ.
"Godkänd såsom avhandling för vinnande av doktorsgrad vid Tekniska
högskolan i Finland."—Note at end.

1. Church architecture—Finland. 2. Building, Brick. I. Title.
20–11612

Library of Congress   NA5693.L5

NL 0377065   DLC 00

Lindberg, Carolus, 1889–
Pohjolan rakennustaide. Porvoo, W. Söderström ₍1931₎
273 p. illus., plates, plans. 26cm.

Bibliography: 259–260.

NL 0377066   NNC-A NN

Lindberg, Carolus, 1889–   ed.
... Rakennustaide ja rakennustekniika; esihis-
torialliset rakennukset, rakennustaiteen historia,
kaupunkien suunnittelu, uudenaikaiset rakennukset,
huonerakennustekniika, kirjoittajat ... Carolus
Lindberg ... Otto- I. Meurman, ... Hilding
Ekelund ... U. Varjo. Toimittaja Carolus Lindberg
... 1126 kuvaa ja 23 liitekuvaa. Porvoo, Helsinki,
W. Söderström osakeyhtiö ₍1938₎
2 p. l., 831 p. incl. illus. (incl. maps, plans)
plates. 25 cm.
At head of title: Keksintögen kirja.

1. Architecture - Hist. 2. Meurman, Otto - I.
3. Ekelund, Hilding. 4. Varjo, U. I. Title.
II. Finnish language - Texts.

NL 0377068   MB

VOLUME 334

Lindberg, Carolus, 1889–
Suomen kirkot, kirjoittanut Carolus Lindberg ... The churches of Finland, by Carolus Lindberg ... Les églises de Finlande, par Carolus Lindberg ... Die kirchen Finnlands, von Carolus Lindberg ... Helsinki ₍Tilgmannin kirjapaino₎ 1939.
1 p. l., 5–63 p. incl. 40 pl. on 21 l. 29½ x 22½ᶜᵐ.
Finnish, English, French and German.
1. Church architecture—Finland. 2. Churches—Finland. I. Title. II. Title: The churches of Finland. III. Title: Les églises de Finlande. IV. Title: Die kirchen Finnlands.

Library of Congress   NA5693.L53   42–6502
                         ₍2₎   726.509471

NL 0377069   DLC

Lindberg, Conrad Emil, 1852–1930.
Apologetics; or, A system of Christian evidence, by Conrad Emil Lindberg ... Rock Island, Ill., Augustana book concern, 1917.
216 p., 1 l. 21½ᶜᵐ.
"Books on apologetics and collateral reading": p. ₍203₎–207.
1. Apologetics—20th cent. I. Title.
                                              17–4485
Library of Congress   BT1101.L5'

NL 0377070   DLC MH-AH PPLT

Lindberg, Conrad Emil, 1852–1930.
Beacon lights of prophecy in the latter days, by Conrad Emil Lindberg ... Rock Island, Ill., Augustana book concern ₍ᶜ1930₎
xiv p., 1 l., 256 p. front. (port.) 19½ᶜᵐ.
"Scripture passages cited": p. 254–256.
1. Bible—Prophecies. 2. Second advent. I. Title.
Library of Congress   BS647.L48   30–24604
Copyright A 27399   ₍3₎   232.12

NL 0377071   DLC PPWe OrP MH-AH ICRL PG1adM

BS2825
.A3L5   **Lindberg, Conrad Emil,** 1852–1930.
Betraktelser öfver Johannis Uppenbarelses, tre första kapitel. Chicago, Engberg & Holmbergs förlag, 1883.
163 p. illus. 16 cm.

NL 0377072   MnHi PPLT

Lindberg, Conrad Emil, 1852–1930.
Christian dogmatics and notes on the history of dogma, by Conrad Emil Lindberg ... tr. from the Swedish by Rev. C. E. Hoffsten, B. D. Rev. and augmented by the author. Rock Island, Ill., Augustana book concern, 1922.
602 p., 1 l. 21½ᶜᵐ.
I. Hoffsten, Conrad Emanuel, 1876–   tr. II. Title.
                                              22–13426
Library of Congress   BT75.L72

NL 0377073   DLC MH-AH PPWe PPLT OrStbM

Lindberg, Conrad Emil, 1852–1930.
Encheiridion i dogmatik jämte dogmhistoriska anmärkningar, af d: r Conrad Emil Lindberg ... Rock Island, Ill., Lutheran Augustana book concern, 1898.
1 p. l., ₍v₎–vii, 467 p. 21½ᶜᵐ.
1. Theology, Doctrinal. 2. Lutheran church—Doctrinal and controversial works. I. Title.
Library of Congress   BT75.L7   C-249 Revised

NL 0377074   DLC PPLT MH-AH

BV
811   **Lindberg, Conrad Emil,** 1852–1930.
.L55   Om dopet. Andra upplagen. New York,
1890a   Författarens Förlag [1890]
          88 p. 18 cm.
          1. Baptism. I.T.

NL 0377075   MH-AH MnHi

BX8013
.L5S9   **Lindberg, Conrad Emil,** 1852–1930.
          Syllabus i konstruktiv luthersk kyrkorättslära; jämte några praktiska anvisningar. Rock Island, Ill., Lutheran Augustana Book Concern ₍förord 1897₎
          48 p. 20 cm.

NL 0377076   MnHi

BX8013
.L5S9   **Lindberg, Conrad Emil,** 1852–1930.
1911   Syllabus i konstruktiv luthersk kyrkorättslära; jämte några praktiska anvisningar. 2. uppl. Rock Island, Ill., Augustana Book Concern ₍förord 1911₎
          46 p. 21 cm.

NL 0377077   MnHi

BX8065
.L48   **Lindberg, Conrad Emil,** 1852–1930.
          Syllabus of Lutheran church polity, by Conrad Emil Lindberg. Rock Island, Ill., Augustana Book Concern [1927]
          144 p. 19 cm.
          1. Church polity. 2. Lutheran Church - Government. 3. Augustana Evangelical Lutheran Church - Government. I. Title. II. Title: Lutheran church polity.

NL 0377078   ICLT

WZ
100   **LINDBERG, David Oscar Nathaniel,**
qL743   **1891–**
          A collection of miscellaneous bio-bibliographical material on this person, together with abstracts, résumés, etc. of his works, may be found on the shelves under the above call number.

NL 0377079   DNLM

Lindberg, David Oscar Nathaniel, 1891–
A manual of pulmonary tuberculosis and an Atlas of thoracic roentgenology. By David O. N. Lindberg ... Springfield, Ill., Baltimore, Md., C. C. Thomas, 1943.
xv, 233 p., 1 l. incl. illus., plates, diagrs. 25½ᶜᵐ.
"First edition."
1. Tuberculosis. 2. Diagnosis, Radioscopic. 3. Chest—Diseases—Diagnosis. 4. Radiography.
                                              43–8027
Library of Congress   RC311.L7₹
                                              616.246

NL 0377080   DLC OU PU-Med OrU-M

Lindberg, Emil, 1850–1920
see   Lindberg, Otto Emil, 1850–1920.

Lindberg, Erik.
Sweden; glimpses of its charm, traditions, and modern progress, by Erik Lindberg. ₍Stockholm₎ The Swedish traffic association ₍1933₎
2 p. l., ₍7₎–127, ₍1₎ p. incl. illus., plates (part col.) 20ᶜᵐ.
1. Sweden—Descr. & trav. 2. Sweden. I. Turisttrafikförbundet, Stockholm.
Library of Congress   DL618.L5   33–34401
                                              914.85

NL 0377082   DLC CtY KyU PPAmSwM MB KyU OLak

Lindberg, Erik. Sweden; glimpses of its charm, tradition, and modern progress.
Johnson, Walter Gilbert, 1905–
Beginning Swedish, by W. G. Johnson ... Rock Island, Ill., Augustana book concern ₍ᶜ1939₎

Law   Lindberg, Erik, member of Landskansliet, Malmöhus, Sweden, ed.
Sweden. *Laws, statutes, etc.*
Lagbok för motorfordonsförare; utgivare: Erik Lindberg. Malmö, Skånetryckeriet ₍1947₎

Lindberg, Erik Gustaf, respondent.
Savitri, en spisod ur den indiska...
see under Bergstedt, Carl Fredrick, 1817– praeses.

4DK   **Lindberg, Ernst**
Fin.   I Åbo på 1800-talet; bilder och
379   minnen. Åbo, Åbo tryckeri och Tidnings aktiebolags förlag, 1921.
          369 p.

NL 0377086   DLC-P4

QC451   **LINDBERG, ERNST.**
.L7   ...The M- and N-series, a spectroscopic study of X-rays... Uppsala, 1931.
          ₍1₎, 74 p. illus., diagrs. 27cm. (Nova acta Regiae societatis scientiarum upsaliensis. ser. IV, v.7, no.7)
          Inaug.-diss.--Upsala.
          Thesis note on added t.-p.
          Bibliographical foot-notes.
          1. Spectrum analysis. 2. X-rays.

NL 0377087   ICU ICJ MH DLC CtY RPB DN-Ob ICRL

Lindberg, Ernst Folke,   ed.
Salaminnen ₍Stockholm₎ Nordiska museet ₍1954₎
          424 p. illus. 21cm. (Svenskt liv och arbete, 20)
          1. Sala, Sweden (City) Hist.

NL 0377088   MnU

VOLUME 334

Lindberg, Esther Adeline
The infinity of true magic squares.
₍Missoula, Mont., Delaneys' bureau of printing,
1950₎
45 p. 23 cm.

NL 0377089 MtU

SD 409
L 5
1915
Lindberg, Ferd.
Om barrträdskulturer i Norrland. Stockholm, Centraltryckeriet, 1915.

48 p. illus. 25 cm. (Skogsvårdsföreningens Tidskrift, 1915. Supplementhäfte, 2)

1. Reforestation - Sweden. 2. Tree planting. 3. Coniferæ. I. Title. (Series: Sveriges Skogsvårdsförbund. Tidskrift, 1915. Supplementhäfte, 2)

NL 0377090 CaBVaU

352.042
L64
Lindberg, Folke Adolf, 1903–
Det europeiska stadsväsendets uppkomst, en blick på den nyare litteraturen. Stockholm, Bonnier, 1938.

53 p. 21cm. (Skrifter utg. av Stadshistoriska institutet)

1. Municipal government in Europe. 2. Cities and towns in Europe.

NL 0377091 MnU CU

Lindberg, Folke Adolf, 1903–
Fogde, råd och menighet, några drag i den svenska stadsförfattningens utveckling under medeltiden och 1500-talet. Stockholm, A. Bonnier, 1941.

34 p. 21 cm. (Skrifter utg. av Stadshistoriska institutet)

1. Local government—Sweden—Hist. (Series: Svenska stadshistoriska institutet. Skrifter)

49–38310*

NL 0377092 DLC MnU

Lindberg, Folke Adolf, 1903–
Hantverkarna. Stockholm, Tidens förlag ₍1947–

v. 24 cm. (Den Svenska arbetarklassens historia)
Bibliographical references included in "Noter" (v. 1, p. ₍241₎–256₎)
Contents.—1. delen. Medeltid och äldre Vasatid.

1. Artisans—Sweden. I. Title. (Series)

HD2346.S85L5
50–22710

NL 0377093 DLC MnU

Lindberg, Folke Adolf, 1903–
Kunglig utrikespolitik; studier och essayer fran Oskar IIs tid. Stockholm, Bonnier ₍1950₎

257 p. illus., ports. 20 cm.
"Källhänvisningar och anmärkningar": p. ₍231₎–₍251₎

1. Sweden—Hist.—Oscar II, 1872–1907. 2. Sweden—For. rel.—1814–1905. I. Title.

DL852.L47
948.5
51–16707

NL 0377094 DLC PU WaU MnU OC1

DL991
.L5K7
Lindberg, Folke Adolf, 1903– joint author.

Kraft, Salomon, 1898–
Linköpings historia, av Salomon Kraft och Folke Lindberg, under medverkan av Thord Lindell, Bengt Cnattingius och Arvid Kugelberg. Utg. genom Westman-Wernerska fonden. ₍Uppsala, 1946₎

Lindberg, Folke Adolf, 1903– ed.
Nordens friket. årg. ₍1₎–6; 28 mars 1940–dec. 1945. ₍Stockholm, 1940–45₎

---

*F601.5
.M66
v.33
Lindberg, Folke Adolph, 1903–
Organizing research in urban history.

(In Minnesota history. Saint Paul, 1953. 26cm. v.33, p.201–207. illus.)

NL 0377097 MnHi

JS2654
.P7
Lindberg, Folke Adolf, 1903– ed.

... Privilegier resolutioner och förordninger för Sveriges städer ... Stockholm, P. A. Norstedt & söner, 1927–

Lindberg, Folke Adolf, 1903–
The Scandinavian countries in international affairs; a selected bibliography on the foreign affairs of Denmark, Finland, Norway, and, Sweden, 1800–1952, by Folke Lindberg and John I. Kolehmainen. ₍Minneapolis₎ Program in Scandinavian Area Studies, University of Minnesota, 1953.

vi, 17 p. 23 cm.
Cover title.

1. Denmark—For. rel.—Bibl. 2. Finland—For. rel.—Bibl. 3. Norway—For. rel.—Bibl. 4. Sweden—For. rel.—Bibl. I. Kolehmainen, John Ilmari, joint author.

Z2551.L55
016.32748
53—62970

OrU Or
NL 0377099 DLC CU MeB NNC TxU NcD PPT OC1W OO OOxM

Lindberg, Folke Adolf, 1903–
Västerviks historia 1275–1718 ... av Folke Lindberg ... ₍Västervik och Stockholm, 1933₎
vii, 496 p. illus. (incl. ports., plan) fold. pl. 25 cm.
Akademisk avhandling—Stockholms högskola.
"Arken 1–23 äro tryckta å A.-b. C. O. Ekblad & c:os boktryckeri, Västervik 1933. Det övriga av boken å Alb. Bonniers boktryckeri, Stockholm 1933."
Published also in v. 1 of Västerviks historia utg. av Västerviks stadsfullmäktige.
"Källor och litteratur": p. 482–494.

1. Västervik, Sweden—Hist.

DL991.V27L5 1933
948.6
34–23882 rev

NL 0377100 DLC PU CtY

Lindberg, Fr.
Ett besök i Amerika, af Fr. Lindberg. Uppsala, A. Sundquist ₍1911₎
131 p. plates, ports. 19½ᵐ.

1. U. S.—Descr. & trav. 2. Baptists. 3. Swedes in the U. S. I. Title.

Library of Congress
E169.L68
39–11675
₍2₎
917.3

NL 0377101 DLC NN

Lindberg, Frederic, respondent.

Linné, Carl von, 1707–1778, praeses.
... Nutrix noverca ... Upsaliæ, typis L. M. Höjer ₍1752₎

[Lindberg, G A]
QK495
R45L5
Rhipsalis. ₍Erlangon, ₍etc.₎ 1889?–93?₎
8 pts. in 1 v. illus. 24cm.
Binder's title.
Contents.—Zum kakteenstudium. Die rhipsalideen. (Separatabdruck aus dr. Paul Arendt's "Monatschrift für kakteenkunde" 1891, augustnummer)—Rhipsalis pulvinigera G. A. Lindberg n. sp. (Sonderabdruck aus "Gartenflora" jahrgang 1889, heft 7)—Rhipsalis regnellii G. A. Lindberg n. sp. (Sonderabdruck aus "Gartenflora" jahrgang 1890, he₍ ft 5)—Lepismium (?) dis-

simile G. A. Lindberg n. sp. (Sonderabdruck aus "Gartenflora" jahrgang 1890, heft 6)—Rhipsalis puniceodiscus G. A. Lindberg. (Aus Gartenflora 1893, XLII ₍in ms.₎)—Rhipsalis hadrosoma nov. spec. Von G. A. Lindberg. (Separat-abdruck aus der "Monatsschrift für kakteenkunde")—Rhipsaliden in Afrika. Von G. A. Lindberg. (Separatdruck. "Monatsschrift für kakteenkunde. 1893, III. jahrg.)—Rhipsalis sarmentacea Otto & Dietr. Von G. A. Lindberg.

1. Cactaceae—Bibl. 2. Rhipsalis. I. Title.

NL 0377104 CSmH

Lindberg, G F illus.
Rygh, O₍luf₎ 1833–1899.
Norske oldsager, ordnede og forklarede af O. Rygh. Tegnede paa træ af G. F. Lindberg ... Christiania, A. Cammermeyer; ₍etc., etc.₎ 1885.

Lindberg, Georgiĭ Ustinovich.
Четвертичный период в свете биогеографических данных. Москва, Изд-во Академии наук СССР, 1955.
334 p. maps (1 fold.) 27 cm.
At head of title: Академия наук СССР. Зоологический институт.
Bibliography : p. ₍318₎–329.

1. Paleontology—Quaternary. 2. Geographical distribution of animals and plants. I. Title. *Title transliterated:* Chetvertichnyĭ period v svete biogeograficheskikh dannykh.

QE741.L5
56–30025

NL 0377106 DLC

Lindberg, Georgiĭ Ustinovich.
₍Ryby ĪAponskogo morı̆a i sopredel'nykh chasteĭ Okhotskogo i Zheltogo moreĭ₎
Рыбы Японского моря и сопредельных частей Охотского и Желтого морей. Ленинград, "Наука," Ленингр. отд-ние, 19
v. illus. 27 cm. (Определители по фауне СССР, 99
3.00rub (v.3₎
USSR 60–VKP (v.3)
At head of title, v. : Академия наук Союза Советских Социалистических Республик. Г. У. Линдберг и З. В. Красюкова.
Bibliography : v. 3, p. ₍445₎–455.
CONTENTS:
ч. 3. Teleostomi XXIX. Perciformes 1. Percoidei (XC. Cem. Serranidae—CXLIV. Cem. Champsodontidae.

1. Fishes—Japan Sea. 2. Fishes—Okhotsk, Sea of. 3. Fishes—Yellow Sea. I. Krasi̇ukova, Zoı̆a Valentinovna, joint author. II. Akademiı̆a nauk SSSR. Zoologicheskiĭ institut. III. Title. IV. Series: Opredeliteli po faune SSSR, 99.

QL281.A4 vyp. 99, etc.
73–303806
₍QL623₎

NL 0377108 DLC

VOLUME 334

PT7090   Lindberg, Gunnar
M6   Förklaringar till Viktor Rydbergs dikter,
no.28   avsedda för gymnasier, seminarier, flickskolor
         och studiecirklar.   Stockholm, Bonnier ₁1927₎
         32 p.   (Skrifter utg. av Modersmålslärarnas
         förening, n:r 28)

         1. Rydberg, Viktor, 1828-1895.

NL 0377109   CU

         Lindberg, Gunnar, 1⁸86-
J684   Uppenbarelsekyrkan i Saltsjöbaden.
+1   Stockholm [P.A.Norstedt] 1937.
1937L   74 p. illus. 22 cm.

         1. Saltsjobaden, Sweden. Uppenbarelsekyrkan.

NL 0377110   CtY

LINDBERG, GUSTAF.
   Hsing-yao and Ting-yao; an investigation and
description of some Chinese T'ang and Sung white
porcelain in the Carl Kempe and Gustaf Lindberg
collections.   (IN: Stockholm. Ostasiatiska samlingarna. Bulletin.
Stockholm. 29cm. n₁o. 25 (1953) p. 19-71.   112 plates)

1. Pottery, Chinese. 2. Pottery,   Chinese--Collections, Private--
Kempe. 3. Pottery, Chinese--   Collections, Private--Lindberg.

NL 0377111   NN

BT1210   Lindberg, Gustaf, 1883-
.L73   ... Kristen agnosticism.   Stockholm, Bokförla-
         get Natur och kultur ₍1945₎
         76, ₍1₎ p.

         1. Agnosticism. 2. Apologetics--20th cent.

NL 0377112   ICU NcD MnU

Lindberg, Gustaf, *1883-*
   Kyrkans heliga år; en historisk-princi-
piell undersokning med särskild hänsyn
till det Svenska Kyrkoaret.   Stockholm...
1937.

   602 p.

NL 0377113   PPLT

BV825   Lindberg, Gustaf, *1883-*
.L74   Nattvarden. 3. upp. Stockholm, Svenska
1946   Kyrkans Diakonistyrelses Bokförlag [1946]
         24p. 19cm.

         1. Lord's supper. I. Title.

NL 0377114   IEG

Lindberg, Gustaf, 1883-
   Die schwedischen missalien des mittelalters; ein beitrag zur
vergleichenden liturgik. I. Kalendarium, proprium de tem-
pore, proprium de sanctis, commune sanctorum ... von Gustaf
Lindberg ... Uppsala, Almqvist & Wiksells boktryckeri-a.-b.,
1923.
   xxiv, 439, ₍1₎ p. facsims. (1 double) 23½ᶜᵐ.
   Akademische abhandlung—Uppsala.
   "Quellen und literatur": p. ₍ix₎-xxi.
   "Notenbeilage": p. ₍427₎-439.
   1. Catholic church. Liturgy and ritual. Missal. 2. Catholic church.
Liturgy and ritual. Sweden. 3. Missals.   I. Title.
                                 ₍Full name: Nils Gustaf Lindberg₎
                                                   34-10139
Library of Congress   BX2015.L5 1923   264.025

NL 0377115   DLC PU PPLT IU MH ICU NjP CtY

Lindberg, Gustaf, 1883-
   Die schwedischen missalien des mittelalters; ein beitrag zur
vergleichenden liturgik ... Von Gustaf Lindberg. Berlin,
Speyer & Peters, 1924-
   v. facsims. (1 double) 23½ᶜᵐ.
   Vol. 1 issued also as author's dissertation, Uppsala.
   "Quellen und literatur": v. 1, p. ₍ix₎-xxi.
   "Notenbeilage": v. 1, p. ₍427₎-439.
   1. Catholic church. Liturgy and ritual. Missal. 2. Catholic church.
Liturgy and ritual. Sweden. 3. Missals.   I. Title.
                                 ₍Full name: Nils Gustaf Lindberg₎
                                                   34-8544
Library of Congress   BX2015.L5 1924
————— Copy 2.
Copyright A—Foreign   25735
                           ₍2₎   264.025

NL 0377116   DLC ICU PPLT PPPD

Lindberg, Gustav Adolf.
   Fragment; några dikter.   Stockholm, Svenska
Andelsförlaget, [1924]
   61† p.   sm. 4°.

NL 0377117   MH

QH7   **Lindberg, Håkan,** 1898-
.S78   Die Biologie von *Pipunculus chlorionae* Frey und die
vol. 45 Einwirkung von dessen Parasitismus auf Chloriona-Arten.
         Helsingforsiae, 1946.
         50 p. illus., tables. 26 cm. (Acta zoologica fennica 45)
         "Literatur": p. 49-50.

         1. Pipunculidae. 2. Parasites—Insects.   (Series)
                                                   A 48-4312*
         Ohio State Univ. Libr.
         for Library of Congress   ₍2₎

NL 0377118   OU MoU DLC ViU PU NcU

Lindberg, Håkan, 1898-
   De bortglömda öarna. Helsingfors, Söderström ₍1955₎
   207 p. illus. 22 cm.

   1. Cape Verde Islands—Descr. & trav.   I. Title.
   DT671.C2L5 1955   57-41715 ‡

NL 0377119   DLC

Lindberg, Håkan, 1898-
   De bortglömda öarna. Strängnäs, Tomas ₍1955₎
   207 p. illus. 22 cm.

   1. Cape Verde Islands—Descr. & trav.   I. Title.
                                            A 56-4342
   Northwestern Univ.   Library
   for Library of Congress   ₍3₎

NL 0377120   IEN

Lindberg, Håkan, 1898-
   Canaricoris, eine neue kanarische Miriden-Gattung.   ₍Hel-
singfors, Akademiska bokhandeln₎ 1951₎
   12 p. illus. 23 cm. (Societas Scientiarum Fennica. Commentationes biologicae, XII, 9)
   Caption title.

   1. Miridae.   (Series: Finska vetenskaps-societeten, Helsingfors.
Commentationes biologicae, XII, 9)
   Q60.F553 vol. 12, no. 9   A 54-6116

   John Crerar Library
   for Library of Congress   ₍1₎†

NL 0377121   ICJ ViU OU PU DLC

Q60   **Lindberg, Håkan,** 1898-
.F553
vol. 14 **Finnländische Kanaren Expedition,** *1947-1951.*
            Entomologische Ergebnisse. Helsingfors ₍Akademiska
         bokhandeln₎ 1953-₍54₎

Q60   Lindberg, Håkan, 1898-
.F553
vol. 14, **Finnish Expedition to the Canary Islands,** *1947-1951.*
no. 1,   Entomologische Ergebnisse der finnländischen Kanaren-
etc.   Expedition, 1947-1951. Helsingfors, 1953-

Q60   Lindberg, Håkan, 1898-
.F553
vol. 3, **Inventa** entomologica itineris hispanici et maroccani, quod a.
no. 4; etc. 1926 fecerunt Harald et Håkan Lindberg. I-
         ₍Helsingfors, 1929-

Lindberg, Håkan, 1898-
   Notes on the biology of dryinids.   ₍Helsingfors, 1950₎
   18, ₍1₎ p. illus. 24 cm.   (Societas Scientiarum Fennica. Com-
mentationes biologicae. x, 15)
   Caption title.
   At head of title: From Tvärminne Zoological Station.
   Bibliography: p. ₍19₎

   1. Dryinidae.   (Series: Finska vetenskaps-societeten, Helsingfors. Commentationes biologicae, x, 15)
   Q60.F553 vol. 10, no. 15   A 54-4876

   John Crerar Library
   for Library of Congress   ₍2₎†

NL 0377125   ICJ ViU OU ICJ

570.57
F49 v.12
         Lindberg, Håkan, 1898-
            Odo Morannal Reuter, 1850-1950: in memory of
         the 100th anniversary of his birth.
         ₍iii₎-viii p. incl. port. (Societas scien-
         tiarum fennica. Commentationes biologicae.
         Helsingfors, 1951. XII, 1)
            Caption title.
            1. Reuter, Odo Morannal, 1850-1913. I. Series:
         Finska vetenskaps societeten, Helsingfors. Com-
         mentationes biologicae, XII, 1.   570.9273

NL 0377126   ICJ

Lindberg, Håkan, 1898-
   ... Ökologisch-geographische untersuchungen zur insektenfauna der felsentümpel an den küsten Finnlands, von Håkan
Lindberg ... Helsingforsiae ₍Oy. Tilgmann ab.₎ 1944.
   3 p. l., ₍5₎-178 p. illus., 4 pl. on 2 l., maps, tables. 26ᶜᵐ. (Acta
zoologica fennica 41 edidit Societas pro fauna et flora fennica)
   "Literatur": p. ₍175₎-178.

   1. Insects—Finland. 2. Insects, Aquatic.
                                            A 46-4742
   Ohio state univ. Library
   for Library of Congress   [QH7.S78 vol. 41]

NL 0377127   OU MoU ViU NcU

VOLUME 334

Lindberg, Håkan, 1898–
On stylopisation of araeopids. Helsingforsiae, 1949.
40 p. illus. 26 cm. (Acta zoologica Fennica, 57)
Bibliography: p. 35–36.

1. Parasites—Leaf-hoppers. 2. Strepsiptera. I. Title.
(Series)
QH7.S78 vol. 57   A 52–5839
Ohio State Univ. Libr.
for Library of Congress   [3]†

NL 0377128 OU MoU DLC DI ViU

Lindberg, Håkan, 1898–
... Der parasitismus der auf *Chloriona*-arten (*Homoptera, Cicadina*) lebenden strepsiptere *Elenchinus chlorionae* n. sp. sowie die einwirkung derselben auf ihren wirt, von Håkan Lindberg. Mit 58 figuren und 7 tabellen ... Helsingforsiae [A.-b. F. Tilgmann] 1939.
1 p. l., 179 p. illus. 25½ᶜᵐ. (Acta zoologica fennica 22, edidit Societas pro fauna et flora fennica)
"Aus der Zoologischen station Tvärminne."
"Zitierte literatur": p. [175]–179.
1. Strepsiptera. 2. Cicada. I. Title.
                                                      A C 39–3496
Ohio state univ. Library
for Library of Congress   [QH7.S78 no. 22]
                        [3]   (590.82)

NL 0377129 OU AAP MoU PU ViU NcU

QH178
.F5N6
Lindberg, Håkan, 1898– ed.

Nordenskiöld-samfundet i Finland.
Skärgårdsboken; författad av finlandssvenska forskare. [Redaktör: Håkan Lindberg] Helsingfors, 1948–

Lindberg, Håkan, 1898–
Verzeichnis der ostfennoskandinischen Homoptera cicadina. Helsingforsiae, 1947.
81 p. map. 26 cm. (Societas pro Fauna et Flora Fennica. Fauna Fennica, 1)

1. Cicadidae. 2. Homoptera—Finland. (Series: Societas pro Fauna et Flora Fennica, Helsingfors. Fauna Fennica, 1)
QL298.F5S6 no. 1   52–20924

NL 0377131 DLC MoU NcD DI

Lindberg, Håkan, 1898–
Verzeichnis der Typen in O. M. Reuters paläarktischen Heteropterensammlung. [Helsingfors, Akademiska bokhandeln, 1951]
34 p. 23 cm. (Societas Scientiarum Fennica. Commentationes biologicae, XII, 14)
Caption title.
1. Heteroptera, Fossil. (Series: Finska vetenskaps-societeten, Helsingfors. Commentationes biologicae, XII, 14)
Q60.F553 vol. 12, no. 14   A 54–6117

John Crerar Library
for Library of Congress   [1]†

NL 0377132 ICJ ViU OU PU DLC

QH 301
F52
v.13
no.18
Lindberg, Håkan, 1898–
Zur Kenntnis der Hemipterenfauna der Azorischen Inseln. [Helsingfors, 1954]
9 p. illus. 24 cm. (Societas Scientiarum Fennica. Commentationes biologicae, XIII, 18)

1. Insects - Azores.

NL 0377133 OU

Lindberg, Håkan, 1898–
Zur Kenntnis der Insektenfauna im Brackwasser des Baltischen Meeres. Helsingfors, 1948.
206 p. maps, diagrs. 24 cm. (Societas Scientiarum Fennica. Commentationes biologicae, x, 9)
Bibliography: p. [202]–206.

1. Insects—Baltic Sea. 2. Insects, Aquatic. (Series: Finska vetenskaps-societeten, Helsingfors. Commentationes biologicae, x, 9)
Q60.F553 vol. 10, no. 9   A 54–4237

Virginia. Univ. Libr.
for Library of Congress   [2]†

NL 0377134 ViU OU PU IU DLC

Lindberg, Håkan, 1898–
... Zur kenntnis der ostasiatischen homopteren; weitere ergebnisse einer von Y. Wuorentaus im jahre 1917 unternommenen forschungsreise, von Håkan Lindberg ... [Helsingfors, 1929]
14 p. pl. 23½ᶜᵐ. (Societas scientiarum fennica. Commentationes biologicae III, 6)
Caption title.
1. Homoptera. 2. Insects—Siberia. I. Wuorentaus, Y.
                                                      A C 33–1277
Title from John Crerar Libr.
Library of Congress   [Q60.F553 vol. 3, no. 6]

NL 0377135 ICJ OU ViU PU PPAmP

820.9
L648
Lindberg, Hanna.
„The shrew". Argbiggans typ i den engelska literaturen intill Shakespere, berättande poesi och prosa. **Tavastehus, 1901.**
178p.

Akademisk avhandling--Hälsingfors.

NL 0377136 IU ICRL

Lindberg, Hans V.
Farmer cooperative audits to accountants, auditors, and the management of farmer cooperatives. Spokane, Wash., H. V. Lindberg, ᶜ1940.
1 p. l., 19 numb. l. 27 x 21½ᵐ.
Reproduced from type-written copy.

1. Agriculture, Cooperative — Societies—Accounting. 2. Agriculture, Cooperative—U. S. I. Title.
Library of Congress   S567.L7 1940   41–27616
                        [2]   334.6

NL 0377137 DLC

Lindberg, Hans V.
Farmer cooperative audits to the management of farmer cooperatives and accountants and auditors. Spokane, Wash., H. V. Lindberg, ᶜ1941.
34 p. 23ᵐ.

1. Agriculture, Cooperative — Societies—Accounting. 2. Agriculture, Cooperative—U. S. I. Title.
Library of Congress   S567.L7 1941   41–27617
                        [2]   334.6

NL 0377138 DLC IdU

Lindberg, Harald, 1871–
Beitrag zur Kenntnis der Käferfauna der Kanarischen Inseln. [Helsingfors, 1950]
20 p. illus. 24 cm. (Societas Scientiarum Fennica. Commentationes biologicae. x, 18)
Caption title.

1. Beetles—Canary Islands. (Series: Finska vetenskaps-societeten, Helsingfors. Commentationes biologicae, x, 18)
Q60.F553 vol. 10, no. 18   A 54–4873

John Crerar Library
for Library of Congress   [2]†

NL 0377139 ICJ ViU OU DLC

Lindberg, Harald, 1871–
Beitrag zur Kenntnis der Käferfauna der Kanarischen Inseln. [Helsingfors, 1950–53]
2 v. illus. 24 cm. (Societas Scientiarum Fennica. Commentationes biologicae. x, 18; XIII, 12)
Caption title.
Imprint on cover: København, Munksgaard, 1951 (v. [1]) and 1954 (v. [2])

1. Beetles—Canary Islands. (Series: Finska vetenskaps-societeten, Helsingfors. Commentationes biologicae, x, 18 [etc.])
Q60.F553 vol. 10, no. 18, etc.   A 54–4873 rev
John Crerar Library
for Library of Congress   [r58c1]†

NL 0377140 ICJ DLC

QK539
.S75
L5
Lindberg, Harald, 1871–
Bidrag till kännedomen om de till Sphagnum cuspidatum-gruppen hörande arternas utbredning i Skandinavien och Finland. Helsingfors, 1899.
26 p. 23 cm. (Acta Societatis pro Fauna et Flora Fennica, t. 18, no. 3)

1. Sphagnum - Finland. 2. Sphagnum - Scandinavia. i. t. ii. s.

NL 0377141 NNBG

Lindberg, Harald, 1871–
Enumeratio plantarum in Fennoscandia orientali sponte et subsponte nascentium. Förteckning öfver örnbunkar och fröväxter vildtväxaude och förvildade i Finland och angränsande delar af Ryssland. Luettelo saninisista ja siemenkasveista jotka kasvavat villeinä tai metsistyneinä Suomessa ja siihen rajoittuvissa osissa Venäjää. [Helsingfors, Söderström, 1901]
79 p. 23 cm.

1. Botany - Finland. 2. Botany - Russia. i. t.

NL 0377142 NNBG

Lindberg, Harald, 1871–
... Die früchte der *Taraxacum*-arten Finnlands, von Harald Lindberg. Mit 38 tafeln. Helsingforsiae, 1935.
22 p. 38 pl. 25½ᶜᵐ. (Acta botanica fennica. 17)
"Literaturverzeichnis": p. [11]–12.

1. Dandelions. 2. Botany—Finland.
                                                      A C 38–1028
John Crerar library
for Library of Congress   [QH7.S76 no. 17]
                        [4]   (580.6)

NL 0377143 ICJ MoU NNBG MU ViU NcU DLC OU PU

Q60
.F553
vol. 3,
no. 4; etc.
Lindberg, Harald, 1871–
Inventa entomologica itineris hispanici et maroccani, quod a. 1926 fecerunt Harald et Håkan Lindberg. I– [Helsingfors, 1929–

Lindberg, Harald, 1871–
Iter Cyprium, contributio ad cognitionem floræ insulæ Cypri. Helsingfors, 1946.
37 p. illus. 30 cm. (Acta Societatis Scientiarum Fennicæ. Nova series B. t. 2, n:o 7)

1. Botany—Cyprus. I. Title. II. Series: Finska vetenskaps-societeten, Helsingfors. Acta Societatis Scientiarum Fennicæ. Nova series B: Opera biologica, t. 2, no. 7.
QH7.F5 t. 2, no. 7   A 48–2471*
New York. Public Libr.
for Library of Congress   [2]†

NL 0377145 NN MoU NNBG MdBJ NcD PU ViU DLC

VOLUME 334

Lindberg, Harald, 1871–
... Itinera mediterranea; ein beitrag zur kenntnis der west-mediterranen flora auf grund eines materials von gefässpflan-zen, gesammelt in Tunesien und Sizilien im jahre 1924 und in Spanien und Marokko im jahre 1926, von Harald Lindberg ... Helsingfors, 1932.
1 p. l., 178 p. plates. 30ᵐᵐ. (Acta Societatis scientiarum fennicæ. nova series b. t. 1, n:o 2)

1. Botany—Mediterranean sea. ₍1. Mediterranean region—Botany₎ ɪ. Title.
                                                    Agr 33–106
Library, U.S. Dept. of   Agriculture 511H36A n. s. b,
                                t. 1, no. 2

NL 0377146   DNAL NNBG ViU

Lindberg, Harald, 1871–
Die nordeuropäischen Formen von Scirpus (Hele-ocharis) paluster L. Mit 2 Tafeln. Helsingfors, 1902.
16 p. 2 plates. 24 cm. (Acta Societatis pro Fauna et Flora Fennica, 23, no. 7)

1. Scirpus paluster. ɪ. t. ɪɪ. s.

NL 0377147   NNBG MH

Lindberg, Harald, 1871–
... Die nordischen *Al hemilla vulgaris*-formen und ihre verbreitung. Ein beitrag zur kenntnis der einwanderung der flora Fennoscandias, mit besonderer rücksicht auf die finländische flora von Harald Lindberg ... Helsingfors, Druckerei der Finnischen literaturgesellschaft, 1909.
2 p. l., 171, ₍1₎ p. 20 pl., 15 maps. 29ᵐᵐ. (Acta Societatis scientiarum fennicæ, tom. XXXVII, n:o 10)
"Literatur-verzeichnis": p. ₍164₎–167.

1. Alchemilla.
                                                    11–173
Library of Congress   QK495.A36L6

NL 0377148   DLC NIC CtY

Q60
.F553   Lindberg, Harald, 1871–
vol. 10,   On the insect fauna of Cyprus. Results of the expedition of
no. 7   1939 by Harald, Håkan and P. H. Lindberg. Helsingfors, 1948–

Lindberg, Harald, 1871–
Taraxacum-former från södra och mellersta Finland. Helsingfors, 1907.
48 p. 24 cm. (Acta Societatis pro Fauna et Flora Fennica, 29, no. 9)

1. Taraxacum - Finland. 2. Compositae. ɪ. s.

NL 0377150   NNBG

Lindberg, Henrik.
To the problem of Masolino and Masaccio, by Henrik Lind-berg. ₍Stockholm, Kungl. boktryckeriet, P. A. Norstedt & söner, 1931₎
2 v. 112 pl. on 56 l. 32½ᶜᵐ.
Akademisk avhandling—Stockholms högskola.
Extra t.-p. with thesis note, inserted in vol. 1.
Vol. 2: Illustrations.
"Literature": v. 1, p. ix–xiii.

1. Masolino da Panicale, Tommaso Fini, known as, 1383–1440. 2. Masaccio, Tommaso Guidi, known as, 1401–1428?
                                                    34–35761
Library of Congress   ND623.M45L5 1931   759.5

CaBVaU
NcU MdBWA OO CtY MiU TNJ MoSW UU NIC GU ViU MtU
NL 0377151   DLC NcD OU OCl PPiU MiDA TxU FU PBm MH

Lindberg, Hugo,   ed.
Teknikern; tidskrift för byggnadskronst
see under title

Lindberg, Hugo, 1887–
En dag i Nürnberg; introduktion till ett vittnesmål. Stockholm, Wahlström & Widstrand ₍1946₎
85 p. 22 cm.

1. War crimes—Trials—Nuremberg, 1945–1946. ɪ. Title.
                                   Full name: Karl Hugo Lindberg.
D804.G42L5   53–34756

NL 0377153   DLC NN

Lindberg, J.
Åkerman, Åke, 1887–
Studien über den kältetod und die kälteresistenz der pflanzen, nebst untersuchungen über die winterfestigkeit des weizens, von dr. A. Åkerman ... unter mitwirkung von magister J. Lindberg ... Lund, Berlingska boktryckeriet, 1927.

Lindberg, J. G.
Kliniska undersoekningar oever depigmenterigen av pupillarranden och genomlysbarheten av iris...
Inaug. diss. Helsingfors, 1917.
Bibl.

NL 0377155   ICRL DNLM

LINDBERG, J. JOHAN.
Papierchromatographie phenolischer Abbauprodukte von Thiolignimen, von J. Johan Lindberg und Terje En-kvist. København, E. Munksgaard, 1953. 23 p. illus. 24cm. (Finska vetenskaps-societeten, Helsingfors. Commentationes physico-mathematicae, 17:4)

Cover title.
Bibliography, p. 22–23.
1. Thiolignin. 2. Phenols. 3. Chromatographic analysis. I. Enkvist, Terje, 1904– . II. Series.   t. 1953.

NL 0377156   NN

Lindberg, Jacob Christian, 1797–1857.
A M. le chevalier P. O. Brøndsted sur quelques médailles cufiques dans le cabinet du Roi de Dane-marck, récemment trouvées dans l'ile de Falster, et sur quelques manuscrits cufiques. Copenhague, 1836.
66 p. 12 pl. 4°.

NL 0377157   CtY PU

284.7
V822Y4   Lindberg, Jacob Christian, 1797–1857.
Andet indlaeg i den visbyske sag tilligemed nye beviser for, at Praesten C. H. Visby... er en falsk laerer og fjende af Christendommen. Afgivet i den Kongelige Lands Over- samt Hof- og Stads-Ret i København, Mandagen d. 16de April 1832. Kiöbenhavn, Wahlske Boghandel, 1832.
62p. 18cm.

1. Visby, Carl Holger, 1801–1811. I. Title.

NL 0377158   IEN

Lindberg, Jacob Christian, 1797–1857.
Bemaerkninger i anledning af Kirkens Gien-maele. Kjøbenhavn, Wahlske Boghandling, 1825.
vi,19p. 22cm.

1. Clausen, Henrik Nicolai, 1793–1877. Kirkens Gienmaele.

NL 0377159   IEN

Lindberg, Jacob Christian, 1797–1857, tr.
Biblen...   see under   Bible. Danish. 1853–56. Lindberg.

LINDBERG, Jakob Christian, 1797–1857.
Commentatio de nummis punicis Sextorum olim Canacae et Concanae tributis. Hauniae,J.H. Schultzii,1824.
pp.44. Plate.   Arc 1423.3

NL 0377161   MH

PJ
4191   Lindberg, Jacob Christian, 1797–1857.
L5   De inscriptione Melitensi Phoenicio-Gracco, commentatio... submittit Jac. Chr. Lindberg; respondente Jano Petro Georgio Jensen. Harniae, Farritius de Tengnagel, 1828.
92 p. fold. facsim. vi pl. 20 cm.

1. Inscriptions, Phenician. 2. Arabic language - Dialects - Malta.

NL 0377162   NRCR PU

Pamph.   LINDBERG, Jacob Christian, 1797–1857.
v.531   Er Dr. Prof. Theol. H. N. Clausen en aerlig laerer i den christne kirke? Et alvorligt spoergsmaal til ...J. Moeller i anledning af hans Yttringer i Nyt theologisk Bibliothek femtende bind. Kjoebenhavn, Wahlske Boghandels Forlag, hos C. Graebe, 1830.
50p. 18cm.

Tredie   uforandrede oplag.

NL 0377163   MH-AH

Lindberg, Jacob Christian, 1797–1857.
Essai sur les Monnaies coufiques frappées par les Emirs de la fam. des Bouides ... in Mém. de la Soc. Rag. des Antiq. du Nord, 1844. Copenhague, 1844.
8°.

NL 0377164   CtY

Lindberg, Jacob Christian, 1797–1857.
Hebraisk grammatik, af Jac. Chr. Lindberg ... 2. forögede oplag. Kjöbenhavn, Wahl, 1828.
4 p.l., 248 p. facsim. 22 cm.
1. Hebrew language - Grammar.

NL 0377165   CU OCH

VOLUME 334

PJ4567 LINDBERG, JACOB CHRISTIAN, 1797-1857.
.L739   Hebreiska grammatikens hufvudreglor med åtföljande
         conjugations- och declinations-tabeller af Jac.Ch.
         Lindberg. Öfversättning. 4.upplagan öfversedd och
         tillökt af Herman Almquist ... Uppsala, W.Schultz
         ₍1866₎
              ₍4₎,97,₍38₎p. 21½cm.

              1.Hebrew language--Grammar.

    NL 0377166   ICU

Lindberg, Jacob Christian, 1797-1857.
     Hebraiske conjugations - og declinations-
tabeller, af Jac. Chr. Lindberg ... Kjöbenhavn,
Wahl, 1827.
     4 p.l., 75 p. 23 cm.
     1. Hebrew language - Inflection.

    NL 0377167   CU

C   LINDBERG, JACOB CHRISTIAN, 1797-1857.
6852   Historiske oplysninger om den danske kirkes
.5   symbolske bøger. Tredie mindeskrift i anledning
       af den augsborgske confessions jubelfest…
       Kjöbenhavn,P.Jorgensen,1830.
            123p.

            Contents--Indledning.--Om det apostolske
       symbol.--Om den nicaenske troesbekjendelse.--
       Om den athanasianske troesbekjendelse.--Om den
       augsborgske confession.--Om Luthers lille cate-
       chismus.

    NL 0377168   ICN

PJ4563 Lindberg, Jacob Christian, 1797-1857.
L53   Hovedreglerne af den hebraiske Grammatik
1835   tilligemed Conjugations- og Declinations-
        Tabeller. Udg. til Brug ved Skole-Underviis-
        ningen. 2. opl. Kjöbenhavn, Paa den
        Wahlske Boghandlings Forlag, 1835-36.
             64,₍36₎ p. tables. 25cm.

             Tables (₍36₎ p. at end) have special t.-p.:
        Hebraiske Conjugations og Declinations-
        Tabeller ... 1836.
        "Grammatiske Arbeider": p.6.

    NL 0377169   CU

Law   Lindberg, Jacob Christian, 1797-1857.

        Stahlfest, Frederik Petrus, 1793-1842.
           Indlæg i den ved den Kongelige Lands-over- samt Hof-
        og stads-ret i Kjøbenhavn paadømte sag: Magister artium
        Lindberg imod etatsraad Fr. Thaarup, som redacteur af
        Dagen. Med nogle bilage. Udg. af etatsraad Thaarup.
        Odense, S. Hempel, 1833.

Lindberg, Jacob Christian, 1797-1857.
     Den kongelige Lands-Overrets samt Hof- og
Stads-Rets Kendelse og Dom i Sagen H.N. Clau-
sen contra N.F.S. Grundtvig. Kjøbenhavn,
Wahl, 1826.
     83p. 18cm.

     1. Clausen, Henrik Nicolai, 1793-1877. 2.
Grundtvig, Nicolai Frederik Severin, 1783-
1872.

    NL 0377171   IEN

Lindberg, Jacob Christian, 1797-1857.
     Libri ecclesiae Danicae Symbolici.
     Hauniae, 1830.

    NL 0377172   NjNbS

Lindberg, Jacob Christian, 1797-1857, ed.

     Den Nordiske kirke-tidende ... Udg. af Jacob Christian
Lindberg ... 1.-   aarg.;
4. jan. 1833.
Kiöbenhavn, Paa udgiverens forlag trykt hos Fabritius de Tengnagel ₍etc.₎, 1833-

Lindberg, Jacob Christian, 1797-1857.

     Müller, Ludvig i. e. Carl Ludvig, 1809-1891.
        Numismatique de l'ancienne Afrique. Ouvrage pré-
     paré et commencé par C. T. Falbe et J. Chr. Lindberg,
     refait, achevé et pub. par L. Müller ... Copenhague,
     Impr. de B. Luno, 1860-74.

Lindberg, Jacob Christian, 1797-1857.
     ₍; ₎ Sur quelques médailles
cufique dans le cabinet du roi de Danemarck rècemment
trouvées dans l'Ile de Falster. Copenhague, 1830, 66 pp.
₍12 pls. 4°.

    NL 0377175   MSaE

Lindberg, Jacob Christian, 1797-1857.
     Trykkefriheden, eller, Indlæg, Domme og
Bilag i Sagen: O.E. Höegh-Guldberg som con-
stitueret Generalfiskal, contra Jac. Chr.
Lindberg, anlagt af det Kongelig Danske Can-
cellie, i Anledning af Skriftet: "Er Dr. Prof.
Theol. H.N. Clausen enserlig Laerer i den
christne Kirke?" Kjöbenhavn, Wahl, 1830.
     iv,394p. 19cm.

    NL 0377176   IEN

943.51 Lindberg, Jacob Christian, 1797-1857.
L893ue   Ueber die Krankheit des Staates und
1830   Cancelleiraths Lornsens Heilmittel.
        Kopenhagen, Gyldendalsche Buchhandlung,
        1830.
             24p. 18cm.

             Bound with Lornsen, Uve Jens. Ueber das
        Verfassungswerk in Schleswigholstein.
        Kiel 1830.

             1. Schleswig-Holstein. Hist. Addresses,
        essays, lectures   I. Title.

    NL 0377177   KU

Lindberg, Jakob Kristian, 1873-   ed.

Dansk industriberetning ... udgivet af Industriforeningen i
København. ₍1.₎—   aarg.; 1906-
København, Trykt hos Nielsen & Lydiche ₍etc.₎ 1907-

HM   Lindberg, Jakob   Kristian, 1873-
136   Magt; en bog om arbejdets ordning ₍af₎
L53   Jak. Kr. Lindberg. ₍Ud. af Dansk forening for
        social oplysning₎ København, Martin, 1933.
             2v. illus. 21cm. (Nyt socialt bibliotek)

             1. Power (Social sciences) 2. Social
        policy 3. Industry and state I. Dansk
        forening for social oplysning II. Title

    NL 0377179   WU

Lindberg, Jakob Kristian, 1873-
     ...Oprettelse af Bedriftsraad i Industrien; Foredrag i "Dansk
Forening for Socialpolitik" den 7. December 1920, af Jak. Kr.
Lindberg... København: H. Jensen, 1921. 12 p. 8°.
(Dansk Forening for Socialpolitik. ₍Skrifter.₎ Hefte 8.)

     1. Employee representation.   2. Series.
     N. Y. P. L.   April 1, 1924.

    NL 0377180   NN

Lindberg, James Christian, 1876-*1937,* comp.
     An anthology of South Dakota poetry, compiled by J. C.
Lindberg and Gertrude B. Gunderson ... Pierre, S. D., J.
Fred Olander company ₍1928₎
     249 p. illus. (ports.) 19ᶜᵐ.

     1. American literature—South Dakota. 2. American poetry (Collec-
tions) I. Gunderson, Mrs. Gertrude (Bertlesen) joint comp. II. Title.
                                                    29-2185
     Library of Congress   PS571.88L5

    NL 0377181   DLC WaS

Lindberg, James Christian, 1876-
     English grammar for secondary schools, by J. C. Lind-
berg ... Pierre, S. D., J. Fred Olander company ₍1923₎
     190 p. 20ᶜᵐ.

     1. English language—Grammar—1870-
                                                    23-12598
     Library of Congress   PE1111.L488

    NL 0377182   DLC

Lindberg, James Christian, ed. and tr.

     Oehlenschläger, Adam Gottlob, 1779-1850.
        An English version of Oehlenschlaeger's Hakon jarl, by
     James Christian Lindberg.
        (In Nebraska. University. University studies. Lincoln, 1905.
     23ᶜᵐ. v. 5, no. 1, p. 39-141)

₍Lindberg, James Christian₎ 1876-   *comp.*
     "Fifteen South Dakota poets: Eva K. Anglesburg, Charlotte
L. Bertlesen, Margarette Ball Dickson ... ₍and others₎ New
York, H. Harrison ₍1930₎
     96 p. 22½ᵐ.

     "Dedicated by the publisher to J. C. Lindberg ... who compiled these
poems."

     1. American literature — South Dakota. 2. American poetry—20th
cent. I. Title.
                                                    31-13268
     Library of Congress   PS571.88L53
     Copyright A 37400   ₍3₎   811.508

    NL 0377184   DLC NBuU IU OU

VOLUME 334

Lindberg, James Christian, 1876–1937.
Posthumous poems by J. C. Lindberg; The dust that was I.
New York, H. Harrison [1937]
92 p. incl. front. (port.) 21½ᶜᵐ.

I. Title: The dust that was I.

Library of Congress   PS3523.I 515 1937   39–30219
——— Copy 2.
Copyright A 132507   [2]   811.5

NL 0377185   DLC

Lindberg, James Christian, 1876–1937, comp.

Tiger lilies, a volume of Doane verse...
Compiled by J.C. Lindberg, chairman, Lucy
M. Sprague, J.E. Taylor. Minneapolis, Minn.,
The Augsburg publishing house [1930?]
xp., 1 ℓ, 3–91 p. 20 cm.

I. Sprague, Lucy Manville (jt.comp.)
II. Taylor, J.E. (jt.comp.) III. Doane college
Crete, Neb. IV. Title.

NL 0377186   RPB OO

Lindberg, James Christian, 1876–1937.
Wenona, and other poems, by J. C. Lindberg. [Aberdeen?
S. D., 1923?]
44 p. 18ᶜᵐ.

I. Title.

30–28845

Library of Congress   PS3523.I 515W4   811.5

NL 0377187   DLC ViU

Lindberg, Jens, ed.

Aasen, Ivar Andreas, 1813–1896.
... Norske minnestykke. Ved Jens Lindberg. Kristiania,
Norsk folkeminnelag, 1923.

Lindberg, Jens, 1917–
Die Jungen der 7a. Nürnberg, Sebaldus-Verlag [1953]
116 p. illus. 20 cm. (Sebaldus Jugend Buch)

I. Title.

PZ33.L48   54–17104 ‡

NL 0377189   DLC

TS1300
.G64
nr. 3,
etc.
Lindberg, Joel.

Measurement of friction between single fibres. Göteborg
[Gumpert] 1947–

Lindberg, Joel.
Relationship between various surface properties of wool
fibers. Göteborg, Elanders boktr., 1953.
13 p. diagrs. 25 cm. (Doktorsavhandlingar vid Chalmers tek-
niska högskola, nr. 9)
Thesis—Chalmers tekniska högskola, Gothenburg, Sweden.
Without thesis statement.
The dissertation is a summary of four papers. Cf. verso of t. p.
Bibliography: p. [14]

1. Wool.   I. Title.   (Series: Gothenburg, Sweden. Chalmers
tekniska högskola. Doktorsavhandlingar, nr. 9)

TS1547.L48   56–41342

NL 0377191   DLC NN

Lindberg, Johan August
see Lindberg, August, 1846–1916.

Lindberg, Johan Edvard, 1865–
Kinaminnen och fältupplevelser, av J. E. Lindberg.   Stockholm, Baptistmissionens bokförlag [1948]   200 p.   illus.
20cm.

580149B. 1. Missions, Foreign—   China.

NL 0377193   NN

Lindberg, Johan Edvard, 1865–
Om kinesernas fädernedyrkan; eller, Tillbedjan
af de dödas andar ... Stockholm [1901]
83 p.   19 cm.

NL 0377194   CtY

Lindberg, Johan Evald.
... Kvalitetsundersökning och kvalitetsbedömning av bröd-
säd. Reseberättelse av J. E. Lindberg ... Stockholm, Statens
reproduktionsanstalt, 1937.
58 p., 2 l. illus. (incl. map, diagr.) 23½ᶜᵐ. (Sweden. Kungliga
lantbruksstyrelse. Meddelanden. n:r 309. n:r 4 ar 1937)
"Litteratur": p. [61]

1. Flour.

Agr 38–326

U. S. Dept. of agr. Library   118w3 no. 309
for Library of Congress   [TX558.W5]

NL 0377195   DNAL

Lindberg, Johannes
Die Konsumgenossenschaftsbewegung in Schweden. Hamburg, 1952
24 p. illus. (Genossenschaftliche Welt, 4)

NL 0377196   MH

Lindberg, Johannes Emanuel, 1881–
Jonas i valfiskens buk.   Stockholm,
Kooperativa förbundets bokförlag, 1951
238 p.   illus., ports.   23cm.

NL 0377197   MnU

Lindberg, Johannes Emanuel, 1881–
Vätö handelsförening under tjugufem år jämte några ros-
lagsbilder och korta data från ett gånget sekel, av Johannes
Lindberg. [Stockholm, Tryckeri aktiebolaget Thule, 1928]
68 p. illus. (incl. ports., map) 23½ᶜᵐ.
On cover: Vätö handelsförening 1903–1928.

1. Vätö handelsförening.

46–36016

Library of Congress   HD3524.V3L5

NL 0377198   DLC

Lindberg, Johannes Vilhelmus, respondent.
De Ellipsi in Lingua Hebraica dissertatio...
see under Emanuelsson, Petr Jakob, 1802–
1888, praeses.

Lindberg, John, 1901–
An attempt to construct international measures of unemployment, by John Lindberg ...
(*In* International labour review, Geneva. October 1932, v. 26,
p. [491]–512)

1. Unemployed—[Statistics] [1. Unemployment—Statistics] 2. Index
numbers (Economics)   I. Title.   L 33–22

Library, U. S. Dept. of   Labor
Library of Congress   [HD4811.I 65 vol. 26]

NL 0377200   DL MiU

JX1975
.A25
1946
II.A.5
Lindberg, John, 1901–

League of nations. *Secretariat. Economic, financial and
transit dept.*
... Food, famine and relief, 1940–1946. Geneva, League of
nations, 1946.

Lindberg, John, 1901–
Foundations of social survival. New York, Columbia
University Press, 1953.
260 p. 23 cm.

1. Sociology.   I. Title.

HM51.L54   301   53–11452 ‡

OOxM PSC RP MB WaU NBuC CaBVa IdU OrU CaBVaU
NL 0377202   DLC IU OC1 NN TU PPPSW NcD TxU PPLas PP

Lindberg, John, 1901–
A general economic appraisal of Libya. New York, United
Nations Technical Assistance Administration, 1952.
vi, 55 p. tables. 28 cm. (United Nations. [Document] ST/TAA/
K/Libya/1)
"United Nations publication. Sales no.: 1952.II.H.2."

1. Libya—Econ. condit.   I. Title.   (Series)
JX1977.A2 ST/TAA/K/Libya/1
——— Copy 2.   HC567.L5L5   54–4950

ScCleU OC1W DPU N IU MBU DNAL
NL 0377203   DLC IdU WaU IaU MB FU NNC OCU PU–W NN

Lindberg, John, 1901–
Some problems in the construction of index numbers of
unemployment, by John Lindberg ...
(*In* International labour review, Geneva. April 1934, v. 29, p. [472]–
499)

1. Index numbers (Economics) 2. Unemployed—Statistics. [2. Unemployment—Statistics]   I. Title.

Library, U. S. Dept. of   Labor   L 34–61
Library of Congress   [HD4811.I 65 vol. 29]

NL 0377204   DL MiU

Lindberg, John, 1901–
Some problems of international employment statistics, by
John Lindberg ...
(*In* International labour review, Geneva. May 1937. v. 35, p. [568]–
642)

1. Labor [and laboring classes—Statistics] [1. Employment—Statis-
tics] 2. Statistics.   I. Title.   L 37–118

U. S. Dept. of labor. Library
for Library of Congress   [HD4811.I 65 vol. 35]

NL 0377205   DL

VOLUME 334

Lindberg, John S.
The background of Swedish emigration to the United States; an economic and sociological study in the dynamics of migration, by John S. Lindberg ...   Minneapolis, The University of Minnesota press, 1930.
xiv, 272 p. 23⁰ᵐ.

1. Sweden—Emig. & immig. 2. U. S.—Emig. & immig. 3. Sweden—Econ. condit. 4. Swedes in the U. S.   I. Title. II. Title: Swedish emigration to the United States, The background of.
Library of Congress   JV6744.L5   30-8155

NcU ICRL MtU WaS OrU CaBVaU OrCS
NL 0377206   DLC NcD OO OC1 MiU OU WaU ViU MH IU MB

Lindberg, Josef.
... Determination of temperature distribution in an incision on a cylindrical conductor, by Josef Lindberg ... Communicated February 27ᵗʰ, 1929, by H. Pleijel and C. Benedicks. Stockholm, Almqvist & Wiksells boktryckeri-a.-b., 1929.
24 p. illus., diagrs. 28½ᵐ. (Kungl. svenska vetenskapsakademiens handlingar. 3. ser., bd. 7, n:o 2)

1. Temperature.   I. Title.
                                            A 30-1050
Title from Univ. of Chi-   Q64.S828 3. ser., vol. 7, no. 2
cago   Printed by L. C.

NL 0377207   ICU MiU

Lindberg, K
Voyage dans le Sud de l'Iran; carnet de route d'un médecin, à la poursuite du ver de Médine. Lund, C. W. K. Gleerup ₁1955₎
331 p. illus. 23 cm.

1. Iran—Descr. & trav. 2. Dracunculus medinensis.   I. Title.
DS258.L48   56-46650 ‡

NL 0377208   DLC OrU WU OU TxU CtY CU ICU

Lindberg, Kaj.
... Über die formale genese des lungenkrebses, von Kaj Lindberg. Mit 557 abbildungen und 3 tabellen im text. Helsingfors ₁Mercators tryckeri aktiebolag₎ 1935.
2 p.l.,₁3₎–400 p.incl.plates,tables.   2 pl.on 1 l. 25ᵐ.
"Aus dem Pathologischen institut der Universität Helsingfors ... und der Pathologischen abteilung am Karolinischen institut in Stockholm ... "
The first part of the author's account of his investigation appeared in 1935 with title: Über die histologie des primären lungenkrebses.
"Literaturverzeichnis"   p.₁393₎–400.
1. Lunge—Cancer.

NL 0377209   MiU CtY CaBVaU

Lindberg, Kaj.
... Über die histologie des primären lungenkrebses, von Kaj Lindberg. Mit 268 abbildungen, 27 diagrammen und 12 tabellen im text. Helsingfors ₁Mercators tryckeri aktiebolag₎ 1935.
3 p.l.,₁3₎–249 p.   illus.,pl.,diagrs.   25ᵐ.
"Aus dem Pathologischen institut der Universität Helsingfors ... und der Pathologischen abteilung am Karolinischen institut in Stockholm ... "
The second part of the author's account of his investigation appeared in 1935 with title: Über die formale genese des lungenkrebses.
"Literaturverzeichnis": p.₁245₎–249.
1. Lunge—Cancer.

NL 0377210   MiU CaBVaU

Lindberg, Karl August
see
Lindberg, August, 1885–

Hp38   **Lindberg, Karl Hilmer**
Sk2   Skeemålets ljudlära ...   Göteborg, W.
L6   Zachrisson, 1906.
2p.,l.,212p. 25½ᵐ.
Akademisk afhandling - Göteborg.
"Ur Bidrag till kännedom om Göteborgs och Bohusläns fornminnen och historia."

1. Swedish language - Dialects - Skoo.

NL 0377212   CtY MnU ICRL MH IEN

Lindberg, Karl Hugo
see **Lindberg, Hugo, 1887–**

Lindberg, Knut
Cyclopides (Crustacés, Copépodes). Bruxelles, 1951.

(In: Exploration hydrobiologique du Lac Tanganyika (1946-1947). Résultats scientifiques. v. 3, fasc. 2, p. 45-91. illus., II pls., map, tables (part fold.) diagr.)

NL 0377214   PPAN

Lindberg (Knut) ₁1892-   ₎. *Étiologie et pathogénie du vitiligo. 324 pp. 8°. Paris, 1922. No. 428.

NL 0377215   DNLM CtY

TK7872   **Lindberg, L., joint author.**
.V3B5
Björkman, J
Development of trochotrons, by J. Björkman and L. Lindberg. Göteborg, Elanders boktr., 1954.

Lindberg, Lars.
Erotiken i svensk skönlitteratur. Stockholm, Bokförlaget Vido ₁1954₎
163 p. 22 cm.

1. Swedish literature—Hist. & crit. 2. Love in literature.   I. Title.
PT9295.L6L5   56-57985 ‡

NL 0377217   DLC MnU NN CU

PC2460 **Lindberg, Lars.**
.L7   Les locutions verbales figées dans la langue française ... Upsal, Impr. Almqvist & Wiksell, 1898.
₁4₎, 117 p. 25ᵐ.
Thèse—Upsala.
"Titres des ouvrages cités": p. ₁116₎–117.

1. French language—Terms and phrases. 2. French language—Idioms, corrections, errors.

NjP NjR
NL 0377218   ICU CU WaU NRU ICRL CtY PU IU MiU NN MH

Lindberg, Lucile.
The democratic classroom; a guide for teachers. New York, Bureau of Publications, Teachers College, Columbia University, 1954.
115 p. 24 cm. (Teachers College studies in education)

1. Classroom management.   I. Title.
LB3011.L5   371.3   54-7854 ‡

OrPS OrSaW OrU CaBVaU Or OU
OrAshS PPT PPPL OrU PBm PSt OCU OC1 OOxM PU-Penn
MiU WaU WaSpG KMK IdU OrCS IdPI MtU OrLgE OrMonO
NL 0377219   DLC KEmT MsSM PBL PPD TU ViU MB NcD PWcT

Lindberg, M₁aja₎.
Karlchens Reise in der Seifenblase; erzählt und illustriert von M. Lindberg.   Berlin: Pestalozzi Verlags-Anstalt₁, 19—?₎.
col'd illus.   4°.
Unpaged.

NL 0377220   NN

Lindberg, Maja.
Karl's journey to the moon, written and illustrated by Maja Lindberg, translated by Siri Andrews. ₁New York and London, Harper and brothers, 1927₎
cover-title, 28 p., 1 l. col. illus. 29ᵐ.
"Printed and made in Germany."

I. Andrews, Siri, tr. II. Title.
Library of Congress   PZ8.L64Ka   28-26081

NL 0377221   DLC PPD PWcT WaSp NN PP OC1 OLak MB

Lindberg, Marie.
Vegetarisk kogebog, med et kapitel om vegetarismen og de almindeligste vegetariske leveregler.   Christiania, Den norske bogmission, n. d.
il.

NL 0377222   OrP

Lindberg, Marie Louise (Lange) 1918–
... Heavy mineral correlation of the Fox hills, Hell creek and Cannonball sediments, Morton and Sioux counties, North Dakota, by Marie Louise Lindberg ... Grand Forks, N. D., 1945.
cover-title, ₁131₎–143 p. incl. illus., tables. 24ᵐ. (North Dakota. Geological survey. Bulletin 19)
"Reprinted from Journal of sedimentary petrology, vol. 14, no. 3 ... 1944."
Bibliography: p. 143.
1. Geology—North Dakota—Morton co. 2. Geology—North Dakota—Sioux co.   I. Title. II. Title: Mineral correlation of the Fox hills, Hell creek and Cannonball sediments.
                                                 G S 45-12
U. S. Geol. survey. Library
for Library of Congress   QE150.M6L4
——— Copy 2.   QE149.A23 no. 19
                          ₁5₎†   (557.84) 553

NL 0377223   DI-GS DLC

Lindberg, Milton Benjamin.
Gog all agog "in the latter days"; Russia and Palestine in the light of Ezekiel 38 and 39, by Milton B. Lindberg ...   Chicago, Ill., The Book store, Chicago Hebrew mission ₁1946₎
38, ₁2₎ p. 19ᵐ.
"First edition, 1938 ... Sixth edition (revised) 1946."

1. Bible—Prophecies—Russia. 2. End of the world.   I. Title.
Library of Congress   BS649.R9L5 1946   46-19620
                            ₁3₎   220.1

NL 0377224   DLC

VOLUME 334

Lindberg, Milton Benjamin.
  Gog all agog "in the latter days"; Russia and Palestine in the light of Ezekiel 38 and 39, by Milton B. Lindberg...   Chicago, Ill., The Book store, Chicago Hebrew mission ₁1947₁   38, ₂2₁ p. 19cm.

  "First edition, 1938...Seventh edition (Revised) 1947."

  ₄1. Prophecies, Biblical.   2. Russia   —Prophecies.

NL 0377225   NN

Lindberg, Milton Benjamin.
  Palestine and the Jew today in the light of prophecy, by Rev. Milton B. Lindberg ...   Los Angeles, Calif., Printed by A. J. Johnson ₁1933₁
  48 p. illus. (incl. maps) diagr. 22ᶜᵐ.

  1. Palestine—Descr. & trav. 2. Bible—Prophecies. 3. Jews in Palestine.

Library of Congress	DS107.3.L715	33–22179
Copyright AA 125661	₂2₁	915.69

NL 0377226   DLC

Lindberg, Milton Benjamin.
  Palestine and the Jew today in the light of prophecy, by Milton B. Lindberg...   Chicago, Chicago Hebrew mission ₁1946₁
  64 p. illus. 19cm.

  12. ed., rev.

  1. Palestine—Colonization.   2. Jews—Restoration.
N. Y. P. L.   December 10, 1948

NL 0377227   NN

Lindberg, Milton Benjamin.
  Palestine today in the light of prophecy, by Rev. Milton B. Lindberg ...   St. Paul, Minn., Virtue printing co. ₁1930₁
  31 p. illus., diagr. 22ᶜᵐ.

  1. Palestine—Descr. & trav. 2. Bible—Prophecies.

Library of Congress	DS107.3.L72	30–19088
—— Copy 2.		
Copyright A 26153	₂2₁	915.69

NL 0377228   DLC

Lindberg, Milton Benjamin.
  Witnessing to Jews; a handbook of practical aids.   Foreword by Torrey M. Johnson.   Chicago, Moody Press ₁1948₁
  95 p. 20 cm.

  "Suitable literature for distribution": p. 81–85. "Books for further study": p. 89.

  1. Missions—Jews.   I. Title.

BV2620.L5	266	48–6474*

NL 0377229   DLC NN

Lindberg, Niels, 1829-1886.
  Grundtvigs politiske stade, af N. Lindberg...
Odense, R. Nielsen, 1876.   xi, 214 p. 18cm.

  1. Grundtvig, Nicolai Frederik Severin, 1783-1872.
  2. Denmark—Politics, 19th cent.

NL 0377230   NN MH-AH IEN

LINDBERG, Niels, 1829-1886.
Templet i Jerusalem och Försoningsdagen
hos Judarne. Öfversättning från Danskan af
Eva Wigström. Stockholm, A.V. Carlson, n.d.

  Plates.   Arc 505.5.32

NL 0377231   MH

Lindberg, Niels, 1829–1886.
  Templet i Jerusalem og Forsoningsdagen hos Jøderne, af Niels Lindberg... Med 3 kobberstukne Tavler.   Kolding: K. Jørgensen, 1880. 111 p.   8°.

                           SCHIFF COLLECTION.

  1. Temples—Jerusalem.   2. Atonement day.
N. Y. P. L.   July 14, 1930

NL 0377232   NN MH

Lindberg, Niels, 1904–
  Idealer og regler i anvendt økonomik. Kjøbenhavn, Nyt nordisk forlag, 1951.
  470 p. 24 cm.

  Thesis—Københavns universitet.
  Bibliography: p. ₁459₁–465.

  1. Economics. 2. Social ethics.   I. Title.

HB72.L5		52–29874

NL 0377233   DLC NN NIC MH NNC MnU CtY

Lindberg, Niels, 1904-
  Nutidens økonomi og fremtidens; betragininger over den statskapitalistiske udvikling. København, Martins forlag, 1954.

  280 p.

NL 0377234   MH

Lindberg, Niels, 1904–
  Prisudvikling og Prispolitik. København, Udg. af Folkeuniversitetsudvalget, i Kommission hos E. Munksgaard, 1942.
  16 p. 20 cm. (Grundrids ved folkelig Universitetsundervisning. Nr. 443)

  "Litteratur": p. ₂2₁

  1. Prices—Denmark.   I. Title.   (Series)

		A 48–4611*
Harvard Univ. Library		
for Library of Congress	₁1₁	

NL 0377235   MH

Lindberg, Nils Gustaf
  see Lindberg, Gustaf, 1883-

PD   Lindberg, Nils Herman
5111   Lärobok i svenska. Lehrbuch der schwedi-
L74   schen Sprache. Rootsi keele öpperaamat.
    Tartu/Dorpat, J. G. Krüger, 1930.
    viii, 155 p. 24cm.

  1. Swedish language—Grammar.

NL 0377237   NIC

Lindberg, Nils Herman, 1894-
... Lehrbuch der schwedischen sprache. 4. umgearb., erweiterte aufl. Göteborg, Riksföreningen för svenskhetens bevarande i utlandet, 1945.
  viii, 235 p.
  "Literaturanweisungen": p. ₂279₃–285.

NL 0377238   ICU

Lindberg, Nils Herman, 1894–
  Lehrbuch der schwedischen Sprache. 5. umgearb., erweiterte Aufl. Göteborg, Riksföreningen för svenskhetens bevarande i utlandet (i kommission) 1950.
  viii, 290 p. map (on lining paper) 22 cm.
  "Literaturnachweis": p. ₂282₁–290.

  1. Swedish language—Grammar. 2. Swedish language—Chrestomathies and readers. I. Title.

		A 51–1053
Minnesota. Univ. Libr.		
for Library of Congress	₂2₁	

NL 0377239   MnU PU

Lindberg, Nils Olov Hugo
  see Lindberg, Olov, 1914–

4QK   Lindberg, O
118   Blomsterstudier. Med förord af V. Adler.
    Stockholm, Wahlström & Widstrand [1904]

NL 0377241   DLC-P4

HD9835   **Lindberg, Olof.**
.S82L5   Näringsgeografiska studier över den svenska pappersindustriens lokalisering. Uppsala, Almqvist & Wiksells boktr., 1951.
  2 v. illus., maps, diagrs. 25 cm. (Geographica; skrifter från Upsala universitets Geografiska institution, nr. 23)
  Akademisk avhandling—Uppsala.
  Extra t. p. with thesis statement, inserted.
  Summary in English.
  "Tryckta källor och litteratur": v. 1, p. ₂241₁–243.
  CONTENTS.—A. Text.—B. Kartor och diagram.

  1. Paper making and trade—Sweden. 2. Industries, Location of. (Series: Uppsala. Universitet. Geografiska institutionen. Geographica, nr. 23)

		A 52–1450
Harvard Univ. Library		
for Library of Congress	₁1₁	

NL 0377242   MH NN MnU DLC ICU MoU

Lindberg, Olov, 1914-
  Chemistry and physiology of mitochondria and microsomes, by Olov Lindberg and Lars Ernster. Wien, Springer, 1954.
  156 p. illus. 26 cm. (Protoplasmatologia: Handbuch der Protoplasmaforschung. Bd. 3: Cytoplasma - Organellen, A: Chondriosomen, Mikrosomen, Sphaerosomen, 4)

  Includes bibliography.

  1. Mitochondria.   2. Protoplasm. I. Ernster, Lars,   joint author. II. Title.

  NBuU NBuC CU-M UU MU N OrU-M MtBC
NL 0377243   WU NcU OU ICU InRenS CSt DNLM ViU NIC

Lindberg, Olov, 1914-
  On the occurrence of propanediol phosphate and its effect on the carbohydrate metabolism in animal tissues. Stockholm, Almqvist & Wiksells boktr., 1946.
  45 p. diagrs. 22 cm. (Arkiv för kemi, mineralogi och geologi, bd. 23 A, n:o 2)
  Cover title.
  Akademisk avhandling—Stockholms högskola.
  Thesis t.-p., with imprint, Uppsala, Almqvist & Wiksells boktr., inserted.
  "References": p. 45.
  1. Phosphates. 2. Metabolism.   (Series)
                            Full name: Nils Olov Hugo Lindberg

QP535.P1L5		52–24070

NL 0377244   DLC CtY

VOLUME 334

Lindberg, Oskar Fredrik, 1887–
(Adagio, string orchestra)

Adagio. Pingst. För stråkorkester. **Partitur och stämmor.** Stockholm, Nordiska musikförlaget (1945)

score (2 p.) and parts. 34 cm.

1. String-orchestra music—Scores and parts.

M1145.L77A3   49–55554*

NL 0377245 DLC

Lindberg, Oskar Fredrik, 1887–
(Chorales, organ)

Fyra orgelkoraler. Stockholm, Nordiska musikförlaget (1944)

7 p. 23 x 31 cm.

CONTENTS.—Gud ej sitt tryckta barn förgäter.—Jesus allt mitt goda är.—Tänk när en gång det töcken har försvunnit.—Helige Ande, låt nu ske.

1. Chorale preludes.

M11.L   48–38426*

NL 0377246 DLC

Lindberg, Oskar Fredrik, 1887–

En gammal kämpavisa från Dalarna, från 1500 talet. Partitur. Stockholm, Nordiska musikförlaget (1945)

score (25 p.) 34 cm.

For orchestra.

1. Orchestral music—Scores. I. Title.

M1045.L74G3   49–52992*

NL 0377247 DLC

Lindberg, Oskar Fredrik, 1887–

Mitt land; (text av) Georg Åhlstad. För piano, orgel (harmonium) solo och manskör. Klaverutdrag (!) Stockholm, Nordiska musikförlaget (1945)

score (24 p.) 31 cm.

1. Choruses, Secular (Men's voices, 4 pts.) with piano and reed-organ. I. Ahlstad, Georg. Mitt land. II. Title.

M1564.L   49–56036*

NL 0377248 DLC

Lindberg, Oskar Fredrik, 1887–   Pingst
see his Adagio.

Lindberg, Oskar Fredrik, 1887–
(Requiem)

Requiem; för soli, kör, orkester och orgel. Partitur. (n. p., *1949)

score (109 p.) 36 cm.

Reproduced from ms.

1. Requiems—Scores.

M2010.L73R4   49–54611 *

NL 0377250 DLC

Lindberg, Oskar Fredrik, 1887–

Sånger under vårdträdet, kantat vid Svenska folkskolans 100-års jubileum. Till text av Helmer V. Nyberg. Utgiven på uppdrag av Läraroganisationernas kommitté. Stockholm, Nordiska musikförlaget (1942)

score (19 p.) 31 cm.

Cover title.
For solo voices (SBar) children's chorus in unison and mixed chorus, with piano and organ acc.

1. Cantatas, Secular—Vocal scores with piano and organ. 2. Folksongs, Swedish. I. Nyberg, Helmer Viktor. II. Title.

M1533.L76S3   48–32133*

NL 0377251 DLC

---

sVM
8
L 74s
   LINDBERG, OSKAR Fredrik, 1887–
(Sonata, organ, G minor) Sonat G-moll för orgel. Stockholm, Nordiska musikförlaget (194–?)
score (17 p.) 23 x 31 cm.

NL 0377252 ICN

Lindberg, Oskar Fredrik, 1887–

Tre dalmålningar. Op. 1. Paritur. (n. p., *1949)

score (77 p.) 36 cm.

Reproduced from ms.
For orchestra.

CONTENTS.—Preludium. Ganglåt.—Natt över skogen.—Lek.

1. Suites (Orchestra)—Scores. I. Title: Dalmålningar.

M1003.L725 op. 1   49–54610*

NL 0377253 DLC

Bh57
68J
   Lindberg, Otto Emil, 1850–1920.
... Hârûn Arraschîd och hans närmaste samtida i historia och saga, af O.E.Lindberg. Göteborg, Wettergren & Kerber, 1900.
xi,175p. 19½cm. (Populärt vetenskapliga föreläsningar vid Göteborgs högskola, XIV)

NL 0377254 CtY

Mc x395
908t
   Lindberg, Otto Emil, 1850–1920.
... Jobs-boken; eller, Lidandets problem på israelitisk mark. Stockholm, A.Bonniers förlag[1908]
4p.ℓ.,94p. 19½cm. (Populärt vetenskapliga föreläsningar vid Göteborgs Högskola. Ny följd, VI)
"Använd litteratur": p.[93]-94.

1. Bible. O.T. Job. x.ser.^

NL 0377255 CtY

4BP
312
   Lindberg, Otto Emil, 1850–1920.
Mohammed och Qoranen. Göteborg, Wettergren & Kerber, 1897.
194 p.

(Populärt vetenskapliga föreläsningar vid Göteborgs Högskola, 6)

NL 0377256 DLC-P4 CtY MH

Lindberg, O(tto) E(mil), 1850–1920.

Semiterna och den alfabetiska skriften. (In: Festskrift tillägnad Oscar Ekman. Göteborg, 1898. 8°. p. 134-151, 1 fac.)

Göteborgs Högskolas årsskrift. Bd. 4.

1. Alphabet (Semitic).—History.
N. Y. P. L.   August 19, 1911.

NL 0377257 NN

Lindberg, Otto E(mil), 1850–1920.

Studier öfver de semitiska ljuden w och y. Akademisk afhandling, Upsala. Lund, Berlingska boktryckeri- och stilgjuteri-aktiebolaget, 1893.
pp. (1), 176 +.

NL 0377258 MH CtY ICRL ICU CU

Lindberg, Otto Emil, 1850–1920.

Studier öfver de semitiska ljuden w och y, af O. E. Lindberg. (Göteborg, D. F. Bonniers förlagsexpedition, 1894)

1 p. L., 176, (3) p. 22ᶜᵐ. (Göteborgs kongl. vetenskaps- och vitterhetssamhälles handlingar. Ny (i. e. 3.) tidsföljd, 28:de häftet)

Issued also as the author's thesis.

1. Semitic languages—Phonology.

Illinois. Univ. Library   A 45–5605
   for Library of Congress   AS284.G7 föl. 3, hft. 28

NL 0377259 IU DLC

Lindberg, O(tto) E(mil), 1850–1920.

Vergleichende Grammatik der semitischen Sprachen. Göteborg: W. Zachrisson, 1897. 2 p.l., xi, 160 p., 1 l. 8°. (Göteborgs Högskolas årsskrift. Bd. 3.)

1. Semitic languages.—Grammar.   2. Phonetics (Semitic).
N. Y. P. L.   August 19, 1911.

NL 0377260 NN RPB MH CtY OCH PU PPDrop NjNbS

Lindberg, Otto G 1886–

My story. Convent Station, N. J., General Drafting Co., 1955.

unpaged. illus. 24 cm.

1. General Drafting Company, inc.

GA407.L5A3   526.8069   56–20520 ‡

NL 0377261 DLC OrCS

Lindberg, Pär Harald.

Bibliotheca zoologica Fenniae. Helsingforsiae, 1937–

70   v. 23 cm. (Acta Societatis pro Fauna et Flora Fennica, 59)

A continuation of Bibliotheca zoologica Fennica. Hrsg. von Zoologen Finlands. Helsingfors, 1900.

CONTENTS.—(1) 1901–1930.—(2) 1931–1940.

1. Zoology—Finland. I. Title. (Series: Societas pro Fauna et Flora Fennica, Helsingfors. Acta, 59 (etc.))

QH7.S7 vol. 59, etc.   55–4840

NL 0377262 DLC MnU CtY

VOLUME 334

87
125
70
Lindberg, Pär Harald
Bibliotheca zoologica Fenniae; opera
annorum 1931-1940; mandatu Societatis pro
Fauna et Flora Fennica curavit Pär Harald
Lindberg. Helsingforsiae, 1953.
ix, 284 p. 24 cm. (Acta Societatis pro
Fauna et Flora Fennica, 70)

1. Zoology - Bibl.[1] 2. Zoology - Finland -
Bibl.[2]

NL 0377263 CtY

Lindberg, Pehr.
Architectura mechanica. Moole boek of eenige opstalle van
moolens neffens haare gronden etc.: getekend door, Pieter Linpergh...uytgegeeven door Iustus Danckerts. Amsterdam: C.
Danckerts[, 1727?]. 6 l. [31] pl. f°.

251536A. 1. Windmills. 2. Dan-   ckerts, Justus, editor.
N.Y.P.L.   August 31, 1926

NL 0377264 NN IU NNE NNC MdBP CtY CU MH

Lindberg, Pehr.
Moole boek, of eenige opstalle von moolens
neffens haare gronden etc. getekend door Pieter
Linpergh ... in plaat-druk nytgegeeven door
Iustus Danckerts. Amsterdam, gedrukt by
Cornelis Danckerts [1686?]
10 p. 32 pls. F°.

NL 0377265 MB

Lindberg, Per, 1890-1944.
Anders de Wahl [av] Per Lindberg och Sten af Geijerstam.
Stockholm, Wahlström & Widstrand [1944]
306 p. plates, ports., facsims. 24 cm.

1. De Wahl, Anders, 1869-   I. Geijerstam, Sten af, joint
author.   Full name: Per August Lindberg.
PN2778.D4L5   927.92   50-49793

NL 0377266 DLC NcD NN WaU ICU MnU

Lindberg, Per, 1890-1944.
August Lindberg, skådespelaren och människan; interiörer
från 80- och 90-talens teaterliv. Stockholm, Natur och kultur
[1943]
452 p. illus., ports. 23 cm.

1. Lindberg, August, 1846-1916.
                                 Full name: Per August Lindberg.
PN2778.L47L5   927.92   50-49794

NL 0377267 DLC NcD NN MnU

Lindberg, Per, 1890-1944.
Bakom masker. Stockholm, Bonnier [1949]
188 p. 20 cm.
Contents.—Några synpunkter på Pär Lagerkvists dramatik.—
Hjalmar Bergman, dramatikern.—Den ökande Hjalmar Bergman.—
Hjalmar Bergmans radiodramatik.—Clownen Jac.—Pirandello som
dramatiker.—Ett teaterbibliotek.

1. Lagerkvist, Pär Fabian, 1891-   2. Bergman, Hjalmar Fredrik
Elgerus, 1883-1931. 3. Pirandello, Luigi, 1867-1936. I. Title.
PT9875.L2Z7   839.746   A 50-4291
Minnesota. Univ. Libi
for Library of Congress   [3]†

NL 0377268 MnU DLC MH NN KU WaU

Lindberg, Per, 1890-1944.
Baletten under fyra sekler. Stockholm, Natur och kultur
[1943]
175 p. illus., ports. 28 cm.

1. Ballet. I. Title.

GV1787.L48   50-48770

NL 0377269 DLC NSyU NN WaU

Lindberg, Per, 1890-1944.
En bok om Per Lindberg
see under title

Lindberg, Per, 1890-1944
Gösta Ekman; skådespelaren och människan. 2. uppl.
Stockholm, Natur och kultur [1942]

311 p. illus., ports.

NL 0377271 MH ICU MnU

Lindberg, Per, 1890-1944.
Gösta Ekman, skådespelaren och människan. 4. uppl.
Stockholm, Natur och kultur [1943]
311 p. illus., ports. 23 cm.

1. Ekman, Gösta, 1890-
PN2778.E4L5 1943   50-49801

NL 0377272 DLC

Lindberg, Per, 1890-1944.
Kring ridån; studier i teaterns utveckling under femtio år,
av Per Lindberg. Stockholm: A. Bonnier[, 1932]. 288 p.
22½ cm.

684012A. 1. Stage—Hist.
N.Y.P.L.   February 23, 1934

NL 0377273 NN MnU WaU

LINDBERG, Per. 1890-1944.
Regiproblem; spridda artiklar. Stockholm,
Wahlström & Widstrand, [1927].
12°. illustr.

NL 0377274 MH

Lindberg, Per, 1890-1944.
... Tillkomsten av Strindbergs "Mäster Olof" jämte en undersökning av de två första texterna, av Per Lindberg. Stockholm, A. Bonnier i distribution [1915]
115 p. 22¾ cm. (Skrifter från Stockholms högskolas litteraturhistoriska seminarium ... 1)

1. *Strindberg, August, 1849-1912. Mäster Olof.
                                                      34-37501
Library of Congress   PT9812.M32L5   839.726

NL 0377275 DLC PU CU CtY NN NjP MH

Lindberg, Peter August, 1863-
Adam; en berättelse, af P. A. Lindberg. Chicago,
P. A. Lindberg & co., 1899.
227 p. 20½ cm.

I. Title.

Library of Congress   PT9995.L5A7   99-4943 Revised

NL 0377276 DLC WaU MnHi

Lindberg, Ramon Iverson.
Fermentation of tobacco [Cincinn., 1939]
6 p.l., 15 numb. l., 1 l. incl. tables.

NL 0377277 OCU

Lindberg, Robert Benjamin, 1914-
The antigenic structure of H. capsulatum, particularly the
yeast phase. Ann Arbor, University Microfilms, 1950 [i. e.
1951]
([University Microfilms, Ann Arbor, Mich.] Publication no. 2412)
Microfilm copy of typewritten ms. Positive.
Collation of the original: v, 130 l. tables.
Thesis—University of Michigan.
Abstracted in Microfilm abstracts, v. 11 (1951) no. 2, p. 220-222.
Bibliography: leaves [125]-130.
1. Histoplasma capsulatum. 2. Antigens and antibodies.
Microfilm AC-1 no. 2412   Mic A 51-156

Michigan. Univ. Libr.
for Library of Congress   [1]†

NL 0377278 MiU DLC

Lindberg, Robert G
Growth, population dynamics, and field behavior in the
spiny lobster, Panulirus interruptus (Randall) Berkeley,
University of California Press, 1955.
157-248 p. plates, maps, diagrs. 26 cm. (University of California publications in zoölogy, v. 59, no. 6)
Bibliography: p. 228-231.

1. Lobsters.   (Series: California. University. University of
California publications in zoology, v. 59, no. 6)
[QL1.C15 vol. 59, no. 6]   A 55-9803

California. Univ. Libr.
for Library of Congress   [5]

NL 0377279 CU MsU MU DLC DI TxU OCU OU FTaSU WaWW

---

cF
870
S23
L5
Lindberg, Ruby
Some Swedes, in early California. [Rock
Island, Ill., Augustana Book Concern, 1953]
3-15 p. 25 cm.

Constitutes the Swedish pioneer historical
quarterly, v. 4, no. 1, Jan. 1953. Title
from 1st article.

NL 0377280 C

Lindberg, S[extus] O[tto] 1835-1889.
... Animadversiones de hypno elegante Hook. et speciebus europæis plagiothecii scripsit S. O. Lindberg. Helsingfors, T. Sederholms boktryckeri, 1867.
1 p. l., [2]-38 p. 21½ cm.
At head of title: Notiser ur Sällskapets pro fauna et flora fennica förhandlingar. IX. 1867.

1. Hypnum elegans. 2. Plagiothecium.

Library of Congress   QK539.P7L   5-24420†

NL 0377281 DLC NNBG

VOLUME 334

Lindberg, S₁extus₁ O₁tto₁ 1835–1889.
Anmärkningar angående *Hypnum vaucheri* och *Eucladium verticillatum* i Bot. not. 1863. Af S. O. Lindberg. ₁Stockholm, I. Hæggströms boktryckeri, 1863₁
4 p. 22½ᶜᵐ.
Caption title.

1. Hypnum vaucheri. 2. Eucladium verticillatum.

Library of Congress   QK537.L72   5–24413†

NL 0377282   DLC

Lindberg, S₁extus₁ O₁tto₁ 1835–1889.
... *Anomodon apiculatus* Br. & Sch. et *Fimbriaria lindenbergii* Cord., novæ floræ Scandinaviæ cives. Describit S. O. Lindberg. ₁Upsala, Kongl. akad. Boktryckeriet, 1865₁
4 p. 21½ᶜᵐ.
Caption title.
At head of title: E diar. "Botaniska notiser," 1865.

1. Anomodon apiculatus. 2. Fimbriaria lindenbergii.

Library of Congress   QK544.S2L   5–24152†

NL 0377283   DLC

Lindberg, S₁extus₁ O₁tto₁ 1835–1889.
Bidrag till mossornas synonymi. Af S. O. Lindberg ... Stockholm, P. A. Norstedt & söner, 1863.
36 p. 21½ᶜᵐ.
Aftryck ur Öfversigt af K. V. A. Förhandl. 1863, n:o 7.
Unfinished; no more published.

1. Botany—Nomenclature. 2. Mosses.

Library of Congress   QK96.L73   5–19593†

NL 0377284   DLC NNBG

588.2
L742B

Lindberg, Sextus Otto, 1835–1889.
₁Bidrag till mossornas synonymi ...
₁ Stockholm, 1863₁
p. 385–418. 23 cm.

Separated from Öfversigt af K. V. A. Förhandl. 1863, n:o 7.
Unfinished; no more published.
1. Botany. Nomenclature. 2. Mosses.

NL 0377285   NcD

Lindberg, S₁extus₁ O₁tto₁ 1835–1889.
... Bryological notes. By S. O. Lindberg, M. D. ₁London, 1871₁
₁65₁–72 p. 21½ᶜᵐ.
Extracted from the Linnean society's Journal.—Botany, vol. XIII, 1873.

1. Mosses.

Library of Congress   QK537.L725   5–24414†

NL 0377286   DLC

Lindberg, S₁extus₁ O₁tto₁ 1835–1889.
... Contributio ad floram cryptogamam Asiæ boreali-orientalis. Auctore S. O. Lindberg ... Helsingforsiæ, ex officina typographica Societatis litterariae fennicae, 1872.
1 p. l., ₁223₁–280 p. 28 x 22½ᶜᵐ.
At head of title: Acta Societatis scientiarum fennicae, x.
Societati exhibita die 19 febr. 1872.

1. Mosses—Asia.

Library of Congress   QK545.J3L   5–23745†

NL 0377287   DLC NcD

, **Lindberg, Sextus Otto, 1835–1889.**
Contributio ad floram cryptogamam Asiæ boreali-orientalis. Auctore S. O. Lindberg ...
(*In* Finska vetenskaps-societeten. Helsingfors. Acta Societatis scientiarum fennicæ. Helsingforsiæ, 1875. 26½ x 22½ᶜᵐ. t. x, p. ₁221₁–280)
"Societati exhibita die 19 febr. 1872."
Also published separately.

1. Mosses—Asia.

New York. Public library   A C 38–2
for Library of Congress   [Q60.F5 vol. 10]
₁4₁   (508)

NL 0377288   NN DLC CaBVaU

QK539
.L4
L5

Lindberg, Sextus Otto, 1835–1889.
De Cryphaeis Europaeis. [Helsingforsiae, 1881]
[71]–75 p. 22 cm.
Caption title.
"Meddel. af Societas pro Fauna et Flora fennica, 6: 1881."

1. Cryphaea arborea. 2. Cryphaea lamyi.
3. Musci. i.t. 4. Leucodontaceae.

NL 0377289   NNBG

Lindberg, S₁extus₁ O₁tto₁ 1835–1889.
De speciebus timmiæ observationes. Auctore S. O. Lindberg. ₁Stockholm, 1864₁
333–338 p. 22ᶜᵐ.
Caption title.
Acad. scient. suec. propos. die 8 junii 1864.
Öfvers. af K. Vet.-akad. förh., 1864, n:o 6.

1. Timmia.

Library of Congress   QK539.T58L   5–24425†

NL 0377290   DLC

Lindberg, Sextus Otto, 1835–1889.
Europas och Nord Amerikas hvitmossor (Sphagna) jämte en inledning om utvecklingen och organbildningen inom mossornas alla tre hufvudgrupper ... Helsingfors, J.C.Frenckell, 1882.

xxxviii, 88 p. 23 cm.
Thesis - K.Alexanders-Universitetet i Finland.

NL 0377291   MH PPAN NcD

Lindberg, S₁extus₁ O₁tto₁ 1835–1889.
Förteckning öfver mossor, insamlade under de svenska expeditionerna till Spitsbergen 1858 och 1861. Af S. O. Lindberg. ⟨Meddelad den 12 december 1866⟩ ₁Stockholm, 1866₁
535–561, ₁1₁ p. 21½ᶜᵐ.
Öfvers. af K. Vet.-akad. förh. årg. 23.

1. Mosses—Spitzbergen.

Library of Congress   QK544.R9L   5–24151†

NL 0377292   DLC NNBG

Lindberg, S₁extus₁ O₁tto₁ 1835–1889.
... Genera europæa hepaticarum secundum novam dispositionem naturalem. ₁Helsingforsiæ, 186–?₁
₁4₁ p. 29ᶜᵐ.
Caption title.

1. Hepaticae.

Library of Congress   QK553.L74   5–37263†

NL 0377293   DLC

Lindberg, Sextus Otto, 1835–1889.
Granskning af mossorna uti Vaillant's Botanicon parisiense, af S. O. Lindberg.
(*In* K. Svenska vetenskaps-akademien, Stockholm. Öfversigt. Stockholm, 1864. 21½ cm. Vol. xx, p. 455–460)

1. Vaillant, Sebastien, 1669–1722. Botanicon parisiense.
2. Bryology.
Q64.S87   vol. 20   5–24163 rev
———— Copy 2, separate.   QK313.V1₁BL5

NL 0377294   DLC

Lindberg, Sextus Otto, 1835–1889.
Hepaticæ in Hibernia mense julii 1873 lectæ a S. O. Lindberg ...
(*In* Finska vetenskaps-societeten, Helsingfors. Acta Societatis scientiarum fennicæ. Helsingforsiæ, 1875. 26½ x 22½ᶜᵐ. t. x, p. ₁465₁–559)
"Societati exhibitum die 28 septembris 1874."
Also published separately.

1. Hepaticae—Ireland.

New York. Public library   A C 38–3
for Library of Congress   [Q60.F5 vol. 10]
₁4₁   (508)

NL 0377295   NN DLC

Lindberg, S₁extus₁ O₁tto₁ 1835–1889.
... *Hepaticæ* in Hibernia mense julii 1873 lectæ a S. O. Lindberg (Societati exhibitum die 28 septembris 1874.) Helsingforsiæ, ex officina typographica Societatis litterariæ fennicæ, 1875.
1 p. l., ₁467₁–559 p. 27ᶜᵐ.
"Acta Societatis scientiarum fennicæ, x."

1. Hepaticae. 2. Botany—Ireland.

Library of Congress   QK558.L74   5–37283†

NL 0377296   DLC NNBG

Lindberg, Sextus Otto, 1835–1889.
Hepaticologiens utveckling från äldsta tider till och med Linné, af S. O. Lindberg. ₁Helsingfors, J. C. Frenckell & sons tryckeri, 1877₁
₁4₁ 51 p. 29ᶜᵐ.
Akademisk afhandling—Helsingfors.

NL 0377297   ICJ MH PPAN NNC ICRL

QK535
.L5

Lindberg, Sextus Otto, 1835–1889.
Historiska data rörande vår kännedom om moss-sporens groning. Program af S. O. Lindberg. Helsingfors, J. C. Frenckell, 1884.
11 p. 27 cm.

1. Musci. 2. Spores (Botany) 3. Botany - History. i.t.

NL 0377298   NNBG

VOLUME 334

Lindberg, S[extus] O[tto] 1835–1889.
Kritisk granskning af mossorna uti Dillenii Historia muscorum. Program af S. O. Lindberg. Helsingfors, J. C. Frenckell & son, 1883.
59, [2] p. 26½ᶜᵐ.
Inbjudningsskrift—Helsingfors.

1. Mosses.   2. Dillenius, Johann Jakob, 1687–1747. Historia muscorum.

Library of Congress   QK537.D57L   5-24140†

NL 0377299   DLC MH CU PPAN

Lindberg, S[extus] O[tto] 1835–1889.
En liten profbit på namnförbistring. Af S. O. Lindberg. Helsingfors, T. Sederholm, 1867.
18 p. 21½ᶜᵐ.

1. Botany—Nomenclature.

Library of Congress   QK96.L74   5-23957†

NL 0377300   DLC

Lindberg, Sextus Otto, 1835–1889.
... Manipulus muscorum primus [secundus] quem scripsit S. O. Lindberg. Helsingfors, T. Sederholms boktryckeri, 1870–74.
2 v. pl. 22 cm.
Notiser ur Sällskapets pro fauna et flora fennica förhandlingar. XI. 1870, XIII. 1874.

1. Bryology.

QK537.L73   5—24415

NL 0377301   DLC

QK537
.L454
Lindberg, Sextus Otto, 1835–1889.
Manipulus Muscorum primus[-secundus. Helsingfors, T. Sederholms boktr., 1871]-74.
2 v. in 1. 1 plate. 24 cm.

Part 2: Notiser ur Sällskapets pro Fauna et Flora Fennica förhandlingar, 13, 1874.

1. Musci. i.t. ii.s: Notiser ur Sällskapets pro Fauna et Flora Fennica förhandlingar, 13.

NL 0377302   NNBG

Lindberg, S[extus] O[tto] 1835–1889.
Monographia metzgeriæ. Auctore S. O. Lindberg ... (Societati exhibita die 3 octobris 1874.) Helsingforsiæ, ex officina typographica Societatis litterariae fennicae, 1877.
48 p. 2 pl. (1 fold.) 22½ᶜᵐ.

1. Metzgeria.

Library of Congress   QK555.M6L   5-37281†

NL 0377303   DLC NNBG

QK555
.M2
L5
Lindberg, Sextus Otto, 1835–1889.
Monographia praecursoria Peltolepidis, Sauteriae et Cleveae. Helsingforsiae, Ex officina J. Simelii, 1882.
15 p. 22 cm. (Acta Societatis pro Fauna et Flora Fennica, t.2, nr.3)

1. Peltolepis. 2. Sauteria. 3. Clevea.
4. Marchantiaceae. 5. Hepaticae. i.t. ii.s.

NL 0377304   NNBG

Lindberg, Sextus Otto, 1835–1889.
... *Musci* Asiæ borealis. Beschreibung der von den schwedischen expeditionen nach Sibirien in den jahren 1875 und 1876 gesammelten moose, mit berücksichtigung aller früheren bryologischen angaben für das russische Nord-Asien, von S. O. Lindberg und H. W. Arnell ... Stockholm, P. A. Norstedt & söner, 1889–90.
2 v. 31ᶜᵐ. (Kongl. svenska vetenskaps-akademiens handlingar. [Ny följd] bd. 23, n:o 5, 10)
CONTENTS.—1. th. Lebermoose.—2. th. Laubmoose.

1. Mosses—Siberia.   I. Arnell, Hampus Wilhelm, 1848–1932.
A 43-167

Chicago. Univ. Library   Q64.S85 bd. 23, no. 5, 10
for Library of Congress

NL 0377305   ICU NN DLC NcD

588.2
L742MD
Lindberg, Sextus Otto, 1835–1889.
... Musci nonnulli scandinavici descripti a S. O. Lindberg ... [Helsingfors, J. Simelii arfvingars tryckeri, 1879]
14 p. 22 cm.

Caption title.
"Meddel. af Societas pro fauna et flora fennica, 5:1879."
"Societati exhibitum die 8 Novembris 1879."

1. Mosses. Scandinavia. I. Societas pro fauna et flora fennica, Helsingfors.

NL 0377307   NcD

Lindberg, S[extus] O[tto] 1835–1889.
... Musci novi scandinavici. Descripsit S. O. Lindberg. Helsingfors, T. Sederholms boktryckeri, 1868.
1 p. l., [255]-299 p. 22ᶜᵐ.
At head of title: Notiser ur Sällskapets pro fauna et flora fennica förhandlinger. IX. 1868.

1. Mosses—Scandinavia.

Library of Congress   QK544.S2L7   5-23731†

NL 0377308   DLC NNBG

Lindberg, Sextus Otto, 1835–1889.
Musci scandinavici in systemate novo naturali dispositi, a S. O. Lindberg. Upsaliae, ex officina Iesaiae Edquist, 1879.
1 p. l., 50 p. 21ᶜᵐ.

1. Mosses. 2. Botany—Scandinavia. [2. Scandinavia—Botany]
Agr 25-1074

Library, U. S. Dept. of   Agriculture 461.31L64

NL 0377309   DNAL PPAN ICJ WaU NcD CU NNBG

Lindberg, Sextus Otto, 1835–1889.   L580.4 L645
Några ord om blomman och blomställningen. Program af S. O. Lindberg. Helsingfors, J. C. Frenckell & son, 1883.
15 p. 26ᶜᵐ.

NL 0377310   ICJ NNBG

Lindberg, S[extus] O[tto] 1835–1889.
Några växtmorfologiska iakttagelser. Af S. O. Lindberg ... [Stockholm, 1865]
501-505 p. 1 double pl. 21½ᶜᵐ.
Caption title.
Meddelade den 16 november 1864.
Öfvers. af K. Vet.-akad. förh., 1865, n:o 7.

1. Botany—Morphology.

Library of Congress   QK641.L74   5-32247†

NL 0377311   DLC

Lindberg, S[extus] O[tto] 1835–1889.
Nya mossor. Beskrifna af S. O. Lindberg. [Helsingfors, Tryckt hos J. Simelii arfvingar, 1870.
[70]-84 p. 23ᶜᵐ.
Caption title.
Öfversigt af Finska vet.-societetens förhandlingar. XII, n:o 2, 1869.

1. Mosses.

Library of Congress   QK537.L74   5-24416†

NL 0377312   DLC NNBG

Lindberg, S[extus] O[tto] 1835–1889.
... Observationes de formis præsertim europæis polytrichoidearum (bryacearum nematodontearum) publice proposuit S. O. Lindberg. Helsingfors, T. Sederholms boktryckeri, 1868.
1 p. l., [91]-158 p. 21½ᶜᵐ.
At head of title: Notiser ur Sällskapets pro fauna et flora fennica förhandlingar. IX. 1867.

1. Polytrichaceae.

Library of Congress   QK539.P78L   5-24421†

NL 0377313   DLC

Lindberg, S[extus] O[tto] 1835–1889.
... Observationes de mniaceis europæis conscripsit S. O. Lindberg. Helsingfors, T. Sederholms boktryckeri, 1868.
1 p. l., [41]-88 p., 1 l. 21½ᶜᵐ.
At head of title: Notiser ur Sällskapets pro fauna et flora fennica förhandlingar. IX. 1867.

1. Mniaceae.

Library of Congress   QK539.M68L   5-24419†

NL 0377314   DLC NcD NNBG

QK539
.H9
L515
Lindberg, Sextus Otto, 1835–1889.
Öfvergång af honorgan till hanorgan hos en bladmossa. [Stockholm, 1879]
75-78 p. 1 plate. 22 cm.
Caption title.
From Öfversigt af Kongl. Vetenskaps-Akademiens Förhandlingar 1879. N:o 5."

1. Hypnum erythrorrhizon. 2. Musci. i.t.

NL 0377315   NNBG

Lindberg, Sextus Otto, 1835–1889.
Om bladmossornas locklösa former. Af S. O. Lindberg. [Stockholm, 1864]
575-588 p. 21½ cm.
Caption title.
Meddelladt den 9 december, 1863.
Öfvers. af K. Vet.-akad. förh., 1864, n:o 10.

1. Bryology.

QK535.L73   5-24148

NL 0377316   DLC NNBG

Lindberg, Sextus Otto, 1835–1889.
Om de europeiska *Trichostomeæ* ... Helsingfors, J. C. Frenckell & son, 1864.
1 p. l., 48 p. 21½ᶜᵐ.
Akademisk afhandling—Helsingfors.

1. Trichostomeae.

Library of Congress   QK539.T82L   5-24426†

NL 0377317   DLC NcD NNBG PPAN

VOLUME 334

Lindberg, Sextus Otto, 1835–1889.
　Om de officinela barkarne. Af S. O. Lindberg ...
ₜStockholm, P. A. Norstedt & söner, 1864ₗ
　50 p. 23½ᶜᵐ.
　Akademisk afhandling—Upsala.
　Caption title.

　1. Materia medica, Vegetable.　2. Bark.

　　　　　　　　　　　　　　　　10–30862†
Library of Congress　　　RS164.L6

NL　0377318　DLC

Lindberg, Sₜextusₗ Oₜttoₗ 1835–1889.
　Om ett nytt fall af acrosyncarpi. Af S. O. Lindberg.
ₜHelsingfors, 1872ₗ
　ₜ43ₗ–58 p. 23ᶜᵐ.
　Caption title.
　Fin. vet. soc. förh. xiv., 1872.
　Bidrag till mosornas morfologi och inbördes systematiska ställning,
p. ₜ46ₗ–58.

　1. Mosses.

Library of Congress　　　QK535.L74　　5–24411†

NL　0377319　DLC

Lindberg, Sₜextusₗ Oₜttoₗ 1835–1889.
　Om ett nytt slägte, *Epipterygium*, bland bladmossorna.
Af S. O. Lindberg. ₜStockholm, 1862ₗ
　599–609 p. 22½ᶜᵐ.
　Caption title.
　Meddeladt den 10 december 1862.
　Öfversigt af K. Vet.-akad. förh. xix., 1862.

　1. Epipterygium.

Library of Congress　　　QK539.E64L　　5–24418†

NL　0377320　DLC

QL35
.A1
L5　Lindberg, Sextus Otto, 1835–1889.
　　Om fruktgömmet hos Cariceae. Helsingfors,
　J. Simelii tryck., 1885.
　　6 p. 22 cm. (Acta Societatis pro Fauna et
　Flora Fennica, t.2, nr.7)

　　1. Cariceae.　2. Cyperaceae.　i.t.　ii.s.

NL　0377321　NNBG

Lindberg, Sₜextusₗ Oₜttoₗ 1835–1889.
　Om rörelsen inom växtriket. Föredrag vid vetenskaps-
societetens årshögtid af S. O. Lindberg. ₜHelsingfors,
1873ₗ
　143–163 p. 23ᶜᵐ.
　Caption title.
　Reprint from Öfversigt af Finska vetenskaps-societetens Förhandlingar,
xv, 1873.

　1. Plants, Irritability and movements of.

　　　　　　　　　　　　　　　　5–36045†
Library of Congress　　　QK771.L74

NL　0377322　DLC

Lindberg, Sₜextusₗ Oₜttoₗ 1835–1889.
　... Plantæ nonnullæ Horti botanici helsingforsiensis de-
scriptæ a S. O. Lindberg. (Societati exhibitum die 19 septembris 1870.) Helsingforsiæ, ex officina typographica
Societatis litterariae fennicae, 1871.
　1 p. l., ₜ121ₗ–133 p.　vi pl.　29½ᶜᵐ.
　Acta Societatis scientiarum fennicae, x.

　1. Botany—Pictorial works.　2. Helsingfors.　Universitet.　Botaniska
trädgården.

Library of Congress　　　QK98.L7　　5–35811†

NL　0377323　DLC MH–A NNBG

Lindberg, Sextus Otto, 1835–1889.
　Plantæ nonnullæ Horti botanici helsingforsiensis, descrip-
tæ a S. O. Lindberg ...
　(*In* Finska vetenskaps-societeten, Helsingfors.　Acta Societatis
scientiarum fennicae. Helsingforsiæ, 1875.　26½ x 22½ᶜᵐ. t. x, p. ₜ119ₗ–
133. vi pl. (part fold.))
　"Societati exhibitum die 19 septembris 1870."
　Also published separately.

　1. Botany—Pictorial works.　2. Helsingfors.　Universitet.　Botaniska
trädgården.

　　　　　　　　　　　　　　　　A C 38–1
New York.　Public library
　for Library of Congress　　　[Q60.F5　vol. 10]
　　　　　　　　　　　ₜ4ₗ　　　　　　　(508)

NL　0377324　NN DLC

Lindberg, Sₜextusₗ Oₜttoₗ 1835–1889.
　Remarks on *Mesotus*, Mitten.　By S. O. Lindberg, м. d.
ₜLondon, 1872ₗ
　ₜ4ₗ p.　21½ᶜᵐ.
　Extracted from the Linnean society's Journal—Botany, vol. xiii, 1873, p.
182–185.

　1. Mesotus.

Library of Congress　　　QK539.M58L　　5–24422†

NL　0377325　DLC

Lindberg, Sₜextusₗ Oₜttoₗ 1835–1889.
　... Revisio critica iconum in opere Flora danica muscos illustrantium.　Auctore S. O. Lindberg ... Helsingforsiæ, ex officina typographica Societatis litterariae fennicae, 1871.
　118 p.　29½ x 23ᶜᵐ.
　At head of title: Acta Societatis scientiarum fennicae, x.
　Societati exhibita die 15 novembris 1870.

　1. Mosses—Denmark.　2. Mosses—Norway.　i. Finska vetenskaps-
societeten, Helsingfors.　ii. Flora danica.

Library of Congress　　　QK544.D4L　　5–23728†

NL　0377326　DLC

Lindberg, Sextus Otto, 1835–1889.
　Revisio critica iconum in opere Flora danica muscos illus-
trantium.　Auctore S. O. Lindberg ...
　(*In* Finska vetenskaps-societeten, Helsingfors.　Acta Societatis
scientiarum fennicae. Helsingforsiæ, 1875.　26½ x 22½ᶜᵐ. t. x, p. ₜ1ₗ–
118)
　"Societati exhibita die 15 novembris 1870."
　Also published separately.

　1. Mosses—Denmark.　2. Mosses—Norway.　i. Flora danica.

　　　　　　　　　　　　　　　　A C 37–3376
New York.　Public library
　for Library of Congress　　　[Q60.F5　vol. 10]
　　　　　　　　　　　ₜ4ₗ　　　　　　　(508)

NL　0377327　NN NNBG DLC

QK553
.L5　Lindberg, Sextus Otto, 1835–1889.
　　Sandea et Myriorrhynchus, nova Hepaticarum
　genera. Helsingforsiae, Ex officina J. Simelii,
　1884.
　　9 p.　21 cm.　(Acta Societatis pro Fauna et
　Flora Fennica, t.2, nr.5)

　　1. Sandea.　2. Myriorrhynchus.　3. Hepaticae.

NL　0377328　NNBG

Lindberg, Sₜextusₗ Oₜttoₗ 1835–1889.
　Spridda anteckningar rörande de skandinaviska mossorna, af S. O. Lindberg.　ₜLund, Berlingska boktryckeriet, 1872ₗ
　16 p.　22ᶜᵐ.
　Caption title.
　At head of title: Aftryck ur Botaniska notiser 1872.

　1. Mosses—Scandinavia.

Library of Congress　　　QK544.S2L74　　5–23732†

NL　0377329　DLC

Lindberg, Sₜextusₗ Oₜttoₗ 1835–1889.
　Uppställning af familjen *Funariaceæ*. Af S. O. Lind-
berg.　ₜStockholm, 1864ₗ
　589–608 p.　21½ᶜᵐ.
　Caption title.
　Meddelad den 9 december 1863.
　Öfvers. af K. Vet.-akad. förh., 1864, n:o 10.

　1. Funariaceae.

Library of Congress　　　QK539.F98L　　5–24424†

NL　0377330　DLC NNBG

Lindberg, Sₜextusₗ Oₜttoₗ 1835–1889.
　Utkast till en naturlig gruppering af Europas blad-
mossor med toppsittande frukt (*Bryineæ acrocarpæ*).
Program af S. O. Lindberg. Helsingfors, J. C. Frenckell
& sons, tryckeri, 1878.
　1 p. l., 39 p.　26ᶜᵐ.

　1. Mosses.

Library of Congress　　　QK537.L75　　5–24417†

NL　0377331　DLC CtY ICRL NNBG PPAN

Lindberg, Sₜextusₗ Oₜttoₗ 1835–1889.
　Utredning af de skandinaviska *Seligeriæ*. Af S. O.
Lindberg.　ₜStockholm, P. A. Norstedt & söner, 1864ₗ
　185–192 p.　21½ᶜᵐ.
　Caption title.
　Meddelad den 9 december 1863.
　Öfvers. af K. Vet.-akad. förh., 1864, n:o 3.

　1. Seligeria.

Library of Congress　　　QK539.S46L　　5–24423†

NL　0377332　DLC NNBG

VOLUME 334

Lindberg, S₍extus₎ O₍tto₎ 1835–1889.
Utredning af Skandinaviens *Porella*-former. Af S. O.
Lindberg. (Aftryck ur Acta Societatis scientiarum fennicae t. ɪx) ₍Helsingfors, 1869₎
1 p. l., ₍329₎–345 p. 29¼ᵐᵐ.

1. Porella. 2. Botany—Scandinavia.

Library of Congress　　QK555.P83L　　5-3782†

NL 0377333　DLC

Lindberg, Sextus Otto, 1835–1889.
Utredning af Skandinaviens *Porella*-former. Af S. O.
Lindberg ...

(*In* Finska vetenskaps-societeten, Helsingfors. **Acta Societatis
scientiarum fennicæ.** Helsingforsiæ, 1871. 26¼ x 22ᵐ. t. ɪX, pars L
p. ₍327₎–345)

"Föredr. d. 15 nov. 1869."
Also published separately.

1. Porella. 2. Mosses—Scandinavia.　　A C 38-926

New York. Public library
for Library of Congress　　[Q60.F5　vol. 9, pt. 1]
　　　　　　　₍4₎　　　　　　　　　　(508)

NL 0377334　NN DLC

Lindberg, Sten G
Bokband i Stockholm under 325 år. ₍Stockholm, 1955₎
26 p. illus. 21 cm.

"Först publicerat i Bokbinderiidkaren nummer 3 och 4 1955 under
titeln Orneringsstilar i Sverige under 325 år."
Summary in English.

1. Bookbinding—Stockholm. ɪ. Title.

Z270.S9L5　　56-33449

NL 0377335　DLC

PQ2067　Lindberg, Sten G. Carl Gustaf Tessin och flickan
.T26F3　　från Fänö.
1955　Tessin, Carl Gustaf, *greve*, 1695–1770.
　　　Faunillane. Malmö, Allhems förlag, 1955.

Lindberg, Stig.
Nyfiken i en strut-öppnar de den så tittar
han ut ...
see under　[Hellsing, Lennart] 1919–

Lindberg, Torgny, 1909–
The treatment of juvenile delinquents in Sweden ₍by₎
Torgny Lindberg and Gerhard Simson. Stockholm, Swedish
Institute, 1951.
54 l. 30 cm.

1. Juvenile delinquency—Sweden. ɪ. Simson, Gerhard, 1902–
joint author. ɪɪ. Title.

58-41869 ‡

NL 0377338　DLC CU

Law　Lindberg, Torgny, 1909–　joint author.

Strahl, Ivar, 1899–
Villkorlig dom och villkorlig frigivning, samt det därtill
anknutna skyddsarbetet, författningar med kommentar av **Ivar
Strahl ... och Torgny Lindberg ...** Stockholm, P. A. Norstedt
& söner ₍1944₎

Lindberg, Torsten.
Suinula tragedin, af Torsten Lindberg.　Tammerfors: Förf.
förlag, 1921.　104 p.　illus. (incl. plan, ports.)　plates.　8°.

1. Finland.—History, 1917.
N. Y. P. L.　　　　　　　　　　July 5, 1923.

NL 0377340　NN

Lindberg, Valter
Suomen kansantulo vuosina 1926-1938. Helsinki, Akateeminen Kirjakauppa ₍1943₎
185 p. tables. (Suomen Pankin. Suhdan-
netutkimusosaston. Julkaisuja, sarja B:1)

"Zusammenfassung" (in German): p. ₍141₎-
146.
Bibliography: p. ₍147₎-152.

NL 0377341　NNC MH-L

Lindberg, Valter.
Utvecklingen av den allmänna inkomstskatten
i Finlands statsskattesystem ... av Valter
Lindberg ... Helsingfors, 1934.
360 p.,1 l. fold.tables,diagrs. 22½ᶜᵐ.
Akademisk avhandling--Helsingfors.
"Litteraturförteckning": p.₍351₎-360.

1.Income tax--Finland.

NL 0377342　MiU OU PU NNC

DL149　Lindberg, Verner, tr.
.D32
Danstrup, John.
A history of Denmark. ₍Tr. into English by Verner
Lindberg₎ Copenhagen, Wivel, 1948.

Lindberg, Vilhelm Axelson.
Modellyachtsbyggnad, av Vilh. Ax: son Lindberg... Stockholm: Wahlström & Widstrand ₍1923₎.　111 p incl. diagrs., illus.,
plates.　8°.

1. Boats—Models.
N. Y. P. L.　　　　　　　　　　February 24, 1925

NL 0377344　NN

4CT　Lindberg, Vivi
384　　v. Wrightarna på Haminanlaks. Helsingfors, Söderström [1926]
101 p.

NL 0377345　DLC-P4

PT9995　Lindberg, Walter
.L52M6　　Mot det hägrande landet; dikter
och drömmar. New York, Nordstjernans
boktr. ₍19--?₎
78 p. illus. 22 cm.

NL 0377346　MnHi

Lindberg, Walter.
The winding road, an autobiography in story form, by
Walter Lindberg. Burlington, Ia., The Lutheran literary
board, 1933.
279 p. 20ᵐᵐ.

ɪ. Title.
Library of Congress　　BX8080.L52A3　　34-1451
──── Copy 2.
Copyright A 68850　　　₍2₎　　　　922.473

NL 0377347　DLC

Lindberg-Dovlette, Elsa.
Främling; boken om Konstantinopel, av Elsa Lindberg-
Dovlette (Prinsessan Mirza Riza Khan). Historier om Astrid-
Anisa, Condjagull och Yasmine.　Stockholm: A. Bonniers
förlag₍, 1929₎.　220 p. col'd, mounted front., col'd, mounted
plates.　8°.

452919A. 1. Fiction, Swedish.　　　2. Constantinople—Social life.
N. Y. P. L.　　　　　　　　　　December 27, 1929

NL 0377348　NN

Lindberg-Dovlette, Elsa.
Der Gesang der dunklen Wasser; ein Buch
von Konstantinopel. Einzig berichtigte
Übertragung aus dem Schwedischen von Heinrich
Goebel. Tübingen, Alexander Fisher Verlag,
1929.
225 p. port.

NL 0377349　WaU

914.961　Lindberg-Dovlette, Elsa.
L64k　　Konstantinopel₎ aus dem Tagebuch einer
jungen Türkin. Berlin, Morawe & Scheffelt
₍1916₎
115 p. (Nordland-bücher ₍15₎)

1. Istanbul - Description. I. Title.

NL 0377350　WaU

Lindberg Nielsen, Carl
see　Nielsen, Carl Lindberg.

Lindberg engineering company, Chicago.

Koebel, Norbert K.
Industrial controlled atmospheres, by Norbert K. Koebel ...
Chicago, Ill., Lindberg engineering company ₍1942₎

₍Lindberga, Alma₎
...Saimnieka meita; skatu luga 5 cēlienos. ₍Rīgā₎ "Latvju
grāmata," 1936. 79 p. 20½cm.
Author's pseud., Alma Liepkalne, at head of title.

1. Drama, Lettish. I. Title.
N. Y. P. L.　　　　　　　　　　December 6, 1938

NL 0377353　NN

VOLUME 334

Lindberga, Alma.
...Uz svešām zemēm; bērnu ludziņa 2 cēlienos, 4 ainās.   Rīgā: Latvijas skolotāju kooperātivs, 1934.   24 p.   17½cm.   (Skolas teātris. nr. 1.)

857833A.   1. Juvenile literature—   Drama, Lettish.   I. Title.
N. Y. P. L.   December 9, 1936

NL 0377354   NN

QP551 **Lindberger, Bertil Julius,** 1886–
.L73   Undersökningar över äggvitefällning med syror och sura saltlösningar ... Stockholm, P. A. Norstedt & söner, 1924.
68 p. incl. xxxi tab., diagrs.   21ᶜᵐ.
Akademisk afhandling—Upsala.
"Litteratur": p. 65–68.

1. Albumin.   2. Precipitation (Chemistry)

NL 0377355   ICU MH ICRL DNLM ICU

Lindberger, Bror Valter Herman.
See
Lindberger, Valter, 1859–

PT9375 **Lindberger, Örjan,** 1912–
L5   Att läsa poesi, ᶜmetoder för diktanalys [av] Örjan Lindberger och
Scandi-   Reidar Ekner.   Stockholm, Svenska bokförlaget, Bonniers [1955]
navian   ix, 165 p.   illus.   (Verdandis skriftserie, 4)
Dept.

1. Swedish poetry - Hist. & crit.   2. Poetry.   I. Ekner, Reidar, joint author.   II. Title.

NL 0377357   CU KU MnU WaU NN

Lindberger, Örjan, 1912–
Gustav Hedenvind-Eriksson.   Stockholm, Kooperativa förbundets bokförlag, 1945.
224 p.   illus., ports.   20 cm.
Bibliography: p. 215.

1. Hedenvind-Eriksson, Gustav, 1880–

PT9875.H42Z7   928.397   50–29556

NL 0377358   DLC NcU TxU WaU PU MnU NNC

Lindberger, Örjan, 1912–
Prometeustanken hos Viktor Rydberg; hans utopiskt liberala förutsättningar och de därav betingade problemställningarna i hans idddiktning.   Stockholm, H. Gebers [1938]
2v. in 1 (507p.)   26cm.
Includes bibliography.

1. Rydberg, Viktor, 1828–1895   I. Title

NIC
NL 0377359   WU NNC ICRL MH ICU MnU NN CtY CU NcU NcD

839.78 **Lindberger,** Örjan, 1912–   ed.
L742sv   Svensk arbetardikt; prosa och poesi från femtio år, utg.1952 till Tidens förlags 40-årsjubileum.   Stockholm, Tidens förlag 1952;
429,ᵢ2ᵢ p.   23 cm.
"För vidare läsning": p.ᵢ431ᵢ

1.Short stories,Swedish.   2.Swedish literature (Selections: Extracts,etc.)   I.Tidens förlag, Stockholm.   II.Title.

NL 0377360   MiU NcD WU IEN MH

PT9260 **Lindberger, Örjan,** 1912–
.S416   **Schück, Henrik,** 1855–1947.
1952   Sveriges litteratur intill 1900.   ᵢPå uppdrag av Svenska akademien reviderats och försetts med upplysningar om nyare litteratur, av Örjan Lindberger;   Stockholm, Geber ᵢ1952ᵢ

Lindberger, Örjan, 1912–   ed.
Ur Verner von Heidenstams diktning
see under   Heidenstam, Verner von, 1859–1940.

Lindberger, Örjan, 1912–
Wergeland och Sverige.   Stockholm, Kooperativa förbundets bokförlag, 1947.
208 p.   24 cm.

1. Wergeland, Henrik Arnold, 1808–1845.

PT8940.L5   839.8216   48–21267*

NL 0377363   DLC WaU MnU

Lindberger, Ruth
Beard family hist. & genealogy.   [Lawrence, Kan., World co.] c1939.   123, ᵢ5ᵢ p.

NL 0377364   OClWHi

Lindberger, Valter, 1859–   615.9 P301
Bidrag till kännedomen om förgiftningarna i Sverige under åren ᵢ1866 1873–1892. .... Af Valter Lindberger, ... Upsala, Almqvist & Wiksells boktryckeri-aktiebolag, 1893.
ᵢ8ᵢ, 117 p. incl. tables.   25ᶜᵐ.
Akademisk afhandling—Upsala.

NL 0377365   ICJ NN PPC DNLM DL IU

Lindbergh, Alfred E., 1912–1921.
The blind Swedish evangel, Rev. A.J. Freeman ... Chicago, [1917]
91 p.   front. port.   19 cm.
Contains translations of Swedish poems.

NL 0377366   RPB

Lindbergh, Anne (Morrow) 1906–
... A Oriente per il nord, alla ricerca della più breve via aerea fra l'America e l'Asia; con numerose cartine del col. Ch. Lindbergh.   Trad. di E. E. Andreani.   Firenze, Marzocco ᵢ1939ᵢ
2 p. l., ᵢviiᵢ–xii, 218, ᵢ2ᵢ p.   front., maps (1 fold.)   22½ᵐᵐ.
At head of title: Anna Morrow Lindbergh.
1. Aeronautics—Flights.   2. Radio in aeronautics.   3. Arctic regions.   4. East (Far East)—Descr. & trav.   I. Lindbergh, Charles Augustus, 1902–   II. Andreani, E. E., tr.   III. Title.   *Translation of North to the Orient.*
ᵢFull name: Anne Spencer (Morrow) Lindberghᵢ
                                                            44–44193
Library of Congress   TL540.L49A32
                             ᵢ2ᵢ   629.133347

NL 0377367   DLC OCl

Lindbergh, Anne (Morrow) 1906–
Ascolta, è il vento, con pref. e carte di Carlo A. Lindbergh.   Milano, V. Bompiani, anno XVIII ᵢ1940ᵢ
380 p.   map.   21 cm.

1. Aeronautics—Flights.   2. São Tiago, Cape Verde Islands.   3. Bathurst, Gambia.   4. Natal, Brazil.
Full name: Anne Spencer (Morrow) Lindbergh

TL540.L49A283   50–2514

NL 0377368   DLC MiD

Lindbergh, Anne (Morrow) 1906–
Flying around the north Atlantic, by Anne Morrow Lindbergh, with a foreword by Charles A. Lindbergh ...   ᵢWashington, National Geographic Society, 1934ᵢ
p. ᵢ259ᵢ–337.   illus.   25½cm.
National Geographic Magazine, Volume LXVI, number three, September, 1934.
Inscribed to Conger Goodyear by the authors.

NL 0377369   NBu OrP WaE

PS
3523   **Lindbergh, Anne (Morrow)** 1906–
I56   Die Gefährtin; ein Erlebnis.   Tübingen,
S75   R. Wunderlich, c1944.
1944   229 p.   19 cm.

Translation of the steep ascent.

NL 0377369–1   CaBVaU

Lindbergh, Anne (Morrow) 1906–
Gift from the sea.   ᵢNew Yorkᵢ Pantheon ᵢ1955ᵢ
127 p.   illus.   21 cm.

1. Life.   I. Title.
Full name: Anne Spencer ᵢMorrowᵢ Lindbergh.

BD435.L52   128   55–5065 ‡

Or OrAshS OrCS OrLgE OrMonO OrP OrSaW OrU
KyLxCB KyU–H Wa WaE WaS IdB WaSp WaSpG IdU WaT WaWW
ODW PBm PPLas PIm PPEB PPT OC1ND MiU KyLx NcD KyMdC
PBa PPT PSt PHC PSC PPL OOxM OC1W NcD NcC IEN OCU
WaS TNJ NBuU TU MB TxU OO MB OC1 PPD PPA OU NN NIC
NL 0377370   DLC MtBC CaBViP CaBVaU IdPI CaBVa MtBuM

Lindbergh, Anne (Morrow) 1906–
Gift from the sea.   ᵢNew Yorkᵢ Pantheon ᵢ1955ᵢ
ᵢ128ᵢ p.   col. illus.   24 cm.

1. Life.   I. Title.
Full name: Anne Spencer (Morrow) Lindbergh.

BD435.L52 1955a   Rosenwald Coll   57–4637

N WaS NBu
NL 0377372   DLC CaBVaU FTaSU MiU KyBB KyU–A OWorP OU

---

128   **Lindbergh, Anne (Morrow)** 1906–
L 64 G.2   Gift from the sea.   Large type edition.
New York, F. Watts ᶜ1955ᵢ
127 p.   illus.   29ᵐᵐ.   (A Keith Jennison book)

NL 0377373   OO WaSp WaT

Lindbergh, Anne (Morrow)
Height, a poem.   (Scribner's, 1928)
From- The Outlook, Feb. 27, 1929
Clipping mounted.

NL 0377374   RPB

Lindbergh, Anne (Morrow) 1906–
Horch—der Wind.   Mit Vorwort und Kartenzeichnungen von Charles A. Lindbergh.   ᵢAus dem Amerikanischen übers. von Karl Eugen Brunner;   Zürich, Orell Füssli ᵢ19—ᵢ
316 p.   front., maps.   21 cm.

1. Aeronautics—Flights.   2. São Tiago, Cape Verde Islands.   3. Bathurst, Gambia.   4. Natal, Brazil.   I. Title.
Full name: Anne Spencer (Morrow) Lindbergh.

TL540.L49A282   629.133347   50–48502

NL 0377375   DLC MiD OCl

VOLUME 334

Lindbergh, Mrs. Anne Morrow
Ich fliege mit meinem Mann... Leipzig, E. P.
Tal, 1937.
239 p. port. maps.

Translation of her "North to the Orient".

NL 0377376   MiD CaBVa

Lindbergh, Mrs. Anne (Morrow) 1906–

Patterson, Jean Rushmore.
Letter to Anne Lindbergh from Jean Rushmore Patterson.
New York, The Lenox hill press, 1940.

Lindbergh, Anne (Morrow) 1906–
Listen! the wind. Tor. McClelland.
Front. maps.

NL 0377378   CaBVa

Lindbergh, Anne (Morrow) 1906–
Listen! the wind, by Anne Morrow Lindbergh. With
foreword and map drawings by Charles A. Lindbergh. New
York, Harcourt, Brace and company [1938]
xii, 275 p. illus. (maps) pl. 21 cm.

Maps on lining-papers.
The story of the flight made by Col. and Mrs. Lindbergh in 1933,
across the Atlantic ocean from Africa to Brazil.
"First edition."

CONTENTS.—pt. 1. Santiago.—pt. 2. Bathurst.—pt. 3. Bound Natal.

1. Aeronautics — Flights. 2. São Tiago, Cape Verde islands. 3.
Bathurst, Gambia. 4. Natal, Brazil. I. Lindbergh, Charles Augustus, 1902– II. Title.

TL540.L49A27   629.133347   38—27808

OrCS OrU OrMonO OrAshS Or
WaTC OrP MtU IdB IdU Wa WaSp OrPR IdU-SB OrSaW WaS
KyWAT DAU MnHi OOxM OC1JC MtBC WaE WaT WaSpG WaWW
NcC TxU CaBVa NcD KyU KEmT CaBVaU KyLx KyU-H KyU-A
NL 0377379   DLC NcRS OC1 TU OU NN CU OO ViU PHC PBm PPT

TL540
.L59A27 Lindbergh, Mrs. Anne (Morrow)
1938b   Listen! the wind...
               New York [1938]
               275p,   21 cm.
               "Third printing, October, 1938"

NL 0377381   DLC

Lindbergh, Mrs. Anne Morrow
Le monde vu de haut; d'Amérique en Chine par
le Cercle polaire... Adaptation de l'anglais
par Hervé Lauwick. [Paris, Plon, °1935.
367 [1] p. port. maps. ("Collection la
Fayette")

Translation of her North to the Orient.

NL 0377382   MiD MH

Lindbergh, Anne (Morrow) 1906–
Muscheln in meiner Hand. [Übersetzt von
Maria Wolff. Die Gedichte übertrug Peter
Stadelmayer] München, R. Piper [c1955]
148 p. 21 cm.
Translation of Gift from the sea.
1. Life. I. Title.

NL 0377383   CoFS

TL540
.L49A38 Lindbergh, Anne Morrow, 1906–
Norröver till orienten; översättning av Gösta
Dahl. Stockholm, P. A. Norstedt [1935]
241 p. front. map. 22 cm.
Original title: North to the Orient.
1. Aeronautics–Flights. 2. Artic regions.
3. East(Far East)–Descr. & trav. I. Lindbergh,
Charles Augustus, 1902– II. Title.

NL 0377384   MB

Lindbergh, Anne (Morrow) 1906–
North to the Orient, by Anne Morrow Lindbergh; with maps
by Charles A. Lindbergh. New York, Harcourt, Brace and
company [1935]
255 p. front., illus. (maps) 21ᵐ.
Maps on lining-papers.
The story of the flight made by Col. and Mrs. Lindbergh in 1931, from
Washington, D. C., to Japan and China.
"First edition."

1. Aeronautics—Flights. 2. Radio in aeronautics. 3. Arctic regions.
4. East (Far East)—Descr. & trav. I. Lindbergh, Charles Augustus,
1902– II. Title.
                                        [Full name: Anne Spencer (Morrow) Lindbergh]
                                                       35—27279

Library of Congress   TL540.L49A3
                               [a44x⁷]   629.133347

OrAshS OrU OrLgE Or
WaT WaTC OrP IdB IdU WaSp OrPR IdU-SB OrSaW WaS OrCS
MB NN ViU OU PU MiU OC1W WaE OrSaW WaWW MtU WaSpG
CU-M CoU KEmT CaBVa CaBVaU FTaSU ICJ OC1 OO ODW DGU
NL 0377385   DLC MtBC DAL MtBuM CU TxU UU NBu KyLx NIC

Lindbergh, Mrs. Anne (Morrow) 1906–
North to the Orient, by Anne Morrow Lindbergh; with maps
by Charles A. Lindbergh. New York, Harcourt, Brace and
company [1935]
255 p. front., illus. (maps) 21ᵐ.
Maps on lining-papers.
The story of the flight made by Col. and Mrs. Lindberg in 1931, from
Washington, D. C., to Japan and China.
"Second printing, August, 1935."

NL 0377387   ViU NcRS NcC NcD

TL540
.L49A3   Lindbergh, Mrs. Anne (Morrow) 1906–
1935b   North to the Orient, by Anne Morrow Lind-
               bergh; with maps by Charles A. Lindbergh. New
               York, Harcourt, Brace and company [1935]
               255 p. front., illus. (maps) 21cm.
               Maps on lining-papers.
               The story of the flight made by Col. and
               Mrs. Lindbergh in 1931, from Washington, D. C.
               to Japan and China.
               "Third printing, August, 1935."

NL 0377388   DLC DN-Ob ViU

TL540
.L49A3   Lindbergh, Mrs. Anne (Morrow) 1906–
1935d   North to the Orient, by Anne Morrow Lind-
               bergh; with maps by Charles A. Lindbergh.
               New York, Harcourt, Brace and company [1935]
               255 p. front., illus.(maps) 21cm.
               Maps on lining-papers.
               The story of the flight made by Col. and
               Mrs. Lindbergh in 1931, from Washington, D.C.,
               to Japan and China.
               "Fifth printing, October, 1935."

NL 0377389   DLC

TL540
.L49A3   Lindbergh, Mrs. Anne (Morrow) 1906–
1935e   North to the Orient, by Anne Morrow Lind-
               bergh; with maps by Charles A. Lindbergh.
               New York, Harcourt, Brace and company [1935]
               255 p. front., illus. (maps) 21cm.
               Maps on lining-papers.
               The story of the flight made by Col. and
               Mrs. Lindbergh in 1931, from Washington, D.C.,
               to Japan and China.
               "Sixth printing, November, 1935."

NL 0377390   DLC

TL540
.L49A3   Lindbergh, Mrs. Anne (Morrow) 1906–
1935h   North to the Orient, by Anne Morrow Lind-
               bergh; with maps by Charles A. Lindbergh.
               New York, Harcourt, Brace and company [1935]
               255 p. front., illus. (maps) 21cm.
               Maps on lining-papers.
               The story of the flight made by Col.
               and Mrs. Lindbergh in 1931, from Washington,
               D. C., to Japan and China.
               "Ninth printing, December 1935."

NL 0377391   DLC

TL540
.L49A3   Lindbergh, Mrs. Anne (Morrow) 1906–
1935l   North to the Orient, by Anne Morrow Lind-
               bergh; with maps by Charles A. Lindbergh.
               New York, Harcourt, Brace and company [1935]
               255 p. front., illus. (maps) 21cm.
               Maps on lining-papers.
               The story of the flight made by Col. and
               Mrs. Lindbergh in 1931, from Washington, D.C.,
               to Japan and China.
               "Tenth printing, December, 1935."

NL 0377392   DLC

TL540
.L49A3   Lindbergh, Mrs. Anne (Morrow) 1906–
1936   North to the Orient, by Anne Morrow Lind-
               bergh; with maps by Charles A. Lindbergh.
               New York, Harcourt, Brace and company [1936]
               255 p. front., illus. (maps) 21cm.
               Maps on lining-papers.
               The story of the flight made by Col. and
               Mrs. Lindbergh in 1931, from Washington, D.C.,
               to Japan and China.
               "Eleventh printing, February, 1936."

NL 0377393   DLC ViU

Lindbergh, Anne (Morrow) 1906–
The steep ascent, by Anne Morrow Lindbergh. New York,
Harcourt, Brace and company [1944]
viii p., 2 l., 120 p. 21ᵐ.
"First edition."

I. Title.
                               [Full name: Anne Spencer (Morrow) Lindbergh]
                                                       44—40062
Library of Congress   PZ3.L643St

Or OrCS InU MH
MB NSyU CoU CSt CaBVa UU OO PSt PPT AU CaBVaU MtBC
Wa OrU ODW OC1 OO OC1W OU OOxM NcD NcRS PV TxU ViU
NL 0377394   DLC WaSpG WaTC WaT WaSp WaS WaE OrSaW OrP

Lindbergh, Anne (Morrow) 1906–
The steep ascent. London, Chatto & Windus, 1945.
108, [1] p. 20 cm.

I. Title.
                               Full name: Anne Spencer (Morrow) Lindbergh.

PZ3.L643St 2   47-25036*

NL 0377395   DLC

Lindbergh, Anne (Morrow) 1906–
Le vent se lève (Listen! The wind) Tr. de l'anglais par
Henri Delgove. Préf. de Antoine de Saint-Exupery. Avant-
propos de Charles Lindbergh. Paris, Corrêa [1939]
xxi, 318 p. plate, map. 19 cm.
The story of the flight made by Col. and Mrs. Lindbergh in 1933 across
the Atlantic Ocean from Africa to Brazil.
CONTENTS.—Santiago.—Bathurst.—Destination: Natal.
1. Aeronautics — Flights. 2. São Tiago, Cape Verde Islands. 3.
Bathurst, Gambia. 4. Natal, Brazil. I. Delgove, Henri, tr. II. Title.
                               Full name: Anne Spencer (Morrow) Lindbergh.

TL540.L49A28   47-42208*

NL 0377396   DLC MnU

VOLUME 334

Lindbergh, Anne (Morrow) 1906–
The wave of the future, a confession of faith ₍by₎ Anne Morrow Lindbergh. New York, Harcourt, Brace and company ₍ᶜ1940₎
3 p. l., 3–41 p. 19½ cm.
"First edition."

1. World war, 1989–1945. I. Title.

Full name: Anne Spencer (Morrow) Lindbergh.

D753.L5 1940   940.53   40–33094

MeB TNJ CoU NIC
PNt PHC NcC NcD OC1W OOxM OC1 CaBVa OrMonO Wa MnHi
IdU IdU–SB IdB WaTC OrP WaE PV OO OU ODW KU–M PPLT
NL 0377397   DLC OrCS OrPR WaS OrU WaSp Or MtBC WaWW

Lindbergh, *Mrs.* **Anne (Morrow)** 1906–
The wave of the future, a confession of faith ₍by₎ Anne Morrow Lindbergh. New York, Harcourt, Brace and company ₍1940₎
3 p. l., 3–41 p. 19½ᵐ.
"Third printing, October, 1940."

NL 0377398   ViU

Lindbergh, *Mrs.* **Anne (Morrow)** 1906–
The wave of the future, a confession of faith ₍by₎ Anne Morrow Lindbergh. New York, Harcourt, Brace and company ₍1940₎
3 p. l., 3–41 p. 19½ᵐ.
"Fifth printing, October, 1940."

NL 0377399   ViU

D
753
L74
Lindbergh, Anne (Morrow) 1906–
The wave of the future; a confession of faith. New York, Harcourt, Brace ₍ᶜ1940₎
41 p. 20cm.
"Sixth printing."

1. World War, 1939–1945. I. Title.

NL 0377400   NIC PPD

B1al6
A64
Lindbergh, *Mrs.* **Anne (Morrow),** 1906–
The wind of privation or the sun of mercy? Radio address by Anne Morrow Lindbergh, December 24, 1940 over the National broadcasting system. Philadelphia, American Friends service committee ₍1940₎
Pamphlet

I.Friends, Society of. American Friends service committee.

NL 0377401   CtY MiU PHi

Lindbergh, Anne (Morrow) 1906–
Zug a szel. [Budapest] Revai, [c1940]
206p.

A mu angol cime: Listen! the wind; tr. by Kosaryne Rez Lola.
Hungarian.

NL 0377402   OC1

Lindbergh, Charles August, 1859–1924.
Banking and currency and the money trust, by Charles A. Lindbergh ... ₍Washington, D. C., National capital press, inc., ᶜ1913₎
318 p. 19ᵐ.

1. Currency question—U. S.—1901–   2. Banks and banking—U. S.
Title.

Library of Congress   HG181.L6   13–13242

NL 0377403   DLC TxU WHi ICU PPAmSwM OC1 ICJ MB

Lindbergh, Charles August, 1859–1924
C.A.Lindbergh, Little Falls, Minnesota, candidate for Congress, Sixth Congressional District. [Washington? 1914?]
70 p. port.

NL 0377404   MH

Lindbergh, Charles August, 1859–
U. S. *Congress. House. Committee on banking and currency.*
... Changes in the banking and currency system of the United States ... Report, together with views of the minority and minority views. ⟨To accompany H. R. 7837.⟩ ₍Washington, Govt. print. off., 1913₎

Lindbergh, Charles August, 1859–1924.
The economic pinch, by C. A. Lindbergh. Philadelphia, Dorrance ₍ᶜ1923₎
249 p. 20ᵐ.

1. U. S.—Econ. condit.—1918–   2. U. S.—Pol. & govt.   I. Title.

Library of Congress   HC106.L7   23–7677

NL 0377406   DLC WaTC CLSU KEmT OU PPAmSwM

Lindbergh, Charles A., 1859–
U. S. *Congress. House. Committee on rules.*
Hearings on House resolution no. 238 authorizing the Monetary commission to investigate financial institutions or corporations and report whether they operate in restraint of trade and in violation of law. Hearings held before the Committee on rules, House of representatives, July 27, 1911. Washington, Govt. print. off., 1911.

323
L742i
Lindbergh, Charles August, 1859–1924.
Invisible government and the consequence of it, speech... in the House of Representatives, July 5, 1916. Washington, 1916.
29p. 24cm.

Cover title.

1. Pressure groups. 2. U.S. Pol. & govt.
I. U.S. 64th Cong. 1st sess. 1915–1916. House.
II. Title.

NL 0377408   IEN

Lindbergh, Charles A., 1859–
U. S. *Congress. House. Committee on claims.*
... Overtime claims of letter carriers ... Report. ⟨To accompany S. 3638.⟩ ... ₍Washington, Govt. print. off., 1910₎

Lindbergh, Charles August, 1859–
Why is your country at war and what happens to you after the war, and related subjects, by Charles A. Lindbergh ... Washington, D. C. ₍National capital press, inc.₎ 1917.
220 p. ports. (incl. front.) 16ᵐ.

1. U. S.—Econ. condit. 2. Banks and banking—U. S. 3. European war, 1914—Economic aspects—U. S. I. Title.

Library of Congress   HC106.2.L5   17–21964

NL 0377410   DLC MB

Lindbergh, Charles August, 1859–1924.
Your country at war and what happens to you after a war, by Charles A. Lindbergh, sr. Philadelphia, Dorrance & company, inc. ₍ᶜ1934₎
215 p. front., plates, ports. 19½ᵐ.
Published in 1917 under title: Why is your country at war and what happens to you after the war, and related subjects.

1. U. S.—Econ. condit. 2. Banks and banking—U. S. 3. European war, 1914–1918—Economic aspects—U. S. I. Title.

Library of Congress   HC106.2.L5 1934   34–5947
—— Copy 2.
Copyright A 70732   ₍3₎   330.973

MoU PSC PPT OU OC1 MiU MB NN ViU
NL 0377411   DLC IdB IdU WaSp WaS Wa Or OrP OrSaW GU

TL540
L49A39
Lindbergh, Charles Augustus, 1902–
Lindbergh, Anne (Morrow) 1906–
... A Oriente per il nord, alla ricerca della più breve via aerea fra l'America e l'Asia; con numerose cartine del col. Ch. Lindbergh. Trad. di E. E. Andreani. Firenze, Marzocco ₍1939₎

Lindbergh, Charles Augustus, 1902–
An account of the visit to Japan of Col. and Mrs. Charles A. Lindbergh
see under The Japan advertiser.

Lindbergh, Charles Augustus, 1902–
Address.
(*In* National education association of the United States. Addresses and proceedings, 1928. p. 806–809)

1. Aeronautics.

Library, U. S. Office of   Education L13.N212 1928   E 31–215

NL 0377414   DHEW

Lindbergh, Charles Augustus, 1902–
Address by Charles A. Lindbergh at the Philadelphia arena, May 29, 1941. New York, N. Y.: The America first committee ₍1941₎ 10 p. 17¼cm.

1. World war, 1939– ——   Neutrality of the U. S. I. America
first committee.
N. Y. P. L.   April 15, 1942

NL 0377415   NN MH

Lindbergh, Charles Augustus, 1902–
Address by Charles A. Lindbergh, Madison square garden, New York city, May 23, 1941. New York, N. Y.: The America first committee ₍1941₎ 10 p. 17½cm.

1. European war, 1939– ——   Neutrality of the U. S. I. America
first committee.
N. Y. P. L.   December 31, 1941

NL 0377416   NN

VOLUME 334

Lindbergh, Charles Augustus, 1902–
Address by Charles A. Lindbergh, Minneapolis, Minn., May 10, 1941. N. Y. C.: The America first committee [1941] 10 p. 18cm.

1. European war, 1939– — Neutrality of the U. S. I. America first committee.
N. Y. P. L.   December 31, 1941

NL 0377417 NN

D743.9 Lindbergh, Charles Augustus, 1902–
.L74   Address, by Charles A. Lindbergh, New York, April 23, 1941. [Chicago, America first committee, 1941] cover-title,14,[1] p. 17cm.

NL 0377418 MnHi

Lindbergh, Charles Augustus, 1902–
Address by Charles A. Lindbergh. St. Louis arena, May 3, 1941. New York, N. Y.: The America first committee [1941] 14 p. 17cm.

1. European war, 1939– — Neutrality of the U. S. I. America first committee.
N. Y. P. L.   December 31, 1941

NL 0377419 NN

WB   Lindbergh, Charles A   1902–
41718 El aguila solitaria. [Traducción de Fernando Trias Beristain] Buenos Aires, Jackson de Ediciones Selectas [1954]
479 p. illus.
English title: The spirit of St. Louis.

NL 0377420 CtY OKentU

LINDBERGH, CHARLES AUGUSTUS
America must stay out of Europe's war and pre serve civilized life here. Washington, D.C., Nat. council for prevention of war, 1939.
cover-title, [6] p.

Speech ... over three national radio networks.
Sept.15, 1939.

NL 0377421 Or

Lindbergh, Charles Augustus, 1902–
America must stay out of Europe's war and preserve civilized life here; speech of Charles A. Lindbergh over three national radio networks, September 15, 1939. Reprinted by the National council for prevention of war... Washington [etc., 1939] 4 l. 23cm.

"Revised copy." — *ms. note.*

1. World war, 1939–1945—Neu-   trality of the U. S. I. National council for prevention of war.
N. Y. P. L.   November 24, 1947

NL 0377422 NN

Lindbergh, Charles Augustus, 1902–
...Chas. Lindbergh'as [As ir lektuvas. Av--leit. Adomavioiaus vertimas.
151p. front.(port.) Kaunas, "Naujo Zodzio" Bves leidinys, 1932.

Lithuanian.

NL 0377423 OC1

Lindbergh, Charles Augustus, 1902–

Carrel, Alexis, 1873–
The culture of organs, by Alexis Carrel and Charles A. Lindbergh; with 111 illustrations. New York, P. B. Hoeber, inc., 1938.

Lindbergh, Charles Augustus, 1902–
The flight of Captain Charles A. Lindbergh from New York to Paris, May 20–21, 1927
see under U.S. Dept. of state.

Lindbergh, Charles Augustus, 1902–
Lindbergh's message; an address delivered by Col. Charles A. Lindbergh at Manhattan center rally April 23, 1941. New York, N. Y.: The America first committee [1941] 10 p. 17cm.

1. European war, 1939– — Neutrality of the U. S. I. America first committee.
N. Y. P. L.   October 31, 1941

NL 0377426 NN CtY

Lindbergh, Charles Augustus, 1902–
Lindbergh's own story of his New York-Paris flight
see under New York times.

Lindbergh, Charles Augustus, 1902–
FOR OTHER EDITIONS
SEE MAIN ENTRY
Lindbergh, *Mrs.* Anne (Morrow) 1906–
Listen! the wind, by Anne Morrow Lindbergh. With fore-word and map drawings by Charles A. Lindbergh. New York, Harcourt, Brace and company [1938]

Lindbergh, Charles Augustus, 1902–.
Mein Flug über den Ozean. (Übers. von Hans Jürgen Soehring. Berlin) Fischer, 1954.

569p.

NL 0377429 PPG OC1

Lindbergh, Charles Augustus, 1902–
Mi aeroplano y yo. ("We") Por Charles A. Lindbergh. Prólogo y revisión por el comandante Ramón Franco, tra-ducción de M. Vallvé. Barcelona, Editorial Mentora, s. a. [1927]
1 p. l., 5–274, [2] p. front., plates, ports. 21ᶜᵐ. [Colección Viajes, aventuras, memorias]

I. Franco Bahamonde, Ramón, 1896–1938, ed. II. Vallvé, Manuel, tr. III. Title.

Library of Congress   TL540.L5A7   43–30702

                      [2]   926.2913

NL 0377430 DLC

Lindbergh, Charles Augustus, 1902–
... Mon avion et moi, ma vie depuis mon enfance jusqu'au len-demain de ma traversée. Préface de Myron T. Herrick ... Tra-duit par Léon Lemonnier. Paris, E. Flammarion [1927]
x, [11]–282 p., 2 l. plates, ports. 18ᶜᵐ.
At head of title: Charles Lindbergh.

1. Aeronautics—Flight. I. Lemonnier, Léon, 1890– II. Title.
Translation of "We."

                            44–38190

Library of Congress   TL540.L5A34

NL 0377431 DLC WaS MnHi NN

Lindbergh, Charles A. , 1902–
Neutrality. Radio address by Col. Charles A. Lindbergh, delivered September 15, 1939 ...
2 p. Q.

YA 5000
J 17   (Congressional speeches, by author)

NL 0377432 DLC

Lindbergh, Charles Augustus, 1902–
... New-York–Parigi senza scalo; traduzione di P. Gerardo Jansen. Milano, A. Mondadori, 1928.
3 p. l., [9]–242 p., 3 l. front., plates, ports. 22½ᶜᵐ.
At head of title: Charles Lindbergh.
"Una breve dimostrazione di come il mondo ammirò Lindbergh (es-posizione di Fitzhugh Green)": p. [179]–242.

I. Jansen, P. Gerardo, tr. II. Green, Fitzhugh, 1888– III. Title.
Translation of "We."

Library of Congress   TL540.L5A5   28–24694

NL 0377433 DLC

WB   Lindbergh, Charles Augustus, 1902–
28399 Non-stop Paris 33 timer, med 16 sider illus-trasjoner. [Oslo] Nasjonalforlaget [1953]
364 p. illus.

Original title: The spirit of St. Louis.

NL 0377434 CtY

Lindbergh, Charles Augustus, 1902–

Lindbergh, *Mrs.* Anne (Morrow) 1906–
North to the Orient, by Anne Morrow Lindbergh; with maps by Charles A. Lindbergh. New York, Harcourt, Brace and company [1935]

Lindbergh, Charles Augustus, 1902–
Of flight and life. New York, Scribner's Sons, 1948.
viii, 56 p. 20 cm.

1. Science—Philosophy. I. Title.

TL540.L5A8   501   48–8089*

ICU IdB MtBC Or OrCS OrP OrU
DSI MeB CoU DAU ViU CaBVa MiU NcC MB TU LU CU GAT
NcGU PU–PSW WaE Wa PPMoI PPGi CU–S KyLxT KyLx TxU
NL 0377436 DLC CaBVaU MB MtU WaTC MiEM WaSpG WaT WaS

Lindbergh, Charles Augustus, 1902–
The radio addresses of Col. Charles A. Lindbergh, 1939–1940 ... [New York, Scribner's Commentator, *1940.
18, [1] p. 22½ᶜᵐ.
CONTENTS. — America and European wars. — Neutrality and war. — The air defense of America.—Our drift toward war.—Our relationship with Europe.

1. European war, 1939– —U. S. 2. European war, 1939– —Ad-dresses, sermons etc. 3. U. S.—For. rel.—1933– I. Title.

Library of Congress   D753.L52   41–867
    ——— Copy 2.
Copyright AA 351548   [4]   940.5373

NL 0377437 DLC OrU

VOLUME 334

Lindbergh, Charles Augustus, 1902–
The Spirit of St. Louis. New York, Scribner, 1953.

562 p. illus. 22 cm.

"A condensation has appeared in the Saturday evening post under the title '33 hours to Paris.'"

1. Spirit of St. Louis (Airplane) 2. Aeronautics—Flights.
I. Title.

TL540.L5A85   53—11546 ‡

*629.109 629.1309

WaS WaSp WaT WaWW WaTC OrAshS
OrLgE CoU MiU MtBC IdU MtU Or OrCS OrP OrU Wa WaE
CU-S KyU-A KyU-N MdBP MoSW UU AU NIC KyU CaBViP
PBL PJA CaBVaU KyMdC CaBVa ICJ DSI KyBB KEmT CoU
MtBuM IdPI NBuC NcD ViU NN TxU TU MB CU PPLas PPFr
PPT NcC MiHM PSC OO OU PV OCU OC1U OOxM PPL OC1W
NL 0377438   DLC OC1 PWcS OC1W KyLx MiU PBa PIm PSt

Lindbergh, Charles Augustus, 1902–
The Spirit of St. Louis. New York, Scribner, 1954 [c1953].

562 p. illus. 22 cm.

"A condensation has appeared in the Saturday evening post under the title '33 hours to Paris.'"

NL 0377440   NBuC

---

*TL540
.L5A4   Lindbergh, Charles Augustus, 1902–
To Bogota and back by air; the narrative of a 9,500 mile flight from Washington, over thirteen Latin-American countries and return, in the single-seater airplane "Spirit of St. Louis." Washington, National Geographic Society, 1928.
2v. in 1 ([529]–602 p.) illus., map, ports. 25cm.

Caption title.
On cover: American flights: To Bogota and back by air.
Reprinted from National geographic magazine, v.53, no.5 (May 1928)

NL 0377442   MnHi

Lindbergh, Charles Augustus, 1902–
我れ等―リンドバーグ半自敍傳 宇都宮爽平譯
遠 東京 文明協會 昭和4 [1929]
6, 144 p. 19 cm.

I. Title.

Title romanised: Warera.

J 66—181

Harvard Univ. Chinese-for Library of Congress   Japanese Library 4515
[1]

NL 0377443   MH-HY

Lindbergh, Charles Augustus, 1902–
"We," by Charles A. Lindbergh; the famous flier's own story of his life and his transatlantic flight, together with his views on the future of aviation, with a foreword by Myron T. Herrick ... New York, London, G. P. Putnam's sons, 1927.

318 p. front., plates, ports. 21 cm.

"A little of what the world thought of Lindbergh, by Fitzhugh Green": p. 233–318.

I. Green, Fitzhugh, 1888–   II. Title.

TL540.L5A3 1927   27—15660

WaS IdU Or WaSpG OrP OrCS OrSaW WaWW WaTC
WaE MoU ICJ OrP CU-S MtU MWA WaT NIC IdB PPFr Wa WaSp
KyU WaU NIC IaU KyLx ViW LU CU DN MU OrPR KEmT NBuC
OCU OCX OC1 OU MH PPT CtY MWiW-C NcRS KyLx OrP ICU
NL 0377444   DLC CaBVa IdPI DAL MB NN ICJ NcD MiU ViU

Lindbergh, Charles Augustus, 1902–
"We", by Charles A. Lindbergh; the famous flier's own story of his life and his transatlantic flight, together with his views on the future of aviation, with an introduction by Myron T. Herrick ... New York & London, G.P. Putnam's sons, 1927.

308p. front., plates, ports., facsims. 26cm.

"Author's autograph edition. One thousand copies of this edition have been printed for sale. Each copy bears the autograph signature of the author. This is no.513. [Signed] G.P. Putnam's Sons [and] Charles A. Lindbergh."
"A little of what the world thought of Lindbergh, by Fitzhugh Green": p.223–308.
Ex libris John Stuart Groves.

I. Green, Fitzhugh, 1888–   II. Title.

NL 0377446   TxU DLC MoSW MH NNC NN NjP MiU NIC OrLgE

Lindbergh, Charles Augustus, 1902–
"We", by Charles A. Lindbergh; the famous flier's own story of his life and his transatlantic flight, together with his views on the future of aviation, with a foreword by Myron T. Herrick ... New York, Grosset and Dunlap, 1928.
318 p. front., plates, ports. 21 cm.

NL 0377447   WaTC

Lindbergh, Charles Augustus, 1902–
"We," by Charles A. Lindbergh; the famous flier's own story of his life and his transatlantic flight, together with his views on the future of aviation, with a foreword by Myron T. Herrick ... New York, London, G. P. Putnam's sons, 1928.
2 p. l., 5–318 p. front., plates, ports. 21 cm.

"First ... and fifth impressions, July, 1927 ... twenty-ninth impression, February, 1928."
"A little of what the world thought of Lindbergh, by Fitzhugh Green": p. 233–318.

NL 0377448   ViU OO OC1

Lindbergh, Charles Augustus, 1902–
"We", by Charles A. Lindbergh; the famous flier's own story of his life and his transatlantic flight, together with his views on the future of aviation, with a foreword by Myron T. Herrick ... New York, London, G. P. Putnam's sons, 1928.
318 p. front., plates, ports. 21 cm.

"First ... and fifth impressions, July, 1927 ... thirtieth impression, March, 1928."
"A little of what the world thought of Lindbergh, by Fitzhugh Green": p. 233–318.

1. Aeronautics—Flights.   I. Green, Fitzhugh, 1888–   II. Title.

28—20118

Library of Congress   TL540.L5A3 1928

NL 0377449   DLC Or

Lindbergh, Charles Augustus, 1902–
"We", by Charles A. Lindbergh; the famous flier's own story of his life and his transatlantic flight, together with his views on the future of aviation, with a foreword by Myron T. Herrick ... New York, London, G. P. Putnam's sons, 1928.
6 p. l., 5–318 p. front., plates, ports. 21 cm.

"First ... and fifth impressions, July, 1927 ... thirty-first impression, June, 1928."
"A little of what the world thought of Lindbergh, by Fitzhugh Green": p. 233–318.

I. Green, Fitzhugh, 1888–   II. Title.

29—2617

Library of Congress   TL540.L5A3 1928 a

NL 0377450   DLC CaBVaU MU PP NRCR

Lindbergh, Charles Augustus, 1902–
We. n.p., Grosset, 1929.

NL 0377451   OrU

Lindbergh, Chas. Augustus, 1902–
"We", by .... the famous flier's own story of his life & his transatlantic flight, together with his views on the future of aviation, with a foreword by Myron T. Herrick....N.Y., Lond., G.P.Putnam's sons, [1930]
318p.

NL 0377452   ODW

Lindbergh, Chas. Augustus, 1902–
"We", lentokoneeni ja mina; kuulun lentajan kertomus omasta elamastaan ja lentoretkestaan Atlantin meren poikki ynna hanen mielipiteensa ilmailun tulevaisuudesta ...suomentanut I.K. Inha. [283p.illus.port.]
Porvoo, Soderstrom, [1927]

NL 0377453   OC1

Lindbergh, Charles Augustus, 1902–
... Wir zwei; im flugzeug über den Atlantik. Leipzig, F. A. Brockhaus, 1927.

159, [1] p. front., plates, ports. 19 cm. (*Half-title:* Reisen und abenteuer. 41)

At head of title : Charles A. Lindbergh.

1. Aeronautics—Flights.   I. Title.   *Translation of "We".*

33—14210

Library of Congress   TL540.L5A35

[2]   926.29

NL 0377454   DLC NN

Lindbergh, Gage, *pseud.*
"Plucky" Lindbergh; incidents in the life of Colonel Charles Lindbergh and brief biography, log of his transatlantic trip and receptions, recording all important facts, by Gage Lindbergh [pseud.] Los Angeles, Calif., Gem publishing company [*1927]
5 p. l., [13]–77 p. 19 cm.

1. Lindbergh, Charles Augustus, 1902–   2. Aeronautics—Flights.
[Gage Lindbergh, pseud. of Gerald R. Gage and James Lindbergh]

27—14266

Library of Congress   TL540.L5L5

NL 0377455   DLC WaTC WaSp MH MiEM MiU DSI

Lindbergh, Gage, pseud.

"Plucky" Lindbergh; incidents in the life of Colonel Charles Lindbergh and brief biography, log of his transatlantic trip and receptions; recording all important facts, by Gerald Gage, 2d ed. Los Angeles, Calif., Wetzel Publ. Co. 1927.
98 p. illus., ports. 19cm.

NL 0377456   ViU IU ICU MtU IdU

LINDBERGH, HENRY.
... Vanhin hurmaa; moottoriurheilun kehitystä ja historiaa... Helsinki, Tammi [1952] 302 p. illus., maps. 21cm.

1. Automobile racing.

NL 0377457   NN

Lindbergh, James, and G. R. Gage.
See
Lindbergh, Gage, pseud. of Gerald R. Gage and James Lindbergh.

VOLUME 334

*F604.1 ₍Lindbergh, Måns Olson₎ 1835-1870.
186811   ₍Staten Minnesota i Nord Amerika. Dess
innebyggare, klimat och beskaffenhet, af
Lgh. ₍Köpenhamn, I.Cokens tryckeri₎1868.
facsim.: 9 sheets. 20x25cm. (first
and last, 20x14cm.)

Photostat (negative) from the original
in the Kungliga Biblioteket in Stockholm.
Each sheet of the facsimile represents
two pages of the original (a verso and

the opposite recto) beginning with the
verso of the title-page and the opposite
recto. Page 1 (the title-page) and 16
are half sheets and represent a recto
and a verso respectively.
Collation of the original (as represented by facsimile): 16 p. 20cm.
Title vignette.

NL 0377460   MnHi

Lindbergh, Zacharias Wilhelm, respondent.
Digerböden dess tidehvarf och dess...
see under Hwasser, Israël, 1790-1860,
praeses.

Lindbergh flies alone; an editorial from the New
York Sun
see under [Anderson, Harold M.]

₍Lindbergh songs, published in commemoration of his flight to
France, May 20-21, 1927₎ ₍New York, etc., 1927-29₎
19 no. in 1 v. ports. 31cm.
For 1 voice with piano acc.
Includes 1 song about his flight to Mexico, and 1 song about Chamberlin and
Lindbergh.
"By the watermelon vine, by Thomas S. Allen," issued with no. 10 (Lindy).
CONTENTS.—Chamberlin and Lindy, by Robert King.—Charlie boy, by Mary Earl.
—Hello Lindy, by Larry Conley and Dave Silverman.—Here he comes, by Earl
Hanbrich.—I owe it all to you, by Lou Klein, Irving Mills and Jimmy McHugh.—
Just Lindy, by E. E. Edstrom.—Like an angel you flew into everyone's heart, by

Jimmy McHugh and Irving Mills.—Lindbergh, by Howard Johnson and Al Sherman.—Lindbergh — the hero of the day, by Chester Escher.—Lindy, by Norman Leigh
and G. L. Cobb.—Lindy, Lindy, by Dok Eisenbourg.—Lone eagle, by George Pianta-
dosi, Jack Glogau and Roy Turk.—Lucky Lindy, by Abel Baer.—Oh, Charlie is my
darling, by Irving Bibo.—Plucky Lindy, by Lou Zoeller and Fred Bernhard.—Plucky
Lindy's lucky day, by Charles Abbott and Dale Wimbrow.—Triumphant Lindbergh;
and "We," by H. J. Lincoln.—Welcome home, by Charles Maduro.—You flew over,
by Charlie Harrison and Joe Verges.

977725A. 1. Songs, English.   American composers—Collections.
2. Lindbergh, Charles Augustus,   1902-   3. Chamberlin, Clarence
Duncan, 1893–   January 19, 1939
N. Y. P. L.

NL 0377464   NN

Lindbergh, the flier of Little Falls ... ₍St. Cloud, Minn.,
1928₎
₍23₎ p. illus. (incl. ports.) 28ᶜᵐ.
Dedication by the classes of nineteen hundred and twenty-eight and
nineteen hundred and twenty-nine of Little Falls high school, Little
Falls, Minn.

1. Lindbergh, Charles Augustus, 1902-   I. Little Falls, Minn.
High school.

Library of Congress   TL540.L5L4
                             CA 28-545 Unrev'd

NL 0377465   DLC WaS PPAmSwM

Lindbergh's own story of his New York-Paris
flight, as published in the New York times,
May 22 and 24, 1927
see under New York times.

Lindblad, Adolf Fredrik, 1801-1878
Bref till Adolf Fredrik Lindblad fran Mendelssohn,
Dohrn...
see under title

Lindblad, Adolf Fredrik, 1801-1878.

Geijer, Erik Gustaf, 1783-1847.
Erik Gustaf Geijers samlade skrifter ... Stockholm, P. A.
Norstedt och söner, 1873-75.

Lindblad, Adolf Fredrik, 1801-1878.   **M.450.235
The heardsman's mountain song. "Pa berget." Composed by A. F.
Lindblad. [Song with accompaniment for the pianoforte.]
[New York. Hall. 185–?] 7 pp. Illustrated title-page. [Amer-
ican edition of Jenny Lind's Swedish melodies.] 35.5 cm.
The text is in English and Swedish.

E165 — T.r. — Songs. With music.

NL 0377469   MB

[Lindblad, Adolf Fredrik] 1801-1878.
Herd Sang, the celebrated Echo song, sung by
Mlle. J. Lind. (Come hither, come hither, my
pretty herd!) [Voice with piano acc.] Philadelphia,
E. Ferrett & Co., [1852]
5 p. F°.

NL 0377470   NN

M 1620   Lindblad, Adolf Fredrik, 1801-1878.
.L74L72   Lieder mit Begleitung des Pianoforte
componiert von A. F. Lindblad aus dem
Schwedischen übertragen von A. Dohrn.
Bonn. Gedruckt bei N. Simrock [1842?]
2 v. in 1.

1. Songs (Medium voice) with piano.

NL 0377471   ICU MB

Lindblad, Adolf Fredrik.   No. 25 in *8050a.730.22
Near. A Swedish song. [With accompaniment for pianoforte.]
Translated from the German by J. S. Dwight.
═ Boston. Russell & Richardson. [185–?] 5 pp. 35½ cm.

L4968 — T.r. — Songs. With music.

NL 0377472   MB

Lindblad, Adolf Fredrik, 1801-1878.
Der Norden-Saal; eine Sammlung schwedischer Volkslieder,
übersetzt von Amalie v. Helwig geborne Freiin v. Imhoff, mit
Begleitung des Pianoforte nach den alten Gesang-Weisen bearbeitet...von A. F. Lindblad...   Berlin: A. M. Schlesinger
₍1827?₎.   Publ. pl. nos. 1435-1436.   2 v. in 1. ob. 4°.
German and Swedish words of first stanza only with music for 1 voice with
piano acc. Complete German text at end of each part.

                                        JUILLIARD FOUNDATION FUND.
1. Folk songs (Swedish). 2. Helvig,   Amalia (von Imhoff) von, 1776-
1831, translator. 3. Title.   October 24, 1923.
N. Y. P. L.

NL 0377473   NN

VM   LINDBLAD, ADOLF FREDRIK, 1801-1878.
1   The post boy's return, Swedish melody.
F 91   ₍New York, W.Hall & son, ca.1850₎
no.13   7p. 34cm.

        Caption title.

NL 0377474   ICN PPAmSwM

LINDBLAD, ADOLF FREDRIK, 1801-1878.

        Schwedische Lieder; mit Begleitung des
Pianoforte. In deutscher Uebertragung mit Beibe-
haltung des Originaltextes von A. E. Wollheim.
Hamburg, Schuberth [ca.1842-48] Pl. no. 493/1117
7 no. in 1 v. 34cm.

        Heft 1, 3, 5-9.

        For voice and piano; German and Swedish words.

        1. Songs, Swedish.

NL 0377476   NN

Lindblad, Adolf Fredrik, 1801- 1878.   No. 10 in.**M.392.38
Ein Sommerabend. [Männerchor.]
(In Steinhausen. Conferenz-Gesänge. Band 2, Heft 1, p. 8. Neu-
wied. [1878.])

E3388 — T.r. — Part songs.

NL 0377477   MB

Lindblad,Adolf Fredrik, 1801-1878.
        Serenade on Adrias sea, (Ro sakta med
gondolen här), barcarolle, sung by Mdlle.Jenny
Lind,composed by Lindblad ... New York, Firth,
Pond & co., c1850.

        8 p. 34cm.

        Caption title.
        Cover title: Jenny Lind's serenade.
        Portrait on title-page.
        Vol.V,no.15: "Music collections".
        1.Vocal music.2.Li   thographs,American.3.Lind,
Jenny,1820-1887-Icon   ography.I.Title.II.Title:
Jenny Lind's serenade.

NL 0377478   MiU-C

HQ   LINDBLAD, Anders, 1849-1908
222   Statistisk undersökning angående
J65s   skörlefvande kvinnors lefnadsförhällanden.
1908   Stockholm, Marcus, 1908.
        80 p. ₍With Johansson, J. E. Statistisk
utredning angående reglementeringen i
Stockholm, 1859-1905. Stockholm, 1908₎

NL 0377479   DNLM

Lindblad, Anders Fredrik, 1888-
        A critical analysis of the factors affecting safety and
economy of operation of the bulk freight vessels of the
Great Lakes, by Anders Fredrik Lindblad ... ₍Ann Ar-
bor? 1924₎
1 p. l., ₍24₎ p. tables, diagrs. (1 fold.) 27½ᶜᵐ.
Various pagings.
Thesis (D. sc.)—University of Michigan, 1923.
Contains four articles reprinted from Marine review, Cleveland, October,
November, December, 1923, February, 1924, and two from Transactions of
the Society of naval architects and marine engineers, v. 30, 1922, v. 31, 1923.
1. Ship-building. 2. Stability of ships. 3. Shipping—Great Lakes.
                                                    24—20667
Library of Congress   VM391.L5 1923
Univ. of Michigan Libr.   ₍25c2₎

NL 0377480   MiU OO OCU OrU IdU DLC

VOLUME 334

Egleston
D623.8
G712
nr.3
Lindblad, Anders Fredrik, 1888–
Experiments with bulbous bows. Göteborg,
N. J. Bumperts bokhandel A B, 1944.
28 p. illus., tables, diagrs. 25cm.
(Gothenburg, Sweden. Statens skeppsprovnings-
anstalt. Meddelanden, nr. 3)

1. Ship-building.

NL 0377481 NNC

Egleston
D623.8
G712
nr.8
Lindblad, Anders Fredrik, 1888–
Further experiments with bulbous bows.
Göteborg, 1948.
20 p. illus., tables, diagrs. 25cm.
(Gothenburg, Sweden. Statens skeppsprovnings-
anstalt. Meddelanden, nr. 8)

1. Ship-building.

NL 0377482 NNC

Lindblad, Anders Fredrik, 1888–
. . . Kryssareakterns användning vid handelsfartyg; några
modellförsök, av Anders Lindblad. Göteborg, 1945. 32 p.
illus. 25cm. (Chalmers tekniska högskola, Gothenburg.
Handlingar. nr. 45.)
Summary in English.

1. Shipbuilding—Experiment   tanks—Sweden—Gothenburg. I. Ser.
N. Y. P. L.   April 23, 1948

NL 0377483 NN NNC

Lindblad, Anders Fredrik, 1888–
. . .Some experiments with models of high speed cargo liners,
by Anders Lindblad. Göteborg, 1943. 34 p. 25cm.
(Chalmers tekniska högskola, Gothenburg. Handlingar. nr. 25.)
"List of references," p. [33]–34.

1. Ships—Resistance. I. Ser.
N. Y. P. L   October 10, 1947

NL 0377484 NN NNC

Lindblad, Anders Fredrik, 1888–
. . .Some experiments with selfpropelled models
of twin screw ships; the influence of longitudinal centre of buoyancy on resistance and
propulsion, by Anders Lindblad. Göteborg,
Erlander, 1951. 24 p. 25cm. (Chalmers
tekniska högskola, Gothenburg. Handlingar.
nr. 110)

1. Ships—Propulsion.   2. Ships—Resitance.

NL 0377485 NN

Lindblad, Axel, 1874–
. . . Einige Versuche über den zweiten Hauptsatz der Wärmelehre, von Axel Lindblad . . . [Uppsala, Almqvist & Wiksells
boktryckeri-a.-b., 1936]
5 p. 1 illus. 23cm. (Arkiv för matematik, astronomi och fysik. bd. 25a,
n:o 15)
Caption title.

NL 0377486 ICJ

Lindblad, Axel, 1874–
Framställning av oljor ur ved genom
hydrering... Stockholm, Svenska bokhandelscentralen a.-b., 1931.
59 p. (Ingeniörsvetenskapsakademiens.
handlingar. nr. 107)

NL 0377487 OU

Lindblad, Axel, 1874–
Is the second law of thermodynamics generally valid for
macroscopic processes? by Dr. Axel Lindblad and Dr. Ragnar
Liljeblad ... Stockholm, Generalstabens litografiska anstalts
förlag [1937]
14 p. illus., diagr. 24cm. (Ingeniörsvetenskapsakademiens handlingar.
nr. 145)

1. Thermodynamics.   I. *Liljeblad, Ragnar, 1885–   joint author.
II. Title.
[Full name: Axel Rudolf Lindblad]
A 38–494
Iowa. State coll. Library
for Library of Congress   [TA4.I 43 no. 145]
[2]   (620.82)

NL 0377488 IaAS DLC OC1

Lindblad, Axel, 1874–
A new static gravity meter and its use for ore prospecting, by
Dr. Axel Lindblad and Dr. David Malmqvist ... Stockholm,
Generalstabens litografiska anstalts förlag, 1938.
52 p. illus., tables, diagrs. 24cm. (Ingeniörsvetenskapsakademiens
handlingar. nr. 146)
"Literature": p. 52.

1. Gravity. 2. Prospecting.   I. Malmqvist, David, joint author.
II. Title: Static gravity meter.
[Full name: Axel Rudolf Lindblad]
A C 38–2976
Iowa. State coll. Library
for Library of Congress   [TA4.I 43 no. 146]
[2]   (620.82)

NL 0377489 IaAS OU

Lindblad, Bertil, 1895–
A condensation theory of meteoric matter and
its cosmological significance, by Bertil Lindblad. (St. Albans, Eng., printed by Fisher,
Knight & co., ltd., 1935)
cover-title, (7) p. 22 cm. (Stockholms
observatorium. Meddelande n:o 18)
("Reprinted from Nature, Vol. 135, page
133, January 26, 1935.")

NL 0377490 DN-Ob

Lindblad, Bertil, 1895–
. . . Contributions to the theory of stellar
systems, by Bertil Lindblad; with 17 figs.
in the text... Stockholm, Almqvist & Wiksells boktryckeri-a.-b., 1936.
64 p. tables, diagrs. 29 cm.
(Stockholms observatoriums Annaler (Astronomiska iakttagelser och undersökningar a
Stockholms observatorium) bd. 12. n:o 4)

NL 0377491 DN-Ob

Lindblad, Bertil, 1895–
. . .Cosmogonic consequences of a theory of the stellar system,
by Bertil Lindblad. With 6 figures in the text ... [Uppsala,
Almqvist & Wiksells boktryckeri-a-b., 1926]
15 p. illus., diagrs. 23cm. (Arkiv för matematik, astronomi och fysik.
bd. 19A, n:o 35)
Caption title.

NL 0377492 ICJ

QB
4
897S83+
v.19
no.9
Lindblad, Bertil, 1895–
Differential motions in dispersion orbits
in the galaxy. Stockholm, Almqvist & Wiksell, 1957.
15 p. illus. 29cm. (Stockholms
observatoriums annaler, bd. 19, no. 9)

1. Milky Way. 2. Orbits. I. Title.
II. Title: Dispersion orbits in the galaxy.

NL 0377493 NIC

QB
351
L74
Lindblad, Bertil, 1895–
Dynamics of stellar systems, lectures at the
University of Michigan, June-July 1950. [Ann
Arbor? 1950]
88 l. diagrs. 28 cm.
Caption title.

1.Stars. 2.Mechanics,Celestial. I.Title.

NL 0377494 MiU

Lindblad, Bertil, 1895–
... The luminosities, individual parallaxes, and motions of B
and A type stars, by Bertil Lindblad and Carl Schalén ... [Upp-
sala, Almqvist & Wiksells boktryckeri-a.-b., 1927]
25, [1] p. incl. tables. 23cm. (Arkiv för matematik, astronomi och fysik.
bd. 20A, n:o 7)
Caption title.

NL 0377495 ICJ

Lindblad, Bertil, 1895–
The luminous surface and atmosphere of the sun.
(In Smithsonian Institution. Annual report, 1950. Washington,
1951. 24 cm. p. 173–182. illus.)
"Seventeenth James Arthur lecture, given under the auspices of
the Smithsonian Institution on April 6, 1950."

1. Sun.
Q11.S66 1950   52–4067

NL 0377496 DLC TxU

Lindblad, Bertil
Note on the distances of the cluster type
variables. Bertil Lindblad.
(Chicago, 1924.)
cover title+(8) p. 24cm.

Astrophys. Journ., 59, 1924, 37–44.

NL 0377497 DN-Ob

Lindblad, Bertil.
Note on the spectroscopic parallaxes of A-type
stars. Bertil Lindblad....
(Chicago, 1924.)
cover title+(5) p. 24cm.

Astrophys. Journ., 59, 1924, 305–309.

NL 0377498 DN-Ob

VOLUME 334

QB
4
S97S83
v.16
no.1+

Lindblad, Bertil, 1895–
   On a theorem in the dynamics of stellar systems. Stockholm, Almqvist & Wiksell, 1950.
   34 p. illus. 29cm. (Stockholms Observatoriums Annaler, Bd. 16, N:o 1)

   1. Astrophysics. I. Series: Stockholm. Astronomiska Observatoriet. Annalen, v.16, no. 1.

NL 0377499 NIC

Lindblad, Bertil, 1895–
   ... On the absolute magnitudes and parallaxes of bright stars determined by the cyanogen criterion, by Bertil Lindblad ... Communicated February 23rd 1927 by H. von Zeipel and Östen Bergstrand. Stockholm, Almqvist & Wiksells boktryckeri-a.-b., 1927.
   23 p. incl. tables, diagrs. 28½ᶜᵐ. (Kungl. svenska vetenskapsakademiens handlingar. 3. ser., bd. 4, n:o 5)

   1. Stars—Magnitudes. 2. Parallax—Stars. 3. Stars—Spectra.
                         A 29–53

Title from Univ. of Chi-   cago Q64.8828 3. ser., vol. 4, no. 5
                        Printed by L. C.

NL 0377500 ICU MiU

Lindblad, Bertil, 1895–
   ... On the cause of the ellipsoidal distribution of stellar velocities, by Bertil Lindblad ... ₍Uppsala, Almqvist & Wiksells boktryckeri-a.-b., 1927₎
   7 p. 23ᶜᵐ. (Arkiv för matematik, astronomi och fysik. bd. 20A, n:o 17)
   Caption title.

NL 0377501 ICJ

Lindblad, Bertil, 1895–
   On the constitution and development of rotating stellar systems. (by)... Bertil Lindblad... (Edinburgh, Neill & Co.. ltd.. 1934)
   cover-title, p. (11)–24. diagrs. 25½ cm. (Stockholms observatorium. Meddelande. n:o 17)
   "Monthly Notices of R.A.S., 1934 November"

NL 0377502 DN–Ob

Lindblad, Bertil, 1895–
   ... On the decrease of star-density with distance from the galactic plane, by Bertil Lindblad ... ₍Uppsala, Almqvist & Wiksells boktryckeri-a.-b., 1926₎
   6 p. 23ᶜᵐ. (Arkiv för matematik, astronomi och fysik. bd. 19B, n:o 15)
   Caption title.

NL 0377503 ICJ

Lindblad, Bertil, 1895–
   ... On the development of spiral structure in anagalactic nebulae, by Bertil Lindblad. With 2 figures in the text ... ₍Uppsala, Almqvist & Wiksells boktryckeri-a.-b., 1930₎
   9, ₍1₎ p. diagrs. 23ᶜᵐ. (Arkiv för matematik, astronomi och fysik. bd. 22A, n:o 11)
   Caption title.

NL 0377504 ICJ

Lindblad, Bertil, 1895–
   ... On the direction of star-streaming (by) Bertil Lindblad. (Edinburgh, Printed by Neill & co., ltd., 1935)
   1 p. 1., p. (69)–77. 25½ cm. (On cover: Stockholms observatorium. Meddelande n:o 25)
   Reprinted from the Monthly notices of the Royal astronomical society, v. 96, no. 1.

NL 0377505 DN–Ob

Lindblad, Bertil, 1895–
   On the distribution of intensity in the continuous spectra of the sun and the fixed stars, and its relation to spectral type and luminosity ... by Bertil Lindblad ... ₍Uppsala, E. Berlings boktryckeri, 1920₎
   2 p. l., 113, ₍1₎ p. pl., diagrs. 24ᶜᵐ.
   Inaug.-diss.—Uppsala.
   "Reprinted from Uppsala universitets årsskrift 1920."

   1. Spectrum, Solar. 2. Stars—Spectra.
                       24–17488

Library of Congress   QB465.L5

NL 0377506 DLC NN IU PHC CtY

Lindblad, Bertil, 1895–
   ... On the distribution of intensity in the continuous spectra of the sun and the fixed stars, and its relation to spectral type and luminosity, by Bertil Lindblad. Uppsala, A.-b. Akademiska bokhandeln ₍1920₎
   2 p. l., 113, ₍1₎ p. pl., diagrs. 24ᶜᵐ. (Uppsala universitets årsskrift 1920. Matematik och naturvetenskap. 1)
   Issued also as the author's thesis, Uppsala.

   1. Spectrum, Solar. 2. Stars—Spectra.
                       A C 39–2061

Minnesota. Univ. Library
for Library of Congress   [AS284.U7 1920]
                    ₍4₎   (378.485)

NL 0377507 MnU PU MoU MiU

QB
4
S97
S83+
v.15
no.9

Lindblad, Bertil, 1895–
   On the distribution of light-intensity and colour in the spiral nebula Messier 63, by B. Lindblad and J. Delhaye. Stockholm, Almquist & Wiksell, 1949.
   26 p. illus. 29 cm. (Stockholms Observatoriums Annaler, bd. 15, no. 9)

   1. Astrophysics. I. Delhaye, Jean, 1921–

NL 0377508 NIC

QB
4
S97S83
v.15,
no.4+

Lindblad, Bertil, 1895–
   On the dynamical theory of spiral structure. Comparison between theory and observation. Stockholm, Almqvist & Wiksell, 1948.
   52 p. illus. 29cm. (Stockholms observatoriums annaler, Bd. 15, no. 4)

   1. Nebulae. I. Series: Stockholm. Astronomiska Observatoriet. Annalen, v. 15, no. 4.

NL 0377509 NIC

QB
4
S97S83+
v.17
no.6

Lindblad, Bertil, 1895–
   On the dynamics of stellar systems, by Bertil Lindblad and Ray G. Langebartel. Stockholm, Almqvist & Wiksell, 1953.
   61 p. illus. 29cm. (Stockholms observatoriums Annaler, Bd.17, n:o 6)

   1. Astrophysics. I. Langebartel, Ray G   jt. auth. II. Series: Stockholm. Astronomiska Observatoriet. Annalen, v.17, no. 6.   III. Title.

NL 0377510 NIC

Lindblad, Bertil, 1895–
   ... On the dynamics of the Andromeda nebula, by Bertil Lindblad ... ₍Uppsala, Almqvist & Wiksells boktryckeri-a.-b., 1939₎
   8 p. diagrs. 23ᶜᵐ. (Arkiv för matematik, astronomi och fysik. bd. 27A, n:o 2)
   Caption title.

NL 0377511 ICJ

Lindblad, Bertil, 1895–
   ... On the dynamics of the stellar system, by Bertil Lindblad. With 9 figures in the text ... ₍Uppsala, Almqvist & Wiksells boktryckeri-a.-b., 1928₎
   28 p. diagrs. 23ᶜᵐ. (Arkiv för matematik, astronomi och fysik. bd. 21A, n:o 3)
   Caption title.
   Bibliographical foot-notes.

NL 0377512 ICJ

Lindblad, Bertil, 1895–
   ... On the dynamics of the system of globular clusters, by Bertil Lindblad ... ₍Uppsala, Almqvist & Wiksells boktryckeri-a.-b., 1926₎
   8 p. 23ᶜᵐ. (Arkiv för matematik, astronomi och fysik. bd. 19A, n:o 27)
   Caption title.

NL 0377513 ICJ

Lindblad, Bertil, 1895–
   ... On the emission and absorption in the H and K lines of calcium in Nova Herculis 1934, by Bertil Lindblad and Yngve Öhman ... ₍Uppsala, Almqvist & Wiksells boktryckeri-a.-b., 1935₎
   5 p. diagrs. 23ᶜᵐ. (Arkiv för matematik, astronomi och fysik. bd. 25B, n:o 4)
   Caption title.

NL 0377514 ICJ

Lindblad, Bertil, 1895–
   ... On the evolution of a rotating system of material particles, with applications to Saturn's rings, the planetary system and the galaxy (by) Bertil Lindblad... (Edinburgh, Neill & co., ltd., 1934)
   1 p. l., p. (231)–240. diagrs. 25½ cm. (On cover: Stockholms observatorium. Meddelande. n:o 13)
   Bibliographical foot-notes.
   "Reprinted from the Monthly notices of the Royal astronomical society, vol. 94, no. 3."

NL 0377515 DN–Ob

Lindblad, Bertil
   On the intensity-distribution in short grating spectra and objective-prism spectra as a function of spectral type and absolute magnitude. By Bertil Lindblad...
   (London, 1923.)
      (10) p. 22½cm.

Astron. Soc. Month. Not., 83, 1922–23, 503–510.

NL 0377516 DN–Ob

Lindblad, Bertil, 1895–
   On the proper motion of the cluster Messier 37. Communicated 13 May 1953
     see under   Lindblad, Per Olof.

VOLUME 334

Lindblad, Bertil, 1895–
... On the relation between the velocity ellipsoid and the rotation of the galaxy, by Bertil Lindblad. With 2 figures in the text ... ₁Uppsala, Almqvist & Wiksells boktryckeri-a.-b., 1929₁

7 p. diagrs. 23ᶜᵐ. (Arkiv för matematik, astronomi och fysik. bd. 21A, n:o 15)

Caption title.
Bibliographical foot-notes.

NL 0377518   ICJ

Lindblad, Bertil, 1895–
... On the rotation theory of the galaxy, by Bertil Lindblad. With 2 figures in the text ... ₁Uppsala, Almqvist & Wiksells boktryckeri-a.-b., 1933₁

12 p. diagrs. 23ᶜᵐ. (Arkiv för matematik, astronomi och fysik. bd. 23A, n:o 18)

Caption title.

NL 0377519   ICJ DN-Ob

Lindblad, Bertil, 1895–
... On the spectrophotometric criteria of stellar luminosity, by Bertil Lindblad and Erik Stenquist. With 28 figures in the text... Stockholm, Almqvist & Wiksell, 1934.

75 p.   illus., tables, diagrs. 29 cm.
(Astronomiska iakttagelser och undersök- ningar a Stockholms observatorium. bd. 11, n:r 12)
Bibliographical foot-notes.

NL 0377520   DN-Ob

Lindblad, Bertil, 1895–
On the spiral orbits in the equatorial plane of a spheroidal disk with applications to some typical spiral nebulæ. Upp- sala, Almqvist & Wiksells boktr., 1927.

18 p. diagrs. 19 cm. (Kungl. Svenska vetenskapsakademiens handlingar, 3. ser., bd. 4, n:o 7)

Meddelanden från Astronomiska observatorium, Upsala, n:o 31.

1. Orbits. 2. Nebulae.   (Series: Svenska vetenskapsakademien, Stockholm. Handlingar, 3. ser., bd. 4, n:o 7. Series: Uppsala. Uni- versitet. Astronomiska observatoriet. Meddelanden, n:o 31)

Q64.S85   ser. 3, bd. 4, no. 7   A 29–55 rev*
———— Copy 3.   QB355.L5

Chicago. Univ. Libr.
for Library of Congress   ₁r59cⁿₜ₎†

NL 0377521   ICU DLC MiU

QB   Lindblad, Bertil, 1895–
4   On the theory of star-streaming, by
S97S83+   Bertil Lindblad and Fernand Nahon.
v.18   Stockholm, Almqvist & Wiksell, 1954.
no.²2   22 p. illus. 29cm. (Stockholms
               Observatoriums Annaler, bd. 18, no.2)

1. Stars--Proper motion. I. Title: Star-streaming. II. Nahon, Fernand, jt. auth. III. Series: Stockholm. Astronomis- ka Observa   toriet. Annalen, bd. 18. no. 2.

NL 0377522   NIC

Lindblad, Bertil
On the use of grating spectra for determining spectral type and absolute magnitude of the stars. Bertil Lindblad.
(Chicago, 1919.)
cover title   (14) p. 24cm.

Astrophys. Journ., 49, 1919, 289-302.

NL 0377523   DN-Ob

Lindblad, Bertil, 1895–
On the velocity ellipsoid and the general star-streaming in the region around the sun ₍by₎ dr. Bertil Lindblad... Edinburgh. Printed by Neill & co;, ltd., 1936.
cover-title, p. (15)-24.   diagr. 25½ cm.
(Stockholms observatorium Meddelande n:o 29)
Monthly notices of R.A.S., 1936 November.

NL 0377524   DN-Ob

Lindblad, Bertil, 1895–
... The orientation of the planes of spiral nebulæ inferred from the dark lanes of occulting matter, by Bertil Lindblad ... ₁Uppsala, Almqvist & Wiksells boktryckeri-a.-b., 1934₁

7 p. 3 pl., diagr. 23ᶜᵐ. (Arkiv för matematik, astronomi och fysik. bd. 24A, n:o 21)

Caption title.
Bibliographical foot-notes.

NL 0377525   ICJ DN-Ob

Lindblad, Bertil, 1895–
... Die photographisch effektive Wellenlänge als Farbenäqui- valent der Sterne, von Bertil Lindblad. Mit 16 Abbildungen im Texte ... ₁Uppsala, Almqvist & Wiksells boktryckeri-a.-b., 1918₁

75, ₁1₁ p. incl. tables, diagrs. 23ᶜᵐ. (Arkiv för matematik, astronomi och fysik. bd. 13, n:o 26)

Caption title.
Bibliographical foot-notes.

NL 0377526   ICJ PHC DN-Ob

LINDBLAD, BERTIL, 1895–
A radar investigation of the delta Aquarid meteor shower of 1950. Göteborg [Gumpert] 1952.   26, [2] p.   illus.   25cm.
(Chalmers tekniska högskola, Gothenburg. Handlingar, nr. 129)

"Avd. Elektroteknik 30."
Bibliography, p. [27].

1. Meteors. 2. Meteors, 1952. I. Series.

NL 0377527   NN

Lindblad, Bertil.
... Radiative equilibrium and solar temperature, by Bertil Lindblad.   (Presented to the Royal society of sci- ence of Upsala February 2nd 1923) Uppsala, E. Ber- lings boktryckeri a.-b., 1923.

2 p. l., 24 p. tables, chart. 29ᶜᵐ. (Nova acta Regiae societatis scien- tiarum Upsaliensis. ser. 4, v. 6, n:o 1)

1. Sun—Temperature. 2. Solar radiation.   I. Title.

                                            A 24–128

Title from John Crerar   Libr. Printed by L. C.

NL 0377528   ICJ PHC NN

Lindblad, Bertil, 1895–
... Researches based on determinations of stellar lu- minosities (second paper) By Bertil Lindblad. (With 10 figures) (Presented to the Royal society of science of Upsala March 5th 1926) Uppsala, Almqvist & Wiksells boktryckeri-a.-b., 1926.

55 p. tables, diagrs. 29 x 22½ᶜᵐ. (Nova acta Regiae societatis scien- tiarum Upsaliensis. Volumen extra ordinem editum 1927)

1. Stars—Magnitudes.

NL 0377529   MiU

Lindblad, Bertil, 1895–
... The rotation of the galaxy... (Milano, 1932)
cover-title, p. (325)-334.   24 cm.
(Stockholms observatorium. Meddelande n:o 7)
"Extrait de "Scientia", mai 1932."

NL 0377530   DN-Ob

Lindblad, Bertil, 1895–
... The small oscillations of a rotating stellar system and the development of spiral arms, by Bertil Lindblad ... ₁Uppsala, Almqvist & Wiksells boktryckeri-a.-b., 1927₁

9, ₁1₁ p. 23ᶜᵐ. (Arkiv för matematik, astronomi och fysik. bd. 20A, n:o 10)

Caption title.

NL 0377531   ICJ

Lindblad, Bertil, 1895–
Spectrophotometric determinations of stellar luminosi- ties; the distances and tangential velocities of stars in the Greenwich polar zone. Uppsala, Edv. Berlings Nya boktr., 1925.

99 p. 29 cm. (Nova acta Regiae Societatis Scientiarum Upsali- ensis, ser. 4, v. 6, n:o 5)
"Presented to the Royal Society of Science Upsala November 7th 1924."
Includes bibliographical references.
1. Stars — Magnitudes. 2. Spectrophotometry.   I. Title. II. Series: Vetenskaps-societeten i Upsala. Nova acta ser. 4, v. 6, n:o 5.

Q64.U6   ser. 4, vol. 6, no. 5   508'.1 s   73–172574
[QB815]   [523.8'22]   MARC

NL 0377532   DLC DN-Ob ICJ IEN NN

Lindblad, Bertil.
... Spectrophotometric methods for determining stellar luminosity, by Bertil Lindblad ... ₁Chicago, 1922₁
cover-title, 34 p. diagrs. 25½ᶜᵐ. (Contributions from the Mount Wilson observatory. no. 228)

At head of title: Carnegie institution of Washington.
"Reprinted from the Astrophysical journal, vol. lv, 1922."

1. Stars—Magnitudes.

Library of Congress   QB4.C32 no. 228   22–19470

NL 0377533   DLC MB OO OU

Lindblad, Bertil, 1895–
Star-streaming and spiral motion in the stellar system ₍by₎ dr. Bertil Lindblad... ₍Edinburgh. Printed by Neill & co., ltd.₎ 1935.
cover-title, p. (663)-671.   diagrs. 25½ cm. (Stockholms observatorium Med- delande n:o 23)
Monthly notices of R.A.S., 1935 June.

NL 0377534   DN-Ob

QB   Lindblad, Bertil, 1895–
4   Star-streaming and spiral structure.
A97S83   Stockholm, Almqvist & Wiksells, 1955.
v.18   20 p. illus. 29cm. (Stockholms obser-
no.6+   vatoriums annaler, bd.18, no.6)

1. Stars--Motion in line of sight. I. Series: Stockholm. Astronomiska Observatoriet. Annaler, bd.18, no.6.

NL 0377535   NIC

Lindblad, Bertil, 1895–
... Star-streaming and the structure of the stellar system ₍first₁-second paper) by Bertil Lindblad ... ₁Uppsala, Almqvist & Wiksells boktryckeri-a.-b., 1925-1926₁

2 v. diagr. 23ᶜᵐ. (Arkiv för matematik, astronomi och fysik. bd. 19A, n:o 21; bd. 19B, n:o 7)

Caption title.

NL 0377536   ICJ

VOLUME 334

Lindblad, Bertil, 1895– joint author.

Curtis, Heber Doust, 1872–
   Das sternsystem, erster teil II, bearb. von Heber D. Curtis,
B. Lindblad, K. Lundmark, H. Shapley. Mit 118 abbildungen
und 2 tafeln. Berlin, J. Springer, 1933.

NL 0377538 DN-Ob

Lindblad, Bertil, 1895–
   ... Über die spiralbildung bei den nebeln.
Von B. Lindblad. (Kiel) 1935.
   3 p. diagrs. 29 cm. (On cover: Stock-
holms observatorium. Meddelande n:o 24)
   Abdruck aus der Astr. nachr. nr. 6156.
(Band 257. – Nov. 1935)

NL 0377539 DN-Ob

Lindblad, Bertil.
   ... The velocity ellipsoid, galactic rotation, and the dimensions of the stellar system. By Professor Bertil Lindblad. (Edinburgh, Neill and co., ltd., 1930)
   1 p. l., p. (503)-516 incl. tables, diagrs.
22½ cm.
   Bibliographical foot-notes.
   "Reprinted from the Monthly notices of the
Royal astronomical society, vol. XC. No. 5."

NL 0377540 DN-Ob

Lindblad, Bertil, 1895–
   Zur theorie der spiralnebel, von B. Lindblad
... Kiel, Druck von C. Schaidt, Inhaber Georg
Oheim, 1935.
   cover-title. (2) p. diagr. 29 x 22½ cm.
(Stockholms observatorium. Meddelande n:o
20)
   "Abdruck aus der Astr. Nachr. Nr. 6090.
(Band 254. – Febr.1935.)"

NL 0377540 DN-Ob

Lindblad, Bertil Anders
      see Lindblad, Bertil, 1895–

948.5
L64 Lindblad, Carl S
         Lödöse stad, samt Ale och Flundre
      härader; historiska minnen och nu-
      varande förhållanden. Göteborg,
      H.L. Bolinders boktr., 1897.

         143 p. illus. 23cm.
         1.Lödöse, Sweden. 2. Ale, Sweden.
      3. Flundre, Sweden.

NL 0377542 MnU

Lindblad, Carl S.
   Skärgårdsbilder. Från Morlanda kyrkor och hembygd.
(Göteborg: the author, 1911) 116 p. illus. 8°.

1. Morlanda, Sweden. 2. Poetry   (Swedish).
N. Y. P. L.   October 19, 1911.

NL 0377543 NN

Lindblad, Elis Wilhelm, 1828–1878, ed.
   Dansk läsebok, jemte anmärkningar och en
kort öfwersigt af literaturhistorien. Örebro, Lindh, 1865.
   374 p. D.

NL 0377544 NcD

Lindblad, Elis Wilhelm, 1828–1878, ed.
   Samlade dikter af P. D. A. Atterbom ...
      see under Atterbom, P[er] D[aniel]
   A[madeus] 1790–1855.

Lindblad, Erik, ed.
   Kronobergs läns hushållningssällskap, 1915–1942.
(Växjö, 1942)
   326 p.

   1. Kronobergs läns hushållningssällskap.
   2. Sweden. Agriculture.

NL 0377546 DNAL

Lindblad, Frank V.
   A few notes on prayer, by Frank Lindblad. Springfield,
Mo., Gospel publishing house (*1927)
   64 p. 19ᵐ.

   1. Prayer.

Library of Congress   BV213.L5   28–13686

NL 0377547 DLC

Lindblad, Frank V.
   The spirit which is from God, by Frank Lindblad ...
Springfield, Mo., Gospel publishing house (*1928)
   4 p. l., 11–271 p. 19½ᵐ.

   1. Holy Spirit. I. Title.

Library of Congress   BT121.L47   28–23509
Copyright A 1053905   (2)

NL 0377548 DLC

Lindblad, Göran, 1894–
   August Strindberg som berättare, studier i hans tidigare prosa ... Stockholm, P. A. Norstedt & söner (1924)
   223, (1) p. 20ᵐ.
   Akademisk avhandling—Lund.
   CONTENTS.—Inledning : An Bosveig.—Från havet. Här och där.—Från
Fjärdingen och Svartbäcken.—Röda rummet.—Det nya riket.—Svenska öden
och äventyr 1882–1883.
   1. *Strindberg, August, 1849–1912.
                     (Full name: Karl Göran Leonard Lindblad)

Library of Congress   PT9816.L5   26–1403

NL 0377549 DLC WaU ICN CtY IU IEN NcD

Lindblad, Göran.
   August Strindberg som berättare; studier i hans tidigare
prosa, av Göran Lindblad... Stockholm: P. A. Norstedt &
Söner (1924). 223 p. 8°.

1. Strindberg, August, 1849–1912.
N. Y. P. L.   January 12, 1925

NL 0377550 NN NjP MH MiU

*Lindblad, Göran, 1894– ed.

Vem är det? Svensk biografisk handbok ... Stockholm, P. A.
Norstedt & söners (1912–

Lindblad, Göran, 1894–
   ... Verner von Heidenstam, av Göran Lindblad
(1.–4. tusendet) Stockholm, A. Bonnier (1913)
   44 p. illus.(port.) 20ᶜᵐ. (Studentföreningen Verdandis småskrifter. 189)

   1.Heidenstam,Verner von,1859–
               (Full name: Karl Göran Leonard Lind-
                                          blad)

NL 0377552 MiU NcD IU

PD5201 Lindblad,Gösta, 1888–
.L7   Abraham Sahlstedt och den svenska substantiv-
         böjningen;ett bidrag till det svenska skriftsprå-
         kets historia av Gösta Lindblad. Lund,Gleerup-
         ska univ.-bokhandeln[1919]
            [2],xvi,265 p. 24ᶜᵐ.
            Added t.-p.with dissertation note Akademisk av-
         handling—Lund)
            "Kronologisk källförteckning":p.[v]–xiii.
            1.Sahlstedt,Abraham Magnusson,1716–1776. 2.Swe-
         dish language—Noun. 3.Swedish language—Declension.

NL 0377553 ICU CtY MH ICRL CU

PT9555 Lindblad, Gösta, 1888–
.L5   Svensk litteratur efter 1900, i urval för
         den högre undervisningen. Stockholm,
         Bonnier (1929)
            290 p.

            "Biografiska och bibliografiska notiser":
         p.(271)–276.

NL 0377554 CU

Ph.D.   Lindblad, Goethe Mansfield.
Po   The background and immediate effects of
'48   the Cripps mission to India. May 1948.
L742   viii,369 l. 29cm.

            Thesis – Univ. of Southern California.
            "Bibliography": l.[361]–369.

            1. Cripps, Sir Stafford, 1889– . 2.
         India – Politics and government, 1765–1947.

NL 0377555 CLSU

AS284 Lindblad, Gustaf.
.L8   Der isländska accenttecknet, en historisk-ortografisk
bd. 48, studie. Lund, C. W. K. Gleerup (1952)
nr. 1   230 p. facsims. 26 cm. (Lunds universitets årsskrift, n. f., avd. 1,
         bd. 48, nr. 1)
            Lundastudier i nordisk språkvetenskap, 8.
            Bibliography : p. (224)–230.
            1. Icelandic and Old Norse languages—Accents and accentuation.
         (Series: Lund. Universitet. Acta Universitatis Lundensis, n. s.
         Lunds universitets årsskrift, n. f., avd. 1, bd. 48, nr. 1. Series: Lunda-
         studier i nordisk språkvetenskap, 8)
            [AS284.L8 bd. 48, nr. 1]   A 53–7397

Chicago. Univ. Libr.
   for Library of Congress   (2)

NL 0377556 ICU MoU MH CU CtY MnU TxU PU DLC

VOLUME 334

Lindblad, Gustaf.
Relativ satsfogning i de nordiska fornspråken. **Lund,**
1943.
210 p. 24 cm. (Lundastudier i nordisk språkvetenskap, 1)
Akademisk avhandling—Lund.
Extra t. p., with thesis statement, inserted.
Summary in German.
Bibliography: p. [202]-210.

1. Scandinavian languages—Syntax.   I. Title.   (Series)

PD1701.L5   55-49676

NL 0377557   DLC ICU MnU NNC NjP NIC TxU

Lindblad, Gustaf.
Relativ satsfogning i de nordiska fornspråken. **Lund,**
1943.
210 p. 24 cm. (Lundastudier i nordisk språkvetenskap, 1)
Issued also as thesis, Lund.
Summary in German.
Bibliography: p. [202]-210.

NL 0377558   LU MH CU

Lindblad, Gustaf.
Studier i Codex regius av Äldre Eddan. With
an English summary. Lund, C.W.K. Glerrup
[1954]
xxiv, 328 p. diagrs., facsims., tables.
24 cm. (Lundastudier i nordisk språkvetenskap,
10)
Bibliography: p. [292]-298.
1. Edda Saemundar. 2. Edda Snorra Stur-
lusonar. Mss. (Codex regius) I. Title.
II. Ser.

NN NNC NjP NIC TxU
NL 0377559   ViU CtY CU OrU CaBVaU ICU InU MH MH-L MnU

Lindblad, Johan Adolph, respondent.
De Essenis schediasma historico-theologicum
cujus specimen primum
see under   Bergström, Erik, 1775-1833,
praeses.

LINDBLAD, Johan Christofer, 1799-1876.
De probatione causarum judiciali in genere
nec non de probatione causarum indirecta.
Upsaliae, 1842.

Diss.

NL 0377561   MH-L

Lindblad, Johan Christofer, 1799-1876.
Läran om bevisning inför rätta enligt
sveriges lag, med fästad upmärksamhet ej
mindre på sveriges gamla lagar och nya
lagförslaget, än ock på fremmande lagstift-
ningar och lagsförslag. Upsala, Leffler
och Sebell, 1842.
265p. 22cm.

NL 0377562   CtY-L

Lindblad, Johan Christofer]
Om dråp och mord; akademisk afhandling...till offentlig
granskning framställd af J. C. Lindblad och W. Wachtmeister
[och H. E. Taube]. Del 1-[2]. Upsala: Palmblad & C[o.], 1832.
1 p.l., 96 p.   8°.
Dissertation, Upsala.
Title-page of Del 2 following page 40. Page 41-48 wrongly bound at end of
pamphlet.

1. Manslaughter.—Jurisprudence,   Sweden. 2. Murder.—Jurispru-
dence, Sweden. 3. Wachtmeister, Wil   helm, grefve. 4. Taube, Henning
Edward, grefve.
N. Y. P. L.   January 24, 1913.

NL 0377563   NN MH-L

Lindblad, Johan Christofer, 1799-1876.
Om prescription enligt Sveriges lag. 2. helt och hållet
omarb. upl. Upsala, Tryckt hos Leffler och Sebell, 1843.
156 p. 21 cm.

1. Limitation of actions—Sweden. 2. Prescription (Law)—
Sweden.

48-30557*

NL 0377564   DLC

Lindblad, Joh[an] Chr[istofer]
Om skyldigheten att bebygga, underhålla och häfda boställen
samt andra hemman, som innehafvas under besittningsrätt.
Akademisk afhandling, som framställes till offentlig granskning...
af J. C. Lindblad och L. Kinmanson [och W. Prinzencreutz].
Upsala: Palmblad & C[o.], 1833.   2 p.l., (3)-56 p.   8°.
Dissertation, Upsala.
In two parts. Title-page of Del 2 inserted between page 28 and 29.

1. Buildings (Public).—Jurisprudence,   Sweden. 2. Kinmanson, Leonard.
3. Prinzencreutz, Wilhelm.
N. Y. L.   January 23, 1913.

NL 0377565   NN

LINDBLAD, Johan Michael, 1817-1893.   7449.15
Betragtninger for unge Gjæster ved Herrens Bord. Konfirmations
gave. Oversat fra den Svenske. Med et Forord af N. Hald. 2det Oplag
Christiania. Malling. 1861. (4), 188 pp. Sm. 12°.

NL 0377566   MB

Lindblad, Johan Mikael, 1817-1893, ed.

Luther, Martin, 1483-1546.
Doct. Martin Luthers skrifter, uti ett efter tidens behof
lämpadt urwal. Öfwersatta af P. A. Sondén och ånyo genom-
sedda af J. M. Lindblad, med tillägg af N. J. Cervin-Steenhoff,
m. fl. ... Stockholm, P. A. Huldberg [1857-58]

Lindblad, Johan Wilhelm, respondent.
De correctione elementorum veneris...
see under   Bergius, Axel Theodor, praeses.

Lindblad, Mrs. Johanna Magdalena (Olson)
see
Lindblad, Mrs. Lina (Olson) 1875-

Lindblad, Johannes, respondent.
... Monumenta politico ecclesiastica ex archiva
Palmskiöldiano
see   Celsius, Olof Olofsson, bp., 1716-
1794, praeses.

Lindblad, Karl Erik.
Noah Webster's pronunciation and modern New England
speech; a comparison. Upsala, Lundequistska bokhandeln;
Cambridge, Harvard University Press [1954]
90 p. 25 cm. (Essays and studies on American language and
literature, 11)
Bibliography: p. [86]-90.

1. English language—Pronunciation. 2. English language—Dialects—New England. 3. Webster, Noah, 1758-1843.   I. Title.
(Series: Uppsala. Universitet. Amerikanska seminariet. Essays
and studies on American language and literature, 11)

PE1137.L5   421.5   A 55-8385
Harvard Univ. Library
for Library of Congress   [2]†

MiU PSt ViU NcD NcGU FTaSU TxU DLC CaBVaU OU MU TU
NL 0377571   MH CU CoU MoU MeB MB ICN NIC IaU NN LU OO

Lindblad, Karl Göran Leonard
see
Lindblad, Göran, 1894-

Lindblad, Mrs. Lina (Olson) 1875-
Thureby prestgård; eller, Fädernas missgerningar, af
Lina Lindblad. [Minneapolis, Posten press, inc.] [1924.
300 p. illus. (port.) 19[cm].

I. Title.
[Full name: Mrs. Johanna Magdalena (Olson) Lindblad]

Library of Congress   PT9995.L515T5 1924   25-2244

NL 0377573   DLC WaU

Lindblad, Matts Adolf, 1821?-1899.
D:r M. A. Lindblads Svampbok, bearbetad af Lars Romell, jämte
anvisningar om svampars insamling, förvaring och anrättning, af
Herman Sandeberg.
= Stockholm. Idun. 1901. (7), 166 pp. Plates. 4 colored plates
in portfolio. 8°.

F4060 — Mushrooms. — Romell, Lars, ed. — Sandeberg, Hermann, ed.

NL 0377574   MB DNAL

Lindblad, M[atts] A[dolf] 1821?-1899.
D:r M. A. Lindblads Svampbok, bearb. af Lars Ro
mell, jämte anvisningar om svampars insamling, förvaring
och anrättning, af Herman Sandeberg ... Stockholm,
C. E. Fritzes K. hofbokhandel [1902]
6 p. l., 166 p. incl. 2 front. 4 fold. col. pl. 22[cm].
Plates separate in case.

1. Mushrooms.
                                                Agr 3-992
Library, U. S. Dept. of   Agriculture 462L64.

NL 0377575   DNAL MiU

Lindblad, Matts Adolf, 1821†-1899.
Monographia lactariorum Sueciae ... Upsaliae, typis
descripsit reg. acad. typographus, 1855.
1 p. l., xvi, 31 p. 22[cm].
Inaug.-diss.—Upsala.

1. Lactaria.
                                                Agr 9-39
Library, U. S. Dept. of   Agriculture 462L643

NL 0377576   DNAL ICRL MH

Lindblad, Matts Adolf, 1821?-1899, respondent.
Rationen sacrificii et sacerdotii sactissimi
salvatoris
see under   Hagberg, Fredrik Theodor,
praeses.

Lindblad, Matts Adolf, 1821?-1899, respondent.

Fries, Elias Magnus, 1794-1878, praeses.
Synopsis fungorum hydnaceorum in Svecia nascentium ...
Upsaliae, Wahlström & c., 1853.

VOLUME 334

Lindblad, Otto
Fyra quartetter för mansröster.
Componerade och tillegnade Ryttmastare;
Axel Toll.   Stockholm, Abr. Hirsch.
n.d.
7 p.

NL 0377579   PPAmSwM

Lindblad, P.
Fasti Skyttiani ...
see under   Almroth, Nicolaus.

QB   **Lindblad, Per Olof.**
4   On the proper motion of the cluster
S97S83 Messier 37. Communicated 13 May 1953
v.18   by Bertil Lindblad and Yngve Öhman.
no.1+   Stockholm, Almqvist & Wiksell, 1954.
        35 p. illus. 29cm. (Stockholms
        Observatoriums Annaler, Bd.18, no.1)

        1. Stars--Clusters. I. Series:
        Stockholm.Astronomiska Observatoriet.
        Annalen,   Bd. 18, no.1.

NL 0377581   NIC

Lindblad, Petrus   respondent.
... Dissertatio de obligatione e pactis...
see under   Boëthius, Daniel, 1751-
1810, praeses.

}P9!   **LINDBLAD,R   GERHARD.**
L72   Studien über den blutzucker bei Astacus fluviatilis
        ... Kristianstad,1931.
        ₃₁,129 p. diagrs. 23cm.
        Akademisk afhandling--Lund.
        Thesis note on added t.-p.
        "Literaturverzeichnis":p.127-129.

        1.Sugar in the body. 2.Blood--Analysis and chem-
        istry.

NL 0377583   ICU OC1W CtY

Lindblad, Ragnar.
Svenska luftvärnet. ₁Stockholm₁ Folkförsvaret förlags
ab ₁1955₁
84 p. illus. 21 cm.

        1. Sweden. Armén. Luftvärnet.

        UF625.L46   59-40568 ‡

NL 0377584   DLC

Lindblad, Tord, 1904-
... Zur theorie der korrelation bei mehrdimensionalen zufälli-
gen variablen, von Tord Lindblad ... Helsingfors, 1937.
81 p. incl. tables. 28½ x 22¼ᶜᵐ. (₁Finska vetenskaps-societeten, Helsingfors₁ Acta Societatis scientiarum fennicæ. n. s., A, t. II, n:o 10)
"Am 24 maj 1937 von E. Lindelöf und L. Ahlfors vorgelegt."
"Literaturverzeichnis" at end of each chapter except the last.

        1. Probabilities.   I. Title: Korrelation bei mehrdimensionalen zufäl-
ligen variablen, Zur theorie der.
                    ₁Full name: Tord Ingul Rudolf Lindblad₁
New York. Public library   A C 39-2158
for Library of Congress   [Q60.F5 n. s., A, vol. 2, no. 10]
                    ₁4₁   (508)

NL 0377585   NN DAS MoU ICU ViU OU

Lindblad, Waldemar
Die bedeutungsentwickelung des praefixes kata in
kompositis.
Inaig. diss. Helsingfors, 1922.
Bibl.

NL 0377586   ICRL PU

Lindblad, Waldemar.
... Die bedeutungsentwickelung des präfixes *kata* in kompositis. Eine semasiologische untersuchung von Waldemar
Lindblad ... (Am 21. april 1922 durch F. W. Gustafsson
und I. A. Heikel eingereicht) Helsingfors, Helsingfors centraltryckeri, 1922.
167 p. 23½ᶜᵐ. (₁Finska vetenskaps-societeten, Helsingfors₁ Commentationes humanarum litterarum. I. 1)
At head of title: Societas scientiarum fennica.

1. Greek language—Suffixes and prefixes.   A C 33-3866
Title from N. Y. Pub.   Libr.
Library of Congress   [P9.F5 vol. 1, no. 1]

        OCU ViU
NL 0377587   NN CaBVaU NBuU IU MiEM NIC NcD PU NcU

Lindblad-Thafvelin, Christina.
Lampskärmar. Teckningar: Elsa Camming. Presenterad
av Året rundt. ₁Stockholm, Tidskriftsböckerna, 1955₁
63 p. 18 cm. (Gör det själv)

1. Lamp shades.

TT897.L5   58-38654

NL 0377588   DLC

Lindblom, Adolf Fredrik, 1898-
Odin, Martin, 1890-
... Iodized oils as an aid to the diagnosis of lesions of the
spinal cord and a contribution to the knowledge of adhesive
circumscribed meningitis, by Martin Odin and Gösta Run-
ström in co-operation with Adolf Lindblom. Stockholm,
Kungl. boktryckeriet, P. A. Norstedt & söner, 1929.

Lindblom, Adolf Fredrik, 1898-
... Über die funktionsfähigkeit der mit pneumothorax artificialis behandelten lunge nach ihrer wiederentfaltung; eine
pathologisch-anatomische und klinische studie, von Adolf F.
Lindblom ... Stockholm, Zetterlund & Thelanders boktryckeri.- a.-b., 1926.
142 p., 1 l. illus., plates. 23½ᶜᵐ. (On cover: Acta medica scandinavica. Supplementum xv)
At head of title: Aus dem Sanatorium Eksjö und der Pathologisch-
anatomischen abteilung des Karolinischen institutes zu Stockholm.
"Literaturverzeichnis": p. 135-142.
1. Tuberculosis. 2. Pneumothorax, ₁Artificial₁
                                        A C 33-2160
Title from John Crerar   Libr. Printed by L. C.

NL 0377590   ICJ DNLM CtY PPC MiU OU

Lindblom, Alexis Eduard, ed.
Botaniska notiser for ar 1839 och 1840-
1846. Lund, Berling; etc., 1841-1849
7 v. in 6. illus.

NL 0377591   OU

Lindblom, Alexis Eduard. In geographicam plantarum
intra Sueciam distributionem adnotata proponit. Lundæ.
1835. 8°. pp. [2], 100+.   5 tables.

NL 0377592   MH-A

LINDBLOM,Alexis Eduard.
Synopsis drabarum Scandinaviae. [Halle],
[1839].

NL 0377593   MH

Mfc77   **Lindblom, Algot.**   ed.
Up7   Akter rörande ärkebiskopvalet i Uppsala
L6   1432 samt striden därom mellan konung Erik
         och Svenska kyrkan. Utgifna af Algot Lindblom.
         Uppsala,Wretmans tryckeri,1903.
         xv,[1],150p. 23cm. (Skrifter utgifna af
         Kyrkohistoriska föreningen. IV: 2)
         "Anförda arbeten": p.[vii].

NL 0377594   CtY MnU NN

S573.485 **Lindblom, Algot.**
St6v   Från Jakobs kyrkoskola till Vasa läroverk;
          Några blad ur en gammal skolas historia, av
          Algot Lindblom.   Stockholm, C.E.Fritze ₁1926₁
          57, xxxv p. illus., plans. 26½cm.

          1. Stockholm. Vasa realskola.

NL 0377595   NNC-T

Lindblom, Algot.
... En omtvistad biskopsstol i Sverge under
kyrkoschismen af A. Lindblom.   Upsala, Almqvist & Wiksells boktryckeri-a.-b., 1902.
28 p.   23 cm.   (In Bidrag till Sverges
medeltidshistoria tillegnade C. G. Malmström
af Historiska seminariet vid Upsala universitet.
14)

NL 0377596   CU PU

Lindblom, Anders Theodor.
In Silii Italici Punica quaestiones ...   Up-
sallae, Almqvist et Wiksell, 1906.
2 p.l., 140 p.   23 cm.
Akademisk afhandling - Upsala.
Bibliographical foot-notes.

NL 0377597   CU CtY PU ICRL

Lindblom, Andreas Adolf Fredrik, 1889-
Antoine Watteau. Stockholm, Norstedt ₁1948₁
122 p. illus. (part col.) ports., facsims. 25 cm. ₁Världskonstens
mästare₁
"Citerade författare": p. 121-122.

1. Watteau, Jean Antoine, 1684-1721.   (Series)

ND553.W3L5   50-16629

NL 0377598   DLC NhD

AM101   **Lindblom, Andreas Adolf Fredrik,** 1889-
.S725
folio   **Stockholm. Nordiska museet.** *Skansen.*
         Bilder från Skansen. Med text av Andreas Lindblom.
         Stockholm, Svensk litteratur ₁1954₁

BX4700   **Lindblom, Andreas Adolf Fredrik,** 1889-   ed.
.B6B5
         Birgittastiftelsen.
         Birgittaboken; med bidrag av Yngve Brilioth ₁et al.₁
         Utg. av Birgittastiftelsen genom Andreas Lindblom.
         ₁Stockholm, Tryckt hos Nordisk rotogravyr, 1954₁

VOLUME 334

Lindblom, Andreas Adolf Fredrik, 1889–
Björsäters stafkyrka och dess målningars ställning inom vår medeltidskonst, af A. Lindblom ... ₍Stockholm, Cederquists grafiska a.-b., 1911₎
37 p. illus., double pl. 23ᶜᵐ.
"Ur Fornvännen 1911."

1. Church decoration and ornament—Sweden. 2. Björsäter, Sweden (Östergötland) Church.

23–3725

Library of Congress   NA5791.B5L5

NL 0377601   DLC

Lindblom, Andreas Adolf Fredrik, 1889–
Björsätersmålningarna. The legends of St. Thomas Becket and of the Holy Cross painted in a Swedish church. Stockholm, Kungl. Vitterhets, historie- och antikvitetsakademien ₍1953₎
79 p. illus., plates. 33 cm.
"Rättelser": slip tipped in.
Summary in English.

1. Björsäter, Sweden (Östergötland) Kyrkan. 2. Thomas à Becket, Saint, Abp. of Canterbury. Legend.

A 53–4524 rev

Harvard Univ. Library
for Library of Congress   ₍r54b²₎

NL 0377602   MH CU MoU NN MnU CtY

Lindblom, Andreas Adolf Fredrik, 1889–   ed.
En bok om Skansen, till hundraårsminnet av Artur Hazelius' födelse, under medverkan av Alarik Behm, Gotthard Gustafsson och Gösta Selling utgiven av Andreas Lindblom. Stockholm, P. A. Norstedt & söner, 1933.
226, ₍2₎ p. col. front., illus. (incl. ports., facsims.) plates (part col.) plans. 28½ᶜᵐ.

1. Stockholm. Nordiska museet. 2. Hazelius, Artur, 1833–1901. I. *Behm, Alarik, 1871– II. *Gustafsson, Gotthard, 1902– III. *Selling, Gösta, 1900– IV. Title. v. Title: Skansen, En bok om.

35–15819

Library of Congress   AM101.S73L5
₍2₎   069.09487

NL 0377603   DLC MnU

DL091
.S89S8
Lindblom, Andreas Adolf Fredrik, 1889–   ed.
Stockholm. Nordiska museet.
En bok om Svindersvik, utg. av Andreas Lindblom. Stockholm, 1953.

NB785
.L74
Lindblom, Andreas Adolf Fredrik, 1889–
Fransk barock- och rokokoskulptur i Sverige; studier. Uppsala, Almqvist & Wiksell, 1923.
181 p. illus., ports., plans.

1. Sculpture--Sweden. 2. Sculpture, Baroque. 3. Sculpture, Rococo. 4. Sculpture, French.

NL 0377605   ICU

Lindblom, Andreas Adolf Fredrik, 1889–
En gammalromansk torntyp från Östergötland. Af Andreas Lindblom. ₍Stockholm, Cederquists graf. a. b., 1909₎
p. ₍178₎–200. illus. (incl. plans) 23ᶜᵐ.
Caption title.
"Ur Fornvännen, 1908."

1. Church architecture—Sweden. 2. Architecture, Romanesque.

22–16668

Library of Congress   NA410.L5

NL 0377606   DLC

ND8375
.L55A46
Lindblom, Andreas Adolf Fredrik, 1889–
De gyllene åren. Stockholm, Norstedt ₍1952₎
176 p. illus., ports. 22 cm.

I. Title.

Minnesota. ₍Univ. Lib₎
for Library of Congress   ₍²₎

A 53–4986

NL 0377607   MnU DLC

Lindblom, Andreas Adolf Fredrik, 1889–
Den₍heliga Birgitta; bildverk i skulptur och måleri från Sveriges medeltid. Stockholm, P.A. Norstedt, 1918.
56p. illus. 30 plates.

1. Birgitta, Saint, of Sweden, d.1373.

NL 0377608   NcU OO NjP

Lindblom, Andreas ₍Adolf Fredrik₎ 1889–
Jacques-Philippe Bouchardon* och de Franska bildhuggarna vid Stockholm slott under rokokotiden av Andreas Lindblom. Uppsala, Almquist & Wiksell Boktryckeri, 1924.
p₍1–6₎ (includ. etching of Bouchardon) p.7–191 (biog. notes p. ₍177₎–183, index p.189–191).

*1711–1745 Court sculptor of Sweden; younger brother of Edme Bouchardon, Court sculptor of France.

NL 0377609   DDO NjP ICU

Lindblom, Andreas, 1889–
Kyrkor i Bankekinds härad. Norra delen ... Konsthistoriskt inventarium, utarbetat av Andreas Lindblom ... Stockholm, Svenska teknologföreningen, 1921.
3 p. l., ₍3₎–98 p., 1 l., ₍99₎–190 p. illus. (incl. plans) 26ᶜᵐ. (Sveriges kyrkor. Östergötland, bd. 1, hft. 1–2)

1. Church architecture - Sweden.

NL 0377610   NNC MH

Lindblom, Andreas Adolf Fredrik, 1889–
Kyrkor i Närke, af A. Lindblom. ₍Stockholm, Centraltryckeriet, 1911₎
cover-title, p. ₍107₎–116. illus. 21½ᶜᵐ.
"Särtryck ur Svenska turistföreningens årsskrift, 1911."

1. Churches—Sweden—Nerike.

27–13874

Library of Congress   NA5791.N5L5

NL 0377611   DLC

Lindblom, Andreas Adolf Fredrik, 1889–
Lille Jonathan. Illustrationer av Einar Norelius. Stockholm, P.A. Norstedt [1948]
105 p. illus. 22 cm.

NL 0377612   PU

Lindblom, Andreas Adolf Fredrik, 1889–
joint author.
Branting, Agnes Margaretha Mathilda, 1862–1930.
Medieval embroideries and textiles in Sweden, by Agnes Branting and Andreas Lindblom ... Uppsala and Stockholm, Almqvist & Wiksells boktryckeri-a.-b., 1932.

LINDBLOM, Andreas Adolf Fredrik, 1889–
Nordtysk skulptur och måleri i Sverige från den senare medeltiden. Utgifvet af K. Vitterhets Historie och Antikvitets Akademien. Stockholm, Wahlström & Widstrand, etc., 1916.
4°. pp. (4), 32. Plates (1 mounted), and other illustr.
"300 exemplar. No.290."
Arkeologiska monografier, No.8, heft 1/2.

NL 0377614   MH CtY NjP PP DDO CU

Lindblom, Andreas Adolf Fredrik, 1889–
... La peinture gothique en Suède et en Norvège; étude sur les relations entre l'Europe occidentale et les pays scandinaves, par Andreas Lindblom ... Introduction—Livres I et II ... ₍Stockholm, Cederquists grafiska aktiebolag, 1916₎
1 p. l., 186 p. illus. (incl. plans) 50 pl. 32½ x 23ᶜᵐ.
At head of title: Académie royale des belles-lettres, d'histoire et d'archéologie.
Thèse—Stockholms högskola.
Translated by S. Harel. cf. Pref.
The complete work (3 p. l., 252 p., 1 l.) published same year.
1. Painting—Sweden. 2. Painting—Norway. 3. Art, Gothic. I. K. Vitterhets, historie- och antikvitetsakademien, Stockholm. II. Harel, Stéphane, tr. III. Title.

36–23105

Library of Congress   ND703.L4 1916   759.8

NL 0377615   DLC

Lindblom, Andreas Adolf Fredrik, 1889–
La peinture gothique en Suède et en Norvège; étude sur les relations entre l'Europe occidentale et les pays scandinaves, par Andreas Lindblom, pub. par l'Académie royale des belles-lettres, d'histoire et d'archéologie de Stockholm ... Stockholm, Wahlström & Widstrand; ₍etc., etc.₎, 1916.
3 p. l., 252 p., 1 l. col. front., illus. (incl. plans) 50 pl. 33 cm.

1. Painting—Sweden. 2. Painting—Norway. 3. Art, Gothic. I. Vitterhets-, historie- och antikvitetsakademien, Stockholm. II. Title.

ND703.L4   24–1703

CaBVaU
NjP OC1 NcU MdBWA CtY OO MiU CU NcD CSt InU CLU
NL 0377616   DLC OC1MA MiU MB NN DDO CtY WaS CaBVaU

Lindblom, Andreas Adolf Fredrik, 1889–
Salaminnen. [Sala, Sweden] Nordiska museet [1954]
424 p. illus., maps. 21cm. (Svenskt liv och arbete n:r 20)

1. Sala, Sweden - Description. I. Title.

NL 0377617   FU

Lindblom, Andreas Adolf Fredrik, 1889–
En stafkyrkotakstol i en romansk stenkyrka, af A. Lindblom. ₍Stockholm, Cederquists graf. a.-b., 1910₎
p. ₍186₎–197. illus. 23ᶜᵐ.
Caption title.
"Ur Fornvännen 1910."

1. Church architecture—Sweden. 2. Architecture, Romanesque. 3. Knista, Sweden. Church.

23–3726

Library of Congress   NA5791.K8L5

NL 0377618   DLC

Lindblom, Andreas Adolf Fredrik, 1889–
Stockholms slott genom seklerna; en konsthistorisk överblick. Uppsala, Almquist & Wiksell ₍1925₎
142 p. illus. (part col.), plans (1 fold.) 20cm.

1. Stockholm. Slottet.

NL 0377619   MnU OO

VOLUME 334

Lindblom, Andreas Adolf Fredrik, 1889–
... Sveriges konsthistoria från forntid till nutid ... Stockholm, Nordisk rotogravyr ₁1944–
    v. col. front., illus. (incl. ports., plans) col. plates. 25½ᵐ.
At head of title: Andreas Lindblom.

1. Art—Sweden—Hist. ɪ. Title.

N7381.L5   709.485   47–2013

CLU CLSU ICU MiD NNC IaU IU
NL 0377620   DLC OU MB OO MdBWA NcD CtY NN PPAmSwM MnU

Lindblom, Andreas Adolf Fredrik, 1889–
    Sveriges konsthistoria från forntid till nutid. Stockholm, Nordisk rotogravyr ₁1947₁
    1000, xiii p. illus., ports., col. plates. 27 cm.
    "Åren 1944 och 1946 utkommit i tre volymer."

1. Art—Sweden—Hist. ɪ. Title.

N7381.L52   709.485   48–24874*

NL 0377621   DLC PPiU

N8375
.L55A3   **Lindblom, Andreas Adolf Fredrik,** 1889–
    Utsikt från Skansen. Stockholm, Norstedt ₁1954₁
    215 p. illus., ports. 22 cm.

ɪ. Title.

                      A 55–2665
Minnesota. Univ. Libr.
for Library of Congress   ₁5₁

NL 0377622   MnU DLC NN

Lindblom, Andreas Adolf Fredrik, 1889–
    Vårt Skansen, av Andreas Lindblom. Stockholm, Åhlén & Åkerlund, 1937.
    ₁80₁ p. illus. (incl. port.) 29ᵐ.
    Includes 67 pages of illustrations. Double plan on end papers.

1. Stockholm. Nordiska museet. ɪ. Title.

Library of Congress   AM101.S73L52   41–39861
                          ₁2₁   708.3

NL 0377623   DLC

Lindblom, Andreas Adolf Fredrik, 1889–
    Vadstena, av Andreas Lindblom. Stockholm: P. A. Norstedt & söner ₁1925₁ 64 p. incl. front. (plan.) illus. 19cm. (Svenska kulturorter. 4.)
    "Litteraturförteckning," p. 64.

1. Vadstena, Sweden. I. Ser.
N. Y. P. L.   March 29, 1940

NL 0377624   NN

NK2190 **Lindblom, Andreas Adolf Fredrik,** 1889–
.L74   ... Vägledning i afdelningen för kyrklig konst, af Andreas Lindblom ... Linköping, Billstens boktryckeri, 1915.
    46 p. plates. 17½ᵐ.
    At head of title: Östergötlands museum.

1. Church decoration and ornament. 2. Christian art and symbolism.

NL 0377625   ICU

Lindblom, Andreas Adolf Fredrik, 1889–
    Västeuropeiska strömningar i Nordens måleri under gotiken. En överblick. Av Andreas Lindblom. ₁Stockholm, Cederquists graf. a.-b., 1915₁
    ₁1₁, ₁254₁–277 p. illus. 23ᵐᵐ.
    On cover: Ur Fornvännen 1914.
    "Deutsche zusammenfassung": p. ₁275₁–277.

1. Painting—Scandinavia. 2. Painting, Medieval.

                         23–3710
Library of Congress   ND703.L5

NL 0377626   DLC

Lindblom, Axel
    ...Hallonviveln (Anthonomus rubi herbst) ett for vissa delar av vart land mycket betydelsefullt skadedjur, av .... Stockholm, O.L. Svanbacks boktryckeri, 1930.– 39pl. illus. (Meddelande n:o 375 fran K. Landtbruksakademien. Centralanstalten for forsoksvasendet pa jordbruksomradet. Landtbruksentomologiska avdelningen n:o 60)

NL 0377627   OU

Lindblom, Axel
    ...Jamforande forsok med insektdodande vinterbesprutningsvatskor for frukttradgarden, av Axel .... Stockholm, O.L. Svanbacks boktryckeri, 1932. 24p. illus. (Meddelande nr 422 fran K. Landtbruks-adademien. Centralanstalten for forsoksvasendet pa jordbruksomradet. Lantbruksentomologiska avdelningen nr 65)

NL 0377628   OU

Lindblom, Axel
    ...Orienterande jamforande forsok med insedtbekampningsmedel, av Axel .... Stockholm, O.L. Svanbacks boltryckeri, 1928. 33p. illus. (meddelande n:o 330 fran K. Landtbruksakademien. Centralanstalten for forsoksvasendet pa jordbruksomradet. Landbruksentomologiska avdelningen n:o 53)

NL 0377629   OU

Lindblom, Axel
    ...Studier rorande frukttradskarbolineum, unsersokningar av frukttradskarbolineumpreparatens praktiska varde och sambandet mellan effektiviteten hos dem och nagra av deras kemiska och fysikaliska egenskaper. Av Axel Lindblom och knut Sjorberg... Stockholm, O.L. Svanbecks boktryckeri, 1931. 28p. (meddelande nr 397 fran K. Landbruks-akademien

    Centralanstalten for forsoksvasendet pa jordbruksomradet. Lantbruksentomologiska avdelnin₅en nr 61. Kemiska av-...)

NL 0377631   OU

Lindblom, Axel
    ...Två undersokningar rorande vetemyggans skadegorelse och ekonomiska betydelse, av Axel.....och J. Muhlow.. Stockholm, O.L. Svanbacks boktryckeri, 1932. 24p. illus. (Meddelande nr 420 fran K. Lantbruksakademien. Centralanstalten for forsoksvasendet pa jordbruksomradet. Landbruksentomologiska avdel'ngen nr 64)

NL 0377632   OU

Lindblom, Bo.
    Vikande helfigur. Stockholm, Wahlström & Widstrand ₁1950₁
    129 p. 20 cm.

ɪ. Title.

                      A 51–3368
Minnesota. Univ. Libr.
for Library of Congress   ₁5₁

NL 0377633   MnU

Lindblom, Charles Edward, 1917–
    America's needs and resources. ₁New York, Anti-Defamation League of B'nai B'rith, 1950₁
    45 p. 23 cm. (Freedom pamphlets)
    Bibliography: p. 41.

1. U. S.—Soc. condit. ɪ. Title.

HN64.L518   309.173   50–3467

NL 0377634   DLC OrU Or OrCS FU OrU NN ViU

353
L742b   **Lindblom, Charles Edward,** 1917–
    Bargaining: the hidden hand in government. Santa Monica, Calif., Rand Corp., 1955.
    iii,44f. 29cm. (Rand Corp. Research memorandum RM-1434-RC)

    1.U.S. - Politics and government - 20th century. I.Title. (Series: Rand Corp. Research   memorandum)

NL 0377635   CLSU N WaU MiU MoU NNC

JF
1351   **Lindblom, Charles Edward,** 1917–
L56   Bargaining: the hidden hand in government ₁by₁ Charles E. Lindblom. Santa Monica, Calif., Rand Corp., 1955.
    iii,44f. (Research memorandum, RM-1434-RC)

    Photocopy (positive) of typescript.

    1. Public administration. 2. U.S.-- Pol. and govt. I. Title.

NL 0377636   UU

HD82
.D28   **Lindblom, Charles Edward,** 1917–   joint author.

Dahl, Robert Alan, 1915–
    Politics, economics, and welfare: planning and politico-economic systems resolved into basic social processes ₁by₁ Robert A. Dahl ₁and₁ Charles E. Lindblom. New York, Harper ₁1953₁

Lindblom, Charles Edward, 1917–
    Some aspects of the interrelationships between labor unions and the competitive price system. Chicago, 1945.
    ii, 394 l. 32 cm.
    Thesis—University of Chicago.
    Typescript (carbon copy)
    Bibliography: leaves 382–394.

1. Trade-unions. 2. Wages. 3. Prices. ɪ. Title.

HD6483.L49   63–39969

NL 0377638   DLC ICU

VOLUME 334

Lindblom, Charles Edward, 1917–
Some aspects of the interrelationships between labor unions and the competitive price system. ₍n. p., 1948₎
671–697 p. 24 cm.
Part of thesis—Univ. of Chicago.
Reprint of an article pub. in the Quarterly journal of economics, v. 62, no. 5, Nov., 1948, under title: The union as a monopoly.
Bibliographical footnotes.
1. Trade-unions. 2. Wages. 3. Prices. I. Title: The union as a monopoly.
HD6483.L5   331.215   A 49–2049*
Chicago. Univ. Libr.
for Library of Congress   ₍1₎†

NL 0377639   ICU DLC CtY NcU

Lindblom, Charles Edward, 1917–
Unions and capitalism. New Haven, Yale University Press, 1949.
xi, 267 p. 21 cm.
Bibliographical references included in "Notes" (p. ₍256₎–262)
1. Trade-unions—U. S. 2. Monopolies—U. S. 3. U. S.—Economic policy. I. Title.
HD6508.L5   331.880973   49–10401*

IdPI IdU MtU MtBC Or OrCS OrStbM OrU OrPR OrPS MB OOxM OCU OC1W OU OO ICU CaBVaU CaBVa CaBViP IdB KEmT PU PSC PPLas PHC PP PBm PPT MiU MB ScU ViU NNC
NL 0377640   DLC WaT Wa WaE WaS WU UU CU NSyU OKentU

Lindblom, Charles Edward, 1917–
Unions and capitalism. ₍c1949₎ ₍2d printing 1950₎

NL 0377641   MiHM

Lindblom, Christian Johannes.
See
Lindblom, Johannes, 1882–

Lindblom, David.
The synchronous stability of parallel operating power stations, by Civilingenjör David Lindblom... Stockholm: A.-B. Gunnar Tislls Tekniska Förlag, 1923. 32 p. pl. 8°.
(Ingeniörsvetenskapsakademien, Stockholm. Handlingar. nr. 22.)
1. Machinery, Electrical—Syn-   chronizing. 2. Series.
N. Y. P. L.   December 18, 1924

NL 0377643   NN OU

PT 9773 .L5R6 **Lindblom, Edel.**
Rosen i Dalhem; eller, En dotter af folket; verklighetsskildring. ₍Minneapolis, J. Leachman & Son, 19--?₎
183 p. 19 cm.

NL 0377644   MnHi

Lindblom, Ernst, 1865–1925.
Linnaea. Poetiskt album af Svensk-Amerikanska publicister
see under title

LINDBLOM, Ernst, 1865–1925.
Mina teatereftnar. Stockholm, C.L.Gullberg, ₍1917₎.
pp.48.
Port.of August Strindberg.

NL 0377646   MH MnU

PT9995 .L54P2 Lindblom, Ernst, 1865–1925.
På försök; fem svensk-amerikanska dikter. Chicago, Enander & Bohmans tryckeri, 1888.
30 p. 18 cm.

NL 0377647   MnHi

E184 .S23L7 Lindblom, Ernst, 1865–
Stjärnbanerets land. Tankar i bunden form. Stockholm,C.L.Gullbergs förlag ₍1910₎
110 p. 20cm.
On cover: Minne af den svensk-amerikanska sångfärden till Sverige.
"En juldröm i Minneapolis": p.₍61₎–64.
"Till Minneapolis": p.₍94₎–97.

NL 0377648   MnHi

Lindblom, Ernst, 1865–1925.
Den svensk-amerikanske Sherlock Holmes. Stockholm, 1908.
155 p.

NL 0377649   WaS

Lindblom, Ernst, 1865–1925.
Svenska teaterminnen från Chicago; anteckningar och anekdoter, av Ernst Lindblom. Stockholm, C. L. Gullberg ₍1916₎
192 p. illus. (incl. ports.) 19½ᶜᵐ.
1. Theater—Chicago. 2. Swedes in Chicago. I. Title.
37–20826
Library of Congress   PN2277.C4L5
₍2₎   792.097731

NL 0377650   DLC PPAmSwM WaU MnU NN MH

Lindblom, Gabriel Axel, tr.
Troil, Uno von, abp. of Upsala, 1746–1803.
Lettres sur l'Islande, par M. de Troil ... Traduites du Suédois. Par M. Lindblom ... Avec figures. A Paris ₍Chez P. Fr. Didot le jeune₎ M.DCC.LXXXI.

₍**Lindblom, George R** ₎
Automobile maintenance and its relation to safe driving. ₍Milwaukee, The Milwaukee safety commission, ᵉ1935₎
16 p. 23ᶜᵐ.
On cover: By George R. Lindblom, general manager, Edwards motor company.
1. Automobiles. 2. Automobiles—Accidents. 3. Automobile drivers. I. Edwards motor company, Milwaukee. II. Title. III. Title: Safe driving.
35–19533
Library of Congress   TL152.L5
Copyright AA 185063   ₍2₎   629.28

NL 0377652   DLC

Lindblom, Gerhard, 1887–1969.
African razors: a preliminary study. Stockholm, 1943.
54 p. illus. 25 cm. (Statens etnografiska museum. Smärre meddelanden, nr. 19)
Bibliography: p. 36–39.
1. Razors. (Series: Stockholm. Statens etnografiska museum. Smärre meddelanden, nr. 19)
GN4.S7 nr. 19   A 54–6553
Columbia Univ.   Libraries
for Library of Congress   ₍a96b₎†

NL 0377653   NNC DLC CtY UU MH ICF ICU IEN CU-SB

Lindblom, Gerhard, 1887–
Afrikanische Relikte und indianische Entlehnungen in der Kultur der Buschneger Surinams, eine vergleichende ethnographische Studie. Mit 29 Textabbildungen und 1 Tafel. Göteborg, Elanders boktr., 1924.
120 p. illus. 26 cm. (Göteborgs kungl. vetenskaps- och vitterhets-samhälles handlingar, 4. följden, 28. bandet ₍no. 1₎)
"Inlämnat den 10 september 1923."
"Zitierte litteratur" p. 111–120.
1. Ethnology—Dutch Guiana. 2. Acculturation. 3. Negroes in Dutch Guiana. I. Series: Göteborgs kungl. vetenskaps- och vitterhets-samhälle. Handlingar, 4. följden, 28. bandet, no. 1.
Full name: Karl Gerhard Lindblom.
AS284.G7 föl. 4,   bd. 28, no. 1   A 48–1859*
Illinois Univ. Library
for Library of Congress   ₍2₎†

NL 0377654   IU CU FU MH PU NN ICU NcU DLC

916.76 L742a Lindblom, Gerhard, 1887–
Afrikanska strövtåg, två års folklivsstudier i Engelska och Tyska Ost-Afrika. Stockholm, A. Bonnier ₍1914₎
333p. illus., fold. map. 23cm.
1. Africa, British East. Descr. & trav. 2. Africa, German East. Descr. & trav.

NL 0377655   IEN WU NNC ICJ

DT425 .L49 Lindblom, Gerhard, 1887–
Afrikanska strövtåg; två års folklivsstudier i Engelska och Tyska Ost-Afrika, av Gerhard Lindblom. Med 53 bilder och 20 planscher i kopparfotogravyr. Stockholm, Åhlén & Åkerlunds förlag ₍1926₎
211 p. illus. 21 cm.
1. Africa, British East—Descr. & trav. 2. Africa, German East—Descr. & trav.

NL 0377656   MB IEN

Lindblom, Gerhard, 1887–
The Akamba in British East Africa; an ethnological monograph by Gerhard Lindblom ... Uppsala, K. W. Appelbergs boktryckeri, 1916.
223 p. 23ᶜᵐ.
Inaug.-diss.—Uppsala.
"List of works referred to": p. ₍215₎–219.
1. Kamba tribe. I. Title.
₍*Full name:* Karl Gerhard Lindblom₎
36–32017
Library of Congress   DT429.L5 1916
₍2₎   572.96765

NL 0377657   DLC PU ICU IU MH MdBJ CU CtY

VOLUME 334

Lindblom, Gerhard, 1887–
... The Akamba in British East Africa; an ethnological monograph, by Gerhard Lindblom. 2d edition, enlarged. Uppsala, Appelbergs boktryckeri aktiebolag, 1920.

xii, 607 p. illus., tables, diagrs. 25 cm. (Archives d'études orientales ... v. 17)

"The first edition of this monograph was published as a university dissertation (discussed publicly at Upsala, May 27th, 1916) ... In the second edition numerous additions are made to the text."
"List of works referred to": p. [585]–592.

1. Ethnology—Africa, British East. 2. Kamba tribe.

A 35—775

Brown Univ. Library
for Library of Congress   [a64b½]

NBC CSt FU
OCU ViU NcD NcU CtY TxU OC1 CtY PPAmSwM FTaSU KyLoU
NL 0377658   RPB CaBVaU IdPI OrU MiU CU NN WU IU MU OU

LINDBLOM, Gerhard.
Die Beschneidung bei den Akamba. Wien, 1927.

p. 100–108, illus., 23 cm.
"Sonderabdruck aus der Zeitschrift "Volkerkunde" heft 4–6 – jahrg. 1927"

NL 0377659   MH-P

Lindblom, Gerhard, 1887–
Carved initiation sticks and bows from Taveta, Kenya Colony. Stockholm, 1950.

30 p. illus. 25 cm. (Stockholm. Statens etnografiska museum. Smärre meddelanden, nr. 23)

Bibliography: p. 22.

1. Initiations (in religion, folk-lore, etc.) 2. Rites and ceremonies—Africa. 3. Bow and arrow. (Series: Stockholm. Statens etnografiska museum. Smärre meddelanden, nr. 23)

Full name: Karl Gerhard Lindblom.

A 54–6272

Columbia Univ.   Libraries
for Library of Congress   [2]

NL 0377660   NNC UU NcD ICF ICU CU-SB

LINDBLOM, Gerhard.
Dragning av metalltrad i Afrika. n.p., 1926.

p. 97–109, 7 illus., 27 cm.
"Avhandlinger Aug. 1926".

NL 0377661   MH-P

Lindblom, Gerhard, 1887–
Einige details in der ornamentik der buschneger Surinams, von K. G. Lindblom. Stockholm [Gernandts boktryckeri a.-b.] 1926.

11 p. illus. 25 cm. (On cover: Riksmuseets etnografiska avdelning. Smärre meddelanden. [n:o 1])

1. Decoration and ornament. Primitive. 2. Decoration and ornament—Africa, West.

Full name: Karl Gerhard Lindblom.

35–14178

Library of Congress   GN4.87 no. 1   (572.082)   571.7

NL 0377662   DLC PU ICF OC1

LINDBLOM, Gerhard.
Einige Parallelen" zum Alten Testament aus Kavirondo (Kenya Colony, Ostafrika). Wien, 1926

p. 158–160, 24 cm.
"Sonderabdruck aus der Zeitschrift "Volkerkunde" heft 7–9–jahrgang 1926."

NL 0377663   MH-P

... Ethnos. v. 1–
- Jan. 1936–
Stockholm; Sweden, Bokförlags aktiebolaget Thule [1936–

Lindblom, Gerhard, 1887–
... Fighting-bracelets and kindred weapons in Africa, by K. G. Lindblom. Stockholm [Gernandts boktryckeri a.-b.] 1927.

32 p. illus. 25 cm. (Riksmuseets etnografiska avdelning. Smärre meddelanden. [n:o 4])

1. Arms and armor, Primitive. 2. Bracelets.

Full name: Karl Gerhard Lindblom

35–14171

Library of Congress   GN4.87 no. 4   (572.082)   399

NL 0377665   DLC PU NSyU OC1 MH

Lindblom, Gerhard, 1887–1969.
... Forskningar bland niloter och bantu i Kavirondo, särskilt med hänsyn till äldere kulturelement. Av G. Lindblom ... Stockholm, Almqvist & Wiksell [1927]
cover-title, p. [249]–272. illus. 23 cm.
At head of title: K. Svenska vetenskapsakademiens årsbok för år 1927.
Bibliography: p. 272.
1. Kavirondo (African people) 2. Africa, British East.

NL 0377666   CU MH

Lindblom, Gerhard, 1887–
... Further notes on the use of stilts, by K. G. Lindblom. Stockholm [Bröderna Lagerström, boktryckare] 1928.

19 p. illus. 25 cm. (Riksmuseets etnografiska avdelning. Smärre meddelanden. n:r 6)

1. Stilts.

Full name: Karl Gerhard Lindblom

35–14173

Library of Congress   GN4.87 no. 6   (572.082)   796.42

NL 0377667   DLC ICF MH PU OC1 NSyU

967.6
L7421
Lindblom, Gerhard, 1887–
I vildmark och negerbyar; Mount Elgon och annorstädes i Ostafrika. Uppsala, J. A. Lindblad [1921]
214 p. illus., fold. map. 23 cm.

1. Africa, British East. Descr. & trav.

NL 0377668   IEN MB

GN422
L742
Lindblom, Gerhard, 1887–
Jakt- och fångstmetoder bland afrikanska folk. Stockholm, V. Petterson, 1925–26.
2 v. illus., maps. 25 cm.
At head of title: Etnografiska riksmuseet.
Bibliography: v. 1, p. [130]–138; v. 2, p. [147]–157.

1. Hunting, Primitive. 2. Hunting – Africa
I. Stockholm. Statens etnografiska museum.

OC1
NL 0377669   CSt-H MH CU MiEM MH-P PU WaU NN DCU CtY

Lindblom, Gerhard, 1887–
... Kamba folklore ... with linguistic, ethnographical and comparative notes, by Gerhard Lindblom. Uppsala, Appelbergs boktryckeri aktiebolag, 1928–

v. 25 cm. (Archives d'études orientales ... v. 20: 1–
Kamba and English.
CONTENTS.—Tales of animals.

I. Title.

[Full name: Karl Gerhard Lindblom]

28–29181

CSt CtY NIC PU OC1 UU
NL 0377670   DLC WaU NSyU IdPI NBC ViU IU CU OU MBU

LINDBLOM, Gerhard.
Läppsmycken i Afrika och särskilt sadana av sten. Stockholm, 1925.

p. 457–466, 5 illus., 24 cm.
"Ur Ymer, tidskrift utgiven av Svenska sällskapet for antropologi och geografi, arg. 1925, h. 3 o. 4".

NL 0377671   MH-P

398.2
L742n
Lindblom, Gerhard, 1887–
Negerhistorier kring lägerelden; afrikanska folkberättelser. Uppsala, J. A. Lindblad [1922]
228 p. illus. 21 cm.

1. Folk-lore. Africa, East. 2. Folk literature. Africa, East.

NL 0377672   IEN

GN419
.A1L5
Lindblom, Gerhard, 1887–
Nose ornaments in Africa. Stockholm, 1945.

56 p. illus., map. 25 cm. (Stockholm. Statens etnografiska museum. Smärre meddelanden, nr. 20)

Bibliography: p. 50–56.

1. Decoration and ornament, African. (Series: Stockholm. Statens etnografiska museum. Smärre meddelanden, nr. 20)

Full name: Karl Gerhard Lindblom.

A 54–6668

Columbia Univ.   Libraries
for Library of Congress   [1]

NL 0377673   NNC DLC CtY MH CU-SB NSyU ViHaI ICF ICU

Lindblom, Gerhard, 1887–
Notes ethnographiques sur le Kavirondo septentrional et la colonie du Kenya (1) Par Gerhard Lindblom. (In Tucuman, Argentine Republic. Universidad. Instituto de etnologia. Revista. Tucuman, 1932. t. II, ent. 2ª, p. [395]–440. illus.)

NL 0377674   OU

Lindblom, Gerhard, 1887–
... Notes on Kamba grammar. With two appendices: Kamba names of persons, places, animals and plants—Salutations. By Gerhard Lindblom. Uppsala, Appelbergs boktrykeri aktiebolag, 1926.

100 p. 25 cm. (Archives d'études orientales ... v. 10)

"The present paper is merely meant to form a supplement to E. Brutser's 'Handbuch der kambasprache' (Berlin, 1906)"—Introd.

[Full name: Karl Gerhard Lindblom]

27–4490

WaU
NL 0377675   DLC CU-S FU MiU ViU OU CSt TxU IU CtY PU

VOLUME 334

GN231
.L5
    Lindblom, Gerhard, 1887–
       The one-leg resting position (nilotenstellung), in Africa and elsewhere. Stockholm, 1949.
       34 p. illus., map. 25 cm. (Stockholm. Statens etnografiska museum. Smärre meddelanden, nr. 22)
       Bibliographical footnotes.

       1. Posture.   (Series: Stockholm. Statens etnografiska museum. Smärre meddelanden, nr. 22)
               Full name: Karl Gerhard Lindblom.
                       A 54–6554
    Columbia Univ.   Libraries
    for Library of Congress   ₍1₎

    NL 0377676   NNC DLC MH-P ICF ICU NSyU UU CU-SB

PL8730 LINDBLOM, GERHARD, 1887–
.L7   ...Outlines of a Tharaka grammar with a list of words and specimens of the language, by Gerhard Lindblom. Upsala₍K.W.Appelberg₎1914.
       53, ₍1₎p. 25cm. (Archives d'études orientales... v.9)

       1.Tharaka language.

       IEN CtY MiU AAP ICarbS
    NL 0377677   ICU OU CU CtY CSt TxU OC1 NN ViU NIC PU

    Lindblom, Gerhard, 1887–
       ... Die schleuder in Afrika und anderwärts, von K. G. Lindblom. Stockholm ₍Gernandts boktryckeri a.-b.₎ 1927.
       31 p. illus., map. (Riksmuseets etnografiska avdelning. Smärre meddelanden. n:o 2)

       1. Slings.   I. Title.
                ₍*Full name:* Karl Gerhard Lindblom₎
                       35–14177
    Library of Congress   GN4.S7 no. 2   (572.082) 399

    NL 0377678   DLC ICF NcD NSyU IU PU OC1 MH-P

    Lindblom, Gerhard, 1887–
       ... The sling, especially in Africa; additional notes to a previous paper, by K. G. Lindblom. Stockholm ₍Lund, H. Ohlssons boktryckeri₎ 1940.
       41 p. illus. (incl. map) 26 cm. (Statens etnografiska museum. Smärre meddelanden, n:r 17)
       Bibliographical foot-notes.

       1. Slings.
       GN4.S7 nr. 17   A 44–1381 rev
    Yale Univ. Library
    for Library of Congress   ₍r64c₎₎†

    NL 0377679   CtY DLC CU-SB ICU ICF MH

LINDBLOM,   Gerhard.
    Some words of the language spoken by the Elgoni people on the east side of Mt.Elgon, Kenya Colony,East Africa. Uppsala,Almquist, 1925.

    p.46-55,26 cm.
    "Extrait,le Monde oriental XVIII,1924"

    NL 0377680   MH-P

    Lindblom, Gerhard, 1887–
       ... Spears and staffs with two or more points, in Africa, by K. G. Lindblom. Stockholm ₍Tryckeri aktiebolaget Thule₎ 1937.
       64 p. illus. (incl. maps) 25 cm. (Statens etnografiska museum (The Ethnographical museum of Sweden, Stockholm) Smärre meddelanden, n:r 14)
       "Published by financial support granted by the Swedish government and the trustees of the late Baron Carl von Platens foundation."—p. ₍4₎
       "Notes" (bibliographical) : p. 44–46.
       1. Spears. 2. Staffs (Sticks, canes, etc.)   I. Title.
                Full name: Karl Gerhard Lindblom.
       GN4.S7 nr. 14   571.5   39–30631

    NL 0377681   DLC CU-SB OC1 PPAmSwM ICU ICF

    Lindblom, Gerhard, 1887–
       ... The spiked wheel-trap and its distribution, by Karl Gerhard Lindblom. Stockholm ₍Bröderna Lagerström, boktryckare₎ 1928.
       30 p. illus. (incl. map) 25ᵐᵐ. (Riksmuseets etnografiska avdelning. Smärre meddelanden. n:r 5)

       1. Trapping. 2. Hunting, Primitive. I. Title. II. Title: Wheel-trap, The spiked.
                ₍*Full name:* Karl Gerhard Lindblom₎
                       35–14170
    Library of Congress   GN4.S7 no. 5   (572.082) 639.1

    NL 0377682   DLC ICF MB MH NSyU OC1 PU DHU

    Lindblom, Gerhard, 1887–
       ... String figures in Africa, by K. G. Lindblom. Stockholm ₍Bröderna Lagerström, printers₎ 1930.
       12 p. 25ᵐᵐ. (Riksmuseets etnografiska avdelning. Smärre meddelanden. n:r 9)

       1. String-figures.
                ₍*Full name:* Karl Gerhard Lindblom₎
                       35–14167
    Library of Congress   GN4.S7 no. 9   (572.082) 793.7

    NL 0377683   DLC NSyU IaU ICF ICU MB PPAmSwM OC1

GN447
.P6L5
    Lindblom, Gerhard, 1887–
       Tubular smoking pipes, especially in Africa. Stockholm, 1947.
       39 p. illus., map. 25 cm. (Stockholm. Statens etnografiska museum. Smärre meddelanden, nr. 21)

       1. Tobacco-pipes. (Series: Stockholm. Statens etnografiska museum. Smärre meddelanden, nr. 21)
                Full name: Karl Gerhard Lindblom.
                       A 54–6555
    Columbia Univ.   Libraries
    for Library of Congress   ₍1₎

    NL 0377684   NNC CtY CU-SB ICF UU DLC

    Lindblom, Gerhard, 1887–1969, joint author.

    Leth, T.
       ... Two kinds of fishing implements: 1. The plunge basket (stülpkorb), in Africa and elsewhere. 2. The circular cast-net in Africa. By T. Leth and K. G. Lindblom. Stockholm ₍Printed by Bröderna Lagerström₎ 1933.

    Lindblom, Gerhard, 1887–
       ... The use of oxen as pack riding animals in Africa, by K. G. Lindblom. Stockholm ₍Bröderna Lagerström, printers₎ 1931.
       77 p., 1 l. illus. 25ᵐᵐ. (Riksmuseets etnografiska avdelning. Smärre meddelanden. n:r 10)

       1. Pack transportation. 2. Oxen.
                ₍*Full name:* Karl Gerhard Lindblom₎
                       35–14166
    Library of Congress   GN4.S7 no. 10   (572.082) 636.2161

    NL 0377686   DLC ICF MB OC1

    Lindblom, Gerhard, 1887–
       ... The use of stilts, especially in Africa and America, by K. G. Lindblom. Stockholm ₍Gernandts boktr. a.-b.₎ 1927.
       40 p. illus. 25ᵐᵐ. (Riksmuseets etnografiska avdelning. Smärre meddelanden. (n:o 3₎)

       1. Stilts.
                ₍*Full name:* Karl Gerhard Lindblom₎
                       35–14172
    Library of Congress   GN4.S7 no. 3   (572.082) 796.42

    NL 0377687   DLC OC1 ICF MH PU PPAmSwM

    Lindblom, Gerhard, 1887–
       ... The use of the hammock in Africa, by K. G. Lindblom. Stockholm ₍Bröderna Lagerström, boktryckare₎ 1928.
       39 p. illus. 25ᵐᵐ. (Riksmuseets etnografiska avdelning. Smärre meddelanden. n:r 7)

       Hammocks.
                ₍*Full name:* Karl Gerhard Lindblom₎
                       35–14169
    Library of Congress   GN4.S7 no. 7   (572.082) 685.534

    NL 0377688   DLC ICF ICU NSyU OC1 DHU PU PPAmSwM

    Lindblom, Gerhard, 1887–1969
       ... Wire-drawing, especially in Africa, by K. G. Lindblom. Stockholm ₍Tryckeri aktiebolaget Thule₎ 1939.
       38 p. illus. (incl map) 25 cm. (Statens etnografiska museum (the Ethnographical museum of Sweden, Stockholm) Smärre meddelanden. n:r 15)

       1. Wire. 2. Drawing (Metal-work) I. Title.
                Full name: Karl Gerhard Lindblom.
       GN4.S7 nr. 15   571.4   39–15976

    NL 0377689   DLC CU-SB ICU IaU NSyU OC1 PU PPAmSwM

S
233
L742b
    Lindblom, Harry
       Bibeln och vetenskapen. Orebro, Mennets vans forlag, 1938.
       79 p.

    NL 0377690   WaE

    Lindblom, Harry, tr.

    Pethrus, Lewi, 1884–
       ... The wind bloweth where it listeth, by Lewi Pethrus ... Translated by Dr. Harry Lindblom. Chicago, Ill., Philadelphia book concern ₍1938₎–

    ₍Lindblom, Johannes₎ 1882–
       The University of Lund.   ₍Lund₎ C W K Gleerup ₍1949₎
       83 p. illus., map. 21cm.
       "Composed, at the request of the principal of the university, by Professor Joh. Lindblom, former principal of Lund university."

       I. Lund, Sweden. Universitet.
    N. Y. P. L.   March 26, 1951

    NL 0377692   NN NjP

    Lindblom, Jakob Axelsson, 1746–1819, respondent.
       ... Caussae impeditae in studiis progressionis see under Ihre, Johan, 1707–1780, praeses.

    Lindblom, Jakob Axelsson, 1746–1819.
       Dissertatio gradualis de carminibus skaldorum see Hesselgren, Johan.
       De carminibus skaldorum.

    Lindblom, Jakob Axelsson. 1746–1819.
       Dissertatio gradualis exhibens historiam
RBS   acidularum Medeviensium. Beskrifning om
143797 Medewi surbrunnar.
       Upsaliae: Joh. Edman, [1785].

    NL 0377695   NNNAM NN

VOLUME 334

[Lindblom, Jakob Axelsson] 1746–1819.
Lexicon latino-svecanum. Latinsk och swensk ord-bok
På konungens befallning utgifwen af Academien i Upsala.
Upsala, Tryckt hos J. Edman, 1790.

2 v. 23½ x 19½ᶜᵐ.

Paged continuously.
Vol. 2 has half-title only.
Dedication signed: Jac. Ax. Lindblom.

1. Latin language—Dictionaries—Swedish. 2. Swedish language—Dictionaries—Latin. i. Upsala. Universitet.

10-25735†

Library of Congress   PD5645.L3L7

NL 0377696   DLC

Z6621
.L75

Lindblom, Jakob Axelsson, 1746–1819.

Linköping, Sweden. Stifts- och läroverksbibliotek.
Linköpings bibliotheks handlingar. Första[-andra] delen
... Linköping, G. W. Lordicer och Björckegrens enka,
1793-95.

Lindblom, Jakob Axelsson, 1746–1819, praeses.
Specimen prius historico-criticum de poematis Ossianis...
Upsala: Typis Edmannianis, 1778. 28 p. 4°.

Dissertation, Upsala (Johan Swartz, respondent.)
Incomplete.

1. Ossian. 2. Swartz, Johan, re-   spondent.
N.Y.P.L.   November 28, 1916.

NL 0377698   NN

Mu
490.6
St93
v.1

LINDBLOM, JOHANNES, 1882-
Altchristliche kreuzessymbolik. Einige bemerkungen zu einer stelle der Bell'schen papyrus-
edition von 1924. Von Joh. Lindblom...
(In Studia orientalia.   Helsingforsiae,
1925. v.1,[102-]113. illus.)

Caption title.

NL 0377699   PU

IM50
L64b

Lindblom, Johannes, 1882-
Boken om Job och hans lidande. Lund, C.W.K.
Gleerup [1940].
372 p. illus. 22 cm.

Bibliographical references included in
"Anmärkningar" (p. [350]-367)

NL 0377700   CtY-D ViRUT NjPT MH

Lindblom, Johannes, 1882-
La composition du livre de Job.
(In Humanistiska vetenskapssamfundet i Lund. Årsberättelse
1944-1945. Lund, 1945. 25 cm. p. 111-305)
Bibliographical footnotes.

1. Bible. O. T. Job—Criticism, interpretation, etc. i. Title.
                            Full name: Christian Johannes Lindblom.
AS284.L85 1944/45   A 50-1333

Cincinnati. Univ. Libr
for Library of Congress   [1]†

NL 0377701   OCU PPWe ICU MH DLC

EY54
Isl
L64d

Lindblom, Johannes, 1882-
Deuterojesaja i den nyfunna Jesaja-handskriften
från Palestina, av Joh. Lindblom. [Lund, Håkan
Ohlssons Boktryckeri, 1950]
[302]-314 p. 26 cm.

Caption title.
"Särtryck ur Svensk teologisk kvartalskrift
1950: 3-4."

1. Bible. O.T. Isaiah.   I. Title.

NL 0377702   CtY-D

EY54
Isl
L64e

Lindblom, Johannes, 1882-
Die Ebed Jahwe-Orakel in der neuentdeckten
Jesajahandschrift (DSIa) von Joh. Lindblom.
Berlin, A. Töpelmann [1951]
[235]-248 p. 23 cm.

Caption title.
"Sonderdruck aus Zeitschrift für die alt-
testamentliche Wissenschaft, Band 63, Heft 3/4."
Bibliographical footnotes.

1. Bible. O.T. Isaiah.   I. Title.

NL 0377703   CtY-D

Lindblom, Johannes, 1882-
Efraim Briem. Minnesord.
(In Humanistiska vetenskapssamfundet i Lund. Årsberättelse
1946-1947. Lund, 1947. 25 cm. p. xvii-xxiii. port.)

1. Briem, Efraim, 1890-1946.
AS284.L85 1946/47   A 50-6541

Cincinnati. Univ. Libr
for Library of Congress   [1]†

NL 0377704   OCU DLC

B
785
.E6L5

LINDBLOM, Johannes, 1882-
Erasmus, Onderzoek naar zijne Theologie en
zijne Godsdienstig Gemoedsbestaan. Leiden,
A.H. Adraini, 1909.

200p.

NL 0377705   WaWW

Lindblom, Johannes, 1882-
Erik Aurelius. Av Joh. Lindblom.
(In Humanistiska vetenskapssamfundet i Lund. Årsberättelse
1935-1936. Lund, 1936. 23½ᶜᵐ. p. [xliii]-lxvii. port.)

1. Aurelius, Erik, 1874-1935.
                            Full name: Christian Johannes Lindblom]
                                        A 44-5097
Cincinnati. Univ. Libr.
for Library of Congress   AS284.L85 1935/36
                            [2]†   (068.485)

NL 0377706   OCU DLC

Lindblom, Johannes, 1882-
Das ewige leben, eine studie über die entstehung der religiösen lebensidee im Neuen Testament von Joh. Lindblom
... Uppsala, A.-b. Akademiska bokhandeln i kommission;
[etc., etc.], 1914.

vi, 252 p. 25½ cm. (On cover: Arbeten utg. med understöd af Vilhelm Ekmans universitetsfond, Uppsala, 15)

1. Future life. i. Title.
                            Full name: Christian Johannes Lindblom.
BT901.L65   22-2285

NL 0377707   DLC CtY CtY-D ICJ IEG MiU NN NcD ViRUT

LINDBLOM, Johannes, 1882-
Gamla Testamentet i kyrka och
teologi. Lund, C.W.K. Gleerups
Foerlag [1939]
47p. 19.5cm. (Skrifter i Teologiska och Kyrkliga Aemnen,15)

NL 0377708   MH-AH NjPT

Lindblom, Johannes, 1882-
... Den gammaltestamentliga religionens egenart; en meto-
dologisk och exegetisk studie, av Joh. Lindblom. Lund,
C. W. K. Gleerup [1935]
77 p. 25½ᶜᵐ. (Lunds universitets årsskrift. n. f., avd. 1, bd. 31, nr. 1)
Bibliographical foot-notes.

1. Bible. O. T.—Theology. 2. Bible—Theology—O. T. 3. Jews—Re-
ligion.
                            [Full name: Christian Johannes Lindblom]
                                        A 36-807
Title from Univ. of Chi-   cago AS284.L96 n. f., avd. 1, bd. 31
Library of Congress   [AS284.L8 n. f., avd. 1, bd. 31]

NL 0377709   OCU CSaT CtY-D OU PU

Lindblom, Johannes, 1882-
Handbok til Nya Testamentet. Stockholm,
P. A. Norstedt, 1917-1923 [v.1,1923]
2v. in 3. 26cm.

1. Bible. N. T. - Commentaries.

NL 0377710   MoSCS

Lindblom, Johannes, 1882-
...Hosea, literarisch untersucht, von Joh. Lindblom... Åbo:
Åbo Akad., 1927. 149 p. 8°. (Åbo Akad. Acta Academiae
Aboensis. Humaniora 5.)

1. Bible. O. T.: Hosea. 2. Ser.
N.Y.P.L.   December 16, 1927

NL 0377711   NN MH OCH

Lindblom, Johannes, 1882–
... Hosea; literarisch untersucht, von Joh. Lindblom ...
Åbo, Åbo akademi, 1928.

3 p. l., 149 p. 24ᶜᵐ. (Acta Academiae aboensis. Humaniora. v.2)
Bibliographical foot-notes.

1. Bible. O. T. Hosea—Criticism, interpretation, etc. 2. Bible—
Criticism, interpretation, etc.—O. T. Hosea.
                            [Full name: Christian Johannes Lindblom]
                                        A C 33-233
Title from Princeton   Univ.
Library of Congress   [AS262.A3 vol. 5, no. 2]

NL 0377712   NjP CtY-D ICN ICMcC MU NIC PU OCl OU

PT9838
.L83

Lindblom, Johannes, 1882-

Lund. Universitet.
Inbjudning till den högtidlighet varmed Lunds universi-
tet den 2. november 1946 firar hundraårsminnet av Esaias
Tegnérs död, utfärdad av universitetets rektor. Bifogad
skrift: Tegnér och Bibeln av Joh. Lindblom. Lund, H.
Ohlssons boktr., 1946.

Lindblom, Johannes, 1882-
Israels religion, I gammaltestamentlid tid.
Stockholm, Svenska Kyrkans Diakonistyrelses
Bokförlag, [1953]

292 p. 23 cm.

1. Jews-Hist.—To A.D.70.
2. Jews - Religion.

NL 0377714   MWalB

VOLUME 334

Lindblom, Johannes, 1882–
 Die Jesaja-Apokalypse in der neuen Jesajahandschrift (DSIa)
 (*In* Humanistiska vetenskapssamfundet i Lund. **Årsberättelse** 1950–1951. Lund, 1951. 25 cm. p. 87–97)

 1. Bible. Manuscripts, Hebrew. O. T. Isaiah. I. Title.
 Full name: Christian Johannes Lindblom.

 [AS284.L85 1950/51]   A 53–5095

 Cincinnati. Univ. Libr'
 for Library of Congress   (3)

NL 0377715   OCU NNJ IEG CtY–D

Lindblom, Johannes, 1882–
 … Die Jesaja-apokalypse, Jes. 24–27, von Joh. Lindblom. Lund, C. W. K. Gleerup; (etc., etc., 1938)
 122 p. 25½ᵐ. (Lunds universitets årsskrift. n. f., avd. 1, bd. 34, nr. 3)

 1. Bible. O. T. Isaiah xxiv–xxvii—Criticism, interpretation, etc.
 (*Full name: Christian Johannes Lindblom*)
                                           A 40–1520

 Chicago. Univ. Library   AS284.L96 n. f., avd. 1, bd. 34, pt. 1
 for Library of Congress   [AS284.L8 n. f., avd. 1, bd. 34]
                 (2)   (378.485)

CtY OCH CCSC ICMcC KyLoS NcU
NL 0377716   ICU PPEB CSt IU OU NNC ViU PU NcU NjP MH

Lindblom, Johannes, 1882–

 Jesu missions-och dopbefallning; Matt. 28: 18–20; tillika en studie över det kristna dopets ursprung. Stockholm, Svenska Kyrkans Diakonistyrelses Bokförlag (1919)
 287p. 23cm.

 1. Bible. N. T. Matthew 28:18–20 – Criticism, interpretation, etc. 2. Baptism.

NL 0377717   MoSCS MH–AH

Lindblom, Johannes, 1882–
 … Jesu religion och historisk kristendom, av Joh. Lindblom. 2.uppl. Stockholm, Sveriges kristliga studentrörelses förlag (1919)
 200 p.   19cm.   (Sveriges kristliga studentrörelses skriftserie. n:r 105)

 1. Jesus Christ. 2. Christianity.

NL 0377718   MnU ICU

BS465   **LINDBLOM, JOHANNES,** 1882–
.L74   Kanon och Apokryfer. Studier till den bibliska kanons historia, av Joh. Lindblom. Stockholm, A.-b. Svenska kyrkans diakonistyrelses bokförlag [1920]
 [7],219 p.   22cm.

 1. Bible—Canon.

NL 0377719   ICU MnU

Lindblom, Johannes, 1882–
 … Die literarische gattung der prophetischen literatur. Eine literargeschichtliche untersuchung zum Alten Testament, von Joh. Lindblom. Uppsala, A.-b. Lundequistska bokhandeln (1924)
 2 p. l., 122 p. 24ᵐ. (Uppsala universitets årsskrift 1924. Teologi. 1)

 1. Bible. O. T. Prophets—Language, style. 2. Bible as literature. 3. Bible—Language, style—O. T. Prophets. I. Title.
                                           A 41–1380
 Minnesota. Univ. Library
 for Library of Congress   [AS284.U7 1924]
                 (2)   (378.485)

NL 0377720   MnU MoU NN PPEB PU OO OClW

Lindblom, Johannes, 1882–
 … Die literarische Gattung der prophetischen Literatur. Eine literargeschichtliche Untersuchung zum Alten Testament, von Joh. Lindblom. Uppsala, A.-b. Lundequistska bokhandeln (1924)
 2 p. l., 122 p. 24ᵐ. (Uppsala universitets årsskrift 1924. Teologi. 1)
 Xeroxed copy, 1967, from original at Union Theological Seminary, New York.
 Bibliographical footnotes.

NL 0377721   ICMcC

Lindblom, Johannes, 1882–
 … Micha; literarisch untersucht, von Joh. Lindblom … Åbo, Åbo akademi, 1929.
 177, (1) p. 23ᵐ. (Acta Academiae aboensis. Humaniora. vi:2)

 1. Bible. O. T. Micah—Criticism, interpretation, etc. 2. Bible—Criticism, interpretation, etc.—O. T. Micah.
                             (*Full name: Christian Johannes Lindblom*)
                                           A C 33–234
 Title from Princeton   Univ.
 Library of Congress   [AS262.A3 vol. 6, no. 2]

PBm PU OO OU OCl
NL 0377722   NjP TNJ–R MU NIC PPiPT KyLoS ICN ICU CtY

Lindblom, Johannes, 1882–   , ed.
 … Observationes strengnenses, utgivna med inledning och kommentar, av Joh. Lindblom och Hilding Pleijel. Stockholm, Svenska kyrkans diakonistyrelses bokförlag (1943)
 222 p., 23ᵐ. (Samlingar och studier till Svenska kyrkans historia. 5)
 "Utgivet med anslag från Humanistiska fonden."
 Summary in German.
 Bibliographi-   cal footnotes.

NL 0377723   NjPT MoSCS

Lindblom, Johannes, 1882–
 Om lifvets idé hos Paulus och Johannes samt i de s. k. Salomos oden, af Johannes Lindblom … Uppsala, Akademiska boktryckeriet, E. Berling, 1911.
 vi p., 1 l., 187 p. 24½ᵐ. (Uppsala universitets årsskrift, 1910. Teologi)

 1. Life. 2. Bible. N. T. Epistles of Paul—Theology. 3. Bible. N. T. Johannine literature—Theology. 4. Bible. O. T. Apocryphal books. Odes of Solomon—Theology. 5. Bible—Theology—N. T. Epistles of Paul. 6. Bible—Theology—N. T. Johannine literature.
                             (*Full name: Christian Johannes Lindblom*)
                                           37–39426 Revised
 Library of Congress   AS284.U7 1910

NL 0377724   DLC MH NIC

BS   **Lindblom, Johannes,** 1882–
505   Om språket i den svenska bibelöversättningen av 1917. (Stockholm) Svenska bokförlaget (1955)
.L5   46 p.   20 cm. (in binder, 22 cm.) (Skrifter utgivna av Nämnden för svensk språkvård, 13)

 Bibliographical footnotes.

 1. Swedish lan-   guage. 2. Bible.
 Swedish. 1917.   I. Title.

NL 0377725   WU WaU NN MH–AH MH ICU

Lindblom, Johannes, 1882–
 Profetismen i Israel, av Joh. Lindblom. Stockholm, Svenska kyrkans diakonistyrelses bokförlag [1934]
 703 p.   21.5 cm.
 Bibliographical references in "Anmärkningar": p. [651]–685.

NL 0377726   NjPT

Lindblom, Johannes, 1882–
 Psalms and Odes of Solomon…
 Uppsala, 1909
  see under Bible. O. T. Apocryphal books. Odes of Solomon. Greek. 1909.

AS284   **Lindblom, Johannes,** 1882–
.L8   The servant songs in Deutero-Isaiah; a new attempt to
bd. 47, solve an old problem. Lund, C. W. K. Gleerup (1951)
nr. 5   114 p.   26 cm. (Lunds universitets årsskrift, n. f., avd. 1, bd. 47, nr. 5)

 Bibliography: p. (105)–109.

 1. Servant of Jehovah. 2. Bible. O. T. Isaiah XL–LV—Criticism, interpretation, etc. (Series: Lund. Universitet. Acta Universitatis Lundensis, n. s. Lunds universitets årsskrift, n. f., avd. 1, bd. 47, nr. 5)
                             Full name: Christian Johannes Lindblom.
                                           A 52–6954
 Chicago. Univ. Libr.
 for Library of Congress   (2)

CtY–D PU MH–AH CBBD DLC
NL 0377728   ICU NRCR PPDrop NjPT NNJ PPLT NIC OU TxU

Lindblom, Johannes, 1882–
 … Skandalon; eine lexikalisch-exegetische untersuchung, von Joh. Lindblom. Uppsala, Almqvist & Wiksells boktryckeri-a.-b., 1921.
 52 p. 24ᵐ. (Uppsala universitets årsskrift 1921. Teologi. 2)

 1. Greek language, Biblical—Semantics. I. Title.
                             (*Full name: Christian Johannes Lindblom*)
 Minnesota. Univ. Library   A C 39–2070
 for Library of Congress   [AS284.U7 1921]
                 (4)   (378.485)

NL 0377729   MnU CBPac IEG MH OCH MoU PU MH–AH

Lindblom, Johannes, 1882–
 … Der sogenannte bauernkalender von Gezer, von Joh. Lindblom … Åbo, Åbo akademi, 1931.
 25 p. illus. 24ᵐ. (Acta Academiae aboensis. Humaniora. vii:5)
 Bibliographical foot-notes.

 1. Calendar, Assyro-Babylonian. 2. Inscriptions—Palestine.
                             (*Full name: Christian Johannes Lindblom*)
 Title from Princeton   Univ.   A C 33–239
 Library of Congress   [AS262.A3 vol. 7, no. 5]

NL 0377730   NjP MU NIC PBm PU OU OCl

Lindblom, Johannes, 1882–
 … Studier till 1541 års Bibel … Lund, C. W. K. Gleerup; Leipzig, O. Harrassowitz (1941–

491.2   **LINDBLOM, Johannes,** 1882–
Swed.   Studier till en ny provoersaettning
L742s   av Syraks Bok; med saerskild hansyn till 1500-talets Svenska bibeloeversaettningsarbete. Stockholm, F.A. Norstedt & Soeners Foerlag (1915)
 153p. 22.5cm.

NL 0377732   MH–AH

LINDBLOM, Johannes, 1882–
 … A study on the Immanuel section in Isaiah; Isa.vii, 1–ix,6.
 57p. 23.5cm. (Scripta Minora, 1957–1958:4)

NL 0377733   MH–AH

VOLUME 334

Lindblom, Johannes, 1882–
Sven Herner: minnesord.
(*In* Humanistiska vetenskapssamfundet i Lund. **Årsberättelse**
1949–1950. Lund, 1950. 25 cm. p. xxix–xxxiv. port.)

1. Herner, Sven, 1865–1949.
Full name: Christian Johannes Lindblom.
[AS284.L85 1949/50]   (068.485)   A 51–1119

Cincinnati. Univ. Libr.
for Library of Congress   (1)

NL 0377734   OCU

Lindblom, Johannes, 1882–
Tegnér och bibeln. Lund, C. W. K. Gleerup (1946)
96 p. 25 cm. (Lunds universitets årsskrift, n. f., avd. 1, bd. 42,
nr. 1)
(Lund. Universitet) Esaias Tegnér; studier till hans person och
verk, nr. 1.
1. Tegnér, Esaias, Bp, 1782–1846. 2. Bible in literature. 3. Bible—
Influence.   (Series: Lund. Universitet. Acta Universitatis lundensis, n. s. Lunds universitets årsskrift, n. f., avd. 1, bd. 42, nr. 1.
Series: Lund. Universitet. Esaias Tegnér; studier till hans person
och verk, nr. 1)
Full name: Christian Johannes Lindblom.
[AS284.L8 bd. 42, nr. 1]   A 48–5936*

Chicago. Univ. Libr.
for Library of Congress   (1)

NL 0377735   ICU PU NcU

Lindblom, Johannes, 1882–
Tegnér och Bibeln
(In Hundraårsminnet av Esaias
Tegnérs död ... 1946)

NL 0377736   ICLT

Lindblom, Johannes, 1882–
The University of Lund. (Lund) C. W. K. Gleerup (1948)
83 p. illus., map. 20 cm.

1. Lund. Universitet.
Full name: Christian Johannes Lindblom.
LF4543.L5   378.485   52–65805

NL 0377737   DLC CU CtY MH

Lindblom, Johannes, 1882–
Zur frage der entstehung des alphabets. Von Joh. Lindblom.
(*In* Humanistiska vetenskapssamfundet i Lund. **Årsberättelse**
1931–1932. Lund, 1932. 23½cm. p. 39–64. illus.)

1. Alphabet.   *(Full name:* Christian Johannes Lindblom)
A 44–5066
Cincinnati. Univ. Libr.
for Library of Congress   AS284.L85 1931/82
(2)†   (068.485)

DLC MH–AH
NL 0377738   OCU TxFTC OU OC1 PPDrop InU TxU GU OCH

Lindblom, Karl Gerhard
see
Lindblom, Gerhard, 1887–

Lindblom, Knut, 1905–
Arthrography of the knee; a roentgenographic and anatomical study. Stockholm, P. A. Norstedt, 1948.
111, (1) p. illus. 25 cm. (Acta radiologica. Supplementum 74)
"References": p. (112)

1. Knee—Wounds and injuries. 2. Diagnosis, Radioscopic.
I. Title.   (Series)
Full name: Knut John Gustaf Lindblom.
A 50–4901

Michigan. Univ. Libr.
for Library of Congress   (2)

NL 0377740   MiU MoU ViU

Lindblom, Knut, 1905–
... A roentgenographic study of the vascular channels of the
skull with special reference to intracranial tumors and arteriovenous aneurysms, by Knut Lindblom.   Stockholm, Kungl.
boktryckeriet, P. A. Norstedt & söner, 1936.
146 p. illus. 25ᶜᵐ. (On cover: Acta radiologica. Supplementum
xxx)
At head of title: From the Roentgen institute of Serafimerlasarettet,
Stockholm. Chief: Professor Gösta Forssell.
Translated by Dr. and Mrs. Clifford Franseen.
Bibliography: p. 142–146.
1. Brain—Blood-vessels. 2. Diagnosis, Radioscopic. 3. Brain—Tumors. 4. Aneurism.   I. Franseen, Clifford Carlton, 1905–   tr. II.
Franseen, Mrs. Clifford Carlton, tr. III. Title: Skull, Vascular channels
of the.
(Full   name: Knut John Gustaf Lindblom)
A C 39–2259
Michigan. Univ. Library
for Library of Congress   (a39d2)

NL 0377741   MiU MoU ViU

Microfilm   Lindblom, Knut, 1905–   joint author.
RC–2
Alström, Carl Henry, 1907–
... Über die lungentuberkulose der geisteskranken, insbesondere der schizophrenen; ihre entstehung, häufigkeit und
bekämpfung, von Carl Henry Alström, Carl Gentz (und)
Knut Lindblom. Kopenhagen, E. Munksgaard, 1943.

Lindblom, Myron.
You that labor, by Myron Lindblom. Columbus, O., The
Wartburg press (1944)
77 p. illus. 18½ᶜᵐ.

1. Christian life—Stories.   I. Title.
44–30697
Library of Congress   BV4515.L5
(2)   244

NL 0377743   DLC NRCR

Lindblom, Nicolaus, respondent.
Dissertatio academica analysi veterum
geometrica. 1746.
see under Duraeus, Samuel, praeses.

Lindblom, Olavi, 1911–
Mikä on totuus. Helsinki, 1951. 80 p.
20 cm. (SAK ajankohtaisia kysymyksiä. 5)

At head of title: MAL–SAK.

1. Trade unions. 2. Trade unions—Finland.

NL 0377745   NN DLC-P4

HD8532   Lindblom, Olavi, 1911– ed.
.S8
Suomen Ammattiyhdistysten Keskusliitto.
Pöytäkirja Suomen Ammattiyhdistysten Keskusliitto
(SAK) r. y. :n kuudennesta varsinaisesta edustajakokouksesta Helsingissä 27.6.1–1.7.1951. Laatineet: Olavi Lindblom ja Uuno Hiironen. (Helsinki, 1953)

Lindblom, Olavus, respondent.
Propitionumine. Dissertatio gradualis de
artificiis mnemonicis... 1746
see under Ekerman, Petrus, praeses.
1696–1763, praeses.

Lindblom, Paul.
Common sense och ändamålsetik i G. E. Moores filosofi.
Lund, C. W. K. Gleerup (1945)
220 p. 23 cm.
Akademisk avhandling—Lund.
Extra t. p. with thesis statement, inserted.
Bibliography: p. 212–220.

1. Moore, George Edward, 1873–
B1647.M74L5   52–64561

NL 0377748   DLC CU ICU NNC

B821
.L56
Lindblom, Paul.
Humanistiska perspektiv, av Paul Lindblom och Georg
Landberg. Stockholm, Ehlin, 1950.
184, (2) p. 19 cm. (Idé & samhälle)
Bibliographies: p. 64, (125)–(136)
CONTENTS.—Humanistiskt minimum, av Paul Lindblom.—Kristen
humanism, av Georg Landberg.

1. Humanism. 2. Christianity.   I. Landberg, Georg, 1897–
joint author. II. Title.
A 51–3070
Chicago. Univ. Libr.
for Library of Congress   (3)

NL 0377749   ICU NN DLC

Lindblom, Paul.
Lång hämnd. Stockholm, P. A. Norstedt (1948)
186 p. 21 cm.

I. Title.
A 49–5418*
Minnesota. Univ. Lib.
for Library of Congress   (1)

NL 0377750   MnU

Lindblom, Paul.
Ofarlig kollision; roman. Stockholm, Norstedt (1950)
242 p. 20 cm.

I. Title.
A 51–4624
Minnesota. Univ. Libr.
for Library of Congress   (3)

NL 0377751   MnU MH

Lindblom, Paul.
Ungdomsvårdsskolorna. På Ungdomsvårdsskoleutredningens uppdrag. Stockholm, Wahlström & Widstrand
(1954)
140 p. illus. 22 cm.

1. Children—Institutional care—Sweden.   I. Title.
HV1237.L5   56–23261 ‡

NL 0377752   DLC NN

VOLUME 334

Lindblom, Theodor.
Bibliskt galleri. Kristi lif. Allmänna konst-
och industriutställningen i Stockholm 1897.
Stockholm, 1897.
6p. illus.

NL 0377753 ICRL ICJ

Lindblom, Torsten
Kraft att leva; en årgång predikningar. Stockholm,
Svenska kyrkans diakonistyrelses bokförlag [1951]

NL 0377754 MH

Lindblom, Yngve.
Han byggde en bro mellan öst och väst; en skildring av
Alexander Duffs livsverk. Stockholm, Harrier ₁1946₎
148 p. 19 cm.

1. Duff, Alexander, 1806-1878.   I. Title.

BV3269.D8L5   63-41473 ‡

NL 0377755 DLC NN

Lindblom, Yngve.
Havet var hans öde; sannsagan om James Cook, värld-
somseglaren, söderhavsöarnas fredlige erövrare. Stockholm,
Harrier ₁1946₎
159 p. illus. 19 cm.

1. Cook, James, 1728-1779—Juvenile literature.

G246.C7L73   63-37125 ‡

NL 0377756 DLC NN

Lindbloom, Harold Seth, 1906-
Colorado citizen, by H. S. Lindbloom and L. T. Sigstad.
Illus. by Paul Busch. Denver, Old West Pub. Co. ₁1955₎
98 p. illus. 26 cm.

1. Colorado—Pol. & govt.   I. Sigstad, Lawrence Truman, 1904-
joint author. II. Title.

JK7825 1955.L5   56-20207 ‡
*320.9788 342.788

NL 0377757 DLC NN MiU

Lindboe, Asbjørn, 1889-
Privat rettergang; voldgiftsprosessen. Oslo, J. G. Tanum, 1944.
224 p. 23 cm.

"Tvistemålsloven. (Lov om rettergangsmåten i tvistemål av 13.
august 1915) 32. kapitel: Voldgift": p. 155-176.   "Tvistemålslovens
øvrige bestemmelser i utdrag": p. 177-224.
Bibliography included in "Forkortelser" (p. ₁9₎)

1. Arbitration and award—Norway.   I. Norway. Laws, statutes,
etc. II. Title.

48-32337*

NL 0377758 DLC

Lindboe, Fredrikke.
Smaabørnenes melodier; 30 ganske lette smaasange for börn.
Kristiania: Carl Warmuth ₁19—?₎.   4 v.   4°.

NL 0377759 NN

Lindboe, Waldemar
Eine neue formel...
Inaug. Diss. Tech. Hoch. Dresden, 1910
Bibl.

NL 0377760 ICRL

Lindboe Bliksted, H
see Bliksted, H   Lindboe.

Lindbohm, Carolus, respondent.
... Dissertatio philiosophica de adquiescentia...
see under   Christiernin, Peter Nikolai,
praeses.

PT9773   ₁Lindbohm, Lars Robert₎
L8S8   Sten sture den yngre; sorgespel. Svenskt
1865   original af Lbm ₁pseud.₎ Stockholm, A.
Bonnier ₁1865₎
120 p.   (Sv₁enska₎ theatern, n:o 158)

NL 0377763 CU

Lindbom, Åke.
Arteriosclerosis and arterial thrombosis in the lower limb,
a roentgenological study. Stockholm ₁Esselte aktiebolag₎
1950.
80 p. illus. 25 cm.   (Acta radiologica. Supplementum 80)

At head of title: From the Roentgen Diagnostic Department of
Karolinska sjukhuset, Stockholm. Chief: Professor Åke Åkerlund.
"References": p. ₁77₎-80.

1. Arteriosclerosis. 2. Thrombosis. 3. Leg—Diseases. 4. Diagnosis,
Radioscopic.   (Series)

Michigan. Univ. Libr.   A 51-2583
for Library of Congress   ₁2₎

NL 0377764 MiU MoU ViU

Lindbom (Isacus)
*De virtute personata. *Upsaliae,* 1742. 3 p.l., 24 pp.,
1 l. 12°.
In: YFH p. v. 2.

NL 0377765 NN

QH9   Lindbom, Olavus, respondent.
.T6
no. 184   Thunberg, Karl Peter, 1743-1828, *praeses.*
Rare bk.   Dissertatio de viribus et usu atropae belladonnae ... Upsaliae, typis Zeipel et Palmblad ₁1817₎

Lindbom, Olavus, respondent.
Remedia guineensia...
see under   Afzelius, Adam, 1750-1837,
praeses.

---

890   LINDBOM, Olof
Box 1   En christelig hoegmaessopredikan,
foerestaellande Jesu Christi sidsta
stunder, haalen foer den christeliga
Guds foersamling i Fellingsbro, paa
Laang=fredagen aar 1748. Waesteraas,
Johann Laur. Horrn, 1767.
60p. 19cm.

Tredje ₁aangen uplagd.

NL 0377768 MH-AH

W1   Lindbom, Oscar, 1883-
LA265   Invärtes medicin, av Oscar Lindbom. Tuberkulos, av
Bd.4   Alf Westergren. 1. uppl. Stockholm, Svensk
1943   bokförlaget [1945]
vi, 130 p. illus. (Lärobok för sjuksköterskeelever,
4)

First published 1943.
1. Internal Medicine - nursing texts 2. Tuberculosis
- nursing texts I. Westergren, Alf, 1891-
Tuberkulos II. Title III. Title: Tuberkulos

NL 0377769 DNLM

W 4   Lindbom, Oscar, 1883-
qS86   Studier över akut leukämi. Stockholm,
1919   Marcus, 1919.
iv, 254 p. illus. (part col.)

Akademisk avhandling - Karolinska institutet,
Stockholm.
Author's autograph presentation copy.
Bibliography: p. 238-253.

NL 0377770 DNLM

Lindbom, Tage Leonard, 1909-
Arbetarrörelsen och kulturen. Stockholm, Arbetarnas
bildningsförbund, 1947.
112 p. 20 cm.

1. Sweden—Intellectual life. 2. Trade-unions—Sweden.
I. Title.

DL635.L5   55-16735 ‡

NL 0377771 DLC NN MH MnU

LINDBOM, TAGE Leonard, 1909-
Atlantis; Idee und Wirklichkeit des Sozialismus.
Frankfurt am Main, Büchergilde Gutenberg [1955]
275 p. 21cm.

1. Socialism, 1945-

NL 0377772 NN

Lindbom, Tage Leonard, 1909-
En beredskapsman ser pa försvaret. [Stockholm] Kooperativa förbundet [1941]

NL 0377773 MH

Lindbom, Tage Leonard, 1909-
Efter Atlantis. Stockholm, Kooperativa förbundets bokförlag, 1951.
277 p. 21 cm.

1. Socialism—Hist.   I. Title.

HX36.L5   52-33700 †

NL 0377774 DLC NN NNC

Lindbom, Tage Leonard, 1909-
Den nya fronten. Stockholm, Kooperativa förbundets
bokförlag, 1949.
160 p. 20 cm.

CONTENTS.—Den demokratiska skolan.—Samhället sådant det håller
på at bli.—Folket och folkrörelserna.—Nya gemenskapsformer.—
Myten och verkligheten.—Den inre fronten.—Fritidens aktiva och
passiva.—Är kunskap makt?—Har vi glömt bort att leka?—Korsets
väg.—Socialismen som tankebyggnad och frälsningslära.—Förnyelse.

1. Social problems. 2. Democracy.   I. Title.

HN18.L5   301.153   50-27762

NL 0377775 DLC

VOLUME 334

Lindbom, Tage Leonard, 1909–
Schweden gestern und heute. Mit einem Anhang über die Wohnungsbau- und Sozialpolitik in Schweden, von Kurt Stern. Hamburg, E. Tessloff [1949]
116 p. plates, ports. 19 cm.

1. Trade-unions—Sweden. 2. Labor and laboring classes—Sweden. 3. Sweden—Pol. and govt.—1905–

HD8578.L5   331   50-33319

NL 0377776   DLC

Lindbom, Tage Leonard, 1909–
Den socialdemokratiska ungdomsrörelsen i Sverige; en historik. Stockholm, Tidens förlag, 1945.
367 p. illus., ports. 24 cm.

"Det socialistiska ungdomsförbundet, Socialdemokratiska ungdomsförbundet med födelsearet 1903 samt Sverges socialdemokratiska ungdomsförbund ... avspegla i sin verksamhet tre huvudskeden i den svenska socialdemokratins historia."

1. Svenska socialistiska ungdomsförbundet. 2. Socialdemokratiska förbundet. 3. Sverges socialdemokratiska ungdomsförbund. I. Title.

DL861.L5   50-57354

NL 0377777   DLC MH-IR IEN ICU MH

Lindbom, Tage Leonard, 1909–
Den socialdemokratiska ungdomsrörelsen i Sverige; en historik. [2. uppl.] Stockholm, Tiden [1952]
367 p. illus., ports. 24 cm.

1. Svenska socialistiska ungdomsförbundet. 2. Socialdemokratiska ungdomsförbundet. 3. Sverges socialdemokratiska ungdomsförbund. I. Title.

[DL861.L   ]   A 54-1807
Harvard Univ. Library
for Library of Congress   [2]

NL 0377778   MH

Lindbom, Tage Leonard, 1909–
Den svenska fackföreningsrörelsens uppkomst och tidigare historia 1872–1900. Stockholm, Landsorganisationen i Sverige, 1938.
421 p. 23 cm. (Landsorganisationen skriftserie, nr. 49)
Akademisk avhandling—Stockholms högskola.
Bibliography: p. 409–416.

1. Trade-unions — Sweden.   (Series: Landsorganisationen i Sverige. Skriftserie, nr. 49)

HD6757.L5   53-54483

NL 0377779   DLC CtY MnU NcD RPB NNC ICRL PPAmSwM

331.88
Sv246l   Lindbom, Tage Leonard, 1909–
Svenska kommunalarbetareförbundet, 1910–1935; historik. [Stockholm, Tryckeriaktiebolaget Tiden, 1935]

252 p. illus., ports. 27cm.
1. Svenska kommunalarbetareförbundet. 2. Municipal officials and employees. Sweden.

NL 0377780   MnU

Lindbom, Tage Leonard, 1909–
Sweden's labor program. New York, League for Industrial Democracy [1948]
61, [2] p. illus., ports. 24 cm. (League for Industrial Democracy Pamphlet series)
"Suggested reading list": p. [62]–[63]

1. Labor and laboring classes—Sweden.   I. Title.   II. Series.

HD8576.L5   331.8   48-1759*

TxU NN PU-PSW
NL 0377781   DLC CaBViP Or OrU CU Mi NcU OO OU ICU

FILM
658   Lindbom, Theodore R
L641s   Supervisory training and employee attitudes. Ann Arbor, Mich., University Microfilms, 1952. ([University Microfilms, Ann Arbor, Mich., Publication no.3637)

Microfilm copy of typescript. Positive.
Collation of the original: vii, 123l. forms, tables.
Thesis—University of Minnesota.
Bibliography: leaves 91–93.

NL 0377782   IU

Lindborg, Arthur E.
Education in the Virgin islands, by Arthur E. Lindborg ... U. S. Department of the interior. Ray Lyman Wilbur, secretary. Office of education. William John Cooper, commissioner. [Washington, U. S. Govt. print. off., 1932]
1 p. l., 4 p. 23⍟. (U. S. Office of education. Leaflet no. 42)

1. Education—Virgin islands of the United States.   I. Title.

U. S. Off. of educ. Library   L111.A53 no. 42   E 32—435
———— Copy 2.   LA505.V8L3
for Library of Congress   L111.A73 no. 42
———— Copy 2.   LA505.V5L5
                [a41e1]   (370.61)   379.7297

NL 0377783   DHEW DLC OrSaW DNW MiU OU

Lindborg, Carl Laurentius.
Om kung fjalar.
Inaug. diss. Upsala, 1869.

NL 0377784   ICRL

517
564e   **Lindborg, Gustaf.**
Elementerna av derivatkalkylen jämte problemsamling.   Uppsala [1911]
68p. diagrs.

NL 0377785   IU

Lindborg, Karin Rigmor Gerda Elisabeth
see Lindborg, Rigmor, 1912–

Lindborg, Olga E.
Bibelberättelser för bruk i söndagsskolans småbarnsavdelning, av Olga E. Lindborg, redigerad av fil. kand. G. Vallinder och Nath. Franklin. Chicago, The Covenant book concern [1922]
128 p. illus. (part col.) 20⍟.
Contains music.

1. Vallinder, Gustav, ed.   II. Franklin, Nath., joint ed.   II. Title.

Library of Congress   BS556.L5   22-16151

NL 0377787   DLC MnHi

Lindborg, Olga E.
Bibelberättelser för bruk i söndagsskolans småbarnsavdelning, av Olga E. Lindborg; redigerad av Nath. Franklin och Gustav Vallinder. Chicago, The Covenant book concern [1923]
128 p. illus. (part col.) 20⍟.
Contains music.
Published also in English.

1. Franklin, Nath., ed.   II. Vallinder, Gustav, joint ed.   III. Title.

Library of Congress   BS556.L5 1923   24-1659

NL 0377788   DLC MnHi

Lindborg, Olga E.
Bible biographies (bibelbiografier) for use in the intermediate department of Sunday schools, prepared in English and Swedish by Olga E. Lindborg, for the Covenant Sunday school committee, Nath. Franklin, editor. Chicago, The Covenant book concern [1922]
3 p. l., [9]–301, [1] p. illus. 20⍟.

1. Franklin, Nath., ed.   II. Title.

Library of Congress   BS605.L5   22-16152

NL 0377789   DLC ICRL

Lindborg, Olga E.
Bible biographies (Bibelbiografier) for use in the intermediate department of Sunday schools, prepared in English and Swedish by Olga E. Lindborg, for the Covenant Sunday school committee; Nath. Franklin, editor. Chicago, The Covenant book concern [1923]
2 p. l., [9]–313 p. illus. 19½⍟.
Half-title: The Covenant graded lessons, intermediate department.

I. Franklin, Nath., ed.   II. Swedish evangelical mission covenant of America.   III. Title.   IV. Title: Covenant graded lessons.

Library of Congress   BS610.S8L5   24-1660

NL 0377790   DLC

Lindborg, Olga E.
Bible biographies (Bibelbiografier) for use in the intermediate department of Sunday schools, prepared in English and Swedish by Olga E. Lindborg, for the Covenant Sunday school committee; Nath. Franklin, editor. Chicago, The Covenant book concern [1924]
3 p. l., [9]–319 p. illus. 19½⍟.
Half-title: The Covenant graded lessons, intermediate department.

I. Franklin, Nath., ed.   II. Swedish evangelical mission covenant of America.   III. Title.   IV. Title: Covenant graded lessons.

Library of Congress   BS610.S8L5 1924   24-31821

NL 0377791   DLC

Lindborg, Olga E.
Bible stories for use in the primary department of the Sunday school, prepared by Olga E. Lindborg for the Covenant Sunday school committee, Nath. Franklin, editor. Chicago, The Covenant book concern [1922]
128 p. illus. (part col.) 20⍟.
Contains music.

1. Franklin, Nath., ed.   II. Title.

Library of Congress   BS551.L45   22-16238

NL 0377792   DLC MnHi

VOLUME 334

Lindborg, Olga E.
Bible stories for use in the primary department of the
Sunday school, prepared by Olga E. Lindborg for the
Covenant Sunday school committee; Nath. Franklin, ed-
itor. Chicago, The Covenant book concern [1923]

128 p. illus. (part col.) 19¼ᶜᵐ.

Contains music.
Published also in Swedish.

I. Franklin, Nath., ed. II. Title.

Library of Congress   BS551.L45 1923   24-1658

NL 0377793   DLC MnHi

Lindborg, Olga E.
... Departmental teachers' manual for the elementary
school. Beginners' department, Primary department, by
Olga E. Lindborg. Intermediate department, history de-
partment, Supplemental outline of Young people's Bible
school and Post graduate school, by G. F. Hedstrand.
Prepared for the Covenant Sunday school committee.
Chicago, The Covenant book concern [1923]

239 p. 20ᶜᵐ.

At head of title: The Covenant graded lessons.
I. Hedstrand, G. F. II. Swedish evangelical mission covenant of America.
III. Title. IV. Title: Covenant graded lessons.

Library of Congress   BV1538.L5   24-1279

NL 0377794   DLC MnHi

Lindborg, Olga E., joint author.
Person, Peter P.
Manual for daily vacation Bible schools, by Peter P.
Person and Olga E. Lindborg. Chicago, Covenant book concern
[*1927]

Lindborg, Olga E., tr.
Boberg, Carl Gustaf, 1859–
The ways of youth, by Carl Boberg; translated from
the Swedish by Olga E. Lindborg. Chicago, Ill, The
Covenant book concern [*1924]

Lindborg, Rigmor, 1912–
Strå och sten; roman. Stockholm, LT:s förlag [1950]
377 p. 20 cm.

I. Title.

Full name: Karin Rigmor Gerda Elisabeth Lindborg.

     A 51-6727

Minnesota. Univ. Lib
for Library of Congress   [2]

NL 0377797   MnU

Linde.
Fischkost — Gemischte Kost. Ein Fischkochbuch für die
feine und die einfache Küche, von Küchenmeister Linde...
Bremen: C. Schünemann [1914]. 78 p., front. (port.), 1 fold. pl.
16°.

1. Cookery.—Fish. 2. Cookery (Ger-   man). 3. Title.
N. Y. P. L.   August 30, 1915.

NL 0377798   NN

341.3
L64v
Linde,
Das völkerrecht im kriege. Vortrag, gehalten am 25. november 1887 vor dem offi-
ziercorps der 1. combinirten infanterie-
brigade. Berlin, 1888.
92p. (Beiheft zum Militär-wochenblatt
hrsg. von v.Löbell. 1888. 2.heft)

Caption title.

NL 0377799   IU MH

4DK
Pol
429
Linde,   van der
Leven en daaden van Johannes
Sobietzki de III, tegenwoordig
-regeerende Koning van Polen; mitsgaders de levens en daaden aller
voorgaande Poolsche en Hungarische
koningen. Amsterdam, J. en T. ten
Hoorn, J. Bouman en A. Dirkse
Oossaan, 1685.
368, 401 p.

NL 0377800   DLC-P4

C.2116 **Linde, A A**
The injurious tendency of the modifying of our navigation laws, made manifest; and the consequent necessity for
revising the concessions made in favor of the navigation
of other nations, clearly proved; with many other points
of considerable interest to the commerce, navigation, and
manufactures of the country, treated of; in communications
addressed to His Majesty's ministers, and principally to the
Right Hon. William Huskisson . . . London, S.Low, 1828.
xx, [38], [21]-216 p. 21.5 cm.

NL 0377801   MH-BA

LINDE, A. DE. Improvement of the Taku bar.
Tientsin [1902] 1 p. l., 23 p. Plans, pl. f°.

NL 0377802   MSaE

Linde, A. de.
———— Report of the Hai-ho River improvement,
and the rivers of Chihli. Tientsin, 1900. 1 p.
l., xiii, 26 p. Illus. 8°.
"Reprinted from the report of 1890."

NL 0377803   MSaE

Linde, Adolph Heinrich, respondent.
...De computatione graduum cognationis ...
see under   Cocceji, Heinrich von, 1644-
1719, praeses.

Linde, Andreas Conrad Putscher, ed.
Denmark. *Ministeriet for kirke- og undervisningsvæsenet.*
Meddelelser angaaende de lærde skoler med dertil hørende
realundervisning i kongeriget Danmark ... Udgivne efter
foranstaltning af Ministeriet for kirke- og undervisningsvæsenet ... Kjøbenhavn, 1879–

Linde, Andreas Conrad Putscher, ed.
Meddelelser angaaende Universitetet og den
Polytekniske laereanstalt for aarene 1857–1863
see under title

LINDE, Andrew, bookseller.
Bibliotheca curiosa; being a catalogue of the
libraries of Messrs. Jager and Brande, and of a
reverend and learned clergyman, consisting of a
great number of scarce and valuable books, [etc..
Which will begin this day to be sold. [London,
1753.]

20 cm. pp.(4),76.

NL 0377807   MH

LINDE, Andrew, bookseller.
A catalogue of curious and usefull books in
all languages and sciences, the most of them
lately imported, [etc.]. Which will be sold very
cheap...on Thursday, December 5, 1754. [London,
1754.]

21 cm. pp.(6),79,(1).

NL 0377808   MH

Linde, Anna, tr.
Couperin, François, 1668–1733.
L'art de toucher le clavecin, par François Couperin. Die
kunst das clavecin zu spielen. The art of playing the harpsichord. Herausgegeben und ins deutsche übersetzt von Anna
Linde; englische übersetzung von Mevanwy Roberts ... Leipzig, Breitkopf & Härtel [*1933]

Linde, Antonius van der, 1833–1897.
Aanteekeningen op het "Ontwerp der spelling voor
het aanstaande Nederlandsch woordenboek". Door dr.
B. Huydecoper [pseud.] ... Nijmegen, C. Klercq, 1863.
47 p. 23ᶜᵐ.

No. 12 in volume of pamphlets with binder's title: Stukken over de spelling, enz.

1. Dutch language—Orthography and spelling.

NL 0377810   MiU

Linde, Antonius van der, 1833–1897.
Antoinette Bourignon; das Licht der
Welt... Leiden, E.J. Brill, 1895.
310 p. facsims. 25ᵐ.

"Anmerkungen und Litteratur": p. [261]–
286.

1 Bourignon, Antoinette, 1616–1680

NL 0377811   NjPT MH-AH

Linde, Antonius van der, 1833–1897.
Balthasar Bekker. Bibliografie door Dr. A. van der
Linde ... 's Gravenhage, M. Nijhoff, 1869.
2 p. l., 57 p. 24½ᵐᵐ.

1. Bekker, Balthasar, 1634–1698—Bibl.

     8-7359

Library of Congress   Z8086.8.L5

TxU MH
NL 0377812   DLC NIC CSt CtY-D MH-AH DNLM NIC NjPT CLU

LINDE, Antonius van der, 1833–1897.
Beginselen van het schaakspel. Utrecht, G.A.
van Hoften, 1876.

20 cm. Port.and other illustr.
"Drukfouten", pp.[132].

NL 0377813   MH OC1 PP NjP

VOLUME 334

Linde, Antonius van der, 1833-1897.

Spinoza, Benedictus de, 1632-1677.
Benedict de Spinoza's Kurzer tractat von Gott, dem menschen und dessen glückseligkeit. Auf grund einer neuen, von dr. Antonius van der Linde vorgenommenen vergleichung der handschriften ins deutsche übersetzt mit einer einleitung, kritischen und sachlichen erläuterungen begleitet von dr. Christoph Sigwart ... Tübingen, H. Laupp, 1870.

Linde, Antonius van der, 1833-1897.
Benedictus Spinoza; bibliografie door Dr. A. van der Linde. 's Gravenhage, M. Nijhoff, 1871.
viii, ii, 113 p. 23ᶜᵐ.

1. Spinoza, Benedictus de, 1632-1677—Bibl.

2-8425

Library of Congress   Z8831.L74

ICJ NcDD
NL 0377815   DLC NjP FU ViAlTh TNJ ViU NNC NcD CtY

¡Linde, Antonius van der¡ 1833-1897.
Bibliografie van Haarlem. Haarlem, F. J. MacDonald, 1867.
2 p. l., 177 p., 1 l. 28ᶜᵐ.
A catalog of Van der Linde's collection.

1. Haarlem—Bibl.   I. Title.

6-8047

Library of Congress   Z2454.H2L5

NL 0377816   DLC ICJ

Linde, Antonius van der, 1833-1897.
Catalogue de la bibliothèque de M. A. Van der Linde...Bruxelles, Chez G.-A. Van Trigt, 1864.
3 p.l., [iii]-xvi, 360 p. 25 cm.
"La vente aura lieu du 7 au 16 avril 1864,..

1. Bibliography—Rare books. 2. Religious literature—Bibl.

NL 0377817   CSmH OCl PPAmP

Linde, A¡ntonius¡ van der, 1833-1897.
David Joris. Bibliografie door Dr. A. van der Linde ... 's Gravenhage, M. Nijhoff, 1867.
xiv p., 1 l., 68 p., 1 l. 24½ᵐᵐ.

1. Joris, David, 1501 or 2-1556—Bibl. 2. Davidists—Bibl.

Library of Congress   Z8457.2.L5

6-14071†

NL 0377818   DLC MH-AH CtY-D NcD NIC MH CtY CBPac

Linde, Antonius van der, 1833-1897.
Das erste Jartausend der Schachlitteratur (850-1880). Berlin, J. Springer, 1881.
112 p.   21 cm.
1. Chess - Bibl.   I. Title.

NL 0377819   MdBP ICN MH NjP OCl PP PPL

Linde, Antonius von der, 1863-
Erste Selbstbiographie [Die älteste...
        see under   Hauser, Kaspar, 1812-1833.

Linde, Antonius van der, 1833-1897.
Geschichte der erfindung der buchdruckkunst; von Antonius von der Linde ... Berlin, A. Asher & co., 1886.
3 v. illus., pl., port., facsim. 33½ x 25ᶜᵐ.
Paged continuously.
Title in red and black.

CONTENTS.—1. bd. Litteratur. Unhistorische ansprüche in Mainz, Strassburg und Feitre. Der holländische Koster mythus.—2. bd. Der Koster mythus ¡forts.—3. bd. Die erfindung der typographie zu Mainz. Beilagen. Register: Register der illustrationen. Litteraturregister. Mythologisches register. Alphabetisches register.

1. Printing—Hist.—Origin and antecedents. 2. Gutenberg, Johann, 1397?-1468. 3. Coster, Lourens Janszoon, ca. 1370-1439?

2-6043

Library of Congress   Z126.L74
                                ¡37b1-¡

        OCl OCU MiU CtY NcD PU PP MU
NL 0377821   DLC MH MB OO ICJ FU ICU MdBP NNC OKentU

Linde, Antonius van der, 1833-1897.
Geschichte und litteratur des schachspiels, von Antonius van der Linde ... Berlin, J. Springer, 1874.
2 v. front. (v. 2) illus., ports. 25¼ᶜᵐ.
Title in red and black.

1. Chess—Hist. 2. Chess—Bibl.

Library of Congress   GV1317.L74

6-3974

NL 0377822   DLC MdBP PP OCH MiU OCl

Linde, A¡ntonius¡ van der, 1833-1897.
Gutenberg. Geschichte und erdichtung. Aus den quellen nachgewiesen von Dr. A. v. d. Linde. Stuttgart, W. Spemann, 1878.
viii, 582 p., 1 l., xcvii, ¡1¡ p. 25½ᵐ.

1. Gutenberg, Johann, 1397?-1468. 2. Printing—Hist.—Origin and antecedents.

Library of Congress   Z126.L72

6-11208

NL 0377823   DLC ICJ CtY OCH MiU MH NN NNGr OO PP PU UU

Linde, Antonius van der, 1833-1897.
The Haarlem legend of the invention of printing by Lourens Janszoon Coster, critically examined by Dr. A. van der Linde. From the Dutch by J. H. Hessels, with an introduction, and a classified list of the Costerian incunabula. London, Blades, East & Blades, 1871.
xxvi p., 1 l., 170 p. fold. tab. 24½ᶜᵐ.

1. Printing — Hist. — Origin and antecedents. 2. Gutenberg, Johann, 1397 (ca.)-1468. 3. Coster, Lourens Janszoon, 1370 (ca.)-1439. I. Hessels, Jan Hendrik, 1836-1907, tr. II. Coster, Lourens Janszoon, 1370 (ca.)-1439. III. Title.

2-6050

Library of Congress   Z126.L745

NL 0377824   DLC OO MU NcD PP CtY PHC MiU OCU ICJ NN

Linde, A¡ntonius¡ van der, 1833-1897.
De Haarlemsche Costerlegende wetenschappelijk onderzocht door Dr. A. van der Linde. 2., omgewerkte uitgaaf. 's Gravenhage, M. Nijhoff, 1870.
5 p. l., 352 p. 23½ᵐ.

1. Printing—Hist.—Origin and antecedents. 2. Coster, Lourens Janszoon, ca. 1370-1439?

Library of Congress   Z126.L744

6-8046

NL 0377825   DLC CtY MH

Linde, Antonius van der, 1833-1897.

Wiesbaden. Nassauische landesbibliothek.
Die handschriften der Königlichen landesbibliothek in Wiesbaden, verzeichnet von dr. A. v. d. Linde ... Wiesbaden, Hofbuchhandlung von E. Rodrian, 1877.

4CT   Linde, Antonius van der, 1833-1897.
346   Kaspar Hauser. ¡
                                18 -
             v. 1

NL 0377827   DLC-P4

CT1098   Linde, Antonius van der, 1833-1897.
.H3L7   Kaspar Hauser, eine neugeschichtliche Legende.
            Wiesbaden, Chr. Limbarth, 1887.
            2 v. in 1. ports., facsims., geneal. table.
            "Chronologische Übersicht und Kaspar-Hauser-Litteratur, 1828-1886. ": p. 325-398.

1. Hauser, Kaspar, 1812-1833.

NL 0377828   ICU NcD DLC-P4 MdBP MH NjP MiU IEN FTaSU

Linde, Antonius van der, 1833-97
Kaspar Hauser und die Kritik [Die gewonnene Schlacht] Wiesbaden, Buchdruckerei von C.Ritter, 1888

120 p. (His Zum Kaspar-Hauser-Schwindel, 2)

NL 0377829   MH

LINDE,Antonius van der,1833-1897.
De kerkvaders der schaakgemeente. Uit het Latijn,Spaansch,Italiaansch,Fransch,Engelsch en Duitsch vertaald,en systematiesch bewerkt. Utrecht,M.S.van Tussenbroek.1875.

22 cm.

NL 0377830   MH NjP OCl

LINDE, ANTONIUS VAN DER, 1833-1897.
Leerboek van het schaakspel, door Dr. A. v. d. Linde ... Utrecht: G.A. van Hoften, 1876. xviii, 301 p. incl. tables. illus. 23½cm.

Bibliographies included.

635256A. 1. Chess, 1876.

NL 0377831   NN PPL MH OCl NjP

Linde, Antonius van der, 1833-1897.
La legende Costérienne de Harlem; nouvel examen critique, précédé d'une introduction historique par M. Ch. Ruelens. Bruxelles, Fr. J. Olivier, 1871.
        fold. table. 24cm.

The second and last fasc. was to be accompanied by the introduction by Ch. Ruelens.

NL 0377832   NNC ICJ

VOLUME 334

Linde, Antonius van der, 1833-1897
Letters relating to chess from Antonius van der Linde, 22 Sept., 1880 - 21 Nov., 1882, and graf Tassilo von Heydebrand und der Lasa, 20 July, 1879 - 3 Feb., 1899.   2v.   [Cleveland, n. d.]

Manuscript letters to John G. White mounted and arranged, with printed title-page.

NL 0377833   OC1

Linde, Antonius van der, 1833-1897.
Michael Servet, een brandoffer der gereformeerde inquisitie, door prof. dr. A. v. d. Linde. Groningen, P. Noordhoff, 1891.

viii, 326 p. 24ᵐ.

"Litteratuur": p. [301]-326.

1. Servetus, Michael, 1509 or 11-1553.

NL 0377834   MiU NN NIC PBa NjPT CtY‑D

Linde, Antonius van der, 1833-1897.
Die Nassauer brunnenlitteratur der Königlichen landesbibliothek zu Wiesbaden
    see under Wiesbaden. Nassauische landesbibliothek.

Linde, Antonius van der, 1833-1897.

Wiesbaden. Nassauische landesbibliothek.
Die Nassauer drucke der Königlichen landesbibliothek in Wiesbaden, beschrieben von Antonius von der Linde. I. 1467-1817. Wiesbaden, Feller & Gecks, 1882.

Linde, Antonius van der, 1833-1897.
De nederlandsche geloofsbelijdenis
    see under Belgic confession.

Linde, Antonius van der, 1833-1897.
Het oudste gezangboek ... Gravenhage, 1869.

NL 0377838   NjNbS

Linde, Antonius van der, 1833-1897.   093 O100
Quellenforschungen zur Geschichte der Erfindung der Typographie. Das Brevarium Moguntinum. Eine Studie von Antonius von der Linde. Wiesbaden, Feller & Gecks, 1884.

[6], 82, [2] p. 23½ᵐ.

NL 0377839   ICJ

Linde, A[ntonius] van der, 1833-1897.

Quellenstudien zur geschichte des schachspiels, von D⁷ A. v. d. Linde. Mit unterstützung der Königl. Akademie der wissenschaften zu Berlin. Berlin, J. Springer, 1881.

vii, [1], 412 p. illus. 19ᵐ.

1. Chess—Hist. 2. Chess—Bibl.

Library of Congress   GV1315.L74   5-2978

NL 0377840   DLC NjP MdBP CtY PP OC1 OCH MiU

Linde, Antonius van de, 1833-1897
Der roch, zur wissenschaftlichen enscheidung einer heraldischen streitfrage. [Berlin, 1874]
31,[5]p.

NL 0377841   OC1 DLC-P4 NjP

Linde, Antonius van der, 1833-1897
Schaakbibliotheek (c.[1850-1875])   [4],89p.
Utrecht, G. A. van Hoften, 1875.

Added title-pages, with German, English, French, and Italian titles.
Interleaved.

NL 0377842   OC1 MH NNC OC1 PPL NjP

Linde, Antonius van der, 1833-1897.
Schaakbibliotheek vroeger toebehoord hebbende aan A. van der Linde.
22 cm.   (In Hague. Koninklijke Bibliotheek. Verslag. 1876. p. 115-194)

NL 0377843   MH

[Linde, Antonius van der] 1833-1897.
De schaakpartijen van Gioachino Greco. Nijmegen, 1865.

NL 0377844   NjP

Linde, Antonius van der, 1833-1897.
Het schaakspel in Nederland, door Dr. A. v. d. Linde. Utrecht: G. A. van Hoften, 1875. 186 p. incl. tables. illus. 23cm.

666387A. 1. Chess—Netherlands.
N.Y.P.L.

FRANK J. MARSHALL CHESS COLL.
October 5, 1933

NL 0377845   NN MH OC1 NjP

Linde, Antonius van der, 1833-1897
Schachlitteratur; bibliographische skizze. 19p. [Im Haag] 1870.

Cover-title.

NL 0377846   OC1 NjP PP

Linde, Antonius van der, 1833-1897.
Das schachspiel des XVI. jahrhunderts. Nach uneditirten quellen bearbeitet von Dr. Antonius van der Linde. Berlin, J. Springer, 1874.

viii p., 1 1., 209 p. illus. 24ᵐ.

CONTENTS.—1. abth. Historisch-bibliographische einleitung.—2. abth. Polerio's Schachwerk nach italienischen handschriften.

1. Chess—Hist. 2. Chess—Bibl.   1. Polerio, Giulio Cesare.

Library of Congress   GV1320.L74   6-3971

NL 0377847   DLC PPL PP OC1 NjP

193
Sch26YL Linde, Antonius van der, 1833-1897.
Schelling's wijsbegeerte der openbaring. Amsterdam, P.M. van der Made, 1862.
1i, 354p. 25cm.

Bibliographical footnotes.

1. Schelling, Friedrich Wilhelm Joseph von, 1775-1854. I. Title.

NL 0377848   TxU

Linde, Antonius van der. Skak paa Island. En kritisk Undersøgelse. I.-III. *Extr. fr.* Nordisk Skaktidende. II. Aargang. Kjøbenhavn, 1874. 8°. pp. 2-14, 37-46, 65-68.
IcLSLA73

NL 0377849   NIC

Linde, Antonius van der, 1833-1897.   199·83 L64
Spinoza. Seine Lehre und deren erste Nachwirkungen in Holland. Eine philosophisch-historische Monographie. ... Von Antonius van der Linde. Göttingen, Van den Hoeck und Ruprecht, 1862.

xxxi, [1], 214, [2] p. 1 fold. table. 24ᵐ.

Inaug.-Diss. —Göttingen.
"Literatur des Spinozismus," p. [171]-214.

NL 0377850   ICJ IEN

Linde, Antonius van der, 1833-1897.
Spinoza. Seine lehre und deren erste nachwirkungen in Holland. Eine philosophisch-historische monographie, von dr. Antonius van der Linde ... Göttingen, Van den Hoeck und Ruprecht, 1862.

xxxi, [1], 214 p., 1 l. 22½ᵐ.

"Literatur des Spinozismus": p. [171]-214.

1. Spinoza, Benedictus de, 1632-1677.

32-32454

Library of Congress   B3998.L5   193.9

NL 0377851   DLC CaBVaU ICJ ViU MH ICU NIC PU OCH

LL62.5 Linde, Antonius van der, 1833-1897.
L641s   De strijdende Gereformeerde Kerk. Een strijdschrift, vooral tegen de Christelijke Afgescheidene Kerk gericht, door A. van der Linde. Amsterdam, W. Clement, 1859.
x, 203 p. 22 cm.

Includes bibliographical references.

1. Christelijke Gereformeerde Kerk. 2. Netherlands - Church history. I. Title.

NL 0377852   CtY-D

Linde, Antonius, van der, 1833-1897.
Studiën van Dr A. van der Linde. Theologie. Bibliographie. Schaakspel. Utrecht, G. A. van Hoften, 1868.

viii, 242, [2] p. incl. 1 illus., tables. 25ᵐ.

Contents.—1. Das Leben Jesu. Historisch-apologetische Beleuchtung der Zeitfrage. (1865.)—2. Livres hollandais imprimés sur vélin (Nov. 1864.)—3. Le siége de Neuss. (Dec. 1864.)—4. Conrad de Altzheim ou Altzey est-il l'auteur du Speculum humanae salvationis? (Dec. 1864.)—5. La première édition du Wonderboeck of David Joris de Gand. 1542. (1866.)—6. Les œuvres de David Joris. (1866.)—7. Sur les collections des voyages des frères de Bry et L. Hulsius. (1866.)—8. De Collectio Weigeliana. Xylografie en typografie. (Jan. 1866.)—9. De Mormonen. Een voorlezing.

(Dec. 1863.)—10. Nekrologie van Z. H. E. G. den Heer Jan Hulst.—11. De duitsche schaaklitteratur van de jaren 1864 en 1865. (1865.)—12. Schaaklitteratur. (1866.)—13. De speloopning van Hampe of de Weener Partij. (1866.) Schaakstudie. Opgedragen aan den weled. zeer geleerden Heer Dr. A. van der Linde, door L. J. Bodding te Nijmegen. 1866.—14. Schaakpartijen. (1865 en 1866.)—15. Het klassieke Raadsheergambiet. §1. Geschiedenis en kritiek. (Nov. 1865.)—16. De oudste zeetochten der Nederlanders. (Jan. 1868.)

NL 0377854   ICJ MH PP PU

[Linde, Antonius van der] 1833-1897.
[Urkundenbuch des Schachspiels].   Utrecht, 1876]
56 p.
Only 2 copies known at the time of his Das erste Jartausend der Schachlitteratur.
Title-page lacking. It is either this title or an entirely unknown v. d. Linde item.—cf. note on fly-leaf by A. Buschke.

NL 0377855   OC1

VOLUME 334

Linde, Antonius van der, 1833-97
Zum Kaspar-Hauser-Schwindel. Wiesbaden, Buchdruckerei von C.Ritter, 1888

2 pt.
Contents: - 1. Kaspar Hauser's erste Selbst-
bibliographie (Die älteste, noch ungedruckte,
Selbstbiographie) - 2. Kaspar Hauser und die Kritik
(Die gewonnene Schlacht)

NL 0377856　MH

QD341　Linde, Arthur von der, 1867-
.P6L6　　Einwirkung von chlor auf orcin.
Marburg, 1893.
48p.
Inaug. diss. Marburg.

NL 0377857　DLC

Linde, August.
...Imanta un Kaupo; wehsturisks nostahsts 8 dseedajumos
wahziski no A. Lindes. Latwiski brihwi atdsejojis Frizis Simsons.
Tukumā: M. Silneeks, 1933.　79 p.　17½cm.

857528A. 1. Poetry, German.　　I. Simsons, Frizis, tr.　II. Title.
N. Y. P. L.　　　　　　　　　　December 15, 1936

NL 0377858　NN

Linde, August.
Imanta und Kaupo. Eine lettische Sage in acht Gesängen,
von A. Linde...　Moskau: E. Liessner & I. Romann, 1891.
84 p.　8°.

1. Poetry, German. 2. Title.
N. Y. P. L.　　　　　　　　　　September 1, 1925

NL 0377859　NN

Linde, Augusta Ärnbäck-Christie
see Ärnbäck-Christie-Linde, Augusta.

Linde, Bernhard, 1886-
Dr. Eduard Beneš; Tšehhoslovakkia Vabariigi teise
presidendi elu võitluses oma rahva iseseisvuse eest. Tallinnas, Kirjastus Varak [1936]
88 p.　illus., ports.　20 cm.　(Sari: Tähtsad mehed ja naised, 3)

1. Beneš, Edvard, Pres. Czechoslovak Republic, 1884-1948.
DB217.B3L48　　　　　　　　　58-52534

NL 0377861　DLC

4PH　Linde, Bernhard, 1886-
Est.　　Heitlikud ilmad; wäikesed skandalid
249　murrangu-aia Eestist.　[　　　　]
'Noor-Eesti', 1913.
82 p.

NL 0377862　DLC-P4

DK511　Linde, Bernhard, 1886-
L163　Loova Kesk-Euroopa poole; kirjanduslikke
L55　ja teatrilisi reisumuljeid Lätist, Poolast,
Tšehhoslovakkiast ja Ungarist. Tartus, Noor-
Eesti Kirjastus [1930]
320 p.　ports.　24 cm.

1. Latvia - Intellectual life. 2. Poland -
Intellectual life. 3. Czechoslovak Republic -
Intellectual life. 4. Hungary - Intellectual
life. I. Title (1)

NL 0377863　CtY

Linde, Bernhard, 1886- ed.
Ungari, koguteos.　114p. front. plate.
Tallinnas, Kirjastus "Varak", 1936.

NL 0377864　OC1

Linde, Bert. de.　Vitranir á vígvellinum.
[Reykjavík], (1916).　4°. pp. (4), *illustr.*

"Sérprentað úr Heimilisblaðinu." Transl. by
Á[rni] Jóh[annsson].　No t.-p.

NL 0377865　NIC

M1621　Linde, Bo.
L56　[
Klockbojen.　[Tekst av Mikael Lybeck.
[Stockholm] Föreningen Svenska Tonsättare
[n.d.]
4 p.　36cm.
Cover title.
Holograph.

1. Songs (Medium voice) with piano.

NL 0377866　CoU

Linde, Bruno Cohn-

see

Cohn-Linde, Bruno.

Linde, C. Hnr., respondent.
Historiola litteraturae Graecae in Svecia...
see under　Fant, Erik Mikael, 1754-1817,
praeses.

Linde, Carl August.
Faust. Eine tragödie. III.theil zu Goethe's
Faust. Von Carl Aug.Linde. Darmstadt, Selbst-
verlag des verfassers, 1887.
vi,114 p.　15½cm.
In verse.

1.Goethe,Johann Wolfgang von. Faust. I.Title.

NL 0377869　MiU CtY NIC

4T-59　Linde, Carl Paul Gottfried Ritter von, 1842-1934.
Aus meinem Leben und von meiner Arbeit;
Aufzeichnungen für meine Kinder und meine
Mitarbeiter.　München, Druck von R. Olden-
bourg [Schlusswort 1916]
148 p.

NL 0377870　DLC-P4

Linde, Carl Paul Gottfried, Ritter von, 1842-1934.
... Carl von Linde zum 90. Geburtstag.
Berlin, 1932.
1 p.l., p.[55]-84.　front. (port.)　21 cm.
(Deutsches Museum Abhandlungen und Berichte...
4. Jahrg., Hft. 3)
Contents: "Aus meinem Leben und von meiner
Arbeit" von Carl Linde. - Veröffentlichungen von
Carl von Linde. - Die Schätze der Atmosphäre. -
Kühlung. - Gegenstände von Carl von Linde und
von der Gesellschaft für Linde's Eismaschinen im
Deutschen Museum.

NL 0377871　CtY

536.5　Linde, Carl Paul Gottfried,Ritter von, 1842-1934.
qL641　Physik und technik auf dem wege zum
absoluten nullpunkte der temperatur.
Festrede gehalten in der öffentlichen
sitzung der K. Akademie der wissenschaften am 16. november 1912 von dr. Carl
v. Linde...　München, Verlag der K.B.
Akademie der wissenschaften in kommission des G. Franz'schen verlags, 1912.

17 p.　27cm.
1. Low temperature research. I. Title.

NL 0377872　MnU PBm OC1

Linde, Carl Paul Gottfried,Ritter von, 1842-1934.
Refrigerating machine of today.
21p.　8°

(Am. Soc. of Mech. Engineers, 1893.
Paper DXLII)

NL 0377873　MWA

Linde, Carl Paul Gottfried,Ritter von, 1842-1934.
Retrospect and prospective consideration on the development of the art of refrigeration.　(In: International Congress of
Refrigeration, II.　Vienna, 1910.　Reports and proceedings. English edition.　Vienna, 1911.　4°.　p. 11-16.)

1. Refrigeration and cold storage.
N. Y. P. L.　　　　　　　　　October 14, 1912.

NL 0377874　NN

Linde, Carl Paul Gottfried,Ritter von, 1842-1934.
Die Schätze der Atmosphäre; Fest-Vortrag aus Anlass der 4.
Jahresversammlung gehalten...in Berlin am 17. Dezember 1907
von...C. von Linde.　[München: F. Bruckmann A.-G.,] 1907.
8 p.　8°.　(Deutsches Museum von Meisterwerken der Naturwissenschaft und Technik.　Vorträge und Berichte.　Heft 1.)

Title from cover.

1. Air. 2. Title.
N. Y. P. L.　　　　　　　　　October 22, 1915.

NL 0377875　NN MB MH

QD399　Linde, Carl von der, 1871-
.L74　　Untersuchungen ueber gechlorte diketo-t-
pentene.
Marburg, 1895.
48p
Inaug. diss. Marburg.

NL 0377876　DLC MH

Linde, Karl von
see Linde, Carl Paul Gottfried Ritter von,
1842-1934.

VOLUME 334

Linde, Karl von der, 1871–
see Linde, Carl von der, 1871–

Linde, David, pseud.

see

Blomberg, David, 1874–

Linde, Dmitriĭ Pavlovich.
Антенно-фидерные устройства. Москва, Гос. энерг.
изд-во, 1953.
100 p. illus. 20 cm. (Массовая радиобиблиотека, вып. 194)

1. Radio—Antennas. I. Title.
Title transliterated: Antenno-fidernye ustroĭstva.

TK6565.A6L48   57–22580 rev ‡

NL 0377880   DLC

Linde, Ebbe, 1897–
Bräsch; dikter. Stockholm, A. Bonnier,
[1924]
90 p.

NL 0377881   MH

Linde, Ebbe, 1897–
... Brott och straff, av Ebbe Linde
... Stockholm, Brand [1930]
94 p., 1 l. 18½cm.
At head of title: Bort med strafflagen

NL 0377882   MH-L NN

Linde, Ebbe, 1897–
Gilgamesj; skådespel för musik. Stockholm, Bonnier
[1946]
91 p. 20 cm.

I. Gilgamesh. II. Title.

PT9875.L593G5   *839.727 839.726   53–26745

NL 0377883   DLC CU

Linde, Ebbe, 1897–
Göteborg; med reproduktioner efter etsningar av Folke
Persson. [2. uppl. Stockholm] Wahlström & Widstrand
[1948]
158 p. illus. 21 cm.

1. Gothenburg, Sweden.
DL991.G6L55 1948   948.6   49–22169*

NL 0377884   DLC MnU NN

Linde, Ebbe, 1897–
Gyllenåsnan. Illustrerad av Helga Henschen. [Stock-
holm] Bonnier, 1949.
125 p. 18 cm.
"Denna transposition av motiv ur Apuleius' bekanta roman 'Metamorphoses' utarbetades från början som hörspel för radio."

I. Title.

A 50–860

Minnesota. Univ. Libr.
for Library of Congress   [3]

NL 0377885   MnU

Linde, Ebbe, 1897–
...Isljuset: Skådespel i tre akter.   Stockholm: A. Bonnier
[1939] 175 p. 20cm.

52048B. 1. Drama, Swedish.   I. Title.
N. Y. P. L.   June 10, 1940

NL 0377886   NN MnU MH

Linde, Ebbe, 1897–
...Senapskornet; skådespel i fem akter. [Stockholm] Clarté
[1934] 226 p. illus. (plans.) 20cm.

761389A. 1. Drama, Swedish.   I. Title.
N. Y. P. L.   July 24, 1935

NL 0377887   NN

Linde, Ebbe, 1897–
... Vad gäller striden ? Några ord om Ryssland och Finland
och vad det ryska överfallet innebär, av Ebbe Linde. Göteborg, Förlagsföreningen bokklubben [1940]
31, [1] p. illus. 21cm. (*On cover:* Demokratiens problem. 1)
At head of title: 2. upplagan.

1. Finland—Soc. condit. I. Title.
                                       41–20804
Library of Congress   HN533.L5
                              [2]   300.1471

NL 0377888   DLC MnU

Linde (Eduard) [1865–   ]. *Ueber Carpain
96 pp., 1 l. 8°. Jurjew, Schnakenburg, 1895.

NL 0377889   DNLM

Linde, Ernst, 1864–
Die Bildungsaufgabe der deutschen Dichtung.
Leipzig, Brandstetter, 1927.
viii,163p. 23cm.

1. German literature. Addresses, essays,
lectures. 2. Literature and society. 3. Literature. Philosophy. I. Title.

NL 0377890   OrU ICarbS InU MH

Linde, Ernst, 1864–
Der darstellende unterricht. Nach den grundsätzen
der Herbart-Zillerschen schule und vom standpunkte des
nicht-Herbartianers. Mit einem anhang: Lehrproben in
darstellender form. Von Ernst Linde. Leipzig, F.
Brandstetter, 1899.
1 p. l., [VI]–vi p., 1 l., 144 p. 21½cm.

1. Herbart, Johann Friedrich, 1776–1841. 2. Ziller, Tuiskon, 1817–1882.
                                       E 11–304
Library, U. S. Bur. of   Education LB648.L64

NL 0377891   DHEW

Linde, Ernst, 1864–
Führer durch die Dramen der Weltliteratur; ausgewählte
Bühnendichtungen im Auszug, von Ernst Linde. Leipzig: E. H.
Mayer, 1914. xx, 826 p. 16°.

1. Drama.—History and criticism.
N. Y. P. L.   September 27, 1919.

NL 0377892   NN RP PU PBL MiD PSt

PN
6114
L5   Linde, Ernst, 1864–
            Führer durch die Dramen der Weltliteratur;
            ausgewählte Bühnendichtungen im Auszug. 2.
            Aufl. Leipzig, F. Brandstetter [1925]
            912p. 17cm.

            1. Drama - Stories, plots, etc. 2. Drama -
            Hist. & crit. I. Title

NL 0377893   WU PP NjP NcWsW

Linde, Ernst, 1864–
Gude, Carl Heinrich Friedrich, 1814–1898.
Gudes Erläuterungen deutscher dichtungen; ausge-
führte anleitungen zur ästhetischen würdigung und un-
terrichtlichen behandlung ... bearb. und hrsg. von Ernst
Linde. Leipzig, F. Brandstetter, 1911–20.

Linde, Ernst, 1864–
Kunst und erziehung: gesammelte aufsätze, von Ernst Linde
... Leipzig, F. Brandstetter, 1901.
vi p., 1 l., 272 p. 20½cm.

1. Education — Addresses, lectures, etc. 2. Esthetics — [Study and]
teaching.
                                       E 11–247
U. S. Off. of educ. Library   LB41.L64
for Library of Congress   [37b1-]

NL 0377895   DHEW MB ICJ

Linde, Ernst, 1864–
Moderne lyrik in schulgemässer behandlung;
mit besonderer berücksichtigung des ästhetischen. Ausgeführte lehrproben zum gebrauch in
niederen und höheren schulen. 3., durchgesehene
aufl. Leipzig, Brandstätter, 1921.
xi, 227 p.

1. German poetry - 19th cent. - History and criticism.

NL 0377896   NNC OrU

VOLUME 334

Linde, Ernst, 1864–
   Die muttersprache im elementarunterricht. Grundzüge für die vermittelung des sprachgehaltes im ersten schuljahre. Von Ernst Linde. Mit einer empfehlung von prof. R. Hildebrand ... Leipzig und Berlin, J. Klinkhardt, 1891.
   vii, [1], 90 p. 20½ᵐ.

1. German language—Teaching—Elementary schools.

E 13–1119

Library, U. S. Bur. of   Education LB1529.G3L6

NL 0377897   DHEW

Linde, Ernst.
   Natur und geist als grundschema der welterklärung; versuch einer kulturphilosophie auf entwicklungsgeschichtlicher grundlage; als unterbau einer künftigen allgemeinen pädagogik, von Ernst Linde. Leipzig, F. Brandstetter, 1907.
   xvi p., 1 l., 655 p. 23½ᵐ.

8–2646

NL 0377898   DLC NN

Linde, Ernst.
Die neueste deutsche lyrik. Lpz., Brandstetter, 1910.

v. 1.

NL 0377899   PU

Linde, Ernst, 1864–
   ... Pädagogische streitfragen der gegenwart, von Ernst Linde. Leipzig, O. Nemnich, 1913.
   4 p. l., [iii]–iv, 252 p. front. (port.) 22½ᵐ. (Die pädagogik der gegenwart ... v. bd.)

1. Education.

E 13–1656

Library, U. S. Bur. of   Education LB775.L62

NL 0377900   DHEW PU

Linde, Ernst, 1864–
   Persönlichkeits-pädagogik; ein mahnwort wider die methodengläubigkeit unserer tage, mit besonderer berücksichtigung der unterrichtsweise Rudolf Hildebrands, von Ernst Linde ... 3. durchgesehene aufl. Leipzig. F. Brandstetter, 1909.
   xv, [1], 247 p. 20½ᵐ.

1. Education. 2. *Hildebrand, Rudolf. 1824–1894.

E 9–382

U. S. Off. of educ. Library   LB1027.L64
for Library of Congress   [a38b1]

NL 0377901   DHEW ICJ

BL65   LINDE, ERNST, 1864–
.A7L7   Religion und kunst; ein vortrag von Ernst Linde... Tübingen, Mohr, 1905.
   [4], 36 p. 21½cm. (Half-title: Lebensfragen... [6])

1. Art and religion.

NL 0377902   ICU MH NN

Linde, Ernst, 1864–
   Vom goldnen baum. Aphorismen zur kunst des lebens und der erziehung, von Ernst Linde ... Leipzig, F. Brandstetter, 1902.
   viii, 134 p. 18½ᵐ.

E 11–305

Library, U. S. Bur. of   Education LB41.L643

NL 0377903   DHEW

Linde, Ernst, 1864–
   Wer hat ein recht auf die volksschule? Grundlagen einer schulpolitik vom freiheitlich-protestantischen, deutsch-nationalen und wissenschaftlich-pädagogischen standpunkt. Von Ernst Linde ... Leipzig, F. Brandstetter, 1906.
   66 p. 21½ᵐ.

1. Church and education—Germany.

E 12–733

Library, U. S. Bur. of   Education LC116.G3L6

NL 0377904   DHEW

Linde, Eugen von der
   Der gute Glaube in der Zwangsvollstreckung ... von Eugen v.d.Linde... Borna-Leipzig, R. Noske, 1928.

   v, 38 p., 1 l. 21cm.
   Inaug.-Diss. - Halle-Wittenberg.
   "Lebenslauf": leaf at end.
   "Literatur": p. v.

NL 0377905   MH-L MiU ICRL

Linde, Fr
   Kurze geschichte der kirchen-reformation in Regensburg. 2. aufl. Nurnberg, Raw, 1843.
   79 p.

NL 0377906   PPLT

LINDE, Fr   , and WAGNER, Emil[e], editors.
   Predigten üb.d.Sonn- u.Festtags-Evangelien d. Kirchenjahres, herausgeg.v.Linde u.Wagner. Bayr. 1847.

   2 Bde.

NL 0377907   MH-AH

Linde, Franz.
   Die betriebs-arbeiter-und wirtschaftsraete des artikels 165 der neuen reichsverfaffung, ihr wesen und ihre rechtliche natur.(Auszug) Inaug.diss. Goettingen,1924.

NL 0377908   ICRL

Linde, Franz, ed.
   Fürsorge des staates, fürsorge der partei; sammlung der gesamten fürsorgevorschriften mit eingehenden erläuterungen, von dr. Franz Linde ... und dr. Ludwig Zimmerle ... 2., neubearb. und wesentlich erweiterte aufl. München und Berlin, C. H. Beck, 1939.

   1 v. 20ᵐ.
   Loose-leaf.

1. Public welfare—Germany—Law. 2. Disabled—Rehabilitation, etc.—Germany. 3. Pensions, Military—Germany. i. Zimmerle, Ludwig, joint ed. ii. Germany. Laws, statutes, etc. iii. Title.

42–44598

NL 0377909   DLC MiU MH CoU CtY MnU

Linde, Franz, of Charlottenburg.
   Die Haftung des Rheders aus fremdem Verschulden nach römischem Recht, nach den Quellen des Mittelalters und nach dem Handelsgesetzbuch ... von Franz Linde ... Berlin, "Gutenberg" Druckerei und Verlag, 1898.
   38 p. 21½cm.
   Inaug.-Diss. - Erlangen.
   Bibliographical footnotes.

NL 0377910   MH-L ICRL NIC

Linde, Franz. writer on art.
   Kunst oder Kitsch? Ein Führer zur Kunst...   Berlin: Julius Bard [cop. 1934] 128 p. illus., pls. (some col'd.) 8°.

1. Art. 2. Title.
N. Y. P. L.   May 7, 1935

NL 0377911   NN IEN NcU

4DB   Linde, Franz Xaver
878   Chronik des Marktes und der Stadt Melk umfassend den Zeitraum von 890 bis 1899 mit besonderer Berücksichtigung der letzten 34 Jahre zusammengestellt. 2. Aufl. Melk, Selbstverlag der Gemeinde Melk, 1900.
   480 p.

NL 0377912   DLC-P4 PPeSchw MH

Linde, Friedrich.
   Etwas über Lautveränderung in der deutschen Sprache. Langensalza, H. Beyer & Söhne, 1904.
   25 p. 8°. (Pädagogisches Magazin. Heft 221)

NL 0377913   NN

Linde, Friedrich
   Die onomatik, ein notwendiger zweig des deutschen sprachunterrichts. Von Fr. Linde. Langensalza, Hermann Beyer, 1900 [i. e. 1902] 52 p. (Pädagogisches magazin, hft. 142)

1. German language - Word formation.

NL 0377914   NNC

Linde, Friedrich A. van der, 1904–
   ...Ihr seid gewarnt; die Flucht aus der französischen Fremdenlegion! Erlebnisse und Erfahrungen eines holländischen Staatsangehörigen...   Dortmund: Im Selbstverlag des Verfassers[, 1931]. 80 p.   port. 8°.

571980A. 1. Foreign legion, French.
N. Y. P. L.   February 19, 1932

NL 0377915   NN

Linde, Friedrich-Wilhelm, 1904–
   ... Gastritis und Ulcus und ihre möglichen Zusammenhänge ...   Marburg, 1934.
   Inaug.-Diss. - Marburg.
   Lebenslauf.
   "Literatur-Verzeichnis": p. 19.

NL 0377916   CtY

VOLUME 334

Linde, Friedrich Wilhelm von der, 1894–
Die Hamburg-Amerika Linie. Berlin, Widder-Verlag, 1930.
90 p. illus., ports. 21 cm. (Stätten deutscher Arbeit, Bd. 2)

1. Hamburg-American line.   I. Title.   (Series)

HE945.H2L5   49–36150*

NL 0377917   DLC IU NN

Linde, Fritz: Aus d. Univ.-Frauenklinik in Bonn. Über Geburtsstörungen bei Ventrofixation. Bonn: Rost 1910. 57 S. 8°
Bonn, Med. Diss. v. 4. Okt. 1910, Ref. Fritsch
[Geb. 18. Dez. 83 Hörde; Wohnort: Dortmund; Staatsangeh.: Preußen; Vorbildung: Städt. Gymn. Dortmund Reife O. 04; Studium: Würzburg 2, München 1, Würzburg 2, Bonn 2, Berlin 1, Leipzig 1, Bonn 2 S.; Coll. 29. Juni 09; Approb. 27. Mai 10.]   [U 11.418]

NL 0377918   ICRL DNLM MBCo

DD218
A2095
Bismarck, Otto, *fürst* von, 1815–1898.
Bismarck, grösse und grenze seines reiches; in selbstzeugnissen und berichten von zeitgenossen dargestellt von Fritz Linde. Mit 4 bildnissen. Leipzig, In der Dieterich'schen verlagsbuchhandlung [1939]

Linde, Fritz, 1900–   ed.

Linde, Fritz, 1900–
Ich, der könig. Der untergang Ludwigs des Zweiten, von Fritz Linde; mit 48 abbildungen der personen und geschichtlichen stätten. Leipzig, G. Kummer   [c1926]
343, [1] p. illus. (facsims.) plates, ports. 18ᶜᵐ.
"Belege": p. [339]–343.

NL 0377920   CtY

Linde, Fritz, 1900–
Ich, der König; der Untergang Ludwigs des Zweiten. 6.–10.Aufl. Leipzig, G.Kummer [c.1926]

NL 0377921   MH

Linde, Fritz, 1900–
Ich, der könig. Der untergang Ludwigs des Zweiten, von Fritz Linde; mit 48 abbildungen der personen und geschichtlichen stätten. Leipzig, G. Kummer [*1928]
343, [1] p. illus. (facsims.) plates, ports. 18ᶜᵐ.
"Belege": p. [339]–343.

1. Ludwig II, king of Bavaria, 1845–1886.   I. Title.
Library of Congress   29–14965
DD801.B387L5

NL 0377922   DLC NcD NN

Linde, Fritz, 1900–
Ich, der König. Der Untergang Ludwigs des Zweiten. Leipzig, G.Kummer [c.1928]
350 p. ports., plates, facsims. 21.5 cm.

NL 0377923   MH

914.33
L743
Linde, Fritz, 1900–
König Ludwig und seine schlösser [von] ... Mit einer lebensskizze "König Ludwig" Leipzig, Georg Kummer [1926]
3v. in 1v. illus. 21cm.

1. BAVARIA – DESCR. & TRAVEL
2. CASTLES   I. Title.

NL 0377924   OWorP

Linde, Fritz, 1900–
Mensch Goethe; ein lebensspiegel, selbstzeugnisse, zeitberichte, schlaglichter aus dem werk; eingeleitet und ausgewählt von dr. Fritz Linde. Stuttgart, Robert Lutz, nachfolger Otto Schramm [*1932]
262 p. plates, ports. 19ᶜᵐ. (*Half-title:* Scheinwerfer ins menschliche. bd. 1)
On verso of t.-p.: 2. auflage.
"Namensverzeichnis": p. 255–262.

1. Goethe, Johann Wolfgang von, 1749–1832.   II. Title.
A 32–1963

Columbia univ. Library
for Library of Congress   [a37b1]

NL 0377925   NNC NcRS

U
444
.507
LINDE, GEORG, 1754–1847.
Artillerievidenskabens begyndessesgrunde for landetatens militaire underviisningsanstalter.   Kjøbenhavn, Brünnich, 1813.
241p. fold.diagrs. 18cm.

NL 0377926   ICN

Linde, Gérard van de.
See
Van de Linde, Gérard, 1840–

Linde, Gerhard, 1905–
... Über den Einfluss der Salvarsanbehandlung der Syphilis auf die Entwicklung späterer quartärer Erkrankungen ...   [Tilsit] 1931.
Inaug.-Diss. – Königsberg.
Lebenslauf.
"Literaturverzeichnis": p. 35.

NL 0377928   CtY

Linde, Gerhard, 1909–
Das wesen des erythema nodosum. ... Zeulenroda, 1935.
Inaug. Diss. – Würzburg, 1935.
Lebenslauf.
Literaturverzeichnis.

NL 0377929   DNLM

[**Linde, Gerrit van de**] 1808–1858.
Gedichten van den Schoolmeester [pseud.] uitg. door Mr. J. van Lennep. 4. druk. Amsterdam, Gebroeders Kraay, 1863.
1 p. l., 5–208 p. 16ᶜᵐ.
CONTENTS.–Iets over den schrijver en zijn dichttrant.–Concept-voorrede.–Epische poëzy.–Dramatische poëzy.–Didactische poëzy.–Bespiegelingen.–Brieven.–Fabels en vertellingen.–Lyrische poëzy.–Mengelpoëzy.

1. Lennep, Jakob van, 1802–1868, ed.   II. Title.
1–6278 Revised

Library of Congress   PT5854.L55G4 1863

NL 0377930   DLC WaS

[**Linde, Gerrit van de**] 1808–1858.
De gedichten van den schoolmeester, uitgegeven door Mr. J. van Lennep... Illustraties van A. de Vries.   Amsterdam, Gebr. Kraay, 1872.
2 p.l., (1) 4–324 p. 8°.
6. ed.

NL 0377931   NN

[**Linde, Gerrit van de,** 1808–58]
De gedichten van den Schoolmeester. Uitg.door J.van Lennep. 7.druk. Met illustraties van A.de Vries. Amsterdam, Kraay, 1875.

NL 0377932   MH

[**Linde, Gerrit van de**] 1808–1858.
De gedichten van den schoolmeester, uitgegeven door Mr. J. van Lennep. Tiende druk. n.p., 1887.
179, iv p. 17 cm.

NL 0377933   CU

839.31
L641d
1902
Linde, Gerrit van de, 1808–1858.
De gedichten van den Schoolmeester; uitg. door J. van Lennep. 12. druk. Met 300 illustraties van Anth. de Vries. Arnhem, Gebrs E. & M. Cohen [1902]
332p. illus. 19cm.
"Iets over den schrijver en zijn dichttrant," by J. van Lennep: p.[315]–326.

I. Lennep, Jakob van, 1802–1868, ed.   II.

NL 0377934   TxU

839.3
N28
v.57–58
[**Linde, Gerrit van de**]
Gedichten van den Schoolmeester [pseud.] met inleiding van J. van Lennep en de oorspronkelijke illustraties. 3. druk ...   [Amsterdam, 1915]
335p. illus. (Nederlandsche bibliotheek [57–58])
Title within ornamental border.

NL 0377935   IU

PT5854
L55G4
1954
Linde, Gerrit van de, 1808–1858.
Gedichten van den Schoolmeester. Een keuze met 7 oorspronkelijke illus. Amsterdam, De Bezige Bij, 1954.
63 p. illus. (Robijnenboekjes, 4)

I. De Schoolmeester. II. Title.

NL 0377936   CU

W 4
L68
1718
L 1
LINDE, Gosuinus van der
Dissertatio medica inauguralis. De diarrhoea ... Lugduni Batavorum, Apud Conradum Wishoff, 1718.
13 p. 22 cm.
Diss. – Leyden.

NL 0377937   DNLM

VOLUME 334

₍Linde, Guillermo₎
Report of manganese deposit, Pirucaua, state of Maranhão,
Brazil. ₍Pará, 1917₎ 5 f. 33cm.

Caption-title.
Dated and signed: Pará, Nov. 26th, 1917, Guillermo Linde.

1. Manganese—Brazil—Pirucaua.
N. Y. P. L.   March 28, 1945

NL 0377938   NN

Linde, Gunnar.
Studier över de svenska sta-namnen. Uppsala, Appel-
bergs boktr., 1951.
291 p. maps. 25 cm. (Studier till en svensk ortnamnsatlas, 9)
Skrifter utg. av Kungl. Gustav Adolfs akademien, 26.
Akademisk avhandling—Stockholms högskola.
Bibliography: p. ₍281₎–291.

1. Names, Geographical—Sweden. 2. Swedish language—Etymology—Names. I. Title. (Series. Series: Gustav Adolfs akademien för folklivsforskning. Skrifter, 26)

PD5576.L5   55–41774

          NN TxU
NL 0377939   DLC CU CtY IU IEN ICU PU MnU NIC NcU OU

4PZ   **Linde, Gunnel**
1306   Lururi. Genfortalt af Inge Aasted.
          Musik af Lasse Eriksson. Omslag og
          illustrationer af Iben Clante. ₍
          Branner og Korch ₍19 ₎
                    88 p.

NL 0377940   DLC-P4

Linde, Hans
     Das dorf: gestalt und aufgabe länd-
lichen zusammenlebens ... Hannover,
M. & H. Schaper, 1954.
     84p., tab., 21.5cm. (Schriftenreihe
     für ländliche sozialfragen, 11)

NL 0377941   RU

HB3595   **Linde, Hans.**
A673   Preussischer Landesausbau; ein Beitrag der
v.7   ländlichen Gesellschaft in Süd-Ostpreussen am
          Beispiel des Dorfes Piassutten, Kreis Ortels-
          burg. Leipzig, S. Hirzel, 1939.
          iv, 94 p. illus. 24ᶜᵐ. (7. Beiheft zum
          Archiv für Bevölkerungswissenschaft und Bevölke-
          rungspolitik)
          "Quellenverzeichnis": p. 92–94.

          1.Piassutten, Ger. 2.Prussia, East (Pro-
          vince) - Popula   tion. 3.Land tenure -
          Prussia, East   (Province) 4.Sociology,
          Rural. I.Title.

NL 0377942   CSt-H CtY NN NcD

Linde, Hans Jürgen von der: Inkorporationen zwischen Aktiengesellschaften und Gesellschaften mit beschränkter Haftung, im Gegensatz zur Fusion von Aktiengesellschaften untereinander. [Ma-
schinenschrift.] IV, 85 S. 4°. — Auszug: Potsdam 1922: Krämer.
4 Bl. 8°
Breslau, R.- u. staatswiss. Diss. v. 31. März 1922   ₍U 22. 1254₎

NL 0377943   ICRL

Linde, Haqvinus, respondent.
     Summo adspirante numine. Dissertatio academica
Merita Jesuitarum in eloqvetiam...
          see under Ekerman, Petrus, praeses.

PA25   **Linde, Harry**
G71d   Studier till Columellas nionde bok, av Harry
no.12   Linde ... Göteborg, Elanders boktryckeri
          aktiebolag, 1936.
          vii, [1], 82, [1] p. 23½cm. (On cover:
          Doktors avhandlingar i latinsk filologi vid
          Göteborgs högskola. serie Fr. O. M. 1926. XII)
          Akademisk avhandling - Göteborgs högskola.
          "Litteraturförteckning": p.[v]–vii.

          1.Columella, Lucius Junius Moderatus. De
          re rustica.   2.Bees - Early works to
          1800.   I.Ser.*

NL 0377945   CLU CU NcD MiU NjP CtY OCU DLC MH

Linde, Heinrich.
     ... Lohntheorie und lohnpolitik der sozialdemokratie. Wien,
Berlin, Verlag für literatur und politik ₍1931₎
     79 p. 22ᶜᵐ.
     At head of title: H. Linde.

     1. Wages—Germany. 2. Socialism in Germany. 3. Sozialdemokra-
tische partei Deutschlands. I. Title.   A 32–117 Revised
New York. Public library
     for Library of Congress   HD5029.L5
                                       ₍r43c2₎†   331.2943

NL 0377946   NN NcD CtY DLC

Linde, Heinrich von der.
     ... Ueber die An-
wendung von ammoniakalischen Quecksilber-
cyanid in der quantitativen Analyse. 42 pp.
8°. *Bern. S. Collin,* 1894.

NL 0377947   DNLM CtY

Linde, Hendrik Martinus van der.
     Het baarmoederslijmvlies op ouderen leeftijd ...
Amsterdam [1936?]
     Dissertation. - Amsterdam, 1936.

NL 0377948   MiU

JR16   Linde, Hendrik van der, 1915–
L743   Credo unam sanctam. ₍n.p.₎Uitgegeven
          door de Oecumenische Jeugdraad in Nederland
          ₍1946?₎
          cover-title,34 numb.ℓ. 31cm.
          Includes bibliographies.

NL 0377949   NNUT

JR14   Linde, Hendrik van der, 1915–
C1948   De eerste steen gelegd. De eerste Assemblée
X   van de Wereldraad van Kerken te Amsterdam,
L641e   1948. Amsterdam, W. ten Have, 1949.
          280 p. illus., ports. 22 cm.

          Bibliography: p. 276–278.

          1. World Council of Churches. 1st Assembly,
Amsterdam,   1948. I. Title.

NL 0377950   CtY-D CtY NNUT MH-AH

Linde, Hendrik van der, *ed.*
     Geloofsinhoud en geloofsbeleving; een peiling binnen Re-
formatie en Katholieke Kerk in Nederland. Onder redactie
van H. van der Linde en F. Thijssen. Utrecht, Het Spectrum, 1951.
     367 p. 22 cm.
     Bibliographical footnotes.

     1. Reformation—Netherlands. 2. Nederlandse Hervormde Kerk—
Relations—Catholic Church. 3. Catholic Church—Relations—Nederlandse Hervormde Kerk. 4. Christian union. I. Thijssen, F., 1904–
joint ed. II. Title.
                                                 A 52–5411
Catholic Univ. of   America. Library
for Library of Congress   ₍4₎

NL 0377951   DCU CtY-D MH-AH NNUT

Linde, Hendrik van der.
     Rome en de una sancta, het oecumenisch vraagstuk en de
arbeid van Rome voor de hereniging der kerken. Nijkerk,
G. F. Callenbach, 1947.
     295 p. 23 cm.
     Academisch proefschrift—Utrecht.
     "Stellingen": p. ₍4₎ inserted.
     "Lijst van geraadpleegde litteratuur": p. 365–389. "Enige tijd-
schriften": p. 389–390.

     1. Ecumenical movement. 2. Catholic Church—Relations.
I. Title.

     BX8.L5 1947a   280   50–27330

NL 0377952   DLC NjP ICU CtY

Linde, Hendrik van der, 1915–
     Rome en de Una Sancta, het oecumenisch vraagstuk en de
arbeid van Rome voor de hereniging der kerken. Nijkerk,
G. F. Callenbach, 1947.
     383 p. 24 cm.
     "Lijst van geraadpleegde litteratuur": p. 353–378.

     1. Ecumenical movement. 2. Catholic Church—Relations.
I. Title.

     BX8.L5   280   49–20422*

NL 0377953   DLC NcD

BX4851   Linde, Hendrik van der, 1915–
.L74   De situatie van de Protestanten in Spanje;
          verslag van een studiereis gemaakt in het
          najaar van 1949 door H. Van der Linde en F.
          Thijssen. 's Gravenhage, Boekencentrum, 1950.
          99 p. (Bijdragen tot de eenheid der Kerk)

          1. Protestants in   ain. 2. Christian union.
          I. Thijssen, F

NL 0377954   ICU CtY-D TxHU NjPT NNUT

JR76   Linde, Hendrik van der, 1915–
L64u   De "Una Sancta" in en na de oorlog. Kort
          verslag van eenige oecumenische litteratuur uit
          de oorlogsjaren, opgesteld ten behoeve van de
          Synodale Urgentie-Commissie der Ned. Herv. Kerk
          in het bevrijde gebied door H. van der Linde,
          opgedragen in de vergadering te Goes, Maart 1945.
          ₍Neerbosch, Boekdrukkerij der Weesinrichting,
          1945₎
          34 p. 19 cm. (De strijdende kerk, no. 1)

NL 0377955   CtY-D

JR36   Linde, Hendrik van der, 1915–
L641w   De wereldraad van kerken; geschiedenis,
          ontwikkeling en toekomst der oecumenische
          beweging. Met een woord van inleiding door
          S.F.H.J. Berkelbach van der Sprenkel.
          Nijkerk, G.F. Callenbach, 1948.
          141 p. table. 20 cm.

          "Vragen en litteratuur": p. 125–141.

          1. Church   union. I. Title.

NL 0377956   CtY-D DLC-P4 MH NNUT

Linde, Henricus van der
     see Arnoldi, Henricus, 1405–1487.

VOLUME 334

Linde, Herman.
A brief history of P.H. Balling's original oil painting of General Ulysses S. Grant, "In the trenches before Vicksburg" and a description of Jas. Fagan's magnificent etching. New York, H. Linde, [190–]
12 l., 1 port. 8°.

NL 0377958 NN

Linde, Hermann,   comp.
Shakespeare-Recitationen. (Frei aus dem Gedächtniss) Ausgewählte Urtheile der Presse.| Düsseldorf, Spiethoff [18--?]
42 p. 22 cm

Bound with Erdman, Preston K. An essay on Shakespeare's Merchant of Venice. 1868, and Himes, John Andrew. An essay on Shakespeare's MacBeth. 1873.

NL 0377959 NjP

Linde, Hermann, 1863–1923, illus.

Rudolf Steiners mysteriendramen ... Dornach, Sektion für redende und musische künste am Goetheanum, 1936.

Linde, Imme.
Kriegserinnerungen eines kindes, von Imme Linde. Leipzig, Koehler & Amelang [1936]
240 p. 19ᶜᵐ.

1. European war, 1914–1918—Personal narratives.   I. Title.

	37-4967
Library of Congress	D640.L49
Copyright A—Foreign	33946
	[2] 940.48243

NL 0377961 DLC

CS71   Linde, Inga Hippe, 1892–
.H667   Family history of Mr. and Mrs. Iver G.
1938   Hippe, pioneers of New Prairie township, Pope Co., Minn. [n.p. 1938?]
12 l. 28cm.

NL 0377962 MnHi

Linde, J   Manuel Garcia de la
    see   Garcia de la Linde, J.   Manuel, d. 1887.

Linde, Johan de.
Anonè. De Europese gemeenschap gedurende de Japanse bezettingstijd. Rotterdam, A. Donker, 1946.
98 p. 20 cm.

1. World War, 1989–1945—Prisoners and prisons, Japanese. I. Title.
D805.J3L5   55-24882
[3]

NL 0377964 DLC CtY NIC NN

FLGZ
148   Linde, Johann.
no.4   ... De compensatione in concvrsv creditorvm ... Giessae, J.J. Braun, 1782.
16p. 20cm.
(Foreign law pamphlet collection, v.148, no.4)

NL 0377965 CtY-L

Linde, Johann Wilhelm, 1760–1840.
Sententiae Iesv Siracidae Graece...
Gedani, 1795
    see under   Bible. O.T. Apocrypha. Ecclesiasticus. Greek. 1795.

Linde, Johann Wilhelm, 1760–1840.
Sittenlehre Jesu des sohns Sirach...
Leipzig, 1782
    see under   Bible. O.T. Apocrypha. Ecclesiasticus. German. 1782. Linde.

Linde, Johannes.
Das Zurueckbehaltungsrecht des Handelsgesetzbuchs für das deutsche Reich vom 10. Mai 1897.
Leipzig, 1902.
Inaug. diss.
Bibl.

NL 0377968 ICRL

Linde, Johannes Cornelis van de, 1884–
De verdeeling der heldere sterren ... door Johannes Cornelis van de Linde ... Rotterdam, Drukkerij M. Wyt & zonen, 1921.
5 p. l., 66 p. incl. tables, diagrs. 23½ᶜᵐ.
Proefschrift—Utrecht.
"Errata" : 1 leaf laid in.

1. Stars—Distribution.   I. Title.
                      36-35808
Library of Congress   QB819.L5 1921 a
               [2]   523.89

NL 0377969 DLC PU ICRL WU TxU NN

Linde, Johannes Cornelis van de.
De verdeeling der heldere sterren, door J. C. van de Linde. Rotterdam, Drukkerij M. Wyt, 1921.
2 p. l., 66 p. tables, diagrs. 24 cm.

1. Stars—Distribution.   I. Title.
QB819.L5   24-16709

NL 0377970 DLC CtY PU

Linde, John, 1737–1781
    see Lind, John, 1737–1781.

Linde, John A   1888–
Linde orthodontic appliances and ... materials illustrating practical procedure in management of malocclusion. New York [1951]
69 p. illus. 23 cm.

1. Dental instruments and apparatus. 2. Teeth—Abnormities and deformities.   I. Title.
RK521.L56   617.64   51-2183
[U. S. Army Med. Libr.: 1. Dental instruments & apparatus. 2. Orthodontia.   WU440 L743o]

NL 0377972 DLC DNLM

Linde, Jonas Otto, 1898–
Elektrische widerstandseigenschaften der verdünnten legierungen des kupfers, silbers und goldes, eine experimentaluntersuchung über die atomaren widerstandserhöhungen und ihre temperatur- und druckabhängigkeit, von J. O. Linde. Lund, H. Ohlssons buchdruckerei, 1939.
96 p. incl. tables, diagrs. 24½ᶜᵐ.
Imprint on cover: Lund, Gleerupska univ.-bokhandeln.
Issued also as author's thesis, Tekniska högskolan, Stockholm.

1. Electric resistance. 2. Alloys.
                      43-41234
Library of Congress   QC611.L47 1939
               [2]   537.5

NL 0377973 DLC CU CtY NNC

PG5022   Linde, Josef, 1789–1834, joint author.
.A3
1879   [Hanka, Václav] 1791–1861.
    Rukopisové zelenohorský a kralodvorský. Staročeskym textem vydal Josef Jireček. V Praze, F. Řivnáč, 1879.

Linde, Joseph I.
----The work of the Infant welfare association of New Haven...[n.p., 1913?]
cover-title, p. 147]- 154. 23 1/2 cm.

NL 0377975 DL

van der Linde (Jules Armand). *Die Gewebsveränderungen im Euter bei Galactophoritis sporadica der Kuh. [Bern.] 1 p. l., pp. 337–362. 2 pl. 8°. Berlin, L. Schumacher, 1906.

NL 0377976 DNLM ICRL PU

KD1371   Linde, Justin Timotheus Balthasar, freiherr von,
.22   1797–1870.
.I56A2   Abhandlungen aus dem deutschen gemeinen civil-
1823   prozesse, mit Berücksichtigung der Preussichen allgemeinen Gerichtsordnung, von Just. Timoth. Balth. von Linde. Bonn, A. Marcus, 1823–
    v.

1. Civil procedure—Prussia. 2. Civil procedure—Germany.   I. Title.

NL 0377977 ICU

Linde, Justin Timotheus Balthasar, freiherr von, 1797–1870.
Auffassung des christlichen seligkeitsdogma's nach katholischem und protestantischem bekenntnisse; ein beitrag zur betrachtung der neuesten kirchlichen ereignisse aus dem standpunkte des rechts und der politik, von dem Kanzler Dr. J. Th.B. von Linde. Mainz, Florian Kupferberg, 1846.
xx, 179 p., 23ᶜᵐ.   (His: Berichtigung confessioneller missverständnisse. 1)

NL 0377978 NjPT

265.62   Linde, Justin Timotheus Balthasar, Freiherr von,
L1   1797–1870.
    Berichtigung confessioneller Missverständnisse. Mainz, Fl. Kupferberg, 1846.
3 pts.
Each pt. has separate t.p.

1. Confession. I. Title.

NL 0377979 TxDaM-P DLC-P4 ICRL

VOLUME 334

₍Linde, Justin Timotheus Balthasar, freiherr
von₎ 1797-1870.
Betrachtung der neuesten kirchlichen
Ereignisse aus dem Standpunkte des Rechts
und der Politik. Von einem rechtsgelehrten
Staatsmann ₍i.e. Justus Timotheus Balthasar
von Linde₎ Mainz, Florian Kupferberg, 1845.
128 p.

NL 0377980   TxDaM DLC-P4

BR856   Linde, Justin Timotheus Balthasar, Freiherr von,
.L53   1797-1870.
1855   Betrachtungen über die Selbstständigkeit und
Unabhängigkeit der Kirchengewalt und Schutz-
pflicht des deutschen Bundes und der Theil-
nehmer an dem westphälischen Frieden samt und
sonders in Deutschland. Gietzen, Ferber, 1855.
xvii, 202 p. 21 cm. (Archiv für das
öffentliche Recht des deutschen Bundes, v.2,
pt. 1)
1. Church and   state in Germany.
2. Religion   Germany. I. Title.

NL 0377981   ViU

Linde, Justin Timotheus Balthasar, *Freiherr von, 1797-1870*
Dissertatio inauguralis exhibens observatio-
nes quasdam de successione germanica imprimis
pactitia. Bonnae, n.d.

(?),22 p. 8°
Diss. --- Bonn, 1820.

NL 0377982   MH-L

AC931   Linde, Justin Timotheus Balthasar, Freiherr von,
.H3   1767-1870.
v. 144   Erwiederung auf die bemerkungen des
Herrn Geh. Raths. Dr. A.A.E. Schleiermacher
ueber den studienplan fuer die Grossh. Hessische
landesuniversitaet zu Giessen... Darmstadt,
Jonghaus, 1843.
69 p. [Haverford-Bauer pamphlets, v. 144,
no. 4]

NL 0377983   DLC

Linde, Justin Timotheus Balthasar, freiherr von,
1767-1870.
De grondlegger van de gewetensvrijheid...
Groningen, P. Noordhoff, 1926.
viii, [141 p.]

NL 0377984   OCl

Linde, Justin Timotheus Balthasar, *Freiherr von*, 1797-
1870.
Lehrbuch des deutschen gemeinen Civilprozesses, von
Timoth. Balth. Linde. Bonn, A. Marcus, 1825.
xxvi, 602 p. 21 cm.
On spine: Lehrbuch des Civilprocesses.
Bibliographical footnotes.

1. Civil procedure—Germany. 2. Roman law. I. Title.
II. Title: Lehrbuch des Civilprocesses.

75-228791

NL 0377985   DLC

4K   Linde, Justin Timotheus Balthasar,
Ger.   Freiherr von, 1797-1870.
1307   Lehrbuch des deutschen gemeinen
Civilprozesses. 2. umgearb. und sehr
verm. Ausg. Bonn, A. Marcus, 1828.
688 p.

NL 0377986   DLC-P4 NN

LINDE, Just[in] Timoth[eus] Balth[asar] von.
Lehrbuch des deutschen gemeinen civilprocesses. 3 te aus. Bonn, 1831.

NL 0377987   MH-L

Linde, Justin Timotheus Balthasar, *freiherr von*, 1797-1870.
Lehrbuch des deutschen gemeinen civilprocesses, von Just.
Timoth. Balth. Linde ... 4., verb. und verm., aufl. ... Bonn,
A. Marcus, 1835.
xxx, 564 p. 21ᶜᵐ.

1. Civil procedure—Germany. 2. Civil procedure (Roman law)

40-21944

NL 0377988   DLC

Linde, Justin Timotheus Balthasar, *freiherr von*, 1797-1870.
Lehrbuch des deutschen gemeinen civilprocesses. Von Just.
Timoth. Balth. von Linde ... 6. verb. und verm. aufl. Bonn,
A. Marcus, 1843.
xx, 586 p. 21ᶜᵐ.
First edition : 1825.
Heraldic stamp (in double state) of F. L. Keller j. u. d. on p. ii.

1. Civil procedure—Germany. 2. Roman law. I. Title.

31-33167

NL 0377989   DLC

₍Linde₎ Justin Timotheus Balthasar, freiherr
von₎ 1797-1870.
Römische Waffen in deutschem Streit; oder:
die Berechtigung des Herrn von Linde in Darmstadt zum Urtheile in den confessionellen
Fragen der Gegenwart. Mannheim, Heinrich
Hoff, 1846.
151 p.
1. Apologetics--19th century. I. Title.

NL 0377990   TxDaM

AC931   Linde, Justin Timotheus Balthasar, freiherr von,
.H3   1797-1870.
v. 69   Staatskirche, gewissensfreiheit und religioese
vereine... Mainz, Rupferberg, 1845.
xxviii, 211 p. [Haverford-Bauer pamphlets,
v. 69, no. 12]

NL 0377991   DLC

SD42   Linde, Justin Timotheus Balthasar, Freiherr von,
L743   1797-1870.
Ueber Abschliessung und Auflösung der Ehe
im Allgemeinen, und insbesondere über
gemischte Ehen. Nebst einigen Erwiederungen
auf des Herrn Freiherrn v.Gagern zweite
Ansprache an die deutsche Nation. Von Dr.
J.T.B. v.Linde ... Giessen,B.C.Ferber,1846.
xviii,₍2₎,169p. 23cm.

NL 0377992   NNUT

LINDE, Justin Timothus Balthasar von.
Ueber religiöse kindererziehung in gemischten
ehen und über ehen zwischen juden und christen, i
nebst beiträgen zur beleuchtung der selbstherr-
lichkeit des grossen geschichtsforschers Schlosser. Giessen, 1847.

NL 0377993   MH-L OCH

AC931   Linde, Justin Timotheus Balthasar, freiherr von,
.H3   1797-1870.
v. 73   Urkundliche berichtigung von Thatsachen...
Mainz, Kupferberg, 1846.
72 p. [Haverford-Bauer pamphlets, v. 74,
no. 2]

NL 0377994   DLC

Linde, Justin Timotheus Balthasar, freiherr von,
1797-1870, ed.
Zeitschrift für civilrecht und prozess. 1.–20. bd. ₍1828–44₎;
neue folge, 1.–22. bd. ₍1845–65₎ Giessen, B. C. Ferber ₍etc.₎
1828–65.

Linde, Karl, respondent.
... Concordiam religionis christianae statvsqve
civilis...
see under   Buddeus, Johann Franz, 1667-
1729, praeses.

LINDE, Karl of Gotha?
De proverbiorum apud tragicos graecos usu.
Gotha, 1896.

4°. pp. 31.
"Wissenschaftliche beilage zu dem progr.des
herzoglichen gymnas. zu Helmstedt,1896,nr.711."

NL 0377997   MH NjP

Linde, Karl, 1899-
Die entwickelung der eisenbahngütertarife nach
dem kriege unter besonderer berücksichtigung der
tarifreform von 1920 und ihrer volkswirtschaftlichen
bedeutung. ... Giessen, 1928. 29 p.
Inaug. Diss. - Giessen, 1928.
Lebenslauf.
Literatur.

NL 0377998   ICRL MiU CtY MH PU

Linde, Kurt, 1899-
Die Rachitis und ihre Auswirkung auf die Zähne
unter besonderer Berücksichtigung der Allgemein-
therapie... [Berlin, 1926]
Inaug.-Diss. - Berlin.
Lebenslauf.
Literatur-Verzeichnis: p. [31-32]

NL 0378001   CtY ICRL

Linde, Kurt, 1907-
... Über angeborenen Totalstar ... Düssel-
dorf, 1934.
Inaug.-Diss. - Münster.
Lebenslauf.

NL 0378002   CtY DNLM

VOLUME 334

Linde, Lars Gustaf, 1825–1890.
   Sveriges ekonomirätt, af Lars Gustaf Linde. Stockholm, P. A. Norstedt & söner [1888]
   2 p. l., vii, 960 p. 22½ᶜᵐ.

1. Sweden—Economic policy.

Library of Congress   HC375.L7   16–19113

NL 0378003   DLC MH

Linde, Lars Gustaf, 1825–1890.
   Sveriges finansrätt, af Lars Gustaf Linde. Stockholm, P. A. Norstedt & söner [1887]
   2 p. l., vii, 704 p. 21½ᶜᵐ.

16–5743

NL 0378004   DLC PU-L

Linde, L ev Rudol'fovich.
   ... Русско-английско-французско-немецкий технический словарь для лесоинженеров. Москва, Гослестехиздат, 1936.
   847, [1] p. 22½ᶜᵐ.
   At head of title: Л. Линде ...
   Added title-pages in German, French and English.
   Prefaces and indexes in Russian, English, French and German.
   1. Forests and forestry — Dictionaries. 2. Lumbering — Dictionaries. 3. Russian language—Dictionaries—Polyglot. 4. English language—Dictionaries — Polyglot. 5. French language — Dictionaries—Polyglot. 6. German language — Dictionaries — Polyglot. i. Title: Технический словарь для лесоинженеров.

Library of Congress   SD126.L5   *0–20405

NL 0378005   DLC OrCS CU ICJ NN DNAL WaT

Linde, Lev Rudol'fovich.
   Technical dictionary for forest engineers: Russian-English-French-German. n.p., Stechert, 1937.

NL 0378006   OrCS

Linde, Lucas de
   Le relationi et descrittioni universali. Bologna, Gioseffo Longhi, 1674

NL 0378007   NcU

Linde, Manuel de Terán, barón de la
   barón de la. ... [Demarcacion de lo pueblos comprehendidos dentro de las qua tro leguas de la frontera de tierra de Francia, y dos de la costa del mar en el principado de Cataluña, formada por los geometras, que entienden alli en las operaciones del castastro para evitar las extracciones fraudulentas de moneda; [Barcelona, 1788] [14]p. 30cm. (Spain. Reales ordenes. 8:4)

NL 0378008   CU-B

Linde, Marianne, 1901–
   Über einen fall von haemangioma cavernosum des zwischenhirns. ... Würzburg, 1934.
   Inaug. Diss. – Tübingen, 1934.
   Lebenslauf.

NL 0378009   OU

Linde, Marie, pseud.
   see Bosman, Elise, 1894–

Linde, Max, 1862–1940.
   ... Edvard Munch und die kunst der zukunft. Berlin, Friedrich Gottheiner [about 1903]
   14 [2] p.   illus., ports., [3] col. pl.   28.5 cm

NL 0378011   PPPM CSt

LINDE, Max, 1862–1940
   Edvard Munch. Neue Ausgabe. Berlin, etc., F. Gottheiner, 1905.
   28 cm.   pp.14, (6).   Colored plates, ports., and illustr.

NL 0378012   MH PPPM

Linde, Max, 1862–1940.
   Edvard Munchs brev fra dr. med. Max Linde.   Oslo, Dreyer, 1954.
   95 p.   illus.   27cm.   (Oslo kommunes kunstsamlinger. Munch-museets Skrifter, 3)
   I. Munch, Edvard, 1863–1944.

NL 0378013   MnU NN

Linde (Max) [1877–]. *Pupillenuntersuchungen an Epileptischen, Hysterischen, und Psychopathischen. [München.] 53 pp. 8°. Leipzig, W. Engelmann, 1907.

NL 0378014   DNLM

LINDE, Max, 1881–
   Der verlust der staatsangehörigkeit durch auswanderung. Inaug.-diss. Tübingen. Hamburg, 1908.

NL 0378015   MH

Linde, Nehemya
   see his later name Allony, Nehemya.

Linde, Nils., joint ed.
   ... Träbyggnadskonst. Stockholm, Lindfors [1938]

Linde, Otto.   543-3 Q601
   Anleitung zur chemischen Untersuchung des Wassers auf seine Brauchbarkeit für den menschlichen Genuss, zu gewerblichen Zwecken etc. Von Dr. O. Linde. 2. Auflage, unter Mitwirkung des Verfassers bearbeitet von Dr. W. Peters, ... Göttingen, Vandenhoeck & Ruprecht, 1906.
   vi, 62 p. 20½ᵐ.

NL 0378018   ICJ PPF ICRL DNLM MWelC

QV
L743r   LINDE, Otto
1906   Repetitorium der Pharmakognosie in Tabellenform; mit besonderer Berücksichtigung des Arzneibuches für das Deutsche Reich.   Göttingen, Vandenhoeck & Ruprecht, 1906.
           195 p. illus.

NL 0378019   DNLM MiU

Linde, Otto.
   Repetitorium der pharmakognosie in tabellenform. Mit besonderer berücksichtigung der Arzneibuches für das Deutsche Reich, bearb. von dr. O. Linde ... 2. ausg., verm. durch einen nachtrag; die durch erscheinen des Arzneibuches v bedingten änderungen ... Göttingen, Vandenhoeck & Ruprecht, 1911.
   xi p., 2 l., 195 p.   illus.   25 cm.

1. Pharmacy.

U. S. Dept. of Agr. Libr.   396L642   Agr 14—432
for Library of Congress   [a48b½]

NL 0378020   DNAL

Linde, Otto zur, 1873–
   ... Gesammelte Werke ...   Gross-Lichterfelde, 1910–1925.
   10 v. in 8   19.5 cm.
   Contents: 1. Abteilung; Gesammelte Gedichte. Bd. I. Thule Traumland. – Bd. II. "Album" und "Lieder der Liebe und Ehe". – Bd. III. Stadt; Vorstadt; Park; Landschaft; Meer. – Bd. IV. Charontischer Mythus. – Bd. V. Wege, Menschen und Ziele. – Bd. VI. Das Buch "Abendrot". – Bd. VII/VIII. Lieder des Leids. – Bd. IX/X. Denken, Zeit und Zukunft.

NL 0378021   CtY IU MH NN

PT
2623   Linde, Otto zur, 1873–1938.
I62   Album; und, Lieder der Liebe und Ehe.   Gross-
A83   Lichterfelde, Charonverlag, 1910.
             142p.   21cm.   (His Gesammelte Werke; 1. Abt.: Gesammelte Gedichte, Bd. 2)

NL 0378022   WU

831.91
H762Yl   Linde, Otto zur, 1873–1938.
             Arno Holz und der Charon, [eine Abrechnung] Zugleich ein Versuch einer Einführung in das tiefere Verständnis vom Wesen des Charon... [Grosslichterfelde] Charonverlag, 1911.
             clixp.

1. Holz, Arno, 1863–1929. 2. Charon, Monatsschrift für modernes geistiges Leben, insbesondere Ref   der Lyrik.
3. Lyrik poetry   Hist. & crit.

NL 0378023   ICarbS Mi NNU NcU

Linde, Otto zur, 1873–1938.
   Charon; Auswahl aus seinen Gedichten. Einführung von Hans Hennecke. München, R. Piper [1952]
   219 p.   port.   22 cm.

i. Title.

A 54–3964

Rochester. Univ. Libr.   PT2623.I 62O4
for Library of Congress   [1]

InU IU PPT CU NNC CSt CtY NcGU
NL 0378024   NRU CaBVaU NcU OU WaU OCU OCl IEN PU

VOLUME 334

PT
2623
I565
D4
Linde, Otto zur, 1873-1938
Denken, Zeit, und Zukunft. Berlin, Charon-
verlag, 1925.
288p. 19cm. (His Gesammelte Werke, 1.
Abt.: Gesammelte Gedichte, Bde. 9, 10)

NL 0378025   WU PU CaBVaU

Linde, Otto zur, 1873-
Gesammelte Gedichte.   Gross-Lichterfelde: Charonverlag,
1910-13. 5 v. in 2.   12°.   (In his: Gesammelte Werke,
Abt. 1.)

Bd. 1. Thule Traumland.
Bd. 2. Album. Lieder der Liebe und Ehe.
Bd. 3. Stadt. Vorstadt. Park. Landschaft. Meer.
Bd. 4. Charontischer Mythus.
Bd. 5. Wege. Menschen und Ziele.

1. Poetry (German).
N. Y. P. L.   February 11, 1915.

NL 0378026   NN

PT2333 Linde, Otto zur, 1873-
.A2L7   Heinrich Heine und die deutsche romantik ...   Freiburg i.
Br., C. A. Wagner's universitäts-buchdr., 1899.
[8], 219, [1] p. 21½cm.
Inaug.-diss.—Freiburg i. Br.
"Litteratur": 1 p. at end.

NL 0378027   ICU InU NIC MiU DLC

PT
2342
L553
1899a
Linde, Otto zur, 1873-1938.
Heinrich Heine und die deutsche romantik. Freiburg i. Br., 1899.
219 p. 26 cm.

Inaug. Diss. - Freiburg i. Br.
Photocopy.
Bibliography: p. [220]

1. Heine, Heinrich, 1797-1856. 2. Ro-
manticism - Germany. I. Title.

NL 0378028   CaBVaU

PT 2623 LINDE,OTTO ZUR,1873-1938
.I57 K9   Die Kügel, Bd. 1.   [Gross-Lichterfelde,
Charonverlag, 1902]
64 p.

No more published?

NL 0378029   InU

PT2623 Linde, Otto zur, 1873-1938.
.IL7K9 Die Kugel; eine Philosophie in Versen.
1909   Gr. Lichterfelde [-Berlin. Charonverlag,
1909.
64 p.

NL 0378030   ICU PU NjP

Linde, Otto zur, 1873-
Die kugel; eine philosophie in versen.
2. sehr verm. aufl. München, R. Piper,
1923.
147 p.

NL 0378031   NNC IaU

PT2623 Linde, Otto zur, 1873-
L1567L5   Lieder des Leids.   Berlin, Charonverlag, 1924.
1924   287 p.   (His Gesammelte Werke, 1.Abt., Bd.7/8)

NL 0378032   CU PU

Linde, Otto zur, 1873-   ed.

Moritz, Karl Philipp, 1757-1793.
... Reisen eines Deutschen in England im jahr 1782, von
Carl Philipp Moritz, herausgegeben von Otto zur Linde. Ber-
lin, B. Behr, 1903.

PT
2623
I565
T5
Linde, Otto zur, 1873-1938
Thule Traumland. Gross-Lichterfelde,
1910.
142p. 21cm. (His Gesammelte Werke;
1. Abt., Gesammelte Gedichte, Bd. 1)

NL 0378034   WU

Linde, Paul.
Gegen Rennenkampf und Joffre; kriegserlebnisse von
der ost- und westfront, hrsg. von Paul Linde. 3. aufl.
Leipzig, Xenien-verlag [1915]
121 p. 19cm.

1. European war, 1914-1918—Fiction.   I. Title.

21-20881

Library of Congress   PT2623.I 57G4 1915

NL 0378035   DLC OrPR CtY NjP DNW IU NN

Linde, Paul.
Der russische sumpf; roman aus dem weltkriege von
1914/15, von Paul Linde. 3. aufl. Dresden, C. Reissner,
1915.
3 p. l, 161 p. 20½cm.

1. European war, 1914-   —Fiction.   I. Title.

20-8188

Library of Congress   PT2623.I 57R8 1915

NL 0378036   DLC

619.9 Linde, Paul, *writer on fish*
L641f   Fischkrankheiten; Krankheiten unserer
Aquarienfische. Leipzig, Urania [1954?]
83, [1] p. illus., col. plates.

1. Fishes - Diseases and pests. I. Title.

NL 0378037   WaU

Linde, Paul, 1881-
De Epicuri vocabulis ab optima Atthide vel
omnino vel notione alienis... Breslau, 1906.
Inaug. - Diss.

NL 0378038   ICRL

Linde, Paul, 1881-
De Epicuri vocabulis ab optima Atthide alienis, scripsit
Paulus Linde. Vratislaviae, M. et H. Marcus, 1906.
3 p. l, 58 p. 23½cm. (Added t.-p.: Breslauer philologische abhand-
lungen, hrsg. von Richard Förster, 9. bd., 3. hft.)
Issued also as the author's inaugural dissertation, Breslau, 1906.

1. Epicurus—Language.   A C 34-3092

Title from Iowa State   Univ.
Library of Congress   [PA25.B8 bd. 9, hft. 3]

OCU IU
NL 0378039   IaU IU MdBJ CU MH NN NjP CtY NcD MiU

PA2061 Linde,Paul, 1881-
.L74   Die fortbildung der lateinischen schulgrammatik
nach der sprachwissenschaftlichen seite hin...
Königshütte,O.S.,1911-12.
2 pt.in 1 v. 19½cm.

Separate,from Programm-Königliches gymnasium
nebst realschule zu Königshütte O.S.

1.Latin language-Study and teaching.

NL 0378040   ICU

PA
2080
L74
1924
Linde, Paul, 1881-
Die Fortbildung der lateinischen Schulgrammatik nach der sprachwissenschaftlicher
Seite hin. Breslau, Trewendt und Granier,
1924.
67 p. 24cm.

"2. Aufl. der Programmabhandlungen
Königshütte 1911-13."

NL 0378041   NIC

LINDE,Paul,1881-
Griechisches lese- und übungsbuch für unter-
tertia mit grammatischem anhang. Von P.Linde
unter mitwirkung von K.Atzert und M.Schlossarek.
Griechisches wortfamilienverzeichnis von Th.
Lehmann. 2e,verbesserte aufl. Breslau,Trewendt
& Granier,1928.

Plates.
Added title-page: Schola graeca. Herausgeber
K.Atzert und M.Schlossarek.

NL 0378042   MH

Linde, Paul, 1881-
Die lateinische laut-, formen- und wortbildungslehre in den
jahre 1920-1927. Von Paul Linde ...
(In Jahresbericht über die fortschritte der klassischen altertums-
wissenschaft ... 1929. Leipzig, 1929. 22cm. 222. bd. (55. jahrg.
3. abt.) p. [59]-91)

1. Latin language—Phonology—Bibl. 2. Latin language—Pronuncia-
tion—Bibl. 3. Latin language—Inflection—Bibl. 4. Latin language—
Word formation—Bibl.
[Full name: Paul Carl Wilhelm Linde]

Rochester. Univ. Library   A 42-2757
for Library of Congress   [PA3.J3 bd. 222]
(880.5)

NL 0378043   NRU

755z Linde, Paul, 1881-
L743   ... Sophokles' Elektra im verhältnis zu der des
Euripides... Königshütte O.- S., R. Giebler,
1910.
17p. 27cm.

Program- K. Gymnasium nebst realschule, Königshütte O.- S.

NL 0378044   CU MH NjP

VOLUME 334

Linde, Paul Franz Emil, 1889–
Zur Kenntnis von Cladothrix dichotoma Cohn. ...
[Jena, 1913]
2 p.l., 26, [1] p.   23.5 cm.
Inaug.-Diss. - Berlin.
Abdruck aus dem Centralblatt für Bakteriologie,
Parasitenkunde und Infektionskrankheiten. II. Abt.
39. Bd. No. 15/17.   Jena, 1913.

NL 0378045   CtY

Linde, Paulus
see   Linde, Paul, 1881–

Linde, Peter Joseph, 1888–
Anholt, skitser af forfatteren. København, E. Myrdahls
bogtr., 1948.
187 p.   illus. 23 cm.

1. Anholt, Denmark—Descr. & trav.

DL271.A6L55   49–20058*

NL 0378047   DLC

Linde, Peter Joseph, 1888–
...Graabrødre Torv. Skitser af Forfatteren.   København,
E. Myrdahl, 1946.   174 p.   illus. 23cm.

424317B. 1. Copenhagen—Streets—   Graabrødre Torv.
N.Y.P.L.   February 25, 1948

NL 0378048   NN MH

Linde, Peter Joseph, 1888–
Julehilsen fra Nørrevold, 1945. [København, 1945] 10 l.
illus.   20cm.
"Teksten forfattet af konservator v. Nationalmuseet Peter Linde."

1. Copenhagen—Hist. 2. Copen-   hagen—Descr. I. Title: Nørrevold,
Julehilsen fra.   November 20, 1950
N.Y.P.L.

NL 0378049   NN

Linde, Peter Joseph
...Det kuriøse København.   København: P. Haase & Søn,
1931. 105 p.   plan. 8°.

617005A. 1. Copenhagen—Hist.
N.Y.P.L.   December 16, 1932

NL 0378050   NN

948.92C7
L6412 Linde, Peter Joseph, 1888–
Langs Kanalen, fra Kongens Nytorv
til Langebro, skitser af forfatteren.
København, E. Myrdahl bogtrykkeri, 1945.

172 p.   illus.   23cm.

1. Copenhagen. Description.

NL 0378051   MnU

Linde, Peter Joseph, 1888–
Latinerkvarteret, skitser af forfatteren. København, E
Myrdahls bogtr., 1949.
182 p. illus. 23 cm.

1. Copenhagen—Descr. & trav.   I. Title.
DL276.L55   914.89   A 50–1669
Minnesota. Univ. Lit.
for Library of Congress   [4]†

NL 0378052   MnU DLC

Linde, Peter Joseph
Minder om den store Ildebrand, 1728, ved Peter Linde.
Kjøbenhavn: Nyt Nordisk Forlag, 1928.   77 p.   illus. (incl.
facsim., plan.)   8°.

411050A. 1. Fires—Denmark—   Copenhagen, 1728.
N.Y.P.L.   May 16, 1929

NL 0378053   NN NIC

Linde, Peter Joseph, 1888–
Pavedømmets minder i Danmark. Skitser af forfatteren.
København, E. Myrdahls bogtr., 1950.
78 p. illus. 23 cm.

1. Christian art and symbolism. 2. Art—Denmark. 3. Popes—Portraits.   I. Title.
N7958.L5   56–43117

NL 0378054   DLC DCU MH NN

Linde, Peter Joseph
Ved Ewalds grav, Trinitatis kirke-
plads; skitser af forfatteren.   København, E. Myrdahl, 1943.

117 p.   illus.   23cm.

1. Ewald, Johannes, 1743–1781.

NL 0378055   MnU

Bu27   Linde, Peter Joseph, 1888–
C7   Vor gamle hovedstad, det København, der
+929L graves frem, ved Peter Linde, Georg Borup
og Arthur G.Hassø. Med originaltegninger
af Charles Christensen og Peter Linde.
København, C.A.Reitzel, 1929.
viii, 392p. illus., plates (part col.) 27cm.

1. Copenhagen - Hist.

NL 0378056   CtY MnU NN

Bj33a   Linde, Ph   van der
+D95   Simaloer (Simeuloeë). Weltevreden, Boekhandel
20   Visser, 1920.
152, iixp. illus., fold.col.maps, fold.facsim.
26cm. (Bureau voor de Bestuurszaken der Buiten-
gewesten, bewerkt door het Encyclopaedisch
Bureau. Mededeelingen. Afl.20)

NL 0378057   CtY

LINDE, Philander von der, pseud.

See MENCKE, Johann Burkhard, 1674–1732.

Linde, Raf van de, *pseud.*
see
Hecke, Rafaël Petrus Kamiel van, 1924–

4PQ   Linde, Rafael de la
Span   Pétalos, poesías. Prólogo del Dr.
919   Fransco Blázquez Bores.   Antequera,
Spain, Impr. "El Progreso, 1954.
1 v. (unpaged)

NL 0378060   DLC-P4

Linde, Richard, *patent attorney.*
Patent- und Erfinderrecht; gesammelte Studien als Beiträge zum Wiederaufbau der technischen Wirtschaft.
Berlin, Verlag Technik, 1949.
111 p. 21 cm.

1. Patent laws and legislation—Germany.

50–23717 rev

NL 0378061   DLC

Linde, Richard, 1860–1926.   3041.221
Alte Kulturstätten: Bilder aus Ägypten, Palästina und Griechen-
land. Mit ... Einschaltbildern und ... Textabbildungen nach
Aufnahmen des Verfassers.
— Berlin. Velhagen & Klasing. 1911. (8). 212 pp. Illus. Plates.
27 cm., in 8s.

H7353 — Palestine. Antiq. — Greece. Antiq. — Egypt. Antiq. — Antiquities.

NL 0378062   MB

Linde, Richard, 1860–
Alte kulturstätten; bilder aus Ägypten, Syrien, Palästina und Griechenland, von prof. dr. Richard Linde.
Mit 125 bildern nach aufnahmen des verfassers. 2. aufl.
Bielefeld und Leipzig, Velhagen & Klasing, 1924.
3 p. l., 201 p. illus., plates. 25¼ᶜᵐ. (Added t.-p.: Monographien zur
erdkunde ... 31)

1. Levant—Descr. & trav.   I. Title.

Library of Congress   DS44.5.L5   26–18191

NL 0378063   DLC NN ICRL PP MiU ICJ MB IU

Linde, Richard, 1860–
De diversis recensionibus Appolonii
Rhodii Argonauticon...Hannoverae.
Typis G.L.Schraderi, 1885.
51p.
Inaug. diss.-Hannover.
Vita.

NL 0378064   MiU CtY ICRL NjP PBm PU OClW

Linde, Richard, 1860–
Die Lüneburger heide, von Dr. Richard Linde. Mit 111
abbildungen nach photographischen aufnahmen des verfassers
und einer farbigen karte. Bielefeld und Leipzig, Velhagen &
Klasing, 1904.
3 p. l., 149 p. illus., plates, fold. map. 25¼ᶜᵐ. (Added t.-p.: Land und
leute, monographien zur erdkunde ... hrsg. von A. Scobel. XVIII)

Title in red and black.
"Literatur": p. [144]

1. Lüneburg Heath—Descr. & trav.   I. Title.

5—8064

Library of Congress   DD491.H34L7

NL 0378065   DLC FMU ICRL MiU NN ICJ

VOLUME 334

Linde, Richard, 1860–
Lüneburger Heide.   Bielefeld, Velhagen,
1905.
Aufl. 2.
153 S.   illus.   4°.

NL 0378066   PPG

Linde, Richard, 1860–
Die Lüneburger heide...   Mit 114
abbildungen nach photographischen aufnahmen des verfassers und einer farbigen
karte.   3.aufl.   Bielefeld und Leipzig,
Velhagen & Klasing, 1907.
153p.   illus. plates, fold. map.
(Added t.p. Land und leute, monographien
zur erdkunde...)

NL 0378067   MiHM

Linde, Richard. 1860–
Die Lüneburger Heide. 4. Auflage.
— Bielefeld. Velhagen & Klasing. 1911. (7), 158 pp. Illus. Por-
trait. Plates. Map. [Land und Leute. Monographien zur Erd-
kunde. 18.] 25½ cm., in 8s.
Literatur, pp. 151, 152.

H8619 — Lueneburger Heath, Prussia. — S.r.

NL 0378068   MB

943.5d   Linde, Richard, 1860–1926
L74ℓ   Die Lüneburger heide... 6.aufl.
Ed.6   Bielefeld, Velhagen, 1921.
152p. illus.,col.plates, map. Q.
(Added t.-p.: Monographien zur erdkunde, 18)
"Literatur": p.146–147.

NL 0378069   IaU OC1

DD 491   Linde, Richard, 1860–1926.
H34 L5   Die Lüneburger Heide. 7. Aufl. Bielefeld.
1924   Velhagen & Klasing, 1924.
153 p. illus., plates (part col.) fold. col.
map. 25 cm. (Monographien zur Erdkunde, 18)
Bibliography: p. 147.

NL 0378070   OU OrU NcU

Linde, Richard, 1860–1926.
Die Niederelbe. Mit 8 Einschaltbildern und 118
Textabbildungen nach Aufnahmen des Verfassers.
Berlin, Velhagen & Klasing, [1908]
4 p.l., 251 (1) p., 1 map, 8 pl. 4°.

NL 0378071   NN

Linde, Richard, 1860–1926.
Die Niederelbe. Mit 8 Einschaltbildern und 118 Textabbildungen nach Aufnahmen des Verfassers. 3. Aufl. Bielefeld, Velhagen, 1909.
251 p. illus. (part col.) fold. col. map. 28 cm.
"Literatur": p. [250]–251.

1. Elbe River and Valley—Descr. & trav. 2. Hamburg—Descr.

DD801.E3L6 1909   49–35855*

NL 0378072   DLC IaU ViU

Linde, Richard, 1860–
Die Niederelbe, von Richard Linde, mit 106 meist ganzseitigen bildern, darunter vier farbigen, nach aufnahmen
des verfassers und einer übersichtskarte. 4. aufl. Bielefeld und Leipzig, Velhagen & Klasing, 1913.
3 p. l., 202 p. illus. (incl. ports.) plates (part col.) fold. map. 25½cm.
(*Added t.-p.:* Land und leute; monographien zur erdkunde ... 28)
"Literatur": p. [201]–202.

1. Elbe River and Valley—Descr. & trav. 2. Hamburg—Descr.

13–13071

Library of Congress   DD801.E3L6

NL 0378073   DLC ICRL MiU OC1 ICJ NN IU

Linde, Richard, 1860–1926,   4862.70
Die Niederelbe. Mit 106 meist ganzseitigen Bildern . . . 6e Auflage.
— Bielefeld. Velhagen & Klasing. 1924. (6), 200 pp. Illus. Plates,
some colored. [Monographien zur Erdkunde. 28.] 24½ cm., in
8s.
Literatur, pp. 199, 200.

NL 0378074   MB ViU

Linde, Richard, 1876–   joint author.

Knoblauch, Oscar, 1862–
Die thermischen eigenschaften des gesättigten und des überhitzten wasserdampfes zwischen 100° und 180° C. I. teil.
Bericht über die bestimmung der dichte des gesättigten und
des überhitzten wasserdampfes zwischen 100° und 180° C.
Von Osc. Knoblauch, R. Linde und H. Klebe.
(*In* Mitteilungen über forschungsarbeiten auf dem gebiete des in-
genieurwesens ... Berlin, 1905. 26½cm. hft. 21, p. [33]–55. tables,
diagrs. (1 fold.))

Linde, Richard, 1876–
Die thermischen eigenschaften des gesättigten und über-
hitzten wasserdampfes zwischen 100° und 180° C. II. teil.
Theoretische folgerungen. Von Richard Linde.
(*In* Mitteilungen über forschungsarbeiten auf dem gebiete des in-
genieurwesens ... Berlin, 1905. 26½cm. hft. 21, p. [57]–92. tables,
diagrs.)
Bibliographical foot-notes.

1. Steam, Superheated. 2. Specific heat.

P O 28–116

Library. U. S. Patent   Office TA3.F732

NL 0378076   DP

Linde, Richard, 1876–
Ueber die thermischen eigenschaften des gesättigten
und überhitzten wasserdampfes zwischen 100° und 180° C.
... Berlin, Buchdr. A. W. Schade, 1904.
44 p. incl. diagrs. diagrs. on fold. pl. 27cm.
Inaug.-diss.—Tech. hochschule, München.

1. Steam, Superheated.
Full name: Richard Franz Ferdinand Linde
9–1421

Library of Congress   TJ272.L7

NL 0378077   DLC CU CtY PU

Linde, Richard von der, 1880–
Über Oxydations- und Reduktionsketten. ... Von Richard von
der Linde ... . Marburg, Universitäts-Buchdruckerei (R. Friedrich), 1902.
75, [1] p. 2 illus., 1 fold. diagr. 23cm.
Inaug.-dis.—Marburg.
"Lebenslauf."

NL 0378078   ICJ ICRL PU

Linde, Richard Wesley Te
see
Te Linde, Richard Wesley, 1894–

QA   Linde, Roelof Johan van der
519   A method for determining the daily variations
L56   in width of a shadow in connection with the time
of the year and the orientation of the over-
shadowing object [by] R.J.v.d. Linde and
J.P.M. Woudenberg. ['s-Gravenhage, Rijksuitgeverij, 1946]
6 p.   illus.
Text in English and German.

NL 0378080   KMK

Linde, Roelof Johan van der.
On the microclimatic properties of sheltered
areas; the oak coppice sheltered area [by]
R.J. van der Linde and J.P.M. Woudenberg.
s'Gravenhage, Staatsdrukkerij- en Uitgeverij-
bedrijf, 1950.
151p. 24cm. (Koninklijk Nederlands
Meterologisch Instituut. Mededelingen en
verhandelingen, no.102, Serie A, 56)
"Verschijnt teven als Mededeling no.10
van het Instituut voor Toegepast Biologisch
Onderzoek in de Natuur."

NL 0378081   TxU DNAL CtY OU DI

Linde, Roelof Johan van der.
The problem of the woodplantings between cultivated
fields; the microclimate of oak-coppice sheltered areas.
Arnhem, G. W. van der Wiel [1951]
159 p. illus. 25 cm.
Proefschrift—Utrecht.
Translated by Mr. Schenkel.
"Stellingen": [2] p. inserted.
Bibliography : p. 157–159.

1. Windbreaks, shelter belts, etc. 2. Bioclimatology.   I. Title:
Woodplantings between cultivated fields.

SB437.L5   54–39230

NL 0378082   DLC OrU MH IU MiU InU OU

Linde, Samuel Bogumił, 1771–1847
De solatus adversus mortis horrores in
Platone & Novs testamento obviis commentatio...
Lipsiae, 1792.
32 p. Diss.

NL 0378083   PBm

Linde, Samuel Bogumił, 1771–1847
Grundsätze der wortforschung angewandt
auf die polnische sprache. Warschau, 1806.
v. 1

NL 0378084   PU

Bonaparte
Collection LINDE, SAMUEL BOGUMIŁ, 1771–1847.
No.13541   O języku dawnych Prusaków; rozbior dzieła
professora Vatera, przez Samuela Bogumiła Linde
Czytany na posiedzeniu publiczném Królewskiego
towarzystwa warszawskiego przyiacioł nauk dnia 26
listopada 1821.   Warszawa, W drukarni Xięży
Piiarów, 1822.
116p. 19cm.

On J.S.Vater's Die sprache der alten Preussen.

NL 0378085   ICN

VOLUME 334

Rare Books Dept. Linde, Samuel Bogumił, 1771-1847.
O statucie Litewskim ruskim językiem i drukiem wydanym, wiadomość ... Warszawie, Nakładem i Drukiem Zawadzkiego i Węckiego Uprzywilejowanych Drukarzy i Xięgarzy Dworu Królestwa Polskiego, 1816.
4 p.ℓ., 218, [20] p. 2 fold. plates. 22cm.

NL 0378086   CU MH PU WU

Hukl6 Al L64 Linde, Samuel Bogumił, 1771-1847.
Słownik języka polskiego, przez M. Samuela Bogumiła Linde ... W Warszawie, W drukarni XX. Piiarów, 1807-14.
4 v. in 6. 25½cm.
Tom 1-2 in two parts each; [tom 3] called "Część III. czyli volumen V"; [tom 4] called "Tom VI."
Vol. 2-5, W Warszawie, U autore; v.6, W Warszawie, U autora i w drukarni Xięży Piiarów.

NL 0378087   CtY MiU ICN ViU DCU MiU CoU

Linde, Samuel Bogumił, 1771-1847.
Słownik języka polskiego przez M. Samuela Bogumiła Linde. Wyd. 2., poprawne i pomnożone. Lwów, W Druk. Zakładu Ossolińskich, 1854-60.
6 v. 30 cm.
"Żywot Samuela Bogumiła Lindego," by August Bielowski: v. 1, p. [15]-39.
"Prawidła etymologii, przystosowane do języka polskiego" (in Polish and German) v. 1, p. [xix]-lxi.

———— Indeks a tergo do Słownika języka polskiego S. B. Lindego pod red. Witolda Doroszewskiego. [Opracowały R. Grzegorczykowa, Z. Kurzowa, J. Puzynina. Wyd. 1. Warszawa, 1965.
392 p. 24 cm. (Wydawnictwa Uniwersytetu Warszawskiego)
At head of title: Uniwersytet Warszawski.
"Pracownia Leksygologiczna przy Katedrze Języka Polskiego UW" mounted on p. 7.
1. Polish language—Dictionaries. 2. Polish language—Glossaries, vocabularies, etc.   I. Bielowski, August, 1806-1876. II. Doroszewski, Witold, ed.   III. Grzegorczykowa, R. IV. Kawyn-Kurzowa, Zofia.   v. Puzynina, Jadwiga. VI. Title.
PG6625.L48 Index   11-2477 rev

    WU NjP MB MH
NL 0378089   DLC CaBVaU NN CoU CtY ICU InU PCamA PSt

Linde, Samuel Bogumił, 1771-1847.
Słownik języka polskiego. Wyd. 3. fotooffsetowe. [Warszawa] Państwowy Instytut Wydawniczy, 1951.
6 v. 28 cm.
Preface and biographical sketch of the author by August Bielowski in v. 1.
Introduction also in French and German.
With reproduction of title pages of 2d ed., 1854-1860.
"Prawidła etymologii, przystosowane do języka polskiego" (Polish and German) v. 1, p. [xix]-lxiv.
Includes bibliographies.
1. Polish language—Dictionaries. 2. Polish language—Etymology—Dictionaries.   I. Title.
PG6625.L5 1951   52-44067

    PSt OCl NcD OU WaU MoU CtY IU C MU
NL 0378090   DLC InU OClW IaU TNJ IEN CSt PU NcU

LINDE, Samuel Gottlieb.

See LINDE, Samuel Bogumił, 1771-1847

LINDE, Samuel Theophilus.

See LINDE, Samuel Bogumił, 1771-1847

Linde, Sibyl H.
Fergal the Great, a short play in one act, by Sibyl H. Linde; adapted from "In the days of the scholars" by Scheumas McManus. San Francisco, Calif., Cincinnati, O., Banner play bureau, inc., c1937.
11 p. 19¼cm.

   I. MacManus, Seumas, 1869-
   II. Title.   In the days of the scholars.
                           38-22689
   Library of Congress   PR6025.A282 I 65
   ———— Copy 2.
   Copyright D pub. 54234   [2]   822.91

NL 0378093   DLC

Linde, Sibyl H.
Shelved for the summer, an English literature review play in one act, by Sibyl H. Linde ... San Francisco, Calif., Cincinnati, O., Banner play bureau, inc., c1937.
12 p. 19¼cm.

   I. Title.
                           38-22707
   Library of Congress   PN6120.A5L48
   ———— Copy 2.
   Copyright D pub. 54237   [2]   812.5

NL 0378094   DLC

Linde, Siegmund, 1847-
Wurzel-parasiten und angebliche bodenerschöpfung in bezug auf die kleemüdigkeit und analoge krankheitserscheinungen bei ungenügendem pflanzenwechsel ... Freiburg in Baden, Universitäts-buchdr. von C. Lehmann, 1880.
2 p. l., 64 p. tab. 20½cm.
Inaug.-diss.—Leipzig.

1. Soil exhaustion. 2. Root parasites. 3. Rotation of crops.
                         Agr 3-404
   Library, U. S. Dept. of   Agriculture 57L64

NL 0378095   DNAL

Linde, Sigm.
Der vermeintliche Opfertod Jesu im Lichte der Evangelien nebst Beitraegen zu der den Weltfrieden foerdernden Zukunftskirche. Berlin, W. Borngraeber Vlg., 1916.
128 p. 22.5 cm.

NL 0378096   MH-AH

Wason BV1561 L74 Linde, Simon van der, 1905-
Kursus agama Christen, terutama untuk pengerdja2 dan anggota2 Geredja Toradja. Rante Pao, 1949.
2 v. in 1. 20 cm.

Cover title.

1. Religious education—Indonesia—Celebes. 2. Protestant churches—Indonesia.

NL 0378097   NIC

GU2 L641l Linde, Simon van der, 1905-
De leer van den Heiligen Geest bij Calvijn; bijdrage tot de kennis der reformatorische theologie. Wageningen, H. Veenman, 1943.
xvi, 256 p. 24 cm.

Proefschrift - Utrecht.
"Stellingen": [4] p. inserted.
Bibliography: p. [249]-253.

1. Calvin, Jean, 1509-1564. 2. Holy Spirit

   MH-AH ICU NjP NjPT CtY
NL 0378098   CtY-D NcU PU MiU MH NcD NNUT NjNbS DCU

Linde, Sven, pseud.
see
Carlborg, Axel.

Linde, Sven, 1847-
Adversaria in Latinos scriptores. Lundæ: E. Malmström, 1899. 1 p.l., 59(1) p. 4°. (Lund. Universitet. Acta universitatis Lundensis. Lunds universitets årsskrift. Bd. 36, afdeln. 1, nr. 3, 1900.)

1. Latin language.
N. Y. P. L.   December 15, 1911.

NL 0378100   NN OCU PU

Linde, Sven, 1847-
...Brevställaren; affärs- & privatkorrespondens, platsansökningar, tjänste- & tjänstgöringsbetyg...av Sven Linde. Genomsedd och granskad av A. Bergström... Uppsala: J. A. Lindblad[, 1924]. 129 p. 12°. (Lindblads handböcker. no. 7.)

1. Letter writing, Swedish. 2. Bergström, A., editor.
N. Y. P. L.   November 17, 1925

NL 0378101   NN

Linde, Sven, 1847-
De Iano summo Romanorum deo. Scripsit Sv. Linde. Lundæ: Typis Berlingianis, 1891. 54 p. 4°. (Lund. Universitet. Acta Universitatis Lundensis. Lunds universitets årsskrift. Tomus 27, afdelning 1[, no. 1].)
Bibliographical footnotes.

1. Janus.
N. Y. P. L.   December 29, 1925

NL 0378102   NN PU

Linde, Sven, 1847-
Emenandatione Plutarcheal. n. p. n.p. 1885-86.
17 p.

NL 0378103   PU

LINDE, Sven, 1847-
Främmande ord i svenska språket; med uttalsbeteckning och förklaringar. [2.uppl.] Stockholm. Fröléen. 1909. 170p. (Fröléens handböcker, nr.4)

NL 0378104   WaS

Linde, Sven, 1847-
Främmande ord i svenska språket; med uttalsbeteckningar och förklaringar av Sven Linde... Uppsala: J. A. Lindblads Förlag [1923]. 168 p. 6. ed. 12°.

146035A. 1. Swedish language.—   Foreign words and phrases.
N. Y. P. L.   October 9, 1924

NL 0378105   NN

Linde, Sven, 1847-
Främmande ord i svenska spraket. [1925]

NL 0378106   NcU

VOLUME 334

439.73 Linde, Sven, 1847–
L641f7   Främmande ord i svenska språket. 7.
           fullständigt omarbetade uppl., utgiven
           av Roland Liljefors. Uppsala, J. A.
           Lindblad [1936]
           173 p.

           1. Swedish language – Foreign words and
           phrases – Dictionaries. I. Title.

NL 0378107   WaU PU

Linde, Sven, 1847–
   Grammatiska och textkritiska undersökningar.   Lund: H.
Ohlsson, 1906. 35 p. 4°. (Lund. Universitet. Acta universitatis Lundensis. Lunds universitets årsskrift. Bd. 40, afdeln.
1, nr. 1, 1904.)

1. Bible.—Criticism (Textual).
N. Y. P. L   December 15, 1911.

NL 0378108   NN PU

Linde, Sven, 1847–
   Grekiska och latinska etymologier.   Lund: E. Malmström,
1898. 1 p.l., 56 p. 4°. (Lund. Universitet. Acta universitatis Lundensis. Lunds universitets årsskrift. Bd. 34, afdeln.
1, nr. 4, 1898.)

1. Greek language.—Etymology.   2. Latin language.—Etymology.
N. Y. P. L.   December 14, 1911.

NL 0378109   NN PU

Linde, Sven, 1847–
   Hermesmythen hos greker och romare, från språkveten-
skaplig synpunkt framstäld af Sven Linde.   Lund: Berlingska
boktryckeri- och stilgjuteri-aktiebolaget, 1892. 80 p. 4°.
(Lund. Universitet. Acta Universitatis Lundensis. Lunds universitets årsskrift. Tomus 28, afdelning 1[, no. 1].)

Bibliographical footnotes.

1. Hermes. 2. Mythology—Com-   parative.
N. Y. P. L.   December 29, 1925.

NL 0378110   NN PU

         Linde, Sven, 1847–
            Indogermanernas högste gud, af Sven Linde ...
Geog   Lund, Gleerupska universitets-bokhandeln [1889]
GN 539   2 p.l., 100 p. 24½ cm. [With Feist, S.
.F 29   Indogermanen und germanen. Halle a.S., 1914]
1914

NL 0378111   MdBJ NIC MnU MH

Linde, Sven, 1847–
   Quaestiones criticae in S. Annaei
Senecae Epistulas morales. n. p. n. p.
1886.

   17 p.

NL 0378112   PU

Linde, S[ven], 1847–
   Quaestiones criticae in Senecam rhetorem.   Lundæ: H.
Ohlsson, 1905. 14 p. 4°. (Lund. Universitet. Acta universitatis Lundensis. Lunds universitets årsskrift. Bd. 40, afdeln.
1, nr. 2, 1904.)

1. Seneca, Marcus Annæus.
N. Y. P. L.   December 15, 1911.

NL 0378113   NN PU

Linde, Sven, 1847–   2981.11
   Quæstiones etymologicæ et grammaticæ, ad exempla Dorica Attico-
rum scriptorum relatæ. Disputatio academica.
Lundae. Berling. 1879. (3), 57, (1) pp. 25 cm., in 4s.

K2254 — Greece. Lang. Ancient Greek. Dialects. Doric.

NL 0378114   MB

Linde, Sven, 1912–
   Studies on the stimulation mechanism of gastric secretion.
Uppsala, 1950.
     92 p. 24 cm. (Acta physiologica Scandinavica, v. 21. Supple-
mentum 74)

     At head of title: ... From the Institute of Physiology, University
of Uppsala, Sweden.
     Akademisk avhandling—Uppsala.
     Extra t. p., with thesis statement, inserted.
     Bibliography: p. 89–92.

     1. Stomach—Secretions.   (Series)

                               Full name: Sven Gustav Linde.

QP193.L46   612.323   51–3042

NL 0378115   DLC CoU ViU NIC

Linde, Theodor, 1831–1894.
   Samling af reskripter, resolutioner samt kollegiale og minis-
terielle skrivelser af mere almindelig interesse, fra 1660 til
1860. Udgiven af Th. Linde ... P. Schjørring ... og O. Al-
green-Ussing ... Kjøbenhavn, G. E. C. Gad, 1862–65.
     2 v. 20ᵐ.
     Vol. 1 has general and special title-pages; v. 2 has special t.-p. only.
     "Vi have ... omarbejdet eller forkortet mangfoldige af de optagne
bestemmelser."—v. 1, p. v.
     CONTENTS.—1. bd. 1660–1835.—2. bd. 1836–1860. Register.
     1. Law—Denmark. 2. Law—Norway. 1. *Schjørring, Peter, 1831–
1913. II. Ussing, Otto Algreen-, 1835–1885. III. Denmark. Laws, statutes. etc. IV. Norway. Laws, statutes, etc. V. Denmark. Sovereigns,
etc. VI. Title.

                                               37–37394

     Library of Congress   [3]   [347.09489] 349.489

NL 0378116   DLC

834L642 Linde, Verena zur, 1871–
Of1913   Feldblumen, gedichte ..   Gr.-Lichterfelde,
          Charonverlag, 1913.
          190p.

NL 0378117   IU

         Linde, Vladimir Vladimirovich, 1878–   ed.
3F553
V8   Kul'tura ...

         Vsesoiuznaia akademiia sel'skokhoziaistvennykh nauk im.
         V. I. Lenina. Komissiia shelkovodstva.
            Культура дубового шелкопряда в СССР; труды совеща-
         ния за 1945–1946 гг. Под ред. В. В. Линде и М. С. Павель-
         евой. Москва, Сельхозгиз, 1948.

NL 0378119   DLC

Linde, Vladimir Vladimirovich, 1878–
   Общая механическая технология волокнистых материа-
лов. Допущено в качестве учебника для вузов текстил.
промышл. Москва, Гос. научно-техн. изд-во текстил., лег-
кой и полигр. промышл., 19—
     v. illus. 23 cm.
     At head of title, v.   : В. В. Линде и Н. И. Труевцев.
     Errata slip inserted. ... v. 2.
     Bibliography: v. 2, p. [373].
     CONTENTS.—
     ч. 2. Прядение шерсти и технология шелка.
     1. Textile industry and fabrics. I. Truevtsev, N. I., joint author.
     II. Title.

            Title transliterated: Obshchaia mekhanicheskaia
            tekhnologiia voloknistykh materialov.

TS1445.L59   54–24405

NL 0378119   DLC

Linde, Vladimir Vladimirovich, 1878–
   Die Seide, von W. W. Linde und P. A. Ossipow. [Übers.
aus dem Russischen von Robert Otto und Herbert Prieb]
Leipzig, Fachbuchverlag, 1954.
     526 p. illus. 24 cm.
     Translation of Технология шелка (transliterated: Tekhnologiia
shelka)
     Bibliography: p. 525–526.

     1. Silk manufacture and trade.   I. Osipov, P. A., joint author.

TS1665.L514   56–19236 ‡

NL 0378120   DLC CU PPF ICJ NN

Linde Janszoon, Gerrit van de

                see

Linde, Gerrit van de, 1808–1858.

741.9   Linde-Walther, Heinrich, 1868–1939
L641p   Plattdeutsche Spruchweisheiten. Mit
           mehrfarbigen Bildern. Vorwort von Alfred
           Richard Meyer. Wolfshagen-Scharbeutz
           (Lübecker Bucht) F. Westphal [°1955]
           [39] p., incl. 31 p. of col. illus.

           1. Caricatures and cartoons 2. Proverbs,
           German I. Meyer, Alfred Richard, 1882–

NL 0378122   MiD MH OCU

Linde Air Products Company.
     The Linde Air Products Company was incorporated in 1907.
After becoming a division of the Union Carbide Corporation, its
name was changed in 1917 to Linde Company. The name was again
changed in 1963 to Linde Division.

Linde Air Products Company.
     Bibliography on oxygen therapy. Rev. ed. New York,
1947.
     99 p. 28 cm.
————— Supplement. New York [1953–
     v. 28 cm.

                               Z6665.O9L5 1947 Suppl.

     1. Oxygen therapy—Bibl.

Z6665.O9L5 1947   016.615221   47–28630 rev*

         NBuG OCl
NL 0378124   DLC CaBVaU ICU ViU IParkA ICJ OU Or

Linde air products company.
Fetherston, Thomas Cook, 1895–   FOR OTHER EDITIONS
                                        SEE MAIN ENTRY
   Cast iron welding by the oxy-acetylene process, compiled by
T. C. Fetherston ... New York, The Linde air products com-
pany, 1925.

The Linde air products company.
[Catalog] no. 184. TS227
[Buffalo? c 1911]   .L6

NL 0378126   DLC

VOLUME 334

Linde air products company.
Current practices for welding aluminum. New York, The
Linde air products company [*1935]
10, [2] p. illus. 28 x 21½ᵉᵐ.

1. Welding. 2. Aluminium. 3. Aluminium alloys. I. Title.

Library of Congress	TS227.L613	36–7969
——— Copy 2.		
Copyright AA 191731	[3]	671

NL 0378127   DLC

Linde air products company.
Design of welded piping. New York, The Linde air prod-
ucts company [*1936]
197, [2] p. incl. illus., tables, diagrs. 24ᵉᵐ.
"This book ... replaces 'Design standards for oxwelded steel and
wrought iron piping', first published in 1929."—Foreword.
Blank pages for "Notes" ([2] at end)
"Design of expansion bends in piping. Bibliography": p. 188.

1. Pipe. I. Title: Welded piping.

| Library of Congress | TS280.L5 | 37–15070 |
| | [5–2] | 671 |

NL 0378128   DLC WaS DI TU MiU OU MB ICJ

Linde air products company.
Design of welded piping. New York: The Linde air products
co. [etc., etc., c1938]   vi, 9–197 p. incl. diagrs., tables.   23cm.
"Bibliography," p. 188.

1. Pipe—Welding. 2. Pipe   fittings.
N.Y.P.L.   September 12, 1941

NL 0378129   NN

Linde air products company.
Design standards for oxwelded steel and wrought iron piping. New York, The Linde air products company [*1929]
67, [1] p. diagrs. 23ᵉᵐ.

1. Pipe. I. Title.

| Library, Smithsonian | Institution | S 30–14 |

NL 0378130   DSI MB OCl IU ICJ

Linde air products company
Design standards for oxwelded steel
and wrought iron piping   N.Y.
The Linde air products co. c1930.

67 p.

NL 0378131   PPD

669.173 The Linde air products company.
L64e   Engineering and management phases of
oxwelded construction; a series of recently published articles and addresses,
reprinted from engineering periodicals.
New York [1925?]
64p. illus., diagrs.

NL 0378132   IU NN

TS227
.L615   **Linde air products company.**
1925   Engineering and management phases of
oxwelded construction, a series of recently
published articles and addresses, reprinted
from engineering periodicals.   <2d ed.,
New York, N. Y., The Linde air products company [1925?]
64 p.   illus., diagrs.   23cm.

1. Welding.   I. Title.

NL 0378133   DLC CU

Linde air products company.
Fabrication of oxwelded piping. New York, The Linde air
products company [*1933]
156, [4] p. incl. illus., tables, diagrs. 23ᵉᵐ.
Blank pages for "Notes" ([4] at end)
"Supersedes 'Fabrication of welded piping designs' published in 1929
and contains much new material."—Foreword.

1. Welding. 2. Pipe. I. Title. II. Title: Oxwelded piping.

		33—36794
Library of Congress	TS227.L628 1933	
	[a36d2]	671

NL 0378134   DLC WaSp WaS MB TU PPD ICJ NN IU

Linde air products company.
Fabrication of oxwelded piping. New York, The Linde
air products company [*1934]
156, [4] p. incl. illus., tables, diagrs. 23ᵉᵐ.
Blank pages for "Notes" ([4] at end)
"Supersedes 'Fabrication of welded piping designs' published in 1929
and contains much new material."—Foreword.

1. Welding. 2. Pipe. I. Title. II. Title: Oxwelded piping.

		35–1741
Library of Congress	TS227.L628 1934	
Copyright A 71582	[2]	671

NL 0378135   DLC PPF

Linde air products company.
Fabrication of oxwelded piping. (3d ed.) New York, The
Linde air products company [*1936]
156, [4] p. incl. illus., tables, diagrs. 23ᵉᵐ.
Blank pages for "Notes" ([4] at end)

1. Welding. 2. Pipe. I. Title. II. Title: Oxwelded piping.

		36–13174
Library of Congress	TS227.L628 1936	
——— Copy 2.		
Copyright A 94775	[3]	671

NL 0378136   DLC

Linde air products company.
Fabrication of oxy-acetylene, welded steel and wrought
iron piping; oxy-acetylene welding steel and wrought iron,
procedure control for installation of piping systems, layout
of templets and pipe joints, data for estimating costs. New
York [etc.] The Linde air products company; Toronto,
Dominion oxygen company, limited [*1940]
64 p. incl. illus., tables, diagrs. 23 cm.
"An abstract of [its] ... 'Fabrication of welded piping.'"—p. 3.

1. Welding. 2. Pipe. 3. Pipe, Steel. I. Title.

| TS227.L628 1940 | 671 | 42—23282 |

NL 0378137   DLC ICU NN

Linde air products company.
Fabrication of welded piping. (4th ed.) New York, The
Linde air products company [*1937]
159, [1] p. incl. illus., tables, diagrs. 23ᵉᵐ.
Blank page for "Notes" at end.
Previous editions have title: Fabrication of oxwelded piping.

1. Welding. 2. Pipe. I. Title. II. Title: Welded piping, Fabrication of.

		38–1053
Library of Congress	TS227.L628 1937	
Copy 2.		
Copyright A 112655	[3]	671

NL 0378138   DLC ICJ

Linde air products company.
Fabrication of welded piping designs. New York, The
Linde air products company [*1929]
86 p. diagrs. 23ᵉᵐ.

1. Pipe.

| Library, Smithsonian | Institution | S 30–15 |

NL 0378139   DSI PPD ICJ NN MB NBuG

LINDE AIR PRODUCTS COMPANY
Flame-hardening; a flexible and efficient
surface-hardening method.   Author c1940?»
9 p.

NL 0378140   Or

Linde air products company.
Fusion welding cast iron ... New York, The Linde air products company; Toronto, Dominion oxygen company, limited
[1942]
11, [1] p. illus. 28 x 21½ᵉᵐ.

1. Welding. 2. Cast-iron. I. Title.

		42–25563
Library of Congress	TT211.L48	
	[3]	671

NL 0378141   DLC

Linde air products company.
Handbook of current practices in operating oxygen therapy
equipment. New York, The Linde air products company
[*1937]
38 p. illus. 19ᵉᵐ.
"Available literature": p. 36–38.

1. Oxygen—Therapeutic use. I. Title.

		40–34285
Library of Congress	RM666.O8L47 1937	
Copyright AA 245689	[2]	615.221

NL 0378142   DLC

Linde air products company.
Handbook of current practices in operating oxygen therapy
equipment. New York, The Linde air products company
[*1938]
38 p. illus. 19ᵉᵐ.
"Available literature": p. 36–38.

1. Oxygen—Therapeutic use. I. Title.

		40–34286
Library of Congress	RM666.O8L47 1938	
Copyright AA 252866	[2]	615.221

NL 0378143   DLC

VOLUME 334

Linde air products company.
Handbook of current practices in operating oxygen therapy equipment. New York, The Linde air products company [*1939]
42 p., 1 l. illus. 19ᵐ.
"Available literature": p. 40–42; "Bibliographical references": p. 42.

1. Oxygen—Therapeutic use.   ɪ. Title.
                                                    39–5876
Library of Congress   RM666.O8L47
Copyright AA 290832   [2]   615.221

NL   0378144   DLC ICJ

Linde air products company.
Handbook of current practices in operating oxygen therapy equipment. New York, The Linde air products company [1940]
46 p., 1 l. illus. 19ᵐ.
"Sixth printing, March, 1940. 15,000."
"Bibliographical references": p. 45.

1. Oxygen—Therapeutic use.   ɪ. Title.
                                                    40–32231
Library of Congress   RM666.O8L47 1940
———— Copy 2.
Copyright AA 332322   [2]   615.221

NL   0378145   DLC IParkA

WB
343
O9   Linde Air Products Company
L743h   Handbook of current practices in operating
1941   oxygen therapy equipment. New York, The Linde
            Air Products Company, [1941].
            46 p., illus., 19 cm.

NL   0378146   IParkA OrU-M

●TS227   (The) Linde air products company.
L624   How to bronze-weld.   New York, The Linde
            air products company [c1935]
            cover-title, 10p.   illus.   28cm. in 30½cm.

1. Welding. 2. Bronze. ɪ. Title.

NL   0378147   NBuG

Linde air products company.
How to bronze-weld cylinder blocks. New York, The Linde air products company [*1933]
cover-title, 11, [1] p. illus. 28ᵐ.

1. Welding.   ɪ. Title.
                                                    A 40–472
Grosvenor library   TS227.L625
for Library of Congress   [2]

NL   0378148   NBuG

Linde air products company.
How to increase efficiency in hand-cutting operations ... **New York**, The Linde air products company; Toronto, Dominion oxygen company, limited, 1942.
23, [1] p. incl. illus., tables, diagrs. 28 x 21½ᵐ.

1. Oxyacetylene welding and cutting.   ɪ. Title.
                                                    42–10979
Library of Congress   TS227.L629
                              [3]   671

NL   0378149   DLC

Linde air products company.
How to wrinkle-bend ferrous and non-ferrous pipe ... New York, The Linde air products company; Toronto, Dominion oxygen company, limited [*1941]
15 p. incl. illus., tables, diagrs. 28 x 21½ᵐ.

1. Pipe.   ɪ. Title.
                                                    42–4509
Library of Congress   TA492.P6L5
                                                    621.8672

NL   0378150   DLC

The Linde Air Products Co.
How welded joints solved pipe lines troubles. 1923.

NL   0378151   PPUG

Linde air products company.
[Instruction bulletins]   New York [c1940–]   v.
diagrs., illus. (incl. charts.)   28cm.

1. Welding, Oxy-acetylene.
N. Y. P. L.   June 30, 1942

NL   0378152   NN

Linde Air Products Company.
Linde metalworking bulletin
      see   Linde welding and cutting progress.

Linde air products company.
The Linde oxwelder.   New York, c1925.
1 v.   26 cm.

NL   0378154   PSt

TS225   Linde air products company
.A187   Linde tips. v. 1–   Aug. 1922–
            [New York] Linde air products company [1922–

The Linde air products company.
[Liquid air, liquid oxygen, liquid air apparatus, nitrogen apparatus, oxygen apparatus, vacuum vessels ?] Buffalo, N. Y., 1910.   TJ992
                                                    .L58

NL   0378156   DLC

Linde air products co.
Maintenance of reciprocating parts.
..N.Y. author c1934.

7 p.

NL   0378157   PPD

Linde air products company.
●TS227   Oil well casings now Lindewelded.   New
L625   York, The Linde air products company [c1935]
            cover-title, 7[1]p.   illus.   28cm.

1. Welding.   2. Oil industries.   I. Title.

NL   0378158   NBuG

Linde air products company.
●TS227   101 uses for the air-acetylene flame.
L628   New York, The Linde air products company, c1934.
            cover-title, 7p.   photos.   30½cm.

1. Acetylene.   2. Welding.   I. Title.

NL   0378159   NBuG PPD

Linde air products company.
Outline training course for aircraft welders. New York, N. Y., The Linde air products company, c1930.
8 p.   diagrs.
TL671.5

NL   0378160   DLC WaS

LINDE AIR PRODUCTS COMPANY.
Oxweld instruction manual; principles and operation of Oxweld oxy-acetylene equipment. New York: The Linde air products co. [c1937] 47 p. incl. diagrs., tables. illus. 23cm.

1. Welding, Oxy-acetylene, 1937. I. Title.

NL   0378161   NN

Linde Air Products Company.
Oxwelded construction for modern piping services.
— New York. [1927.] 77 pp. Illus. 23 cm.

NL   0378162   MB TU MiD

Linde Air Products Company
Oxwelded construction for modern piping services. New York, N. Y., The Linde Air Products Company [*1929]
77, [2] p. illus. 23½ᵐ.

NL   0378163   ICJ CU DLC

Linde air products company.
Oxwelded construction for modern piping services. New York, N. Y., The Linde air products company [*1930]
77 p. illus. 23ᵐ.

1. Welding. 2. Pipe. ɪ. Title.
                                                    30–23789
Library of Congress   TS227.L63
Copyright AA 49473   [3]   671

NL   0378164   DLC WaS

Linde Air Products Company.
Oxwelded roof trusses
      see under   Moss, Herbert Henry, 1889–

VOLUME 334

Linde air products company.
The oxwelder's handbook; instructions for welding and cutting by the oxy-acetylene process. 14th ed. completely rewritten. New York [etc.] The Linde air products company; Toronto, Dominion oxygen company, limited [*1937]

iv, 5–331 p. illus. 23ᶜᵐ.

Previous edition has title: The oxwelder's manual.
"Supplementary reading" at end of some of the chapters.

1. Welding. 2. Metal-cutting. I. Title.
37–3713

Library of Congress   TS227.L635 1937
——— Copy 2.
Copyright A 103520   [3]   671

NL 0378166   DLC OC1 OU

Linde air products company.
The oxwelder's handbook; instructions for welding and cutting by the oxy-acetylene process. 14th ed. completely rewritten. New York [etc.] Linde air products company; Toronto, Dominion oxygen company, limited [*1938]

iv, 5–331 p. illus., diagrs. 23ᶜᵐ.

Earlier editions have title: The oxwelder's manual.
"Supplementary reading" at end of some of the chapters.

1. Oxyacetylene welding and cutting. 2. Metal-cutting. I. Title.
40–34844

Library of Congress   TS227.L635 1938
Copyright AA 257621   [2]   671

NL 0378167   DLC

Linde air products company.
The oxwelder's handbook; instructions for welding and cutting by the oxy-acetylene process. 15th ed. New York [etc.] The Linde air products company; Toronto, Dominion oxygen company, limited [*1939]

iv, 5–331 p. illus., diagrs. 23ᶜᵐ.

Earlier editions have title: The oxwelder's manual.
"Supplementary reading" at end of some of the chapters.

1. Oxyacetylene welding and cutting. 2. Metal-cutting. I. Title.
40–34845

Library of Congress   TS227.L635 1939
Copyright AA 314879   [15]   671

NL 0378168   DLC MtBC IdPI OrP NcRS PP OLak OO OU OC1

---

ar W
45611
Linde air products company.
The oxwelder's manual; instructions for welding and cutting by the oxy-acetylene process. 12th ed. rev. New York [c1932]

228 p. 23cm.

Earlier editions published by Oxweld Acetylene Co., New York.

NL 0378169   NIC CaBVa WaPS

Linde air products company.
The oxwelder's manual; instructions for welding and cutting by the oxy-acetylene process. 13th ed. rev. New York, The Linde air products company [*1934]

228 p. illus., diagrs. 23ᶜᵐ.

"Supplementary reading" at end of some of the chapters.

1. Oxyacetylene welding and cutting. 2. Metal-cutting. I. Title.
CA 34—1011 Unrev'd

Library of Congress   TS227.L635 1934
[a45b1]   671

NL 0378170   DLC PSt MB

Linde air products company.
Oxwelding brass and bronze, including: Welding of commercial yellow brass pipe. New York, The Linde air products company [193–?]
10 p. illus. 29 cm.
1. Oxyacetylene welding and cutting. 2. Pipe.

NL 0378171   CU

Linde air products company.
The oxy-acetylene handbook; a manual on oxy-acetylene welding and cutting procedures. New York, N. Y. [etc.] The Linde air products company; Toronto, Dominion oxygen company, limited [1943]

xiv, [2], 587, [1] p. illus., diagrs. 24ᶜᵐ.

"Supersedes and replaces 'The oxwelder's manual'—which in more recent years has appeared as 'The oxwelder's handbook'."—Foreword.

1. Oxyacetylene welding and cutting. 2. Metal-cutting. I. Title.
43–18214

Library of Congress   TS227.L638
671

CtY MtBuM OrP WaSp IdB WaSpG Or
OU ViU OCU OrStbM MiEM MiHi IdPI CaBVaU WaS WaT OrCS
NL 0378172   DLC PSt PRosC NcRS NcC NcD PSC OC1 OEac

669.173
Ox9
1945
Linde Air Products Company.
The oxy-acetylene handbook; a manual on oxy-acetylene welding and cutting procedures. New York [1945]
587p. illus., diagrs. 24cm.

"Supersedes and replaces 'The oxwelder's manual'—which in more recent years has appeared as 'The oxwelder's handbook'." Foreword.

NL 0378173   KU

669.173
Ox9
1947
Linde Air Products Company.
The oxy-acetylene handbook; a manual on oxy-acetylene welding and cutting procedures. New York [1947]
587p. illus., diagrs. 24cm.

"Supersedes and replaces 'The oxwelder's manual'—which in more recent years has appeared as 'The oxwelder's handbook'." Foreword.

NL 0378174   KU

TS227
L56
Engin.
Lib.
Linde air products company.
The oxy-acetylene handbook; a manual on oxy-acetylene welding and cutting procedures. New York, N.Y. [etc.] The Linde air products company; Toronto, Dominion oxygen company, limited [1951]
xiv, [2], 587, [1] p. illus., diagrs.

"Supersedes and replaces 'The oxwelder's manual' – which in more recent years has appeared as 'The oxwelder's handbook'." – Foreword.

NL 0378175   CU NN

CU
OU
Linde Air Products Company.
The oxy-acetylene handbook; a manual on oxy-acetylene welding and cutting procedures. New York [1954, *1943]
595 p. illus. 25 cm.

1. Oxyacetylene welding and cutting. 2. Metal-cutting. I. Title.
TS227.L638 1954   *671.522   54–1836 ‡

NL 0378176   DLC CU OU

Linde Air Products Company.
Oxy-acetylene tips.
see Linde tips.

The Linde air products company.
Oxy-acetylene welding. Buffalo, N. Y., The Linde air products co. [*1911]
cover-title, 26 p. 22½ᶜᵐ.

1. Welding.
11–25683

Library of Congress   TS227.L64

NL 0378178   DLC

LINDE air products company.
The oxygen lance in blast furnace and steel plants. 3d ed. rev. New York, c1925.

44 p. diagrs.

NL 0378179   MH

TN707
.L5
1926
Linde air products company.
... The oxygen lance in blast furnace and steel plants. 3d ed., rev., 4th printing. New York, N. Y., The Linde air products company, c1926.
44 p. illus., diagrs. 19cm.

At head of title: Applications of oxygen in major industries: iron and steel.

NL 0378180   DLC Or

WB
343
O9
L743o
1943
Linde Air Products Company
Oxygen therapy handbook. New York, [c1943].
55 p., illus., 19 cm.

1. Oxygen therapy.

NL 0378181   IParkA

WB
343
O9
L743o
1949
Linde Air Products Company
Oxygen therapy handbook. Second Edition, 1949.
60 p., illus., 22 cm.

1. Oxygen therapy.

NL 0378182   IParkA

W 6
P3
LINDE Air Products Company.
Oxygen therapy handbook. [3d ed.] New York [1954, c1953]
62 p. illus.
1. Oxygen - Therapeutic use

NL 0378183   DNLM NNC IParkA

W 6
P3
LINDE Air Products Company
Physiology of anoxia; the basis of inhalation therapy ... produced with the collaboration of Alvan L. Barach [et al.] New York [c1943]
24 p. illus.
"Adapted from the motion picture of the same title."
1. Oxygen deficiency I. Barach, Alvan Leroy, 1905–

NL 0378184   DNLM

VOLUME 334

RC645.A6
L64
    Linde air products company.
      Physiology of anoxia; the basis of inhalation
therapy, adapted from the motion picture of the
same title ...　New York, Linde air products
company ₍c1943₎
      28 p.　illus. (incl. diagrs.)　23ᶜᵐ.

      "Both the motion picture and this booklet
were produced with the collaboration of Alvan L.
Barach ... Walter M. Boothby ... Arno B. Luck-
hardt ... Carl F. Schmidt ... ₍and₎ Ralph M.
Waters ..."

NL　0378185　 NNC

RC645.A6
L64
1955
    Linde Air Products Company.
      Physiology of anoxia; the basis of inhalation
therapy, adapted from the motion picture of the
same title.　New York ₍c1955₎
      23 p.　illus.

      "Both the motion picture and this booklet
were produced with the collaboration of Alvan
L. Barach ₍and others₎"

NL　0378186　 NNC-M

    Linde air products company.
      Precautions and safe practices.　Operation of oxy-acetylene
equipment.　Handling oxygen and acetylene cylinders.　Safe
practices in welding and cutting.　New York: Linde air products
co. ₍c1939₎　56 p.　illus.　23cm.

      1. Welding, Oxy-acetylene—Safety　 measures and appliances.　2. Metal
cutting.
N. Y. P. L.　 September 29, 1943

NL　0378187　 NN MiD DLC

    Linde air products co.
      Precautions & safe practices: operation
oxy-acetylene equipment, handling oxygen & acetylene cylinders, safe practices in welding & cutting.　N.Y., The Linde air products co.;
Toronto, Dominion oxygen co., lt., [1941]
56p.

NL　0378188　 OU WaS

    Linde air products company.
      Precautions and safe practices in the storage, care and han-
dling of oxy-acetylene welding and cutting equipment.　New
York, The Linde air products company ₍ᶜ1934₎
      24 p.　17½ᶜᵐ.
      Bibliography included in the foreword.

      1. Welding.　2. Metal-cutting.　 ɪ. Title.　ɪɪ. Title: Oxy-acetylene
welding and cutting equipment.
                             36–9365
    Library of Congress　 TS227.L645
                  ₍3₎   671

NL　0378189　 DLC OrP Or OU

671.522
L743p
    Linde Air Products Company.
      Precautions and safe practices in
welding and cutting with oxy-acetylene
equipment.　New York [1953, c1939]
      56p.　illus.　23cm.

      Cover title.

      1.Oxyacetylene welding and cutting.
2.Metal cutting. I.Title.

NL　0378190　 CLSU

    Linde air products co.
      Prest-o-weld instruction manual; directions for
operating welding and cutting equipment.　N. Y.
₍The Author₎ ᵒ1935.
      23 p. illus.

      Earlier ed.: Prest-o-weld manual, by Oxweld
acetylene co.

NL　0378191　 MiD

    Linde air products co.
      Prest-o-weld instruction manual; principles
and operation of Prest-o-weld oxy-acetylene
equipment.　N. Y. ₍The Author₎ ᵒ1935.
      43 p. illus.

NL　0378192　 MiD

D669.11
L643
    ₍Linde air products company₎
      Preventing welding and cutting fires.　₍New
York, Linde air products company, 193–?₎
      15, ₍1₎ p. illus. 18ᶜᵐ.

      1. Fire prevention. 2. Welding. 3. Oxyacety-
lene and cutting. I. Title.

NL　0378193　 NNC

    The Linde air products company.
    ₍1910?₎ The production of the lowest temperatures and
machines for the liquefaction of gases and the
mechanical separation of gaseous mixtures.
    [Buffalo ? N. Y., c1910].

NL　0378194　 DLC

8035A
.94
    Linde Air Products Company, New York.
      [Publications on welding and related
operations.　New York, c1939-41]
      26 pamphlets.　28 cm.

      1. Welding—Collected works.
2. Oxyacetylene welding and cutting.

NL　0378195　 MB

    Linde air products company
      Purox instruction manual, principles and opera-
tion of purox oxy-acetylene equipment.　N. Y.
₍The Author₎ ᵒ1935.
      39 p. illus.

NL　0378196　 MiD

    Linde air products company.
      The purox manual; instructions for welding and cutting by
the oxy-acetylene process.　2d ed.　New York, The Linde air
products company ₍ᶜ1931₎
      150 p. illus., diagrs. 23ᶜᵐ.

      1. Welding.　2. Metal-cutting.　 ɪ. Title.
    Library of Congress　 TS227.L65 1931　 31–34115
    ——— Copy 2.
    Copyright A 45269　 671

NL　0378197　 DLC

RM666
.O8L5
    Linde air products company.
      Recent trends in oxygen therapy, with
bibliography.　New York [c1931]
      32 p.　illus.　23 cm.
      Bibliography: p. 24-32.

NL　0378198　 DLC

    Linde air products company.
      Recommended practices for gas cutting of structural steel.
New York, The Linde air products company ₍ᶜ1934₎
      cover-title. 16 p.　diagrs. 20½ᶜᵐ.

      1. Oxyacetylene welding and cutting.　ɪ. Title.　ɪɪ. Title: Gas cut-
ting of structural steel.
                             38–8885
    Library of Congress　 TS227.L653
                                672

NL　0378199　 DLC NN

TS227
.W545
    Linde air products company.
      Wilson, Wilbur M., 1881–
      ... Residual stresses in welded structures; a report of an in-
vestigation conducted by the Engineering experiment
station, University of Illinois, in cooperation with the Chicago bridge and iron company and the Linde air products
company, by Wilbur M. Wilson ... and Chao-chien Hao ...
₍Urbana₎ University of Illinois ₍1946₎

    Linde air products company.

      Fetherston, Thomas Cook, 1895–
      Sheet metal welding by the oxy-acetylene process, compiled
by T. C. Fetherston ...　New York, The Linde air products
company, 1925.

    Linde air products company.
      Sheet metal welding fundamentals, including:
instruction outline for welding light-gauge
sheet and tubing.　New York, The Linde air
products company ₍c1940₎
      15, ₍1₎ p. diagrs. 28ᶜᵐ.
      1. Welding. 2. Sheet-metal work.

NL　0378202　 NNC

    Linde air products company.
      Stack-cutting speeds the production of identical parts ...
New York, The Linde air products company ₍ᶜ1941₎
      11 p.　illus., diagrs. 28 x 21½ᶜᵐ.

      1. Oxyacetylene welding and cutting.　2. Sheet-metal work.　ɪ. Title.
                             42–3682
    Library of Congress　 TS227.L654
                  ₍2₎   672

NL　0378203　 DLC

    Linde air products company.
      Step by step in oxwelding a crank case.　New York,
N. Y., The Linde air products company ₍ᶜ1925₎
      2 p. l., 12 p. illus. 27ᶜᵐ.
      "2nd. printing."

      1. Welding.　ɪ. Title.　ɪɪ. Title: Crank case, Oxwelding a.
                            CA 25–1197 Unrev'd
    Library of Congress　 TT211.L5

NL　0378204　 DLC

VOLUME 334

Linde air products company.
Step by step in oxwelding a cylinder block. **New York,**
N. Y., The Linde air products company [*1925]
2 p. l., 12 p. illus. 27ᶜᵐ.
"2nd. --inting."

1. Welding. 2. Cylinders. i. Title. ii. Title: Crank case, Oxwelding a.

Library of Congress   TT211.L53   CA 25–1196 Unrev'd

NL 0378205   DLC

Linde air products company.
The testing and qualification of welding
operators. New York, The Linde air products
company [c1935]
23, [1] p. illus., diagrs. 23ᶜᵐ.

1. Welding.

NL 0378206   NNC OrP

Linde air products company.
The testing and qualification of welding operators. New
York: Linde air products co. [1938] 23 p. illus. 23cm.

1. Welding.
N.Y.P.L.   September 27, 1943

NL 0378207   NN

LINDE AIR PRODUCTS COMPANY.
Unionmelt welding; an electric welding process.
[New York] Developed by the Linde air products co.
[c1938] 75 p. incl. diagrs., tables. illus. 29cm.

1563B. 1. Welding, Electric.

NL 0378208   NN WaS

Linde Air Products Company
Use of oxygen in steelmaking. [New York]
1947.
43 l. illus.

Cover-title.
With this is bound the author's Oxygen
production and distribution.

NL 0378209   OCl

669.173 Linde air products company
L64u2   Useful information and tables covering
oxy-acetylene pipe welding and pipe
data. 2d. ed.   New York, 1923.
51p. tables(part fold.) diagrs.

NL 0378210   IU PU-Sc

Linde air products company.
The utility of carbide residue. New York, The Linde air
products company, Unit of Union carbide and carbon corporation [*1935]
cover-title, 21 p. illus. 18ᶜᵐ.

1. Carbides—By-products. i. Title.
                                           A 40–2238
Grosvenor library   TP770.L5
   for Library of Congress   [2]

NL 0378211   NBuG Or

Linde air products co.
The utility of carbide residue. N.Y., The
Linde air products co., Unit of Union carbide & c
carbon corp. [c1939]
19,[1] p. illus

NL 0378212   OU

Linde Air Products Company.
Welding and cutting manual; how to use your oxy-acetylene outfit. New York [1949]
208 p. illus. 24 cm.

1. Oxyacetylene welding and cutting.

TS227.L655   671   49–6662*

OU NcD TU OCl
NL 0378213   DLC CaBVa CaBVaU OrP Wa WaT OrCS MtBC

Linde Electric welding progress.
      see   Linde welding and cutting progress.

Linde metalworking bulletin
      see   Linde welding and cutting progress.

Linde tips. v. 1–   Aug. 1922–
[New York] Linde air products company [1922–
v. in   illus. (incl. diagrs.) 27–30½ cm.
Monthly, Aug. 1926–Apr. 1942; quarterly, July 1942–
Title varies: Aug. 1922–Apr. 1946, Oxy-acetylene tips (varies)
July 1946–   Linde tips.

1. Oxyacetylene welding and cutting—Period. i. Linde air products
company.

TS227.A187   671   32–11627 rev

MiU NN NBuG OrCS WaS ICJ OrP TU MMeT
NL 0378216   DLC WvU MiD TxU NNC MB ICJ OCl OU OCU

Linde welding and cutting progress. v.1–
1950?–
Long Island, N.Y., Union Carbide Corporation,
Linde Division.

Crerar set begins with v.11, no.3, May 1960.
Title varies: 1950?–Nov.1958, Linde metalworking bulletin; Dec.1958–Aug.1961, Metalworking
bulletin; Sept.1961–1968, Linde electric welding
progress.
   I. Union Carbide Corporation. Linde Division.
II. Linde electric   ing progress. III. Metalworking bulletin.

NL 0378217   ICJ P DP ICJ

Lindeberg, A
Vainolaista vastaan. [Kuvat tk. A. Lindebergin, teksti
Martti Santavuoren. Helsinki, Söderström, 1943]
48 plates (in portfolio) 42 cm.
Cover title.

1 World War, 1939–1945—Pictorial works.   i. Santavuori.
Marttl.

NC269.L5S3   54–45816

NL 0378218   DLC

PT9773   Lindeberg, Anders, 1789–1849.
L85   Samlade arbeten. Stockholm, L.J. Hjerta, 1835.
1835   2 v.

NL 0378219   CU

Z944.05
L641   [Lindeberg, Anders] 1789–1849.
          Äro de nya händelserna i Frankrike[till
          Europas lycka eller olycka? Politisk gissning. Stockholm, Tryckt hos O. Grahn,
          1815.

          24 p. 18cm.

1. Europe. Hist. 1789–1815. I. Title.

NL 0378220   MnU

Lindeberg, Anders. Betraktelser under en resa i Danmark, Tyskland och Ungern. Stockholm. 1841. sm. 8°.

NL 0378221   MH CtY

4DL Swed. [Lindeberg, Anders] 1789–1849.
-200   Bidrag till sveriges historia efter den 5 november 1810. Stockholm, Tryckt hos L.J. Hjerta,
            1839.
            2 v.

NL 0378222   DLC-P4

[Lindeberg Anders] 1789–1849.
Blanka, tragedi i fem akter. [In verse] Svenskt
original. Stockholm, Fr. B. Nestius, 1822.
1 p.l., v (1), 64 p. 8°.

NL 0378223   NN

[Lindeberg, Anders] 1789–1849.
Fågel blå; dramatiserad folksaga... Stockholm, O. Grahn,
1815. 50 p. 20cm.

1. Drama, Swedish. I. Title.   Card revised

NL 0378224   NN

[Lindeberg, Anders] 1789–1849.
Fågel blå. Dramat iserad-folksaga i fem akter.
Stockholm, 182–?
1 p.l., 275–313 p. 12°.

NL 0378225   NN

Z944.05
W16bmaeS [Lindeberg, Anders] 1789–1849.
          Försök till en characteristik af Napoleon
          och hans tidehvarf. Stockholm, Tryckt
          hos O. Grahn, 1815.

          56 p. 18cm.

          Bound with: Märkwärdiga handlingar
          hörande till historien om Napoleon Bonapartes fångenskap. 1822.
1. Napoléon I, Emperor of the French, 1769–1821.

NL 0378226   MnU

VOLUME 334

[Lindeberg, Anders] 1789–1849.
Midsommarsaftonen: skådespel i 4 akter.
Svenskt original. [In verse] Stockholm, L.J.
Hjerta, 1834.
3 p.1 (1) 4–82 p. 8°.

NL 0378227   NN CtY

323.2   Lindeberg, Anders, 1789–
1641r   Revolution och republik. Stockholm,
L. J. Hjerta, 1838.
95 p.

1. Revolutions. I. Title.

NL 0378228   WaU

4DL Swed. [Lindeberg, Anders] 1789–1849.
-90   Sverige år 1809 och år 1832. Stockholm,
Tryckt hos C. Deleen, 1832.
137.

NL 0378229   DLC-P4

---

4 DL   [Lindeberg, Anders] 1789–1849.
Swed.   Swerige i framtiden. Fortsättning af Sverige
-91   år 1809 och år 1832. Stockholm, Elméns &
Granbergs Tryckeri, 1833.
174. p.

NL 0378230   DLC-P4

[Lindeberg, Anders.] 1789-1849.
Svensk biografi. Del 1. Stockholm: O. Grahn, 1818. 1 v.
8°.

Del 1. Medeltidens märkvärdigaste personer.

1. Biography (Swedish). 2. Title.
N. Y. P. L.   June 12, 1913

NL 0378231   NN

[Lindeberg, Anders, 1789-1849]
Toni, dram i tre akter, efter en verklig händelse
på S.Domingo. Svenskt original. Stockholm, Ecksteinska
boktr., 1832

84 p.

NL 0378232   MH

LINDEBERG, Anders, 1789-1849
Zunker Carl; historisk roman fran birger
jarls tidehvarf. Stockholm, N.H.Thomson, 1847.

3 vol. (NYA svenska Parnassen, III.)

NL 0378233   MH

Lindeberg, Carl Johan, 1815-1900
Novitiæ floræ scandinavicæ. i.
Göteborg. 1858. sm. 8°. pp. 24. 2 plates.

NL 0378234   MH-A

Lindeberg, Carl Johan, 1815-1900, respondent.

Fries, Elias Magnus, 1794-1878.
Plantarum vascularium in regione Mæleri orientali-boreali
sponte crescentium synopsis ... Upsaliae, P. Hanselli, 1848.

Lindeberg, Carl Johan, 1815-1900.
Ruborum Sueciae disposito monographico-
critica...
see under   Arrhenius, Johan Peter, 1811-
1889, praeses.

J406   Lindeberg, Erik Frederik Leopold, 1889–
.R15
1938:12,   Sweden. *Sakkunniga angående fastighetstaxering*, 1938–1943.
... Undersökning av taxeringsutfallet beträffande jordbruks-
fastighet å landsbygden enligt beredningsnämndernas förslag
vid 1938 års fastighetstaxering. Stockholm, I. Hæggströms
boktryckeri, a. b., 1938–43.

J406   Lindeberg, Erik Fredrik Leopold, 1889–
.R15
1943:39   Sweden. *Norrlandsutredningen*, 1940.
... Utredning angående Norrlands näringsliv, förberedande
undersökning, verkställd av 1940 års Norrlandsutredning.
Stockholm, Iduns tryckeri aktiebolag, Esselte ab., 1943.

839.746   Lindeberg, Giovanni, 1883-
N832ZL   Ludvig Nordströms utvecklingshistoria;
vägen till totalismen. En studie. Stockholm,
A. Bonnier [1933]
154 p. 19 cm

1. Nordström, Ludvig Anselm, 1882-

NL 0378239   NcD TxU CU MnU

PD   Lindeberg, Giovanni, 1883- , ed.
5117   Södra Norrlands diktare; läsebok.
L54   Uppsala, J. A. Lindblad [1932]

1. Swedish language - Readers. I. Title.

NL 0378240   WaU

Lindeberg, Giovanni, 1883-
Svenska diktarsilhuetter, av Giovanni Lindeberg. Stock-
holm: O. Eklund [1923]. 103 p. 8°.
Contents: Till läsaren. Ur Tegnérs religiösa diktning. Viktor Rydberg. En
blick på Strindbergs religiösa utveckling. Heidenstam. Sagoförtäljerskan. Selma
Lagerlöfs Jerusalem. Gustav Fröding. Erik Axel Karlfeldt. Karl-Erik Forsslund.
Dan Andersson. Gunnar Hede.

1. Swedish literature—Hist. and criticism, 19th–20th cent. 2. Tegnér, Esaias, 1782-
1846. 3. Rydberg, Viktor, 1828-1895. 4. Strindberg, August, 1849-1912. 5. Heidenstam, Verner von, 1859- . 6. La-   gerlöf, Selma Ottiliana Lovisa,
1858- . 7. Fröding, Gustaf,   1860-1911. 8. Karlfeldt, Erik Axel,
1846- . 9. Forsslund, Karl   Erik, 1872-   10. Andersson,
Dan. 11. Hede, Gunnar.
N. Y. P. L.   March 10, 1925

NL 0378241   NN

Lindeberg, Giovanni, 1883-
Svenska diktarsilhuetter; andra samlingen.
Stockholm, Eklund, 1924.
90 p.
Innehåll: Till läsaren. Wallin och psalmboken.
Ett drag i Geijers bild. Fredrika Bremer. Viktor
Rydbergs reformatoriska gärning. Livstrons
sierska - Ellen Key. Vitalis Norströms kulturkri-
tik. Ivan Oljelunds ställning till.

NL 0378242   WaS

Lindeberg, Gösta, 1910-
Krigsfinansiering och krishushållning i Karl
xii:s Sverige. Stockholm, H.Geber [1946]

57 p. illus. 21 cm. (Det levande förflutna;
svenska historiska foreningens folkskrifter, 9)
Full name: Sten Gösta Lindeberg.

NL 0378243   MH MnU

Lindeberg, Gösta, 1910 -
Svensk ekonomisk politik under den görtzka perioden.
Lund, C. W. K. Gleerup [1941]
xxiv, 394 p. 25 cm.
Akademisk avhandling—Lund.
Extra t. p., with thesis statement, inserted.
Bibliography: p. xiii–xxii.

1. Sweden—Economic policy. 2. Görtz, Georg Heinrich, friherre
von Schlitz, called von, 1668-1719.

HC374.L5   53–51244

NL 0378244   DLC MiU CtY NjP ICU NNC InU NN MH CU Mnl

Lindeberg, Gösta Giovanni, 1911–
Studies on the middle lamella of the flax fibre, by Gösta
Lindeberg and Paul W. Lange. Introduction by Thor
Svenzon. Stockholm, Generalstabens litografiska anstalts
förlag, 1948.
41 p. illus. 25 cm. (Ingeniörsvetenskapsakademiens handlingar,
nr. 198)
"References": p. 39–41.

1. Flax.   I. Lange, Paul William, 1915-   joint author. II.
Svenzon, Thor, 1908-   (Series: Ingeniörsvetenskapsakademien,
Stockholm. Handlingar, nr. 198)

Iowa. State Coll. Libr.   A 49–1835*
for Library of Congress

NL 0378245   IaAS OU NNC

Lindeberg, Gösta Giovanni, 1911–
... Über die physiologie ligninabbauender bodenhymenomy-
zeten; studien an schwedischen *Marasmius*-arten, von Gösta
Lindeberg. Uppsala, A.-b. Lundequistska bokhandeln [1944]
183 p. incl. tables, diagrs. 25½ᶜᵐ. (Symbolae botanicae upsalienses
VIII: 2. Arbeten från botaniska institutionerna i Uppsala)
Summary in English.
"Literaturverzeichnis": p. [173]–183.

1. Hymenomycetes. 2. Soil micro-organisms. 3. Lignin. 4. Biological
chemistry.

            A 46–3451
Iowa. State coll. Library
for Library of Congress   [2]

NL 0378246   IaAS NNBG MoU NNC OU DLC

Lindeberg, Gunnar, 1912-
... Über konstitutionell bedingte Über- und
Untermassigkeit normal ausgetragener Neugebore-
ner ... Radebeul-Dresden, 1937.
Inaug. - Diss. - Leipzig.
Lebenslauf.
Full name: Sven Gunnar Lindeberg.

NL 0378247   CtY

VOLUME 334

Lindeberg, Gustaf Wilhelm, 1878–
Missionskunskap; kortfattad lärobok ...
Stockholm, Svenska kyrkans diakonistyrelses bokförlag [1933]
93 p. 18 cm.

NL 0378248   CtY

Lindeberg, Gustaf Wilhelm, 1878–
Protestantismen i Japan 1859–1913, historisk-princi-
piell undersökning av G. W. Lindeberg. Lund, H. Ohlssons boktryckeri, 1918.
2 p. l., ₍iii₎–iv p., 1 l., 246 p. 24ᶜᵐ.
Added t.-p. with thesis note: Akademisk avhandling—Lund.
"Litteraturförteckning": p. ₍243₎–246.

1. Protestant churches—Japan. 2. Missions—Japan. I. Title.

Library of Congress   BR1305.L5   20–22359

NL 0378249   DLC CtY-D MH-AH ICU

Lindeberg, Karl Johan
    see Lindeberg, Carl Johan, 1815–1900.

Lindeberg, Harrie Thomas, 1880–   joint author.

Albro, Lewis Colt.
    Domestic architectvre, pvblished for private distribv-
tion by Lewis Colt Albro and Harrie T. Lindeberg, New
York. ₍Cambridge, Presswork by the University press₎
1912.

Lindeberg, Harrie Thomas, 1880–
    Domestic architectvre of H. T. Lindeberg, with an introdvc-
tion by Royal Cortissoz. New York, W. Helbvrn inc., 1940.
    xvi p., 1 l., 310 p., 1 l. incl. col. front., illus. (incl. plans) col. plates.
37½ x 29ᶜᵐ.
    Includes 304 pages of illustrations.
    "1000 copies of this edition have been printed."

1. Architecture, Domestic—U. S. 2. Architecture, Domestic—Designs
and plans.

Library of Congress   NA737.L5A43   41–1933
——— Copy 2.
Copyright   ₍6₎   728.0973

NL 0378252   DLC OrU MU NIC FMU PP PU-FA OU OCU OCl

PT   Lindeberg, Hjalmar Kristian Ferdinand, 1866–
9773   Anders Lindeberg; hans liv och verksamhet.
.L49   Biografisk studie. Stockholm, Norstedt
Z68   ₍1918₎
            256 p. illus., ports. 22 cm.

Includes bibliography.

1. Lindeberg, Anders, 1789–1849

NL 0378253   WU MnU

Lindeberg, Hjalmar Kristian Ferdinand, 1866–
    Görtz, ett offer för enväldet; politisk
studie. Stockholm, Norstedt ₍1925₎
    164 p. illus., ports., facsims.

1. Sweden - History. 2. Görtz, Georg
Heinrich von, 1668–

NL 0378254   WaU InU PBa NN MH

---

4 DL   Lindeberg, Hjalmar Kristian Ferdinand, 1866–
Swed.   Prinsen av Wasa, hans levnad och samtimennes-
-265   teckning. Stockholm, P. A. Norstedt [1921]
            287 p.

NL 0378255   DLC-P4

Lindeberg, Jarl Waldemar, 1876–1932.
    ... Note sur le problème isopérimétrique, par J. W. Linde-
berg. Helsingfors, Imprimerie de la Société de littérature
finnoise, 1915.
    5 p. 29 x 23ᶜᵐ. (₍Finska vetenskaps-societeten. Helsingfors₎ Acta So-
cietatis scientiarum fennicæ. t. XLVI. n° 3)

1. Calculus of variations.

                                    AC 38–1503
New York. Public library
for Library of Congress   [Q60.F5 vol. 46, no. 3]
                ₍4₎   (508)

NL 0378256   NN DLC

Lindeberg, Jarl Waldemar, 1876–1932.
    Sur l'integration de certaines equations aux deriv-
es partielles. Helsingfors, 1900.
    In. Diss.

NL 0378257   ICRL

Lindeberg, Jarl Waldemar, 1876–1932.
    ... Sur les maxima et minima d'une fonction de deux inté-
grales définies, par J. W. Lindeberg. Helsingfors, Imprimerie
de la Société de littérature finnoise, 1914.
    21 p. 29 x 23ᵐᵐ. (₍Finska vetenskaps-societeten, Helsingfors₎ Acta
Societatis scientiarum fennicæ. t. XLIV, n° 5)

1. Functions. 2. Maxima and minima.

                                    AC 38–1492
New York. Public library
for Library of Congress   [Q60.F5 vol. 44, no. 5]
                ₍4₎   (508)

NL 0378258   NN DLC

Lindeberg, Knut Mauritz, 1848–1914.
    Historisk oefversigt af teorierna for singulaera
solutioner till ordinaera differential eqvationer.
    Inaug. diss. Upsala, 1875.

NL 0378259   ICRL

Lindeberg, Knut Mauritz, 1848–1914.
Jäderin, Edvard, 1852–1923.
    ... Komparationer emellan Sveriges meterprototyp och tre
statens institutioner tillhöriga hufvudlikare och normalmått,
utförda af Edv. Jäderin och K. Lindeberg och redigerade af
Edv. Jäderin ... Stockholm, P. A. Norstedt & söner, 1895.

NL 0378261   ICJ

Lindeberg, Knut Mauritz, 1848–1914.   530.2 N902
    Öfningsuppgifter till begagnande vid undervisningen i fysik vid
de allmänna läroverken, utgifna af K. M. Lindeberg, ... Med
25 figurer. Upsala, W. Schultz, [1879].
    (4), 139 p. diagr. 21½ᶜᵐ.

Lindeberg, Märta, ed.
    Gästrikland; hembygdsbok. Utgiven under redaktion av Märta
Lindeberg... Uppsala, J. A. Lindblad ₍1946₎ 368 p. illus.
21cm.

394171B. 1. Gästrikland, Sweden.
N. Y. P. L.   November 13, 1947

NL 0378262   NN ICU

Z943.2R739
L641   Lindeberg, Peter, 1562–1596.
            Aus Petri Lindenbergii, Rostocker
        Chronicken, kurtzer, an etzlichen Orthen
        aber vermehrter, Ausszug, begreiffend
        etzliche darin enthaltene Bürgerliche
        Sachen, so auff eigen Kosten zum Druck
        befodert hat, H.M.J. ₍i.e. Heino Meyer der
        Jünger₎ Rostock, Jacobus Riecheln, 1677.

        3 pt. in 1 v. 16cm.

        Pt. ₍2₎: Kurtze Beschreibung, des H.

        Römischen wie auch der vornehmesten Welt-
        Reiche und Republiqven; pt. ₍3₎: Weise,
        Christian. Fundamentall Historie.
            With this is bound Lübeck. Laws, sta-
        tutes, etc. Statuta und Stadt-Recht. 1657.

NL 0378264   MnU

Lindeberg, Peter, 1562–1596.
                                Carmen nup-
tiale. 2 pp. (Latein. litteraturdenkmaeler des 15 u. 16
iahrh. v. 7, p. 48.)

NL 0378265   MdBP

Lindeberg, Peter, 1562–1596.
    Petri Lindebergii ...₍Chronicon rostochiense posthu-
mum quinque libris absolutum ... Rostochii, imprimebatur typis S. Myliandri, 1596.
    174, ₍18₎ p. 20ᶜᵐ.
    "Exsequiae Petri Lindebergii P. L. civis rostochiensis & chronici huius
auctoris": ₍18₎ p. at end.
    Ed. by Nicolaus Petreus.

1. Rostock—Hist. I. Petræus, Nicolaus, 1569–1641, ed.   4–32090

Library of Congress   DD901.R8L7

NL 0378266   DLC MH PU ICU

Lindeberg, Peter, 1562–1596.
    Commentarii rerum memorabilium in Europa ab anno
octuagesimo sexto, usq₍ ad præsentem nonagesimum primum gestarum, quibus summorum virorum, Joannis Re-
giomontani, Joannis Stœfleri, Henrici Ranzovii, & multo-
rum aliorum de anno potissimum mirabili prædictiones
corroborantur & confirmantur: auctore Petro Lindebergio,
ex bibliothecâ Ranzoviana collecti. Hamburgi, ex officinâ
J. Wolffij, 1591.
    8 p. l., 176, ₍1₎ p. incl. illus., 1 port., 1 fold. pl. 20ᶜᵐ. ₍With his Chroni-
con rostochiense posthumum. Rostochii, 1596₎
    1. Europe—Hist.—1517–1648.
                                    4–29110

Library of Congress   DD901.R8L7

NL 0378267   DLC ICU DFo CtY

---

*GC5   Lindeberg, Peter, 1562–1596.
16412   Petri Lindebergii Epigrammata in vrbes, et
596c   viros aliqvot clarissimos, quorum in
        Hodoeporico suo mentionem ordinè facit, quibus
        in fine nonnulla alia sunt addita.
            Rostochii typis Myliandrinis. Anno
        CIƆIƆXXXCVII.
            4°. [24]p. 18cm.
            Signatures: A-C⁴.
            Bound with his Chronicon rostochiense, 1596.

NL 0378268   MH

VOLUME 334

Lindeberg, Peter, 1562-1596, supposed author.

₍Rantzau, Henrik₎ 1526-1598.
Genealogia ranzoviana, primvm pvblicata, anno Domini M.D.LXXXV. ... ₍Hamburgi, 1585₎

DL188
.8
.R32L5   Rantzau, Henrik, 1526-1598.
Rosenwald   Henrici Ranzovii De somnijs, eorumque euentibus liber,
Coll.   cui accesserunt eiusdem H. R. quatuor filiorum, at unius filiae
... nunnulla epitaphia, & monumentorum quorundam Ranzouianorum descriptiones, cum quibusdam alijs in fine additis epigrammatibus. Rostochii, Typis S. Myliandri, 1591.

Lindeberg, Peter, 1562-1596.
Historica rervm in Evropa ab anno octvagesimo sexto ad praesentem nonagesimvm primum gestarum narratio ... Ex ... Henrici Ranzovii bibliotheca, summo studio à Petro Lindebergio collecta ... Hambvrgi, Excudebat Iac. Wolfius, impensis Pauli Brachfeldii, 1591.
₍12₎, 176, ₍7₎ p. illus. 20 cm.

NL 0378271   NNC

Lindeberg, Peter, 1562-1596.
Hypotyposis arcium, palatiorum, librorum, pyramidum, obeliscorum, cipporum, molarum, fontium, monumentorum & epitaphiorum, ab illustri & strenuo viro Henrico Ranzovio ... conditorum, cum nonnullis eorum ectypis partim aeneis, partim ligneis, & in fine additis epigrammatibus. Francofurti, Apud I. Wechelum, 1592.
321 p. illus., ports. 22 cm.
Henrik Rantzau's copy. The original binding bearing his name and arms and dated 1597 mounted inside present covers.
With this is bound: Rantzau, Henrik. De somnijs. Rostochii, 1591.
1. Rantzau, Henrik, 1526-1598.   I. Title.

DL188.8.R32L5   Rosenwald Coll.   48-38512*

NL 0378272   DLC CtY ICN ICU NjP

Lindeberg, Sten.
Exhibition of drawings by the Swedish painter Ernst Josephson... January 11-February 22, 1948. see under   The American Swedish Historical Museum, Philadelphia.
American Swedish historical foundation presents an exhibition of drawings...

Lindeberg, Walter.
... Über den einfluss der thymektomie auf den gesamtorganismus und auf die drüsen mit innerer sekretion, insbesondere die epiphyse und hypophyse ... Tartu (Dorpat) Typographie J. Mällo, 1924.
71 p. illus., iv pl. 23½ᶜᵐ.
Thesis—Dorpat.
On t-p: Folia neuropathologica estoniana Tartu (Dorpat) vol. II, 1924.
"Literaturverzeichnis": p. 68-71.
1. Thymus gland. 2. Endocrinology.   I. Folia neuropathologica estoniana.   II. Title.
Library of Congress   QP187.L5
                                              31-1933
                          ₍2₎   612.43

NL 0378274   DLC PPC

Lindeblad, Assar, 1800-1848.
Dikter. Lund, Berlingska boktryckeriet, 1832-
1 v. 21.5 cm.

NL 0378275   CtY

Lindeblad, Assar, 1800-1848.
Fosterländska sånger. Götheborg, C.M. Ekbohrn, 1843.
2 p.l., 7-65 p., 1 l. 19.5 cm.

NL 0378276   CtY

Lindeblad, Assar, 1800-1848.
Henric Schartaus lefnad och lära. Af Assar Lindeblad.
2. tillökade uppl. Med ett bihang innehållande utdrag af några förut otryckta bref, embetspåminnelser och ett predikoutkast. Stockholm, Huldberg & komp:s boktryckeri, 1864.
97 p., 1 l. 19ᶜᵐ.
"Schartaus skrifter": p. ₍61₎-78.
With this are bound: ₍Åberger, Gustaf₎ Om schartauanismen i lära och lefverne från Schartaus tid till våra dagar. Stockholm ₍1901₎ and Schartau, Henric. Anteckningar föranledde af åtskilliga ställen i den Heliga Skrift. Lund, 1886.
1. Schartau, Henric, 1757-1825.

                                          35-29543
Library of Congress   BX8080.S22L5 1864   922.4485

NL 0378277   DLC MH-AH

BV2086
.L74   ₍Lindeblad, Assar₎ 1800-1848.
The missionary, by a Swedish nightingale.
London, Aylott and Jones, 1852.
23 p. 17 cm.

1. Missions—Poetry.

NL 0378278   IEG

Lindeblad, Assar, 1800-1848.
Religiösa sånger. Götheborg, C.M. Ekbohrn, 1843.
19.5 cm.

NL 0378279   CtY

Lindeblad, Assar, 1800-1848.
Svenska sången; akademiska föreläsningar.
Lund, Tryckt i Lundbergs och Lönnegrens Officin, 1832.
xv, 221 p.

1. Swedish poetry - Addresses, essays, lectures. I. Title.

NL 0378280   WaU

Div.S.   Lindeboom, A   M
923.2492   Dr. A. Kuyper in "Jan Rap en zijn maat," door A. M. Lindeboom. ₍n. p., 1952?₎
K97LIN   ₍1₎ l. 25 cm.
Caption title.
"Gereformeerd theologisch tijdschrift. Overdruk."

1. Kuyper, Abraham, 1837-1920.

NL 0378281   NcD

Lindeboom (Evert). *Over de eigenwarme in koorts. viii. 42 pp. 8°. *Utrecht*, 1862.

NL 0378282   DNLM

Lindeboom, F   T   Diemer-
see Diemer-Lindeboom, F   T

Lindeboom, Fenna Tjeerdina.
De ontwikkeling van het strafstelsel in Sovjet-Rusland, 1917-1937. Rotterdam, 1937.
231 p. 25 cm.
Proefschrift—Vrije Universiteit, Amsterdam.
"Stellingen": ₍2₎ leaves inserted.
Bibliography: p. 227-231.

1. Criminal law—Russia. 2. Criminal procedure—Russia. 3. Juvenile delinquency—Russia.   I. Title.

                                          55-52087
NL 0378284   DLC OCU

Lindeboom, Gerrit Arie.
Hippocrates. Antwerpen, Uitgeverij Het Kompas, 1948.
71 p. illus., port. 21 cm.
"Literatur": p. 70-71.

1. Hippocrates.

R126.H8L55   926.1   53-21159

NL 0378285   DLC DNLM CtY-M OU NjP

Lindeboom, Gerrit Arie.
Kuyper over de geneeskunde. Kampen, J. H. Kok, 1955.
20 p. 25 cm.
"Oorspronijlik verschenen in het tijdschrift 'Geloof en wetenschap.'"
Includes bibliography.

1. Kuyper, Abraham, 1837-1920. 2. Medicine—Philosophy.

R723.L55   60-21538 ‡

NL 0378286   DLC DNLM NcD

Div.S. Lindeboom, Gerrit Arie
922.8146
S491LI   Michaël Servet (1511-1553) en de ontdekking van de kleine bloedsomloop, door G. A. Lindeboom. ₍n. p., 1954?₎
13 p. port., facsims. 24 cm.

Caption title.
Also numbered ₍696₎-708 p.
"Overgedrukt uit het Ned. Tijdschrift voor Geneeskunde. Jaargang 98, No. 11 - Zaterdag 13 Maart 1954."
Bibliography: p. 13.
1. Servetus,   Michael, 1509 or 11-1553.

NL 0378287   NcD

Lindeboom, Gerrit Arie.
Nieren en zwangerschap, door dr G. A. Lindeboom ... Met een voorwoord van prof. M. A. van Bouwdijk Bastiaanse.
Amsterdam, Uitgeversmaatschappij Holland, 1941.
267 p. incl. tables, diagrs. 4 pl. on 2 l. 25 cm.
"Literatuurlijst": p. ₍229₎-252.

1. Kidneys—Diseases. 2. Pregnancy, Complications of.

RG484.L5   A F 47-6119
Minnesota. Univ. Libr.
for Library of Congress   ₍1₎†

NL 0378288   MnU DNLM ViU IU ICRL DLC

VOLUME 334

QV
250
L743n
1944
LINDEBOOM, Gerrit Arie
De nieuwe chemotherapie in de praktijk. 2. herziene druk.
Amsterdam, Uitgeversmij. Holland, 1944.
112 p. illus.
1. Chemotherapy

NL 0378289   DNLM

QV
250
L743n
1946
LINDEBOOM, Gerrit Arie
De nieuwe chemotherapie in de praktijk. 3. herziene druk.
Amsterdam, Uitgeversmij Holland, 1946.
130 p. illus.
1. Chemotherapy

NL 0378290   DNLM

W 1
VE468
19/21
1949
LINDEBOOM, Gerrit Arie
De ontwikkeling der geneeskunde in haar betekenis voor de zielszorg, door G. A. Lindeboom ₍et al.₎ Rotterdam, Donner, 1949.
61 p. (Vereniging ter Bevordering van de Geestelijke Volksgezondheid op Gereformeerde Grondslag. Geschriften en referaten, 19/21)
Lectures delivered at the annual meeting of the Vereniging ter Bevordering van de Geestelijke Volksgezondheid op Gere-

formeerde Grondslag on 9 Oct. 1948.
Contents. —Psychosomatische geneeskunde, door G. A. Lindeboom. —Psychotherapie en zielszorg, door J. G. Fernhout. —Geloof en suggestie, door F. J. Tolsma.
1. Medicine - Pastoral 2. Psychosomatic medicine   Series: Vereniging

voor Geestelijke Volksgezondheid op Gereformeerde Grondslag. Geschriften en referaten, 19/21

NL 0378293   DNLM

Lindeboom, Gerrit Arie.
De ziel der geneeskunde. Haarlem, Erven F. Bohn, 1950.
24 p. 23 cm.
Rede—Vrije Universiteit, Amsterdam (aanvaarding van het ambt van hoogleraar in de geneeskunde) 1950.
Includes bibliography.

1. Medicine, Psychomatic.   I. Title.

RC49.L5   59-25557

NL 0378294   DLC DNLM

Lindeboom (Joh.) *De dysphagiæ speciebus recte distinguendis. iv, 68 ₍p₎. 8°. *Traj. ad Rhenum, N. van der Monde* 1835.

NL 0378295   DNLM

BX9480
.G72L6
Lindeboom, Johannes, 1882-1958.
Austin Friars; geschiedenis van de Nederlandse Hervormde Gemeente te Londen, 1550-1950.
's-Gravenhage, M. Nijhoff, 1950.
xii, 203 p. plates, facsims. 25½ cm.

Bibliographical footnotes.

NL 0378296   NjR CtY TNJ-R TxFS

Lindeboom, Johannes, 1882–
Austin Friars; history of the Dutch Reformed Church in London, 1550-1950. Translation from the Dutch by D. de Iongh. The Hague, Nijhoff, 1950.
xv, 208 p. plates, facsims. 26 cm.
Bibliographical footnotes.

1. London. Dutch Reformed Church.

BX9480.G72L62   284.242   57-38878

NL 0378297
OrP CU IEN NNUT GU CaBVaU
RPB TNJ Vi CSt PPiPT IaU CtY-M MH NIC CtY-D MU MB IU
DLC OrU ICN InU WaU MH-AH MiU NcD NjPT

Lindeboom, Johannes, 1882-1958.
De beteekenis van methodische geschiedvorsching voor de beoefening der dogmengeschiedenis en der zedekunde ... Leiden, A. H. Adriani, 1914.
31 p.   24 cm.
Bibliography: p. [30]-31.
Inaugural address - Groningen, Rijks-Universiteit.

NL 0378298   ViHarEM

Lindeboom, Johannes, 1882–
Het bijbelsch humanisme in Nederland, door dr. J. Lindeboom. Leiden, A. H. Adriani, 1913.
viii, 280 p. 24½ᶜᵐ.

1. Humanism. 2. Netherlands—Church history.   I. Title. II. Title: Humanisme, Het bijbelsch.

Library of Congress   BR904.L7   13-21840 rev.

NL 0378299   DLC OrU MH-AH NIC CU CtY MiU

BR
900
N281
v.3
Lindeboom, Johannes, 1882-
De confessioneele ontwikkeling der reformatie in de Nederlanden. 's-Gravenhage, M. Nijhoff, 1946.
116 p. (Kerkhistorische studien behoorende bij het Nederlandsch Archief voor Kerkgeschiedenis, deel 3)
Bibliographical footnotes.

1. Netherlands - Church history. I. Title. II. Series: Nederlands Archief voor Kerkgeschiedenis. Kerkhistorische studien. v.3.

NL 0378300   InGo NcD ICN NNUT
CLU IaU CtY-D CU NjPT NIC MoSCS MH CSaT

Lindeboom, Johannes, 1882-
Dr. G. van der Leeuw ...
see under title

GR8
L64ler
Lindeboom, Johannes, 1882-1958
Erasmus, onderzoek naar zijne theologie en zijn godsdienstig gemoedsbestaan. Leiden, A.H. Adriani, 1909.
x, 200 p. 25 cm.

Proefschrift - Leiden.
"Stellingen": ₍5₎ p. bound in at end.
Bibliographical footnotes.

1. Erasmus, Desiderius, d.1536.

NL 0378302   CtY-D WaWW NIC ICN OO

GR8
L641e
Lindeboom, Johannes, 1882-1958
Erasmus van Rotterdam, door J. Lindeboom.
Amsterdam, Lankamp & Brinkman, 1936.
46 p. port. 23 cm.

Bibliography: p. 46.

1. Erasmus, Desiderius, d.1536.

NL 0378303   CtY-D MH ViHarEM

Lindeboom, Johannes, 1882–

Banning, Willem, 1888–   ed.
Europeesche geest, inhouden en vormen van het cultuurleven der europeesche wereld ; onder redactie van dr W. Banning en dr J. D. Bierens de Haan, met medewerking van de hoogleeraren dr. J. N. Bakhuizen van den Brink, dr. J. Lindeboom, dr H. J. Pos ₍en anders₎, ... Arnhem, Van Loghum Slaterus' uitgevers-mij n. v., 1939.

BR350
F7L5
Lindeboom, Johannes, 1882-
Een franc-tireur der Reformatie: Sebastiaan Franck. Arnhem, Van Loghum Slaterus, 1952.
54p. port., facsim. 21cm. (Gastmaal der eeuwen; taferelen uit de cultuurgeschiedenis van Europa, 19)

Includes bibliography.

1. Franck, Sebastian, 1499-1542.

NL 0378305   IaU CSaT GEU-T MiU NNUT NjPT ICN MH-AH

Lindeboom, Johannes, 1882–
Frederik Adolf van der Marck, een achttiende-eeuwsch leeraar van het natuurrecht. 's-Gravenhage, M. Nijhoff, 1947.
xii, 217 p. port. 24 cm.
"Legenda": p. ₍xi₎-xii. Bibliographical footnotes.

1. Marck, Frederik Adolf van der, 1719-1800.

50-21489

NL 0378306   DLC OU MH CtY

Lindeboom, Johannes, 1882–
Geert Groote's preeksuspensie, een bijdrage tot zijn geestelijke plaatsbepaling, door J. Lindeboom ... Amsterdam, Noord-hollandsche uitgevers maatschappij, 1941.
cover-title, 35, ₍1₎ p. 23½ᶜᵐ. (Mededeelingen der Nederlandsche akademie van wetenschappen, Afdeeling letterkunde. Nieuwe reeks, deel 4, no. 4)

1. Groote, Gerard, 1340-1384.

A 46-4749

Cleveland. Public library
for Library of Congress

NL 0378307   OCl CtY-D

Lindeboom, Johannes, 1882–   ed.

Reitsma, Johannes, 1837–1902.
Geschiedenis van de hervorming en de hervormde kerk der Nederlanden, door dr. J. Reitsma ... Vierde, herziene druk, bezorgd door dr. J. Lindeboom ... Utrecht, Kemink & zoon, n. v., 1933.

VOLUME 334

Lindeboom, Johannes, 1882–
Geschiedenis van het vrijzinnig protestantisme, door dr.
J. Lindeboom ... Huis ter Heide (U.) N. v. uitgevers-
maatschappij "De Wachttoren", 1929–35.
3 v. 21ᶜᵐ. ("Het handboek"; bibliotheek van wetenschappelijke
geschriften over den godsdienst, onder redactie van G. A. van den Bergh
van Eysinga. G. van Duyl, H. T. de Graaf, G. Horreüs de Haas en
J. Lindeboom)
Imprint varies: v. 2–3, Assen, Van Gorcum & comp. n. v.
CONTENTS.—I. (Tot Lessing) Het ontstaan van het neo-protestan-
tisme.—II. De ontwikkeling van het vrijzinnig protestantisme sedert
Lessing tot en met het ontstaan van het modernisme.—III. Het vrijzinnig
protestantisme sedert 1870.
1. Protestantism—Hist.   2. Liberalism (Religion)—Hist.   I. Title.

Library of Congress   BX4805.L5   36–15286

                                             284

NL 0378309   DLC NjNbS ICMcC MH-AH

LINDEBOOM, Johannes, 1882–
Godsdienst en kerk. ₍Delft₎
Uitgegeven in opdracht van den
Vrijzinnig Protestantschen Radio
Omroep door de Uitgeversmaatschappij
"De Tijdstroom" ₍1929₎
10p. 22.5cm. (Wat gelooven en
denken Vrijzinnige Protestanten?5)

NL 0378310   MH-AH

BR145 Lindeboom, Johannes, 1882–   joint author.
.B16
        Bakhuizen van den Brink, Jan Nicolaas, 1896–
Handboek der kerkgeschiedenis, door dr J. N. Bakhuizen
van den Brink ... en dr J. Lindeboom ... 's-Gravenhage, D. A.
Daamen, 1942–

Lindeboom, Johannes
...Humanisme en reformatie, door Prof. Dr. J. Lindeboom.
Haarlem: De Erven F. Bohn, 1919. 52 p. 8°. (Synthese.
Deel 5, no. 1.)

Cover-title.

1. Humanism. 2. Series.
N. Y. P. L.   September 9, 1920.

NL 0378312   NN

Lindeboom, Johannes, 1882– ed.

Nederlandsch archief voor kerkgeschiedenis ... 1.–7. deel
₍1884₎–99; nieuwe ser.. 1– deel, 1900–
's-Gravenhage, M. Nijhoff, 1885–19

Lindeboom, Johannes, 1882–
Oorsprong en geschiedenis van den naam protestant, door
J. Lindeboom ... Amsterdam, Noord-Hollandsche uitgevers
maatschappij, 1940.
cover-title. 31 p. 23½ᶜᵐ. (Mededeelingen der Koninklijke nederlandsche akademie van wetenschappen, Afd₍eeling₎ letterkunde. Nieuwe
reeks, deel 3, no. 2)

1. Protestantism—Hist.

Cleveland. Public library   A 41–2496
for Library of Congress   [AS244.A51 n. s., vol. 3, no. 2]

                                             (068.492)

NL 0378314   OCl ViHarEM MH-AH NNUT

Lindeboom, J[ohannes] 1882–
De psychologische beteekenis der richtings-
verschillen. Door Prof. Dr. J. Lindeboom.
Baarn, Hollandia, 1924

41p. 24cm. (Levensvragen)

1. Church history. 2. Schism. I. Title.

NL 0378315   ViHarEM

Lindeboom, Johannes, 1882–
St. Willibrord's Roomsche reizen. Amsterdam, Noord-
Hollandsche Uitg. Mij., 1948.
13 p. 24 cm. (Mededeelingen der Koninklijke Aka-
demie van Wetenschappen. Afd. Letterkunde. Nieuwe reeks, deel
11, no. 5)
Cover title.
Pages also numbered 145–157.
Bibliographical footnotes.
1. Willibrord, Saint, Bp. of Utrecht, d. 738.   I. Title.   (Series:
Akademie van Wetenschappen, Amsterdam. Afdeeling voor de Taal-,
Letter-, Geschiedkundige en Wijsgeerige Wetenschappen. Verslagen
en mededeelingen. Nieuwe reeks, deel 11, no. 5)
AS244.A51 n. r., deel 11, no. 5   A 52–7404
——— Copy 2.   BX4700.W56L55

Chicago. Univ. Libr.
for Library of Congress

NL 0378316   ICU DLC

Lindeboom, Johannes, 1882–
De satyren naar aanleiding van het "Liber conformitatum." Amsterdam, Noord-Hollandsche Uitg. Mij., 1944.
14 p. 24 cm. (Mededeelingen der Nederlandsche Akademie van
Wetenschappen, Afd. Letterkunde, nieuwe reeks, deel 7, no. 6)
Cover title.
1. Albizzi, Bartolommeo, d. 1401. Liber conformitatum. 2. Alberus,
Erasmus, d. 1553. Alcoran franciscanorum. 3. Francesco d'Assisi,
Saint, 1182–1226.   (Series: Akademie van Wetenschappen, Amsterdam. Afdeeling voor de Taal-, Letter-, Geschiedkundige en Wijsgeerige Wetenschappen. Verslagen en mededeelingen, nieuwe reeks,
deel 7, no. 6)
AS244.A51 n. r., deel 7, no. 6   A 51–3304

Cleveland. Public Libr.
for Library of Congress   ₍2₎†

NL 0378317   OCl DLC

AS244
.A51
n. r.,   **Lindeboom, Johannes,** 1882–
deel 18,   De "Satyres chrestiennes de la cuisine papale" en hun
no. 1   auteur. Amsterdam, Noord-Hollandsche Uitg. Mij., 1955.
16 p. 24 cm. (Mededeelingen der Koninklijke Nederlandse Akademie van Wetenschappen. Afd. Letterkunde. Nieuwe reeks, deel 18
no. 1)
Cover title.
1. Viret, Pierre, 1511–1571. Satyres chrestiennes de la cuisine
papale. 2. Badius, Conrad, 1510?–1562? supposed author. Satyres
chrestiennes de la cuisine papale.   I. Title.   (Series: Akademie
van Wetenschappen, Amsterdam. Afdeeling voor de Taal-, Letter-,
Geschiedkundige en Wijsgeerige Wetenschappen. Verslagen en mededeelingen, nieuwe reeks, deel 18, no. 1)
[AS244.A51 n. r., deel 18, no. 1]   A 55–5639

Chicago. Univ. Libr.
for Library of Congress   ₍2₎

NL 0378318   ICU DLC

BT
1315   Lindeboom, Johannes, 1882–1958
.L74   Stiefkinderen van het Christendom, door
dr. J. Lindeboom ... 's-Gravenhage, M. Nijhoff,
1929.
2 p. l., ₍vii₎–xi, 392 p. 25ᶜᵐ.
Bibliographical foot-notes.

1. Heresies and heretics. 2. Sects. I. Title.

NL 0378319   MiU NcD ViHarEM CtY ICU

Lindeboom (L.) De beteekenis van het chris-
telijk geloof voor de geneeskundige wetenschap,
in 't bijzonder voor de psychiatrie. 38 pp. 8°.
Heusden, A. Gezelle. 1887.

NL 0378320   DNLM

Lindeboom, Lucas, 1845–1933.
Gedenkt den Sabbatdag dat gij dien heiligt.
Leiden, 1888.

NL 0378321   NjNbS

RJ5   Lindeboom, Lucas, 1845–1933.
L641g   Godgeleerden. Door L. Lindeboom. Heusden, A.
Gezelle Meerburg, 1894.
83 p. 25 cm.

Rede – Kampen (Op den 39ˢᵗᵉⁿ jaardag der Theol.
School van de Geref. Kerken in Nederland) 1893.
Includes bibliographical references.

1. Theology – Methodology. I. Title.

NL 0378322   CtY-D

Pamph   LINDEBOOM, Lucas, 1845–1933.
v.424   Heb de Waarheid en den vrede Lief. Open
Brief aan Dr. A. Kuyper...alsmede aan de
"Heraut"-lezers en alle Gereformeerden in
den lande. Leiden, D. Donner, 1880.
70, xviiip. 23.5cm.

NL 0378323   MH-AH NcD

Lindeboom, Lucas, 1845–1933.
De Leiding des heiligen Geestes... Kampen,
1902.

NL 0378324   NjNbS

Lindeboom, Lukas.
Parlementaire schadelsostelling. Rotterdam,
1916.
Proefschrift ——— Vrije Universiteit ₍te Amster-
dam₎

NL 0378325   MH-L

Lindeborg, Robert Gust, 1910–
Water requirements of certain rodents from xeric and
from mesic habitats. ₍Ann Arbor₎ 1948.
Microfilm copy of typewritten ms. Made in 1948 by University
Microfilms (Publication no. 1061) Positive.
Collation of the original: iii, 124 l. diagrs.
Thesis—Univ. of Michigan.
Abstracted in Microfilm abstracts, v. 8 (1948) no. 2, p. 156–157.
"Literature cited": leaves 92–97.

1. Water in the body. 2. Mice.
Microfilm AC–1 no. 1061   Mic A 48–160*

Michigan. Univ. Libr.
for Library of Congress   ₍2₎†

NL 0378326   MiU DLC

QH431 Lindeborg, Robert Gust₍ 1910–
A1M5   Water requirements of certain rodents from
no.58   xeric and mesic habitats. Ann Arbor, Mich.,
1952.
32 p. diagrs., tables. 26 cm. (Michigan.
University. Laboratory of Vertebrate Biology.
Contributions no. 58).
"Literature cited": p. 30–32.

1. Rodentia. I. Title. (Series).

NL 0378327   DI

VOLUME 334

Lindeborn, Jan, 1630-1696.
Historia; sive, Notitia episcopatus Daventriensis ex ecclesiarum membranis, monasteriorum tabulis, authenticis annotatis & classicis authoribus eruta ac publici juris facta a Joanne Lindebornio. Coloniae Agrippinae, sumptibus J. à Metelen, 1670.
8 p. l., 556, ₍2₎ p.   19½ᵐᵐ.

1. Deventer—Church history.

NL 0378328   MiU ICN

HQ728 **LINDEBORN, JAN,** 1630-1696.
.L7   In matrimonii sacramentum notæ catecheticæ annotatæ a Joanne Lindeborn, quibus, dispositio quâ ad nuptias accedendum, quæ prolium habenda cura, & quid exigat fœdus conjugale, breviter explicatur... Coloniæ, pro A. ab Eynden, 1675.
[16], 184 p.   16cm.
Added t.-p., engr.

1. Marriage.

NL 0378329   ICU PU

BX   **Lindeborn, Jan,** 1630-1696.
2264   In poenitentiae sacramentum notae catecheticae, quibus eruditur poenitens, quam oris confessionem, cordis contritionem, & operis satisfactionem sacerdotalis absolutio requirat, annotatae a Joanne Linderborn.... Coloniae, pro Arnoldo ab Eynden, 1677.
[14], 221 p.

1. Confession. 2. Penance.   I. Title

NL 0378330   CU-L

Lindeborn, Jan, 1630-1696.
De leeder Jacobs. De maegden, die Godt met opzet van eeuwige reinigheit, in de weereld dienen, toe-gevast van den eerw. heere Joannes Lindeborn. Uit het Latijn, door den autheur van nieuws oversien ende verbetert, in het Neder-duidsch vertaelt. Door den eerw. heere Adrianus Terlou ... T'Antwerpen, by Michiel Cnobbert voor Joachim à Metelen, 1670.
₍22₎, 389, ₍4₎ p. plate. 17cm.

Added engraved t.-p. reads: De leeder van Jacob ...

NL 0378331   NNC

JG62   **Lindeborn, Jan,**   1630-1696.
L641   Scala Jacob, virginibus Deo cum proposito
K⁴²L   perpetuæ continentiae in seculo famulantibus
Restricted applicata, a ... Joanne Lindeborn ...
Circulation Antverpiae, Prostant apud J. à Metelen, Anno
M. DC. LXVI.
11 p. l., 351, ₍1₎ p. 18 cm.

Translation of Ladder Jacobs.

Restricted   1. Women in Christianity. 2. Women's work in
Circulation the church. 3. Jansenists - Works (to 1800)
4. Jansenists in the Netherlands. I. Title.
Imprints file (Author and date)

NL 0378333   CtY-D

CS   **Lindebraekke, H**
919   Slegtstavler vedkommende Kristoffer Sjurdssen
H48   og Marta Sjurdsdatter Hjeltnes's slegt. Bergen, Centraltrykkeriet, 1915.
1915   85 p. 23 cm.

1. Hjeltnes family. I. Title.

NL 0378334   WHi

Lindebrække, Sjur, 1909-
Eiendomsrett og konkursbeslag; prinsipielle synspunkter i løsøreomsetningen. Bergen, F. Beyers bok- og papirhandel, Forlagsavdelingen, 1946.
228 p. 24 cm.

"Forkortede litteraturhenvisninger": p. ₍226₎-228.

1. Bankruptcy—Norway.   I. Title.

50-22370

NL 0378335   DLC

Lindebrække, Sjur.
Liberal-økonomiske fremtidslinjer. ₍København₎ Erhvervenes oplysningsråd ₍1951₎
29 p. illus. 21 cm.

1. Denmark—Pol. & govt.—1947-   I. Title.

DL258.L55   55-22757 ‡

NL 0378336   DLC

Lindebraekke, Sjur
Oversikt over negotiable dokumenter og andre omsetningspapirer, av Sjur Lindebrekke ... Oslo, Skrivemaskinstua ₍1939₎
₍4₎, 2-54 numb. l. 29½cm.
Reproduced from typewritten copy.

NL 0378337   MH-L

Lindebraekke, Sjur, 1909-
Tillit og tillitspolitikk. [Kragerø?, 1953]
95 p.

NL 0378338   MH

Lindebro, Ricard.
Politi i fangenskab, 19. september 1944-4. maj 1945. København, Nyt nordisk forlag, 1948.
253 p. 23 cm.

1. World War, 1939-1945—Prisoners and prisons, German. 2. World War, 1939-1945—Personal narratives, Danish. 3. Police—Norway.   I. Title.

D805.G3L52   50-17855

NL 0378339   DLC

Lindebrog, Friedrich
see
Lindenbrog, Friedrich, 1573-1648.

GV362 **Lindeburg, Franklin Alfred,** 1918-
L5   Organization and operation of supervision of physical education for boys in large secondary school systems in California. ₍Berkeley, 1952₎
vii, 471 l. diagrs., tables.

Thesis (Ed.D.) - Univ. of California, June 1952.
Bibliography: p. 249-253.

NL 0378341   CU

Lindeck, Stephan August, 1864 –
Ueber das electromotorische verhalten von amalgamen.
Inaug. diss. Strassburg, 1888 (Leipzig).

NL 0378342   ICRL DLC MH

Lindeck, Stephan August, 1864-   ed.

Zeitschrift für instrumentenkunde. Organ für mittheilungen aus dem gesammten gebiete der wissenschaftlichen technik. Hrsg. unter mitwirkung der Physikalisch-technischen reichsanstalt von E. Abbe ... Fr. Arzberger ... ₍etc.₎
Berlin, J. Springer,

Lindecke, Alfred.
Kohle, Wasser, Dampf. Leipzig, Fachbuchverlag, 1955.
144 p. illus. 19 cm.

1. Steam-boilers—Handbooks, manuals, etc.   I. Title.

TJ289.L62   56-31978 ‡

NL 0378344   DLC MiU

LINDECKE, Hans.
Der strafrechtliche schutz des deponenten gegen missbräuchliche stimmrechtsausübung auf grund sammeldeponierter aktien. Leipzig, 1933.
pp. 4-41.
Inaug.-diss. --- Leipzig.

NL 0378345   MH-L ICRL

AC831 **Lindecke, Karl.**
H3   Zur Behandlung er neueren Dichter im
1896   deutschen Unterrichte in der Prima.
Halberstadt, Doelle, 1896.
Stack   20 p.
"1896. Progr. Nr. 238."
Programmschrift - Königliches Dom-Gymnasium Halberstadt.
Accompanies Schulnachrichten.

1. German literature - Study and teaching.

NL 0378346   CSt

Lindecke, Konrad, Tierarzt: Arbeiten aus d. med. Veterinärkl. d. Univ. Gießen. Die Erkrankungen der Vormägen des Rindes und ihre Beeinflussung durch Veratrin. Mit 22 Tab. Cöthen-Anh. 1913: Schettler. 89 S. 8°
Gießen, Veterinär-Med. Diss. v. 18. Sept. 1913, Ref. Gmeiner
[Geb. 18. Juni 86 Edderitz; Wohnort: Gießen; Staatsangeh.: Anhalt; Vorbildung: G. Köthen Reife 07; Studium: Dresden TiH. 8 S.; Rig. 30. Mai 13.]
[U 13. 1931]

NL 0378347   ICRL PU MH DNLM

Lindecke, Otto,
Die aussichten der konsumvereine und der kleinhandlerischen interessenverorande.
Inaug. diss. Basel, 1904.
Bibl.

NL 0378348   ICRL

VOLUME 334

Lindecke, Otto.   334-57
Die Aussichten der Konsumvereine und der kleinhändlerischen
Interessenverbände, von Dr. Otto Lindecke. Basel, Kommissions-
Verlag von Helbing & Lichtenhahn vorm. Reich-Detloff, [1904].
104 p. 25ᶜᵐ.
"Literatur der behandelten Fragen," p. [103]-104.

NL 0378349   ICJ MiU CtY PU

Lindecke, Otto.
Die Beschaffung der zweiten Hypotheken mit
Hilfe der Gemeinden. Städtische Anstalten für
zweite Hypotheken. Verfasst im Auftrage des
"Rheinischen Vereins für Kleinwohnungswesen"
vom Generalsekretär Dr. Otto Lindecke. Düsseldorf, Verlag von Schmitz & Olbertz, 1913.
103 p.   24 cm.
1. Mortgages - Germany.

NL 0378350   CtY

Lindecke, Otto.
... Das genossenschaftswesen in Deutschland, von Dr.
Otto Lindecke ... Leipzig, G. J. Göschen, 1908.
144 p. 15½ᶜᵐ. (Sammlung Göschen. [384])
"Literatur": p. [4]

1. Association and associations—Germany. 2. Cooperation—Germany.
                                                   8-23904
Library of Congress   HD3498.L5

NL 0378351   DLC ICJ

Lindecker, Werner
Untersuchungen der zusammenhänge bei der
retuschelosen herstellung einer autotypie nach
einem photographischen halbtonbild. ... Solothurn,
1939.   34 p.
Inaug. Diss. - Techn. Hochschule Zürich, 1939.

NL 0378352   ICRL CtY

Lindecrantz, Erik Magnus, 1727-1788.
Canis familiaris, 21 dec. 1753.

NL 0378353   PPAN

Lindecrantz, Erik Magnus, 1727-1788, respondent
Linné, Carl von, 1707-1778, praeses.
... Cynographia ... Upsaliæ, exc. L. M. Höjer [1753]

Lindecrantz, Erik Magnus, 1727-1788, respondent.
... Dissertatio medica, sistens partem
priorem classis primae remediorum opht hal-
micorum ... 1756
        see under   Aurivillius, Samuel, praeses.

Lindedal, Ammon
Hp36   Vanliga främlingsord i svenskan, alfabetiskt
L64   ordnade under deras ursprungsord, med uttals-
       beteckning och förklaringar; etymologisk
       uppslags- och lärobok, av Ammon Lindedal
       och Hildegard Lundberg. Göteborg,
       Etymologisk uppslagsboks förlag[1939]
       392p. 25cm.
       On cover: Etymologisk uppslagsbok över främlingsord i
svenskan.

       1. Swedish language - Dictionaries.
       2. Swedish language · Etymology. cdu

NL 0378356   CtY CU MnU NN NNC

Lindefjeld, Nanna
    see
    Lindefjeld-Hauge, Nanna, 1896-

Lindefjeld-Hauge, Nanna, 1896-
...Antikkens guder og helter, m ytologiske skisser og fritt for-
talte sagn med navne- og slektsregister. Innledning av Emil
Smith. Oslo, J. W. Cappelen [1947] 232 p. illus. 21cm.
"Kilder," p. 232.

438251B. 1. Mythology, Greek.
N. Y. P. L.   May 9, 1949

NL 0378358   NN

Lindefjeld-Hauge, Nanna, 1896-
    Seks dage. Kristiania, H. Aschehoug & co. (W. Nygaard)
1919.
    104 p. 20 cm. kr3.40

    I. Title.
    PT8950.L65S4 1919   20-6699

NL 0378359   DLC

967.5
L743s   Lindegaard, A   E   A
         Soldaterliv i Congo, 1897-1900. Kjøben-
         havn, Nyt Nordisk Forlag, A.Busck, 1928.
         199p. illus.,fold.map. 23cm.

         1. Congo, Belgian. Descr. & trav. I. Title.

NL 0378360   IEN NN WU

AS284
L82   **Lindegård, Bengt.**
bd. 45,   Anthropologische Untersuchung mittelalterlicher Skelett-
nr. 9   funde aus dem Aussätzigenspital St. Jörgen in Åhus, von
         Bengt Lindegård und Folke Löfgren. Lund, C. W. K. Glee-
         rup [1949]
         56 p. 7 plates, diagrs., tables. 26 cm. (Lunds universitets års-
         skrift, n. f., avd. 2, bd. 45, nr. 9)
         Kungl. Fysiografiska sällskapets handlingar, n. f., bd. 60, nr. 9.
         "Literatur": p. [55]-56.
         1. Craniology—Sweden. 2. Jaws.   I. Löfgren, Folke, joint author.
         (Series: Lund. Universitet. Acta Universitatis Lundensis, n. s.
         Lunds universitets årsskrift, n. f., avd. 2, bd. 45, nr. 9.   Series:
         Fysiografiska sällskapet i Lund. Acta. Handlingar, n. f., bd. 60, nr.
         9)
                                                   A 50-6406
         Chicago. Univ. Libr.
         for Library of Congress   [2]

NL 0378361   ICU DLC

Lindegård, Bengt.
    A new racial character of the lower jaw; a theoretical an-
thropological investigation, by Bengt Lindegård and Bertil
Sonesson. Lund, C. W. K. Gleerup [1952]
    17 p. diagrs. 26 cm. (Lunds universitets årsskrift, n. f., avd. 2,
    bd. 48, nr. 8)
    Kungl. Fysiografiska sällskapets handlingar, n. f., bd. 63, nr. 8.
    Bibliography : p. 17.
    1. Jaws. 2. Ethnic types.   I. Sonesson, Bertil, joint author.
    (Series: Lund. Universitet. Acta Universitatis Lundensis, n. s.
    Lunds universitets årsskrift, n. f., avd. 2, bd. 48, nr. 8. Series: Fysio-
    grafiska sällskapet i Lund. Acta ... Handlingar, n. f., bd. 63, nr. 8)
    [AS284.L82 bd. 48, nr. 8]   A 53-7459

    Chicago. Univ. Libr.
    for Library of Congress

NL 0378362   ICU MH-P TxU

Lindegård, Bengt.
    Variations in human body-build; a somatometric and X-
ray cephalometric investigation on Scandinavian adults.
[Translated by L. James Brown] Copenhagen, Munksgaard,
1953.
    163 p. illus., diagrs. 24 cm. (Acta psychiatrica et neurologica,
supplementum 86)
    "References": p. [159]-163.

    1. Anthropometry—Scandinavia.   I. Title.   (Series: Acta
psychiatrica et neurologica Scandinavica. Supplementum 86)

GN57.S33L52   573.6   54-2319 rev

NL 0378363   DLC MiU DNLN NIC MH-P ViU

Lindegård, Mai, 1919-
    Andere Tage kommen, Roman [von] Synnøve Christensen
[pseud.] Zürich, Pan-Verlag [1944]
    377 p. 21 cm.
    "Titel der Originalausgabe 'Det kommer dagar efter dessa.' Über-
setzt aus dem Schwedischen von Anna Helfenberger-Hallberg. Manuskript in Norwegisch."

    I. Title.

    PT8950.L652K64   47-23389 rev*

NL 0378364   DLC

PT   Lindegård, Mai, 1919-
8950   Der kommer dage efter disse [af] Synnøve
L652   Christensen [pseud.] Oversat af Lorentz
K613   Albeck-Larsen. [1. opl.] Aalborg, Asbo
         Forlag [1946]
         298 p. 22 cm.

NL 0378365   WU IEN

Lindegård, Mai, 1919-
    Det kommer dagar efter dessa, roman av Synnöve Chris-
tensen [pseud.] Översättning från det norska manuskriptet
av Dagny Henschen. Stockholm, Ljus [1943]
    265 p. 22 cm.

    I. Title.

    PT8950.L652K6   839.8236   44-50966 rev 2*

NL 0378366   DLC

Lindegård, Mai, 1919-
    Døtrene Lindeman ; roman fra rokokkotiden. [Av] Syn-
nøve Christensen [pseud.] Oslo, Gyldendal, 1955.
    367 p. 24 cm.

    I. Title.

                                            A 56-3524
    Minnesota. Univ. Libr.
    for Library of Congress

NL 0378367   MnU OrP WaU OCl KyU CU WU NN IaDL

Lindegård, Mai, 1919-
    Ich bin eine norwegische Frau, Tatsachenbericht [von]
Synnøve Christensen [pseud.] Zürich, Humanitas Verlag
[1943]
    297 p. 21 cm.
    "Übersetzung aus dem Schwedischen von Anna Helfenberger-Hall-
berg. Manuskript in Norwegisch."

    1. Norway—Hist.—German occupation, 1940-1945. 2. World War,
1939-1945—Personal narratives, Norwegian.   I. Title.

    D811.5.L544   47-38352 rev*

NL 0378368   DLC

VOLUME 334

Lindegård, Mai, 1919–
Ich bin eine norwegische frau; tatsachen-
bericht. Zürich, Humanitas verlag, [c1944]
297 p.

NL 0378369 MiD

Lindegård, Mai, 1919–
Ja, jag är en norsk kvinna, av Synnöve Christensen
[pseud.] Oversättning från det norska manuskriptet.
Stockholm, Ljus förlag [1943]
271 p. 20 cm.

1. Norway—Hist.—German occupation, 1940–1945. 2. World War,
1939–1945—Personal narratives, Norwegian. I. Title.

D811.5.L54   940.53481   44–27105 rev 2*

NL 0378370 DLC

Lindegård, Mai, 1919–
Ja, jeg er en norsk Kvinde [af] Synnöve
Christensen [pseud.] Kobenhavn, Student-
ernes Efterretningstjeneste, 1944.
83p. 30cm.

Besaettelsestidens illegale Blade og
Bøger.
Mimeographed.

NL 0378371 IEN MH

Lindegård, Mai, 1919–
Jeg lever videre, roman. Oslo, Gyldendal, 1940.
208 p. 20 cm.

I. Title.

PT8950.L652J4   839.8236   47–36337 rev*

NL 0378372 DLC CU NN

Lindegård, Mai, 1919–
Kaleidoskop; noveller [av] Synnøve Christensen [pseud.]
Oslo, Gyldendal, 1950.
199 p. 20 cm.

I. Title.

PT8950.L652K3   A 51–3345 rev
Minnesota. Univ. Libr.
for Library of Congress   [r52b1]†

NL 0378373 MnU NcU NN DLC

Lindegård, Mai, 1919–
Mor Maria, roman [av] Synnøve Christensen [pseud.]
Oslo, Gyldendal, 1947.
256 p. 22 cm.

1. Mary, Virgin—Fiction.   I. Title.

PT8950.L652M6   48–15960 rev*

NL 0378374 DLC CU WU NcU NN MnU

Lindegård, Mai, 1919–
Nasaretin Maria; romaani. Jyväskylä. K.J.
Gummerus. 1951.
262 p.
By Synnöve Christensen, pseud.

NL 0378375 WaS

Lindegård, Mai, 1919–
Norway is my country, by Synnöve Christensen [pseud.]
London, Collins, 1943.
160 p. 19 cm.

Translation of Ja, jag är en norsk kvinna.

1. Norway—Hist.—German occupation, 1940–1945. 2. World War,
1939–1945—Personal narratives, Norwegian.   I. Title.

D811.5.L543   940.53481   44–4882 rev 2*

NL 0378376 DLC

Lindegård, Mai, 1919–
Sønn av første ekteskap [av] Synnøve Christensen [pseud.]
Oslo, Gyldendal, 1945.
313 p. 20 cm.

I. Title.

PT8950.L652S6   47–16408 rev*

NL 0378377 DLC CU

Lindegård, Mai, 1919–
Sono una donna norvegese, relazione di fatti
avvenuti di Synnöve Christensen [pseud.]   [Milano]
A. Mondadori, 1946.
229 p.   (Medusa, vol. CLX)

NL 0378378 DLC

Lindegård, Mai, 1919–
Verbrannte Herzen. Roman [von] Synnöve Christensen
[pseud.] Zürich, Pan-Verlag [1945, *1946]
215 p. 21 cm.

"Aus dem Schwedischen übertragen von Anna Helfenberger-Hallberg."

I. Title.

PT8950.L652A85   839.8236   47–29030 rev*

NL 0378379 DLC

Lindegård, Margit Inger
see Lindegård, Mai, 1919–

LS281
.A3l   Lindegaard Petersen, Valdemar, 1877–
v.7–8   Kampstillingen mellem kirke og stat i Fran-
             krig, 1789–1906. Aarhus Universitetsforlaget,
             1935–36.
             2 v. (Acta Jutlandica, VII–VIII. Supple-
mentum)
             Contents.—1. 1789–1870.—2. 1870–1906.

1. Church and state in France.

NL 0378381 ICU MiU RPB

Pamph.   LINDEGAARD PETERSEN, Valdemar, 1877–
v.530   Den protestantike kirke i Frankrig
             under Germinalloven (1802–52). Koebenhavn,
             Schoenberg, 1907.
             173p. 24.5cm.

Afhandling -- Copenhagen.

NL 0378382 MH-AH

Pamph.   LINDEGAARD PETERSEN, Valdemar, 1877–
v.514   Le protestantisme français sous la loi
             de décembre 1905. Paris, Bureaux de la
             Revue chrétienne [1908?]
             12p. 23.5cm.

Cover-title.

NL 0378383 MH-AH

Lindegger, Albert, 1904–
see his pseudonym: Lindi.

Lindegger (Charles) [1893–   ]. *Recherches
organométriques sur le foie des nourrissons
atrophiques et leurs conséquences. 36 pp.
8°. Paris, 1923.

NL 0378385 DNLM CtY

Lindegger, Gaspard, 1855–
——— * Contribution à l'étude de gros rein poly-
kystique et son opération. 87 pp. 4°. Paris,
1896. No. 357.

NL 0378386 DNLM

Lindegger (Gaspard) [1855–   ]. * Ein Fall
von Nephrectomie einer multilocullären Cysten-
niere. 48 pp. 8°. Strassburg. C. Goeller. 1894.

NL 0378386-1 DNLM MH

Lindegger, Marianne.
Die Rechte des Mündels im schweizerischen ZGB, insbesondere der Ausschluss der Vertretungsmacht des Vor-
mundes, das eigene Handeln und die Mitwirkung des Bevor-
mundeten. Bern, 1952.
ix, 77 p. 23 cm.

Diss.—Bern.
"Erschienen als Heft 290 der 'Abhandlungen zum schweizerischen
Recht,' neue Folge."
Bibliography: p. vi–ix.

1. Guardian and ward—Switzerland.   I. Title.

54–42407

NL 0378387 DLC MH-L

Lindegger, T.
Die Anwaltschaft im Gebiete des Kantons Aargau. Eine
rechtshistorische Studie. Aarau: H. R. Sauerländer & Co., 1911.
x, 93 p. 8°.

Dissertation, Zurich. Bibliography, p. viii–x.

1. Criminal law, Switzerland : Aargau.
N. Y. P. L.   April 18, 1913.

NL 0378388 NN ICRL MH

Lindegren, Alina Marie, 1887–
Education and service conditions of teachers in Scandinavia, the Netherlands and Finland, by Alina M. Lindegren,
specialist in western European education ... Federal security agency, Paul V. McNutt, administrator. U. S. Office of
education, John W. Studebaker, commissioner. Washington, U. S. Govt. print. off., 1941.
vii, 149 p. incl. maps, tables. 23 cm. (U. S. Office of education.
Bulletin 1940, no. 9)
Bibliography at end of each section.
1. Teachers—Scandinavia. 2. Teachers—Netherlands. 3. Teachers—Finland. 4. Teachers, Training [of]—Scandinavia. 5. Teachers,
Training [of]—Netherlands. 6. Teachers, Training [of]—Finland.
I. Title.
L111.A6 1940, no. 9   371.1094
——— Copy 2.   LB1723.L5   E 41—78
U. S. Office of Education.   Library
for Library of Congress   [a60x1]†

NL 0378389 DHEW NcC PBm DLC

VOLUME 334

Lindegren, Alina Marie.
Education in Germany, by Alina M. Lindegren, specialist in western European education ... United States Department of the interior, Harold L. Ickes, secretary. Office of education, J. W. Studebaker, commissioner. Washington, U. S. Govt. print. off., 1939.
xii, 145 p. illus., plans, tables. 23 cm. (U. S. Office of education. Bulletin 1938, no. 15)
Bibliography: p. 143–145.
1. Education—Germany.—1933–
[L111.A6 1938, no. 15]   E 39—153
—— Copy 2.   [LA722.L72]

U. S. Office of Education.   Library
for Library of Congress   ₍a57k1₎

OCU ODW
NL 0378390   DHEW WaWW OrU DLC MH NcC PBm OU OOxM

Lindegren, Alina Marie, 1887–
Education in Sweden. ₍Washington₎ Federal Security Agency, Office of Education ₍1952₎
viii, 90 p. illus. 24 cm. (₍U. S.₎ Office of Education. Bulletin, 1952, no. 17)
Bibliography: p. 81–83.

1. Education—Sweden. 2. ₍Higher education—Sweden₎   (Series)
L111.A6 1952, no. 17   370.9485   E 53–17
—— Copy 2.   LA901.8.L55

U. S. Office of Education.   Library
for Library of Congress   ₍12₎†

NL 0378391   DHEW OrStbM PP PBm PU-Penn PPPL PPD DLC

LA721
.P7
Lindegren, Alina Marie, joint author.

Prange, Gordon William, 1910–
Education in the German Federal Republic ₍by Gordon W. Prange and Alina M. Lindegren. Washington ₍U. S. Dept. of Health, Education, and Welfare, Office of Education, Division of International Education ₍1954₎

Lindegren, Alina Marie.
... Institutions of higher education in Denmark, by Alina M. Lindegren, specialist in western European school systems, Office of education ... Washington, U. S. Govt. print. off., 1934.
ix, 126 p. 23ᶜᵐ. (U. S. Office of education. Bulletin, 1934, no. 13)
At head of title: United States Department of the interior, Harold L. Ickes, secretary. Office of education, George F. Zook, commissioner.
Bibliography: p. 117.
1. Education, Higher. ₍1. Higher education—Denmark₎ 2. Universities and colleges—Denmark.   i. Title.
U. S. Off. of educ. Library   L111.A6 1934, no. 13   E 35—18
—— Copy 2.   LA877.L5
for Library of Congress   L111.A6 1934, no. 13

NL 0378393   DHEW WaWW OrU PPT OU OCU ODW OC1 DLC

Lindegren, Alina Marie.
Institutions of higher education in Norway, by Alina M. Lindegren, specialist in western European school systems, Office of education ... United States Department of the interior. Harold L. Ickes, secretary. Office of education, George F. Zook, commissioner. Washington, U. S. Govt. print. off., 1934.
vii, 96 p. fold. chart. 23ᶜᵐ. (U. S. Office of education. Bulletin 1934, no. 2)
Bibliography: p. 89.
1. Education, Higher. ₍1. Higher education—Norway₎ 2. Universities and colleges—Norway.
Library, U. S. Office of   Education LA896.L24   E 34—440
—— Copy 2.   L111.A6 1934 no. 2
Library of Congress   [L111.A6 1934 no. 2]

NL 0378394   DHEW WaWW PP PBm MiU OCU OU OC1

Lindegren, Alina Marie.
... Institutions of higher education in Sweden, by Alina M. Lindegren, specialist in western European school systems, Office of education. United States Department of the interior. Ray Lyman Wilbur, secretary. Office of education. William John Cooper, commissioner. Washington, U. S. Govt. print. off., 1932.
v, 45 p. 23ᵐᵐ. (U. S. Office of education. Pamphlet no. 32. July, 1932)
Bibliography: p. 45.
1. Universities and colleges—Sweden. 2. Education, Higher. ₍2. Higher education—Sweden₎   i. Title.
E 32—600
U. S. Off. of educ. Library   L111.A54 no. 32
—— Copy 2.   LA908.L24
for Library of Congress   L111.A75 no. 32
—— Copy 2.   LA907.5.L5
                    ₍u40k1₎

OC1 OO DLC
NL 0378395   DHEW WaWW WaTC OrSaW MB PPT OCU ODW OU

₍Lindegren, Alina Marie₎ 1887–
Studies on the Far East at universities and colleges in the United States. Division of comparative education, Federal security agency, U. S. Office of education. Washington, 1942.
cover-title, ₍3₎–31 p. incl. tables. 26½ᶜᵐ.
Mimeographed.
"By Alina M. Lindegren."—p. ₍3₎

1. ₍Civilization, Oriental—Study and teaching₎ 2. East (Far East)—₍Study and teaching₎ 3. Universities and colleges—U. S.—Curricula. 4. ₍Eastern question (Far East)₎   i. Title.
                                        E 42–328
U. S. Off. of educ. Library
for Library of Congress   CB251.L4
                                        950.02

NL 0378396   DHEW OO DLC

LINDEGREN, ANNA.
Albert Blombergsson, en hälsingemålarei förra århundradet.   (IN: Gammal Hälsingekultur. Hudiksvall. 22cm. 1933. p. 114–155. illus., ports.)

1. Blombergsson, Albert, 1810–1875.

NL 0378397   NN

Lindegren, August, illus.
... Les maisons souveraines de l'Europe see under Wrangel, F₍redrik₎ U₍lrik₎ grefve.

Lindegren, Axel Johan, 1860–
Konsten och samhället, vardagslivets estetik; med flera uppsatser, av Axel Lindegren... Stockholm: Bröderna Lagerström, 1913. 2 p.l., (i)viii–x p., 1 l., 173 p., 1 l. 8°.
Contents: Konsten och samhället. Stilbegreppets innebörd. Stilkänslans nydaning. Vardagslivets estetik. Om färgstil. Scenkonstens tidsenliga förnyelse. Nutida svensk bildkonst (fragment). Husbyggnadskonst. Nationella strävanden i den nutida svenska husbyggnadskonsten. Arkitekturminnesvård. Ödekyrkan.

1. Art.—Essays and misc. 2. Art   (Swedish). 3. Stage. 4. Title.
N. Y. P. L.   October 23, 1917.

NL 0378399   NN MH

Lindegren, Carl Clarence, 1896– , joint author.
Walker, John Charles, 1893–
Further studies on the relation of onion scale pigmentation to disease resistance. By J. C. Walker ... and Carl C. Lindegren ...
(*In* U. S. Dept. of agriculture. Journal of agricultural research. vol. XXIX, no. 10, November 15, 1924, p. 507–514. 25ᶜᵐ. Washington, 1925)

Lindegren, Carl C., joint author.
Rose, Dean Humboldt, 1878–
Phytophthora rot of pears and apples. By Dean H. Rose ... and Carl C. Lindegren ...
(*In* U. S. Dept. of agriculture. Journal of agricultural research. vol. XXX, no. 5, March 1, 1925, p. 463–468. illus., col. pl. 25ᵐᵐ. Washington, 1925)

Lindegren, Carl Clarence, 1896–
Two hitherto unreported diseases of stone fruits. By C. C. Lindegren ... and Dean H. Rose ...
(*In* U. S. Dept. of agriculture. Journal of agricultural research. vol. xxviii, no. 6, May 10, 1924, p. 605–605. 25 cm. Washington, 1924)
Contribution from Bureau of plant industry (G—405)
Published October 14, 1924.

1. Alternaria. 2. Botrytis. 3. Cherry—Diseases ₍and pests₎ 4. Peach—Diseases ₍and pests₎ i. Rose, Dean Humboldt, 1878– joint author.
                                        Agr 24–851 rev
U. S. Dept. of Agr. Libr.   1Ag84J vol. 28
for Library of Congress   ₍r40e‡₎

NL 0378402   DNAL OC1 OO OU

Lindegren, Carl Clarence, 1896–
The yeast cell, its genetics and cytology. 1st ed. St. Louis, Educational Publishers, 1949.
1 v. (various pagings) illus. 24 cm.
Developed from a series of lectures given at the University of Washington, Seattle, in 1947.
Bibliography: 7 p. at end.

1. Yeast.   i. Title.

QR151.L66   589.2361   49–11233

OrCS CU CaBVaU OrU IdU WaU
ViU NNC NcD NcRS PPLas ICJ AU IdPI MtBC WaSpG
NL 0378403   DLC PU PSt PPF ICU OU DI TxU OC1W TU CU

Lindegren, Carl Clarence, 1896–
The yeast cell, its genetics and cytology. 1st ed. St. Louis, Educational Publishers, 1949.
1 v. (various pagings) illus. 24 cm.
Developed from a series of lectures given at the University of Washington, Seattle, in 1947.
Bibliography: 7 p. at end.
Photoreproduction.   Ann Arbor, Mich., University Microfilms, 1970.

NL 0378404   INS

Lindegren, Carl Johan , 1770–1815.
Samlade arbeten. Stockholm, Carl Delén, 1805–1807.
3 v.

NL 0378405   WaU CU MH

Lindegren, Carl Johan, 1770–1815
L'amant aveugle, comedie en deux actes de Chas. Lindegren. [Tr. en francais par Mlle. R. Du Puget] (In Chef-d'oeuvre des theatres etrangers... tr. en francais. 1823. v.25, p. 415–456)

NL 0378406   OU

Lindegren, Carl Johan, 1770–1815
L'aventurier, comedie en quatre actes de Chas. Lindegren. [Tr. en francais par Mlle. R. Du Puget] (In Chefs-d'oeuvre des theatres etrangers...tr. en francais. 1823. v.25, p.[311]–413)

NL 0378407   OU

Lindegren (CARl JoHan)
*De philosophiæ in historia usu. Upsaliae, [1791]. 16 pp. 4°.
In: BAC p. v. 4.

NL 0378408   NN

Lindegren (CARl JoHan)
*De præcipuis eruditorum vitiis. Upsalia, 1788. 16 pp. 4°.
In: YAM p. v. 2.

NL 0378409   NN

[Lindegren, Carl Johan] 1770–1815.
Den försonade fadren. Drame i tre acter. Svenskt original. Stockholm, A. Nordström, 1795.
3 p.l., 66 p. 16°.

NL 0378410   NN

VOLUME 334

Lindegren, Erik, 1910–1968.
ABC of lettering and printing types. New
York, Museum Books, Inc. [n.d.–
2v. illus.

Contents:--[v.1] Lettering--[v.2] Printing
types--

NL 0378411   MtBC

839.7169   Lindegren, Erik, 1910–
L641A2   Dikter, 1942-1947.   Stockholm, A.
1953   Bonnier, 1953.
           99p. 20cm.

NL 0378412   KU DCU OC1 IEN NNC NcD PU MH CU

Lindegren, Erik, 1910–   ed.
40 [i.e. Fyrtio]-talslyrik. Utg. av Erik
Lindegren och Karl Vennberg. Stockholm,
A. Bonnier [1946]
131 p.   20 cm.
1. Swedish poetry--20th cent.   I. Vennberg,
Karl Gunnar, 1910–   ed. II. Title.

NL 0378413   NIC

Lindegren, Erik,   ed.
40-tals-lyrik, utgiven av Erik Lindegren och Karl Vennberg. Stockholm,
A. Bonnier [1947]

131 p.   20cm.

1. Swedish poetry. Collections.
I. Vennberg, Karl,   jt. ed.

NL 0378414   MnU

Lindegren, Erik, 1910–
I speglarnas sal
see under Blomdahl, Karl Birger, 1916–

Lindegren, Erik, 1910–
Im Saale der Spiegel
see under Blomdahl, Karl Birger, 1916–

Lindegren, Eric, 1910–
In the hall of Mirrors
see under Blomdahl, Karl-Birger, 1916–

Lindegren, Erik, 1910–
Mannen utan väg; dikter. Ny uppl. Stockholm,
Bonnier, 1945

85 p.

NL 0378418   MH MnU

PT   Lindegren, Erik, 1910–
9875   Posthum ungdom; dikter. Stockholm, A.
L597   Bonnier [c1935]
P6   58p. 20cm.

NL 0378419   WU MnU

Lindegren, Erik, 1910–
Sviter, dikter. Stockholm, A. Bonnier [1947]
86 p. 22 cm.

I. Title.

Full name: Johan Erik Lindegren.

PT9875.L597S9   48-27358*

NL 0378420   DLC WaU NcD CtY

411   [Lindegren, Erik] 1910-1968.
L643v   Våra bokstäver, hur de utvecklats och fått
1952   sin nuvarande form. [Illustrationer Knut
        Grane, manuskript Erik Lindegren och Gustaf
        Bondeson. Göteborg] Wezäta [1952]
        27p. illus. 23cm. (Wezätas skriftserie
        nr. 5)

1. Alphabet. I. Grane, Knut
II. Bondeson, Gus-   taf

NL 0378421   KU

Lindegren, Erik, 1910–1968.
Vinteroffer. Stockholm, Bonnier [1954]
81 p. 24 cm.
Poems.

I. Title.

Full name: John Erik Lindegren.

PT9875.L597V5   55-17954 ‡

NL 0378422   DLC NcU WU ICU NcD WaU MnU NN OC1

Lindegren, H   comp.
Palmgrenska samskolan, 1876-1901; några minnen
samlade och utgifna af H. Lindegren ... Stockholm,
Tryckt hos E. Westerberg, 1901.
199, [1] p. 23cm.
"Redogörelse för undervisningskursen i lefvande språk i Palmgrenska
samskolan 12 juni-1 juli 1899, af Gunnar Norlander": p. [187]-199.
Several of the above essays were later translated into German and appeared in Palmgren's "Erziehungsfragen." Altenburg, O. Bonde, 1904.
CONTENTS.— Förord.—Palmgrenska samskolan.—Pedagogiska uppsatser
af K. E. A. H. Palmgren]
1. Teaching. 2. Stockholm. Palmgrenska samskolan. I. Palmgren,
Karl Edvard Abraham Henning, 1840–   II. Nordlander, Gunnar.

                                          7-41560
Library of Congress   LA909.S7L5

NL 0378423   DLC

Lindegren, Johan, 1842-1908
Fuga, piano
Fuga uti fri stil för piano. Stockholm, pa Musikal-
iska konstföreningens förlag [1866?]

Score (6 p.)
Bd.with his Sonata, piano, op.2

NL 0378424   MH

Lindegren, Johan, 1842-1908
Quintets, strings, F major
Kvintett för 2 violiner, 2 altvioliner och violon-
cell. Stockholm, Musikaliska konstföreningen [1908]

Score (39 p.) & 5 pts.

NL 0378425   MH

Lindegren, Johan, 1842-1908
Sonatas, piano, op.2
Stor sonat (canon) för piano. Op.2. Stockholm,
Hirsch, pa Musikaliska Konstföreningens förlag [1867?]

Score (31 p.)
Bd.with his Fugue, piano

NL 0378426   MH

Lindegren, Johan Erik
see Lindegren, Erik, 1910–1968.

Lindegren, Karl.
Kampen mellan Öst och Väst; den världspolitiska utvecklingen efter 1945. [Stockholm] LTs förlag [1952]
208 p. 20 cm. (Vårt forum, 3)

1. World politics—1945–   2. Sweden—For. rel.—1905–
I. Title.

D843.L5   56-29456 ‡

NL 0378428   DLC MnU

Lindegren, Karl Johan
see Lindegren, Carl Johan, 1770-1815.

Lindegren, *Mrs.* Signe.
Ingrid's holidays, by Signe Lindegren; translated from the
Swedish by Caroline Schleef; illustrated by Vera Neville.
New York, The Macmillan company, 1932.
4 p. l., 238 p. front., illus. 19½ᵐ.

I. Schleef, Caroline, tr. II. Title.

Library of Congress   PZ7.L658 In   32-11563
—— Copy 2.
Copyright A 51132   [3]   839.7369

NL 0378430   DLC NN MB PJA OC1W OC1

f711.409471
L743h   Lindegren, Yrjö, d.1952.
        Helsingin keskus; keskusalueen
        asemakaavaedotus 1954. Helsingfors
        centrum; förslag till stadsplan för det
        centrala området. [Helsinki, Tilgmann,
        1955]
        87p., [11]ℓ. illus. plans(part fold. part col.)
        30cm. (Helsingin kaupungin julkaisuja, no.3)

        "Professor Lindegren had as collaborator

        Architect Erik Kråkström, who completed the
        task after the death of Professor Lindegren ..."
        Text in Finnish and Swedish, with summaries in
        English.
        "The new centre of Helsinki", by Alvar Aalto,
        11ℓ. at end.

        1.Cities and towns – Planning – Helsingfors.
        I.Kråkström, Erik. II.Title. (Series)

NL 0378432   CLSU NNC MH

Lindehn, H. A. W.
Biographical sketch [of Viktor Rydberg].
(In Rydberg, A. V. Roman days. Pp. v-xxi. New York, 1879.)

NL 0378433   MB MdBP

VOLUME 334

917.481 Lindehn, H   A   W
L641i   Illustrerad hand-bok till Philadelphia
Sw   och dess omgifningar, särskildt för dem
         som besöka Verldsutställningen 1876...
         C.P. Thore [°1875]
         159p. illus.

1. Philadelphia -   Descr. - Guide-books.

NL 0378434   PP

Lindehn, H   A   W
    Illustrerad hand-bok till Philadelphia
och dess omgifningar, särskildt för dem som
besöka verldsutställningen 1876, jemte veg-
ledning till Washington, New York, Boston,
Niagara, Chicago, med flera platser.
New York, Chas. P. Thore & co., 1876.
    180 p.

NL 0378435   PPAmSwM

Lindeholz, Herbert, 1908–
    Die nutzverwaltung nach 15 Abs. 2 REG. ...
Würzburg, 1937.   68 p.
    Inaug. Diss. - Halle-Wittenberg, 1937.
    Lebenslauf.
    Verzeichnis des verwendeten schrifttums.

NL 0378436   ICRL

Lindeijer, Egberta Johanna.
    De bacterie-ziekte van den wilg veroorzaakt door
Pseudomonas saliciperda N. sp. ...   Baarn,
N. V. Hollandia, 1932.
    6 p.l., [3]–82 p.   illus., plates, tables.
25 cm.
    Proefschrift - Amsterdam.
    Contains English summary.
    "Literatuurlijst": p. [80]–82.

NL 0378437   OrCS CtY

Lindeijer, Evart Willem.
    Explosiviteit van gasmengsels ...   Worme-
oveer, 1935.
    Proefschrift - Leiden.

NL 0378438   CtY

Lindeiner, Hans Erdmann von, 1883–
    Konservativismus, von Hans Erdmann von Lindeiner-
Wildau...   (In: Harms, B., editor. Volk und Reich der
Deutschen.   Berlin, 1929.   8°.   Bd. 2, p. [35–]61.)

560065A. 1. Conservatism—   Germany.
N. Y. P. L.   December 28, 1931

NL 0378439   NN

Lindeiner, Hans Erdmann von, 1883–
    Wie der Gewaltfriede aussieht. Von H. E. v. Lindeiner-
Wildau...   Berlin: Deutschnationale Schriftenvertriebsstelle,
G.m.b.H.[, 1919.]   7 p.   8°.   (Deutschnationale Volkspartei.
Deutschnationale Flugschrift. Nr. 17.)

1. Versailles, Treaty of, 1919.   2. Ser.
N. Y. P. L.   July 11, 1927

NL 0378440   NN

Lindeiner von Wildau, Hans Erdmann von.
    See
Lieneiner, Hans Erdmann von, 1883–

Lindeken, Carl L
    A decade of plant spray oil research, an index
to the 1930–1940 literature on this subject, by
Carl L. Lindeken ...   [Richmond, Calif.,
Standard oil company of California [1941]
    cover-title, 18 numb. l.   28 cm.
    Mimeographed.

NL 0378442   OrCS

DT87   Lindekens, B., tr.
.5
.C32   Capart, Jean, 1877–
        Tout-ankh-Amon, door Jean Capart, met de medewerking
    van Marcelle Werbrouck, E. Bille-de Mot, Jeanne M. Taupin
    [en] Pierre Gilbert. Geautoriseerde vertaling door B. Linde-
    kens. Brussel, A. Manteau n. v.; [etc., etc.] 1944.

Lindekens, René.
    Ta mort ne t'appartient pas. [Paris] Dutilleul [1955]
    78 p. 22 cm.
    A novel.

    I. Title.
                                    A 57–290

Illinois. Univ. Library
for Library of Congress   [8]

NL 0378444   IU

Lindekruis, T., pseud.
    see Aarts, Antoon, 1902–

Lindekugel, Erich, 1906–
    Gesamtvollmacht. ... 1934.   47 p.
    Inaug. Diss. - Rostock, 1934.
    Lebenslauf.
    Bibliography.

NL 0378446   ICRL

Lindekugel, Walter, 1910–
    ... Ueber die Magenverweildauer einer
Probemahlzeit zu Beginn und am Ende einer
Nordseekur...   Hamburg, 1935.
    Inaug.-Diss. - Hamburg.
    Lebenslauf.
    "Literatur": p. 7.

NL 0378447   CtY MiU

Lindel, Johan L.
    Disputatio medica inauguralis, de vipera.
Trajecti ad Rehenum, [1690]
    1 p.l., 22 p., 1 l. 1 pl.   sm 4°.
    Title-page mutilated; printer's name and
date wanting. Plate cut off bottom.

NL 0378448   DLC

Lindel, Johann, ed.
    Sammlung der Polizei-Verordnungen, Orts-
statuten und sonstigen Bestimmungen für die
Stadt Königshütte O.-S.
        see under Królewska Huta, Silesia. Ordi-
nances, etc.

Lindelauf, J.
    La ready-méthode pour l'enseignement des langues modernes
... par J. Lindelauf ... [Français] Den Haag et Groningen,
The International company limited, Ready school of languages; [etc., etc., °1933–
    v. illus. 22½cm.

1. French language — Grammar — 1870–   2. French language—
Conversation and phrase books. I. Title.   33–36410
    Library of Congress   PC2111.L716
    Copyright A—Foreign   21626
                                    [2]   448.24

NL 0378450   DLC

Lindelauf, J.
    Die ready-methode zum erlernen fremder sprachen ... von
J. Lindelauf ... [Deutsch] Den Haag and Groningen, The
International company limited, Ready school of languages;
[etc., etc., °1932–
    v. illus. 23cm.

1. German language—Grammar—1870–   2. German language—
Conversation and phrase books. I. Title.   33–32410
    Library of Congress   PF3111.L49
    Copyright A—Foreign   20385
                                            438.24

NL 0378451   DLC

x475   Lindelbach, Michael, 15th cent.
L641p   Praecepta latinitatis.   Heidelberg [Printer
1486   of Lindelbach] 15 Dec. (xviij. kl'as ianuarij)
        1486.
        [72]l., the last blank. 4°. 20.6cm.
                    Goff L195
        Leaf [1ª] (t.p.): Precepta latinitatis ex
    diuersis oratory atq poetarum codicibus tracta.
    Brit. Mus. Cat. (XV cent.) III, p.667
    (IA.12912); Goff L223.
    Capital-spaces, some with guide-letters;

NL 0378452   IU

Lindelius, Lars Axel Magnus.
    Jesaias tjuguattonde kapitel. oefversaettning med
anmaerkningar.
    Inaug. diss. Upsala, 1863.

NL 0378453   ICRL

Lindell, Allan.
    Tillverkning av bilmotordetaljer. Örebro, Verkstadstek-
nik, Högre tekniska läroverket, 1953.
    80 l. illus. 29 cm.

1. Automobiles—Motors.   I. Örebro, Sweden. Högre tekniska
läroverket. II. Title.
                                        A 59–680
Detroit. Public Library
for Library of Congress   [8]

NL 0378454   MiD

Lindell, Arne.
    Carcinoma of the uterine cervix; incidence and influence
of age. A statistical study. [From the Swedish by
Catherine Djurklou] Stockholm, 1952.
    102 p. illus. 25 cm. (Acta radiologica. Supplementum 92)
    Akademisk avhandling—Karolinska institutet, Stockholm.
    Without thesis statement.
    At head of title: From the Gynecological Department (Director:
Hans-Ludvig Kottmeier) of the Radiumhemmet, Stockholm.
    Bibliography: p. [97]–102.

1. Uterus—Cancer.   I. Title.   (Series)
                                        A 54–1364
Wisconsin. Univ. Libr.
for Library of Congress   [2]

NL 0378455   WU MoU DNLM ViU

VOLUME 334

Lindell, August, 1862–
   Bidrag till historien om Norrbottens läns bebyggande och odling ... af August Lindell ... ₍Malmö, Stenström & Bartelsons boktryckeri, 1900₎
   96 p. 21½ᵐᵐ.
   Akademisk afhandling—Lund.
   "Använda arbeten och handlingar": p. ₍3₎–₍4₎

   1. Norrbotten, Sweden.
                              ₍Full name: Nils August Lindell₎
                                                36–28685
   Library of Congress   DL971.N6L5 1900
                              ₍2₎   948.8

   NL 0378456   DLC CtY

LINDELL, Carl E
   Massage and your health. ₍Portland, Or., 1949₎
   31 p. illus.
   1. Massage

   NL 0378457   DNLM

Lindell, Carl H₍olger₎.
   Construction of high voltage bushing & a study of insulator flashovers...
   ₍Cin.₎, 1929. [4], 59 l. pl.
   Thesis, Univ. of Cincinnati Electrical Engineer, 1929.

   NL 0378458   OCU

Lindell, Emil, 1854–
   Bibliotheca linnæana—works by or relating to Carolus Linnæus, his predecessors, contemporaries and pupils, with sequels—from the library of Emil Lindell ... **Växjö, Smålandspostens** boktr. a.-b., 1932.
   123, ₍1₎ p. 23½ᵐᵐ.

   1. Linné, Carl von, 1707–1778—Bibl.   i. Title.
                              ₍Full name: Emil Vilhelm Lindell₎
                                                34–9463
   Library of Congress   Z8508.L75
                                                012

   NL 0378459   DLC NNBG MoSB CtY

Lindell, Emil Vilhelm
   see Lindell, Emil, 1854–

Lindell, Gustaf.
   Bronislawa: dramatisk dikt i fem akter. Stockholm, Bergs boktryckeri, 1894.
   124 p. 12°.

   NL 0378461   NN

Law   Lindell, Ingvar, ed.

Sweden. *Laws, statutes, etc.*
   Den nya sjukförsäkringen; redogörelse för den år 1946 beslutade sjukförsäkringsreformen, av Rolf Broberg, Ingvar Lindell ₍och₎ Yngve Samuelsson. Stockholm, Norstedt ₍1947₎

Lindell, Nils August
   see
Lindell, August, 1862–

Lindell, Per Gustaf Edvard, 1842–1902, ed.
   Autografier och porträtt af framstaende personer ...
   see under title

Lindell, Per Gustaf Edvard, 1842–1902.
   Föredrag om likbränning. Stockholm, I. Marcus, 1882.
   16 p.

   NL 0378465   ICJ

Lindell, Per Gustaf Edvard, 1842–1902.
   ... Likbränning eller begrafning? Af Per Lindell ... (4. tusendet.) Stockholm, A. Bonnier ₍1891₎
   24 p. 19 cm. (Studentföreningen Verdandis småskrifter ₍4. bd.₎, 31)
   CONTENTS.—Öfversikt af likbränningsreformen.—Likbränningens företräden.—Invändningar mot likbränningen.

   1. Cremation.   i. Title.
   AC50.U73 nr. 31   24—25036

   NL 0378466   DLC

Lindell, Per Gustaf Edvard, 1842–1902.
   Likbränningen jemte öfriga grafskick, af Per Lindell. Med 124 figurer och 2 tabeller. ₍Stockholm₎ C. E. Fritzes k. hofbokhandel ₍1888₎
   ₍4₎ 434 p. illus., II fold. tables. 23ᵐᵐ.

   NL 0378467   ICJ ICRL

Lindell, Per Gustaf Edvard, 1842–1902.
   Likbränningen och dess införande i Sverige. Stockholm, A. L. Normans boktryckeri-aktiebolag, 1885.
   11 p.

   NL 0378468   ICJ

Lindell, Per Gustaf Edvard, 1842–1902. 614.62 P501
   Likbränningens rättsliga ställning i olika länder af Per Lindell.
   Stockholm, Iduns tryckeri aktiebolag, 1895.
   81, [1] p. 21½ᵐᵐ.
   "Separataftryck ur Meddelanden från Svenska likbränningsföreningen, n:o 20."

   NL 0378469   ICJ

Lindell, Per Gustaf Edvard, 1842–1902.
   Om likbränning. Stockholm, Gernandts boktr. aktiebolag, 1885.
   8 p.

   NL 0378470   ICJ

Lindell, Ruth Beauchamp ("Mrs. Edward E. Lindell")
   The Civil war experiences of Thomas J. Beauchamp. [Roseburg, Oregon?, n.d.]
   16 p.   port.

   NL 0378471   KyU

Lindell, Selma A., joint author.

Schorling, Raleigh, 1887–
   ... Instructional tests in algebra, adjusted for pupils of varying abilities, comprising fifty-two goals, by Raleigh Schorling, John R. Clark & Selma A. Lindell. Experimental ed. 1925. Ann Arbor, Mich., G. Wahr, 1925.

Lindell, Selma A., joint author.

Schorling, Raleigh, 1887–
   Modern algebra; second course, by Raleigh Schorling ... John R. Clark ... and Selma A. Lindell ... Yonkers-on-Hudson, N. Y., World book company, 1929.

Lindell, Thord Axel Frithjof, 1904–   *ed.*
   I Östergötland; prosa och poesi. ₍Redaktion: Thord Lindell och Harriet Alfons. Uddevalla₎ Forum ₍1953₎
   191, ₍1₎ p. illus. 19 cm.
   Bibliography: p. 191–₍192₎

   1. Östergötland, Sweden, in literature.   i. Alfons, Harriet, joint ed. ii. Title.
                                                A 54–5694
   Minnesota. Univ. Libr.
   for Library of Congress   ₍1₎

   NL 0378474   MnU CtY

Lindell, Thord Axel Frithjof, 1904–
   Östergötland; en rapsodi i färg. A rhapsody in colour. Linköping, H. Carlsons bokhandel ₍1954₎
   unpaged. illus. 30 cm.

   1. Östergötland, Sweden—Descr. & trav.—Views.
   DL971.O8L5   54–44500 †

   NL 0378475   DLC MnU

Lindell, Thord Axel Frithjof, 1904–   *comp.*
   Östgötahistorier. Med Förord av Sven Jerring. Stockholm, Wahlström & Widstrand ₍1946₎
   182 p. illus. 22 cm.

   1. Folk-lore—Sweden—Östergötland.   i. Title.
   GR225.L55   49–18014*

   NL 0378476   DLC PU

948.5
L641 LINDELL, Thord Axel Frithjof, 1904–
         Svensk historia, av Thord Lindell och Herbert Lagerström. Stockholm, Ehlins ₍1946–₎

         v. illus. 19cm. ₍Folkbildningsserien₎

         Contents.– Del I. Sveriges historia före 1809, av Thord Lindell.
         1. Sweden. History. I. Lagerström, Herbert, 1894–   Jt. author.

   NL 0378477   MnU

Lindell Railway Company
   Defendant's record [1894?]
      see under
Adams Electric Railway vs. the Lindell Railway Company.

Lindelöf, Ernst Leonard, 1870–
   ... Le calcul des résidus et ses applications à la théorie des fonctions, par Ernst Lindelöf ... Paris, Gauthier-Villars, 1905.
   vi p., 1 l., 141, ₍2₎ p. diagrs. 25½ᵐᵐ. (Collection de monographies sur la théorie des fonctions, pub. sous la direction de M. Émile Borel)

   1. Functions.
   Library of Congress   QA331.L6   11—18518

   MiU OU ViU PPT PBm MB ICJ
   NL 0378479   DLC MtBC CU MoU NcD TU NjP OC1W OCU

VOLUME 334

Lindelöf, Ernst Leonard, 1870–
Le calcul des résidus et ses applications à la théorie des fonctions. New York, Chelsea Pub. Co., 1947.
vi, 141 p. 22 cm. (Collection de monographies sur la théorie des fonctions)

1. Functions. (Series)

QA331.L6 1947   517.5   47–11966

NNC ViU OCU OC1JC MiEM OrPR IdPI IdU NNCoCi-G
NL 0378480   DLC CaBVaU OrCS IEdS NBuU NcRS MiU TxU

Lindelöf, Ernst Leonard, 1870–
Commentationes in honorem Ernesti Leonardi Lindelöf ...
see under title

Lindelöf, Ernst Leonard, 1870–
... Demonstration élémentaire de l'existence des intégrales d'un système d'équations différentielles ordinaires, par Ernst Lindelöf. ₁Helsingforsiæ, ex Officina typographica Societatis litterariæ fennicæ, 1896₁
13 p. 30 x 24ᶜᵐ. (₁Finska vetenskaps-societeten. Helsingfors₁ Acta Societatis scientiarum fennicæ. t. xxi, nᵒ 7)

1. Differential equations. 2. Integrals.
A C 38–127

New York. Public library
for Library of Congress   [Q60.F5 vol. 21, no. 7]
₁4₁   (508)

NL 0378482   NN DLC

Lindelöf, Ernst Leonard, 1870–
Einführung in die höhere analysis zum selbststudium und für studierende der ersten semester, von Ernst Lindelöf ... Nach der ersten schwedischen und zweiten finnischen auflage deutsch herausgegeben von Egon Ullrich ... Mit 84 figuren im text. Leipzig und Berlin, B. G. Teubner, 1934.
ix, 526 p. diagrs. 23 cm.

1. Calculus. I. Ullrich, Egon, 1902– tr.
QA303.L58   517   A C 34–3690

Yale Univ. Library
for Library of Congress   ₁a53e₁†

NL 0378483   CtY CU NN NcRS PU-Math MoU DLC

Mathematics
D517
L64
Lindelöf, Ernst Leonard, 1870–
Einführung in der höhere analysis zum selbststudium und für studierende der ersten semester. Nach der ersten schwedischen und zweiten finnischen aufl. deutsch hrsg. von Egon Ullrich. 2. aufl. Leipzig, Teubner, 1950.
ix, 526 p. diagrs.
1. Calculus. 2. Functions. I. Ullrich, Egon, 1902– tr.

NL 0378484   NNC PBL NcD MH NBuU MnU OO

Lindelöf, Ernst Leonard, 1870–
...Finlands svenska landskommuner; statistiska uppgifter sammanställda av Ernst Lindelöf. Helsingfors: Söderström & Co., 1923. 85 p. incl. tables. 3 col'd pl. 8°. (Samfundet Folkhälsan i svenska Finland. Skrifter. ₁nr.₁ 2.)

1. Statistics, Vital—Finland, 1810–   1910. 2. Emigration and immigration—Finland, 1893–1910. 3. Ser.
N.Y.P.L.   February 4, 1925

NL 0378485   NN InU

517
L64i
Lindelöf, Ernst Leonard, 1870–
Inledning till den högre analysen, af Ernst Lindelöf ... Stockholm, Albert Bonniers förlag ₁1912₁
1 p.ℓ., viii, 615, ₁1₁ p. 22½cm.

1. Mathematical analysis.

NL 0378486   ViW IU

Lindelöf, Ernst Leonard, 1870–
Kutsu kuulemaan sitä julkista esitelmää jonka Helsingin Yliopiston geologian ja mineralogian professori filosofiantohtori Matti Rufus Sauroma
see under   Helsinki. Yliopisto.

Lindelöf, Ernst Leonard, 1870–
... Mémoire sur certaines inégalités dans la théorie des fonctions monogènes et sur quelques propriétés nouvelles de ces fonctions dans le voisinage d'un point singulier essentiel, par Ernst Lindelöf ... ₁Helsingforsiæ, ex Officina typographica Societatis litterariæ fennicæ, 1909₁
35 p. 29½ x 23ᵐᵐ. (₁Finska vetenskaps-societeten, Helsingfors₁ Acta Societatis scientiarum fennicæ. t. xxxv, nᵒ 7)
"Présenté le 21 septembre 1908."

1. ₁Functions, Monogenic₁
A C 38–1226

New York. Public library
for Library of Congress   [Q60.F5 vol. 35, no. 7]
₁4₁   (508)

NL 0378488   NN DLC

518
L64m
Lindelöf, Ernst Leonard, 1870–
Mémoire sur la théorie des fonctions entières de genre fini. Helsingfors, Société de lit-térature finnoise, 1902.
79p. (Acta Societatis scientiarum fennicae. t.XXXI, no.1)

Présenté le 16 décembre 1901.

NL 0378489   IU

Lindelöf, Ernst Leonard, 1870–
... Mémoire sur la théorie des fonctions entières de genre fini, par Ernst Lindelöf ... ₁Helsingforsiæ, ex Officina typographica Societatis litterariæ fennicæ, 1903₁
1 p. l., iv, 79 p. 29½ x 23ᵐᵐ. (₁Finska vetenskaps-societeten, Helsingfors₁ Acta Societatis scientiarum fennicæ. t. xxxi, nᵒ 1)
"Présenté le 16 décembre 1901."

1. ₁Functions, Holomorphic₁
A C 38–938
Provisional

New York. Public library
for Library of Congress   [Q60.F5 vol. 31, no. 1]
₁4₁   (508)

NL 0378490   NN DLC ViU

518
L64q
Lindelöf, Ernst Leonard, 1870–
... Quelques applications d'une formule sommatoire générale ... Helsingfors, Societé de littérature finnoise, 1902.
46p. (Acta Societatis scientiarum fennicae, t.XXXI, no.3)

NL 0378491   IU

Lindelöf, Ernst Leonard, 1870–
... Quelques applications d'une formule sommatoire générale, par Ernst Lindelöf ... ₁Helsingforsiæ, ex Officina typographica Societatis litterariæ fennicæ, 1903₁
1 p. l., 46 p. incl. tab., diagrs. 29½ x 23ᵐᵐ. (₁Finska vetenskaps-societeten, Helsingfors₁ Acta Societatis scientiarum fennicæ. t. xxxi, nᵒ 3)
"Présenté le 17 mars 1902."
Bibliographical foot-notes.

1. Series.
A C 38–940

New York. Public library
for Library of Congress   [Q60.F5 vol. 31, no. 3]
₁4₁   (508)

NL 0378492   NN DLC ViU

Lindelöf, Ernst Leonard, 1870–
... Remarques sur l'intégration numérique des équations dif-férentielles ordinaires, par Ernst Lindelöf ... Helsingfors, 1938.
21 p. incl. tables. 28½ x 22ᶜᵐ. (₁Finska vetenskaps-societeten, Helsingfors₁ Acta Societatis scientiarum fennicæ. n. s. A, t. II, n:o 13)
"Présenté à la société le 18 octobre 1937."

1. Differential equations. I. Title: L'intégration numérique des équations différentielles ordinaires.
A C 39–2160

New York. Public library
for Library of Congress   [Q60.F5 n. s., A, vol. 2, no. 13]
₁4₁   (508)

NL 0378493   NN ViU

Lindelöf, Ernst Leonard, 1870–
... Remarques sur un principe général de la théorie des fonctions analytiques, par Ernst Lindelöf ... ₁Helsingforsiæ, ex Officina typographica Societatis litterariæ fennicæ, 1899₁
39 p. incl. tables. 29½ x 23ᵐᵐ. (₁Finska vetenskaps-societeten, Helsingfors₁ Acta Societatis scientiarum fennicæ. t. xxiv, nᵒ 7)
"Présenté à la société le 18 avril 1898."

1. Functions.
A C 38–151

New York. Public library
for Library of Congress   [Q60.F5 vol. 24, no. 7]
      (508)

NL 0378494   NN PPAmP

Lindelöf, Ernst Leonard, 1870–
... Sur l'intégration de l'équation différentielle de Kummer, par Ernst Lindelöf. ₁Helsingforsiæ, ex Officina typographica Societatis litterariæ fennicæ, 1893₁
31 p. 29½ x 23ᶜᵐ. (₁Finska vetenskaps-societeten, Helsingfors₁ Acta Societatis scientiarum fennicæ. t. xix, nᵒ 1)

1. Differential equations. I. Kummer, Ernst Eduard, 1810–1893.
A C 38–106

New York. Public library
for Library of Congress   [Q60.F5 vol. 19, no. 1]
₁4₁   (508)

NL 0378495   NN

Lindelöf, Ernst Leonard, 1870–
... Sur la forme des intégrales des équations différentielles au voisinage des points singuliers, par Ernst Lindelöf ... ₁Helsingforsiæ, ex Officina typographica Societatis litterariæ fennicæ, 1897₁
26 p. 29½ x 23½ᶜᵐ. (₁Finska vetenskaps-societeten, Helsingfors₁ Acta Societatis scientiarum fennicæ. t. xxii, nᵒ 7)
"Présenté à la société le 18 janvier 1897."
Bibliographical foot-notes.

1. Differential equations, Linear. 2. Differential equations. Partial.
A C 38–136

New York. Public library
for Library of Congress   [Q60.F5 vol. 22, no. 7]
₁4₁   (508)

NL 0378496   NN DLC ViU

VOLUME 334

Lindelöf, Ernst Leonard, 1870–
... Sur le mouvement d'un corps de révolution roulant sur un plan horizontal, par Ernst Lindelöf. ₍Helsingforsiæ, ex Officina typographica Societatis litterariæ fennicæ, 1895₎

18 p. 29½ x 23½ᶜᵐ. (Finska vetenskaps-societeten, Helsingfors₎ Acta Societatis scientiarum fennicæ. t. xx, nº 10)

1. Kinematics.

New York. Public library   A C 37-2252
for Library of Congress [Q60.F5 vol. 20, no. 10]

(508)

NL 0378497 NN

Lindelöf, Ernst Leonard, 1870–
Sur les systèmes complets et le calcul des invariants différentiels des groupes continus finis ... Helsingfors, Impr. de la Société de littérature finnoise, 1893.

1 p. l., 62 p. 29½ x 23½ᶜᵐ.

Inaug.-diss.—Helsingfors.

1. Differential invariants.

Library of Congress QA381.L74 4–24232

NL 0378498 DLC NcU RPB

Lindelöf, Ernst Leonard, 1870–
... Sur les systèmes complets et le calcul des invariants différentiels des groupes continus finis, par Ernst Lindelöf. ₍Helsingforsiæ, ex Officina typographica Societatis litterariæ fennicæ, 1895₎

1 p. l., 62 p. 29½ x 23½ᶜᵐ. ₍Finska vetenskaps-societeten, Helsingfors₎ Acta Societatis scientiarum fennicæ. t. xx, nº 1)

Issued also as the author's thesis, Helsingfors.
Bibliographical foot-notes.

1. Differential invariants. 2. Groups, Continuous. 3. Transformations (Mathematics)

New York. Public library A C 37-2245
for Library of Congress [Q60.F5 vol. 20, no. 1]

(508)

NL 0378499 NN

Lindelöf, Ernst Leonard, 1870–
... Sur un cas particulier du théorème de M. Picard relatif aux fonctions entières, par Ernst Lindelöf ... ₍Stockholm, Kungl. boktryckeriet, 1903₎

p. ₍101₎–104. 23ᶜᵐ. (Arkiv för matematik, astronomi och fysik. bd. 1 ₍no. 6₎)

Caption title.

NL 0378500 ICJ

Lindelöf, Ernst Leonard, 1870–
... Sur un principe général de l'analyse et ses applications à la théorie de la représentation conforme, par Ernst Lindelöf ... Helsingfors, Imprimerie de la Société de littérature finnoise, 1915.

35 p. diagrs. 23ᶜᵐ. ₍Finska vetenskaps-societeten, Helsingfors₎ Acta Societatis scientiarum fennicæ. t. xlvi, nº 4)

"Présenté le 17 mai 1915."
Bibliographical foot-notes.

1. Surfaces, Representation of.

New York. Public library AC 38-1504
for Library of Congress [Q60.F5 vol. 46, no. 4]

₍4₎ (508)

NL 0378501 NN DLC

Lindelöf, Ernst Leonard, 1870–
... Über die ermittelung der genauigkeit der beobachtungen bei der analyse periodischer erscheinungen und in der methode der kleinsten quadrate, von Ernst Lindelöf. ₍Helsingforsiæ, ex Officina typographica Societatis litterariæ fennicæ, 1902₎

1 p. l., 34 p. 29½ x 23½ᶜᵐ. ₍Finska vetenskaps-societeten, Helsingfors₎ Acta Societatis scientiarum fennicæ. t. xxix, nº 9)

1. Periodicity. 2. Least squares.

New York. Public library A C 38-172
for Library of Congress [Q60.F5 vol. 29, no. 9]

(508)

NL 0378502 NN DLC

Lindelöf, Ernst Leonard, 1870–
Pipping, Hugo, 1864–
... Über die theorie der vocale, von dr. Hugo Pipping. ₍Helsingforsiæ, ex Officina typographica Societatis litterariæ fennicæ, 1895₎

Lindelöf, Gustaf, tr.
Schleich, Karl Ludwig, 1859–1922.
Hågkomster om Strindberg, av Carl Ludwig Schleich. Bemyndigad översättning av Gust. Lindelöf. Stockholm, Björck & Börjessen ₍1917₎

Pamph. LINDELOEF, Johan August
v.523 Den kateketiska undervisningen i
Finland ifraan reformationen intill den
stora ofreden. Historisk teckning...
Helsingfors, Frenckell & Son, 1858.
96p. 20.5cm.

NL 0378505 MH-AH

---

621 LINDELOEF, Johan August
L745omn Om naad och frihet. Synodal-afhandling.
1880 Helsingfors, Finska Litteratur-saells-
kapets tryckeri, 1880.
86p. 21cm.

No.1 in a bound volume.

NL 0378506 MH-AH

Lindelöf, Laurent Léonard.
 see Lindelöf, Lorenz Leonard, 1827–1908.

Lindelöf₍ Leonard₎ konetehdas osakeyhtiö,
Helsingfors
Lindelöfin Konetehdas 1886–1946
 see under Öller, Ragner, 1893–

Lindelöf, Lorenz Leonard, 1827–1908.
Bestämning af den komets bana, som den 6 Mars 1855 upptäcktes af Secchi i Rom. Helsingfors, J. C. Frenckell, 1855.
27 p. 24cm.

Thesis, Kejserliga Alexanders-Universitetet i Finland.
Volume of pamphlets.

NL 0378509 NNC

Science
523.6
Z17 **Lindelöf, Lorenz Leonard,** 1827–1908.
De orbita cometae qui anno 1664 apparuit disputationem academicam ... praeside Nath. Gerh. a Schultén ... auctor Laur. Leonh. Lindelöf ... Helsingforsiae, typis Frenckelli-anis, 1854.
30 p. tables.

NL 0378510 NNC

Lindelöf, Lorenz Leonard, 1827–1908.
Détermination analytique de la forme des ondes lumineuses élémentaires. Par L. L. Lindelöf ...

(*In* Finska vetenskaps-societeten, Helsingfors. Acta Societatis scientiarum fennicæ. Helsingforsiæ, 1861. 26½ x 22½ᶜᵐ. t. vi, p. ₍25₎–31)

"Lu le 4 avril 1859."

1. Light, Wave theory of.

New York. Public library A C 37-2211
for Library of Congress [Q60.F5 vol. 6]

(508)

NL 0378511 NN

Lindelöf, Lorenz Leonhard, 1827–1908. 516 Byes
Lärobok i analytisk geometri, af Dr. L. Lindelöf, ... Med 93 i texten intryckta träsnitt. Tredje upplagan. Stockholm, A. Bonnier, [1877].
288, ₍2₎ p. diagrs. 21½ᶜᵐ.

NL 0378512 ICJ DLC-P4

Lindelöf, Lorenz [Leonard], 1827–
Leçons de calcul des variations, par L. Lindelöf, ... , rédigées en collaboration avec M. l'abbé Moigno. Imprimées aux frais de l'Université de Helsingfors (Finlande). Paris, Mallet-Bachelier, 1861.
xvi, 352 p. 23ᶜᵐ.

NL 0378513 ICJ CU InU IaAS CtY MWelC NjP DN-Ob

Lindelöf, Lorenz Leonard, 1827–1908.
Minnes-tal öfver professor emeritus, kanslirådet d:r Nathan. Gerh. af Schultén, hållet vid Finska vetenskaps-societetens årshögtid den 29 april 1861, af L. Lindelöf.

(*In* Finska vetenskaps-societeten, Helsingfors. Acta Societatis scientiarum fennicæ. Helsingforsiæ, 1861. 26½ x 22½ᶜᵐ. t. vi. 19 p.)

Colophon: Helsingfors, Tryckt hos H. C. Friis, 1861.
List of published works of N. G. af Schultén: p. 15–19.

1. Schultén, Nathanaël Gerhard af, 1794–1860.

New York. Public library A C 37-2226
for Library of Congress [Q60.F5 vol. 6]

(508)

NL 0378514 NN

Lindelöf, Lorenz Leonard, 1827–1908.
Note supplémentaire sur les polygones au plus petit périmètre circonscrits à une ellipse
 see under his Sur les polygones au plus petit périmètre ...

Lindelöf, Lorenz Leonard, 1827–1908.
Observations faites en Espagne pendant l'éclipse totale du soleil, le 18 juillet 1860, par L. Lindelöf ...

(*In* Finska vetenskaps-societeten, Helsingfors. Acta Societatis scientiarum fennicæ. Helsingforsiæ, 1861. 26½ x 22½ᶜᵐ. t. vi, p. ₍559₎–563 incl. tables)

"Lu le 3 déc. 1860."

1. Eclipses, Solar—1860.

New York. Public library A C 37-2222
for Library of Congress [Q60.F5 vol. 6]

(508)

NL 0378516 NN

Lindelöf, Lorenz Leonard, 1827–1908.
Ilmatieteellinen keskuslaitos.
Observations météorologiques publiées par l'Institut météorologique central de la Société des sciences de Finlande. 1881/82–1899/1900. Kuopio, 1893–95; Helsingfors, 1904–09.

VOLUME 334

QC989
.R5F65

Lindelöf, Lorenz Leonard, 1827–1908.

Suomen tiedeseura.

Observations météorologiques publiées par la Société des sciences de Finlande. Année 1873–1880. Helsingfors, Impr. de la Société littéraire finlandaise, 1875–83.

Lindelöf, Lorenz Leonard, 1827–1908.

Quelques formules relatives à la courbure moyenne d'une courbe fermée. Par L. Lindelöf ...

(*In* Finska vetenskaps-societeten, Helsingfors. Acta Societatis scientiarum fennicæ. Helsingforsiæ, 1871. 26½ x 22ᶜᵐ. t. IX, pars I, p. ₍361₎–365)

Caption title.
"Lu le 19 avril 1870."

1. Curves.

A C 38–980

New York. Public library
for Library of Congress   [Q60.F5 vol. 9, pt. 1]

(508)

NL 0378519   NN DLC

Lindelöf, Lorenz Leonard, 1827–1908.

... Recherches sur les polyèdres maxima, par L. Lindelöf ... ₍Helsingforsiæ, ex Officina typographica Societatis litterariæ fennicæ, 1899₎

47 p. diagrs. 29½ x 23ᶜᵐ. (₍Finska vetenskaps-societeten, Helsingfors₎ Acta Societatis scientiarum fennicæ. t. xxiv, nº 8)

"Présenté le 18 avril 1896."

1. Polyhedra.

A C 38–152

New York. Public library
for Library of Congress   [Q60.F5 vol. 24, no. 8]

(508)

NL 0378520   NN

Lindelöf, Lorenz Leonard, 1827–1908.

Remarques sur les différentes manières d'établir la formule $\frac{d^2z}{dxdy} = \frac{d^2z}{dydx}$ Par L. Lindelöf ...

(*In* Finska vetenskaps-societeten, Helsingfors. Acta Societatis scientiarum fennicæ. Helsingforsiæ, 1867. 26½ x 21½ᶜᵐ. t. VIII, pars I, p. ₍205₎–213)

"Lu le 22 janvier 1866."

1. Differential equations.

A C 37–3370

New York. Public library
for Library of Congress   [Q60.F5 vol. 8, pt. 1]
₍4₎   (508)

NL 0378521   NN DLC

Lindelöf, Lorenz Leonard, 1827–1908.

Statistisk undersökning af ställningen i finska ecklesiastik-statens enke- och pupillkassa den 1 maj 1884. Af L. Lindelöf.

(*In* Finska vetenskaps-societeten, Helsingfors. Acta Societatis scientiarum fennicæ. Helsingforsiæ, 1888. 29 x 23½ᶜᵐ. t. XV, p. ₍209₎–239 incl. tables)

1. Civil service pensions—Finland. 2. Clergy—Finland—Salaries, pensions, etc.

A C 38–21

New York. Public library
for Library of Congress   [Q60.F5 vol. 15]

(508)

NL 0378522   NN

Lindelöf, Lorenz Leonard, 1827–1908.

Statistiska beräkningar angående finska civilstatens enke- och pupillkassa. Af L. Lindelöf.

(*In* Finska vetenskaps-societeten, Helsingfors. Acta Societatis scientiarum fennicæ. Helsingforsiæ, 1885. 29 x 23ᶜᵐ. t. XIV, p. ₍1₎–83 incl. tables)

Continued in next column

Continued from preceding column

1. Civil service pensions—Finland.

A C 38–4

New York. Public library
for Library of Congress   [Q60.F5 vol. 14]

(508)

NL 0378523   NN DLC

Lindelöf, Lorenz Leonard, 1827–1908.

Sur la figure apparente d'une planète, par L. Lindelöf ...

(*In* Finska vetenskaps-societeten, Helsingfors. Acta Societatis scientiarum fennicæ. Helsingforsiæ, 1871. 26½ x 22ᶜᵐ. t. IX, pars I, p. ₍185₎–199. diagrs.)

"Lu le 27 janvier 1868."

1. Planets—Figure.

A C 38–922

New York. Public library
for Library of Congress   [Q60.F5 vol. 9, pt. 1]
₍4₎   (508)

NL 0378524   NN DLC

Lindelöf, Lorenz Leonard, 1827–1908.

Sur les limites entre lesquelles le caténoïde est une surface minima, par L. Lindelöf ...

(*In* Finska vetenskaps-societeten, Helsingfors. Acta Societatis scientiarum fennicæ. Helsingforsiæ, 1871. 26½ x 22ᶜᵐ. t. IX, pars I, p. ₍353₎–360 incl. tables)

Caption title.
"Lu le 24 janvier 1870."

1. Catenary. 2. Surfaces, Minimal.

A C 38–929

New York. Public library
for Library of Congress   [Q60.F5 vol. 9, pt. 1]
₍4₎   (508)

NL 0378525   NN DLC

Lindelöf, Lorenz Leonard, 1827–1908.

Sur les maxima et minima d'une fonction des rayons vecteurs menés d'un point mobile à plusieurs centres fixes. Par L. Lindelöf ...

(*In* Finska vetenskaps-societeten, Helsingfors. Acta Societatis scientiarum fennicæ. Helsingforsiæ, 1867. 26½ x 21½ᶜᵐ. t. VIII, pars I, p. ₍189₎–203)

"Lu le 22 janvier 1866."

1. Maxima and minima. 2. Vector analysis.

A C 37–3369

New York. Public library
for Library of Congress   [Q60.F5 vol. 8, pt. 1]
₍4₎   (508)

NL 0378526   NN DLC

Lindelöf, Lorenz Leonard, 1827–1908.

... Sur les polygones au plus petit périmètre circonscrits à une ellipse donnée, par L. Lindelöf. ₍Helsingforsiæ, ex Officina typographica Societatis litterariæ fennicæ, 1903₎

13 p. incl. tab., diagrs. 29½ x 23ᶜᵐ. (₍Finska vetenskaps-societeten, Helsingfors₎ Acta Societatis scientiarum fennicæ. t. xxxi, nº 4)

—— ... Note supplémentaire sur les polygones au plus petit périmètre circonscrits à une ellipse, par L. Lindelöf. ₍Helsingforsiæ, ex Officina typographica Societatis litterariæ fennicæ, 1906₎

8 p. 28 x 23½ᶜᵐ. (₍Finska vetenskaps-societeten, Helsingfors₎ Acta Societatis scientiarum fennicæ. t. xxxii, nº 5)

—— ... Deuxième note supplémentaire sur les polygones au plus petit périmètre circonscrits à une ellipse, par L. Lindelöf. ₍Helsingforsiæ, ex Officina typographica Societatis litterariæ fennicæ, 1908₎

9 p. 28½ x 23ᶜᵐ. (₍Finska vetenskaps-societeten, Helsingfors₎ Acta Societatis scientiarum fennicæ. t. xxxiii, nº 3)

1. Polygons. 2. Ellipse.

A C 38–941

New York. Public library
for Library of Congress   [Q60.F5 vol. 31–33]

(508)

NL 0378528   NN DLC ViU

Lindelöf, Lorenz Leonard, 1827–1908.

... Sur les polygones de Poncelet, par L. Lindelöf ... ₍Helsingforsiæ, ex Officina typographica Societatis litterariæ fennicæ, 1909₎

15 p. diagrs. 29½ x 23ᶜᵐ. (₍Finska vetenskaps-societeten, Helsingfors₎ Acta Societatis scientiarum fennicæ. t. xxxv, nº 10)

"Extrait d'un ouvrage posthume."

1. Polygons. 2. Poncelet, Jean Victor, 1788–1867.

A C 38–1228

New York. Public library
for Library of Congress   [Q60.F5 vol. 35, no. 10]
₍4₎   (508)

NL 0378529   NN DLC

Lindelöf, Lorenz Leonard, 1827–1908.

Théorie des surfaces de révolution à courbure moyenne constante. Par L. Lindelöf.

(*In* Finska vetenskaps-societeten, Helsingfors. Acta Societatis scientiarum fennicæ. Helsingforsiæ, 1863. 26½ x 22½ᶜᵐ. t. VII, p. ₍345₎–372. pl. (diagrs.))

"Lu le 1 décembre 1862."

1. Rotating masses of fluids. 2. Surfaces of constant curvature. I. Title: Surfaces de révolution.

A C 37–2234

New York. Public library
for Library of Congress   [Q60.F5 vol. 7]

(508)

NL 0378530   NN

Lindelöf, Lorenz Leonard, 1827–1908.

Trajectoire d'un corps assujetti à se mouvoir sur la surface de la terre sous l'influence de la rotation terrestre, par L. Lindelöf.

(*In* Finska vetenskaps-societeten, Helsingfors. Acta Societatis scientiarum fennicæ. Helsingforsiæ, 1888. 29 x 23ᶜᵐ. t. XVI, p. ₍369₎–428 incl. tables. fold. pl. (diagrs.))

1. Centrifugal force.

A C 38–37

New York. Public library
for Library of Congress   [Q60.F5 vol. 16]

(508)

NL 0378531   NN

Lindelöf, Lorenz Leonard, 1827–1908.

... Ueber die verbesserungen und die genauigkeit der von Hevelius mit seinem grossen sextanten gemessenen sternabstände; ein beitrag zur geschichte der astronomischen instrumente, von mag. L. L. Lindeloef ... ₍1853?₎

p. ₍33₎–42. fold. table. 21.5ᶜᵐ.

Caption title.
"Aus den Mélanges mathematiques et astronomiques, t. II."

1. Sextant. 2. Hevelius, Johannes, 1611–1687.

NL 0378532   NNC

PB10
.N413
vol. 5

Lindelöf, Uno Lorenz, 1868–1944, ed.

Catholic church. *Liturgy and ritual. Psalter. Bosworth psalter.*

Die altenglischen glossen im Bosworth-psalter (Brit. mus. ms. Addit. 37517) von U. Lindelöf.

(*In* Neuphilologischer verein, Helsingfors. Mémoires de la Société néo-philologique de Helsingfors. Helsingfors, 1909. 23ᶜᵐ. v. p. ₍137₎–₍231₎)

Lindelöf, Uno Lorenz, 1868–

Beiträge zur kenntnis des altnorthumbrischen.

(*In* Neuphilologischer verein, Helsingfors. Mémoires de la Société néo-philologique à Helsingfors. Helsingfors, 1893. 23ᶜᵐ. I, p. ₍219₎–302)

Signed: Uno Lindelöf.

1. Anglo-Saxon language—Dialects—Northumbrian.

A C 37–1590

Chicago. Univ. Library   PB10.N5 vol. 1
for Library of Congress   [PB10.85 vol. 1]

(408.2471)

NL 0378534   ICU NIC

VOLUME 334

Lindelöf, Uno Lorenz, 1868–   ed.
Gautier *d'Épinal, 13th cent.?*
Les chansons de Gautier d'Épinal; édition critique par
U. Lindelöf et A. Wallensköld.
(*In* Neuphilologischer verein, Helsingfors. Mémoires de la Société
néo-philologique à Helsingfors. Helsingfors, 1902. 23ᶜᵐ. III, p. [265,-
[320].)

Lindelöf, Uno Lorenz, 1868–
Elements of the history of the English language, by Uno
Lindelöf ... translated by Robert Max Garrett ... [Seattle]
University of Washington, 1911.

4 p. l., [15]–128 p. 20ᶜᵐ. (*Half-title:* University of Washington publications in English, vol. I)

1. English language—Hist.   I. Garrett, Robert Max, 1881–   tr.

Library of Congress   PE1075.L5   11–15053 Revised

OO NN PSC PHC ViU
NL 0378536   DLC IdU MtU OrP Wa OrU OCU MiU OU OCl

Lindelöf, Uno Lorenz, 1868–
Engelska språkets ortografi i historisk belysning... Av U.
Lindelöf. Helsingfors: Söderström & Co., 1923. 18 p. 8°.
(Finska Vetenskaps-Societeten, Helsingfors. Årsbok. bd. 2, B,
nr. 1.)

1. English language—Spelling.
N. Y. P. L.   August 30, 1926

NL 0378537   NN

Lindelöf, Uno Lorenz, 1868–
... English verb-adverb groups converted into nouns, by
U. Lindelöf. (Communicated February 22, 1937) [Helsing-
fors, 1937]

41 p. 24ᶜᵐ. ([Finska vetenskaps-societeten, Helsingfors] Commen-
tationes humanarum litterarum. IX, 5)
Caption title.
At head of title: Societas scientiarum fennica.
Bibliography: p. 2–3.

1. English language—Noun.
New York. Public library   A C 37–2750
for Library of Congress   [P9.F5 vol. 9, no. 5]
                                              (406.2)

NL 0378538   NN KMK NBuU NIC NcD PU OU OCU ViU

Lindelöf, Uno Lorenz, 1868–1944.
Finnland ...   Berlin [1918]
56 p.   20 cm.   (Kriegsschriften des
Kaiser-Wilhelm-Dank, Verein der Soldatenfreunde.
Hft. 126/127)

NL 0378539   CtY

Lindelöf, Uno Lorenz, 1868–
Finnland, von Professor Dr. U. Lindelöf...   Berlin: Verlag Kameradschaft, Wohlfahrtsges. m.b.H. [1919.] 56 p. 12°.
(Kaiser-Wilhelm-Dank, Verein der Soldatenfreunde. Kriegsschriften. Heft 126/127.)

On cover: Unterm Eisernen Kreuz, 1914–1918.

1. Finland. 2. Series.
N. Y. P. L.   June 25, 1924

NL 0378540   NN

Lindelöf, Uno Lorenz, 1868–
... Glossar zur altnorthumbrischen Evangelienübersetzung in
der Rushworth-handschrift (die sogenannte Glosse Rushworth²) Von Uno Lindelöf ... [Helsingforsiæ, ex Officina
typographica Societatis litterariæ fennicæ, 1897]

2 p. l., 104 p. 29½ x 23½ᶜᵐ. ([Finska vetenskaps-societeten, Helsing-
fors] Acta Societatis scientiarum fennicae. t. XXII, n° 5)

1. Anglo-Saxon language—Dialects—Northumbrian. 2. Bible. N. T.
Gospels. Anglo-Saxon—Glossaries, vocabularies, etc. 3. Bible. Anglo-
Saxon—Glossaries, vocabularies, etc.—N. T. Gospels.

New York. Public library   A C 38–134
for Library of Congress   [Q60.F5 vol. 22, no. 5]
                                              [508]

DLC ViU
NL 0378541   NN NIC CLSU NcD PBm CtY OClW MiU OCU

PE1101 Lindelöf, Uno Lorenz, 1868–
.L7   Grunddragen af engelska språkets[historiska
ljud- och formlära af Uno Lindelöf...   Helsingfors,W.Hagelstam[1895]
[4],108 p. 19½ᶜᵐ.
"Föreliggande kortfattade framställning...ut-
gör en omarbetning af föreläsningar,hållna vid
härvarande universitet vårterminen 1894."-Förord.

NL 0378542   ICU PBm MH

PE1585 LINDELÖF,UNO LORENTZ,1868–
.A5D9   Grunddragen af engelska språkets; historiska
ljud- och formlära. Andra omarbetade upplagan.
Helsingfors [Lilius & Hertzberg] 1911.
122 p.

1. English language—Hist. 2. English language—
Etymology. I. Title.

NL 0378543   InU

Lindelöf, U[no Lorenz].
Grundzüge der Geschichte der englischen Sprache.   Leipzig: B. G. Teubner, 1912.   v, 141 p.   8°.

1. English language—History.
N. Y. P. L.   June 21, 1912.

NL 0378544   NN ICU WaU MH IU

Ia603 Lindelöf, Uno Lorenz, 1868–
911Lb   Grundzüge der Geschichte der englischen
Sprache. Leipzig,B.G.Teubner,1920.
148p. 21cm.
Unveränderter anastatischer Nachdruck.

1. English language - History.

NL 0378545   CtY

Lindelöf,Uno Lorentz,1868–
Grundzüge der geschichte der englischen
sprache,von U.Lindelöf ... 2.,erweiterte und
verbesserte aufl. Leipzig und Berlin,B.G.
Teubner,1928.
vi,160 p. 19½ᶜᵐ.

1.English language—History.

NL 0378546   MiU PBm PU OCU RPB NNU TxU

Lindelöf, Uno Lorenz, 1868–   ed.
Oxford. University. *Bodleian library. Mss. (Junius 27)*
Die handschrift Junius 27 der Bibliotheca Bodleiana, von
Uno Lindelöf. Helsingfors, Helsingforser centraldruckerei,
1901.
(*In* Neuphilologischer verein, Helsingfors. Mémoires de la Société
néo-philologique à Helsingfors. Helsingfors, 1902. 23ᶜᵐ. III, p. [1,-73])

Lindelöf, Uno Lorenz, 1868–1944, ed.
Der Lambeth-Psalter [Helsingfors, 1909–1914]
see under   Bible. O.T. Psalms. Anglo-
Saxon. 1909–1914.

PR3581 Lindelöf, Uno Lorentz, 1868–
.L72   ... Milton. Helsingfors, H. Schildt [1920]
[4], 110 p. incl. front., ports. 22ᶜᵐ. (*Half-title:* Biografier, IX)
At head of title: U. Lindelöf.

1. Milton, John, 1608–1674.

NL 0378549   ICU IU CtY MH

Lindelöf, Uno Lorenz, 1868–   ed.
Rituale Ecclesiae Dunelmensis
see under   Catholic Church. Liturgy and
ritual. Collectar. [Durham ritual]

Lindelöf, Uno Lorenz, 1868–
Some observations on the English adjective formations in
-ative and -atory. Helsingfors, 1944.

20 p. 24 cm. (Societas Scientiarum Fennica. Commentationes
humanarum litterarum, XIII, 4)
Caption title.

1. English language—Adjective. 2. English language—Word formation. (Series: Finska vetenskaps-societeten, Helsingfors. Commentationes humanarum litterarum, XIII, 4)

P9.F5 t. 13, no. 4   A 48–8874*
Pennsylvania. Univ.   Library
for Library of Congress   [2]†

NL 0378551   PU NN ViU KMK NBuU NIC NcD TxU DLC

Lindeloof, Uno Lorenz
Die sprache des rituals von Durham. Helsingfors,
1890.
In. Diss.

NL 0378552   ICRL

Lindelöf, Uno Lorenz
Die sprache des Rituals von Durham; ein beitrag zur altenglischen grammatik. Helsingfors, J. C. Frenckell & sohn, 1890.
pp. (1), v, (1), 125 +.

Durham Ritual[

OO PBm
NL 0378553   MH TU NIC CU MnU NcD OCU MiU OClW OCl

Lindelöf, Uno Lorenz, 1868–
... Studien zu altenglischen Psalterglossen, von Un
Lindelöf ... Bonn, P. Hanstein, 1904.

2 p. l., 123, [1] p. 22½ᶜᵐ. (Bonner beiträge zur anglistik, hft. XIII)

1. Catholic church. Liturgy and ritual. Psalter. Anglo-Saxon.
I. Title. II. Psalter glossen.

                                              5—5224
Library of Congress   PE25.B6 vol. 13

NN
NL 0378554   DLC NjP ViU OClW OCU MiU OU OO PU PBm

VOLUME 334

Lindelöf, Uno Lorenz, 1868–
... Die südnorthumbrische mundart des 10. jahrhunderts; die sprache der sog. glosse Rushworth², von dr. Uno Lindelöf ... Bonn, P. Hanstein, 1901.

vii, 152 p. 23½ᵐ. (Bonner beiträge zur anglistik ... Hft. x)

"Litteraturangaben": p. 151–152.

1. Anglo-Saxon language—Dialects—Northumbrian. 2. Anglo-Saxon language—Glossaries, vocabularies, etc. 3. Bible. N. T. Gospels. **Anglo-Saxon—Language, style.** 4. Bible. Anglo-Saxon—Language, style—N. T. Gospels.

Library of Congress   PE25.B6 vol. 10   2–19502

ViU PBm
NL 0378555   DLC NjP NcU OClW OU MH NN OCU MiU PU

Lindelöf, Uno Lorenz, 1868–1944.
... Versbau und sprache des mittelenglischen stabreimenden gedichtes "The wars of Alexander," see under Steffens, Heinrich.

Lindelöf, Uno Lorenz, 1868–1944.
... Wörterbuch zur interlinearglosse des Rituale Ecclesiae dunelmensis, von dr. Uno Lindelöf.

(*In* Bonner beiträge zur anglistik ... Bonn, 1901. 22½ᵐ. hft. IX, p. 105–220)

1. Anglo-Saxon language—Glossaries, vocabularies, etc. 2. Anglo-Saxon language—Dialects—Northumbrian. 3. Durham ritual.

12–22411

Library of Congress   PE25.B6 vol. 9

NL 0378557   DLC NIC OU OCU OClW MH NN

Lindelöf och co., *Göteborg.*
Handbok för textilmannen. 4. uppl. Göteborg ₍1949₎
125 p. 15 cm.

1. Textile industry and fabrics—Tables, calculations, etc.

TS1451.L57 1949   51–34204

NL 0378558   DLC

Lindelof, Friedrich von, 1794–1882.
Deutsche Reichsgeschichte, insbesondere historische Entwickelung des deutschen öffentlichen Rechts in gedrängter Uebersicht. Giessen, G. F. Heyer, 1827.

xii, 356 p. geneal. tables. 21 cm.

Bibliographical footnotes.

1. Holy Roman Empire—Constitutional law. 2. **Administrative law—Germany.** I. Title.

78–226405

NL 0378559   DLC CtY

Lindelof, Friedrich von, 1794–1882.   **Ger 95.8**
Grundriss des deutschen staatsrechts mit beigefügten quellen- und litteratur-belegen. Giessen, G. F. Heyer, 1828.
nar. 12°. pp. iv, 76.

Germany—Laws, etc.—Hist.

NL 0378560   MH CtY

Oga48
838ℓ **Lindelof, Friedrich, Freiherr von,** 1794–1882.
Von dem Rechte der Bundes-Austrägalgerichte, Wiedereinsetzung in dem vorigen Stand gegen Fristversäumnisse zu ertheilen. Darmstadt, 1838.
iv, 64p. 22cm.

NL 0378561   CtY

Lindelof, Otto Julius Swenson, 1852–
A trip to the north pole; or, The discovery of the ten tribes as found in the Arctic ocean, and published by O. J. S. Lindelof, owner and proprietor ... Salt Lake City, Tribune printing company, 1903.
200 p. illus. 17½ x 13ᵐ.

1. Israel—Ten lost tribes—Fiction.   I. Title.
                                                           4–71 Revised

Library of Congress   PZ3.L644T

NL 0378562   DLC ICJ

CS929 **Lindeman, A   E**
.S213   Släktregister öfver släkten Sandblad
1914   med dess utgreningar upprättadt af A.E. Lindeman ... Östersund, Östersunds-postens tryckeri aktiebolag, 1914.
31 p. 23cm.

"Släktnamnet Sandblad" är taget efter gården Sandtorp i Äggby församling i Warnhems pastorat i Skaraborgs län."

NL 0378563   MnHi

Lindeman, Adolf. Unter Islands Gletschern. Reutlingen, Ensslin & Laiblin. [1924]. 16°. pp. 160.
"Der Sammlung Weltfahrer. Bücher der Abenteuer und Reisen. 6. Band." A novel.

NL 0378564   NIC

4HE **Lindeman, Berndt Adolf**
849   Ny vägvisare genom storfurstendömet Finalnd, med stöd af de tillförlitligaste vägauppgifter af landets samtelige herrar guvernörer, meddelte åren 1845, 1846 och 1847, sistnämnde år. Helsingfors, J. Simelii arfvingar, 1848.
150 p.

NL 0378565   DLC-P4

WZ LINDEMAN, Caspar, d. 1538₎
240   Caspar Lindeman bonarum artium & medicinae doctor
L743d instituto medicae facultatis Lipsicae publica disceptatione
1523   definita hic decreta adferet die, quem prefiniet. Lipsiae, In aedibus Valentini Schumanni, 1523.
[28] p. 20 cm.
Signatures: A–B⁴, C⁶.
Contains 205 propositions.
According to the author's preface (sig. A1ᵛ–A2ᶠ) these are drawn from the first six books of Galenus' Methodus medendi

1. Galenus. Methodus medendi

NL 0378566   DNLM

759.949 **Lindeman, Catharinus Marius Anne Alettus.**
L743o   De oorsprong, ontwikkeling en beteckenis van het romanisme in de nederlandsche schilde kunst. Utrecht, A. Oosthoek, 1928.
₍151₎–247p. 27cm.

Proefschrift—Utrecht.
Includes only last chapter of a work by Joachim A. Wtewael.

1. Painting, Dutch.   I. Title.

NL 0378567   UU ICRL MH

Lindeman, Catharinus Marius Anne Alettus.
Joachim Anthonisz Wtewael, door Dr. C. M. A. A. Lindeman...met een voorwoord van Prof. Dr. W. Vogelsang. Utrecht: A. Oosthoek, 1929.   278 p.   front. (port.), 72 pl., geneal. table.   4°.

Plates printed on both sides.

421844A. 1. Uitewaal, Joachim,   1566–1638. 2. Paintings, Dutch
N. Y. P. L.   and Flemish.   August 28, 1929

IaU MdBJ MiU OClMA IU MoU
NL 0378568   NN MH CU CtY OU ICU MiDA KU CSt NNU WaU

Lindeman, David S
A survey of the Greensboro retail trading area, under the auspices of the city of Greensboro. Directed by the Commercial development bureau of the Greensboro Chamber of commerce and the Trade promotion committee of the Greensboro retail merchants association. Conducted by David S. Lindeman, Assisted by W. A. Williams and others.
Greensboro, N.C., The Greensboro Chamber of commerce, 1933.
3 p.l.,61 ;. incl. maps, tables, diagrs. 27½cm.

NL 0378569   DL

Lindeman, Diego Villa y

see

Villa y Lindeman, Diego.

Lindeman, Eduard Christian, 1885–1953.

Brown, Thomas Kite, 1885–   *ed.*
Adult education for social change; a handbook for leaders and members of discussion groups, forums, and adult classes. Prepared by the Swarthmore seminar with an introduction by Eduard C. Lindeman. Edited by Thomas K. Brown, jr. ₍Philadelphia, Pa., 1936₎

Lindeman, Eduard Christian, 1885–

American eugenics society.
American eugenics. Addresses: Eduard C. Lindeman, Arthur E. Morgan. Round table discussions and papers: Eduard C. Lindeman, Will Durant, Margaret Sanger, Sidney Goldstein, Joseph K. Folsom, Dorothy Wiehl, Marie E. Kopp. Being the proceedings at the annual meeting and round table conferences of the American eugenics society ... New York city, May 7, 1936. ₍New York? 1936?₎

Lindeman, Eduard Christian, 1885–
... Boys' and girls' clubs; a course of study in boys' and girls' club leadership for county normal training classes, by E. C. Lindemann ... Pub. by Fred L. Keeler, the superintendent of public instruction. ₍Lansing, 1919₎

63 p. diagrs. 23ᵐ. (Michigan. Dept. of public instruction. Bulletin no. 26, 1919)

1. Boys—Societies and clubs. 2. Girls—Societies and clubs. 3. Agricultural clubs. I. Michigan. Dept. of public instruction. II. Title.

Library, U. S. Bur. of   Education LB1600.L64   E 20–371

NL 0378573   DHEW

Lindeman, Eduard Christian, 1885–
... The church in the changing community, by Eduard C. Lindeman ... New York city, The Community church of New York ₍1929₎

cover-title, 32 p. 19ᵐ. (Community religion series, no. 4)

At head of title: Community religion.

1. City churches. I. Title. II. Title: Community religion.

                                                           A 35–530

Title from Columbia   Univ. Printed by L. C.

NL 0378574   NNC

VOLUME 334

Lindemann, Eduard Christian, 1885-1953.

1901
LI3834c
   College characters; essays and verse.
Port Huron, Mich., Riverside Printing Co.
[1911]
Harris
Collection
   143 p. illus. 20 cm.

NL 0378575   RPB MiU

HD2745
.H3
Lindeman, Eduard Christian, 1885-

Hader, John Jay.
   Committees, their purposes, functions and administration,
by John J. Hader and E. C. Lindeman ... New York, N. Y.,
American management association, °1929.

Lindeman, Eduard Christian, 1885-
   The community; an introduction to the study of community leadership and organization [by] Eduard C. Lindeman ... New York, Association press, 1921.
   ix, 222 p. 19½ cm.

   1. Community organization. 2. Church and social problems.
I. Title.
   HM131.L5   22—293

   NN MB MH PU NjNbS
   OU OCU MiU WaTC OrP MtU Or ViU NcD PBm PHC PPT ICJ
NL 0378577   DLC TxU UU IEG OKentU ICRL MoU OCl ODW

DU1
.I5
1929 a
vol. xvi
Lindeman, Eduard Christian, 1885-

Conference as an agency of industrial progress. I. Conference
method in the administration of labor law [by] Joseph P.
Chamberlain ... II. Conference method in handling industrial disputes in the men's clothing industry [by] Sidney
Hillman ... III. Conference method in employee representation plans and procedures [by] Eduard C. Lindeman ...
Preliminary papers prepared for the third general session of
the Institute of Pacific relations to be held at Kyoto, Japan,
October 28th to November 9th, 1929. [New York?], American council, Institute of Pacific relations, 1929.

JC423
.S66
1951
Lindeman, Eduard Christian, 1885-

Smith, Thomas Vernor, 1890-
   The democratic way of life; an American interpretation,
by T. V. Smith and Eduard C. Lindeman. A new and completely rev. ed. [New York, New American Library [1951]

Lindeman, Eduard Christian, 1885-   joint
      author.
Hader, John Jay.
   Dynamic social research, by John J. Hader and Eduard C.
Lindeman ... London, K. Paul, Trench, Trubner & co., ltd.;
New York, Harcourt, Brace and company, 1933.

PS1602
.L5
Lindeman, Eduard Christian, 1885-   ed.

Emerson, Ralph Waldo, 1803-1882.
   ... Emerson, the basic writings of America's sage, edited
by Eduard C. Lindeman ... New York, Penguin books, inc.
[1947]

BT
771
L56
Lindeman, Eduard Christian, 1885-1953.
   Faith for a new world. [n. p.]
1943.
   71 l. 29 cm. (Rauschenbusch lectures, Colgate-Rochester Divinity
School, Rochester, N. Y., 1943)
   1. Faith. 2. Christianity -
20th cent. I. Title. (Series)

NL 0378582   NRCR

Lindeman, Eduard Christian, 1885-
   Group reading; an experiment and an invitation, by Eduard C.
Lindeman. [New York, 1940] 12 f. 28cm.

Caption-title.
Reproduced from typewritten copy.

N. Y. P T   1. Reading aloud.   February 27, 1942

NL 0378583   NN

Lindeman, Eduard Christian, 1885-
   How to use The wonderful world of books
in discussion groups and classes. [1953?]
[8] p.

   1. Books and reading. I. Stefferud, Alfred.
The wonderful world of books.

NL 0378584   NNC Or

Lindeman, Eduard Christian, 1885-
   In what direction is America moving? An
analysis of present trends in politics, government, economic and social organization, by
Eduard C. Lindeman. [New York, Council for
social action of the Congregational Christian
churches, 1946]
   30 p. illus. (Social action, v. 12, no. 6,
June 15, 1946)
   1. U.S. - Politics and government.

NL 0378585   NNC

Lindeman, Eduard Christian, 1885-
   Leisure—a national issue; planning for the leisure of a democratic people, by Eduard C. Lindeman ... New York, Association press, 1939.
   61 p. 23ᵐ.

   1. Leisure.   I. Title.
                                                40-4754
   Library of Congress   GV51.L5
   ——— Copy 2.
   Copyright AA 320618   [5]   331.84

   OU OCl
NL 0378586   DLC OrU Or OrP CU ViU PBm PSt PU NcD

HV28
.L5A2
Lindeman, Eduard Christian, 1885-1953.
   Letters, 1923-35.
   47 items.

   In Portland State College Library Special Collections.
Author and teacher of sociology and social research at
the New York School of Social Work and other institutions.
Three letters to Herbert Croly, 1924, and 44 letters
(chiefly personal) to Mrs. Leonard K. Elmhirst (Dorothy
Payne Whitney, formerly Mrs. Willard Straight) benefactress
and trustee of the New York School of Social Work. Include
issues from Christian citizenship, New York; The Inquiry,
New York; and a reprint of Lindeman's article "Industrial
technique and social ethics," from Survey graphic, Aug. 1 2 .
Gift of Betty Lindeman Leonard, 1964.

NL 0378587   OrPS

Lindeman, Eduard Christian, 1885-
   The meaning of adult education, by Eduard C. Lindeman
... New York, New Republic, inc., 1926.
   3 p. l., ix-xx, 222 p. 19 cm.
   "References": p. [205]-213.

   1. Education of adults.   I. Title.
   LC5215.L5   26—22085

   Or
   NcRS OClW NN WaTC ICJ OrP MtBC WaSp OrU OrCS CaBVaU
NL 0378588   DLC ViU MB ICJ TU NcD PU PPFr OCl WaU

LC
5215
L5
Lindeman, Eduard Christian, 1885-1953.
   The meaning of adult education, by Eduard C. Lindeman
... New York, New Republic, inc., 1926 [1 .e .1935, c1926]
   3 p. l., ix-xx, 222 p. 19 cm.
   "References": p. [205]-213.

NL 0378589   NSyU

Lindeman, Eduard Christian, 1885-1953.
   Mental hygiene and the moral crisis of
our time. Austin, Hogg Foundation for
Mental Hygiene, University of Texas [c1952]
   18 p.

   1. Mental hygiene. 2. U.S.--Moral conditions.
I. [Hogg Foundation for Mental Health.
II. Title. x I.

NL 0378590   CaOTP Or

Lindeman, Eduard Christian, 1885-1953.
   Minimum requirements for peace; an outline
for discussion, by Eduard C. Lindeman. [New
York] New York school of social work, Columbia
university. [1944?]
   1 p.   28 cm.
   Caption title.

NL 0378591   DPU

Lindeman, Eduard Christian, 1885-
   Palestine—test of democracy ... New York, Christian council on Palestine, American Palestine committee [1945]
   8 p. 19ᵐ.

   1. Zionism. 2. Jewish question.
                                              A 46-2733
                                              Brief cataloging
   Harvard univ. Library
   for Library of Congress

NL 0378592   MH OCH NcD NN NNZi

Lindeman, Eduard Christian, 1885-
   A people's war and a people's peace [by] Eduard C. Linde-
man. New York, Society for ethical culture [1942]
   15 p. 20½ᵐ.
   "A radio talk over station WQXR under the auspices of the New
York society for ethical culture, May 31, 1942."—p. 3.

   1. World war, 1939-   —U. S. 2. World war, 1939-   —Peace.
I. New York society for ethical culture. II. Title.
                                              42-25292
   Library of Congress   D742.U5L5
                                              940.5373

NL 0378593   DLC

LC225
.N32
Lindeman, Eduard Christian, 1885-   ed.

National council of parent education.
   Problems for parent educators ... Edited by Eduard C.
Lindeman and Flora M. Thurston ... New York City, Na-
tional council of parent education [1929]-1931.

VOLUME 334

Lindeman, Eduard Christian, 1895–   et al.
    Problems of America, a group of articles on
        social adjustment
            see under title.

[Lindeman, Eduard Christian] 1885–
    ... Recreation and rural health. [Washington, Govt. print.
off., 1920]
    14 p. 23ᶜᵐ. ([U. S.] Bureau of education. Teachers' leaflet no. 7)
    Caption title.
    At head of title: Department of the interior. Bureau of education.
Washington, D. C.

    1. Recreation. 2. Hygiene, Rural. 3. Games.   I. Title.
U. S. Off. of educ. Library
for Library of Congress   E 20–546 Revised
——— Copy 3.   L111.A57 no. 7
                     LB3081.L5

NL 0378596   DHEW DLC OrCS OrU WaWW PPT

GV53
.A5
1937

Lindeman, Eduard Christian, 1885–
    U. S. *Interdepartmental committee to coordinate health and
        welfare activities.*
        Report of the Technical committee on recreation. Interde-
    partmental committee to coordinate health and welfare activi-
    ties, 1937. [Washington, 1937]

Lindeman, Eduard Christian, 1885–
    Social discovery; an approach to the study of func-
tional groups, with an introduction by Herbert Croly.
By Eduard C. Lindeman. New York, Republic publishing company, 1924.
    xxvii p., 2 l., 3–375 p. 18½ᶜᵐ.

    1. Sociology. 2. Social psychology.   I. Title.
Library of Congress   HM51.L55   24–13608

CaBVaU OrPR CaBVa ICJ NN
ODW OU OrP MB MtU NN Or ViU WaWW MH OCU OrCS GU OrU
NL 0378598   DLC ScU NIC TU KEmT CU PU PCC OCl OO

Lindeman, Eduard Christian, 1885–
    Social education; an interpretation of the principles and
methods developed by the Inquiry during the years 1923–
1933, by Eduard C. Lindeman ... New York, New republic,
inc., 1933.
    xix, 233 p. diagrs. 18½ᶜᵐ. (*On cover:* The New republic series)
    "Inquiry publications": p. 207–226.

    1. The Inquiry, New York. 2. Social surveys. 3. Social problems.
I. Title.
Library of Congress   HN29.L5   33–35687
    Copy 2.
Copyright A 65884   [5]   309.173

PU NN MB WaE OrP MtBC Or WaS OrCS CaBVaU NSyU WaU
NL 0378599   DLC OCU NIC WU CU NBuU NcD OU PPT PP

Lindeman, Eduard Christian, 1885–
    Some unsolved problems of rural education from the
viewpoint of sociology.

    (*In* National education association of the United States. Addresses
and proceedings, 1922. p. 1110–1121)

    1. Rural schools—U. S.

Library, U. S. Bur. of   E 24–304
                    Education

NL 0378600   DHEW

Lindeman, Eduard Christian, 1885–
    Upon what does peace depend? By Eduard C. Lindeman.
New York, N. Y., Carnegie endowment for international peace,
1941.
    19, [1] p. 21½ᶜᵐ.

    "An address delivered ... at the New York school of social work,
February [1941]"

    1. World war, 1939–   —Peace.   I. Carnegie endowment for inter-
national peace. II. Title.   —Peace.
Library of Congress   D816.5.L55   44–20963
                                           940.531

NL 0378601   DLC UU Or DNAL

Lindeman, Eduard Christian, 1885–   joint
author.   FOR OTHER EDITIONS
                                SEE MAIN ENTRY
Anderson, Nels, 1889–
    Urban sociology; an introduction to the study of urban com-
munities, by Nels Anderson ... and Eduard C. Lindeman ...
New York, F. S. Crofts & co., 1935.

Lindeman, Eduard Christian, 1885–
    Varieties of family relationships and some pedagogical im-
plications, by Eduard C. Lindeman. New York, National council of parent education, 1934.
    19 p. diagrs. 21½ᶜᵐ.

    1. Family.   I. Title.

                                           A 38–261
Teachers college library,   Columbia univ.
for Library of Congress   [2]

NL 0378603   NNC-T OrCS

Lindeman, Eduard Christian, 1885–
    Wealth & culture, by Eduard C. Lindeman; a study of
one hundred foundations and community trusts and their
operations during the decade 1921–1930; with 8 charts, 3
graphs, and full statistical tables. New York, Harcourt,
Brace and company [*1936]
    5 p. l., vii–ix, 185 p. incl. illus., tables, diagrs. 23½ x 22½ cm.
    "Notes on a foundation bibliography": p. 51–54.

    1. Endowments—U. S. 2. Wealth—U. S. 3. Culture. 4. Social
surveys.
    AS911.A2L5   061   36—27179

ICJ OrSaW WaTC
ViU ICJ Ok MsU KEmT NBuU ICRL MB OrU MtU WaS Or
NL 0378604   DLC NcD PPT PU OClW OU OCU ODW OO NN

Lindeman, Eduard Christian, 1885–
joint author.
Hader, John J.
    What do workers study? An analysis of the content of
workers' education in the United States and Great Britain for
the years 1920 to 1927 inclusive, with some comparative notes
of workers' education in Germany. [By] John J. Hader and
Eduard C. Lindeman. New York, The Workers education bureau press, 1929.

Lindeman, Eduard Christian, 1885–1953.
    Workers' education and the public libraries, by E. C. Linde-
man ... New York, Workers' education bureau of America,
1926.
    19 p. 18½ᶜᵐ. (*On cover:* Workers' education pamphlet series, no. 7)

    1. Labor and laboring classes—Education. [1. Education of workers]
2. Education of adults. 3. Libraries.   I. Title.

                                           L 27—4
U. S. Dept. of labor. Libr.
for Library of Congress   Z711.2.L74

DLC MB
NL 0378606   DL Or OrU WaS OrP WHi MiU OO OU OCl IU

TN404
.C4N4
1913

Lindeman, Einar.
    Canada. *Mines branch* (1901–1936)
    ... Austin Brook iron-bearing district, New Brunswick
by Einar Lindeman, M. E. Ottawa, Government printing
bureau, 1913.

Lindeman, Einar.
    ... Le district ferrifere de Moose–Mountain,
Ontario
        see under   Canada. Mines branch (1901–
1936)   [Supplement]

Lindeman, Einar.
    Les gisements de fer d'Austin Brook au Nou-
veau-Brunswick
        see under   Canada. Mines branch (1901–
1936)   [Supplement]

Lindeman, Einar.
    ... Gisements de magnétite le long de la ligne
du Central Ontario Railway
        see under   Canada. Mines branch (1901–
1936)   [Supplement]

Lindeman, Einar.
    ... Les gisements de magnétite près de
Calabogie
        see under   Canada. Mines branch (1901–
1936)   [Supplement]

Lindeman, Einar.
    ... Gisements de minerais de fer de la mine
Bristol
        see under   Canada. Mines branch (1901–
1936)   [Supplement]

Lindeman, Einar.
    ... Iron ore deposits of the Bristol mine, Pontiac county,
Que. Magnetometric survey, etc., by E. Lindeman ...
Magnetic concentration of ores, by Geo. C. Mackenzie ...
Ottawa, Government printing bureau, 1910.
    15 p. II pl. (incl. front.) 2 fold. maps, 2 fold. tab. 24½ cm. (Can-
ada. Department of mines. Mines branch. Bulletin no. 2)

    1. Iron ores—Quebec (Province) 2. Ore-deposits—Quebec (Prov-
ince)   I. Mackenzie, George C., 1877–
    TN26.A35 no. 2   G S 10—481
U. S. Geol. Survey. Libr.
for Library of Congress   [a66d½]†

NNC DLC
NL 0378613   DI-GS MtBuM ViU CU MoU WaS CaBVaU PPAN

TN404
.C4B8
1909

Lindeman, Einar.
    Canada. *Mines branch* (1901–1936)
    ... Iron ore deposits of Vancouver and Texada Islands,
British Columbia, by Einar Lindeman, M. E. Ottawa, Government printing bureau, 1909.

TN404
.C3A5
1917

Lindeman, Einar.
    Canada. *Mines branch* (1901–1936)
    ... Iron ore occurrences in Canada, in two volumes, comp.
by E. Lindeman ... and L. L. Bolton ... Introductory by
A. H. A. Robinson ... Ottawa, Government printing bureau,
1917.

VOLUME 334

TN404
.C4O5
1918

Lindeman, Einar.

Canada. *Mines branch* (1901–1936)
... Magnetite occurrences along the Central Ontario railway, by E. Lindeman. Ottawa, Government printing bureau, 1913.

TN404
.C4O5
1914

Lindeman, Einar.

Canada. *Mines branch* (1901–1936)
... Magnetite occurrences near Calabogie, Renfrew county, Ontario, by E. Lindeman. Ottawa, Government printing bureau, 1914.

Lindeman, Einar.
... Moose mountain iron-bearing district, Ont., by E. Lindeman. Ottawa, Government printing bureau, 1914.

v, 14, xviii p. diagrs. *and* 8 fold. maps in portfolio. 24½ᵐ.

At head of title : Canada. Department of mines ... Mines branch.
In lower right corner of t.-p.: no. 303.
"Reports and maps of economic interest published by the Mines branch."—xviii p.

1. Iron mines and mining—Ontario. I. Canada. Dept. of mines. Mines branch. II. Title.

G S 14–786 Revised 2

U. S. Geol. survey. Library   402 (100) C24
for Library of Congress   [TN404.C4O5 1914 a]

NL 0378618   DI-GS Or PPAN NcU NIC NjP ICJ MB NN

Lindeman, F   L   von
see Lindemann, F   L   von.

Lindeman (Ferd. P.) [1877-   ]. *Casuistischer Beitrag zur Frage der angeborenen klappenförmigen Verengerung der Pars prostatica urethræ. 36 pp., 3 pl., 1 l. 8°. Jena, A. Kämpfe. 1904.

NL 0378620   DNLM NN MH ICRL

[Lindeman, Gregory]
The rise and progress of the Province of St. Joseph...
see under title

Lindeman, Hans Thorvald, 1867-
see
Lindeman, Thorvald, 1867-

QE75
.C5
no. 235

Lindeman, Harold Burns, 1899–
Sodium carbonate brine and trona deposits in Sweetwater County, Wyoming. Washington, 1954.

10 p. illus., maps, tables. 27 cm. (U. S. Geological Survey. Circular 235)

"Correction sheet" : slip inserted.
"Literature cited" : p. 10.

1. Sodium. 2. Mines and mineral resources—Wyoming—Sweetwater Co. I. Title: Trona deposits in Sweetwater County, Wyoming.   (Series)

[QE75.C5 no. 235]   G S 54–277

U. S. Geol. Survey. Libr.
for Library of Congress   [2]

NL 0378623   DI-GS DLC

W 4
F86
1937

Lindeman, Heinz Olaf, 1912-
Lässt sich Farbenuntüchtigkeit durch Neophanglâser beheben? Mit einem kurzen Beitrag zur Erkennung Farbenuntüchtiger bei der Musterung und ähnlichen Reihenuntersuchungen. Freiburg i. Br., 1937.
8 p.

Inaug.-Diss. - Freiburg.
Published also in Klinische Monatsblätter für Augenheilkunde 1937, Bd. 99, Heft 2, S. 224.

Bibliography: p. 8.

NL 0378625   DNLM

Lindeman,   Henri.
Botsingen van electronen met waterstofatomen. ..
Amsterdam, 1933.
Inaug. Diss. - Utrecht, 1933.

NL 0378626   ICRL CtY OU

788.45
L64h

Lindeman, Henry.
The Henry Lindeman method for saxophone: the physical factors; the musical factors.   New York, Mills Music, Inc. [*1934]
47 p. music. 30 cm.

Cover title.

1. Saxophone--Methods.   I. Title.

NL 0378627   LU

Lindeman, Iosif Karlovich, ed.

[RUSSIA] Pushkin, Aleksandr Sergeevich, 1799–1837.
... Пѣснь о вѣщемъ Олегѣ. Точная копія рукописи поэта. Съ 21 рисункомъ въ текстѣ. Разборъ баллады и объяснительныя къ ней примѣчанія написалъ ... I. К. Линдеманъ. Для старшихъ классовъ среднеучебныхъ заведеній. Москва [Т-во скоропечатни А. А. Левенсонъ] 1915.

DK651
.T68L5
1905

Lindeman, Iosif Karlovich.
Разборъ свѣдѣній, сообщаемыхъ Пальмквистомъ о Торжкѣ; докладъ, читанный на 2. Областномъ археологическомъ съѣздѣ, съ присовокупленіемъ отвѣта критикамъ и указателя. Тверь, Тип. Губ. правленія, 1905.
16 p. illus. 26 cm.

1. Torzhok, Russia. 2. Palmquist, Erich, 1650 (ca.)–1676. I. Title.
Title transliterated: Razbor sv1ĕdĕniĭ, soobshchaemykh Pal'mkvistom.

DK651.T68L5 1905   56–52889 ‡

NL 0378629   DLC

Lindeman, J   C
Het onderzoek van gerstrassen aan de korrel. [Rotterdam, 1947]
197–214 p. illus. 25 cm. (Mededelingen van het Nationaal Comité voor Brouwgerst, 1947–13)

1. Barley.   I. Title.

SB191.B2L5   59–50096 ‡

NL 0378630   DLC

Lindeman, Jan Christiaan.
Boomlijst; overzicht van de meest voorkomende boomsoorten in het noordelijk gedeelte van Suriname.   [Suriname?], 1954]
48 l.   35cm.

1. Trees—Guiana, Dutch.

NL 0378631   NN DNAL

Lindeman, Jan Christiaan.
The vegetation of the coastal region of Suriname. Utrecht, Drukkerij en Uitg.-Mij. v/h Kemink, 1953.
x, 135 p. illus., fold. col. maps, tables. 24 cm.
Part of the illustrative matter in pocket.
Proefschrift—Utrecht.
Bibliography: p. 130–135.

1. Botany—Dutch Guiana. 2. Botany—Ecology. 3. Marshes. I. Title.

QK938.M3L5   54–32789

NL 0378632   DLC DSI ICRL NNBG NIC CtY

Lindeman, Jan Christiaan.
Voorlopig overzicht van de bostypen in het noordelijk deel van Suriname, door J. C. Lindeman en S. P. Moolenaar. Paramaribo, Dienst's Lands Bosbeheer, 1955.
54 p. illus., fold. map. 24 cm.
Part of illustrative matter in pocket.
Bibliography : p. 53–54.

1. Forests and forestry—Dutch Guiana. 2. Forest ecology. 3. Plant communities.   I. Moolenaar, S. P., joint author. II. Title.

SD168.D8L5   58–38686

NL 0378633   DLC

Lindeman (Joh.) * De morbo retrogrado. 26 pp. 1 l. 4°. [Halla], typ. C. A. Zeitleri. [1697].

NL 0378634   DNLM

HD2709
.N322
no. 4

Lindeman, John, joint author.

Taylor, Wayne Chatfield, 1893–
The Creole Petroleum Corporation in Venezuela, by Wayne C. Taylor and John Lindeman, with the collaboration of Victor Lopez R. [Washington, National Planning Association, 1955]

Lindeman, John.
The Philippine American Life Insurance Company, by John Lindeman, with the collaboration of Naty Osorio Aguinaldo. [Washington, National Planning Association, 1955]
ix, 91 p. illus., tables. 23 cm. (Case study in an NPA series on United States business performance abroad, 3)

1. Philippine American Life Insurance Company.   (Series: National Planning Association. Case study in an NPA series on U. S. business performance abroad, 3)

HD2709.N322 no. 3   A 55–10308
Mount Holyoke Coll.   Library
for Library of Congress   [a59b1]†

OrCS OrPR WaS DLC
ViU TU PPD OCU OC1W MoU AAP NcU DS CU WaTC MtBC
NL 0378636   MsSM NcGU ScU MB NN NcD TxU NIC MH-BA

395
L642
1948

Lindeman, Johs.
Kjemi for fagskulane til landbruket. Nynorsk utg. ved Anton Røstad.   Oslo, Gyldendal, 1948.
208 p.

1. Chemistry, Agricultural.   I. Tufte, Per   , joint author. II. Røstad, Anton, ed.

NL 0378637   DNAL

VOLUME 334

Līndeman , K₍arl₎ E₍duardovīch₎ *1844-*
Гессенская муха. Монографія профессора К. Э. Линдеманъ. Черниговъ, Земская типографія, 1889.

1 p. l., 115, ₍1₎ p. 27ᶜᵐ.

₍Hessian fly. A monograph₎
Изданіе редакціи "Земскаго сборника Черниговской губ."

1. Hessian fly.   Agr 4-690

Library, U. S. Dept. of   Agriculture, no. 428L64.

NL 0378638   DNAL

Lindeman, Karl Éduardovích, 1844-
Die Hessenfliege (Cecidomyia destructor Say) in Russland. Moscou, 1887.

103 p. 8°.

NL 0378639   MH-Z

Lindeman, Just, 1822-1894.
It Heitelân. Frysk folksliet. Ien- en fjouwerstimmich mei piano- en oargellieding. Musyk fen J. Lindeman... Wirden fen J. L. van der Burg... Ljouwert: R. van der Velde ₍n. d.₎ 2 l. 33cm.

For 1 voice with piano accompaniment. Also for 4 mixed voices with organ accompaniment. Friesian words.
First line: Dèr't de dyk it lân omklammet.

1. Songs, National—Netherlands   —Friesland. I. Burg, Jan Linses van der, 1864-1905. It Heitelân.
N. Y. P. L.   September 20, 1943

NL 0378640   NN

Līndeman , K₍arl₎ E₍duardovīch₎ *1844-*
Хлѣбный жукъ. (Anisoplia austriaca). Отчетъ, представленный г. Министру государственныхъ имуществъ, К. Э. Линдеманомъ... Москва, Типографія М. Н. Лаврова и к°, 1880.

1 p. l., v, ₍1₎, 144 p. 27ᶜᵐ.
Grain weevil (Anisoplia austriaca) Report presented to the minister of Imperial domains ...
"Литература": p. 141-144.
Печатано по распоряженію Департамента земледѣлія и сельской промышленности Министерства государственныхъ имуществъ.

1. Anisoplia austriaca.   Agr 4-690

Library, U. S. Dept. of   Agriculture, no. 427L64.

NL 0378641   DNAL

Lindeman, Karl Éduardovích, 1844-
Die schädlichsten Insekten des Tabak in Bessarabien. Moscou, 1888.

67 p. 8°.

NL 0378642   MH-Z

Lindeman, Karl Éduardovích, 1844-
... Прекращеніе землевладѣнія и землепользованія поселянъ собственниковъ. Указы 2 февраля и 13 декабря 1915 года и 10, 15 іюля и 19 августа 1916 года и ихъ вліяніе на экономическое состояніе южной Россіи. Составилъ К. Э. Линдеманъ... Москва, Тип. К. Л. Меньшова, 1917.

384 p. 24ᶜᵐ.

At head of title: На правахъ рукописи.

1. Land tenure—Russia—Law. 2. European war, 1914-1918—Law and legislation — Russia. 3. Russia — Foreign population. 4. Germans in Russia. I. Title.

         37-32965

Library of Congress

NL 0378643   DLC

Lindeman, Karl Eduardovich, 1844–
... Von den deutschen kolonisten in Russland; ergebnisse einer studienreise 1919-1921, von professor dr. Karl Lindeman ... Stuttgart, Ausland und heimat verlagsaktiengesellschaft, 1924.

123 p. front. (port.) 24½ᶜᵐ. (Schriften des Deutschen ausland-instituts, Stuttgart. A. Kulturhistorische reihe ... bd. 14)

1. Germans in Russia.

Library of Congress   DK43.L5   25-25041

NL 0378644   DLC LU CU MH-AH NN OB1C-M

Lindeman, Karl Éduardovich, 1844-
... Законы 2-го февраля и 13-го декабря 1915 г. (объ ограниченіи нѣмецкаго землевладѣнія въ Россіи) и ихъ вліяніе на экономическое состояніе южной Россіи. Составилъ К. Э. Линдеманъ ... Москва, Тип. К. Л. Меньшова, 1916.

233, III p. 22½ᶜᵐ.

At head of title: На правахъ рукописи.

1. Land tenure—Russia—Law. 2. European war, 1914-1918—Law and legislation — Russia. 3. Russia — Foreign population. 4. Germans in Russia.

         37-32966

Library of Congress

NL 0378645   DLC

Lindeman, L
Het nationalisme van de N. S. B., een documentatie over het tijdvak: einde 1931-zomer 1939, verzameld door L. Lindeman. 3. druk. Leiden, Uitgave Nenasu ₍1940₎.

361 p., 1 l. front. (port.) illus. (maps) 5 pl. 25ᶜᵐ.

1. Netherlands—For. rel.—1830— 2. Netherlands—Defenses. 3. Nationaal-socialistische beweging der Nederlanden.

         46-36099

Library of Congress   DJ285.L5 1940

NL 0378646   DLC CLU MiU CU CtU NN

JN5985
N5L74
ed.4
Hoover
Library

Lindeman, L.
Het nationalisme van de N.S.B.; een documentatie over het tijdvak: einde 1931 - zomer 1939, verzameld door L. Lindeman. 4. druk. Utrecht, NENASU ₍1939₎.

361 p., 1 l. front.(port.) illus.(maps) 5 pl. 25ᶜᵐ.

1.Nationaal-socialistische beweging der Nederlanden. I.Title.

NL 0378647   CSt-H

DJ
285
L5
1943

Lindeman, L
Het nationalisme van de N.S.B., een documentatie over het tijdvak: einde 1931-zomer 1940, verzameld door L. Lindeman. 5. druk. Utrecht, Nenasu, 1943.
361 p. illus. 25 cm.

1. Netherlands - For. rel. - 1830 - 2. Netherlands - Defenses. 3. Nationaal-socialistische beweging der Nederlanden. I. Title.

NL 0378648   CaBVaU

Lindeman, L
Het socialisme van de N. S. B., een documentatie over het tijdvak: einde 1931-zomer 1940, verzameld door L. Lindeman, Leiden, Uitgave Nenasu ₍1941₎.

331 p. front., 1 illus., plates, ports. 25ᶜᵐ.

"Dit boek vormt met het in de maand maart 1940 uitgekomen deel 'Het nationalisme van de N.S.B.' één geheel."—Ter inleiding.

1. Nationaal-socialistische beweging der Nederlanden.

         46-38866

Library of Congress   DJ285.L53

NL 0378649   DLC OU NNC ICU CU MiU NN

Lindeman, L
Het socialisme van de N.S.B., een documentatie over het tijdvak: einds 1931-zomer 1940, verzameld door L. Lindeman. 2. druk. Utrecht, Uitgave Nenasu [1941]

331 p. front., 1 illus., plates, ports. 25 cm.
"Dit boek vormt met het in de maand maart 1940 uitgekomen deel 'Het nationalisme van de N.S.B.' één geheel." - Ter inleiding.
1. Nationaal-socialistische beweging der Nederlanden.

NL 0378650   CU

Bt29j
941Lc

Lindeman, L
Het socialisme van de N.S.B., een documentatie over het tijdvak, einde 1931-zomer 1940, verzameld door L. Lindeman. 3. druk. Utrecht, Nederlandsche Nationaal-socialistische Uitgeverij Nenasu, 1943.
331p. illus., port. 25cm.
"Dit boek vormt met het in de maand Maart 1940 uitgekomen deel 'Het nationalisme van de N.S.B.' één geheel."- Ter inleiding.

NL 0378651   CtY

LINDEMAN, Ludvig Mathias, *1812-1887, ed.*
AEldre og nyere norske Fjeldmelodier samled og bearbeidede for Pianofor. Ie, IIet Bind; IIIle Hefte. 2 Bde. & 1 Hefte. Christiania. [1853-67.]

f°.

NL 0378652   MH CtY

Lindeman, Ludvig Matthias, 1812-1887, editor.
Ældre og nyere norske fjeldmelodier; samlede og bearbeidede for pianoforte af Ludvig M. Lindeman. Christiania: C. Warmuths musikforlag ₍, 1879₎. Publ. pl. no. N. M.-F. 327 Kra., C. 327 W. 3 v. in 1. f°.

Arranged for piano, with interlinear Norwegian, or Norwegian dialect, words. Illustrated t.-p.

456461A. 1. Folks songs, Norwegian.
N. Y. P. L.   February 18, 1930

NL 0378653   NN MH OU NNC

Lindeman, Ludvig Matthias, 1812-1887.

Bugge, Sophus, 1833-1907, ed.
Gamle norske folkeviser. Samlede og udgivne af Sophus Bugge. Kristiania, Feilberg & Landmark, 1858.

LINDEMAN, Ludvig Mathias, *1812-1887,*
Halvhundrede norske Fjeldmelo dier harmoniserede for Mand[]stemmer. Udgione af det Norske Selskab. Kristiano 1862.

4°. pp. viii., 44.

NL 0378655   MH

LINDEMAN, Ludvig Matthias, *1812-1887.*
Indberetning om den af ham i maanedern juli og august 1848 med offentligt stipendium foretagne reise for at optegne folkemelodier. [Christiania, 1850.]

pp. (30). 4 pp. of music.
Norske univ.-og skole-annaler, 1850. 2en raekke, V. 481-510.

NL 0378655-1   MH

VOLUME 334

Lindeman, Ludv[ig] Matthias, 1812–1887.
Koralbog indeholdende melodier til salmebog for lutherske kristne i Amerika, til Landstads, Synodens og andre salmeboeger, udsatte for blandet kor, orgel eller pianoforte... med et tillaeg samlet og ordnet af Oluf Glasoe. Udgivet after forlagskomiteens foranstaltning. Minneapolis, Minn., Augsburg pub. house, 1899.
236 p. 4°. cop.

NL 0378656   DLC IU NNUT PU

Lindeman, Ludvig Matthias, 1812–1887.
Melodier til Biskop J. N. Skaars Lovsange og aandelige viser, af Ludv. M. Lindeman. Kristiania: O. By's Musikforlag, 190–?].
Publ. pl. no. O. B. 100. 9 p. f°.

For piano, with superlinear Norwegian words.
Stamped below imprint: Optaget i Norsk Musikforlag.

1. Hymns, Norwegian. 2. Skaar,   JUILLIARD FOUNDATION FUND.
Lovsange og aandelige viser.   Johannes Nilsson, pr.
N. Y. P. L.   October 7, 1929

NL 0378657   NN

M2140
.N6164   Lindeman, Ludvig Mattias, 1812–1887
Melodier til Brorsons Svanesang; for piano eller orgel med underlagt tekst. Jubilæums-utgave.
Kristiania, J. W. Cappelens Forlag [1912]
16,3–108 p. front.(port.) illus., music. 28cm.

"Ludv. M. Lindeman, 1812–1887, og Melodierne til Brorsons Svanesang; ved O. A. Lindeman" p. 5–9.
"Ludv. M. Lindeman og Kirkemusikken i vort land; ved Peter Lindeman": p. 10–13.

NL 0378658   IaDL

M1772
.L74   Lindeman, Ludvig Matthias, 1812–1887
Melodier til Kristoffer Hagenes sange for skolen og hjemmet; gjennemseede af Ludv. M. Lindeman. 3die øgede opl. Kristiania, P. T. Mallings Boghandels Forlag [1894]
115 p. music. 13½cm.

NL 0378659   IaDL

Lindeman, Ludvig Matthias, 1812–1887.
Mit følge; digt...
see under Bjørnson, Bjørnstjerne, 1832–1910.

M2172
.L5   Lindeman, Ludvig Mattias, 1812–1887.
Norsk messebog indeholdende formler og melodier, saavel til den almindelige som til den lutherske Messe samt de tilhorende menighedssvar, ved Ludv. M. Lindeman; 2. förbedrede udgave. Christiania, Jacob Dybwad, 1885.
36 p. music. 23½ cm.

I. Norske kirke. Liturgy and ritual. I. Title.

NL 0378661   ICLT

Lindeman, Ludvig M[athias], 1812–1887.
Norske fjeld-melodier harmonisk bearbeidede. Christiania, P. T. Malling, [1840].
5 pt. 4°.
Pt. 1 is "2te oplag."

Folksongs–Norwegian.

NL 0378662   MH

Lindeman, Ludvig Matthias, 1812–1887.
Landstad, Magnus Brostrup, 1802–1880, ed.
Norske folkeviser, samlede og udgivne af M. B. Landstad ... Christiania, C. Tönsberg, 1853.

Lindeman, Ludvig Matthias, 1812–1887.
Vig, Ole, 1824–1857, comp.
Sange og rim for det norske folk. Samlet og med anmærkninger ledsaget af O. Vig. (Med melodier af L. M. Lindeman.) Udgivet af "Selskabet for folkeoplysningens fremme" som tillægshæfte til "Folkevennens", 3die aargang. Kristiania. Trykt i P. T. Mallings bogtrykkeri, 1854.

Lindeman, Ludvig Matthias, 1812–1887, compiler.
30 norske Kjæmpevisemelodier med fuldstændig text, harmoniserede for 3 lige stemmer (2 tenorer og bas eller 2 sopraner og alt), af Ludv. M. Lindeman. (Texten besørget af cand. J. E. Nielsen.) Christiania: J. W. Cappelens forlag, 1863. 91 p. 21½cm.

Norwegian words; music for 2 T. and B. or 2 S. and A.

1. Folk songs, Norwegian.   II. Nielsen, Johan Eberhard Colbjørnsen,
1827–   II. Title: Norske   kjaempevisemelodier.
N. Y. P. L.   June 1, 1933

NL 0378665   NN NcD

Lindeman, Ludvig Matthias, 1812–1887.
34 Psalme-Melodier af Kingos Gradual, 1699. Harmoniseret for Orgel eller Pianoforte, af Ludv. M. Lindeman... Christiania: C. Warmuth's Musikforlag, pref. 1875]. Publ. pl. no. C. W. 191. 23 p. 4°.

Danish words; music for 4 voices.

1. Hymns, Denominational—Lutheran   JUILLIARD FOUNDATION FUND.
Danish. (3) Kingo, Thomas Hansen,   Church—Denmark. 2. Hymns,
N. Y. P. L.   1634–1703.
                                     October 11, 1929

NL 0378666   NN

M 9
L55 V3   Lindeman, Ludvig Matthias, 1812–1887.
[Variations on He who will suffer God to guide him, organ]
Variasjoner til koralen Hvo ene lader Herren rade, for piano eller orgel. [Drammen, Norway, Harald Lyche, c1952]

11 p. 23 x 31 cm. (Edition Lyche, Nr. 227)

1. Variations (Organ)

NL 0378667   OU

QD393
.L74   Lindeman, Ludwig.
Ueber stickstoff-verbindungen des anthracens. Freiburg, 1880.
30p.
Inaug. diss. Freiburg.

NL 0378668   DLC

Lindeman, Marcella, joint author.
Miller, Henry J.
... Behavior of molybdenum as resistor in the electric furnace, by Henry J. Miller and Marcella Lindeman ... New York, American institute of mining and metallurgical engineers, inc., °1927.

Lindeman, Marie von, d. 1903.
Die rathende Freundin; Mitgabe für junge Mädchen beim Eintritt in's Leben. Von Marie von Lindeman. Zweite vermehrte Auflage. Köln am Rhein: J. P. Bachem [1893] xl, 177 p. 17cm.

Added t.-p. illustrated in colors.

6939B. 1. Girls.
N. Y. P. L.   January 23, 1940

NL 0378670   NN

NL 0378671   ICN MH

Lindeman, Moritz Karl Adolf, 1823–1908.
Die arktische fischerei der deutschen seestädte 1620–1868. In vergleichender darstellung von Moritz Lindeman. Mit zwei karten von A. Petermann ... Gotha; J. Perthes, 1869.
vi, 118 p. 2 maps. 28cm. (In Petermanns mittheilungen. Gotha, 1871. Ergänzungsband vi, ergänzungsheft no. 26)

1. Fisheries—Arctic regions. 2. Whaling. 3. Germany—Indus.—Hist.
I. Title.

Library of Congress   G1.P44   5–32564

NL 0378672   DLC MoU ViU NIC MiU OU NN

Lindeman, Moritz Karl Adolf, 1823–1908.
Beiträge zur statistik der deutschen seefischerei. Im auftrage der Sektion für küsten- und hochseefischerei bearb. von ... M. Lindeman ... Berlin, W. Moeser hofbuchdr., 1888.
v, 247 p. incl. tables (1 fold.) 25½ cm.

1. Fisheries—North Sea. 2. Fisheries—Germany. I. Deutscher
seefischerei-verein, Berlin.

Library of Congress   SF271.L6   9–25512

NL 0378673   DLC MH

Lindeman, Moritz Karl Adolf, 1823–1908, ed.
Deutsche geographische blätter ... Hrsg. von der Geographischen gesellschaft in Bremen ... bd. 1– Bremen, 1877–19

Lindeman, Moritz Karl Adolf, 1823–1908.
Finnland und seine bewohner. Eine historisch-geographische skizze von Moritz von Lindeman. Mit einem vorwort von dr. Karl Andree. Leipzig, C. B. Lorck, 1855.
x p., 1 l., 143 p. 17cm. (Added t.-p.: Conversations- und reisebibliothek)

1. Finland. I. Title.

                                          1–6383
Library of Congress   DK449.L7

NL 0378675   DLC PPG

Lindeman, Moritz Karl Adolf, 1823–1908.
Die gegenwärtige Eismeer-Fischerei und der walrang, von Dr. phil. Moritz Lindeman. Berlin, O. Salle, 1899.
vii, 134 p. incl. tables. 34½cm. (Added t.-p.: Abhandlungen des Deutschen Seefischerei-Vereins ... Bd. IV)

NL 0378676   ICJ MH

VOLUME 334

Lindeman, Moritz [Karl Adolf]1823-1908.
Gesetzgebung und Einrichtungen im Interesse des Auswanderungswesens in Bremen.
(In Verein fuer Socialpolitik. Schriften. 52. Pp. 415-431. Leipzig, 1892.)

E2478 — Bremen, Germany. Emig.

NL 0378677 MB

Lindeman, Moritz [Karl Adolf]1823-1908. Mitteilungen über den bayrischen wald, (iii). [Bremen. 1885.] 8°. Map.
Deutsche geographische blätter, 1885, viii, 1-30.

NL 0378678 MH-A

HE945 Lindeman, Moritz Karl Adolf, 1823-1908.
.N8L7 Der Norddeutsche Lloyd. Geschichte und handbuch.
(Ge) Bearb. von dr. phil. Moritz Lindeman ... Bremen, C. Schünemann, 1892.
xxi, [1], 487, [1] p. front., illus., plates (part fold.) maps (part fold.) tables (part fold.) diagrs. (part fold.) 22cm.

1. North German Lloyd steamship company, Bremen.

NL 0378679 ICU MdBP MH-BA

Lindeman, Moritz Karl Adolf, 1823-1908.
Die seefischereien, ihre gebiete, betrieb und erträge in den jahren 1869-1878. Von Moritz Lindeman. Mit zwei karten ... Gotha, J. Perthes, 1880.
v, [1], 95, [1] p. illus., fold. map. 28cm. (*In* Petermanns mittheilungen. Gotha, 1880. Ergänzungsband XIII, ergänzungsheft no. 60)

1. Fisheries.

5-32588

Library of Congress G1.P44

NL 0378680 DLC NN MoU ViU PPL OU MiU

Lindeman, Moritz [Karl Adolf], 1823-1908.
Nb83 Urbegriffe der Wirtschaftswissenschaft.
L641 Arbeit, Wert (Gebrauchs- und Tauschwert), Geld,
904 Preis: Wirtschaft, Wirtschaftswissenschaft, von Dr.philos.Moritz Lindeman. Dresden,O.V.Böhmert, 1904.
xi,248p. 25cm.

1.Economics
2.Economics - His+

NL 0378681 CtY NNC ICJ NN

Lindeman, Moritz Karl Adolf, 1823-1908, ed.
G630
.G4G4
Geographische gesellschaft in Bremen.
Die zweite deutsche nordpolarfahrt in den jahren 1869 und 1870 unter führung des kapitän Karl Koldewey. Hrsg. von dem Verein für die deutsche nordpolarfahrt in Bremen ... Leipzig, F. A. Brockhaus, 1873-74.

TA1
.M69 Lindeman, Myrl A
no.50
1944 Automotive engine performance with various compression ratios and fuels [by] Myrl A. Lindeman, and Thomas E. Murphy. [Minneapolis] 1944.
28 p. illus. 28cm. (Minnesota. University. Institute of Technology. Engineering Experiment Station. Technical paper, no. 50)

1. Automobiles—Motors. 2. Gas and oil engines—Testing. I. Murphy, Thomas E., joint author. II. Title. III. Ser.

NL 0378683 ViU

TA1
.M69 Lindeman, Myrl A
no.48
1944 Valve guide leakage in an automotive engine [by] Myrl A. Lindeman, and Burton J. Robertson. [Minneapolis] 1944.
22 p. illus. 28cm. (Minnesota. University. Institute of Technology. Engineering Experiment Station. Technical paper, no. 48)
Bibliography: p. 22.

1. Valves. 2. Automobiles—Motors. I. Robertson, Burton J., 1882- joint author. II. Title. III. Ser.

NL 0378684 ViU

Lindeman, Ole Andres, 1768-1855?
Pièces pour le clavecin par Ole-Andres Lindeman. Paris, 1861.
2 p.l., 11 p. (music) 35 cm. (In Trésor des pianistes, v. 16)
"Notice biographique de O.-A. Lindeman": 1st preliminary leaf.

NL 0378685 CtY-Mus

M2140 Lindeman, Peter
N6 Melodier til "Kirkeklokken" let udsatte for blandet kor, orgel eller piano af Peter Lindeman. Udgive: Birger Hall. Kristiania, J.Bjørnstads bog- og nodetrykkeri, 1890.
xii,240p. 21cm.
On cover: Melodier til Kirkiklokken med Tillaeg.
On t.p.: "Hovedkommission hos Marius Lund."

1. Hymns, Norwegian. I. Hall, Birger II. Title.

NL 0378686 IaU

Lindeman, Peter.
Praktisk skole for orgel og harmonium. Op. 17. 15.-16. oppl. Oslo, Aschehoug, 1950-
v. 32 cm.
Principally exercises.

1. Organ—Methods. 2. Organ—Studies and exercises. 3. Reed-organ—Methods. 4. Reed-organ—Studies and exercises. I. Title.

MT182.L55 M 57-1387

NL 0378687 DLC

Lindeman, Raymond Laurel, 1915-
Ecological dynamics in a senescent lake ... by Raymond L. Lindeman ... [Notre Dame, Ind., The University press, 1941]
cover-title, [1], 636-673 p. incl. 1 illus., tables, diagrs. 22½cm.
Portion of thesis (PH. D.)—University of Minnesota, 1941.
"Third in a series of papers, 'Ecological studies of a senescent lake'."
"Reprinted from 'The American midland naturalist' vol. 26, no. 3 ... November, 1941."
The reprint has title: Seasonal food-cycle dynamics in a senescent lake.
Vita: p. [3] of cover.
"References": p. 671-673.

1. Fresh-water biology. 2. Lakes. I. Title.

42-24892

Library of Congress QH98.L52

NL 0378688 DLC

Lindeman, Seeley.
The know-how of salesmanship. [1st ed.] New York, Pageant Press [1953]
33 p. 21 cm.

1. Salesman and salesmanship. I. Title.

HF5438.L59 658.85 53-12692 ‡

NL 0378689 DLC OCl NN

Lindeman, Sidney O.
The generals go to war, by S. O. Lindeman; a study of advertising and sales methods of a fast-growing industry. [Greensboro, N. C., Business publications co., °1930]
4 p. l., [13]-116 p. port. 20½cm.
"A study of advertising and selling methods used in connection with electric refrigeration."—p. [13]

1. Refrigeration and refrigerating machinery. 2. Advertising—Refrigeration and refrigerating machinery. I. Title.

30-18027

Library of Congress HF6161.R35L5
Copyright A 24763 [658.8962157] 659.1

NL 0378690 DLC OCl

TP854N
L74 Lindeman, Thorvald, 1867-
Norske glasvaerker; et bidrag til disses
Corning Museum of Glass Library historie, av Thv. Lindeman... Trondhjem, F. Brun, 1928. 104 p. illus. 24 cm. (Det Kgl. norske videnskabers selskabs skrifter 1927. Nr. 8)
"Literaturfortegnelse": p. 98-100.

912. 1. Glass factories—Norway. 2. Manufacture of glass—Norway.

NL 0378691 NCorniC NN

Lindeman, Thorvald, 1867-
... Torv, av Thv. Lindeman. Med 8 tekstfigurer og zusammenfassung. Kristiania, I kommission hos H. Aschehoug & co., 1922.
32 p. tables, diagrs. 24cm. ([Norway] Norges geologiske undersøkelse. [Skrifter] nr. 105)
Statens raastofkomite. Publikation nr. 5.
"Zusammenfassung": p. 28-32.
1. Peat.

[*Full name:* Hans Thorvald Lindeman]

G S 23-190 Revised

Library, U. S. Geological Survey (581) B no. 105
Library of Congress QE281.A2 nr. 105

NL 0378692 DI-GS MiU NIC DLC

Lindeman, Thorvald, 1867-
Den Trønderske familie Lindeman. Samlet og skrevet for familien av Thv.Lindeman. Trondhjem, Janssen, 1924
75 p. illus.

NL 0378693 MH

Lindeman, Thorvald, 1867-
Ueber einige neue salze des antipyrins und über die einwirkung von epichlorhydrin auf phenole.... Jena, Frommannsche buchdr., 1891.
31,[1] p. 24 cm. [Jena. Universität. Dissertationen. v. 22, no. 9]
Inaug.-diss. - Jena.
[Full name: Hans Thorvald Lindeman]

NL 0378694 CU ICRL PU MH

VOLUME 334

Lindeman, Trygve Henrik, 1896–
Lærebok i taktering for kor-dirigenter, av Trygve Lindeman ... Oslo, H. Aschehoug & co. (W. Nygaard) 1939.
56 p., 1 l. illus. (incl. music) diagrs. 20½ᶜᵐ.

1. Conducting, Choral.   I. Title.
42–489 Revised

Library of Congress   MT88.L56L4

NL 0378695   DLC

730.77
L641
Lindeman, Trygve Henrik, 1896–
Tonetreffing og musikkdiktat. Oslo, H. Aschehoug, 1951.
55p. music. 22 cm.

1. Ear-training. I. Title.

NL 0378696   OrU

Lindeman, Trygve Henrik, 1896–
Tonetreffing og musikkdiktat. Oslo, Aschehoug, 1951.
66 p. music. 21 cm.

1. Sight-singing. 2. Musical dictation.   I. Title.

MT870.L679   M 53–1635

NL 0378697   DLC OrU

Lindeman, Verlus Frank, 1902–
The physiology of the crustacean heart. I. The effect of various ions upon the heart rhythm of the crayfish, *Cambarus clarkii*. II. The effect of lithium, ammonium, strontium, and barium ions upon the heart rhythm of the crayfish, *Cambarus clarkii*. By Verlus Frank Lindeman ... (Chicago, 1930)
1 p. l., (1), 576–592, 395–410 p. diagrs. 23½ᶜᵐ.
Thesis (PH. D.)—University of Iowa, 1930.
"Reprints from Physiological zoölogy, vol. 1, no. 4 ... October, 1928, vol. 2, no. 3 ... July, 1929."
"Literature cited": p. 592, 410.
1. Heart. 2. Ions. 3. Crayfish. 4. Physiological chemistry.
31–2\0984
Library of Congress   QP111.L65 1930
Univ. of Iowa Libr.
———— Copy 2.   [595.3841] 591.11

NL 0378698   IaU DLC

Lindeman, Willem.
Over de beteknis van phosphaat in de photosynthese van *Lemna minor* L. 's-Gravenhage (1952)
83 p. diagrs., tables. 25 cm.
Proefschrift—Amsterdam.
Summary in English.
"Stellingen": leaf inserted.
Bibliography: p. 79–83.

1. Photosynthesis. 2. Phosphates. 3. Lemna minor.

QK882.L5   56–16945

NL 0378699   DLC CtY

Lindeman, Włodzimierz, 1867–
... Iperyt. Warszawa, Wojskowy instytut naukowo-wydawniczy, 1929.
xi, 322 p., 2 l. illus., plates (part col.) diagrs. 25ᶜᵐ.
At head of title: Dr. med. Wł. Lindeman ...

1. Gases, Asphyxiating and poisonous.   I. Title.
CA 31–574 Unrev'd

Library of Congress   RA1245.L5

NL 0378700   DLC NN CU CSt-H NcD IU

Lindeman, Woldemar.

See

Lindeman, Włodzimierz, 1867

Lindemann.
Fünfjährige Registrierungen über Luftdruck, Temperatur, relative Feuchtigkeit und Sonnenschein an der Landes-Wetterwarte zu Dresden. 1906–1910. Von Dir. Ass. Lindemann... (Magdeburg,) 1912. 193–203 p. 8°.
Caption-title.
Excerpt: Das Wetter, Sept. 1912.

1. Meteorology, Germany:
N. Y. P. L.   Dresden, 1906–10.
July 13, 1916.

NL 0378702   NN

Lindemann, oberlehrer, Conitz
    see Lindemann, J   Hermann.

Lindemann, A
Formenlehre des ägyptischen Nomen und Verbums auf Grund ausseraegyptisches und koptisches Transcriptionen neu zusammengestellt. [n.p., 19—]
2 v. 30 cm.
Manuscript.

NL 0378704   RPB

PJ1181
.L5
Lindemann, A
[Studies in Egyptian verbs. n.p., 19—]
4 v. in 5. 33 cm.
Manuscript.
Contents.–
2. Das zweiradikalige Nomen und Berbum im Aegyptischen.– 3. Das Dreiradikale Nomen und Verbum.– 4. Die Vier und mehrradikaligan Nomen.– 5. Die Nisbeformen.

NL 0378705   RPB

Lindemann, A., fl. 1899.
Die markthallen Berlins, ihre baulichen anlagen und betriebseinrichtungen, im auftrage des magistrats dargestellt von A. Lindemann ... Berlin, J. Springer, 1899.
2 p. l., 90 p., 1 l. illus., 33 pl. (part fold., part col. and incl. plans) 39½ᶜᵐ.

1. Berlin—Markets.   I. Title.
Agr 13—2224

U. S. Dept. of agr. Library   280.3L64
for Library of Congress   HF5474.G4B55

NL 0378706   DNAL ICJ CU

D921
.L5
Lindemann, A   J
Sketches from my travels in Continental Europe. (Milwaukee, 1922)
3 p. l., 115 p. illus. 20 cm.

1. Europe—Descr. & trav.   I. Title.

NL 0378707   T

Lindemann (A.J,) & Hoverson Co., Milwaukee, Wis
THE LINDEMANN STOVES AND RANGES; A CATALOGUE ... [n.p., 1905]
180 p. illus.

WISCONSIN: INDUSTRIES: STOVES
LINDEMANN (A.J.) & HOVERSON CO.: CATALOGS
title

NL 0378708   WHi

Lindemann, Ada, 1904–
Ueber trinkwasserdesinfektion durch clorinaheyden.
Inaug. Diss.   Kiel [1930]
Bibl.

NL 0378709   ICRL CtY

(v)
DD233
G373
v.2:9
Lindemann, Adolf.
Betrüger und Betrogene. Leipzig, G. Kürsten [1920]
29 [i.e. 34] p. 22cm. ([German pamphlets on the Revolution of 1918 and subsequent events, v.2:9])

1. Germany – Hist. – Revolution, 1918.
2. Corruption (in politics) – Germany. 3. Leipzig – Hist.   I. Title.

NL 0378710   CSt-H

Lindemann, Adolf.
Untersuchungen über die beeinflussung der länge der von einem Righi'schen erreger ausgesandten elektrischen wellen durch drähte, welche der primärleitung angehängt werden ... Leipzig, J. A. Barth, 1900.
24 p. diagrs. 23ᶜᵐ.
Inaug.-diss.—Rostock.

1. Electric waves.
8–3223

Library of Congress   QC665.L72

NL 0378711   DLC CtY

---

fl. 1869.
Lindemann (Adolf,) Ueber die Nerven der Kehlkopfschleimhaut. 16 pp., 1 pl. 8°. Leipzig, E. Polz, 1869.

NL 0378712   DNLM ICRL

Lindemann, Adolf, 1879–
Deutschlands erster Admiral, historischer Roman. Köln, K. Schroeder [1939]
408 p. illus., ports. 19 cm.

1. Brommy, Karl Rudolf, 1809–1860—Fiction.

PT2623.I 5713D4   52–46926

NL 0378713   DLC CU CtY

Lindemann, Adolf, 1879–
Jürgen Wullenwever; Erzählung aus der deutschen Hansezeit. Reutlingen, Ensslin & Laiblin [1942]
302 p. illus. 22 cm.
"Zeittafel": p. 299–300.

1. Wullenwever, Jürgen, 1492?–1537—Fiction.

PT2623.I 5713J8   50–49046

NL 0378714   DLC

VOLUME 334

Lindemann, Albert Clarence.
　　A lapidary machine: its development and use for
industrial arts laboratories... 1941.
　　Thesis - Ohio state university, 1941.

NL 0378715　　OU

Lindemann, Alfred, joint author.
　　Liefmann, Harry.
　　Der einfluss der hitze auf die sterblichkeit der säuglinge
in Berlin und einigen anderen grossstädten (New York,
München, Essen Ruhr) von H. Liefmann ... und Alfred
Lindemann ... mit 33 kurventafeln. Braunschweig, F.
Vieweg & sohn, 1911.

Lindemann, Alfred.
　　Die verantwortlichkeit des schriftleiters einst
und jetzt. ... Erlangen, 1936. 43 p.
　　Inaug. Diss. - Erlangen, 1936.

NL 0378717　　ICRL CtY

Lindemann, Alfred, *1883-* appr. Arzt: Aus d. bakteriol. Labor. d.
hygien. Univ.-Inst. Bonn. Das Schicksal der Bakterien
im Dünndarm. Bonn 1909: Eisele. 44 S. 8°
Bonn, Med. Diss. v. 6. Febr. 1909, Ref. Finkler
[Geb. 13. März 83 Essen (Ruhr); Wohnort: Crefeld; Staatsangeh.: Preußen;
Vorbildung: Gymn. Essen Reife O. 02; Studium: Freiburg i. B. 3, Würzburg 2,
Marburg 2, Bonn 1, Berlin 3 S.; Coll. 6. Febr. 09; Approb. 31. Aug. 08.]
　　　　　　　　　　　　　　　　　　　[U 09. 35]

NL 0378718　　ICRL DNLM MBCo

Lindemann (Andreas). *De partu præterna-
turali, quem sine matris aut fœtus sectione ab-
solvere non licet operatori.* 34 pp. sm. 4°.
Gottingæ, E. Luzac [1756].

NL 0378719　　DNLM PPC

Lindemann, Anna
　　Frauen schreiben; 12 Novellen deutscher Erzählerinnen; mit
Illustrationen erster deutscher Künstler; dargereicht von Anna
Charlotte Lindemann. Berlin: Reimar Hobbing und Dom-
Verlag[, cop. 1932]. 255 p. pl., port. 8°.
　　Contents.—Baum, V. Die Strandwache.—Berend, A. Der Hirt vom Berge.
Der Schein.—Dill, L. Der indische Ring. Seltsame Liebespaare.—Forbes-Mosse, I.
Das werbende Herz.—Huch, R. Köln.—Schanz, F. Irenes Fahrt ins Glück.—Seidel, I.
Die Flöte.—Viebig, C. Das Kind.—Zobeltitz, M. v. Die Kakteen der Selene Denecke.

1. Short stories
N. Y. P. L.　　　　　　　　　　　　　　　May 10, 1933

NL 0378720　　NN InU NRU

Lindemann, Anna, editor.
　　Unsere Ernährung in der Kriegszeit. Neun Vorträge, gehalten bei dem Lehrkurs des Nationalen Frauendienstes in Stutt-
garter Landesgewerbemuseum, 22.–24. Februar 1915. Im Auftrage des Nationalen Frauendienstes Stuttgart, hrsg. von Anna
Lindemann. Berlin: W. Kohlhammer, 1915. vii, 162 p., 1 fold.
chart. 8°.
　　Addresses by Dr. Rosa Kempf, Eleonore Ingelfinger, Anna Lindemann,
Hermine Kiehnle, Irmgard Zipperling, H. Müller, Dr. R. Nübling and Garten-
bauinspektor Schönberg.

1. Food.—Dietary studies and nu-　trition investigations. 2. European war, 1914- .—Food supply,　Germany. 3. Nationaler Frau-
endienst, Stuttgart. 4. Title.
N. Y. P. L.　　　　　　　　　　　　　April 11, 1916.

NL 0378721　　NN CSt-H

4HQ
465
Lindemann, Anna
　　Die Zukunft der Kriegswitwe.
Berlin, A. Collignon, 1915.
　　46 p.

　　(AGV Schriften)

NL 0378722　　DLC-P4

Lindemann (Antonius). *De hæmoptysi.* 16
pp. 8°. *Mosachii, C. Wolf, [1834].*

NL 0378723　　DNLM

Lindemann, Arno: Die Behandlung des Pemphigus durch
intravenöse Salvarsaninfusion. Borna-Leipzig 1912: Noske.
23 S. 8°
Jena, Med. Diss. v. 12. Nov. 1912, Ref. Stintzing
[Geb. 15. Febr. 79 Köthen i. A.; Wohnort: Dresden; Staatsangeh.: Anhalt;
Vorbildung: Stadtgymn. Halle a. S. Reife O. 98; Studium: Halle 4, Leipzig 5,
Halle 4 S.; Coll. 7. Nov. 12; Approb. 1. März 11.]　　　　　[U 12. 5363]

NL 0378724　　ICRL PPAmP DNLM MBCo

Lindemann, Arno, 1899-
　　Die morphologische und chemische blutuntersuchung
u. ihre diagnostische bedeutung für die otologie.
... Königsberg Pr., 1926. 19 p.
　　Inaug. Diss. - Königsberg Pr., 1926.
　　Lebenslauf.
　　Literatur.

NL 0378725　　DNLM

Lindemann (August) [1880-]. *Beiträge
zur funktionellen Herzdiagnostik.* 60 pp.,
1 l. 8°. *Würzburg, A. Borst, 1905.*

NL 0378726　　DNLM ICRL

RD523
L642
1941
Lindemann, August, 1880-
　　Die chirurgie des gesichts, der mundhöhle
und der luftwege, von August Lindemann, Georg
Lange und H. Frenzel. Berlin, Urban, 1941.
　　p. illus., 11 col. plates.

　　"Sonderausgabe aus: Die chirurgie. 2. auflage. Herausgegeben von Martin Kirschner und
Otto Nordmann."

　　1. Face - Surgery. 2. Surgery, Plastic.
3. Trachea - Surgery. 4. Larynx - Surgery.

NL 0378728　　NNC DNLM NNC-M

RD523
L643
1920/22
Lindemann, August, 1880-
　　Die chirurgisch-plastische versorgung der
weichteilschäden des gesichtes. Leipzig,
Vogel, 1920-22,
　　p. [45]-112, [181]-208. illus.

　　"Separatabdruck aus der Deutschen zeitschrift
f. chirurgie, 160. bd, 170. bd."

　　1. Face - Surgery.

NL 0378729　　NNC NNC-M

Bruhn, Chr., *ed.*
　　Die gegenwärtigen behandlungswege der kieferschuss-
verletzungen; ergebnisse aus dem Düsseldorfer lazarett
für kieferverletzte (Kgl. reservelazarett). Unter ständi-
ger mitwirkung von Friedrich Hauptmeyer ... **Max Kühl**
... dr. med. August Lindemann ... hrsg. von prof. **Chr.
Bruhn** ...
　　Wiesbaden, J. F. Bergmann, 1915

WU
280
L743g
1950
LINDEMANN, August, 1880-
　　Die Geschwülste der Mundhöhle, der
Kiefer und des Gesichtes, von August
Lindemann und Otto Lorenz. Stuttgart,
Wissenschaftliche Verlagsgesellschaft,
1950.
　　283 p. illus.
　　1. Jaws - Neoplasms 2. Mouth -
Neoplasms I. Lorenz, Otto, 1909-

NL 0378731　　DNLM NNC-M NNC ICJ DLC

Lindemann, August, 1880- ed.
　　Leitfaden der chirurgie und orthopädie des mundes und der
kiefer, unter mitwirkung von prof. dr. Wilhelm Haberling-
Düsseldorf, dozent dr. Herbert Hofrath-Düsseldorf, prof. dr.
Paul Huebschmann-Düsseldorf [u. a.] ... herausgegeben von
dr. August Lindemann ... Leipzig, H. Meusser, 1938-
　　v. illus., diagrs. 23½ᶜᵐ.

1. Mouth—Surgery. 2. Jaws—Surgery. 3. Orthopedia. I. Title.
　　　　　　　　　　　　　　　　　　　　　　　　　　　39-33085
Library of Congress　　RD523.L5
　Copyright A—Foreign　　40977
　　　　　　　　　　　　　　　　　　　　　　　　　　　617.52

NL 0378732　　DLC NNC DNLM

W 1
ME8237
Heft 5
1949
LINDEMANN, August, 1880-
　　Zur chirurgisch-plastischen Deckung
der Weichteildefekte des Gesichtes, von
August Lindemann und Otto Lorenz.
Berlin, Urban & Schwarzenberg, 1949.
　　30 p. illus. (Monographien der
"Medizinischen Klinik," Heft 5)
　　1. Face - Surgery 2. Surgery -
Plastic I. Lorenz, Otto, 1909-
Series: Medizinische Klinik.
Monographien, Heft 5

NL 0378733　　DNLM NNC

Lindemann, August S.
　　Administration of industrial education, state and municipal.
　　(*In* National education association of the United States. Journal of
proceedings and addresses, 1908. p. 1060-1065)

1. Industrial education—U. S.

　　　　　　　　　　　　　　　　　　　　　　　　　　E 9-295
Library, U. S. Bur. of　　　　　　　Education

NL 0378734　　DHEW OU

Lindemann, Aug. W ed.
　　Schreiblesefibel für deutsche Elementar-
Schulen. Columbus, Ohio, Lutherische Verlags-
handlung, 1885.

NL 0378735　　MH

VOLUME 334

Lindemann, Bernhard, 1871–
... Erdbild und erdzeitalter; eine geologische formationskunde, von dr. B. Lindemann, mit 117 abbildungen im text ... Leipzig, P. Reclam jun. [*1930]
2 v. illus. 15½ᶜᵐ. (Bücher der naturwissenschaft. 34.–35. bd.)
On cover: Reclams universal-bibliothek nr. 7086–7091.
Contents.—v. 1. Vom archäischen zeitalter bis zur trias.—v. 2. Von der rät-lias-zeit bis zur gegenwart.

1. Geology, Stratigraphic. 2. Paleontology.   I. Title.
Library of Congress   QE651.L65   31–6579
Copyright A—Foreign   10778
                                [2]   551.7

NL 0378736   DLC MB

Lindemann, Bernhard, 1871–
... Die erde; eine allgemeinverständliche geologie Stuttgart, Kosmos [etc., ᶜ1912–
v. illus., plates (partly col.) maps. 26½ᶜᵐ.

1. Geology.

Library of Congress   QE31.L7   12–10620

NL 0378737   DLC CU MiU MB

Lindemann, Bernhard, 1871–
...Die Erde; eine allgemeinverständliche Geologie. Bd 1– Stuttgart: Kosmos, Gesellschaft der Naturfreunde[, cop. 1925–   ] v. col'd front. (v. 1), diagrs., illus. (incl. plans, maps), plates (part col'd).   2. ed.   4°.
Printed in double columns.
Plates printed on both sides.
Contents: Bd. 1. Geologische Kräfte.   1925.

1. Geology. 2. Title.
N. Y. P. L.   April 26, 1926

NL 0378738   NN CU

Lindemann, Bernhard, 1871–
Geologie der deutschen landschaften, von dr. B. Lindemann ...   Stuttgart, Kosmos, Gesellschaft der naturfreunde, 1914.
1 p. l., [v]–viii, 368 p.   illus. (incl. maps) plates (part. col., part. double)   26 cm.
In double columns.
"Literverzeichnis: p. vi–viii.
1. Geology–Germany.

NL 0378739   CU

QE   Lindemann, Bernhard, 1871–
31   Geologische Kräfte. Mit 7 Farbdruck-
L71   tafeln, 19 Schwarztafeln u. 322 Abbildungen.
        Stuttgart, Kosmos [etc., ᶜ1912].
            408,[18]p.   illus.,plates (part col.,
        1 double),   maps(1 double),   diagrs.
        (Die Erde; eine allgemeinverständliche
        Geologie [von] Dr. B. Lindemann, Bd. 1)

            1. Geology.

NL 0378740   UU

551.43
L641k
Geol   Lindemann, Bernhard, 1871–
Lib'y   Kettengebirge. Kontinentale Zerspaltung
        und Erdexpansion.   Jena. G. Fischer, 1927.
        iv,[1],186p. illus. 25cm.

        1. Mountains – Europe. 2. Geology,
        Structural. 3. Geology – Europe.

NL 0378741   TxU MH CU MH-GS

LINDEMANN, Bernhard, 1871–
Ueber einige wichtige vorkommnisse von körnigen carbonatgesteinen etc.   Inaug.-diss. München.   Stuttgart, 1904.

NL 0378742   MH PU

Lindemann, Carl August, 1893–
Die feindliche bestimmung der kriegskonterbande ... von Carl August Lindemann ...   Münster i. Westf., F. Coppenrath, 1917.
101 p.   20½ᶜᵐ.
Inaug.-diss.—Erlangen.
"Literatur": p. [5]–7.

1. Contraband of war.   I. Title.
                                    42–28443
Library of Congress   JX5231.L5

NL 0378743   DLC MH PU ICRL NIC CtY NN

Lindemann, Carl August Siegfried
    see   Lindemann, Siegfried, 1880–

Lindemann, Carl Felix, 1868–
Die bestrebungen zur erhaltung der boden-fruchtbarkeit von ihren ersten anfängen bis zur landwirtschaftlichen hochkultur der Römer ...   Scheibenberg, Buchdr. von K. A. Richter, 1900.
4 p. l., [5]–161, [1] p.   21ᶜᵐ.
Inaug.-diss.—Heidelberg.
Lebenslauf.
"Benutzte litteratur": p. [14]–16.

1. Agriculture—Hist.
                                    12–5028
Library of Congress   S421.L6

NL 0378745   DLC PU IU ICRL CtY

Lindemann, Carl Hugo, 1867–
Arbeiterpolitik und wirtschaftspflege in der deutschen städteverwaltung.   Von dr. H. Lindemann (C. Hugo) ...   Stuttgart, J. H. W. Dietz nachf. (g. m. b. h.) 1904.
2 v.   24ᶜᵐ.
Contents.—1. bd. Arbeiterpolitik.—2. bd. Wirtschaftspflege.

1. Municipal ownership—Germany. 2. Labor and laboring classes—Germany. 3. Municipal government—Germany.
                                    5–27656 Revised
Library of Congress   HD4659.L5

NL 0378746   DLC NIC CU PU CtY MiU ICJ MH NN

Lindemann, Carl Hugo, 1867–
Arbeiterpolitik & wirtschaftspflege in der deutschen städteverwaltung.   Stuttgart, Dietz, 1909.
2v.   2nd ed.

NL 0378747   OClW

Lindemann, Carl Hugo, 1867–
Gb22   De dialecto ionica recentiore ...
1   Scripsit Hugo Lindemann ... Kiliae,1889.
L64   Pamphlet
        Diss. inaug. – Kiel.
        Vita.

NL 0378748   CtY ICRL NIC ICU MH RPB NjP CU PU

Lindemann, Carl Hugo, 1867–
... Die deutsche stadtgemeinde im kriege, von dr. Hugo Lindemann ...   Tübingen, Mohr, 1917.
2 p. l., 94 p.   24ᶜᵐ.   (Kriegswirtschaftliche zeitfragen ... 6/7)

1. European war, 1914–   —Germany. 2. European war, 1914–
—Hospitals, charities, etc.
                                    21–20169
Library of Congress   HC286.2.K7   no. 6/7

NL 0378749   DLC NN

[**Lindemann, Carl Hugo**] 1867–
Die deutsche städteverwaltung; ihre aufgaben auf den gebieten der volkshygiene, des städtebaus und des wohnungswesens; von C. Hugo [pseud.]   Stuttgart, J. H. W. Dietz nachf. (g. m. b. h.) 1901.
xii p., 2 l., 512 p. fold. plan.   23½ᶜᵐ.

1. Municipal government—Germany. 2. Sanitation. 3. Hygiene, Public.
I. Title.
                                    2–23292 Revised
                JS5399.L7

NL 0378750   DLC NIC ICJ NBuU PSC ICJ MiU

Lindemann, Carl Hugo, 1867–
Die deutsche städteverwaltung; ihre aufgaben auf den gebieten der volkshygiene, des städtebaus und des wohnungswesens, von dr. H. Lindemann (C. Hugo)   2. verb. und verm. aufl. Stuttgart, J. H. W. Dietz nachf., 1906.
xii p., 2 l., 622 p.   24ᶜᵐ.

1. Municipal government—Germany. 2. Sanitation. 3. Hygiene, Public.
                                    11–28460 Revised
Library of Congress   JS5399.L7 1906

NL 0378751   DLC FU OClW ICJ MH NN

Lindemann, Carl Hugo, 1867–   ed. and tr.
Howell, George, 1833–1910.
Die englische gewerkvereins-bewegung. Nach G. Howell's "The conflicts of capital and labour" von C. Hugo [pseud.]   Stuttgart, J. H. W. Dietz, 1896.

                            Carl
*GC9   Lindemann, Hugo, 1867–
R4574   Erinnerung an Rainer Maria Rilke, geschrieben
LIn75   bei der Nachricht von seinem Tode.
v.17(1)   (In Das Inselschiff.   Leipzig, 1935.   23.5cm.,
        in case 25cm.   XVII.Jahrg.,1.Hft.,p.14–18)

            Ritzer K149.

NL 0378753   MH

Lindemann, Hugo i.e. Carl Hugo, 1867–
                                    joint author.
Stegmann, Carl.
Handbuch des socialismus. Von dr. jur. Carl Stegmann und dr. phil. C. Hugo [pseud.]   Zürich, Verlagsmagazin (J. Schabelitz) 1897.

Lindemann, Carl Hugo, 1867–   ed.

Handwörterbuch der kommunalwissenschaften, herausgegeben von Josef Brix ... dr. Hugo Lindemann ... dr. Otto Most ... dr. Hugo Preuss ... [und] dr. Albert Südekum ...   Jena, G. Fischer, 1918–24.

VOLUME 334

Lindemann,   Carl Hugo, 1867–
... . Kommunale Arbeiterpolitik. Von Hugo Lindemann.
Berlin, Buchhandlung Vorwärts, 1905.
61 p. 20½ᶜᵐ. (*In* Sozialdemokratische Gemeindepolitik, Heft 2.)

NL 0378756   ICJ

Lindemann, Carl Hugo, 1867–   ed.
Kommunales jahrbuch ... 1.–6. jahrg., 1908–1913/14; ₍7.
jahrg.₎ (kriegsband) 1919; neue folge, 1.– bd., 1927–
Jena, G. Fischer, 1908–

352.043
L6423
Lindemann, Carl Hugo, 1867–
Die neue gemeindeordnung; eine kritik, von
dr. H. Lindemann. Stuttgart, J. H. W. Dietz
nachf., 1903.
2 p. l., 80 p. 23½ᶜᵐ.
1. Municipal government - Germany.

NL 0378758   NNC

Lindemann, Carl Hugo, 1867–
Die religioesen kommunistischen Gemeinden in Nordamerika.
(In: K. Kautsky. Die Vorläufer des neueren Sozialismus. Stutt-
gart, 1895. Bd. 1, Theil 2, p. 863–890.)
Die Geschichte des Sozialismus in Einzeldarstellungen.

1. Communism U. S.,
N. Y. P. L.   June 19, 1912.

NL 0378759   NN PU MB

Lindemann, Carl Hugo, 1867.
**Der sozialismus in Frankreich im 17.
und 18. jahrhundert.**

NL 0378760   PU

Lindemann, Carl Hugo, 1867–
Sozialrechtliches jahrbuch. hrsg. von den direktoren des
Forschungsinstitutes für sozialwissenschaften der stadt
Köln : Theodor Brauer, Christian Eckert, Hugo Lindemann,
Leopold von Wiese ; redaktion : Theodor Brauer. Berichte,
materialien, untersuchungen zum werdenden sozialrecht,
vornehmlich über berufsorganisationswesen, industrie, pädagogik und lohngestaltung ... Mannheim ₍etc.₎ J. Bensheim-
er, 1930–

Lindemann, Hugo i. e. Carl Hugo, 1867–
joint author.
Stegmann, Carl.
... Справочная книга социалиста. Гуго ₍pseud.₎ и
Штегмана ... Пер. съ нѣмецкаго подъ ред. В. Я.
Вуточарскаго ₍pseud.₎ и Л. З. Марковича ... С.-Па-
тербургъ, Тип. "Общественная польза", 1906–

₍Lindemann, Carl Hugo₎ 1867–
Städteverwaltung und munizipal-sozialismus in England, von C. Hugo ₍pseud.₎ Stuttgart, J. H. W. Dietz,
1897.
xii, 300 p. 20ᵐᵐ.

1. Municipal government—Gt. Brit. 2. Municipal ownership—Gt. Brit.
3. London—Pol. & govt. I. Title.

Library of Congress   JS3118.L7
                                      6-34891 Revised

NL 0378763   DLC MB OO ICJ

JS
3118
.L5
Lindemann, Carl Hugo, 1867–
Städteverwaltung und Munizipal-Sozialismus
in England. 2. Aufl., mit einem neuen
Vorwort. Stuttgart, J. H. W. Dietz, 1906.
300 p. 20cm. (Internationale Bibliothek,
Bd. 27)

1. Municipal government - Gt. Brit.
2. Municipal ownership - Gt. Brit. 3. London - Pol. & govt. I. Title

NL 0378764   WU NN MH

Lindemann,   Carl Hugo, 1867–
... . Die städtische Regie. Von Dr. H. Lindemann. Berlin,
Buchhandlung Vorwärts, 1907.
64 p. 21ᶜᵐ. (*In* Sozialdemokratische Gemeindepolitik, Heft. 6.)

NL 0378765   ICJ NN

Lindemann,   Carl Hugo, 1867–
... . Steuern und Gebühren. Von Hugo Lindemann. Berlin,
Buchhandlung Vorwärts, 1906.
48 p. 20½ᶜᵐ. (*In* Sozialdemokratische Gemeindepolitik, Heft 5.)

NL 0378766   ICJ

Lindemann, Carl Hugo, 1867–
Ueber Begriff und Bedeutung der Kommunalwissenschaft;
Antrittsvorlesung an der Technischen Hochschule zu
Stuttgart. Nebst Führer durch die kommunalpolitische
Literatur. Berlin, Verlag: Buchhandlung Vorwärts
Singer, 1916
100 p. (Sozialdemokratische Gemeindepolitik; Kommu-
nalpolitische Abhandlungen, 18)

NL 0378767   MH

Lindemann, Carl Hugo, 1867–
Wohnungsstatistik. (Verein für Socialpolitik. Schriften.
Leipzig, 1901. 8°. ₍v.₎ 94, p. 261–384.)

1. Habitations.—Statistics, Germany.
N. Y. P. L.   April 4, 1913.

NL 0378768   NN

Lindemann,   Carl Hugo, 1867–
... . Zur Litteratur über die Wohnungsfrage. Von Dr. H.
Lindemann, ...
3 pts. (*In* Archiv für soziale Gesetzgebung und Statistik. Berlin, 1902–1907.
24½ᶜᵐ. 17. Band, p. ₍508₎–540, 19. Band, p. 694–725, 25. Band, p. 714–761.)

NL 0378769   ICJ

Lindemann, Charles, 1906–
... Contribution à l'étude de la "non-fréquen-
tation scolaire"; ses causes, ses remèdes...
Paris, 1930.
Thèse - Univ. de Paris.
"Bibliographie": 47–48 p.

NL 0378770   CtY

Lindemann, Christa.
Die feststellung der blutmässigen abstammung
bei ehelichen und unehelichen kindern. ...
Düsseldorf, 1937.   35 p.
Inaug. Diss. - Erlangen, 1937.
Verzeichnis der benutzten schriften.

NL 0378771   DLC

Lindemann, Christoph Friedrich Heinrich, d. 1816.
Geographische und statistische beschreibung der insel
Minorka. Bei einem langen aufenthalte daselbst aufgezeichnet, von C. F. H. Lindemann ... mit sieben kupfern
und einer landcharte. Leipzig, Weygandschen buchhandlung, 1786.
5 p. l., iv, 192 p. 7 pl. (1 fold.) fold. map, fold. table. 17ᶜᵐ.
Title vignette.

1. Minorca—Descr. & trav.

NL 0378772   MiU ICU

Lindemann, Christoph Friedrich Heinrich, d. 1816.
Versuch einer neuen liturgie vornehmlich in
rücksicht des nachmittagigen Gottesdienstes
für die jugend. Lüneburg, Herold und Wahl-
stab, 1808.
By F. H. Lindemann.

NL 0378773   MH

Lindemann, Curt.
...Gibt es ein eigenes Wirtschaftsstrafrecht? Von Dr. Curt
Lindemann. Jena: G. Fischer, 1932. iv, 94 p. 24½cm.
(Jena. Universität. Institut für Wirtschaftsrecht. Schriften.
Nr. 12.)
"Verzeichnis der benutzten Literatur," p. 91–94.

1. Legislation, Economic—Germany.   2. Criminal law—Germany. I. Ser.
N. Y. P. L.   November 3, 1933

NL 0378774   NN NNC

Lindemann, Curt, 1889–
Konjugierte punkte bei widerstandsaufgaben der
variationsrechnung... Breslau, H. Fleischmann,
1917.
3 p. l., 59 p., 1 l. diagrs. on 3 l. 22 cm.
(German mathematical dissertations. Breslau.
v. 9)
Inaug.-diss.—Breslau.
Lebenslauf.

NL 0378775   RPB CtY IU MH ICRL

Lindemann, E   H.
The practical guide and receipt book, for distillers,
wine-growers, druggists, manufacturers of wines, liquors,
cordials, etc. ... San Francisco, M. Weiss, book and job
printing, 1875.
1 p. l., ₍5₎–41, ₍1₎ p. illus. 13¼ᶜᵐ.

1. Liquors.

Library of Congress   TP612.L74   8-25453†

NL 0378776   DLC

RARE
PA
6568
.A4
1825
Lindemann, Eduard,
De Punicis Plautinis. Lipsiae,
G. Nauck, 1837.
48 p.
Bound with Plautus, T. M.
Aulularia. Coloniae ad Rhenum,
1825.
#Plautus, Titus Maccius.
Poenulus.
#Carthaginians.
(A)De Punicis Plautinis.

NL 0378777   MoU PU

Lindemann, Eduard, 1842–1917.
Helligkeitsmessungen der Bessel'schen Plejaden-
sterne. St.-Pétersbourg, Académie Imp. des
Sciences, 1884.
29 p. 33ᶜᵐ. (Mémoires de l'Académie Impériale des
Sciences de St.-Pétersbourg. 7. sér. t. 32, no.6)

1. Pleiades. 2. Stars—Radiation. 3. Bessel, Friedrich
William, 1784–1846. I. Ser.

NL 0378778   ViU CtY MdBP DNC

VOLUME 334

Z5156
.P98

Lindemann, Eduard, 1842–1897, comp.

Pulkovo. Glavnaía astronomicheskaía observatoriía.
Librorum in bibliotheca Speculae pulcovensis anno 1858
exeunte contentorum catalogus systematicus. Edendum
curavit et praefatus est Otto Struve ... Petropoli ₍typis
Academiae imperialis scientiarum petropolitanae; etc., etc.₎
1860–80.

———

Lindemann, ·Ed₍uard₎ 1842–1897.
Photometrische bestimmung der grössenclassen der
Bonner durchmusterung. Von Ed. Lindemann ... St.
Pétersbourg, Impr. de l'Académie impériale des sciences,
1889.

2 p. l., iii p., 1 l., 162 p. 35 x 26¼ᶜᵐ. (Supplément II aux Observations
de Poulkova)

1. Stars—Magnitudes.

Library of Congress   ₍28e1₎   6–17079†
QB4.P98

NL 0378780   DLC ICU NIC CU OU ICJ NjP

———

Lindemann, Eduard, 1842–1897.
Über den Lichtwechsel des Sterns V Cygni.
St. Petersbourg, 1884.
(16) p. 22cm.

St. Petersb., Acad. Sci. Melanges, 6, 1881–88,
p. 215–230.
St. Petersb., Acad. Sci. Bull., 29,   , p. 302–314.

NL 0378781   DN-Ob

———

Lindemann, Eduard, 1842–1897.
Über eine von Prof. Ceraski angedeutete persönliche
Gleichung bei Helligkeitsvergleichungen der
Sterne.
St. Petersbourg, 1890.
(6) p. 28cm.

St. Petersb., Acad. Sci. Melanges, 7,   , p. 83–88.

NL 0378782   DN-Ob

———

Lindemann, Eduard, 1842–1897.
Über helligkeitsbestimmungen v. fixsternen
... Zollnerschen photometer
Pulkowa, 1874

NL 0378783   NjP

———

Lindemann, Eduard, 1842–1917.
Verzeichniss von 42 neuen rothen Sternen.
St. Petersbourg, 1878
(10) p. 22cm.

St. Petersb., Acad. Sci. Melanges, 1874–81, p. 565–574.

NL 0378784   DN-Ob

———

Lindemann, Eduard, 1842–1917.
Zweites Verzeichniss neuer rother Sterne 1882.
St. Petersbourg, 1883.
(4) p. 22cm.

St. Petersb., Acad. Sci. Melanges, 6, 1881–88,
p. 103–106.

NL 0378785   DN-Ob

Lindemann, Eduard, 1842–1917.
Zur Beurtheilung der veränderlichkeit rother
Sterne. St.-Pétersbourg, Académie Imp. des
Sciences, 1882.
10 p. 33ᶜᵐ. (Mémoires de l'Académie Impériale des
Sciences de St.-Pétersbourg. 7. sér. t.30, no.4)

1. Stars, Variable.   I. Ser.

NL 0378786   ViU CtY DNC

———

Lindeman, Eduard Emanuilovich, 1825–1900.
3ᵉʳ Bericht über den Bestand meines Herbariums.
Moscou, 1885.
8°.

NL 0378787   CtY

———

Lindemann, Éduard Émanuilovich, 1825–1900.
Flora Chersonensis. Auctore Eduardo a Lindemann ...
Odessae, Тип. Б. Г. Ульриха (П. А. Зеленаго) 1881–82.
2 v. in 1. 24ᶜᵐ.

"Приложеніе къ VI т. Записокъ Новор. общ. естествоиспытателей."
"Index autorum in hoc opere citatorum" : vol. 1, p. ₍xliv₎–liv.

1. Botany—Russia—Kherson. ₍1. Kherson, Russia—Botany₎
I. Title.

Agr 14—522

U. S. Dept. of agr. Library   459.2L64
for Library of Congress   ₍a41b1₎

NL 0378788   DNAL MH-A MH PPAN ICJ

———

Emanuilovich, 1825–1900
LINDEMANN, Eduard
Florula Elisabethgradensis. Moscou 1867–72.

2 parts, 8vo., with Supplement. II.
From Bulletin de la Société impériale des
naturalistes de Moscou.

NL 0378789   MH

———

Lindemann, Eduard Emanuilovich, 1825–1900.
——— Index plantarum quas in variis Rossiae provinciis
hucusque invenit et observavit. [Moscou. 1860.] 8°.
Bulletin de la Société impériale des naturalistes de Moscou, 1860, xxxiii,
77–190.

NL 0378790   MH-A MH

———

Emanuilovich, 1825–1900.
Lindemann, Eduard ^ Nova revisio florae urskianae
[Cum " addenda." Moscou. 1865.] 8°.
Bulletin de la Société impériale des naturalistes de Moscou, 1865, xxxviii,
pt. 1, pp. 172–206, 600–601.

NL 0378791   MH-A MH

———

Emanuilovich, 1825–1900.
Lindemann, Eduard ^ Prodromus florarum Tschernigovianae, Mohilevianae, Minskianae nec non Grodnovianae.
From Bulletin de la Société impériale des naturalistes de Moscou, 1850,
xxiii, 445–547.

NL 0378792   MH-A

———

Lindemann, Eduard Emanuilovich, 1825–1900.
——— Supplementum. Mosquae. 1868. 8°. pp. 26.
Reprinted from Bulletin de la Société impériale des naturalistes de Moscou, 1868, xli, pt. 1, pp. 114–137.

NL 0378793   MH-A

Emanuilovich, 1825–1900.
LINDEMANN, Eduard
Uebersicht der bisher in Bessarabien aufgef.
Spermatophyten. [Moskau.] O. Weigel, Kat.107.
[1880.]

Zusatz, [Moskau, 1881.]

NL 0378794   MH

———

₍**Lindemann, Else (Arnheim)**₎ 1895–
... Hand am pflug, roman. Leipzig, H. Eichblatt ₍1942₎
225, ₍1₎ p. 18¼ cm.
Author's pseud., Else Jung, at head of title.

I. Title.

PT2623.I 5714H3   47–41676

NL 0378795   DLC CtY CU IU

———

₍**Lindemann, Else (Arnheim)**₎ 1895–
Die Jensensippe, aus dem Tagebuch einer Mutter ₍von₎ Else
Jung ₍pseud.₎ Leipzig, H. Eichblatt ₍1943, *1942₎
227 p. 19 cm.

I. Title.

PT2623.I 5714J4   A F 47–7026*
California. Univ. Libr.
for Library of Congress   ₍1₎†

NL 0378796   CU CtY DLC

———

Lindemann, Else (Arnheim) 1895–
... Jungfer Barbara; erzählung eingeleitet und herausgegeben
von professor dr. Karl Plenzat. Leipzig, H. Eichblatt
₍1942₎
72 p. 18¼ᶜᵐ. ₍Eichblatts deutsche heimatbücher, hrsg. von professor
dr. Karl Plenzat, 154/155₎
Author's pseud., Else Jung, at head of title.

I. *Plenzat, Karl, 1882–   ed. II. Title.

PT2623.I 5714J8   833.91   A F 47–2056
Yale univ. Library
for Library of Congress

NL 0378797   CtY DLC CU

———

Lindemann, Else (Arnheim) 1895–
Minchen und Jaromir. Bilder von Else Wenz-Vietor. Zwei
märchen von tieren in versen von Else Jung-Lindemann
₍pseud.₎ München, Braun & Schneider, *1936.
23 p. col. illus. 25 cm.

CONTENTS.—Das bienchen Minchen.—Der schlangentöter Jaromir.

I. Wenz-Viétor, Else, illus. II. Title.

PZ34.3.L5   831.91   37–37445 rev

NL 0378798   DLC

———

Lindemann (Emily). *Ueber den Abfall der
Nabelschnur, mit besonderer Berücksichtigung
der anatomischen Verhältnisse derselben. 31
pp. 12°. Berlin, H. S. Hermann, [1880].

NL 0378799   DNLM

———

Lindemann, Emil, 1857–
Das deutsche Helgoland, von dr. E. Lindemann ... Mit
112 abbildungen. Berlin-Charlottenburg, Vita, deutsches
verlagshaus ₍*1913₎
2 p. l., ₍ix₎–xv, 271 p. incl. illus., plates, ports., maps, diagrs. front., plates
(part col.) fold. maps. 25½ᶜᵐ. M. 7
A revision of Die nordseeinsel Helgoland in topographischer, geschichtlicher,
sanitärer beziehung ... 1889.
"Literatur": p. 259–265. "Karten von Helgoland": p. 265–267.

1. Helgoland.

Library of Congress   DD491.H4L7   ₍a₎–24858

NL 0378800   DLC NN

VOLUME 334

Lindemann, Emil, 1857–
—— Neuere Behandlungsmethoden des chronischen Gelenkrheumatismus. 21 pp. 8°. Berlin, 1901.
Forms 151 Hft. of: Berl. Klinik.

NL 0378801   DNLM

Lindemann, Emil, 1857–
Die Nordseeinsel Helgoland in topographischer, geschichtlicher, sanitärer Beziehung, von Dr. Emil Lindemann.... Berlin: A. Hirschwald, 1889. 116 p. charts, front. 23cm.

"Literatur," p. [91]–95.

176646B. 1. Helgoland.
N.Y.P.L.   October 26, 1942

NL 0378802   NN MH DNLM CU

Lindemann, Emil, 1857–
Die Nordseeinsel Helgoland in topographischer, geschichtlicher, sanitärer Beziehung, von Dr. Emil Lindemann, ... Mit 2 lithographirten Tafeln, 4 Karten, 9 Tabellen. Zweite vermehrte Auflage. Berlin, A. Hirschwald, 1890.
[8], 147, [2] p. incl. tables. 11 pl., 4 maps (1 fold., incl. front.) 23cm.
"Kurzer Auszug aus der alten Bolzendahl'schen Chronik," p. [117]–139.
"Literatur," p. [91]–95.

NL 0378803   ICJ MH ICN

Lindemann, Emil, 1857–
Das öffentliche Gesundheitswesen Helgolands. Von Dr. Lindemann. Berlin: R. Schoetz, 1913. 57 p., 3 pl. 8°. (Prussia. Medizinalabteilung des Ministeriums des Innern Veröffentlichungen aus dem Gebiete der Medizinalverwaltung. Bd. 2, Heft 4.)

1. Hygiene (Public), Germany: Helgoland. 2. Series.
N.Y.P.L.   April 2, 1919.

NL 0378804   NN

Lindemann, Emil, 1857–
—— Das Seeklima, die Eigenschaften und physiologischen Wirkungen desselben durch eigene Beobachtungen erläntert. 32 pp. 8°. Leipzig, B. Konegen, 1893.

NL 0378805   DNLM

Lindemann, Emil, 1857–
—— Seeklima und Seebad, eine wissenschaftliche Abhandlung, nebst einer Zusammenstellung der gesammten Seebadeliteratur. 3 p. l., 76 pp. roy. 8°. Berlin, H. Brieger, 1894.

NL 0378806   DNLM

Lindemann, Emil, 1857–
Zur pathogenese des icterus neonatorum. Halle, S. Plötz, 1883.
37 p., 1 l. 8°.
Inaug. - diss.-Halle.

NL 0378807   ICRL

Lindemann, Erich, 1888– Studien zur Biologie der Teichgewässer. Berlin: Borntraeger 1915. 87 S., 1 Kt. 4°(8°) ¶Aus: Zeitschrift f. Fischerei u. deren Hilfswissensch. Breslau, Phil. Diss. v. 28. Aug. 1915, Ref. Pax
[Geb. 8. Mai 88 Güstrow; Wohnort: Breslau; Staatsangeh.: Mecklenburg-Schwerin u. Preußen; Vorbildung: RG. Güstrow Reife 07; Studium: München 2, Berlin 2, Rostock 5 S.; Rig. 29. Juli 14.]   [U 15. 1558]

NL 0378808   ICRL MH NcD PU

Lindemann, Erich, 1894– Arzt: Hypertrophische Lebercirrhosen im Kindes- und Säuglingsalter. Aus d. 2. inn. Abt. d. Augusta-Victoria-Krankenh. Berlin-Schöneberg. ⟨Dir.: Glaser.⟩ [In Maschinenschrift.] 53, 8 S. 4°(2°). — Auszug: Berlin (1920): Ebering. 2 Bl. 8°
Berlin, Med. Diss. v. 22. Nov. 1920, Ref. His
[Geb. 4. Okt. 94 Eberswalde; Wohnort: Eberswalde; Staatsangeh.: Preußen; Vorbildung: Friedrichs-G. Berlin Reife 14; Studium: Berlin 9. Königsberg 2, Berlin 1 S.; Coll. 22. Nov. 14; Approb. 1. Okt. 20.]   [U 20. 1359]

NL 0378809   ICRL

Lindemann, Erich, 1904–
Ueber bis-ortho-nitrobenzoylcyanid und die umwandlung von optische aktiver o-nitromandelsaeure in optische aktives dioxindol.
Inaug. diss. Berlin, 1927.

NL 0378810   ICRL CtY

Lindemann, Erich, 1913–
Das problem des deutschordensburgtypus. ...
Berlin, Triltsch & Huther, 1938.
22.5 cm.
Inaug. Diss. - Berlin, 1938.
Lebenslauf.
Literatur.

NL 0378811   ICRL CtY MH

Lindemann, Ernst: Die rechtliche Natur der Liegenschafts-Zwangsversteigerung. Bochum 1914: Stumpf. VIII, 62 S. 8°
Erlangen, Jur. Diss. v. 9. März 1914, Ref. Oertmann
[Geb. 12. Mai 85 Gelsenkirchen; Wohnort: Berlin; Staatsangeh.: Preußen; Vorbildung: G. Gelsenkirchen Reife 05; Studium: Marburg 1, Freiburg 1, Leipzig 1, Münster 3 S.; Rig. 22. Dez. 13.]   [U 14. 350]

NL 0378812   ICRL NIC

Lindemann, Ernst August 1880–
Ueber extragenitale ulcera mollia. Berlin, G. Schade, 1908.
28 p., 2 l. 8°.
Inaug. - Diss.- Berlin.
Bibl.

NL 0378813   ICRL DNLM

Lindemann, F
Das Gemeindeschulwesen der Deutschen Evangelisch-Lutherischen Synode von Missouri, Ohio u. a. St. auf der Weltausstellung in St. Louis, ... 1904
see under   Lutheran Church--Missouri Synod. Committee on School-Exhibition.

Lindemann, F.
How to teach elementary geography. A short series of papers, comp. for the use of teachers in our parochial schools. By Prof. F. Lindemann ... St. Louis, Mo., Concordia publishing house, 1895.
50 p. 18¼ᵐᵐ.
"Aids and apparatus": p. 46–50.

1. Geography—Teaching—Elementary schools.
                                             E 11–57
Library, U. S. Bur. of   Education LB1583.L64

NL 0378815   DHEW

HX8015
.L55   Lindemann, F
1901   Was sagen die Worte? Worterklärung des Lutherschen Katechismustextes. St. Louis, Mo., Concordia Pub. House, 1901.
v, 44 p. 19cm.

1. Lutheran Church—Catechisms and creeds—Study and teaching. I. Title.

NL 0378816   ViU

Lindemann, F   L   von.
Meine Gefangenschaft im Russland in den Jahren 1812 und 1813; ein Blick in Russlands Grösse und Herrlichkeit. 2.Aufl. Gera, F.Schumann, 1835.

NL 0378817   MH

R
5   LINDEMANN, FELIX.
.506   Die Bestrebungen zur Erhaltung der Boden-Fruchtbarkeit von ihren ersten Anfängen bis zur landwirtschaftlichen Hochkultur der Römer. Scheibenberg, K.A.Richter,1900.
161p. 22cm.

"Benutzte Literatur": p.[14]–16.

NL 0378818   ICN

374
L64b   Lindemann, Feodor, 1867–
Beiträge zur geschmacksbildung; ein buch zur besinnung und belehrung.
Leipzig, 1917.
126p. illus. (Ordentliche veröffentlichung der pädagogischen literaturgesellschaft: Neue bahnen)

NL 0378819   IU

Lindemann, Feodor, 1867–   joint author.
TT180
.W4
t.2–3   Beulig, Paul.
... Holzarbeit in der volksschule ... bearbeitet von P. Beulig und F. Lindemann. Leipzig, Quelle & Meyer, 1928–29.

Lindemann, Feodor, 1867–   ed.
QA11
.L4
Lebensvoller Unterricht.
Leipzig, Durr, 19

Lindemann, Feodor, 1867–   joint ed.
Mit modellierholz, schere und kreide
see under   Löffler, A   ed.

371.3   Lindemann, Feodor, 1867– ed.
L64ln   Neue bahnen der volksschularbeit; pädagogischer wegweiser hrsg. in verbindung mit Johannes Springer, Abert Böltger ... [u.a.] im auftrag der pädagogischen literaturgesellschaft "Neue bahnen" von F. Lindemann und R. Schulze ... Leipzig, 1923.
3v. in 1. illus.

Bibliographies interspersed.

NL 0378823   IU

VOLUME 334

Lindemann, Feodor, 1867–   ed.

TT180
.W4
Werkunterricht in der volksschule, lehrgang und stoffsammlung für papp- und holzarbeit, herausgegeben von P. Beulig, P. Grünert, F. Lindemann. teil 1–3. Leipzig, Quelle & Meyer, 1928–29.

Lindemann, Ferd. P., 1877–
see Lindeman, Ferd. P., 1877–

Lindemann, Ferdinand, 1852–1939.
... Die biegungsflächen einer gegebenen fläche, von F. Lindemann. Vorgetragen am 5. februar 1921. München, Verlag der Bayerischen akademie der wissenschaften, 1921.

42 p. 28ᶜᵐ. (Abhandlungen der Bayerischen akademie der wissenschaften. Mathematisch-physikalische klasse. XXIX. bd., 3. abh.)

1. Geometry, Differential.
[Full name: Karl Louis Ferdinand Lindemann]

Title from Princeton   Univ.   A C 33–2742
Library of Congress   [AS182.M817]

NL   0378826   NjP NIC OU OCU NN

Lindemann, Ferdinand, 1852–
Gedächtnissrede auf Philipp Ludwig von Seidel, gehalten in der öffentlichen sitzung der K. B. Akademie der wissenschaften zu München am 27. märz, 1897 von Ferdinand Lindemann ... München, K. B. Akademie, 1898.

84 p. 28ᶜᵐ.

1. Seidel, Philipp Ludwig von, 1821–1896.
[Full name: Karl Louis Ferdinand Lindemann]
15–25790 Revised
Library of Congress   Q143.S45L5

OC1W MB MdBP
NL   0378827   DLC CtY NjP DSI ICRL DNC PPAN OU

Lindemann, Ferdinand, 1852–1939.
Lehren und lernen in der mathematik. Rede beim antritt des rektorats der Ludwig-Maximilians. Universität gehalten am 26. november 1904 von dr. Ferdinand Lindemann. München, C. Wofl & sohn, 1904.

32 p.   27 cm.
1. Mathematics – Study and teaching.

NL   0378828   CU MH NN

Lindemann, Ferdinand, 1852–
... Das problem der verbiegung von flächen, von F. Lindemann. München, Verlag der Bayerischen akademie der wissenschaften, 1932.

27 p. 29½ᶜᵐ. (Abhandlungen der Bayerischen akademie der wissenschaften. Mathematisch-naturwissenschaftliche abt. n. f., hft. 13. 1932)

1. Surfaces, Deformation of.
[Full name: Karl Louis Ferdinand Lindemann]

Title from Princeton   Univ.   A C 32–277
Library of Congress   [AS182.M817 n.f., hft. 13]
[2]

NL   0378829   NjP PPAmP PU MB OU OCU

517.32 Lindemann, Ferdinand, 1852–1939.
L64t   Theorie der bestimten integrale und der analytischen darstellung willkürlicher functionen bei prof. Lindemann. München. Wintersemester 1894/95.   [München? 1894?]
216p.

Manuscript notes by Mr. Landau 1894/95.

NL   0378830   IU

QA244 Lindemann, Ferdinand, 1852–
.L74   Über den sogenannten letzten Fermat'schen satz, von Ferdinand Lindemann ... Leipzig, Veit & comp., 1909.
iv, [1], 82 p. 23ᶜᵐ.

1. Fermat's theorem. 2. Numbers, Theory of.

NL   0378831   ICU NNU TxU TU PU IU

AS
182   Lindemann, Ferdinand, 1852–
M9615+   Ueber die Bewegung der Elektronen, von
v.23   F. Lindemann.
no.4–5   (In Akademie der Wissenschaften, Munich. Mathematisch-physikalische Klasse. Abhandlungen. Munich. 28cm. 23. Bd. (1906–09) p. [233]–375. illus.)

Contents.––1. T. Die translatorische Bewegung.––2. T. Stationäre Bewegung.

NL   0378832   NIC NN

Lindemann, Ferdinand, 1852–1939.
... Über die bewegung von massenpunkten, die dem Newton'schen anziehungsgesetze unterworfen sind (problem der n körper), von F. Lindemann. München, Verlag der Bayerischen akademie der wissenschaften, 1935.

31, [1] p. 29½ᶜᵐ. (Abhandlungen der Bayerischen akademie der wissenschaften. Mathematisch-naturwissenschaftliche abt. n. f., hft. 28. 1935)

1. Potential, Theory of.
[Full name: Karl Louis Ferdinand Lindemann]
A C 35–1670
Title from Princeton   Univ.
Library of Congress   [AS182.M817]

NL   0378833   NjP DN-Ob PU PPAmP MiU OCU OU

Lindemann, Ferdinand i. e. Karl Louis Ferdinand, 1852–
Über unendlich kleine bewegungen und über kraftsysteme bei allgemeiner projectivischer massbestimmung ... Leipzig, Druck von B. G. Teubner, 1873.

90 p., 1 l.   24ᶜᵐ.
Inaug.-dis.—Erlangen.
"Besonderer abdruck aus dem VII bande der Mathematischen annalen."

1. Screws, Theory of.

Library of Congress   QA841.L74   5–18206†

NL   0378834   DLC

Lindemann, Ferdinand, 1852–1939.
Untersuchungen über den Fermatschen satz, von Ferdinand Lindemann.   München, Im selbstverlage des verfassers, 1928.
32 p.   tables.   23 cm.
1. Fermat's theorem.

NL   0378835   CU OU

Lindemann, Ferdinand i. e. Karl Louis Ferdinand, 1852–
Untersuchungen über den Riemann-Roch'schen satz ... Leipzig, Druck von B. G. Teubner, 1879.
1 p. l., 40 p. 23ᶜᵐ.
Akademische antrittsschrift—Freiburg.

1. Functions, Abelian.

Library of Congress   QA345.L74   5–31339†

NL   0378836   DLC

Lindemann, Ferdinand, 1852–
... Eine verallgemeinerung des umkehr- und des teilungsproblems der Abel'schen integrale nebst geometrischen anwendungen, von F. Lindemann. München, Verlag der Bayerischen akademie der wissenschaften, 1933.

45, [1] p. 29½ᶜᵐ. (Abhandlungen der Bayerischen akademie der wissenschaften. Mathematisch-naturwissenschaftliche abt. n. f., hft. 19, 1933)

1. Functions, Abelian. 2. Functions, Theta.
[Full name: Karl Louis Ferdinand Lindemann]

Title from Princeton   Univ.   A C 34–170
Library of Congress   [AS182.M817]

NL   0378837   NjP DNC PU OU OCU MB

Lindemann, Ferdinand, 1852–   ed.

FOR OTHER EDITIONS
SEE MAIN ENTRY
Clebsch, Alfred, 1833–1872.
Vorlesungen über geometrie mit besonderer benutzung der vorträge von Alfred Clebsch, bearb. und hrsg. von dr. Ferdinand Lindemann ... 2., verm. aufl. Leipzig, B. G. Teubner, 1906–

*Lindemann, Ferdinand, 1852–   tr.

Picard, Émile, 1856–
... Das wissen der gegenwart in mathematik und naturwissenschaft; autorisierte deutsche ausgabe, mit erläuternden anmerkungen, von F. und L. Lindemann. Leipzig und Berlin, B. G. Teubner, 1913.

*Lindemann, Ferdinand, 1852– tr.

Poincaré, Henri, 1854–1912.
... Wissenschaft und hypothese. Autorisierte deutsche ausgabe mit erläuternden anmerkungen von F. und L. Lindemann. 3. verb. aufl. Leipzig, B. G. Teubner, 1914.

Q175   Lindemann, Ferdinand, 1852–1939, tr.
.P76
1914   Poincaré, Henri, 1854–1912.
... Wissenschaft und methode; autorisierte deutsche ausg. mit erläuternden anmerkungen, von F. und L. Lindemann. Leipzig und Berlin, B. G. Teubner, 1914.

LINDEMANN, Ferdinand, 1852–
Zur geschichte der polyeder und der zahlzeichen. n.p., [1897].

Without title-page. Caption title.
"Sitzung der math.-phys.classe vom 5. dezember 1896," pp.625–758.

NL   0378842   MH

517.85
L743z Lindemann, Ferdinand, 1852–1939.
Zur Theorie der automorphen Funktionen. München, Druck der Akademischen Buchdruckerei, 1900–01
2pts. in 1v.

Cover title.
"Aus den Sitzungsberichten der mathematisch-physikalischen Classe der...Akad. d. Wiss. Bd. XXIX, 1899, Heft III" [und; Band XXX, 1900, Heft III.

1. Functions,   Automorphic.

NL   0378843   ICarbS

VOLUME 334

LINDEMANN, Ferdinand, 1852-1939.
Zur theorie der spectrallinien. München,
1902.

NL 0378844　　MH-C

WG
18185
Lindemann, Frederick, 1886-
Über das Dulong-Petitsche Gesetz. [Berlin]
1911.
54 p. illus.

Inaug.-Diss. - Berlin.

NL 0378845　　CtY PU

Lindemann, Frederick Alexander, *viscount Cherwell*
see
Cherwell, Frederick Alexander Lindemann, *viscount*, 1886-
1957.

Lindemann, Frederick Herman, 1891-
The cross and the garden, by Fred H. Lindemann.　New
York, Chicago, E. Kaufmann, inc. [1941]
114, [13] p.　20½ᵐ.

Thirteen blank pages at end for "Notes".
"A series on the seven words from the cross": p. 57-114.

1. Lenten sermons. 2. Jesus Christ—Seven last words.　3. Lutheran
church—Sermons. 4. Sermons, American.　I. Title.
[Full name: Frederick Herman Otto Lindemann]
41-2742
Library of Congress　　BV85.L48
——— Copy 2.
Copyright　　252.6

NL 0378847　　DLC

Lindemann, Frederick Herman, 1891-
In remembrance of Me; twelve communion addresses, by
Fred H. Lindemann.　New York, The Lutheran press [1937]
xiii p., 2 l., 3-123 p.　20ᵐ.

1. Communion sermons. 2. Lutheran church—Sermons.　3. Sermons,
American.　I. Title.
[Full name: Frederick Herman Otto Lindemann]
38-1721
Library of Congress　　BX8073.L5
——— Copy 2.
Copyright A 113063　　265.3

NL 0378848　　DLC IU

Lindemann, Frederick Herman, 1891-
Thy King cometh, sermons preparing for the Lord's Supper.　New York, E. Kaufmann [1948]
144 p. 21 cm.

1. Lord's Supper—Sermons. 2. Lutheran Church—Sermons.　3. Sermons, American.　I. Title.
Full name: Frederick Herman Otto Lindemann.

BX8073.L517　　265.3　　49-15818*

NL 0378849　　DLC

Lindemann, Frederick Herman, 1891-
Till He come, a study of the Lord's Supper.　New York,
E. Kaufmann [1948]
124 p. 21 cm.

1. Lord's Supper—Lutheran Church. 2. Lord's Supper—Hist.
I. Title.
Full name: Frederick Herman Otto Lindemann.

BX8073.L518　　265.3　　49-15819*

NL 0378850　　DLC

Lindemann, Frido, 1880-
Die operntexte Philippe Quinaults vom literarischen standpunkte aus betrachtet ... von Frido Lindemann ...　Leipzig,
1904.
4 p. l., 139, [1] p.　22½ᵐ.

Inaug.-diss.—Leipzig.
Bibliography: verso of 2d prelim. leaf.
Vita.

1. Quinault, Philippe, 1635-1688.
[Full name: Hermann Heinrich Wilhelm Frido Lindemann]
10-21734 Revised
Library of Congress　　ML1727.2.Q16L4

NL 0378851　　DLC NcU PU ICRL CtY CU

PT
2623
.I54
W57
Lindemann, Frido, 1880-
Wir wandeln; Gedichte.　Leipzig, Seele
[1906]
113p. 19cm.

NL 0378852　　TNJ InU

LINDEMANN, Friedrich,　　*7
Geschichte der Ev.-luth. Zions-Gemeinde, zu Boston, Mass.
West Roxbury, 1889. 19 pp. Illus. Portrs. 8°.

NL 0378853　　MB

Lindemann, Friedrich, 1792-1845.
Brevis expositio de tribus summorum tragi-
corum poetarum fabulis earumque comparationis.
Pars prior.　[n.p.] 1851.
Full name: Johann Friedrich Lindemann.

NL 0378854　　NjP

Lindemann, Friedrich, 1792-1854, *ed.*
Corpus grammaticorum latinorum veterum collegit, auxit,
recensuit ac potiorem lectionis varietatem adiecit Fridericus
Lindemannus sociorum opera adiutus ...　Lipsiae, sumptibus
B. G. Teubneri et F. Claudii, 1831-40.
4 v. in 3.　2 pl., 2 tab., diagrs.　27½ x 23½ᵐ.
Of v. 4 only fasc. 1 has been published.
CONTENTS.—tom. I. Donatum, Probum, Eutychium, Arusianum Mes-
sium, Maximum Victorinum, Asperum, Phocam continens. 1831.—tom.
II. Pauli Diaconi excerpta et Sex. Pompeii Festi fragmenta continens.
1832.—tom. III. Isidori Hispalensis episcopi Etymologiarum libros xx.
continens. 1833. Accedunt tabulae tres lapidi inscriptae.—tom. IV.
Flavium Sosipatrum Charisium et Diomedem continens. fasc. I. Chari-
sius.

1. Latin language—　　Grammar—Early to 1500.
Library of Congress　　PA6139.G7 [1831]　　7-27473

PU MiU OCU OO ViU MiD NjP
NL 0378855　　DLC CaBVaU MdBP NIC NNG PPT NcD MsU

Lindemann, Friedrich, 1792-1854.
... De Horatii epistola ad Pisones quae inscribitur de arte poetica.　Zittaviae, ex off. Seyferti, 1840.
1 p.l., 25 p.　26 cm.
Program - Gymnasium, Zittavia (Schulnachrichten)
With this is his De Horatii epistola ad Pisones
dissertatio altera, from the Novorum munerum
auspicia in Gymnasio Zittaviensi ...　Zittaviae
[1840] 1 p.l., 17 p.　facsim.　26 cm.

NL 0378856　　CU

Bonaparte
Collection　LINDEMANN, FRIEDRICH, 1792-1854.
No.2650　　De latinae linguae accentibus; libellum primum
in publico proposuit simulque solennes ludos lite-
rarios Schroederianos anniversaria memoria cele-
brandos indixit Fridericus Lindemann.　Lipsiae,
C.Tauchnitz,1816.
38p.　21½cm.

NL 0378857　　ICN NN

LINDEMANN, Friedrich, 1792-1854.
Emendationes ad Rhesum atque eiusdem fabulae
interpretatio Teutonica. [Progr.]　Zittaviae,
ex officina Seyferti, [1834.]
pp. (2), 50.

NL 0378858　　MH

[Lindemann, Friedrich] 1792-1854, ed.
Fragmentum excerptorum de adverbio ex
codice Lugdunensi descriptum.　[Zittaviae, ex
officina Seyferti, 1822]
27 p.　25 cm.　(Ineditorum Latinorum, pt.
1)
Caption title.
1. Latin language - Syntax.　I. Title.

NL 0378859　　MdBP

Lindemann, Friedrich, 1792-1854, ed.
Gradus ad Parnassum; sive thesaurus Latinae...
see under　Conrad, Julius.

Lindemann, Friedrich, 1792-1845.
Lectionum Ciceronianarum specimen I.　n.p.,
1830.

NL 0378861　　NjP

Lindemann, Friedrich, 1792-1854.
Memoriam Keimanni in Gymnasio Zittaviensi
A.D. XXIII, novembris pie concelebrandeam
indicit Fridericus Lindemann, dir.　Zittaviae,
typis Seyfertianis [1825]
6 p.　22 cm.
Caption title: De hiatu in versibus Horatii
lyricis.

NL 0378862　　CU

PA2333　Lindemann, Friedrich, 1792-1854.
.L7　　Novus thesaurus latinae linguae prosodiacus; sive, Gradus
ad Parnassum instauratus ad optimas editiones emendatus
utramque et veterem et recentiorem prosodiam complectens
singulis vocabulis accentus repraesentans curante Friderico
Lindemann ...　Zittaviae et Lipsiae, impensis J. D. Schöpsii;
[etc., etc.] 1827-28.
2 v.　20ᵐ.

1. Latin language—Metrics and rhythmics—Dictionaries.

NL 0378863　　ICU

PA27　LINDEMANN,FRIEDRICH,1792-1854.
.L74　　Friderici Lindemanni Orationes selectae.　Lipsiae,
apud C.H.F.Hartmannum,1831.
[8],275,[2]p.　21½cm.

1.Classical philology--Collected works.

NL 0378864　　PU ICU

Lindemann, Friedrich, 1792-1854.
Pauca de usu aquae frigidae in re medica apud
veteres.　Zittaviae [1838]

NL 0378865　　NjP

VOLUME 334

LINDEMANN, Friedrich, 1792-1854.
Scena Plautina ex Curculione emenata. [Progr.
(ZITTAU - 1845,)

4°, pp. 1-10.   Lip 26.815.

NL 0378866   MH

PA6121   LINDEMANN, FRIEDRICH, 1792-1854, ed.
.A7L7   Selecta e poetis latinis carmina ad initiandos
poesi romana tironum animos collegit, recensuit, praefatus est Fridericus Lindemann... Lipsiae, sumtibus
I.C.Hinrichsii, 1823.
2 v. in 1. 20½cm.

1. Latin poetry--Collections.

NL 0378867   ICU

Lindemann, Friedrich, 1792-1854, ed.
Vitae duumvirorum Tiberi Hemster shusii...
see under   Ruhnkenius, David, 1723-1798.

Lindemann, Friedrich, 188)-
Der schrankfachvertrag.
Inaug. Diss. Leipzig, 1908
Bibl.

NL 0378869   ICRL

PT2623
.I572F4 Lindemann, Friedrich, 1898-
1934   Feldwebel zoff...
Berlin, c1934
1 pam.   12°
Mimeographed

NL 0378870   DLC

833.9
L743h Lindemann, Friedrich, 1898-
Herbstschuld; Novelle. Bremen, C. Schünemann [1924]
47p. 17cm.   [Die Garbe]

NL 0378871   IEN

PT2623
.I572I6 Lindemann, Friedrich, 1898-
1935   In luv und lee die liebe...
Berlin, c 1935
1v.   12°
Mimeographed

NL 0378872   DLC

Lindemann, Friedrich, 1898-   Die kluge
ML50   Wirtin.
.H6596K5
1942   Hinrichs, Hajo.
(Die kluge Wirtin. Libretto. German)

Die kluge Wirtin; ein heiteres Opernspiel. Worte von
Friedrich Lindemann. Berlin, A. Bennefeld, °1942.

Lindemann, Friedrich, 1898-
König im moor, roman von Friedrich Lindemann. Berlin,
Ullstein (°1936)
246, (1) p. 1 l. 19½ᵐ.

I. Title.   36-18848
Library of Congress   PT2623.I 5716K6 1936
Copyright A—Foreign   32070
(2)   833.91

NL 0378874   DLC PPG

PT2623
.I572K7 Lindemann, Friedrich, 1898-
1936   Kreuzerbesuch...
Berlin, c 1936
1v.   12°

NL 0378875   DLC

Lindemann, Friedrich, 1898-
Koninklijk koopman. Vertaald door Jef de Leau en G.
Klaass. Den Haag, Uitgeverij Boot (194-)
308 p. illus., col. plate. 22 cm.
Translation of Sohn seiner Firma.

I. Title.
PT2623.I 5716S63   48-43407*‡

NL 0378876   DLC

Lindemann, Friedrich, 1898-
... Koninklijk koopman. 2. druk. 's-Gravenhage, Uitgeverij
Boot (1944)
308, (1) p. illus. 21ᵐ.
"Nederlandsche vertaling door Jef de Leau en G. Klaass van Sohn
seiner firma."

I. Leau, Jef de, tr. II. Title.
PT2623.I 5716S63   A F 47-3485
Yale univ. Library
for Library of Congress

NL 0378877   CtY DLC

Lindemann, Friedrich, 1898-
Lichter der heimat...
Das volksbuch von Iolanthe; mit vielen zeichnungen von
Horst von Möllendorff. Berlin, Drei masken verlag, a. g.
(°1935)

NL 0378878 (?)

Lindemann, Friedrich, 1898-
Ein Mann ging von Bord. [cop. 1930.]

NL 0378879   NN OC1

Lindemann, Friedrich, 1898-
De nobiskroog; geschichten vun Friedrich
Lindemann. Bremen, C. Schünemann [1923]
55 p.   18 cm.
Contents.-De nobiskroog.-Dodendanz.-De hexe
un de dood.

NL 0378880   CU MH

Lindemann, Friedrich, 1898-
Sohn seiner Firma. [3.Aufl. Braunschweig] Vieweg
[c.1939]

NL 0378881   MH

Lindemann, Friedrich, 1898-
Das Problem der Verbiegung von Flächen.
Von F. Lindemann
see under   Lindemann, Ferdinand, 1852-
1939.

Lindemann, Friedrich, 1898-
Sohn seiner Firma; Roman eines hanseatischen Kaufmanns.
Bremen, Döll [1954]

NL 0378883   MH CtY

Lindemann, Friedrich, 1898-
Der streit um die 'Betty Bonn', roman eines geheimnisvollen
schiffes von Friedrich Lindemann. Berlin, Ullstein (°1935)
240, (1) p. 20½ᵐ.

I. Title. II. Title: Die 'Betty Bonn'.
Library of Congress   PT2623.I 5716S7 1935   36-269
Copyright A—Foreign   29125
                                             833.91

NL 0378884   DLC NN

Lindemann, Friedrich, 1898-   tr.

Chesterton, Gilbert Keith, 1874-
Ein streitgespräch zwischen George Bernard Shaw und G.
K. Chesterton, unter vorsitz von Hilaire Belloc, vorwort zur
deutschen ausgabe von Rudolf Kayser. Bremen, C. Schünemann, 1930.

Lindemann, Friedrich Heinrich
see   Lindemann, Christoph Friedrich
Heinrich, d. 1816.

Lindemann, Friedrich Wilhelm, 1900-
... Dauerresultate nach Herznaht bei Schuss-
und Stichverletzungen ... Wuppertal-Elberfeld,
1931.
Inaug.-Diss. - Kiel.
Lebenslauf.
"Literaturverzeichnis": 14-15 p.

NL 0378887   CtY

DS
710   Lindemann, Fritz.
.L74   Im Dienste Chinas; mein Anteil an seinem
Aufbau. Erinnerungen aus den Jahren 1929-
1940. Peking, Im Selbstverlage des Verfassers, 1940.
630 p.   illus.

1.China--Descr.& trav. 2.China--Soc.
condit. 3.Soldiers--Germany--Correspondence,
reminiscences, etc. I.Title.

NL 0378888   MiU FTaSU MH WU

Lindemann, Fritz.
... Versuche über die morphium-urethannarcose ...
Berlin, Druck von L. Schumacher, 1910.
22 p. 25ᵐ.
Inaug.-diss.—Bern.
"Literatur": p. 20-22.
"Sonder-abdruck aus der Zeitschrift f. exp. pathologie u. therapie. 7.
bd."

1. Morphine. 2. Urethane.
                                             Agr 11-617
Library, U.S. Dept. of   Agriculture 396L64

NL 0378889   DNAL DNLM

VOLUME 334

W 4
M96
1951
LINDEMANN, Fritz, 1923-
Todesursachen nach Kropfoperationen.
₍München₎ 1951.
51 ℓ.
Inaug.-Diss. - Munich.
1. Thyroid gland - Surgery

NL 0378890   DNLM

Lindemann, G
Illustrierter Führer durch Lüneburg und seine
Umgebung, mit einem Plan der Stadt. Text von
G.Lindemann. 2.durchgesehene Aufl. Lüneburg,
Herausgegeben vom Reichsbund deutscher Papier-
und Schreibwarenhändler Ortsgruppe [19-]

48 p. illus., plan. 15.5 cm.

NL 0378891   MH

Lindemann, Gabriele: Zur Prognose und Therapie des fieber-
haften Aborts. Leipzig 1914: Lehmann. 38 S., 7 Tab. 8°
Leipzig, Med. Diss. v. 29. Mai 1914, Ref. Zweifel
[Geb. 2. Mai 86 Osnabrück; Wohnort: Hamburg; Staatsangeh.: Preußen; Vor-
bildung: RG. Quakenbrück Reife 07; Studium: Straßburg 1, Leipzig 9 S.;
Coll. 20. Mai 14; Approb. 31. Aug. 13.] [U 14. 2328]

NL 0378892   ICRL DNLM CtY

Lindemann (Georg.) *Ueber die Organisa-
tionsvorgänge bei der chronischen Pneumonie
33 pp. 8°. Strassburg, J. H. E. Heitz, 1888.

NL 0378893   DNLM MH

Lindemann,Georg,1902-
Ueber die verdauungskraft des gesunden,kranken
und operierten magens ein beitrag zu den me-
thoden der quantitativen pepsinbestimmung.
Inaug.diss. Rostock,1928.
₍Borna-Leipzig.₎

NL 0378894   ICRL

Lindemann, Gisela.
Das begnadigungs- und abolitionsrecht und seine
ausuebung im gegenwaertigen kriege. (Auszug)
Inaug. diss. Goettingen,n.d.

NL 0378895   ICRL

Lindemann, Gottfried, 1898-
Ueber einen fall von milchig getruebter aszites-
fluessigkeit. Leipzig, 1924.
Inaug.-Diss.

NL 0378896   ICRL

347.65
L743D
Lindemann, Gottfried Ferdinand, 1744-1804.
De translatione fevdorvm ad clericos.
Lipsiae, Ex officina Loeperia ₍1767?₎
46 p. 20 cm.

Diss. inaug. - Leipzig.
Bibliographical footnotes.
1. Inheritance and succession. Holy Roman
Empire. 2. Feudal law. Holy Roman Empire. 3.
Clergy. Holy Roman Empire. I. Title.

NL 0378897   NcD MH

Lindemann, Gottfried Ferdinand, reichsfreiherr
von, 1744-1804.
Procancellarivs ... inavgvrationem
doctoralem ...
see under   Küstner, Christian Wilhelm,
1721-1785.

Lindemann, Günther.
Heilpflanzen; eine Beschreibung der wichtigsten Heil-
kräuter und ihre Anwendung in gesunden und kranken Tagen. Text zum Bilderatlas von M. H. Mülberger. Ravens-
burg, O. Maier ₍1954₎
99 p. illus., 20 col. plates. 21 cm.
In portfolio.

1. Botany, Medical. 2. Botany—Germany. I. Title.

QK99.L53   55-42740

NL 0378899   DLC NBuU WaU DNLM

PN2658
.D8A45
Lindemann, Gustav.

Dumont, Louise, 1862-1932.
Lebensfeiertag, Briefe an Gustav Lindemann. Hrsg. von
Otto Brües. München, K. Alber, 1948.

Lindemann, H.
Die ermordung des Herzogs Ludwig von Baiern...
Inaug. Diss. Rostock, n.d.

NL 0378901   ICRL

Lindemann, H
Wen trifft die Schuld? Betrachtungen über Ursachen und Ent-
stehung des Ausstandes der Ruhrbergleute [in Bochum] im
Januar und Februar 1905. Von Landrichter H. Lindemann,
... . Essen, O. Radkes Nachf. Thaden & Schmemann, 1905.
[4], 99 p. 22½ cm.

NL 0378902   ICJ

Lindemann (H. J.) Klimatische Curorte.
Nach eigenen Erfahrungen und Beobachtungen.
vi (1 l.), 88 pp. 8°. Erlangen, F. Enke, 1874.

NL 0378903   DNLM

Law

Lindemann, Hans, ed.

Germany (Democratic Republic, 1949-) Laws, statutes, etc.
Die Jugend in der Gesetzgebung der Deutschen Demokra-
tischen Republik. Auf Anregung des Amtes für Jugendfra-
gen beim Stellvertreter des Vorsitzenden des Ministerrates
Walter Ulbricht der Regierung der Deutschen Demokrati-
schen Republik, wurde die Gesetzsammlung von Hans Lindemann zusammengestellt. Berlin, Deutscher Zentralverlag
₍1955₎

Lindemann, Hans, writer on Mohammedanism.
Der Islam im aufbruch, in abwehr und angriff, von professor Hans Lindemann; mit 1 karte und 4 kunstdrucktafeln.
Leipzig, F. Brandstetter, 1941.
84 p. front., plates, group port., double map. 24½ cm.

1. Mohammedanism. 2. Panislamism.

DS38.L5   297   46-28998 rev

NL 0378905   DLC NcD CtY NjP ICU NN

Lindemann, Hans; Beiträge zur Chemie des Arsens. ₍Analyt.
Untersuchungen u. Gleichgewichts-Studien.₎ Dortmund
1910: Krüger. 46 S. 8°
Münster, Phil. Diss. v. 20. Juni 1911, Ref. Thiel
[Geb. 7. Nov. 79 Wetter a. R.; Wohnort: Münster i. W.; Staatsangeh.:
Preußen; Vorbildung: Städt. Gymn. Dortmund Reife O. 02; Studium:
München 1, Würzburg 6, Münster 8 S.; Rig. 18. Juni 10.] [U 11. 3970]

NL 0378906   ICRL MH CtY PU

Lindemann, Hans; Untersuchungen in der Reihe des Cumarins
und des Benzimidazols. Marburg 1913: Köster & Schell.
61 S. 8°
Marburg, Phil. Diss. v. 17. Juli 1913, Ref. Zincke
[Geb. 6. Jan. 90 Hamburg; Wohnort: Marburg; Staatsangeh.: Hamburg; Vorbildung: OR. auf d. Uhlenhorst Hamburg Reife 08; Studium: Straßburg 4,
Marburg 7 S.; Rig. 4. Juni 13.] [U 13. 4362]

NL 0378907   ICRL MH CtY PU

Lindemann, Hans, 1902-
Der kampf gegen den tarifvertrag ... Halle,
1933. 46 p.
Inaug. Diss. -Berlin, 1933.
Lebenslauf.
Bibliography.

NL 0378908   ICRL PU CtY

Lindemann, Hans, 1905-
Die sondergötter in der apologetik der Civitas Dei Au
gustins ... München, A. Küspert, 1930.
78, ₍2₎ p. 23ᶜᵐ.
Inaug.-diss.—Munich.
Lebenslauf.
"Literatur-verzeichnis": p. ₍5₎-₍6₎

1. Augustinus, Aurelius, Saint, bp. of Hippo. De civitate Dei.

NL 0378909   MiU CU PU CtY MH

---

ar W
2393
Lindemann, Hans, 1907-
Das Becken der Steissteratomträger. Düsseldorf, Nolte, 1939.
18 p. 22cm.

Diss.--Göttingen, 1938?

NL 0378910   NIC

Lindemann, Hans Adalbert, 1882—
Filosofía social del futuro; diálogos sobre problemas ibero-
americanos. Buenos Aires, Edición Problemas de América,
distribución exclusiva de Editorial Americalee, 1943.
3 p. l., 11-249, ₍4₎ p. 20½ᶜᵐ.
At head of title: Hans A. Lindemann.

1. Spanish America—Civilization. I. Title.

A 43-3402

Harvard univ. Library
for Library of Congress   ₍2₎

NL 0378911   MH KU CU NcU

Lindemann, Hans Adalbert, 1882-
...Lenguaje y filosofía. El lenguaje: foco central de la dis-
cusión filosófica moderna. Buenos Aires, Edición Problemas
de América ₍1946₎ 258 p. 21cm.

"Bibliografía," p. 255-258.

383109B. 1. Language—Philosophy.
N. Y. P. L.   September 11, 1950

NL 0378912   NN LU

VOLUME 334

Lindemann, Hans Adalbert, 1882–
... Pláticas filosóficas entre un sabio, un poeta y un filósofo. ¡Santiago de Chile¡ Zig-zag ¡1940¡

252 p. port. 21ᵐ. (Added t.-p.: Biblioteca de cultura; director: José del C. Gutiérrez)

At head of title: Hans A. Lindemann.
"Bibliografía": p. ¡245¡–252.

I. Title.

42–20408

Library of Congress   B3286.L63P5
                          ¡2¡   198.9

NL 0378913   DLC OOxM

Lindemann, Hans Adalbert, 1882–
... Weltgeschehen und welterkenntnis. Baden bei Wien, R. M. Rohrer ¡*1937¡

xviii, 421 p. 23½ᵐ.

At head of title: Hans A. Lindemann.

I. Title.

40–15095

Library of Congress   B3286.L63W4 1937
                                                         198.9

NL 0378914   DLC CU CtY

Lindemann, Hans Ulrich Meyer-
        see Meyer-Lindemann, Hans Ulrich.

Lindemann, Hans Walter, 1911–
        Die erfolge der operativen behandlung der netzhautablosung ... 1935.   24 p.
        Inaug. Diss. – Greifswald, 1935.
        Lebenslauf.
        Literaturverzeichnis.

NL 0378916   MiU

Lindemann (Heinrich). *Ueber die ge-
sundheitsgemässeste Methode der Beseitigung
menschlicher Excremente. .34 pp. 8°. *Halle*,
W. Plötz, 1868.

NL 0378917   DNLM

Lindemann, Heinrich
———. Ueber Netzhautentzündungen bei Allge-
meinleiden und ihren diagnostischen Werth. 27
pp. 8°. *Würzburg, I. M. Richter*, 1877.

NL 0378918   DNLM ICRL PPAN

LINDEMANN, Heinrich, b. 1800.
De codicibus Bibliothecae zwiccaviensis. Pt. III. De tribus codicibus Boethii De consolatione philosophiae. Zwiccaviae, 1827.

sm. 4°. pp. 18. (Progr. d. lyceum.)

NL 0378919   MH

Lindemann, Heinrich, b. 1800, ed.
        Gradus ad Parnassum Latinum
        see under Aler, Paul, 1656–1727, ed.

PA6553   Lindemann, Heinrich, b. 1800.
1859   Index zu Ovid's Verwandlungen. Mit besonderer rücksicht auf die ausgabe des verfassers ... Leipzig, W. Engelmann, 1859.
            ¡1¡, 116 p.

            1. Ovidius Naso, Publius. Metamorphoses.
            2. Ovidius Naso, Publius--Dictionaries, indexes, etc.

NL 0378921   ICU

Lindemann, Heinrich, b. 1800.
        Materialien zu aufgaben lateinischer verse. Leipzig, C. H. F. Hartmann, 1830–33.
        2 pt.

        Exempla, quae in versus Latinos transferenda Germanice pro-
posuit Henricus Lindemann Latine. Zuiccaviae, typis Hoeferi, 1830–1833.
        2 pt.

NL 0378922   MH CU PBm PU

Lindemann, Heinrich, 1886–
        ... Über polydactylie beim einhufer ... Kiel, Druck von Vollbehr & Riepen, 1909.
        50, ¡2¡ p. II pl. 23½ᵐ.

        Inaug.-diss.—Leipzig.
        Lebenslauf.
        "Literaturverzeichnis": p. ¡45¡–50.

        1. Hoof. 2. Polydactylism.

U. S. Dept. of agr. Library   444L64   Agr 10—1670
for Library of Congress   ¡a41b1¡

NL 0378923   DNAL DNLM ICRL CtY

Lindemann, Heinrich, 1902–
        Untersuchungen über Wirkungsbedingungen und Wirkungsbereich der oxydierenden Fermente der Hämolymphe von Insekten ... [n.p., 1926]
        Inaug.-Diss. – Hamburg.
        Lebenslauf.

NL 0378924   CtY MiU

Lindemann, Heinrich Simon, 1807–1855.
        Die denkkunde, oder die logik. Von dr. H. S. Lindemann ... Solothurn, Jent & Gassmann, 1846.
        xvi, 240 p. illus. 20½ᶜᵐ.

        1. Logic.

NL 0378925   MiU PU CU KAS MH

LINDERMANN, Heinrich Simon, 1807–1855.
Die Lehre vom Menschen oder die Anthropologie. Ein Handbuch für Gebildete aller Stände. 2 Abth. Zürich. 1844.

NL 0378926   MH

B   LINDEMANN, HEINRICH SIMON, 1807–1855.
247   Uebersichtliche darstellung des lebens und der wissenschaftlehre Carl Chr. Fdr. Krause's, und dessen standpunktes zur Freimaurerbrüder-
475   schaft… München, Fleischmann, 1839.
            112p.

NL 0378927   ICN MH

I   LINDEMANN, HEINRICH SIMON, 1807–1855.
4   Unsere zeit vom standpunkte der erziehung und andeutungen zum besserwerden… München, 1837.
506   36p.

            "Aus der bayerischen Nationalzeitung zum besten der kleinkinderbewahranstalten in der vor-
stadt Au abgedruckt."

NL 0378928   ICN

Lindemann, Heinrich Walther
        see Lindemann, Walther, 1886–

Lindenberg, Heinz.
        Grundbuchberichtigung aus fremdem recht… Hannover, 1930.   66 p.
        Inaug. Diss. Göttingen, 1930.
        Bibliography.

NL 0378930   ICRL

Lindemann, Heinz, 1905–
        Gesichtsfisteln dentalen ursprungs… Berlin, 1932.   20 p.
        Inaug. Diss. Berlin, 1932.
        Lebenslauf.
        Bibliography.

NL 0378931   CtY

Lindemann, Helmut.
        Generäle machen Politik; eine Studie. ¡1. Aufl.¡ Bonn, Brüder Auer, 1952.
        198 p. 19 cm.

        1. Military history.   I. Title.

D25.5.L5   904   54–16271 ‡

NL 0378932   DLC WU NcD MiU MH NN CtY

Lindemann, Helmut, 1911–
        Über die Anwendung von Salvarsanpräparaten bei akuten entzündlichen Prozessen der Mundhöhle ... Borna-Leipzig, 1935.
        Inaug.-Diss. – Leipzig.
        Lebenslauf.
        "Literatur": 29–32 p.

NL 0378933   CtY

Lindemann, Helmut, 1912–
        Die verfassungsrechtliche stellung der britischen Krone. ... 1937.   36 p.
        Inaug. Diss. – Berlin, 1937.
        Lebenslauf.
        Literaturverzeichnis.

NL 0378934   ICRL CtY

Lindemann (Henricus F.) *De sensu caloris.
29 pp. 8°. *Halis, typ. orphanotrophei*, 1857. C.

NL 0378935   DNLM

VOLUME 334

Lindemann, Henriette (Schmidt), 1830–1915.
Dreissig Jahre nach Backfischchens Kaffeekränzchen. Vier Erzählungen für junge Mädchen von Henriette Schmidt. Mit Illustrationen von H. Graube. Berlin: Schreiter'sche Verlagsbuchhandlung₁ 1888₁. 157 p. front., illus. 12°.

167524A.   1. Fiction, German.   2. Title.
N. Y. P. L.   June 10, 1925

NL 0378936   NN

Lindemann, Henriette (Schmidt), 1830–1915.
In Backfischchens Kaffeekränzchen. Vier Erzählungen von Henriette Schmidt. Mit 4 Farbdruckbildern nach Aquarellen, von H. E. Kepler. Stuttgart: E. Hänselmann₁ 1886₁. 164 p. col'd front., col'd plates. 21cm.

659037A.   1. Fiction, German.   I. Kepler, H. E., illustrator.
II. Title.
N. Y. P. L.   March 5, 1934

NL 0378937   NN IEN

PT   **Lindemann, Henriette (Schmidt),** 1830–1915.
2623   Die erste Reise, und andere Erzählungen
I625   für die Jugend von H. Schmidt-Lindemann.
E7   Neue Stereotyp-Ausg. Lahr ₁Ger.₁ New York,
        E. Kaufmann ₁1904₁
        64p. 18cm.

NL 0378938   WU

Lindemann, Henry, 1888–
Love is strong as death; messages from the lives of Bible characters, by H. Lindemann ... Grand Rapids, Mich., Zondervan publishing house, 1934.
80 p. 20ᶜᵐ.

1. Bible—Biog.   I. Title.   II. Title: Bible characters.
                  ₁Full name: Henry William Lindemann₁

Library of Congress   BS571.L5   36–10847
—— Copy 2.
Copyright A 92983   221.92

NL 0378939   DLC

Lindemann, Henry, 1883–
Martin Luther, man of God; selected essays. ₁1st ed.₁ New York, Exposition Press ₁1955₁
102 p. 21 cm.

1. Luther, Martin, 1483–1546.
           Full name: William Henry Lindemann.

BR325.L477   922.443   55–10299 ‡

NL 0378940   DLC PU MH–AH PP OCl PJB

Lindemann, Herbert, 1900–
Das verhalten verschiedener erbsensorten zu verschiedenen stuetzpflanzen im gemengbau. Inaug. diss. Koenigsberg, 1928.
Bibl.

NL 0378941   ICRL MH CtY

Lindemann, Herbert,
Der stimmvertrag. Inaug. Diss. Leipzig, 1930.

NL 0378942   ICRL

Lindemann, Herbert Fred, 1909–
Dead or alive; a series of sermons for Lent and Easter. Saint Louis, Concordia Pub. House ₁1955₁
120 p. 19 cm.

1. Lenten sermons. 2. Easter—Sermons. 3. Lutheran Church—Sermons. 4. Sermons, American. I. Title.

BV4277.L5   252.6   55–9894 rev ‡

NL 0378943   DLC

Lindemann, Herbert Fred, 1909–
Bible. *O. T. Psalms. English. 1940. Authorized.*
The Psalter of the Authorized version of the Scriptures; set to the Gregorian Psalm tones and supplied with proper antiphons, prepared by the Rev. Herbert Lindemann ... Minneapolis, Minn., Augsburg publishing house ₁°1940₁

Lindemann, Hermann.
A pocket-dictionary of the English and German languages. 2d edition. Taschenwörterbuch der englischen und deutschen Sprache. 2. Auflage.
— London ₁etc.₁. Grevel & Co. ₁etc.₁. 1912. 2 v. in 1. ₁Methode Toussaint-Langenscheidt.₁ 15½ cm., in 8s.
Contents. — 1. English-German. 2. German-English.

H9728 — Germany. Lang. Dict. Englisn.ᵣ — Methode Toussaint-Langenscheidt. English-German.

NL 0378945   MB WaS WaU LNHT

PF3640   **Lindemann, Hermann.**
.L6   A pocket-dictionary of the English and
1913   German languages, giving the pronunciation
        according to the phonetic system of Toussaint-
        Langenscheidt. 2d rev. ed. London, H.
        Grevel; New York, International News Co.
        ₁1913?₁
          2 v. 16cm. (Toussaint-Langenscheidt method)
         Added t. p. in German.
         Half-title: Fonolexika Langenscheidt ...   SET INCOMPLETE

         1. English langu   age—Dictionaries—
         German. 2. German   language—Dictionaries—
         English.

NL 0378946   ViU PPCi

Lindemann, Hermann.
... Taschenwörterbuch der englischen und deutschen sprache, mit angabe der aussprache nach dem phonetischen system der methode Toussaint-Langenscheidt ... Zusammengestellt von dr. Hermann Lindemann ... Berlin-Schöneberg, Langenscheidt ₁1911–12₁
2 v. 16ᶜᵐ. (Methode Toussaint-Langenscheidt)
Contents.—1. t. Englisch-Deutsch. 2. t. Deutsch-Englisch.

1. English language—Dictionaries—German. 2. German language—Dictionaries—English.

Library of Congress   PF3640.L6   12–3626

NL 0378947   DLC OrCS ViU OKentU CU PSt PU–W OCl

PF3640   **Lindemann, Hermann.**
.L6
1913   Taschenwörterbuch der englischen und
        deutschen Sprache, mit Angabe der Aussprache
        nach dem phonetischen System der Methode
        Toussaint-Langenscheidt. 2. Revidierte Aufl.
        Berlin-Schöneberg, Langenscheidt ₁1913?₁
         2 v. 16cm. (Methode Toussaint-Langenscheidt)
         Added t. p. in English: A pocket-dictionary ...
        London, H. Grevel; New York, International News Co.

         1. English language—Dictionaries—German. 2.
        German language—Dic   tionaries—English.

NL 0378948   ViU

Lindemann, Hermann.
Taschenwörterbuch der englischen und deutschen Sprache, mit Angabe der Aussprache nach dem phonetischen System der Methode Toussaint-Langenscheidt... 3. revid. Aufl. Berlin-Schöneberg, Langenscheidt ₁°1912₁
v. 16 cm. (Methode Toussaint-Langenscheidt)
CONTENTS.—1. T. Englisch-Deutsch.

1. English language—Dictionaries—German.

PF3640.L63   55–47525

NL 0378949   DLC MH LNHT

Lindemann, Hermann.
... Taschenwörterbuch der englischen und deutschen Sprache, mit Angabe der Aussprache nach dem phonetischen System der Methode Toussaint-Langenscheidt ... Berlin: Schöneberg Langenscheidtsche ₁cop. 1911₁ 2 v. 8. rev. ed. 16°. (Methode Toussaint-Langenscheidt.)
Binder's title: Langenscheidts Taschenwörterbücher.
v. 1. Englisch-deutsch.
v. 2. Deutsch-englisch.

1. Dictionaries.   2. German language   —Dictionaries.
N. Y. P. L.   June 6, 1935

NL 0378950   NN

Lindemann, Hermann.
Taschenwörterbuch der englischen und deutschen Sprache. 11. rev. Ausgabe. Berlin, Langenscheidt ₁c1911₁

v. 2
Added t.p. in English
Contents: 2. Deutsch-English

NL 0378951   MH

LINDEMANN, Hermann.
Taschenwörterbuch der englischen und deutschen Sprache. Mit Angabe der Aussprache nach dem phonetischen System der Methode Toussaint-Langenscheidt. Teil II. 13ᵉ revidierte Aufl. Berlin-Schöneberg, G. Langenscheidt, ₁cop. 1911₁.

"Methode Toussaint-Langenscheidt."
Added title-page in English.
Contents: Pt. II. Deutsch-Englisch.

NL 0378952   MH OU MiU

Lindemann, Hermann.
Taschenwörterbuch der englischen und deutschen Sprache mit Angabe der Aussprache nach dem phonetischen System der Methode Toussaint-Langenscheidt Zweiter Teil Deutsch-Englisch. 14 rev. Aufl. Berlin, Langenscheidt, 1911.
xLviii, 506p. 16cm.

NL 0378953   NcU

Lindemann, Hermann.
Taschenwörterbuch der englischen und deutschen Sprache. Mit Angabe der Aussprache nach dem phonetischen System der Methode Toussaint-Langenscheidt. Teil II. Zusammengestellt von Hermann Lindemann. 15. revidierte Aufl. Berlin, Langenscheidtsche Verlagsbuchhandlung (G. Langenscheidt) G.m.b.H. ₁c.1911₁

xlviii, 506 p. 16 cm.
At head of title: Methode Toussaint-Langenscheidt.
Added title page in   English.
Contents: – 2. Deutsch-Englisch.

NL 0378954   MH

VOLUME 334

Lindemann, Hermann, gerichtsassessor.
Der nicht rechtsfähige verein
see under   Lindemann, Hermann,
landgerichtsrat.

Lindemann, Hermann, *landgerichtsrat*.
Der nicht rechtsfähige verein. Von Hermann Lindemann
... und Hermann Lindemann ... Berlin, F. Siemenroth, 1910.
4 p. l., 124 p.   21½ᵐ.

1. Association and associations—Germany. 2. Persons (Law)—Germany.   I. Lindemann, Hermann, gerichtsassessor.   II. Title.
38-36121

NL 0378956   DLC

Lindemann, Hermann, *novelist*.
... Menschen auf der flucht, roman. Berlin, Büchergilde
Gutenberg, 1934.
2 p. l., 7-234 p.   19½ᵐ.

I. Title.
Library of Congress   PT2623.I 572M4 1934   34-34728
Copyright A—Foreign   25639

833.91

NL 0378957   DLC CtY

Lindemann, Hermann Heinrich Wilhelm **Frido**
see   Lindemann, Frido, 1880-

Lindemann, Hermann Theodor, 1875-
Alphonse Daudet als Humorist ...   Meiningen,
1896.
94 p.   23.5 cm.
Inaug. - Diss. - Leipzig.
Vita.
Benützte Werke, p. [4]

NL 0378959   CtY ICRL

Lindemann (Hermannus Wilhelmus) * De
gonorrhoea. 21 pp. 4°. *Göttingen, H. M. Grapé,*
1790.
In: COLLECT. diss. med. in Acad. Gotting., 1790, i, pt. 1.

NL 0378960   DNLM NNNAM

Lindemann, Hermannus Wilhelmus
Entwurf die vorzüglichsten Krankheiten
der Soldaten im Felde schneller und glücklicher
zu heilen. xxxii, 235 pp. 8°. *Berlin, C. F.*
Himburg, 1799.

NL 0378961   DNLM

Lindemann (Hermannus Wilhelmus)
Magazin auserlesener medicinischer Abhandlungen von berühmten französischen Aerzten gesammelt und übersetzt. 2 p. l., 330 pp.,
1 pl. 12°. *Berlin, G. A. Lange, 1797.*
See also, *Vodere* [F[rançois]-E[mmanuel]). Ueber
den Kropf [etc]. 8°. *Berlin, 1796.*

NL 0378962   DNLM

Lindemann, Howard Gordon.
State teachers' association officers... ₅Columbus₎ Ohio state university, 1930.
90 numb. l.
Thesis.

NL 0378963   OU

LINDEMANN, Hubert, *1864–*
Des hl. Hilarius von Poitiers "Liber mysteriorum." Eine patristisch-kritische studie.
Münster i.W., Aschendorff, 1905.

vii, 120p.   24 cm.

NL 0378964   MH PU

Lindemann, Hubert, 1864-   *ed.*
Florilegii hebraici lexicon quo illius vocabul
latine et germanice versa continentur. Friburgi
Brisgoviae, S. Ludovici Americae [etc.] B. Herder
1914.
[4]1.,82p.

NL 0378965   OCl

Lindemann, Hubert, 1864-   ed.
Florilegium Hebraicum. Friburgi Brisg.,
Herder, 1912
see under   Bible. O. T. Hebrew.
Selections. 1912.

Lindemann, Hugo.
Die sieben schlösser des Melik Schah, orientalische märchen
frei bearbeitet von Hugo Lindemann. Potsdam, G. Kiepenheuer, 1926.
174, ₍2₎ p. 16½ᵐ.   (*Half-title:* Die liebhaberbibliothek)

I. Title.
Library of Congress   PT2623.I 57385 1926   30-2085

NL 0378967   DLC NN

Lindemann, Hugo, *1867 –*
see
Lindemann, Carl Hugo, 1867-

W 4
G59
1940
LINDEMANN, Ingeborg, 1916-
Beitrag zur Kenntnis typischer
Mehrfach-Missbildungen; Akrodyskephalia
splanchnocystica dysphalangica.
Hannover, 1940.
13 p.
Diss. - Göttingen.
1. Abnormalities

NL 0378969   DNLM NIC

Lindemann, J   Hermann.
Über des Herodot religiöse Weltansicht.
Vom Oberlehrer Lindemann.   [Conitz, 1833]
p. [3]-11.   25 cm.
Caption-title.
Programm - K. Gymnasium zu Conitz in
Westpreussen.

NL 0378970   CtY

Lindemann, J   Hermann.
Über die religiös-sittliche Lebensansicht des
Xenophon ...   Conitz, 1843.
22 p.   4°.   [In "Dissertations: Xenophon,"
v.1]

NL 0378971   CtY

Gu5
25
Lindemann, J   Hermann
Vier Abhandlungen über die religiös-sittliche
Weltanschauung des Herodot, Thucydides und
Xenophon und den Pragmatismus des Polybius ...
Berlin, Amelang'sche Sortiments-Buchhandlung,
1852.
94p.   18½cm.

NL 0378972   CtY IEN

Lindemann, James Earl, 1927–
The process and efficacy of short-term nondirective group
psychotherapy with hospitalized schizophrenic patients.
Ann Arbor, University Microfilms ₍1955₎
(₍University Microfilms, Ann Arbor, Mich.₎   Publication no. 11,829)
Microfilm copy of typescript. Positive.
Collation of the original : 106 l. tables.
Thesis—Pennsylvania State University.
Abstracted in Pennsylvania. State University. Abstracts of doctoral dissertations, v. 17 (1954) p. 690-694.
Bibliography : leaves 91-94.
1. Group psychotherapy. 2. Schizophrenia. I. Title: Nondirective
group psychotherapy with hospitalized schizophrenic patients.
Microfilm AC-1   no. 11,829   Mic 56-5180
Pennsylvania. State   University. Library
for Library of Congress   ₍1₎†

NL 0378973   PSt DLC

Lindemann, Joachim.
Die Stralsunder Memorial-Bücher Joachim
Lindemanns und Gerhard Hannemanns, 1531-1611.
Zum erstenmale aus den Handschriften hrsg. und
mit Einleitung, Inhaltsverzeichniss, Bemerkungen
und Wörtererklärungen begleitet von E.H. Zober.
Stralsund, Löffler, 1843.
xvii, 228 p.   (Mohnike, G.C.F. Stralsundische
Chroniken, 2)

NL 0378974   MH IEN

A30
W7
1679L
Lindemann, Joachim, 1662-1694, author and
respondent.
De obligatione conscientiae. Wittenbergae,
1679.
Diss. - Wittenberg (G.Schwartze, praeses)

I. Schwartze, Georg, 1651-1695, praeses.

NL 0378975   CtY

A30
R7
1698L
Lindemann, Joachim, 1662-1698, **praeses**.
De pantosophiae humanae lineamentis ...
Rostochii[1698]
Diss. - Rostock (J.Stoef, respondent **and**
author)

NL 0378976   CtY

Lindemann, J[ohann] C[hristoph] W[ilhelm] 1827-
1879.
Amerikanisch-Lutherische Schul-Praxis.
2. Aufl. St. Louis, Mo., Lutherischer Concordia-Verlag, 1888.
368 p.   O.

NL 0378977   PPLT

VOLUME 334

Lindemann, Johann Christoph Wilhelm, 1827–1879.
Deutsche grammatik für seminare, höhere bürgerschulen und oberklassen gehobener gemeindeschulen. Von J. C. W. Lindemann. St. Louis, Mo., A. Wiebusch u. sohn, 1868.
xi, 156 p. 22ᶜᵐ.

1. German language—Grammar—1800–1870.

34-8681

Library of Congress   PF3109.L5   435

NL 0378978   DLC MiU

L[indemann] Johann Christoph Wilhelm, 1827–1879.
Der deutsche katechismus vor tausend jahren. Katechetische denkmäler aus der ältesten deutschen christlichen zeit, gesammelt von J. C. W. L.   St. Louis, 1868.
18 p.   23 cm.

NL 0378979   RPB

Lindemann, Johann Christoph Wilhelm, 1827–1879, comp.
D[okto]r Martin Luther als Erzieher der Jugend
   see under   Luther, Martin, 1483–1546.

Lindemann, Johann Christoph Wilhelm, 1827–1879.
BX8070   Evangelisch-Lutherische Katechismus-Milch. 75
.L7K7   kurze Katechesen über Dr. Martin Luthers Kleinen
1885   Katechismus, nach der Erklärung Joh. Konr. Dietrichs. Aus dem Nachlasse des J. C. W. Lindemann...   St. Louis, L. Lange, 1885.
vi, 376p. front. (port.) 24cm.

1. Lutheran Church - Catechisms and creeds.
1. Dieterich, Conrad, 1575–1639.

NL 0378981   FMU PPLT

Lindemann, Johann Christoph Wilhelm, 1827–1879, ed.
Evangelisch-lutherisches schulblatt. Monatsschrift für erziehung und unterricht. Hrsg. von der Deutschen evangelisch-lutherischen synode von Missouri, Ohio und anderen staaten ... 1.– jahrg.; sept. 1865–
St. Louis, Mo., A. Wiebusch u. sohn [etc.] 1866–19

Lindemann, Johann Friedrich, 1792–1854.
   see   Lindemann, Friedrich, 1792–1854.

Lindemann, Johann Friedrich, 1898–
   see   Lindemann, Friedrich, 1898–

Lindemann, Johann Gottfried Ludwig. Dissertatio inauguralis medica de cortice peruviano. Helmstadii. 1757. sm. 4°. pp. 26, [6].

NL 0378985   MH-A DNLM

Lindemann, Johann Gottlieb.
   Geschichte der Meinungen älterer und neuerer Völker, im Stande der Roheit und Cultur, von Gott, Religion, und Priesterthum, nebst einer besondern Religionsgeschichte der Aegypter, Perser, Chaldäer, Chinesen, Indianer, Phönicier, Griechen und Römer &c. wie auch von der Religion der wilden Völker, als: Brasilianer, Mexicaner, Peruaner &c...   Theil 1–7.   Stendal: bey Franzen und Grosse, 1784–95.   7 v. in 4.   8°.

   Sabin 41289.
The titles of v. 2–7 vary slightly from that of v. 1, and all contain the name of the author, not found on that of v .1.

1. Religion.—History and origin.   2. Religion (Indian-American).
N. Y. P. L.   August 20, 1924

NL 0378986   NN MnU MH

Lindemann, Johann Wilhelm, 1828–1879
   see   Lindemann, Wilhelm, 1828–1879.

PT35   Lindemann, Johannes, 1888–
.A1   Über die alliteration als kunstform im
v.32   volks- und spielmannsepos... von Johannes
   Lindemann...   Breslau, A. Favorke, 1914.
   62p., 1 l. 23cm. [German language and
   literature dissertations. v.32]
   Inaug.-diss. - Breslau.
   Lebenslauf.
   "Quellen und literatur": p. [5]–8.

   1. Alliteration. 2. German poetry - Versification.

NL 0378988   NNU-W MH IU MiU CtY ICRL PU

Lindemann (Julius [Wilhelm Ernst]) [1864–]. *Spina bifida, mit Berücksichtigung eines geheilten Falles. 32 pp., 1 l. 8°. Bonn, C. Georgi. 1889.

NL 0378989   DNLM CU PPC

Lindemann, Karl, 1878–
   Die rhein und ruhr haefen bei Duesburg...
   Inaug. diss. Wuerzburg, 1908. (Bonn)
   Bibl.

NL 0378990   ICRL MH

Lindemann, Karl August, 1893–
   see   Lindemann, Carl August, 1893–

Lindemann, Karl Eduardovich
   see
Lindeman, Karl Eduardovich, 1844–

Lindemann, Karl Felix, 1868–
   see   Lindemann, Carl Felix, 1868–

Lindemann, Karl Louis Ferdinand
   see
Lindemann, Ferdinand, 1852–1939.

Lindemann, Kelvin, 1911–
   En aften i kolera-aaret [af] Alexis Hareng [pseud.]   København, C. Andersen, 1953.
   167 p. 24 cm.

   I. Title.   Full name: Kelvin Edvard Thybo Lindemann.

PT8175.L52A64   55-20778 rev ‡

NL 0378995   DLC OrP NcD MH NN MnU OC1 CU

Lindemann, Kelvin, 1911–
   ...Alt Levende lyser; Roman ...   Kjøbenhavn: Nyt nordisk Forlag, A. Busck, 1938. 230 p. 22½cm.

2799B. 1. Fiction, Danish. I. Title.
N. Y. P. L.   August 17, 1939

NL 0378996   NN WU CU

Lindemann, Kelvin, 1911–
   ... Den frihet väl kan bära ... Stockholm, Tidens förlag [1943]
   323, [1] p. 22 cm.

   "Från danskan av Knut Stubbendorff."
   "Danska originalets titel: Den kan vel frihed bære."

   1. Bornholm—Hist.—Fiction.   I. Stubbendorff, Knut Bertil, 1898–tr. II. Title.
        Full name: Kelvin Edvard Thybo Lindemann.

PT8175.L52K4   839.8136   47-41408 rev

NL 0378997   DLC MH MnU

4PT   Lindemann, Kelvin, 1911–
Dan.-   Gyldne kaeder. [København] S. Hasselbalch,
5000   1948.
   334 p.

NL 0378998   DLC-P4 PPULC MH C NN MnU

Lindemann, Kelvin, 1911–
   En haandfuld babies. København, W. Hansen, 1931.
   160 p. 22 cm.

   I. Title.   Full name: Kelvin Edvard Thybo Lindemann.

PT8175.L52H2 1931   32-9019*

NL 0378999   DLC

4PT   Lindemann, Kelvin, 1911–
Ger.   Das Haus mit dem grünen Baum, Roman.
573   [Einzig berechtigte Übertragung von Erwin Magnus]
   Berlin, Universitas Verlag [1948]
   443 p.

NL 0379000   DLC-P4 PPULC

Lindemann, Kelvin, 1911–
   The house with the green tree. Translated by Henry Alexander. New York, L. B. Fischer [1944]
   348 p. maps (on lining papers) 22 cm.

   I. Title.   Full name: Kelvin Edvard Thybo Lindemann.

PZ3.L6444Ho   839.8136   44-5522 rev*
   [r5711]

NL 0379001   DLC CaBVaU Or WaS PSt OLak OOxM OC1 NcU

VOLUME 334

Lindemann, Kelvin, 1911–
Huset med det grønne træ. [København] Hasselbalch,
1942

455 p. map

NL 0379002　　MH

Lindemann, Kelvin, 1911–
Huset med det gröna trädet, roman av Kelvin Lindemann,
översättning av K. Stubbendorff. 4. uppl. Stockholm,
Tiden [1943]

479, [1] p. 23 cm.

"Danska originalets titel : Huset med det grønne træ."

I. Stubbendorff, Knut Bertil, 1898–　tr.　II. Title.

Full name: Kelvin Edvard Thybo Lindemann.

PT8175.L52H88　　　　　　　46–16503 rev

NL 0379003　　DLC ICU

Lindemann, Kelvin, 1911–
... Huset med det grønne træ. [København] L. Hasselbalch, 1944.

455 p. fold. map. 22 cm.

"Copyright 1942."
"Denne bog blev–sammen med Michael Tejn: 'Drømmen og virkelig-
heden'–vinder at Hasselbalchs jubilæums-konkurrence 1942."

I. Title.

Full name: Kelvin Edvard Thybo Lindemann.

PT8175.L52H8　　　　　　　47–21899 rev

NL 0379004　　DLC WaS NN IU OrP WaE MnU

Lindemann, Kelvin, 1911–
Isertin kauppahuone, romaani, suomentanut
Ilta Boisen...
(Tanskankielinen alkuteos: Huset med det
grønne træ. (English title: The house with the
green tree)

NL 0379005　　OC1

Lindemann, Kelvin, 1911–
... Den kan vel frihed bære ... [København] S. Hasselbach, 1943.

239 p. illus. (map) 22 cm.

"Baggrunden for handlingen i denne roman er det svenske overfald
paa Bornholm i 1645 og øens stilling under svensk herredømme mellem
de to dansk-svenske krige 1657–58 og 1658–60."

1. Bornholm—Hist.—Fiction.　I. Title.

Full name: Kelvin Edvard Thybo Lindemann.

PT8175.L52K3　　　839.8136　　44–1595 rev

NL 0379006　　DLC NN MnU PU

Lindemann, Kelvin, 1911–
... Den kan vel frihed bære ... [København] S. Hasselbalch, 1945.

238 p. illus. (map) 22 cm.

"Copyright 1943."
"Baggrunden for handlingen i denne roman er det svenske overfald
paa Bornholm i 1645 og øens stilling under svensk herredømme mellem
de to dansk-svenske krige 1657–58 og 1658–60."

1. Bornholm—Hist.—Fiction.　I. Title.

Full name: Kelvin Edvard Thybo Lindemann.

PT8175.L52K3 1945　　　　　47–22365 rev

NL 0379007　　DLC

Lindemann, Kelvin, 1911–
Lykkens tempel. København, Hasselbach, 1949.

174 p. 22 cm.

I. Title.

Full name: Kelvin Edvard Thybo Lindemann.

PT8175.L52L9　　　　　　　50–34761 rev

NL 0379008　　DLC MH NN KyU MnU

Lindemann, Kelvin, 1911–
Maja rohelise puuga, romaan. Toronto,
Canada, Orto [1954]
448p.

Estonian.

NL 0379009　　OC1

Lindemann, Kelvin, 1911–
Min rejse til Rusland, og andre alvorlige betragtninger.
[København, S. Hasselbalch, 1949.

82 p. 20 cm.

I. Title.

Full name: Kelvin Edvard Thybo Lindemann.

PT8175.L52M5　　　　　　　50–20281 rev

NL 0379010　　DLC WaU NN IU

Lindemann, Kelvin, 1911–
Det ostindiske spisestel. Tegninger af Mads Stage.
[Sønderborg, 1954?]

53 p. illus. 22 cm.

I. Title.

Full name: Kelvin Edvard Thybo Lindemann.

　　　　　　　　　　　　　A 55–7494 rev

Minnesota. Univ. Libr.
for Library of Congress　　[r57b?]

NL 0379011　　MnU

Lindemann, Kelvin, 1911–
The red umbrellas. New York, Appleton-Century-Croft
[1955]

214 p. 21 cm.

Translation of En aften i kolera-aaret.

I. Title.

Full name: Kelvin Edvard Thybo Lindemann.

PZ3.L6444Re　　　　　　　55–11352 rev ‡

WaS WaSp WaT OrCS
PP IU TxU CU ViU NcGU CaBVa CaBVaU Or OrMonO WaE
NL 0379012　　DLC WaU FTaSU PBm PSt OO OC1 OCU PPL

Lindemann, Kelvin, 1911–
Vi skal nok blive berømte; roman. Kjøbenhavn, Nyt
nordisk forlag, 1933.

208 p. 22 cm.

"Tilkendt H. C. Andersen-mindemedaljen 1933."

I. Title.

Full name: Kelvin Edvard Thybo Lindemann.

PT8175.L52V5 1933　　　　　41–30656 rev*

NL 0379013　　DLC NN CU

Lindemann, Kelvin Edvard Thybo
see Lindemann, Kelvin, 1911–

W 4
M961
1953
LINDEMANN, Klaus, 1928
Die sog. ATPase-Aktivität von
Rattenherzhomogenaten und ihre
Förderung durch embryonalen
Herzextrakt.　München, 1953.
27 *l.* illus.
Inaug.-Diss. - Munich.
1. Muscles - Physiology
2. Pyrophosphatases

NL 0379015　　DNLM

Lindemann, Klaus A
Behörde und Bürger; das Verhältnis zwischen Verwal-
tung und Bevölkerung in einer deutschen Mittelstadt.
Darmstadt, E. Roether, 1952.

213 p. 23 cm. (Gemeindestudie des Instituts für Sozialwissen-
schaftliche Forschung, Darmstadt. Monographie 8)

1. Darmstadt—Officials and employees. 2. Municipal officials and
employees—Germany—Case studies. I. Title.

JS5530.D32L5　　　　　　　54–44077 ‡

NL 0379016　　DLC FTaSU OU NN IU NIC ICU MH MiU PU TxU

Lindemann, Konrad.
Der berufstand der unterhaltungsmusiker in Hamburg, von
dr. Konrad Lindemann.　Hamburg, Hansischer gildenverlag,
1938.

77 p., 1 l. 23ᶜᵐ. (On cover: Volk und gemeinschaft; soziologische
schriftenreihe, hrsg. von prof. dr. A. Walther.　3)

The author's inaugural dissertation, Hamburg.
"Schrifttum": leaf at end.

1. Musicians—Hamburg. 2. Music as a profession.　I. Title.

Library of Congress　　ML283.8.H19L5　　41–27521

NL 0379017　　DLC

832.9109
L743m
Lindemann, Konrad, comp.
Das moderne völkische Drama; Grundsätzliches
und Proben.　Paderborn, F. Schöningh [1934?]
175p.　(Der Deutsche Quell)

Schöninghs Textausgaben, 146.

1. German drama--20th cent.--Hist. & crit.
2. German drama--20th cent.--Collections.
3. National socialism. I. Title.

NL 0379018　　ICarbS

Law
Lindemann, Kurt, ed.

Saxony, Lower. *Laws, statutes, etc.*
Die Niedersächsische Gemeindeordnung mit Ausführungsbestimmungen. Erläutert von Kurt Lindemann. Hannover, R. Boorberg, 1955.

WE
725
L743e
1953
LINDEMANN, Kurt, *surgeon.*
Die Erkrankungen der Wirbelsäule,
von Kurt Lindemann und Hans Kuhlendahl.
Stuttgart, Enke, 1953.
xii, 376 p. illus.
1. Spine - Diseases I. Kuhlendahl,
Hans

NL 0379020　　DNLM

1894–
Lindemann, Kurt, Kammergerichtsref.: Die Eigentümer-
Nebenleistungshypothek. [In Maschinenschrift.] 100 S.
4°(2°). — Auszug: (Potsdam) 1921: (Stein). 7 S. 8°
Breslau, R.- u. staatswiss. Diss. v. 26. Sept. 1921, Ref. Fischer

[Geb. 20. Jan. 96 Charlottenburg; Wohnort: Berlin-Dahlem; Staatsangeh.:
Preußen; Vorbildung: Bismarck-G. Berlin-Wilmersdorf Reife 14; Studium:
Oxford 1, Berlin 6 S.; Rig. 31. Jan. 21.]
[U 21. 296

NL 0379021　　ICRL

VOLUME 334

Lindemann, Kurt, 1407–
Deutscher Heliand; ein Traumspiel, von Kurt Lindemann...
Grossdeuben bei Leipzig: F. M. Meiner₁, 1926?₁.   63 p.   2. ed.
12°.

309679A.   1. Drama, German.   2. Title.   August 20, 1927

NL   0379022   NN DLC-P4

Lindemann, Kurt, 1907–
... Der tod des erlösers, spiel für ein neues theater in 12
teilen.   Erste auflage.   Landsberg (Warthe) K. Pfeiffer
jun., 1932.
72 p.   20½ cm.

i. Title.
                 A C 33–57 rev
Vassar College. Library
for Library of Congress   ₁r61c2₁

NL   0379023   NPV

---

‡Lindemann (Lambert). *Ueber die Verhältnisse der Bonner Brunnen mit besonderer Berücksichtigung der Frage, woher sie ihr Wasser
beziehen. 24 pp., 1 l. 8°. Bonn, J. F. Carl-
haus. [1860].

NL   0379024   DNLM MH

Lindemann, Frau Lisbeth (Küssner) joint tr.

Picard, Émile, 1856–
... Das wissen der gegenwart in mathematik und naturwissenschaft; autorisierte deutsche ausgabe, mit erläuternden anmerkungen, von F. und L. Lindemann. Leipzig und
Berlin, B. G. Teubner, 1913.

Lindemann, Frau Lisbeth (Küssner) joint tr.

Poincaré, Henri, 1854–1912.
... Wissenschaft und hypothese.   Autorisierte deutsche
ausgabe mit erläuternden anmerkungen von F. und L.
Lindemann. 3. verb. aufl. Leipzig, B. G. Teubner, 1914.

Lindemann, Lisbeth (Küssner) joint tr.

Q175
.P76   **Poincaré, Henri,** 1854–1912.
1914   ... Wissenschaft und methode; autorisierte deutsche ausg.
mit erläuternden anmerkungen, von F. und L. Lindemann.
Leipzig und Berlin, B. G. Teubner, 1914.

Lindemann, Liselotte, 1909–
Ueber extremitäten gangrän bei diphtherie. ...
Breslau, 1935.
Inaug. Diss. - Breslau, 1935.
Lebenslauf.
Literatur.

NL   0379028   MiU

792
L74v   Lindemann, Mrs. Louise (Dumont)
       1862–1932
       Vermächtnisse; hrsg. von Gustav
Germ.   Lindemann.   Düsseldorf, Bagel, 1932.
       209p. D.

       Half-title: Reden und schriften.

       1. Theater. German.   I. Lindemann, Gustav,
ed.   II. Title.

NL   0379029   IaU

Lindemann, Ludwig, 1906–
... Über die Bedeutung und Häufigkeit warziger
Veränderungen der Körperdecke.   Nach den Er-
fahrungen an dem Material der Berliner Universi-
täts-Hautklinik während der Jahre 1930–1936 ...
Berlin [1937]
Inaug.-Diss. - Berlin.
Lebenslauf.
"Literatur"₁ p. 16.

NL   0379030   CtY

Lindemann, M.
De Agathonis oratione quae est in Convivio
Platonico.   n.p., 1871.

NL   0379031   NjP

Lindemann, Martha.
Die Heiraten der Romanows und der deutschen Fürstenhäuser
im 18. und 19. Jahrhundert und ihre Bedeutung in der Bündnis-
politik der Ostmächte, von Dr. Martha Lindemann.   Berlin
₁etc.₁ F. Dümmler, 1935.   176 p.   pl., ports.   23½cm.   (Das
Reich und Mitteleuropa. Bd. 2.)

"Quellenverzeichnis," p. 170–176.

817463A.   1. Romanov, House of.   2. Marriage, Royal—Russia.
3. Marriage, Royal—Germany.   I. Ser.
                                  April 7, 1937

NL   0379032   NN NBuU MH CU

Lindemann (Max). *Beiträge zur Chirurgie des Magens. [Erlangen.] 28 pp., 1 l. 8°.
*Nürnberg. G. Hessdolph. 1892.

NL   0379033   DNLM

Lindemann, Max, 1888–
Die Rückversicherung ...   Greifswald, 1920.
Inaug. - Diss. - Greifswald.
Lebenslauf.

NL   0379034   CtY PU

Lindemann, Max, 1900–
... Ein Beitrag zur chirurgischen Behandlung
der Nephritis dolorosa ...   Hamburg, 1925.
22 cm.
Inaug. - Diss. - Hamburg.
At head of title: Aus dem Städtischen Kranken-
haus 1 Hannover, Chirurgische Abteilung. (Prof.
Dr. Kappis)
Lebenslauf.
Literatur-Verzeichnis: p. [13]–15.

NL   0379035   CtY

Lindemann (Max) [1901–]. *Ein pri-
märes hepatocelluläres Lebercarcinom, ka-
suistischer Beitrag zur Klinik des primären
Lebercarcinoms. [Leipzig.] 28 pp. 8°.
Wernigerode, W. Bergmann, 1925.

NL   0379036   DNLM CtY ICRL

LINDEMANN, Max, 1902–
A. Untersuchungen in der Jndigogruppe.
B. Zur kenntnis der bildung von aldehyden aus
säurehydraziden. Inaug.-diss., München.
[Straubing, J. Wagner, 1926].

pp. 51–.
"Lebenslauf",

NL   0379037   MH-C CtY

---

ar W   Lindemann, Max Friedrich August, 1886–
34326   Die Radioaktivität der Atmosphäre in Kiel
und ihre Abhängigkeit von meteorologischen
Faktoren.   ₁Kiel? 1911₁
     32 p.   illus.   24cm.

     Inaug.-Diss.--Kiel.

     1. Solar radiation.   2. Radioactivity.
3. Atmosphere.

NL   0379038   NIC ICRL DNLM CtY PU MH DAS

LINDEMANN, ODA.
Trucking past and present; an essay [written] as a
senior English assignment at Rutherford high school,
Rutherford, New Jersey. Washington, American
trucking associations [1954?] 14 p. 28cm.

Cover title.
Bibliography, p. 13.

1. MOTOR TRUCKS--U. S.   L American trucking associations, inc.

NL   0379039   NN

Lindemann, Otto.
Beitraege zur kenntnis der einwirkung...
Inaug. diss. Dresden, 1909. Techn. Hoch.

NL   0379040   ICRL

Lindemann, Otto.
Das revolutionäre Heer.   Mit geschichtlich politischen
Ergänzungen.   Hrsg. von Heinrich Laufenberg und Fritz
Wolffheim. Hamburg, Kommistischer Kulturverlag, 1920.
46 p. 21 cm.

1. Germany—Defenses.   i. Title.

UA712.L49   57–51508

NL   0379041   DLC

Law   Lindemann, Otto, 1871–   ed.

Germany. *Laws, statutes, etc.*
Ausführungsgesetz zum Bürgerlichen Gesetzbuche vom 20.
September 1899 nebst einem Anhang: Verordnung zur Aus-
führung des Bürgerlichen Gesetzbuchs vom 16. November
1899.   Nach dem Tode des früheren Herausgebers P.
Siméon, erläutert von Otto Lindemann. 4. Aufl. Berlin,
W. de Gruyter, 1930.

VOLUME 334

Lindemann, Otto, 1871– ed.
... Gesetz, betreffend das urheberrecht an werken der literatur und der tonkunst. Vom 19. juni 1901. Text-ausgabe mit einleitung, anmerkungen und sachregister nebst einem anhang, enthaltend die Berner uebereinkunft vom 9. september 1886 und das Pariser zusatzabkommen vom 4. mai 1896, von Otto Lindemann ... Berlin, J. Guttentag, 1901.

136 p. 13½ᶜᵐ. (Guttentag'sche sammlung deutscher reichsgesetze. nr. 60)

1. Copyright—Germany. 2. Copyright, International. 3. Bern copyright convention, 1886. 4. Bern convention, 1886—Revision, 1896. I. Title.

Library of Congress   Z586.L74   2–6168
(a234)

NL 0379043   DLC

Eur
Ger
.26C69
1907
Lindemann, Otto, 1871– ed.
Gesetz, betreffend das Urheberrecht an Werken der Literatur und der Tonkunst. Vom 19. juni 1901. Text-ausgabe mit einleitung, anmerkungen und sachregister nebst einem anhang, enthaltend die Berner übereinkunst vom 9. september 1886 und das Pariser zusatzabkommen vom 4. mai 1896, von Otto Lindemann. 2. aufl. Berlin, J. Guttentag, 1907.
152p. 13cm. (Guttentag'sche sammlung deutscher reichs- gesetze, nr. 60)

NL 0379044   ViU-L

Lindemann, Otto, 1871– ed.
... Gesetz, betreffend das urheberrecht an werken der literatur und der tonkunst. Von 19. juni 1901. In der fassung der [!] gesetzes vom 22. mai 1910. Textausg. mit einleitung, anmerkungen und sachregister nebst einem anhang, enthaltend die revidierte Berner übereinkunft vom 13. november 1908, von Otto Lindemann ... 3. aufl. Berlin, J. Guttentag, 1910.

2 p. l., (7)–155 p. 13½ᶜᵐ. (Guttentag'sche sammlung deutscher reichs- gesetze. nr. 60)

I. Germany. Laws, statutes, etc., 1888– (William II)

15–22385

NL 0379045   DLC

Lindemann, Otto, 1871– ed.
... Gesetz, betreffend das urheberrecht an werken der litera- tur und der tonkunst vom 19. juni 1901 (in der fassung des gesetzes vom 22. mai 1910) nebst der revidierten Berner übereinkunft vom 13. november 1908. Erläutert von ... Otto Lindemann ... 4. verm. und verb. aufl. Berlin und Leipzig, W. de Gruyter & co., 1921.

1 p. l., (5)–171, (1) p. 15½ᶜᵐ. (Guttentagsche sammlung deutscher reichsgesetze, nr. 60)

1. Copyright—Germany. 2. Copyright, International.   I. Germany. Laws, statutes, etc., 1888–1918 (William II) II. International copyright union. III. Title.

28–4157

NL 0379046   DLC

LINDEMANN, Otto, 1871– ed.
Die gesetzgebung über polizeiverordnungen in Preussen. Berlin, 1904.

24°.
"Guttentag'sche sammlung preussischer gesetze. nr. 36."

NL 0379047   MH-L

Lindemann, Otto, 1871– ed.
... Die gesetzgebung über polizeiverordnungen in Preussen. Textausgabe der einschlägigen gesetzesbestimmungen mit ein- leitung, anmerkungen und sachregister, von Otto Lindemann ... 2. aufl. Berlin, J. Guttentag, 1912.

1 p. l., 5–189 p. 15½ᶜᵐ. (Guttentag'sche sammlung preussischer ge- setze. nr. 36)

1. Police—Prussia.   I. Prussia. Laws, statutes, etc. II. Title.

30–18618

NL 0379048   DLC

Lindemann, Otto, 1871– ed.
... Grunderwerbsteuergesetz mit den ausführungsbestimmun- gen, erläutert von geheimem oberjustizrat Otto Lindemann ... Berlin und Leipzig, Vereinigung wissenschaftlicher verleger, W. de Gruyter & co., 1919.

1 p. l., (5)–141 p. 15½ᶜᵐ. (Guttentagsche sammlung deutscher reichsge- setze. nr. 139)

"Verzeichnis der abkürzungen": p. 6–7.

I. Germany. Laws, statutes, etc. II. Title.

21—1588

NL 0379049   DLC

Lindemann, Otto, 1871– joint ed.

Germany. *Laws, statutes, etc.*
Das reichsgesetz über die angelegenheiten der freiwil- ligen gerichtsbarkeit, unter mitwirkung von Eugen Ebert ... erläutert von Heinrich Dudek ... (und) Otto Lindemann ... 2. verm. und verb. aufl. Breslau, M. & H. Marcus, 1908.

Lindemann, Otto, 1871– ed.
Das Reichsgesetz über die Zwangsversteigerung und die Zwangsverwaltung, nebst dem Einführungs- und Preussischen Ausführungsgesetze,.... Breslau, 1905
see under Germany. Laws, statutes, etc.

Lindemann, Otto, 1871– ed.
... Reichs-kostenordnung (Verordnung über die kosten in angelegenheiten der freiwilligen gerichtsbarkeit und der zwangsvollstreckung in das unbewegliche vermögen) vom 25. november 1935, erläutert von geh. oberjustizrat Otto Linde- mann ... Berlin und Leipzig. W. de Gruyter & co., 1936.

1 p. l., 5–196, (1) p. incl. tables. 15½ᶜᵐ. (Guttentagsche sammlung deutscher reichsgesetze. nr. 198)

1. Costs (Law)—Germany.   I. Germany. Laws, statutes, etc. II. Title.

36–20800

NL 0379052   DLC

LINDEMANN, Otto, 1871– ed.
Sammlung der wichtigsten preussischen straf- gesetze, nebst einem anhang: gesetz betr. den erlass polizeilicher strafverfügungen vom 23 april 1883. Berlin, 1903.

24°
"Guttentag'sche sammlung preussischer gesetze. nr. 34."

NL 0379053   MH-L

Lindemann, Otto, 1871– ed.
Sammlung der wichtigsten preussischen strafgesetze nebst einem anhang: Gesetz, betr. den erlass polizeilicher strafver- fügungen vom 23. april 1883. Ergänzungsband zur Gutten- tag'schen sammlung preussischer gesetze. Text-ausg. mit an- merkungen und sachregister von Otto Lindemann ... 2. aufl. Berlin, J. Guttentag, 1912.

1 p. l., 5–372 p. 16ᶜᵐ. (Guttentag'sche sammlung preussischer ge- setze. nr. 34)

1. Criminal law—Prussia. 2. Police—Prussia.   I. Prussia. Laws, statutes, etc. II. Title.

30–16845

NL 0379054   DLC

Lindemann, Otto, 1871– ed.
... Umsatzsteuergesetz mit den ausführungsbestim- mungen des Bundesrats, erläutert von geheimem oberjus- tizrat Otto Lindemann ... Berlin, J. Guttentag, 1918.

1 p. l., 5–211 p. 16ᶜᵐ. (Guttentagsche sammlung deutscher reichsge- setze. nr. 132)

"Verzeichnis der abkürzungen": p. 6–7.
Contains forms.

I. Germany. Laws, statutes, etc. II. Title.

21–1585

NL 0379055   DLC

Lindemann, Otto, 1879–
Der Bergsee; ein vorspiel vnd zwei akte...
see under   Bittner, Julius, 1874–1939.

M1735
.S
Case
Lindemann, Otto, 1879– arr.

Schultze, Norbert, 1911–
(Lili Marleen; arranged)

Lili Marleen, musik av Norbert Schultze, svensk text: Gu- nilla; tysk text: Hans Leip. (Stockholm) Carl Gehrmans mu- sikförlag; Berlin, Apollo-verlag (1940)

Lindemann, Otto, 1879– arr.
Lucedia; Legende aus heidnischer Zeit ...
see under   Giannini, Vittorio, 1903–

M24
.D685S7
Lindemann, Otto, 1879– arr.

Dostal, Nico.
(Spanische Skizzen ; arr.)

Spanische Skizzen; Suite (in 4 Sätzen. Klaviersatz von Otto Lindemann) Magdeburg, Heinrichshofen (1943) Pl no. H. V. 13452.

Lindemann, Otto, 1879–
A village Romeo and Juliet
see under   Delius, Frederick, 1862–1934.

Lindemann, Otto, 1890–
Die Arbeitsverhältnisse und die Arbeiterpolitik in der chemi- schen Industrie ... von Otto Lindemann ... Berlin: J. Särchen, 1928. xii, 157 p. incl. tables. 8°.

Dissertation, Hamburg.
Lebenslauf, p. 157.
Bibliography, p. v–vii.

441155A. 1. Chemical workers—   Germany.   October 21, 1929

NL 0379061   NN CtY MiU MH-BA ICJ CU

Lindemann. Otto-Friedrich: Die Zulässigkeit der Abtretung und Pfändung des Grundbuchberichtigungsrechts und der Geltend- machung des Zurückbehaltungsrechts gegenüber dem Berichti- gungsberechtigten. [Maschinenschrift.] IV, 78 S. 4°. — Auszug: o. O. 1921. 2 Bl. 8°
Breslau, R.- u. staatswiss. Diss. v. 10. Jan. 1922   (U 23. 1136)

NL 0379062   ICRL

VOLUME 334

4
Music
2940

Lindemann, Paul

   Alle Hampelmänner tanzen, lustiges
Intermezzo.   Salon-Orchester.   Berlin,
Edition Lindemann ₍c1930₎
    score (5 p.) and   parts

NL 0379063   DLC-P4

Lindemann (Paul). *Statistischer Beitrag
zur Behandlung der Placenta prævia. 30 pp.
₍8°. Würzburg, Becker, 1894.

NL 0379064   DNLM

Lindemann, Paul.
   Ueber den wert der leukocytenkurve in der
kriegschirurgie ... Tübingen, Laupp, 1916.
   cover-title, p. 608-636.   diagrs.

   "Sonderabdruck aus 'Bruns' Beiträge zur klinischen chirurgie' ... band CI, heft 5 (24.
kriegschirurgischen heft; kriegschirurgisches
band V, heft 5)"

NL 0379065   NNC

Lindemann, Paul, *Bürgermeister.*
  ----Die städtische säuglingsfürsorge in
Magdeburg im halbjahre april-oktober
1908. I. Allgemeiner verwaltungsbericht,
von Bürgermeister Paul Lindemann...
II. Ärstlicher bericht, von prof. dr.
Martin Thiemich...Leipzig und Wien, F.
Deuticke, 1909.
   2 p. l., 54 p.   tables.   25 1/2 cm.
(Ergebnisse der säuglingsfürsorge...
3. heft)

NL 0379066   DL DNLM

Lindemann, Paul, 1881-1938.
   Ambassadors of Christ, by Paul Lindemann ... St. Louis,
Mo., Concordia publishing house, 1935.
   iv p., 1 l., 161 p.   19½ cm.

   1. Pastoral theology—Lutheran church.   I. Title.

   BV4010.L56   250   35—5924

NL 0379067   DLC PPWe

₍Lindemann, Paul₎ 1881-
   Christian stewardship and its modern implications. St.
Louis, Mo., Concordia publishing house ₍1933₎
   46 p.   22½ᶜᵐ.

   On cover: A reprint of the doctrinal paper read by Rev. Paul Lindemann of St. Paul, Minn., at the meeting of the Atlantic district of the
Ev. Luth. synod of Missouri, Ohio, and other states.

   1. Stewardship, Christian.   I. Title.

   Library of Congress   BX8066.L46C5   34—5992
                                248

NL 0379068   DLC

Lindemann, Paul, 1881-
   A conference with God; a book of sermons, by Paul Lindemann ... Minneapolis, Minn., Augsburg publishing house
₍1937₎
   viii p., 1 l., 307 p.   20½ᶜᵐ.

   1. Lutheran church—Sermons. 2. Sermons, American.   I. Title.

   Library of Congress   BX8066.L45C6   37—10287

   Copyright A 105738   252.041

NL 0379069   DLC

Lindemann, Paul, 1881-
   Festival days; sermons for special occasions, by Paul Lindemann ...   Minneapolis, Minn., Augsburg publishing house
₍*1935₎
   ix, 166 p.   20½ᶜᵐ.

   1. Festival-day sermons. 2. Lutheran church—Sermons. 3. Sermons,
American.   I. Title.

   Library of Congress   BV43.L48   38-4757

   Copyright A 114185   252.6

NL 0379070   DLC PPLT

Lindemann, Paul, 1881-*1938.*
   Fundamental questions, by Paul Lindemann ...   New York,
N. Y., American Lutheran publicity bureau ₍1937?₎
   23 p.   18ᶜᵐ.

   1. Christianity—20th cent.   I. Title.   37-20558

   Library of Congress   BR125.L7345
                                 230

NL 0379071   DLC

Lindemann, Paul, 1911-
   Heimat und Volkstum in der deutschen Tagespresse...von
Schriftleiter Paul Lindemann...   Düsseldorf: Weickert & Ko-
blo, 1937.   61 p.   21cm.

   Inaugural-Dissertation — Köln, 1936.
   Lebenslauf.
   "Literaturverzeichnis," p. 60-61.

   1. Journalism—Germany.   2. Patriotism, Local—Germany.
                                      July 13, 1938

NL 0379072   NN CtY NNC

Lindemann, Paul ₍Hermann Georg₎ 1877-
   ... Über osteogenesis imperfecta ... Berlin, Buchdruckerei von G. Schade (O. Francke) ₍1903₎
   29, ₍3₎ p. 21ᵐᵐ.

   Inaug.-diss.—Berlin.
   Lebenslauf.
   "Litteratur": 1 p. following p. 29.

   1. Bones—Diseases.   7-40633†

   Library of Congress   QM691.L74

NL 0379073   DLC DNLM CtY

Lindemann, Reinhold.
   Begegnung. ₍3. Aufl.₎   Freiburg, Herder
₍1952₎
   13 p. 27 plates (part col.) 19 cm. (Der
Bilderkreis. 21)
   1. Salutations in art.

NL 0379074   NN

Lindemann, Reinhold.
   Hölderlin heute.   Berlin, Minerva-Verlag, 1948.
   187 p. 19 cm.   (Clavis)
   Bibliographical references included in "Nachwort" (p. 187)

   1. Hölderlin, Friedrich, 1770-1843.

                                      A 50-4914

   Harvard Univ. Library
   for Library of Congress

NL 0379075   MH DLC-P4 TxU CU ICU IU CaBVaU

Lindemann, Reinhold.
   Kreuz und Eros. Paul Claudels Weltbild im "Seidenen
Schuh." Frankfurt am Main, J. Knecht ₍1955₎
   188 p. port. 20 cm.

   "Die Zitate sind der deutschen Übersetzung des 'Seidenen Schuh'
von Hans Urs v. Balthasar entnommen."

   Contents.—Das Erosthema im Abendland.—Divina commedia.—
Kraftfelder.—"Afrikas Ruf."—Fegefeuer Mogador.—Gegenstimmen.—
Der gekreuzigte Eros.—Sternbild der Liebe.—Weitereroberung und
Restitution.

   1. Claudel, Paul, 1868-1955. Le soulier de satin.   I. Title.
                                    A 56-2585

   Illinois. Univ. Library
   for Library of Congress

NL 0379076   IU OrU CU MiU MH NN NIC NcU

DE9
B64I5

Lindemann, Richard
   Beiträge zur Charakteristik K.A. Böttigers
und seiner Stellung zu J.G. von Herder.
Anhangsweise sind bisher ungedruckte Briefe
Caroline Herders an Böttiger beigegeben
worden.   Görlitz, A. Foerster, 1885.
   iv,148 p.

   Bibliographical footnotes.

NL 0379077   CU OC1W

Lindemann, Richard, 1860-
   De substantiae, attributorum, modorum apud
Spinozam ratione et cohaerentia. Halis Saxon-
num, 1884.
   35 p. 23cm.

   Thesis, Halle.
   Volume of pamphlets.

NL 0379078   NNC OCH NIC ICRL

Lindemann, Richard, 1886-
   Die Haftung des Niessbrauchers eines
Vermögens für die Zinsen der Schulden
des Bestellers. § 1088 B.G.B. ... von
Richard Lindemann ... Berlin, H. Klo-
kow, 1913.
   5 p.l., 3-43 p.   22cm.

   Inaug.-Diss. - Erlangen.
   "Literaturverzeichnis": 3d-4th prelim.
leaves.

NL 0379079   MH-L NIC ICRL

LINDEMANN, Robert, 1879-
   Über die wärmewirkungen oszillatorischer kon-
densatorentladungen im primären und sekundären
kreise. Inaug.-diss., Göttingen. Leipzig,
1903.

   Diagrs.
   "Lebenslauf", after p. 70.   Phys 3500.8

NL 0379080   MH CtY

D40
.L745

LINDEMANN, ROBERT ALFRED, 1922-
   Important factors in the colonial history of
Rhode Island influencing her participation in the
revolutionary movement. ₍Typewritten ms.₎
Bloomington, Indiana, 1952.
   3+170 p.

   Thesis (Ph.D.)—Indiana University

   1.Rhode Island—Colonial period 2.Rhode Island—
Revolution

NL 0379081   InU

VOLUME 334

BS3650 Lindemann, Rudolf, *1852-1909*.
.A5L7 ... Die echtheit der paulinischen hauptbriefe gegen Steck's umsturzversuch vertheidigt, von Rudolf Lindemann ... Zürich, Schröter & Meyer, 1889.

{8} 56 p. 21ᶜᵐ. (Neutestamentliche studien und kritiken. Hrsg. von prof. dr. G. Volkmar. 1. hft.)

1. Bible. N. T. Epistles of Paul—Evidences, authority, etc. 2. Steck, Rudolf, 1842- Der Galaterbrief, nach seiner echtheit untersucht.

NL 0379082   ICU NjPT MH

Lindemann, Rudolf, 1907-
Emissionsspektrographische aluminiumbestimmung in Aschen biologischer materialien. ... 1935.
Inaug. Diss. - Techn. Hochsch. Berlin, 1935.
Lebenslauf.
Bibliography.

NL 0379083   ICRL

Lindemann, Rudolf, 1907-
Verfahren zur zerstörungsfreien Werkstoffprüfung, von R. Lindemann und M. Pfender. {1. Aufl.} Berlin, G. Siemens, 1948.

76 p. illus. 21 cm. (Fortschritte der Technik, 6)
"Schrifttumsverzeichnis": p. 71-76.

1. Non-destructive testing.   I. Pfender, M., 1907-   joint author.
II. Title.   (Series)

TA406.5.L55   51-29265

NL 0379084   DLC

TA410   Lindemann, Rudolf, joint author.
.V8   *1907-*
      Vaupel, Otto.
      Zerstörungsfreie Werkstoffprüfung mit Röntgen- und Gammastrahlen, von Otto Vaupel unter Mitarbeit von Rudolf Lindemann. Mit einem Vorwort von Rudolf Berthold. Frankfurt am Main, O. Salle, 1944.

Lindemann, Rudolf, 1909-
... Über Schmelzlamellen ... Leipzig, 1936.
Inaug. - Diss. - Leipzig.
Lebenslauf.
Full name: Rudolf Heinrich Richard Lindemann.

NL 0379086   CtY

Lindemann, Ruth.
... Der begriff der conscience im französischen denken, von Ruth Lindemann. Jena und Leipzig, W. Gronau, 1938.

4 p. l., 124 p. 24½ᶜᵐ. (Berliner beiträge zur romanischen philologie, hrsg. von Ernst Gamillscheg und Emil Winkler. bd. VIII, 2)
The author's inaugural dissertation, Heidelberg.
"Literatur": p. 122-124.

1. Conscience. 2. Consciousness. 3. Semantics. 4. Philosophy, French.
I. Title.

Library of Congress   PC13.B47 bd. 8, no. 2
                                                          39-9791

NL 0379087   DLC PPT PBm

Lindemann, Siegfried, *1880-* cand. cam., a. Naumburg a. S.: Das wirtschaftliche Gebahren der modernen Gesellschaftsformen in den verschiedenen Gewerbezweigen nach den Ergebnissen der Konkursstatistik. Halle a. S. 1911: John. 129 S. 8°
Halle, Phil. Diss. v. 17. Juni 1911, Ref. Conrad
[Geb. 16. Febr. 80 Erfurt; Wohnort: Hannover; Staatsangeh.: Preußen; Vorbildung: Gymn. Naumburg Reife O. 98; Studium: Jura Heidelberg 3, München 1, Halle 2, Staatswiss. Halle 3 S.; Rig. 1. März 11.] [U 11. 1863

NL 0379088   ICRL PU CtY MiU MH NN

PT35   Lindemann, Theodor, 1890-
.A1   Versuch einer formenlehre des Hürnen
v.32   Seyfrid, mit heranziehung des neugefundenen Strassburger druckes von 1563... von Theodor Lindemann...   Halle a.S., E. Karras, 1913.
      3 p.l., 82 p., 1 l. 22cm. {German language and literature dissertations. v.32}
      Inaug.-diss. - Rostock.
      Lebenslauf.
      Published also, with the 24 wood-engravings of the 1563 edition, Halle a. S., M. Niemeyer, 1913.
      "Literatur"   3d prelim. leaf.

      1. Siegfried. Das lied vom hürnen Seyfrid.

NL 0379090   NNU-W ICRL ICU MH PU

Lindemann, Theodor, *1890-*
Versuch einer Formenlehre des Hürnen Seyfrid. Mit den 24 Holzschnitten des neuentdeckten Strassburger Druckes von 1563 als Anhang. Halle a. S.: M. Niemeyer, 1913. 4 p.l., 82 p., 11 pl. 8°.

1. Siegfried. 2. German language   (New-High).
                                                          May 1, 1914.

NL 0379091   NN OCl MiU IU MH CtY InU CU NjP CaBVaU

Lindemann, Theodor, 1906-
Beitrag zum Luzernebau im mittleren Ostdeutschland auf Grund von Versuchsergebnissen. Giessen, 1940.

244-283 p. illus. 23 cm.
Diss.—Giessen.
"Diese Arbeit erscheint zugleich in der Zeitschrift 'Pflanzenbau,' Jahrgang 16, Heft 7, Seite 243-283."
Vita.
Bibliography: p. 282-283.

1. Alfalfa.   I. Title: Luzernebau im mittleren Ostdeutschland.

SB205.A4L5   51-49519

NL 0379092   DLC

Lindemann, Thomas, 1575-1632, praeses
... Synoptica exegesis contractus mutui succinctas ac dilucidas decisiones, & resolutiones quaestionum variarum ad hanc materiam pertinentium, & inter alias monetariarum, conclamato hocce cauponio seculo, magno Reipubl. malo controversarum exhibens. Rostochi, prostat in Bibliopolio Hallervordiano, 1624.

104 (i.e. 124) p. 18cm.

Diss. - Rostock (Nicolaus Schütze, Matthias Kleist and Balthasar Gloxin, respondents)
Three dissertations, the 1st and 3d having added title-pages.
Paged in part.
Contents.-Dissertatio I. De mutuo, ejusdem definitionem & caussam efficientem exhibens.- {Dissertatio II.} De

vera et genuina mutui et imprimis nummi essentia.-Dissertatio III. De fine et effectu mutui, quaestionum de condictione certi, aestimatione rei mutuo datae, aliâsve debitae, nec non ratione interesse & usurarum cotidiè emergentium resolutiones breves, uti & enodationes legum difficiliorum circa hanc materiam occurrentium exhibens.

NL 0379095   MH-L MiU-L

Lindemann, Thomas, 1575-1632, praeses.
... Utilissimam reconventionis materiam exhibentem ... Rostochi, J. Pedanus {n.d.}

{24} p. 19cm.
Diss. - Rostock (Heinrich Sibrandt, respondent)

NL 0379096   MH-L

PT   Lindemann, Treumund
2623   Fantasieen. Leipzig, P.G. Kummer,
1625   1826.
F35   iv, 204 p. front. 19 cm.
1826

NL 0379097   CaBVaU

Lindemann, Vladimir.
Soviet forestation: agricultural and social significance. New York, Research Program on the U. S. S. R., 1952.

57 p. maps, diagrs. 28 cm. ({East European Fund; Mimeographed series, no. 25)
Cover title.
Text in Russian.

1. Afforestation—Russia.   I. Title.   (Series)

DK1.E35 no. 25   53-21566

NL 0379098   DLC NNC NN TxU DNAL

Lindeman, Vladimir Karlovich, 1868-
... Zur Lehre von den Funktionen der Niere, von Prof. W. Lindemann ...

(In Ergebnisse der Physiologie. 14. Jahrg., p. 618-656. tables. 1914)
Literatur: p. 618-620.

NL 0379099   ICJ

Lindemann, W   C
Radio Rube's collection of hill country ballads and comic songs
                see under Kennedy, Tom, comp. and ed.

4BR-   Lindemann, Walter.
192   Die proletarische Freidenker-Bewegung; Geschichte, Theorie and Praxis [von] Walter und Anna Lindemann.   Leipzig, Freidenker-Verlag, 1926.
      84 p.

NL 0379101   DLC-P4

Lindemann, Walter.
Schwestern-Lehrbuch zum Gebrauch für Schwestern und Krankenpfleger, von Privatdozent Dr. Walter Lindemann, ... Mit zahlreichen Abbildungen im Text. Wiesbaden, J. F. Bergmann, 1918.
xii, 323, {1} p. incl. illus., diagrs. 25ᶜᵐ.

NL 0379102   ICJ PPC ICRL

WP   LINDEMANN, Walter, *physician*
100   Grundlagen der gynäkologischen
L743g   Ausbildung; kurzgefasstes Lehrbuch für
1922   Studierende. München, Bergmann, 1922.
      ix, 173 p. illus.

NL 0379103   DNLM PPC

VOLUME 334

Lindemann, Walther.
Beitraege zur biologischen bedeutung der lipode, besonders fuer die sexualfunktion des weibes. Inaug. diss. Halle, 1915. (Leipzig).
Bibl.

NL 0379104   ICRL DNLM

Lindemann, Walther, Aus d. physiol. Inst. zu Halle. Zur Kenntnis der Autolyse. Halle a.S. 1911: Kaemmerer. 17 S. 8°
Halle, Med. Diss. v. 29. Juli 1911, Ref. Bernstein
[Geb. 22. März 86 Halle a. S.; Wohnort: Halle; Staatsangeh.: Preußen; Vorbildung: Latina Halle Reife O. 05; Studium: Halle 10 S.; Coll. 2. Aug. 10; Approb. 3. Juli 11.]   [U 11. 1779

NL 0379105   ICRL MiU DNLM MBCo

Lindemann, Werner, 1883–
Die Haftung des Luftschiffers nach geltendem Reichsrecht... von Werner Lindemann...   Borna-Leipzig: R. Noske, 1914.
viii, 54 p.   8°.

Dissertation, Erlangen.
Bibliography, p. [vii–]viii.

1. Aeronautics—Jurisp.—Germany,   1914.
September 10, 1928

NL 0379106   NN NIC ICRL MH CtY MH-L

Lindemann, Wilhelm.
Der lokomotivrahmen als starrer balken auf federnden stützen. Ein beitrag zur bestimmung der lastverteilung von lokomotiven. Berlin, Buchdruckerei A. W. Schade, 1904.
1 p. l., 31 p. 3 fold. diagr. 26½ x 21ᶜᵐ.
Inaug.-diss.—Technische hochschule, Braunschweig.

1. Locomotives.
7—27426

Library of Congress   TJ608.L6

NL 0379107   DLC ICJ

Lindemann, Wilhelm.
Ueber die Unglücksfälle und Berufskrankheiten der Minen- und Tunnelarbeiter.   (In: Internat. Congress on Hygiene and Demography, 15. Washington, 1912. Transac. Washington, 1913. 8°. v. 3, p. 673–690.)

1. Mines, etc.—Accidents. 2. Miners   —Diseases. 3. Tunneling—Hygiene. 4. Occupations—Diseases of.   October 25, 1917.

NL 0379108   NN

4
Music
2991

Lindemann, Wilhelm, musician.
Deutschland über alles, Gott erhalte Franz den Kaiser, Ouverture zum Vaterländischen Schauspiel, Radetzky, von Wilhelm Lindemann qta. Fritze Bollmann.   Berlin, C. M. Roehr, c1916.
parts.

NL 0379109   DLC-P4

Lindemann, Wilhelm, *musician*.

Gross-Deutschland "Sieg Heil!", Marsch.
Postillion-Liedermarsch, die Post im Walde.
Berlin, W. Lindemann c 1939

parts
Plate no. Wi. Li. 138

NL 0379110   NN PP MB CtY MH IaU

Lindemann, Wilhelm, of Magdeburg.
Kritische Darstellung der Verhandlungen Papst Innocenz III. mit den deutschen Gegen-königen. I. Abt. Bis zur offenen Erklärung Innocenz für Otto IV. (1201) ... Magdeburg, Baensch, 1885.
21 p.

Programm des mit Gymnasialklassen verbundenen Real-Gymnasiums in Magdeburg.

NL 0379111   NNC CU

Lindemann, Wilhelm, surgeon.
Über partielle fussamputationen.   Jena, W. Ratz, 1876.
46 p. 8°.
Inaug. - Diss. - Jena.

NL 0379112   DNLM ICRL

Lindemann, Wilhelm, 1828–1879.
Angelus Silesius, Johannes Scheffler; bild eines convertiten, dichters, und streittheologen aus dem 17. jahrhundert. Freiburg im Breisgau, Herder, 1876.
nar. 12°. pp. (6), 170. (Sammlung historischer bildnisse, 3ᵉ serie, 8.)

Scheffler||Series|

NL 0379113   MH MnCS NN MWelC OClJC CU

Lindemann, Wilhelm, 1828–1879.
Blumenstrauss von geistlichen gedichten des deutschen mittelalters, den freunden religiöser dichtung gewidmet, von W. Lindemann. Freiburg im Breisgau, Herder, 1874.
xv, 529, [1] p.   17½ cm.

NL 0379114   KAS

Lindemann, Wilhelm, 1828-1879.
Für die Pilgerrise, ein album von religiösen dichtungen gesammelt. Freiburg im Breisgau, Herder, 1878.
264 p.

NL 0379115   OClJC

Lindemann, Wilhelm, 1828–1879.
Geistliche dichtungen der neuzeit. Hrsg. von W. Lindemann. Freiburg im Breisgau, Herder, 1871.
x, 193 p. 19 cm.

NL 0379116   KAS OClJC

830.9
L743g

Lindemann, Wilhelm, 1828–1879.
Geschichte der deutschen Literatur.
Freiburg, Herder, 1866.
714 p. 22 cm.

1. German literature—Hist. & crit.

NL 0379117   ICarbS

Lindemann, Wilhelm, 1828–1879.
Geschichte der deutschen literatur von den ältesten zeiten bis zur gegenwart, von Wilhelm Lindemann. 2., überarbeitete und verm. aufl. ... Freiburg im Breisgau, Herder, 1869.
vii, 711 p. 23 cm.

1. German literature—Hist. & crit.
23–28446

Library of Congress   PT95.L5 1869

NL 0379118   DLC CaBVaU OClStM

Lindemann, Wilhelm, 1828–1879.
Geschichte der deutschen literatur. Freiburg, Herder, 1866. v. 3 only.   4 aufl., 1876 v. 3
5 aufl., 1879.   v. 3

NL 0379119   MWelC OCU

Lindemann, Wilhelm, 1828-1879.
Geschichte der deutschen Litteratur. 6. Aufl., nach dem Tode des Verfassers hrsg. und teilweise neu bearb. von Joseph Seeber.   Freiburg im Breisgau; St. Louis, Mo., Herder, 1889.
xii, 976 p.   24 cm.

1. German literature - History and criticism. I. Seeber, Joseph,   ed.

NL 0379120   KAS OClJC PLatS

Lindemann, Wilhelm, 1828–1879.
Wilhelm Lindemanns Geschichte der deutschen litteratur. 7. aufl. Herausgegeben und teilweise neu bearbeitet von dr. p. Anselm Salzer. Freiburg im Breisgau, St. Louis, Mo. [etc.] Herder, 1898.
x, 1115 p. 24½ cm.

1. German literature—Hist. & crit. I. Salzer, Anselm, 1856–   ed.
3–25299

Library of Congress   PT80.L6 1898

NL 0379121   DLC OrStbM NjP NIC PU MoSU

Lindemann, Wilhelm, 1828–1879.
Wilhelm Lindemanns Geschichte der deutschen literatur. 8. aufl. Hrsg. und teilweise neu bearb. von Dr. Max Ettlinger. Freiburg im Breisgau, St. Louis, Mo., Herder [etc.] 1906.
xiv, 1083 p. 26 cm.

1. Ettlinger, Max, 1877–   ed.
6-46308

NL 0379122   DLC MB CU PBm OCX

Lindemann, Wilhelm, 1828–1879.
Geschichte der deutchen Literatur. 9. und 10. Aufl. Hrsg. und teilweise neu bearb. von Max Ettlinger. Freiburg im Breisgau, Herder, 1915.
2 v. illus. plates. facsims. 23 cm.

1. German literature—Hist. & crit. I. Title.

NL 0379123   ICarbS CU MH ICN GU MH

VOLUME 334

Lindemann, Willy, 1901–
Zur behandlung der blutungen aus magenduodenalgeschwueren und nach operativen eingriffen am magen.
Inaug. diss., Rostock, 1926.
Bibl.

NL 0379124   ICRL

Lindemann, Wilhelm, 1905–
Die deutsche margarineindustrie und die öffentliche margarinepolitik bis 1935. ...
Eisfeld i. Thür., 1936.   171 p.
Inaug. Diss. – Erlangen, 1936.
Lebenslauf.
Literaturverzeichnis.

NL 0379125   ICRL CtY NN

4K Lindemann, Wilhelm, 1912–
Ger   Das Soester Strafrecht bis zum
946   Beginn des 16. Jahrhunderts. Pölitz,
Pom., 1939.
71 p.

NL 0379126   DLC-P4

Lindeman, Włodzimierz, 1867–
Toksykologja chemicznych środków bojowych. Warszawa, Wojskowy Instytut Naukowo-Wydawniczy, 1925.
285, xxv p.   17 illus., 12 col. plates.   23 cm.
Bibliography: p. xxi-xxv.
L. C. copy imperfect: t. p., p. xxv mutilated.

1. Gases, Asphyxiating and poisonous—War use.   I. Title.
UG447.L53   59–56942

NL 0379127   DLC

Lindemann-Frommel, Karl August, 1819–1891, illus.
Gregorovius, Ferdinand Adolf, 1821–1891.
Die insel Capri, von F. Gregorovius. Mit bildern und skizzen von K. Lindemann-Frommel. Holzschnitte aus den xylographischen anstalten von R. Brend'amour, F. A. Brockhaus, gebrüder Dalziel und G. Flegel. Leipzig, A. Dürr, 1868.

Lindemann-Frommel, Karl August, 1819–1891, illus.
[Skizzen und bilder aus Rom und der umgegend.
Stuttgart, 1851–60]
42 pl. in Portfolio obl f°

NL 0379128   DLC MH

914.56 Lindemann-Frommel, Karl August, 1819–1891, illus.
L64v   Vignetten aus Rom ... Rom [etc.?] 185-?]
2 l. front., 4 pl.

1. Rome (City)—Descr.—Views.

NL 0379129   IU

Lindemans, G   J
De theosofie, haar wezen en haar waarde. Amsterdam, H. J. W. Becht [1949]
xxxiii, 198 p. 24 cm. (Athenæum-bibliotheek)

1. Theosophy.
BP565.L73   A 50–1255
Chicago. Univ. Libr.
for Library of Congress   †

NL 0379130   ICU DLC CtY

Lindemans, Jan, 1888–
Album Dr. Jan Lindemans
see under title

Lindemans, Jan, 1888–
Bijdragen tot de geschiedenis en de beteekenis van de vlaamsche persoonsnamen, door dr. Jan Lindemans ...
Turnhout, Drukkerij J. van Mierlo-Proost, 1944–
v. 19 cm.
"Bibliographische verantwoording": v. 1, p. 9–12.

1. Names, Personal—Flemish. 2. Flemish language—Etymology—Names.
CS2375.F5L5   A F 50–63
Chicago. Univ. Libr.
for Library of Congress   †

NL 0379132   ICU CtY DLC

LINDEMANS, JAN, 1888–
Brabantsche plaatsnamen. Leuven, Vla. top. vereeniging, 1932–51. 9 v. maps (part fold.) 26cm. (Toponymica. 2)

[Deel] 4–12.
Vols. 10–12 issued by: Instituut voor naamkunde.
Vol. 9: electrostatic reproduction.

CONTENTS.—4. Baardegem.—5. Beersel.—6. Beert.—7. Belgem.—8. Bekkerzeel.—9. Drogenbosch, door J. Lindemans en C. Theys.—10. Dworp, door J. Lindemans en C. Theys.—11. Bellingen.—12. Bogaarden.

1. Geography—Names—Belgium—Brabant. I. Series.

NL 0379134   NN MH

Lindemans, Jan, 1888–
Brabantse persoonsnamen in de xiii° en de xiv° eeuw.
Leuven, Instituut voor Naamkunde, 1947.
x, 55 p. 25 cm. (Anthroponymica 1: Onomastica Neerlandica)

1. Names, Personal—Belgium—Brabant. 2. Names, Personal—Dutch. 3. Dutch language—Etymology—Names. I. Title. (Series: Anthroponymica, 1)
CS2529.B7L55   49–25764 rev*

NL 0379135   DLC NN PU NIC MoU

LINDEMANS, JAN, 1888–
Het cijnsboek van Duyst; excerpten en aanteekeningen, door J. Lindemans en E. van der Linden.
Leuven, Vla. top. vereeniging, 1931. 52 p. 26cm. (Toponymica. 3)
Bibliographical footnotes.
1. Geography—Names—Belgium—Uccle. 2. Geography—Names—Belgium—Saint Gilles. 3. Geography—Names—Belgium—Ixelles. I. Linden, E. van der, joint author. II. Series.
III. Linden, E. van der.

NL 0379136   NN

Lindemans, Jan, 1888–
Fêtes et jeux de Flandre et de Wallonie.
31, [1]p. Courtrai, Éditions de Chez nous [1926]

NL 0379137   OCl

Lindemans, Jan, 1888–
... Hoe maak ik mijn stamboom op, kleine inleiding tot de vlaamsche familiegeschiedenis. 3. druk. Antwerpen [etc.]
N. v. Standaard-boekhandel, 1943.
80 p. incl. illus. (coats of arms) geneal. tables, diagr. 18½ cm.
Appeared in Nieuw Vlaanderen during 1941 with title Over vlaamsche familiegeschiedenis, under the pseudonym Jan van der Hameyde. cf. Voorwoord.

1. Genealogy. 2. Names, Personal—Flemish. 3. Flemish language—Etymology—Names. III. Title.
CS19.L5 1943   A F 47–67
Wisconsin. Univ. Libr.
for Library of Congress   †

NL 0379138   WU DLC NN

Lindemans, Jan, 1888–
Plaats- en persoonsnamen in oude cijnsboeken; proeve van bewerking naar het renteboek der St.Baafsabdij te St.-Lievens-Houtem, XVe eeuw, door J.Lindemans. Leuven Inst. Vla. Toponymie, 1941
47 p. (Toponymica; bijdragen en bouwstoffen, 8)

I. Sint-Lievens-Houtem, Belgium. II. Ghent. Saint Bavon (Benedictine abbey)

NL 0379139   WU NN

Lindemans, Jan, 1888–
Toponymie van Asse. 's-Gravenhage, M. Nijhoff, 1952.
223 p. maps (1 fold.) 25 cm. (Nomina geographica Flandrica; studiën en monographieën over Vlaamse plaatsnaamkunde. Monographieën 5: Onomastica Neerlandica)
Bibliography: p. [79]–84.

1. Names, Geographical—Belgium—Asse. 2. Dutch language—Etymology—Names. I. Title. (Series: Nomina geographica Flandrica; studiën en monographieën over Vlaamsche plaatsnaamkunde. Monographieën, 5)
DH414.L48   A 53–5007
Yale Univ. Library
for Library of Congress   [a56c½]†

NL 0379140   CtY NIC MH MB NN DLC

Lindemans, Jan.
Toponymie van Opwijk, door dr. Jan Lindemans. 's-Gravenhage, N. v. M. Nijhoff, 1931.
3 p. l., [ix]–xii, 219, [1] p. incl. maps. fold. map. 25½ cm. (Added t.-p.: Nomina geographica flandrica; studiën en monographieën over vlaamsche plaatsnaamkunde ... Monographieën. 1)
"Bronnen": p. 15–18.

1. Names, Geographical—Belgium—Opwijk. I. Title.
A C 36–4938
Title from Yale Univ.   Printed by L. C.

NL 0379141   CtY MB CtY NN

Lindemans, Jan, 1888–
Toponymische verschijnselen; geografisch bewerkt, door dr. J. Lindemans ... 's-Gravenhage, M. Nijhoff, 1942–
v. fold. maps. 23 cm. (Added t.-p.: Nomina geographica flandrica; studiën en monographieën over vlaamsche plaatsnaamkunde ... Studiën v)
Bibliography included in "Bijlagen" of v. 1.
CONTENTS.—I. De -heemnamen en -ingeformaties. De kouternamen.

1. Names, Geographical—Flemish. 2. Flemish language—Etymology—Names. I. Title.

A 46–863
Yale univ. Library
for Library of Congress

NL 0379142   CtY NN MH

VOLUME 334

Lindemans, Jan, 1888–
... Vakwoordenlijst der hopteelt, door dr. Jan Lindemans ... Alfons de Jaegher ... en i' Paul Lindemans ... Wetteren, Boekdrukkerij J. de Meester en zonen, 1928.

195 p. illus. 25⁰. (Koninklijke vlaamsche academie voor taal- en letterkunde. ₍Uitgaven. VI. reeks. Bekroonde werken. 45₎)

"Lijst der fransche vakwoorden": p. ₍155₎–166. Engelsche vakwoordenlijst": p. ₍167₎–181. "Duitsche vakwoordenlijst": p. ₍182₎–195. Bibliography included in "Inleiding" (p. ₍3₎–9)

1. Hops—Dictionaries—Flemish. I. Jaegher, Alfons de, joint author. II. Lindemans, Paul, joint author.

45–51459

Library of Congress   SB295.H8L5

NL 0379143   DLC ICU

Lindemans, L
Taalgebruik in gerechtszaken. In deze verhandeling werd de stof bijgehouden tot 1 Februari 1955. ₍Brussel, F. Larcier, 1955–

1 v. (loose-leaf) 27 cm.

Binder's title: Algemene practische rechtsverzameling. Includes bibliography.

1. Belgium—Languages. 2. Law—Language.   I. Title. II. Title: Algemene practische rechtsverzameling.

58–22629

NL 0379144   DLC

30.6
L64
Bl.2
Lindemans, Paul.
Bedrijfscontrole en boekhouden op de boerderij. 2. uitg.   Lier [Belgium] N.V. Jozef van In & Co, 1952.
72 p.

First ed. appeared in Landbouwkundig tijdschrift, June 1949 (105.2 Or5)

1. Agriculture. Accounting.

NL 0379145   DNAL

96
L64
Lindemans, Paul.
Bloementeelt op de landelijke huishoudschool.   Antwerpen, De Sikkel, 1954.
99 p.

1. Floriculture. Sweden.

NL 0379146   DNAL

Lindemans, Paul.
Geschiedenis van de landbouw in België. Antwerpen, De Sikkel, 1952.

2 v. illus., plates. 25 cm.

Slip mounted on t. p. of v. 2 has imprint: 's-Gravenhage, M. Nijhoff. Includes bibliographies.

NL 0379147   ViU DNAL NN ViU PU NN MnU MH WU

DB40
1770
L5
₍Lindemayr, Maurus₎ 1723–1783.
₍Kurzweiliger Hochzeit-Vertrag nach der natürlichen ob der Ennserisch-Bäurischen Mund- und Denkungsart in gebundener Rede zu Unterhaltung Ihro Königl. Hoheit, der Durchlauchtigsten Frau, Frau Maria Antonia ... als höchst dieselben den 23. April 1770 in dem Stifte Lambach übernachteten. Steyr, Gedruckt bey G.Menhardt, 1770.
43 p. 20cm.
Title and text within ornamental borders.
Imperfect copy: p. 39-40 torn, with loss of some text.

NL 0379148   CSt

Lindemayr, Maurus, 1723–1783.
... Sämtliche Dichtungen in obderennsischer Volksmundart./Mit einer biographisch-literarischen Einleitung und einem kurzgefassten Idiotikon, hrsg/ von Pius Schmieder. Linz, H. Korb, 1875.
418p. 18cm.

I. Schmieder, Pius, 1834–1918, ed.

NL 0379149   NcD NcU CU

Lindemayr, Maurus, 1723–1783.
Zwei Singspiele von P. Maurus Lindemayr; Die durch die Todesfurcht vertriebene Saufsucht des liederlichen Hansen; Hans in der Klause, eine komische Oper in II Acten. Mitgeteilt von Moriz Enzinger. (Euphorion. Stuttgart, 1930. 8⁰. Bd. 31, p. 34–95.)

1. Drama, German. 2. Enzinger,   Moriz, 1891–   , editor.
September 26, 1930

NL 0379150   NN

W 1
WI214
Bd. 6
1954
LINDEMAYR, Walther
Arzneimittelexantheme. Wien, Maudrich, 1954.
91 p. (Wiener Beiträge zur Dermatologie, Bd. 6)
1. Drugs - Experimental studies
2. Skin - Reactions   Series

NL 0379151   DNLM

W 4
G453
1940
LINDEMEIER, Wilhelm Heinrich, 1910-
Experimentelle Untersuchungen über die diuretische Wirkung einiger Theophyllinpräparate im Vergleich zu Euphyllin. Giessen, Klein, 1940.
40 p. illus.
Diss. - Giessen.
1. Aminophylline 2. Diuretics & diuresis 3. Theophylline

NL 0379152   DNLM CtY-M

Lindemeyer, Albert.
Zusammenarbeit auf biblischen Bekenntnisgrund. Zurich, Zwingli-Verlag [1948]
24 p. (Kirchliche Zeitfragen, Heft 21)

NL 0379153   MH-AH

Lindemeyer, Georg.
Die Wiedereinsetzung (Rehabilitation) unter besonderer Berücksichtigung der §§ 50-52 des Vorentwurfs und der §§110-112 des Gegenentwurfs. Berlin: A. W. Schade, 1913. 88 p. 8⁰.
Dissertation, Erlangen.
Bibliography, p. 5-7.

1. Rehabilitation.—Jurisprudence,   Germany.
December 18, 1913.

NL 0379154   NN ICRL NIC MH-L MH

Lindemeyer, Julius.
Jesu historia enligt den Heliga Skrift. Stockholm, Carlson [1881]
2 pts. in 1 v. 21.5 cm.
Original title: Geschichte Jesu nach der Heiligen Schrift.

NL 0379155   MH-AH

Lindemeyer, Karl, 1900 –
Die Fieberthermometerindustrie auf dem Thüringer Walde; eine Untersuchung ihrer wirtschaftlichen und sozialen Verhältnisse, von Dr. Karl Lindemeyer... Jena: G. Fischer, 1927
110 p. 8⁰. (Jena. Universität. Wirtschaftswissenschaftliches Seminar. Abhandl. Bd. 17, Heft 5.)

Bibliography, p. ₍109–₎110.

1. Thermometer, Clinical—Trade and   stat.—Germany—Thuringia. 2. Ser.
June 30, 1927

NL 0379156   NN ICRL CU PU ICJ CtY MB MH

LINDEMEYER, Rudolf, ₍1899-
"Die souveranität des königs"; studien zu den staatsanschauungen' im Frankreich Richelieu's. Inaug.-diss.,Berlin. [Kirchhain N.L.,Zahn & Baendel],1929.

NL 0379157   MH PU ICRL OU CtY

Lindemuth, A.C.
Telephone mergers illegal, address. Chicago, The International Independent Telephone Association [1908]
12 p. 22 cm.
1. Telephone. Addresses, essays, lectures.

NL 0379158   NIC MH

Lindemuth (Arnold) [1880–   ]. *Beitrag zur Entstehung der Poliomyelitis anterior acuta nach Trauma. 19 pp. 8⁰. München, C. Wolf & Sohn. 1908.

NL 0379159   DNLM

Lindemuth (Heinrich) [1883–   ]. *Neue Versuche zur Begründung der rationellen Rektalernährung. 31 pp. 8⁰. Halle a. S., C. A. Kaemmerer & Co., 1908.

NL 0379160   DNLM ICRL MH MiU

MANN
SB
323
L74
Lindemuth, Hugo.
Gemüsebau auf Gartenbeeten. Berlin, K. Siegismund, 1900.
3 v. illus. 19 cm. (Gartenbau-Bibliothek, Bd. 15, 18, 11)

1. Vegetables. 2. Vegetable gardening. I. Title. ₍II. Series: Gartenbau-Bibliothek, Bd. 11, etc. ₎

NL 0379161   NIC DNAL

Lindemuth, Hugo. Handbuch des obstbaues auf wissenschaftlicher und praktischer grundlage. Berlin. 1883. 8⁰. Illustr.

NL 0379162   MH-A CU-A

VOLUME 334

MANN
SB
425
L74
Lindemuth, Hugo.
　　Schönblühende Knollengewächse. Berlin, K.
Siegismund ₁1900₎
　　58 p. 20 illus. 19 cm. (Gartenbau-
Bibliothek, Bd. 29)

　　1. Tubers. I. Title. ₁II. Series₎

NL 0379163　　NIC

MANN
SB
425
L74S
Lindemuth, Hugo.
　　Schönblühende Zwiebelgewächse. Berlin,
K. Siegismund ₁1900₎
　　64 p. 30 illus. 19 cm. (Gartenbau-
Bibliothek, Bd. 13)

　　1. Bulbs. I. Title. ₁II. Series₎

NL 0379164　　NIC

Lindemuth, Hugo.
　　Studien über die sogenannte panaschüre und über
einige begleitende erscheinungen. illus., 2 pl.
　　Landw. jahrb. bd. 36, p. 807-862.　　Berlin, 1907.

　　1. Hybrids. 2. Hybridization. 3. Grafting. 4. Variation in foliage.

　　Library, U. S. Dept. of　　Agriculture　　Agr 8-344

NL 0379165　　DNAL

Lindemuth, Hugo.
　　Ueber vegetative bastarderzeugung durch impfung.
4 pl.
　　Landw. jahrb. bd. 7, p. 887-939.　　Berlin, 1878.

　　1. Grafting. 2. Hybrids and hybridization.

　　Library, U. S. Dept. of　　Agriculture　　Agr 4-1371

NL 0379166　　DNAL OkU

Lindemuth, Margarethe, 1914–
　　Das lettisch-deutsche Verhältnis vor dem Weltkriege auf
Grund der lettischen Presse unter besonderer Berücksichti-
gung der Jahre 1905-1907. ₁Heidelberg₎ 1944.
　　137 l. 29 cm.
　　Inaug.-Diss.—Heidelberg.
　　Vita.
　　Bibliography: leaves 125-137.

　　1. Germans in Latvia. 2. Latvia—Pol. & govt.　　I. Title.

　　DK511.L165L5　　　　50-49156

NL 0379167　　DLC

Lindemuth, Wm. H.
₁Thisted, Valdemar Adolph₎ 1815-1887.
　　A message from a lost soul; or, Letters from hell; with
an introductory chapter on Hell as God has revealed it
in His word, by Rev. R. A. Torrey, and a concluding chapter on Heaven, the home of the redeemed, by Rev. Wm. H.
Lindemuth. Philadelphia, P. W. Ziegler co. ₁°1906₎

Linden, A　　J
　　Songs for common schools by A.J. Linden.
Chicago, [c1914]
　　75 p.　ports.　23 cm.

NL 0379169　　RPB

Linden, A　　J　　ter.
　　Stoomwerktuigen en ketels. Delft, Delftsche Uitg. Mij.,
1949.
　　116 p. illus. 25 cm. (Handleidingen bij het onderwijs aan de
Technische Hogeschool te Delft, no. 86)
　　Bibliography : p. ₁5₎

　　1. Steam engineering.　I. Title.　(Series: Delft. Technische
Hoogeschool. Handleidingen no. 86)

　　TJ275.L5　　　　50-57304

NL 0379170　　DLC

Linden, A　　　v.d., pseud., ed.
　　Geheime wissenschaften
　　　see under title

Linden, A. v. d., pseud., tr.

Brandes, Georg Morris Cohen, 1842-1927.
　　Die hauptströmungen der litteratur des neunzehnten jahrhunderts. Vorlesungen, gehalten an der Kopenhagener universität von G. Brandes. Uebers. und eingeleitet von Adolf
Strodtmann ... Charlottenburg, H. Barsdorf, 1897-1900.

Linden, A　　v　　d　　, pseud.
　　Das Heine–Grab auf dem Montmartre.
Von A. v.d. Linden. Mit 2 Abbildungen.
Leipzig, H. Barsdorf, 1898.
　　1 p.l., 40, [3] p.　incl. 1 illus., double plate.
21.5 cm.
　　1. Heine, Heinrich – Monuments, etc.

NL 0379173　　CtY CU NcD NN NjP OCH

Linden, A. v. d., pseud., ed. and tr.

Wilhelmine, *consort of Frederick William, margrave of Bay-*
reuth, 1709-1758.
　　Memoiren der königlich preussischen prinzessin Friederike
Sophie Wilhelmine, markgräfin von Bayreuth, schwester Friedrichs des Grossen. Vom jahre 1709-1742. Von ihr selbst
geschrieben ... 10. aufl., fortgeführt bis zum jahre 1758. Mit
dem porträt der markgräfin. Leipzig, H. Barsdorf, 1899.

BF1623
.R7J42
Linden, A. v. d., pseud., tr.

Jennings, Hargrave, 1817-1890.
　　Die rosenkreuzer; ihre gebräuche und mysterien, von H. Jennings, übersetzt von A. v. d. Linden ... Mit ca. 300 illustrationen und 12 tafeln, mit ausführlichem namen- und sachregister ... Berlin, H. Barsdorf, 1912.

Linden, Ada, pseud.
　　see Förster, Luise.

Linden, Adolph F.
　　A history of the Seattle banks, a record of
the growth of the Seattle banks, comp., ed., and
pub. by Adolph F. Linden.　Seattle, Washington
Print. Co., c1910.
　　4 p.l., 148 p.　tables.　20 x 35 cm.

NL 0379177　　CaBViP CaBViPA

Linden, Adriaan Leo Victor Lambert van der.
　　De Europeaan in de maleische literatuur ... door Adriaan
Leo Victor Lambert van der Linden ... Meppel, Drukkerij
en uitgeverszaak B. ten Brink ₁1937₎
　　4 p. l., 458 p. 24½ᵐ.
　　Proefschrift—Utrecht.
　　"Inhoudsopgave der bronnen" : p. ₁453₎-455.
　　"Stellingen" (2 p.) laid in.

　　1. Malay literature.　I. Title.　　　　42-40953

　　Library of Congress　　PL5130.5.L5

NL 0379178　　DLC NN ICU CtY

Linden, Adrien.
　　Causeries enfantines et récréatives.
　　Paris. Delagrave. [1879.] 10 v. in 1. Colored plates. [Petite
bibliothèque des connaissances utiles.] 12°.
　　Contents. — Le mouton. — Le blé. — Le papier. — Le bœuf. — La houille.
— Défenseurs de l'agriculture. — Le verre. — La pierre. — Le bois. —
Inventions et découvertes.

　　F4657 — France. Lang. Reading. — S.r. — T.r.

NL 0379179　　MB MH

Linden (Albert [Hubert Nicolaus]).　"Hat das
enge Becken einen Einfluss auf die Entstehung
des Geschlechts? 18 pp., 1 l. 8°.　Marburg,
E. C. Friedrich, 1886.

NL 0379180　　DNLM PPC

Linden, Albert van der, 1913–
　　... Des tendances régionales dans la musique, par Albert
Vander Linden.　Bruxelles, G. van Campenhout ₁1937₎
　　cover-title, 11, 4 p. 25½ cm.　(Bibliothèque d'études régionales, pub.
sous la direction de Félicien Leuridant.　No. 14)
　　Double paging.
　　"Les danses des provinces belges" : 4 p. at end.

　　1. Nationalism in music. 2. Regionalism. 3. Dancing—Belgium.

　　ML3545.L5　　　　781.7　　　　40-21200 rev

NL 0379181　　DLC

ML 410 LINDEN,ALBERT VAN DER,1913–
.M325 L74　La légende d'un psaultier perdu de Samuel
　　Mareschall. Anvers, N.V. de Nederlandsche
　　Boekhandel, 1945.
　　308-317 p. illus.

　　"Extrait de Hommage a Charles van den Borren."
　　Author's autograph.
　　Cover title.

　　1. Mareschal,Samuel,1554-1640. I. Title.

NL 0379182　　InU

VOLUME 334

Linden, Albert van der, 1913–
Octave Maus et la vie musicale belge (1875–1914) ₍Bruxelles, Palais des académies, 1950₎
155 p. 25 cm. (Académie royale de Belgique. Classe des beaux-arts. Mémoires. Collection in 8°, t. 6, fasc. 2)
CONTENTS.—Sources.—Octave Maus.—L'art moderne.—Les "xx" et la "Libre Esthétique."—Conclusion.—Annexes: 1. Lettres de Vincent d'Indy à Octave Maus. 2. Lettres des compositeurs à Octave Maus. 3. Extraits de presse relatifs aux concerts des xx et de la Libre Esthétique. 4. Table des comptes rendus de l'art moderne sur les concerts des xx et de la L. E.
1. Maus, Octave, 1856–1919. 2. Concerts—Belgium.
[AS242.B3416 t. 6, fasc. 2]　　　A 51–1546

Stanford Univ. Library
for Library of Congress

NL 0379183　　CSt MdBP MB IaU NN ICN TxU ICU

Linden, Albrecht von Heyden—
　　see Heyden-Linden, Albrecht von, 1872–

Linden, Alexandra, tr.
Andreev, Leonid Nikolaevich, 1871–1919.
The red laugh, fragments of a discovered manuscript, by Leonidas Andreief; tr. from the Russian by Alexandra Linden. New York, Duffield & company ₍1915₎

PZ3
.G678
Th
Linden, Alexandra, tr.
Gor'kiĭ, Maksim, 1868–1936.
Three of them, by Maxim Gorky; translated by A. Linden. 4th popular ed. London, T. F. Unwin, 1905.

Linden, Alfred.
Der einfluss von frachtgestaltung und verkehrswegen auf den absatz der Ruhrkohle, von dr. Alfred Linden. Münster (Westf.) Wirtschafts- und socialwissenschaftlicher verlag e. v. für den buchhandel Kommissions-verlag von G. Fischer, Jena, 1938.
19, ₍1₎ p. 22½ᶜᵐ. (Added t.-p.: Verkehrswissenschaftliche forschungen aus dem Verkehrs-seminar an der Westf. Wilhelms-universität zu Münster i. W., hrsg. in verbindung mit ... Otto Most von ... Paul Berkenkopf, hft. 12)
"Vortrag auf einladung des Verkehrs-seminars an der Universität Münster am 18. februar 1938."—p. 5.
1. Coal trade—Ruhr river and valley. 2. Coal—Ruhr river and valley—Transportation.　I. Title.

Library of Congress　　HD9553.7.R8L5
　　　　　　　　　　　　　　　42–29009

NL 0379187　　DLC NN

Linden, Alvin.
The finishing of gunstocks and notes on the conversion of the 1917 Enfield rifle, by Alvin Linden. Being the third booklet in a series devoted to the design and assembly of custom-built firearms.
₍Plantersville, S.C., Small-arms technical publishing company, 1941₎
46 p. (A Samworth booklet on firearms, no. 3)

NL 0379188　　OC1

683
qL744
Linden, Alvin.
Firearm design & assembly ... ₍Georgetown, S.C., T.G. Samworth, 1943–ᵧ ₎
v. illus. 27cm. (Samworth booklet on firearms, nos.1–)
Cover-title.
Includes pattern sheets 1– .
Imprint varies.
Contents:—₍v.1₎ The inletting of gunstock blanks as applied to modifications of the Springfield rifle.—₍v.2₎ The shaping of inletted blanks with notes on some alterations to the model 70 Winchester rifle.—₍v.3₎ The finishing of gunstocks and notes on the conversion of the 1917 Enfield rifle.

NL 0379189　　N CaBVaU Wa MiD

Linden, Alvin.
The inletting of gunstock blanks as applied to modifications of the Springfield rifle, by Alvin Linden. Being the first booklet in a series devoted to the design and assembly of custom-built firearms.
₍Plantersville, S.C., Small-arms technical publishing company, 1941₎
38 p. (A Samworth booklet on firearms, no.1)

NL 0379190　　OC1 CU-B

Linden, Alvin.
The shaping of inletted blanks with notes on some alterations to the model 70 Winchester rifle, by Alvin Linden. Being the second booklet of a series devoted to the design and assembly of custom-built firearms.
₍Plantersville, S.C., Small-arms technical publishing company, 1943₎
54 p. (A Samworth booklet on firearms, no.2)

NL 0379191　　OC1

Linden, Annie.
"Gold"; a Dutch-Indian story, by Annie Linden. New York, The Century co., 1896.
3 p. l., 258 p. 19½ᶜᵐ.

I. Title.

　　　　　　　　　　　　　　　7–19014
Library of Congress　　PZ3.L645G

NL 0379192　　DLC PPL

Linden, Arie Cornelis van der.
De microbiologische aminozuurbepaling en haar toepassing bij de analyse van menselijk globine op verschillende leeftijden. Bergen op Zoom, P. Harte, 1949.
100 p. diagrs. 24 cm.
Proefschrift—Amsterdam.
Summary in English.
"Stellingen": ₍2₎ p. inserted.
Bibliography: p. ₍97₎–100.
1. Amino acids. 2. Globin.　I. Title.

QP801.A5L5　　612.01533　　51–16454

NL 0379193　　DLC DNLM

Linden, Arthur van der, composer.
El concours de Pinsons; comédie-vaudeville in ein acque ...
　　see under Linden, Frédéric van der.

Linden, August Robert von der.
Die Strafrechtsanalogie in Carpzovs Practica criminalis. Bonn, L. Röhrscheid, 1947.
FL6　viii, 41 p. 21ᶜᵐ. (Bonner rechtswis-
B7173r senschaftliche Abhandlungen. Heft 43)
no.43
1. Criminal law. 2. Carpzov, Benedict, 1595–1666. Practica nova imperialis Saxonica rerum criminalium.　I. Title. Series.

NL 0379195　　MiU-L NNC

Linden, Auguste.
Children's trials; or, The little rope-dancers, and other tales. Translated from the German of Auguste Linden, by Trauer Mantel. Boston: Crosby, Nichols & co. ₍etc., etc.₎ 1855. 238 p. col'd front., col'd plates. 17½cm.
Plates are lithographs printed by S. W. Chandler & bro., Boston.
CONTENTS.—Flodvard and Ermena.—Gabrielle.—The gray woman of Scharfenstein.—Mother Ingeborg and her children.—The true son.

895300A. 1. Juvenile literature—　Fiction, German. I. Trauermantel, pseud., tr. II. Title.
　　　　　　　　　　　　　　February 15, 1938

NL 0379196　　NN MB OKentU

Linden, Auguste.
Children's trials: or, The little rope-dancers and other tales. Translated from the German of Auguste Linden, by Trauer Mantel ₍pseud.₎ Boston, Crosby, Nichols, 1859. 238 p. illus.

I. Trauermantel, pseud., tr. II. Title.

NL 0379197　　NNC

Linden, Auguste.
Titania; tales and legends, tr. from the German by Trauermantel. [4], 236p. col.front., col. plates. Boston, Crosby, Nichols & co.; ₍etc., etc.₎ 1857.

NL 0379198　　OC1 CtY

PZ663
.L675
1864
Linden, Auguste.
Titania; tales and legends, translated from the German ... by Trauermantel ₍pseud.₎ Boston, Crosby and Nichols, 1864.
236 p. col. front.

I. Title. II. Trauermantel, pseud., tr.

NL 0379199　　ICU CtHT-W

Linden, Bernard Arthur, 1892–
... Food poisoning from a streptococcus in cheese, by B. A. Linden, W. R. Turner and Charles Thom, microbiological laboratory, Bureau of chemistry, United States Department of agriculture ... Washington, Govt. print. off., 1926.
1 p. l., 6 p. incl. tables. 23ᶜᵐ.
At head of title: Treasury department. United States Public health service. Hugh S. Cumming, surgeon general.
Reprint no. 1100 from the Public health reports, v. 41, no. 32, August 6, 1926 (p. 1647–1652)
Running title: Poisoning from streptococcus in cheese.
1. Cheese—Bacteriology. I. Turner, Wendell R., joint author. II. Thom, Charles, 1872– joint author. III. U. S. Public health service. Public health reports. Reprint 1100. IV. Title. V. Title: Poisoning from a streptococcus in cheese.

Library of Congress　　RA1260.L5
　　　　　　　　　　　　　　　26–27579

NL 0379200　　DLC OU MiU

Linden, Bernard Robert, 1926–
The radial equations and their approximate solutions for the ground state of the nuclear three-body problem with the inclusion of tensor forces. 1951.
120 l.
Thesis – Ohio State University.

NL 0379201　　OU

VOLUME 334

W 4
L68
1774
L.1
LINDEN, Bernardus van
Specimen pathologico-medicum inaugurale de immodica
mentis exercitatione ... Lugduni Batavorum, Apud
Andream Coster, 1774.
29 p. 24 cm.
Diss. - Leyden.

NL 0379202   DNLM

Law
Lindén, Birger, ed.

Sweden. *Laws, statutes, etc.*
Kulturvård och arkivväsen, av Gösta Berg ₍och₎ Birger
Lindén. Stockholm, Norstedt ₍1952₎

Lindén, Bror.
Dalska namn- och ordstudier, gällande särskilt Mora
tingslag och Österdalsområdet. Uppsala, Appelbergs
boktryckeriaktiebolag, 1947-
v. illus., maps (part fold.) 25 cm.
Vol. 1, Akademisk avhandling—Uppsala.
Extra t. p., with thesis statement, inserted in v. 1.
"Arkivkällor och litteratur samt förkortningar": v. 1, p. ₍vii₎-xvi.
CONTENTS.—1. Serieordnade smärre studier. Första serien.

1. Names, Geographical — Sweden — Dalecarlia. 2. Swedish language—Etymology.   I. Title.

DL971.D2L5   50-18101

NL 0379204   DLC MH-P MnU PU CU ICU NN MH

Linden, C. A. Huguenot van der
see   Huguenot van der Linden, C. A.

Linden, C   G   van der.
Le pigeon voyageur; historique, origines du pigeon
voyageur, anatomie, valeur sportive élevage et alimentation,
maladies, vol, dressage. Paris, Payot, 1950.
186 p. illus. 23 cm. (Bibliothèque scientifique)

1. Homing pigeons.   I. Title.

Missouri. Univ. Libr.   A 51-5963
for Library of Congress

NL 0379206   MoU MeU

Linden, C. v. d., and M. S. Wytema.
Met Hr. Ms. K XIII naar Nederlandsch-Indië; een onderzee-
boottocht van meer den 20.000 zeemijlen, door C. v. d. Linden en
M. S. Wytema... Met voorwoord en medewerking van Prof.
Dr. Ir. F. A. Vening Meinesz. Met ca. 100 illustraties naar foto's
en eenige routekaartjes. Amsterdam: Scheltens & Giltay₍,
1927₎. 252 p. front. (facsim.), map, plates. 8°.

Plates printed on both sides.

371833A.   1. Voyages and travels,   1900-   . 2. Submarine boats,
1926.   3. Wytema, M. S., jt. au.   November 15, 1928

NL 0379207   NN IU

Linden, Mme C   van der.
Tableaux anciens, antiquités. Sculptures, ivoires, meubles,
tapisseries...porcelaines de la Chine...vieux Delft...manuscrits
enluminés; collection Mme. C. van der Linden, d'Anvers...
Vente aux enchères publiques les 14, 15 et 16 juin 1938 dans la
grande salle des ventes de la maison Frederik Muller & cie...
Amsterdam. ptie. 1- ₍Amsterdam, 1938₎ v. illus.
30cm.

1. Art—Collections, Private—   Linden. I. Muller, Frederik, &
compagnie, Amsterdam.   May 23, 1945

NL 0379208   NN PPULC DSI

Linden (Car. Philip. Henr.) [1793-   ]. * De
febre hydrocephalica. 52 pp. sm. 8°. *Berolini,*
typ. J. F. Starckii, [1817].

NL 0379209   DNLM PPC

Linden, Carel Hendrik van der
Experimenteele therapie van phosgeenvergiftiging.
... 's-Gravenhage, 1937.   86 p.
Inaug. Diss. - Utrecht, 1937.
Litteratuurlijst.

NL 0379210   ICRL CtY-M

Linden, Catharina van der
De visgier. Arnhem, Van Loghum Slaterus, 1955

Poems

NL 0379211   MH

F516
L5
Linden, Charles.
Narrative of an excursion in eastern Florida,
during the winter of 1866-67, by Chas. Linden ...
Buffalo, N. Y., Beinecke ₍1₎ & Zesch, 1871.

86p.   21½cm.

1. Florida.   Description.

NL 0379212   NBuG NBuHi Nh

QD431
.L6
Linden, Charles Florent van der, 1876-
Synthetische versuche mit benzoylalaninazid.
Heidelberg, 1903.
43p.
Inaug. diss. Heidelberg.

NL 0379213   DLC PU CtY

Linden, *Mrs.* Charlotte E   "Mrs. Henry Linden,"
1859-
Autobiography and poems ₍by₎ Mrs. Henry Linden.
₍3d ed.₎ Springfield, O. ₍1907?₎
1 p. l., 64 p. 15ᶜᵐ.
Title vignette (portrait)
Cover-title: Scraps of time.

I. Title: Scraps of time.

18-8036
Library of Congress   PS3523.I 52A6 1907

NL 0379214   DLC

LINDEN, CHRISTA.
DEUTSCHE LANDSCHAFT UM DIE WEIHNACHTSZEIT,
EINE STIMMUNGSBILD MIT WORTEN VON CHRISTA
LINDEN. BERLIN, EIGENTUM DER AUSLANDS-ABTEILUNG
DES LICHTBILD-DIENSTES, 19-
18P.

NL 0379215   MH

Linden, Clarence.
Our general. By Col. C. Linden ... Philadelphia, Barclay & co. ₍187-?₎
1 p. l., 19-20, iv, 21-201 p. front., plates. 24½ᶜᵐ.
On cover: A work of absorbing interest, whose characters are real personages.

1. U. S.—Hist.—Civil war—Fiction.

Library of Congress   PZ3.L646O   7-20109†

NL 0379216   DLC

Linden, Clarence.
Our general. By Col. C. Linden ... Philadelphia, Barclay
& co. ₍1872 ₎
1 p. l., 19-20, iv, 21-201 p. front., plates. 24½ᶜᵐ.
On cover: A work of absorbing interest, whose characters are real
personages : **wanting** (rebound)

NL 0379217   ViU NjP ViU MB

FILM
4274
PR
v.2
reel
L8
Linden, Clarence
Our general. By Col. C. Linden... Phila.,
Barclay ₍1872₎
19-201 p.   illus. (Wright American fiction,
v.II, 1851-1875, no.1553, Research Publications Microfilm, Reel L-8)

1. U. S. - Hist. - Civil War - Fiction.
I. Title.

NL 0379218   CU PSt

Linden, Cornelis Over de, 1811-1874. Oera Linda boek
see Oera Linda bok.

Linden, Cornelis van der, 1839-1918.
₍Leiden ontzet. Libretto. Dutch₎

Leiden ontzet! (1574) Groote opera in 5 bedrijven (6
tafereelen) door E. van der Ven... Iuziek von C. van der
Linden. Amsterdam, Holdert ₍189-?
79 p. 16 cm.

1. Operas—Librettos.   I. Ven, Ernest van der. Leiden ontzet.
II. Title.

ML50.L7367L4   74-247731

NL 0379220   DLC

Linden, Cornelis van der, 1839-1918.
Een nieuwe vorm voor een zeeschip, met uitslaande platen,
door C. Over de Linden... Helder: S. Giltjes, 1856. 1 p.l.,
viii p., 1 l., 53 p., 1 l., 3 fold. diagr. 8°.

1. Shipbuilding.   October 12, 1916.

NL 0379221   NN

BL
1216
L56
Linden, Cornelius Wilhelmus Josef van der.
The concept of Deva, by C. W. J. van der
Linden. Utrecht, Vesta ₍1954₎
v.

Proefschrift - Utrecht.
Includes bibliography.
Contents.- 1. In the Vedic age of the Indian
literature.

NL 0379222   WaU CaBVaU MiU MH NNC NiC CtY OCl NN

VOLUME 334

Linden, D. van der, tr.

PT2617
.E853
D52   **Hesse, Max René.**
Dietrich en de wereldbeheerscher, roman. Vertaling van
D. van der Linden. Amsterdam, Van Ditmar [1943]

Linden, D. van der, tr.

PT2647
.E612
L44   **Welk, Ehm,** 1884–
De levensklok van Gottlieb Grambauer, de biecht van een
ongekunsteld gemoed, roman. Vertaling van D. van der
Linden. Antwerpen, Van Ditmar [1944]

Linden, Diederick Wessel.
—— An experimental and practical enquiry
into the ophthalmic, antiscrophulous, and nervous properties of the mineral water of Llan-
gybi, in Carnarvonshire; to which is annexed an
essai on the prize question proposed by the Royal
Academy of Bordeaux, for the year 1767, on the
subject of analizing mineral waters.   ii, v, ii, 90
pp., 1 l.   8°.   *London, J. Everingham, 1767.*

NL 0379225   DNLM

Linden (Diederick Wessel). An experimental
dissertation on the nature, contents, and virtues
of the Hyde saline purging water, commonly
called the Hyde spaw, near Cheltenham in
Gloucestershire. In which is proved from facts,
that these waters are of the same nature and
considerably richer in salts than those of Cheltenham; and the various distempers in which
they are salutary fully set forth and demonstrated to be in every respect superior to the
Cheltenham water; with directions for drinking
and bathing. viii, 66 pp., 1 pl., 3 l. 8°. *London, W. Owen & R. Fiddes, 1751.*

NL 0379226   DNLM WU

Linden, Diederich Wessel.
Gründliche chemische Anmerkungen über Herrn
D. Schüttens Physikalische Nachricht, wie auch
über des Herrn von Welling Opvs mago-cabbalis-
ticvm. Diesen sind beygefügt nützliche medici-
nische Nachrichten von der Kraft der Mistel gegen
die Epilepsie. Aus dem Englischen übersetzt und
erleutert. Amsterdam, 1746.

NL 0379227   WU

Linden, Diederick Wessel.
A letter to William Hooson, a Derbyshire
miner. Shewing the mistakes, and errors, com-
mited in his lately publish'd miners dictionary. With a preface setting forth the reasons for making the said publick. By Diederick Wessel Linden, M.D. Chester: Printed
and sold by J. Page ... and
by Joseph Gittins in Holywell, 1747.
72 p. 19½ᶜ. [With Hooson, William. The
miners dictionary   ... Wrexam, 1747.]

WILLIAM
ANDREWS
CLARK
MEMORIAL
LIBRARY

NL 0379228   CLU-C MH CtY NNNAM

Linden, Diederick Wessel.
Lettres sur la minéralogie et la métallurgie pratiques.
Tr. de l'anglois de M. Diederick-Wessel-Linden ... Paris,
Durand [etc.] 1752.
11 p. l., 201, [1] p. 18½ᶜᵐ.

1. Mineralogy. 2. Metallurgy.
                                        G S 15–761

Library, U.S. Geological   Survey 409 L641F

NL 0379229   DI–GS WU ICU PPC

Linden, Diederick Wessel.
——. A medicinal and experimental history and
analysis of the Hanlys-Spa saline, purging, and
chalybeate waters near Shrewsbury; with new
discoveries from practical knowledge and critical remarks on the efficacy of these, and the
same kind of mineral waters.   iv, iii, ii, 132 pp.
8°.   *London, J. Everingham, 1768.*

NL 0379230   DNLM

LINDEN, Diederick Wessel.
Proposals for printing by subscription, an
analytical examination of the nature, virtues
and contents of the bath waters, taken from
experiments. [London? 1761].

sm. 4°. pp. (2), 6.

NL 0379231   MH

Z622
L642   Linden, Dietrich Wessel
Three letters on mining and smelting; in
which a method is laid down, whereby these
useful sciences may be greatly improved, to
which is added, a fourth letter; setting
forth, a discovery of an easy method to
secure ships bottoms from worms. London,
George Keith, 1750.
[4], 96 p. 19cm.
1. Mines and mineral resources. 2. Smelting.

NL 0379232   MnU MH–BA CtY

615.79
L744   Linden, Diederick Wessel.
A treatise on the origin, nature, and
virtues of chalybeat waters and natural hot
baths. With a physico-chemical analysis,
and medicinal description of the mineral
waters at Tunbridge — and the celebrated
waters at Cleves in Germany. Likewise,
directions for the preparation and use of
artificial, hot, mineral-water-baths. To
which is added, an appendix on the selter
water — a dissertation on Baron Schwanberg's
liquid shell,

with the process for preparing the same.
London, T. Osborne, 1748.
xx, 337 p. plates. 21 cm.

1. Mineral waters. Gt. Brit. 2. Mineral
waters. Cleves, Ger. I. Title.

NL 0379234   N NNC PPC PPL

Linden, Diederick Wessel.
A treatise on the origin, nature, and virtues
of chalybeat waters, and natural hot-baths. With a
description of the mineral waters in England and
Germany. Likewise directions for the preparation
and use of artificial, hot, mineral-water baths.
To which is added, and appendix, on the Selter
water; with many remarks, especially on its mix-
ture with tar-water. And also a dissertation on
Baron Schwanberg's liquid-shell; with the process
for preparing the same. To which are annexed, occasional remarks and queries on the Glastonbury
waters. With copper-plates. By Diederick Wessel
Linden, M.D. 2d ed. London, Printed for D. Browne
and J. Ward, 1755.
xx[4],341[7]p.   front.,illus.,fold.diagr.
21cm.

NL 0379235   MoU CtY–M MH WU DNLM

RBS104.   Linden, Diederick Wessel.
A treatise on the origin, nature,
and virtues of chalybeat waters...
3.ed. London: J. Pottinger, 1759.

NL 0379236   NNNAM

MN
615.79
L744ℓ   Linden, Diederick Wessel.
A treatise on the three medicinal
mineral waters at Llandrindod, Radnorshire,
South Wales with some remarks on mineral
and fossil mixtures, in their native veins
and beds; at least as far as respects their
influence on water. London, Printed by
J. Everingham and T. Reynolds for the author,
and sold by W. Owen, 1756.
xliv, 336 p. front. 21 cm.
With this is bound Wall, John, m.d.
Experiments and   observations on the
Malvern   waters. [London,
1757]

1. Mineral waters. Llandrindod Wells, Wales.
I. Title.

NL 0379238   N NIC DNLM CtY–M IU WU

Linden, Dirk Arie van der, 1919–
...Totdat de atoombom viel... Friesche jongens in Japansche
krijgsgevangenschap: in de Japansche gevangenkampen op Java,
aan den doodenspoorweg in Thailand, als slaven in de Japansche
mijnen. Utrecht, P. den Boer, 1946. 99 p. front. 19cm.

1. World war, 1939–1945—Prison-   ers and prisons, Japanese.
                                        January 21, 1948

NL 0379239   NN NIC

Linden, Edmund.
Sofia; a tale of the lower Rio Grande, by Edmund Linden. San Antonio, Tex., T. Kunzman, printer, 1920.
29 p. 19¼ᵐ.

I. Title.

Library of Congress   PZ3.L6462So   20–21003

NL 0379240   DLC TxU

Linden, Edmund.
Zur klinik der Grippe-Encephalitis. (Auszug.)
Inaug. Diss. Bonn, 1922

NL 0379241   ICRL

Lindén, Eeva.
Kaakkois-hämeen murteiden äännehistoria. 1. Konsonan-
tisto. Helsinki, 1942.
xx, 202 p. 22 cm.

Thesis—Helsingfors universitet.
Published also as v. 1 of Suomalaisen Kirjallisuuden Seuran toimi-
tuksia, 219. osa.
Bibliography: p. [190]–199.

1. Finnish language—Dialects—Tavastland. I. Title.

PH293.T3L5 1942a   53–51545

NL 0379242   DLC NNC InU NN CtY

Lindén, Eeva.
Kaakkois-hämeen murteiden äännehistoria. Helsinki
[Suomalaisen Kirjallisuuden Seuran Kirjapaino] 1942.
2 v. 22 cm. (Suomalaisen Kirjallisuuden Seuran toimituksia,
219. osa)

Vol. 1 issued also as thesis, Helsingfors universitet.
Bibliography: p. [190]–199.

1. Finnish language—Dialects—Tavastland. I. Title. (Series:
Suomalaisen Kirjallisuuden Seura, Helsingfors. Toimituksia, 219.
osa)

PH293.T3L5 1942   53–51544

NL 0379243   DLC MH CLU NNC

VOLUME 334

Linden, Em   van der.
Het Belgische handelsrecht, schematisch bewerkt voor het
middelbaar onderwijs, herzien door G. Swinnen. Lier, Drukkerij J. van In ₍194₋₎
91 p. 27 cm.

1. Commercial law—Belgium.   I. Title.

54–30882 ‡

NL 0379244   DLC MH NNC

LINDEN, Emile vander.
Du patronage des condamnés libérés et de
leur réhabilitation dans la société. Louvain,
C.Fonteyn;Paris,F.Fetscherin & Chuit,1885.
pp.52. 8°.

NL 0379245   MH-L

Linden, Erich, 1904-
Die haftung der berufsvereine fuer unzulaessige
kampfhandlungen.
Inaug. diss. - Erlangen, 1928. (Coburg. 1929)
Bibl.

NL 0379246   DLC PU

Linden, Ernst.
Der Prairie-Vogel. Eine Erzählung aus den Wildnissen des
westlichen Amerika. Nach Murray, für die Jugend bearbeitet,
von Ernst Linden... Zweite Auflage. Reutlingen: Ensslin und
Laiblin ₍1884₎ 221 p. col'd front., col'd plates. 21cm.

810382A. 1. Fiction, German.   2. Indians, N. A.—Fiction. I. Murray,
Sir Charles Augustus, 1806–1895.   The prairie-bird. II. Title.
                                      December 31, 1936

NL 0379247   NN

ar W   **Linden, Ernst C**
1531   Gen.-Major von Steuben, Das Steuben-
Fest und das Steuben-Denkmal in Baltimore,
Md. Baltimore, Kroh, 1878.
39 p. 23cm.

1. Steuben, Friedrich Wilhelm von,
1730-1794.

NL 0379248   NIC NN

**Linden, Ernst Ludwig Franz Heinrich, *freiherr von*, 1806-
1885.**
Betrachtungen über zeitfragen, von Ernst baron von Linden.
Augsburg, In commission der v. Jenisch und Stage'schen
buchhandlung, 1861.
24 p. 21ᶜᵐ.
CONTENTS.—Die politischen gänge in Oesterreich.—Reformen.—Die
politischen gänge in Deutschland.—Nachtrag.

1. Austria—Pol. & govt.—1848-1866. 2. Germany—Pol. & govt.—
1848-1870. I. Title.
                                      36–34887
Library of Congress   DB86.L5

NL 0379249   DLC

LINDEN, Ernst Ludwig Franz Heinrich, freiherr von, *1806-1885*
Kritische beleuchtung unserer politischen
zustände. Augsburg, K. Kollman, 1851.
pp. viii, 32.

NL 0379250   MH

DD 225 **LINDEN,ERNST LUDWIG FRANZ HEINRICH,Freiherr**
.L74   **von,1806-1885**
Die Wiedergeburt des Deutschen Reiches;
ein Nachtrag zur Schrift "Der Europäische
Krieg etc." von Ernst Baron von Linden.
Zürich, Druck von J. Schabelitz, 1878.
79 p.

1. Germany—Pol. & govt.—1871- .

NL 0379251   InU

DG256 **Linden, Eugen.**
.7   De bello civili Sullano ... Friburgi Brisigavorum, C. A.
.L7   Wagner, 1896.
68 p. 21ᶜᵐ.
Inaug.-diss.—Freiburg i. B.

1. Sulla, Lucius Cornelius, surnamed Felix, B. C. 138-78. 2. Rome—Hist.—
Republic, B. C. 265-30.

NL 0379252   ICU NjP ICRL

PA6953 **Linden, Eugen.**
1905   Präparation zu Virgils Äneide ... Gotha, F. A.
Perthes, 1905-13.
3 v. in 1.
Vol.1-2, 2. aufl., 1913.

1. Vergilius Maro, Publius--Dictionaries, indexes, etc. 2.   Latin language--Dictionaries
--German.

NL 0379253   ICU CtY

LINDEN (F. A. C. VAN DER) & COMPAGNIE, Hamburg.
100 [hundert] Jahre Lack und Farbe...   [Hamburg, 1928?]
16 f.   illus.   17 x 22cm.

NL 0379254   NN

Linden, Fl   van der.
Over belasting, en meer bepaaldelijk over gemeentebelastingen.
's Gravenhage, W. P. van Stockum en zoon, 1875.
vii, [3]-164 p. 24ᶜᵐ.
Introduction signed: Fl. v. d. Linden.
Includes a review of the taxation theory of Lorenz von Stein.
Bibliographical foot-notes.

NL 0379255   ICJ ICU NN

Linden, Frank.
A layman's creed, describing the awakening of a fundamentalist,
by Frank Linden; embodying the substance of a letter to the
author's friend G. B. Merritt, Ph.D., Ottawa, Kansas.   Fall
River, Mass., Better life foundation ₍1943₎ 31 p.   illus.
19cm.

263880B. 1. Apologetics, Christian.   2. Merritt, G. B.
                                          December 17, 1945

NL 0379256   NN

₍Linden, Frank₎
The secret of a long and active life and how to enjoy it ...
presenting the condensed views, advices and counsel of qualified biologists, physicians, dietitians and specialists, consulted;
combined and rendered by the author in an explanatory tenet ...
₍Boston, Better life foundation, 1942₎
4 p. l., 64 p. illus., 2 port. (incl. front.) 20½ᵐ.
On cover: By Frank Linden.
CONTENTS.—We and our cells.—A new ten commandments.
1. Hygiene. 2. Longevity.   I. Title.
                                          43–654
Library of Congress   RA776.L738
                                          618

NL 0379257   DLC OrCS

Linden, Frans van.
... The full secret about the knowledge of carrier- and home-
pigeons decorated with engravings in natural colours ... by
Frans van Linden ... tr. by Mr. R. Coulon. 1st ed. Antwerp,
1925.
127, ₍4₎ p. illus., col. plates. 20½ᵐ.

1. Pigeons.   I. Coulon, R., tr.
                                          Agr 29-1496
Library, U. S. Dept. of   Agriculture 413L642

NL 0379258   DNAL

Linden, Franz.
Sozialismus und religion. Konfessionssoziologische unter-
suchung der Labour party, 1929-1931. Von dr. Franz Linden.
Mit einer karte und 3 handschriftlichen beilagen. Leipzig,
B. Tauchnitz, 1932.
178 p., 2 l. illus. (map, facsims.) 24ᵐ. (Added t.-p.: Kölner angli-
stische arbeiten ... 17. bd.)
"Literaturnachweis": p. ₍174₎-178.

1. Socialism in Great Britain. 2. Socialism, Christian. 3. Labor
party (Gt. Brit.) I. Title.
                                          33–4222
Library of Congress   HX246.L55
                                          335.1

NL 0379259   DLC OrCS MoU NcD NN

Linden, Franz, ₍1892-₎ Ueber angeborene Spaltbildung an Fuß und
Hand (bei einem Individuum.) [In Maschinenschrift] 25 S.
4°(2°). — Auszug: Marburg 1920: Hamel. 6 S. 8ᵇ
Marburg, Med. Diss. v. 30. Aug. 1920 [1921], Ref. Läwen
[Geb. 10. Jan. 92 Gelsenkirchen; Wohnort: Marburg; Staatsangeh.: Preußen;
Vorbildung: G. Gelsenkirchen Reife 12; Studium: Freiburg 3, Leipzig 10,
Marburg 3 S.; Coll. 29. Okt. 19; Approb. 11. Okt. 19.]   [U 21. 5008]

NL 0379260   ICRL

Pam.   **Linden, Fred van der, 1883-**
Coll.   Colonialisme et colonisation. Glembloux,
36390   J. Duculot, 1952.
30 p. 25 cm.

"Extrait du Bulletin de l'Institut royal
colonial belge, t. XXIII, fasc. 3, 1952."
Bibliographical footnotes.

1. Colonialism. 2. Colinization. I. Title.

NL 0379261   NcD RPB

916.75   **Linden, Fred. van der, 1883-**
L744c   Le Congo, les noirs et nous. Paris, A.
Challamel, 1909.
389p. illus. 25cm.

1. Congo, Belgian. Descr. & trav.

NL 0379262   IEN CtY CU

VOLUME 334

Linden, Fred. van der, 1883–
... Le Congo, les noirs et nous. ₂2. éd.₎ Paris, A.
Challamel, 1910.
389 p. incl. illus., plates. front. (port.) plates, map. 25½ᵐ.
Author's name given as Fritz van der Linden.

1. Kongo, Belgian—Descr. & trav.

12–26832

Library of Congress   DT646.L6

NL 0379263   DLC FU NcD NBuU MBU GU ICJ

Linden, Fred. van der, 1883–
Contes des tropiques; histoires congolaises
₂par₎ Fritz Des Tilleuls. Bruxelles, Association des écrivains belges, 1914.
193 p. 19cm.
Error in imposition: pp.81, 84, 85, 88, 89,
92, 93, 96 printed twice; pp.82, 83, 86, 87,
90, 91, 94, 95 wanting.

NL 0379264   IEN

HC591
K7L74
Linden, Fred. van der, 1883–
Rapports sur la crise économique au Congo
belge et en Afrique equatoriale française,
présentés par Fred van der Linden et Du
Vivier de Streel. ₂Paris, 1930₎
50 p. 22cm.
At head of title: Comité franco-belge
d'études coloniales. Compte rendu de la
réunion du 19 décembre 1930.

1. Congo (Leopoldville) - Econ. condit.

NL 0379265   CSt-H

DT
641
.B93
v.31
no.3
Linden, Fred. van der, 1883–
Les territoires d'outre-mer et la communauté
européenne. ₂Bruxelles, 1953₎
52 p. (Institut royal colonial belge. Section
des sciences morales et politiques. Mémoires.
Collection in-8°, t.31, fasc.3)
Includes bibliography.

1. Congo, Belgian--Econ.condit. 2. European
Economic Community.

NL 0379266   MiU MH NNC NN MH-P CtY ICU NIC

Linden, Frédéric van der.
El concours dé Pinsons; comédie-vaudeville in ein acque de
F. van der Linden. Musique d'Arthur van der Linden. Mons:
Boland & fils, 1910. 35 p. 16°. (Bibliothèque populaire des
auteurs wallons montois.)

1. Drama (Walloon). 2. Linden,   Arthur van der, composer. 3. Title.
June 13, 1911.

NL 0379267   NN

LINDEN, Fredrik ter.
Einsam. Male quartette.
=   Boston. Whipple. [1881.] 3 pp. [Select songs.] F°.
The words are in German and English.

Sheet D 561   Oct. 14 ₎

NL 0379268   MB

Linden, Frederick, *pseud.*
see
Parker-Rhodes, Arthur Frederick Parker, 1914–

Linden, Friedrich Otto zur.
Melchior Hofmann, ein prophet der wiedertäufer. Mit 9 beilagen. Haarlem, de erven F. Bohn, 1885.
pp. xxii, 477 +. (Teylers Godgeleerd Genootschap. Verhandelingen. Nieuwe serie, 11, ii.)

Hofmann||Series|

PHC IaU NIC NcD TNJ-R
NL 0379270   MH MH-AH CSt OU NNUT NRCR MoSCS ViHarEM

Linden, Fritz van der
see Linden, Fred. van der, 1883–

TK301
L5
Linden, G   J   J   van der.
Electrische meetinstrumenten. Amsterdam, Uitgeversmij,
voorheen Van Mantgem & De Does ₂1949₎
155 p. diagrs., tables. 21 cm. (Polytechnische bibliotheek, 107)

1. Electric meters. (Series)

A 50–7025

Mass. Inst. of Tech.   Library
for Library of Congress

NL 0379272   MCM DLC

Linden, Georg.
...Arische und semitische Dichtung. Bonn: K. Schroeder,
1925. 163 p. 4°.
"Nur zur Abkürzung sollen hier Juden und Araber als Semiten, die anderen
Völker aber als Arier bezeichnet werden." p. 2.

1. Poetry—Hist. and crit. 2. Arabic   literature—Poetry—Hist. 3. Poetry,
Hebrew—Hist. and crit. 4. Litera-   ture, Comparative.
December 9, 1926

NL 0379273   NN TU PPDrop MH

Linden, Gijsbertus Martinus van der, 1812–
1888.
... Continens quaestiones juridicas ...
defendet Gysbertus Martinus van der Linden
... Lugduni Batavorum, H.W. Hazenberg,
1836.
4 p.l., 49, ₂5₎ p. 20½cm.
Diss.- Leiden.
Bibliographical footnotes.

NL 0379274   MH-L

BX3493
Z6D5
Linden, Gilbert L. H. van der, 1903–

Sangers, Willem Chr   Hub   1915–
De Kruisheeren te Diest, 1845–1945 ₂door₎ W. Sangers ₂en₎
G. van der Linden, met voorwoord van J. Gessler. Diest,
Lichtland, 1945.

Linden, Gijsbertus Martinus van der, 1812–1888.
Pleitredenen ...
see under Hoevenaar, H   P
complainant.

Linden, Göran.
Förvärv och förlust av medlemskap i ekonomisk förening.
Stockholm, C. E. Fritzes kungl. Hovbokhandel ₂1952₎
ix, 272 p. 25 cm.
Akademisk avhandling—Stockholms högskola.
Extra t. p., with thesis statement in full, inserted.
Bibliography: p. 263–268.

1. Agriculture, Cooperative—Sweden. 1. Title.

55–36076

NL 0379277   DLC IEN MH MnU CtY MH-L NIC TxU

Linden, Gustav, fl. 1808.
Der neue Proteus. Ein Original-Lustspiel in vier Aufzügen.
Von Gustav Linden. Für die k. k. Hoftheater. Wien: J. B.
Wallishausser, 1808. 135 p. 16°.

612216A. 1. No subject. I. Title.
November 2, 1932

NL 0379278   NN IEN

Linden, Gustav von.
Der Sieg des Judenthums über das Germanenthum. Eine
Widerlegung der W. Marr'schen Polemik in historischer und allg-
meiner Beziehung; zugleich eine Mahnung an das deutsche Volk
und an die deutschen Fürsten, von Gustav von Linden... Leipzig: G. Körner, 1879. vi, 41 p. 2. ed. 8°.

1. Marr, Wilhelm, b. 1819: Der Sieg   des Judenthums über das Germanenthum. 2. Jews in Germany—Apolo-   getic writings.
March 20, 1929

NL 0379279   NN NIC OCH

4HE-50
Linden, H   V   D
Eenige aanteekeningen omtrent den postdienst
sedert 1650 te   Rotterdam en
de gebouwen, waarin deze werd uitgevoerd.
's Gravenhage, Der Posterijen, Telegrafie en
Telefonie, 1929.
36 p.

NL 0379280   DLC-P4 NN

NA 6082
L55
1931
Lindén, Haakon
De heliga symbolerna och Egyptens byggnadskonst. Helsingfors, F. Tilgmann, 1931.
195 p. illus.

1. Architecture, Egyptian. 2. Architecture, Ancient. 3. Temples - Egypt. I.
Title.

NL 0379281   CaBVaU

Lindén, Haakon.
"Tarmo-affären", av Haakon Lindén. Helsingfors, Söderström & c:o förlagsaktiebolag, 1919.
119 p. illus. (ncl. ports.) 18.5 cm.
1. Tarmo (Ice breaker) 2. Finland - History -
Revolution, 1917–1918 - Foreign participation.

NL 0379282   CSt-H

PT 2623
.I59 B3
LINDEN, HANNS
Bauern-Acht; Charakterbild in fünf Aufzügen.
München, the author, 1881.
87 p.

NL 0379283   InU

VOLUME 334

Linden, Hans.
   Die von der Panzerkompanie
      see under   Becker, W

Linden, Hans Jürgen
   Landser lachen; Erlebtes und Erlauschtes zwischen Front
und Etappe. Darmstadt, Teich [1954]

NL 0379285   MH

Linden, Heinrich.
   Kann Geschäftsführungs- und Vertretungsbefugnis dem ein-
zigen Komplementar der Kommandit-Aktien-Gesellschaft entzo-
gen werden, und hat dieser im Falle der Entziehung einen An-
spruch auf Auflösung? Berlin: R. Trenkel, 1910.   51 p.   8°.

   Doctoral dissertation, Erlangen.
   Bibliography, p. 5-7.
   Gift of the University.

1. Companies (Joint stock).—Juris-   prudence, Germany.
                           N. Y. PUBLIC LIBRARY December 29, 1910.

NL 0379286   NN ICRL MH-L NIC MH

Linden, Heinrich von der
   Deutsche heldensagen, der jugend erzählt, mit
farbendruckbildern nach aquarellen von Otto
Försterling. 4. aufl. [2],221,[1]p. col.front.
col.plates. Leipzig, O. Drewitz nachfolger
[n.d.]

NL 0379287   OCl

AC   Linden, Heinz von der
831   Die rechtsstellung des unternehmers und die
     des führers des betriebes nach dem gesetz zur
     ordnung der nationalen arbeit. ... Eisfeld i.
     Thür., 1936.   51 p.
        Inaug. Diss. - Erlangen, 1936.
        Literaturverzeichnis.

NL 0379288   ICRL CtY NNC

Linden, Hendrik van der.
   De cope; bijdrage tot de rechtsgeschiedenis van de open-
legging der Hollands-Utrechtse laagvlakte. (Avec résumé
en français) Assen, Van Gorcum [1955]
   xv, 400 p. maps. 25 cm.
   Proefschrift—Utrecht.
   "Stellingen": [2] leaves inserted.
   Bibliography: p. xiii-xv.
   —— Bijlagen. Topografische kaart. Kaart van Rijnland
van 1687. [Assen, Van Gorcum, 1955]
   2 fold. maps (1 col.) 25 cm.
   Issued in portfolio.
   1. Land tenure—Netherlands—Law—Hist.

                                              66-55787

NL 0379289   DLC IU MH-L MiU-L

Bd.w.   [Linden, Henricus Antonides van der] 1546-1614.
PA   Carmen Henrici Antonii Nerdeni [pseud.] in
3893   sententiam hoc tempore obseruatu utilissimam
M3   Disce contemnere & contemni ... Franekerae,
1599   Excudebat Aegidius Radaeus, 1586.
Cage
        A-G⁴. 4to.
        Includes music.

NL 0379290   DFo

229.2   Linden, Henricus Antonides van der, 1546-1614.
T551   Henrici Antonii Nerdeni De correctione fratrum
     ecclesiastica aphorismi.   [Franekerae] in Acade-
     mia franekerana, excudebat Ægidius Radæus, Ordi-
     num Frisiæ typographus, 1611.
        [74]p. 19cm.   [With Bible--O.T.--Apocrypha--
     Tobit--Latin--Paraphrases. Henrici Antonii Ner-
     deni, Adolescentia, sev Exilivm. Franekeræ, 1611]
        Signatures: *⁴, A-H⁴(A¹ blank) I².
        Title vignette; initial.
        1. Nederlandsche hervormde kerk--Discipline.
     I. Title: De correctione fratrum ecclesiastica
     aphorismi.

NL 0379291   IU

Linden, Henry.
   A lover's revery on New Year's eve. A poem. By Henry
Linden. Minneapolis, Minn., 1889.
   cover-title, [8] p. 14ᶜᵐ.

   I. Title.

   Library of Congress   PS2246.L53   28-4761

NL 0379292   DLC

Linden, *Mrs.* Henry
          see
Linden, *Mrs.* Charlotte E   "Mrs. Henry Linden,"
   1859-

TP345   Linden, Henry Robert, 1922-   comp.
.R5
   Riesz, Charles Homer, 1914-
      Cracking catalyst activity in the presence of hydrogen
   sulfide; an exploratory study, using the steam-propane reaction, of the activities of metallic cracking catalysts. Prepared from the experimental data of C. H. Riesz and J. J. S.
   Sebastian, by H. A. Dirksen, H. R. Linden [and] E. S. Pettyjohn. Sponsored by the Gas Production Research Committee of the American Gas Association. Chicago, Institute
   of Gas Technology, 1953.

Linden, Henry Robert, 1922-
   Prevention and resolution of tar emulsions in high-Btu
oil gas production, by H. R. Linden [and] R. Parker. Sponsored by the Gas Production Research Committee of the
American Gas Association. Chicago, Institute of Gas Technology, 1953.
   16 p. illus. 28 cm.
   At head of title: Institute of Gas Technology. Interim report.

   1. Cracking process. 2. Tar. 3. Emulsions.   I. Parker, Rose-
mary, 1928-   joint author. II. Chicago. Institute of Gas Technology. III. Title.
   TP690.L55   *665.53   53-9513 ‡

NL 0379295   DLC NN DI

Linden, Henry Robert, 1922-
   Production of natural gas substitutes by pressure hydrogasification of oils, by H. R. Linden, J. J. Guyer [and] E. S.
Pettyjohn. Sponsored by the Gas Production Research Committee of the American Gas Association. Chicago, Institute
of Gas Technology, 1954.
   35 p. illus. 28 cm. (Institute of Gas Technology. Interim report)

   1. Gas as fuel.   I. Title. II. Title: Gas substitutes by pressure
hydrogasification.
   TP751.5.L5   *662.67   55-4074 ‡

NL 0379296   DLC NN DI MB

Linden, Henry Robert, 1922-
   Selection of oils for high-Btu oil gas, by H. R. Linden
[and] E. S. Pettyjohn. Chicago, Institute of Gas Technology, 1952.
   48 p. illus. 28 cm. (Institute of Gas Technology. Research
bulletin, 12)
   A PAR plan activity of the American Gas Association.

   1. Gas manufacture and works. 2. Petroleum products. 3. Cracking process.   I. Title. II. Title: High-Btu oil gas.
   TP751.7.L55   *665.77   52-11225 ‡

NL 0379297   DLC OrPR UU KMK OU ViU DI TxU

Linden, Herbert, joint ed.
                                        FOR OTHER EDITIONS
                                          SEE MAIN ENTRY
Gütt, Arthur, 1891-   *ed.*
   Blutschutz- und ehegesundheitsgesetz; Gesetz zum schutze
des deutschen blutes und der deutschen ehre und Gesetz zum
schutze der erbgesundheit des deutschen volkes, nebst durch-
führungsverordnungen sowie einschlägigen bestimmungen,
dargestellt, medizinisch und juristisch erläutert von dr. med.
Arthur Gütt ... dr. med. Herbert Linden ... [und] amtsgerichtsrat Franz Massfeller ... Anhang: Reichsbürgergesetz
mit übersichtstafeln und erläuterungen ... 2., unveränderte
aufl. München, J. F. Lehmann, 1937.

Linden, Herbert.
   ... Deutsche bevölkerungspolitik, die
grundlage unserer rassischen zukunft, von dr.
Herbert Linden ... Erfurt, K. Stenger [c1938]
   25 p. (Volk und wissen, hrsg. von professor dr. Hanns v. Lengerken, bd. 12)

NL 0379299   NNC CU

Law   Linden, Herbert, ed.
                                        FOR OTHER EDITIONS
                                          SEE MAIN ENTRY
Germany. *Laws, statutes, etc.*
   Gesetz zum Schutze der Erbgesundheit des deutschen
Volkes (Ehegesundheitsgesetz) ... Gesetz zum Schutze des
deutschen Blutes und der deutschen Ehre ... Reichsbürgergesetz ... [nebst Verordnungen] Erläuterte Textausg. in
einer Bearbeitung von H. Linden und W. Franke. Bielefeld, W. Bertelsmann [1937]

Linden, Herbert.
   ... Grundlagen der erb- und rassenpflege. 1. Volkskunde. Von
direktor dr. Burgdörfer. 2. Erbkunde. Von prof. dr. Boehm
... 3. Rassenkunde. Von dr. Friese ... 4. Gesetzliche grundlagen der erb- und rassenpflege, von oberregierungsrat dr.
Linden. Berlin, C. Heymann, 1936.

Linden, Herman Otto van der.
   Banda en zijne bewoners. Dordrecht, Blussé en van
Braam, 1873.
   73 p. 22 cm.

   1. Banda Islands.   I. Title.
   DS647.B25L5   57-51601 ‡

NL 0379302   DLC CU CtY NIC MH NN

[LINDEN, Herman Otto van der.]
   Emigratie naar Oost-Indië. ['s Gravenhage,
1874.]
   pp. 15
   "Overgedrukt uit den Volke-Almanak, jaargang
1875, uitgegenen doorde Maatschappij; Tot nut
van't algemeen."
   Signed: H.O. van der Linden.

NL 0379303   MH

VOLUME 334

Linden, Herman vander, 1868–
    Album historique de la Belgique, par H. van der
Linden ... et H. Obreen ... avec une préface de Henri
Pirenne.   Bruxelles, G. van Oest & cᵉ, 1912.

    3 p. l., 104 p. plates, ports. 29½ᶜᵐ.

    1. Belgium—Hist.   I. Obreen, Henri, joint author.
                                                              16–20579
        Library of Congress   DH424.L5

NL 0379304   DLC ICU MiU

Linden, Herman Vander, 1868–
    Alexander Vi. and the demarcation of the
maritime and colonial domains of Spain and
Portugal, 1493–1494, by H. Vander Linden.
New York, The Macmillan company, 1916
    20 p.

    Reprinted from the american historical
review, Vol. XXII., no. 1, Oct. 1916.

NL 0379305   MiU-C

Linden, Herman vander, 1868–
    Anglo-Belgian relations, past and present, by Herman
vander Linden ... and Paul Hamelius ...   London, Constable
and company ltd., 1918.

    117 p.   19 cm.

    1. Gt. Brit.—For. rel.—Belgium. 2. Belgium—For. Rel.—Gt. Brit.
    I. Hamelius, Paul, 1868–1922, joint author.   II. Title.

        DH569.G7L5   19—11595

NL 0379306   DLC MiU OU CtY FMU OClW ICJ MB NN DNW

Linden, Herman vander, 1868–
    Belgium, the making of a nation, by H. vander Linden
... tr. by Sybil Jane.   Oxford, The Clarendon press, 1920.

    356 p.   maps.   20ᶜᵐ.

    "Chapters 13, 14, and 15 were specially written for the English edition."

    1. Belgium—Hist.   I. Jane, Sybil, tr.   *Translation of* Vue
générale de l'histoire de Belgique.

        Library of Congress   DH523.L8   20–9824

        ⁿᵃᵗᶜ
        OO OC1 NjN ICJ NN MB NNC DAU CaBVaU WaS WaSp OrP
NL 0379307   DLC CU-S NIC MeB CtY PPT OrStbM MiU OC1W

Linden, Herman van der, 1868–
    L'expansion coloniale de l'Espagne jusqu'au début du XIXᵉ siècle.
(In Histoire de l'expansion coloniale des peuples européens. Pp.
239–436. Bruxelles. 1907.)

    G6606 — Spain. Colo. — Spain. Hist.

NL 0379308   MB

Linden, Herman van der, 1868–
    ***** Les gildes marchandes dans les Pays-Bas au Moyen Age, par Her-
man vander Linden, ...   Gand, Librairie Clemm (H. Engelcke
successeur), 1896.

    [8], 126 p. 25½ᶜᵐ.
    Bibliographical foot-notes.

NL 0379309   ICJ OClW MiU NIC MoU MH NN CtY

Linden, Herman vander, 1868–
    ... L'hégémonie européenne, période italo-espagnole, par
Herman Vander Linden ...   Paris, E. de Boccard, 1936.

    xI, 470 p., 1 l. 23ᶜᵐ. (Histoire du monde, publiée sous la direction de
m. E. Cavaignac. t. x)

    1. Europe—Hist.—1492–1648.   I. Title.
                                                              36–11591
        Library of Congress   D20.H52 t. 10
                                                         (909) 940.2

NL 0379310   DLC NIC NN OCU OU ICU

Linden, Herman van der, 1868–   joint author.

Lannoy, Charles de, 1868–
    ... Histoire de l'expansion coloniale des peuples européens
            Bruxelles, H. Lamertin; [etc., etc.] 1907–

Linden, Herman vander, 1868–
    ... Histoire de la constitution de la ville de Louvain au
moyen âge, par Herman vander Linden ...   Gand, Clemm
(H. Engelcke, successeur) 1892.

    viii p., 1 l., 194 p. 24ᶜᵐ. (Université de Gand. Recueil de travaux
pub. par la Faculté de philosophie et lettres. 7. fasc.)

    "Appendices. I. Chartes concernant la gilde de Malines (1276) et celle
de Louvain (1221) II. La Charte des apaisanteurs ou paismakers. III. La
paix de 1363. IV. La Charte constitutionnelle de 1378. V. La paix de
1383": p. [160]–194.

    1. Louvain — Hist. 2. Louvain — Pol. & govt. 3. Louvain—Charters,
grants, privileges.
                                                              13–3536
        Library of Congress   JS6048.L61

NL 0379312   DLC NN PU

Linden, Herman vander, 1868–

Lannoy, Charles de, 1868–
    A history of Swedish colonial expansion, by Charles De
Lannoy ... translated from the French. Newark, Department
of history and political science, University of Delaware, 1938.

Linden, Herman vander, 1868–
    Itinéraires de Charles, duc de Bourgogne, Marguerite
d'York et Marie de Bourgogne (1467–1477) par Herman
vander Linden. Bruxelles, M. Lamertin, 1936.

    4 p. l., 87, [1] p. 30½ᶜᵐ. [Académie royale des sciences, des lettres et
des beaux arts de Belgique, Brussels. Commission royale d'histoire.
Publications in-quarto. 51]

    1. Charles le Téméraire, duke of Burgundy, 1433–1477. 2. Margaret,
of York, consort of Charles the Bold, duke of Burgundy, 1466–1503. 3.
Marie, duchess of Burgundy, 1457–1482. 4. Netherlands—Hist.—House
of Burgundy, 1384–1477.   I. Title.
                                                              37–33294
        Library of Congress   DH403.A2 vol. 51
                                                    (949.30062) 949.201

NL 0379314   DLC NcD GU MoU FU NIC NN ICU OC1W CaBVaU

Linden, Herman vander, 1868–
    Itinéraires de Marie de Bourgogne et de Maximilien d'Au-
triche (1477–1482) par Herman vander Linden. Bruxelles,
M. Lamertin, 1934.

    xiv, 125 p. 31ᶜᵐ. [Académie royale des sciences, des lettres et des
beaux-arts de Belgique, Brussels. Commission royale d'histoire. Publications in quarto. 50]

    "Liste des sources citées en abrégé": p. [Ix]–xiv.

    1. Marie, duchess of Burgundy, 1457–1482. 2. Maximilian I, emperor
of Germany, 1459–1519. 3. Netherlands—Hist.—House of Habsburg,
1477–1556.   I. Title.
                                                              35–9746
        Library of Congress   DH403.A2 vol. 50
                                    DH180.L5
                                                    (949.30062) 923.1492

        OU NN
NL 0379315   DLC CaBVaU GU MoU FU NIC ICU NcD OC1W

Linden, Herman vander, 1868–
    Itinéraires de Philippe le Bon, duc de Bourgogne (1419–1467)
et de Charles, comte de Charolais (1433–1467), par Herman vander Linden.   Bruxelles, Palais des Académies, 1940. x, 533 p.
31cm.

    On cover: Académie royale de Belgique. Commission royale d'histoire...
    "Ce volume remplace, en partie, le tome 1ᵉʳ de la Collection des voyages des souve-
rains des Pays-Bas que Gachard publiait en 1876."
    Bibliography, p. viii–x.

    355653B. 1. Itineraries—Netherlands.   2. Itineraries—France. 3. Philip
the Good, duke of Burgundy, 1396–   1467. 4. Charles the Bold, duke of
Burgundy, 1433–1477. I. Académie   royale des sciences, des lettres et des
beaux arts, Brussels. Commission   royale d'histoire.
                                                         December 11, 1946

        NNC NIC ICN
NL 0379316   NN CaBVaU IU MH CtY PU NcD ICU NjP FU

Linden, Herman vander, 1868–   ed.

Lodewijk van Velthem, fl. 1293–1326.
    Lodewijk van Velthem's voortzetting van den Spiegel histo-
riael (1248–1316) opnieuw uitgegeven door Herman vander
Linden en Willem de Vreese ...   Brussel, Hayez, drukker der
K. Academie van België, 1906–38.

Linden, Herman vander, 1868–
    Mélanges d'histoire offerts à Henri Pirenne par ses anciens
élèves et ses amis à l'occasion de sa quarantième année d'enseignement à l'Université de Gand 1886–1926 ...   Bruxelles,
Vromant & cᵉ, 1926.

LINDEN, HERMAN VANDER, 1868–
    Notice sur Henri Pirenne, membre de l'Acade-
mie.   Bruxelles, Palais des Académies, 1950.
    66p. front.(port.) 20cm.

    Bibliography: p. 21–66.
    "Extrait de l'Annuaire de l'Académie royale
de Belgique 1950."

NL 0379319   ICN

Linden, Herman vander, 1868–
    ... Vue générale de l'histoire de Belgique. Paris,
Payot & cⁱᵉ, 1918.

    3 p. l., [9]–287 p. 19ᶜᵐ. fr. 4.50
    At head of title: H. vander Linden.

    1. Belgium—Hist.
        Library of Congress   DH523.L7   18–21774

NL 0379320   DLC CaBVaU CSt NN CSt-H

Linden, Hermann.
    Die Chirurgie des Magens, und ihre.
Indikationen, einschliesslich Diagnostik.
12 Vorlesungen ...   Berlin, Enslin, 1896.
    312 p.   22 cm.
    I. Kuttner, L.

NL 0379321   MBCo

PT 2623 LINDEN, HERMANN, 1896–
.I53 G3   Gesichter der Zeit; ein Buch der Tatsachen.
           Dresden, C. Reissner, 1929.
           202 p.

NL 0379322   InU

VOLUME 334

Linden, Hermann, 1896–   *comp.*
Joseph Roth, Leben und Werk; ein Gedächtnisbuch, von Hermann Kesten [et al.], gesammelt von Hermann Linden. Köln, G. Kiepenheuer, 1949.
254 p. ports. 31 cm.
Selections: p. 65–233.
"Werke": p. 251–252.

1. Roth, Joseph, 1894–1939.

PT2635.O84Z6   928.3   50–24395

NL 0379323   DLC CSt NcD FTaSU TxU NcU ICarbS OCl IU

Linden, Hermann, 1896–
Retter Tod, Ein Akt.   Frankfurt a. M., Berlin, Siebener Verlag, 1921.
20 S.

NL 0379324   NjP

Linden, Hermann, 1896–
...Schauspieler und Herzogin; ein Traumspiel.   **Hannover,** Wolf Albrecht Adam Verlag [1924]   41 p.   25cm.
No. 262 of an autographed edition of 300 copies.

1. Drama, German.   I. Title.
                                                June 30, 1947

NL 0379325   NN

Linden, Heyden Albrecht von
see   Heyden-Linden, Albrecht von, 1872–

338.47678
L744p   Linden, Horacio de.
Por las tierras del caucho.   Buenos Aires, Sociedad Geográfica Americana, 1946.
110 p.   illus.   18 cm. (Colección Nadir. Serie D. Miscelánea, 6)
At head of title: Horacio J.T. de Linden.

1. Rubber industry and trade--Latin America. I. Title.

NL 0379327   ICarbS

Linden, Ilse.
Fanny Elssler, die Tänzerin des Biedermeier. Nach Briefen und zeitgenössischen Berichten zusammengestellt. Berlin, Ullstein, 1921.

118 p. (Die fünfzig Bücher, 30)

NL 0379328   MH PPC ICarbS NN

808.6
L641   Linden, Ilse,   ed.
Der letzte brief: eine sammlung letzter briefe; hrsg. und eingeleitet von Ilse Linden.   Berlin, 1919.
131p.

"Literatur-verzeichnis": p.129-[132]

NL 0379329   IU InU

Linden, Ilse.
... Literarische visionen, essays, A. D. 1920; mit 5 original-lithographien von Charlotte Berend. Berlin, Oesterheld & co. [1920]
100 p. ports. 25ᶜᵐ.
CONTENTS.—Lichtenberg.—Bürger.—Lenz.—Gottschedin.—Sheridan.—Jean Paul.—A. W. Schlegel.—W. v. Humboldt.—Bettina.—Schleiermacher.—Rahel.—E. T. A. Hoffmann.—Karoline Bauer.—Andersen.—Stifter.

1. Authors, German.   I. Title.

Library of Congress   PT155.L5   44–21902
                                                   830.4

NL 0379330   DLC WaU CtY OrU RPB MH

Linden, Ilse, ed.
Ottilie von Goethe; ein Porträt aus Dokumenten
see under   Goethe, Ottilie (von Pogwisch) von, 1796–1872.

Linden, Ilse von der, 1914–
... Rassetypen und Prognathismus; eine Untersuchung an Schädeln der Völkerwanderungszeit ... Lengerich i. W., 1937.
Inaug. – Diss. – München.
Lebenslauf.

NL 0379332   CtY

MKA2
L642b   **Lindén, Ingemar**
Biblicism, apokalyptik, utopi; adventismens historiska utformning i USA samt dess svenska utveckling till o. 1939. Uppsala [Stockholm, Distributed by Almquist and Wiksell] 1971.
494 p. diagrs. maps. 25 cm. (Studia historico-ecclesiastica Upsaliensia, 19)

Acta Universitatis Upsaliensis.
"Summary in English: Biblicism, apocalyptic, utopia. The historical development of Adventism in the United States and in Sweden to about 1939."
Bibliography: p. 466–486.

1. Adventists – History. 2. U.S. – Church history. 3. Sweden – Church history. I. Title. II. Title: Biblicism, apocalyptic, utopia. III. Series: Uppsala. Universitet. Acta Universitatis Upsaliensis. IV. Series: Studia historico-ecclesiastica Upsaliensia, 19.

NL 0379334   CtY-D

[Linden, Ingyärd Marya] 1894–
The life cry, anonymous. New York, The Macaulay company [*1933]
312 p. 19ᶜᵐ.

I. Title.
Library of Congress   PZ3.L64622Li   33–3297

NL 0379335   DLC

Linden J   H   van der.
Een brief over: "Zekerheid. Twee brieren var Ph. R. Hugenholtz, predikant te Amsterdam". Amsterdam, J. H. & G. van Heteren, 1864.
34 p. 8°.

NL 0379336   NN

SB   **Linden, J.**   van der.
229   Java-Zucker; Geschichte, Pflanzungen,
J4   Fabrikat. Aarau, Verlag der AZ-Presse,
L74   1946.
         80 p. illus., maps. 30 cm.

"Quellenverzeichnis": p. 80.

1. Sugar-cane – Java. 2. Sugar – Manufacture and refining – Java. I. Title.

NL 0379337   NIC DNAL CtY

Wason   **Linden, J   van der.**
BV3355   "Den Javanen een Javaan" (zendeling J.
L74   Wilhelm van Poerworedjo, 1883–1892) Hoenderloo, Uitg. vanwege de Zendingsstudie-Raad door de drukkerij van de stichting, 1947.
           30 p. 19cm. (Lichtstralen op den akker der wereld, no. 2)

1. Wilhelm, J   2. Missions--Java. I. Title.

NL 0379338   NIC

Linden, J   van der
Moeder. Wageningen, Zomer & Keuning [1952]

NL 0379339   MH

Hfm   **Linden, Jacobus Petrus van der.**
es220   Alphonse Esquiros de la bohème romantique à la république sociale. Heerlen, Winants, 1948.
           237p. illus., ports. 24cm.
           Proefschrift - Nijmegen.
           "Verschijnt als nummer 2 van de Parcival-reeks".
           "Stellingen" ([3]p.) inserted.
           "Bibliographie": p.220-230.

CU-S
NL 0379340   CtY NRU RPB MiU NNC InU CaBVaU MH CU NjP

346.1   **LINDEN, Jacobus van der,** 1852–1926.
L744h   Het heilige land bezien bij het licht van Bijbel en historie. Met twintig autotypiën. Kampen, Kok, 1915.
           304p. illus., front.(port.) 24cm.

NL 0379341   MH-AH

Linden, Jakob, 1853–1915.
Hilfsbuch zum einheitskatechismus. Zweite auflage. Bearbeitet von Theodor Mönnichs. München, Kösel und Pustet, 1925.
219 p.

NL 0379342   OClJC

Linden, Jakob,   1853–
Katholischer Katechismus für die Vereinigten Staaten von Nordamerika. Catechism of the Catholic religion.   St. Louis, Herder, 1915.
xiv, xiv, 153, 153 p. 19 cm.
German and English on opposite pages.

NL 0379343   PLatS

VOLUME 334

Linden, Jakob, 1853-1915.
The truth of the Catholic religion; an explanation of its fundamental doctrines and of the essential points of difference between Catholic and Protestant belief, by James Linden, s. j. St. Louis, Mo., and London, B. Herder book co., 1923.
v, 99 p. 19ᶜᵐ.

I. Title.

Library of Congress   BX1751.L73   23-16561

NL 0379344   DLC WaSpG TxDaM-P DCU OC1JC OCX OC1ND

BT
1107   **Linden, Jakob,** 1853-1915.
.L5   Kleine Apologetik; oder Begründung des kath. Glaubens. Ein Leitfaden für den Unterricht an höheren Lehranstalten und zum Privatstudium für Gebildete, von J. Schmitz [pseud.] 9., unveränderte Aufl. Regensburg, New York, F. Pustet, 1912.
127 p. 20 cm.

1. Catholic Church - Apologetic works.
I. Title.

NL 0379345   WU

Linden, Jakob, 1853-
Der mittlere deharbesche Katechismus ... fünfte auflage. Regensburg, Pustet, 1909.
152 p. D.

NL 0379346   NcD

Linden, Jakob, S.J., 1853-1915.
Stundenbilder. Kurzgefasste Katechesen zu P. Lindens Religionsbüchlein für die Unterklassen. Bearbeitet von Georg Schreiner. 2 verb. Aufl. München, Josef Küsel & Friedrich Pustet, 1922.
xi, 191p. 19cm.

1. Catechisms, German. I. Schreiner, Georg, Father, ed. II. Title.

NL 0379347   PLatS

Linden, James.
The mechanics lien law, of Illinois. Review and practical suggestions, by James Linden ... [Chicago, Press of Monitor printing company] *1896.
2 p. l., 78 p. 15½ᶜᵐ.
"Law of 1895": p. 45-76.

1. Mechanics' liens—Illinois. I. Illinois. Laws, statutes, etc. II. Title.
Library of Congress   31-30437

NL 0379348   DLC

Linden, James, 1853-1915
see Linden, Jakob, 1853-1915.

Linden, James Vincent.
Christian peace; radio address delivered Jan. 27, 1941. over...K.G.A. Spokane, Wash. [Inland Empire Outlook, n. d.]
[6] p.

NL 0379350   WaSpG

Linden, James Vincent,
Come with me to Mass. Chicago, Paluch [1951]
123 p.

NL 0379351   WaSpG IMunS

Linden, James Vincent.
God's boy Tommy. N.P., n.d.
16 p.

NL 0379352   WaSpG

Linden, James Vincent,
My rosary, [Chicago, Paluch, 1954]
160 p. (Lumen books)
Autographed by author.

NL 0379353   WaSpG

Linden, James Vincent.
On the way back home. Chicago, Ill., Paluch, c1947.
139p

NL 0379354   WaSpG

Linden, James Vincent,
On the way back home. [Chicago, Paluch, 1949]
139 p.
3d ed.
Autographed by Author.

NL 0379355   WaSpG

Linden, Jan Antonides van der
see Linden, Johannes Antonides van der, 1609-1664.

Linden, Jan Rudolf Anne Cort van der
see Cort van der Linden, Jan Rudolf Anne, 1858-

Linden, Jan van der, d. 1638.
Cort verhael oft tractaet van de contagieuse sieckte de peste. Die sessendertich Jaren gepractiseert ende hem gheexerceert heeft, binnen de voorseyde stadt, soo in't cureren, preserveren, als door hem bemerct, bevonden ende bee experimenteert. Antwerpen, G. Verdussen, 1634.
69 p. 16°.

NL 0379358   DNLM

Linden, Jan van der, d. 1638
Heerlyke en gelukkige reys naer het Heylig Land en stad van Jerusalem, beschreeven en bereyst door Broeder Jan van der Linden (Pater van de Cellebroeders te Antwerpen) in 't jaer ... 1633. ... Maestricht, G. B. van Gulpen [1634-45]
2 pts. in 1.

NL 0379359   NNC DCU-H

Linden, Jan van der, d. 1638.
Heerlyke ende gelukkige reyze nae het heylig Land ende Stad van Jeruzalem... deel 1-2. tot Gend: J. Begyn, [1740?]
2 v. bd. in one.

NL 0379360   OCH

LINDEN, Jan VAN DER, d. 1638.
Het wederkeeren oft tweede deel van de heerlycke onde gheluckighe reyse naer het H. Landt ende de stadt van Jerusalem beschreven ende bereyst door broeder Jan vander Linden, 1633.. Antwerpen, by de weduwe van H.Verdussen, [after 1717].
sm.4°. pp. 52. Wdcts.

NL 0379361   MH

Linden, Jan van der, 1907-
Die entstehungsgeschichte der mission der niederländischen reformierten kirchen. ... Tübingen, 1934. 76 p.
Inaug. Diss. - Tübingen, 1934.
Lebenslauf.
Bibliography.

NL 0379362   ICRL NIC CtY

Linden, Jane, *pseud.*
see
Walton, Pamela Yendys, 1918-

Linden, J[ean Jules] 1817-1898.
Hortus Lindenianus. Recueil iconographique des plantes nouvelles introduites par l'établissement de J. Linden ... au Jardin royal de zoologie, et d'horticulture, à Bruxelles. 1.[-2.] livr. Bruxelles, M. Hayez, 1859-60.
3 p. l., 25 p. 11 col. pl. (2 fold.) 27½ᶜᵐ.
No more published.

1. Brussels. Jardin royal de zoologie et d'horticulture. I. Title.
Agr 6-1919

Library, U. S. Dept. of   Agriculture 452L643

NL 0379364   DNAL MBH PPHor

VOLUME 334

Linden, Jean Jules, 1817-1898.

Lindley, John, 1799-1865.
Orchidaceæ Lindenianæ; or, Notes upon a collection of orchids formed in Colombia and Cuba, by Mr. J. Linden. By John Lindley ... London, Bradbury and Evans, 1846.

NL 0379366   DNAL NN MBH MiU PPAN

Linden, Jean Jules, 1817-1898.
Pescatorea. Iconographie des orchidées par J. Linden ... avec la collaboration de mm. J. E. Planchon ... M. ₁₁-G. Reichenbach fils ... G. Luddemann ... 1. v. Bruxelles, M. Hayez, 1860.

unp. 48 col. pl. 45½ᶜᵐ.

3 p. l. Each plate is accompanied by one or two pages of descriptive text.

1. Orchidaceæ.   ɪ. Planchon, Jules Émile, 1823-1888.   ɪɪ. Reichenbach, Heinrich Gustav, 1823-1889.   ɪɪɪ. Luddemann, G.

Agr 5—828

U. S. Dept. of agr. Library   452.3L642
for Library of Congress   ₁a40b1₁

NL 0379367   MH-A

Linden, Jean Jules, 1817-1898
Prix-courant de l'establishment d'introduction pour les plantes nouvelles de J. Linden, a Bruxelles. Introductions de 1855.

52 p. (Printemps, Été et Automne de 1855)

NL 0379367   MH-A

Linden, Jean Jules, 1817-1898.
——— and Planchon, Jules Émile. Troisième voyage de J. Linden dans les parties intertropicales de l'Amérique, au Venezuela, dans la Nouvelle-Grenade, à la Jamaïque et dans l'île de Cuba, exécuté par ordre du gouvernement belge, 1841-1845. Pt. i. Botanique. Plantae columbianae. Tom. 1. Bruxelles. 1863. 8°.

NL 0379368   MH-A

87C16
EL4
Linden, Joannes Albertus Maria van der.
Een speciaal gebruik van de ablativus absolutus bij Caesar; een onderzoek op structurele grondslag. 'S-Gravenhage, Uitgeverij Excelsior ₁1955₁
125 p.

Thesis, Amsterdam.
Summary in French.
Bibliography: p. 119-124.

NL 0379369   NNC MH

438.6
L642
LINDEN, Johanna.
Bei uns zu hause; ein kinderbuch... bilder von Ernst Kutzer... bd. ₁Graz, etc.₁ Österr. pädäg. verlag

v. col. illus. 24 cm.

Title-page illustrated in colors.
"Zum unterrichtsgebrauch an allgemeinen Volksschulen als klassenlesestoff allgemein zugelassen."
1. German language. Chrestomathies and readers. I. Kutzer, Ernst, 1880-   illus. II. Title.

NL 0379370   MnU

R128   Linden, Johannes Antonides van der, 1609-1664.
.7   Johannis Antonidæ Van der Linden, De hemicrania menstrua, historia et consilium ...   Lvgdvni Batavorvm, apud Johan. Elsevirium, 1660.
.L7

11 p. l., 92, ₁4₁ p. 20¼ᶜᵐ. ₁With his Meletemata medicinæ, 1660₁

1. Hemicrania.

NL 0379371   ICU PPULC CtY-M MiU DNLM

Linden, Johannes Antonides van der, 1609-1664.
... De lactibus, sive, lacteis venis quarto ... see under Aselli, Gaspare, 1581-1626.

NON-CIRC.
History Collection
Linden, Johannes Antonides van der, 1609-1664.
Ioannis Antonides van der Linden, De scriptis medicis libri duo. Quibus praemittitur D. Petrvm Tvlpivm manuductio ad medicinam. Amstelredami, apud Iohannem Blaev, 1637.
₁52₁, 559, ₁26₁ p. 19 cm.

First ed.
On the t.p. the signature "Nat: Highmore".
There is one short note (p. 90) in the same hand, and crosses against various titles.
Printer's device; initial.

1. Medicine—15th-18th centuries—Bibliography
I. Title: De scriptis medicis libro duo.

NL 0379373   CU-M CaBVaU

Linden, Johannes Antonides van der, 1609-1664.
Ioh. Antonidæ vander Linden ... De scriptis medicis libri dvo. Editio altera, auctior & emendatior. Amstelredami: apud Iohannem Blaev, 1651. 8 p.l., 688 p., 14 l. 12° in eights.

1. Medicine.—Bibliography. 2. Title.

June 16, 1915.

NL 0379374   NN OU MiU DNLM

Linden, Johannes Antonides van der, 1609-1664.
... De scriptis medicis libri duo. Editio altera, auctior & emendatior. Amstelredami, apud Iohannem Blaev, 1651.
Microfilm copy, made in 1960 of the original in Vatican. Biblioteca vaticana. Positive.
Negative in Vatican. Biblioteca vaticana.
Collation of the original as determined from the film: 8 p.l. 671, ₁45₁ l.
The first edition issued in Amsterdam in 1637. The third   "tertia parte auct." in 1662.

1. Medicine—bibliography. (Series: ₁Manuscripta, microfilms of rare and out-of-print books. List 15, no. 49₁)

NL 0379376   MoSU NcU

Linden, Johannes Antonides van der, 1609-1664.
Ioh. Antonidæ vander Linden ... De scriptis medicis libri dvo. Editio tertia & tertia auctior. Amstelredami, I. Blaev, ɔɪɔ. ɪɔ C. LXII.

8 p. l., 755, ₁36₁ p. 20¼ᶜᵐ.

Title vignette.

1. Medicine—15th-18th cent.—Bibl.

35—36002

Library of Congress   Z6659.L74   016.61

CtY-M PPC CtY MnU-B DNLM MoSU CaBVaU WU
NL 0379377   DLC PPJ CLU-M NcD-MC KU-M ICU MoSB PPL

Linden, Johann Antonides van der.
De scriptis medicis, libre duo, quorum prior, omnium tam veterum quam recentiorum ... scriptorum medicorum consummatissimum catalogum continet... posterior vers Cynosuram medicam sive Rerum & materiarum indicem... erhibet... continuati...₂ .. purgati a G.A. Mercklino Norimbergae, Enateri, 1680.

NL 0379378   PU

Linden, Johannes Antonides van der, 1609-1664.
Conring, Hermann, 1606-1681.
Hermanni Conringii introductio in universam artem medicam singulasqve ejus partes ex publicis ejus præcipue lectionibus olim concinnata nunc vero additamentis necessariis aucta continuata ad nostra tempora praecipuorum scriptorum serie. Accesserunt Johannis Rhodii, aliorumqve in arte principum virorum consimilis argumenti commentationes. Cura ac studio Guntheri Christophori Schelhammeri ... cum præfatione Friderici Hoffmanni ... de studio medico recte pertractando et ejus probatissimis auctoribus. Halæ & Lipsiæ, apud E. G. Crugium, 1726.

NL 0379380   DNLM NNNAM

W 6
P3
v.2561
no. 10
LINDEN, Johannes Antonides van der, 1609-1664, praeses
Hippocratis de circuitu sanguinis, exercitatio II. ...
Lugduni Batavorum, Apud Johannem Elsevirium, 1659.
₁8₁ p. 19 cm.
Diss. - Leyden (N. A. Bartels, respondent)

1. Bartels, Nikolaus Adolf, fl. 1659, respondent

NL 0379380   DNLM NNNAM

Linden, Johannes Antonides van der, 1609-1664, tr.
Hippocrates.
Hippocrates on airs, waters, and places. The received Greek text of Littré, with Latin, French, and English translations by eminent scholars ... London, Printed—not for sale—by Wyman & sons, 1881.

NL 0379382   DNLM

64₁.   Linden (Johannes Antonides) van der,
24ᶜ.   Historiæ ægrotorum vigintiquinque. 12 l.
₁Leyden?₁, 1651.

NL 0379382   DNLM

R126
.H5
1665
Rare bk.
Linden, Johannes Antonides van der, 1609-1664, ed.
Hippocrates.
Magni Hippocratis Coi opera omnia. Græce & latine edita, et ad omnes alias editiones accommodata. industriâ & diligentiâ Joan. Antonidæ vander Linden ... Lugduni Batavorum, apud Danielem, Abrahamum & Adrianum à Gaasbeeck, 1665.

Linden, Jan Antonides van der, 1609-1664.
Lindenius renovatus, sive, Johannis Antonidæ van der Linden De scriptis medicis libri duo: quorum prior, omnium, tam veterum, quàm recentiorum, latino idiomate, typis unquam expressorum scriptorum medicorum, consummatissimum catalogum continet; posterior verò cynosuram medicam, sive, rerum & materiarum indicem, omnium titulorum vel thematum medicorum potiorum loca communia alphabetico hâcque novâ demum editione primùm adornato ordine suis loculis ita comprehendentem exhibit, ... : à postremæ editionis anno ᴍ ᴅᴄ.ʟxɪɪ usque ad praesentem continuati ... à Georgio Abrahamo Mercklino, ... Norimbergæ, impensis J. G. Endteri, 1686.
2 vol. in 1. front. 19½x15½ᶜᵐ.
Vol. 2 title reads: Cynosura medica, sive, De scriptis medicis liber II.

DNLM KU-M PPiU-D OC1W-H
NL 0379384   ICJ MiU WU-M MnU PPC WaU NNC PPPH CU-M

VOLUME 334

Linden, Johannes Antonides van der, 1609-1664.
17th Cent.   Medicina physiologica, nova curataque methodo
ex optimis quibusque auctoribus contracta ...
Amstelaedami, Apud Joh. à Ravestein, 1653.
4p. l., 884p. 20cm.

1. Medicine - 15th-18th cent.   2. Medicine - Practice.
3. Physiology - Early works to 1800.

NL   0379385   CtY-M WaU DNLM PPL WU-M PPJ

Linden, Johannes Antonides van der, 1609-1664.
Ioa. Antonidæ van der Linden, med. professoris, Me-
dvlla medicinæ, partibus quatuor comprehensa. ɛ 1.
Franekeræ, apud Uldericum Balck, acad. typogr. & Joh.
Fabiani Deüring, 1642.
8 p. l., 350, 192, 183-380 p. 14½ᶜᵐ.
No more published.
CONTENTS.-De medico futuro necessariis, oratio.-Manuductio ad me-
dicinam. Ed. 3.-Medvllæ medicinæ pars prima, physiologica.-Medvllæ
medicinæ pars altera, pathologica.

1. Medicine.

Library of Congress   R128.7.L74   7-22964†

NL   0379386   DLC

R128   Linden, Johannes Antonides van der, 1609-1664.
.7   Johannis Antonidæ Van der Linden ... Meletemata medi-
.L7   cinæ Hippocraticæ.   Lugduni Batavorum, J. Z. Baronius,
1660.
4 p. l., 399, ₁1₎ p. 20½ᶜᵐ.
With this is bound *his* De hemicrania menstrua. 1660.

1. Medicine—Early works.

NL   0379387   ICU CtY-M DNLM

W 4   LINDEN, Johannes Antonides van der, 1609-1664, praeses.
L68   Mulieris colicae historia. lib. III. Epid. sect. II. aegr. IX.
1652   proposita, & exposita ... Lugduni Batavorum, Ex officina
L. 1   Francisci Hackii, 1652.
[18] p. 20 cm.
Published also in Linden's Selecta medica, Lugduni Batavorum,
1656, p. 208-241, under title: Tisameni colica.
Thesis -- Leyden (Pierre Caulier, respondent)

L. Caulier, Pierre, fl. 1652, respondent

NL   0379388   DNLM

R
135   Linden, Johannes Antonides van der, 1609-1664, comp.
L74   Johannis Antonidae vander Linden ... Selecta
medica, et ad ea exercitationes batavae. Lvgdvni
Batavorvm, Apud J. Elsevirivm, 1656.
6 p. l., 772, ₅56₎ p. 20 cm.

1. Medicine, Greek and Roman.

NL   0379389   MiU NIC PPL PPJ NNNAM PPiU ICJ DNLM

LINDEN, Johannes Antonides VAN DER, 1609-1664, ed.
Tractatvs eorum, qui post Spigelivm natomiam
invento aliqvo majoris usus adaerunt. Gasparis
Aselli. Gvilelmi Harveü. Johannis Valaei.
Amsterdami, 1645.

f°.

NL   0379390   MH

LINDEN, Johannes van der, 1756-1835.
Algemeene manier van procedeeren in civiele
en crimineele zaaken. In den Haag, 1799.

Same. Alphabetisch register. Leyden, 1800.

NL   0379391   MH-L

Linden, Johannes van der, 1756-1835.
... De jure viduarum ... submittit
Joannes van der Linden ... Lugduni
Batavorum, J. Hasebroek et T. Haak,
1774.

2 p. l., 64, ₄₎ p. 24cm.

Diss.- Leiden.

NL   0379392   MH-L

Linden, Johannes van der, 1756-1835.

Law

Netherlands (*United provinces, 1581-1795*) *Laws, statutes,
etc.*
Groot placaatboek, vervattende de placaaten, ordonnantien en edicten van de hoog mog. heeren Staaten generaal der
Vereenigde Nederlanden; en van de edele groot mog. heeren
Staaten van Holland en Westvriesland; mitsgaders van de
edele mog. heeren Staaten van Zeeland ... ₁15. Junij, 1097-
19. Jan., 1795₎ 's Gravenhage, 1658-1770; Amsterdam,
1795-96.

Linden, Johannes van der, 1756-1835.
Institutes of Holland; or, Manual of law,
practice, and mercantile law, for the use of
judges, lawyers, merchants, and all who wish to
have a general view, of the law, by Mr. Joannes
Van Der Linden ... Tr. from the original
Dutchby Sir Henry Juta ... ed ed.   Cape Town,
[etc.] J. C. Juta & co., 1897.
lxxxi, 515 p.   21.5 cm.

NL   0379394   CtY-L MH

Linden, Johannes van der, 1756-1835.
Institutes of Holland, or Manual of law, practice, and
mercantile law, for the use of judges, lawyers, merchants, and all who wish to have a general view of the
law. By Mr. Joannes van der Linden ... Tr. from the
original Dutch by Sir Henry Juta ... 5th ed. Capetown
₁etc.₎ J. C. Juta & co., 1906.
lxxxi, 515, ₁1₎ p. 22ᶜᵐ.

1. Law—Netherlands. ₁1. Dutch law₎ 1. Juta, Sir Henry Herbert,
1857?– tr. 11. Title.
12-26545

NL   0379395   DLC WaU-L

Linden, Johannes van der, 1756-1835.

Balasingham, Kadirvalepillai.
Institutes of the laws of Ceylon ... By K. Balasingham ...
Jaffna, Ceylon, S. Ragunath & co.; ₁etc., etc.₎, 1906–

Linden, Johannes van der, 1756-1835.
Institutes of the laws of Holland, by Johannes
van der Linden.   Amsterdam, Printed in the
year 1806, and now translated by order of the
Right Honourable The Earl Bathurst, by J.
Henry. London, Printed for J. and W. T.
Clarke, 1828.
735 p.   22 cm.

NL   0379397   OU PU-L MH

LINDEN, Johannes van der, 1756-1835.
Institutes of the Laws of Holland; translated
by G. T. Morice. Bks. 1, 2, selections from Bk.
3 and Bk. 4, ch. 1, section 11-14.   2d. ed.
Cape Town, ₁pref. 1922₎.

NL   0379398   MH-L PU-L

[Linden Johannes van der] 1756-1835.
Judicial, Practical and Mercantile Guide of
British Guiana. By Van der Linden. 1814.
Title from F. Cundall's "Bibliography of the
West Indies," 1909, no. 1512 a.
The author was probably Johannes van der
Linden, the compiler of similar works.

Linden, Johannes van der, 1756-1835.
Korte schets der form van procedeeren, voor
de hoven van justitie in Holland gebruikelyk.
Voor eenige jaaren door een voornaam en kundig
practizyn zaamgesteld; en nu overzien, en in
't licht gegeven. In 's-Gravenhaage, by Johannes Mensert, 1781.
viii, 224 p.

Volume of pamphlets.

NL   0379400   NNC

Linden, Johannes van der, 1756 -1835.

Delany, E   P.
Leading cases on Van der Linden's Institutes of Holland; a digest of decisions based on Van der Linden with
index and references. 2d ed., by E. P. Delany ... and
E. Chas. F. Hutton ... Johannesburg and Pretoria, 1907.

Linden, Johannes van der, 1756-1835.
Legal, practical and mercantile manual for the use of judicial
officers, practitioners, merchants, and all who desire a general
view of legal knowledge, by Mr. Joannes van der Linden ...
generally known as Van der Linden's Institutes of the laws
of Holland. Books I., II., III., chs. I.-VII. and book IV., ch. I.;
being the parts required for the law certificate and civil service
law examinations, and containing all that is useful for practitioners; tr. with notes explanatory of difficulties and showing
how far the text is applicable at the present time, and with

references to modern cases, by George T. Morice ... Cape
Town, T. M. Miller, 1914.
xxiv, 400 p. 22ᶜᵐ.

1. Law—Netherlands. 2. Law—Africa, South.   1. Morice, George
Thomas, ed. and tr.
15-4681

NL   0379403   DLC PPB GU-L WaU-L CSt-Law

Linden, Johannes van der, 1756-1835.
Legal, practical, and mercantile manual ⟨koopmans
handboek⟩ for the use of judicial officers, practitioners,
merchants and all who desire a general view of legal
knowledge, by Mr. Joannes van der Linden ... generally
known as Van der Linden's Institutes of the laws of Holland, books I., II., selections from book III., and book IV.,
ch. I., sections 11-14, containing the parts required for
the law certificate and civil service law examinations, and
all that is useful for practitioners, tr. with notes, includ-

ing references to modern cases, by George T. Morice ...
2d ed., brought up to date and with a sketch of South
African procedure. Cape Town, T. M. Miller ₁pref. 1922₎
xxii, 348 p. 22½ᶜᵐ.
Binder's title: Van der Linden's Institutes, with notes.

1. Law—Netherlands. ₁1. Dutch law₎ 2. Law—Africa, South. 3. Civil
procedure— Africa, South. 4. Criminal procedure — Africa, South. 5.
Courts—Africa, South. ₁6. Roman-Dutch law₎ 1. Morice, George
Thomas, ed. and tr.
24-9249

NL   0379405   DLC CtY

VOLUME 334

Linden, J₍ohannes₎ van der, 1756–1835.
Het leven van Buonaparte. Door M'. J. van der Linden ... Amsterdam, J. Allart, 1802.
2 p. l., 434, viii p. front. (port.) 4 fold. pl. 22½ᶜᵐ.

1. Napoléon I, emperor of the French, 1769–1821. 2. France—Hist.—1789–1815.
4–13536

Library of Congress   DC205.L75

NL 0379406   DLC

Linden, Johannes van der, 1756–1835.
Merula, Paulus, 1558–1607.
Pauli G. F. P. N. Merulæ J. C. Manier van procederen, in de provintien van Hollandt, Zeelandt en West-Vrieslandt, belangende civile zaaken ... vergadert uit alle ordonnantien, privilegien, instructien, missiven, acten, apostillen, enz. tot dien einde in de honderd jaaren herwaards by de hooge overheid, of van wegen dezelve uitgegeven: alles met civile en canonyke rechten, nevens der rechtsgeleerden zoo nieuwe als onde meeningen bevestigd: eerst in den jaare 1705 ... vermeerdert door M'. Gerard de Haas. Mitsgaders nu op nieuw overgezien, verbetert, en considerabel verm. door Mrs. Didericus Lulius, en Joannes van der Linden ... Leiden, S. en J. Luchtmans; ₍etc., etc.₎ 1781–83.

Linden, Johannes van der, 1756–1835.
₍Lulius, Diderik₎ *supposed author.*
Rechtsgeleerde memorie, waar in onzydig onderzogt word de gegrondheid der klagten van den koning van Groot-Brittannien, over de geheime correspondentie tusschen Amsterdam en de Americaansche colonien: en wyders wederlegt word de zaakelyke inhoud van zeker tractaatje, geintituleert, Het politicq systema van de regeering van Amsterdam ... ₍n. p.₎ 1781.

4 K
10417
Linden, Johannes van der, 1756–1835.
Regtsgeleerd, practicaal en koopmans handboek, ten dienste van regters, practizijns, kooplieden, en allen, die een algemeen overzicht van regtskennis verlangen. Amsteldam, J. Allart, 1806.
588 p.

NL 0379410   DLC–P4 CtY NN MH–L MiU–L

Linden, Johannes van der, 1756–1835.
Repertorium of Generaal register over de negen deelen van het Groot placaatboek. Zoo volgens de jaar-en-dagteekeningen als volgens de orde van het alphabet; eerst over de zes deelen in den jaare 1752 uitgegeven: en nu over de verdere deelen aangevult en verbeterd door Mr. Joannes van der Linden ... Amsterdam, J. Allart, 1797.
14 p. l., 25–668 p. 39ᶜᵐ.
1. Netherlands—Pol. & govt. 2. Law—Netherlands. 3. Netherlands—Hist.—Sources. I. Netherlands. United provinces, 1581–1795. Staten generaal. Groot placaatboek. II. Title.
1–23360

Library of Congress   J391.A2   Index

NL 0379411   DLC

Law

Linden, Johannes van der, 1756–1835.
Voet, Joannes, 1647–1713.
The selective Voet; being the Commentary on the Pandects, Paris edition of 1829, and the Supplement to that work by Johannes van der Linden. Translated with explanatory notes and notes of all South African reported cases by Percival Gane. Durban, Butterworth, 1955–

Linden, Johannes van der, 1756–1835.
Table générale alphabétique et raisonnée des matières, contenues dans les codes Napoléon, de procédure civile, de commerce, d'instruction criminelle, et pénal. Algemeen register der voornaamste zaken, voorkomende in het Wetboek Napoleon, Wetboek van civiele regtsvordering, Wetboek von koophandel, Wetboek van strafvordering, en het Wetboek van het strafregt. Door mr. Joannes van der Linden ... Haag, J. Allart ₍1813₎.
v. 22ᶜᵐ.
CONTENTS.—1. stuk. Français.
1. Law—France—Indexes. 2. Law—Netherlands—Indexes. I. France. Laws, statutes, etc. (Indexes) II. Netherlands (Kingdom of Holland, 1806–1813) Laws, statutes, etc. (Indexes)
14–21554 Revised

NL 0379413   DLC

Linden, Johannes van der, 1756–1835, tr.
₍Galard de Terraube, Louis Antoine Marie Victor de, *marquis*₎ 1765–1840.
Tafereel van Cayenne, of Fransch Guiana: naar het Fransch; door mr. Joannes van der Linden ... Leyden, A. en J. Honkoop, 1800.

Linden, Johannes van der, 1756–1835.
Verhandeling over de judicieele practijcq, of form van procedeeren, voor de hoven van justitie in Holland gebruikelijk, voor eenige jaaren door een voornaam en jundig practizijn bij wegen van een korte schets zaamgesteld: vervolgens in den jaare 1781. in 'i licht gegeven: en nu geheel overzien, verbeterd en uitgebreid door Mr. Joannes van der Linden... Leyden, A. en J. Honkoop, 1794–98.
2 v.   22.5 cm.

NL 0379415   CtY–L MH PU–L

Linden, Johannes van der, 1756–1835.
Van der Linden's manual commonly known as the Institutes; translated and annotated by Sir Henry Juta ... Cape Town ₍etc.₎ Juta & co., ltd., 1920.
xxvii, 144 p. 22½ᶜᵐ.
"This book contains all of the Institutes that can be of any use to students."

1. Law—Netherlands. ₍1. Dutch law₎ ₍2. Roman-Dutch law₎ I. Juta, Sir Henry Hubert, 1857–   tr. II. Title: Institutes.
27–21419

NL 0379416   DLC CtY

Linden, Johannes van der, 1756–1835.
Verhandeling over de judicieele practijcq, of form van procedeeren, voor de hoven van justitie in Holland gebruikelijk. Voor eenige jaaren door een voornaam en jundig practizijn bij wegen van een Korte schets zaamgesteld: vervolgens in den jaare 1781, in 't licht gegeven: en nu geheel overzien, verbeterd en uitgebreid door m'. Joannes van der Linden ... 2. druk. Amsterdam, De erven H. Gartman, 1829.
2 v. 23ᶜᵐ.
First published, 1781, under title: Korte schets der form van procedeeren voor de hoven van justitie in Holland gebruikelyk.
1. Courts—Netherlands. 2. Civil procedure—Netherlands.
17–12683 Revised

NL 0379417   DLC

Linden, John, Cleveland.
Baunscheidtism; or, a new exanthematic method of cure... Trans. from the German by T.G. Glewell. 13th ed.   Cleveland, Linden, 1874.
268 p.

NL 0379418   PPC PPULC

Linden, John, Cleveland,
Lehrbuch der exanthematischen heilmethode, auch bekannt unter dem namen Baunscheidtismus ... 14. aufl. nebst einem anhange: Das auge und das ohr ... von John Linden ... Cleveland. O., ₍Publishing house of the Evangelical association₎ 1877.
xvi, 301 p. front. (port.) illus. 20½ᶜᵐ.

1. Baunscheidtism. 2. Eye—Diseases and defects. 3. Ear—Diseases.

Library of Congress   RM129.L73   7–8411†

NL 0379419   DLC DNLM

WBC   LINDEN, John, Cleveland.
L744m   Lehrbuch der exanthematischen
1883   Heilmethode, auch bekannt unter dem
Namen Baunscheidtismus. 1. Ausg. der
15. Aufl., nebst einem Anhange: Das
Auge und das Ohr ... ₍Cleveland, Pub.
House of the Evangelical Assn.₎ 1883.
xvi, 301 p. illus. port.
Translation of Manual of the
exanthematic method of cure.

NL 0379420   DNLM

Linden, John, Cleveland.
Lehrbuch der exanthematischen heilmethode, auch bekannt unter dem namen Baunscheidtismus. Nebst einem anhange: Das auge und das ohr, deren krankheiten und heilung durch die exanthematische heilmethode ... Von John Linden ... Gänzlich umgearb. und vielfach verm. 25. aufl. ₍Cleveland, Evangelical press, 1915₎
xvi, 425, 4, 14 p. front. (port.) illus. 20ᶜᵐ.
"Wird auch in der englischen sprache herausgegeben."
"Beachtungswerte auszüge aus meiner korrespondenz": p. 195–425.
1. Baunscheidtism. 2. Eye—Diseases and defects. 3. Ear—Diseases.
16–12003

Library of Congress   RM129.L73 1915

NL 0379421   DLC

Linden, John, Cleveland,
Manual of the exanthematic method of cure, also known as Baunscheidtism. 14th ed., with an appendix on "The eye" and "The ear" ... thoroughly rev. and enl. By John Linden. ₍Cleveland, O., Publishing house of the Evangelical association₎ 1878.
xvi, 332 p. front. (port.) illus. 20½ᶜᵐ.

1. Baunscheidtism. 2. Eye—Diseases and defects. 3. Ear—Diseases.
7–8412

Library of Congress   RM129.L74

NL 0379422   DLC OU ICJ

Linden, John, Cleveland.
Manual of the exanthematic method of cure, also known as Baunscheidtism. With an appendix on "The eye" and "The ear," their diseases and treatment by means of the exanthematic method of cure ... By John Linden ... Thoroughly rev. and enl. ... 25th ed. ₍Cleveland, Evangelical press₎ 1915.
xvi, 402, 4, 12 p. front. (port.) illus. 20ᶜᵐ.
"Published also in the German language."
"Important extracts from my correspondence": p. 218–402.
1. Baunscheidtism. 2. Eye—Diseases and defects. 3. Ear—Diseases.
16–12002

•Library of Congress   RM129.L74 1915

NL 0379423   DLC DNLM ICJ

Linden, John, Cleveland.
Manual of the exanthematic remedy, also known as Baunscheidtism. With an appendix; for the practical use of everyone. By John Linden ... Thoroughly rev. ... 28th ed. ₍Cleveland, Central publishing house₎ 1931.
157 p. front. (port.) illus. 20½ᶜᵐ.
"Published also in the German language."
Earlier editions have been published under the title: Manual of the exanthematic method of cure.

1. Baunscheidtism. I. Title: The exanthematic remedy.

Library of Congress   RM129.L74 1931   31–29786
Copyright A 41,70
615.814

NL 0379424   DLC

VOLUME 334

Lindén, John, 1867- 1914.
Beiträge zur Kenntniss des westlichen Theiles des russischen Lapplands. Von John Lindén... ₍Helsingfors, 1894.₎ 24 p. map, pl. 8°. (Fennia. ₍v.₎ 9, ₍no.₎ 6.)

1. Kola peninsula. 2. Meteorology,   Russia: Lapland. 3. Series.
June 26, 1923.

NL 0379425   NN

Lindén, John, 1867-1914.
Beiträge zur Kenntniss des westlichen Theiles des russischen Lapplands
In Wissenschaftliche ergebnisse der finnischen expeditionen nach der halbinsel Kola in den jahren 1887-1892.

XA Lindén, John, 1867-1914.
.C76 Bidrag till kännedomen om vegetation och flora inom Enontekis lappmarks björk- och fjällregioner. ₍Helsingfors, 1943₎
v.63:1 82 p. 24 cm. (Acta Societatis pro Fauna et Flora Pennica, 63, no. 1)

Caption title.
"Företal" signed: Ernst Häyrén.

1. Botany - Finland - Enonteki lappmark.
2. Botany - Lapland. 3. Phytosociology - Finland - Enonteki   lappmark. i. t. ii. s.

NL 0379427   NNBG

DA999 Linden,John M.
.L74   ...Mary Stuart and the casket letters...
[Chicago]1903.
6 l.,12 numb.l. 28½ᶜᵐ.
Typewritten.
Thesis(D.B.)--University of Chicago(Dept.of church history)
Bibliography:5th-6th prelim.leaves.

1.Mary Stuart,queen of the Scots,1542-1587.

NL 0379428   ICU

Linden (Josef) [1887-   ]. *Ueber die Erfolge der Röntgen- und Salvarsanbehandlung bei Mycosis fungoides. 67 pp. 8°. Bonn, H. Trapp. 1916.

NL 0379429   DNLM CtY ICRL

Linden, Joseph, 1785-1852.
Das abfahrtgeld, mit rücksicht auf die bestehenden freizügigkeits-verträge. Von Joseph Linden. Wien, J. B. Wallishauffer, 1827.
111 p. 20cm.

1. Taxation. I. Title.

NL 0379430   NcD

Linden, Joseph, 1785-1852.
Abhandlungen über cameral- und fiscalämtliche gegenstände, als: caducitäten, amortisationen von urkunden und öffentlichen creditspapieren, vierten pfenning, münzsachen, punzirungssachen und feingehalt, tabaksachen, postsachen, lottosachen, cautionen, instructionen für die fiskalämter und cameralrepräsentanten; nebst einer besondern abhandlung über adelsanmassungen ... Wien, C.Gerold, 1834.
xviii, 408 p. fold. diagr. 21 cm.

1.Austria - Finance. 2.Industry and state - Austria.

NL 0379432   MH-BA MiU

Linden, Joseph, 1785-1852.
Beilagen zu dr. Joseph Linden's Grundsteuerverfassung in den deutschen und italienischen provinzen der Österreichischen monarchie...
Wien? 184-?
2 pts. in 1.

NL 0379433   MiU

Linden, Joseph, 1785-1852.
Das früher in Oesterreich übliche gemeine und einheimische Recht nach der Paragraphenfolge des neuen bürgerlichen Gesetzbuches; ein Handbuch für Justitzmänner bey Entscheidung älterer Rechtsfälle. Wien, Im Verlage der Geistingerschen Buchhandlung, 1815-20.
3 v. in 1. 20 cm.
Includes bibliographical references.

1. Civil law—Austria—Cases. I. Title.

79-282832

NL 0379434   DLC MH-L MiU-L

Linden, Joseph, 1785-1852.
Die grundsteuerverfassung in den deutschen und italienischen provinzen der österreichischen monarchie, mit vorzüglicher berücksichtigung des stabilen katasters. Von Dr. Joseph Linden ... Wien, F. Volke, 1840.
2 v. fold. tables, fold. pl. 22½ᶜᵐ.

1. Land—Taxation—Austria. 2. Taxation—Austria.

8-7118†

Library of Congress   HJ4342.L7

NL 0379435   DLC MiU

Linden, Joseph, 1785-1852.
Das österreichische Frauenrecht. Wien, C. Gerold, 1834.
2 v. in 1. 20 cm.
Includes bibliographical references.

1. Woman—Legal status, laws, etc.—Austria. I. Title.

74-258451

NL 0379436   DLC CLU ICJ

Linden, Js. van der.
Waarheen met onze moeite en ons verdriet? Een woord ter bestiering en bemoediging in deze bange tijden, door Js. van der Linden... 's-Gravenhage: Firma Wed. C. Oranje ₍1914₎.
16 p. 8°.

Title from cover.

1. European war, 1914- .—Sermons.

January 2, 1915.

NL 0379437   NN

Lindén (K. E.) *Kliniska studier öfver rosen. [Clinical studies on erysipelas.] 75, xxxi pp., 2 pl. 4°. Helsingfors, J. C. Frenckell & Son.1885.

NL 0379438   DNLM ICRL

Lindén, Karl, 1907-
Prognostic and therapeutic aspects of urogenital tuberculosis. ₍Translated by L. J. Brown₎ Lund, 1950.
215 p. illus. 24 cm. (Acta chirurgica Scandinavica. Supplementum 158)
At head of title: From the Department of Surgery ... and the Department of Roentgen-Diagnostics, Lasarettet, Lund, Sweden. Akademisk avhandling—Lund.
Without thesis statement.
Bibliography : p. ₍211₎-215.

1. Genito-urinary organs—Tuberculosis. i. Title. (Series)
Full name: Karl Axel Ture Lindén

A 57-4908

Wisconsin. Univ. Libr.
for Library of Congress

NL 0379439   WU OkU-M ViU ICRL DNLM

Lindén, Karl August.
...40 Tafeln; die Form moderner Grabsteine mit Bronze- u. Eisen-Schmuck, mit einem Vorwort von Dipl. Gartenbau-Inspektor Kuhk... Berlin: O. Baumgärtel₍, 1931₎. 2 l. 40 pl. sq. f°.

573518A. 1. Monuments, Sepulchral.

June 2, 1932

NL 0379440   NN

Lindén, Karl Eberhard, 1847-1927.
... Förhållanden och sjukvård under kriget i Finland, 1788-1790, av K. E. Lindén. Helsingfors, Helsingfors centraltryckeri och bokbinderi aktiebolag, 1920.
293 p. map. 22ᶜᵐ. (Bidrag till kännedom af Finlands natur och folk, utgifna af Finska vetenskaps-societeten. h. 74, n:o 2)

1. Russo-Swedish war, 1788-1790. 2. Russo-Swedish war, 1788-1790—Medical and sanitary affairs.

A C 37-586

Wisconsin. Univ. Library   [Q60.F55 vol. 74, no. 2]
for Library of Congress   (067.1)

NL 0379441   WU NN NcU

DL790 LINDÉN,KARL EBERHARD,1847- 1927.
.L75   Sjukvård och läkare under kriget 1808-1809,af K.E. Linden. Helsingfors[Tidnings- & tryckeri-aktiebolagets tryckeri]1908.
ix,229,[1]p. ports. 23cm. (Half-title:Skrifter utg. af Svenska litteratursällskapet i Finland. LXXXV)
With Ljunggren,C.J. Skildring af krigshändelserna i Öster-och Västerbotten 1808-1809. Helsingfors,1903.
1.Russo-Swedish war,1808-1809--Hospitals,charities, etc. 2.Finland--Hist.--Russian conquest,1808-1809.

MdBJ OU NNC GU NN
NL 0379442   ICU NIC MoU DLC-P4 NcD MH MnU PPAmSwM

91.41 Linden, L   van der.
L64   Verslag over het Onderzoek betreffende de aspergeteelt in de provincie Antwerpen. ₍Mechelen, 1954₎
68 p.

1. Asparagus. I. Antwerp (Province)
Bedrijfsvoorlichtingsdienst voor de Tuinbouw.

NL 0379443   DNAL

VOLUME 334

Lindén, Lars. Wilhelm Felix, 1923–
The effect of stellate ganglion block on cerebral circulation in cerebrovascular accidents. Uppsala, 1955.
110 p. illus. 24 cm. (Acta medica Scandinavica. Supplementum 301)
Bibliography: p. [97]–110.

1. Brain—Blood vessels. 2. Apoplexy.   I. Title.   (Series)

Ohio State Univ. Libr.
for Library of Congress
A 55–8032

NL 0379444   OU ViU DNLM

W 1   LINDÉN, Lars   Wilhelm Felix, 1923–
AN3095   Relation of blood volume to fat content
v. 44   of the body and blood volume deficits in
1955   surgical patients. [Tr. from the Finnish.]
Suppl. 7   Turku, 1955.
92 p. illus. (Annales chirurgiae et gynaecologiae Fenniae, v. 44, supplementum 7)
1. Blood volume 2. Fats   Series

NL 0379445   DNLM

Linden, Leon Mathias, 1878–
A concord of sweet notes, by Leon M. Linden; with a preface by Charles J. O'Malley ... 1st ed. Chicago, J. S. Hyland & co., 1908.
159 p. incl. front. (port.) 18¾ cm.

8–5206

NL 0379446   DLC NN

813   LINDEN, LIELE.
L642c   Chestnut Wood. A tale. By Liele Linden ...
New-York, London, D. Appleton and company, 1854.
2v. 20cm.

NL 0379447   TxU MB NN MH RPB MB NjP

FILM   Linden, Liele.
4274   Chestnut Wood: A tale...   New York,
PR   Appleton, 1854.
v.2   2 v. (359, 360 p.)   (Wright American fiction,
reel   v.II, 1851–1875, no.1554, Research Publica-
L8   tions Microfilm, Reel L–8)

NL 0379448   CU

Linden, Liele.
Holiday afternoons; or, the commandments illustrated. By Leile Linden...
Boston, New England S. S. union, 1854.
vi, [7]–251 p.

NL 0379449   OO LLafS

Linden, Lilla, compiler.
Linden harp... A rare collection of popular melodies, adapted to sacred and moral songs, original and selected, for Sabbath and other schools, and the home circle. Also, a manual of musical instruction. By Lilla Linden. Middletown, Conn.: C. M. Thayer [cop. 1855]. 160 p. illus. 24°.
Words with music for 3 voices.

1. Hymns. 2. Title.

December 19, 1919.

NL 0379450   NN NBuG N NcD NNUT

M1628.5   Linden, Lilla, comp.
L5   Linden harp: a rare collection of popular
melodies, adapted to sacred and moral songs,
original and selected ... Also, a manual
of musical instruction. By Lilla Linden ...
New York, Printed for the author, 1855.
2p.ℓ.,160p.   illus.   15cm.
Added title-page.

NL 0379451   NBuG CtU CoU RPB

-VM   LINDEN, LILLA,   comp.
2193   Linden harp: a rare collection of popular
L 74L   melodies. Adapted to sacred and moral songs,
1856   original and selected. Illustrated. Also, a
manual of musical instruction... New-York, D.
Burgess & co., 1856.
160p.   16½cm.
For children.

NL 0379452   ICN MH NjR NNUT

Linden, Lilla, comp.
Linden harp: a rare collection of popular
melodies adapted to sacred and moral songs, original and selected, illustrated; also, a manual
of musical instruction.   N.Y., Ivison &
Phinney, 1857.
160p.   16cm.

NL 0379453   PPPrHi RPB

Linden, Lucien, 1854–
Iets over orchideën en hun cultuur in onze
kassen voor hollandsche tuinlui. Vrij bewerkt
naar het Fransch van Lucien Linden's "Les orchidées exotiques." Amsterdam, G.P.Tierie, 1903.
123 p. plates. 21 cm.
"Aanbevolen door de 'Nederlandsche orchido-
philen-club' aan alle liefhebbers van orchideën".

NL 0379454   MH

Linden, Lucien, 1854–   ed.
Le Journal des orchidées; guide pratique de culture dirigé et
publié par Lucien Linden ... 1.–7. année (no. 1–165); 15
mars 1890–16 jan. 1897. Gand, Imprimerie E. Vander-
haeghen, 1890–96.

Linden, Lucien, 1854–   ed.
Lindenia; iconographie des orchidées. v. 1–17; [août?] 1885–
déc. 1901. Gand, Imprimerie E. Vander Haeghen [etc.]
1885–1901.

Linden, Lucien, 1854–
Les orchidées exotiques et leur culture en
Europe par Lucien Linden, A. Cogniaux [et]
G. Grignan. Bruxelles, 1894.
xiv, 1019 p. illus., plates, port. 28 cm.
Bibliography: p. [102]–109.
1. Orchids - Europe. 2. Orchid culture.

NL 0379457   CaBVaU MB MBH MH-A MH PPAN

Bonaparte   Linden, M   C   van der.
Collection   Grammaire allemande; ou, Methode
No. 9634   facile pour apprendre la langue alle-
mande, par la comparaison avec le
flamand... Malines,1850.   Q.
"Dialogues familiers...d'après Mei-
dinger": p.395–462. (Text in German,
Flemish and French, in parallel columns)

NL 0379458   ICN

Bon.   LINDEN, M   C   VAN DER.
Call.   Nouvelle grammaire anglaise à l'usage des
No.11211   collèges et des pensionnats. Bruxelles,Ch.-
J.-A.Greuse,1851.
xi,384p. 18cm.
Many of the exercises in English, Dutch
and French.

NL 0379459   ICN

Linden, M   L   M   van der
De grondverhuring door inlanders aan niet-
inlanders op Java en Madoera. Vastgesteld
bij de ordonnantie van 27 augustus 1900
(Staatsbl. no. 240) bewerkt door M. L. M. van
der Linden (Multavidi) Rotterdam, Masereeuw,
& Bouten, 1907.
335 p.
1. Leases - Dutch East Indies.

NL 0379460   NNC NIC CtY WU

Linden, Margaret.
Pasha the Persian, by Margaret Linden; illustrations by
Milt Gross. [New York, C. Kendall, inc.,1936]
108 p. illus. 23½ cm.
"First edition."

I. Gross, Milt, 1895–   illus. II. Title.

PZ3.L64623Pas   37—1672

NL 0379461   DLC

Linden, Maria, Gräfin von, 1869–1936.
Die Assimilationstätigkeit bei Schmetterlings-Puppen, von
Prof. Dr. Gräfin von Linden ... Mit 14 Figuren im Text und 3
Tafeln. Leipzig, Veit & Comp., 1912.
164 p. illus, III pl. (part fold.), diagrs. 24½cm.
Bibliographical foot-notes.

NL 0379462   ICJ IdU MH PPAN NIC NjP

Linden, Maria, gräfin von, 1869–
Eimer, Gustav Heinrich Theodor, 1843–1898.
Die entstehung der arten auf grund von vererben
erworbener eigenschaften nach den gesetzen organischen
wachsens. Ein beitrag zur einheitlichen auffassung der
lebewelt, von dr. G. H. Theodor Eimer ... Jena, G.
Fischer, 1888–1901.

Linden, Maria Gräfin von, 1869–1936.
Die Entwicklung der Skulptur und der Zeichnung
bei den Gehäuseschnecken des Meeres. Tuebingen, 1896.
Inaug.-Diss. - (Leipzig)

NL 0379464   ICRL

VOLUME 334

Linden, Maria, *gräfin von, 1869–1936.*
Parasitismus im tierreich, von prof. dr. gräfin von Linden ... Braunschweig, F. Vieweg & sohn, 1915.
viii, 214 p., 1 l. illus., VII (i. e. 8) pl. (1 fold.) 22^{cm}. (Added t.-p.: Die wissenschaft ... bd. 58)
Part of plates cover both sides of leaf.
"Literaturverzeichnis": p. 207–208.

1. Parasites.

Library, U. S. Dept. of   Agriculture   436L645   Agr 22–542

NL 0379465   DNAL MiU UU PU PPC ICJ MdBP

Linden, Maria Anna Wilhelmine Luise Karoline Elise Kamilla Olga Amalie Pauline, gräfin von
see   **Linden, Maria, gräfin von, 1869–1936.**

MB5
L642s   **Linden, Martin,** 1893–   ed.
        Sändebud till Sinims land; svenska missionens i Kina 60-års berättelse. Stockholm, Svenska missionens i Kina förlag [1947]
        172 p. ports., map. 21 cm.

NL 0379467   CtY-D

Linden, Maurice E
        Architecture for psychogeriatric installations [n.p.] American Psychiatric Association, 1953.
        20p. 28 cm.

NL 0379468   NRCR

BF1413   **Linden, Maximilian Joseph, Freiherr von.**
.L74   Handschriften für Freunde geheimer Wissen-
Rare   schaften zum Druck befördert von M. J. F. v.
Bk   L**. Wien, A. Blumauer, 1794–
        v. plates.

        1. Occult sciences. 2. Occult sciences—Bibl. I. Title.

NL 0379469   ICU WU

Z5784
.M9M6   **Linden, Michael.**
1952   **Motion Picture Association of America.**
        Books into films [by] Michael Linden, librarian. Rev. Washington, 1952.

Linden, Michael.
        Motion picture censorship; a selected bibliography on the artistic, educational, psychological, and legal aspects of film censorship. 1951.
        7 l.

        1. Moving-pictures - Censorship - Bibliography.

NL 0379471   NNC

Linden, Michael; *1885–* Neuere Reduktionsmethoden zur quantitativen Bestimmung des Traubenzuckers im Harne. Rostock 1912: Adler. 30 S. 8°
Rostock, Med. Diss. v. 25. Juni 1913, Ref. Martius
[Geb. 16. Dez. 85 Meckenheim b. Bonn; Wohnort: Ludwigslust; Staatsangeh.: Preußen; Vorbildung: Gymn. Euskirchen Reife M. 04; Studium: Bonn 2, Würzburg 3, München 3, Rostock 2 S.; Coll. 24. Mai 12; Approb. 1. Juli 13.]
[U 12. 6676

NL 0379472   ICRL MH

Linden, Oliver, *pseud.*
see
Abrahams, Doris Caroline, 1901–

Linden, Oscar.
        Columbia is free. . . . [Song, with pianoforte accompaniment.] Written by W. Dexter Smith, Jr. Music by Oscar Linden. Boston. Russell & Co. 1865. 5 pp. 33 cm.

K7900 — Double main card. — Linden, Oscar. (M1) — Smith, William Dexter, 1838–1909. (M2) — T.r. (1)

NL 0379474   MB

Linden, Oskar, pseud.
        See
[Wimmer, Adolph] 1857–

Linden, P   C   van der.
        Klinische en proefondervindelijke studies in verband met de ziekten van de slagaders der ledematen. Brugge, Drukkerij Sinte Katharina, 1940–
        v. diagrs. 26 cm.
        Proefschrift (ter verkrijging van de graad van geaggregeerde van het hooger onderwijs)—Ghent.
        Over title.
        "Stellingen": v. 1, [1] p. inserted.
        "Literatuur": v. 1, p. [125]–130.
        CONTENTS.—deel 1. Proefondervindelijke onderzoekingen over de gebruikelijke contraststoffen bij arteriographie.

        1. Arteries—Diseases.
RC691.L5   52–38880

NL 0379476   DLC OrU DNLM NIC IU CtY

MANN
QP   **Linden, P   C   van der.**
101   Proefondervindelijke onderzoekingen over de
L74P   gebruikelijke contraststoffen bij arteriographie. Brugge, Sinte Katharina, 1940.
        130 p. diagrs. 26 cm. (Half title: Klinische en proefondervindelijke studies in verband met de ziekten van de slagaders der ledematen, deel 1)

        Proefschrift--Gent.
        At head of title: Uit de heelkundige kliniek der Rijksuniversi   teit te Gent.

        1. Blood - Pressure. I. Title. [II. Series: Klinische en proefondervindelijke studies in verband met de ziekten van de slagaders der ledematen, deel 1]

NL 0379478   NIC DNLM

        Linden, Peter, 1895–
        Der tod des benefiziaten in Rom ... Bonn, 1937.
        30 p.
        Inaug. Diss. - Bonn, 1937.
        Lebenslauf.
        Schrifttum.

NL 0379479   ICRL

Linden, Peter, 1895–
        Der tod des benefiziaten in Rom; eine studie zu geschichte und recht der päpstlichen reservationen, von dr. theol. Peter Linden. Bonn, L. Röhrscheid, 1938.
        xvi, 284 p. 23½^{cm}. (Added t.-p.: Kanonistische studien und texte, hrsg. von A. M. Koeniger ... bd. 14)
        Issued also in part as inaugural dissertation, Bonn.
        "Schrifttum": p. [viii]–xvi.

        1. Benefices, Ecclesiastical. I. Title.   39–19536

Library of Congress   BX1955.L5
                            254

NL 0379480   DLC

Linden (Peter [Lambert]) [1868–   ]. *Aktinomykose. 80 pp., 2 l. 8°. Bonn, J. Bach Wwe., 1892.

NL 0379481   DNLM

Linden, Pierre Léonard van der
        see
Vanderlinden, Pierre Léonard, 1797–1831.

Linden, Pieter Wilhelm Adriaan Cort van der
        see   Cort van der Linden, Pieter Wilhelm Adriaan, 1846–1935.

Linden, Pieter Willem Jacob Henri Cort van der
        see
        Cort van der Linden, Pieter Willem Jacob Henri, 1893–

Linden, R   A   D   Cort van der
        see
        Cort van der Linden, R   A   D.

        Linden, R.A.
        Map of Washington's Birthplace from a Survey, 1879. Published, May, 1897.

NL 0379486   MHi

BX   Linden, Raymund, 1904–
7406   Die Regelobservanz in der Rheinischen
.Z5   Kapuzinerprovinz von der Gründung bis zur
R4   Teilung, 1611–1668 ... Münster i. W., Druck der
L7   Aschendorffschen Buchdruckerei, 1935.
        x p., 1 l., 143, [1] p. 23cm.
        Inaug.-Diss.--Münster.
        "Quellen- und Literaturverzeichnis": p. [vii]-x.
        Lebenslauf.
        1. Capuchins. Rheinische Provinz. I. Title.

NL 0379487   DCU

VOLUME 334

Linden, Raymund, *1904–*
... Die regelobservanz in der Rheinischen kapuzinerprovinz von der gründung bis zur teilung, 1611–1668, von p. dr. Raymund Linden ... Münster i. W., Aschendorff ₍1936₎

x p., 1 l., 149, ₍1₎ p. illus. (map) 24½ᵐᵐ. (Franziskanische studien, beiheft 16)

"Quellen- und literaturverzeichnis": p. ₍vii₎–x.

1. Capuchins. Rheinische provinz. I. Title. 37–5896

Library of Congress BX3134.L5

271.36094342

NL 0379488 DLC OClW

HJ
4639
L744a
1951

LINDEN, Robert
Arzt und Steuern von A–Z, ein zeitnahes Nachschlagewerk für den freiberuflichen Arzt, Zahnarzt und Dentisten; auch für die übrigen freien Berufe geeignet. 3. neubearb. und erweiterte Aufl. Mainz, Kirchheim, 1951.
92 p.
1. Dental economics 2. Income tax 3. Medical economics

NL 0379489 DNLM IEN-D

HJ
4639
L744a
1955

LINDEN, Robert
Arzt und Steuern von A–Z; ein zeitnahes Nachschlagewerk für den freiberuflichen Arzt, Zahnarzt und Alle übrigen Heilberufe. 5., neubearb. und erweiterte Aufl. unter Berücksichtigung der Steuerreform ab 1955. Mainz, Kirchheim, 1955.
88 p.
1. Dental economics 2. Income Tax 3. Medical economics

NL 0379490 DNLM MH-L

Linden, Robert.
Steuer-ABC für den selbständigen Handwerker; ein zeitnahes Nachschlagewerk für den selbständigen Handwerker und die übrigen Gewerbetreibenden, unter Berücksichtigung der Einkommensteuerreform 1950; der neue Einkommensteuertarif 1950 ist enthalten. H. Luchterhand ₍Vorwort 1950₎

88 p. 21 cm.

1. Taxation—Germany (Federal Republic, 1949–   )—Popular works. I. Title.

55–31496 ‡

NL 0379491 DLC

PG2640
L744

Linden, S   W
Pocket-dictionary of the English and Russian languages ₍by₎ S. W. Linden and Th. Kawraisky. Leipzig, O. Holtze's Nachf., 1909.
461, 445 p. 15cm.
Added t.p. in Russian.
Lettered on cover: Angliĭsko-russkiĭ i russko-angliĭskiĭ slovar'.

Hoover
Library

1. English language - Dictionaries - Russian. 2. Russian language - Dictionaries - English. I. Kawraiskiĭ,   Fedor Fedorovich, 1866– II. Title.

NL 0379492 CSt-H NN CtY NcU

PG 2640
L5
1920

Linden, S   W
Pocket-dictionary of the English and Russian languages ₍by₎ S. W. Linden and Th. Kawraisky. 5d ed. Leipzig, O. Holtze, 1920–
v. 15 cm.

Added t. p. in Russian.
Contents. – 1. pt. English-Russian.

1. English language - Dictionaries - Russian. I. Kawraiskiĭ, F   F   joint author. II. Title.

NL 0379493 OU

Linden, S. W.
... Pocket-dictionary of the English and Russian languages ... 4th ed. Leipzig, Otto Holtze's nachfolger, 1922.
2 v. in 1.

NL 0379494 OrPR

Linden, Simeon, tr.

₍Smidovich, Vikentiĭ Vikent'evich₎ 1867–
The memoirs of a physician; translated from the Russian of Vikenty Veressayev ₍pseud.₎ by Simeon Linden; with an introduction and notes by Henry Pleasants, jr., M. D. New York, A. A. Knopf, 1916.

839.5L6422
OS

Lindén, Staffan, 1926–
Staffans stollar; en årskrönika i bild. årg.;   Uppsala, Lindblads.

v. illus. 19cm.

NL 0379496 MnU

Linden, Théodore, illus.

Pauphilet, Albert.
La tétralogie de Richard Wagner, transposée par Albert Pauphilet; illustrations en couleurs de Théodore Linden. Paris, H. Piazza ₍1938₎

LINDEN, W. *Nachbehandlung schmerzhafter und eitriger Prozesse in der Zahnheilkunde unter Berücksichtigung von Yatren ₍Heidelberg₎ 35p. 8°. Konstanz, 1930.

NL 0379498 DNLM

W 6
P3

LINDEN, W   zur
Infantile paralysis (polio) its recognition & treatment. London, New Knowledge Books ₍1954₎
20 p.
1. Anthroposophy 2. Poliomyelitis - Treatment

NL 0379499 DNLM

Linden, W   H   van der.
Stamboek der familie Boelen. Amsterdam, Druk: De Bussy ₍1941₎

248 p. illus., ports., map, coats of arms, facsims., geneal. tables. 30 cm.

1. Boelen family.

CS829.B562 1941 61–56940

NL 0379500 DLC NIC MH

Linden, Walter, *1902–*
Eisenbahn und Konjunktur, von Dr. Walter Linden, ... Karlsruhe, G. Braun, 1926.

[4], 99, ₍1₎ p. incl. tables. 25ᵐᵐ. (*In* Wirtschaftsstudien. Neue und erweiterte Folge der Volkswirtschaftlichen Abhandlungen der badischen Hochschulen, 7. Band.)

"Literatur," p. [97]–99.

NL 0379501 DNLM IU NN ICJ ICU

LINDEN, WALTER, 1902–
Der Fremdenverkehr in den mitteldeutschen Grossstädten. Halle, Gebauer-Schwetschke A.-G., 1927. 36 p. incl. tables, charts. (Halle, Germany. Statistisches Amt. Beiträge zur Statistik der Stadt Halle, Heft 35)

"Von... Walter Linden verfasst."—Pref.

1. Tourist industry—Germany. Central. I. Series.

NL 0379502 NN

Linden, Walter, 1902–
₍...₎ Gegenwartsprobleme des strassengüterverkehrs; drei vorträge, gehalten auf der generalversammlung 1954 der Arbeitsgemeinschaft güterfernverkehr im bundesgebiet von ... W. Linden ... A. Gutersohn und ... H. Krüger. Bielefeld, Kirschbaum ₍1955₎

2 p.l., 7–51 p. 21cm. (Schriftenreihe der Arbeitsgemeinschaft güterfernverkehr im bundesgebiet, heft 2)

NL 0379503 MH-L

HE
249
.L74

Linden, Walter, 1902–
Koordinierungsausschüsse im Personenverkehr; Gedanken und Anregungen zur Rationalisierung des Verkehrsdienstes. Nach einem Vortrag, gehalten auf der Sitzung des Ausschusses Verkehr der Arbeitsgemeinschaft Rationalisierung, am 25. November 195X in Dusseldorf. Dortmund, Verkehrs- und Wirtschaftsverlag ₍1953₎
152, ₍2₎ p. 25 cm. (Arbeitsgemeinschaft für Rationalisierung des Landes Nordrhein-Westfalen. ₍Schriftenreihe₎ Heft 4)
Bibliography: p. ₍153–154₎
1. Transportation   —Germany (Federal Republic, 1949–   2. Transportation—Passenger traffic.

NL 0379504 MiU

Linden, Walter, 1902–
Der Werkverkehr mit Kraftfahrzeugen in der Verkehrspolitik unserer Zeit; Tatsachen und Probleme um die Individualisierung des Güterverkehrs. np [1949]

NL 0379505 MH

B2949
.Z9
v.5

Linden, Walter, 1904–
Solger und Hegel, bemerkungen aus anlass eines vergleiche ihrer aesthetischen schriften. Hamburg, 1938.
47 p.
Diss.—Hamburg.

₍Hegel, Georg Wilhelm Friedrich, 1770–1831—Pamphlets. v.5, no.5₎

1. Solger, Karl Wilhelm Ferdinand, 1780–1819.

NL 0379506 ICU CtY OrU

VOLUME 334

PT1731
.A6
1943

Linden, Walther, 1895–1943, ed.

Grimmelshausen, Hans Jacob Christoffel von, 1625–1676.
Der abenteuerliche Simplicissimus, von Jakob Christoffels von Grimmelshausen. Nach der ausgabe von Philipp Lenz herausgegeben von Walther Linden. Leipzig, P. Reclam jun. ₁1943₎

NL 0379508   IaAS NcD PBL MH CtY NNC CU

Linden, Walther, 1895–1943.
... Alexander von Humboldt; weltbild der naturwissenschaft, von dr. Walther Linden. Hamburg, Hoffmann und Campe ₍1940₎

93 p. 19ᶜᵐ. (Added t.-p.: Geistiges Europa; bücher über geistige beziehungen europäischer nationen, herausgeber A. E. Brinckmann)

1. *Humboldt, Alexander, freiherr von, 1769–1859. I. Title.

                A 41–2163
Iowa. State coll. Library
for Library of Congress

NL 0379508   IaAS NcD PBL MH CtY NNC CU

Linden, Walther, 1895–
Alexander von Humboldt; Weltbild der Naturwissenschaft. Hamburg ₍1942₎
92p. (Geistiges Europa; Bücher über geistige beziehungen europäischer Nationen)

NL 0379509   ICRL PPG IaU

WB
65100

Linden, Walther, 1895–
Alexander von Humboldt, a jeho světový názor přírodovědný. [Přeložil Fr. Štěpánek. 1. vyd.] Praha, Orbis, 1945.
51 p. 21 cm.

1. Humboldt, Alexander, Freiherr von, 1769–1859.

NL 0379510   CtY

830.9
L74a

Linden, Walther, 1895–
...Arteigene dichtung unserer zeit. Leipzig, Eichblatt , 1935.
28p. D. (Bildung und nation ₍55–56₎)

NL 0379511   IaU CU CtY NN

Linden, Walther, 1895–
... Aufgaben einer nationalen literaturwissenschaft. München, C. H. Beck, 1933.
4 p. l., 65, ₍1₎ p. 22ᶜᵐ.

1. Criticism. 2. Literature—History and criticism. 3. German literature—History and criticism. I. Title.   A C 33–4423
Title from New York   Univ. PT81.L7 Printed by L. C.

NL 0379512   NNU PPT OkU CU CtY MiU ODW OCU OO IU

Linden, Walther, 1895–
... Aufgaben einer nationalen literaturwissenschaft. 2., unveränderter abdruck. München, Beck, 1933.
4 p. l., 65, ₍1₎ p. 22ᶜᵐ.

"Die vorliegende schrift ₍ist₎ in gewissen sinne eine allgemeine einleitung in meine 'Geistesgeschichte des deutschen realismus', deren erster band in diesem jahre erscheinen wird."—Vorwort.

1. German literature—Hist. & crit.—Theory, etc. 2. Literature—Philosophy. 3. Literature and state. I. Title.   34–17055
Library of Congress   PT49.L5 1933
Copyright A—Foreign   24288
                     830.1

NL 0379513   DLC

Linden, Walther, 1895–   joint ed.

Korff, Hermann August, 1882–   ed.
Aufriss der deutschen literaturgeschichte nach neueren gesichtspunkten, in verbindung mit E. Ermatinger, P. Merker, G. Müller ₍u. a.₎ ... herausgegeben von H. A. Korff und W. Linden. 2. aufl. Leipzig und Berlin, B. G. Teubner, 1931.

PT2432
.Z8L7

Linden, Walther, 1895–
... Conrad Ferdinand Meyer, entwicklung und gestalt. München, C. H. Beck, 1922.
₍5₎, 249 p. 21½ᶜᵐ.

1. Meyer, Conrad Ferdinand, 1825–1896.

     PPT PSt UU
     CaBVaU ODW OCU MiU MH OU RPB PHC OC1W PU NcD CtY
NL 0379515   ICU OrU CU TU CLSU NIC ICarbS GU MBU

Linden, Walther, 1895–1943.
Deutsche Dichtung am Rhein; Literaturgeschichte der fränkischen Rheinlande. Ratingen, A. Henn ₍1944₎
482 p. 24 cm. (Rheinische Bücherei)

1. German poetry—Hist. & crit. 2. German literature—Rhine River and Valley. (Series)
PT3803.R5L5   A 48–8653*
Pennsylvania. Univ.   Library
for Library of Congress   †

NL 0379516   PU LU CtY CU WU IU DLC

Linden, Walther, 1895–1943.
Eindrucks- und Symbolkunst, herausgegeben von dr. Walther Linden. Leipzig, P. Reclam jun., 1940.
314 p. port. 21 cm. (Added t.-p.: Deutsche literatur; sammlung literarischer kunst- und kulturdenkmäler in entwicklungsreihen ... Reihe ₍23a₎: Vom naturalismus zur neuen volksdichtung ... bd. 2)

CONTENTS.—I. Symbolkunst: Friedrich Nietzsche.—II. Eindruckskunst; Liliencron, Dauthendey.—III. Die umkehr des naturalismus: Conradi, Holz.—IV. Kampf zwischen Trieb und Geist: Richard Dehmel.

1. Naturalism in literature. 2. Symbolism in literature. 3. Impressionism. 4. German literature—19th cent. I. Title.
PT1101.D3   reihe 23a, bd. 2   830.9
                      A 44–2152
Western Reserve Univ.   Library
for Library of Congress   ₍61m₎†

     MdBJ NIC NBC DLC MU GU GASC CaBVaU MtBC AAP
NL 0379517   OC1W ViU MsU PSC OCU OU OO NN LU PU ICU

830
G599
tF.Y53

Linden, Walther, 1895–1943₎
Faust und Wilhelm Meister; von Kampf und Wechselbeziehung dichterischer Symbole. ₍Heidelberg, C.Winter, n.d.₎ p.₍255₎–267. 23cm.

Caption-title.
"Sonderabdruck aus ₍sic₎ dem Jahrgang XX der Germanisch-romanischen Monatsschrift."

1. Goethe, Johann Wolfgang von. Faust. 2. Goethe, Johann Wolfgang von. Wilhelm Meister. I. Title.

NL 0379518   CLSU

Linden, Walther, 1895–   ed.

Sulger-Gebing, Emil, 1863–1923.
... Gerhart Hauptmann, von prof. dr. Emil Sulger-Gebing. Vierte verbesserte und vermehrte auflage, bearbeitet von dr. Walther Linden. Leipzig und Berlin, B. G. Teubner, 1932.

PT96
.K57
1943

Linden, Walther, 1895–1943.

Klöpzig, Walther, 1889–
Geschichte der deutschen Literatur nach Entwicklungsperioden. 5. Aufl. Leipzig, P. Reclam jun. ₍1943₎

Linden, Walther, 1895–1943.
... Geschichte der deutschen literatur von den anfängen bis zur gegenwart. Leipzig, P. Reclam jun. ₍1937₎
490 p. col. front., plates, ports., facsims. 23 cm.

1. German literature—Hist. & crit.
PT85.L55   830.9   A C 38–195 rev
Rochester. Univ. Libr.
for Library of Congress   ₍r64c₎†

     OCU DLC
NL 0379521   NRU WaWW OC1W PBm PPT NcD CtY CU TxU

Linden, Walther, 1895–
... Geschichte der deutschen literatur von den anfängen bis zur gegenwart. 2., erweiterte aufl. Leipzig, P. Reclam jun. ₍1940₎
528 p. col. front., plates, ports., facsims. 23ᶜᵐ.

1. German literature—Hist. & crit.
                   46–39388
Library of Congress   PT85.L55 1940
                   830.9

NL 0379522   DLC OU FU TxDaM ICU NjP PSC

Linden, Walther, 1895–
... Geschichte der deutschen literatur von den anfängen bis zur gegenwart. 4. aufl. Leipzig, P. Reclam jun. ₍1942₎
528 p. plates, ports., facsims. 23ᶜᵐ.

1. German literature—Hist. & crit.
                   46–39387
Library of Congress   PT85.L55 1942
                   830.9

NL 0379523   DLC CLU IaU MiD NNC MB MoU

Linden, Walther, 1895–
... Geschichte der deutschen literatur von den anfängen bis zur gegenwart. 5. aufl. Leipzig, P. Reclam jun. ₍1944₎
1 p. l., ₍5₎–525 p. 23ᶜᵐ.

1. German literature—Hist. & crit.
                   A 46–3224
Yale univ. Library
for Library of Congress   PT85.L55 1944
           †   830.9

NL 0379524   CtY NRU CU IU WU DLC PU

Linden, Walther, 1895–1943.

Bielschowsky, Albert, 1847–1902.
Goethe, sein leben und seine werke, von Albert Bielschowsky; neubearbeitet von Walther Linden ... München, C. H. Beck, ₍1928₎

VOLUME 334

Linden, Walther, 1895–
Goethe und die deutsche gegenwart, von Walther Linden. Berlin, Bong & co. [°1932]
3 p. l., 5–69, [1] p., 1 l. front. (port.) 20½ᶜᵐ.
On cover: Zum Goethe-jahr 1932.

1. Goethe, Johann Wolfgang von, 1749–1832.   I. Title.
Library of Congress   PT2166.L5   32–17827
Copyright A—Foreign
                                                          928.3

PPG OC1W ODW MiU OCU NNC MH
NL 0379526   DLC CaBVaU OrU NBuU OrU CU CtY ICU PSC

Linden, Walther, 1895–
... Goethes leben und werk, von Walther Linden. Mit 26 abbildungen. Bielefeld und Leipzig, Velhagen & Klasing, 1937.
vi, 178 p. incl. front., illus., ports. 17½ᶜᵐ. (Deutsche ausgaben, hrsg. von L. Gruenberg und P. Habermann. bd. 286)
Advertisements: p. 171–178.

1. Goethe, Johann Wolfgang von—Biography.
                                                          A C 38–1293
Rochester. Univ. Library   PT2051.L7
for Library of Congress

NL 0379527   NRU NcD

Linden, Walther, 1895–
Heinrich von Kleist, der dichter der völkischen gemeinschaft, von Walther Linden. Leipzig, P. Reclam [°1935]
76, [2] p. 16ᶜᵐ. (On cover: Reclams universal bibliothek, nr. 7293)

1. Kleist, Heinrich von, 1777–1811.
Library of Congress   PT2379.L5   35–17914
Copyright A—Foreign   28279
                                                          928.3

NL 0379528   DLC NNC NcD NcU CtY CU

Linden, Walther, 1895–
Heinrich von Kleist, der Dichter der völkischen Gemeinschaft. 2., durchgesehene Aufl. Leipzig, P.Reclam[1940]
77p. 16cm. (Reclams Universal-Bibliothek. 7293)
Pamphlet

NL 0379529   CtY

Linden, Walther, 1895–   ed.
Luther, Martin, 1483–1546.
Luthers kampfschriften gegen das judentum; herausgegeben von dr. Walther Linden. Mit 11 abbildungen auf tafeln. Berlin, Klinkhardt [°1936]

Linden, Walther, 1895–1943, ed.
Naturalismus, herausgegeben von dr. Walther Linden. Leipzig, P. Reclam jun., 1936.
295 p. port. 21½ x 16 cm. (Added t.-p.: Deutsche literatur; sammlung literarischer kunst- und kulturdenkmäler in entwicklungsreihen ... hrsg. von dr. H. Kindermann. Reihe [23a,]: Vom naturalismus zur neuen volksdichtung ... bd. 1)
Contents.—Naturalistische theorie.—Naturalistische lyrik.—Naturalistische epik.—Naturalistische drama.

1. Naturalism in literature.   2. German literature—19th cent.
PT1101.D3   reihe 23a, bd. 1   830.822   38—630

OC1 NN GU MsU ViU AAP
NL 0379531   DLC MtBC OrU CU MU NBC ScU PU PSC OO OU

Y
A 95   LINDEN, WALTHER, 1895–
.9795   Studien zum Wigamur. Überlieferung und
            sprache. Halle,Noske,1920.
            61p.

            "Benutzte literatur": p.[3]

NL 0379532   ICN MH OC1 CU

Linden, Walther, 1895–1943, ed.
Meyer, Conrad Ferdinand, 1825–1898.
Wandlungen der gedichte Conrad Ferdinand Meyers, ausgewählt von dr. Walther Linden. Berlin, Junker und Dünnhaupt, 1935.

ar W   Linden, Wilhelm.
53189   Ist der Papst Souverän? Neuss a. Rhein,
no.5   Druck der Allgem. Rheinischen Volkszeitung,
            1898.
                64 p. 22cm.

            Inaug.-Diss.---Erlangen.

NL 0379534   NIC MH NNC ICRL

Linden, Wilhelm: Thrombose und Embolie in der Gynäkologie. Gummersbach 1915: (Luyken). 56 S. 8°
Gießen, Med. Diss. v. 18. Mai 1916, Ref. Opitz
[Geb. 9. Juli 91 Gummersbach; Wohnort: Gelsenkirchen; Staatsangeh.: Preußen; Vorbildung: OR. Gummersbach Reife 09; Studium: Marburg 5, Bonn 1, Leipzig 1, Gießen 3 S.; Coll. 31. Juli 14; Approb. 22. Aug. 14.] [U 16. 912

NL 0379535   ICRL DNLM

Linden, Wilhelm Helmuth Elias de Heydensee   Heyden-Linden, Wilhelm Helmuth Elias de, 1842–

Linden, Wilhelm jur, 1896–
Ueber ungewoehnlich lange dauer der biermerschen krankheit. (Auszug).
Inaug. diss., Rostock, 1923.

NL 0379537   ICRL

Linden, Willem Damasus van der, 1525–1588
see
Lindt, Willem Damasus van der, 1525–1588

Linden, Wolfgang, 1905–
Nachbehandlung schmerzhafter und eitriger Prozesse in der Zahnheilkunde unter Berücksichtigung von Yatren ... Konstanz, 1930.
Inaug. – Diss. – Heidelberg.
Lebenslauf.
"Literatur": p. 31–34.

NL 0379539   CtY

Linden van den Heuvell (Hendrik Ludwijn) Klinische en physiologische waarnemingen omtrent Adonis vernalis en adonidine. [Leyden.] 2 p. l., 80 pp. 8°. Haarlem, J. F. Haeseker & Co., 1883.

NL 0379540   DNLM

Linden van Spranckhuysen, Johannes van der, 1766–1855.
Proeve eener vrije behandeling Van den Heidelb. Catechismus in den geest Van het gezuiverd Christendom, overeenkomstig het beginsel der Kerkhervorming. Groningen, 1825.

NL 0379541   NjNbS

889   LINDEN VAN SPRANCKHUYSEN, Johannes van der,
V949p   1766–1855.
1854   Kerkelijke toespraak, bij gelegenheid van
no.8   het afsterven van den weleerwaardigen heer
            Albertus Lofvers...Groningen, Van Boekeren
            1843.
                23p. 22cm.

            No.8 in a bound volume of sermons and
            addresses by various authors.

NL 0379542   MH-AH

Linden, Hannover, Ger.
Haushaltspläne der stadt Linden ...
[Linden]
    v. 28½ᶜᵐ.

1. Budget—Linden, Hannover, Ger.
Library of Congress   HJ9049.L52   32–7457
                                                          352.1094353

NL 0379543   DLC

027.4749   Linden, N.J. Free Public Library.
L64   Report. 1st–   1928–   Linden,
N.J., 1928–
                v. 21–29 cm.

            1. Libraries—New Jersey.

NL 0379544   LU DHEW CU

Linden, N.J. Ordinances, etc.
Building code of the city of Linden, New Jersey. 1925 ... Compiled by Jules Verner ... Passed June 22nd, 1925 ... Approved June 23rd, 1925 ... [Linden] Linden Observer [1925]
2 p. l., 272, [2] p. illus. 20½ x 12ᶜᵐ.

1. Building laws—Linden, N. J.   I. Verner, Jules, comp.
                                                          37–9173
Library of Congress   TH225.L53 1925
                                                          692.90074984

NL 0379545   DLC

Linden, N.J. Ordinances, etc.
Ordinances of the city of Linden, Union county, New Jersey. June, 1926. [Linden] Linden Observer [1926]
cover-title, 71, [1] p. incl. tables, forms. 23ᶜᵐ.

I. Title.
                                                          39–8334
Library of Congress   JS997.L4A5 1926

NL 0379546   DLC

VOLUME 334

Linden gravel mining co.
...R.W. Sargent, respondent, v. the Linden
gravel mining co. (a corporation) appellant
see under   Irwin, Charles F

Linden harp ... A rare collection of popular
melodies
see under   Linden, Lilla, comp.

AC901   Linden lead company.
.W4   Charter of the Linden lead company, with
vol. 4, geological reports and certificates relative to
no. 21 the same.   Pittsburgh, Printed by W.S. Haven,
Office   1854.
23 p.   22.5 cm.   [Wells pamphlets, v. 4,
no. 21]

NL 0379549   DLC

Linden leaves; published by the students of Lindenwood College,
Saint Charles, Missouri.
v.
₁St. Charles, 19   ob. 8°.
v. illus.

1. Colleges and universities.—Stu-   dent publications: Annuals, U. S.:
Lindenwood College.
October 15, 1921.

NL 0379550   NN DHEW

Linden-Museum, *Stuttgart*
see Stuttgart. Museum für Länder- und Völkerkunde.

The Linden waltz
see under   Czerny, Carl, 1791-1857.

Lindenau, August von
see Lindenau, Fr. August von.

QB36   Lindenau, Bernhard August von, 1780-1854.
Z27A4 Zach, Franz Xaver, *freiherr* von, 1754-1832.
... Briefe Franz Xaver freiherrn von Zach, direktors der
Herzoglichen sternwarte am Gotha-Seeberg und seines nach-
folgers Bernhards von Lindenau, von 1791-1816, an p. Martin
Alois David, adjunkt und direktor der Königlichen Prager
sternwarte. Mit unterstützung des Masarykfondes beim
Čechoslovakischen national-forschungsrate, aus dem Archiv
der Prager sternwarte, herausgegeben von Otto Seydl. Prag,
Königl. Böhm. gesellschaft der wissenschaften, 1938.

Lindenau, Bernhard August von, 1780-1854.
Investigatio nova orbitae a Mercurio circa solem descriptae;
accedunt tabulae planetae ex elementis recens repertis et theoria
gravitatis illustr. de Laplace constructae. Auctore Bernhardo de
Lindenau.   Gothae: In Libraria Beckeriana, 1813.   40, xliv p.
incl. tables.   28cm.

With this is bound his: Tabulae Veneris... Gothae, 1810.

1. Mercury (Planet)—Orbit,   1813.   *Revised*
January 25, 1937

NL 0379555   NN DN-Ob MB MdBP NIC PHC MiU NjP

Lindenau, Bernhard August von, 1780-1854.
Tables barométriques pour faciliter le calcul
des nivellements et des mesures des hauteurs
par le baromètre, par Bernard de Lindenau.
Gotha, R.Z.Becker, 1809.
lxv p.,1 ℓ.,170 p.,1 ℓ.   22½cm.

1.Barometric hypsometry—Tables.
QC896.L74

NL 0379556   MiU ICU NN PPAmP

Lindenau,Bernhard August von,1780-1854.
Tabulae Martis novae et correctae ex theoria
gravitatis clarissimi de La Place et ex observationibus recentissimis erutae. Auctore Bernhardo de Lindenau.   Eisenberg, in libraria
Schoeniana, 1811.
26,xlix p.incl.tables.   26 x 22cm.

1.Mars (Planet)—Tables.
QB376.L74

NL 0379557   MiU DN-Ob NNC NjP PHC PPAmP NN MB MH

Lindenau,Bernhard August von,1780-1854.
Tabulae Veneris novae et correctae ex theoria gravitatis clarissimi de La Place et ex
observationibus recentissimis in Specula astro-
nomica seebergensi habitis erutae. Auctore Bernhardo de Lindenau. Sumtibus serenissimi ducis
Saxo-Gothani. Gothae, in libraria Beckeriana,
1810.
1 p.ℓ.,32,L p,incl.tables (part.fold.)   30 x 23cm.

1.Venus (Planet)—Tables.
QB372.L74

NL 0379558   MiU DNC MH NN PPAmP

Lindenau, Bernhard August von, 1780-1854.   *3322.2.1841.1
Versuch einer neuen Bestimmung der Nutations- und Aberrations-
Constanten aus beobachteten Geraden-Aufsteigungen des Polaris.
(In Koeniglich-preussische Akademie der Wissenschaften. Mathe-
matische Klasse. Abhandlungen. 1841, pp. 1–63. Berlin. 1843.)

H3268 — Pole-star. — Nutation. — Aberration.

NL 0379559   MB NIC DN-Ob

LINDENAU,Curt W F von.
Der Beresina-Uebergang des kaisers Napoleon
unter besonderer berücksichtigung der theilna-
hme der badischen truppen. Ein vortrag,gehal-
ten in der Garnison Freiburg i.Br. Berlin,
Mittler und sohn, 1896.

pp. 50. nap (in pocket at end)
Errata slip, inserted.

NL 0379560   MH CtY

LINDENAU, Curt W   F von.
Drei infanterie-angriffe Friedrichs des
Grossen in ihrer bedeutung für den heutigen in-
fanterie-angriff; ein vortrag am Friedrich-
stage 1911 der garnison Erfurt gehalten. Berlin
Ernst Siegfried Mittler und sohn, 1911.

pp. 42. Plans.   Ger 4295.1.10

NL 0379561   MH

Lindenau, Curt W   F   von
Emperor Napoleon's crossing of the
Beresina with particular reference to the
part taken in it by the Baden troops.
Berlin, Mittler, 1896.
36p.

Translation of his Beresina - Uebergang.
du Kaisers Napoleon...

NL 0379562   MBU

Lindenau, Ernst von.
Die arbeiter unter der Räte-Republik
(Soziale Föderative Sowjetrepublik) in
Russland. Nach authentischen quellen
dargestellt ...   [Nürnberg, Curt Stockhausen, 1919]
[8] p.   23.5 cm.

NL 0379563   NcD

Lindenau, Ernst von, compiler.
Was Jedermann wissen muss über Deutschlands Heer u.
Flotte; Einteilung, Stärke und Standorte der einzelnen Truppen-
körper, nebst Vergleich mit den Heeren unserer Feinde. Ver-
zeichnis unserer Kriegsschiffe, deren Grösse, Besatzung &c.
Zusammengestellt von Ernst von Lindenau...   Nürnberg: C.
Stockhausen ₁1915₎.   29(1) p., 1 l.   nar. 12°.

Title from cover.

1. Army (German), 1915. 2. Navy   (German), 1915. 3. European war,
1914.—Military statistics. 4. Eu-   ropean war, 1914-   .—Naval statistics.
5. Title. 6. Title: Deutschlands Heer   u. Flotte.
September 22, 1915.

NL 0379564   NN CtY

LINDENAU, Ernst von.
Was man wissen muss vom bolschewismus (Spart-
akismus), nach authentischen quellen dargestellt
Nürnberg, C.Stockhausen, [1917?].

NL 0379565   MH

Lindenau, Ernst von.
Was man wissen muss vom Bolschewismus (Spartakismus-
Kommunismus) Nach authentischen Quellen dargestellt.
3. Aufl. Nürnberg, C. Stockhausen ₁1919₎
48 p. 23 cm.

1. Communism—Russia. I. Title.

DK266.L55 1919   52-55476

NL 0379566   DLC MiU NN IU

D515   Lindenau, Ernst von.
L744   Zum kampf auf's letzte sind wir herausgefor-
dert! Worte zur beherzigung von Ernst von Lindenau... ₁Nürnberg, C. Stockhausen, 1918?₎
₁8₎ p. 22cm.

1.European war, 1914-1918 - Germany. 2.
European war, 1914-1918 - Peace proposals and
settlements.   I.Title.

NL 0379567   CSt-H:

VOLUME 334

U
438
.506
LINDENAU, Fr. AUGUST VON.
Anleitung zu dem Unterrichte der Rekruten der Cavallerie auf der Reitbahne, vorzüglich für die Unteroffiziers bestimmt. Leipzig, A. F. Böhme, 1804.
112p. fold.diagr. 19cm.

NL 0379568   ICN

4UE-19 Lindenau, Fr. August von.
Entwurf zu einer Anweisung, wie das Benehmen eines Cavalleristen, bey Gefechten in zerstreuter Ordnung, in Friedenszeiten zu lehren und zu üben sey. Nebst einem Anhang über den Angriff der Cavallerie en Front auf Cavallerie. Leipzig, A. F. Böhme, 1806.
116 p.

NL 0379569   MH DLC-P4

Lindenau, Gotske
see Lindenow, Godske, d. 1612.

Lindenau, Günter, 1913–
Die verfassung der Mark Brandenburg unter der regierung des kurfürsten Georg Wilhelm und seines Ratgebers Graf zu Schwarzenberg im Hinblick auf die überwindung ständischer verhältnisse durch den brandenburgisch-preussischen obrigkeitsstaat.
...72 p.
Inaug. Diss. - Kiel,[1936]
Lebenslauf.
Schrifttum.

NL 0379571   ICRL ICJ

Lindenau, Heinrich, 1872–   ed.
Deutsche strafrechts-zeitung. Zentralorgan für das gesamte strafrecht, strafprozessrecht und die verwandten gebiete in wissenschaft und praxis des in- und auslandes ... 1.–   jahrg.;
apr. 1914
Berlin, O. Liebmann, 1914–

Lindenau, Heinrich, 1872–
Kriminalinspektor dr. Stretter, eine polizeigeschichte von Heinrich Lindenau. Berlin, O. Liebmann, 1924.
148 p. 19½ᶜᵐ. (*Added t.-p.*: Schattenbilder des lebens, eine roman reihe)

I. Title.
Library of Congress   PT2623.I 575K7 1924   25–606

NL 0379573   DLC

HV8031
.N6
Lindenau, Heinrich, 1872–   ed.
Niceforo, Alfredo, 1876–
Die kriminalpolizei und ihre hilfswissenschaften, von prof. dr. A. Niceforo ... eingeleitet und erweitert von dr. H. Lindenau ... Mit 300 illustrationen nach original-photographieen. Gross-Lichterfelde-Ost, P. Langenscheidt [1909.

Lindenau, Karl Friedrich von, 1742–1817.
Lindsay, *Hon.* Colin, 1755–1795.
Extracts from Colonel Tempelhoffe's History of the seven years war: his remarks on General Lloyd: on the subsistence of armies; and on the march of convoys. Also a treatise on winter posts [by K. F. Lindenau] To which is added a narrative of events at St. Lucie and Gibraltar, and of John duke of Marlborough's march to the Danube, with the causes and consequences of that measure ... By the Honourable Colin Lindsay ... London, T. Cadell, 1793.

Z355.4
I642
Lindenau, Karl Friedrich von, 1742–1817.
Ueber die höhere preussische Taktik, deren Mängel und zeitherige Unzweckmässigkeit nebst einer dagegen vorgetragnen richtigern und zweckmässigern Methode. Leipzig, J.G. Beygang, 1790

v. 20cm.

1. Tactics.

NL 0379576   MnU

4UD-52 Lindenau, Karl Friedrich von, 1742–1817.
Über Winterpostirungen.   Leipzig, J. G. Beygang, 1789.
360 p.

NL 0379577   DLC-P4 ICN

Lindenau, Kurt W. F. von
see Lindenau, Curt W. F. von.

Lindenau, Max, 1885–
Beiträge zur altindischen rasalehre, mit besonderer berücksichtigung des Nâtyaśâstra des Bharata Muni. vi,[2],100,[2]p. Leipzig, Druck von G. Kreysing, 1913.

Inaug.-diss. - Leipzig.
Lebenslauf.
Literatur: p.vii.

NL 0379579   OC1 PU CtY MH ICRL ICU

PK3791
.B3Z8L7
(S)
Lindenau, Max, 1885–
Bhāsa-studien. Ein beitrag zur geschichte des altindischen dramas von dr. Max Lindenau. Leipzig, G. Kreysing, 1918.
vi,[7]–51 p. 24ᶜᵐ.

1. Bhāsa. 2. Sanskrit drama—Hist. & crit.

NL 0379580   ICU NjP MH OC1 NN CtY PU HU

Lindenau, Max, 1885–
Spuren griechischen Einflusses im Schauspielbuch (Nâtyaśâstra) des Bharata Muni? Von Max Lindenau. (In: Festschrift Ernst Windisch zum siebzigsten Geburtstag...dargebracht. Leipzig, 1914. 4°. p. 38–42.)

1. Bharata.

August 16, 1916.

NL 0379581   NN

Lindenau, Max, 1885–
Ein vedischer Lobgesang auf die Mutter Erde als die grosse Allgottheit (Atharvaveda XII, 1). Von Max Lindenau... (In: Beitraege zur Literaturwissenschaft und Geistesgeschichte Indiens. Bonn, 1926. 8°. p. [248]–258.)

Caption-title.

306131A. 1. Vedas. Atharva-veda.

November 21, 1927

NL 0379582   NN

Lindenau, Oskar Paul, 1874–
... Untersuchungen von rinderaugen, insbesondere über die ametropie dieser sehorgane ... Stuttgart, Druck der Union deutsche verlagsgesellschaft, 1909.
3 p. L, 47 p., 1 l. col. pl. 22ᶜᵐ.
Inaug.-diss.—Bern.
Vita.
Sonderabdruck aus "Monatshefte für praktische tierheilkunde": xx. bd.
"Literatur": p. 44–47.

1. Ametropia. 2. Cattle. Anatomy and physiology.

Agr 10–1197

Library, U. S. Dept. of   Agriculture 411.641

NL 0379583   DNAL CU DNLM

Lindenau (Paul) [1851–   ]. *Ein Fall von Magenerweiterung wegen Stenose des Pylorus, bedingt durch ein Ulcus simplex pylori. 32 pp. 8°. *Berlin, G. Lange*, [1876].

NL 0379584   DNLM ICRL

Lindenau (Rudolphus). *De staphyloraphia, adjectis duobus operationis speciminibus. 28 pp. 8°. *Gryphiæ, F. G. Kunile*, 1800.   c.

NL 0379585   DNLM

Lindenau, Ursula Zoege (von Manteuffel) von Trebra–
see Zoege von Manteuffel, Ursula Frau von Frebra Lindenau, 1850–1910.

Lindenau-Museum, *Altenburg, Ger.*
see Altenburg, Ger. Staatliches Lindenau-Museum.

Tz
799.3
I642s
Lindenau Schützenverein, Lindenau, Tex.
Statuten des Lindenau Schuetzen-Vereins zu Lindenau, Texas. [New Braunfels, Tex.] Neu-Braunfelser Zeitung [1927]
16p. 16cm.

Cover title.
German and English.

NL 0379588   TxU

Lindenbach, Camillo, Freiherr Komers von
see Komers von Lindenbach, Camillo, Freiherr.

VOLUME 334

Lindenbach, Hugo, Freiherr von Komers
   see   Komers-Lindenbach, Hugo,
Freiherr von.

Lindenbaum (Aïdla). *De la sclérodermie
généralisée ches l'enfant. 43 pp. 8°.
Genève. 1911.

NL   0379591   DNLM

DL644
.7
.L5
Lindenbaum, Arne, 1892–
    Okrönta härskarinnor på Stockholms slott. Stockholm,
C. E. Fritze [1952]
    248 p. illus., ports. 22 cm.

    CONTENTS.—Karin Månsdotter.—Cecilia Vasa.—Ebba Brahe.—
Aurora Königsmarck.—Hedvig Taube.—Lolotte Forsberg.—Ulla och
Sophie von Fersen.—Magdalena Rudenschöld.—Sophie Hagman.—
Charlotte Slotsberg.—Giovanna Bassi.—Flickorna Löf.—Henriette
Widerberg. —Emilie Högqvist.—Helga de la Brache.—Charlotte
Strandberg.—Elise Hwasser.—Marie Friberg.—Ellen Hartman.

    1. Sweden—Court and courtiers. 2. Sweden—Kings and rulers.
3. Women in Sweden.   I. Title.

                      A 53–4985
Minnesota. [Univ. Libr.]
for Library of Congress

NL   0379592   MnU WaU NN DLC

PN2777
.S7
Lindenbaum, Arne, 1892–   joint ed.
Sundström, Einar, 1885–   *ed.*
    Svenska konstnärer inom teaterns, musikens och filmens
värld; huvudredaktör, Einar Sundström ... för teateravdelnin-
gen, Arne Lindenbaum ... för musikavdelningen, Åke Vretblad
... Stockholm, Bokförlaget Mimer a.-b. [1943]

Lindenbaum, Bernhard Hesterbrink-
   see   Hesterbrink-Lindenbaum, Bernhard,
1900–

QD258
.L6
Lindenbaum, Ernst, 1884–
    Vanadinpentoxyd als oxydationsbeschleuniger
insbesondere fuer zucker zu oxalsaure durch
salpetersaure.
Frankfurt a. M. 1906.
    27p.
    Inaug. diss. Giessen.

NL   0379595   DLC MH PU DNLM

B610.24
H15H675l
Lindenbaum, Laurentius Gustavus, respondent.
    ...Observationes clinicas circa
curationem quartanae... Pro doctoris
gradu... Halae Magdeburgicae, Typis
J. C. Hilligeri, 1728.
    24 p.   20 cm.
    Inaug. Diss. - Halle (Friedrich
Hoffmann, praeses)

    I.Hoffmann, Friedrich, 1660-1742, praeses.

NL   0379596   MnU-B DNLM

Lindenbaum, Robert, 1898–
    Das alte Haus, Roman. Karlsbad, A. Kraft [1943]
    334 p. 20 cm.

    I. Title.

PT2623.I 576A7   833.91   A F 48–416*
Illinois. Univ. Library
for Library of Congress   †

NL   0379597   IU CtY NN CU DLC

LINDENBAUM, ROBERT, 1898–
    Dörflicher Lobgesang; Gedichte und Erzählungen.
Umschlagzeichnung: Toni Schönecker. Geislingen
(Steige), Egerland-Verlag [1955?] 79 p. 1 illus. 21cm.
(Bücher der Egerländer. Bd. 17)

NL   0379598   NN

Lindenbaum, Robert, 1898–
    ... Gutshäuser, drei erzählungen. Reichenberg,
Sudetendeutscher verlag, F. Kraus, [c1940]
    156, [1] p.   19 cm.
    Contents.—Gutshäuser.—Der letzte bauer.—
Geschichten um Oedt.

NL   0379599   CtY

Lindenbaum, Robert, 1898–
    ... Gutshäuser, drei erzählungen. Reichenberg, Sudeten-
deutscher verlag, F. Kraus, 1941.
    156, [1] p. 19ᶜᵐ.
    "3.–14. tausend."
    CONTENTS.—Gutshäuser.—Der letzte bauer.—Geschichten um Oedt.

    I. Title.
PT2623.I 576G8   833.91   A F 46–894
Columbia univ. Libraries
for Library of Congress   †

NL   0379600   NNC DLC IEN

Lindenbaum, Robert, 1898–
    Gutshäuser; Drei Erzählungen. Reichenberg,
F.Kraus [1943]

NL   0379601   MH

Lindenbaum, Robert, 1898–
    Land der Äcker, Roman. Karlsbad, A. Kraft [1938]
    300 p. 20 cm.

    I. Title.
PT2623.I 576L3   50–49175

NL   0379602   DLC IEN NNC

Lindenbaum, Robert, 1898–
    Land der Äcker; Roman. Karlsbad, A. Kraft [1943]
    296 p. 20 cm.

    I. Title.
PT2623.I 576L3   1943   55–49667 ‡

NL   0379603   DLC CU CtY MH NN

LINDENBAUM, ROBERT, 1898–
    Das Lied von der Eger; uraufgeführt an der Eger-
quelle am 18. Juli zum Ausklang des Egerlandtages
1955. Geislingen (Steige), Egerland-Verlag [1955]
18 p. 19cm. (Bücher der Egerländer. Bd. 14)

    1. Drama, German. 2. Eger river and valley, Czechoslovakia--Hist.--
Drama. I. Series. II. Title.

NL   0379604   NN

LINDENBAUM, ROBERT, 1898–
    Morgenruf, Gedichte von Robert Lindenbaum.
Eger: Verlag der literarischen Adalbert–Stifter–Gesellschaft, 1929. 66 p. 18cm. (Sudetendeutsche Sammlung. [Nr.]12.)

    632325A. 1. Poetry, German. I. Title.

NL   0379605   NN MH

Lindenbaum, Robert, 1898–
    September in Böhmen; Haberspirker Chronik. Karlsbad,
A. Kraft [1940]
    127 p. 19 cm.

    I. Title.
PT2623.I 576S4   833.91   49–35971*

NL   0379606   DLC

Lindenbaum, Robert, 1898–
    Eine Spanne Zeit; Gedichte. Karlsbad, A. Kraft, 1941.
    63 p. 18 cm. (Volksdeutsche Reihe, Nr. 46)

    I. Title.
PT2623.I 576S7   831.91   53–50205

NL   0379607   DLC

Lindenbaum, Robert, 1898–
    Zwischen gestern und heute, Roman. Karlsbad, A. Kraft
[1942]
    468 p. 19 cm.

    I. Title.
PT2623.I 576Z48   A F 47–6967*
California. Univ. Libr.
for Library of Congress   †

NL   0379608   CU CtY NN DLC

W 4
S89
1933
Lindenbaum, Sarah, 1908–
    Étude sur l'assistance médico-sociale
aux enfants infirmes de la motricité dans
différents pays. Strasbourg, Goeller,
1933.
    40 p. (Strasbourg. Université. [Faculté
de médecine] Thèse. 1933. no. 41)

    Bibliography: p. 39-40.

NL   0379609   DNLM CtY

Lindenbaum, Seymour Joseph
    An investigation of the Goldberger model
for the interaction of high energy nucleons
with a heavy nucleus. [New York] 1951.
    66 l. diagrs. (part fold.) 29cm.

    Thesis, Columbia university.
    Bibliography: l. 63.

NL   0379610   NNC

VOLUME 334

Lindenbaum, Simon, 1878-
Ueber die einwirkung von 2.3-dibrom-a-naphtochinon...
Inaug. diss. Berlin, 1901.

NL 0379611   ICRL PU

W 4
B29
1950
LINDENBAUM, Stefania
Über die Möglichkeiten einer klinischen
Diagnose bei aneurysma arterio-venosum
des Kleinhirns. ₁Basel, Volksdruckerei,
1950.
27 p.
Inaug.-Diss. - Basel.
1. Aneurysm - Arteriovenous
2. Cerebellum

NL 0379612   DNLM

Der Lindenbaum deutsche Volkslieder
see under Hesse, Hermann, 1877-1972,
comp.

Lindenbaur, Aloys.
Die göttliche Lehr-Auktorität in der katholischen Kirche. Im Gegensatz zur anarchischen Lehrfrei-
heit ausser der Kirche. Oder: der historische und
mythische Christus. Augsburg, B. Schmid, 1845.

328 p. 22 cm.
Bound with his: Das Schiff Petri und seine
Fahrst durch den Strom der Jahrhunderte. Augsburg,
J. A. Schlosser, 1846.
1. Church - Authority. 2. Jesus Christ. 3. Reformation. I. Schubert, Gotthilf Heinrich von, 1780-
1860. II. Title.

NL 0379614   PLatS

4BR-136 Lindenbaur, Aloys.
Das Schiff Petri und seine Fahrt durch
den Strom der Jahrhunderte. Augsburg,
J.A. Schlosser, 1846.
342 p.

NL 0379615   DLC-P4 PLatS

Lindenbaur, Aloys
Das Schiff Petri und seine Fahrt durch den
Strom der Jahrhunderte. 2. Aufl. Augsburg,
J. A. Schlosser's Buch- und Kunsthandlung,
1847.
342p. 22cm.

1. Church - Addresses, essays, lectures.

NL 0379616   InStme

Lindenbaur, Aloys.
Ueber die gegenwärtige Stellung der katholisch-
en Kirche zu den von ihr getrennten Confessionen.
Oder die Frage: Ist eine Vereinigung oder Gemeinschaft mit den von uns getrennten Confessionen
möglich? Augsburg, B. Schmid, 1844.

161 p. 22 cm.
Bound with his: Das Schiff Petri und seine
Fahrt. Augsburg, J.A. Schlosser, 1846.

1. Christian union.

NL 0379617   PLatS

Lindenbein, A
Erklärung der offenbarung des Johannes...
Braunschweig, 1890.

NL 0379618   ODW

Lindenbein, A
Erklärung der Offenbarung des Johannes;
ein Beitrag zur Förderung ihres Gebrau-
ches in der Gemeine… 2. Aufl.   Braunschweig, C.A. Schwetschke, 1895.
11, 182 p.   23ᵐ.

NL 0379619   NjPT

S141
3
L642
Lindenbein, Werner, 1902-
Beitrag zur Cytologie der Charales ...
Berlin,1927.
Inaug.-Diss. - Kiel.
Lebenslauf.
"Sonderabdruck aus 'Planta', Bd.4."
"Literatur": p.465-466.

NL 0379620   CtY ICRL MH

Lindenberg, B
Geschichte der israelitischen Schule zu
Markisch Friedland...
Markisch Friedland, the author, 1855.
66 p.

NL 0379621   OCH

Lindenberg, C.
Die Briefmarken von Baden unter Benutzung amtlicher Quellen
bearbeitet.
= Berlin. Brendicke. 1894. vi, (1), 171 pp. 16°.

E3848 — Baden. Postage stamps. — Postage stamps.

NL 0379622   MB

Lindenberg, C   *2237.135
Die Briefumschläge der deutschen Staaten, unter Benutzung amt-
licher Quellen. Heft 1-15.
= Berlin. Brendicke. 1892-95. 2 v. and unbound parts. Illus. 16°.
Contents. — Band 1, Heft 1. Braunschweig. 2. Mecklenburg-Schwerin und
Mecklenburg-Strelitz. 3. Lübeck. 4. Thurn und Taxis. 5, 6. Norddeutscher
Postbezirk. Band 2, Heft 7. Oldenburg. 8. Baden. 9. Hamburg und Bremen.
10. Sachsen. 11, 12. Hannover. Band 3, Heft. 13. Bayern. 14, 15. Württem-
berg.

E3890 — Germany. Postage stamps. — Envelopes.

NL 0379623   MB PSt

Lindenberg, C.

Germany. *Reichs-postmuseum, Berlin.*
Katalog der markensammlung des Reichs-postmuseums. Im
auftrage des Reichs-postamts bearb. von C. Lindenberg. Berlin, Reichsdruckerei, 1888.

HD7889
P7L54
1901
Lindenberg, Carl
Das preussische Gesinderecht im Geltungsbereiche der
Gesindeordnung vom 8. november 1810, bearb. von C. Linden-
berg. 6. Aufl. des gleichnamigen Posseldt'schen Buches.
Berlin, H.W. Müller, 1901.
viii, 159 p.

1. Master and servant - Prussia. 2. Servants - Laws, regulations, etc. - Prussia. I. Posseldt, H.

NL 0379625   CU

Lindenberg, Carl.
Das preussische gesinderecht im geltungsbereiche der Gesindeordnung vom 8. november 1810, bearb. von C. Lindenberg ... 8. aufl. des gleichnamigen Posseldtschen buches. Berlin, H. W. Müller, 1912.
viii, 160 p. 18ᵐ.
"Die bearbeitung des vom amtsgerichtsrat Posseldt herausgegebenen
Gesinderechts, das zum ersten male im jahre 1882 erschienen ist, habe
ich nach dem tode des herausgebers von der zweiten im jahre 1885 not-
wendig gewordenen auflage ab in die hand genommen."—Vorwort zur
5. aufl.
1. Master and servant—Prussia.   I. Posseldt, H.   II. Title.
37-23031

NL 0379626   DLC

Lindenberg, E   ed.
Inleiding tot die Afrikaanse letterkunde,
onder redaksie van E. Lindenberg, met medewerking van R. Pheiffer ₁et al.₎ Pretoria en
Kaapstad, Academica, 1965.
110 p. illus.

1. Afrikaans literature - Hist. and crit.

NL 0379627   NNC

Lindenberg, Edouard, 1908–
Comment lire une partition d'orchestre. Préf. d'Arthur
Honegger. Paris, Heugel, °1952.
31 p. illus. 19 cm.

1. Score reading and playing.   I. Title.

MT85.L6   52-35123 ‡

NL 0379628   DLC IU NcU FTaSU

W 4
M961
1952
LINDENBERG, Ellen, 1927-
Der Einfluss des Laktoflavins auf die
experimentelle Bleivergiftung. ₁München₎
1952.
32ℓ.
Inaug.-Diss. - Munich.
1. Lead poisoning
2. Riboflavin - Effects

NL 0379629   DNLM

Lindenberg, Ernst: Ueber das Erscheinen eines vierten Molaren im
Gebiss des Menschen und Ueberzahl der Zähne im allgemeinen.
[Maschinenschrift.] 69 S. 4°. — Auszug: Greifswald 1922: Adler.
4 S. 8°
Greifswald, Med. Diss. v. 24. März 1922   [U 22. 3413

NL 0379630   ICRL

Lindenberg, Ernst, 1887-
Die dingliche Surrogation beim Vermögen
im Bürgerlichen Gesetzbuch ... von Ernst
Lindenberg ... Heidelberg, C. Pfeffer,
1912.
58 p., 2 l. 21½cm.
Inaug.-Diss. - Heidelberg.
"Lebenslauf": 2d leaf at end.
"Literatur": p.₁6₎-7.

NL 0379631   MH-L MH ICRL

Lindenberg, Ernst, 1903-
Autarkie und wirtschaftliche expansion ...
68 p.
Inaug. Diss. - Heidelberg, n.d.
Lebenslauf.

NL 0379632   ICRL CtY

VOLUME 334

Lindenberg, Felix.
Die Asphalt-Industrie. Eine Darstellung der Eigenschaften der natürlichen und künstlichen Asphalte und deren Anwendung in den Gewerben, Künsten und in der Bautechnik. Von Felix Lindenberg .... Mit 46 Abbildungen. Wien und Leipzig, A. Hartleben, [1906].
x, [2], 320 p. 46 illus. incl. diagrs. 19½cm. (*On cover:* Chemisch-technische Bibliothek. Band 294.)

NL 0379633   ICJ NN PPF NIC ICRL

DD   Lindenberg, Friedrich Wolfgang
253.5   Heil unserem Führer! Das Hitlerbuch eines
L54   Hitlerjungen. Reutlingen, Enszlin &
Laiblins (1935)
112 p.   illus.   22cm.

1. Nationalsozialistische Deutsche Arbeiter-Partei. Hitlerjugend 2. Youth - Germany - Societies, etc. I. Title

NL 0379634   WU DLC-P4

Lindenberg, Fritz.
...Das Antennenrecht des Mieters, von Fritz Lindenberg... Berlin: Deutsch-literarisches Institut[, 1932]. 31 p. 20cm. (Deutsche Radio-Bücherei. Bd. 48.)

1. Radio—Antennae. 2. Radio—   Jurisp. I. Ser.   October 20, 193*

NL 0379635   NN

Lindenberg, Fritz
Heimarbeit in der holzspielwarenindustrie des oberen erzgebirges. ... Dresden, 1936.   49 p.
Inaug. Diss. - Leipzig, 1936.
Schrifttum.

NL 0379636   ICRL

Lindenberg, Fritz, 1901-
Was lehrt die statistik ueber die zunahme des alkoholismus in der nachkriegszeit?
Inaug. diss. Bonn, 1925.
Bibl.

NL 0379637   ICRL CtY

Lindenberg, G   respondent.
... Testium numerus ...
see under Geissler, Friedrich, 1636-1679, praeses.

Lindenberg, Georg.

Stenglein, Melchior, 1825-1903.
M. Stengleins Kommentar zu den strafrechtlichen nebengesetzen des Deutschen Reichs. 4. aufl. völlig neubearb. in gemeinschaft mit dr. A. Hoffmann ... dr. E. Trautvetter ... dr. W. Cuno ... von Ludwig Ebermayer ... Franz Galli ... Georg Lindenberg ... Berlin, O. Liebmann, 1911-13.

Lindenberg, Gottlieb Friedrich, respondent.
... De intercessione foeminarum pro capite damnatis ...
see under   Carmon, Jakob, 1677-1743, praeses.

Lindenberg, Gustav.
...Die Lebensfrage der Gesangspädagogik im neuen Deutschland. Leipzig: F. Kistner & C. F. W. Siegel, 1935.   30 p.
18½cm.
"28920."

894270A. 1. Singing—Study and   teaching—Germany.   July 14, 1937

NL 0379641   NN

QD369 **Lindenberg, Gustav.**
Ueber trimethylandiaminkobaltisalze.
Leipzig, 1906.
42p.
Inaug. diss. Zuerich.

NL 0379642   DLC ICRL

Lindenberg, H.

Hankel, Wilhelm Gottlieb, 1814-1899.
Elektrische untersuchungen, von W. G. Hankel ... Leipzig, S. Hirzel, 1856-99.

Lindenberg, Hans, Medizinalprakt.: Aus d. städt. Krankenh. Moabit. (I. inn. Abt. Klemperer.) Neuere Versuche in der Behandlung der perniziösen Anaemie. (Berlin 1910: Blanke.) 28 S. 8°
Berlin, Med. Diss. v. 14. Okt. 1910, Ref. Kraus
[Geb. 13. Jan. 87 Berlin; Wohnort: Berlin; Staatsangeh.: Preußen; Vorbildung: Kölln. Gymn. Berlin Reife O. 05; Studium: Berlin 5, München 1, Berlin 2, Freiburg i. B. 2 S.; Coll. 13. Okt. 10.]   [U 11. 103

NL 0379644   ICRL CtY DNLM

4D-1213 Lindenberg, Harald.
Kasernenhof und Feldquartier; ein Vierteljahrhundert deutsches Soldatentum.   Stuttgart, Union Deutsche Verlagsgesellschaft [19]
63 p.

NL 0379645   DLC-P4

Lindenberg, Heinrich Richard, 1846-
Über methylamidorppopionsaure und die bildung von homokreatin.
Leipzig, 1875.
Dissert.

QD319
.L74

NL 0379646   DLC

Lindenberg, Heinrich Richard Walter, 1895-
see Lindenberg, Walter, 1895-

Lindenberg, Herman Albert, 1839-
The acanthus leaf applied to the various styles. 20 gelatine plates from originals by Herm. Lindenberg ...   New York, A. Gerbel, 1903.
1 p. l., 20 pl. 34 x 26½ᵐ.

1. Design, Decorative—Plant forms.   I. Title.   3-11995 Revised

Library of Congress   NK1565.L7

NL 0379648   DLC PSt PPMoI PPD MiU OC1 MB

Lindenberg, Herman Albert, 1839-
Development and distinction of all styles of ornaments; instruction for compounding ornaments and their essential adornment indispensible to the art trade.   New York, Hessling & Spielmeyer [1890?]
6 pts. in 1 vol.   plates.   16½x26cm.

NL 0379649   NBuG OC1MA

Lindenberg, Herman Albert. 1839-
Development and distinction of all styles of ornaments. Instruction for compounding ornaments and their essential adornment indispensible to the art trade.
— New York. Hessling & Spielmeyer. [1894.] 6 v. in portfolio. 8°, obl.

F6999 — Drawing. — Design.

NL 0379650   MB

Lindenberg, Herman Albert. 1839-
Shields, foliated heads & animals.   Series 2.
— New York. Hessling & Spielmeyer. 1895. 8 v. in portfolio. 8°, obl.

F7040 — Drawing. — Design.

NL 0379651   MB WaS

Lindenberg, Hermann Meyer-
see
Meyer-Lindenberg, Hermann.

Lindenberg, Hugo A.
Jabs and gems, by Hugo A. Lindenberg.   Cincinnati, The Caxton press, 1924.
112 p. illus. 18½ᵐ.

1. Jewelry trade. I. Title.

Library of Congress   PN6231.J4L5   24-7629

NL 0379653   DLC

Lindenberg (Joannes Carolus). "De curatione febrium intermittentium per remedia exaestuantia infida et nociva. 22 pp. 4°. *Halæ, stanno Hendeliano.* [1774].

NL 0379654   DNLM

VOLUME 334

Lindenberg (Joh. Daniel). *Diss. sistens observationem de partu laborioso. 23 pp. 4°. *Giessae Hassorum. J. G. Braun.* [1781].

NL 0379655   DNLM

Lindenberg, Johan.
Peggy schenkt thee; tooneelspel in één bedrijf, door Johan Lindenberg.   Amsterdam: N. V. van Holkema & Warendorf[, 1931]. 24 p. 22cm.

677056A. 1. Drama, Dutch. I. Title.
November 24, 1933

NL 0379656   NN

Lindenberg, Johan.
Rechter David; een wonderlijke gebeurtenis in een bedrijf, door Johan Lindenberg.   Haarlem: N. v. Gebr. van Staden [1938] 31 p. 19cm.   (Tooneelfonds "Bredero.")

1. Drama, Dutch. I. Title.
June 20, 1940

NL 0379657   NN

Lindenberg, Johann Bernhard Wilhelm, 1781-1851.
... Commentationem ad ivris lvbencensis lib. II. Tit. 1: de testamentis et legatis, qvam ... defendet Joann. Bernhard. Guilielm. Lindenberg ... Goettingae, typis Henrici Dieterich [1805]
74, [2] p. 21cm.
Inaug. diss.- Göttingen.

NL 0379658   MH-L

q
QK Lindenberg, Johann Bernard Wilhelm, 1781-1851.
553 Monographie der Riccieen, von J.B.W. Linden-
G65 berg ... Bei der Akademie eingegangen den 28.
1843 Februar 1836. [Breslau, 1836-37?]
HHC-HS   p.[361]-504, 504a-m. 19 col. plates. 29cm.

Bound with Gottsche, K.M. Anatomisch-physiologische Untersuchungen über Haplomitrium Hookeri ... [Breslau, 1843]
"Nachträge ... (Bei der Akademie eingegangen am 12. August 1836, 11. Februar und 19. März 1837)": p.504a-m.

Detached from Deutsche Akademie der Naturforscher. Nova acta ... v.18, pt.1.

1. Riccia. I. Title.

NL 0379660   TxU ICU PU-B NcD DLC-P4 WaU

588.3 Lindenberg, Johann Bernhard Wilhelm, 1781-
L642s   1851.
1839   Species hepaticarum. Recensuit, partim descripsit iconibusque illustravit Ioh. Bernh. Guil. Lindenberg ...   Bonnae, Henry et Cohen, 1839-51.
2v. (various paging) 67 col. plates. 30cm.

Issued in 11 fasc., 1839-51.
Pt.1 (164p.) has special title page: Monographia   hepaticarum generis

Continued in next column

Continued from preceding column

plagiochilae. Auctore Ioh. Bernh. Guil. Lindenberg. Bonnae, sumptibus Henry & Cohen, 1844.
Pt.2 (78p.) has special t.p.: Species hepaticarum. Recensuerunt, descripserunt iconibusque illustraverunt I.B.G. Lindenberg et C.M. Gottsche. Fasc VI. Iungermannicae. Trichomanoideae. Lepidozia. Bonnae, impensis   Henry et Cohen, 1846.

Pt.3 (118p.) issued without special t.p., but with caption title: Mastigobryum ... This copy has a special t.p. supplied in ms., bearing the date 1851.
1. Hepaticae. I. Gottsche, Karl Moritz, 1808-1892, jt. auth. II. Title. III. Title: Monographia hepaticarum generis plagiochilae.

NL 0379663   KU CU CtY PPAN NNC ViU MB MiU DNAL

Lindenberg, Johann Bernhard Wilhelm, 1781-1851, joint author.
Gottsche, Karl Moritz, 1808-1892.
Synopsis hepaticarum. Coniunctis studiis scripserunt et edi curaverunt C. M. Gottsche ... J. B. G. Lindenberg ... et C. G. Nees ab Esenbeck ... Hamburgi, sumtibus Meissnerianis, 1844[-47]

Lindenberg, Johann Bernhard Wilhelm, 1781-1851
Synopsis hepaticarum Europaearum, adnexis observationibus et adnotationibus criticis illustrata, auctore I. B. G. Lindenberg... Bonnae, Sumtibus Academiae Caes. L. C. naturae curiosorum, venditur apud Eduardum Weberum, Bibliopolam, 1829.
133 p. 2 pl. 28cm.

1. Hepaticae. Europe.

NL 0379665   NcD WaU NNC PU-B ViLxW

Lindenberg, Johann Friedrich, respondent.
Dissertatio moralis philosophica de vitae genere see under   Pauli, Gottfried Wilhelm, praeses.

Lindenberg, Kurt: Forstwirtschaft und Holzindustrie Deutschlands im Kriege und die Aussichten nach dem Friedensvertrage. [Maschinenschrift.] XVII, 169 S. m. Taf. 4°. — Auszug: Greifswald 1922: Adler. 26 S. 8°
Greifswald, R.- u. staatswiss. Diss. v. 1. April 1922   [U 22. 9461]

NL 0379667   ICRL PU

Lindenberg (Leopoldus Fridericus, [1821-]. *De asthmatis pathologia et formis. 39 pp. 8°. *Berolini, typ. Friedlanderiana.* [1843].

NL 0379668   DNLM

Lindenberg, Ludwig, 1884-
Leben und schriften David Fassmanns (1683-1744) mit besonderer berücksichtigung seiner totengespräche... Berlin, Ebering [1937]
143 p. 23 cm.

Inaug.-diss. - Berlin.
Lebenslauf.
"Benutzte literatur": p.142-143.

1.Fassmann, David, 1683-1744.

NL 0379669   NjP CtY ICRL NIC NN NNC

Lindenberg (Oscar). *Zwei Fälle von Herzen mit vier Semilunarklappen der Arteria pulmonalis. 25 pp. 8°. *Würzburg, A. Boenler* 1893.

NL 0379670   DNLM

Lindenberg, Otto Friedrich Hans, 1872-
50 jahre geschichte einer spekulationsbank. Ein beitrag zur kritik des deutschen bankwesens, von dr. Otto Lindenberg ...   Berlin, A. W. Hayn's erben, 1903.
2 p. l., 246 p. 23½cm.

1. Disconto gesellschaft, Berlin.   I. Title. II. Title: Spekulationsbank, 50 jahre geschichte einer.

16-7806

Library of Congress   HG3060.B54D62

NL 0379671   DLC CU ICU ICJ

Lindenberg, Otto Friedrich Hans, 1872-
Die zweckmässigkeit der psychischen vorgänge wirkung der vorstellungshemmung ... Berlin, C. Duncker [1894]
3 p. l., [3]-64, [2] p. 25 cm. [Breslau. Universität. Dissertationen. v. 14, no. 3]
Inaug.-diss. - Breslau.
Lebenslauf.

NL 0379672   CU ICU NjP CtY PU IU

Lindenberg, Paul, 1859-
Alt-Berlin, mit einleitung.   Berlin, 1904.

NL 0379673   NjP

1692 Lindenberg, Paul, 1859-
.586   Auf deutschen pfaden im Orient... Berlin, Dümmler, 1902.
320 p. illus. 22 cm.

1.Levant-Descr.& trav.

NL 0379674   NjP

LINDENBERG, Paul, 1859-
Aus dem Paris der dritten Republik. Bilder und Skizzen. 2tes Bändchen.
Leipz. Reclam. [1893.] 116 pp. [Universal-Bibliothek. 3055.] 16.

NL 0379675   MB

Lindenberg (Paul) 1859- A Bei Robert Koch. pp. 12, 35. 4°. [*Leipzig*, 1891.]
Cutting from: Gartenlaube, Leipz., 1891.

NL 0379676   DNLM

VOLUME 334

Lindenberg, Paul, 1859–
Beim armee-oberkommando Hindenburgs; ein neues kriegsbuch, von Paul Lindenberg. 1.–6. tausend. Stuttgart, A. Bonz & comp., 1915.
191, ₁1₎ p. 18ᶜᵐ.
CONTENTS. – Beim armee-oberkommando Hindenburgs. – Aus dem kriegstagebuche bis mitte september. – Die winterkämpfe an der ostpreussischen grenze. – Stimmungen und eindrücke.

1. European war, 1914– —Personal narratives. 2. European war, 1914– 15–24030
Library of Congress   D551.L46
                             1.284B

NL 0379677   DLC CtY NjP IU DNW

DD878   Lindenberg, Paul, 1859–
L5   Berlin.   Leipzig, P. Reclam jun. ₁1883?₎
        v.   (Universal-Bibliothek, 1870
2004, 2131)

Contents. –
v.2. Die National-Galerie. –
v.4. Stimmungsbilder. – v.5. Neu-Berlin.

NL 0379678   CU

Lindenberg, Paul, 1859–
Berlin in wort und bild, von Paul Lindenberg. Mit 244 illustrationen von O. Gerlach ₍etc.₎ Berlin, F. Dümmler, 1895.
viii, 612 p. illus. 24ᶜᵐ.

Subject entries: 1. Berlin—Descr. 2. Berlin—Soc. life & cust.
                                    3–2418
Library of Congress, no.   DD878.L74.

NL 0379679   DLC

Lindenberg, Paul, 1859–
Berliner geflügelte worte; eine sammlung Berliner worte und redensarten. 2. aufl.
[2],70p. Berlin, H. Lazarus, 1887.

NL 0379680   OCl

Lindenberg, Paul, 1859–
Berliner Polizei und Verbrechertum.
Leipzig, Reclam. [1892]
192 p. [Universal-Bibliothek, 2996, 2997]

NL 0379681   MB MiU

Lindenberg, Paul, 1859–
…Das Buch der Kaiserin Auguste Viktoria… Berlin-Schmargendorf: W. Andermann, 1927. 255 p. front., plates (incl. ports.). 4°.

Plates printed on both sides.

330284A. 1. Augusta Victoria, em   press consort of William II, German emperor, 1858–1921.
                                          November 22, 1927

NL 0379682   NN

Lindenberg, Paul, 1859–1943.
Das Buch vom Feldmarschall Hindenburg. Mit 160 Abbildungen, u. a. nach Gemälden und Zeichnungen von Ludwig Manzel ₍et al.₎ Oldenburg i. O., G. Stalling, 1920.
372 p. illus. 24 cm.

1. Hindenburg, Paul von, Pres. Germany, 1847–1934.

DD231.H5L55   52–55274 ‡

NL 0379683   DLC NcD DNW ICJ MH PPCS IMunS

LINDENBERG, Paul, 1859–
Charles Ier, roi de Roumanie, préface de Georges de Dubor. 2e éd. Paris, libr. H. Le Soudier, 1913.

Ports., facsim., and other illustr.

NL 0379684   MH

831.08   Lindenberg, Paul, 1859–1943, ed.
L744D   Dem Kaiser! Deutsche Dichter-Gaben; hrsg. von Paul Lindenberg. Erfurt, F. Bartholomäus ₁1879₎
         128 p. 23 cm.

1. Wilhelm I, German Emperor, 1797–1888.
Poetry. I. Title.

NL 0379685   NcD

Lindenberg, Paul, 1859–
… Es lohnte sich, gelebt zu haben, erinnerungen. Berlin, Vorhut-verlag O. Schlegel ₍ᶜ1941₎
370 p. front. (port.) 22ᶜᵐ.

I. Title.
                                          46–31914
Library of Congress   DD231.L55A3
                                              928.3

NL 0379686   DLC CLU

DR87   Lindenberg, Paul, 1859–1943.
L5   Ferdinand I.; das Buch vom Zaren der Bulgaren. Zum 25. Regierungs-Jubiläum des Zaren Ferdinand I. den deutschen Schulen in Bulgarien, gewidmet von Wilhelm Walther und Friedrich Wilhelm Pflüger. ₍Berlin, O. Elsner, 19––₎
        131 p. illus., ports. 25ᶜᵐ.

1. Ferdinand I, Czar of Bulgaria, 1861–1948.

NL 0379687   CSt

Lindenberg, Paul, 1859–
Ferdinand I, König der Bulgaren. Berlin, G. Bernstein, 1911.
168 ₍1₎ p. illus. ports.

NL 0379688   MiD MH

DR 87   LINDENBERG, PAUL VON, 1859–
.L 74   Ferdinand I. König der Bulgaren. 2. verm Aufl. Berlin-Charlottenburg, C. Hamel, 1918.
          222 p. illus.

1. Ferdinand I, Czar of Bulgaria, 1861–1948.

NL 0379689   InU

Lindenberg, Paul, 1859–1943.
Fritz Vogelsang. Abenteuer eines deutschen Schiffsjungen in Kiautschou… Mit 4 Farbenbildern nach Aquarellen von Willy Werner… Berlin, F. Dümmler, 1899. 288 p. illus. 24cm.

NL 0379690   NN

Lindenberg, Paul, 1859–1943.
Gegen die Russen mit der armee Hindenburgs, von Paul Lindenberg … Leipzig, S. Hirzel, 1914.
180, ₍2₎ p. front. (port.) 22 cm.
"Zur veröffentlichung zugelassen vom Stellvertretenden generalstab, abteilung III B."

1. European war, 1914–1918—Campaigns—Eastern.
                                          15—2264
Library of Congress   D551.L5

NL 0379691   DLC PPG NN NjP

Lindenberg, Paul von, 1859–
Gegen die Russen mit der armee Hindenburgs, von Paul Lindenberg … Leipzig, S. Hirzel, 1915₍ᶜ1914₎
180, ₍2₎ p. front. (port.) 22ᶜᵐ.
"Zur veröffentlichung zugelassen vom Stellvertretenden generalstab, abteilung III B."

NL 0379692   CU MB CtY NN CSt-H

Lindenberg, Paul, 1859–
Generalfeldmarschall von Hindenburg, von Paul Lindenberg. Mit einem Bildnis nach einem Gemälde von Hugo Vogel. Stuttgart: A. Bonz & Comp. ₍1918₎ 102 p. front. (port.) 12°.

3080A. 1. Hindenburg, Paul Lud-   wig Hans Anton von Beneckendorff und von, 1847–
                                          March 18, 1921.

NL 0379693   NN

Lindenberg, Paul, 1859–
Das heutige Bulgarien, von Paul Lindenberg … Stuttgart, A. Bonz & comp., 1915.
148 p. front., illus. (incl. ports.) 19ᶜᵐ.

1. Bulgaria.
                                          23–3416
Library of Congress   DR55.L5

NL 0379694   DLC

DD231   Lindenburg, Paul, 1859–1943, eᵈ
.H5H618   FOR OTHER EDITIONS
1926   SEE MAIN ENTRY
        Hindenburg-Denkmal für das deutsche Volk, hrsg. von Paul Lindenberg. Mitarbeiter: General d. Inf. von Eisenhart Rothe ₍et al.₎ Künstler: Karl Bauer ₍et al.₎ Berlin, C. A. Weller, 1926.

VOLUME 334

Lindenberg, Paul, 1859–1943, *ed.*
Hindenburg-Denkmal für das deutsche Volk, hrsg. von Paul Lindenberg und Walter Bloem. Mitarbeiter: Walter Bloem [et al.]. Berlin, C. A. Weller [193–?]

367–480 p. illus. 33 cm.

CONTENTS.—Die erste Präsidentschaft (1925–1932) von Walter Bloem.—Die zweite Präsidentschaft, von Walter Bloem.

1. Hindenburg, Paul von, Pres. Germany, 1847–1934. I. Bloem, Walter, 1868– II. Title.

DD231.H5L554   52–55494

NL 0379696   DLC

[Lindenberg, Paul] 1859–
Julius Pintsch; Blätter der Erinnerung. Berlin, Privatdruck, 1914.
88 p. illus., plates, ports.

Signed at end: Paul Lindenburg.

NL 0379697   MH-BA

Lindenberg, Paul, 1859–1943.
Kaiserin Auguste Viktoria. Ein deutsches Volksbuch. Mit einem Vorwort der Kaiserin Hermine, neuem unveröffentlichtem Material. Berlin, E. C. Etthofen [*1933]
418 p. ports. 18 cm.

1. Auguste Viktoria, consort of William II, German Emperor, 1858–1921.

DD229.7.L56   923.143   49–43308*

NL 0379698   DLC PPG OC1 NN

Lindenberg, Paul, 1859–1943.
923.1497   König Ferdinand von Bulgarien. Berlin,
F347L   Verlags-Anstalt Augustin, 1917.
192 p. illus., ports. 22 cm.

1. Ferdinand I, Czar of Bulgaria, 1861–1948. I. Title.

NL 0379699   NcD MH

Lindenberg, Paul, 1859–
923.1498   **König Karl von Rumänien ... Mit einer**
C292   **Heliogravure und über 100 Illustrationen.**
I-L   Berlin, F. Dümmler, 1906.
vii, 369 p. illus., ports. 22½ cm.

Includes bibliography.

1. Carol I, King of Rumania, 1839–1914.

NL 0379700   NcD FMU WU

Lindenberg, Paul, 1859–
König Karl von Rumänien, ein lebensbild dargestellt unter mitarbeit des königs, von Paul Lindenberg ... Berlin, Hafen-verlag g. m. b. h., 1923.
2 v. front. (port.) illus. 22½ᶜᵐ.
"Literatur": v. 2, p. 348.

1. Carol I, king of Rumania, 1839–1914.

Library of Congress   DR255.L5   25–13778

NL 0379701   DLC CLU OU MiU OC1 NN

Lindenberg, Paul, 1859–
Med Hindenburgs armé mot Ryssarna ... Bemyndigat översattning. Stockholm [1915]
20.5 cm.

NL 0379702   CtY

Lindenberg, Paul, 1859–1943.
Das neue Bulgarien 1887–1912; Studien und Streifzüge. Berlin, F. Dümmler, 1912.
153 p. illus., ports. 25 cm.

1. Bulgaria.

DR85.L6   A 13–362 rev*

Columbia Univ.   Libraries
for Library of Congress   [r52b¼]†

NL 0379703   NNC NIC CtY DLC

---

fT440   Lindenberg, Paul, 1859–
C1L5   Pracht-Album photographischer Aufnahmen der
1896   Berliner Gewerbe-Ausstellung 1896, und der Sehenswürdigkeiten Berlins und des Treptower Parks... Text von Paul Lindenberg unter Mitwirkung von H. Lichtenfelt [et al.] Berlin, The Werner Co., [1896?]
191p. illus. 33cm.

1. Berlin – Exhibitions. I. Title: Berliner Gewerbe-Ausstellung 1896. II. Lichtenfelt, H

NL 0379704   IaU MB DLC-P4 NN

[Lindenberg, Paul] 1859–
Reichsparteitag in Nürnberg, 1934.   Dresden: M. O. Groh,
1934.   205 p.   col'd front., illus., ports.   4°.

1. Nazis. 2. Title.

November 22, 1935

NL 0379705   NN

G 440
L5   Lindenberg, Paul, 1859–
Um die Erde in Wort und Bild. Berlin, Ferd. Dümmlers Verlagsbuchhandlung, 1900.
2 v. illus.

Library has volume 2 only.

1. Voyages around the world. I. Title.

NL 0379706   TxHU NjP

Lindenberg, Paul, 1859–1943.
Unter Habsburgs fahnen gegen Italien; kriegserlebnisse von Paul Lindenberg ... 1.–8. tausend. Stuttgart, A. Bonz & comp., 1915.
223 p. front. (port.) plates. 19 cm.

1. European war, 1914–1918—Campaigns—Italo-Austrian. I. Title.

D569.A2L5   21–4236 rev

NL 0379707   DLC CSt-H DNW MiU

LINDENBERG, Paul, 1859–
Unter Hindenburgs siegreichen fahnen; erzählung aus dem weltkrieg 1914/1915. Berlin, Schreitersche verlagsbuchhandlung, [19–].

Ports. and plates.   H 863.114.10

NL 0379708   MH

Lindenberg, Paul, 1859–
Wir denken seiner; zum 75. geburtstage des kaisers, **von Paul Lindenberg.** Mit einem beitrag der kaiserin Hermine und 17 abbildungen aus neuster zeit. Berlin, Phönix-verlag, Carl Siwinna [*1934]
32 p. incl. front., plates, ports. 24ᵐᵐ.

1. Wilhelm II, German emperor, 1859–

A C 34–2307

Title from N. Y. Pub.   Libr.   Printed by L. C.

NL 0379709   NN

Lindenberg, Paul P
Das Postwesen Palastinas vor der britischen besetzung. Wien, 1926.
46 p. (Die Postmarke veröffentlichungen der postmarke Wien Nr. 1.)

NL 0379710   PPDrop

Lindenberg, Sidney J
Supervision in social group work, by Sidney J. Lindenberg ... foreword by Arthur L. Swift, jr. ... New York, Association press, 1939.
xiv, 141 p. 21ᵐ.

1. Group work, Educational and social. I. Title.

30–34170

Library of Congress   HV41.L5
[a44k2]   361.8

PPT PBm OCU OO OC1 OU
NL 0379711   DLC Wa WaOB CaBVaU OKentU OrPS MiU CU

Lindenberg (W.) *Ueber zwei Fälle von Lupus aus der chirurgischen Klinik zu Erlangen. [Erlangen.] 32 pp., 1 pl. 8°. Celle, W. Gross-gebauer, 1888.

NL 0379712   DNLM

1895–
Lindenberg, Walter. Über kongenitale Muskeldefekte der Nackenmuskulatur. [Maschinenschrift.] 30 S. 4° [Lag nicht vor.] — Auszug: Leipzig 1922: Lehmann. 6 S. 8°
Leipzig, Med. Diss. v. 8. Aug. 1922   [U 24. 7373]

Full name: Heinrich Richard Walter Lindenberg.

NL 0379713   ICRL DNLM

Lindenberg, Willi: Affektionen der Tränenwege bei Oberkieferverletzungen. [Maschinenschrift.] 41 S. 4°. — Auszug: Berlin (1922): Ebering. 2 Bl. 8°
Berlin, Med. Diss. v. 15. Mai 1922   [U 22. 396]

NL 0379714   ICRL

QD341   Lindenberg, Willy.
.A8L7   Beitraege zur kenntniss des p-xylylhydrazins, des pikryl-, o-p-dinitrophenyl- und 2-nitro-5-chlorphenyl-p-xylylhydrazins und der derivate der letzteren.
Freiburg, 1900.
54p.
Inaug. diss. Freiburg.

NL 0379715   PU

VOLUME 334

VL
354 Lindenberg, Wladimir, 1902–
L744a Die ärztliche und soziale Betreuung des
1948 Hirnverletzten. Leipzig, Thieme, 1948.
iv, 85 p. illus. (part col.)

Bibliography: p. [84]–85.

1. Brain – Wounds and injuries – Complications and sequels 2. Personality –
Disorders

NL 0379716   DNLM

153.7
L744m Lindenberg, Wladimir, 1902–
Mysterium der Begegnung. München, E.
Reinhardt [1929]
255p. illus.

1. Self. 2. Experience.   I. Title.

NL 0379717   ICarbS

Lindenberg, Wladimir, 1902–
So sieht es der Patient; Briefe und Selbstschilderungen
von Hirnverletzten. Berlin, Berliner medizinische
Verlagsanstalt [1954]

NL 0379718   MH

Lindenberg, Wladimir, 1902–
Tragik und Triumph grosser Ärzte. Ulm/Donau, J.
Ebner [1948]
196 p. 20 cm. (Forschung und Humanität, Grundlagen und Ziele
der Naturerkenntnis, 4. Bd.)
"Literaturverzeichnis": p. 189–193.

1. Physicians–Biog. 2. Medicine–Hist.   (Series)

R134.L5   926.1   49–12673*

NL 0379719   DLC DNLM

Lindenberg, Wladimir, 1902–
Ueber blutdrucksteigerung und apoplexie.
Inaug. diss. Bonn, 1928. (1929)
Bibl.

NL 0379720   ICRL CtY

4PN–371 Lindenberg, Wladimir, 1902–
Die Unvollendeten; Lebensläufe früh
verstorbener Dichter. Hamburg, H.
Dulk [c1948]
382 p.

NL 0379721   DLC–P4 TNJ KU NNC InU NN

Lindenberg-Steiner, Mona Lisa.

See

Steiner, Mona Lisa.

Lindenberg, Ger. Aerologisches Observatorium.
Die Arbeiten des Preussischen Aeronautischen Observa-
toriums bei Lindenberg. 1.–17. Bd.; 1905–[1931] Braun-
schweig, F. Vieweg.
16 v. illus., maps, charts, diagrs., tables. 33 cm.
Supersedes its Ergebnisse der Arbeiten am Aeronautischen Ob-
servatorium.
Title varies: 1905–10, Ergebnisse der Arbeiten des Königlich
Preussischen Aeronautischen Observatoriums bei Lindenberg (varies
slightly)
Other slight variations in title.
Issued by the observatory under its earlier name: Preussisches
Aeronautisches Observatorium.

Editors: 1905–13, R. Assmann.—1914–31, H. Hergesell.
Superseded by Ergebnisse der Arbeiten des Aeronautischen Obser-
vatoriums bei Lindenberg, 1932–33, published by the Preussisches
Meteorologisches Institut.
L. C. set incomplete: vol. 14 wanting.

1. Meteorology in aeronautics. 2. Meteorology—Germany—Lindenberg. 3. Aeronautics in meteorology. I. Assmann, Richard, 1845–
1918, ed. II. Hergesell, Hugo, 1859–1938, ed. III. Lindenberg, Ger.
Aerologisches Observatorium. Ergebnisse der Arbeiten. IV. Title.

TL558.G4L5   31–4970 rev 2

NL 0379724   DLC MBdAF ICU MCM

QC989
.G2265 Lindenberg, Ger. Aerologisches Observatorium.

Germany (*Democratic Republic, 1949–*   ) *Meteorologi-
scher und Hydrologischer Dienst.*
Deutsches meteorologisches Jahrbuch. 1946–
Berlin, Akademie-Verlag [etc.]

Lindenberg, Ger. Aerologisches Observatorium.
Ergebnisse der aerologischen Tagung vom 3.
bis 6. Juli 1921
see under   Hergesell, Hugo, 1859–1938, ed.

Lindenberg, Ger. Aerologisches Observatorium.
Ergebnisse der Arbeiten am Aeronautischen Observa-
torium. 1900/01–1903/04. Berlin, A. Asher.
3 v. illus., charts, diagrs., tables. 33 cm. (Veröffentlichungen
des Königlich Preussischen Meteorologischen Instituts)
Superseded by its Die Arbeiten des Preussischen Aeronautischen
Observatoriums bei Lindenberg.
Edited by R. Assmann and A. Berson.

1. Meteorology—Germany. 2. Aeronautics in meteorology.
3. Balloons. I. Assmann, Richard, 1845–1918, ed. II. Berson, Arthur,
1895–1942, ed. III. Title.

QC879.L48   31–4969 rev*

NL 0379727   DLC MH

Lindenberg, Ger. Aerologisches Observatorium.
Ergebnisse der Arbeiten ... im Jahre 1905/07.
Herausgegeben von Richard Assmann.   Braunschweig, Vieweg, 1906–1908.
3 v. Illus. Plates. Maps. Plans. Charts.
32 cm. , in 4s.
Meteorological observations.

NL 0379728   MB

Lindenberg. Aerologisches Observatorium.
Flugsicherung Sommer 1928. Lindenberg.
1928.
v. p. 30 cm.
Manifolded.
52007

NL 0379729   DAS

Lindenberg, Ger. Aerologisches observatorium.
Höhenwetterdienst und luftverkehr. Herausgegeben im
auftrage des direktors des Aeronautischen observatoriums
Lindenberg vom höhenwetterdienst. [Beeskow i. M., Druck:
G. Knüppel & Haeseler, 1927]
22, [2] p. illus. (incl. map) diagrs. 22½ cm.

1. Meteorology in aeronautics. 2. Aeronautics in meteorology.
I. Title.

TL556.L43   629.1324   33–37885 rev

NL 0379730   DLC NN DAS

Lindenberg. Ger. Aerologisches
Observatorium.
Kurzer Monatsbericht. 1922–1929
plates. 35 cm.

NL 0379731   DAS

Lindenberg. Aerologisches   Observatorium.
Mittelungen. p.1–197   Aug. 1920.
May 1929.
(Lindenberg. 1920–29)
33½ cm.

NL 0379732   DAS

Lindenberg, Ger. Aerologisches Observatorium.
Die Wettersicherungsmassnahmen fur die ein-
zelmen Strecken des deutschen Luftverkehrs.
Lindenberg. 1928.
unp. 30cm.

NL 0379733   DAS

Lindenberg, Ger. Aeronautisches Observatorium
see Lindenberg, Ger. Aerologisches
Observatorium.

Lindenberg, Ger. Aerologisches Observatorium. *Leitung
des Flugwetterdienstes*
see
Prussia. *Leitung des Flugwetterdienstes.*

Lindenberg, Ger.   **Geschäftss** *telle für flugtechnik.*
Luftschrauben-untersuchungen der Geschäftsstelle für flugtechnik des Sonderausschusses der Jubiläumsstiftung der
deutschen industrie, von dr.-ing. F. Bendemann ... München und Berlin, R. Oldenbourg, 1911–18.
3 v. diagrs. (part fold.) 31½ x 24cm.
Vols. [2–3] have title: Luftschrauben-untersuchungen; berichte der
Geschäftsstelle für flugtechnik ...
On t.-p. of v. [3]: Drittes abschliessendes heft, hauptsächlich beear-
tet von dr.-ing. Carl Schmid.
"Systematische versuche. (Nach dissertation [Die luftschraube am
stand, Technische hochschule, Karlsruhe, 1915] von dr.-ing. C. Schmid)":
v. [3], p. 6–29.
CONTENTS.—[1. hft.] Aus dem bericht I für 1908/10. Aus dem bericht II für 1910/11.—   [2. hft.] Berichte für 1911–12.—
[3. hft.] Berichte für   1913–15.
1. Propellers, Aerial.   I. Bendemann, Friedrich, 1874–
II. Schmid, Carl, 1884–   III. Title.   32–7052
Library of Congress   TL705.L5   629.13

NL 0379736   DLC NN

Lindenberg, Ger.   Internationale kommission für wissenschaftliche luftschiffahrt
see International Aerological Commission.

**Lindenberg, Ger. Preussisches Aeronautisches Observa-
torium**
see
Lindenberg, Ger. Aerologisches Observatorium.

Lindenberger, Fritz, 1891–
... Appendicitis und Gravidität ...
Berlin, [1919]
20 p. , 2 l. 21.5 cm.
Inaug.-Diss. – Berlin.
Lebenslauf.

NL 0379739   CtY

VOLUME 334

Lindenberger, Gerhard, 1910–
... Unterkieferresektionen bei Carcinomen und Sarkomen, unter besonderer Berücksichtigung der Fälle aus der chirurgischen Klinik in Tübingen aus den Jahren 1920–1934 ... [Leonberg-Stuttgart, n. d.]
Inaug.-Diss. - Tübingen.
Lebenslauf.
"Literaturverzeichnis": p. 17.

NL 0379740   CtY OU DNLM

W 4   LINDENBERGER, Heinz, 1927–
M96   Die Behandlung des Hirnabszesses,
1951   einschliesslich des subduralen Empyems
unter besonderer Berücksichtigung der thorakogenen und posttraumatischen Abszesze. [München] 1951.
52 *l.*
Inaug.-Diss. - Munich.
1. Brain - Abscess

NL 0379741   DNLM

Lindenberger, Herbert Samuel, 1929–
Georg Trakl: the development of his poetic world. Ann Arbor, University Microfilms [1955]
([University Microfilms, Ann Arbor, Mich.] Publication no. 12,996)
Microfilm copy of typescript. Positive.
Collation of the original : 237 l.
Thesis—University of Washington.
Abstracted in Dissertation abstracts, v. 15 (1955) no. 10, p. 1854–1856.
Vita.
Bibliography : leaves 225–231.
1. Trakl, Georg, 1887–1914.
Microfilm AC–1 no. 12,996   Mic 55–556

Washington Univ.,   Seattle. Library
for Library of Congress   ·†

NL 0379743   WaU CU IU DLC

Lindenberger, Hermann.
Die reichsrechtliche behandlung des wander-buchhandels in Deutschland ... Leonberg, Druck von S. Lindenberger, 1901.
1 p. l., 82 p. 22½ᶜᵐ.
Inaug.-diss.—Tübingen.

1. Booksellers and bookselling—Colportage. 2. Liberty of the press.
2—25136
Library of Congress   Z313.L74

NL 0379744   DLC

LINDENBERGER, Joannes Baptista. O. S. B.
Adm. rdo. perillustri, rraenobile ac multum strenuo dño Sebastiano Lustrier de Liebenstain [poem]. Viennae Austriae, apud G. Gelbhaar, [1623?].
sm. 4°. pp. (8).   Ott 372.8

NL 0379745   MH

Lindenberger, Joannes Baptista, O.S.B.
Reverendissimo ... Georgio Placido Federer ... cum 1622 in abbatem eligeretur (monasterii ad D. Lambertum in Altenburg) ... epos sacrabat J. B. Lindenberger. Viennae Austriae, apud Gregorium Gelbhaar, 1624.
[7] p. 20 cm.

NL 0379746   PLatS

Lindenberger, *Mrs.* Ruth (Eason) 1899–
Beard family history and genealogy, by Ruth Lindenberger. [Lawrence, Kan., Printed by the World company] °1939.
121, [1] p. ports. 26½ᶜᵐ.

1. Baird family.
[Full name: *Mrs.* Ruth Winifred (Eason) Lindenberger]
39—12566
Library of Congress   CS71.B166 1939

NL 0379747   DLC P Or MtHi KyHi WHi NcD

[E   LINDENBERGER, Mrs. RUTH (EASON) 1899–
7   The Eason record, and allied families of
.E 12925 Rierson, Crain, Chandler, Toler, Zumwalt,
Howard, Phillips, etc.   Topeka, Kan., 1951.
38, [5], 10 *l.* 29cm.

NL 0379748   ICN NN

Lindenberger, Ruth (Eason) 1899–
The Eason record, and allied families of Rierson, Crain, Chandler, Toler, Zumwalt, Howard, Phillips, etc. [n. p., 1952?]
1 v. 30 cm.

1. Eason family. 2. U. S.—Geneal.
Full name: Ruth Winifred (Eason) Lindenberger.
CS71.E1324 1952   52—35013 ‡

NL 0379749   DLC

Lindenberger, S   A
Streams from the valley of Berachah.
N.Y. Christian Alliance Pub. co., n.d.
160 p.

NL 0379750   OO

Lindenberger aus Leonberg, Gerhard
see Lindenberger, Gerhard, 1910–

Lindenbergh, Pieter Cornelis, 1896–
Bijdrage tot oordeelkundig beheer van het duinwaterkapitaal ... door Pieter Cornelis Lindenbergh ... Leiden, N. v. boek- en steendrukkerij Eduard IJdo [1941]
xi, 188 p. incl. illus., maps, profiles, tables, diagrs. 24 cm.
Proefschrift—Technische hoogeschool, Delft.
Vita : p. [182]
"Literatuurlijst": p. [177]–181.

1. Leyden—Water-supply. 2. Leidsche duinwater maatschappij. 3. Water, Underground—Netherlands.
TD277.L5   G S 47–342
U. S. Geol. survey. Library
for Library of Congress   †

NL 0379752   DI-GS DLC

Lindenbichel, Johann Nep. Rainer von
see Rainer von Lindenbichel, Johann Nepomuk

Lindenblatt, C. W.
De hospitalitate et hospitio veterum.
n. p., 1825.

NL 0379754   NjP

Lindenblatt, Hellmut: Ueber Kriegsmelanosen. [Maschinenschrift.]
89 S. 4°. — Auszug: Breslau [1924]: Goldstein. 2 Bl. 8°
Breslau, Med. Diss. v. 20. Sept. 1924   [U 24. 1691

NL 0379755   ICRL

Lindenblatt, Johannes.   Ger 517.5.2
Jahrbücher Johannes Lindenblatts, oder Chronik Johannes von der Pusilie, officials zu Riesenburg, zum erstenmal herausgegeben von Johannes Voigt und Friedrich Wilhelm Schubert. Königsberg, in der Universitäts-buchhandlung, 1823.
pp. xxxiv, 407 +.

Teutonic knights||.

NL 0379756   MH CU-W NjP CU

ar X   Lindenblatt, Johannes, of Wriezen.
1148   Der Conflict zwischen Juden und Römern
no.20   von seinen Anfängen bis zur Niederlage des Cestius Gallus 64 vor Chr. bis 66 nach Chr. Wriezen, Tesch, 1870.
42 p. 26cm.

"Dritter Jahresbericht über die höhere Bürgerschule zu Wriezen."
No. 20 in a vol. with binder's title: Programmes: Roman history. II.

NL 0379757   NIC NjP

Lindenblatt, Kurt: Das Asylrecht der politischen Verbrecher nach Völkerrecht unter besonderer Berücksichtigung des deutschen Auslieferungswesens. Potsdam 1910: Krämer.
51 S. 8°
Würzburg, Jur. Diss. v. 20. Aug. 1910, Ref. Meurer
[Geb. 11. Okt. 85 Freienwalde z. O.; Wohnort: Potsdam; Staatsangeh.: Preußen; Vorbildung: Gymn. Potsdam Reife O. 04; Studium: Königsberg 5, Freiburg i. B. 1 S.; Rig. 25. Juli 10.]   [U 11. 4511

NL 0379758   ICRL MH NN CtY

Lindenblatt, Leo
Ueber gehaeufte kleine anfaelle. (Auszug)
Inaug. diss. Koenigsberg, 1925

NL 0379759   ICRL

Lindenblatt (Rud. Guil.) *De hydrarthro.
36 pp. 8°. Gryphiæ, F. G. Kunike. [1845].

NL 0379760   DNLM

Lindenblatt, Wolfgang, 1919–
Das Bildungsproblem in den Augen deutscher Akademiker zur Zeit der Weimarer Republik. München, 1952.
170 l. 29 cm.
Typescript (carbon)
Inaug.-Diss.—Munich.
Vita.
Bibliography : leaves 168–169.

1. Education—Germany. I. Title.
LA721.8.L55   55–18797

NL 0379761   DLC

VOLUME 334

Lindenborn (Adolf). *Ueber den Petersilien-
kampher und das Apiin. 24 pp. 8°. *Würzburg,
F. E. Thein, 1867.*
C.

NL 0379762   DNLM

Lindenborn (Adolph). *Ueber fibröse Uterus-
polypen. [Heidelberg.] 56 pp. 8°. *Mainz,
H. Prickarts, 1895.*

NL 0379763   DNLM PPC

PT 2424 [Lindenborn, Heinrich] 1712-1750.
L55 W4   Der die Welt beleuchtende Diogenes;/die Fehler
1742a   und Thorheiten der Menschen in biblisch-, his-
torisch-, poetisch- und sittlichen lustig- und
ernsthaften Sin- und Traum-Bildern etc. darstel-
lend. Anderte Auflag. Cölln, G. A. Schauberg,
1742-
|v. 17 cm.

NL 0379764   OU MH

Lindenborn, Heinrich, 1712-1750.
    Neues Gott und dem Lamm geheiligtes Kirchen-
und Hauss- Gesang der auf dem dreyfachen Wege der
Volkommenheit nach dem Himmlischen Jerusalem
wandernden Tochter Sion, die Glaubens Geheimnisse
und Fest-Täge, nach der biblischen Geschichte und
Kirchen-Ordnung vorstellend ... Zum Erstenmal in
Truck verlegt.   Cölln am Rhein, Gereon Arnold
Schauberg, 1741.
    8 p. l., 615, [8] p.   14 cm.
    207 hymns. with music.
    Published anonymously.

NL 0379765   NNUT

IVU31 [Lindenborn, Heinrich.] 1712-1750.
L74   *Neues Gott und dem Lamm geheiligtes Kirchen-
[1750?   und Hauss-Gesang der auf dem dreyfachen Wege der
Vollkommenheit nach dem himlisch-Jerusalem wandern-
den Tochter Sion, die Glaubens Geheimnisse und
Fest-Täge, nach der Biblischen Geschichte und
Kirchen Ordnung vorstellend... Zum Drittenmal in
Druck verlegt.
Cölln am Rhein, Schaubergische Buchdruckerey, [1750?]
656, [10] p.   14 cm.

    207,(really 209) hymns; with music.

NL 0379766   NNUT

Lindenborn (Hermann). *Allgemein-patho-
logische Betrachtungen über das Vorkommen
und die Bedeutung der Unreinlichkeit der Geisteskranken. [Wurtzburg.] 45 pp. 8°. *Berlin, L. Schumacher, 1886.
Repr. from: Arch. f. Psychiat., Berl., 1886. xvii, 2. Hft.

NL 0379767   DNLM ICRL

Lindenborn (Karl) [1880-]. *Ueber Carcinom des Pharynx mit Einschluss der
Tonsillen und seine Behandlung. [Heidel-
berg.] 58 pp., 1 l. 8°. *Tübingen, H. Laupp,
jr., 1904.

NL 0379768   DNLM ICRL

MW10 Lindenborn, M
L642a   Actueele zendingsvragen in Ned.-Indië.
Oegstgeest, Zendingsbureau, 1922.
22 p. 23 cm.

    1. Indonesia - Missions. 2. Nederlandse
Hervormde Kerk - Missions - Indonesia. 3.
Christianity and other religions - Islam.
I. Zendingsbureau, Oegstgeest. II. Title.

NL 0379769   CtY-D

MQ54 Lindenborn, M
L642a   Allah Akbar, door M. Lindenborn. [Rotterdam]
J.M. Bredé, 1920.
26 p. illus. 19 cm. (Lichtstralen op den
akker der wereld [26. jaarg.] 1920, 2)

    1. Missions to Muslims. 2. Christianity and
other religions - Islam. I. Title. II. Series.

NL 0379770   CtY-D NIC

NH4 Lindenborn, M
L642b   Bidden en werken in verband met zending. Door
M. Lindenborn. [Rotterdam, J.M. Bredée, 1904]
23 p. 19 cm. (Lichtstralen op den akker der
wereld [10. jaarg., 1904] 1)

    1. Missions - Hortatory works. I. Title.

NL 0379771   CtY-D

MW19 Lindenborn, M
Z29   Jan Lambrecht Zegers; zendeling van Indramajoe,
Xʂ64j   1870-1890. Uit zijn dagboek geteekend door M.
Lindenborn. [Rotterdam, Nederlandsche Zendings-
vereeniging, n.d.]
87 p. illus., ports. 20 cm.

    1. Zegers, Jan Lambrecht, 1845-1919. 2. Java-
Missions. 3. Missions, Dutch. 4. Nederlandsche
Zendingsvereeniging. 5. Indramayu, Java - Mis-
sions. I. Zegers, Jan Lambrecht, 1845-1919.

NL 0379772   CtY-D

MQ54 Lindenborn, M
L642m   Mohammad Rasul Allah, door M. Lindenborn.
Rotterdam, Ned. Zendingsvereeniging [n.d.]
32 p. illus. 20 cm.

    1. Missions to Muslims. 2. Christianity and
other religions - Islam. I. Title.

NL 0379773   CtY-D

Wason Lindenborn, M
Pamphlet   Pionierswerk door zendeling H. van der
B   Klift op Zuid-Oost Celebes. [Rotterdam]
124   J.M. Bredée [1918]
32 p. illus. 19 cm. (Lichtstralen op
den akker der wereld, 4)

    1. Missions--Celebes. 2. Klift, H van
der.

NL 0379774   NIC

MW19 Lindenborn, M
V588   Een welbesteed leven. J. Verhoeven, de vader
Xʂ64w   van Tjideres. Door M. Lindenborn. Oegstgeest,
Zendingsbureau, 1923.
32 p. illus., port. 22 cm.

    1. Verhoeven, J   d.1922. 2. Java - Mis-
sions. 3. Missions to Muslims. 4. Missions,
Dutch. 5. Nederlandsche Zendingsvereeniging.
6. Tijderes, Java. I. Title. SA(2)

NL 0379775   CtY-D NIC

Nye500 Lindenborn, M
I61   West-Java als zendingsterrein der Neder-
L642   landsche Zendingsvereeniging. Utrecht, Zendingsstudieraad; in den handel gebracht door
Algemeene Boekhandel voor Inwendige- en Uitwendige zending, Den Haag [1922]
xi, 192 p. illus. 20 cm. (Onze zendings-
velden)

    1. Missions - West Java (Province) 2. West
Java (Province) I. Ser.

NL 0379776   CtY ICU CLU HU

MW19 Lindenborn, M
L642w   West-Java als zendingsterrein der Nederlandsche zendingsvereeniging. Utrecht,
Uitg. door den Zendingsstudieraad; in den
handel gebracht door Algemeene boekhandel
voor inwendige- en uitwendige zending, Den
Haag [1923]
xi, 192 p. illus. 21 cm. (Onze zendings-
velden, 3)

    Bibliography: p. [viii]-xi.

NL 0379777   CtY-D CLU WU

Wason Lindenborn, M
BP172   Zendingslicht op den Islam. Den Haag,
L74   Boekhandel van den Zendingsstudie Raad [1918?]
xi, 184 p. 23 cm.

    1. Mohammedanism--Relations--Christianity.

NL 0379778   NIC CtY-D NN CtY InU MH-AH

Lindenborn, Walter: Tierhalterhaftung bei Vermögen unter Verwaltung. [Maschinenschrift.] xiii, 58 S. 4°. — Auszug: (Cassel
[1923]: Scheel) 1 Bl. 8°
Marburg, Jur. Diss. v. 20. Juli 1923   [U 23. 8813

NL 0379779   DLC

Lindenbrog, Erpold, 1540-1616.
    Chronica von dem scheutzlichen Kriege welchen
die Cimbri mit dem Römischen Volcke ganzer acht
Jahr geführet ... Durch Erpoldum Lindenbruch.
Hamburg, J. Wolff, 1589.
    1 v. (unpaged) 20 cm.
    1. Cimbri. 2. Imprints - Hamburg, 1589.
3. Imprints - Wolff, Jacob, 1589. I. Title.

NL 0379780   MdBP

    Lindenbrog, Erpold, 1540-1616, ed.

BX1538
.B6H5   **Historia archiepiscoporum bremensium.**
    Historia archiepiscoporvm bremensivm, a tempore Karoli
Magni vsqve ad Karolvm IIII. Id est, à Willehado omnium
archiepiscoporum bremensium primo, vsque ad Gothafredum
XXXII. ab incerto auctore deducta, & nunc primum in lucem
edita. Ex bibliotheca generosi ac illustris domini Henrici Ran-
zovii producis cimbrici; studio & operâ Erpoldi Lindenbrvch.
Lvgdvni Batavorvm, ex officina Plantiniana, apud Franciscum
Raphelengium, 1595.

    Lindenbrog, Erpold, 1540–1616.
    Historia compendiosa ac svccincta serenissimorvm
Daniæ regvm: ab incerto auctore conscripta; nunc vero
usque ad Christianvm IIII. deducta, primumque in lucem
edita, opera & studio Erpoldi Lindenbrvch. Lvgdvni
Batavorvm, ex officina Plantiniana, apud Franciscum
Raphelengium, 1595.

    2 p. l., 64 p., 2 l. 21ᶜᵐ.

    1. Denmark—Kings and rulers. 2. Denmark—Hist. I. Title.

                                  24-30600

    Library of Congress   DL147.L5

NL 0379782   DLC InU ViU IaU CtY NN NIC

VOLUME 334

Lindenbrog, Erpold, 1540-1616.
Historia compendiosa ac svccincta serenis-
simorvm Daniae regvm: ab incerto auctore conscripta, nunc vero usque ad Christianvm IIII.
deducta, primumque in lucem edita, opera &
studio Erpoldi Lindenbrvch. Lvgdvni Batavorvm,
Ex officina Plantiniana, 1595.
Microfilm copy, made in 1962, of the original
in Vatican. Biblioteca vaticana. Positive.
Negative film in Vatican. Biblioteca
vaticana.

Collation of the original, as determined
from the film: 1 p. *l.*, 64, [4] p.
1. Denmark--Kings and rulers. 2. Denmark--
Hist. I. Title. (Series: [Manuscripta, microfilms of rare and out-of-print books. List 41,
no. 12])

NL 0379784   MoSU OU

Lindenbrog, Erpold, 1540-1616.
HISTORIA compendiosa ac svccincta serenissi-
morum Daniae regum; ab incerto auctore conscripta; postea vero ad Christianum IV. deducta antehac in lucem edita, opera-studio
Erpoldi Lindenbruck ([STEPHANIUS, S. J. De regno Daniae, etc., 1629.]
24°. pp.102-172.)   Scan 419.1

NL 0379785   MH

Lindenbrog, Erpold, 1540-1616, ed.
Historica narratio. De origine gentis Danorum
et de regibus eiusdem gentis: et eorumdem rebus
gestis ... usque ad Ericum Menuit CXVII. ...
compendiose olim conscripta ab Erico Daniae rege
... Edita ab Erpoldo Lindenbruch. [Hamburg],
1603.
iv, 60 p.   19.5 cm.

NL 0379786   CtY

Lindenbrog, Erpold, 1540-1616.
Index in Donatum. (In Terentius Afer, Publius. P. Terentii Carthaginiensis Afri Comoediae
sex, ex recensione Lindenbrogii... 1774. v.2,
supplementary pp. [1]-22)

NL 0379787   PPiU

Lindenbrog, Erpold, 1540-1616, ed.
M. Adami Historia ecclesiastica...
see under   Adamus, Bremensis, 11th cent.

Lindenbrog, Erpold, 1540-1616.   Ger 435.26
Newe vermehrte chronica von dem grossmechtigsten ersten
deudschen keyser Carolo Magno, seinem jnnerlichen wandel und
privat leben oder sitten, *etc.* und seinen grossen thaten, so wol ge-
waltigen kriegen zusammen gezogen durch Erpoldum Lindenbruch.
Hamburg, [colophon: H. Steinbach, typis Hered. I. Wolffii], 1593.
sm. 4°. ff. (12), 276, (4). Coats of arms and other woodcuts.

Charlemagne|Print. spec.||

NL 0379789   MH

Lindenbrog, Erpold, 1540-1616.   L943.02
Scriptores rervm Germanicarvm septentri-   H481c
onalivm, vicinorvmqve popvlorvm diversi...
Qvibvs accedvnt variorvm pontificvm, imper-
atorvm, regum & ducum diplomata & priuilegia... Studio atque opera Erpoldi Lindenbrogi. Cum indice rerum & verborum satis
locuplete... Francofvrti, Ex officina
typographica M. Beckeri, 1609.
307p. 32cm. [With Helmoldus. Chronica
Slaorum... Francofvrti, 1581]

NL 0379790   IEN PU

Lindenbrog, Erpold, 1540-1616.
Scriptores rervm germanicarvm septentrionalivm, vicinorvmqve popvlorvm diversi ... qvibvs accedvnt variorvm pontificvm, imperatorum, regum & ducum diplomata
& priuilegia ... Studio atque opera Erpoldi Lindenbrogi
... Francofvrti, typis C. Rôtelii, sumptibus G. Fitzeri,
1630.
3 p. l., 307, [4] p. 32cm.

1. Scandinavia—Hist. 2. Europe, Northern—Hist.

Library of Congress   DL45.L7   5-6181†

NL 0379791   DLC

Lindenbrog, Erpold, 1540-1616.
Scriptores rerum Germanicarum Septentrio-
nalium, vicinorumque populorum, veteres
diversi, quibus continentur historia ecclesiastica et religionis propagatio gestaeque
Saxonum, Sclavorum, Wandalorum, Danorum,
Norwegorum, Svedorum &c. situs denique &
natura omnium quae in septentrione sunt
regionum, ipsarumque gentium vetustis temporibus mores ac religiones. Praeterea
variorum pontificum, imperatorum, regum

et ducum diplomata et privilegia. Omnia
ad fidem vett. codd. emendata & aucta, partim etiam primùm ex archivis prolata. Cum
novo auctario et indice rerum & verborum
fatis locuplete. Quid in hac editione nova
praestitum sit, declarat praefixa praefatio
Jo. Alberti Fabricii. Scriptorum nomina
atque seriem proxima post praefationem pa-

gina indicabit. Hamburgi, C. Liebezeit,
1706.
[24],276,[4] p. port. (His Scriptores
septentrionales ... [v.1])

1. Scandinavia – Hist. 2. Europe, Northern – Hist. I. Fabricius, Johann Albert,
1668-1736. II. Title.

PPL MnU InU PU NNG NRU OCl
NL 0379794   CLU ICN ICU MH NN MiU OCl CtY MdBP WU

Lindenbrog, Friedrich, 1573-1648, ed.
Ammiani Marcellini, Rerum gestarum...
see under   Ammianus Marcellinus.

Lindenbrog, Friedrich, 1573-1648.
Pedo, Albinovanus.
C. Pedonis Albinovani Elegiæ III, et fragmenta, cum inter-
pretatione et notis Jos. Scaligeri, Frid. Lindenbruchii, Nic.
Heinsii, Theod. Goralli [pseud.] et aliorum. Amstelædami,
apud Davidem Mortier, MDCCXV.

Lindenbrog, Friedrich, 1573-1648, ed.
Codex legvm antiqvarvm, in qvo continentvr: Leges
Wisigothorvm. Edictvm Theodorici regis. Lex Bvrgvn-
dionvm. Lex Salica. Lex Alamannorvm. Lex Baivva-
riorvm. Decretvm Tassilonis dvcis. Lex Ripvariorvm.
Lex Saxonvm. Anglorvm et Werinorvm. Frisionvm.
Longobardorvm. Constitvtiones sicule sive neapolitanae.
Capitvlare Karoli M. et Hlvdowici impp. &c. Quibus
accedunt Formule solennes priscæ publicorum privatorum-
que negotiorum, nunc primum editae: et glossarivm ... Ex

bibliotheca Frid. LindenbrogI. J. C. Francofvrti, apud
Ioannem & Andream Marnios & consortes, CIↃIↃCXIII.
12 p. l., 1570, [2], p. 314 cm.
Title vignette (coat of arms) : printer's mark at end.
"Karoli Magni et Hlvdovici Pii ... capitvla, sive leges ecclesiasticæ
et civiles; ab Ansegiso abbate & Benedicto Levita collectæ, lib. VII":
p. [823]-1204.
"Formvlæ exorcismorvm ad maleficia reprimenda": p. [1299]-1310.
"Frid. LindenbrogI, i. c. Glossarivm sive interpretatio rervm vocvm-
qve difficilivm et obscvriorvm": p. [1348]-1499.
1. Law, Germanic. 2. Law—Germany. 3. Law—Naples. I.
Ansegisus, Saint, abbot of Fontenelle, d. 833. II. Benedictus, levita,
ca. 850. III. Holy Roman   empire. Laws, statutes, etc. IV.
Naples (Kingdom)   Laws, statutes, etc. v. Title.
                                                              4—32112

OClW PU-L NIC WaU-L
NL 0379798   DLC N KU PPD MH ViU NjP PU ViU-L CLL NN

Lindenbrog, Friedrich, 1573-1648, ed.
Diversarvm gentivm historiae antiqvae scriptores tres. Iornandes ... De regnorvm ac tem-
porvm svccessionibus. Eivsdem Historia de
origine Gothorvm. Isidorvs Hispalens. De Go-
this, Wandalis, & Suevis. Eivsdem Chronicon
regum Wisigothorvm. Pavli Warnefridi F. Diaconi De gestis Longobardorvm lib. VI. Frid.
Lindenbrogivs recensuit, & observationibvs
illustravit. Hambvrgi, Apud Michaelem Herin-
givm, 1611.
[12], 379, [2] p. 23cm.

NL 0379799   NNC NjP PU MH WU PLatS

Lindenbrog, Friedrich, 1573-1648.
Fr. Lindenbrogi Observationes in Ammianum
Marcellinum et in eundem Collectanea variarum
lectionum. Hamburgi, Apud M. Hlvdovicum
Frobenium, 1609.
276p. 21cm.

Bound with: Ammianus Marcellinus. Ammiani
Marcellini Rerum gestarum qui de XXXI.
supersunt libri XVIII. Hamburgi, 1609.

1. Ammianus   Marcellinus.

NL 0379800   TxU InU

Lindenbrog, Friedrich, 1573-1648.
Aetna (Latin poem, 1st cent.)
P. Cornelii Severi Ætna, & quæ supersunt fragmenta, cum
notis et interpretatione Jos. Scaligeri, Frid. Lindenbruchii &
Theod. Goralli [pseud.] Accessit Petri Bembi Ætna. Am-
stelædami, apud Davidem Mortier, MDCCXV.

Lindenbrog, Friedrich, 1573-1648, ed.   DG511
Paulus Diaconus, 720 (ca.)-797?   .P55
Pavli Warnefridi Langobardi filii, diaconi foroivliensis, De 1595
gestis Langobardorum libri VI., ad mss. & veterum codicum
fidem editi. Lvgdvni Batavorvm, ex officina Plantiniana, apud
Franciscum Raphelengium, 1595.

Lindenbrog, Friedrich, 1573-1648, ed.   PA6755
Terentius Afer, Publius.   .A2
Pvblii Terentii Carthaginiensis Afri Comoediæ N. VI et 1602
in eas Ælii Donati et Evgraphii commentaria. Fr. Linden-
brvchivs collatis mss. veteribusque exemplaribus recensuit,
auxit, & observationibvs inlustravit, adiecto indice vberrimo.
Parisiis, Ex Officina Plantiniana; Apud H. Perier. 1602.

VOLUME 334

Lindenbruch, Erpoldus
    see   Lindenbrog, Erpold, 1540-1616.

Lindenbruchius, Fridericus
    see
Lindenbrog, Friedrich, 1573-1648.

Lindenburg, Cornelis Willem Hendrinus.
    Duitse spraakkunst. Heidelberg, J. Groos, 1942.
        vii, 243 p. 20 cm. (Methode Gaspey-Otto-Sauer)
    —— Sleutel bij de Duitse spraakkunst. Heidelberg, **J.**
    Groos, 1942.
        40 p. 20 cm. (Methode Gaspey-Otto-Sauer)
                                        PF3112.5.L5 Key

    1. German language—Self-instruction. 2. German language—Text-
books for foreigners—Dutch.   (Series: Method Gaspey-Otto-Sauer)

    PF3112.5.L5   50-52734

    NL 0379806   DLC ICRL

Lindenburg, Cornelis Willem Hendrinus.
    Kleine niederländische sprachlehre für
    schul- privat- und selbstunterricht. 10.
    aufl. Heidelberg, J. Groos, 1950.
        vii, 188 p. 20 cm. (Methode Gaspey-
    Otto-Sauer)
    "An die stelle der 'Kleinen niederländischen
    sprachlehre' von Valette tritt mit vorliegendem
    werke eine ganz neue bearbeitung." - Vorwort.

    NL 0379807   NcD PU

ML
3003   Lindenburg,Cornelis Willem Hendrinus.
.L74   Het leven en de werken van Johannes Regis
       ... door Cornelis Willem Hendrinus Lindenburg
       ... Amsterdam, "De Spieghel" [1939?]
           4 p.l., 105 p.; 14 p.(music) front.,illus.(music)
       25 x 19ᶜᵐ.
           Proefschrift—Utrecht.
           Also published without thesis note.
           Bibliographical foot-notes.
           "Bijlage: Het motet 'O admirabile commercium'":
       14 p.at end.
           "Stellingen" (iii p.) laid in.
           1.Regis,Johannes,15th cent.

    NL 0379808   MiU NIC ICU NjP

Lindenburg, Cornelis Willem H.
    Het leven en de werken van Johannes Regis, door dr. C. W.
    H. Lindenburg. Amsterdam, "De Spieghel"; [etc., etc., 1939;
        3 p. l., 105 p.; 14 p. (music) front., illus. (music) 25 x 19ᶜᵐ.
        Bibliographical foot-notes.
        Errata slip laid in.
        "Bijlage: Het motet 'O admirabile commercium' " : 14 p. at end.

    1. Regis, Johannes, 15th cent.   40-24621

    Library of Congress   ML3003.L74L3
                                            927.8

    NL 0379809   DLC OU MiU CLU MH NcU

LINDENBURG, CORNELIS Willem Hendrinus.
    Het leven en de werken van Johannes Regis.
Amsterdam,"De Spieghel" [1939] 103,14 p. illus., music.
25 x 19cm.

    Film reproduction. Negative.
    "Bijlage: Het motet 'O admirabile commercium, " 14 p. at end.
    Bibliographical footnotes.

    1. Regis, Johannes, 15th cent.

    NL 0379810   NN

Lindencrona, Carolus Johannes
    De ludo scacchorum ...
    Inaug. Diss. Lund, 1849

    NL 0379811   ICRL

Lindencrona, E. A. F., respondent.
    Upplysningar til Sveriges mynthistoria
        see under Hildebrand, Bror Emil,
    1806-1884, praeses.

Law   Lindencrona, Gustaf, 1912-   ed.

    Sweden. *Laws, statutes, etc.*
        Utlänningslagen jämte dithörande författningar. Med
    kommentar av Johan Björling [och] G. Lindencrona. Utg.
    av Statens nämnd för utgivande av förvaltningsrättsliga
    publikationer. [Stockholm, 1955]

Lindencrona, Per Alvar Haldan, 1903–
    ... Blixtkrig mot Sverige. [Stockholm] Centralkommittén
    för det frivilliga försvarsarbetet, Ab. Seelig & c:o i distribu-
    tion [1943]
        136 p. illus., maps (1 fold.) 19ᶜᵐ.
        At head of title: Per Lindencrona.
        "Tidigare införd som en artikelserie i tidskriften Folk och försvar ...
    Boken redogör i populär form för hur ett blixtkrig mot Sverige kan
    tänkas äga rum och de åtgärder som därvid vidtagas från såväl de
    militära som de civila myndigheternas sida."—Förord.

        1. Sweden—Defenses.   I. Centralkommittén för det frivilliga förs-
    varsarbetet (Sweden) II. Title.
                                            45-12876
    Library of Congress   UA790.L48
                                            355

    NL 0379814   DLC WaU

Lindencrone, Anna Lillie (Greenough) Hegermann-
    see Hegermann-Lindencrone, Lille
    (Greenough) Moulton, 1844-1928.

Lindencrone, Cai Ditlev Hegermann-
    see Hegermann-Lindencrone, Cai Ditlev,
    1807-1893.

Lindencrone, Frederik Hegermann-
    see
Hegermann-Lindencrone, Frederik, 1840-

Lindencrone, Johan Frederik, tr.
    Folke-eventyr, samlede af brødrene Grimm
        see under Grimm, Jakob Ludwig Karl,
    1785-1863.

Lindencrone, Knud Hegermann-
    see Hegermann-Lindencrone, Knud.

Lindencrone, Lillie de Hegermann-
    see   Hegermann-Lindencrone, Lillie
    (Greenough) Moulton, 1844-1928.

Lindencrone, Louise (Lindencrone) Hegermann-
    see   Hegermann-Lindencrone, Louise
    (Lindencrone) 1778-1853.

Lindencrone, Mette Louise Christine Frederike
    Hegermann-
        see   Hegermann-Lindencrone, Mette Louise
    Christine Frederike.

Lindendorf, H., pseud.
    see Siecke, Hedwig, 1847-1923?

HC331   **Lindener, Boris Aleksandrovich.**
.A65   *Raboty ...*
    Akademiíà nauk SSSR. *Komissiíà po izucheniíù estest-*
    vennykh proizvoditel'nykh sil Soíùza.
        Работы Российской академии наук в области исследо-
    вания природных богатств России; обзор деятельности
    КЕПС за 1915–21 гг. Составил Б. А. Линденер. Петро-
    град, Российская гос. академическая тип., 1922.

W 6   LINDENER, Johann Ferdinand
P3   Dissertatio medica inauguralis de phrenitide ... Harderovici,
v.1937   Apud Johannem Moojen, 1759.
no.9   8 p. 24 cm.
             Diss. - Harderwijk.

    NL 0379825   DNLM

Lindener, Johann Georg, respondent.
    ...De substitutionibus...
        see under   Bernbeck, David Philipp,
    praeses.

Lindener (Justus Franciscus). * De fame ca-
nina. 24 pp. sm. 4°. *Halæ Magdeb., ex off. Hen-*
deliana. [1760?]

    NL 0379827   DNLM PPC

Lindener, Karl Friedrich, respondent.
    De remedio syndicatvs adversvs sententias
    camerae imperii exercitatio
        see under   Boehmer, Georg Ludwig,
    1715-1797, praeses.

Lindener, Karl Friedrich, respondent.
    Testamenti signati et svbscripti a
    testibvs in involvero
        see under   Böhmer, Georg Ludwig,
    1715-1797, praeses.

VOLUME 334

Lindener, Michael, d. 1562.
Michael Lindeners Rastbüchlein und Katzipori, hrsg. von Franz Lichtenstein. Tübingen, Litterarischer verein in Stuttgart, 1883.

2 p. L. 219 p. 21½ᶜᵐ. (Added t.-p.: Bibliothek des Litterarischen vereins in Stuttgart. ₁bd.₁ CLXIII)

Collection of facetiae.
"Neues über M. Lindener ₁Sein tod. Zwei bilderbogen₁," additional notes by J. Bolte in v. 217 of this collection.

1. German wit and humor. I. Lichtenstein, Franz, 1852–1884, ed. II. Title: Rastbüchlein. III. Title: Katzipori.

Library of Congress   PT1101.L5 vol. 163
2—9437

```
       MiU OC1 OCU OU MH MB OC1W
NL  0379830      DLC PU OrCS MdBP CU MoU GU NjP NcD PBm
```

₁Lindener, Michael₁ d. 1562.
Tid fordriff. En skøn lystig selskabs bog eller huilebog: ₁huor vdi findis smuck snack oc lystige fabeler, som ere historier lige. Tilsammenscreffuen, alle dem til villie oc tieniste, som vandre oc reyse til lands oc vands, at forlyste sig, oc at fordriffue tiden met. København, 1921.

120, ₁8₁ p. 16ᶜᵐ. (Half-title: Forening for boghaandværks smaa bøger)
"Nærværende udgave er paa Forening for boghaandværks vegne besørget af underbibliotekar R. Paulli."—Udgiverens efterskrift.

I. German wit and humor. I. Paulli, Richard Jakob, 1890–   ed. II. Title.
24–19274

Library of Congress   PT1743.L7R34

```
NL  0379831      DLC NN
```

Lindener, Wilhelm August.
＊De communicatione vasorum mammariorum cum epigastricis.
Halae Magdeb, typ. Salfeldianis,[1748]
4 l. 30p. 5 l. 4°.

```
NL  0379832      NNNAM DNLM PPC
```

Lindenfeld (Berta). ＊Contribution à l'étud₁ des fonctions du nerf spinal. 46 pp., 1 l. 8°. Genève. 1908.

```
NL  0379833      DNLM
```

Lindenfeld, D.
"Efrusi." Eine auflösung der räthselhaften profezeiung Daniels cap. 8. betreff der erlösung Israels. In zwei theile₁n₁ 1. th. "Ohel hachaim"—"Das zelt des lebens". 2. th. "Sukas David"—"Die hütte Davids". Verfasst von D. Lindenfeld ... ₁Illok₁ Wortman's "Erste Illoker buchdr.", 1885.

34 p. 21ᶜᵐ.

1. Bible. O. T. Daniel—Criticism, interpretation, etc. 2. Jews—Restoration. I. Title.
CA 25–301 Unrev'd

Library of Congress   BS649.J5L5

```
NL  0379834      DLC
```

Lindenfeld (Leopold). ＊Ueber einen Fall von traumatischem rechtsseitigem Chylothorax. 25 pp. 8°. Zürich, Leemann & Co., 1919.

```
NL  0379835      DNLM
```

Lindenfeld, Mihály.
Naplóbizonylatos könyvelési rendszer a könnyuiparban
    see under   Hungary. Könnyuipari Minisztérium.

Lindenfeld, Peter.
Internal pair production of gamma rays from π-absorption. Ann Arbor, University Microfilms ₁1954₁
(₁University Microfilms, Ann Arbor, Mich.₁ Publication no. 8717)
Microfilm copy of typescript. Positive.
Collation of the original: 37 l. diagrs., tables.
Thesis—Columbia University.
Abstracted in Dissertation abstracts, v. 14 (1954) no. 9, p. 1442.
Bibliographical footnotes.

1. Gamma rays. 2. Mesotrons. I. Title.

Microfilm AC–1   no. 8717   Mic A 55–3364

Columbia Univ.   Libraries
for Library of Congress   †

```
NL  0379837      NNC DLC
```

Lindenfeld, Wilhelm.
Carcinom bei lupus erythematodes.   (Auszug).
Inaug. diss. Braunschweig, 1920.

```
NL  0379838      ICRL
```

Die Lindenfeldin.
    Poetisches Linden-Gebüsche ...
    see under title

Lindenfels, J B von
Johannes Wit gen. von Dörring als Theaterrecensent, bewundert von J.B. von Lindenfels. Alton, 1827

```
NL  0379840      MH
```

Spec.
Arnold Lindenfels, Joseph Benedict, 1762–1833.
Z 104   Den hemmelige skrivekonst; eller, Chiffrer-
L 5   og dechiffrer-konsten, isaerdeleshed practiskt oplyst ved et nyt transpositionschiffre, der, formedelst dets utallige afvexlinger, i forening med den største simpelhed og lethed, kan gjøres aldeles uopløseligt, endog for den, som har opfundet det. Ledsaget af en forerindring, en indledning og et tillaeg. Kjøbenhavn, F. Brummers Forlag, 1819.
xl, 294 p. 13 fold. plates. 22 cm.
J. S. Galland, Bibl. of cryptology, p. 112.
1. Ciphers.   2. Cryptography.

```
NL  0379841      MoSW PU NN NIC CtY
```

PT 2424 LINDENFELS,LUISE VON
₁L36 B59   Bilder des Lebens und der Natur, in einfachen ernsten Dichtungen. Sulzbach, Seidel, 1844.
134 p.

```
NL  0379842      InU
```

4k   Lindenfels, Philip Meyster von
9557   Speoulvm notariorvm; das ist, Notariat Spiegel vnd ausführlicher Bericht vom Ampt der Notarien, so wol in gemein als sonderlich in Beschreibung der Contracten, Testamenten vnd letzten Willen, auch gerichtlicher Acten vnd andern solchen drey Hauptstücken anhängigen Sachen, wie auff dem vierdten Blat zusehen. Auss den beschriebenen keyserlichen Rechten, auch dess

H. Reichs Constitutionen vnd Abschieden, Keyserlicher Cammergerichts Ordnung vnd vortrefflicher Rechtsgelehrten Schrifften mit Eynführung der Chur- vnd Fürsten, auch anderer Herrschafften vnd Städt, publicirter Landt vnd Stadt Rechten, Reformationen vnd Ordnungen sonderlich auch

Continued in next column

Continued from preceding column

sächsischen Rechtens vnd anderer vnbeschriebenen Bräuch vnd Gewonheiten. Nicht allein den Notariis, sondern auch allen den jenigen, so sich in vnd ausserhalb Gerichts in Schreiben, Rahten vnd Reden gebrauchen lassen, zum besten zusammen getragen vnd in fünff Büchern gantz verstandtlich vnnd

ordentlich Theorice vnd Practice beschrieben, von newem vbersehen vnd an vielen Orten mit nützlichen Additionibus vnd distincto Charactere der Allegaten verb., jetzo zum vierdten mal in Truck verfertigt sampt einer Rethorica der hochteutschen Spraach wie dieselb in Reden vnd Schreiben

jetziger Zeit vblichem Stylo gemäss nach derselben Kunst eygentlichen vnnd gewissen Reguln zugebrauchen, dissmals von newem in Truck geben. Meyntz, Gedruckt bey B. Lippen, 1616.
840 p.

```
NL  0379847      DLC-P4
```

Lindenhagen, Julius.
Die zur Bearbeitung des Holzes angewendeten Werkzeugler-Maschinen. Ein Handbuch für Bau-, Möbel- und Modell-Tischler, Drechsler, Zimmerleute, Pianoforte-Fabrikanten, Wagner, Böttcher u. s. w.; bearbeitet von Julius Lindenhagen... Weimar: B. F. Voight, 1862. xii, 87 p. 7 pl. 12°. (Neuer Schauplatz der Künste und Handwerke. Bd. 69.)

204430A. 1. Woodworking machin-   ery. 2. Ser.
April 13, 1926

```
NL  0379848      NN
```

GD561 Lindenhayn, Hans, 1878–
₁L861₁   Beitraege zur kenntnis der diazoverbindungen. Jena, 1903.
38p.
Inaug. diss. Jena.

```
NL  0379849      DLC MH PU
```

Lindenhayn, Hans.
Landwirtschaftliches aus den Vereinigten Staaten von Nordamerika, von Dr. phil. Hans Lindenhayn...   Dippoldiswalde, Sa.: C. Jehne, 1925. iv, 62 p. diagrs., illus. 8°.
Bibliographical footnotes.

I. Agriculture—U. S.
April 9, 1927

```
NL  0379850      NN
```

Lindenhayn (Josephus). ＊Probabilia aliquot de acidorum in corpus humanum viribus. 32 pp. 8°. Regimontii, typ. academicis Hartungianis, ₁1869₁.

```
NL  0379851      DNLM
```

Lindenheim (Æmilius) [1819–]. ＊De catarrhi natura nec non aetiologia. 25 pp., 2 l. 8°. Berolini, typ. fratrum Schlesinger, [1843].

```
NL  0379852      DNLM
```

VOLUME 334

Lindenheim, Hans, 1880-
Ueber die durch graviditaet verursachte cystenbildung
in uterusmyomen.
Inaug. diss. Leipzig, 1906. (Berlin)
Bibl.
32 pp.

NL 0379853   ICRL CtY DNLM

Lindenheim, Norman, joint ed.

Henry, George McClellan, 1877-   ed.
Pennsylvania digest of decisions, being a digest of all the
reported decisions of the Supreme, Superior and county courts
for the years 1906 to 1929 inclusive, edited by George M.
Henry ... This digest connects with the decisions digested in
Vale's Digest volumes 1–10 inclusive, also Pepper and Lewis'
Digest of decisions 23 volumes and C. R. A. supplement volumes 1 and 2 ... Newark, N. J., Soney & Sage co.; Philadelphia, Pa., George T. Bisel co., 1931.

Lindenhout, H. van 't, 1836–1900.
In memoriam. Mevrouw H. van 't Lindenhout
see under   [Lindenhout, Johannes van 't]
1836–1918.

UD4   Lindenhout, Jacob van 't
L64
Bladzijden uit mijn leven. Nijmegen: P.J.
Milborn, n.d.
168p. 22cm

NL 0379856   NjNbS

Lindenhout, Jacob van 't.
De landbouw in Amerika. Een verhandeling over den
Amerikaanischen landbouw, voor landbouwers en allen,
die belang in den landbouw stellen. Door J². van 't Lindenhout ... Nijmegen, P. J. Milborn ₁188-?₁
48 p. incl. 3 pl. 19ᶜᵐ. ₁With Lindenhout, Johannis van 't. Zes weken
tusschen de wielen. 2. druk. Nijmegen ₁1886?₁₁

1. Agriculture—U. S.

Library of Congress   E184.D9L7   5–11249

NL 0379857   DLC

Lindenhout, J₁ohannes₁ van 't, 1836 - 1918.
Eenige gedachten over Amerikaanische toestanden.
Enkele raadgevingen aan landverhuizers door J. van 't
Lindenhout ... Nijmegen, P. J. Milborn ₁188-?₁
2 p. l., 80 p. 19ᶜᵐ. ₁With his Zes weken tusschen de wielen. 2 druk.
Nijmegen ₁1886?₁₁

1. U. S.—Descr. & trav.
5–11250
Library of Congress   E184.D9L7

NL 0379858   DLC

999.4   [LINDENHOUT, Johannes van 't] 1836-1918.
L744   In memoriam. Mevrouw H. Van 't Lindenhout,
L744i   1836-1900./ Nijmegen, Milborn [1900?]
148p. front. (port.) 22cm.

NL 0379859   MH-AH

818   LINDENHOUT, Johannes van 't, 1836-1918.
L744z   Na vijf-en-twintig jaren. Levensherin-
L744n   neringen. Nijmegen, Milborn [1888]
1888   350p. ports. 21.5cm.

Vierde druk.

NL 0379860   MH-AH

Lindenhout, J₁ohannes₁ van 't, 1836 - 1918.
Zes weken tusschen de wielen, of De Hollanders in
Amerika. Door J. van 't Lindenhout. 2. druk. Nijmegen, P. J. Milborn ₁1886?₁
3 p. l., 304 p. 10 pl., 2 port. (incl. front.) 19ᶜᵐ.

1. U. S.—Descr. & trav. 2. Dutch in the U. S.

Library of Congress   E184.D9L7   5–11251

NL 0379861   MH

Lindenhout, Johannes van't, 1836 - 1918.
Zes weken tusschen de wielen; of, De Hollanders in Amerika,
door J. van't Lindenhout.   Nijmegen: P. J. Milborn ₁1886?₁.
2 p.l., 304 p., 10 pl., 2 port. (incl. front.).   3. ed   12°.

NL 0379862   NN

Lindenhurst galleries
Catalogue of the collection of pictures
by the old masters of the early English
schools & Mihály Munkácsy, compiled from the
latest biographies, encyclopedias ' museum catalogues, by Ecsiter. ₁Phila., ₁riv. pr., 1904.₁
121 p

NL 0379863   PPPM

Lindenia; iconographie des orchidées. v. 1–17; ₁août?₁ 1885–
déc. 1901. Gand, Imprimerie E. Vander Haeghen ₁etc.₁
1885–1901.
17 v. col. plates (part fold.) 36½ᶜᵐ. monthly (irregular)
Edited by Lucien Linden and others.
Vols. 11–17 called also 2. sér., v. 1–7.
No more published.
"Table des planches contenues dans les dix premiers volumes": v. 10,
p. 108–112.

1. Orchids.   ɪ. Linden, Lucien, 1854–   ed.
43–33472
Library of Congress   SB409.A1L5
584.15

NL 0379864   DLC TU MH TxReTR FU PPAN

Map   Lindenkohl, Adolphus, 1833-1904.
G   Map of the Albemarle and Chesapeake
3792   canal, connecting Chesapeake Bay with
C5   Currituck, Albemarle, and Pamplico
1881   sounds and their tributary streams.
L5   Fairfield canal and New Berne & Beau-
fort canal. 14th ed., rev. Washington,
1881.
col. map 70 x 50 cm.

Scale 1 inch to 8 miles.

NL 0379865   NIC

Lindenkohl, Adolphus, 1833-1904.
Map of the Albemarle and Chesapeake Canal
connecting Chesapeake Bay with Currituck,
Albemarle and Pamlico Sounds and their tributary streams. By Marshall Parks, President... 16th ed., revised and corrected.
Compiled and drawn by A. Lindenkohl.
Wash. ₁Albemarle and Chesapeake Canal Co.₁
1885.
72 x 50 cm.
Scale of miles 3 to an inch.

NL 0379866   NcU

Lindenkohl, Adolphus, 1833-1904.
Map of the Albemarle and Chesapeake
Canal connecting Chesapeake Bay with
Currituck, Albemarle and Pamlico Sounds
and their tributary streams... compiled
and drawn by A.& H. Lindenkohl.   20th
ed.   Wash., Norris Peters Company
for Albemarle and Chesapeake Canal
Company, 1902.
Scale of miles 8 to an inch
28 X 19 3/4

NL 0379867   NcU

Lindenkohl, A₁dolphus₁, 1833-.904.
Notes on the model of the Gulf of Maine constructed for
the United States fish commission. By A. Lindenkohl.
(*In* Bulletin of the United States fish commission for 1883. Washington,
1883. 23ᶜᵐ. vol. III, p. 449–454)

1. Gulf of Maine.
F 12-403
Library, U. S. Bur. of   Fisheries

NL 0379868   DI OO CaBVaU

LINDENKOHL, Adolphus, 1833-1904.
Solution of the "Three-Point Problems by determining the Point of Intersection of a Side
of the Given Triangle with a Line from the
Opposite Point [ ] the Unknown Point. (U.S.
COAST SURVEY. Report of the Superintendent,
etc.,during the Year 1869,1872.

4°, p. 235.) Plate.
"Appendix No. 14."

NL 0379869   MH

Lindenkohl, A₁dolphus₁, 1833-1904.
Das spezifische gewicht des meerswassers im Nordost-
Pacifischen ozean im zusammenhange mit temperatur-
und strömungszuständen. Von A. Lindenkohl ... ₁Go-
tha, 1897₁
7 p. fold. map. 27½ x 23ᶜᵐ.

Caption title.
Abdruck aus Dr. A. Petermanns Geogr. mitteilungen 1897, heft xɪɪ.

1. Sea-water. 2. Pacific Ocean.
6-4094
Library of Congress   GC151.L74

NL 0379870   DLC

Lindenkohl, Adolphus, 1833-1904.   ᴹMap 1020.80
The United States: southern part. [Map.] From the latest sur-
veys.
Cassel. Freyschmidt. 1865. Size, 16⅞ X 21¼ inches. Scale,
1 :3000000 (or, 47.4 miles to 1 inch). Folded.
Statistics on the back.

K6084 — South, The. Geog. Maps.

NL 0379871   MB

VOLUME 334

Lam 1
Lindenkohl, G
Ueber das Volks-Schul- und Unterrichtswesen in Sicilien. Vorlesung gehalten am 15. Mai 1857 in Cassel zum Besten des Gustav-Adolph-Vereines ... Kassel, O.Bertram, 1857.
Pamphlet

NL 0379872   CtY

Lindenlaub, Georg.
Der alte und der neue Glaube: Der Wodanswanderer, von Georg Lindenlaub; Winfried, von Liselotte Heise. 13. Aufl. Langensalza, J. Beltz [1937]
80 p. illus. 19 cm. (Geschichte in Erzählungen, geschichtliche Arbeitshefte, Heft 9/10)
"Diese beiden Erzählungen ... finden sich in dem Werke 'Geschichtsunterricht in neuen Geiste, 2. Teil: Germanische Frühgeschichte.'"
1. Germanic tribes—Religion. 2. Bonifacius, originally Winfried, Saint, Abp. of Mainz, 680–755.   I. Heise, Liselotte.   II. Title. (Series)
BL865.L5 1937   51–50905

NL 0379873   DLC

4PT
Ger. -1077
Lindenlaub, Georg.
Der tolle Hugbald, eine Erzählung aus der Zeit vor etwa 2000 Jahren. 22. Aufl. Langensalza, J. Beltz [
34 p.   (Geschichte in Erzählungen, geschichtliche Arbeitshefte, Heft 5)

NL 0379874   DLC-P4

189.4
A116sY
L
Lindenkohl, Georgius Steph.
De Petri Abaelardi libro Sic et Non commentatio. Dissertatio inauguralis quam amplissimo philosophorum Marburgensium ordini ad summos in philosophia honores rite capessendos offert Georgius Steph. Lindenkohl. Marburgi Cattorum, typis Elwerti academicis, 1851.
35 p.   22cm.
1. Abailard, Pierre, 1079-1142.

NL 0379875   TxDaM DLC MH CtY

Lindenlaub, Th.
Université de Strasbourg; origines, historique, réorganisation et projets d'agrandissement. Paris, Hachette & cie, 1879.
(4), 50 p.
"Extrait des publications de la Société pour l'étude des questions d'enseignement supérieur."

NL 0379876   MH

Lindenmaier, Friedrich.
Die stellvertretung im servituten...
Inaug. Diss. Rostock, 1903
Bibl.

NL 0379877   ICRL MH

Lindenmaier, Fritz, 1881–   ed.
Nachschlagewerk des Bundesgerichtshofs [von] Lindenmaier [und] Möhring. München, Beck [1951–
v. (loose-leaf) 22 cm.
L. C. copy imperfect: t. p. and preliminary matter wanting; title from cover.
1. Law reports, digests, etc.— Germany (Federal Republic, 1949–   )   I. Germany (Federal Republic, 1949–   ) Bundesgerichtshof.   II. Title.
57–31067

NL 0379878   DLC ICU NNC CU

Lindenmaier, Fritz, 1881–   ed.
Das Patentgesetz
see under
Germany (Federal Republic, 1949–   ) Laws, statutes, etc.

TS73
.T1
1944
Lindenmaier, Fritz, 1881–   ed.
Germany. *Laws, statutes, etc.*
Das Patentgesetz vom 5. mai 1936; fortführung des von reichsgerichtsrat dr. Heinrich Krausse verfassten erläuterungsbuchs des früheren gesetzes; 3. aufl., ergänzt und teilweise neubearb. von dr. Franz Katluhn ... nach dem tode des bearbeiters mit zusätzen entsprechend der rechtsentwickelung bis zum erscheinen versehen von dr. Fritz Lindenmaier ... Berlin, C. Heymann, 1944.

Law
Lindenmaier, Fritz, 1881–   ed.
Germany (*Federal Republic, 1949–*   ) *Laws, statutes, etc.*
Schiffahrtsrecht; Textsammlung wichtiger reichs- und bundesrechtlicher Vorschriften und Bedingungen der See- und Binnenschiffahrt, hrsg. von Kurt von Laun und Fritz Lindenmaier, unter Mitwirkung von Otto Rudolf von Laun. München, Beck, 1953.

Z1009
.B45
abt. 5
Lindenmaier, Henrica Maria, ed.
Berlin. Deutsches auslandswissenschaftliches institut.
... Bulgarien. bd. 1–   1939/42–
Leipzig, O. Harrassowitz, 1942–

Lindenmaier, Werner, 1903–
Die elektrolyse von ammoniumsalzen der fettsaeuren.
Inaug. diss. Basel, 1929
Bibl.

NL 0379883   ICRL MH CtY MiU

---

ar W
491
Lindenmann, Adolf, 1923–
Beiträge zur Kenntnis der Isochinolinalkaloide. Basel, B. Birkhauser, 1949.
[1880]–1891 p. 23cm.
Diss.—Basel. Verkürzte Fassung.
1. Alkaloids.

NL 0379884   NIC

Lindenmann, Alfred, 1922–
Bäume und Sträucher im Nachbarrecht. Zürich, Juris-Verlag, 1950.
103 p. 22 cm.
Inaug.-Diss.—Bern.
Vita.
Bibliography: p. 99–102.
1. Adjoining landowners—Switzerland.   I. Title.
51–16711

NL 0379885   DLC

Rs10
B944
Lindenmann, Elizabeth, 1915–
Studien in der 1,4-Diphenylbutanreihe ... Zofingen, 1945.
Inaug.-Diss. – Basel.

NL 0379886   CtY MH IEN

W 4
Z96
1951
LINDENMANN, Jean, 1924–
Versuche mit Ultraschall an Drosophila-Eiern; Analyse der erhaltenen Absterbekurven. Basel, Karger, 1951.
p. [415]-435.
Cover title.
Inaug.-Diss. – Zürich.
Reprinted from Schweizerische Zeitschrift für allgemeine Pathologie und Bakteriologie, V. 14, Nr. 4, 1951.
Summary in English, French, German, and Italian.
1. Drosophila 2. Supersonic waves

NL 0379888   DNLM

Lindenmann, R
Die Helvetier im kampfe um ihre freiheit und um die nationale ehere; eine exegetisch-historische studie.
Fehraltorf, Selbstverlag des verfassers, 1898.
147 p.

NL 0379889   OClW

Lindenmann, Walter Karl, 1920–
Untersuchungen zur postembryonalen Entwicklung schweizerischer Orchesellen. Genève, 1950.
353–428 p. illus. 25 cm.
Inauguraldiss.—Basel.
Vita.
"Separatabdruck aus Revue suisse de zoologie, Bd. 57, Heft 2, 1950."
Bibliography: p. 425–428.
1. Orchesella. 2. Insects—Development.
QL503.C6L5   52–38870

NL 0379890   DLC NIC CtY

W 4
M96
1953
LINDENMAYER, Helmut, 1928–
Klinische Beobachtungen über das Blutbild bei der Hepatitis epidemica und ihren Folgezuständen. [München] 1953.
41 ℓ.
Inaug.-Diss. – Munich.
Typewritten copy.
1. Hepatitis - Infectious

NL 0379891   DNLM

VOLUME 334

Lindenmayr (Josef). Die Vergiftungen, deren Erkenntnis, Vorbeugung und das gegen sie gerichtete Heilverfahren, für Mediciner, Aerzte, Thierärzte, Apotheker und gebildete

Laien, tabellarisch dargestellt. 29 pp., 3 tab. 12º. Wien, J. Safář, 1896.

NL 0379892   DNLM MH

Lindenmayer, Otto, 1880–
Die strafrechtliche und zivilrechtliche lehre der einziehung.
Inaug. Diss. Heidelberg, 1907 (Stuttgart)
Bibl.

NL 0379893   ICRL

Lindenmayr (Emericus P.) * Hippocrates homo, philosophus, medicus. 34 pp., 1 l. 8º. Buda, typ. Reg. Univ. Hung., 1832.

NL 0379894   DNLM

Lindenmayr, Emericus P
RA887   Die Mineralquellen bei Buziás in der serbischen
B9   Woiwodschaft mit dem temeser Banate. Temesvár,
856L   Beichel, 1856.
84, iiip. 18cm.

1. Physical medicine – Hydrotherapy – Buziás, Serbia (Yugoslavia)

NL 0379895   CtY-M

WAA   LINDENMAYR, Emericus P
L748s   Serbien, dessen Entwickelung und
1876   Fortschritt im Sanitäts-Wesen, mit
Andeutungen über die gesammten
Sanitäts-Verhältnisse im Oriente.
Temesvar, Csanáder Dioecesan-
Buchdruckerei, 1876.
xi, 439 p.

NL 0379896   DNLM

Lindenmayr, Josef.
Das Gifttrias Arsen, Blei und Quecksilber, die Erwürger der gewerblichen Arbeiter. Eine Flugschrift technischen und sozial-politischen Inhalts, von Dr. med. Josef Lindenmayr, mit einem Vorwort von Dr. Georg v. Schulpe... Dresden: "Globus," 1916. xvi, 42 p. incl. tables. New ed. 8°. (Bibliothek für Volks- und Weltwirtschaft. Heft 18.)

1. Occupation.—Diseases.   2. Schulpe, Georg von, 1867– . 3. Series.   June 1, 1921.

NL 0379897   NN

Lindenmayr (Max). * Ueber Entstehung und Heilung der Blasen-Scheiden-Fisteln. 32 pp. 8º. Salzbach, J. E. von Seidel, 1845.

NL 0379898   DNLM

Lindenmeyer. Wie ernähren wir unsre Kinder kräftig, gesund und billig? Praktische Anleitung zur Ernährung des Kindes in gesunden und kranken Tagen, [etc.] 17 pp. 8º. Stuttgart, G. Hohl, 1884.

NL 0379899   DNLM

Lindenmeyer, Albert.
Regeneratio; das neu-machende Handeln Gottes am Menschen und an der Welt.   Zürich, Zwingli-Verlag ₍c1943₎
42p. (Kirchliche Zeitfragen, Heft 5)

Bibliographical footnotes.

1. Regeneration (Theology) I. Series.

NL 0379900   TxFTC MH-AH

Lindenmeyer, Albert.
Zusammenarbeit auf biblischem Bekenntnis-grund.   Zürich, Zwingli-Verlag ₍c1948₎
24p. (Kirchliche Zeitfragen, Heft 21)

1. Interdenominational cooperation. I. Title. II. Series.

NL 0379901   TxFTC DCU

Lindenmeyer, Eugen, 1915–
SL25   ... Bestimmung des Gesamteiweisses im
3   Liquor cerebrospinalis ... Basel [1944]
L642   Inaug.-Diss. – Zürich.
"Sonderdruck aus "Monatsschrift für Psychiatrie und Neurologie",Vol.109,Nr.2."

NL 0379902   CtY DNLM

Lindenmeyer, Franciscus Xaverius, O.F.M. Conv.
Verbum abbreviatum seu Theses theologico-Scotistae de Ineffabili Incarnati Verbi Mysterio, rationibus pro & contra breviter propositas, quas Praeside P. Adriano Mayer ... defendendas susceper-unt VV. & RR. P. Franciscus Xaverius Lindenmeyer ... & F. Joannes Chrysostomus Widmar de Uberlinga ... Herbipoli, Typis Joannis Michaelis Kleyer, 1721.
63 p. 16 cm.
Bound with: Borg, P.H.: Tractatus De Deo. Herbipoli, Typis H. Engmann, 1705.
1. Incarnation. 2.   Sacraments. I. Widmar, Joannes Chrysostomus,   O.F.M. Conv.

NL 0379903   PLatS

Lindenmeyer, Georg Christian Ludwig
see   Lindenmeyer, Ludwig, 1762-1820.

Lindenmeyer, Harold F.
What does the Patent Office Scientific Library have to offer the chemist.   [Wash., Govt., 1954]
8 p. 27 cm.

NL 0379905   PPD

Lindenmeyer, Helmut, 1904–
Die ethische Begründung der Prohibition...von Helmut Lindenmeyer... Erlangen, 1927.   ix, 98 p.   8°.

Dissertation, Erlangen.
Lebenslauf, at end.
Bibliography, p. ₍vii₎–ix.

386651A. 1. Prohibition.   December 19, 1928

NL 0379906   NN ICRL MH CtY PU MiU

Lindenmeyer, Johann Christian Ludwig
see   Lindenmeyer, Ludwig, 1762-1820.

Lindenmeyer, Julius.
Das göttliche Reich als Weltreich. Nach der heiligen Schrift ...   Tübingen, 1869.
22.5 cm.

NL 0379908   CtY

Lindenmeyer, Julius, Dr.-Ing.
Die stapelfaser sniafil, ihre verarbeitung nach dem baum-wollverfahren vom rohstoff bis zum veredelten gewebe, unter besonderer berücksichtigung der fasereigenschaften, von dr.-ing. Julius Lindenmeyer. 24 abbildungen und 20 zahlentafeln. München und Berlin, R. Oldenbourg, 1931.
vi, 94 p., 2 l. illus., tables (part fold.) diagrs. 24ᶜᵐ.
"Quellen": p. ₍93₎–94.

1. Silk, Artificial. I. Title.

Library of Congress	TS1688.L5	31-17877
Copyright A—Foreign	11796	
		677.463

NL 0379909   DLC NN

Lindenmeyer, Julius, Dr.-Ing.
Die verarbeitung der stapelfaser,, Sniafil" nach dem baumwollverfahren im grossbetrieb vom rohstoff bis zum veredelten gewebe unter besonderer berücksichtigung der fasereigenschaften
Inaug. Diss. München, 1930.
Bibl.

NL 0379910   ICRL

Lindenmeyer, Ludwig, 1762-1820
Jahrbuch meines Lebens. Nach der Handschrift hrsg. von K.Esselborn. Darmstadt, Schlapp, 1927
xvi, 415 p. (Hessische Volksbücher, 61-65)

NL 0379911   MH

333L64   **Lindenmeyer, Ludwig,** 1762-1820.
₍1803   Gedichte...   Frankfurt am Main, 1803.
220p.

Title vignette, engr.

NL 0379912   IU NNUT

PT 2424   **LINDENMEYER, Ludwig,** 1762-1820.
.L38 A17   Gedichte. Wien, F. Haas, 1806.
1806   218 p. front.

NL 0379913   InU

VOLUME 334

4K
2942 Lindenmeyer, Marius
Les fiançailles et les promesses de mariage dans le droit et la jurisprudence. Vevey, 1901.
220 p.

NL 0379914   DLC-P4

Lindenmeyer (Otto). "Beitrag zur Kenntnis der strangförmigen Gebilde im Glaskörper. 24 pp. 8°. *Tübingen, F. Pietzcker,* 1900.

NL 0379915   DNLM ICRL

Otto
Lindenmeyer,ᴧ Ueber paradoxe Lidbewegungen. 39 pp. 8°. *Halle a. S., C. Marhold,* 1904.
Forms Heft 6, Bd. v. of Samml. zwangl. Abhandl. a. d. Geb. d. Augenh., Halle a. S., 1904.

NL 0379916   DNLM

Lindenmeyer, Otto

—— Ueber Schrotschussverletzungen des Auges. 28 pp. 8°. *Halle a. S., C. Marhold,* 1902.
Forms 1. Hft., v. 5, of : Samml. zwangl. Abhandl. a. d. Geb. d. Augenh.

NL 0379917   DNLM

Lindenmeyer, Paul Henry, 1921–
An investigation of the structure and related properties of certain organic nitro compounds ... 1951.
102 numb. l.
Thesis (PH. D.) - Ohio state university, 1951.

NL 0379918   OU

621.94 Lindenmeyer, Ray S
L637o Operating an engine lathe   Chicago, Ill.,
Science and mechanics, 1944.
64p. illus., port., diagrs.

1. Lathes. I. Title.

NL 0379919   IU

Lindenmeyer, Walter
Hochverzug in der baumwoll-verarbeitung vom rohstoff bis zum veredelten gewebe.
Inaug. diss. Muenchen, Techn.Hoch., 1929
Bibl.

NL 0379920   ICRL

Lindenmeyer, Walter.
Hochverzug in der baumwoll-verarbeitung vom rohstoff bis zum veredelten gewebe, von dr.-ing. Walter Lindenmeyer; mit 17 tafeln im anhang. München und Berlin, R. Oldenbourg, 1929.
viii, 96 p. 4 fold. pl. (diagrs.) 13 fold. tab. 24ᶜᵐ.
Also issued as inaugural dissertation, Technische hochschule, München.
Errata slip laid in.
"Quellen": p. [94]-96.

1. Cotton spinning.

Library of Congress   TS1577.L55   30-4226

NL 0379921   DLC NN ICJ

Lindenmeyr, Carl E., joint author.

Vertrees, Joseph Hodgen, 1887–
Human problems in production supervision, by Joseph H. Vertrees ... Ann Arbor, Mich., Printed by Edwards brothers, inc., ᶜ1941.

Lindenmeyr, Henry, & Sons.
Belgrade cover.   New York [1912].   14 l.   8°.
Title from cover.

1. Book covers.
                                        February 27, 1912.

NL 0379923   NN

Lindenmeyr, Henry, & Sons.
Bonds; a short story of investments on paper, and paper as an investment.   New York: H. Lindenmeyr & Sons, 1927.   6 l.   8°.
Printed at the Rudge press.

331046A. 1. Paper—Catalogues.
                                        October 28, 1927.

NL 0379924   NN

Lindenmeyr, Henry, & Sons.
Buckeye covers.   New York [1912].   15 l.   8°.
Title from cover.

1. Book covers.
                                        February 27, 1912.

NL 0379925   NN

Lindenmeyr, Henry, & Sons.
Catalog & price list; the Lindenmeyr lines.   [New York, 1923?]   xvi, 211 p.   12°.
Cover-title.
Six blank leaves at end, for notes.
Contains prices of various grades of papers and cardboards.

311490A. 1. Paper—Catalogues.
                                        August 19, 1927.

NL 0379926   NN

Lindenmeyr, Henry, & Sons.
New shades of Belgrade cover papers.   New York [1912].
7 l.   8°.

1. Book covers.
                                        February 27, 1912.

NL 0379927   NN

The LINDENMEYR library of print shop helps.
New York, H. Lindenmeyr.   no.   19cm.

1. Printing, Practical. I. Lindenmeyr, Henry, & sons.

NL 0379928   NN

W 4
M96 LINDENMÜLLER, Robert, 1927–
1955 Ergebnisse experimenteller Untersuchungen am isolierten Nerv-Muskel-Präparat von Warmblütern.   München, 1955.
46 l. illus.
Inaug.-Diss. - Munich.
1. Myasthenia gravis 2. Nerves - Experimental studies

NL 0379929   DNLM

634.9
U583s Lindenmuth, A   W
no.11 Forest fire damage appraisal procedures and tables for the northeast. By A.W. Lindenmuth, Jr. and others.   Asheville, N.C., Southeastern Forest Experiment Station, 1951.
cover-title, 28 p. illus. 21cm.   (U.S. Forest Service. Southeastern Forest Experiment Station. Station paper no.11)

NL 0379930   DAS

Lindenmuth, A   W   Jr.
1951 forest fires and fire danger in Maryland

see under

U.S. Southeastern Forest Experiment Station, Asheville, N.C.

Lindenmuth, John Michael.
Family journal of John Michael Lindenmuth. Also a birth register of his family and his generation. n.p., n.d.
23 p.

NL 0379932   PHi

Lindenov, Christoffer, 1639–1697.
The first Triple Alliance; the letters of Christopher Lindenov, Danish envoy to London, 1668–1672. Tr. and ed. with an historical introduction by Waldemar Westergaard. Copenhagen, Rosenkilde and Bagger, 1947.
lxxviii, 528 p. 25 cm.
Errata slip inserted.
"Works cited": p. [507]-509.

1. Triple Alliance, 1668. 2. Europe—Hist.—1648–1715—Sources. I. Westergaard, Waldemar Christian, 1882–   tr.

D273.5.L5 1947a   940.22   48-13414*

NL 0379933   DLC CaBVa

Lindenov, Christoffer, 1639–1697.
The first Triple alliance; the letters of Christopher Lindenov, Danish envoy to London, 1668–1672, translated and edited with an historical introduction by Waldemar Westergaard ... New Haven, Yale university press; London, G. Cumberlege, Oxford university press, 1947.
4 p. l., [vii]-lxxviii, 528 p. 24 cm.
"Works cited": p. [507]-509.

1. Triple alliance, 1668. 2. Europe—Hist.—1648–1715—Sources. I. Westergaard, Waldemar Christian, 1882–   tr.

D273.5.L5   940.22   47—3557

ICU TxU InU ViU MB
NL 0379934   DLC WaSpG OrU MH PP OO NcD PV PU ViU-L

VOLUME 334

Lindenov, Harald.
The etiology of deaf-mutism with special references to heredity ... Copenhagen, Munksgaard, 1945.

268 p. illus. 25½ᶜᵐ.

Thesis—Copenhagen.
"Translated from Danish, by Axel Andersen."
Summaries in English and Danish.
"References": p. ₍203₎–268.

1. Deaf. ₍1. Deaf-mutism—Etiology and pathogenesis₎ 2. Heredity of disease. ₍2. Deaf-mutism—Heredity₎ ɪ. Andersen, Axel, tr. ɪɪ. Title.

RF320.L5   617.8   Med 46–219 †

U. S. Army medical library   [W4C78]
for Library of Congress   ₍a47d1₎†

DNLM
NL 0379935   DNAL DLC CLSU ICU PU MnU PPC CtY ICU MH

Lindenow, Godske, d. 1612.
Drie uoyagien gedaen na Groenlandt
see under [La Peyrère, Isaac de]
1594–1676.

832.9
L744e   **Lindenrode, Gustav Adolf von.**
Die Erzählungen eines Toten. Dresden, Aurora, 1918.
84p. 19cm.

NL 0379937   IEN

Lindenschatt, H(ermann) V(ictor): Aus d. Chir. Klinik zu Bonn. Über spontane Ruptur des Darmes. Bonn 1914: Eisele. 45 S. 8°
Bonn, Med. Diss. v. 8. Aug. 1914, Ref. Garrè
[Geb. 17. Juli 89 Warschau; Wohnort: Bonn; Staatsangeh.: Rußland; Vorbildung: OR. Warschau Reife 08, Erg. Moskauer-Lehrbez. 13; Studium: Bonn 10 S.; Rig. 4. Aug. 14.]   [U 14. 1495

NL 0379938   ICRL DNLM MH

Lindenschatt (Srul-Meier) [1888–　].*Ueber den Einfluss der OH- und H-Jonen auf die Komplementablenkung und das differente Verhalten verschieden hoch erhitzter Sera bei der Komplementfixierung. 39 pp., 2 l. 8°.
Heidelberg, J. Hörning, 1913.

NL 0379939   DNLM ICRL MH

Lindenschmid, Hans.
Fehdebrief an Eitel Schelm von Bergen.
15.Sept. 1490. [Ulm, Johann Reger, 1490]
Kat. der Einblattdrucke 962. Goff L–224.

NL 0379940   DLC

Lindenschmidt, Heinrich.
Schliemann's ausgraben in Troja und Mykenae. Mainz, 1878.

NL 0379941   RPD

Lindenschmidt, Mihály.
A verbászi német nyelvjárás alaktana irta Lindeschmidt Mihály. Budapest, Magyar tudományos akadémia, 1905.
37 p., 1 l. 23 cm. (On cover. Magyarországi német nyelvjárások ... 2. füzet.)
Bibliography: p. [3]
1. German language - Dialects - Verbász, Hungary.

NL 0379942   CU

Lindenschmit, Ludwig, 1809–1893, ed.

Archiv für anthropologie; zeitschrift für naturgeschichte und urgeschichte des menschen ... 1.– bd.; 1866– Braunschweig, F. Vieweg und sohn, 1866–19

Lindenschmitt, Ludwig. 1809–   *4072.167
Ein auf dem Schlossplatz in Mainz gefundenes Elfenbeinrelief. Plate. (In Studien aus Kunst und Geschichte Friedrich Schneider ... gewidmet ... Pp. 411–415. Freiburg im Breisgau. 1906.)

G4605 — Mainz, Germany. Antiq. — Ivory.

NL 0379944   MB

₍Lindenschmit, Ludwig₎ 1809–1893.
Ein deutsches hügelgrab aus der letzten zeit des heidenthums. ₍Mainz, 1852₎
16 p. illus.,2 col.plates. (Abbildungen von alterthümern des Mainzer museums, hrsg. vom Verein zur erforschung der rheinischen geschichte und alterthümer, 4.hft.)

Caption title.
Signed: Ludwig Lindenschmit.

1. Mounds – Germany. I. Title.

NL 0379946   CU

Lindenschmit, Ludwig, 1809–1893, joint author.
Das germanische Todtenlager bei Selzen in der Provinz Rheinhessen
see under Lindenschmit, W[ilhelm] 1806–1848.

Lindenschmit, Ludwig, 1809–1893.
Handbuch der deutschen alterthumskunde. Übersicht der denkmale und gräberfunde frühgeschichtlicher und vorgeschichtlicher zeit. Von L. Lindenschmit. In drei theilen. ɪ. th. Die alterthümer der Merovingischen zeit. Mit zahlreichen eingedruckten holzstichen. Braunschweig, F. Vieweg und sohn, 1880–1889.

xii, 514 p., 1 l. illus., xxxvii pl. 24½ᶜᵐ.

No more published.
Bibliography: p. 64–67.
1. Germany—Antiq.

3–25626

Library of Congress   DD51.L74

NL 0379948   DLC PU MH OC1W CtY MdBP NjP

NK5107
L74   **Lindenschmit, Ludwig,** 1809–1893.
Neuerwerbungen des Mainzer Altertumsvereins. p. 135–139. illus., plate. 29 cm.

Extracted from: Mainzer Zeitschrift, v. 3, 1908.
Photocopy (negative)

11000. 1. Glassware, Roman--Rhineland. I. Mainzer Zeitschrift, v. 3, 1908.

NL 0379949   NCorniC

Lindenschmit, Ludwig, 1809–1893.

Mainz. Römisch-germanisches zentral-museum.
Das Römisch - germanische central - museum, in bildlichen darstellungen aus seinen sammlungen. Hrsg. im auftrage des Vorstandes von dem conservator, L. Lindenschmit, sohn. Mainz, V. v. Zabern, 1889.

Lindenschmit, Ludwig, 1809–1893.
Tracht und bewaffnung des römischen heeres während der kaiserzeit, mit besonderer berücksichtigung der rheinischen denkmale und fundstücke. Dargestellt in zwölf tafeln und erläutert von Ludwig Lindenschmidt. Braunschweig, F. Vieweg und sohn, 1882.

2 p.l., 29, ₍1₎ p. xɪɪ pl. 27ᶜᵐ.

"Der text ist . . . von meinem neffen Heinrich Lindenschmidt redigirt und von mir revidirt worden."—Note on p. 3, signed: Ludwig Lindenschmidt.

1. Arms and armor, Roman. 2. Rome—Army. ɪ. Lindenschmidt, Heinrich.

NL 0379951   MiU MH OCU ICU PU MdBP CU NIC DLC-P4

[Lindenschmit, Ludwig] 1809–1893.
Über eine besondere Gattung von Gewandnadeln aus deutschen Gräben des V. und VI. Jahrhunderts. n.p.
16 p.

NL 0379952   PU

Lindenschmit, Ludwig, 1809 - 1893.
Die vaterländischen alterthümer der fürstlich hohenzoller'schen sammlungen zu sigmaringen. Mainz, 1860.
4°

NL 0379953   NN

Lindenschmit, W₍ilhelm₎ 1806–1848.
Das germanische todtenlager bei Selzen in der provinz Rheinhessen, dargestellt und erläutert von den gebrüdern W. und L. Lindenschmit ... Mainz, V. v. Zabern, 1848.

2 p. l., 54 p. illus., 23 pl. (22 col., 1 fold.) fold. plan. 25ᶜᵐ.

ɪ. Lindenschmit, Ludwig, 1809–1893, joint author.

5–2903†

NL 0379954   DLC MH-P

Lindenschmit, Wilhelm, 1806–1848.
Die Raethsel der Vorwelt, oder Sind die Deutschen eigewendert? Mainz, Seifert, 1846.
86 s.

NL 0379955   PPG

VOLUME 334

Lindenschmitt, Wilhelm, 1829–
Schiller-Gallery, from the original drawings
see under Förster, Erwin.

LINDENSCHMITT, Wilhelm, painter. 1829–
Shakespeare und die englische Literatur. 1564–1864. [Photograph
von J. Albert. Mit Schlüssel.]
München, 1864. Text, folded leaf. 8°: Pl. 19 x 27½ inches.
Inserted in the volume of text is a clipping from the Athenæum, dated March 10
1864, describing the picture.
The photograph is kept in G. cabinet.

NL 0379957   MB

Lindenskov-Samuelsen, Georg.
...Sól og sirm; yrkingar.   Tórshavn: A/S Færø amtsti-
dendes bogtrykkeri, 1930.   31 p.   18½cm.

642608A. 1. Poetry, Faroese. I. Title.
                                              June 1, 1933

NL 0379958   NN MH

Lindenspür, Georg Ludwig,   respondent.
... Ad ordinationes politicas...
see under Besold, Christoph, Praeses.

Oepb0
639L
Lindenspür, Georg Ludwig
Trias discursuum. I. De arcanis imperii
monarchici, contra monarchomachos. II. Mo-
nita politica ad Avream bvllam Caroli IV.
Imp. III. Analysis pacis religionis. Auctore
Georgio Lvdovico Lindenspiro ... Ingolstadii,
typis Gregorii Haenlini, 1639.
17 p.ℓ., 615, [5] p. 13 cm.
Signatures:)(¹²')(()(⁶A–Ee¹²Dd⁶( )()(₆ and
V₁₂ blank).

1. Political science – Early works to 1800.

NL 0379960   CtY

Lindenstädt, Adalbert Joachim, 1910–
Die verlängerung der wahlperiode des deutschen reichstags und der deutschen landtage auf
dem wege der verordnung ... von Adalbert Joachim Lindenstädt ... Quakenbrück, C. Trute, 1933.
vi, 75 p., 1 l.   22cm.

Thesis, Freiburg i. Br.
"Literaturverzeichnis": p. 73–75.

1. Germany. Reichstag. 2. Germany – Constitutional law.

NL 0379961   NNC CtY PU MiU ICRL

LINDENSTÄDT, GEORG.
146 Bass-Etüden für Piano-Akkordeon. 146 bass
studies for piano-accordion. Leipzig, D. Rahter
[c1937] 75 p. 32cm. (Elite edition no. 927)

Title and explanatory text in German, French and English.

1. Accordion--Studies and exercises.

NL 0379962   NN

LINDENSTÄDT, GEORG.
Neue Piano-Akkordeon Schule.   Leipzig, A.J.,
Benjamin [c1931] 138 p. 31cm. (Elite edition, No. 695)

Title and text in German, English and French.

1. Accordion--Methods.   I. Title.

NL 0379963   NN

Lindenstead, Arthur.   650.942 Q500
H738   Sketches from commercial life in England. Preceded by an introductory sketch on the historical development of the city of
London, by Arthur Lindenstead, ... With 25 illustrations and
2 maps. Leipzig, Rengersche Buchhandlung, Gebhardt & Wilisch,
1905.
[4], 146, [2], 58 p. front., illus., 4 fold. pl., 1 fold. map, 1 fold. plan. 22cm.

NL 0379964   ICJ

Lindenstead, Arthur.   5586.113
Sketches from professional life in England.
— Marburg. Elwert. 1909. (4), 185, (1) pp. 23 cm., in 8s.
There are notes in German.

H3983 — T.r. — Professions. — England. Manners.

NL 0379965   MB

Lindenstead, Arthur.   396.048 L64
H738   .... Woman in domestic, social, and professional life: being
glimpses from woman's world. By Arthur Lindenstead, ...
Berlin, E. S. Mittler und Sohn, 1906.
iv, [2], 178 p. 20cm. (Sammlung von Lehrmitteln für Fach- und Fortbildungsschulen.)

NL 0379966   ICJ

PT2424
.I37I25
1875
Lindenstedt, Friedrich.
Das Märchen von den sieben Raben und der
treuen Schwester; eine Dichtung nach Moritz
von Schwind's gleichnamigem Bilde. Mit Titelbild, Initialen und Vignetten von Georg und
Theodor Schweissinger. 2. Aufl. Leipzig,
L. Zander, 1875.
64 p. illus. 28cm.

I. Title. II. Title: Die sieben Raben.
III. Schwind, Mori   tz, ritter von, 1804–
1871. Das Märchen   von den sieben Raben
und der treuen Schwester.

NL 0379967   OCU

Lindenstein (Louis) [1879–   ]. *Beitrag
zur Lehre von der Fütterungs-Tuberkulose
nebst 21 Fällen von primärer Darmtuberku-
lose aus dem path.-anat. Institut des Krankenhauses Friedrichshain, Berlin. 98 pp. 8°
Würzburg, F. Staudenraus, 1904.

NL 0379968   DNLM ICRL

Lindenstjerna, Wolf, Freiherr von Ceumern-
see Ceumern-Lindenstjerna, Wolf,
Freiherr,von, 1904–

LINDENSTRAUSS, ILSE.
On women's law in Israel. [Tel-Aviv, Women's
international Zionist organisation, Instruction and
information center] 1949. 29 p. 21cm.

1. Woman--Legal status--Israel (State). I. Women's international Zionist
organisation, Instruction and   information center.

NL 0379970   NN

Lindenstrauss, Leo: Die rechtliche Stellung der Staatsratsmitglieder.
[Maschinenschrift.] v, 75 S. 4°. — Auszug: Berlin 1923: Pincus.
2 Bl. 8°
Breslau, R.- u. staatswiss. Diss. v. 1. Mai 1923   [U 22.1000

NL 0379971   ICRL

Lindenstruth, Ernst Ludwig.
Marktformen und betriebliche Absatzpolitik; eine betriebswirtschaftliche Auseinandersetzung mit der Marktformen-
lehre. Winterthur, P. G. Keller, 1954.
115 p. 21 cm.
Issued also as thesis, Handelshochschule, St. Gall, Switzerland.
Bibliography: p. 110–115.

1. Competition. 2. Marketing. I. Title.

HB771.L5 1954   56–38479

NL 0379972   DLC NN

Lindenstruth, Otto
Untersuchungen über die bakteriziden Eigensch-
affen des Entozons gegenüber psychrophilen Keim-
en und seine Verwendbarkeit als Eiszusatzmittel
bei der Frischhaltung von Fischen.
Giessen, 1940.
Inaug. Diss. - Giessen

NL 0379973   CtY-M

Brll1
1
1910
Lindenstruth, Wilhelm, 1885–
Der Streit um das Busecker Tal. Ein Beitrag
zur Geschichte der Landeshoheit in Hessen ...
Giessen,1910.

Diss. - Giessen.
Lebenslauf.
"Erscheint als Sonderabdruck aus den Mitteilun-
gen des Oberhessischen Geschichtsvereins Bd.18.
Den zweiten Teil (nebst Anhang) wird der nächste
Band dieser Zeitschrift bringen."
Bibliographical foot-notes.

NL 0379974   CtY PU ICRL MH NN

624.42
L64c
Lindenthal, Gustav, 1850 - 1935.
— The continuous truss bridge over the Ohio
river at Sciotoville, Ohio, of the Chesapeake
and Northern Ohio railway ... with discussion by
Messrs. C. A. P. Turner, T. Kennard Thomson [and
others] [New York, 1922]
cover-title, p.[910]–975. plates, tables,
diagrs.(part fold.)
At head of t.-p.: American society of civil engineers.
"Reprinted from Transactions; vol.LXXXV, p.910
(1922)."

NL 0379975   IU

VOLUME 334

Lindenthal, Gustav, 1850-1935.
Multnomah County, Oregon, preliminary
plans for proposed new bridges over the
Willamette River at Portland, Oregon.
Author, 1925.

4 blue-prints.

NL 0379976   OrP

[Lindenthal, Gustav,] 1850-
The North River bridge; how to finance it, and who should
build it. [New York, 1918.] 14 p. 8°.

Signed: Gustav Lindenthal.

1. New York City—Bridges—North   river. 2. Title.
                                                    October 15, 1925

NL 0379977   NN

[Lindenthal, Gustav] 1850-
The proposed New York city terminal railroad, including North River bridge and grand terminal station
in New York city. [New York] Johnston print [1887]

cover-title, [4] p. 23½°°.

Signed: Gustave Lindenthal. New York ... 1887.
"This report is printed, not as a publication, but simply for convenience
of the promoters of the project and for their exclusive use."

1. Railroads—New York (City)   2. New York (City)—Bridges.

Library of Congress   TF308.N7L7   6-23505†

NL 0379978   DLC

Lindenthal, Gustav, 1850-
Railroad terminal plans as a part of the port problem
of New York; a study, by Gustav Lindenthal ... [New
York] 1919.

17 p. 23°°.

1. Railroads—New York (City)—Stations.   2. New York (City)—Har
bor.   3. [Railroads—Terminals—New York (City)]

                                                    A 19-595

Title from Bureau of   Railway Economics. Printed by L. C.

NL 0379979   DBRE

Lindenthal, Gustav, 1850-
A rational form of stiffened suspension bridge. By Gustav
Lindenthal... With discussion... [New York,] 1905.   93 p.,
5 fold. diagr., 1 pl.   illus. (incl. diagr.)   8°.

Cover-title.
Repr.: Amer. Soc. of Civil Engineers. Transac. v. 55.

1. Bridges (Suspension).
                                                    September 8, 1917.

NL 0379980   NN

Lindenthal, Gustav, 1850-1935
...Ross Island bridge, Portland, Oregon:
high level cantilever design, max.
clearance 123', general elevation.   diagr
New York, n. pub. 1924.

At head of title: Multnomah county,
Oregon.

NL 0379981   OrP

Lindenthal, Gustav, 1850-1935
...Sellwood bridge, Portland, Oregon:
general elevation & plan.   diagr.   n. pub.
1924.

At head of title: Multnomah county,
Oregon.

NL 0379982   OrP

Lindenthal, Gustav, 1850-1935.
... A sound scientific money system as cure for unemployment, by Gustav Lindenthal.   Original treatise written in
1922, revised in September, 1933.   Boston, The Stratford company [*1933]

51 p.   25°°.   (The Stratford booklets)

1. Currency question—U. S.   2. Money—U. S.   I. Title.   II. Title:
Money system.

Library of Congress   HG538.L63   34-8692

Copyright A 67423   332.40973

NL 0379983   DLC MB OC1

Lindenthal, Israel Levy.
The Sacred Scriptures in Hebrew
and English...   London, 1844-
see under   Bible. O. T. Hebrew.
1844.

770z   Lindenthal, Josef.
L744   ... Horaz und die römische dramatik, von professor Josef Lindenthal ... Oberhollabrunn,
M. Jordan, 1905.
25p.   23cm.
Program - K. K. Staats-gymnasium, Oberhollabrunn
(35. jahresbericht)

NL 0379985   CU MH PU CSt NjP

PA   Lindenthal, Josef.
6826   Ist das V. Buch der Aneis nach dem
L74   VI. geschrieben?   Oberhollabrunn, 1904.
30 p.   23cm.

Accompanies "Programm" (Jahres-Bericht)
--K. K. Staat -Gymnasium, Oberhollabrunn.

1. Vergilius Maro, Publius.   Aeneis--
Chronology of the books.

NL 0379986   NIC IU MH NjP CU

Lindenthal (Julius Alexend.) [1801-]. *De
diagnosi vulnerum thoracis quaedam.   53 pp.   8°.
*Berolini, formis Brüschebianis. 1826.

NL 0379987   DNLM

JC269   Lindenthal, Walther, 1886-   tr.
.B44   Berggrav, Eivind Josef, bp., 1884-
Der staat und der mensch.   Autorisierte übersetzung aus dem
norwegischen von Walter Lindenthal.   Stockholm, New York
[etc.] Neuer verlag [1947]

Lindenthal, Walter, 1886-
Ueber vorzeitige Loesung eines Hausarzt-
vertrages und deren rechtliche Folgen ...
[von] Walter Lindenthal ...   Berlin, G.
Buschhardt, 1911.

51 p.   22½cm.

Inaug.-Diss. - Heidelberg.
"Lebenslauf": p. 51.
"Literatur": p. 3-5.

NL 0379989   MH-L ICRL MH

Lindenthaler, Christine.
Die ferne höhe, eine sommergeschichte von Christine
Lindenthaler.   Mit bildschmuck von Frz. Kulstrunk.
Reichenberg, Gebrüder Stiepel [1923]

250 p.   19cm.

Vignettes.

I. Title.

Library of Congress   PT2623.I 58F4 1923   23-12324

NL 0379990   DLC

NA1036   Lindenthaler, Michael
S28.25   Deutsche Kirchenkunst in St. Wolfgang
W3   [Kurzgefasste Beschreibung von
L5   Konservat. Dr. Mich. Lindenthaler]
St. Wolfgang, S. Gastberger [192-?]
[14] p.   18cm.

Cover title.
German, English and French.

NL 0379991   MWiCA

Lindenwald, Hermann von Czetsch-
see
Czetsch-Lindenwald, Hermann von, 1901-

LD7251   Lindenwood college, St. Charles, Mo.
.S181a   Alumnae bulletin.
St. Charles, Mo., 1936.
1 v.   23 cm.

NL 0380001   DLC

Lindenwood college. St. Charles, Mo.
Alumnae directory ... 1918.

St. Charles, Mo. (Lindenwood college) 1918.
1 v. phot.   23 cm.   (Lindenwood
college vol. 87, Apr. 1918; no. 12.

NL 0380002   DHEW

Lindenwood college, Saint Charles, Mo.
Annual catalogue.   1858-

NL 0380003   NjP

Lindenwood college, *St. Charles, Mo.*
Annual register ... Lindenwood college for young ladies
...
St. Louis,
v. plates. 22½cm.

                                    CA 9-1513 Unrev'd

Library of Congress   LD7251.S18

NL 0380004   DLC

VOLUME 334

Lindenwood college, St. Charles, Mo.
  A book of views of Lindenwood college ...
(Jefferson City, Mo., Hugh Stephens press,
1922)
  48 pl. 28 x 20½ cm.

NL 0380005   DHEW

Lindenwood college, St. Charles, Mo.
  A book of views of Lindenwood college.
Founded 1827, St. Charles, Mo. (St. Charles
Mo., 1924.)
  (48) p. plates. 28 cm. (On verso of
cover: Lindenwood college, (bulletin) pt.2,
vol. 93. no.9.)

  Plates printed on both sides.

NL 0380006   DHEW

LD   Lindenwood College, St. Charles, Mo.
7251   Catalog.
.S134   St. Charles, Mo.
L742   (Its Bulletin v.130, no.11

NL 0380007   MiU

Lindenwood College, St. Charles, Mo.
  Linden leaves
        see under title

Lindenwood college, St. Charles, Mo.
  The newer Lindenwood, in commemoration
of the dedication of Roemer hall
        see under Templin, Lucinda de Leftwich.

Lindenwood Conference on International
  Relations, Lindenwood College, St. Charles,
  Mo., 1950
        see Conference on International Relations,
  Lindenwood College, 1950.

Lindeque, Barend Gerhardus, 1899–
  Afrikaanse taaloefeninge vir (i) Junior-sertifikaat "A" (ii)
Junior en senior-matriek "B" (iii) Laer en hoër taaleksamen.
Deur B. G. Lindeque ... 8. druk. Pretoria, J. L. van Schaik,
beperk, 1944.
  298, (1) p. 18ᶜᵐ.

  1. Afrikaans language—Composition and exercises.

New York. Public library   A 46–733
  for Library of Congress   PF861.L48 1944

NL 0380011   NN DLC

Lindeque, Lydia.
  Trek op die skerm. Pretoria, J.L. Van Schaik,
bepk., 1941.

  163 p. ports. 19.5 cm.

NL 0380012   MH

DA145 **Lindequist, Björn,** 1890–
.L7   Beiträge zur geschichte des römischen Britanniens ... Zü-
      rich, Gebr. Leemann & co., 1916.
        117, (1) p. 22ᶜᵐ.
        Inaug.-diss.—Zürich.
        Lebenslauf.
        "Literaturverzeichnis": p. (114)-117.

        1. Gt. Brit.—Hist.—Roman period, B. C. 55–A. D. 449.

NL 0380013   ICU ICRL

Lindequist (Carl Henrik). *Om fungus me-*
  dullaris. 50 pp. 8°. *Helsingfors, J. C. Frenckell*
  & Son, 1840.

NL 0380014   DNLM

Lindequist, Friedrich von, 1862–
  Deutsch-Ostafrika als siedelungsgebiet für Europäer,
unter berücksichtigung Britisch-Ostafrikas und Nyassa-
lands. Bericht der 1908 unter führung des damaligen
unterstaatssekretärs dr. von Lindequist nach Ostafrika
entsandten kommission ... München und Leipzig, Duncker & Humblot, 1912.
  ix, 114 p. fold. map. 23ᶜᵐ. (*Added t.-p.:* Schriften des Vereins für
  sozialpolitik. 147. bd., 1. t. Die ansiedelung von Europäern in den tropen.
  1. bd.)

  1. Africa, German East. 2. Africa, British East. 3. Nyasaland.

                                           13–14849

  Library of Congress   HB5.V4 vol. 147, pt. 1

NL 0380015   DLC IEN CtY CU ViU ICJ NN OU OO

Lindequist, (Friedrich) **von,** 1862–
  Die Kolonien. (Deutschland unter Kaiser Wilhelm II.
Berlin, 1914. 4°. Bd. 1, p. 415-449.)

  1. Colonies, etc. (German), 1888-1913.

                                    March 27, 1914.

NL 0380016   NN

Lindequist, Gustaf.
  Om riksdagen i Stockholm 1644.
  Inaug. diss. Upsala, 1857.

NL 0380017   ICRL

Lindequist, Olaf Carl Friedrich von, 1844–
  Gedenkblätter zur Rang-Liste des Kaiser Alexander
Garde-Grenadier-Regiments No.I. Berlin, 1884. [Berlin,
1884]

NL 0380018   MH

Lindqvist, Johan, 1823–1898.
  Om den norske qvægavl. Indberetning til
Departementet for det indre af Johan Lindeqvist.
Christiania, C. Grøndahl, 1857.

NL 0380019   CtY

Lindeqvist, Johan, 1823–1898.
  Optegnelser under en landbrugsreise gjennem det syd-
lige Norge i sommeren 1855, af Johan Lindeqvist ...
Christiania, Trykt hos C. Schibsted, 1856.
  28 p. 2 fold. pl. 21½ᶜᵐ.

  1. Agriculture—Norway.

                                           12–5709

  Library of Congress   S469.N9L74

NL 0380020   DLC CtY MH

Lindeqvist, K.O.
      see Lindeqvist, Kaarle Olavi.

Lindeqvist, Kaarle Olavi.
  Isonvihan aika Suomessa. Porvoo, W. Söderström (1919)
  727 p. fold. maps. 22 cm.
  Bibliographical footnotes.

      1. Finland—Hist. I. Title.

  DK457.L5   67–52296

NL 0380022   DLC

Lindeqvist, Kaarle Olavi
  Pikku vihan aika Suomessa, kirjoittanut K.O.
Lindeqvist. Hämeenlinnassa, Hämeen sanomain
osakeyhtiön kirjapaino, 1889
  65, xxiv p.

NL 0380023   MH

Lindeqvist, K. O.
  Suomen historia. Porvoossa, [1906]
  471 p. illus. map.

NL 0380024   WaS

LINDEQVIST, K. O.
  Suomen historia. 2. painos. Porvoossa,
W. Söderström [1916] xv, 491 p. illus., ports. 26cm.

  1. Finland—Hist.

NL 0380025   NN

Lindeqvist, K. O.
  Suomen historia, kirj. K. O. Lindeqvist. 3. painos. Porvoo, W. Söderström (1926)
  xvi, 558 p. illus., maps, ports. 26 cm.

  1. Finland—Hist. I. Title.

  DK451.L6 1926   67–52620

NL 0380026   DLC

Lindeqvist, K. O.
  Suomen oloista ison vihan aikana.
  Inaug. diss. Helsingfors, 1886.

NL 0380027   DLC

Lindeqvist, Kaarle Olavi
  Yleinen historia; vanha aika, kirjoittanut K.O.
Lindeqvist. Tampere, Wesanderin kirjakauppa, Arnold
Carnberg [1900]
  [1]–144 p.
  HCL copy imperfect: all after p. 144 wanting

NL 0380028   MH

VOLUME 334

Lindeqvist, K. O.
Yleinen historia.
Porvoossa, Soderstrom, 1902.
2 v.

NL 0380029   OC1

Lindeqvist, Kaarle Olavi
Yleinen historia, Kirjoittamut K.O.Lindeqvist. Porvoossa, Söderström [1903-05]

2 v. illus.
Contents: 1.Vanha- ja Keski-aika.- 2.Uusi aika

1. History

NL 0380030   MH WaS

LINDER,
Catalogue de livres la plupart rares et curieux de feu M. Linder, dont la vente aura lieu le lundi 20 novembre, et les 7 jours suivants, maison Silvestre par le ministere de Me Levillain. Paris, François, 1865.
187p. 23cm.

Bookplate: Bibliotheca Lindesiana.

NL 0380031   ICN

---

*PS
509
B3L64h

Linder, A   Carl
Hurricane; a spectacle for Antonin Artaud. [Flint? Mich.]
Printed at Fenian Head Centre Press [19--]
broadside. 41 x 14cm.

Poem.

NL 0380032   CLU

Linder, Åke.
Tall oil refining. Stockholm, Generalstabens litografiska anstalts förlag, 1952.
56 p. illus. 25 cm. (Ingenjörsvetenskapsakademiens handlingar, nr. 207)

Includes summary.
Bibliography: p. 52-56.

1. Wood-oil.   I. Title.   (Series: Ingenjörsvetenskapsakademien, Stockholm. Handlingar, nr. 207)
[TA4.I 43 nr. 207]   A 52-9947

Iowa. State Coll. Lib. for Library of Congress

NL 0380033   IaAS NN DNAL OU

Linder, Albert, 1901-
L330.53 n.s.
B39 v.2
Die schweizerischen Grossbanken, von Dr. Albert Linder.
Bern, Stämpfli & cⁱᵉ, 1927.
x, 242 p. incl. tables. 25½ᶜᵐ. (Added t.-p.: Beiträge zur schweizerischen Wirtschaftskunde ... Neue Folge, 2. Heft)
Another copy, issued as the author's inaugural dissertation, Basel, has call number L378.494 BaO1 1926
"Literatur- und Quellennachweis": p. vii-ix.

NL 0380034   ICJ NNUW CtY NN PU ICRL MiU MH

ML647
.L74
1954

Linder, Alf, 1907-
Preludiering. vid Alf Linder och Ingemar Gabrielsson. Stockholm, Nordiska Musikförlaget [1954]
49p. music. 28cm.

1. Organ music--Hist. & crit. 2. Organs--Canons, fugues, etc. I. Gabrielsson, Ingemar, joint author. II. Title.

NL 0380035   IEG

Linder, Alfred.
...Kunstseide; Wissenswertes für den Textil-Fachmann und Kaufmann. Basel: B. Wepf & Cie., 1930. 53 p. incl. diagrs., tables. illus. (incl. port.) 2. ed. 8°.

567961A. 1. Silk, Artificial.   February 2, 1932

NL 0380036   NN

•Linder, Alfred, 1853-
[Enselmino, of Treviso, 14th cent., supposed author.
Plainte de la Vierge en vieux vénitien; texte critique précédé d'une introduction linguistique et littéraire, par Alfred Linder ... Upsala, Impr. E. Berling, 1898.

Linder, Andreas, respondent.
... Dissertationis historicae, de liturgia...
see under   Arrhenius, Laurentius, 1680-1730, praeses.

Linder, Ane Gurli (Peterson)
see   Linder, Gurli, 1865-1947.

Linder, Anna.
Vårt psalmboksarv; det svenska fromhetslivets urgamla vårdträd, av Anna Linder... Uppsala: J. A. Lindblad [1934]
160 p. 21½cm.

763176A. 1. Hymns, Swedish—Hist.   August 5, 1935

NL 0380040   NN

D610
Z81
Box 68

Linder, Armin, 1914-
Didaktische behandlung störungstheoretischer fragen. Biel, Graphische anstalt Schüler, 1944.
19 p. diagrs.

Thesis, Bern.
Bibliography: p. 19.

NL 0380041   NNC CtY

Linder, Arthur, 1904-
Methoden zur berechnung von volkssterbetafeln ...
Bern, 1934. 85 p.
Inaug. Diss. - Bern, 1934.
Lebenslauf.
Bibliography.

NL 0380042   ICRL PU CtY

Linder, Arthur, 1904-
Planen und Auswerten von Versuchen; eine Einführung für Naturwissenschafter, Mediziner und Ingenieure. Basel, Birkhäuser, 1953.
182 p. illus. 25 cm. (Lehrbücher und Monographien aus dem Gebiete der exakten Wissenschaften. Reihe der experimentellen Biologie, Bd. 13)
Bibliography: p. 171-172.

1. Experimental design. I. Title.

KyU
NL 0380043   CtY IEN OrU NIC MBdAF ICJ DNLM PU OU

Linder, Arthur, 1904-
Statistische methoden für naturwissenschafter, mediziner und ingenieure, von Arthur Linder ... Basel, Birkhäuser [1945]
150 p. diagrs. 24½ᶜᵐ. (Half-title: Lehrbücher und monographien aus dem gebiete der exakten wissenschaften, 6. Mathematische reihe, bd. III)
"Literaturverzeichnis": p. 185-186.

1. Statistics.
Library of Congress   HA29.L76   46-18542
                                    311.2

NL 0380044   DLC PPCP NBC CtY NcD CU OU OrCS OrU

Linder, Arthur, 1904-
Statistische Methoden für Naturwissenschafter, Mediziner, und Ingenieure. 2., erweiterte Aufl. Basel, Birkhäuser, 1951.
288 p. illus. 25 cm. (Lehrbücher und Monographien aus dem Gebiete der exakten Wissenschaften. Mathematische Reihe, Bd. 3)

1. Statistics.   I. Title.
HA29.L76 1951   311.2   51-35103 ‡

NL 0380045   DLC NjP ICJ TxU DNAL NcD

M
1734
.L74
19--

Linder, August,   comp.
Deutsche Weisen; die beliebtesten Volks- und geistlichen Lieder für Klavier mit vollständigem Text. Neue, verb.Aufl. Stuttgart, A.Auer's Musikverlag [19--?] Pl.no.A.30 A.
271 p. 28 cm.

1.Song-books, German. I.Title.

NL 0380046   MiU

943
Ref.85
L744z
L745jo

LINDER, August Gottlieb
Johannes Linder; Lebensbild eines Predigers der Basler Kirche aus der ersten Haelfte dieses Jahrhunderts. Nach dessen Briefen und Tagebuechern geschildert von August Gottlieb Linder. Basel, Bahnmaier (C. Detloff), 1880.
viii, 320p. front. (port.) 22.5cm.

NL 0380047   MH-AH CtY

Linder, Béla.
JX1974
L744
Kell-e katona? A militarizmus csödje. Tanulmány a leszerelésröl, irta Linder Béla. Budapest, Lantos A. Bizománya [1919]
111,[1] p. 21ᶜ.

1.Armies. 2.Disarmament. 3.Austria - Army. 4.Hungary - Army. 5.Hungary - Hist. - Revolution - 1918   -1919. I.Title.

NL 0380048   CSt-H

VOLUME 334

Linder, C   E
The salutary relation between Christian
doctrine and Christian life, Rev. C.E. Linder.
Columbus, Ohio, The Lutheran Book Concern, n.d.
32 p

NL 0380049   NRCR

QC278
.L5   Linder, C   T
1950
The measurement of low temperatures.
East Pittsburgh, Westinghouse Research
Laboratories [1950]
26 p., 27-   20 diagrs. 28cm. (Research
report R-944   -A)
Includes   graphies.

1. Low temperature research. I. Title. II.
Ser.

NL 0380050   ViU NNC NIC NN

Linder, Carl Alfred

see

Linder, Alfred, 1853-

---

ar V
11237   Linder, Carl Wilhelm, 1825-1882.
Carmina Latina. Upsaliae, Wahlstroem,
1855.
54 p. 19cm.

"Carmina poetarum graecorum latine
reficta": p. [3]-15.

1. Latin poetry, Medieval and modern.

NL 0380052   NIC PU

---

ar W
14354   Linder, Carl Wilhelm, 1825-1882.
De rerum dispositione apud Antiphontem
et Andocidem oratores Atticos commentatio.
Upsaliae, Acad. Typographus, 1859.
87 p. 22cm.

1. Antiphon, orator. 2. Andocides.

NL 0380053   NIC MH OCU PBm CU NjP DLC

---

17   Linder, Carl Wilhelm, 1825-1882.
De vi et ratione ... ex novo testamento
repetenda. Commentaio theologica. Lundae,
H. Ohlsson, 1866.
47 p. 8°.

NL 0380054   DLC

---

f792.0938   Linder, Carl Wilhelm, 1825-1882.
L744d   Dionysos-Theatern i Athen. Om re-
sultaterna af de senast anställda gräf-
ningarna å platsen för Dionysos-Theatern
i Athen. Stockholm, I.Marcus, 1865.
24p. plates. 30cm.

"Ur Tidskrift för Byggnadskonst och
Ingeniörvetenskap."

1.Athens.   Theater of Dionysus.

NL 0380055   CLSU NNC CtY

Linder, Carl Wilhelm, 1825-1882, ed.
Hyper Euxenippou eisangelias apologia ...
see under   Hyperides.

Linder, Carl Wilhelm, 1825-1882.
Ὑπερ Ξου Hyperidis oratoris Attici
pro Euxenippo in Polyeuctum oratio.
Upsaliae, 1856.

17 p.

NL 0380057   PU

Linder, Carl Wilhelm, 1825-1882.
Några ord om skolfrågan i Norden, af C. W. Linder ...
Stockholm, Tryckt hos A. L. Norman, 1868.
1 p. l., 47, [1] p. 22cm. [With Pedagogisk tidskrift, Stockholm, 1868.
v. 4]

"Aftryck ur Nordisk tidskrift."
Supplement to v. 4 of Pedagogisk tidskrift.

1. Education—Sweden. 2. Education—Norway.   i. Pedagogisk tidskrift. Supplement.

26-10432

Library of Congress   L46.P35   vol. 4

NL 0380058   DLC

LINDER, C[arl] W[ilhelm], 1825-1882.
Om Grekernes theater och skådespel; föreläsningar hållna i Stockholm under vintern.1864-
1865. Stockholm, P.A. Norstedt & söner,1865.

Diagrs.   Class 1568.65

NL 0380059   MH

PA445   Linder, Carl Wilhelm, 1825-1882.
.S9L7   Svenskt-Grekiskt lexikon. Utgifvet af C. W.
Linder och C. A. Walberg. Upsala, Lundequistska
Bokhandeln [1862]
535 p.

1. Swedish language--Dictionaries--Greek.

NL 0380060   ICU

Q67
S404   Linder, Charles, 1879-   comp.

Schweizerische Naturforschende Gesellschaft.
Bibliographie der Schweizerischen Naturforschenden Gesellschaft, 1931-1940. Verhandlungen, Nekrologe, Denk-
schriften. Bern, Buchdr. Büchler, 1944.

Linder (Christoph). *Lues congenita unter
dem Bilde einer hereditären Ataxie (Fried-
reich-Marie) verlaufend. [Basel.] 23 pp.
8°. Berlin, S. Karger, 1922.

NL 0380062   DNLM CtY ICRL

620.69   Linder, Clarence H.
L744f   The future of the professions:
engineering and applied science.
New York, General Electric Co.,
Public Relations Services Division, 1954
18p. illus. 23 x 10cm.

1.Engineering as a profession.
I.General Electric Company.

NL 0380063   CLSU PPD

Linder, Conraad Burger.
Christelikheid en nasionalisme in die opvoeding. Johannesburg, Afrikaanse Pers-Boekhandel, 1946.
181 p. 19 cm.

1. Church and education in Africa, South. 2. National socialism.
I. Title.
LC433.S6L5   55-35359 ‡

NL 0380064   DLC

Linder, David Hunt.
—— Botanical report of Liberia. [Cambridge. 1930.]
1. 8°. Map and other illustr.
"Reprinted from the Report of the Harvard-African expedition upon
the African republic of Liberia and the Belgian Congo," pp. 513-568.

NL 0380065   MH-A

LINDER, David H[unt].
The development of certain helicosporic fungi
Imperfecti in relation to environmental condi-
tions and to classification. [Dissertation,
Harvard University], 1926.

Typewritten. 1.8°. ff. (3), 98†. Plates and
charts.
"Bibliography", at end.
"Summary", in pocket,at end.

NL 0380066   MH

Linder, David Hunt.
Lichens. 1934.
(California academy of sciences,
San Francisco. Proceedings, v. 21, # 18)

NL 0380067   OrU

Linder, David Hunt.
... Marine fungi
see under   Barghoorn, Elso Sterrenberg,
1915-

QK
625   Linder, David Hunt.
M74   A monograph of the helicosporous Fungi im-
L74   perfecti [by] David H.Linder ... [St.Louis,
1929]
cover-title,227-388 p.   illus.(incl.charts)
pl.12-31. 24 cm.

"Reprinted from Annals of the Missouri
botanical garden 16: 227-388. September 1929."

1.Helicosporium.

NL 0380069   MiU ICarbS NcU

VOLUME 334

F386
.C64
1955

Linder, Dorothy A., joint author.

Clark, Joseph Lynn, 1881–
The story of Texas, by Joseph L. Clark ₍and₎ Dorothy A. Linder. With maps and pencil drawings by E. M. Schiwetz. Boston, Heath ₍ᶜ1955₎

Linder, E.
Der interkonfessionelle religionsunterricht in der schule. Vortrag, gehalten am 23. oktober 1884 im Freisinnigen schulverein, von E. Linder ... ₍n. p., 1884?₎
16 p. 20½ᶜᵐ.
Caption title.

1. Church and education—Switzerland.   I. Title.

E 12–734

Library, U. S. Bur. of   Education   LC116.S9L6

NL 0380071   DHEW

Linder, Edward.
Spoils of marriage, by Edward Linder, L. L. B. ₍and₎ Nathan Goldberg ... Los Angeles, Calif., Publix publishing co. ₍ᶜ1931₎
285 p. 20½ᶜᵐ.

I. Goldberg, Nathan, joint author.   II. Title.

32–769

Library of Congress   PZ3.L646258p

NL 0380072   DLC

Linder, Erik.
...Den svenska mekaniska verkstadsindustriens utveckling intill krigsutbrottet; utredning verkställd på uppdrag av Tull- och traktatkommittén, av Erik Linder. Stockholm, 1923. iv, 435 p. incl. tables. illus. (charts.) 8°. (Sweden. Statens offentliga utredningar. 1923. ₍nr.₎ 31.)

At head of title: Tull- och traktatkommitténs utredningar och betänkanden XVIII.

1.̓ Iron—Manufacture—Sweden.   2. Machinery—Trade and stat.—
Sweden. 3. Ser.
October 6, 1928

NL 0380073   NN MH-L

Linder, Erik, *1891–*
Snedögd terror, Sumatra i krigstid. Stockholm, H. Geber ₍1946₎
174 p. 21 cm.

1. World War, 1939–1945—Sumatra. 2. World War, 1939–1945—
Personal narratives, Swedish.   I. Title.

D767.7.L5   52–51393 ‡

NL 0380074   DLC NN NIC

Linder, Erik Hjalmar, 1906–
... England hösten 1942, reportage från en resa. Stockholm, Saxon & Lindström ₍1942₎
144 p. plates, ports. 21½ᶜᵐ.
At head of title: Erik Hj. Linder.
"Huvudparten av dess innehåll består av artiklar, som under oktober ₍1942₎ publicerades i Svenska morgonbladet."—p. ₍5₎

1. World war, 1939–1945—Gt. Brit.   I. Title.

₍Full name: Gustaf Erik Hjalmar Linder₎
44–9432 Revised

Library of Congress   DA587.L5
₍r46c2₎   940.5342

NL 0380075   DLC NN

Linder, Erik Hjalmar, 1906–
Fyra decennier av nittonhundratalet. Stockholm, Natur och Kultur ₍1952₎
xx, 814 p. illus., facsims. (part fold.)
(Ny illustrerad svensk litteraturhistoria. v. 5)

Bibliography: p. 739–775.

1. Swedish literature - 20th cent. - Hist. and crit. I. Tit

NL 0380076   NNC

Linder, Erik Hjalmar, 1906–
Guds pennfäktare och andra essayers. Stockholm, Natur och kultur ₍1955₎
194 p. 20 cm.
CONTENTS.—Från Dante till Graham Greene.—Dostojevskij och vi.—Guds pennfäktare.—T. S. Eliot och mognaden.—Mörker och ljus hos Mauriac.—Graham Green, en kättersk ortodox.—Från Strindberg till Lars Ahlin. — Sven Lidmans förvandlingar. — Barabbas och de stora symbolerna.—Inte ett altare i vanlig bemärkelse.—Religion hos Olle Hedberg.—Gunnar Edman.—Lars Ahlin och Fromma mord.—Efterskrift.

1. Literature—Addresses, essays, lectures.   I. Title.
Full name: Gustaf Erik Hjalmar Linder
A 56–981

Illinois. Univ. Library
for Library of Congress

NL 0380077   IU WaU NN CU

Linder, Erik Hjalmar, 1906–
... Hjalmar Bergman, en profilteckning. Stockholm, A. Bonnier ₍1940₎
233 p. 19¼ᶜᵐ.
At head of title: Erik Hj. Linder.
Bibliography : p. 223–224.

1. Bergman, Hjalmar Fredrik Elgerus, 1883–1931.
₍Full name: Gustaf Erik Hjalmar Linder₎
42–145 Revised
Library of Congress   PT9875.B53Z7

NL 0380078   DLC MnU CtY

Linder, Erik Hjalmar, 1906–
Hjalmar Bergmans ungdom, liv och diktning till och med 1910. Stockholm, Bonnier, 1942.
407 p. 22 cm.
Akademisk avhandling—Stockholms högskola.
"Otryckta källor" : p. 388–389.
"Bibliografi" : p. 393–398.

1. Bergman, Hjalmar Fredrik Elgerus, 1883–1931.
Full name: Gustaf Erik Hjalmar Linder.
PT9875.B53Z72   53–52510

NL 0380079   DLC NcD PU NNC TxU CU

Linder, Erik Hjalmar, 1906–
Hjalmar Bergmans ungdom; liv och diktning til och med 1910. Stockholm, A. Bonnier ₍1942₎

407 p. ports. 22cm.

"Bibliografi": p. 393–398.

1. Bergman, Hjalmar Fredrik Elgerus, 1883–1931.

NL 0380080   MnU MH ICU NIC NcU

Linder, Erik Hjalmar, 1906–
Hjalmar Gullberg, av Erik Hjalmar Linder...   Stockholm, P. A. Norstedt & söner ₍1946₎ 43 p. 20cm.
Works of Hjalmar Gullberg, p. ₍44₎

1. Gullberg, Hjalmar, 1898–
February 27, 1950

NL 0380081   NN MH WaU CU MnU

Linder, Erik Hjalmar, 1906–   *ed.*
I Närke; prosa och poesi. ₍Redaktion: Erik Hj. Linder och Lennart Berglund. Stockholm, Forum ₍1954₎
192 p. illus. 19 cm.

1. Närke, Sweden, in literature. 2. Swedish literature (Collections)
I. Berglund, Lennart, joint ed. II. Title.
Full name: Gustaf Erik Hjalmar Linder.
A 55–4974

Minnesota. Univ. Libr.
for Library of Congress

NL 0380082   MnU WU

Linder, Erik Hjalmar, 1906–

PT9260
.S4
1926

Schück, Henrik, 1855–1947.
Illustrerad svensk litteraturhistoria, av Henrik Schück och Karl Warburg. 3., fullständigt omarb. uppl., utg. av Henrik Schück. Stockholm, H. Geber ₍1926–49₎

380.9485
L643

Linder, Erik Hjalmar, 1906–
Jämförande undersökning rörande allmän och enskild affärsverksamhet i Sverige. På begäran av Internationella handelskammaren verkställd genom försorg av Svenska nationalkommissionen. Stockholm, K.L. Beckmans boktr., 1929.

129 p. tables 24cm.
1. Sweden. Commerce. I. International Cham -ber of Commerce.
Swedish
National Committee.

NL 0380084   MnU

IC32
pam

Linder, Erik Hjalmar, 1906–
... Kristet kulturarbete i vår tid; föredrag vid Fria Kristna riksmötet i Stockholm den 16 mars 1950. Stockholm,Gummessons bokförlag ₍1950₎
29,₍1₎p. 20cm. (On cover: Focus)

NL 0380085   NNUT

Linder, Erik Hjalmar, 1906–
Mänskligt och kristet; litterära betraktelser, mer eller mindre. Uppsala, J.A. Lindblad ₍1940₎

179 p. 21cm.

NL 0380086   MnU

WC
11822

Linder, Erik Hjalmar, 1906–
Möte med Indien. [Stockholm]Rabén & Sjögren [1954]

1. India - Descr. & trav. - 1950–1975.

NL 0380087   CtY NN

PT9260
.N9

Linder, Erik Hjalmar, 1906–

Ny illustrerad svensk litteraturhistoria. ₍Huvudredaktör, E. N. Tigerstedt₎ Stockholm, Natur och kultur ₍1955–58₎

VOLUME 334

Linder, Erik Hjalmar, 1906–
Religiöst minimum. Stockholm, Wahlström & Widstrand ₁1945₎
239 p. 22 cm.

1. Civilization, Christian. ɪ. Title.
Full name: Gustaf Erik Hjalmar Linder.

BR115.C5L48   52–64557

NL 0380089   DLC

Linder, Erik Hjalmar, 1906–   supposed author.
Snedögd terror
     see under   Linder, Erik, 1891–

Linder, Erik Hjalmar, 1906–
Sommarresa till diktens städer. Med teckningar av Gunnar Brusewitz. ₁Malmö₎ Allhem ₁1955₎
106 p. illus. 24 cm.

1. Sweden—Descr. & trav. 2. Sweden in literature. ɪ. Title.
Full name: Gustaf Erik Hjalmar Linder.

Minnesota. Univ. Libr   A 56–6437
for Library of Congress

NL 0380091   MnU WaU

PT9275   Linder, Erik Hjalmar, 1906–
L5   Stenarna där barn jag lekt, och andra
studier och käserier. Stockholm, Jonson &
Winter ₁1942₎
256 p. illus.

1. Swedish literature – 20th cent. – Hist.
& crit. I. Title.

NL 0380092   CU NcD MH MnU

Linder, Erik Hjalmar, 1906–
... Sveriges neutralitetspolitik, fakta och dokument, av Erik Hj. Linder. Stockholm ₁Kooperativa förbundets bokförlag₎ 1943.
63 p. 19ᶜᵐ. (Världspolitikens dagsfrågor, 1943, nr. 1–2 ... Utrikespolitiska institutets broschyrserie)

1. World war, 1939–1945—Sweden. 2. Sweden—Neutrality.
₁*Full name:* Gustaf Erik Hjalmar Linder₎
46–17494

Library of Congress   D754.S8L5

NL 0380093   DLC CtY WaU

Linder, Ernest Gustaf, 1902–
The dissociation of water in the glow discharge ... by Ernest Gustaf Linder ... ₁Minneapolis, 1931₎
cover-title, p. 679–692. 1 illus., diagrs. 25½ᶜᵐ.
Thesis (ᴘʜ. ᴅ.)—Cornell university, 1931.
From Physical review, v. 38, no. 4, Aug. 15, 1931.

1. Dissociation. 2. Electric discharges through gases. 3. Water.
—— Copy 2. S.
Library of Congress   QD561.L5 1931   32–14742
          541.39

NL 0380094   DLC CU OU NIC

Linder, Ernst, 1868– *1943*
Efter sexton år; en återblick på mitt deltagande i Finlands frihetskrig ₁av₎ Ernst Linder. Stockholm: V. Pettersons bokindustriaktiebolag, 1935. 357 p. incl. tables. charts, 3 maps, plates, port. 25½cm.
Maps in pocket.

837360A. 1. Finland—Hist.—Revo-   lution, 1917–1918. I. Title.
                         September 29, 1936

NL 0380095   NN CSt-H

Linder, Ernst, 1868–
Från Finlands frihetskrig, av Ernst Linder... Stockholm: P. A. Norstedt & Söner ₁1920₎. 231 p. maps, plates, port. 8°.

1. European war, 1914– .—Cam-   paigns, East. 2. Finland.—History.
1918.   May 31, 1922.

NL 0380096   NN CSt-H

Linder, Ernst, 1868–
Kring Finlands andra frihetskrig; strödda minnen från min verksamhet. Stockholm, Norstedt [1942]

NL 0380097   MH

4DK   Linder, Ernst, 1868–
Fin   Kuudentoista vuoden takaa;
284   katsaus toimintaani Suomen Vapaussodassa. Suomentanut Kapteeni S. Frey. Helsingissä, Kustannusosakeyhtiö Otava [1936]
        343 p.

NL 0380098   DLC-P4

DK 459   LINDER, ERNST, 1868–
.L 745   Muistelmia Suomen vapaussodasta. Suomentanut Kalle Väänänen. Helsingissä, Otava ₁1921₎
        312 p. illus., maps.

NL 0380099   InU CSt-H

Linder, Ernst, 1868– *1943*
Problemet Sverige—Finland; några uttalanden, av Ernst Linder. Andra upplagan. ₁Stockholm: Distribution: Seelig & c:o, 1939₎ 55 p. 22½cm.

Reprinted from Aftonbladet 3/10, 1920, 6/12, 1927.

1. Sweden—For. rel.—Finland.   2. Finland—For. rel.—Sweden.
                                    May 2, 1941

NL 0380100   NN MH

E168   Linder, Estrid.
1917l   Tretton kapitel om en lucklig resa; Amerika, Japan, Kina, Sibirien. Andra upplagan. Stockholm, A. Bonniers Förlag. ₁1920₎
        299 p. illus. 23cm.

        Includes music (p.62)

NL 0380101   MnHi

Linder, Estrid.
Tretton kapitel om en lycklig resa; Amerika, Japan, Kina, Sibirien, av Estrid Linder. Stockholm: A. Bonnier ₁1920₎. 299 p., 1 l. illus. (incl. ports.) 2. ed. 8°.

1. Voyages and travels, 1900–
                                 November 8, 1920.

NL 0380102   NN

1926   **Linder, Evald**
L1x26t   The troubadour, and other poems. [1st ed.] New York, Poets Press ₁c1941₎
      48 p. 22 cm.

NL 0380103   RPB NN

Linder, Felix.
Technik im Haus; was man in der Wohnung, Haus und Garten selber reparieren, installieren und werken kann, von Felix Linder ... Wien, Humboldt-Verlag ₁1948₎ viii, 151 p. illus. 19cm.

479240B. 1. Repairing. 2. Receipts.
                                 April 18, 1949

NL 0380104   NN

Linder, Felix.
Technik im Haus; was man in der Wohnung, Haus und Garten selber reparieren, installieren und werken kann. Zürich, Fraumünster-Verlag ₁°1948₎
viii, 151 p. diagrs. 19 cm.

1. Repairing. ɪ. Title.

TT151.L6   50–31866

NL 0380105   DLC DNAL InU

Judaica   Linder, Fintanus, 1725–1785.
Fme20   P. Fintani Linderi ... Opus grammaticum
755L: ebraeum ad solidam s. linguae intelligentiam methodo analytica ducens; cui accedit Lexicon ebraeo-latinum ad Genesin ... Ulmae, Impensis Johannis Conradi Wohleri, 1755.
      2p.l., [iii]-lxii p., 4l., 288, 159p. 18cm.

NL 0380106   CtY

PJ 4563   Linder, Fintanus, 1725–1785.
L55   ... Opus Grammaticum Ebraeum ad
1756   solidam S. Linguae intelligentiam methodo analytica ducens; cui accedit Lexicon Ebraeo-Latinum ad Genesin ... Ulmae, Impensis Johannis Conradi Wohleri, 1756.
      lxii, 288, 159 p. 18 cm.
      Lexicon Ebraeo-Latinum ad Genesin has special title page and is separately paged.

      1. Hebrew language—Grammar
2. Hebrew language—Dictionaries—Latin. I. Title II. Title: Lexicon Ebraeo-Latinum ad Genesin.

NL 0380107   OU

PJ4563   Linder, Fintanus, 1725–1785.
.L74   Sonnenfelsii Lapis Lydius cum Opere grammatico Ebraeo Fintani Linderi collisus, ac comminutus ... curante ejusdem operis auctore. Ulmae, Impensis J. C. Wohleri, 1758.
      121 p. (With his Opus grammaticum Ebraeum)

      1. Sonnenfels, Alois, d. 1768.

NL 0380108   ICU

VOLUME 334

Linder, Folke Fritiof, 1904–
Contributions to the morphology and the taxonomy of the Branchiopoda Anostraca. Uppsala, Almqvist & Wiksells boktr., 1941.

104–302 p. illus. 26 cm.

Cover title.
Inaug.-diss.—Uppsala.
Title page, with thesis statement, inserted.
"Reprinted from Zoologiska bidrag från Uppsala. Band 20."
"References": p. [297]–302.

1. Anostraca.

QL395.8.A5L5   595.323   49–38240*

NL 0380109   DLC CtY NNC IU

Q11
U55
v.102
no.3291
Linder, Folke Fritiof, 1904–
Contributions to the morphology and taxonomy of the Branchiopoda Notostraca, with special reference to the North American species. Washington, D. C., 1952.
69 p. illus., plates, diagrs., tables. 25 cm. (U.S. National Museum. Proceedings, v. 102, no. 3291).
Cover title.
"Literature cited": p. 66–69.

1. Branchiopoda.   (Series).

NL 0380110   DI

S22
0641
25
Linder, Folke Fritiof, 1904–
... Über Nebaliopsis typica G.O.Sars, nebst einigen allgemeinen Bemerkungen über die leptostraken ... Copenhagen, C.A.Reitzel; [etc., etc.]1943.
38p. illus.(incl.map)plate. 31½cm. (The Carlsberg foundation's oceanographical expedition round the world 1928–30 and previous "Dana"-expeditions ... Dana-report no.25)
"Literaturverzeichnis": p.37.

NL 0380111   CtY CU

WB
7
qL744
LINDER, Forrest Edward, 1906–
[Collection of papers]
The Library has a collection of miscellaneous papers by this author kept as received. These papers are not listed or bound separately.

NL 0380112   DNLM

Linder, Forrest Edward, 1906–
... Manual de estadística vital, con un prólogo del dr. Rafael Schiaffino ... Montevideo, Ministerio de salud pública, 1942.

cover-title, xiii, 72 p., 3 l. incl. tables, forms. 26ᶜᵐ.

On cover: Reprinted by Bureau of the census, Division of vital statistics, Washington, D. C.
"[Traducido] por el br. Adolfo Morales."—p. xii.
"Bibliografía": 1st leaf at end.

1. Vital statistics.   I. U. S. Bureau of the census.   II. Uruguay. Ministerio de salud pública.   III. Morales, Adolfo, tr.

          44–427
Library of Congress   HB881.L5
          312

NL 0380113   DLC CU-S NIC NNUN

Linder, Forrest Edward, 1906–

U. S. *Bureau of the census.*
... Sixteenth census of the United States: 1940. Vital statistics rates in the United States, 1900–1940. By Forrest E. Linder, assistant chief statistician for vital statistics and Robert D. Grove, social science analyst. Prepared under the supervision of Halbert L. Dunn, M. D., chief statistician for vital statistics. Washington, U. S. Govt. print. off., 1943.

HA201
1940
.A573
Linder, Forrest Edward, 1906–

U. S. *Bureau of the Census.*
Las tasas demográficas en los Estados Unidos de América, 1900–1940. Traducción española de los capítulos I a IV del volumen inglés Vital statistics rates in the United States, 1900–1940, by Forrest E. Linder and Robert D. Grove. Washington, Instituto Interamericano de Estadística, Unión Panamericana [1950]

HA201
1940
.A57
Linder, Forrest Edward, 1906–

U. S. *Bureau of the Census.*
Vital statistics rates in the United States, 1900–1940, by Forrest E. Linder, assistant chief statistician for vital statistics and Robert D. Grove, social science analyst. Washington, U. S. Govt. Print. Off., 1943.

PT
3825
L5
Linder, Franz.
Aus den hohen Tauern; tiroler Volkssagen, von Fr. Linder. Mit Bildern von Hugo Grimm. Innsbruck, Verlagsanstalt Tyrolia [1925]
350p.

1. Tales, Austrian—Tyrol.   I. Title.

NL 0380117   UU ICN ICarbS MH OC1

Linder (Franz). *Ein Fall von Narbenstenose und Membranbildung im Kehlkopf nach O'Dwyer'scher Intubation.* [Wurtzburg.] 38 pp. 8°. München, A. Gradinger, 1897.

NL 0380118   DNLM ICRL

Linder (Franz) [1885–]. *Ueber Hydrops foetus.* 23 pp., 2 pl. 8°. München, Kastner & Callwev. 1913.

NL 0380119   DNLM PPWi CtY

Linder, Franz, 1902–
Das spanische markt- und börsenwesen unter besonderer berücksichtigung der ferias und lonjas ... Berlin und Bonn, F. Dümmler [1929?]
4 p.l., 118 p. 25ᶜᵐ.
Inaug.-diss.—Würzburg.
Lebenslauf.
"Literaturangabe": p.115–118.

1. Stock exchange—Spain.

NL 0380120   MiU NN PU MH ICRL CtY

TF28
.U5
1947
Linder, Fred E.

U. S. *Railway Mission in Mexico.*
The United States Railway Mission in Mexico [a summary report] by Fred E. Linder. Washington, Institute of Inter-American Transportation [1947]

Linder, Fredrik William

see

Linder, William, 1876–

Linder, Friedrich, 1899–
Die Gesundheitsverhältnisse in den Steiltälern des Schwarzwaldes im Vergleich zu seinen freigelegenen Höhenorten ... Freiburg i. Br., 1936.
Inaug.-Diss. - Freiburg.
Lebenslauf.

NL 0380123   CtY MiU

Linder, Friedrich, 1910–
... Leukoplakia oris und Karzinom ... Freiburg im Breisgau, 1933.
Inaug.-Diss. - Freiburg.
Lebenslauf.
"Literaturangabe": p. [25]–29.

NL 0380124   CtY

W 4
E461
1939
Linder, Fritz, 1913–
Ueber angeborene Epuliden und die verschiedenen Deutungen ihres histologischen Bildes mit Berücksichtigung der Myoblastenmyome des Erwachsenen. Heidelberg, Burkhardt, 1939.
40, [3] p.

Inaug.-Diss. - Heidelberg.
Bibliography: p. [41–42]

NL 0380125   DNLM

LINDER, G.
Auslegung der gesichte vom ersten Tier — in der Offenbarung Johannis. Liestal, Lüdin, 1907.

NL 0380126   MH

M2023
.C2 O6
Linder, G. Emil.

Carlson, Fritz Al.

The open door, a sacred cantata for soprano, tenor, bass and baritone solos with four and eight part choruses, ladies' trios, male choruses ... Lyrics by G. Emil Linder; music by Fritz Al. Carlson ... Omaha, Neb., F. A. Carlson [1939]

Linder, Gisela, 1914–
... Zahnheilkundliches in deutschen Sprichwörten und Redensarten ... Köln, 1938.
Inaug.-Diss. - Köln.
Lebenslauf.
"Literaturverzeichnis": p. 33–34.

NL 0380128   CtY

LINDER, Gottfried.
Zwei Männerchöre. Op. 17.
Stuttgart. Ebner. [1889?] 11 pp. L. 8°.
Contents. — Pfingstmorgen. — Reiterlied.

NL 0380129   MB

943
Ref
Box 3
LINDER, Gottlieb, 1842–1912.
Ambrosius Kettenacker und die Reformation in Riehen-Bettingen; ein neuer Beitrag zur Basler Reformationsgeschichte von G. Linder. Basel, H. Georg, 1883.
56p. 23cm.

NL 0380130   MH-AH CBGTU NjPT NNUT

VOLUME 334

Linder, Gottlieb, 1842-1912.
Die reformationsgeschichte einer dorfgemeinde ...
Halle a. S., Verein für reformationsgeschichte, 1889.
50 p. 12°. (Schriften für das deutsche volk, 3)

G–153

NL 0380131   DLC MoSCS MH-AH NjPT PPLT NNUT OCU MH

**M350
S84L5** **Linder, Gottlieb,** 1842-1912.
Simon Sulzer und sein Antheil an der Reformation im Lande Baden, sowie an den Unions-
bestrebungen.   Heidelberg, C.Winter's Uni-
versitätsbuchhandlung, 1890.
170p. 23cm.

1. Sulzer, Simon, 1508-1585. 2. Reformation – Germany – Baden.

NcD InU OU
NL 0380132   IaU CSt NjP CBPac WU MiDW MH-AH CtY-D

Linder, Grace.

Ohio. State university, *Columbus. Dept. of home economics.*
... Effect of gas pressure on natural gas cooking operations
in the home, based on tests made in the laboratory of the Department of home economics, the Ohio state university, Columbus, Ohio, under the direction of Edna Noble White ... Grace
Linder ... and Samuel S. Wyer ... Columbus, The University,
1918.

Z
673
.S97 Linder,Greta, 1888–
no.24 Bibliotekarieyrket; en orientering för
aspiranter och biblioteksstyrelser. ₁Lund,
Bibliotekstjänst₎ 1947.
23 p. 22 cm. (Sveriges allmänna biblioteksförenings småskrifter,n:r 24)
Cover title.

1.Library science as a profession.
Full name: Ingrid Gurli Margareta Linder.

NL 0380134   MiU

Linder, Greta
Bibliotekarieyrket en orientering för aspi-
ranter och biblioteksstyrelser. 2. upplagan.
₁Örebro, Bibliotekens försäljningscentral₎
1949.
cover-title, 22 p. (Sveriges Allmänna
bibliotek förenings småskrifter. No. 29)

1. Library science. 2. Libraries – Sweden.

NL 0380135   NNC

Z
673
.S97 Linder,Greta.
no.48 Folkbibliotekarieyrket. 3.omarbetade uppl.
Lund, Bibliotekstjänst, 1955.
24 p. 22 cm. (Sveriges allmänna biblioteksförenings småskrifter,nr 48)

1.Library science as a profession.

NL 0380136   MiU

Linder, Greta, 1888–   FOR OTHER EDITIONS
SEE MAIN ENTRY
... **Nordisk** litteraturfortegnelse; ræsonnerende katalog over
litteratur til studiet af danske, norske og svenske forhold
samt over dansk, norsk og svensk skønlitteratur, af ... T.A.
Døssing, Kobenhavn ... Trygve Aalheim, Kristiania ... Fr.
Hjelmqvist og ... Greta Linder, Stockholm. ₁Kristiania,
Raadhustrykkeriet a/s₎ 1921.

Linder, Greta, 1888–
Om handbokssamlingar och referensarbete i folkbiblioteken.
Föredrag vid Sveriges allmänna biblioteksförenings årsmöte
1930. Av andre biblioteskonsulenten Greta Linder. ₁Stock-
holm, 1931₎ p. ₁305₎–318. 25cm.
Caption-title.

1. Libraries—Reference work.
September 26, 1950

NL 0380138   NN

Linder, Greta, 1888–
... Swedish books for American libraries,
1932-33, compiled by Greta Linder ... on the
basis of the annotated lists published by the
Swedish government library commission ... ₁1935₎
₁2₎ p. 25cm.

"Reprinted from the American-Scandinavian review, March, 1935."
Caption title.

1.Bibliography - Best books - Swedish literature
2.Swedish literatu   re - Bibliography.

NL 0380139   NNC

Linder, Greta, 1888–
Thomas Døssing. Lund, Carl Bloms Boktryckeri, 1954.
31 p. port.

1. Døssing, Thomas, 1882–

NL 0380140   NNC MnU

Linder, Gurli, 1865- 1947.
Kvinnofrågen i Sverige, 1845-1905.
Stockholm, Wahlstroem, [1905]
59 p.

NL 0380141   PU MiD

DL976 Linder, Gurli, 1865–
.L55   På den tiden. Några bilder från 1870-talets
Stockholm. Stockholm, Albert Bonnier ₁1924₎
374p. illus.

1. Stockholm - Biography. I. Title.

NL 0380142   NcU

Linder, Fru Gurli, 1865–
På den tiden; några bilder från 1870-
talets Stockholm... 2. uppl. Stockholm, A. Bonnier ₁1925₎

374 p., 1 *l.* illus. (incl. ports.)
20cm.

1. Stockholm. Social life and customs.

NL 0380143   MnU

**304.7
L643** **LINDER, Fru Gurli,** 1865–   ed.
Qvinnan och dess bestämmelse – för
hundra år sedan. Tre uppsatser från
1800-talets början, med en efterskrift,
utg. av Gurli Linder. Stockholm,
P.A. Norstedt & söner ₁1914₎
2 p.ℓ., 55, ₁1₎ p. 21cm.
With reproduction of original t.-p.
of the first essay: Betraktelser öfver
qvinnan och dess bestämmelse, Stockholm,
Tryckt i Marquardska tryckeriet, 1811.

"Efterskrift" states that "Betraktelser"
was probably by Jenny Elisabeth Charlotta
von Breda, and may have been a translation from English.
Contents.– Betraktelser öfver qvinnan
och dess bestämmelse.– Ur Journal för
litteraturen och theatern, 1810; Bref
från ett fruntimmer till dess wän, rörande principen wid unga flickors uppfostran. Pro-   spektus till en ny
pensionsinrätt-   ning till unga frun-
timmers upp-   fostran.– Efterskrift,
af Gurli Linder

1. Woman. History and condition.
2. Education of women. I. Title.
II. Title: Betraktelser öfver qvinnan
och dess bestämmelse. III. Breda, Jenny
Elisabeth Charlotta, b.1795, supposed
author.

NL 0380146   MnU

Linder, Gurli, 1865–
Sällskapsliv i Stockholm under 1800 och 1890
talen. Några minnes bilder. Stockholm, Norstedt.
1918.
174 p

NL 0380147   PPAmSwM

**PN58
.L73** **LINDER,Fru GURLI,**1865- 1947
Våra barns fria läsning, av Gurli Linder. Stockholm,
P.A.Norstedt & söner[1916]
viii,237 p. 20cm.
"För denna bok använd facklitteratur":p.[vii]-viii.

1.Children's literature.

NL 0380148   ICU MiD

**028
L643v4** Linder, Gurli, 1865- 1947.
Våra barns nöjeslänsning. Stockholm,
A. Bonnier ₁1902₎
103 p. (Populär-vetenskapliga afhand-
lingar, 24)

NL 0380149   MiD IU

Linder, Gustaf Erik Hjalmar
see
Linder, Erik Hjalmar, 1906–

**Hky
L6453
E5** Linder, Hans Rudolf, 1921–
Eirene; Hymnus einer Sehnsucht. Basel,
Papillons-Verlag[1953]
28p. 20cm.
One of an ed. of 120 copies.
Werkstatt-Drucke 1953.

NL 0380151   CtY

VOLUME 334

Linder, Hans Rudolf, 1921-

Gedichte ⟨von⟩ Hans Rudolf Balmer, Robert H. Blaser,
Florian Egger, Max Freivogel, Fritz Hindermann ⟨und⟩
Hans R. Linder. Basel, Turm-verlag ⟨1940⟩

Linder, Hans Rudolf, 1921-
Lautréamont, sein Werk und sein Weltbild.
Affoltern am Albis, Buchdruckerei J.Weiss, 1947.

Dissertation - Basel.

NL 0380153   MH NNU InU NjP NN LU IEN NIC NNC ICU

Linder, Harold F
    Economic relations between Eastern and Western Europe.
⟨Based on an address made before the National Conference
on U. S. Foreign Policy on Oct. 30. Washington, Division
of Publications, Office of Public Affairs, 1951⟩
    759-762 p. 26 cm. (U. S. Dept. of State. Publication 4300. Euro-
pean and British Commonwealth series, 32)
    "Reprinted from the Department of State bulletin of November 12,
1951."
    1. Europe—Comm.   I. Title.   (Series: U. S. Dept. of State.
Publication 4300. Series: U. S. Dept. of State. European and British Commonwealth series, 32)

    HF3496.L5   382   52–60206

NL 0380154   DLC

W 4   Linder, Hedwig (Sandrock) 1913-
H46   Familiäres Auftreten von Kiemengangsfisteln.
1939   ⟨Heidelberg?⟩ 1939.
           31 p. 1 illus.

    Inaug.-Diss. - Heidelberg.
    Bibliography: p. 27-29.

NL 0380155   DNLM

Linder, Hermann, Dr.med. (Zürich)
    ... Ein Fall von akuter lymphatischer
Leukaemie ...   Zürich, 1924.
    23 cm.
    Inaug.-Diss. -.Zürich.

NL 0380156   CtY DNLM

Linder, Hermann, *writer on biology.*
    Biologie des Menschen, von Hermann Linder und Eugen
Hübler. Mit 93 Abbildungen, 2 Schwarz- und 4 Bunttafeln
gezeichnet von Hermann Huber und vielen Vignetten und
Tabellen sowie einem Anhang "Beobachtungen und Versuche." Stuttgart, J. B. Metzler, 1951.
    216 p. illus. 25 cm.

    1. Man. 2. Anatomy, Human. 3. Physiology.   I. Title.

    QP34.L65   612   52–66098

NL 0380157   DLC

Linder, Hermann,⟨ 1889-⟩ Beiträge zur Kenntnis der Plesiosaurier-
Gattungen Peloneustes und Pliosaurus. Nebst Anh.: Über
d. beiden ersten Halswirbel der Plesiosaurier. Jena: Fischer
1913. 73 S., 4 Taf. m. je 1 Erl.-Bl. 4° ¶ Auch als: Geol.
u. paläontol. Abhandlungen. Bd 15. N. F. Bd 11, H. 5.
Tübingen, Naturwiss. Diss. v. 18. Juni 1912, Ref. v. Koken
    [Geb. 25. April 89 Ebingen i. W.; Wohnort: Tübingen; Staatsangeh.: Württem-
berg; Vorbildung: OR. Magdeburg Reife 08; Studium: Tübingen 2, Leipzig 2,
Göttingen 2, Tübingen 4 S.; Rig. 18. Juni 12.]
                                                    [U 13.463⁴]

NL 0380158   ICRL PPAN MiU

Linder, Hermann, 1889-
    ... Beiträge zur kenntnis der plesiosaurier-gattungen
Peloneustes und *Pliosaurus.* Nebst anhang: **über die
beiden ersten halswirbel der plesiosaurier,** von **Hermann
Linder** ... mit 4 tafeln und 40 textfiguren. **Jena,** G.
Fischer, 1913.
    73, ⟨1⟩ p., 4 l. illus., IV pl. 31ᶜᵐ. (Geologische und palæontologische
abhandlungen ... n. f. bd. XI ... hft. 5)
    "Literaturzeichnis": p. 71.

    1. Plesiosauria.

                                                    13–18946
    Library of Congress   QE1.G492 n. f., bd. 11, hft. 5

NL 0380159   DLC FU CU ICRL NN.MB

Linder, Hjalmar
    De svenske lagmännens ställning till
konung och folk till och med år 1347.
I. ... af Hjalmar Linder ... Upsala,
E. Berling, 1875.
    1 p.l., 38 p. 21½cm.

    Akademisk afhandling - Upsala.

NL 0380160   MH-L ICRL

Linder, Isaak Maksovich.
    А. Д. Петров, первый русский шахматный мастер. 2.
доп. изд. Москва, Физкультура и спорт, 1955.
    245 p. illus., ports. 21 cm.

    First ed. published in 1952 under title: Александр Дмитриевич
Петров (transliterated: Aleksandr Dmitrievich Petrov)
    Bibliography: p. 239–⟨242⟩

    1. Petrov, Aleksandr Dmitrievich, 1794-1867.
                            Title transliterated: A. D. Petrov.

    GV1439.P4L5 1955   56–44264 rev

NL 0380161   DLC

Linder, Isaak Maksovich.
    Александр Дмитриевич Петров, первый русский шах-
матный мастер. ⟨Москва, Физкультура и спорт, 1952.
    126 p. illus., ports. 22 cm.

    Includes bibliographies.

    1. Petrov, Aleksandr Dmitrievich, 1794-1867.
                        Title transliterated: Aleksandr Dmitrievich Petrov.

    GV1439.P4L5   53–24785 rev

NL 0380162   DLC

371.8   Linder, Ivan H
L54o   Our war-time experience should establish coun-
        seling as a major influence in the high school.
        A program of high school counseling, by Ivan H.
        Linder.   Palo Alto, Calif., Palo Alto senior
        high school, 1944.
           45 numb.l. incl.charts, diagrs.

        Reproduced from typewritten copy.
        "Helpful aids to counseling": leaves 44-45.

        1. Counseling. I. Title.

NL 0380163   IU OC1 CU

Linder, Jerome Gladden.
    The wartime industrial safety problem
in the United States ... ⟨Phila.⟩ 1943.

NL 0380164   PU

Linder, Johan
    see
Lindestolpe, Johan, 1678-1724.

Linder, Johannes, 1790-1853.
    Johannes Linder; Lebensbild eines Predigers
der Basler Kirche ...
    see under Linder, August Gottlieb.

Linder, Josef.
    St. Gallerland in Bildern

see under

St. Gall, Switzerland (Canton). Regierungsrat.

BS413   Linder, Joseph
C8   Commentarius in Librum Daniel, quem exaravi
1931   Josephus Linder. Parisiis, P. Lethielleux,
pt.2   1939.
v.23   ix,548p. 24cm. (Cursus Scripturae Sacrae.
        Sectio altera. Commentarii in Vetus Testamen-
        tum, 23)
           Bibliography: p.[1]-15.

           1. Bible. O.T. Daniel - Commentaries. I.
        Title. II. Series: Cursus Scripturae Sacrae,
        pt.2, v.23.

NNUT
NL 0380168   InStme CtY-D NbHCR DDO PPWe OrStbM MBtS

Linder, Josephine.
    Down friendship road, by Josephine Linder. New York
House of Field, inc., 1941.
    68 p. 19¼ᶜᵐ.

    Poems.

    I. Title.   42–14973
    Library of Congress   PS3523.I 582D6
                                                    311.8

NL 0380169   DLC

Linder, Karl.

Rikli, Martin Albert, 1868-
    ... Von den Pyrenäen zum Nil; natur- und kulturbilder
aus den mittelmeerländern; mit beiträgen von pfarrer
K. Linder und dr. H. Weilenmann. Bern und Leipzig,
E. Bircher, aktiengesellschaft ⟨1926⟩

Linder, Karl Wilhelm
    see Linder, Carl Wilhelm, 1825-1882.

Linder, Karol.
    Dawne wojsko polskie w ilustracji; ⟨album. Wyd. 1.
Warszawa, Wydawn. Ministerstwa Obrony Narodowej,
1955.
    95 p. illus. 22 x 31 cm.

    1. Poland — History, Military — Pictorial works. 2. Poland.
Armia—Uniforms.   I. Title.

    UA829.P7L5   62–49441

NL 0380172   DLC CtY

VOLUME 334

Linder, Knut Sextus Ludvig.
see
Linder, Ludvig, 1862-

Linder, Kurt.
Die Verwandlungen der Mary Wigman.   Freiburg im Breisgau: Urban Verlag, cop. 1929.   53 p.   pl., port.   8°.

1. Wigman, Mary.   2. Title.

July 8, 1930

NL 0380174   NN NjP NcD TU

Linder, L   comp.
Bibliografisk förteckning över innehållet i Svenska Skogsvårdsföreningens/(Föreningens för skogsvård) publikationer, 1902-1919; jämte utförligt register över det förtecknade innehållets gruppindelning samt författarregister med kortfattade biografiska anteckningar och uppgifter om författarskap; utarb. av L. Linder, utg. under medverkan av Professor G. Schotte. Stockholm, Centraltryckeriet, 1920.
288, 3 p. 25½cm.

NL 0380175   NcD

JU83
.1948   Linder, Leo J
Insecure America.   New York, Progressive Party, [1948]
15 p.   illus.   21 cm.

Cover title.

1. Campaign literature, 1948 - Progressive party (1948)

NL 0380176   WHi

Linder, Leslie.
The Beatrix Potter papers at Hill Top. A catalogue of the manuscripts, miscellaneous drawings and papers at Hill Top, Sawey, belonging to the National Trust. Privately compiled by L. Linder, 1954. Pp. 54. 29.6x 21cm.

NL 0380177   CaOTP

Linder, Leslie
Safe working loads of lifting tackle. 2d ed. London, Testing Dept. of Coubro & Scrutton, ltd., 1952.
344 p.   illus.

1. Hoisting machinery - Safety measures. I. Coubro &   Scrutton. Testing Dept. II. Title.

NL 0380178   OrP

Linder, Louise S   .
We need churches...   Philadelphia [etc.] Judson press [c1948] 91 p. 25cm. (Judson keystone series)

Bibliography, p. 91.

1. Education, moral and religious--Outlines, syllabi, etc.

NL 0380179   NN

Linder, Ludvig, 1862-
...Bidrag till kännedomen om Messenii tidigare lif, 1579 (c.) - 1608. Af Ludvig Linder.   Lund: Berlingska boktryckeri- och stilgjuteri-aktiebolaget, 1894. 66 p. 4°. (Lund. Universitet. Acta Universitatis Lundensis. Lunds universitets årsskrift. Tomus 29, afdelning 1, no. 4.)
Bibliographical footnotes.
At head of title: Meddelanden från det Literaturhistoriska seminariet i Lund, utgifne af Henrik Schück.

1. Messenius, Johannes, 1579-1636.
N.Y.P.L.   December 28, 1925

NL 0380180   NN CtY

Linder, Ludvig, 1862-   FOR OTHER EDITIONS SEE MAIN ENTRY
Stockholm.   Kungliga biblioteket.
... Svenska samlingens katalogsignaturer 1919. Stockholm, Kungl. boktryckeriet, P. A. Norstedt & söner, 1919.

Linder, Manfred, 1912-
Über Speichelsteine ...   Heidelberg, 1935.
Inaug.-Diss. - Heidelberg.
Lebenslauf.
"Literaturverzeichnis": p. 16-17.

NL 0380182   CtY

Linder, Maria G.
Kawin, Ethel.
A comparative study of nursery-school versus a non-nursery-school group, by Ethel Kawin and Carolyn Hoefer, assisted by Edna Mohr, Maria G. Linder, and Marian W. Taylor, based upon studies made by the Elizabeth McCormick memorial fund and the Institute for juvenile research assisted by the Behavior research fund. Chicago, Ill., The University of Chicago press [1931]

Linder, Marianne.
Brunnarna. [Dikter] Stockholm, Bonnier [1950]
91 p. 20 cm.

I. Title.
Minnesota. Univ. Libr.   A 51-565
for Library of Congress

NL 0380184   MnU NN

Linder, Marianne.
Chonchet, djävulen och döden; dikt. Stockholm, Bonnier [1954]
110 p. 20 cm.

I. Title.
Minnesota. Univ. Libr.   A 54-5098
for Library of Congress

NL 0380185   MnU

Linder, Marianne.
De röda lutorna. [Dikter] Stockholm, Bonnier [1951]
108 p. 20 cm.

I. Title.
                          A 52-1316
Minnesota. Univ. Lit.
for Library of Congress

NL 0380186   NN MH MnU

Linder (Marie Louise). *Ueber das Verhalten von Blutdruck, Temperatur und Puls in den menstruellen Phasen. [Basel.] 54 pp. 8°. Berlin. E. Ebering. 1921.

NL 0380187   DNLM CtY MiU

LINDER, MARK.
Chip off the old block; or, The lifer. A crime series [for] television. Episode 1-[20]. [New York? 1950-?] 1 v. 28cm.

Typescript.

1. Television scripts, American. 2. Television--Scripts, American.

NL 0380188   NN

Linder, Max
Freies oder gebundenes mandat ein beitrag zur theorie der staatsrechtlichen stellung des abgeordneten... Kallmünz, 1932.   101 p. Inaug. Diss. Erlangen, 1932.
Bibliography.

NL 0380189   ICRL PU CtY

PN1997
L584   Linder, Max.
Sette anni di guai. A cura di Aldo Buzzi. [Milano, Editoriale Domus, 1945]
x, 119 p. illus. 20cm. (Cineteca Domus in volumi 7)

1. Sette anni di guai (Motion picture)

NL 0380190   GU IaU CLSU IEN

W 4
R29
1944   Linder, Max, 1918-
Zur Kenntnis der extramedullären Plasmozytome ... Basel, Ganzmann, 1944.
25 p. illus.

Inaug.-Diss. - Basel.

NL 0380191   DNLM

338.54
L744a   Linder, Moritz.
Die Asche der Millionen, vor, während und nach der Krise vom Jahre 1873.   Wien, W. Frick, 1883.
112p. 25cm.

1. Depressions. 1873. Austria. I. Title.

NL 0380192   IEN ICJ ICU

VOLUME 334

Linder, Nachman Zebi Hirsch, 1791–1851.
הכמת המספר. הסבון הפשום (ארימפעטיק) והאלנעברא הפרטי
והכללי. ווארשא. בדפוס י. לעבענזאהן. תרט״ו.
W Warszawie, 1854.
138 p. 21 cm.

1. Mathematics.   *Title transliterated:* Ḥokhmat ha-mispar.

QA39.L499   52–51753

NL 0380193   DLC

Linder, Nachman Zebi Hirsch, 1791–1851.
לוחות המגבילים מן המספרים הטבעים ... עם ביאורם,
אופני תוצאותם, ודרך שמושם. קאניגסבערג, תרי״ד.
Königsberg ₁1854₎
xi, 57, 48 p. 20 cm.

1. Logarithms.   *Title transliterated:* Luḥot ha-magbilim ...

QA55.L56   51–50517

NL 0380194   DLC

Linder, Nils i. e. Nikolaus, 1835–1904, ed.

Nordiske filologmøde. *4th, Copenhagen, 1892.*
Forhandlinger paa det fjerde Nordiske filologmøde i København den 18–21 juli 1892, udgivne af C. Jørgensen ... Tillæg: Berättelse om förhandlingarna vid det tredje Nordiska filologmötet i Stockholm 10–13 augusti 1886, af Nils Linder. København, Gyldendalske boghandels forlag (F. Hegel & søn) 1893.

Linder, Nils i.e.Nikolaus, 1835–1904.
Heimskringla. 1869–1872
    see under   Snorri, Sturluson, 1178–1241.

Linder, Nils i. e. Nikolaus, 1835–1904, ed.

Nordisk familjebok; konversationslexikon och realencyklopedi, innehållande upplysningar och förklaringar om märkvärdiga namn, föremål och begrepp ... Stockholm, Expeditionen af Nordisk familjebok ₁1876–99₎

PD5837 Linder, Nils i.e. Nikolaus, 1835–1904.
.S7L7   Om allmogemålet i Södra Möre härad af Kalmar län ... Uppsala, W. Schultz' boktryckeri, 1867.
xii, 202, ₁1₎ p. 23ᶜᵐ.
Akademisk afhandling—Uppsala.
"Förkortningar": p. ix–xii.

NL 0380198   ICU ICRL

Linder, Nils i.e. Nikolaus, 1835–1904.
Om -er, -r, -ar och -or såsom pluraländelser för neutrala substantiver i svenska språket. Stockholm, Norstedt [1890]
101 p.

NL 0380199   MH ICU

PD5261 Linder, Nils i.e. Nikolaus, 1835–1904.
L5   Om tilltalsord i svenska språket. Föreläsning ... den 20 februari 1884. Stockholm, A.Bonnier ₁1884₎
45 p.

1. Swedish language – Pronoun.   2. Salutations.

NL 0380200   CU MH

Linder, Nils i.e. Nikolaus, 1835–1904.
Om uppfostran hos forntidens nordboar. Föreläsning, hållen på Wet.-akad:s hörsal d. 1 Dec. 1869. Extr. fr. Läsning för folket. XXXVI. årg. 1870. pp. 145–174. IcB3L747

NL 0380201   NIC

PD5143 Linder, Nils i.e. Nikolaus, 1835–1904.
.L74   Regler och råd angående svenska språkets behandling i tal och skrift. Af N. Linder. Stockholm, Tryckt i Centraltryckeriet, 1882.
₁1₎, 64 p. 19ᶜᵐ.

1. Swedish language—Grammar.   2. Swedish language—Orthography and spelling.

NL 0380202   ICU

Linder, Nils i.e. Nikolaus, 1835–1904.
Regler och råd angående svenska språkets behaldling i tal och skrift. Omarbetning ... Stockholm, Norstedt, 1886.
(5), 237 p. 8°.

NL 0380203   MB WaU MH ICN CU

439.76 Linder, Nils i.e. Nikolaus, 1835–1904.
L744S   Svenska språket i modern diktkonst; en studie. Stockholm, C. E. Fritzes kongl. hofbokhandel i kommission ₁1902₎
71 p. 22 cm.

1. Swedish language. Rhythm. 2. Swedish language. Versification. I. Title.

NL 0380204   NcD WaU NcU CU

PT Linder, Oliver Anderson, 1862–1939.
9995   Glada grin; bläcksudderier på vers och
.L55052 prosa, af Olle Bark ₍pseud.₎ Chicago, Reliable Supply & Card Co. ₁1890?₎
32 p. illus. 17 cm.

"Andra häftet."

NL 0380205   MnHi

Linder, Oliver Anderson, 1862–1939.
I västerland; stycken på vers och prosa af Oliver A. Linder. Rock Island, Ill., Augustana book concern ₍1914₎
320 p. front. (port.) 20ᶜᵐ. $1.00

I. Title.

Library of Congress   14–21217

NL 0380206   DLC WaSp NN MnHi WaU

Linder, Oscar, and E. C. Frost.
Specifications and tests of glue.
(In American Society for Testing Materials. Proceedings. Vol. 14, part 2, pp. 508–519. [Philadelphia.] 1914.)

K4397 — Glue. — Jt. auth.

NL 0380207   MB

LINDER, O[scar] 1829–
Des dépots lacustres du vallon de Saucats. Bordeaux, 1872.
pp. 139 – 215. Table.
"Extrait des Actes de la Société linnéenne de Bordeaux, t. XXV 64 11[ ]1872."

NL 0380208   MH PPAN

Linder, Oscar, 1829–
Du nombre des freins qu'il convient d'introduire dans les trains de chemin de fer, par M. Linder ... ₍Paris? 18—?₎ 32 p. incl. tables. 4°.
Caption-title.

498286A. 1. Brakes.   October 3, 1930

NL 0380209   NN

Linder, Oscar, 1829–
Du nombre des freins qu'il convient d'introduire dans les trains de chemin de fer, par M. Linder ... Bordeaux, G. Gounouilhou, 1870.
cover-title, 32 p. 25ᶜᵐ.

1. Railroads—Brakes. ₁1. Brakes₎ I. Title.

                      A 29–716
Title from Bureau of   Railway Economics TF415.L64
                Printed by L. C.

NL 0380210   DBRE PPAmP CtY

Linder, Oscar, 1829–
Étude sur les terrains de transport du département de la Gironde suivie de considérations sur la formation du terrain quaternaire en général, par M. Linder ... Bordeaux, Coderc, Degreteau et Poujol, 1868.
136 p., 1 l. diagrs. 25ᶜᵐ.
Extrait des Actes de la Société linnéenne de Bordeaux, t. xxvi, 5° livraison.

1. Geology—France—Gironde. 2. Geology, Stratigraphic—Quaternary.

                     G S 15–580
Library, U. S. Geological   Survey 352(540) L64

NL 0380211   DI-GS

Linder, ₍Oscar₎ 1829–
Note sur les variations séculaires du magnétisme terrestre par M. Linder ... Bordeaux, G. Gounouilhou, imprimeur, 1869.
20 p. diagrs. 24ᶜᵐ.
"Extrait des Mémoires de la Société des sciences physiques et naturelles de Bordeaux, tome VII."

1. Magnetic variations, Secular.

                         5–31422†
Library of Congress   QC828.L74

NL 0380212   DLC

VOLUME 334

Linder, Oscar, 1880–
Ueber die entzuendungstemperaturen der mischungen von metallen und schwefel.
Inaug. diss. Berlin, 1901.

NL 0380213   ICRL PU MH

JN
4930
.L74
Linder, Otto.
Die entstehung der verwaltungsrechtspflege des geheimen rats in Württemberg, von dr. Otto Linder. Berlin, Junker und Dünnhaupt verlag, 1940.
109 p. 24½ᶜᵐ. (Added t.-p.: Neue deutsche forschungen ᵣbd. 287.₎ abteilung staats–, verwaltungs–, kirchen–, völkerrecht und staatstheorie. bd. 20)
"Schrifttumsverzeichnis": p. ₍106₎–109.)

1. Württemberg. Geheimrat. 2. Administrative law—Württemberg.

NL 0380214   MiU CU MH-L

Linder, Paul
Keisarillisen kaartin upseerina. Helsingissä, Kustannusosakeyhtiö Otava [1938]
367 p. illus.

NL 0380215   MH

Linder, Paul, 1871–
Die direkte Volksgesetzgebung im schweizerischen Staatsrecht. Erster Teil: Geschichte ... ₍von₎ Paul Linder ... Opponenten: ... Otto Loening ... Kurt Genzmer. Halle a. S., Buchdruckerei des Waisenhauses, 1905.
3 p. l., 91, ₍2₎ p. 21½ᶜᵐ.
Inaug.-Diss. - Halle-Wittenberg.
No more published?
"Lebenslauf": p. ₍92₎.
Bibliographical footnotes.

NL 0380216   MH-L NNC CtY ICRL

Linder, Ragnar.
Det var Bohus bataljon. ₍En minnesbok över försvarsberedskapen i väst-Sverige 1939–1945₎ Granskad av Försvarsstaben. Stocksund, Egilsförlaget, Seelig i distribution ₍1948₎
317 p. illus., ports. 28 cm.

1. World War, 1939–1945—Sweden. 2. Sweden. Armén. Bohus bataljon. I. Title.
D754.S8L53   51-29439

NL 0380217   DLC

Linder, Ralph F.
The grocer's idea book, edited by Ralph F. Linder ... New York, The Progressive grocer ₍ᶜ1937₎
vii, 200 p. illus. 22½ᵐ.

1. Grocery trade. I. Title.
Library of Congress   HF6201.G7L5   37-20424

Copyright A 109196   658.9414

NL 0380218   DLC Or PP OU OCl

Linder, Ralph F.   ed.
New idea book for food merchants, edited by Ralph F. Linder. New York, N. Y., The Progressive grocer ₍ᶜ1941₎
119 p. illus. 31 x 23½ᵐ.

1. Grocery trade. 2. Advertising—Grocery trade. 3. Salesmen and salesmanship. I. The Progressive grocer. II. Title.
                                            41-24540
Library of Congress   HF6161.G8L5
                                            658.9414

NL 0380219   DLC WaS NN PPD PP OCl

Linder, Raymond Marcel, 1920–
Contribution à l'étude de l'α-amino- et des α, α'-diamino-anthracènes et de leurs dérivés. Saignelégier, Impr. "Le Franc-Montagnard," 1947.
56 p. 23 cm.
Thèse—École polytechnique fédérale, Zürich.
Curriculum vitae.
Bibliographical footnotes.

1. Anthracene.

QD393.L75   51-41020

NL 0380220   DLC CtY CdU

PZ8
.F498
Dan
Linder, Remo E.

Finst, Rudy.
The dancing queen, written by Rudy Finst, illustrated by Jean Tack, produced under the direction of Remo Linder. ₍Sheboygan Falls, Wis., Newcomer-Linder, 1944₎

NL 0380221

Linder, Richard.
Bismarcks stellung zur revolution; ein beitrag zur kenntnis seiner politischen anschauungen. Auf grund authentischer äusserungen bearb. von Richard Linder. Wolfenbüttel, Heckner [1920]
2 p. l., 71 p. 22.5 cm.

NL 0380222   CSt-H MH

DK511
L3L55
Linder, Richard, 1867–
Zur älteren Livländischen Reimchronik. Leipzig, 1891.
76 p. 22ᵐ.
Inaug.-Diss. - Leipzig.
Vita.
"Ausgaben, Übersetzungen, Literatur": p. 17–20.
Full name: Friedrich Karl Ludwig Richard Linder.
1. Livländische Reimchronik. 2. Livonia - Hist.

NL 0380223   CSt NIC ICU MH NjP ICRL InU

Linder, Richard, fl. 1938
...Die schwedische Landbevölkerung unter dem Einfluss der Industrialisierung, von Richard Linder. Greifswald: L. Bamberg, 1938. 127 p. incl. tables. illus. (charts.) 24½ cm. (Nordische Studien... 20.)

"Diese Arbeit hat der... Universität Leipzig als Dissertation vorgelegen."
"Literaturverzeichnis", p. 5–7.

1. Sweden—Population. 2. Cities—Growth—Sweden. 3. Villages—Sweden. 4. Industries—Sweden.
                                            November 6, 1939

NL 0380224   NN NIC ICU

Linder, Robert.
Die gruendung der aktiengesellschaft nach franzoesischem recht.
Inaug. diss. - Erlangen, 1929. (München)
Bibl.

NL 0380225   DLC PU

Linder, Roscoe George, 1892–
An evaluation of the courses in education of a state teachers college by teachers in service, by Roscoe George Linder ... New York city, Teachers college, Columbia university, 1935.
viii p., 1 l., 156 p., 1 l. 23ᵐ.
Thesis (PH. D.)—Columbia university, 1936.
Vita.
Published also as Teachers college, Columbia university, Contributions to education, no. 664.
An evaluation of the topics of the education, psychology, and sociology courses offered at the Western Illinois state teachers college, Macomb. cf. p. 9.
"List of textbooks, outlines, and syllabi analyzed": p. 141–142. Bibliography: p. 149–156.
1. Illinois. State teachers college, Macomb—Curricula. 2. Education—Study and teaching. 3. Teachers, Training of. I. Title.
                                            36-12500
Library of Congress   LB1861.M42 g 1936
Columbia Univ. Libr.   370.7322

NL 0380226   NNC DLC PU-Penn OOxM OU MiU OCU

Linder, Roscoe George, 1892–
An evaluation of the courses in education of a state teachers college by teachers in service, by Roscoe George Linder ... New York city, Teachers college, Columbia university, 1935.
viii p., 1 l., 156 p. 23½ᵐ. (Teachers college, Columbia university. Contributions to education, no. 664)
Issued also as thesis (PH. D.) Columbia university.
An evaluation of the topics of the education, psychology, and sociology courses offered at the Western Illinois state teachers college, Macomb. cf. p. 9.
"List of textbooks, outlines, and syllabi analyzed": p. 141–142. Bibliography: p. 149–156.
1. Illinois. State teachers college, Macomb—Curricula. 2. Education—Study and teaching. 3. Teachers, Training of. I. Title.
                                            36-12499
Library of Congress   LB1861.M42 g 1935
———— Copy 2.   LB5.C8 no. 664
Copyright A 94807   370.7322

PU-Penn PBm MB ViU
NL 0380227   DLC KEmT PSt OrP OrCS OrU OrMonO WaTC

Linder, Roscoe George, 1892–
The individual child; a study guide, prepared by R. G. Linder ... Ann Arbor, Mich., Edwards brothers, inc., 1940.
iii, 42 numb. l. 28 x 21½ᵐ.
Reproduced from type-written copy.
Includes bibliographies.

1. Child study. I. Title.
Library of Congress   HQ772.L5   41-4790

Copyright AA 354949   [159.9227?2] 136.7002

NL 0380228   DLC

Linder, Rudolf, 1892–
Das technische problem von ort und zeit in den dramen und dramatischen theorien Otto Ludwigs ... von Rudolf Linder ... Basel, Schweighauserische buchdruckerei, 1918.
84 p. 23ᵐ.
Inaug.-diss.—Basel.
Vita.

1. Ludwig, Otto, 1813–1865. 2. Drama—Technique.
                                            21-15549
Library of Congress   PT2426.Z5L5

NL 0380229   DLC IU PU CtY MiU

Linder, Ruth Loss.

Brigham, Albert Perry, 1855–1932.
... Our home state and continent ₍by₎ Albert Perry Brigham ... and Charles T. McFarlane ... Wyoming edition ₍by₎ Ruth Loss Linder ... New York, Cincinnati ₍etc.₎ American book company ₍ᶜ1938₎

VOLUME 334

Linder, Samuel Ernest, 1868–

Hatschek, Emil, *ed.*
Klassische arbeiten über kolloide lösungen; arbeiten von H. Schulze, C. Winsinger, S. E. Linder, H. Picton, Francesco Selmi, F. Selmi und A. Sobrero, hrsg. von Emil Hatschek, mit einer abbildung im text. Leipzig, Akademische verlagsgesellschaft m. b. h., 1926.

NL 0380232   MiD

Linder, Sophie, illus.
Lob eines tugendsamen Weibes; Sprüche Salomonis XXXI, 1. 10–31; zwanzig Zeichnungen von Sophie Linder, mit einleitendem Vorwort von J. J. Balmer-Rinck. 3. Aufl. Gotha, F. A. Perthes, 1873.
[4] p. 20 plates.

NL 0380232   MiD

PT9816 Linder, Sten Ingvar, 1900–
.L74   ... August Strindberg ... Stockholm, A. Bonnier [1942]
79, [1] p. (Studentföreningen Verdandis Småskrifter. N:r.445)

NL 0380233   ICU MH

AS284 Linder, Sten Ingvar, 1900–
874   August Strindberg. Stockholm, A. Bonnier
no.445   [1949]
79, [1] p. (Studentföreningen Verdandis Småskrifter. N:r.445)

NL 0380234   CU

Linder, Sten Ingvar, 1900–
Berit Spong. Stockholm, P.A. Norstedt & söner [1944]

23 p.   20cm.

1. Spong, Berit, 1895–

NL 0380235   MnU CU

Linder, Sten Ingvar, 1900–
... Bo Bergman, av Sten Linder. Stockholm, A. Bonnier [1940]
64 p. 18ᶜᵐ. (Student-föreningen Verdandis småskrifter. N:r 431)
Label mounted on cover: Litteratur-serien.
Bibliography: p. 64.

1. *Bergman, Bo, 1869–
41–15808
Library of Congress   PT9875.B52Z7
839.7169

NL 0380236   DLC CU

Linder, Sten Ingvar, 1900–
Ernst Ahlgren i hennes romaner; ett bidrag till det litterära åttitalets karakteristik, av Sten Linder ... Stockholm, A. Bonnier [1930]
5 p. l., [7]–429 p. 22½ᶜᵐ.
Issued also as akademisk avhandling, Uppsala.
"Litteraturförteckning": p. [415]–420.

1. Benedictsson, Fru Victoria Maria (Bruzelius) 1850–1888.
33–22011
Library of Congress   PT9733.Z5L5
928.397

ICU
NL 0380237   DLC NcU NcD WU CtY NN PU ICRL IU TxU

Linder, Sten Ingvar, 1900–
Ibsen, Strindberg och andra; litteraturhistoriska essäer [av] Sten Linder. Stockholm, A. Bonnier [1936]
299 p. ports. 20 cm.

1. Scandinavian literature. Addresses, essays, lectures. I. Title.

NL 0380238   NcD NNC WaU CtY CU ICU MnU IU IEN

Linder, Sven Vilhelm, 1887–1947, *ed.*
Palästinische Volksgesänge. Aufgezeichnet und gesammelt von Sven Linder. Aus dem Nachlass hrsg. und mit Anmerkungen versehen von Helmer Ringgren. Mit einem Beitrag vom Herausgeber: Die Volksdichtung und das Hohe Lied. Uppsala, Lundequistska bokhandeln [1952–55]
2 v. 25 cm. (Uppsala universitets årsskrift 1952: 5, 1955: 9)
In Arabic (transliterated) and German.
Bibliography: v. 1, p. [116]–118; v. 2, p. [125]
1. Arabic poetry (Collections) 2. Folk-songs, Arabic—Palestine I. Ringgren, Helmer, 1917– II. Ringgren, Helmer, 1917– Die Volksdichtung und das Hohe Lied. III. Title. (Series: Uppsala. Universitet. Årsskrift. 1952: 5 [etc.])
AS284.U7 1952, no. 5, etc.   A 55–3712 rev

Minnesota. Univ. Libr.
for Library of Congress   [r56c2]†

PPDrop CtY NIC NNUT NjPT DLC NN MnU NNJ
NL 0380239   MnU MoU KyLoS TxFTC IEG OC1 OU PU

Linder, Sven Vilhelm, 1887–
Sauls Gibea ... Uppsala, Almqvist & Wiksells boktryckeri-a.-b., 1922.
vi, [2], 232 p., 1 l. 8 pl. (incl. map) 22½ᶜᵐ.
Akademisk avhandling—Uppsala.
Plates printed on both sides.

1. Gibeah, Palestine. 2. Palestine—Historical geography. 3. Saul, king of Israel.
26–22642
Library of Congress   DS110.G55L5

NL 0380240   DLC KyLoS MoSCS CtY PU ICU

Linder, Sven Vilhelm, 1887– 1947.
Studier till Gamla Testamentets föreställningar om Anden, av Sven Linder ... Uppsala, Almqvist & Wiksells boktryckeri-a.-b.; [etc., etc.,] 1926,
4 p. l., 177 p. 25½ᶜᵐ. (On cover: Arbeten utg. med understöd av VII helm Ekmans universitetsfond, Uppsala. 32)
"Förkortningar": 4th prelim. leaf.

1. Holy Spirit.
27–11401
Library of Congress   BT121.L5

NL 0380241   DLC CU CtY PU MiU OCH ICJ NN

QD341 Linder, Theodor.
.H9L7   Beitraege zur kenntnis des ortho-xylols.
Freiburg, 1895.
51p.
Inaug. diss. Freiburg.

NL 0380242   DLC

Linder (THEODOR *and* Håkansson (J. E.)
*Carmina Suecana, Latine reficta. [Parts I–II.] *Upsaliæ*, 1842–47. 2 pts. nar. 8°.
In: N10p. v. 2.

NL 0380243   NN

Linder, Thomas.
... Property valuations and the tax assessor
see under   Connecticut. Tax commissioner.

Linder, Tom, 1887–
Timetable of Bible prophecy, and Strong meat (Hebrews 5:12) [Atlanta, T. Linder Pub. Co., 1947]
xiv, 412 p. 3 fold. col. diagrs. 24 cm.
Errata slip inserted.

1. Bible—Prophecies—Chronology. I. Title. II. Title: Strong meat.
BS649.C5L46   220.1   47–28698*

NL 0380245   DLC

Linder, Ulla Elisabeth, 1873–
Adeljunkrar, krigare och bönder, av Ulla Linder... Stockholm: Åhlen & Åkerlunds förlag [, 1927]. 338 p. 2. ed. 12°.
Contents: Förord. Vargskallet i Drättingeskogen. Sången ur det fördolda. Den Guds röst kallar. De tunga stegen. Jorden bär fagra blommor. Den svåra vintern.

1. Fiction, Swedish. 2. Title.   June 6, 1928

NL 0380246   NN

PT9875 Linder, Ulla Elisabeth, 1873–
.L508   Guld; roman från spekulationsraseriets
1909   dagar (1907–1908) 2. uppl. Stockholm, H. Geber [1909]
302 p. 19 cm.

NL 0380247   MB

Linder, Ulla Elisabeth, 1873–
Magdalena Leijonstierna; roman från svenskt sextonhundratal; av Ulla Linder. Stockholm: Åhlen & Åkerland [, 1924]. 286 p. 12°.

1. Fiction, Swedish. 2. Title.   June 18, 1925

NL 0380248   NN

Linder, Ulla Elisabeth, 1873–1954.
Mot undergången; kulturhistorisk roman. Stockholm, Geber [1904]
330 p.

NL 0380249   WaU

PT9875 Linder, Ulla Elisabeth, 1873–1954.
L5742V2   Vågsvall; roman. Stockholm, H. Gebers förlag [1910]
243 p.

NL 0380250   CU

Linder, Usher F   1809–1876.
Reminiscences of the early bench and bar of Illinois. By General Usher F. Linder. With an introduction and appendix, by the Hon. Joseph Gillespie. Chicago, The Chicago legal news company, 1879.
406 p. 20ᶜᵐ.

1. Lawyers—Illinois. 2. Illinois—Biog. I. Gillespie, Joseph, 1809–1885.
5–36849
Library of Congress   F540.L65

NL 0380251   DLC ICN ICJ MnHi ViU–L OU Nh MeB OC1WHi

VOLUME 334

Linder, Usher F 1809–1876.
Reminiscences of the early bench and bar of Illinois. By General Usher F. Linder. With an introduction and appendix by the Hon. Joseph Gillespie. 2d ed. Chicago, The Chicago legal news company, 1879.
406 p. 20ᶜᵐ.

1. Lawyers—Illinois. 2. Illinois—Biog. I. Gillespie, Joseph, 1809–1885.
Library of Congress   F540.L65 1879 a   46–35005

NL 0380252   DLC NcD MWA Nh OU DI ICJ WaU-L NjP

Linder, Vilhelm, 1855–   FOR OTHER EDITIONS
SEE MAIN ENTRY
Sweden. *Vintersjöfartskommittén för Norrland.*
Betänkande II angående åtgärder för underlättande av vintertrafiken utmed Norrlandskusten och på de norrländska hamnarna, enligt nådigt uppdrag den 13 februari 1917 avgivet av Vintersjöfartskommittén för Norrland. Stockholm, I. Marcus' boktryckeri-aktiebolag, 1919.

Linder (Wilhelm) [1891–   ]. *Zur Behandlung der Pyodermien. 28 pp., 1 l. 8°.
.Breslau. 1918

NL 0380254   DNLM ICRL

W 4
M96
1954
LINDER, Wilhelm, 1919–
Bisherige Erfahrungen der Cortisontherapie. [München] 1954.
87 ℓ.
Inaug.-Diss. - Munich.
1. Cortisone

NL 0380255   DNLM

---

*Linder, William, 1876–

Sweden. *Justitiedepartementet.*
Betänkande och förslag rörande dödsstraffets avskaffande avgivet den 14 januari 1920 av den utav chefen för Justitiedepartementet jämlikt nådigt bemyndigande den 21 augusti 1919 tillkallade sakkunnige. Lund, Berlingska boktryckeriet, 1920.

Linder, William J
The history of wave guides. [Berkeley, 1947]
iv, 75 numb. l. mounted illus. 30 cm.
Report presented to the Graduate Seminar in Electrical Engineering of the University of California, spring term, 1947.
Bibliography: p. 67–75.

NL 0380257   CU

Linder, Willy, 1922–
Der Verhältnislohn; betriebswirtschaftliche Studie über eine neue Entlöhnungsform. Winterthur, P. G. Keller, 1955.
183 p. illus. 24 cm.
Inaug.-Diss.—Zürich.
Vita.
Bibliography: p. 12–19.

1. Wages. 2. Profit-sharing. I. Title.
HD4911.L55   58–19925

NL 0380258   DLC NNC CtY

NVR
L744
Linder, Willy, 1922–
Der Verhältnislohn; betriebwirtschaftliche Studie über eine neue Entlöhnungsform. Zürich, Schulthess, 1955.
181 p. illus. (Mitteilungen aus dem Handelswissenschaftlichen Seminar der Universität Zürich, Hft. 101)

Includes bibliography.
Issued also as thesis - Zürich.

NL 0380259   MH-BA NNU

Linder-Jaeggin, Sylvia.
...Hinder der guldige Tür; es hämpfeli Wiehnachtsvärsli. Bern, A. Francke [1948] 41 p. 18cm.

1. Poetry, Swiss-German. Switzerland—Bern. 3. Christmas—
I. Title.   2. German language—Dialects—
Poetry, songs, hymns, etc., German.

NL 0380260   NN CtY

LINDER-KNECHT, ANNA, 1895–
Heimatantlitz. [Erzählungen] Feldkirch, Montfort-Verlag [c1952] 136 p. 20cm.

I. Title.

NL 0380261   NN

4
Music
1778
Linder-Lienz, Anton

Tirol, mein Vaterland. Für gemischten chor bearb. von Bruno Graf. Wien, C. Haslinger [   ]
Pl. no. H.654.
score (3 p.) and   parts

NL 0380262   DLC-P4

Linderbauer, Benno, 1863–1928.   Lc 40-440
De verborum mutuatorum et peregrinorum apud Ciceronem usu et compensatione. [Progr. Metten, 1892–93.]
2 pt.

Cicero—Lang.||

NL 0380263   MH NjP CU NIC

Linderbauer, Benno, 1863–1928.

Benedictus, *Saint, abbot of Monte Cassino.*
S. Benedicti Regula monachorum, herausgegeben und philologisch erklärt von Benno Linderbauer, o. s. b. Metten, Verlag des Benediktinerstiftes, 1922.

Lindefbauer, Benno, 1863–1928, ed.

Benedictus, *Saint, abbot of Monte Cassino.*
S. Benedicti Regula monasteriorum; edidit, prolegomenis, apparatu critico, notis instruxit Benno Linderbauer, o. s. b. ... Bonnae, sumptibus Petri Hanstein, 1928.

PA
2349
L74
Linderbauer, Benno, 1863–1928.
Studien zur lateinischen Synonymik. Landshut, J. Thomann'sche Buch- und Kunstdruckerei, 1904.
64 p. 22cm.

Accompanies "Programm"(Jahresbericht)—Humanistische Gymnasium im Benediktinerstifte Metten.
1. Latin   language--Synonyms.

NL 0380266   NIC NjP

Linderberg, Carl.
Kort beskrifning öfver staden Falun och Stora Kopparbergs grufvan, med bifogade kartor och vuer. Utgifven af Carl Linderberg... Stockholm: Tryckt hos C. Delén, 1804. 54 p. 3 charts (incl. front.), plates. 23cm.

157397B. 1. Copper—Mines and   mining—Sweden—Falun. 2. Falun,
N. Y. P. L.   Sweden—Hist.
June 5, 1942

NL 0380267   NN PPAmSwM PBa

922.243
K43L
Linderberg, Fernando, 1854–1914.
Biskop Ketteler og socialismen i Tyskland ... København, Forlagt af V. Pios Boghandel, 1913.
406 p. 22½cm.

1. Ketteler, Wilhelm Emmanuel, Freiherr von, Bp., 1811–1877 2. Church and social problems. Catholic Church

NL 0380268   NcD

Linderberg, Fernando, 1854–1914.
Fyrst Krapotkin og den ideelle Anarkisme. Kjøbenhavn, Lehmann & Stage, 1904.
40 p. 8°.
Repr.: For kirke og kultur.

NL 0380269   NN

Linderberg, Fernando.
Grundtvigianismen og Underklassen; udvidet gengivelse af et foredrag paa Vennemødet i Grundtvigs Hus den 13de oktober 1908. [n.p. 1908?]
22p. 22cm.

Caption title.

1. Grundtvigianism.

NL 0380270   IEN

Linderberg, Fernando, 1854–1914.
Henry George og hans Social-Program... Af Fernando Linderberg. København: K. Jørgensen, 1889. 147 p. front. (port.) 12°.

1. George, Henry, 1839–1897.   2. Single tax. 3. Single tax—Denmark.
May 17, 1926

NL 0380271   NN CtY

LB
675
K58
L4
Linderberg, Fernando
Kristen Mikkelsen Kold; en levnetstegning. Rønne, Colbergs boghandels forlag, 1882.
132p. 21cm.
"Saertryk af Folkebladet."
Bound with Nygård, Frederik. Kristen Kold. [Odense, 1914]

1. Kold, Christen Mikkelsen, 1816–1870

NL 0380272   WU

VOLUME 334

Linderberg, Fernando
Kvoekernes Moensterstat. (William rex.: II)
Copenhagen, 1888.
92 p

NL 0380273   PHi

Linderberg, Fernando.
Professor Werner Sombart og den
socialistiske arbejderbevaegelse.
Kjøbenhavn, Lehmann & Stage, 1897.

78 p.   22cm.

1. Sombart, Werner, 1863-1941.

NL 0380274   MnU

Linderberg, Fernando, 1854-1914, ed.
Sociale kendsgerninger ...   København,
see under title

DL
199
.8
B53L74

Linderberg, Fernando, 1854-1914.
Statsminister Andreas Peder Bernstorf.
Kolding, ¡Danmark¿ K. Jørgensen, 1886.
79 p. illus. 19cm.

1. Bernstorff, Andreas Peter, greve,
1735-1797.

NL 0380276   NIC

Linderberg, Fernando, 1854-1914.
William Penn. Kolding, 1889
88 p

¡Danish.¿

NL 0380277   PHi

Linderberg, Peder Theodor Fernando.
See
Linderberg, Fernando, 1854-1914.

Linderboom, Gerrit Arie.
Encephalographie ...   Amsterdam,
[1930?]

NL 0380279   MiU

941.46
L743c

LINDERBOOM, Johannes, 1882-
De confessioneele ontwikkeling der
Reformatie in de Nederlanden. 's-Gravenhage, Nijhoff, 1946.
116p. 24cm. (Kerkhistorische Studien
behoorende bij het Nederlandsch Archief
voor Kerkgeschiedenis, 3)

NL 0380280   MH-AH

Linderborg, Charles G., tr.

Mathews, William, 1818-1909.
På lifvets vädjobana, eller, Vinkar om rätta vägen
till framgång och utmärkelse, af professor William
Mathews. Oversättning af C. G. Linderborg. Chicago,
Enander & Bohmans tryckeri, 1881.

Linderer, C   J   d. 1840.
Einige wohlmeinende worte ueber den
grossen werth und die nothwendigkeit der zaehne.
... n.p., n.p., ¡1818¿
8 p

NL 0380281   PU-D

Linderer, C   J   d. 1840.
Handbuch der Zahnheilkunde, enthaltend Anatomie und
Physiologie, Materia medica dentaria und Chirurgie, nach eige-
ner drei und vierzigjährigen Erfahrung und vielfältigen Be-
obachtungen dargestellt von C. J. Linderer sen. ... und Joseph
Linderer ... Mit achtzehn lithographirten Tabellen. Berlin,
Schlesinger'sche Buch- und Musikhandlung, 1837.

viii, 502 p. XVIII fold. pl. 19¼ᶜᵐ.

"Titel der Bücher, die in diesem Werke angeführt sind": p. 492–493.

NL 0380282   ICJ PU-D

RK50
.L74

LINDERER, C   J   d. 1840.
Handbuch der zahnheilkunde, enthaltend anatomie und
physiologie, materia medica dentaria und chirurgie ...
dargestellt von C. J. Linderer ... und Joseph Linderer ...
Berlin, Schlesinger, 1842-48.
2 v. plates (part fold.) 21cm.
¡Bd.1¿2.verm.und veränderte aufl.von J.Linderer;
bd.2,von Joseph Linderer(sub-title varies)

1.Teeth--Diseases.

NL 0380283   ICU PU-D PPDC DNLM

Linderer, C   J   d. 1840.
Lehre von den gesammten zahnoperation
nach den besten quellen und eigener vier-
sigjährigen erfahrung. Ber., ¡Brandes, pr.,¿
1834
319 p

NL 0380284   PU-D

Linderer, Eduard.
Berliner Hauswirth und Miether. Volksstück
mit Gesang und Tanz in 3 Abtheilungen und 6
Bildern. Musik von ... Louis Schmid. Berlin,
1861.
46 p.   8°.

NL 0380285   NN

Linderer, Eduard.
Eine Berliner Putzmacherin. Posse
mit Gesang in 1 Akt. Musik von A. Conradi.
Berlin, Meyer & Janke, [18--?]
28 p.   8°.

NL 0380286   NN

WB
25226

Linderer, Eduard
Die Geheimnisse von Berlin, Volksstück mit
Gesang und Ballet in 3 Akten und 7 Bildern,
von Eduard Linderer und Ferdinand Richter.
Musik von G. Steffens. Hamburg, Krüger &
Diehl [n.d.]
75p.
Without the music.

I. Richter, Ferdinand   joint author. cdu

NL 0380287   CtY

Linderer, Eduard
Hurrah! Hier ist Polterabenc! Ein strausschen
von Polterabenc-dichtungen ernsten und launigen
inhalts, nebst dichtungen zu silbernen und
goldenen hochzeiten und toasten, gewunden von
Eduard Linderer. 16. verm. aufl.
Berlin, S. Mode's verlag (Gustav Mode) n.d.
128 p.

NL 0380288   OCl

Linderer, Eduard.
Der rathgeber auf landpartieen, oder die quelle
des vergnügens im freien. Von Eduard Linderer.
2. aufl.   Berlin, A. Kiessling [1867]
126, [2] p.   15 cm.
1. Amusements.

NL 0380289   CU

Linderer, Eduard.
Seifen-Fritze. Original-Posse mit Gesant
in 1 Akt. Musik von A. Conradi. Berlin,
Meyer & Janke, [18--?]
24 p.   8°.

NL 0380290   NN

TX537
.S6

Linderer, Elinore Olivia (Thompson) 1911-
joint author.

¡Southerland, Fitzhugh Lee, 1904-
Questions and answers on government inspection of processed
fruits and vegetables. Washington, D. C., Production and
marketing administration, 1946.

WU
L744e
1842

LINDERER, Joseph, 1809-1878
Die Erhaltung der eignen Zähne, in
ihrem gesunden und kranken Zustande.
Berlin, Hirschwald, 1842.
64 p.   WU L744e

NL 0380292   DNLM

B617.6
L643

Linderer, Joseph, 1809-1878.
Die Zahnheilkunde nach ihrem
neuesten Standpunkte; ein Lehrbuch
für Zahnärzte und Aerzte.   Erlangen,
J.J. Palm und E. Enke, 1851.

xii, 482 p.   illus.   24cm.

Bibliography: p. 345-480.
1. Dentistry.   I.Title.

NL 0380293   MnU PU-D MiU

VOLUME 334

Linderer, Oscar.
... Schuster Faust und seine Grete. Komische Scene mit Duett. (Im Berliner Jargon) (Mel.: "Am grünen Strand der Spree") von Oscar Linderer ... Berlin, O. Linderer [1880?]
[4] p.   26 cm.   (Komische Vorträge, No. 20)
Without music.

NL 0380294   CtY

Linderer, Robert, 1824–1886.
Er ist Baron, oder: Im Geheimratsvriertel. Schwank in 1 Akt.   Mühlhausen i Thür, G. Danner, [1904?]
24 p.   12°.   (Vereinstheather. No. 180)

NL 0380295   NN

Linderer, Robert, 1824–1886.
Pietsch in: Robert der Teufel; burleske Solo-Scene mit Gesang. Nach Levassor. Berlin, E. Bloch, 1859.
13+ p.
(In Komische Solo-Scenen für Herren und Damen. Bd. 1. Berlin [18-])

NL 0380296   MH

Linderer, Robert, 1824–1886.
Ra-Ta-Tschin. Grosse chinesische Burleske mit Gesang und Tanz in 1 Akt und 2 Bildern, von Robert Linderer. Musik von G. Michaelis...   Berlin: E. Bloch [185-?]   24 p.   16cm.

904507A. 1. Drama, German.   I. Title.
October 11, 1937

NL 0380297   NN

Linderer, Robert, 1824–1886.
Der schoenste mann im regiment. Lustspiel in 1 akt, von Robert Linderer. Musik von Richard Thiele. Berlin, Bloch [1885]
40 p

NL 0380298   PPTU

LINDERER, ROBERT, 1824–1886.
Unsere Marine. Posse mit Gesang in 1 Akt. Von Robert Linderer. Musik von Richard Thiele. Zweite Auflage. Berlin: E.Bloch [1903] 42 p. 18½cm. (Eduard Blochs Theater-Korrespondenz. Nr. 197.)

Without music.

883427A. 1. Drama, German.   I. Title.

NL 0380299   NN PPTU

Linderer, Robert, 1824–1886.
Unsere ulanen. Berlin, Bloch [1890]
52 p

NL 0380300   PPTU

Linderer, Robert, 1824–1886.
Welche Lust Soldat zu sein! Solo-Scene für einen Herrn. 3. Aufl.   Berlin, E. Bloch [19-]   12 p.   18cm.   (Edouard Bloch's Dilettanten-Bühne)

1. Monologues, German.   I. Title.

NL 0380301   NN

Linderer, Robert, 1824–1886.
Wen heirathen? oder: Wer die wahl hat, der hat auch die qual. Soloscherz von Robert Linderer. Berlin, E. Bloch, 1860.
12 p. 17ᶜᵐ. (Eduard Bloch's Dilettanten-bühne. nr. 29)

I. Title.

28-31227

Library of Congress   PT2424.L38W4   1860

NL 0380302   DLC MH

Linderer, Robert, 1824–1886.
Wen heirathen? Oder: Wer die Wahl, hat die Qual. Solo-Scherz.   Berlin, Eduard Bloch, [1863?]
16 p.   16°.   (Eduard Bloch's Dilettanten-Bühne. no. 29)

NL 0380303   NN

Linderfelt, Klas August, 1847–1900.
Eclectic card catalog rules; author and title entries, based on Dziatzko's "Instruction" compared with the rules of the British museum, Cutter, Dewey, Perkins and other authorities, with an appendix, containing a list of oriental titles of honor and occupations, by Klas August Linderfelt ...   Boston, C. A. Cutter, 1890.
viii, 104 p.   25ᶜᵐ.
Interleaved.

1. Cataloging.

Library of Congress   Z695.L74   1-36560

NL 0380304   OO MiU TU DNR MiHM MB ICJ NN
DLC OrU CaBVaU MoU TxU NjP PPL PBm OU

FILM
025.31
L744e
Linderfelt, Klas August, 1847–1900.
Eclectic card catalog rules; author and title entries, based on Dziatzko's Instruction, compared with the rules of the British Museum, Cutter, Dewey, Perkins and other authorities, with an appendix, containing a list of oriental titles of honor and occupations.   Boston, C. A. Cutter, 1890.

Microfilm copy (negative) made in 1958 by the University of Illinois Library.
Collation of the original: viii, 104p.

NL 0380305   IU CU

Linderfelt, Klas August, 1847–1900.
The game of preference or Swedish whist. With a bibliography of English whist. By Klas August Linderfelt. Milwaukee, Priv. print. [Riverside printing co.] 1885.
52 p.   16½ᶜᵐ.
"Seventy-five copies printed for private distribution, of which this is no. 56."
Bibliography: p. 41-48.

1. Preference (Game)   2. Whist—Bibl.

5-26435†

Library of Congress   GV1291.P8L7

NL 0380306   DLC NIC ICRL PPL MiU MH

[Linderfelt, Klas August] 1847–1900.
Katalog der Buecher im deutscher Sprache
see under   Milwaukee. Public Library.

O.R.
025.3
L744L
Linderfelt, Klas August, 1847–1900.
List of Oriental titles and occupations, with their signification. [Boston, C. A. Cutter, 1890]
76-97 p.   25 cm.
Caption title.
From his Eclectic card catalog rules; author and title entries, based on Dziatzko's "Instruction" compared with the rules of the British Museum ...
Xerox copy. Durham, N. C., Duke University Library, 1963.

1. Cataloging of Oriental literature.   2. Names, Personal.   (Cataloging)   3. Titles of honor and nobility.   Orient.

NL 0380309   NcD

Linderfelt, Klas August, 1847–1900.
Milwaukee. Public library.
Reports on the proposed library and museum building for the city of Milwaukee, December, 1890, by K. A. Linderfelt, librarian of the Public library, and Adolph Meinecke, trustee of the Public museum. Milwaukee, Trustees of the Public library and the Public museum, 1890.

Linderfelt, Klas August, 1847–1900.
Caspar, Carl Nicolaus Joseph Matthias, ed.
Die stadt Milwaukee. Führer durch Deutsch-Athen für fremde und einheimische ... Ein souvenir an das 24. bundes-sängerfest des N. A. Sängerbundes, Milwaukee, 21.–25. juli 1886 ... Reich illustrirt. Nebst zehn ansichten aus der vogel-perspective nach direkter aufnahme, sowie einem neuen stadtplan und einer neuen karte von Milwaukee County ... Milwaukee, Wis., Caspar & Zahn, herausgeber, 1886.

PM
8952
.I5
Linderfelt, Klas August, 1847–1900.
Volapük; an easy method of acquiring the universal language constructed by Johann Martin Schleyer. Prepared for the English-speaking public on the basis of Alfred Kirchhoffshoffs Hilfsbuch, with the addition of a key to the exercises and a Volapük-English and English-Volapük vocabulary. Milwaukee, C. N. Caspar, H. H. Zahn, 1888.
130 p.   17 cm.

On cover: The universal language: Volapük.

NL 0380312   MnHi CtY NN PPL DN

Linderfelt, Klas August, 1847–1900.
Volapük. An easy method of acquiring the universal language constructed by Johann Martin Schleyer. Prepared for the English speaking public on the basis of Alfred Kirchhoff's Hilfsbuch with ... key to the exercises and a Volapük-English and English-Volapük vocabulary. [2d edition.] Milwaukee. Caspar. 1888. (2), 130 pp. 16°.

M9961 — Volapük. Grammar. — Linderfelt, Klas August. — Kirchhoff, Alfred, 1838–

NL 0380313   MB CU DLC OCl MiU

VOLUME 334

LINDERFELT, KLAS AUGUST, 1847-1900.
Volapuk, an easy method of acquiring the universal
language constructed by Johann Martin Schleyer,
prepared for the English-speaking public on the
basis of Alfred Kirchhoff's Hilfsbuch, with the
addition of a key to the exercises and a Volapuk-
English and English-Volapuk vocabulary. 3. ed.
Milwaukee, C. N. Casper, H.H. Zahn, 1888.
130 p. 17cm.

Film reproduction. Positive.

1. Volapuk. I. Kirchhoff, Alfred, 1838-1907. Volapuk Hilfsbuch.

NL 0380315   NN

Linderfelt, Klas August, 1847-1900.
Volapük, an easy method of acquiring the universal
language ... Ed. 4.   Milwaukee, Caspar, 1888.

NL 0380316   OrP

...Linderhof. [München, 1888.] plates. obl. f°.
Binder's title.
At head of title: Die bayerischen Koenigsschloesser.
Mounted photographs.

299858A. 1. Palaces—Germany—Lin-   derhof. 2. Interior decoration, German.   3. Rococo.
                                          July 11, 1927

NL 0380317   NN

LINDERHOLM, C   LINCOLN.
State of Michigan highway financing, by C. Lincoln
Linderholm... New Brunswick, N.J., 1938. 40 f.
facsim. 27½cm.

Reproduced from typewritten copy.
Thesis—American institute of banking, 1938.
"Bibliography," f. 39-40.

1. Highway finance—U.S.—Michigan.

NL 0380318   NN

Linderholm, Clara C
... Establishing and operating a stationery and office-sup-
ply store ... by Clara C. Linderholm. Written under the
supervision of General products section, Industry division,
Office of domestic commerce, United States Department of
commerce ... Washington, D. C., U. S. Govt. print. off.
[1946]
v, 30 p. illus. diagrs. 23½ cm. ([U. S. Bureau of foreign and
domestic commerce] Industrial (small business) series no. 44)
At head of title : United States Dept. of commerce ...
Bibliography : p. 29-30.
1. Stationery. 2. Office equipment and supplies.
T7.U62 no. 44   46—26830
            (650.82) 658.95146
            HF6201.S75L5

         OrCS CaBVaU
NL 0380319   DLC WaSp MH-BA OClCC Mi MB WaS OrP

Linderholm, Clara C
... Establishing and operating an automatic merchandising business ... by Clara C. Linderholm, under the direction
of Curtis E. Anderson ... Washington, D. C., U. S. Dept. of
commerce [1946]
v, 41, p. incl. illus., forms. 23 cm. ([U. S. Bureau of foreign and
domestic commerce] Industrial (small business) series no. 58)
At head of title: United States Dept. of commerce ...
"Suggested reading material": p. 40-41.

1. Vending machines.
T7.U62 no. 58   658.87   46—27599
                        HF5483.L5

       Mi PPD OrCS CaBVaU
NL 0380320   DLC WaT WaSp WaS MB PP PPTU OClCC NIC

RN46   Linderholm, Emanuel, 1872-1937.
H229   Adolf von Harnack. En återblick på hans
X   livsverk. Av Em. Linderholm. [n.p., 193-?]
v.1   155-242, 33-52 p. facsim., port. 22 cm.
no.10   (In Harnack, Adolf von. [Pamphlets, v. 1,
          no. 10])

          Caption title.
          Detached from Religion och kultur, 1930-31.
          Bibliographical references included in
          footnotes.

          1. Harnack, Adolf von, 1851-1930.

NL 0380322   CtY-D

LINDERHOLM, Emanuel, 1872-1937.
Gustaf Vasa, och reformationen i Sverige.
Stockholm, Tryckeriaktiebolaget Fylgia, 1917.

pp. 62.   Scan 2636.16

NL 0380323   MH

BV   Linderholm, Emanuel, 1872-1937.
178
L5   Der Hauptgottesdienst; ein Vorschlag.
          Uppsala, Almqvist & Witfells [1925]
          14p.
          With this are bound Fendt, Leonhard. Die
          Bedeutung der Liturgie für die Persönlich-
          keit und Arbeit des Predigers. 1930. Knolle,
          Theodor. Bindung und Freiheit in der litur-
          gischen Gestaltung. 1932. Frick, Heinrich.

          Evangelische Liturgie. 1926. Macholz,
          Waldemar. Der Gottesdienst evangelischer
          Konsequenz. 1931.

NL 0380325   MoSCS

BX8067   Linderholm, Emanuel, 1872-1937.
.A51AL7
          (Das Jahr der Kirche in Lesungen und Gebeten.
          E. Linderholm] Neues Evangelienbuch, deutsch von
          Th. Reissinger in 2.Aufl., verm. und Überarbei-
          tet mit W. Knevels und G. Mensching von Rudolf
          Otto. Gotha, L. Klotz, 1927.
          xxvi, 377 p. 23 cm.
          1. Lectionaries. I. Linderholm, Emanuel,
          1872-1937. II. Otto, Rudolf, 1869-1937.
          III. Title.

NL 0380326   ICU MH-AH NcD IaU PPLT

LINDERHOLM, Emanuel, 1872-1937.
Neues evangelienbuch; gebete und bibellesung-
en für den offentlichen Gottesdienst für schul
und einzelzndacht. Deutsch von Th.Reissinger
mit geleitwort von Otto. Gotha, Perthes,1924.

xxix, 112p. 18 cm.

NL 0380327   MH

PD5701   Linderholm, Emanuel, 1872-1937.
.S93   Nordisk magi; studier i nordisk religions-
v.20   och kyrkohistoria. I. Urnordisk magi. Stock-
          holm, P. A. Norstedt, 1914.
          157 p. (Svenska landsmål ock svenskt folk-
          liv. [2.ser.] B.20)
          No more published?

NL 0380328   ICU

GR225   Linderholm, Emanuel, 1872-
.L5   Nordisk magi; studier i nordisk religions-ock
          kyrkohistoria. Stockholm, P. A. Norstedt,
          1918-
          v. illus. 22½ cm. (Svenska landsmål
          och svenskt folkliv, no. 20)

          Contents. - v. 1. Urnordisk magi. -

          1. Folklore -   Sweden. I. Title.

NL 0380329   NjR NIC

LINDERHOLM, Emanuel, 1872-
Om den kristna statskyrkans uppkomst. 2a upp-
logan. Uppsala, A. B. Akademiska. bolehandeln
[1914].

NL 0380330   MH CtY

943   LINDERHOLM, Emanuel, 1872-1937
Pen   Pingstroerelsen dess foerutsaettningar
L744pi   och uppkomst. Ekstas, under och apok-
          alyptik i Bibel och nytida folkreligio-
          sitet. Stockholm, Bonnier, [1924]
          315p. 19.5cm.

          With this is bound his Pingstroerelsen
          i Sverige.

NL 0380331   MH-AH

943   LINDERHOLM, Emanuel, 1872-
Pen   Pingstroerelsen in Sverige. Ekstas,
L744pi   under och apokalyptik i nutida Svensk
          folkreligiositet. Stockholm, Bonner
          [1925]
          351p. 19.5cm.

          Bound with his: Pingstroerelsen, dess
          foerutsaettningar och uppkomst.

NL 0380332   MH-AH NN

Linderholm, Emanuel, 1872-
... Problemställningar och arbetsuppgifter i nutida svensk
teologi, af Emanuel Linderholm. Uppsala, A.-b. Akademiska
bokhandeln [1921]
1 p. l., 62 p. 24cm. (Uppsala universitets årsskrift 1921. Teologi. 1)

1. Theology—Study and teaching—Sweden. 2. Religious education—
Sweden. 3. Sweden—Religion. I. Title.
                           [Full name: Johannes Emanuel Linderholm]
                                                  A C 39-2069
Minnesota. Univ. Library
for Library of Congress   [AS284.U7 1921]
                                                  (378.485)

NL 0380333   MnU IEG MH MoU PU

PD5701   Linderholm, Emanuel, 1872-1937.
.S93   ...Signelser ock besvärjelser från medeltid ock
ser.B   nytid samlade ock utgivna av Emanuel Linderholm.
v.41   Stockholm, P. A. Norstedt & söner [1917-40]
          viii,478,[1] p. 24cm. (Svenska landsmål ock
          svenskt folkliv. B.41. Archives des traditions
          populaires suedoises. B.41)
          Added t.-p. and summary in French.

          1. Incantations, Swedish. 2. Prayers.

NL 0380334   ICU NIC

VOLUME 334

Linderholm, Emanuel, 1872–   ed.

BR1653
.R6A3

Rosén, Sven, 1708–1750.
Skrifter och bref af Sven Rosén, samlade och utgifna af Emanuel Linderholm. Uppsala & Stockholm, Almqvist & Wiksells boktryckeri-a.-b. [1910]

LINDERHOLM, EMANUEL, 1872–1937.
De stora häxprocesserna i sverige; bidrag till svensk kultur- och kyrkohistoria. Första delen. Uppsala, J. A. Lindblad [1918] xii, 272 p. 22cm.

No more published. --cf. Svenska män och kvinnor.
Bibliography, p. [xi]–xii.
Contents. --Del 1. Inledning. Bohuslän.

1. Witchcraft--Trials--Sweden.

NL 0380336   NN ICJ NIC ICRL

Linderholm, Emanuel, 1872–
Sven Rosén och hans insats i frihetstidens radikala pietism. Bilaga: Skrifter och bref af Sven Rosén ... af Emanuel Linderholm ... Uppsala & Stockholm, Almqvist & Wiksells boktryckeri-a.-b. [1911]

xxxii, 430, [1] p. 23½cm.
Akademisk afhandling--Uppsala.
"Bilaga" wanting.
"Fullständig förteckning öfver källor och litteratur": p. [xix]–xxxi.

1. Rosen, Sven, 1708–1750. 2. Pietism.
[Full name: Johannes Emanuel Linderholm]

Library of Congress   BX4983.R8L7   12–10528 Revised

NL 0380337   DLC NN PU CtY CU

Linderholm, Emanuel, 1872–1937.
Svensk Evangeliebok; boener och Bibeltexter foer den offentliga Gudstjaensten skola och enskild andakt.   Stockholm, Svenska Andelsfoerlaget [1920]
366 p.   19.5 cm.

NL 0380338   MH-AH NcD

764.9   LINDERHOLM, Emanuel, 1872–
Luth   Tankar och foerslag rocrande Svenska
L744ta   Kyrkans ritual utg. av. Birger Edmar.
1938   Uppsala, Almqvist & Wiksell, 1938.
202,viii,8p. music. 24cm.

Contains also: "Utdrag ur...G. Brandts analys av Em. Linderholms 'Svensk Hoegmaessa'

NL 0380339   MH-AH

BR1650   Linderholm, Emanuel, 1872–1937
.L74   Teologi och pietism; studier till den pro-
1914   testantiska teologiens ställning till pietismen
in: Uppsala, A.-B. Akademiska Bokhandeln [1914]
GTS   106p. 24cm.
Bibliographic footnotes.
Särtryck ur kyrkhistorisk årsskrift 1914.
1. Pietism--Hist. 2. Theology, Doctrinal--Hist. I. Title.

NL 0380340   IEG ICU

Linderholm, Håkan.
Active transport of ions through frog skin with special reference to the action of certain diuretics; a study of the relation between electrical properties, the flux of labelled ions, and respiration.   Uppsala, 1952.

144 p. 23 cm. (Acta physiologica Scandinavica, v. 27. Supplementum 97)

Akademisk avhandling--Uppsala.
Extra t. p., with thesis statement, inserted.
Bibliography: p. [140]–144.

1. Electrophysiology. 2. Diuretics and diuresis.   I. Title.
(Series)

QP341.L5   312.4641   54–383

NL 0380341   DLC IdPS NjR NIC DNLM CU ViU

Linderholm, Helmer, 1916–
Bagare; berättelser från förr. Stockholm, Hökerberg [1953]
181 p. 20 cm.

1. Bakers and bakeries.   I. Title.
Full name: Sven Gottfrid Helmer Linderholm.

A 54–4308

Minnesota. Univ. Libr.
for Library of Congress

NL 0380342   MnU

Linderholm, Helmer, 1916–
Berget och lågorna. Stockholm, Hökerberg [1952]
226 p. 22 cm.

I. Title.
Full name: Sven Gottfrid Helmer Linderholm.

A 53–3956

Minnesota. Univ. Libr.
for Library of Congress

NL 0380343   MnU

Linderholm, Helmer, 1916–
...Hör, skällorna!   Helsingfors, Söderström & c:o [1947]
269 p.   22cm.

436655B. 1. Fiction, Swedish-Finfion. I. Title.   nish. 2. World war, 1939–1945--Fiction.
April 23, 1948

NL 0380344   NN

Linderholm, Helmer, 1916–
Svedjefolket. Stockholm, Hökerberg [1951]
243 p. 22 cm.

I. Title.
Full name: Sven Gottfrid Helmer Linderholm.

A 52–1224

Minnesota. Univ. Libr.
for Library of Congress

NL 0380345   MnU

Linderholm, Hermannus.
De venaesectionis usu et abusu in pleuritide. Gryphiswaldiae, Rose, 1777.
24 p.
Diss.

NL 0380346   PPC DNLM

Linderholm, Johannes Emanuel

see

Linderholm, Emanuel, 1872–

Linderholm, Magnus Gustaf, 1799–1839, respondent.

QH9
.T6
no. 254   Thunberg, Karl Peter, 1743–1828, *praeses.*
Rare bk.   De geo urbano dissertatio botanico-medica ... Upsaliæ, excudebant Palmblad & c. [1827]

Linderholm, Olavus, respondent.
Dissertatio academica de Fennonibus...
see under   Fant, Erik Mikael, 1754–1817, praeses.

Linderholm, Sven Gottfrid Helmer
see Linderholm, Helmer, 1916–

Linderman, Frank Bird, 1868–1938.
Plenty-Coups, *Crow chief,* 1848–1932.
American: the life story of a great Indian, Plenty-Coups, chief of the Crows, by Frank B. Linderman. Illustrated by H. M. Stoops. New York, John Day Co. [1930]

Linderman, Frank Bird, 1868–
Beyond law, by Frank B. Linderman. New York, The John Day company [1933]
3 p. l., 3–250 p., 1 l. 19½cm.

I. Title.
Library of Congress   PZ3.L6463Be   33–25688

NL 0380352   DLC MB MtU

Linderman, Frank Bird, 1868–1938.
Blackfeet Indians; pictures by Winold Reiss; story by Frank B. Linderman. [St. Paul, Printed by Brown & Bigelow, 1935]
3 p. l., 9–65, [5] p. incl. col. illus., col. plates. 31 cm.

"The Great northern railway asked Frank Bird Linderman ... to write the story of the Blackfeet."--Foreword.

1. Siksika Indians. 2. Indians of North America--Portraits.   I.
*Reiss, Winold, 1886–   illus.   II. Great northern railway.   III. Title.

E99.S54L5   970.3   35–17050
ND237.R33A5

OrLgE CaBViPA IdU
OClW PP PPL OrP MtU WaT IdU MtBC WaSp WaS OrCS OrU
NL 0380353   DLC NN ViU OCU OU MiU OKentU NBuG FU OCl

[Linderman, Frank Bird, 1868–1938.
Blackfeet Indians of Glacier national park ... St. Paul, Minn., Brown & Bigelow, *1940.
cover-title, 11, [1] p. 24 col. il. 32cm.

A portfolio containing 24 reproductions of paintings of Blackfeet Indians by Winold Reiss and pamphlet (11, [1] p.) with title, "Out of the north, a brief historical sketch of the Blackfeet Indian tribe, by Frank B. Linderman." An earlier edition, published in 1935 under title, Blackfeet Indians; pictures by Winold Reiss; story by Frank B. Linderman, has the same text and 49 plates.
"Prepared and published by the Great northern railway company."

1. Siksika Indians. 2. Indians of North America--Portraits.   I.
*Reiss, Winold, 1886–   illus.   II. Great northern railway.   III. Title.

Library of Congress   E99.S54L5 1940   41–12000
ND237.R33A5 1940
970.3

NL 0380354   DLC IU

VOLUME 334

Linderman, Frank Bird, 1868–
Bunch-grass and blue-joint, by Frank B. Linderman.
New York, C. Scribner's sons, 1921.

ix p., 1 l., 115 p. front. 17½ᶜᵐ.

Poems.

i. Title.
Library of Congress   PS3523.I 535B8 1921   21–12267

 OrP MtHi OrPR MtU Wa MtBuM
NL 0380355   DLC NN OC1W OC1 PRosC PU KU–RH MU ViU

Linderman, Frank Bird, 1868–
Bunch-grass and blue-joint.   1924 ₍c1921₎

NL 0380356   MtBC

Linderman, Frank Bird, 1868–
A calendar of historic events of the state of Montana,
by Frank B. Linderman ... ₍Dew Lodge, Mont., Printed
by J. Smith, ᶜ1914₎

1 p. l., 40 p. 23ᶜᵐ. $0.50

1. Montana—Hist.   i. Title.

Library of Congress   F731.L74   14–2488

NL 0380357   DLC

323.6   **Linderman, Frank Bird,** 1868-1938.
L64g Good citizenship; charter day address.
 Missoula, Mont., 1919.
  cover-title, 15p. illus., port.
 (University of Montana bulletin. State
 University series, no.221)

NL 0380358   IU DLC OO MH

Linderman, Frank Bird, 1868-1938.
How it came about stories, by Frank B. Linderman ⟨Co-
skee-see-co-cot⟩ Illustrated by Carle Michel Boog. New York,
C. Scribner's sons, 1921.

viii p., 3 l., 3–221 p. col. front., illus., col. plates. 21ᶜᵐ.

1. Animals, Legends and stories of.   i. Title.
Library of Congress   PZ10.3.L64Ho   21–15946

NL 0380359   DLC MtBuM MtU PP

Linderman, Frank Bird, 1869-1938.
How it came about stories, by Frank B. Linderman
⟨Co-skee-see-co-cot⟩ Illustrated by Carle Michel
Boog. New York, Scribner, 1926.   viii, 221 p.
illus. 21cm.

1. Animals—Legends and stories. I. Title.

NL 0380360   NN

Linderman, Frank Bird, 1868–
Indian lodge-fire stories, by Frank B. Linderman ⟨Co-
skee-see-co-cot⟩ illustrated by Charles M. Russell ... New
York, Chicago ₍etc.₎ C. Scribner's sons ₍ᶜ1918₎

117 p. incl. front., illus. 18½ᶜᵐ. (Lettered on cover: Scribner series of
school reading) $0.56

"The stories included in this volume are taken from 'Indian why stories,' a collection of tales told me by the older men of the Blackfeet, Chippewa, and Cree tribes."—Note to the reader.

1. Siksika Indians—Legends. 2. Chippewa Indians—Legends. 3. Cree
Indians—Legends. 4. Folk-lore, Indian. i. Title.

Library of Congress   E98.F6L68   18–18518

NL 0380361   DLC MtHi OrP PP OEac

Linderman, Frank Bird, 1868-1938.
Indian Old-man stories; more sparks from War Eagle's
lodge-fire, by Frank B. Linderman ⟨Co-skee-see-co-cot⟩ illustrated by Charles M. Russell ⟨Cah-ne-ta-wah-see-na-e-ket⟩ ...
New York, C. Scribner's sons, 1920.

xx p., 3 l., 3–169 p. col. front., illus., col. plates. 21ᶜᵐ.

Illustrated t.-p., in colors.

1. Folk-lore, Indian. 2. Chippewa Indians—Legends. 3. Cree Indians—Legends. i. Title. ii. Title: Old-man stories.

Library of Congress   E98.F6L69   20–19248

 MtBC IdU IdPS IdB CaBVaU
 WaPS WaS WaSp WaSpG WaT WaTC WaWW OrP OrCS MtU
 OO OC1 NcU PP CtY NN WaU MnU MoU OrU ICN Wa WaE
NL 0380362   DLC MtHi MtBuM OrU-M OrSaW OrStbM Or

Linderman, Frank Bird, 1868-1938.
Indian why stories; sparks from War Eagle's lodge-fire,
by Frank B. Linderman ⟨Co-skee-see-co-cot⟩ illustrated by
Charles M. Russell ⟨Cah-ne-ta-wah-see-na-e-ket⟩ ... New
York, C. Scribner's sons, 1915.

xvi, 236 p. col. front., illus., col. plates. 21 cm.

Illustrated t.-p., in colors.
"Tales told me by the the older men of the Blackfeet, Chippewa
and Cree tribes."—Pref.

1. Siksika Indians — Legends. 2. Chippewa Indians — Legends.
3. Cree Indians—Legends. 4. Folk-lore, Indian. i. Title.

E98.F6L7   15—19292

 PSC PWcT NN OC1 MtU Or GU OU NcU
NL 0380363   DLC ICN MiDU WaS TxU KMK MiU MoU NcD

Linderman, Frank Bird, 1868–
Kootenai why stories, by Frank B. Linderman ⟨Co-
skee-see-co-cot⟩ illustrated by Charles Livingston Bull.
New York, Blue Ribbon books ₍c1926₎   (A Burt book.)

xx p., 1 l., 166 p. col. front., col. plates. 21ᶜᵐ.

NL 0380364   OU

Linderman, Frank Bird, 1868-1938.
Kootenai why stories, by Frank B. Linderman ⟨Coskee-
see-co-cot⟩ illustrated by Charles Livingston Bull. New
York, C. Scribner's sons, 1926.

xx p., 1 l., 166 p. col. front., col. plates. 21 cm.

1. Kutenai Indians—Legends. 2. Folk-lore, Indian. i. Title.

E99K85L5   26—16371

 MtBC CaBViP MtHi CaBViPA WaWW CaBVaU
NL 0380365   DLC PPL PWcT PPD OC1h OC1 MtU WaSp WaS

Linderman, Frank Bird, 1868–
Lige Mounts: free trapper, by Frank B. Linderman,
with illustrations by Joe De Yong. New York, C. Scribner's sons, 1922.

viii p., 2 l., 330 p. front., plates. 21ᶜᵐ.

i. Title.
Library of Congress   PZ3.L6463Li   22–18893

NL 0380366   DLC MtHi MtU MtBuM PHatU MB MiU

Linderman, Frank Bird, 1868–
Morning light (Lige Mounts: free trapper) by Frank B.
Linderman, with decorations by Joe De Yong. New York,
The John Day company ₍ᶜ1930₎

viii p., 1 l., 330 p., 1 l. 21ᶜᵐ.

Tail-pieces.
"First published under the title of Lige Mounts: free trapper."

i. Title.

Library of Congress   PZ3.L6463Mo   30–26946

 NcC PV OC1
NL 0380367   DLC WaT WaS WaSp CaBViPA IdU MtU CU-B

Linderman, Frank Bird, 1868–
Old man coyote (Crow), by Frank B. Linderman; illus-
trated by Herbert Morton Stoops. New York, The John
Day company ₍ᶜ1931₎

254 p., 1 l. incl. front., illus. 21 cm.

1. Crow Indians—Legends. 2. Indians of North America—Legends.
i. Title.

E99.C92L6   398.21097   31—34529

 MH OC1 OC1W PP PWcT PBm IdU-SB OrU OrPS IdU
NL 0380368   DLC MtHi WaSp OrP MtU CaBVaU MoU MB Or

398.2 Linderman, Frank Bird, 1868–
L642o Old man coyote (Crow) Illustrated by Herbert
1932 Morton Stoops. New York, Junior Literary
  Guild, 1932.
   254p. illus. 21cm.

  1. Crow Indians--Legends. 2. Indians of
 North America--Legends. I. Title.

NL 0380369   IU MtBC

Linderman, Frank Bird, 1868-1938.
On a passing frontier; sketches from the Northwest, by
Frank B. Linderman. New York, C. Scribner's sons, 1920.

5 p. l., 3–214 p. 19 cm.

Contents.—In the name of friendship.—Was Chet Smalley honest?—The medicine keg.—The throw-away dance.—Jake Hoover's
pig.—A gun trade.—The whiskey peddler.—The post-office at Wolftail.—Jew Jake's Monte.—At the bar.—Pap's pinto.—The bullet's
proof.—The Indian's god. — Bravery. — What followed a sermon.—
Cranks.—The flying Dutchman.

i. Title.
Library of Congress   PZ3.L64630n   20—10052

 MtHi MtBC OrU WaSpG
NL 0380370   DLC PPL PPM OO NN MB CaACG ICN WaSp

Linderman, Frank Bird, 1868–1938.
On a passing frontier; sketches from the Northwest. New
York: Charles Scribner's Sons, 1922. 214 p.   12°.

Contents: In the name of friendship. Was Chet Smalley honest? The medicine
keg. The throw-away dance. Jake Hoover's pig. A gun trade. The whiskey peddler.
The post-office at Wolftail. Jew Jake's Monte. At the bar. Pap's pinto. The bullet's
proof. The Indian's God. Bravery. What followed a sermon. Cranks. The flying
Dutchman.

i. Title. 2. Northwest—Fiction.   January 17, 1930

NL 0380371   NN

Linderman, Frank Bird, 1868–1938.
Out of the north; a brief historical sketch of the Blackfeet
Indian tribe... ₍n. p.₎ Great northern railway co., 1947. 11 p.
28cm.

1. Indians, N. A.—Tribes—   Blackfoot. I. Great northern railway company (U.S.) II. Title.

NL 0380372   NN MtBC WaS WaT MtU

VOLUME 334

Linderman, Frank Bird, 1868–

E90
P56L7

Plenty-coups, chief of the Crows. The life
story of a great Indian, by Frank B. Linderman.
London, Faber & Faber limited [1930]

316p. 21cm.

"Thumb-print of Plenty-coups, chief of the
Crows", [p. 9]

Maps on lining papers.

1. Plenty-coups, Crow chief, 1848– 2.
Crow Indians. I. Title.

NL 0380373   NBuG MH DCU

Linderman, Frank Bird, 1868–

Red mother, by Frank B. Linderman; illustrated by Herbert
Morton Stoops. New York, The John Day company [*1932]

256 p. illus. 21¼cm.

The life story of Pretty-shield, a medicine-woman of the Crows.

1. Pretty-shield, Crow Indian. 2. Indians of North America—Women.
3. Crow Indians. I. Title.

Library of Congress   E90.P88L5   32–27272

Copyright A 56305   970.2

OrCS OrPR
CaBVaU MoU TxU NIC WaT MtBC Wa WaSp MtHi Or WaS
NL 0380374   DLC OC1 OrP MtU PPGi PHC CoU WHi NN MB

Linderman, Frank Bird, 1868–1938.
Red mother. N. Y., Day, c1933.
Illus.

NL 0380375   NcC

Linderman, Frank Bird, 1868–1938.
Stumpy, by Frank B. Linderman; illustrated by H. M.
Stoops. New York, The John Day company [*1933]

3 p. l., 3–147, [1] p. front. illus. 23¼cm.

1. Chipmunks. I. Title.

Library of Congress   PZ10.3.L64St   33–5477

00
NL 0380376   DLC MtU WaS Or NN PJA PP OLak OC1h NN

Linderman, George P   1838–

Autobiography of Rev. George P. Linderman; an account of his life, labors and travels. [Binghamton, N. Y.]
Priv. print. [press of Vail-Ballou co.] 1911.

2 p. l., 149 p. front. (port.) 20cm. $1.00

12–2210

NL 0380377   DLC

NJ 47
.L 9
no. 17

Linderman, Henry Richard, 1825–1879.
Catalogue of a valuable collection of
United States coins, embracing dollars of
eighteen hundred and four, 1836 (both varieties), 1838, 1839, 1851, 1853, etc., the
quarter dollar of 1827, half cents of 1831,
1836, 1840–48, and 1852, together with pattern pieces and assay medals, formed by the
late Dr. Henry R. Linderman ... To be sold
at auction ... by Messrs. Bangs & co. ...
New York ...   June 28, 1887 ...
Catalogue by   Lyman H. Low & co.,
17th sale.   Boston, T. R. Marvin

Continued in next column

Continued from preceding column

& son, printers, 1887.
19 p. 25cm.

188 items.

1. Coins, American.   2. Coins - Catalogs.
3. Medals.   I.   Low, Lyman Haynes,
1845–1924. II.   Bangs, firm,
auctioneers,   New York.

NL 0380379   MdBJ

NJ 47
.S 43
1888 a

Linderman, Henry Richard, 1825–1879.
... Catalogue of a valuable collection
of United States coins, embracing dollars
of eighteen hundred and four, 1836, (both
varieties) 1838, 1839, 1851, 1852, etc. ...
together with experimental pieces and
assay medals, formed by the late Dr. Henry
R. Linderman ... To be sold at public
auction ... by Bangs & co. ... on ... February 28, 1888 ... Catalogued by the Scott
stamp & coin co., l'd. ... [New York?] 1888.
2 p.l., [41]–52 p. 24cm.

At head of   title: ... 84th sale.
188 items.

NL 0380380   MdBJ;

Linderman, Henry Richard, 1825–1879.
Circular letter in relation to American medals
and cabinet coins. n.t.-p. [1867]
12°

(U.S. Treas. Dept. Mint.)

NL 0380381   NN

Linderman, Henry Richard, 1825–1879.
A consideration of the
propositions for the re-monetization of
silver.
New York, 1877.
24 p.   YA 21581

NL 0380382   DLC

Linderman, Henry Richard, 1825–1879.
A consideration of the propositions
for the remonetization of silver. Being
an extract from "Money and Legal Tender"
by Henry R. Linderman, Director of the
U.S. Mint. New York, G. P. Putnam's Sons,
182 Fifth Avenue, 1878.
24 p. 19 cm.

NL 0380383   OFH

Linderman, Henry Richard, 1825–1879.
Dr. John J. Linderman and Linderman family notes.
(*In* New Jersey Historical Society. Proceedings. New series,
vol. 8, no. 4, pp. 301–306. Newark, N. J. 1923.)

N1o58 — Linderman family. — Genealogy. Linderman.

NL 0380384   MB

Linderman, Henry Richard, 1825–1879.
The free coinage of gold, and its importance in connection
with the resumption of specie payments and commerce of the
United States. By H. R. Lindermann ... Philadelphia, 1872.

cover-title, 7 p. 23¼cm.

1. Currency question—U. S.

Library of Congress   HG551.L74   CA 7—2204 Unrev'd

NL 0380385   DLC IU

Linderman, Henry Richard, 1825–1879.
Money and legal tender in the United States, by H. R.
Linderman ... New York, G. P. Putnam's sons, 1877.

x, 173 p. 19 cm.

1. Currency question—U. S.

HG501.L5   5–41953

ICJ MH NcD WaU CU
NL 0380386   DLC WaS PHi ViU-L PPL PPTU NjP MdBP

Linderman, Henry Richard, 1825–1879.
Money and legal tender in the United States, by H. R.
Linderman ... New York, G. P. Putnam's sons, 1878.

x, 173 p. 19cm.

1. Currency question—U. S.

                           6–16852

Library of Congress   HG501.L6

NL 0380387   DLC PP PPFr OCU

332.4973
L643m
1879

Linderman, Henry Richard, 1825–1879.
Money and legal tender in the United
States. New York, Putnam's, 1879 [c1877]
x,173p. 18cm.

Appendix: p.[123]–173.

1. Currency question. United States.

NL 0380388   KU NN NjN OO PHC

332.46
L744p

Linderman, Henry Richard, 1825–1879.
The proposed mint. An argument in favor of
its location in St. Louis, and answers to questions. Submitted by Dr. H.R. Linderman,
director of the United States mint at Washington.
St. Louis, Chancy R. Barns, printer, 1875.
20p. front., fold. map. 24cm.

1. Mints – U.S. I. Title.

NL 0380389   LNHT DLC

Linderman, Henry Richard, 1825–1879.
U. S. *Treasury dept. Wastage commission.*
Report upon the wastage of silver bullion in the melter
and refiners department of the mint of the United States.
July 25, 1872. Washington, Govt. print. off., 1872.

Linderman, Wanda Taylor.
The outdoor book
    see under   Camp fire girls.

VOLUME 334

Z7161
.C65

Linderman, Winifred B.

Columbia University. *School of Library Service.*
    Guide to social science literature, for use in connection
with Library service 119 and 219. Prepared by Winifred B.
Linderman, associate in Library Service. 1st ed. New York,
°1954.

H62
.C5845

Linderman, Winifred B.

Columbia University. *School of Library Service.*
    Outline for the course in social science literature, **Library**
service 119. Prepared by Winifred B. Linderman. **Prelim.**
ed. New York, 1952.

F776
.C67

Linderman company, inc., Denver.

Colorado. *State historical society.*
    History of Colorado, prepared under the supervision of the
State historical and natural history society of Colorado; James
H. Baker, editor ... Le Roy R. Hafen, PH. D., associate editor ...
Denver, Linderman co., inc., 1927.

BM
747
Y6L5.5

Lindermann, Simon Abraham
    Der Ewige ist Gott! Eine N'ila-
Predigt, gehalten in der Synagoge zu
Neu-Stettin am Versohnungstage d. J.
5624. Neu-Stettin, 1863.
    10 p.   21 cm.

    1. Yom Kippur sermons. I. Title

NL 0380395   OCH

Lindermann, Simon Abraham.
    שריד בערכין, כולל ביאורים והנהות על ספר הערוך. מהארן.
בדפוס צ. דאמבראווסקי. תר"ל; ₍Thorn, 1870;

    84 p. 20 cm.
    Added t. p.: Sarid ba-arachin; Erläuterungen und Scholien zum
Aruch.

    1. Nathan ben Jehiel, 1035 (ca.)-1106. 'Arukh. I. Title.
        Title transliterated: Sarid ba-'arakhin.

PJ4935.N35L5   5G—49305

NL 0380396   DLC CtY

Lindermayer, Anton. Euboea; eine naturhistorische skizze. ₍Moscou. 1855.] 8°.
    *Bulletin de la Société impériale des naturalistes de Moscou, 1855, xxviii,
pt. 1, pp. 401-451.*

NL 0380397   MH-A MH

598.2
L64v

Lindermayer, Anton.
    Die Vögel Griechenlands. Ein Beitrag zur
Fauna dieses Landes, von Ritter A. Lindermayer.
Passau, Druck von F. W. Keppler, 1860.
    188p. 22cm.

    1. Birds—Greece.

NL 0380398   IU MB PPAN CtY

Lindermayer, Antonius Hermannus.
    Sistens epidemiam tussis convulsivae ac
morbillorum anno 1832-33 observatam.
Monachii, Giesser, 1833.
    28 p.
    Diss.

NL 0380399   PPC

Lindermayr, Georg, editor.
    Sozialismus und Bayerische Volkspartei. Vorträge gehalten
im Dezember 1918 in Augsburg, veranstaltet von der Ortsgruppe
Augsburg des Volksvereins für das katholische Deutschland,
herausgegeben von Georg Lindermayr... Augsburg: Sekre-
tariat der Bayerischen Volkspartei für den Kreis Schwaben, 1918.
iv, 114 p.   8°.
    Contents: Vorwort. WAGNER, G. Der Sozialismus als Weltanschauung; Der
Sozialismus als Wirtschaftssystem. ROST, H. Sozialismus, Ehe und Familie. HART-
MANN. Sozialismus und Kirche. MAYER, J. Sozialismus und Schule. HEBEL, B. Sozialismus und Bauernstand. IMLER, J. Sozialismus und Arbeiterschaft. SCHARNAGEL, K.
Sozialismus und Mittelstand. GEIGER, S. Sozialismus, Papsttum, Weltkrieg und Völker-
friede. HAAS, A. Das Programm der Bayerischen Volkspartei.

    1. Socialism. 2. Bayerische   Volkspartei.
                                                  April 12, 1927

NL 0380400   NN

Lindermayr, Maurus.
    Maurus Lindermayr's Dichtungen in ob der ennsischer
Volksmundart, von Verehrern seiner Muse gesammelt.
Linz, K. K. priv. akademischen Kunst-,Musik- und
Buchhandlung, 1822. 195 p. 19cm.

    546724B. 1. German language—Dialects—Austria—Ens.

NL 0380401   NN DLC-P4

---

von Lindern (Frants Balthasar) [1682-1755].
    De vermibus. 52 pp. sm. 4°. *Jena, lit. Kreb-*
sius, [1707].

NL 0380402   DNLM

Lindern, Franz Balthasar von, 1682–1755.
    Hortus alsaticus; plantas in Alsatia nobili, inprimi
circa Argentinam sponte provenientes, menstruo, qu
singulæ florent, ordine designans, annexo charactere, loc
natali, ac florum colore, additis aliquibus iconibus, æri ad
vivum incisis, ut et aliis ad botanices doctrinam rite addi-
scendam pertinentibus, in usum botanophilorum excur-
siones facientium conscriptus a Franc. Balthasare von
Lindern ... Argentorati, impensis J. Beckii, 1747.
    8 p. l., 302, ₍74; p. xii pl. 18ᵐᵐ.
    1. Alsace-Lorraine. Botany.
                                                  Agr 5-113

    Library, U. S. Dept. of   Agriculture   459L642H.

NL 0380403   DNAL MH-A MoSB

Lindern, Franz Balthasar von, 1682-1755.
    Medicinischer passe-par-tout; oder, Haupt-
Schlüssel. Aller und jeder kranckheiten des
menschlichen Leibes, welcher uns entdecket,
wie dieselbe bestens zu erkennen, und sicher zu
curiren seyen. Samt einer Vorrede D. Georg
Heinrich Behrs. Von der deutsch-geschriebenen
Artzney-Bücher Nothwendigkeit und Nutzbarkeit.
Strassburg, 1739.
    Bound with Carl, J. S. Erfahrungs-Grunde von
des Blutlassens. Flensburg und Altona, 1739;
Stahl, G. E. Gründliche Abhandlung von Abschaf-

fung des Mitzbrauchs. Coburg, 1739; and
Clauder, C. E. Gereralia praxeos medicae
feliciter instituendae momenta. Chemnicii,
1729.

NL 0380405   WU OrU-M CtY-M

Lindern, Franz Balthasar von, 1682-1755.
    Speculum veneris noviter politum: das
ist neu-ausgeputzter Venus-Spiegel oder
Beschreibung der meisten Venus-Kranckheiten.
Strassburg, J.Beck, 1736.
    ₍5ℓ.₎536p.₍8ℓ.₎ 167mm. 8vo.   NcD-MC

    1.Venereal diseases. 2.Sex disorders.
(Chronol: 1736. Printer: Beck, Johann)

NL 0380406   NcD-MC DNLM

Lindern, Frantz Balthasar von, 1682-1755.
    ——, Speculum veneris, oder Venus-Spiegel, vor-
stellend wie die Venus-Kranckheiten überhaupt
wo kein Medicus noch Chirurgus zu gegen, im
Fall der Noth, ein jeder für sich selbsten curiren
auch die sonst gewöhnliche Salivations-Cur
gantz leicht ohne einige Gefahr verrichten kan,
nach der sichersten Methode aus eigener Praxi
aufgezeichnet und entworfen. 6 p. l., 376 pp.,
8 l. 12°. *Strassburg, J. Beck, 1732.*

NL 0380407   DNLM OCl

QZJ
L64

Lindern, Franz Balthasar von, 1682-1755.
    Speculum veneris; oder, Venus spiegel, Das ist
richtige beschreibung aller venerischen kranckheiten nach deren ursprung so wohl als auch cur...wie
auch explication durch vielfaltige experientz ap-
probirter specificorum, von Francisco Balthasare
von Lindern... III.auflage. Strasburg, Johannes
Beck, 1743.
    5 p.l.,3-64,₍22;,612,₍28; p. front. 17½cm.

    Title in red and black.

NL 0380408   WU DNLM WU-M CtY-M

WZ
260
L745S
1751

Lindern, Franz Balthasar von, 1682-1755.
    Speculum veneris; oder, Venus-Spiegel,
worinnen sich einjeder besehen, und was für
abscheuliche Zufälle von einer unreinen Liebe
sich äussern, wahrnehmen, auch im Fall der
Noth, in Ermanglung eines habilen Medici
oder Chirurgi, sich selbsten Rath schaffen
kan. Nebst einigen merckwürdigen Begebenhei-
ten und einem Unterricht einiger approbirten
Specificorum durch vielfältige Erfahrung an
das Licht gestellet... 4. neuverm. Aufl.
Strassburg,   Verlegts Johannes Beck,
1751.

    Stamped on verso of t.-p.: J. K. Proksch.

    1. Sex Behavior. 2. Sex Disorders. 3.
Venereal Diseases. I. Title. II. Title:
Venus-Spiegel.

NL 0380410   WU-M

Lindern, Franz Balthasar von, 1682–1755.
    Tournefortius alsaticus, cis et trans Rhenanus; sive,
Opusculum botanicum ope cujus plantarum species, genera ac differentias, præprimis, circa Argentoratum, locis
in vicinis cis & trans Rhenum sponte in montibus, valli-
bus, sylvis, pratis in & sub aquis nascentes, spatioque
florentes tyro sub excursionibus botanicis facil-
lime dignoscere suæque memoriæ in nominibus impri-
mendis, ex principiis Tournefortii consulere possit, otio
privato conscriptum ac aliquibus tabulis æneis illustratum
à Franc. Balthasare von Lindern ... Argentorati, impensis H. L. Stein, 1728.
    8 p. l., 160, ₍8; p. v pl.   18ᵐᵐ.
    1. Alsace-Lorraine.   Botany.
                                                  Agr 5-114
    Library, U. S. Dept. of   Agriculture   459L642.

NL 0380411   DNAL NIC MH-A MoSB ICJ

VOLUME 334

Lindern, Georg von.
Wie komme ich zlu einem Familienwappen? Mit einer kurzgefassten Einführung in die Wappenkunde. 2., erweiterte Aufl. Leipzig, Hachmeister & Thal [1937]
48 p. coats of arms. 17 cm. (Lehrmeister-Bücherei, Nr. 1012)

1. Heraldry. I. Title.

CR23.L5 1937   50–53769

NL 0380412   DLC

Lindern, Paul von.
Quelques aspects économiques et politiques de la radio-diffusion, par Paul von Lindern ... Paris, Librairie générale de droit & de jurisprudence, R. Pichon et R. Durand-Auzias, administrateurs, 1934.
3 p. l., [3]–178 p., 1 l. incl. tables, diagrs. 25ᶜᵐ.
"Bibliographie": p. [3]–4.

1. Radio broadcasting.
                                              A C 35–2896
Title from N. Y. Pub.   Libr.   Printed by L. C.

NL 0380413   NN ICU

Linderot, Sven Harald Larsson, 1889–
Bönder och arbetare. Stockholm, Arbetarkulturs förlag, 1943.
24p. 19cm. (Dagspolitik, 11)

1. Communism – Sweden 2. Sveriges kommunistiska parti I. Title

NL 0380414   WU MH

Linderot, Sven Harald Larsson, 1889–
Bondefrågan i Sverge; till diskussionen om samverkan mellan arbetare och bönder. Stockholm, Arbetarkulturs förlag, 1943.
166 p. 20 cm.

1. Farmers—Sweden. 2. Agriculture—Economic aspects—Sweden. I. Title.
HD765.L5   52–54153 ‡

NL 0380415   DLC MH

Linderot, Sven Harald Larsson, 1889–
Debatten Linderot-Erlander i Stockholms konserthus 19. april 1948. 2. uppl. Stockholm, Arbetarkulturs förlag, 1948.
48 p. 19 cm.

1. Sweden—Pol. & govt.—1905–   2. Socialism in Sweden.
I. Erlander, Tage Fritiof, 1901–
DL868.L5 1948   49–53821*

NL 0380416   DLC

Linderot, Sven Harald Larsson, 1889–

DL868
.5
.E7 **Erlander, Tage Fritiof, 1901–**
Demokrati eller folkdemokrati; disputationen Erlander-Linderot i Stockholms konserthus den 19. april 1948. Stockholm, Tidens förlag, 1948.

JN
7995   **Linderot, Sven Harald Larsson, 1889–**
K6   Ny kurs [av] Sven Linderot. Stockholm,
L5   Arbetarkulturs förlag, 1943.
       39p.   19cm. (Dagspolitik, 15)

1. Sveriges kommunistiska parti I. Title

NL 0380418   WU MH

Linderot, Sven Harald Larsson, 1889–
Samling kring efterkrigsprogrammet; koncentrerat referat av S.Linderots och H.Hagbergs tal i remissdebatten. Stockholm, Arbetarkulturs förlag [1946]
31 p. illus. (Dagspolitik, 24)

NL 0380419   MH

Linderot, Sven Harald Larsson, 1889–
Svensk arbetarrörelse i brytningstid; tal och skrifter i urval. [Under redaktion av Knut Bäckström] Stockholm, Arbetarkulturs förlag, 1949.
528 p. port. 22 cm.

1. Labor and laboring classes—Sweden—Hist. 2. Socialism in Sweden. 3. Communism—Sweden.   I. Title.
HD8576.L53   331.082   A 50–4618
Minnesota. Univ. Libr.
for Library of Congress   †

NL 0380420   MnU DLC NN

Linderot, Sven Harald Larsson, 1889–
Tal på kommunistiska partiets konferens den 10-11 jan.1942. Stockholm, Arbetarkulturs förlag, 1942
19 p. (Dagspolitik, 1)

NL 0380421   MH

4BR
510   **Linderoth, Fred**
Den svenska kyrkan; kyrkokunskap för kyrka, skola och hem.av Fred Linderoth och Sven Norbrink. 4. omarbetade uppl. Stockholm, Svenska kyrkans diakonistyrelses bokförlag [1952]
512 p.

NL 0380422   DLC-P4 MH

Linders, Edvard, 1884– *ed.*
Lag angående förbud mot införsel till riket av varor med oriktig ursprungsbeteckning den 4 juni 1913, med förklarande anmärkningar och sakregister utgiven av Edvard Linders ... Stockholm, P. A. Norstedt & söner [1930]
138 p. 19½ᶜᵐ.
Cover-title: Lag ang. oriktig ursprungsbeteckning.

1. Marks of origin. I. Sweden. Laws, statutes, etc. II. Title: Lag angaende oriktig ursprungsbeteckning.
[Full name: Edvard August Ansgar Linders]
                                              36–21258
Library of Congress   HD3625.5.L5   338.4

NL 0380423   DLC

AS284   **LINDERS, FRANS JOSUA, 1882–**
.L9   Bidrag till kännedomen om den kommunala beskatt-
v.18   ningen och vissa därmed sammanhängande ekonomiska och demografiska förhållanden i Sveriges landskommuner under åren 1918-1928, av F.J.Linders ... Malmö, Förlags-aktiebolagets i Malmö boktryckeri, 1933.
[1],165 p.incl.tables,diagrs. 25½cm. (Half-title: Skrifter utgivna av Fahlbeckska stiftelsen, XVIII)

1. Sweden--Stat. 2. Taxation--Sweden.

NL 0380424   ICU NN DLC-P4 MH NIC

HB2707 **LINDERS, FRANS JOSUA, 1882–**
.L7   Demografiska studier rörande svenska kyrkans prä-sterskap. Del I... Uppsala,Almqvist & Wiksells bok-tryckeri,1925.
xxiii,278 p.incl.tables,diagrs. 24½cm.
Akademisk afhandling--Uppsala.
"Litteraturförteckning":p.[272]-277.
Résumé(in French):p.[166]-176.

1. Clergy--Sweden.

NL 0380425   ICU CtY PU ICRL MH

Linders, Frans Josua, 1882–
... Formulas, tables, and graphs concerning the addition of two normal frequency curves, by F. J. Linders. Uppsala, Almqvist & Wiksells boktryckeri-a.-b., 1936.
39 p. diagrs. 24ᶜᵐ. (Uppsala universitets årsskrift 1936:3)
Series title also in French.

1. Frequency curves. 2. Statistics. I. Title.
Minnesota. Univ. Library   A C 39–2907
for Library of Congress   [AS284.U7 1936]
                                              (378.485)

NL 0380426   MnU MoU PU OU

Linders, Frans Josua, 1882–   *joint ed.*
Lundborg, Herman Bernhard, 1868– *ed.*
... The racial characters of the Swedish nation, Anthropologia suecica MCMXXVI, with the collaboration of the staff of the institute and other scientists ed. by H. Lundborg ... [and] F. J. Linders ... Uppsala, To be distributed by Almqvist & Wiksell; New York, G. E. Stechert & co.; [etc., etc., 1926]

Linders, Frans Josua, 1882–
... En statistisk undersökning rörande vid Uppsala universitet under åren 1909-1934 avlagda filosofiska ämbetsexamina, särskilt rörande studietidens längd, av F. J. Linders och F. E. Lander. Uppsala, Almqvist & Wiksells boktryckeri-a.-b., 1936.
110 p. incl. illus., tables (part fold.) diagrs. 24ᶜᵐ. (Uppsala universitets årsskrift 1936:9)
Title in French on verso of t.-p.; series title and "Index" also in French.
1. Uppsala. Universitet—Degrees. 2. Degrees, Academic—Sweden.
I. Lander, Frans Elvir, 1899–   joint author. II. Title.
Minnesota. Univ. Library   A C 39–2913
for Library of Congress   [AS284.U7 1936]
                                              (378.485)

NL 0380428   MnU PU

Linders, Frans Josua, 1882–
... Über die Bewegung eines kleinen Planeten in der Nähe der Lagrange'schen Dreieckspunkte, von F. J. Linders ... [Uppsala, Almqvist & Wiksells boktryckeri-a.-b., 1908]
29 p. 23ᶜᵐ. (Arkiv för matematik, astronomi och fysik. bd. 4, no 20)
Caption title.
At head of title: Meddelande från Lunds Astronomiska observatorium.

NL 0380429   ICJ

Linders, Jacob, 1868–
Sweden. *Fattigvårdslagstiftningskommittén.*
... Barnavårdslagstiftningen ... Stockholm, Tryckt hos P. Palmquist, 1921.

VOLUME 334

Linders, Jacob, 1868–

Sweden. *Fattigvårdslagstiftningskommittén.*
... Förslag till lag om behandling af alkoholister, afgifvet af den af Kungl. Majt. den 21 juni 1907 tillsatta Kommitté för utarbetande af förslag till förändrad lagstiftning angående fattigvården samt angående lösdrifvares behandling m. m. Stockholm, Tryckt hos P. Palmquists aktiebolag, 1911.

Law

Sweden. *Laws, statutes, etc.*
Lag om fattigvården den 14. juni 1918 med förklaringar, hänvisningar, prejudikat och sakregister av Jacob Linders. 10. uppl. utg. av Eric Wahlberg. Stockholm, Norstedt ₁1951₎

Linders, Jacob, 1868–   ed.

Law

Sweden. *Laws, statutes, etc.*
Lag om fattigvården den 14. juni 1918 och andra författningar, som beröra fattigvårdsstyrelsernas verksamhet; med förklaringar, hänvisningar, prejudikat, formulär och sakregister, utgiven av Jacob Linders ... 6. uppl. Stockholm, P. A. Norstedt & söner ₁1929₎

Linders, Johan
     see   Lindestolpe, Johan, 1678-1724.

Linders, Olof.
**** Die Formelzeichen. Ein Beitrag zur Lösung der rrage der algebraischen Bezeichnung der physikalischen, technischen und chemischen Grössen. Von Olof Linders ... . Leipzig, Jäh & Schunke, 1905.
[4], 96 p.   28ᶜᵐ.

NL 0380435   ICJ DBS

Linders, Olof.
**** Die für Technik und Praxis wichtigsten physikalischen Grössen in systematischer Darstellung sowie die algebraische Bezeichnung der Grössen, physikalische Masssysteme, Nomenklatur der Grössen und Masseinheiten. Von Olof Linders ... . Mit 43 Textfiguren. Leipzig, Jäh & Schunke, 1904.
xii, 396 p.   43 diagr., 2 fold. tables.   22ᶜᵐ.

NL 0380436   ICJ DBS PPF

Linders, Olof.
Zur klarstellung der begriffe masse, gewicht, schwere und kraft von Olof Linders.   Leipzig, Jaeh & Schunke (Rossberg'sche buchhandlung) 1905.
22 p.   23 cm.

NL 0380437   DBS

Linderstrøm-Lang, C. F.
Commentar til Q. Horatii Flacii Opera. Kjobenhavn, 1898-1900.

NL 0380438   NjP

871   Linderstrøm-Lang, C   F
T3p.Yli   P. Terentii Afri Phormio (Commentar)
...   Kobenhavn, 1893.
 112p.

NL 0380439   IU

Linderstrøm-Lang, Kaj, 1896-
— On the ionisation of proteins.   29 pp. 8°. Copenhague, H. Hagerup, 1924.
Forms No. 7, v. 15 of Compt.-rend. trav. Lab. Carlsberg.

NL 0380440   DNLM

Linderstrøm-Lang (Kaj. On the salting-out effect. 65 pp. 8°. Copenhague, H. Hagerup, 1924.
Forms No. 4, v. 15 of Compt.-rend. trav. Lab. Carlsberg.

NL 0380441   DNLM

Linderstrøm-Lang, Kaj, 1896-
Proteins and enzymes.   Stanford, Stanford University Press, 1952.
vi, 115 p. illus. 23 cm. (Lane medical lectures, 1951)
Stanford University publications. University series. Medical sciences, v. 6.
Includes bibliographies.

1. Proteins. 2. Enzymes.   (Series. Series: Stanford University. Stanford University publications. University series. Medical sciences, v. 6)

Full name: Kaj Ulrik Linderstrøm-Lang.

QP551.I48   612.015   52–5979 ‡
                     AS36.L57 vol. 6

         PSt ViU TU PPASDA NNC-M NcD
NL 0380442   DLC MtU IdPS Or CU GU DNLM PPTU OU

Linderstrøm-Lang, Kaj, 1896–
Studier over kasein; om kaseinets fraktionering, af K. Linderstrøm-Lang. København, H. Hagerup, 1929.
2 p. l., 111 p. fold. tab., diagrs. 23½ᶜᵐ.
Thesis—Copenhagen.
"Litteraturfortegnelse": p. ₁106₎–109.

1. Casein.
                    ₁Full name: Kaj Ulrik Linderstrøm-Lang₎
                                32–25081
Library of Congress   QP551.L5 1929   547.S

NL 0380443   DLC ICRL CtY MiU

Linderup, Hans Christian, 1763-1809.
De første grunde af den rene mathematik. Forsøg til en laerebog for skoler, ved Hans Christian Linderup ... Kiøbenhavn, Forlagt af direktør J.F.Schultz, 1799-1803.
2 v. fold.plates (diagrs.) 18ᶜᵐ.

1.Mathematics--Text-books.   I.Title.

NL 0380445   MiU

Linderup,Hans Christian,1763-1809.
De første grunde af den rene mathematik. Forsøg til en laerebog for skoler,ved Hans Christian Linderup. Tvende dele. Anden,ved flere betydelige forandringer og tillaeg forbedrede,og med en kort afhandling om de krumme linier,der almindelig kaldes keglesnitte,forøgede udgave ... Kiøbenhavn, Trykt og forlagt af directeur J.F.Schultz, 1807.
2 v.in 1.   VII fold.pl.(diagrs.) 18ᶜᵐ.
Vol.2 without t.-p.

1.Mathematics--Text-books.   I.Title.

NL 0380446   MiU

Lindes, August Wilhelm, 1800-1862.
— Beiträge zur gerichtlichen Chemie. Enthaltend: I. Die Ermittelung der Mahlstener-Defraudationen. II. Die Unterscheidung von Leinen und Baumwolle in gemischten Geweben. III. Ueber die Auffindung des Arseniks in Leichen. 1 p. l., 103 pp. 8°. *Berlin, L. Oehmigke,* 1853.

NL 0380447   DNLM MH

Lindes, August Wilhelm, 1800-1862.
Chemische Farbenlehre für Maler, Tapetenfabrikanten und Farbwaarenhändler ... Weimar, B. F. Voigt, 1861.
x, 79 p. 19 cm. (Neuer Schauplatz der Künste und Handwerke, 250. Bd.)

1. Pigments. 2. Colors. 3. Varnish and varnishing.   (Series)
                                                   P O 52–269
U. S. Patent Office.   Library TP935.L5
for Library of Congress

NL 0380448   DP NN

Lindes, August Wilhelm, 1800-1862.
Handbuch der saffian-fabrikation. Ein sicherer leitfaden, wie der schönste saffian auf die einfachste und vortheilhafteste weise bereitet wird. Herausgegeben von dem professor Lindes und dem saffian-fabrikanten Carl Bräutigam... Berlin, J.Springer, 1860.
vi,140 p.   front.(mounted samples)   20cm.

1. Leather industry and trade.   I. Bräutigam, Carl.   II. Title.

NL 0380449   DP CaBVaU

QV   LINDES, August Wilhelm, 1800-
L744p   Praktische Anleitung zu den
1849   wichtigsten gerichtlich-chemischen und
           sanitäts-polizeilichen Untersuchungen;
           für Physiker, Aerzte und Apotheker.
           Berlin, Oehmigke, 1849.
           x, 238 p.

NL 0380450   DNLM MoSU IU DP PPC

Lindes,August Wilhelm,1800-1862.
Praktische anleitung zur prufung und werthbestimmung der wichtigsten im handel vorkommenden dungemittel. Zunachst fur landwirthe. Berlin, 1855.

No.9 in volume lettered: Pamphlets. Agriculture. v.4.

NL 0380451   MiU

Lindes, August Wilhelm, 1800-1862.
₁Lindes,₎ — Ueber die Auffindung des Arseniks bei gerichtlich-chemischen Untersuchungen. 24 pp. 8°. *Berlin, A. W. Hayn,* 1846. — Bound with : Königsstadt. Realschule zu Berlin. Jahresbericht. 4°. *Berlin,* 1846.

NL 0380452   DNLM

QV   LINDES, August Wilhelm, 1800-   ed.
L744v   Vollständige Sammlung aller Gesetze
1836   und Verordnungen, welche in Bezug auf
           das Apothekenwesen für die Königlich
           Preussischen Staaten erlassen sind.
           Berlin, Oehmigke, 1836.
           viii, 526 p.
              I. Prussia. Laws, statutes, etc.

NL 0380453   DNLM

VOLUME 334

QV
L744v
1843

LINDES, August Wilhelm, 1800-   ed.
Vollständige Sammlung aller Gesetze und Verordnungen, welche in Bezug auf das Apothekenwesen für die Königlich Preussischen Staaten erlassen sind. 2. verm. und verb. Aufl. Berlin, Oehmigke, 1843.
x, 546 p.   QV L744v
I. Prussia. Laws, statutes, etc.

NL 0380454   DNLM OCU

QVA
L745v
1846

LINDES, August Wilhelm, 1800-
Vollständiges Wörterbuch zur sechsten Ausgabe der Pharmacopoea Borussica. 2., verm. und verb. Ausg. Berlin, Schultze, 1846.
vii, 163 p.   QVA L745v
I. Pharmacopoea Borussica

NL 0380455   DNLM ICJ

Lindes (Ernestus) [1836-]. *De aqua pota-lonia. 32 pp. 8°. *Berolini, G. Lange, [1859].

NL 0380456   DNLM

Adelmann
QL
838
L74
1865a

Lindes, Georg.
Ein Beitrag zur Entwicklungsgeschichte des Herzens. Dorpat, Druck von H. Laakmann, 1865.
vi, 59 p. 2 plates.
Thesis--Tartu.
Photocopy of the copy in the National Library of Medicine. vi, 59 l. 22 cm.
1. Heart. 2. Embryology.

NL 0380457   NIC MH WU-M DNLM

LINDES, Wilhelm

See LINDES, August Wilhelm, 1800-1862.

Linde's Eismaschinen A.-G., Wiesbaden.
.... Geschichte der gesellschaft für Linde's eismaschinen A.-G. Wiesbaden. Herausgegeben zum jubiläum der gesellschaft für Linde's eismaschinen A.-G. Wiesbaden, 1929.
192 p.
Above title: 50 Jahre kaltetechnik, 1879-1929.

NL 0380459   NN

Lindesay, Sir David, fl. 1490-1555
see
Lindsay, Sir David, fl. 1490-1555.

Lindesay, David, Bp. of Brechen, d. 1641?
see   Lindsay, David, Bp. of Edinburgh, d. 1641?

LINDESAY, FREDERICK, 1792-1871.
The Lindesays of Loughry, county Tyrone; abstract from a manuscript book, written early in the nineteenth century by Frederick Lindesay and presented to his nephew, John Lindesay, the seventh owner of Loughry and Tullyhogue, with a preface, signed and dated June 16, 1834. Morden, Surrey, Issued for private family circulation, by E. H. Godfrey, 1951. 141. . 27cm.

This abstract does not include those portions of the manuscript included in The Lindesays of Loughry, county Tyrone; a genealogical history, compiled by Ernest H. Godfrey, 1949.

1. Lindesay family. I. Godfrey, Ernest Henry, 1862-

NL 0380463   NN

Lindesay, George. Rambles in Norsk Finmarken. 14 pp. (Forts. Rev. n. s. v. 56, 1894, p. 671.)

NL 0380464   MdBP

Lindesay, Mrs. Harriot Hester (Williams-Wynn) d. 1878, ed.

Williams-Wynn, Charlotte, 1807-1869.
Extracts from letters and diaries of Charlotte Williams Wynn. Privately printed. London, Trübner & co., 1871.

Lindesay, Mrs. Harriet Hester (Williams-Wynn) d. 1878, ed.
Memorials of Charlotte Williams-Wynn.
see under Williams-Wynn, Charlotte, 1807-1869.

NL 0380466   CtY

Lindesay, John, fl. 1732.
RES.   *De calore.
Bd.Pam.   Edinburgi: [C.Elliot, & G.Robinson], 1732,
v.618   [44] p. 21 cm.

NL 0380467   NNNAM

Lindesay, John, fl. 1732.
Dissertatio inauguralis de calore. 1732.
(Smellie's Thes. med. , vol. 1, p. 83-126. Edin. 1788)

NL 0380468   MB DNLM

B610.24
Ed4
1805
v.4

Lindesay, John, fl. 1805.
De febre remittente Indiae Occidentalis ... Edinburgi, Excudebant A. Neill et Socii, 1805.
[6], 51 p. 21 cm. (In Edinburgh. University. Dissertationes medicae, 1805, v.4)
Inaug. Diss. - Edinburgh.

NL 0380469   MNU-B DNLM

Lindesay, Mrs. Marie (Batterham) 1862-
The first shearing, by M. Batterham Lindesay. Richmond, Va., Whittet & Shepperson, 1904.
1 p. l., 11 p., 1 l., [13]-299 p. 20½-.
Poems.

I. Title.
                                    4-18022 Revised
Library of Congress   PS3523.I 54F5   1904
                            [r41b2]   -811.5

NL 0380470   DLC Nc NcU NN NcC FTaSU NcRS NcD ViU

Lindesay, Patrick
see Lindsay, Patrick, d. 1753.

Lindesay, Robert, of Pitscottie
see Lindsay, Robert, 1532-1578.

Mac8
1716
L64

[Lindesay, Thomas] Abp. of Armagh, 1656-1764
The insolence of the dissenters against the Establish'd Church exemplified in a memorial given in to the Lords Justices of Ireland, by his Grace the Lord Primate, and the Lord Bishop of Down and Connor ... London, J. Baker, 1716.
43p. 19cm.

NL 0380473   CtY

WX
2
GS8
L6L3a

LINDESBERG, Sweden. Lasarettet
Årsberättelse.
Lindesberg [19--?]-
v.

NL 0380474   DNLM

W 2
GS8.2
L7S7a

LINDESBERG, Sweden. Stads- och sjukstuguläkare
Årsberättelse från Landstingets sjukvårdsinrättningar i Lindesberg, samt Lindesberg stad och Hälsovårdsnämnd. Lindesberg [19--?]-
v.
1. Hospitals - Sweden - Lindesberg
2. Public health - Sweden - Lindesberg

NL 0380475   DNLM

Lindesberg, Sweden. Stadspedagogien.
Redogörelse för allmänna läroverken och pedagogierna i Vestmanland ...
see under Västmanland, Sweden.

Lindesie, A.
The Gospel of grace. By A. Lindesie...
Lond., Paris & N.Y., Cassell & Company, [1883]
xv, (1) 164 p.   19 cm.

YA 26634

NL 0380477   DLC MiD

VOLUME 334

Lindesie, A
Reconciliation, an argument for Chirstian faith.
London, pref. 1882.

NL 0380478   ODW

Lindeskog, Gösta, 1904–
Bibeln och den nyare forskningen ....
Uppsala, J. A. Lindblad [1941]
207 p.   20 cm.
"Litteraturhanvisningar": p. [198]-203.

NL 0380479   NjPT

Lindeskog, Gösta, 1904–
Handbok i bibelkunskap. Stockholm, Natur och kultur
[1952]
406 p.   23 cm.
Bibliographical references: p. [389]-397.

1. Bible—Introductions.
Full name: Gösta Rudolf Edvard Lindeskog.

BS475.L5   55-27557

NL 0380480   DLC CtY-D MH-AH

LINDESKOG, Gösta, 1904–
Inledning till Nya Testamentet, av Gösta Lindeskog, Anton Fridrichsen, Harald Riesenfeld. Stockholm, Svenska Kyrkans Diakonistyrelses Bokförlag
[1951]
383p.

NL 0380481   MH-AH NjPT

Lindeskog, Gösta, 1904–
Jesus och judarna. Stockholm, Svenska
kyrkans diakonistyrelses bokförlag [1940]
186 p.   20 cm.

NL 0380482   CtY-D

Lindeskog, Gösta, 1904–
Die Jesusfrage im neuzeitlichen Judentum; ein Beitrag zur
Geschichte der Leben-Jesu-Forschung ... von Gösta Lindeskog
... Uppsala: Almqvist & Wiksells boktryckeri-a.-b., 1938.
xi, 369 p.   24½cm.   (Upsala, Sweden. Universitet. Teologiska
seminariet. Arbeiten und Mitteilungen aus dem Neutestament-
lichen Seminar zu Uppsala. [Nr. 8])
Inaugural-Dissertation — Uppsala, 1938.
Bibliographies included.

999527A. 1. Jesus Christ in Jewish   literature. I. Ser.
August 17, 1939

NL 0380483   NN OCH MH CtY ICRL PPDrop

Lindeskog, Gösta, 1904–
... Die Jesusfrage im neuzeitlichen Judentum; ein beitrag zur
geschichte der leben-Jesu-forschung, von Gösta Lindeskog.
Leipzig, A. Lorentz; Uppsala, A. B. Lundquist, 1938.
xi, 369, [1] p. 24½cm. (Arbeiten und mitteilungen aus dem Neutestamentlichen seminar zu Uppsala, hrsg. von A. Fridrichsen. VIII)
"Jüdische bibliographie": p. [328]-362; "Angeführte nicht-jüdische
literatur": p. [363]-369.

1. Jesus Christ—Jewish interpretations. 2. Jesus Christ—Biog.—Hist.
& crit. I. Title.
39-29599
Library of Congress   BM620.L53
296

NL 0380484   DLC FU NjPT MB OCH NjP CCSC

Lindeskog, Gösta, 1904–
Studien zum neutestamentlichen Schöpfungsgedanken.
Uppsala, Lundequistska bokhandeln [1952–
v.   25 cm.   (Uppsala universitets årsskrift 1952: 11
Bibliography: v. 1, p. [273]-287.

1. Creation.   I. Title.   (Series: Uppsala. Universitet. Års
skrift, 1952: 11)
Full name: Gösta Rudolf Edvard Lindeskog.
AS284.U7 1952, no. 11, etc.   A 55-3673

Minnesota. Univ. Libr.
for Library of Congress   [a56b]†

ViAlTh MH-AH PPiPT MoU
NL 0380485   MnU DLC NN NIC CtY OCH CtY-D DCU NjPT

BS500
.L74 Lindeskog, Gösta, 1904–
Svenska exegetiske Disputationer under 1800-
Talet. Uppsala, A.-B Lundequistska; Leipzig,
Harrassowitz [1941]
43 p.   25 cm.   (Uppsala Universitets Aar-
skrift 1941: 7, 17)

At head to title: Festskrift utgiven av
Teologiska Fakulteten i Uppsala 1941 till 400-
Aarsminnet av Bibelns Utgivande paa Svenska,
1541.
Bibliography: .9-43.

NL 0380486   IEG

Lindesmith, Alfred Ray, 1905–
... The nature of opiate addiction ... by Alfred Ray
Lindesmith ... [Chicago] 1937.
1 p. l., 11, 82-85, 104-151, 203-226 p. 24cm.
Part of thesis (PH. D.)—University of Chicago, 1937
Lithoprinted.
"Private edition, distributed by the University of Chicago libraries,
Chicago, Illinois."

1. Opium habit.   I. Title.   II. Title: Opiate addiction.
38-11949
Library of Congress   RC369.L5 1937
Univ. of Chicago Libr.
613.82

NL 0380487   ICU DLC NIC CU NcD OU OCIW OCU ViU

Micro
RC   Lindesmith, Alfred Ray, 1905–
369   The nature of opiate addiction.   Chicago,
.L56   Dept. of Photoduplication, University of
Govt.   Chicago Library, 1937.
Doc.   Microfilm copy (positive) of typescript.
Bu.   Collation of the original:
Thesis (Ph.D.) - University of Chicago.
Includes bibliography.

1. Opium habit. I. Title. II. Title:
Opiate addiction.

NL 0380488   NBuU

Lindesmith, Alfred Ray, 1905–
Opiate addiction. Bloomington, Ind., Principia Press,
1947.
ix, 238 p.   24 cm.
Bibliography: p. 222-232. Bibliographical footnotes.

1. Opium habit. [1. Opium addiction] I. Title.
RC369.L52   613.82   Med 48—1380
U. S. National Library   of Medicine,
for Library of Congress   [a60f½]†

PJB
MiU Wa IU GU CU AU TU NNC OrPR CaBVaU TxU ICU ViU
NL 0380489   DNLM OkU-M DLC WaSp CaBVa OrU OrLgE

Lindesmith, Alfred Ray, 1905–
Social psychology, by Alfred R. Lindesmith and Anselm
L. Strauss. New York, Dryden Press [1949]
xvi, 549 p. illus. 22 cm. (The Dryden Press sociology publica-
tions)
Includes bibliographies.

1. Social psychology.   I. Strauss, Anselm L., joint author.

HM251.L477   301.15   49-9196*

OC1JC OC1W PLFM CoDCC TU IdU OrCS OrPR
NL 0380490   DLC OrU ICU WaSpG WaWW OrPS PU PSt TxU

Lindesmith, Alfred Ray, 1905–
Social psychology, by Alfred R. Lindesmith
and Anselm L. Strauss.   New York, Dryden
Press [1950, c1949]
xvi, 549 p. illus.   22 cm.   (The Dryden
Press sociology publications)
Includes bibliographies.

NL 0380491   CU

Lindesmith, Alfred Ray, 1905–
Social psychology, by Alfred R. Lindesmith
and Anselm L. Strauss.   New York, Dryden
Press [1954, c1949]
xvi, 549 p.   illus.   22 cm.   (The Dryden
Press sociology publications)
Includes bibliographies.

NL 0380492   NcRS

Lindestam, Lennart.
Lärobok i deklarationsteknik och skattelagstiftning
Göteborg, Gumpert [1953]
96 p. illus. 20 cm. (Göteborgs handelsinstituts lärokssserie, 18)

1. Income tax—Sweden—Law. 2. Taxation—Sweden—Law.
I. Title.
56-35523
NL 0380493   DLC MH-L

610
L7ud Lindestolpe, Johan, 1678-1724.
Johannis Linder ... De venenis in genere, & in
specie exercitatio ... Lugduni Batavorum, Apud
Andream Dyckhuisen, 1708.

267, [32] p. 13½cm.

NL 0380494   PCarlD PPCP NNNAM

Lindestolpe, Johan, 1678-1724.
Johan Linders Flora wiksbergensis, eller Ett register
uppå de träd / buskar / örter och gräs / som innom en
fierdings wåg kring suurbrunnen Wiksberg, antingen på
åkrar sås / eller wildt wexa / med theras brukeligaste
namn på latin och på swensko. Stockholm, Tryckt hoos
sal. J. G. Matthiæ, Kongl. ant. archivi boktryckarens
enckia, af J. L. S. Horn, fact., 1716.
2 p. l., 42 p. 15cm.

1. Botany—Sweden.

9-3937
Library of Congress   QK327.L68

NL 0380495   DLC KMK

VOLUME 334

Lindestolpe, Johan, 1678–1724.
Johan Linders Flora wiksbergensis, eller Ett register vppå the träd, buskar, örter och gräs, som innom en fierdings wåg kring surbrunnen Wiksberg, antingen på åkrar sås, eller wildt wäxa, med theras brukeligaste namn på latin och på swensko. Stockholm, Tryckt hos J. L. Horrn, 1728.
2 p. l., 42 p. 17¼ᵐ.
First edition, 1716.
1. Botany—Sweden.
9–351
Library of Congress   QK327.L7

NL   0380496   DLC

Lindestolpe, Johan, 1678–1724.
Tanckar Om Frossan Och Kin-Kina Barken. Stockholm, J. G. Matthiae, 1717.
58 p.   8 vo.

NL   0380497   RPJCB

Lindestolpe, Johan, 1678–1724.
Tanckar om Skörbugg och Rogfubben. Stockholm, Joh. L. Horrn, 1721.
2 p. l., 68 p.   17. cm.
1. Scurvy.

NL   0380498   CtY-M

Lindeström, Carl, 1762–1820.
DL991
.S597A7
Almqvist, Sven Paulus, 1699–1780.
Diarium Unnarydense; en småländsk sockenkrönika. Med inledning och kommentarer av Paul Wilstadius. ₍Falun, 1950₎

Lindeström, Carolus, respondent.
Dissertatio historica de meritis Jacobi Ulphonis, archiepiscopi upsaliensis...
      see under   Fant, Erik Mikael, 1754–1817, praeses.

Lindeström, Johannes, respondent.
... Dissertatio academica de dependentia mentis a corpore in percipiendo...
      see under   Christiernin, Peter Nikolai, 1725–1799, praeses.

Lindeström, Johannes, respondent.
... Dissertatio gradualis de necessitate vitae post hanc futurae...
      see under   Christiernin, Peter Nikolai, 1725–1799, praeses.

Lindeström, Peter Mårtensson, 1632–1691.
Geographia Americae with an account of the Delaware Indians, based on surveys and notes made in 1654–1656, by Peter Lindeström; translated from the original manuscript with notes, introduction and an appendix of Indian geographical names with their meanings, by Amandus Johnson ... Philadelphia, The Swedish colonial society, 1925.
xliv, 418 p. plates, ports., fold. maps, facsims. (part fold.) 22¼ᵐ.
Bibliography: p. 291–298.
1. New Sweden. 2. Delaware Indians. 3. Indians of North America—Names. 4. Canary Islands—Descr. & trav.   i. Johnson, Amandus, 1877—tr. ii. Swedish colonial society. iii. Title.
Library of Congress   F167.L73
25–11200

ViW CU TxU NSyU PP OrP
NL   0380503   DLC PPAmSwM MiU PPL PHC PU NcU ICN NIC

Lindeström, Peter Mårtensson, 1632–1691.
Nova Suecia: Eller de Swenskas revier in India Occidentali.   La nouvelle Suede; ou, La reviere des Suedois dans les Indes Occidentales.   n. d.

NL   0380504   PPAmP

Lindeström, Peter Mårtensson, 1632–1691.
Per Lindeströms resa till Nya Sverige, 1653–1656, skildrad av honom själv i hans handskrift "Geographia Americæ eller Indiæ occidentalis beskrijffningh", med 27 illustrationer och 3 kartor, utgiven av Nils Jacobsson ... Stockholm, Wahlström & Widstrand ₍1923₎
200 p. illus. (incl. ports., map, facsim.) 22½ᵐ.
The facsimile is a reproduction of the t.-p. of "Geographia Americæ".
"Litteratur": p. 23.
1. New Sweden. 2. Delaware Indians.   i. Jacobsson, Nils Maurits Valdemar, 1873–   ed. ii. Title: Geographia Americæ.
37–34681
Library of Congress   F167.L72
917.51

NL   0380505   DLC CU WaU CtY MH NNG NN ICU ICN

DG83
.1
.L74
(C1)
LINDET, FERNAND.
...De l'acquisition et de la perte du droit de cité romaine.   De l'acquisition et de la perte de la qualité de Français...   Paris, Impr. Moquet, 1880.
[3]–379 p.   24cm.
Thèse--Faculté de droit de Paris.
Bibliographical foot-notes.

1. Citizenship--Rome.   2. Citizenship--France.

NL   0380506   ICU MH CtY NIC

Lindet, Gaston Aimé Léon
see
Lindet, Léon, 1857–1918.

Lindet, Jean Baptiste Robert
see
Lindet, Robert, 1749 (ca.)–1825.

Lindet, Leon, 1857–1929.
La Bière.   Paris, Gauthier-Villars, 1892.
206 p.

NL   0380509   PPF

*Lindet, Leon, 1857–1929.
International congress of applied chemistry. *8th, Washington and New York, 1912.*
Compte rendu de la Commission internationale d'analyses au VIIIᵐᵉ Congrès international de chimie appliquée tenu à New-York en 1912.   Bericht der Internationalen analysenkommission an den VIII Internationalen kongress für angewandte chemie in New York, 1912.   Report of the International committee on analyses to the VIIIth International congress of applied chemistry at New-York, 1912, par m. L. Lindet ... Paris, Impr. Belin frères, 1912.

Lindet, Léon, 1857–
Contribution à l'étude des matières albuminoïdes solubles du lait.   Par MM. Lindet et L. Ammann.
Ann. Inst. nat. agron. sér. 2, tome 5, p. 283–296.   Paris, 1906.

1. Milk. Albuminoid constituents.   i. Ammann, Louis, joint author.
Library, U. S. Dept. of   Agriculture   Agr 12–1985

NL   0380511   DNAL

Lindet, Léon, 1857–
Dosage de la matière grasse dans les crèmes.
Ann. sci. agron. année 32 (sér. 4, année 4) p. 1–6.   Paris, 1915.

1. ₍Butter fat₎ 2. Cream.
Library, U. S. Dept. of   Agriculture   Agr 16–494

NL   0380512   DNAL

Lindet, Léon, 1857–
L'emploi du lait et l'industrie laitière chez les peuples anciens.
Ann. Inst. nat. agron. sér. 2, tome 9, p. 203–240.   Paris, 1910.

1. Milk. 2. Dairying. History.
Library, U. S. Dept. of   Agriculture   Agr 12–1986

NL   0380513   DNAL

Lindet, Léon, 1857–   3593·19r
— L'esprit et le cœur de l'enfant.
— Paris. Belin. 1910. 166, (1) pp. Illus. 22 cm., in 8s.

H3305 — Children. Study.

NL   0380514   MB

Lindet, Léon, 1857–
Évolution des grains de fécule dans le tubercule de pomme de terre, par L. Lindet ... et P. Nottin ... illus.
Ann. Inst. nat. agron. t. 17, p. 25–54.   Paris, 1923.

1. Starch.   i. Nottin, Paul, 1883–   joint author.
₍Full name: Gaston Aimé Léon Lindet₎
Library, U. S. Dept. of   Agriculture 105.3 In8 tome 17   Agr 24–236

NL   0380515   DNAL

Lindet, Léon, 1857–1929.
Évolution des industries qui transforment les produits agricoles; introduction au cours professé à l'Institut national agronomique, par m. L. Lindet ... Paris, Librairie de L'enseignement technique, 1920.
2 p. l., ₍7₎–159 p. 19ᵐ.

1. ₍Agricultural industries₎ 2. Agriculture—France. ₍2. France—Agriculture₎
U. S. Dept. of agr. Library   33.17L64   Agr 21–500
for Library of Congress   ₍a41b1₎

NL   0380516   DNAL ICJ

VOLUME 334

Lindet, Léon, 1857–　　joint author.

Girard, Aimé, 1830–1898.
　... Le froment et sa mouture. Traité de meunerie, d'après un manuscrit inachevé de Aimé Girard ... par L. Lindet ... Paris, Gauthier-Villars, 1903.

Lindet, Léon, 1857–
　Influence des éléments de la farine bise sur la formation du gluten et sur la panification. Par MM. Lindet et L. Ammann.
　Ann. Inst. nat. agron.　sér. 2, tome 4, p. 249–260.　　Paris, 1905.

　1. Flour.　ɪ. Ammann, Louis, joint author.

　Library, U. S. Dept. of　　Agriculture　　Agr 12–1987

NL　0380518　DNAL

Lindet, Léon, 1857–
　... Le lait et la science.　Paris, Payot, 1923.
　3 p. l., ₉–144 p. 18₁ᶜᵐ. (La renaissance agricole, directeur Prosper Gervaise ...)

　1. Dairying. ₍1. Dairy₎
　　　　　　　　　　　　　　　　Agr 26–153
　Library, U. S. Dept. of　　Agriculture 44L64L

NL　0380519　DNAL

Lindet, Léon, 1857–
　Notice sur la vie et les travaux de Aimé Girard.　port.
　Ann. Inst. nat. agron.　sér. 2, tome 6, p. 197–224.　　Paris, 1907.

　1. Girard, Aimé i. e. Claude Aimé.

　Library, U. S. Dept. of　　Agriculture　　Agr 12–1988

NL　0380520　DNAL

Lindet, Léon, 1857–
　Principes de l'industrie laitière. Le lait, la crème, le beurre, les fromages, par L. Lindet ...　Paris, Gauthier-Villars, 1907.
　x, 347, ₍1₎ p. illus. 25₄ᶜᵐ.
　"Index alphabétique": p. ₍341₎–347.

　1. Dairy.
　　　　　　　　　　　　　　　Agr 7–2136
　Library, U. S. Dept. of　　Agriculture 44L64

NL　0380521　DNAL ICJ NN

HC276
S678
v.123
　Lindet, Léon, 1857–
　　La reconstitution des industries agricoles après la guerre, par M.L.Lindet ₍et M.Naudet₎
　　(In Société d'encouragement pour l'industrie nationale, Paris.　Bulletin... Paris, 1925. 28cm. t.135, p.₍526₎–540)
　　"Conférence faite devant la Société d'encouragement pour l'industrie nationale... 8 juin 1925."
　　Separate number.
　　Contents.– Avant-propos.– La reconstitution des sucreries, par ₍M₎ Lindet et Naudet.– La reconstitution des distilleries, par M.Lindet.– La reconstitution des brasseries.
　　1.Agriculture – France. 2.France – Economic conditions – 1918–　I.Naudet, II. Title.

NL　0380522　CSt–H

Lindet, Léon, 1857–
　Sur la maturation des fromages par MM. Léon Lindet ... et Louis Ammann ... avec la collaboration de M. Houdet ...
　Ann. Inst. nat. agron.　sér. 2, tome 3, p. 223–240.　　Paris, 1904.

　1. Cheese. Ripening.　ɪ. Ammann, Louis, joint author.　ɪɪ. Houdet, V., joint author.

　Library, U. S. Dept. of　　Agriculture　　Agr 12–1989

NL　0380523　DNAL

Lindet, Léon, 1857–
　Sur le dosage de la cellulose dans les farines et la recherche de leur degré de blutage.
　Ann. sci. agron.　année 31 (sér. 4, année 3) no. 4, p. 145–149. Paris, 1914.

　1. Flour–₍Cellulose content₎　2. Flour–₍Bolting₎

　Library, U. S. Dept. of　　Agriculture　　Agr 14–1243

NL　0380524　DNAL

Lindet, Léon, 1857–
　Sur le pouvoir électif des cellules végétales vis à vis du dextrose et du lévulose.
　Ann. Inst. nat. agron.　sér. 2, tome 10, p. 49–68.　　Paris, 1911

　1. Plant nutrition.　2. Dextrose.　3. Levulose.

　Library, U. S. Dept. of　　Agriculture　　Agr 12–1990

NL　0380525　DNAL

Lindet, Léon, 1857–
　Sur le pouvoir rotatoire des proteines extraites des farines de céréales par l'alcool aqueux.　Par MM. Lindet et L. Ammann.
　Ann. Inst. nat. agron.　sér. 2, tome 6, p. 233–242.　　Paris, 1907.

　1. Cereals. Protein content.　ɪ. Ammann, Louis, joint author.

　Library, U. S. Dept. of　　Agriculture　　Agr 12–1991

NL　0380526　DNAL

LINDET, Léon, 1857–
　Sur les combinaisons des chlorures et bromures acides avec les chlorures et bromures d'or. [Thèse.] Paris, Gauthier-Villars, 1886.
　4°.　　　　　　　　　　　　Chem 105.59

NL　0380527　MH

Lindet, Léon, 1857–
　Sur les formes que le phosphore et le calcium affectent dans la caséine du lait.
　Ann. Inst. nat. agron.　sér. 2, tome 11, p. 213–222.　　Paris, 1913.

　1. Casein.

　Library, U. S. Dept. of　　Agriculture　　Agr 13–1733

NL　0380528　DNAL

Lindet, Léon, 1857–
　Sur les matières albuminoïdes solubles du lait ...　Par L. Lindet.
　Ann. Inst. nat. agron.　sér. 2, tome 5, p. 283–296; tome 12, 273–298. Paris, 1906–13.
　1st memoir has title: Contribution à l'étude des matières albuminoïdes solubles du lait. Par MM. Lindet et L. Ammann.

　1. Milk–Albuminoid constituents.　ɪ. Ammann, Louis, joint author.

　Library, U. S. Dept. of　　Agriculture　　Agr 12–1985 Revised

NL　0380529　DNAL

Lindet, Léon, 1857–1929.
　Travaux publiés par M. Lindet.
　Ann. Inst. nat. agron.　sér. 2, tome 1, p. 404–406.　　Paris, 1903.

　　　　　　　　　　　　　　　Agr 12–1992
　Library, U. S. Dept. of　　Agriculture

NL　0380530　DNAL

DC
141
F87+
v.79
　Lindet, Robert, 1749 (ca.)–1825.
　Attentat et crimes de Louis, dernier roi des Français.　₍Paris? 1792?₎
　40 p.　20cm.

　1. Louis XVI, king of France, 1754–1793.

NL　0380531　NIC

Lindet, Robert, 1749 (ca.)–1825.
　Bericht dem National-convent abgelegt, in der sitzung des vierten tags der sans-culottiden des zweyten jahrs, im namen der vereinten ausschüsse des öffentlichen wohls, der allgemeinen sicherheit, und der gesetzgebung über die innerliche lage der republik, von Robert Lindet ... ₍n. p.₎ Im dritten jahre der republik ₍1794₎
　104 p.　17ᶜᵐ.
　1. France–Hist.–Revolution–Sources.　2. France–Pol. & govt.–Revolution.　ɪ. France.　Convention nationale, 1792–1795.
　　₍Full name: Jean Baptiste Robert Lindet₎
　　　　　　　　　　　　　　　44–30914
　Library of Congress　　DC175.L53

NL　0380532　DLC MH

DC
141
F87+
v.127
　Lindet, Robert, 1749–1825.
　Compte rendu des dépenses qu'il a faites dans les différentes missions qu'il a remplies.
　₍Paris, Impr. nat., an 3, i.e. 1795₎
　6 p.　22cm.

NL　0380533　NIC

944.04
L64d
　Lindet, Robert, 1749 (ca.)–1825.
　Discours prononcé sur les dénonciations portées contre l'ancien Comité de salut public et le rapport de la Commission des 21.
　₍Paris, Impr. nationale, an III (1795)₎
　126p.　22cm.

　Caption title.
　At head of title: Convention nationale.

NL　0380534　IU

VOLUME 334

Lindet, Robert, 1749 (ca.)-1825.
    Exposition des motifs qui ont déterminé
Robert Lindet, député du département de l'Eure
à la Convention nationale, à voter pour l'arrestation de 32 membres de la convention
nationale. ₍Paris, Impr. du Journal des
débats, 1793₎
    22 p. 20 cm.

    Caption title.
    "Suppl. au   Journal des débats."

    1. France. History. Revolution, 1792-1795.
    2. France. Convention nationale, 1792-1795.

NL 0380536   NcD CtY NIC MH

DC   Lindet, Robert, 1746-1825.
141   Exposition des motifs qui ont déterminé
F87+   Robert Lindet...à voter pour l'arrestation
v.273 de 32 membres de la Convention Nationale.
       ₍Paris, Vatar, 1793₎
         47 p. 22cm.

NL 0380537   NIC NjP

Lindet, Robert, 1749 (ca)-1825.

    —— Fragmens d'une lettre contenant un précis
    de ₍sa₎ conduite politique, tracé par lui-même. ₍In
    ₍Serieys, A.₎ Carnot. 1816.₎

NL 0380538   NIC

Lindet, Robert, 1749(ca.)-1825.
    Present state of France, presented to the
National Convention. London, 1794.

NL 0380539   PPL-R

Lindet, Robert, 1749 (ca.)-1825.
    Projet de décret présenté au nom des Comités
de salut public, d'agriculture et de commerce, dans
la séance du 14 brumaire ...
        see under France. Convention nationale,
1792-1795.

Lindet, Robert, 1749(ca)-1825.
Projet de décrets contre les perturbateurs du repos
public. [P, 1791?]

    3 p.

NL 0380541   MH

Lindet, Robert, 1749 (ca.)-1825.
    ... Rapport fait à la Convention nationale, dans la séance du
4°. des sans-coulottides de l'an 2°. au nom des comités de salut
public, de sûreté générale et de legislation réunis, sur la situation intérieure de la République; par Robert Lindet ... ₍Paris,
Imprimerie nationale, 1794?₎
    26 p. 21⅛ᵐ.
    Caption title.
    At head of title: Convention nationale.
    No. 1 of a collection of pamphlets lettered: Révolution française.
Convention nationale. Rapports ... an II.
    I. France. Convention nationale, 1792-1795.
                    ₍Full name: Jean Baptiste Robert Lindet₎
    Library of Congress   DC177.R45
                                            4-27420

NL 0380542   DLC NIC CtY MH NjP

Lindet, Robert, 1749(ca.)-1825.
    Rapport fait dans la séance du 4,°
des Sans-culotides de l'an II ₍20 septembre
1794₎ au nom des comités de salut public, de
sûreté générale, & de législation, réunis, sur
la situation intérieure de la république; par
Robert ₍Lindet. ₍Montauban: chez Fontane₎
père & fils, 1794.₎ 37 p.   DFD p.v.144, no.

NL 0380543   NN

Lindet, Robert, 1749(ca.)-1825.
                    Rapport fait dans
    la séance du 4° des sans-culotides de l'an 2° ₍20
    Sept. 1794₎ au nom des comités de salut public, de
    sûreté générale et de législation réunis, sur la situa-
    tion intérieure de la république.
    Paris, an 3 ₍1794₎.   21ᵇ. pp. 33.
    At head of title: Convention nationale.

NL 0380544   NIC

DC   Lindet, Robert, 1749-1825.
141   Rapport qui à précédé l'acte énonciatif
F87+   des crimes de Louis Capet.   Paris, Impr.
v.79   nat., 1793.
         22 p. 20cm.

       Reprinted in Archives Parlementaires, v.
       54, p. 740.

NL 0380545   NIC NN

DC   Lindet, Robert, 1749-1825.
141   Réponse à ceux qui lui reprochent 1°
F87+   d'avoir parlé des évènemens du 31 mai dans
v.513 le mois de juillet 1793...₍Paris? 1794₎
         12 p. 22cm.

       In defense of his political behavior.

NL 0380546   NIC

Lindet, Robert, 1749(ca.)-1825.
    Report on the internal situation of the Republic.
On the 4th of the sans-culotides the second year of
the French Republic. [n.p., 1794]
    57 p.   22 cm.   [20 septembre 1794]
    1. France - Hist. - Revolution, 1794.

NL 0380547   NIC

DC   Lindet, Robert, 1749-1825.
141   Robert Lindet à la Convention nationale.
F87+   ₍Paris, Impr. nat., an 3, i.e. 1795₎
v.513   14 p. 22cm.

       In his own defense.
       At head of title: Convention nationale.

NL 0380548   NIC

Lindet, Robert Thomas
    see
Lindet, Thomas, 1743-1823.

₍Lindet, Thomas₎ 1743-1823.
    Adresse de la Convention Nationale ₍pour
expliquer les motifs des mesures de sûreté
générale prises le 2 de ce mois contre divers
membres de la Convention, 26 Juin 1793₎
    ₍Paris, Impr. Nat., 1793₎
    10 p. 22cm.

    Reprinted in Archives Parlementaires, v.
67, p. 515-517.

NL 0380550   NIC

Lindet, Thomas, 1743-1823.
    ... Correspondance de Thomas Lindet pendant la consti-
tuante et la législative (1789-1792), publiée par Amand
Montier. Paris, Au siège de la Société, 1899.
    3 p. l., ₍III₎-xvi, 393 p. front. (port.) 26ᵐ.
    At head of title: Société de l'histoire de la révolution française.
    "Les documents que nous publions ne comprennent ... que la corre-
spondance de Thomas Lindet avec la municipalité de Bernay et son
frère Robert."—Introd., p. x.
    "Bibliographie des œuvres imprimées de Thomas Lindet": p. ₍xv₎-xvi.
    1. France—Hist.—Revolution, 1789-1792. 2. France. Assemblée na-
tionale constituante, 1789-1791. 3. France. Assemblée nationale législative, 1791-1792. I. Montier, Amand, 1845-   ed. II. Société de
l'histoire de la révolution française, Paris.
                                    ₍Full name: Robert Thomas Lindet₎
    Library of Congress   DC146.L65A3   33-18851
                                                    923.244

NL 0380551   NIC NcU InU MeB NBC MH NjP CtY OClW ICU NcD
              DLC PBm FTaSU OO IEN CSt CU MU FU PU

Lindet, Thomas, 1743-1823.
    ... Discours ... sur les dénonciations portées
contre l'ancien Comité de salut public et le Rapport
de la Commission des 21 ... ₍Paris, 1795₎
    126 p.

NL 0380552   NjP

LINDET, ₍Thomas₎,   ,1743-1823.
    Instruction pastorale de Monsieur Lindet,
évêque du département de l'Eure à l'occasion
des troubles civils & religieux. ₍Evreux, J.J.
L. Ancelle, 1792.₎

    pp. 54.
    Without title-page. Caption title.
                    Fr 1328.297.56

NL 0380553   MH

Lindet,₍   Thomas, Bp., 1743-1823.
    Lettre... aux religieuses des monastères
de son diocèse.   Evreux, Ancelle, 1791.
    16 p., 20ᵐ.

NL 0380554   NjPT

Lindet,   Thomas, Bp., 1743-1823.
    Lettre circulaire... au clergé de son
diocèse.   Evreux, Ancelle, 1791.
    33 p., 20ᵐ.

NL 0380555   NjPT

Lindet, Thomas, 1743-1823
    Lettre pastorale de monsieur l'évêque de l'Eure aux
fidèles de son diocèse. [Evreux, 1791]

    44 p.

NL 0380556   MH

VOLUME 334

Lindet, Thomas, 1743-1823
Mandement de l'évêque de l'Eure aux fidèles de son diocèse. [Evreux, 1791]

13 p.

NL 0380557   MH

Lindet, Thomas, 1743-1823
Mandement de l'évêque de l'Eure pour faire chanter le Te Deum en action de grâces de l'heureuse convalescence du roi. [Evreux, 1791]

4 p.

NL 0380558   MH

Lindet, Thomas, 1743-1823
Opinion sur la prestation du serment ordonnée par le décret du 27 novembre. P, 1790

15 p.

NL 0380559   MH

Lindet, Thomas,   1743-1823.
Opinion sur la résolution du 22 nivôse. [Paris, Imprimerie nationale, 1798]

8 p.
At head of title: Corps législatif. Conseil des anciens.

NL 0380560   MH

Lindeux, Simone
Contribution à l'étude de la silicose. Paris, 1942.
Thèse - Paris

NL 0380561   CtY

Lindevall, C[arl] A[ugust] 1863-
Kristendomen i förnuftets och den moderna forskningens ljus; eller, Kan en bildad nutidsmänniska fasthålla den traditionella uppfattningen af Bibeln såsom Guds ord och kristendomen såsom en religion af öfvernaturligt ursprung. Alla uppriktiga sanningssökare tillägnad af C. A. Lindevall ... [Boston, Svenska tryckeriet] 1904.

292 p. 18cm.

5-2933†

NL 0380562   DLC MnHi WaU PPAmSwM PP

Lindevall, Carl August, 1863-
Reminiscences of an old clergyman, and other narratives and sketches drawn from real life, also narratives of numerous visions and other phenomena from the "unseen" world, claimed by trustworthy persons to be real experiences, indicating that there is a spiritual and supersensible world, and that human personality survives bodily death, committed to writing and edited by C. A. Lindevall ... [Rock Island, Ill., Augustana book concern, 1936]

231 p. 20 cm.
1. Sweden—Soc. life & cust. 2. Visions. I. Title.

BX8080.L55A35   922.473   37—1734

NL 0380563   DLC PPLT PP WaT WaSp

Lindewall, Arvo
Lehtiä. Superior, Wis., Työmies print [192?]
95 p.

NL 0380564   MiD

Lindewall, Peter Johann, respondent.
Disputatio philosophica de lumine lunari   ...
see under   Humerus, Bonde.

Lindewood, William

see

Lyndwood, William, bp. of St. David's, 1375?-1446

HV6727   Lindey, Alexander, 1896-   joint author.
.E7
Ernst, Morris Leopold, 1888-
The censor marches on; recent milestones in the administration of the obscenity law in the United States, by Morris L. Ernst & Alexander Lindey. New York, Doubleday, Doran & company, inc., 1940.

Lindey, Alexander, 1896-   joint author.
Ernst, Morris Leopold, 1888-
Hold your tongue! Adventures in libel and slander. By Morris L. Ernst and Alexander Lindey. New York, W. Morrow & company, 1932.

Law   Lindey, Alexander, 1896-   joint author.
                                FOR OTHER EDITIONS
                                SEE MAIN ENTRY
Ernst, Morris Leopold, 1888-
Hold your tongue! The layman's guide to libel and slander. A fascinating exploration of the realm of defamation, including an analysis of ideological, racial and religious libels, by Morris L. Ernst and Alexander Lindey. [Rev. ed.] New York, Abelard Press [1950]

Lindey, Alexander, 1896-
Motion picture agreements annotated; a manual of contract forms covering every phase of the motion picture industry ... With digests of cases applicable thereto. Albany, M. Bender, 1947.

xiii, 1039 p. 26 cm.
Bibliography: p. 920-925.
1. Moving-pictures—Law—U. S.—Forms.   I. Title.

48-5127*

NL 0380570   DLC CLSU PPB

Lindey, Alexander, 1896-
Plagiarism and originality. [1st ed.] New York, Harper [1952]

xv, 366 p. 22 cm.
Bibliography: p. 343-353.

1. Plagiarism.

PN167.L5   *808.06 029.6   51-11934

wa OrP OrCS OrU MtBC IdPS CaBVaU CaBVa WaU-L WaWW
NL 0380571   DLC TU MiU OU MH MB NN WaTC WaT WaS WaE

Lindey, Alexander, 1896-
Separation agreements and ante-nuptial contracts; their preparation, execution, operation, interpretation and enforcement and the role they play in judicial separation and divorce; comprehensive annotated forms, variants of typical clauses, marriage settlements, reconciliation agreements, deeds of trust guaranties, etc., by Alexander Lindey ... Albany, N. Y., New York, N. Y., M. Bender & company, incorporated, 1937.

xiv, 764 p. 24cm.
Text on front lining-paper.
Bibliography: p. 698.
1. Marriage law—U. S. 2. Divorce—U. S. 3. Separation (Law)—U. S. 4. Forms (Law)—U. S.   I. Title.

37-3306

PPTU-L ViU-L
NL 0380572   DLC IdU OrU-L WaU-L MoU NcD PPB PU-L

Lindey, Alexander, 1896-
Separation agreements and ante-nuptial contracts: preparation, execution, operation, interpretation, enforcement, role in judicial separation and divorce. Tax considerations. Related forms including variants of typical clauses, marriage settlements, reconciliation agreements, escrows and trusts, bonds and notes, guaranties. Rev. and rewritten ed. Albany, M. Bender, 1953.

xii, 920 p. 26 cm.
Bibliography: p. 859-866.

——————Special supplement, covering the changes made by the Internal revenue code of 1954. Albany, M. Bender, 1954.

7 p. 24 cm.

1. Marriage law—U. S. 2. Divorce—U. S. 3. Separation (Law)—U. S.   I. Title.

*301.42 392.5   54-2 rev

TxU PPT
NL 0380574   DLC WaU-L TxU NBuU CU PU-L PPB ICU TU

The Lindfield reporter, or Philanthropic magazine ...
v. 1-
Jan. 1835-
Lindfield [Eng.] Printed by W. Eade at the Schools of Industry, 1836-
v. maps. 22cm. monthly.

Vol. 1 lacks title-page.
Edited by William Allen?
Continues the Philanthropist (London)
Ceased publication with v. 1, no. 24, Dec. 1842.

NL 0380575   NNC PHC MH-BA

---

de Lindfors (Mme.) [1880-   ]. *Traitement de la syphilis du nouveau-né par les injections mercurielles. 47 pp. 8°. Montpellier. 1906. No. 18.

NL 0380576   DNLM

Lindfors, Aili (Thesleff) 1882-   ed.
Min far; kända män skildrade av sina barn. Helsingfors, Söderström [1948]

262 p. illus., ports. 22 cm.

1. Finland—Biog. 2. Fathers.   I. Title.

DK448.L55   50-21724

NL 0380577   DLC NN

VOLUME 334

Lindfors, Aili (Theslöf), 1882–   , ed.
Mor och vi; 25 kända män och kvinnor om sina mödrar. Under redaktion av Aili Lindfors.   Helsingfors, Söderström & c:o ₁1947₁   190 p.   ports.   22cm.

457627B.   1. Finland—Biog.   I. Title.
August 11, 1949

NL 0380578   NN

Lindfors, Anders Otto, 1781–1841.
Anders Otto Lindfors; en pioniär för kropps-kultur i Sverige
see under   Lindfors, Torsten, 1884–   ed.

₁781–1841₁
Lindfors, Anders Otto, ∧ Dissertatio hi-storica de Civitate Jomensi, cujus particu-las, in Academia Lundensi olim exhibitas, in unum redegit auctor Andr. O. Lindfors. Lundæ, 1811. 4°. pp. (2) + 75. IcF61J711

NL 0380580   NIC

Lindfors, Anders Otto,1781–1841.
Dissertatio historica de personis dialogi Ciceroniani de oratore; pars prior. Londini, Gothorum, 1801.
32 p

Univ. of Lund. Ph.D.Diss.

NL 0380581   PU

Lindfors, Anders Otto, 1781–
Fullständigt swenskt och latinskt lexicon, för-fattadt af And. Otto Lindfors ...   Lund, J. Berlingska boktryckeriet, 1815–24.
2 v.
"Af [Prof. El. Lindfors] ... äro ... bokstäf-werna O och P samt en del af S (till Sm) författade."-Pref., v. 2.
Swedish words with Latin equivalents.
Contents.- Förra delen. [A–L] - Senare delen. [M–Ö]
1. Swedish language - Dictionaries - Latin.

NL 0380582   CU

DG
76
L5
1830
Lindfors, Anders Otto, 1781–1844.
Handbok i romerska antiqviteterna. 2. förbattrade uppl. Örebro, N. M. Lindh, 1830.
510 p. illus.

1. Rome - antiquities. I. Title.

NL 0380583   WaU

Lindfors, And₁ers₁ Otto, 1781 – 1844.
Inledning till isländska litteraturen och dess historia under medeltiden. Lund, I. Berling, 1824.
pp. (8), 194 +.

NL 0380584   MH NN CtY NIC CU

Lindfors, Axel Otto, 1852–1909, ed.
Linné, Carl von, 1707–1778.
Linnés dietetik, på grundvalen af dels hans eget originalut-kast till föreläsningar: Lachesis naturalis quæ tradit diætam naturalem, och dels lärjungeanteckningar efter dessa hans föreläsningar: Collegium diæteticum; på uppdrag af Medi-cinska fakulteten i Uppsala ordnad och utgifven af A. O. Lindfors. Uppsala, Akademiska boktryckeriet, E. Berling, 1907.

Lindfors, Axel Otto, 1852–1909.   570.9250 L648
Några Linné-studier, af A. O. Lindfors. Uppsala & Stockholm, Almqvist & Wiksells boktryckeri-A.-B. [1907].
[4], 59 p. 19½ x 15ᶜᵐ.

NL 0380586   ICJ NN

WI
L745o
1889
LINDFORS, Axel Otto, 1852–1909
Om tuberculosis peritonei med särskildt afseende på diagnos och operativ behandling. Ett bidrag till bukens kirurgi. ₁Lund, Ohlsson, 1889₁
149 p.

NL 0380587   DNLM

Lindfors, Axel Otto, 1852–1909.
Sägner och bilder; en samling dikter. Stockholm, W. Billes bokförlagsaktiebolag, [1898]
Illustr.
"Rättelser", at end.

NL 0380588   MH

Lindfors, Axel Otto, 1852–1909.
Smärre dikter, af Axel Otto Lindfors. Lund, C. W. K Gleerup, 1887.
4 p. l., 202 p. 19½ᶜᵐ.

15-16498

NL 0380589   DLC

QM691
L64
1898
Lindfors, Axel Otto, 1852–1909.
Zur lehre von den angeborenen hirnbrüchen und deren chirurgischer behandlung. Leipzig, Breitkopf und Härtel, 1898.
cover-title, 44 p. illus. (Sammlung kli-nischer vorträge. Gynäkologie nr. 80)

"Litteratur": p. 42–44.

1. Brain - Surgery. 2. Encephalocele. I. Sammlung klinischer vorträge. Gynäkologie nr. 80.

NL 0380590   NNC NNC-M

Lindfors, Axel Torsten
see Lindfors, Torsten, 1884–

MT231
.L5
Lindfors, Eula Ashworth.
The majors and their relatives; complete scale family in one octave form and principal triads in all keys. Fischer ed. New York, J. Fischer ₁c1946₁
31 p. 31cm.
Publisher's pl. no.: 8218–30

1. Musical intervals and scales. I. Title.

NL 0380592   MB OrU Mi

Lindfors, Eula Ashworth, arr.
Songs I sing in Sunday-school, in easy arrangements for young musicians; compiled, arranged and illustrated by Eula Ashworth Lindfors. Boston, Mass., The Boston music company ₁1944₁
v, ₁1₁, 3–39 p. illus. 30 x 23ᶜᵐ.
Publisher's plate no.: B. M. co. 10172.
For piano solo; includes interlinear words and brief descriptive notes.

1. Piano music, Juvenile—Arrangements. 2. Hymns, English. I. Title.
Library of Congress   M1378.L56S6   44–47115
783.7

NL 0380593   DLC

Lindfors, Johan Otto.
De epistola Jacobi adversaria... Acce-dunt Theses X.   Lundae, Typis Berlingi-anis, 1864.
37 p. 20ᵐ.

NL 0380594   NjPT

Lindfors, Johan Otto.
Om Guldbracteater. Archaeologiska Anteckningar.   Lund, 1846.
18 p. pl. 4°.

NL 0380595   CtY

Lindfors, Per.
Musikens mästare. Helsingfors, Holger Schildt ₁1946₁
314 p. illus., ports., music. 24 cm.
Contents.—Johann Sebastian Bach.—Georg Friedrich Händel.—Joseph Haydn.—Wolfgang Amadeus Mozart.—Ludwig van Beethoven.—Robert Schumann.

1. Composers, German.
ML390.L65   927.8   47–29315*

NL 0380596   DLC CLU NN

Lindfors, Thore, 1889–
Forsok med utsadesbetning utforda 1924–30, av Thore Lindfors...
Stockholm, O. L. Svanbacks boktryckeri, 1931.
49 p. (Meddelande nr. 390 fran K. Landtbruks-akademien, Centralanstalten for forsoksvasendet pa jordbruksomradet. Avdelningen for lantbruksbotanik nr 49)

NL 0380597   OU

Lindfors, Thore, 1889–
En ny gurksjukdom fororsakad av Venturia cucumerina n. sp. av Thore Lindfors ... Linkoping, Billstens boktryokeri, 1919.
10 p. (K. Landtbruks-akademien, Centralanstal-ten for forsoksvasendet pa jordbrucksomradet. Meddelande n₁r 193. Botaniska avdelningen n₁o 17)

NL 0380598   OU

VOLUME 334

Lindfors, Thore, 1889–
On vissnesjuka hos gurkor fororsaked
av Verticillium alboatrum Bkc. & Berth. ...
Av Thore Lindfors.
Stockholm, Ivar Haeggstroms boktryckeri, a.b., 1917
14 p. (K. Landtbruks-akademien, Centralanstalten
for forsoksvasendet pa jordbruksomradet.
Meddelande n:r 159. Botaniska avdelningen n:r 13)

NL 0380599 OU

Lindfors, Thore, 1889–
Sjukdomar hos våra odlade växter, av Thore Lindfors ...
Stockholm, P. A. Norstedt & söners ₁1927₁
109 p. xx pl. (2 col.) on 10 l. 19¼ᶜᵐ.

1. Botany—Pathology. ₁1. Vegetable pathology₁
₁Full name: Karl Magnus Thore Lindfors₁

Agr 29–1056

Library, U. S. Dept. of   Agriculture 464L642

NL 0380600 DNAL

QK627 **Lindfors, Thore, 1889–**
A1L68   Studien über den entwicklungsverlauf bei einigen rostpil-
zen aus zytologischen und anatomischen gesichtspunkten ...
Uppsala, Almqvist & Wiksells boktryckeri, 1924.
₃₁, 84 p. illus., v pl. 23ᶜᵐ.
Inaug.-diss.—Upsala.
"Särtryck ur Svensk botanisk tidskrift, 1924, bd. 18, h. 1."
"Literaturverzeichnis": p. 78–81.

1. Uredineae.

NL 0380601 ICU MH CtY ICRL

Lindfors, Thore, 1889–
Studier över fusarioser... av Thore Lindfors...
Linkoping, Billstens boktryckeri, 1920.
(K. Landtbruks-akademien, Centralanstalten
for forsoksvasendet pa jordbruksomradet.
Meddelande n:r 203 Botaniska avdelningen n:r 19)

NL 0380602 OU

371.73   LINDFORS, Torsten, 1884–   ed.
L643l   Anders Otto Lindfors; en pionär för
kroppskultur i Sverige. Under medverkan
av Ewert Wrangel... Oswald Holmberg...
₁och₁ Ivan Carlsson... Utg. av Torsten
Lindfors. Stockholm, Lindfors bokförlag ₁1934₁
viii p., 2 l., 3–228 p. illus.,
plates, ports., facsim. 19cm.
"Av denna bok är utgiven en privatupp-
laga, ej avsedd för försäljning, numrerad I–XXX, samt en bibliofilupplaga för

bokhandeln, numrerad 1–1450.₁, N;o 1405."
Contents.- Disputationer från åren
1803–1805, av Anders Otto Lindfors
₁praeses₁ Översatta från latinet, av Ivan
Carlsson.- Kommentar, av Ivan Carlsson.-
Den lingska gymnastiken i dess historiska
sammanhang, av Oswald Holmberg.- Anders
Otto Lindfors och götismen; hans livs-
gärning och betydelse, av Ewert Wrangel.

1. Swedish gymnastics. 2. Physical educa-
tion and training. 3. Lindfors, Anders
Otto, 1781–1841, praeses. I. Wrangel, Ewert
Henrik Gabriel, 1863–   II. Holmberg,
Oswald, 1882–   III. Carlsson, Ivan.

NL 0380605 MnU NN

Lindfors, Torsten, 1884–   *ed.*
Boken om lastbilen; bilarnas bok. ₁Redaktionskommitté:
Torsten Lindfors, huvudredaktör, et al. Stockholm₁ Lindfors ₁1953₁
454 p. illus. 28 cm.

1. Motor-trucks. I. Title.

Full name: Axel Torsten Lindfors.

TL230.L52   55–58853 ‡

NL 0380606 DLC MiD NN

DL867   Lindfors, Torsten, 1884–   ed.
.G8
Gustaf V, konung av Sverige. In memoriam. ₁Redaktör:
Torsten Lindfors. Stockholm, Lindfors, 1951₁

---

*Lindfors, Torsten, 1884–
... **Gustaf V**, konung av Sverige. Minnesskrift med anledning
av konung Gustaf v:s 25-åriga regering och hans 75-årsdag.
₁Stockholm, Lindfors, 1933₁

DL867   Lindfors, Torsten, 1884–
.V28
... **Vår konung**, 1858 ¹⁶⁄₆ 1943. Minnesskrift med anledning av
konung Gustaf v:s 35-åriga regering och hans 85-årsdag.
₁Stockholm, Lindfors, 1943₁

---

*Lindfors, Torsten, 1884–
... **Vår konung** och hans gärning. Minnesskrift med anledning av konung Gustaf v:s 25-åriga regering och hans
75-årsdag. ₁Stockholm, Lindfors, 1933₁

Lindfors, Torsten, 1884–
Villasamhallen och sportstuguomraden i
Stockholmstrakten. Stockholm, H.W.
Tullbergs forlag, 1930.
192 p. illus.

NL 0380611 PPAmSwM

PC259   Lindfors-Nordin, Elsa, G
L56   "Berne, Berner"; expressions rabelaisiennes
étude historique et étymologique, suivie d'un
Commentaire de E. Gemillscheg. Stockholm,
A.B. Magn. Bergvalls [1948]
30 p. 23cm.
Author's autograph presentation copy.

1. French language - Etymology. I.
Title.

NL 0380612 CoU OrU OClW CU NIC   MH OCU

398.4   Lindfors-Nordin, Elsa G
L7451   "Issant de Brisse" [par] E.G. Lindfors-
Nordin. Stockholm, Magn. Bergvalls Förlag
[1952]
46p.

1. Bisse serpent. 2. Serpent (in heral-
ry). 3. Serpents (in religion, folk-lore,
etc.) I. Title.

NL 0380613 IEN

Lindfors-Nordin, Elsa G
Jul, den hundrabladiga gúl, gulis, gueules. Stockholm,
Bergvall, i distribution ₁1955₁
40 p. 23 cm.

1. Swedish language—Etymology. I. Title.

A 57–6359

Minnesota. Univ. Libr.
for Library of Congress

NL 0380614 MnU

Lindfors bokförlag a. b., *Stockholm.*
Frihet och försvar. ₁Stockholm₁ Lindfors bokförlag a. b.
₁1941₁
6 p. l., 5–464 (i. e. 466) p., 1 l. illus. (incl. ports.) port., diagrs. 30¼ᶜᵐ.
Illustrated lining-papers.
Half-title between p. 80 and 81 not included in paging.
"Utgiven i samarbete med Esselte a. b."—1st prelim. leaf.
CONTENTS.—Målet, Sveriges frihet.—Möjligheterna, Sveriges re-
surser.—Medlen, Sveriges försvartåtgärder: Krigsmaktens nydaning.
Det frivilliga försvarets utveckling. Hemfrontens beredskap. Försvar-
sandans härdning.—Framtiden.

1. Sweden—Defenses. 2. World war, 1939–   —Sweden. I. Esselte
a. b., Stockholm. II. Title.

44–15438

Library of Congress   UA790.L5

335

NL 0380615 DLC

Lindfors bokforlag a.b., Stockholm.
Frihet och försvar. ₁Boken om vår beredskap. Stockholm₁
Lindfors ₁1941₁
464 p. illus., ports. 31 cm.
"Utöver normalupplagan är bokverket ... tryckt för bokälskare i
en specialupplaga på trehundrasextio exemplar, försedda med H. M.
Konungens originalfotografi."
CONTENTS.—Målet: Sveriges frihet.—Möjligheterna: Sveriges re-
surser.—Medlen: Sveriges försvaratgärder: Krigmaktens nydaning.
Det frivilliga försvarets utveckling.—Hemfrontens beredskap.—
Försvarsandans härdning.—Framtiden.

1. Sweden—Defenses.

A 48–2904*

Harvard Univ. Library
for Library of Congress

NL 0380616 MH NNUN

Lindforss, Carl Mårten
Käytännöllinen oppikirja Venäjän kielessä.
Mukailemalla toimitti K. M. Lindforss. 4:s
parannettu painos. Helsingissä, Edlund [1898]
306 p.

NL 0380617 MH

I.Wolstedt, Fredericus, respondent.

NL 0380618 DNLM

NL 0380619 DNLM

NL 0380620 DNLM

VOLUME 334

Lindforss, R.
De gente antiqua Troll
see under title [Supplement]

QD445 Lindgaard, Christian.
.C41?   Ueber diphenylaminderivate und azine.
Wiesbaden, 1893.
48p.
Inaug. diss. Basel.

NL 0380622   DLC PU

4PZ   Lindgaard, Erna
532   Blandt drenge og piger i Afrika.
København, O. Lohse, 1954.
60 p.

NL 0380623   DLC-P4

Lindgaard, Otto.
Jensen abdicerer! Lystspil med Sange i 1 Akt, af Otto Lindgaard. København: P. Branner, 1937.   36 p.   18½cm.

Without music.

1. Drama, Danish.   I. Title.   March 14, 1939

NL 0380624   NN

Lindgaard, Otto.
Kærlighed i Krostuen; Lystpil i 1 Akt, af Otto Lindgaard. København: Jespersen og Pios Forlag, 1931.   45 p.   12°.

581908A.   1. Drama, Danish.   I. Title.
         April 30, 1932

NL 0380625   NN

Lindgaard, Otto.
Rullekonens Tøs; Lystspil med Sange i 1 Akt, af Otto Lindgaard. Musik af Forfatteren. København: P. Branner, 1933.   87 p.   18½cm.

Without music.

753162A.   1. Drama, Danish.   I. Title.   May 16, 1935

NL 0380626   NN

LINDGEN, Erich.
Die breslauer strafrechtspflege unter der Carolina und der gemeinen strafrechtswissenschaft bis zum inkrafttreten der Josephina von 1708. Breslau, Priebatschs buchhandlung, [1939].
8°   Ill.
"BEITRÄGE zur geschichte der stadt Breslau", 8.

NL 0380627   MH-L

Lindgen, Erich.
Kleine Staatsbürgerkunde [Staats- und Verfassungsrecht] von Erich Lindgen und M. Grosser. Hrsg. von Dr. Kämmerer. Goslar, E. Herzog [*1951]
116 p.   21 cm.
Published also as Bd. 16 of Kleine Fachbuchreihe für den Post- und Fernmeldedienst, under title: Staats- und Verfassungsrecht.

1. Germany (Federal Republic, 1949–)—Constitutional law—Compends.   I. Grosser, Meinhardt, joint author.   II. Title.

53–30316 ‡

NL 0380628   DLC

Lindgen, Erich.
Kleine Staatsbürgerkunde. [Staats- und Verfassungsrecht] Unter Mitarbeit von M. Grosser. Hrsg. von Ludwi Kämmerer. 2. neu bearb. und erweiterte Aufl. Goslar, I Herzog [1955, *1951]
197 p.   diagrs.   21 cm.
Published also as v. 16 of Kleine Fachbuchreihe für den Post- und Fernmeldedienst, under title: Staats- und Verfassungsrecht.

1. Germany (Federal Republic, 1949–)—Constitutional law—Compends.   I. Grosser, Meinhardt, joint author.   II. Title.

56–3390

NL 0380629   DLC MH-L

Lindgen, Erich.
Staats- und Verfassungsrecht, von Erich Lindgen und Meinhardt Grosser; durchgesehen und hrsg. von Dr. Kämmerer. Goslar, E. Herzog [1951]
116 p. (p. 116 advertisement)   21 cm.   (Kleine Fachbuchreihe für den Post- und Fernmeldedienst, Bd. 16)
Bibliography: p. 112.

1. Germany (Federal Republic, 1949–)—Constitutional law—Compends.   I. Grosser, Meinhardt, joint author.   II. Title.

52–27954

NL 0380630   DLC

Lindgens, Arthur.
Afrika aufs Korn genommen; mit Büchse und Kamera durch Ostafrika. Hamburg, P. Parey [1953]
289 p.   illus.   26 cm.

1. Africa, British East—Descr. & trav.   I. Title.

DT425.L4   916.76   54–19335 ‡

NL 0380631   DLC CU MoU NN

Lindgens, Arthur.
Sorglose Stunden. Mit 211 photographischen Natururkunden des Verfassers aus der Wildbahn. Stuttgart, Franckh [1948]
269 p.   illus.   26 cm.

1. Hunting—Europe.   2. Game and game-birds—Europe.   I. Title.

SK35.L5   50–21218

NL 0380632   DLC DI

799.2
L745s.2   Lindgens, Arthur.
Sorglose Stunden. Mit 211 photographischen Naturkunden des Verfassers aus der Wildbahn. [2. Aufl.] Stuttgart, Franckh [1953]
269p.   illus.   25cm.

1. Hunting.   2. Game and game birds.   3. Hunting. Pictorial works.   I. Title.

NL 0380633   IEN

Lindgens, Arthur.
Wild, bild und kugel, von dr. Arthur Lindgens, mit 202 photographischen natururkunden des verfassers aus der wildbahn. Berlin, Globus verlag g. m. b. h. [1937]
232 p.   illus., fold. pl.   27½ᵐ.
"1. bis 5. tausend."

1. Animals, Habits and behavior of.   2. Photography of animals.   3. Game and game-birds—Germany.   I. Title.

Library of Congress   SK271.L5   38–38470
Copyright A—Foreign   38442
                             799.28

NL 0380634   DLC

LINDGENS, ARTHUR.
Wild, Bild und Kugel.   Stuttgart, Franck' [1949]
231 p.   illus.   26cm.

1. Animals—Habits and behavior.   2. Photography of animals.   3. Game—Germany.

NL 0380635   NN

Lindgens, Joachim, 1927–
Die Räume der §§ 123, 243 Nr. 2, 306 StGB. München, 1955.
127, [8] l.   29 cm.
Typescript (carbon copy)
Inaug.-Diss.—Munich.
Vita.
Bibliography: leaves [128]–[137]

1. Unlawful entry—Germany (Federal Republic, 1949–) 2. Burglary—Germany (Federal Republic, 1949–) 3. Arson—Germany (Federal Republic, 1949–)

58–31646

NL 0380636   DLC

Lindgren, A. W.
Hämeenmaa.   Turussa, 1864.
(1) 92 p.   18°.   (Kuwaelmia suomen maakunnista, v)
Account of Tavastland, Finland.

NL 0380637   NIC

Lindgren, Adolf, 1846–1905.
Drei harmonische Studien, von Dr. Adolf Lindgren. Herausgegeben nach dem Tode des Verfassers.   Leipzig: F. Schuberth Jr. [1910.]   73 p.   diagrs., illus. (incl. music.)   8°.
"Die Studie sind früher in Musik, Centralblatt…1883 und Allgemeine Musik-Zeitung…1886/87 erschienen."

352643A.   1. Harmony.   January 28, 1929

NL 0380638   NN

Lindgren, Adolf, 1846–1905.
Illustreret musikhistorie; en fremstilling for nordiske laesere
see under   Panum, Hortense.

Lindgren, Adolf, 1846–1905.
Musikaliska studier.   Stockholm, Gehrman [1896]
244 p.

NL 0380640   MH

VOLUME 334

Lindgren, Adolf, 1846–1905.
..., Om polskemelodiernas härkomst, av Adolf Lindgren. ₍Stockholm, Kungl. boktryckeriet, 1893₎
27 p. 23½ᶜᵐ. ₍Nyare₎ bidrag till kännedom om de svenska landsmålen ock svenskt folkliv xii. 5)
Caption title.
Forms part of 48. hft. of the whole series.

1. Polonaise. 2. Dance music, Swedish.
₍Full name: Karl Adolf Lindgren₎
Library of Congress   PD5001.S9 48. hft., xii. 5   23–3858

NL 0380641   DLC MiU NN OC1

Lindgren, Adolf 1846–1905, ed.
Svensk musiktidning
see under title

Lindgren, Adolf, 1846–1905.
Svenska hofkapellmästare, 1782–1882; ett bidrag till
operahusets hundraårsminnen. Stockholm [Huss & Beer]
Central-Tryckeriet, 1882
150 p. ports.

NL 0380643   MH

'611.81 Lindgren, Åke Georg Helge, 1909–
L745k   Die kapillare angioarchitektonik der isogenetischen grosshirnrinde des erwachsenen menschen. Morphologische und quantitative beziehungen zwischen angio-, zyso- und myeloarchitektonik sowie einige pathologische aspekte ...   Helsingfors ₍Merators tryckeri₎ 1940.
101p. illus.

"Literaturverzeichnis": p.₍100₎-101.

1. Brain--Blood-vessels.

NL 0380644   IU-M DNLM

Lindgren, Åke Georg Helge, 190.
... On the amount of blood in the peripheral vascular system in some pathological conditions, especially peritonitis, by Åke G. H. Lindgren. Helsingfors, Mercators tryckeri aktiebolag, 1935.
102 p. incl. tables, diagr. 24 cm. (*On cover:* Acta chirurgica scandinavica ... Supplementum xxxix)
At head of title: From the Pathological department of the Caroline institute, Stockholm.
Issued also as the author's thesis, Karolinska mediko-kirurgiska institutet, Stockholm.
"Literature": p. ₍99₎–102.
1. Vascular system. 2. Capillaries. 3. Peritonitis.
A C 36—1573
John Crerar Library
for Library of Congress   ₍a57c1₎

NL 0380645   ICJ MiU ViU

Lindgren, Anna Josephine, 1887–
Afterglow, life and letters of Josephine Princell, by Anna J. Lindgren. ₍Chicago, Free church publications, °1937₎
148 p. front., plates, ports., facsims. 20ᶜᵐ.

1. °Princell, Mrs. Josephine (Lind) 1844–1937. i. Title.
Library of Congress   BX8080.P75L5   38–737
Copyright A 112582   922.473

NL 0380646   DLC OrU ICN

Lindgren, Anna Josephine, 1887–
Charlotte A. Cary; gentlewoman of God--molder of character. Chicago, Free Church Publications [1939]

283 p. front. (port.) illus. (ports.)

NL 0380647   CLamB

Lindgren, Anna Josephine, 1887–
In His presence, by Anna J. Lindgren ... Chicago, The Bible institute colportage ass'n ₍°1934₎
116 p. 18ᶜᵐ.

1. Meditations. i. Title.
Library of Congress   BV4832.L5   35–3604
Copyright A 70301   242

NL 0380648   DLC

Lindgren, Anna Josephine, 1887–
In His presence. Chicago, Moody [c1934]

122 p. (The Colportage library, no. 221)

With this is bound: Growing with our children, by Gertrude Nystrom; Your questions answered, by Dorothy Haskin; The Christian Home, by Norman v. Williams.

NL 0380649   CLamB

Lindgren, Anna Josephine, 1887–
... With Him.   Chicago, Ill., Chicago-Bladet ₍n.d.₎
128 p. 18ᶜᵐ.

NL 0380650   NjPT

Lindgren, Anton Markus.
Der naturwissenschaftliche Unterricht bei Fellenberg im Zusammenhange seiner Grundanschauungen und seiner Erziehungsunternehmung. Bern, P. Haupt ₍1955₎
817 p. 23 cm.
Bibliography: p. 302–311.

1. Fellenberg, Philipp Emanuel von, 1771–1844.
LB675.F3L5   56–3054

NL 0380651   DLC CtY NNC NN NIC MH

Lindgren, Arne, 1910–
Den vita grinden.   ₍Karlstad, Tryckeri Ab. Värmlands folkblad, 1953₎
59 p. 18 cm.

i. Title.
Full name: Karl Arne Lindgren.
A 53–7230
Minnesota. Univ. Libr.
for Library of Congress

NL 0380652   MnU

ƒ839.7 **Lindgren, Astrid (Ericsson) 1907–**
L6å3a   **Alla vi barn i Bullerbyn.   ₍Stockholm₎**
Sw   **Rabén & Sjögren ₍1946₎**
108p.

NL 0380653   PP

Lindgren, Astrid (Ericsson) 1907–
Bill Bergson, master detective; translated from the Swedish by Herbert Antoine. Illustrated by Louis S. Glanzman. New York, Viking Press, 1952.
200 p. illus. 21 cm.

i. Title.
PZ7.L6585Bi   52–12922

OC1 PP
NL 0380654   DLC Or OrMonO OrP OrU WaS MoU MiU

Lindgren, Astrid (Ericsson) 1907–
Bill Bergson lives dangerously; translated from the Swedish by Herbert Antoine. Illustrated by Don Freeman. New York, Viking Press, 1954.
214 p. illus. 21 cm.

i. Title.
PZ7.L6585Bg   54–4337
Library of Congress

NL 0380655   DLC OOxM WaS OrP Or

Lindgren, Astrid (Ericsson) 1907–
Boken om Pippi Långstrump. Med teckningar av Ingrid Vang Nyman. ₍Stockholm₎ Rabén & Sjögren ₍1952₎
232 p. col. illus. 24cm.

NL 0380656   MiDW

ƒ839.7 Lindgren, Astrid Ericsson, 1907–
L63j   Jag vill också gå i skolan, berättad av Astrid Lindgren. Ritad av Birgitta Nordenskjöld. ₍Stockholm₎ Rabén Sjögren ₍1951₎
₍19₎ p. col. illus.

1. Swedish books   I. Title

NL 0380657   MiD

ƒ839.7 **Lindgren, Astrid (Ericsson) 1907–**
L6å3k   **Känner du Pippi Långstrump? Bilderbok**
Sw   **av Astrid Lindgren och Ingrid Nyman.**
₍Stockholm₎ Rabén & Sjögren ₍1947₎
24p.

NL 0380658   PP

4PT   Lindgren, Astrid (Ericsson) 1907–
Swed-   Kati i Amerika; illustrerad av Gobi.
5064   Stockholm, Bonnier [1950]
188 p.

NL 0380659   DLC-P4

Lindgren, Astrid (Ericsson) 1907–
Kati i Paris. Stockholm, Bonnier ₍1953₎
141 p. 20 cm. (Önskeböckerna, 113)

i. Title.
PT9875.L598K3   54–15338

NL 0380660   DLC

VOLUME 334

LINDGREN, ASTRID (ERICSSON), 1907–
Meisterdetektiv Blomquist; ein lustiges Spiel um Gauner, Juwelen, Polizei und einen grossen Detektiv. Für Kinder geschrieben. [Deutsche Bearbeitung: Kurt Peters. 1. Aufl.] Hannover, Verlag Schaffende Jugend [1951] 50 p. 21cm. (Schriftenreihe Laienspiel, 10)

Film reproduction. Negative.
I. Juvenile literature--Drama. Swedish--Translations into German. I. Title.

NL 0380661 NN

---

j839.7
L643m
Sw
Lindgren, Astrid (Ericsson) 1907–
Mera om oss barn i Bullerbyn. [Omslag och illustrationer av Ingrid Vang Nyman] [Stockholm] Rabén & Sjögren [1949] 135p.

NL 0380662 PP

---

j839.7
L643mi
Sw
Lindgren, Astrid Ericsson, 1907–
Mio, min Mio. [Illustrationer och omslag: Ilon Wikland] Stockholm, Rabén & Sjögren [°1954] 189p.

NL 0380663 PP

Lindgren, Astrid (Ericsson) 1907–
Pippi Longstocking; translated from the Swedish by Florence Lamborn. Illustrated by Louis S. Glanzman. New York, Viking Press, 1950.
158 p. illus. 21 cm.

I. Title.

PZ7.L6585Pi 50–10396

ScU MiU MB MU ICU MsSM
NL 0380664 DLC WaSp OO OrPS OCl OrP WaS Or CaBVaU

Lindgren, Astrid (Ericsson) 1907–
Pippi Longstocking; translated from the Swedish by Florence Lamborn. Illustrated by Louis S. Glanzman. New York, Viking Press, 1951.
158 p. illus. 21 cm.

NL 0380665 ViU

LINDGREN, ASTRID (ERICSSON), 1907–
Pippi Longstocking. [Translated by Edna Hurup; illustrated by Richard Kennedy. London; New York] Oxford university press. 1954. 120 p. illus. 21cm.

I. Hurup, Edna. tr. II. Title. III. Hurup, Edna.

NL 0380666 NN

---

aL63p
1955
Lindgren, Astrid (Ericsson) 1907–
Pippi Longstocking. Translated from the Swedish by Florence Lamborn. Illustrated by Louis S. Glanzman. Special ed. Eau Claire, Wis., E. M. Hale [c1950, 1955] 158p. illus. 21cm.

"Cadmus books."

I. Glanzman, Louis S., illus. II. Title.

NL 0380667 IU

Lindgren, Astrid (Ericsson) 1907–
La princesse de Couricoura; traduction de Marie Loewegren. Illustrations de Marianne Clouzot. Paris, Hachette [1953]
252 p. illus. 18 cm. (Bibliothèque rose illustrée)

I. Title.

PZ23.L64P7 54–25492 ‡

NL 0380668 DLC

Lindgren, Bengt.
Tambimetoden; lärobok för den elementära musikundervisningen; illustrerad av Peter Norrman. Stockholm, Ehlins [19—]
51 p. illus., music. 30 cm.
Method for the tambi, a Swedish plectral instrument.

1. Tambi—Methods.

MT647.L5 55–4821C

NL 0380669 DLC

WG
3696
Lindgren, Birger.
Sur "le cas d'exception de M.Picard" dans la théorie des fonctions entières. Uppsala, 1903.
38 p.

Thèse - Uppsala.

NL 0380670 CtY NcU RPB

Lindgren, Bo Gunnar, ed.
Kök

see under

Berg, Ing-Marie.

Lindgren, Carl Folke Gunnar

see

Lindgren, Gunnar, 1909–

Lindgren, Charles.
Breaking the money power, by Charles Lindgren. Chicago, Ill., The Progressive press, 1912.
25 p. 22½cm. $0.10

1. Banks and banking—U. S. 2. Money—U. S. I. Title.

Library of Congress HG2481.L5 12–11721

NL 0380673 DLC IEN ICJ

Lindgren, Charles.
The new salesmanship and how to do business, by Chas. Lindgren. Rev. ed., with valuable additions, by J. M. Fitzgerald ... Chicago, Laird & Lee [°1911]
3 p. l., xxxv, [1], 5–162 p. col. front., illus. 20cm. $1.00

1. Salesmen and salesmanship. 2. Mail order business. I. Fitzgerald, J. M., ed.

HF5438.L6 1911 11–29868

NL 0380674 DLC NIC NN

Lindgren, Charles.
The new salesmanship and how to do business by mail, by Chas. Lindgren ... Chicago, Laird & Lee [°1909]
3 p. l., 5–190 p. front., illus. 19½cm. $1.50

1. Salesmen and salesmanship. 2. Mail order business.

Library of Congress HF5438.L6 10–622

NL 0380675 DLC ICJ PPComm

Lindgren, Clarence William, 1901–
Automotive and construction equipment. [Edited by A. A. Sorenson. Washington? 1951]
xii, 287 p. illus., maps. 29 cm.
"Bibliography of natural disasters": p. 240.

1. Motor-trucks. 2. Motor buses. 3. Transportation, Automotive. 4. Building machinery. I. Title.

TL230.L53 629.284 51–1708

NL 0380676 DLC TU DI ViU OrP WaS WaT MtBC OrCS CU

Lindgren, David Leonard, 1906–
... Factors influencing the results of fumigation of the California red scale [by] D. L. Lindgren.
(In Hilgardia. Berkeley, Calif., 1941. 24cm. v. 13, no. 9, p. 491–511 incl. tables, diagrs.)
"Literature cited": p. 511.

1. Fumigation. 2. Aonidiella aurantii. A 41–1833

California. Univ. Libr.
for Library of Congress [S1.H5 vol. 13, no. 9]
(630.5)

NL 0380677 CU

Lindgren, David Leonard, 1906–
The respiration of insects in relation to the heating and the fumigation of grain ... by David Leonard Lindgren ... [St. Paul, 1935]
cover-title, 32 p. diagrs. 22½cm.
Thesis (PH. D.)—University of Minnesota, 1935.
Vita.
Published also as Technical bulletin 109, September 1935, of the Minnesota Agricultural experiment station.
"Literature cited": p. 31–32.

1. Insects—Physiology. 2. Respiration. 3. Grain. 4. Farm produce—Storage. 5. Fumigation.

Library of Congress QL495.L5 1935 36–16037
Univ. of Minnesota Libr.
[631.563] 632.7

NL 0380678 MnU CU DLC

Lindgren, David Leonard, 1906–
... The stupefaction of red scale, *Aonidiella aurantii*, by hydrocyanic acid [by] D. L. Lindgren.
(In Hilgardia. Berkeley, Calif., 1938. 24cm. v. 11, no. 5, p. [211]–225 incl. tables, diagrs.)
"Literature cited": p. 225.

1. Aonidiella aurantii. 2. Hydrocyanic acid. I. Title. A 38–1087

California. Univ. Libr.
for Library of Congress [S1.H5 vol. 11, no. 5]
(630.5)

NL 0380679 CU DLC

LINDGREN, Donald & Steinhart, Arden.
Art museums - museums.
[Seattle. 1949?] 26p. illus. plans.

Reproduced from typewritten copy.
An undergraduate paper by architecture students at the University of Washington.

NL 0380680 WaS

VOLUME 334

Lindgren (E[mil]). A brief description of massage and the Swedish movement cure. 15 pp. 8°. *Washington, H. L. McQueen,* [1892].

NL 0380681   DNLM

Lindgren, Erik.
Handbuch der Neurochirurgie

see under

Olivecrona, Herbert, 1891- ed.

Lindgren, Erik.
A pneumographic study of the temporal horn with special reference to tumours in the temporal region. [Translated by Inez Hultgren] Stockholm [Norstedt] 1948.
151 p. illus. 25 cm. (Acta radiologica. Supplementum 69)
At head of title: From the Roentgen Dept. of the Seraphimer Hospital, Stockholm.
Akademisk avhandling—Karolinska institutet, Stockholm.
Extra t. p., with thesis statement, inserted.
"References": p. 149–151.
1. Temporal bone—Tumors. 2. Diagnosis, Radioscopic. I. Title: Temporal horn. (Series)

A 50–6424

Michigan. Univ. Libr.
for Library of Congress

NL 0380683   MnU DNLM MoU ViU

Lindgren, Erik, *ed.*
Röntgenologie, einschliesslich Kontrastmethoden. Berlin, Springer, 1954.
vii, 296 p. illus. 28 cm. (Handbuch der Neurochirurgie, 2. Bd.)
Bibliography: p. 251–278.

1. Skull—Radiography. 2. Brain—Radiography. 3. Spine—Radiography. (Series)
RC386.5.L5   55–33315

NL 0380684   DLC OC1W-H OU

PD5640
.W5
1931

Lindgren, Erik, 1844–1899.
             FOR OTHER EDITIONS
             SEE MAIN ENTRY

Wenström, Oscar Edmund, 1845–1902.
Engelsk-svensk ordbok, utarbetad af Edmund Wenström och Erik Lindgren. 2. stereotyperade uppl. Stockholm, P. A. Norstedt & söner [1931]

335
L643

LINDGREN, Erik, *1844-1899*.
    Handbok i svenska trädgårdsskötseln, utg. af Erik Lindgren, Axel Pihl och Georg Löwegren. Stockholm, S. Flodin [1874-77 (v.1, 1877)]

    6 pt. in 2 v. illus. 21cm.

    Pt. 1-3, 2d ed.
    1. Gardening in Sweden. I. Pihl, Axel, jt. author. II. Löwegren, Georg, 1833-1919, jt. autho[r]

NL 0380686   MnU

SB
99
S8
L5

Lindgren, Erik, 1844-1899.
    Handbok i svenska trädgårdsskötseln, utgifven af Erik Lindgren, Axel Pihl och Georg Löwegren. Stockholm, Sigfried Flodin [1877-1883]
    7 v. in 1. illus.

    Each vol. has special t. p.

NL 0380687   WaU

[L]indgren, Ernest.
    The art of the film, an introduction to film appreciation. London, G. Allen and Unwin [1948]
    xiv, 242 p. plates. 22 cm.
    "Select bibliography": p. 195–196.

1. Moving-pictures. I. Title.
PN1995.L47   791.4   48–23227*

   CaBVaU IdPI OrCS MtBC
   CtY Vi OU OOxM NIC TU OO Or OrP OrU WaS WaE WaT MH
NL 0380688   DLC PSt IdB CaBVa OKentC CLSU ICU NNC MB

Lindgren, Ernest.
The art of the film, an introduction to film appreciation. London, G. Allen and Unwin. New York, Macmillan [1955]
xiv, 242 p. plates. 22 cm.   791.4 195–196
"Select bibliography": p.

NL 0380689   MdBJ MiU

Lindgren, Ernest.
    ... The cinema, by Ernest Lindgren ... [London] Pub. for the Association for education in citizenship by the English universities press ltd [1944]
    cover-title, 23, [1] p. 16¼ᵐᵐ. (Unless we plan now ... handbooks for discussion groups, no. 10)
    Bibliography: p. 22–23.

1. Moving-pictures. I. Title.
                    45–7162
Library of Congress   PN1995.L5
                    791.4

NL 0380690   DLC NN

Lindgren, Ethel John, joint ed.

Bartlett, Frederic Charles, 1887– *ed.*
    The study of society; methods and problems, edited by F. C. Bartlett, M. Ginsberg, E. J. Lindgren, and R. H. Thouless. London, K. Paul, Trench, Trubner & co., ltd. [1939]

308t
L7449

Lindgren, Frank Ty, 1924-
    Physical and chemical studies of human serum lipoproteins. [Berkeley, 1955]
    iii, 59 ℓ. illus., diagrs., tables.

    Thesis (Ph. D. in Biophysics) - Univ. of California, June 1955.
    Bibliography: leaves 42-44.

    1. Blood plasma. 2. Lipids. 3. Proteins.

NL 0380692   CU

Lindgren, Frans Gustaf.
Tjuguandra psalmen af psaltaren.
Inaug. diss. Upsala, 1872.

NL 0380693   ICRL

Lindgren, Gunnar, 1909- supposed author.
    ... Autoxidation of diethyl ether and its inhibition by diphenylamine
       see under   Lindgren, Gunnar Olof, 1914-

Lindgren, Gunnar, 1909–
    ... Falbygden och dess närmaste omgivning vid 1600-talets mitt, en kulturgeografisk studie ... av Gunnar Lindgren .. Uppsala, Appelbergs boktryckeri-aktiebolag, 1939.
    3 p. l., [v]–xvi, 198 p. illus. (incl. plans) fold. maps, tables, diagrs. 26ᶜᵐ. (Added t.-p.: Geographica; skrifter från Upsala universitets Geografiska institution ... Nr. 6)
    Akademisk avhandling—Uppsala.
    "Källor och litteratur": p. [ix]–xiii.
    "Zusammenfassung": p. [193]–198.
    1. Västergötland, Sweden. 2. Anthropo-geography—Sweden—Västergötland. I. Title.
            [Full name: Carl Folke Gunnar Lindgren]
                       42–43489
Library of Congress   GF615.V3L5

NL 0380695   DLC TxU MH CtY MnU MoU

RD1
.A22
no.110

Lindgren, Gunnar Olof, 1914-
    Autoxidation of diethyl ether and its inhibition by diphenylamine; a chemical, biological and clinical study of some practically important problems concerning the protection of anesthetic ether against disintegration. Stockholm, 1935.
    190 p. 24 cm. (Acta chirurgica Scandinavica. Supplementum 110)

    Bibliography: p. [188]–190.

NL 0380696   AAP

Lindgren, Gunnar Olof, 1914–
    Autoxidation of diethyl ether and its inhibition by diphenylamine; a chemical, biological and clinical study of some practically important problems concerning the protection of anesthetic ether against disintegration. Stockholm, 1946.
    190 p. 24 cm. (Acta chirurgica Scandinavica, suppl. 110)
    "References": p. [188]–190.

1. Ether (Anesthetic) 2. Oxidation. (Series)
          Full name: Gunnar Olof Afred Lindgren
                         A 49–7888
John Crerar Library
for Library of Congress

NL 0380697   ICJ ViU IU PPPCPh InU CaBVaU

Lindgren, Gustaf, *ed.*
En bok om Prins Eugen, av 22 författare. Uppsala, J. Lindblad [1948]
    237 p. illus., ports. 23 cm.

1. Eugen Napoleon Nicolaus, Prince of Sweden, 1865-1947. I. Title.
           Full name: Gustaf Helge Lindgren
ND793.E8L5   927.5   50–195[?]

NL 0380698   DLC OC1 NhD NN

VOLUME 334

Lindgren, Gustaf.
Försvar mot kupp och blixtkrig ₍av₎ Gustaf Lindgren ₍och₎ Axel Strindberg. ₍Stockholm, Bokhandelsdistribution: Seelig, 1951₎
43 p. map. 21 cm.

1. Sweden—Defenses.   I. Strindberg, Axel, 1910–
II. Title.
Full name: Gustaf Helge Lindgren.
UA790.L53   51–37188

NL 0380699   DLC NN

Lindgren, Gustaf.
Gustaf Wilhelm Palm, 1810–1890. [Stockholm, P.A.Norstedt & söner, 1934]

xii, 352 p. illus. 29 cm. (Sveriges allmänna konstförenings publikation, 43)
Katalog över G.W.Palms oljemålningar, p.269–339.

NL 0380700   MH NIC CU NN OO MnU

Lindgren, Gustaf.
Landskapsmålaren Gustaf Wilhelm Palm, 1810–1890 ... av Gustaf Lindgren ... Stockholm ₍Kungl. boktryckeriet, P. A. Norstedt & söner₎ 1933.

xii, 352 p. incl. front. (port.) illus. col. plates. 29 x 22½ᶜᵐ.
Akademisk avhandling—Uppsala.
"Katalog över G. W. Palms oljemålningar": p. ₍267₎–339.
"Käll- och litteraturförteckning": p. 340–344.

1. Palm, Gustaf Wilhelm, 1810–1890.
₍Full name: Gustaf Helge Lindgren₎
34–41753

Library of Congress   ND793.P3L5 1933 [759.85] 927.5

NL 0380701   DLC CU PU IU CtY

Lindgren, Gustaf.
Papper på bordet; bidrag till försvarsberedskapens historia, av Gustaf Lindgren. Stockholm, 1947. 58 p. 21cm.

I. Defense—Sweden.
N. Y. P. L.   July 15, 1949

NL 0380702   NN

Jat79   Lindgren, Gustaf.
S48   Prince Eugen's Waldemarsudde. Stockholm,
+949L   A.Bonniers,1949.
137p.(chiefly illus.,part col.,ports.) 32cm.

1. Waldemarsudde, Sweden (Castle) 2. Eugen Napoleon Nicolaus, Prince of Sweden, 1865–1947.

NL 0380703   CtY

W.C.L.   Lindgren, Gustaf.
728.R2   Prins Eugens Waldemarsudde. Stockholm, A. Bonnier,
L745P   1948.
137 p. illus. (part col.) ports. 32 cm.

1. Valdemarsudde, Djurgården, Stockholm. 2. Eugen Napoleon Nicolaus, Prince of Sweden, 1865–1947. I. Title.
Full name: Gustaf Helge Lindgren.
NA7781.S83L5   A 50–6741
Harvard Univ. Librar
for Library of Congress   ₍1₎†

NL 0380704   MH DLC CU NcD

708.85   Lindgren, Gustaf.
W144L5   Prins Eugens Waldemarsudde; a guide. Stockholm ₍P. A. Norstedt & Söner₎ 1949 87 ₍7₎p. illus, plans.

1.Valdemarsudde, Djur-garden, Stockholm.
2.Eugen, prince of Sweden, 1865–1947.
I.Title

NL 0380705   MiD-A MH

Lindgren, Gustaf.
Prins Eugens Waldemarsudde, a guide by Gustaf Lindgren ... Stockholm, n.p., 1952. 84 p. illus. 17 cm.

NL 0380706   PPAmSwM

Lindgren, Gustaf Axel Herman, 1863–1930, ed.
Samfundet S:t Eriks årsbok. 1903–
see under Samfundet Sankt Erik, Stockholm.

Lindgren, Gustaf Axel Herman, 1863–1930.
Svenska kyrkor, skildrade af Gustaf Lindgren... Femtiotre illustrationer under medverkan af John Kindborg. Stockholm, J. Seligmann ₍1895₎

3 p.l., 3–78, ₍2₎ p. incl. illus., plates. 28cm.

Plates printed on both sides.

1. Churches in Sweden.   I. Title.

NL 0380708   MnU

Lindgren, Gustaf Birch-
see
Birch-Lindgren, Gustaf, 1892–

Lindgren, Gustaf Helge
see Lindgren, Gustaf.

Lindgren (H. J.). Barnsjukhuset i Lund en ny afdelning af Malmöhus läns sjukvårdsinrättningar derstädes. 52 pp., 5 ch. 8°. Lund, Berling, 1900.

NL 0380711   DNLM

LINDGREN, HANS.
Further tests with models of coasters, by Hans Lindgren and Axel O. Warholm. Göteborg, Gumpert, 1955.
46 p. diagrs., tables. (Meddelanden från Statens Skeppsprovningsanstalt, Göteborg, nr.35)

1. Ship models - Testing. 2. Ship resistance. I. Warholm, Axel O   joint author. II. Title.

NL 0380712   GAT

LINDGREN, HANS,   ed.
The influence of propeller clearance and rudder upon the propulsive characteristics, by the staff of SSPA. Göteborg, Gumpert, 1955.
25 p. diagrs., tables. (Meddelanden från Statens Skeppsprovningsanstalt, Göteborg, nr.33)

Bibliography: p.25.

1. Ship propulsion. I. Gothenburg, Sweden. Statens Skeppsprovningsanstalt. II. Title.

NL 0380713   GAT

Lindgren, Harry Arthur, 1888–
Cattle marketing investigation at Portland, Oregon, by H. A. Lindgren and E. L. Potter. Corvallis, Ore., 1927.
15, ₍1₎ p. illus., tables, diagr. 23ᶜᵐ. (Oregon. Agricultural experiment station, Corvallis. Station bulletin 229)

1. Domestic animals. 2. Cattle trade—Oregon.   I. Potter, Ermine Lawrence, 1884–   II. Title.
A 27–574
Title from Oregon Agr.   College. Printed by L. C.
₍3₎

NL 0380714   OrCS MB OrU OrPR

Lindgren, Harry Arthur, joint author.
Potter, Ermine Lawrence, 1884–
... Cost of producing mutton and wool on eastern Oregon ranges, by E. L. Potter and H. A. Lindgren. Corvallis, Ore., 1925.

Lindgren, Harry Arthur, joint author.
Potter, Ermine Lawrence, 1884–
... Cost of producing pork, by E. L. Potter, H. A. Lindgren, and A. W. Oliver. Corvallis, Ore., 1924.

Lindgren, Harry Arthur, 1888–
Feeding wheat to hogs in the Columbia Basin and Blue Mountain Counties in Oregon in connection with the national defense program. Corvallis, 1941.
8 p
(Oregon. College of agriculture, Extension Service. Extension bulletin no. 582.)

NL 0380717   PP

Lindgren, Harry Arthur, 1888–
Lamb marketing investigations in western Oregon ₍by H. A. Lindgren and E. L. Potter₎ Corvallis, Ore., 1930.
15 p. illus., tables. 23ᶜᵐ. (Oregon. Agricultural experiment station, Corvallis. Station bulletin 265)

1. Sheep.   I. Potter, Ermine Lawrence, 1884–   joint author.
II. Title.
[S105.E2 no. 265]   A30–1170
Title from Oreg. Agr.   College. Printed by L. C.
₍3₎

NL 0380718   OrCS OrU OrPR

VOLUME 334

Lindgren, Harry Arthur, 1888–   joint author.

Jardine, James Tertius, 1881–
... Management of range grazing land, by J. T. Jardine,
H. A. Lindgren ₍and₎ E. L. Potter. Corvallis, Or., Oregon
agricultural college, Extension service, 1927.

NL 0380720   OrCS OrP

Lindgren, Harry Arthur, 1888–
Report on the feasibility of grazing livestock
on the cutover timber lands of Columbia and Clat-
sop counties, Oregon, by H.A. Lindgren ... ₍Cor-
vallis, Ore.₎1935₎
cover-title, 19 p. incl. 2 maps. 28cm.

Mimeographed.
"This material has been assembled from information supplied by branches of the United States
Forest service; Farm crops department and Extension service, Oregon state college; Agricultural
and livestock agent, S.P. & S. railway company;
members of the county courts of Columbia and Clat-
sop counties; and private timber owners". -Cover.

NL 0380720   OrCS OrP

Lindgren, Harry Arthur, 1888–
Swine management in Oregon, by H. A. Lingren ₍!₎ and
A. W. Oliver. Corvallis, Oregon state system of higher education, Federal cooperative extension service, Oregon state college, 1941.

20 p. illus. 23ᶜᵐ. (Oregon. State agricultural college, Corvallis.
Federal cooperative extension service₎ Extension bulletin 550)
Cooperative extension work in agriculture and home economics,
Wm. A. Schoenfeld, director.

1. Swine.   I. Oliver, Alfred Weaver, 1894–   joint author.
II. Title.

Oreg. st. agr. coll. Library   S537.O7A5 no. 550   A 41–4504
for Library of Congress   (630.717)

NL 0380721   OrCS

PT8890   Lindgren, Hellen, 1857-1904.
L55   Henrik Ibsen, i hans lifskamp och hans verk.   Stockholm,
             Wahlström & Widstrand [1903]
             180 p.

1. Ibsen, Henrik, 1828-1906.

NL 0380722   CU Or IEN OOxM MH InU

B   Lindgren, Hellen, 1857-1904.
R9413ℓ   Johan Ludvig Runeberg; ett skaldeporträtt ...
             Stockholm, Aktiebolaget Ljus, 1904.
             163p.

1. Runeberg, Johan Ludvig, 1804-1877.

NL 0380723   IU NN MnU

PN516   Lindgren, Hellen, 1857-1904.
L5   Några diktareporträtt, essayer.   Stock-
            holm, Ljus, 1907.
            269 p.

Contents.- Henryk Sienkiewicz.- Leo N. Tol-
stoi.- Romantismen i Frankrike.- Voltaire och
hans strid mot fördomarne i religion och
samhälle.- Emile Zola.- Gunnar Wennerberg
som gluntarnes skald.- Sagoskalden Hans
Christian Andersen.

NL 0380724   CU

839.91364   Lindgren, Hellen, 1857-1904.
M   Sagoskalden Hans Christian Andersen. 2. uppl.
              Stockholm, A. Bonnier [1907]
              27 p. port.   20 cm.   (Studentföreningen Verdandis
              småskrifter. 86)

Includes bibliography.

I. Andersen, Hans Christian, 1805-1875. (Series:
Uppsala. Universitet. Studentföreningen Verdandi.
Småskrifter, 86)

NL 0380725   N CU NcD Or

Lindgren, Hellen, 1857-1904.
   Skalder och tänkare; litterära essayer, af Hellen Lindgren.
Stockholm, C. & E. Gernandt ₍1900₎
   404 p. incl. ports. 19½ᶜᵐ.
   CONTENTS.—Fredrika Bremer.—Carl Snoilsky.—August Strindberg.—
Henrik Ibsen och svenskarne.—William Shakespeare och hans senaste
skandinaviska biografer.—Thomas Carlyle.—Rudyard Kipling och hans
Djungelbok.—Robert Browning.—Molière.—Honoré de Balzac.—Bröderna
Goncourt.—Alphonse Daudet.

1. Literature, Modern—Addresses, essays, lectures.   I. Title.
                                                              33–22941
Library of Congress   PN516.L5   804

NL 0380726   DLC NcU WU MH CU CtY NjP

PT9361   Lindgren, Hellen, 1857-1904.
L5   Sveriges vittra storhetstid, 1730-1850.   Stockholm, Nor-
          stedt [1895-]
             v.

Contents. - Förra delen. 1. Frihetstiden.   2. Gustaf IIIˢ tid och
eftergusta vianerna. -

1. Swedish literature - 18th cent. - Hist. & crit.   2. Swedish
literature - 19th cent. - Hist. & crit.

NL 0380727   CU PU NjP

PN   Lindgren, Hellen, 1857-1904.
516   Vittra storman; kritiker och Porträtt.
L54   Stockholm, Carl Deleen & Comp. [1894]
           161 p.

1. Literature, Modern - Addresses, essays,
lectures. I. Title.

NL 0380728   WaU

LINDGREN, Henr₍ik₎ G₍erhard₎.
   Aristophanis comoedia quae ΠΛΟΥΤΟΣ inscribitur.
Diss. Upsaliae, excudebant Regiae Acad. Typ.,
[1834].

Pamphlet.

NL 0380729   MH

PJ   Lindgren, Henrik Gerhard.
6703   De lingua Neo-Arabica disquisitio.
L74   Upsaliae, Regia Academia ₍1829₎
           44 p. 22cm.

1. Arabic language.

NL 0380730   NIC CtY NN

Lindgren, *Henrik Gerhard.*
   Tusen och en natt
      see under Arabian nights. Swedish. 1854.

Lindgren, Henry Clay, 1914–
   The art of human relations. ₍1st ed.₎ New York, Hermitage House ₍1953₎
   287 p. 22 cm.

1. Interpersonal relations.   I. Title.

BF636.L49   150.13   53—7387 ‡

Or OrAshS OrLgE OrP Wa WaT W-S NBuU
ViU PPPL NcC NN OCl MiD ICU IEG NcD MiU CaBVa CaBVaU
NL 0380732   DLC KyLxCB KyLx TU OU OOxM OClW PPT PSt

BF636   Lindgren, Henry Clay, 1914–
L49   The art of human relations.   New York,
Also   Hermitage House [1954, c1953]
in   287 p.   22cm.
Col

1. Interpersonal relations.   I. Title.

NL 0380733   CoU CU NBuU

Lindgren, Henry Clay, 1914–
   Effective leadership in human relations. ₍1st ed.₎ New
York, Hermitage House ₍1954₎
   287 p. 22 cm.

1. Leadership.   I. Title.

BF637.L4L5   301.155   54—10898 ‡

OrPS Wa WaS WaE WaT
PU-W PPT PPPL DI OU MiU ViU CaBVa CaBVaU Or OrCS
NL 0380734   DLC NN MB OOxM PP TxU PHC OCU OO PCC

Lindgren, Henry Clay, 1914–
   Mental health in education. New York, Holt ₍1954₎
   561 p. illus. 22 cm.

1. Education of children. 2. Mental hygiene. I. Title.

LB1131.L48   371.71   54—6610 ‡

OrPS OrAshS IdPI
OCU OO NcD PSt MiU DNLM PU-Penn PSC OrP WaSpG
Or OrCS OrLgE OrMonO OrSaW OrU WaS PBm PJB PPPL
ODW PP KEmT MB WaU WaT WaWW CaBVa CaBVaU IdU MtU
NL 0380735   DLC NcGW TxU ViU TU PIm PPD OU OOxM

Lindgren, Henry Clay, 1914–
   The mental hygiene of personal and social
adjustment ...   [1951]
   2 parts.

NL 0380736   CaBVaU

VOLUME 334

Lindgren, Henry Clay, 1914–
Psychology of personal and social adjustment. New York, American Book Co. ₁1953₎
481 p. illus. 22 cm.
"Based on ₁the author's₎ Personal and occupational adjustment ... and The mental hygiene of personal and social adjustment."

1. Psychology. I. Title.

BF131.L49   150   53–10186 ‡

WaSpG OrSaW WaSp
OrAshS OrPS TU NIC IaAS NcD ViU WU-M KEmT WaWW
PPEB OC1U OOxM OC1JC OkU-M CaBVa CaBVaU IdPI OrCS
NL 0380737   DLC TxU OC1W OU NcRS PPLas PPT PIm DI

Lindgren, Hjalmar, 1897–
Studia Curtiana ... scripsit ... Hjalmar Lindgren ... Upsaliae, typis descripserunt Almqvist & Wiksell soc., 1935.
xv, 102 p. 24½ᶜᵐ.
Commentatio academica—Uppsala.
"Index editionum" : p. ₁ix₎ ; "Index codicum" : ₁x₎ ; "Index librorum" : p. ₁xi₎–xv.

1. Curtius Rufus, Quintus.
₁Full name: Hjalmar Zakarias Lindgren₎
37–20804

Library of Congress   PA6378.L5 1935
                ₍2₎   878.8

NL 0380738   DLC CtY IU MnU ICU PU

Adelmann
QL
965   **Lindgren, Hjalmar Ossian,** 1837–1919.
L74   Studier öfver däggdjursägget. (Med en
           tafla) Lund, F. Berling, 1876.
           136 p. plate. 25cm.

           Diss.—Lund.

           1. Ovum. 2. Embryology—Mammals.

NL 0380739   NIC

Lindgren (Hjalmar Ossian), 1837–19₍₎. Studier öfver lifmodrens byggnad hos menniskan. 44 pp., 4 pl. 8°. ₍Stockholm, P. A. Norstedt & Söner, 1897.₎
Repr. from : Med. Arch., Stockholm, 1866–7, iii, no. 13.

NL 0380740   ICRL DNLM

Lindgren, Hjalmar Zakarias
    see   Lindgren, Hjalmar, 1897–

Lindgren, Homer Dorr, joint author.

Collins, George Rowland, 1894–
Business argumentation, by G. Rowland Collins ... and Homer D. Lindgren ... New York city, N. Y., C. W. Russell ₁1923₎

PSC
1. Speeches, addresses, etc.   I. Title.
Library of Congress   PN6122.L5
                                          26–11774

OC1 OO ODW MiU NN PSC PPGi
NL 0380743   DLC PPT WU NcU OrP WaS MtBC NcRS OOxM

Lindgren, Homer Dorr, comp.
Modern speeches, compiled by Homer D. Lindgren ... Rev. ed. New York, F. S. Crofts & co., 1930.
xv, 514 p. 21ᶜᵐ.

1. Speeches, addresses, etc.   I. Title.
Library of Congress   PN6122.L5 1930   31–15445
——— Copy 2.
Copyright A 38869   ₍3₎   825.9108

PWcS PPAp ViU MH
NL 0380744   DLC WaS CaBVa OrSaW Or MtBC OrP KMK NcD

Lindgren, Hugo.
Handbok för guldsmeder. Stockholm, Sveriges juvelerare- och guldsmedsförbund, 1949.
381 p. illus., col. coats of arms. 22 cm.
"Lagar och förordningar" : p. ₁299₎–375.

1. Goldsmithing. 2. Goldsmithing—Sweden. 3. Hall-marks. I. Sweden. Laws, statutes, etc.

TS725.L54   52–16273

NL 0380745   DLC NN

Lindgren, Hugo Mauritz, 1872–

Finland. *Socialstyrelsen.*
... Arbetarskydd och arbetarvälfärd, föredrag hållna vid föreläsningsdagarna för kommunala yrkesinspektörer under nov.–dec. år 1919. Helsingfors, Statsrådets tryckeri, 1920.

Lindgrén, Hugo Mauritz, 1872–

Finland. *Socialstyrelsen.*
... Työväensuojelus ja työväenhuolto, kunnallisia amonattientarkastajia varten marras- ja joulukuussa 1919 järjestetyillä luentopäivillä pidetyt esitelmät. Helsinki, Valtioneuvoston kirjapaino, 1920.

325.761
L643   **Lindgren, Ida (Nibelius)** 1829–ca. 1909.
          Ida Lindgrens, f. Nibelius, bref
          fran nybyggarhemmet i Kansas, 1870–
          1881. Malmö, Skanska lithografiska
          aktiebolaget, 1911.

          107 p.   illus., ports   24cm.

          1. Swedes in Kansas.

NL 0380748   MnU MnHi

LINDGREN, IDA (NIBELIUS), 1829–1909.
Brev från nybyggarhemmet i Kansas, 1870–1881.
[Stockholm] Riksföreningen för svenskhetens bevarande i utlandet. 86 p. illus., ports. 23cm. (Svenska spår och insatser i främmande land. 5)

1. Swedes in the U.S.—Kansas.

NL 0380749   NN

Lindgren, Inga.
Angina pectoris; a clinical study with special reference to neurosurgical treatment. Stockholm, 1950.
208 p. illus. 24 cm. (Acta medica Scandinavica. Supplementum 243)
Bibliography : p. ₁131₎–141.

1. Angina pectoris. 2. Nervous system, Sympathetic—Surgery. (Series)

Ohio State Univ. Libr.
for Library of Congress   ₍3₎
                                         A 52–421

NL 0380750   OU ViU PU-Hosp

Lindgren, J., joint author.

Zeipel, Hugo von, 1873–
... Photometrische untersuchungen der sterngruppe Messier 37 (N. G. C. 2099) von H. v. Zeipel und J. Lindgren ... Stockholm, Almqvist & Wiksells boktryckeri-a.-b., 1921.

Lindgren, Jakob Axel, 1845–1915.
Bidrag till den svenska pietismens historia. I. Pietismen i Stockholm 1702–1721 ... af dr. Jakob Axel Lindgren ... Upsala, Akademiska boktryckeriet, E. Berling, 1879.
1 p. l., 119, ₍1₎ p. 22½ᵐ.
Akademisk avhandling—Uppsala.
No more published.

1. Stockholm—Church history. 2. Pietism—Sweden.
                                                         36–28860
Library of Congress   BX4982.88L5
                ₍2₎   273.7

NL 0380752   DLC PPLT MH-AH

Lindgren, Jakob Axel, 1845–1915.
Nahums profetia. oefversaettning med anmarkningar. Inaug. diss. Upsala, 1872.

NL 0380753   ICRL

Lindgren, Joannes Gustavus
    see   Lindgren, Johann Gustav.

Lindgren, Johan, respondent.
Fries, Elias Magnus, 1794–1878, *praeses.*
Symbolæ gasteromycorum ad illustrandam floram svecicam ... Lundæ, Ex officina Berlingiana, 1817–18.

Lindgren, Johan August, 1868–1943.
...Minnen ur min levnad; anteckningar ur en gjutares liv. Stockholm, Tidens förlag ₁1944₎ 171 p. illus. 22cm. (Arbetarnas kulturhistoriska sällskap. Skrifter. Ny följd, nr. 2)

1. Metal workers—Sweden.   I. Ser.
N. Y. P. L.   October 31, 1950

NL 0380756   NN

Lindgren, Johan Erik
    see
Lindgren, Erik, 1844–1899.

VOLUME 334

Lindgren, Johann Gustav.
De viis intestinis ad systema uropoeticam.
[Dorpat], ex off. acad. J. C. Schünmanni,
1824.
50 p.   8°.

NL 0380758   DNLM

WI
L748e
1831
LINDGREN, Johann Gustav.
Der epidemische Brechdurchfall, beo-
bachtet zu Nishni-Nowgorod.   Dorpat,
Schünmann, 1831.
54 p.

NL 0380759   DNLM

Lindgren, Johann Gustav.
Ueber die Entwickelung der Hospital-
klinik an einigen Universitäten Russlands.
Kasan, 1850.
2 p. l., 84 p.   8°.

NL 0380760   DNLM

WC
262
L745v
1848
LINDGREN, Johann Gustav.
Versuch einer Nosologie der Cholera
orientalis. Kasan, Kaiserliche
Universitäts-Typographie, 1848.
vii, 235 p.
WC262 L745v

NL 0380761   DNLM

Lindgren, John
see   Lindgren, John Waldemar.

RS51
L5
Biology
Library
Lindgren, John, 1844-
Läkemedelsnamn, ordförklaring och historik.
Lund, Gleerupska universitets-bokhandeln
[1918]
xv, 450 p.   illus.

Bibliography: [ix]-xiii.

1. Materia medica - Dictionaries.   I.
Title.

NL 0380763   CU ICJ WU

QV
qL745s
1902
LINDGREN, John, 1844-
Svenska läkemedelsnamn. [2. uppl.
Lund] Möller [1902]
85 p.

NL 0380764   DNLM

Lindgren, John Axell
see   Lindgren, John, 1844-

Lindgren, John Waldemar.
AUGUST Palm, den svenska socialdemokratins
banbrytare. Stockholm, Tidens Förlag, 1931.

22 cm. Ports., facsims. and other illustr.
Contents: August Palm. Några biografiska
anteckningar av John Lindgren. - Ur en agitators
liv av August Palm.

NL 0380766   MH

Lindgren, John Waldemar.
August Palm; den svenska socialdemokratins banbrytare.
Stockholm, Tidens förlag [1946]
73 p. illus. 16 cm. (Lilla biblioteket)

1. Palm, August Theodor, 1849-1922.

HX337.P3L5   63-34985 ‡

                    [1]

NL 0380767   DLC

DL859
P3L5
Lindgren, John Waldemar.
August Palm.   Stockholm, Folket i Bilds
förlag, 1950.
95 p.   illus., ports.   (Banerförare)

1. Palm, August Theodor, 1849-1922.

NL 0380768   CU WU InU WaU

Lindgren, John Waldemar.
Från Per Götrek till Per Albin; några drag ur den
Svenska socialdemokratiens historia. Stockholm, Bonnier
[1936]
278 p. illus., ports., facsim. 20 cm. (Orientering i aktuella
ämnen)
Bibliography: p. 271.

1. Sveriges socialdemokratiska arbetareparti. 2. Sweden—Pol. &
govt.   I. Title.   (Series)

DL658.8.L5   51-52268

NL 0380769   DLC OrP NN MnU MH

DL
658.8
L5
1946
Lindgren, John Waldemar.
Från Per Götrek till Per Albin; några drag
ur den Svenska socialdemokratiens historia.
[2. uppl.] Stockholm, Bonnier [c1946]
278 p. illus., ports., facsims (Orientering
i aktuella ämnen)

NL 0380770   WaU

DL870
.H8L5
Lindgren, John Waldemar.
Per Albin Hansson i svensk demokrati. Stockholm, Ti-
dens förlag [1950-
v. illus. (part col.) ports., facsims. 27 cm.
CONTENTS.—1. delen. 1892-1920.

1. Hansson, Per Albin, 1885-1946.

                                        A 51-566

Minnesota. Univ. Libr.
for Library of Congress   [1]

NL 0380771   MnU MH

Lindgren, John Waldemar.
... Det Socialdemokratiska arbetarpartiets uppkomst i
Sverige 1881-1889, av John Lindgren ... Stockholm, Bokför-
lags-a.-b. Tidens tryckeri, 1927.
349 p., 1 l. 22ᶜᵐ. (Skrifter utgivna av Arbetarnas kulturhistoriska
sällskap. bd. 1)
Akademisk avhandling—Uppsala.
"Källor och litteratur": p. [321]-340.

1. Socialism in Sweden. 2. Sveriges socialdemokratiska arbetareparti.
I. Title.   35-30415 Revised
Library of Congress   HX337.L5 1927
                        [r45c2]   335.09485

NL 0380772   DLC CU MnU NN MH ICU PU

Lindgren, John Waldemar.
... Svenska metallindustriarbetareförbundets historia ...
[Stockholm, Tryckeriaktiebolaget Tiden, 1938-
v. illus. (incl. ports., facsims.) 24½ᶜᵐ.
At head of title: John Lindgren.
CONTENTS.—I. 1888-1905.

1. Svenska metallindustriarbetareförbundet.
                                              44-50013
Library of Congress   HD6759.M5L5
                        [2]   331.88171

NL 0380773   DLC NN MnU

Lindgren, John Waldemar.
Varför Sverige icke är republik. Stockholm,
Tidens Förlag [1955]
61 p. (Lilla biblioteket)

1. Sweden - Politics and government - 1905-
2. Sweden - History - 1905-

NL 0380774   NNC CtY NN

Lindgren, Jonas Valfrid, 1859-1932.
Burträskmålets grammatik. Ljudfysiologisk översikt, ak-
sentlagar, vokallagar ... Av Jonas Valfrid Lindgren ...
Stockholm, Kongl. boktryckeriet. P. A. Norstedt & söner,
1890.
165, [1] p. 24ᶜᵐ.
Akademisk avhandling—Uppsala.
From Svenska landsmål och svenskt folkliv, XII, 1.

1. Swedish language — Dialects—Burträsk. 2. Swedish language—
Phonology.   I. Title.
                                              36-30133
Library of Congress   PD5817.B8L5 1890
                        [2]   439.778

NL 0380775   DLC CU

Lindgren, Jonas Valfrid, 1859-1932.
... Burträskmålets grammatik. 1. häftet ... Stock-
holm, Kongl. boktryckeriet, P. A. Norstedt & söner, 1890.
165, [1] p. 23½ᶜᵐ. (Bidrag till kännedom om de svenska landsmålen
ock svenskt folkliv XII. 1)
Akademisk avhandling—Uppsala.
Forms part of 43. hft. of the whole series.
"Burträsk ... är beläget i Västerbotten."—Förord.

1. Swedish language—Dialects—Västerbotten.   I. Title.
                                              26-345
Library of Congress   PD5001.S9 43 h. XII. 1

NL 0380776   DLC OCl NN

VOLUME 334

Lindgren, Jonas Valfrid, 1859-1932.
Dansk och norsk grammatik. Stockholm,
P. A. Norstedt [1894]
88 p. 22 cm.
1. Danish language - Grammar. 2. Norwegian language - Grammar.

NL 0380777   CU

439.85 Lindgren, Jonas   Valfrid, 1859-1932.
L64d   Dansk och norsk grammatik. 2.upplagan.
Stockholm, 1915.
93p.

NL 0380778   IU

HG3180
.G34G4

Lindgren, Jonas Valfrid, 1859-1932.
Fyhrvall, Carl Oscar, 1846-
... Gefle stads sparbank ... Historik. På grundvalen af
ett manuskript af rektor J. V. Lindgren utarbetad af Oskar
Fyhrvall. [Stockholm, Kungl. hofboktryckeriet, Iduns
tryckeri-a.-b., 1904]

PD5826
.L5

Lindgren, Jonas Valfrid, 1859-1932.
Ordbok över Burträskmålet. Utg. av D. O. och Margareta
Zetterholm. Uppsala, A. B. Lundequist [1940]
vii, 167 p. map. 25 cm. (Skrifter utg. genom Landsmålsarkivet i
Uppsala, ser. A : 3)

1. Swedish language—Dialects—Burträsk. 2. Swedish language—
Dictionaries.   I. Zetterholm, Delmar Olof, 1905–   ed.   II. Title.
(Series: Uppsala. Landsmålsarkivet. Skrifter, ser. A : 3)

A 48–4501*

Harvard Univ. Library
for Library of Congress   [2]

NL 0380780   MH NNC ICU CtY NN DLC

Lindgren, Kaj August, 1908-
...I bågens tid. Helsingfors, H. Schildt [1948] 92 p.
19cm.

1. Poetry, Swedish-Finnish.   I. Title.
N. Y. P. L.   February 27, 1950

NL 0380781   NN

Lindgren, Kaj August, 1908-
Ett blad är vänt; dikter. Helsingfors,
H. Schildt [1935]
68 p.

NL 0380782   WaU

Lindgren, Kaj August, 1908-
Dikterna om Finlands kamp. 4. upplagan. Stockholm, A.
Bonnier [1940]

Lindgren, Kaj August, 1908-   tr.

PT9786
.Z5V517

Viljanen, Lauri Sakari, 1900-
Runeberg och hans diktning, 1804-1837. [Bemyndigad
översättning av Kaj Lindgren] Lund, C. W. K. Gleerup
[1947]

Lindgren, Kaj August, 1908-

839.7172
L745S

Stig fram, vårt land...; dikter [av] Kaj
Lindgren. 2. uppl. Helsingfors, H. Schildt
[1942]
89 p. 20 cm.

NL 0380785   NcD

Lindgren, Kaj August, 1908-
...Tall i storm; dikter. Helsingfors, H. Schildt [1944], 126 p.
illus. 20cm.

403685B. 1. No subject. I. Title.
N.Y. P. L.   September 17, 1947

NL 0380786   NN MH

Lindgren, Kaj August, 1908-

Trä-orgel; dikter [av] Kaj Lindgren. Helsingfors, H. Schildt [1937]
73 p. 20 cm.

NL 0380787   NcD

Lindgren, Kaj B
Die Apokope des mhd.-e in seinen verschiedenen Funk-
tionen. Helsinki, 1953.
225 p. map, diagrs., tables. 25 cm.
Thesis—Helsingfors universitet.
Bibliography : p. [7]-10.

1. German language—Middle High—German—Vowels.   I. Title.

PF4089.L5   56-27498

NL 0380788   DLC InU ICU TxU MiU NIC NNC CtY

Lindgren, Kaj B
MHD. genetivformen auf -ens. (Helsinki,
1954)
(667)-672 p. 26 cm. (Suomalaisen
tiedeakatemian Toimituksia. Annales Academiae scientiarum fennicae, sarja/ser. B, nid. /
tom. 84, 32)
Caption title.

NL 0380789   PU

Lindgren, Karl Adolf
see
Lindgren, Adolf, 1846-*1905*.

Lindgren, Karl Arne
see
Lindgren, Arne, 1910-

4:1.2
164

Lindgren, L   A   H
Generalregister till fauna och flora,
1906-1945. Uppsala, Almqvist & Wiksells,
1950.
118 p.

1. Sweden. Zoology. 2. Sweden. Botany.
I. Title: Fauna och flora.

NL 0380792   DNAL

Lindgren (LAURENT[IUS] AX[ELIUS])
*Nemeorum Pindari ode prima, versione et notis illus-
trata. *Upsaliae,* 1803. 2 p.l., 12 pp. 4°.
In: NEW p. v. 1.

NL 0380793   NN

Lindgren, Lawrence Frithof, joint comp.
FOR OTHER EDITIONS
SEE MAIN ENTRY
Peltier, George Leo, 1888-   *comp.*
Laboratory manual for general bacteriology, compiled by
George L. Peltier ... Carl E. Georgi ... [and] Lawrence F.
Lindgren ... (2d ed.) New York, J. Wiley & sons, inc.;
London, Chapman & Hall, limited, 1939.

Lindgren, Lennart.
The lower parts of the uterus during the first stage of
labour in occipito-anterior vertex presentation; studies by
means of intrauterine tokography. [Stockholm, 1955]
79 p. illus., diagrs. 25 cm. (Acta obstetricia et gynecologica
Scandinavica, v. 34. Supplementum 2)
"From the Department of Women's Diseases ... Sabbatsberg Hos-
pital, Stockholm, Sweden."
Errata leaf inserted.
Bibliography : p. [69]-79.

1. Uterus, Pregnant. 2. Labor (Obstetrics)   I. Title. (Series)

A 55–7351

Rochester. Univ. Libr.   RG1
for Library of Congress   [2]

NL 0380795   NRU DNLM MoU ViU

813
L6435m

Lindgren, Lydia.
My heart in my throat; the story of a strange
captivity. New York, W. Faro, 1932.
716p. port. 24cm.

NL 0380796   TxU NN Vi

Lindgren, Lydia C
Vinterrosor; samlade dikter. Seattle,
Washington, 1930.
150 p. illus., port.

NL 0380797   WaU

Lindgren, Maj Levander-
see
Levander-Lindgren, Maj, 1917-

Lindgren, Martin, 1910-
... Zur Frage der Verschleppung des Collum-
carcinoms ... Berlin, [1938]
Inaug.-Diss. - Berlin.
Lebenslauf.
"Literatur": p. 14.

NL 0380799   CtY

VOLUME 334

Lindgren, Nils.
Jbb   Bertil Bull Hedlund; en monografi ...
178   Stockholm, E. Lund, 1943.
     2p.ℓ., vii-viii, 222p., 1ℓ. incl. illus., plates,
ports. 19½cm.
     "Bibliografi": p. 220-221.

NL 0380800   CtY

Lindgren, Nicol. Udalricus, respondent.
     Acta et litterae ad historiam suecanam...
    see under   Geijer, Erik Gustaf, 1783-1847,
praeses.

ND793   Lindgren, Nils.
.H4L5   Bertil Bull Hedlund. Stockholm, Norstedt ₁1952₎
     192 p. illus., plates (part col.) 29 cm.

     1. Hedlund, Bertil Bull, 1893-

              A 53-4523

Harvard Univ. Library
for Library of Congress   ₁‡₎

NL 0380802   MH CU MnU WU NIC NN DLC

Lindgren, Nils.
     Gösta Adrian-Nilsson. ₁Stockholm₎ Rabén & Sjögren
₁1949₎
     221 p. illus., col. plates, ports. 27 cm.

     1. Adrian-Nilsson, Gösta, 1884-

     ND793.A3L5   50-34284

NL 0380803   DLC NhD MoU

Lindgren, Nils.
     ... Knut Ander ...   Linköping, [1933]
     1. Ander, Knut.

NL 0380804   CtY

₁YA   Lindgren, Nils Gustaf.
₂₈70   Beitrag zur kenntniss der spongienfauna des
    Malayischen archipels und der chinesischen Meere.
... [Jena, 1898.]
     378p.

NL 0380805   DLC ICRL PU

Wason   Lindgren, Nils Gustaf.
QL372.5   Beitrag zur Kenntniss der Spongienfauna
L74   des malayischen Archipels und der chinesi-
schen Meere. Upsala, Harald Wretman, 1900.
     96 p. illus. 23 cm.

     Diss.--Uppsala.

     1. Sponges--Malay Archipelago. 2. Spon-
ges--China Sea. I. Title: Spongienfauna
des malayischen Archipels und der chinesischen Meere.

NL 0380806   NIC CtY CaBVaU

Lindgren, Olga.
     Trumman ljuder i Tanganyika. Helsingfors, Taborför-
laget ₁1948₎
     175 p. 19 cm.

     1. Missions--Tanganyika Territory.   I. Title.

     BV3625.T3L5   53-30202 ‡

NL 0380807   DLC

---

*BJ   Lindgren, Oscar.
1588   Lifvets sidor och karaktär. Kennedy,
.L5   Minn., 1909.
     139 p. illus., port. 18 cm.

     Title page in typescript.

     1. Conduct of life. I. Title.

NL 0380808   MnHi MnU

Lindgren, Per.
     Sabotageverksamhet; medel och motåtgärder. Stock-
holm, Riksförbundet för Sveriges försvar ₁1944₎
     80 p. illus. 19 cm. (Medborgarkunskap om riksförsvaret, 18)

     1. Sabotage.   (Series)

     UB273.L5   50-45115 rev

NL 0380809   DLC

UB270   Lindgren, Per.
.B4

     Bernhardsson, Carl Olof.
       Spionpolisen går på jakt. Sakkunnig medhjälpare: Per
Lindgren. Stockholm, Natur och kultur ₁1952₎

Lindgren, Percy.
     The mesencephalon and the vasomotor system; an experi-
mental study on the central control of peripheral blood flow
in the cat. ₁Translated by Stanley H. Vernon₎ Stockholm,
1955.
     189 p. illus., diagrs. 23 cm. (Acta physiologica Scandinavica, v.
35. Supplementum 121)
     Bibliography: p. 183-189.

     1. Nervous system, Vasomotor.   (Series)

             A 57-602

Chicago. Univ. Libr.
for Library of Congress   ₁2₎

     DNLM NIC
NL 0380811   ICU CoU OkU-M DNAL PU-Med ViU CU RPB

Lindgren, Ralph Melvin, 1904-   joint author

Scheffer, Theodore C   1904-
     Some minor stains of southern pine and hardwood lumber
and logs. By T. C. Scheffer ... and R. M. Lindgren ...
     (*In* U. S. Dept. of agriculture. Journal of agricultural research.
v. 45. no. 4. Aug. 15, 1932. p. 233-237. 23½cm. Washington, 1932)

Lindgren, Ralph Melvin, 1904-
     Some relations and effects of fungi causing blue-stain of
wood ... by Ralph Melvin Lindgren ... ₁Washington, 1942₎
     35 p. 4 pl. on 3 l., diagrs. 23ᶜᵐ.
     Thesis (PH. D.)--University of Minnesota, 1937.
     Technical bulletin no. 807, March 1942 of the U. S. Dept. of agricul-
ture, with thesis t.-p. and Vita on p. ₁2₎-₁3₎ of cover. Cover-title: Temperature, moisture, and penetration studies of wood-staining ceratostomellae in relation to their control.
     "Literature cited": p. 34-35.

     1. Wood-staining fungi. 2. Ceratostomella.

             44-35632

     Library of Congress   TA422.L5

NL 0380813   DLC

TA422   Lindgren, Ralph Melvin, 1904-   joint
.S35   author.
     Scheffer, Theodore Comstock, 1904-
     ... Stains of sapwood and sapwood products and their con-
trol, by Theodore C. Scheffer ... and Ralph M. Lindgren ...
Washington, D. C., United States Dept. of agriculture ₁1940₎

Lindgren, Ralph Melvin, 1904-
     ... Temperature, moisture, and penetration studies of
woodstaining *Ceratostomellae* in relation to their control ...
Washington, D. C., U. S. Dept. of Agriculture ₁1942₎
     cover-title, 35 p. illus. 23 cm. (U. S. Dept. of agriculture. Tech-
nical bulletin no. 807)
     Contribution from Bureau of plant industry.
     "Literature cited": p. 34-35.

     1. Ceratostomella. ₁1. Ceratostomellae₎

     S21.A72 no. 807   589.2351   Agr 42-159 rev
     U. S. Dept. of Agr. Libr.   1 Ag84Te   no. 807   Brief cataloging
     for Library of Congress   ₁r50e₎₁†

NL 0380815   DNAL DLC WaWW PPT PPAN PP

Lindgren, Robert.
     Flodsystemet Mackenzie. ₁Helsingfors, 1912.₎   73, 4 p.
8°.   (Geografiska föreningen i Finland. Meddelanden. ₁v.₎ 9.)

     1. Mackenzie river, Canada.
     N. Y. P. L.   January 8, 1913.

NL 0380816   NN

Lindgren, Roy Alexander, 1899-
     ... Some observations regarding refractories for iron blast
furnaces, by Roy A. Lindgren.
     (American institute of mining and metallurgical engineers. Tech-
nical publication no. 752, *in* Mining technology. New York, 1937.
23ᶜᵐ. Jan. 1937. v. 1, no. 1. 16 p. incl. illus., 2 tab., diagrs.)
     "References": p. 16.

     1. Refractory materials. 2. Blast-furnaces.

             P O 38-52

     U. S. Patent office. Library   TN1.A492
     for Library of Congress   [TN1.A525   no. 752]
             ₁3₎

NL 0380817   DP DLC

4SF-148   Lindgren, S   O
     Riistanhoitajan käsikirja. Helsingissä,
Kustannusosakeyhtiö Otava [1943]
     272 p. (Suomen Yleisen Metsästäjäliiton
julkaisufa, n:o 10)

NL 0380818   DLC-P4

Lindgren, Sören, 1935-
     Ornament. ₁Dikter. Helsingfors₎ Schildt ₁1954₎
     31 p. 18 cm.

     I. Title.

             A 55-3992

     Minnesota. Univ. Libr.
     for Library of Congress   ₁‡₎

NL 0380819   MnU

VOLUME 334

Lindgren, Stig.
... Eine studie über depressive sekretionsanomalien des magens; auf grund eines vom bevölkerungsstandpunkt einheitlichen materials aus der provinz Västerbotten im nördlichen Schweden, von Stig Lindgren ... Lund, H. Ohlssons buchdruckerei, 1932.
viii, 235 p. pl., tables (1 fold.) diagrs. 23½ᶜᵐ. (*On cover:* Acta medica scandinavica. Supplementum xlviii)
At head of title: Aus der Medizinischen abteilung des Krankenhauses zu Umeå.
German translation by Konrad and Thea Flex.
"Litteraturverzeichnis": p. ₍218₎–235.
1. Stomach—Diseases. 2. Stomach—Secretions. I. Flex, Konrad, tr. II. Flex, Thea, joint tr.

A C 33–2180

Title from John Crerar Libr. Printed by L. C.
₍2₎

NL 0380820   ICJ PPCP MiU

Lindgren, Torgny.
Sveriges mynt, 1719–1776. Stockholm ₍Kungl. Vitterhets-, historie- och antikvitetsakademien₎ 1953.
xii, 158 p. 39 plates. 27 cm.
At head of title: Kungl. Myntkabinettet.

1. Coins, Swedish. I. Stockholm. Statens historiska museum. Myntkabinettet. II. Title.

CJ3175.L5   54–32454

NL 0380821   DLC CtY NN MnU

Lindgren, Udalricus, respondent.
De jure majestatis aggratiandi meditationes...
see under Boëthius, Jacob Edvard, praeses.

Lindgren, Uno.
Heraldik i svenska författningar; en vapenrättslig översikt från medeltiden till våra dagar. Lund, C. W. K. Gleerup ₍1951₎
179 p. plates (1 col.) 25 cm. (Skrifter utg. av Fahlbeckska stiftelsen, 37)
Summary in German.
Bibliography: p. ₍81₎–96.
1. Heraldry—Sweden. I. Title. (Series: Lund. Universitet. Fahlbeckska stiftelsen. Skrifter, 37)

CR662.L5   54–15938

NL 0380823   DLC MH MnU ICU NN

Lindgren, Verner.
Twenty years of economic reconstruction in Finland; a survey of conditions during the period of independence, by Verner Lindgren ... ₍Helsinki, Keskuskirjapaino, 1938₎
HC337.5
F5L74
59 p., diagrs. 24½ᶜᵐ.
Caption title.
On cover: Reprinted from Unitas, quarterly review of the Oy pohjoismaiden yhdyspankki ab Nordiska föreningsbanken Finland.
1. Finland - Economic conditions - 1918-
2. Reconstruction (1914-) - Finland.
I. Title.

36–13425

NL 0380824   CSt-H CSt NNC MH OU OCl DS WaS NSyU

Lindgren, W   E   von.
Die grundbegriffe des staatsrechts. Versuch einer juristischen construction des staats und der staatsgewalt, von W. E. v. Lindgren. Leipzig, Breitkopf und Härtel, 1869.
2 p. l., 196 p. 21½ᶜᵐ.
1. Constitutional law. 2. Administrative law. 3. Law—Philosophy. I. Title.

36–13425

NL 0380825   DLC NN MH-L PU

Lindgren, Waldemar, 1860–1939.
... Age of the auriferous gravels of the Sierra Nevada, with a report on the flora of Independence Hill, ₍by₎ Waldemar Lindgren ₍and₎ F. H. Knowlton₎
cover-title, 881–906 p. 23 cm. [Pamphlets on California geology. v. 2, no. 25]
Reprinted from the Journal of geology, v. 4, no. 8. Nov.-Dec. 1896.
I. Knowlton, Frank Hill, 1860-

NL 0380826   CU

Lindgren, Waldemar, 1860–1939.
... Biographical memoir of George Perkins Merrill, 1854–1929, by Waldemar Lindgren. Presented to the academy at the annual meeting, 1935.
(*In* National academy of sciences, Washington, D. C. Biographical memoirs. City of Washington, 1937. 23ᶜᵐ. vol. XVII, 2d memoir, p. ₍31₎–53. front. (port.))
Issued also separately.
"Bibliography of George P. Merrill. 1879–1930, compiled by Margaret W. Moodey": p. 42–53.
1. Merrill, George Perkins, 1854–1929. I. Moodey, Margaret W.

30–31255

Library of Congress   Q141.N2 vol. 17, 2d memoir

NL 0380827   DLC OU

Lindgren, Waldemar, 1860–1939.
... Boise folio, Idaho ₍by Waldemar Lindgren₎ ... Washington, D. C., U. S. Geological survey, 1898.
cover-title, 7 p. 4 col. maps. 55 x 47 cm. (U. S. Geological survey. Geologic atlas of the United States. Library ed. Fol. 45)
Lat. 43°30'–44°, long. 116°–116°30'; scale 1: 125,000; contour interval 100 ft.
1. Geology—Idaho—Maps. I. Title.

G1201.C5U5 vol. 45   G S 7–213
U. S. Geol. Survey. Libr.
for Library of Congress   ₍a58g½₎†

NL 0380828   DI-GS WaWW PPAmP PBa DLC

Lindgren, Waldemar, 1860–1939.
The character and genesis of certain contact-deposits.
(In Posepný. The genesis of ore-deposits. 2d edition. Pp. 716–733. New York, 1902.)

E4905 — Ores, Deposits of.

NL 0380829   MB

G1201
.C5U5
vol. 129
Map Div.
₍Lindgren, Waldemar₎ 1860–1939.
... Clifton folio, Arizona. ₍By Waldemar Lindgren₎ ... Washington, D. C., U. S. Geological survey, 1905.
cover-title, 13, ₍1₎ p. illus. 4 maps. 55 x 47 cm. (U. S. Geological survey. Geologic atlas of the United States no. 129)
Lat. 33°–33° 15', long. 109° 15'–109° 30'; scale 1 : 62,500; contour interval 100 ft.
1. Geology—Arizona—Graham co.—Maps.

G S 7—297
U. S. Geol. Survey. Libr
for Library of Congress   ₍a51f½₎

NL 0380830   DI-GS WaWW PBa PPAmP DLC

₍Lindgren, Waldemar₎ 1860–1939.
... Colfax folio, California. ₍By Waldemar Lindgren₎ ... Washington, D. C., U. S. Geological survey, 1900.
cover-title, 10 p. 4 col. maps. 55 x 47 cm. (U. S. Geological survey. Geologic atlas of the United States. Library ed. Fol. 66)
Lat. 39°–39°30', long. 120°30'–121°; scale 1 : 125,000; contour interval 100 ft.
1. Geology—California—Maps. I. Title.

G1201.C5U5 vol. 66   G S 7–234 rev
U. S. Geol. Survey. Libr.
for Library of Congress   ₍r55h¾₎†

NL 0380831   DI-GS DLC WaWW OKentU PBa

Lindgren, Waldemar, 1860–1939.
... Contributions to mineralogy from the United States Geological survey, by F. W. Clarke ...
see under Clarke, F₍rank₎ W₍igglesworth₎ 1847-

Lindgren, Waldemar, 1860–1939, joint author.

Melville, William Harlow.
... Contributions to the mineralogy of the Pacific coast, by William Harlow Melville and Waldemar Lindgren. Washington, Govt. print. off., 1890.

Lindgren, Waldemar, 1860–1939.
... The copper deposits of the Clifton-Morenci district, Arizona, by Waldemar Lindgren. Washington, Govt. print. off., 1905.
375, v p. illus., xxv pl. (incl. col. maps, part fold., 1 in pocket) diagrs. 29½ x 23ᶜᵐ. (U. S. Geological survey. Professional paper no. 43)
Subject series: A, Economic geology, 57; B, Descriptive geology, 68.
Issued also as House doc. no. 199, 59th Cong., 1st sess.
Literature : p. 30–32.
1. Copper ores—Arizona.

G S 6—326
U. S. Geol. survey. Library
for Library of Congress   QE75.P9
—— Copy 2.   TN443.A6L7
                        ₍a41h1₎

NN MB ICJ PP
NL 0380834   DI-GS OrCS OrU WaS MiU OU OCl OO PPAmP

Lindgren, Waldemar, 1860–1939.
... A geological reconnaissance across the Bitterroot Range and Clearwater mountains in Montana and Idaho, by Waldemar Lindgren. Washington, Govt. print. off., 1904.
123, III p. illus., 15 pl. (incl. maps) 29½ x 23ᶜᵐ. (U. S. Geological survey. Professional paper no. 27)
Subject series: A, Economic geology, 35; B, Descriptive geology, 39.
"Maps and literature": p. 10–11.
1. Geology—Montana. 2. Geology—Idaho.

G S 4—156
U. S. Geol. survey. Library   (200) B no. 27
for Library of Congress   QE75.P9 no. 27
—— Copy 2.   QE103.L74
                        ₍a40g1₎

MtHi WaS OrU OrCS IdPI
NL 0380835   DI-GS DLC OCl PU PP PPAmP PBa OO OU MiU

Lindgren, Waldemar, 1860–1939.
... Geology and gold deposits of the Cripple creek district, Colorado, by Waldemar Lindgren and Frederick Leslie Ransome. Washington, Govt. print. off., 1906.
xix, 516, v p. illus., xxix pl. (part fold., incl. maps, plans, diagrs.) 29½ x 23ᶜᵐ. (U. S. Geological survey. Professional paper no. 54)
Subject series: A, Economic geology, 76; B, Descriptive geology, 95.
Two folded maps and folded plan in pocket.
Issued also as House doc. no. 921, 59th Cong., 1st sess.
"Description and petrology of the metamorphic and igneous rocks, by L. C. Graton": p. 41–113.
"Literature": p. 15–17.
1. Gold mines and mining—Colorado—Cripple creek. 2. Geology—Colorado—Cripple creek district. I. Ransome, Frederick Leslie, 1868–1935, joint author. II. Graton, Louis Caryl, 1880-
U. S. Geol. survey. Library
for Library of Congress   QE75.P9 no. 54   G S 7—1
—— Copy 2.   TN423.C7L6
                        ₍a43k1₎   (557.3)

DLC PP PPAN MB ICJ
NL 0380836   DI-GS OrCS OrU WaS MiU OU ODW OO OCl

Lindgren, Waldemar, 1860-
... Geology and mineral deposits of the National mining district, Nevada, by Waldemar Lindgren. Washington, Govt. print. off., 1915.
58 p. illus., plates, fold. maps, diagrs. 23ᶜᵐ. (U. S. Geological survey. Bulletin 601)
1. Geology—Nevada. 2. Mines and mineral resources—Nevada.

G S 15—666
Library. U. S. Geological   Survey (200) E no. 601
—— Copy 2.

OU MiU ICJ MB NN
NL 0380837   DI-GS WaWW CU-B NBuU PPAN PPComm OCl

VOLUME 334

Lindgren, Waldemar, 1860–1939.
... Geology and ore deposits of the Tintic mining district, Utah, by Waldemar Lindgren and G. F. Loughlin, with a historical review by V. C. Heikes. Washington, Govt. print. off., 1919.
282 p. illus., xxxix pl. (part col., part fold.; incl. maps, plan, profiles, diagrs.) on 28 l., fold. tab. 29ᶜᵐ. (U. S. Geological survey. Professional paper 107)
At head of title : Department of the interior.
Three maps, plan, 2 profiles and diagram in pocket.
1. Geology—Utah. 2. Mines and mineral resources—Utah.   I. Loughlin, Gerald Francis, 1880–   joint author.   II. Heikes, Victor Conrad, 1867–
                                                          G S 19—70
U. S. Geol. survey. Library   (200) B no. 107
  for Library of Congress   QE75.P9 no. 107
——— Copy 2.   TN24.U8L7
                                    ₍a41n₎

NL 0380838   DI-GS OrCS OrU WaWW PP PPAN ICJ MB NN

Lindgren, Waldemar, 1860–1939.
Gold and silver deposits in North and South America. By Waldemar Lindgren ...
(*In* Smithsonian institution. Annual report. 1917. Washington, 1919. 23½ᶜᵐ. p. 147–173. illus. (maps))
Reprinted from the Transactions of the American institute of mining engineers, v. 55, p. 883–909 (1917)
1. Gold mines and mining—North America. 2. Gold mines and mining—South America. 3. Silver mines and mining—North America. 4. Silver mines and mining—South America.
Library of Congress   Q11.S66 1917
                                              20–5153

NL 0380839   DLC WaS ICJ

Lindgren, Waldemar, 1860–1939.
... The gold and silver veins of Silver City, De Lamar and other mining districts in Idaho, by Waldemar Lindgren ... Washington, Govt. print. off., 1900.
cover-title, 65–256 p. 29 pl. (part fold., part col., incl. maps, plans) diagrs. 29½ x 23ᶜᵐ.
Extract from the 20th annual report of the U. S. Geological survey, 1898–99, pt. III.
1. Gold mines and mining—Idaho. 2. Silver mines and mining—Idaho.
                                              G S 6—1082
Library, U. S. Geological   Survey

NL 0380840   DI-GS IdU WaS PPAmP PP MB

Lindgren, Waldemar, 1860–1939.
... The gold belt of the Blue mountains of Oregon, by Waldemar Lindgren ... Washington, Govt. print. off., 1902.
cover-title, p. 551–776. 16 pl. (incl. fold. map) diagr. 29½ x 23ᶜᵐ.
Extract from the 22d annual report of the U. S. Geological survey, 1900–1901, pt. II.
1. Gold mines and mining—Oregon.
                                              G S 6—1121
U. S. Geol. survey. Library   431(285) qL64
  for Library of Congress   ₍a40b1₎

NL 0380841   DI-GS OrMonO OrHi WaS PBa PPAmP MiU OCl

Lindgren, Waldemar, 1860–1939.
The gold deposits of Dahlonega, Ga. Plates. Map. Geological section.
(In Graton, Louis C. Reconnaissance of some gold and tin deposits of the Southern Appalachians. Pp. 119–128. Washington. 1906.)

G48c6 — Dahlonega, Ga. Mines. — Gold. Mining, etc.

NL 0380842   MB

Lindgren, Waldemar, 1860–1939.
... The gold-quartz veins of Nevada City and Grass Valley districts, California, by Waldemar Lindgren. Extract from the Seventeenth annual report of the ₍U. S. Geological₎ survey, 1895–96. Pt. II—Economic geology and hydrography. Washington, Gov't print. off., 1896.
cover-title, 262, 851–864 p. illus., xxiv pl. (partly fold., partly col., incl. maps) diagrs. 29½ x 23ᶜᵐ.
1 map in pocket.
Literature : p. 15–17.
1. Gold mines and mining—California—Nevada Co. 2. Geology—California—Nevada Co.
                                              G S 6–404
Library, U. S. Geol.   survey

NL 0380843   DI-GS WaS CtY MB PBa PPAmP MiU

Lindgren, Waldemar, 1860–1939.
... The gold-silver veins of Ophir, California, by Waldemar Lindgren ... Washington, Gov't print. off., 1895.
cover-title, 243–284 p. 2 col. pl. (incl. fold. map) 29½ x 23ᶜᵐ.
Extract from the 14th annual report of the director of the U. S. Geological survey, 1892–93, pt. II.
1. Gold mines and mining—California. 2. Silver mines and mining—California.
                                              G S 6–1031
Library, U. S. Geol.   survey

NL 0380844   DI-GS WaS MdBP PBa PPAmP MiU

Lindgren, Waldemar, 1860–1939.
The igneous geology of the Cordilleras and its problems.
(*In* Problems of American geology. Pp. 234–286. New Haven. [1918.])

M1631 — Igneous rocks. — Rocky Mountains. Geol. and paleon.

NL 0380845   MB PPAN

Lindgren, Waldemar, 1860–1939.
... Marysville folio, California ₍by Waldemar Lindgren and H. W. Turner₎ ... Washington, D. C., U. S. Geological survey, 1895.
cover-title, ₍2₎ p. 4 col. maps. 55 x 47 cm. (U. S. Geological survey. Geologic atlas of the United States. Library ed. Fol. 17)
Lat. 39°–39°30′, long. 121°30′–122° ; scale 1 : 125,000; contour interval 100 ft.
1. Geology—California—Maps.   I. Turner, Henry Ward, 1857–   joint author.   II. Title.
G1201.C5U5 vol. 17   G S 7–185
U. S. Geol. Survey. Libr.ʳ
  for Library of Congress   ₍a58b½₎†

NL 0380846   DI-GS DLC WaWW OKentU PBa OClJC

Lindgren, Waldemar, 1860–1939.
Metasomatic processes in fissure-veins. By Waldemar Lindgren ... Author's ed. ₍n. d.₎ 1900.
cover-title, 115 p. illus. 23½ᶜᵐ.
A paper read before the American institute of mining engineers, at the Washington meeting, February, 1900.
                                              G S 15–762
Library, U. S. Geological   Survey 411 L64

NL 0380847   DI-GS

Lindgren, Waldemar, 1860–1939.
Metasomatic processes in fissure-veins. Illus.
(In Pošepný. The genesis of ore-deposits. 2d edition, pp. 498–612. New York, 1902.)

E490₍ — Lodes.   July 23,   1902

NL 0380848   MB

Lindgren, Waldemar, 1860–1939.
Mineral deposits, by Waldemar Lindgren ... New York ₍etc.₎ McGraw-Hill book company, inc., 1913.
xv, 883 p. illus., diagrs. 24 cm.
1. Ore-deposits.   I. Title.
                                              13—19128
Library of Congress ʳ   TN263.L7

MtU CaBViP WaSpG
PBm ViU ICJ NN MB CU KMK OrP MtU MtBuM CaBVaU Or
NL 0380849   DLC OKentU OClW DSI NcRS NjP MiHM PPAN

Lindgren, Waldemar, 1860–1939.
Mineral deposits, by Waldemar Lindgren ... 2d ed., rev., enl. and entirely reset. New York, McGraw-Hill book company, inc. ; ₍etc., etc.₎ 1919.
xviii, 957 p. illus. (incl. maps) diagrs. 23½ᶜᵐ. $5.00
Bibliographical foot-notes.
1. Ore-deposits.   I. Title.
                                              19—11570
Library of Congress   TN263.L7 1919

TU CU MH MiU MB NRU OKentU
NL 0380850   DLC MH MiHM ICJ NjP ViU OCl OO OU MiU PU

Lindgren, Waldemar, 1860–1939.
Mineral deposits, by Waldemar Lindgren ... 3d ed., rev., enl. and entirely reset. New York ₍etc.₎ McGraw-Hill book company, inc., 1928.
xx, 1049 p. illus. (incl. maps) diagrs. 23½ᶜᵐ. $7.00
Bibliographical foot-notes.
1. Ore-deposits.   I. Title.
                                              28—4768
Library of Congress   TN263.L7 1928

Or CaBVa PPT MiHM
ViU DAL ICJ PHC PU PBm MtU OrP WaTC IdU OrPR OrSaW
NL 0380851   DLC MtU OU CU NcRS TU MiU OO OCl OCU

Lindgren, Waldemar, 1860–1939.
Mineral deposits, by Waldemar Lindgren ... 4th ed., rev. and reset. New York and London, McGraw-Hill book company, inc., 1933.
xvii, 930 p. illus. (incl. maps) diagrs. 23½ᶜᵐ.
Bibliographical foot-notes.
1. Ore-deposits.   I. Title.
                                              33—24760
Library of Congress   TN263.L7 1933
                         ₍a42k1₎   553.1

Or WaSp WaS CaBVaU WaT Wa IdU MtBuM CaBViP MtBC MtU
NBuC MiU OKentU NcD TU PPT PBm PHC ViU ICJ MiHM IdB
NL 0380852   DLC IdPI OrPS OrU OrCS CLSU MeB CU MB UU

Lindgren, Waldemar, 1860–1939.
... The mining districts of the Idaho basin and the Boise ridge, Idaho, by Waldemar Lindgren. With a report on the fossil plants of the Payette formation, by Frank Hall Knowlton ... Washington, Govt. print. off., 1898.
cover-title, p. 617–744. 16 pl. (incl. maps, part fold.) 29½ x 23ᶜᵐ.
Folded map in pocket.
Extract from the 18th annual report of the U. S. Geological survey, 1896–97, pt. III.
Literature : p. 626–628.
1. Mines and mineral resources — Idaho. 2. Paleobotany — Idaho.   I. Knowlton, Frank Hall, 1860–1926.
                                              G S 6–1065
U. S. Geol. survey. Library   431(283) qL64
  for Library of Congress   ₍a37b1₎

NL 0380853   DI-GS IdU MB PPAmP PBa CU-B MiU

Lindgren, Waldemar, 1860–1939.

Hill, James Madison, 1884–
... The mining districts of the western United States, by James M. Hill, with a geologic introduction, by Waldemar Lindgren. Washington, Govt. print. off., 1912.

VOLUME 334

[Lindgren, Waldemar] 1860–1939.
... Nampa folio, Idaho-Oregon. [By Waldemar Lindgren
and N. F. Drake] ... Washington, D. C., U. S. Geological
survey, 1904.

cover-title, 5 p. 2 col. maps, diagrs. 55 x 47 cm. (U. S. Geological
survey. Geologic atlas of the United States. Library ed. No. 103)
Lat. 43°30'–44°, long. 116°30'–117°; scale 1 : 125,000; contour interval 100 ft.

1. Geology—Idaho—Maps.　i. Drake, Noah Fields, 1864–　joint
author.　ii. Title.
G1201.C5U5　vol. 103　　　　　　　G S 7–271 rev
U. S. Geol. Survey.　Libr.
for Library of Congress　　[r55c2]†

NL　0380855　　DI-GS WaWW PBa PPAmP DLC

[Lindgren, Waldemar] 1860–1939.
... Nevada City special folio, California. [By Waldemar
Lindgren] ... Washington, D. C., U. S. Geological survey,
1896.

cover-title, 7 p. 9 col. maps. 55 x 47 cm. (U. S. Geological survey. Geologic atlas of the United States. Library ed. Fol. 29)
Lat. 39°10'22"–39°13'50", long. 121°01'35"–121°05'05", and lat.
39°13'50"–39°17'16", long. 120°57'05"–121°03'45"; scale 1 : 14,400; contour interval 20 ft.

1. Geology—California—Nevada co.—Maps.　i. Title.
G1201.C5U5　vol. 29/　　　　　　　G S 7–197 rev
U. S. Geol. Survey.　Libr.
for Library of Congress　　[r55c2]†

NL　0380856　　DI-GS WaWW ViU DI OKentU PBa OC1JC DLC

Lindgren, Waldemar, 1860–1939.
... The ore deposits of New Mexico, by Waldemar Lindgren,
Louis C. Graton and Charles H. Gordon. Washington, Govt.
print. off., 1910.

361 p. illus., xxii pl. (part fold., part col., incl. maps) 30ᶜᵐ. (U. S.
Geological survey. Professional paper 68)
Plate 1 in pocket.
"Valencia county, by F. C. Schrader": p. 134–140.
"Sandoval county, by F. C. Schrader and L. C. Graton": p. 140–162.
"Grant county, by L. C. Graton, W. Lindgren and J. M. Hill": p. 295–
848.
1. Mines and mineral resources—New Mexico.　i. Graton, Louis
Caryl, 1880–　ii. Gordon, Charles Henry, 1857–1934.　iii. Schrader,
Frank Charles, 1860–　iv. Hill, James Madison, 1884–　v. Title.
G S 10—443
U. S. Geol. survey.　Library　　(200) B　no. 68
for Library of Congress　　QE75.P9　no. 68
——— Copy 2.　　　　　　　TN24.N6L5
　　　　　　　　　　　　[a41j1]　　　　　　(557.3)

DLC ICJ MB ODW
NL　0380857　　DI-GS OrCS OrU WaS PU OC1 OO MiU OU NN

Lindgren, Waldemar, 1860–1937.

Bancroft, Howland, 1883–
... The ore deposits of northeastern Washington, by
Howland Bancroft, including a section on the Republic
mining district, by Waldemar Lindgren and Howland
Bancroft. Washington, Govt. print. off., 1914.

Lindgren, Waldemar, 1860–1939.
... Ore deposits of the Jerome and Bradshaw mountains
quadranges, Arizona, by Waldemar Lindgren. With statistical notes by V. C. Heikes. Washington, Govt. print. off., 1926.

ix, 192 p. illus., 28 pl. (incl. fold. maps, fold. diagrs.) plans, tables.
23ᶜᵐ. (U. S. Geological survey.　Bulletin 782)
At head of title: Dept. of the interior.
Two maps folded in pocket.
Bibliographical foot-notes.

1. Geology—Arizona.　2. Mines and mineral resources—Arizona.　3.
Ore-deposits—Arizona.　i. Heikes, Victor Conrad, 1867–　ii. Title.
iii. Title: Jerome and Bradshaw mountains quadrangles, Arizona.
G S 26—290
U. S. Geol. survey.　Library　　(200) E　no. 782
for Library of Congress　　QE75.B9　no. 782
——— Copy 2.　　　　　　　TN24.A6L5
　　　　　　　　　　　　[a41p1]

NL　0380859　　DI-GS PPComm PPAN OC1W ICJ DLCOO OU MiU

[Lindgren, Waldemar] 1860–1939.
... Placerville folio, California. [By Waldemar Lindgren
and H. W. Turner] ... Washington, D. C., U. S. Geological
survey, 1894.

cover-title, [2] p, 1 l. 4 col. maps. 55 x 47 cm. (U. S. Geological
survey.　Geologic atlas of the United States.　Library ed.　Fol. 3)
Lat. 38°30'–39°, long. 120°30'–121°; scale 1 : 125,000; contour interval 100 ft.

1. Geology—California—El Dorado co.—Maps.　2. Geology—California—Amador co.—Maps.　i. Turner, Henry Ward, 1857–
joint author.　ii. Title.
G1201.C5U5　vol. 3　　　　　　　G S 7–171 rev
U. S. Geol. Survey.　Libr.
for Library of Congress　　[r55b2]†

NL　0380860　　DI-GS PBa OC1JC OKentU FU WaWW DLC

Lindgren, Waldemar, 1860–1939.

Problems of American geology; a series of lectures dealing
with some of the problems of the Canadian shield and of the
Cordilleras, delivered at Yale university on the Silliman
foundation, in December, 1913, by William North Rice,
Frank D. Adams, Arthur P. Coleman, Charles D. Walcott,
Waldemar Lindgren, Frederick L. Ransome, William Diller
Matthew. New Haven, Yale university press; [etc., etc.]
1915.

TN43　Lindgren, Waldemar, 1860–1939.
A5L7　...The production of gold and silver in 1904.
Washington, 1905.

NL　0380862　　DLC

[Lindgren, Waldemar]
The production of gold and silver in 1906.
Washington, Gov't. P't'g. Off., 1907.
265 p.　8°.　(U. S. Geol. Surv.)
Advance chap. fr. the Mineral resources
of U. S., 1906.

NL　0380863　　NN

Lindgren, Waldemar.
The production of gold and silver in 1907.
Washington, Govt. Prtg. Off., 1908.
27 p.　8°.　(U. S. Geolog. Survey)
Advance chap. from Mineral Resources
of the U. S., 1907.
By Lindgren, Waldemar and McCaskey, H. D.

NL　0380864　　NN

LINDGREN, Waldemar, 1860–1939.
..The production of gold and silver in 1908.
Washington, 1909.

By Waldemar Lindgren and Hiram Dryer Mc
Caskey.

NL　0380865　　MH-C MH

[Lindgren, Waldemar] 1860–1939.
... Pyramid Peak folio, California. [By Waldemar Lind-
gren] ... Washington, D. C., U. S. Geological survey, 1896.

cover-title, [2], 5, [1] p. 4 col. maps, diagr. 55 x 47 cm. (U. S. Geo-
logical survey.　Geologic atlas of the United States.　Library ed.
Fol. 31)
Lat. 38°30'–39°, long. 120°–120°30'; scale 1 : 125,000; contour in-
terval 100 ft.
Description of the gold belt, by G. F. Becker, H. W. Turner and
Waldemar Lindgren : 2 p. at beginning.

1. Geology—California—Maps.　i. Title.
G1201.C5U5　vol. 31　　　　　　　G S 7–199 rev
U. S. Geol. Survey.　Libr.
for Library of Congress　　[r55b2]†

NL　0380866　　DI-GS WaWW PBa DLC

Lindgren, Waldemar, 1860–1939.

Graton, Louis Caryl, 1880–
... Reconnaissance of some gold and tin deposits of the southern Appalachians, by L. C. Graton; with notes on the Dahlonega mines, by Waldemar Lindgren. Washington, Govt. print.
off., 1906.

Lindgren, Waldemar, 1860–1939.
... Report of progress in the geological resurvey of the Cripple creek district, Colorado; by Waldemar Lindgren and Frederick Leslie Ransome. Washington, Govt. print. off., 1904.

36, v p. 23½ᶜᵐ. (U. S. Geological survey.　Bulletin no. 254)
Subject series : A. Economic geology, 49 ; B. Descriptive geology, 61.

1. Geology—Colorado—Cripple creek district.　2. Mines and mineral
resources—Colorado.　3. Gold mines and mining—Colorado—Cripple
creek.　i. Ransome, Frederick Leslie, 1868–1935.
G S 5–33
Library, U. S. Geological　　Survey
Library of Congress　　QE75.B9　no. 254
——— Copy 2.　　　　　TN24.C6L7
　　　　　　　　　　[a36g1]

OU OO ODW OC1 MiU ICJ NN
NL　0380868　　DI-GS NBuU CU-B NjP WaS WaWW PPAN PPAmP

Lindgren, Waldemar, 1860–1939.

Bewick, Moreing & co.
Reports on the Moorlort goldfields, ltd. Loddon Valley goldfields, ltd. Option blocks (Consolidated deep
leads, ltd.) Victorian deep leads, ltd. By Bewick, Moreing & co. [London, Crowther & Goodman, printers, 1904]

Lindgren, Waldemar, 1860–1939.
... Reprints from Placerville, Sacramento, and Jackson
folios, California [nos. 3, 5, and 11] by Waldemar Lindgren,
and H. W. Turner ... Washington, D. C., U. S. Geological
survey, 1914.

cover-title, 9 p.　3 maps, diagr.　55 x 47 cm.
Scale 1 : 125 000.
Contour interval 100 and 50 feet.
At head of title: ... Department of the interior.　United States
geological survey ...　Geologic atlas of the United States.
First printed in 1894.

1. Geology—California—Maps.　i. Turner, Henry Ward, 1857–
Joint author.　ii. U. S. Geological survey.
G S 14—477
U. S. Geol. Survey.　Libr.　　(200) fHI
for Library of Congress　　[a48b2]

NL　0380870　　DI-GS

Lindgren, Waldemar, 1860–1939.
[Reprints from the American journal of
science]　1892–97.
4 v. in 2.　23 cm.　[Pamphlets on
California geology.　v. 2, no. 21–24]
Contents. - The gold deposit at Pine Hill,
California. - The auriferous veins of Meadow
Lake, Cal. - An auriferous conglomerate of
Jurassic age from the Sierra Nevada. - The
granitic rocks of the Pyramid Peak district.

NL　0380871　　CU

Lindgren, Waldemar, 1860–1939.
... Research in processes of ore deposition, by Waldemar
Lindgren ... New York, American institute of mining and
metallurgical engineers, inc., °1928.

1 p. l., 14 p.　23ᶜᵐ. (American institute of mining and metallurgical
engineers.　Technical publication no. 78. Class I, Mining geology,
no. 12)
"References": p. 14.
Bibliographical foot-notes.

1. Ore-deposits.　2. Geology, Economic.

P O 29–120
Library, U. S. Patent　　Office　TN1.A49
Library of Congress　　TN1.A525　no. 78

NL　0380872　　DP ViU

VOLUME 334

[Lindgren, Waldemar] 1860-1939.
... Sacramento folio, California. [By Waldemar Lindgren] ... Washington, D. C., U. S. Geological survey, 1894.
cover-title, [2] p., 1 l. 4 col. maps. 55 x 47 cm. (U. S. Geological survey. Geologic atlas of the United States. Library ed. Fol. 5)
Lat. 38°30'-39°, long. 121°-121°30'; scale 1:125,000; contour interval 100 ft.

1. Geology—California—Maps. I. Title.
G1201.C5U5 vol. 5 G S 7-173 rev
U. S. Geol. Survey. Libr. for Library of Congress [r55b2]†

NL 0380873 DI-GS PBa OKentU WaWW DLC

[Lindgren, Waldemar] 1860-1939.
... Silver City folio, Idaho. [By Waldemar Lindgren and N. F. Drake] ... Washington, D. C., U. S. Geological survey, 1904.
cover-title, 6 p. 3 col. maps. 55 x 47 cm. (U. S. Geological survey. Geologic atlas of the United States. Library ed. No. 104)
Lat. 43°-43°30', long. 116°30'-117°; scale 1:125,000; contour interval 100 ft.

1. Geology—Idaho—Maps. I. Drake, Noah Fields, 1864- joint author. II. Title.
G1201.C5U5 vol. 104 G S 7-272 rev
U. S. Geol. Survey. Libr. for Library of Congress [r55c2]†

NL 0380874 DI-GS PBa DLC WaWW

F862 .3 P148 v. 4:4 x
Lindgren, Waldemar, 1860-1939.
The silver mines of Calico, California. Author's ed. [n. p.] 1887.
18 p. fold. map. 23cm. [Pamphlets on California mines, v. 4, no. 4]
Cover title.
"Transactions of The American Institute of Mining Engineers, Scranton meeting, February, 1887."
Provenance: Joseph LeConte.

1. Silver mines and mining - California - Calico. (Series)

NL 0380875 CU-B

Lindgren, Waldemar, 1860-1939.
... Smartsville folio, California [by Waldemar Lindgren and H. W. Turner] ... Washington, D. C., U. S. Geological survey, 1895.
cover-title, [2], 3, [1] p. 4 col. maps, diagr. 55 x 47 cm. (U. S. Geological survey. Geologic atlas of the United States. Library ed. Fol. 18)
Lat. 39°-39°30', long. 121°-121°30'; scale 1:125,000; contour interval 100 ft.

1. Geology—California—Maps. I. Turner, Henry Ward, 1857- joint author. II. Title.
G1201.C5U5 vol. 18 G S 7-186
U. S. Geol. Survey. Libr. for Library of Congress [a58c½]†

NL 0380876 DI-GS DLC WaWW OrPS OKentU FU PBa

Lindgren, Waldemar, 1860-1939.
... Succession of minerals and temperatures of formation in ore deposits and magmatic affiliations, by Waldemar Lindgren. New York, American institute of mining and metallurgical engineers, inc., °1936.
23 p. 23cm. (American institute of mining and metallurgical engineers. Technical publication no. 713. Class I, Mining geology, no. 60)
"Literature": p. 22-23.

1. Ore-deposits. I. Title.
P O 36-50
Library, U. S. Patent Office TN1.A49
Library of Congress [TN1.A525 no. 713]
[2]

NL 0380877 DP

Lindgren, Waldemar, 1860-1939.
... The Tertiary gravels of the Sierra Nevada of California, by Waldemar Lindgren. Washington, Govt. print. off., 1911.
226 p. illus., xxviii pl. (part fold., part col., incl. maps) 29½ cm. (U. S. Geological survey. Professional paper 73)
Folded plate, folded map in pocket.
"Flora of the auriferous gravels of California, by F. H. Knowlton": p. 57-64.
"Literature": p. 12-13.

1. Geology—California. 2. Gold mines and mining—California. I. Knowlton, Frank Hall, 1860-1926. II. Title.
G S 11-567
U. S. Geol. Survey. Libr. (200) B no. 73
for Library of Congress QE75.P9 no. 73
——— Copy 2. TN423.C2L5
[a50k½]

NL 0380878 PU PPAN DLC DI-GS OrCS OrU NN MB ICJ MiU ODW OO OU

Lindgren, Waldemar, 1860-1939.
... Tests for gold and silver in shales from western Kansas, by Waldemar Lindgren. Washington, Govt. print. off., 1902.
21, iii p. 23½cm. (U. S. Geological survey. Bulletin no. 202)
Subject series: A, Economic geology, 18.

1. Gold. 2. Silver ores—Kansas. 3. Assaying. I. Title.
G S 5-743
U. S. Geol. survey. Library for Library of Congress QE75.B9 no. 202
——— Copy 2. TN413.K2L6
[a42b1]

NL 0380879 DI-GS WaWW WaS PU PPAN ODW OC1 DLC OO OU

[Lindgren, Waldemar] 1860-1939.
... Truckee folio, California. [By Waldemar Lindgren] ... Washington, D. C., U. S. Geological survey, 1897.
cover-title, [2], 5, [1] p. 4 col. maps, diagr. 55 x 47 cm. (U. S. Geological survey. Geologic atlas of the United States. Library ed. Fol. 39)
Lt. 39°-39°30', long. 120°-120°30'; scale 1:125,000; contour interval 100 ft.
Description of the gold belt, by G. F. Becker, H. W. Turner and Waldemar Lindgren: 2 p. at beginning.

1. Geology—California—Maps. I. Title.
G1201.C5U5 vol. 39 G S 7-207 rev
U. S. Geol. Survey. Libr. for Library of Congress [r55b2]†

NL 0380880 DI-GS DLC WaWW OKentU PBa

[Lindgren, Harry Arthur] 1888-
... Types of hogs marketed and consumer demand in Oregon. Corvallis, Agricultural experiment station, Oregon state agricultural college, 1932.
cover-title, 14 p., 1 l. illus., tables, diagrs. 23cm. (Oregon. Agricultural experiment station. Station bulletin 297)
Caption title: By H. A. Lindgren, A. W. Oliver, and E. L. Potter.

1. Swine. I. Oliver, Alfred Weaver, 1894- joint author. II. Potter, Ermine Lawrence, 1884- joint author. III. Title. IV. Title: Hogs marketed and consumer demand in Oregon, Types of.
A 32-1981
Title from Oreg. Agr. College
Library of Congress [S105.E2 no. 297]
[4]

NL 0380881 OrCS OrU OrPR

Lindgren, Waldemar, 1860-1939.
... The water resources of Molokai, Hawaiian islands, by Waldemar Lindgren. Washington, Govt. print. off., 1903.
62 p., 1 l. IV pl. (incl. map) 23cm. (U. S. Geological survey. Water-supply and irrigation paper no. 77)
Subject series: O, Underground waters, 19.

1. Water-supply—Hawaiian islands—Molokai.
G S 5-46
Library, U. S. Geological Survey TC801.U2
Library of Congress
——— Copy 2. GB832.H4L7
[a36b1]

NL 0380882 DI-GS OrU OrCS OO OC1 MiU PU ODW ICJ MB

LINDGREN, Wilhelm de.
De conatu delinqendi. Specimen 1. Lipsiae, n.d.
29 + (1) p.

NL 0380883 MH-L

Lindgren, William Marcellous.
Canada: the League of Nations and the U.N.O. ... A thesis...The University of British Columbia April, 1946.

NL 0380884 CaBVaU

Lindh (Alrik). * Om alkoholinsprutningar vid underlifsbräck. 70 pp., 1 l. 8°. Halmstad, F. D. Gernandtska, 1882.

NL 0380885 DNLM

Lindh, Axel Edvin, 1888-
Experimentelle Untersuchungen über die K-Röntgen-Absorptionsspektra der Elemente Chlor, Schwefel und Phosphor. Lund, 1923
Akademische Abhandlung - Lund

NL 0380886 MH-C ICRL CtY ICU DLC

Lindh, Axel Edvin, 1888-
Röntgenspektroskopie, von Axel E. Lindh ... Mit 197 abbildungen. Leipzig, Akademische verlagsgesellschaft m. b. h., 1930.
vii, 436 p. incl. illus., tables, diagrs. 25 cm. (Added t.-p.: Handbuch der experimentalphysik ... hrsg. von W. Wien ... und F. Harms ... bd. 24, 2. t.)
"Druckfehlerberichtigung" (1 leaf) laid in.
"Literaturverzeichnis": p. [392]-425.
Bibliographical foot-notes.

1. X-rays. 2. Spectrum analysis.
P O 30-51
U. S. Patent Office. Libr. QC481.L745
for Library of Congress [QC21.W7 bd. 24]
[a48r37f½]

NL 0380887 NN MH ViU DP CaBVaU NcU NIC PSC PPT OO OU OCU MiU

QC481 .L75 (G1)
Lindh, Axel Edvin, 1888-
Röntgenspektroskopie, von Axel E. Lindh ... Mit 197 abbildungen.
[Ann Arbor, Mich., J. W. Edwards, 1948.
vii, 436 p. incl. illus., tables, diagrs. 25 cm. (Added t.-p.: Handbuch der experimentalphysik ... hrsg. von W. Wien ... und F. Harms ... bd. 24, 2. t.)
~~"Druckfehlerberichtigung" (1 leaf) laid in.~~
"Literaturverzeichnis": p. [392]-425.
Bibliographical foot-notes.

1. X-rays. 2. Spectrum analysis.
P O 30-51
U. S. Patent Office. Libr. QC481.L745
for Library of Congress [QC21.W7 bd. 24]
[a48r37f½]

NL 0380888 DP ICU

Lindh, Axel Edvin, 1888-
Die Struktur der $K\beta_1$- Linie des Schwefels (erste-zweite Mitteilung) von Axel E. Lindh und Osvald Lundquist ... [Uppsala, Almqvist & Wiksells boktryckeri-a.-b., 1924]
2 v. tables, diagrs. 23cm. (Arkiv för matematik, astronomi och fysik. bd. 18, n:o 14, p. [3]-11; bd. 18, n:o 34)
Caption title.
Pt. 2 has title: Über die Struktur der $K\beta_1$-Linie der Elemente Schwefel und Phosphor.

NL 0380889 ICJ

VOLUME 334

Lindh, Axel Edvin, 1888–
Über die K-Röntgenabsorptionsspektra der Elemente Kalium und Calcium, von Axel E. Lindh. Mit 1 Figur im Texte ...
(*In* Arkiv för matematik, astronomi och fysik. ₍Uppsala, 1924₎ 23ᶜᵐ. bd. 18, n:o 14, p. ₍12₎–17 incl. tables, diagr.)

NL 0380890   ICJ

Lindh, Axel Edvin, 1888–
... Untersuchungen über die *Kβ,*– Linie des Chlors, von Axel E. Lindh und Osvald Lundqvist. Mit 1 Figur im Texte ...
₍Uppsala, Almqvist & Wiksells boktryckeri-a.-b., 1924₎
5, ₍1₎ p. incl. tables, diagrs. 23ᶜᵐ.   (Arkiv för matematik, astronomi och fysik. bd. 18, n:o 35)
Caption title.
Bibliographical foot-notes.

NL 0380891   ICJ

Lindh, Carl,   ed.
Huuss-apoteek, och Läkie-book, zwar uths allehanda hälsosamma rådh, och påmånga meñis kior offta proberade läkedommar... Tillsamman draget aff the beste authoribus... Wiisingzborg,[Truckt] aff Hans HögGrefl:Nåd: Booktr:Johann Kankel,₍1675.₎
4p.ℓ.,285,[9]p. 16 1/2cm.
1.Medicine, Popular. 2.Medicine - Formulae, receipts, prescriptions.

NL 0380892   CtY-M CtY

Lindh (Daniel). Om nervsystemets verkningar i synnerhet i menniskokroppen. 66 pp. 8°. *Helsingfors. J. C. Frenckel & Son, 1839.*

NL 0380893   DNLM

UA799 **LINDH,ERIK.**
.L74 Kongliga Björneborgs regemente. Anteckningar om Satakunda knektars del i Sverige-Finlands krigshistoria av Erik Lindh. Helsingfors [Mercators tryckeri aktiebolag,1928]
xii,344 p. illus.(incl.port.)plans,fold.tab. 23cm.
(Half-title:Skrifter utgivna av Svenska litteratursällskapet i Finland. CCIV)
"Källförteckning":p.[338] -344.
1.Kongliga Björneborgs regemente.

GU NNC
NL 0380894   ICU MH NN NcD MnU MdBJ NIC OU CLU MoU

CS884 **Lindh, Erik, ed.**
.S45 **Släktbok.**
ny följd ₍v.₎ 1–   1941–
Helsingfors.

LINDH, GUNNAR.
EXPERIMENTELL JAMFORELSE MELLAN LOSSIERCEMENT OCH STANDARDCEMENT I CEMENTBRUK (EXPERIMENTAL COMPARISON BETWEEN LOSSIER-CEMENT AND SWEDISH STANDARD-CEMENT IN CEMENT MORTAR) STOCKHOLM, 1954. 40 P. ILLUS.
STOCKHOLM. TEKNISKA HOGSKOLAN. SVENSKA FORSKNINGS--INSTITUTET FOR CEMENT OCH BETONG. MEDDELANDEN (BULLETINS) NO. 31. SUMMARY IN ENGLISH.

Continued in next column

Continued from preceding column

1. CEMENT--TESTING. TITLE. SERIES.

NL 0380897   GAT

90.41 **Lindh, Hanna.**
L64 Lärobok i trädgårdsskötsel för folkskolor
Ed.2 och fortsättningsskolor.   2. uppl. Stockholm, Norstedt [1950]
71 p.

1. Gardening. Sweden. 2. School gardens.

NL 0380898   DNAL

Lindh, Jacobus, respondent.
Linné, Carl von, 1707–1778, *praeses.*
... Dissertatio diætetica, de pingvedine animali ... Upsaliæ ₍1759₎

Lindh, Lennart, joint author.
Aspelund, Helge, 1897–
Über die Darstellung von Barbitursäuren mit Magnesiummethylat als Kondensationsmittel, von Helge Aspelund und Lennart Lindh. Åbo, Åbo akademi, 1940.

Lindh, Nils Johan Bertil, 1878–
Möten mellan Öst och Väst; studier i samtida rysk utrikespolitik. Stockholm, Kooperativa förbundets bokförlag, 1949.
330 p. 22 cm. (Skrifter utg. av Utrikespolitiska institutet, 6)

1. Russia—For. rel. I. Title. (Series: Utrikespolitiska institutet, Stockholm. Skrifter, 6)

DK267.L48   50–32207

NL 0380901   DLC

Lindh, Theodor, 1833–1904.
Dikter. Helsingfors, T. Sederholm, 1862.
146 p.

NL 0380902   WaU

Lindh, Theodor, 1833–1904.
Dikter. Stockholm, Bonnier ₍1875₎
340 p.

NL 0380903   WaU NcD

Lindh, Theodor, 1833–1904.
839.7169 Konung Birger och hans bröder; sorgespel i
L745K   fem akter. Borgå, G. L. Söderström ₍1864₎
132 p. 21 cm.

1. Birger, King of Sweden, 1280?–1321. Drama. I. Title.

NL 0380904   NcD

Lindh, Theodor, 1833–1904.
839.7169 Maria af Skottland; sorgespel i 5 akter.
L745M   Borgå, G. L. Söderström ₍1865₎
148 p. 20 cm.

1. Mary Stuart, Queen of the Scots, 1542–1587. Drama. I. Title.

NL 0380905   NcD WaU

Lindhagen, Agnes Byström-
see
Byström-Lindhagen, Agnes.

Lindhagen, Albert
see
Lindhagen, Claes Albert, 1823–1887.

Lindhagen, Anna Jakobina Johanna, 1870–1941.
I nationalitetsfrågan, av Anna Lindhagen. Stockholm, Svenska andelsförlaget ₍1917₎
15 p. 18½ᶜᵐ.

1. Nationalism and nationality. I. Title.

21–16698
Library of Congress   JC311.L65

NL 0380908   DLC

LINDHAGEN,Anna Jakobina Johanna, 1870–1941.
Idyller och utsikter;bilder från Stockholms natur och bebyggelse. Stockholm,Wahlström & Widstrand,₍1925₎.
25 cm. Illustr.

NL 0380909   MH

Lindhagen, Anna Jakobina Johanna, 1870–1941.
Om belgierna nu, av Anna Lindhagen ... Stockholm, Tidens förlag, 1915.
95, ₍1₎ p. Illus. 19½ᶜᵐ.
On cover: 2. uppl.
"Säljes till förmån för nödlidande belgier."
CONTENTS.—Belgien.—I landsflykt.—Besinna vad som hänt.

1. Belgium—Hist.—German occupation, 1914–1918. 2. European war, 1914–1918—Refugees. I. Title.

20—23570
Library of Congress   DH682.L5

NL 0380910   DLC NN NjP

VOLUME 334

Lindhagen, Anna Jakobina Johanna, 1870-
1941, comp.
Témoignages suédois, 1914-1919, ras-
semblés par Melle Anna Lindhagen et avec
une préface de la b^nne Marika Stiernstedt.
[Stockholm, Impr. E. Westerberg, 1919]
61, [7] p. illus. 21.5 cm.
Extracts from Poul Bjerre, Anton Blanck,
Nils Edén, Carl Ericson, and others.
1. European war, 1914-1918 - Sweden.
2. European war, 1914-1918 - Public opinion.
I. Title.

NL 0380911 CSt-H

Lindhagen, Anna Jakobina Johanna, 1870-
1941.
Vad vi tänkte; minnen. Stockholm,
Natur och kultur [1941]

249 p. 22cm.

NL 0380912 MnU

Lindhagen, Arthur, 1884-

Sweden. *Ådalskommissionen.*
Berättelse avgiven av den av Kungl. Maj:t tillsatta Kommissionen för undersökning rörande oroligheterna i Gud-
mundrå m. fl. kommuner av Västernorrlands län maj 1931.
[Stockholm, Kungl. boktryckeriet, P. A. Norstedt & söner,
1931]

DL991   Lindhagen, Arthur, 1884-   joint ed.
.G6S9
Svenska turistföreningen, *Stockholm.*
... En bok om Göteborg, redigerad av Carl-Julius Anrick,
Arthur Lindhagen och Mårten Stenberger. Stockholm [Cen-
traltryckeriet] 1931.

Lindhagen, Arthur, 1884-   joint ed.

Svenska turistföreningen, *Stockholm.*
... En bok om Stockholm; redigerad av Carl-Julius Anrick,
Ezaline Boheman och Arthur Lindhagen. Stockholm, 1929.

Law   Lindhagen, Arthur, 1884-   ed.

Sweden. *Laws, statutes, etc.*
Den nya arvslagen jämte dithörande författningar, med
förklaringar utg. av Arthur Lindhagen och Erik Lind.
Stockholm, Norstedt [1929]

Lindhagen, Arthur, 1884-   joint ed.

Stenbeck, Einar, 1881-   *ed.*
Den nya förmynderskapslagen jämte dithörande författnin-
gar, med förklaringar utgiven av Einar Stenbeck och Arthur
Lindhagen ... Stockholm, P. A. Norstedt & söner [1924]

Lindhagen, Arthur, 1884-   ed.
Law   FOR OTHER EDITIONS
SEE MAIN ENTRY
Sweden. *Laws, statutes, etc.*
Överförmyndares skyldigheter; en handledning jämte
fullständig lagtext och formulär, av Arthur Lindhagen. 2.,
omarb. uppl., ombesörjd av Gösta Walin. Stockholm,
Norstedt [1950]

Lindhagen, Arvid, 1856-1926.
... Distingsfullmånen; en astronomisk-historisk studie, av
Arvid Lindhagen ... [Uppsala, Almqvist & Wiksells boktryc-
keri-a.-b., 1922]
10 p. 23^cm. (Arkiv för matematik, astronomi och fysik. bd. 17, n:o 17)
Caption title.

NL 0380919 ICJ

Lindhagen, Arvid, 1856-1926.
... Länge und Alter des Mondes in den Kalendarien des Mittelalters, von Arvid Lindhagen ... [Uppsala, Almqvist & Wiksells boktryckeri-a.-b., 1914]
27, [1] p. incl. tables. 23^cm. (Arkiv för matematik, astronomi och fysik.
bd. 9, n:o 36)
Caption title.

NL 0380920 ICJ CSdS

Lindhagen, Arvid, 1856-1926.
... Die Neumondansätze eines Tiroler Holzkalenders aus dem
Mittelalter, von Arvid Lindhagen ... [Uppsala, Almqvist &
Wiksells boktryckeri-a.-b., 1921]
9, [1] p. incl. tables. 23^cm. (Arkiv för matematik, astronomi och fysik.
bd. 16, n:o 1)
Caption title.
Bibliographical foot-notes.

NL 0380921 ICJ CSdS

Lindhagen, Arvid, 1856-1926.
... Die Neumondtafel des Robertus Lincolniensis, herausgegeben und erläutert von Arvid Lindhagen ... [Uppsala, Almqvist & Wiksells boktryckeri-a.-b., 1916]
41, [1] p. incl. tables. 23^cm. (Arkiv för matematik, astronomi och fysik.
bd. 11, n:o 2)
Caption title.
Bibliographical foot-notes.

NL 0380922 ICJ

Lindhagen, Arvid, 1856-1926.
... Om calendaria perpetua efter gamla stilen med
rättade gyllental, af Arvid Lindhagen. Uppsala, Almqvist & Wiksells boktryckeri; [etc., etc.] 1912.
cover-title, 41 p. incl. tables. 21^cm.
Reprint from Arkiv för matematik, astronomi och fysik. bd. 7. n:o 23.

1. Calendar. 2. Calendars, Runic.
[Full name: Carl Arvid Lindhagen]
25-23954
Library of Congress   CE91.L5

NL 0380923 DLC ICJ

Lindhagen, Arvid, 1856-1926.
... Om den Gaussiska påskformeln, af Arvid Lindhagen ...
[Uppsala, Almqvist & Wiksells boktryckeri-a.-b., 1908]
12 p. 23^cm. (Arkiv för matematik, astronomi och fysik. bd. 5, n:o 3)
Caption title.

NL 0380924 ICJ

Lindhagen, Arvid, 1856-1926.
... Om grunderna för vår tideräkning, en studie af Arvid
Lindhagen ... [Uppsala, Almqvist & Wiksells boktryckeri-
a.-b., 1908]
21 p. incl. tables. 23^cm. (Arkiv för matematik astronomi och fysik. bd. 4,
n:o 25)
Caption title.

NL 0380925 ICJ

Lindhagen, Arvid, 1856-1926.
... Der schwedische Kalender seit dem Jahr 1700, von Arvid
Lindhagen ... [Uppsala, Almqvist & Wiksells boktryckeri-a.-
b., 1909]
9 p. incl. tables. 23^cm. (Arkiv för matematik, astronomi och fysik. bd. 5,
n:o 18)
Caption title.
Bibliographical foot-notes.

NL 0380926 ICJ

Lindhagen, Arvid, 1856-1926.
Studier öfver gamma-funktionen och några
beslägtade transcendenter ... Upsala,
Almqvist & Wiksell, 1887.
3 p.l., 57 p. tables, diagr. 26 cm.
(Swedish mathematical dissertations.
Uppsala, v. 5)
Akademisk afhandling - Upsala.
Bibliographical foot-notes.

NL 0380927 RPB CU ICRL

Lindhagen, Arvid, 1856-1926.
... Undersökning af månkalendern i Nidaros-breviariet, af
Arvid Lindhagen ... [Uppsala, Almqvist & Wiksells boktryc-
keri-a.-b., 1917]
21, [1] p. incl. tables. 23^cm. (Arkiv för matematik, astronomi och fysik.
bd. 13, n:o 2)
Caption title.
Bibliographical foot-notes.

NL 0380928 ICJ

Lindhagen, Arvid, 1856-1926.
... Der xylographische Kalender des Johann von Gmunden,
von Arvid Lindhagen ... [Uppsala, Almqvist & Wiksells boktryckeri-a.-b., 1917]
13 p. 23^cm. (Arkiv för matematik, astronomi och fysik. bd. 13, n:o 1)
Caption title.
"Literatur": p. 13.

NL 0380929 ICJ

Lindhagen, Arvid, 1856-1926, joint author.

[Höjer, Nils Jakob] 1853-1923.
Yttrande i läroverksfrågan, på uppdrag af Statsrådet och
chefen för Kungl. ecklesiastikdepartementet afgifvet den 20
juni 1899. Stockholm. I. Hæggströms boktryckeri, 1899.

JX   Lindhaven, Carl Albert, 1860-1946.
1953   Alla folks frihet, hela världens fred;
L5   ett testamente. Stockholm, Bokförlaget
natur och kultur [c1942]
88p. 22cm.
Includes bibliography.

1. Peace 2. Liberty I. Title

NL 0380931 WU

VOLUME 334

Lindhagen, Carl Albert, 1860–1946.
Demokrati. Stockholm, A. Bonnier ₁1917₁
272 p. 20 cm. (*His* Drömmar och stridslinier, 4)

1. Democracy. 2. Representative government and representation.
JC423.L544   49–35890*

NL 0380932   DLC NN NjP

Lindhagen, Carl Albert, 1860–*1946*.
Drömmar och stridslinier. ₁v.₁   Stockholm: A. Bonnier
·   v.   12°.
Contents:

₁v.₁ 4. Demokrati.

NL 0380933   NN DLC-P4 MH

Lindhagen, Carl Albert, 1860–*1946.*
I revolutionsland, av Carl Lindhagen. Stockholm,
Ahlén & Åkerlund ₁1918₁
253 p. 19¼ᶜᵐ.
"Upplevelser och intryck från tre resor i början av år 1918, den ena
2–28 januari till Ryssar, den andra 3–6 februari till Lappar, den tredje 22
februari–12 mars till Finnar."—Förord.

1. Russia—Hist.—Revolution, 1917–   2. Finland—Hist.—Revolution,
1917–   I. Title.
Library of Congress   DK265.L45
21–5192

NL 0380934   DLC

Lindhagen, Carl Albert, 1860–*1946.*
Jordfrågan. Några riksdagsmotioner jämte ett företal af Carl
Lindhagen. Stockholm, A. Bonnier, [1907].
xxxii, 210 p. 24½ᶜᵐ.

NL 0380935   ICJ

HM   **Lindhagen, Carl Albert,** 1860–*1946.*
36.5   Krigsväsendets avrustning och folkförbundets
L5   fulländning ₁av₁ Carl Lindhagen. Stockholm,
Svenska freds- och skiljedomsföreningen,
1924.
219p. 21cm.

1. War and society 2. Democracy 3. Neutrality I. Title

NL 0380936   WU

Lindhagen, Carl Albert, 1860–1946.
Carl Lindhagens memoarer ... Stockholm, A. Bonnier
₁1936–39₁
3 v. front. (v. 3) illus., plates, ports. (1 col.) facsims., fold. plans.
25½ cm.
"Claes Albert Lindhagen": v. 2, p. 17–116.

1. Stockholm—Pol. & govt. 2. Sweden—Pol. & govt. 3. Lindhagen,
Claes Albert, 1823–1887.
DL865.L48A3   44–28696 rev

NL 0380937   DLC NN MnU TxU OCl WU

Lindhagen, Carl Albert, 1860–*1946.*
Norrlandsfrågan, af Carl Lindhagen. Stockholm, Kungl.
boktryckeriet, P. A. Norstedt & söner, 1906.
iv, 73 p. 20½ᵐ. (*On cover:* Skrifter utgifna af Frisinnade lands-
föreningen. iv)
Imprint on cover: Stockholm, O. A. Liljegren (i distribution)

1. Land tenure—Norrland, Sweden. 2. Agriculture—Economic aspects—Sweden—Norrland.
46–31526

Library of Congress   HD709.N6L5

NL 0380938   DLC MH PU

Lindhagen, Carl Albert, 1860–*1946.*
... På vikingastråt i västerled, en Amerikaresa. Stockholm,
Wahlström & Widstrand, 1926.
208 p. 22½ᵐ.
At head of title: Carl Lindhagen.

1. U. S.—Descr. & trav. I. Title.
39–11674
Library of Congress   E169.L685
₁2₁   917.3

NL 0380939   DLC

Lindhagen, Carl Albert, 1860–1946.
La paix mondiale; choix de discours de Carl Lindhagen...
Stockholm, A. Bonnier, 1939.   34 p.   26cm.

1. War and peace, 1914–1937.   2. War and peace, 1938–
N. Y. P. L.   December 27, 1949

NL 0380940   NN

Lindhagen, Carl Albert, 1860–1946.
Psykiatrin och rättsskipningen.   Stockholm,
[1930]
71 p.

NL 0380941   MH-L

Lindhagen, Carl Albert, 1860–*1946.*
Den sociala jordfrågan just nu, av Carl Lindhagen.   Stockholm: Tidens förlag, 1928.   29 p.   12°.

422792A. 1. Land—Sweden, 1928.
N. Y. P. L.   August 8, 1929

NL 0380942   NN

Lindhagen, Carl Albert, 1860–1946.
₁Speeches and motions made by Carl Lindhagen in the Riksdagen of Sweden relating to a federation of the northern nations
for peace, to disarmament, to a solution of the Jewish problem,
etc.₁ ₁Stockholm, 1938₁   5 nos. in 1 v.   28cm.
Swedish. Includes ms. notes in English. A partial English translation, also in ms.,
7 l. inserted at end.
Excerpts from: Sweden. Riksdagen. Ridsdagens protokoll. 1938, Första kam-
maren and bihang.

SCHWIMMER-LLOYD COLL.
1. War and peace—Hist. of the   peace movement—Sweden. I. Sweden.
Riksdagen. Riksdagens protokoll.
N. Y. P. L.   August 30, 1948

NL 0380943   NN

Lindhagen, Carl Albert, 1860–*1946.*
Systemet Europa; fredsmotioner vid 1915 års riksdag, av
Carl Lindhagen. Stockholm, Fram ₁1915₁
69 p. 20ᵐ.
Errata slip inserted.
Contents.—Nationernas rätt.—Världsspråket.—Världsparlament och
världsregering.—Skandinavisk avrustningsallians.—Skandinaviens parla-
ment och utrikespolitiken.

1. Nationalism and nationality. 2. Language, Universal. 3. International organization. 4. Scandinavianism. I. Title.
22–4874
Library of Congress   DL57.L5

NL 0380944   DLC NjP NN CtY

DL868
.5
.L5   **Lindhagen, Carl Albert,** 1860–1946.
Tal som ålderspresident i Riksdag och Stadsfullmäktige.
₁Sammanställd av Ture Nerman₁ Stockholm, Natur och
kultur ₁1950₁
188 p. port. 20 cm.

1. Sweden—Pol. & govt.—Addresses, essays, lectures. 2. Stockholm—Pol. & govt.—Addresses, essays, lectures. I. Nerman, Ture,
1886–   ed.
A 51–3367
Minnesota. Univ. Libr.
for Library of Congress   ₁3₁

NL 0380945   MnU DLC

JN   **Lindhagen, Carl Albert,** 1860–*1946.*
7995   Vad vill det nya partiet? ₁Av₁ Carl Lind-
S88   hagen. Stockholm, Folkets förlag ₁1917₁
L4   83p. 23cm.
Cover title.

1. Sveriges socialdemokratiska vänsterparti
2. Sweden - Pol. & govt. - 1905–1950 I. Title

NL 0380946   WU

W   LINDHAGEN, Carl Albert, 1860–1946.
740   Vetenskapen och rättsskipningen.
L745v En inlaga till justitieombudsmannen.
1930   Sthlm ₁i. e. Stockholm₁ Ahlström,
1930.
69 p.
1. Feron, Carl Teodor, 1861–
2. Psychiatry - Jurisprudence Title

NL 0380947   DNLM

Lindhagen, Carl Arvid
see
Lindhagen, Arvid, 1856–*1926.*

Lindhagen, Carl Jacob Johannes, respondent.
Chirurgiska iakttagelser...
see under Bergstrand, Carl Henrik, 1800–
praeses.

Lindhagen, Carl Jacob Joh., respondent.
Läran om feber...
see under Hwasser, Israël, 1790–1860,
praeses.

VOLUME 334

Lindhagen, Curt.
Ἐργάζεσθαι Apc 18 : 17, Hes. 48 : 18, 19. Die Wurzel ϭαχ
im NT and AT. Zwei Beiträge zur Lexikographie der
griechischen Bibel. Uppsala, Lundquistska bokhandeln
₍1950₎
69 p. 25 cm. (Uppsala universitets årsskrift 1950: 5)
"Literaturverzeichnis": p. ₍57₎-62.
1. Greek language, Biblical—Lexicography.   (Series: Uppsala.
Universitet. Årsskrift, 1950: 5)
                                    Title transliterated: Ergazesthai.
[AS284.U7 1950, no. 5]   A 52–10370

Minnesota. Univ. Libr.
for Library of Congress   ₍2₎

NL 0380951   MnU IEG MoU NN PU DLC PPDrop

Lindhagen, Curt.
The servant motif in the Old Testament; a preliminary
study to the Ebed-Yahweh problem in Deutero-Isaiah.
Uppsala, Lundequistska bokhandeln, 1950.
xv, 336 p. 25 cm.
Inaug.-diss.—Uppsala.
Extra t. p., with thesis statement, inserted.
Bibliography: p. ₍292₎-325.

1. Servant of Jehovah.   i. Title.

BS1199.S4L5   224.1   51–18973

NL 0380952   DLC PPDrop CtY-D NcD PPWe NNJ OCH

Lindhagen, Daniel Georg, 1819-1906.
Astronomiens grunder; fri bearbetning efter
Delaunay "Jours elementaire d'astronomie, med
andringar och tillägg.
Stockholm, (1858-61.)
3 pts. in 1 v. 20cm

NL 0380953   DN-Ob

Lindhagen, Daniel Georg, 1819-1906.
Bericht an den Herrn Director der Haupt-Sternwarte über die im
Sommer 1850 ausgeführte Expedition nach dem norwegischen
Finnmarken.
(In Struve. Exposé historique des travaux. Pp. 25-34. St.-
Pétersbourg. 1852.)
Reprinted from the Bulletin of the Imperial Academy of Sciences, St.
Petersburg, vol. 9, 1851.

F6422 — Finmark. Geod.

NL 0380954   MB

Lindhagen, Daniel Georg, 1819-1906.
Förändring i magnetnålens declination och
inclination i Reikiavík
see under   La Roche Poncié, Jules de.

Lindhagen, Daniel Georg, 1819-1906.
... Geodätische azimuthbestimmung auf der sternwarte
in Lund und trigonometrische verbindung der sternwarte
mit dem hauptdreiecksnetz des K. Generalstabes. Von
D. G. Lindhagen ... Stockholm, K. boktryckeriet, P. A.
Norstedt & söner, 1891.
36 p. tables, diagrs. 21½ᶜᵐ.
Bihang till K. Svenska vet.-akad. Handlingar. band 17, afd. i., n:o 7.

1. Azimuth. 2. Lund. Universitet. Observatoriet.

                                    CA 9–1936 Unrev'd
Library of Congress   QB207.L7

NL 0380956   DLC

Lindhagen, D₍aniel₎ G₍eorg₎, 1819-1906.
Geografiska ortbestämningar på Spetsbergen af Prof. A. E.
Nordenskiöld; beräknade och sammanställda af D. G. Lind-
hagen. Stockholm: P. A. Norstedt & Söner, 1863. 47 p. f°.
(Kongliga Svenska Vetenskaps-Akademien. Handlingar. Ny
följd. Bd. 4, no. 5.)

1. Spitsbergen.—Topography.   2. Nordenskiöld, A. E.
N. Y. P. L.   December 26, 1911.

NL 0380957   NN

Lindhagen, D₍aniel₎ G₍eorg₎, 1819-1906.
Komparationer mellan Struves dubbel-toise och den för
Svenska Vetenskaps-Akademiens räkning förfärdigade kopian af
densamma. Stockholm: P. A. Norstedt & Söner, 1863. 10 p.
f°. (Kongliga Svenska-Vetenskaps-Akademien. Handlingar.
Ny följd. Bd. 4, no. 4.)

1. Triangulation.—Instruments.   2. Struve, Friedrich Georg Wilhelm.
N. Y. P. L.   December 29, 1911.

NL 0380958   NN

Lindhagen, Daniel Georg, 1819-1906.
... Längenbestimmungen zwischen den sternwarten in Stockholm, Kopenhagen und Christiania ausgeführt von C. F.
Fearnley, F. C. Schjellerup und D. G. Lindhagen, bearbeitet
von D. G. Lindhagen ... Stockholm, P. A. Norstedt & söner,
1890.
52 p. incl. tables. 31ᶜᵐ. (Kongl. svenska vetenskaps-akademiens
handlingar. ₍Ny följd₎ bd. 24, n:o 4)
1. Longitude. 2. Svenska vetenskapsakademien, Stockholm. Observatoriet. 3. Copenhagen. Universitet. Astronomisk observatorium. 4.
Oslo. Universitet. Astronomiske og magnetiske observatorium. i.
Fearnley, Carl Frederik, 1818-1890. ii. Schjellerup, Hans Karl Frederik
Kristian, 1827-1887.
                                                    A 43–179
Chicago. Univ. Library
for Library of Congress   Q64.S85 bd. 24, no. 4
                                    ₍3₎†

NL 0380959   ICU DLC NN DN-Ob

Lindhagen, D₍aniel₎ G₍eorg₎, 1819-1906.
Om terrestra refractions theorie. n. t.-p.   (Kongliga
Svenska Vetenskaps-Akademien. Handlingar.   Stockholm:
1858. f°. Ny följd. Bd. 1, p. 395-439.)

1. Light.—Refraction. 2. Hori-   zon.—Size of objects at.
N. Y. P. L.   January 6, 1912.

NL 0380960   NN

Lindhagen (Em.). Tuberkulosens bekäm-
pande medelst dispensärer. 96 pp. 8°.
Stockholm, F. Skoglund [1910].

NL 0380961   DNLM PPHPI

Lindhagen, Nils.
Grafikboken av Nils Lindhagen ₍och₎ Rolf
Rude. ₍Stockholm₎ Utg. av Folket i bilds
förlag och Folkrörelsernas konstframjande ₍1954₎
71 p. illus. 22 cm.

Contents. - De konstgrafiska metoderna, av
Rolf Rude. - Grafikens historia, av Nils Lind-
hagen.
Bibliography: p. 67.

1. Engraving. 2. Engraving. History. I.
Rude, Rolf.
Wesleyan University Library

NL 0380962   CtW

NL 0380963   00 OClMA

Lindhagen, Nils.
N7071   Konst hos Freia och Marabou. Introd. av.
F7/L5   Alf Rolfsen; katalog av Nils Lindhagen.
f   Oslo, 1955.
1 v. (chiefly plates, part col.) 35cm.

1.Art - Freia, Norway. 2.Art - Marabou,
Denmark. I.Title. II.Rolfsen, Alf, 1895-

NL 0380964   CSt

Lindhagen, Nils.
N5274
.F7
Freia chocolade fabrik, A/s, Oslo.
Painting and sculpture at Freia and Marabou. Introd. by
Alf Rolfsen. Catalogue by Nile Lindhagen. Oslo, 1955.

GV1060
.5
.L5   Lindhagen, Sven Albert, 1896-
Drömmilare och drömgränser. Stockholm, Tidens förlag
₍1955₎
246 p. illus. 22 cm.

1. Track-athletics.   i. Title.
                                                A 56–4132
Ohio State Univ. Libr.
for Library of Congress   ₍8₎

NL 0380966   OU DLC

GV854
.L56   Lindhagen, Sven Albert, 1896-
Från Pava-Lasse till Mora-Nisse. Stockholm, Tidens förlag ₍1953₎
334 p. illus. 22 cm.

1. Skis and skiing. i. Title.
                                                A 54–2911
Ohio State Univ. Libr.   GV85tL5
for Library of Congress   ₍4₎

NL 0380967   OU NN DLC

GV841
.5
.L5   Lindhagen, Sven Albert, 1896-
Mina 13 olympiader. Stockholm, Tidens förlag ₍1952₎
318 p. illus. 22 cm.

1. Olympic games—Revival, 1896-   i. Title.
                                                A 53–6764
Ohio State Univ. Libr.
for Library of Congress   ₍3₎

NL 0380968   OU DLC

VOLUME 334

Lindhagen, Sven Albert, 1896–
Rekordmän på kolstybb. Stockholm, Tidens förlag ₍1954₎
271 p. illus. 22 cm.

1. Track-athletics. I. Title.

A 55–6087

Ohio State Univ. Libr.   GV1060
for Library of Congress   ₍3₎

NL 0380969   OU NN

LINDHAGEN, TEODOR, 1863–
Professor Franz Delitzsch; en af Israels bästa
vänner. Stockholm, Israelsmissionens bokförlag
[1913] 37 p. front. (port.) 18cm.

Microfiche (neg.) 1 sheet. 11 x 15cm. (NYPL FSN 14,706)

1. Delitzsch, Franz Julius,   1813–1890.

NL 0380970   NN

Lindhal, Johan Harald Josua, 1844–1912.

Illinois. *Geological survey.*
Geological survey of Illinois, A. H. Worthen, director ...
Published by authority of the Legislature of Illinois. ₍Spring-
field, State journal steam press, etc., 1866–90.

Lindhamer, Hedwig, *compiler.*
Die Wohlfahrtseinrichtungen Münchens. Zusammengestellt von
Hedwig Lindhamer. Herausgegeben vom Verein für Frauen-
interessen. 195 p. O. München: A. Schupp, [1901].

NL 0380972   ICJ NN MH

Lindhamer, Hedwig.
Die wohlfahrts-einrichtungen Münchens, bearb. von
Hedwig Lindhamer. Hrsg. vom Statistischen amt der
stadt München, unter mitwirkung des Vereins für frauen-
interessen. 3. durchgesehener abdruck. München, L.
Lindauersche buchhandlung (Schöpping) 1908.
xx, 112 p. 21½cm. ₍Einzelschriften des statistischen amtes der stadt
München. nr. 6₎

1. Munich—Benevolent and moral institutions and societies. I. Munich.
Statistisches amt. II. Verein für fraueninteressen, Munich. III. Title.

14–19937

Library of Congress   HV280.M89L5

NL 0380973   DLC NN ICJ

Lindhamer, Luise, 1875–
Wortstellung im griechischen. Eine unter-
suchung über die spaltung syntaktisch eng
zusammengehöriger glieder durch das verbum ...
Borna-Leipzig, Buchdruckerei R. Noske, 1908.
77 p., 1 l. 24 cm.
Inaug.-diss. - München.
Vita.
"Verzeichnis des für die untersuchung beige-
zogenen materials": p. [5]–6.

NL 0380974   CU PU MH PPDrop NjP

Lindhammer, Johann Ludwig.
Der von dem h[eiligen] Evangelisten Luca
beschriebenen Apostel-Geschichte ausführliche
Erklärung und Anwendung ... Halle, Waysenhaus
see under Bible. N.T. Acts. Ger-
man. 1735. (also 1734)

P17   Lindhard, Annelise.
F5   Det "Gothiske" Element i Engelsk Kultur i det 18. Aarhundrede.
no. 194   København, P. Branner, 1943.
96 p.   (Studier fra sprog- og Oldtidsforskning, udg. af det
Filologisk-Historiske Samfund.   nr. 194)

"Noter" (bibliographical): p. [89]–93; "Bibliografi": p. [94]–96.

1. Gt. Brit. - Civilization.

NL 0380976   CU MH NN ICU

633.7   Lindhard, E
L64d   Dyrkningsforsøg med alsikekløver, hvid-
kløver, humle-sneglebaelg og gul rund-
baelg.   København, 1912.
43p.   (62. beretning fra Statens
forsøgsvirksomhed i plantekultur.)

Saetryk af Tidsskrift for landbrugets-
planteavl, 19. bind.

NL 0380977   IU

Lindhard, J
Brug af kalk og kunstgødning i U. S. A., af J. Lindhard
og E. J. Nørgaard Pedersen. Udg. ved Udenrigsministeriets
foranstaltning. ₍København, I kommission hos det Kgl.
Danske landhusholdningsselskab₎ 1955.
54 p. illus. 24 cm. (Teknisk bistand under Marshallplanen,
TA 36–234)

1. Fertilizers and manures. 2. Soil conservation—U. S. I. Title.
(Series)

Purdue Univ. Library   A 56–5929
for Library of Congress   ₍3₎

NL 0380978   InLP DNAL ScCleA

AS281   Lindhard, Jens, joint author.
.D215
bd. 28,   Bohr, Niels Henrik David, 1885–
nr. 7   Electron capture and loss by heavy ions penetrating
through matter, by Niels Bohr and Jens Lindhard. København, I kommission hos Munksgaard, 1954.

Lindhard, Jens.
Energy loss in matter by fast particles of low charge,
by J. Lindhard and M. Scharff. København, I kommission
hos Munksgaard, 1953.
31 p. diagrs. 24 cm. (Det Kgl. Danske videnskabernes selskab.
Matematisk-fysiske meddelelser, bd. 27, nr. 15)
Bibliography: p. 31.

1. Nuclear physics. I. Scharff, M., joint author. II. Title.
(Series: Danske videnskabernes selskab, Copenhagen. Matematisk-
fysiske meddelelser, bd. 27, nr. 15)

AS281.D215 bd. 27, nr. 15   A 53–7966 rev

Columbia Univ.   Libraries
for Library of Congress   ₍r55c2₎†

NL 0380980   NcC DLC ViU TxU OU MU

Lindhard, Jens.
On the properties of a gas of charged particles. ₍Køben-
havn, I kommission hos Munksgaard, 1954.
57 p. 25 cm. (Det K. Danske videnskabernes selskab. Matematisk-fysiske meddelelser, bd. 28, nr. 8)
Bibliography: p. 57.

1. Ionization of gases.   Series (contents)

₍AS281.D215 bd. 28, nr. 8₎   A 54–7900

Columbia Univ.   Libraries
for Library of Congress   ₍2₎

NL 0380981   NNC DLC TxU FTaSU OU ViU MU MB

Lindhard, Jens Peter Johannes
see
Lindhard, Johannes, 1870–

Lindhard, Johannes, 1870–
Den almindelige (fysiologiske) gymnastiktheori, af J. Lindhard.
113417   1.–[3.] hefte. ... . [København], C. Larsen, 1915–1916.
3 vol. in 1. 27 pl. 22½cm.
"Trykt som manuskript."

NL 0380983   ICJ

Lindhard, Johannes, 1870–
... Contribution to the physiology of respiration under the
arctic climate, by J. Lindhard. (With one plate) 1910.
(*In* Meddelelser om Grønland. København, 1917. 28cm. bd. XLIV,
p. ₍75₎–175 incl. tables. pl. I (fold. diagr.))
Danmark-ekspeditionen til Grønlands nordøstkyst, 1906–1908. bd. IV,
nr. III.
Bibliographical foot-notes.

1. Respiration. 2. Arctic regions—Climate.

₍Full name: Jens Peter Johannes Lindhard₎
A C 39–2478
John Crerar library
for Library of Congress   [Q115.D39 vol. 44]
₍4₎   (508)

NL 0380984   ICJ TxU NN DLC

Lindhard, Johannes, 1870–
Funktionsuntersuchungen an den lungen des menschen mit-
tels gasanalytischer methoden. Von J. Lindhard ... (Mit 13
abbildungen.)
(*In* Abderhalden, Emil, ed. Handbuch der biologischen arbeitsmethoden ... Berlin, 1920–   25cm. abt. V, Methoden zum studium der funktionen der einzelnen organe des tierischen organismus.
t. 4, II (1927) p. ₍1581₎–1628. illus., diagrs.)
Bibliographical foot-notes.

1. Lungs.   A C 36–3754
Title from Ohio State   Univ.
Library of Congress   [QH324.A3 1920 abt. 5, t. 4, II]
₍2₎   (574.072)

NL 0380985   OU

Lindhard, Johannes, 1870–
... Health conditions on the Danmark expedition, by J. Lindhard ...
(*In* Meddelelser om Grønland. København, 1913. 28cm. bd. XLI,
p. ₍457₎–468. pl. XXIV (fold. diagr.))
Danmark-ekspeditionen til Grønlands nordøstkyst, 1906–1908. bd. I,
nr. IV.

1. Danmark-ekspeditionen til Grønlands nordøstkyst, 1906–1908.
I. Title.

₍Full name: Jens Peter Johannes Lindhard₎
A C 39–2445
John Crerar library
for Library of Congress   [Q115.D39 vol. 41]
₍4₎   (508)

NL 0380986   ICJ MB TxU PPAN NN

Lindhard, Johannes, 1870–
... Investigations into the conditions governing the temperature of the body, by J. Lindhard. 1910.
(*In* Meddelelser om Grønland. København, 1917. 28cm. bd. XLIV,
p. ₍1₎–53. diagrs. (1 fold.))
Danmark-ekspeditionen til Grønlands nordøstkyst, 1906–1908. bd. IV,
nr. I.

1. Temperature, Animal and human. 2. Arctic regions—Climate.

₍Full name: Jens Peter Johannes Lindhard₎
A C 39–2476
John Crerar library
for Library of Congress   [Q115.D39 vol. 44]
₍4₎   (508)

NL 0380987   ICJ MB PPAN TxU NN DLC

VOLUME 334

W 6
P3

LINDHARD, Johannes, 1870-
Nogle gymnastiske Stillingers
Indvirkning paa Brystkassen. København,
Graebe, 1924.
96 p. illus.
Cover title.
English summary.
Reprinted from Meddelelser fra
Universitets gymnastikteoretiske Labora-
torium, Nr. 1-2, 1924.
Author's autograph presentation copy.

NL 0380988   DNLM

WB
541
L745n
1944

LINDHARD, Johannes, 1870-
Nogle Undersøgelser angaaende den
svenske Sygegymnastiks Oprindelse.
København, Munksgaard, 1944-45.
2 v. illus., ports.
1. Branting, Lars Gabriel, 1799-1881
2. Ling, Hjalmar Fredrik, 1820-1886
3. Ling, Per Henrik, 1776-1839
4. Gymnastics - Medical - Hist.
5. Swedish gymnastics

NL 0380989   DNLM CtY-M

Lindhard, Johannes, 1870-
... Nogle undersøgelser over den respiratoriske kvotient
under kortvarigt muskelarbejde, af J. Lindhard. København,
Andr. Fred. Høst & søn, Bianco Lunos bogtrykkeri, 1927.
27, [1] p. diagrs. 24cm. (Kgl. danske videnskabernes selskab. Biologiske meddelelser. vi, 7)
"Literaturhenvisninger": p. [28]

1. Respiration.

Title from Stanford Univ.   A C 35-447
Library of Congress   [AS281.D212 vi, 7]
[2]

NL 0380990   CSt MoU PPAmP MiU NN

Lindhard, Johannes, 1870-
... On the function of the motor end-plates in skeletal muscles, by J. Lindhard. København, Andr. Fred. Høst & søn,
Bianco Lunos bogtrykkeri, 1924.
30 p. illus. 24cm. (Kgl. danske videnskabernes selskab. Biologiske
meddelelser. iv, 3)
"List of authors": p. 29-30.
1. Electrophysiology. 2. Muscle. 3. Nerves. i. Title: The function
of the motor end-plates in skeletal muscles.
[Full name: Jens Peter Johannes Lindhard]
Stanford univ. Library   A C 35-443 Revised
for Library of Congress   [AS281.D212 iv, 3]
[r42c2]

NL 0380991   CSt NN MiU PPAmP MoU

Lindhard, Johannes, 1870-
... On the origin of the initial heat in muscular contraction,
by J. Lindhard and Jens P. Möller. København, Andr. Fred.
Høst & søn, Bianco Lunos bogtrykkeri a/s, 1930.
21 p. diagrs. 24cm. (Kgl. danske videnskabernes selskab. Biologiske
meddelelser. viii, 8)
"References": p. 21.
1. Muscles. i. Möller, Jens Peter, 1899- joint author. ii. Title:
The origin of the initial heat in muscular contraction.
[Full name: Jens Peter Johannes Lindhard]
Stanford univ. Library   A C 35-453 Revised
for Library of Congress   [AS281.D212 viii, 8]
[r37c2]   (574.082)

NL 0380992   CSt MoU PPAmP MiU

Lindhard, Johannes, 1870- ed.

Physiological papers, dedicated to Professor August Krogh,
PH. D., L. L. D. Copenhagen, Levin & Munksgaard, 1926.

Lindhard, Johannes, 1870-   joint author.
... Potentialschwankungen bei...
see under   Asmussen, Erling, 1907-

Lindhard, Johannes, 1870-
Der Skeletmuskel und seine Funktion, von J. Lindhard ...
Mit 109 Abbildungen.
(*In* Ergebnisse der Physiologie. München. 1931. 26½cm. 33. Bd., p. [337]-557.
illus., diagrs.)
"Literaturverzeichnis": p. [337]-344.

NL 0380995   ICJ

Lindhard, Johannes, 1870-
... Some investigations on the fluctuations in the number of
white blood corpuscles in the capillaries and the causes of these
fluctuations, by J. Lindhard. 1910.
(*In* Meddelelser om Grønland. København, 1917. 28cm. bd. xliv,
p. [55]-74. diagrs.)
Danmark-ekspeditionen til Grønlands nordøstkyst. 1906-1908. bd. iv,
nr. ii.

1. Blood—Corpuscles and platelets. 2. Arctic regions—Climate.
[Full name: Jens Peter Johannes Lindhard]
A C 39-2477
John Crerar library
for Library of Congress   [Q115.D39 vol. 44]
[4]   (508)

NL 0380996   ICJ DLC NN TxU MB

Lindhard, Johannes, 1870-
Den specielle gymnastikteori, af J. Lindhard. 3. omarb. og
forøgede udg. København, Levin & Munksgaard, 1927.
4 p. l., 413 p. illus. 25cm.
"Udg. med bidrag af Universitetets fritrykskonto."

1. Gymnastics.
Library of Congress   GV461.L7 1927   27-9059
Copyright A—Foreign   33617

NL 0380997   DLC DNLM ICJ

Lindhard, Johannes, 1870-
The theory of gymnastics, by J. Lindhard, with a preface
by Svend Holtze. London, Methuen & co. ltd. [1934]
viii p., 1 l., 359, [1] p. illus., diagrs. 22½cm.
"Originally published in Danish under the title 'Den specielle gymnastikteori'."

1. Swedish gymnastics.
Library of Congress   GV467.L72   35-2043
[3]   613.71

NL 0380998   DLC OrU DNLM IU NN

Lindhard, Johannes, 1870-

The theory of gymnastics, with a preface
by Svend Holtze. 3d ed. London, Methuen
& co. [1949]

viii p., 1 l., 359 [1] p.

NL 0380999   CaBVaU

Lindhard, Johannes, 1870-
Undersøgelser angaaende hjærtets minutvolumen i hvile og
under arbejde. af J. Lindhard. [København] I kommission
hos C. Larsen, 1914.
4 p. l., 131 p. diagrs. 25cm.
Thesis—Copenhagen.

1. Heart. 2. Blood—Circulation. 3. Respiration.
[Full name: Jens Peter Johannes Lindhard]
37-9600
Library of Congress   QP101.L55 1914
[2]   612.171

NL 0381000   DLC DNLM PPC NjP CtY IU

Lindhard, Knud.
Klingende spil; af den danske militærmusiks historie.
København, Levin & Munksgaard, 1932.
124 p. illus., music. 24 cm.
Bibliography: p. [123]-124.

1. Military music, Danish—Hist. & crit.   i. Title.

ML1342.L5   59-56180

NL 0381001   DLC

Lindhardt, Marie, 1894-
The statistics of pulmonary tuberculosis in Denmark,
1925-1934; a statistical investigation on the occurrence of
pulmonary tuberculosis in the period 1925-1934, worked out
on the basis of the Danish National Health Service file of
notified cases and of deaths. Copenhagen, E. Munksgaard,
1939.
179 p. maps, diagrs., tables. 26 cm. (Acta tuberculosea scandinavica. Supplementum 3)
Tr. by W. E. Calvert. cf. Pref.
Summary in Danish.
"References": p. [173]-179.
1. Tuberculosis—Denmark.   i. Calvert, William Ernest, 1887-
tr.   (Series)
A 48-4346*
John Crerar Library
for Library of Congress

NL 0381002   ICJ MoU NNC NcU

Lindhardt, N   P.
... Grethe, en kærlighedshistorie. København og Kristiania, Gyldendal, Nordisk forlag, 1919.
163, [1] p. 18½cm.   kr. 5.75
"Oplag: 1250 eksemplarer."

i. Title.
Library of Congress   PT8175.L53G7 1919   20-6588

NL 0381003   DLC

Lindhardt, Parker.
Carry-overs and carry-backs; an analysis of the net operating
loss deduction and unused excess profits credit adjustment provisions of the Internal revenue code and their effect upon post-
war planning, prepared by Parker Lindhardt ... with the advice and assistance of Frederick W. Platz. [New York] Washington publications, inc. [1944]
1 p. l., vi, 94, 6 p. 21½cm.
Cover-title: Carry-overs and carry-backs explained and illustrated for
corporations, individuals, partnerships, husbands and wives (joint returns)
1. Income tax—U. S.—Law.   i. Platz, Frederick W., joint author.
ii. Title.
Library of Congress °   HJ4653.L6L5   45-12109
336.243

NL 0381004   DLC

Lindhardt, Poul Georg, 1910-
En dansk sognepræst Morten Pontoppidan.
København, Det Danske forlag, 1954.
159 p.   port.   23cm.

1.Pontoppidan, Morten Oxenbøll,1851-1931.

NL 0381005   NN

VOLUME 334

BX8034
.A25L5
Lindhardt, Poul Georg, 1910–
Fem Aalborg-bisper. ₍Festskrift i anledning af 400 års-
dagen for bispestolens overflytning til Aalborg₎ Aalborg,
F. og L. C. Lauritzen, 1954.
253, ₍5₎ p. illus., ports. 26 cm.
Bibliographical references in "Noter" (p. 252–₍254₎)

1. Bishops—Aalborg (Diocese) 2. Aalborg, Denmark (Diocese)—
Biog.

A 55–10510

Minnesota. Univ. Libr.
for Library of Congress

NL 0381006   MnU DLC

—

284.1
G889Bl **Lindhardt, Poul Georg,** 1910–
Grundtvig; an introduction.   London,
S.P.C.K., 1951.
141p.

Bibliography: p.137–139.

1. Grundtvig, Nicolai Frederik Severin,
1783–1872.

NL 0381007   ICarbS ICU NIC KyLxCB CtY-D MiD WU NNC

—

4BR **Lindhardt, Poul Georg,** 1910–
626 Kirken igår og idag. København,
H. Hirschsprung, 1955.
214 p.

NL 0381008   DLC-P4 NcD

—

Lindhardt, Poul Georg, 1910–
Morten Pontoppidan. ₍Aarhus₎ Universitetsforlaget, 1950–
v. port. 25 cm. (Acta Jutlandica ; aarsskrift for Aarhus universitet, XXII, 1. Teologisk serie, 4
Bibliography: v. 1, p. ₍7₎–₍9₎

1. Pontoppidan, Morten Oxenbøll, 1851–   (Series: Aarhus,
Denmark. Universitet. Acta Jutlandica; aarsskrift, XXII, 1
AS281.A34   vol. 22, pt. 1, etc.   52–18186

NL 0381009   DLC MH-AH PU MoU

—

Lindhardt, Poul Georg, 1910–
Morten Pontoppidan; en dansk sognepræst. København,
Danske forlag, 1954.
150 p. illus. 22 cm.
"Bygget på professor P. G. Lindhardts tre bind Pontoppidan-
studier: Præsten Dines Pontoppidan, Morten Pontoppidan I og Morten
Pontoppidan II."

1. Pontoppidan, Morten Oxenbøll, 1851–1931.

BX8080.P6L5   54–39619 ‡

NL 0381010   DLC MnU NcD CU

—

BR972 **Lindhardt, Poul Georg,** 1910–
L5 Den nordiske kirkes historie. Kjøbenhavn, Nyt nordisk
forlag, 1945.
321 p. 25 cm.
"Literatur": p. ₍310₎

1. Scandinavia—Church history. I. Title.

BR972.L5   49–34671*

NL 0381011   DLC CPBL ICU PPLT CtY-D MH CU

—

Lindhardt, Poul Georg, 1910–
Peder Hersleb; studier over dansk-norsk kirke- og kultur-
historie i første halvdel af det 18. århundrede. København,
G. E. C. Gad, 1939–
v. 26 cm.
Thesis—Copenhagen.
Bibliographical footnotes.
Contents.—I. 1689–1737.

1. Hersleb, Peder, 1689–1757.

BX8080.H47L5   63–56541

NL 0381012   DLC MH ICU NjP PPLT CtY NNC MH-AH NIC IU

—

069D
AA
v.20
Lindhardt, Poul Georg, 1910–
Praesten Dines Pontoppidan, 1814–1879.
København, Munksgaard, 1948.
91 p. front. (port.) 25cm. (Acta jutlandica. Aarsskrift for Aarhus universitet,
20: 1)

Bibliographical footnotes.

1. Pontoppidan, Dines, 1814–1879.

NL 0381013   NNC ICU MH-AH

—

Lindhardt, Poul Georg, 1910–
Religion og evangelium; fem
folkelige foredrag. København,
H. Reitzel, 1954.

103 p. 20cm. (Mennesket i
tiden, 12)

1. Religion. Essays. I. Title.

NL 0381014   MnU

—

198
K47L51 **Lindhardt, Poul Georg,** 1910–
Søren Kierkegaards angreb på folkekirken.
₍Aarhus₎ Aros, 1955.
16p. 24cm.

1. Kierkegaard, Søren Aabye, 1813–1855.

NL 0381015   IEN MH-AH MnU

—

Lindhardt, Poul Georg, 1910–
Vækkelser og kirkelige retninger i Danmark. København, Danske forlag ₍1951₎
253 p. illus., ports. 23 cm.
Bibliography: p. 249–₍251₎

1. Revivals—Denmark. 2. Danske Folkekirke—Parties and movements. 3. Denmark—Church history. I. Title.

BR986.L5   52–18739

NL 0381016   DLC

—

Lindhaus, Wilhelm, 1912–
... Ohrmuschelkarzinome ... Lengerich
i. W., 1937.
Inaug.-Diss. - Münster.
Lebenslauf.

NL 0381017   CtY

—

Lindhausen, Justus Lunzer, Edler von.
See
Lunzer, Justus.

—

Lindhé, Curt, 1908–
...Fiskafänge. Helsingfors, H. Schildt ₍1944₎   180 p.
illus. 20cm.

480940B. 1. Fishing—Sweden
N. Y. P. L.   July 7, 1950

NL 0381019   NN

—

Lindhé, Curt, 1908–
Fiskarknep.   Stockholm, Wahlström &
Widstrand ₍1953₎   135 p.   23cm.

1. Fishing—Anecdotes, facetiae, satire, etc.

NL 0381020   NN MoU

—

Lindhé, Curt, 1908–
Rötmånadsfiske. Med illustrationer av Uno Stallarholm.
Stockholm, Wahlström & Widstrand ₍1949₎
181 p. illus. 22 cm.

I. Title.

A 50–859
Minnesota. Univ. Libr.
for Library of Congress   ₍5₎

NL 0381021   MnU NN

—

414
L642 **Lindhé, Curt,** 1908–
Semesterfiske.   Stockholm, Wahlström &
Widstrand ₍1955₎
177 p.

1. Fishing. Sweden. 2. Fishing. Implements
and appliances.

NL 0381022   DNAL

—

Lindhé, Frederika Vilhelmina.
See
Lindhé, Wilma, 1877–

—

Lindhe, Olof.
...Hur vi är i våra drömmar; vårt drömmedvetande och dess
förhållande till vårt vakenmedvetande. En fenomenologisk
studie. Med förord av prof. John Landquist. ₍Stockholm₎
Natur och kultur ₍1947₎   253 p.   22cm.
"Litteraturförteckning," p. 251–253.

448635B. 1. Dreams.
N. Y. P. L.   February 24, 1949

NL 0381024   NN MnU

—

Lindhé, Sten.
Under blågul flagg på spärrade hav. Stockholm, Lindfors bokförlag [1945]

NL 0381025   MH

VOLUME 334

Lindhé, Sven.
The postage stamps, post cards, letter cards, official & local issues of Sweden; being the most complete and exhaustive catalogue of the "stamps of Sweden" ever published in any language. Staffordshire, S. A. Wood ₁189₋₎

29 p. illus. 18 cm.

1. Postage-stamps—Sweden—Catalogs.

HE6185.S82L47   59–56702 ‡

NL 0381026   DLC

Lindhé, Vilma.
See
Lindhé, Wilma, 1877–

Lindhé, Wilma, 1877–
Från flydda tider; barndoms- och ungdomsminnen, upptecknade av Wilma Lindhé... Stockholm: Åhlén & Åkerlund ₁1917₎. 271 p.   illus. (incl. ports.) 8°.

1. No subject.
N. Y. P. L.   December 7, 1920.

NL 0381028   NN

Lindhé, Wilma, *1877–*
Gårdens dotter, roman.   Göteborg.
Åhlen & Åkerlunds, 1912.

NL 0381029   WaSp

839.74   **Lindhé, Wilma, *1877–***
L644u   Ulla Grip; en berättelse från förra
århundradet.   Cedar Rapids, Iowa, N.F.
Hansen Pub. Co., 1916.
112p. 20cm.

NL 0381030   OrU

Lindhé, Wilma, 1838–1922.
Vid gasken och dagsljus; bilder ur teater-lifvet. Stockholm, S.Flodin, [1885].

NL 0381031   MH

LINDHÉ, WILMA, *1838–1922.*
Mödrar, skådespel i tre akter.   Göteberg,
Göteborgs tryckeri, 1887.
74 p.

NL 0381032   Or

Lindheim,
Les chambres de bonnes
see under   Rimbaut, Hippolite.

943.6   **Lindheim,Alfred,ritter von,1836–*1913*.**
K2   Erzherzog Carl Ludwig,1833–1896.Ein
L74   lebensbild,hrsg. von Alfred von Lindheim.
Wien, K.K.Hof–und staatsdruckerei, 1897.
viii,384 p.   front.(port.)illus.(incl.
ports.,tables) col.pl., 2 tab.(1 double,
1 fold.) 27½ cm.

NL 0381034   Mi MH WU NjP

Lindheim, Alfred, *ritter von, 1836–1913*.
Saluti aegrorum. Aufgabe und Bedeutung der Krankenpflege im modernen Staat. Eine sozial-statistische Untersuchung von Alfred von Lindheim. Zweite Auflage. Leipzig und Wien, F. Deuticke, 1905.
334p.

NL 0381035   ICRL ICJ NN DNLM PPC

WS   **Lindheim, Alfred, Ritter von, 1836–1913**
100   Saluti juventutis. Der Zusammenhang
qL745s   körperlicher und geistiger Entwicklung in
1908   den ersten zwanzig Lebensjahren des Menschen;
eine sozial-statistische Untersuchung. 2.
Aufl. Leipzig, Deuticke, 1908.
xi, 564 p. illus. (part col.)

Bibliography: p. ₁563₋564.
Contains signature of Dr. J. Y. Haberman.

NL 0381036   DNLM PPC DHEW NN ICJ NN CtY ICU

Lindheim, Alfred, *ritter von*, 1836–1913.
Saluti senectutis. Die bedeutung der menschlichen lebens-dauer im modernen staate. Eine sozial-statistische unter-suchung von Alfred von Lindheim. II. aufl. Leipzig und Wien, F. Deuticke, 1909.
xii, 501 p. incl. tables. 25½ᶜᵐ.
"Literaturverzeichnis": p. ₁xi₋xii.

1. Age. 2. Longevity. 3. Population. 4. Kings and rulers. 5. Hy-giene, Public. 6. Vital statistics.   I. Title.

36–19514

Library of Congress   HB1531.L5 1909   312

NL 0381037   DLC GU NIC ICU NN PPC CU ICJ CtY

4K   **Lindheim, Alfred, *Ritter* von, 1836**
3083   –1913.
Das Schiedsgericht im modernen
Civilprocesse. Wien, Manz k. u. k.
Hof-Verlags- und Universitäts-Buchhandlung, 1891.
167 p.

NL 0381038   DLC-P4

LINDHEIM, Alfred, *ritter von, 1836–1913*.
Das schiedsgericht im modernen civilprocesse.
2te auf. Wien, 1894.

NL 0381039   MH-L

4K.   **Lindheim, Alfred, Ritter von, 1836–1913.**
Ger.   Das Schiedsgericht im modernen Civil-
206   processe. 3. verm. Aufl.   Wien, Manz,
1894.
192 p.

NL 0381040   DLC-P4

LINDHEIM, Alfred, ritter von, 1836–*1913*.
Zwei briefe über das österreichische actien-gesetz. Wien, .1874.

NL 0381041   MH

Lindheim, Bogislav von, ed.
PE285
.P6D8   **Durham glossary of names of plants.**
Das Durhamer Pflanzenglossar, lateinisch und altenglisch.
Kritisch hrsg. und erläutert von Bogislav von Lindheim.
Bochum-Langendreer, H. Pöppinghaus, 1941.

Lindheim, Bogislav von.
Studien zur sprache des manuskriptes Cotton Galba E IX; enthaltend eine darstellung der sprache des ersten und fünf-ten schreibers des genannten manuskriptes bzw. der texte Ywain and Gawain, The seven sages of Rome, The pricke of conscience, von dr. Bogislav von Lindheim. Wien und Leip-zig, W. Braumüller, 1937.
xiii, 130 p., 1 l. 24ᶜᵐ. (Added t.-p.: Wiener beiträge zur englischen philologie ... hrsg. von dr. Friedrich Wild ... LIX. bd.)
Issued in part as inaugural dissertation, Vienna, under title: Die sprache des Ywain und Gawain und des Pricke of conscience. cf. Vorwort.

"Bibliographie": p. ₁1₎

1. English language—Middle English (1100–1500) 2. British museum. Mss. (Cotton Galba E IX) 3. Ywain and Gawain. 4. Seven sages. English. Middle English. 5. Rolle, Richard, of Hampole, 1290?–1349. The pricke of conscience.

Library of Congress   PR13.W5 bd. 59   38–22173
——— Copy 2.   PE631.A1L5
Copyright A—Foreign   37101
                              ₁8₎   (420.82) 427.02

PBm PHC OC1W NN
NL 0381044   DLC FTaSU OrCS MU ICarbS NcD GU FU PU

Lindheim, Mrs. Irma L   1886–
The immortal adventure, by Irma L. Lindheim, introduc-tion by Dr. Stephen S. Wise, illustrated by J. Benor-Kalter ... New York, The Macaulay company ₁ᶜ1928₎
279 p. front., plates. 23½ᶜᵐ.
Maps on lining-papers.

1. Palestine—Descr. & trav.   I. Title.   28–7962
Library of Congress   DS107.3.L6

OC1Tem OO OC1 MB KyRE
NL 0381045   DLC WaS Or WaSp OrP NcU UU FTaSU NIC

Lindheim, Simon, 1686–1760.
De diversa origine Finlandorum et Lapponum observations.   ₁Upsala, 17–₎
Caption-title.
Extract from Acta Societatis regiae scien-tiarum.

NL 0381046   OC1 PPAN

Lindheim, Wilhelm von.
Bw27D   Russland im Jahre der Weltausstellung 1873.
+874L   Beiträge zur Entwicklungsgeschichte des Czaren-
reiches. Wien,C.Gerold's Sohn,1874.
vi,237p. fold.map,tables. 28cm.

1. Russia. cdu

NL 0381047   CtY

VOLUME 334

Lindheim, Wilhelm von.
　　Russland in der neuesten zeit; statistische und ethnographische mittheilungen.˙ Wien, C. Gerold's sohn, 1876.
　　pp. (5), 88.

Russia—Statistics‖

NL 0381048　　MH NN CtY InU

FILM
388.46
L64s
Lindheim, Wilhelm von.
　　Strassenbahnen in Belgien, Deutschland, Grossbritannien und Irland, Frankreich, Italien, Oesterreich-Ungarn, den Niederlanden, Niederländisch-Indien, der Schweiz und den verschiedenen Staaten von Amerika. Statistisches und Finanzielles, unter besonderer Berücksichtigung der Wiener Verhältnisse. Wien, C. Gerold's Sohn, 1888.
　　iv, 132p.
　　Microfilm (negative) Paris, Bibliothèque nationale, Service photographique, 1973.
　　1 reel. 35mm.

NL 0381049　　IU

Lindheimer, Cornelius, respondent.
　　... De impugnatione testamenti fraterni per qverelam inofficiosi ...
　　　　see under　Fuchs, Johann Heinrich, 1664-1727, praeses.

LINDHEIMER, Ferdinand, 1803-1879.
　　Aufsätze und abhandlungen von Ferdinand Lindheimer in Texas. Herausgegeben von einem seiner schüler [Gustav Passavant.] Frankfurt a.M., T. Wentz, 1879.

NL 0381051　　MH TxU MH-A

Lindheimer, Ferdinand, 1803-1879.
　　Plantae Lindheimerianae; an enumeration of F. Lindheimer's collection of Texan plants ...
　　　　see under　Engelmann, George, 1809-1884.

Lindheimer, Franz P., 1870-
　　Beiträge zur geschichte und kritik der neukantischen philosophie. Erste reihe: Hermann Cohen ... Bern, Druck von C. Sturzenegger, 1900.
　　2 p. l., 104 p. 23ᶜᵐ.
　　Inaug.-diss.—Bern.

　　1. Kant, Immanuel, 1724-1804. 2. Cohen, Hermann, 1842-

1-G-1997

Library of Congress　　　B3216.C44L7

NL 0381053　　DLC NjP ICU NIC PU NN

Lindheimer, Franz P　　, 1870-
　　Karl Boland; roman; umschlag von Edmund Edel. Berlin, 1902.

NL 0381054　　PPL

Lindheimer, Franz P　　1870-
　　... Leben, lieben, singen. Gedichte ... Heidelberg, J. Hörning, 1896.
　　4 p. l., (3)-192 p. 20ᶜᵐ.
　　At head of title: Franz Lindheimer.

I. Title.

29-19596

Library of Congress　　PT2623.I 585L4　1896

NL 0381055　　DLC NjP

Lindheimer, Friedrich, d. 1822.
　　Die leihbibliothek; ein lustspiel in zwey akten, von dr. Fridrich Lindheimer.
　　Franfurt am Main, J. L. E. Zessler, 1798.
　　128 p.

NL 0381056　　OU

PT 2424
.L39 L5
LINDHEIMER, FRIEDRICH,　d 1822.
　　Die Leihbibliothek; ein Lustspiel in zwey Acten.　Grätz, 1799.
　　96 p.

NL 0381057　　InU

1887-
Lindheimer, Friedrich, Referendar: Die §§ 7 bis 9 des Gesetzes über den Verkehr mit Kraftfahrzeugen vom 3. Mai 1909. Frankfurt a. M. 1913: Voigt & Gleiber. 57 S. 8°
Marburg, Jur. Diss. v. 9. Sept. 1913, Ref. André
[Geb. 22. Jan. 87 Frankfurt a. M.; Wohnort: Frankfurt; Staatsangeh.: Preußen; Vorbildung: Goethe-G. Frankfurt Reife 05; Studium: Heidelberg 2, Berlin 2, Marburg 2 S; Rig. 24. Juli 13.]　　　　　　[U 13. 1123]

NL 0381058　　ICRL

Lindheimer, Georg Wilhelm, respondent.
　　... De iure mercedis opificum in concursu creditorum ...
　　　　see under　Böhmer, Georg Ludwig, 1715-1797, praeses.

Lindheimer, Johann Gerhard.
　　... De principe legibus soluto ... Giessae, Typis E.H.Lammers (n.d.)
　　24 p.　21ᶜᵐ.
FL6　　Diss. - Giessen, 1747.
D613　　Vol.3, no.23 of a collection with binder's
v.3　　title: Dissertationes juridicae.
no.23

　　1. Kings and rulers (Roman law) I. Title.

NL 0381060　　MiU

Lindheimer, Leopold, firm, Frankfurt am Main.
　　Ein Rückblick anlässlich des fünfzigjährigen Jubiläums der Firma Leopold Lindheimer, auf ihre Entwicklung und auf das Leben ihres Begründers; 1834-1914. Frankfurt am Main, 1914.
　　84 p.　illus., ports., facsims.

NL 0381061　　NNC

Lindheimer, Otto.
　　Aquarien.
　　illus., pls., plans.　(In Handbuch der Architektur. Th. 4. Entwerfen, Anlage und Einrichtung der Bebäude. Halb-Bd. 6, Heft 4, p. 454-471.　Darmstadt, 1893)
　　Bibliography, p. 471.

NL 0381062　　MB

Lindheimer, Otto.
　　Turnanstalten. Illus. Plans.
　　(In Handbuch der Architektur. Th. 4. Entwerfen, Anlage und Einrichtung der Gebäude. Halb-Band 6, Heft 1, pp. 289-311. Darmstadt. 1889.)
　　Literatur, pp. 309, 311.

K8694 — Gymnasiums. Construction.

NL 0381063　　MB

Lindheimer, Siegfried, 1844-
　　De disivnctiva obligatione ... defendet ... Sigifredvs Lindheimer ... Adversariorvm partes svscipient Pavlvs Holdheim ... Felix Kavfmann ... Ioannes Tovrnier ... Berolini, G. Lange [1867]
　　35 p.　19½cm.
　　Diss. - Berlin.
　　"Avctoris vita": p. 34.

NL 0381064　　MH-L

Lindhjem, Anna.
　　105 [i. e. Hundrede og fem] kirkesangere år 1950. Fredrikstad, C. Hanssens trykkeri og bokbinderi, 1952.
　　29 p. 21 cm.

　　1. Singers, Norwegian. I. Title.

ML106.N6L5　　　　　56-27667 ‡

NL 0381065　　DLC NN MH

Lindhjem, Anna.
　　...Norges orgler og organister til og med 1914... Skien, Fremskridts boktrykkeri, 1916.　xxxi, 374 p. 19cm.

At head of title: Tilegnet norges organister.

　　1. Organ—Hist.—Norway. 2. Organists—Norway.

NL 0381066　　NN

W 4
M22
1953
LINDHOF, Helmut, 1927-
　　Tierexperimentelle Untersuchungen über das Verhalten der Bluteiweisskörper nach Subsidon-Infusionen. [Mainz] 1953.
　　40 ℓ. illus.
　　Inaug.-Diss. - Mainz.
　　1. Blood proteins 2. Blood substitutes

NL 0381067　　DNLM

W 4
1896
1941
Lindhoff, Lucy, 1915-
　　Beitrag zur Frage der Phlebolithen in Varizen. München, Wolf, 1941.
　　14, [5] p. illus.

　　Inaug.-Diss. - Munich.
　　Bibliography: p. [17]

NL 0381068　　DNLM

VOLUME 334

[Lindholm, Anna Chandler] 1870–
The black pearl of passion, by Dorothy Fay [pseud.] ...
New York, The Galleon press [*1936]
218 p. 19½°.

    ɪ. Title.

Library of Congress   PZ3.L64634B1   36–10013

NL 0381069   DLC

[Lindholm, Anna Chandler] 1870–
Mad morning moonlight of Hawaii, by Dorothy Fay [pseud.]
... Los Gatos, Calif. [*1932]
xi, 80 p. incl. front., plates. 22½°.

Poems.
"The birds of paradise ... by Carolyn Louise Lindholm Fitzgerald":
p. 73–74.

    ɪ. Title.

Library of Congress   PS3523.I 55M3 1932   33–7555
—— Copy 2.
Copyright A 59960   811.5

NL 0381070   DLC

[Lindholm, Anna Chandler] 1870–
Wind and trees and other poems, by Dorothy Fay [pseud.]
[San Francisco, V. F. Pollak printing co., *1930]
viii, 287 p. 21½°.

    ɪ. Title.

Library of Congress   PS3523.I 55W5 1930   31–23421
—— Copy 2.
Copyright A 39908   811.5

NL 0381071   DLC

HC 337   LINDHOLM, ARTUR J
.F5 K5   Bidrag till kännedom om Finlands ekonomiska tillstand under tidskiftet 1634-1654.
Helsingfors, 1892.
156+13 p.

Akademisk afhandling—Helsingfors.

1. Finland—Econ. cond.

NL 0381072   InU ICRL DLC CtY NNC

TC425   Lindholm, C. F.
.S4A53   Pennsylvania. *Dept. of Forests and Waters.*
    Water resources investigations relating to the Schuylkill
River Restoration Project, October 1947–December 1949, by
W. F. White and C. F. Lindholm. Prepared in cooperation
with the U. S. Dept. of the Interior, Geological Survey.
Harrisburg, 1950.

Lindholm, Charles.
    Konsten och tiden. Stockholm, Fahlcrantz & Gumælius
[1950]
241 p. 23 cm.

    1. Art—Philosophy. 2. Aesthetics.   ɪ. Title.

                  A 51–2015

Harvard Univ. Library
for Library of Congress   [1]

NL 0381074   MH NN

4PT   Lindholm, Dan.
Nor.-   Små sagn om store ting. Illustrert av
82   Hans G. Sørensen. Dreyer, [1949]
45 p.

NL 0381075   DLC-P4

Lindholm, Disa, 1916–
...Djupare— Helsingfors, Söderström & c:o [1948]   92 p.
22cm.

    1. Poetry, Swedish-Finnish.   ɪ. Title.
N. Y. P. L.   February 27, 1950

NL 0381076   NN

6879   Lindholm, Einar.
E   Über die Verbreitung und Verschie-
v.36   bung von Spektrallinien. Experimentelle
no.1   und theoretische Beiträge. Uppsala,
Almqvist & Wiksell, 1942.
94 p. illus. 25cm.

Diss.--Stockholm.

1. Spectrum analysis.

NL 0381077   NIC MBdAF ViU CU CtY NcD

PA2293   LINDHOLM, ELMO.
.L78   Stilistische studien zur erweiterung der satzglie-
der im lateinischen, von Elmo Lindholm. Lund, H.
Ohlssons buchdr., 1931.
xii, 225, [2] p. 25½cm.
"Literatur": p. [vii]-xii.

1. Latin language—Syntax.

NL 0381078   ICU ICRL CtY CU OClW MiU DCU MH OCU MnU

Lindholm, Ernst, 1915–
    Byn på grytbottnen. [Stockholm] Arbetarkultur [1953]
154 p. 22 cm.

    ɪ. Title.

                  A 53–6572

Minnesota. Univ. Libr
for Library of Congress   [1]

NL 0381079   MnU

Lindholm, Ernst, 1915–
    Hägrande stad. Stockholm, Arbetarkulturs
förlag, 1955.
214 p.

NL 0381080   KyU

Lindholm, Ferdinand, 1883–
    ... Étude de la loi de Beer sur l'absorption dans le spectre
infrarouge, par F. Lindholm. Avec 4 planches et 4 figures dans
le text ... [Uppsala, Almqvist & Wiksells boktryckeri-a.-b.,
1911]
12 p. diagrs. 23°°.   (Arkiv för matematik, astronomi och fysik. bd. 7,
no 2)

Caption title.
At head of title: ... Meddelande från Uppsala univ. Fysiska institution.
Bibliographical foot-notes.

NL 0381081   ICJ

Lindholm, Ferdinand, 1883–
Exploration de la haute atmosphere par
avion...
4p. illus. 31½ cm.
45378

NL 0381082   DAS

Lindholm, Ferdinand, 1883–
    ... Extinction des radiations solaires dans l'atmosphère ter-
restre; étude basée sur les observations spectrobolometriques
faites à l'Institut de physique d'Upsala pendant l'année 1912,
par F. Lindholm ... Upsala, A.-b. Akademiska bokhandeln,
1913.
2 p. l., 93 p. incl. tables. pl., diagrs. 29°°.   (Nova acta Regiæ societatis
scientiarum upsaliensis. ser. IV, v. 3, n. 6)

NL 0381083   ICJ CtY NN DBS PU DAS MH

Lindholm, Ferdinand, 1883–
Klimat och vaderleksforhallanden.
Stockholm. 1923.
p.87-107. illus. figs. 23½ cm.
44065

NL 0381084   DAS

Lindholm, Ferdinand, 1883–
    ... Messungen der Ultraviolettstrahlung der Sonne in Stock-
holm, van F. Lindholm und G. Cronheim ... [Uppsala, Almqvist & Wiksells boktryckeri-a.-b., 1939]
5 p. diagr. 22°°.   (Arkiv för matematik, astronomi och fysik. bd. 27a,
no 2)
Caption title.
"Literatur": p. 5.

NL 0381085   ICJ

Lindholm, Ferdinand, 1883–
    ... Mesures actinométriques pendant l'éclipse solaire du 17 av-
ril 1912, par F. Lindholm. Avec 5 figures dans le texte ...
[Uppsala, Almqvist & Wiksells boktryckeri-a.-b., 1912]
11, [1] p. incl. tables, diagrs. 23°°.   (Arkiv för matematik, astronomi och
fysik. bd. 8, no 21)
Caption title.
At head of title: ... Meddelande från Uppsala universitets Fysiska institution.
Bibliographical foot-notes.

NL 0381086   ICJ

Lindholm, Ferdinand, 1883–
    Normalwerte der Gesamtstrahlung und der
auf die Cadmiumzelle wirksamen Ultra-
violettstrahlung der sonne fur Is vos. 1929.
p. 5-32. figs. 22 cm.

NL 0381087   DAS

Lindholm, Ferdinand, 1883–
Observations pyrheliometriques faites a
Stockholm pendant l'eclipse des 20-21 sout. 1914.
1919.

NL 0381088   DAS

VOLUME 334

Lindholm, Ferdinand, 1883–
Om vertikal temperaturgradient,
ome her sontala temperatur-och Luft-
tahetsgradienter samt em molnigh-
etsfordelningen over Everige.
(Uppsala 1926.(
p. 169–187. figs. 22cm.

NL 0381089   DAS

Lindholm, Ferdinand, 1883–

Physical-meteorological observatory at
Davos (Switzerland.)
6p. illus. 25½cm.

NL 0381090   DAS

**Rhb5
S6
A173
3**

Lindholm, Ferdinand, 1883–
Propagation to great distance of airwaves from
the explosion at Oslo on December 19th 1943 as an
indication of conditions in the upper atmosphere.
[Stockholm, Centraltryckeriet, 1946]
[240]–252p. charts. 25cm. (Sveriges Meteo-
rologiska och Hydrologiska Institut. Meddelanden
ser.B, nr.3)
Cover title.

NL 0381091   CtY

Lindholm, Ferdinand, 1883–
Registrierbeobachtungen der Hesschen
Ultray-Strahlung auf Muottas-Muraigl
(2456 m).
II. Mitteilung. Leipzig. 1929.
p.141–163. figs. 22½ cm.
49767

NL 0381092   DAS

Lindholm, Ferdinand, 1883–
... Registrierbeobachtungen der kosmischen Ultrastrahlung
im Meeresniveau, Stockholm, von F. Lindholm. Mit 5 Figuren
im Text ... [Uppsala, Almqvist & Wiksells boktryckeri-a.-b.,
1932]
20 p. incl. tables, diagrs. 23ᶜᵐ. (Arkiv för matematik, astronomi och
fysik. bd. 23A, n:o 4)
Caption title.
Bibliographical foot-notes.

NL 0381093   ICJ

Lindholm, Ferdinand, 1883–

Das Schweizerische Forschungsinstitut für
Hoongebirskslima und Tuberkulose in Davos.
Abt. I: Das Physikalisch-meteorologisch
Observatorium. 1929.
20p. plates. 23 cm.
By Lindholm, F., and Morikofer, W.

NL 0381094   DAS

Lindholm, Ferdinand, 1883–
... Sur l'insolation dans la Suède septentrionale, par F.
Lindholm ... Stockholm, Almqvist & Wiksells boktryckeri-
a.-b., 1919.
24 p. incl. tables, diagr. 31½ᶜᵐ. (Kungl. svenska vetenskapsakademiens handlingar. bd. 60, n:o 2)

1. Solar radiation.   I. Title: L'insolation dans la Suède septentrionale.
            A 28–2128
Title from Univ. of Chi-   cago Q64.S828 vol. 60, no. 2
                 Printed by L. C.

NL 0381095   ICU NN DAS

**QC879
L5**

Lindholm, Ferdinand, 1883–
... Sur la structure thermique de l'atmosphère au-dessus de
la Suède méridionale; sondages faits par avion en 1924 et 1925,
par F. Lindholm. Stockholm [Uppsala, Almqvist & Wiksells
boktryckeri-a.-b.] 1927.
41, [1] p. incl. illus., tables, diagrs. 32ᶜᵐ. ([Sweden] Statens meteorologisk-hydrografiska anstalt. Meddelanden. bd. 3, n:o 10)

1. Atmosphere, Upper.   2. Meteorology—Sweden.
       [Full name: Vilhelm Ferdinand Valdemar Lindholm]

QC879.L5   28–10683 rev

NL 0381096   DLC NN

Lindholm, Ferdinand, 1883–
Swedish Polar Year Expedition, Sveagruvan, Spitzbergen, 1932–1933. General introduction. Terrestrial magnetism. Published under the direction of the Swedish National
Committee for Geodesy and Geophysics. Stockholm, 1939.
77 p. illus., maps, tables. 31 cm.
Leader of the expedition: Ferdinand Lindholm.

1. Magnetism, Terrestrial—Spitsbergen.   I. Svenska national-
kommittén för geodesi och geofysik.   II. International Polar Year.
2d, 1932–33.   III. Title.
    Full name: Vilhelm Ferdinand Valdemar Lindholm.

QC825.8.L5   52–55017

NL 0381097   DLC MH

Lindholm, Ferdinand, 1883–
... Synoptiska väderlekskartor i navigationens tjänst, av
F. Lindholm. Med 7 figurer och en stationskarta. Stockholm
[Kungl. boktryckeriet, P. A. Norstedt & söner] 1925.
1 p. l., 16 p. incl. illus., tables, charts. 32ᶜᵐ. ([Sweden] Statens
meteorologisk-hydrografiska anstalt. Meddelanden. bd. 3, n:o 3)

1. Meteorology—Charts, diagrams, etc.   I. Title.
       [Full name: Vilhelm Ferdinand Valdemar Lindholm]

QC878.L5   26–687 rev

NL 0381098   DLC NN

Lindholm, Ferdinand, 1883–
Temperaturens och lufttathetens variation med hojden (Uppsala. 1925.)
p. 51–69. illus. 23cm.

NL 0381099   DAS

[Lindholm, Ferdinand] 1883–
Terrestrial magnetism
    see h/s   Swedish Polar Year
Expedition Sveagruvan, Spitzbergen, 1932–
1933. General introduction.

Lindholm, Ferdinand, 1883–
Vara vaderleksforutsagelser. Stockholm. 1926.
16 p. figs. 17 cm.
45924

NL 0381101   DAS

**HX
833
L518**

Lindholm, Fredrik, 1861–
El anarquismo; según las fuentes guegas y
extranjeras, por Federico Lindholm. Versión
directa del sueco, prólogo y notas por Emilio
Miñana. Madrid, Centro Editorial de Góngora,
1906.
159p. illus. 21cm.
Translation of Anarkismen.
Bibliographical footnotes.
1. Anarchism and anarchists   I. Title

NL 0381102   WU CSt-H CU

Lindholm, Fredrik, 1861–   *ed.*
Nationalhymner och soldatsånger under världskriget
på originalspråket och i översättning, jämte uppgifter om
deras tillkomst, diktare och tonsättare; utg. av Fredrik
Lindholm. Stockholm, P. A. Norstedt & söner [1916]
2 p. l., 122 p. 20ᶜᵐ.
Signature note: Lindholm, Sången under världskriget.

1. National songs.   2. War-songs.   I. Title.
          [Full name: Johan Fredrik Lindholm]
                       22–2203
Library of Congress   PN6110.H3L5

NL 0381103   DLC

[LINDHOLM, Fredrik] 1861–
Nya regimen inom de k. teatrarne. Af Cato
Minor. Stockholm, Bokförlagsföreningen Svea,
1885.

    pp. 27.

NL 0381104   MH

Lindholm, Helge, 1886–1926, and K. G. T. Bergquist.
Kommunal affärsverksamhet i de svenska städerna, av Helge
Lindholm och Gillis Bergquist. Stockholm, 1924. vii, 332 p.
incl. tables. 8°. (Sweden. Statens offentliga utredningar.
1924, [nr.] 45.)
Prepared according to an agreement between the Svenska stadsförbundet and
Socialiseringsnämnden.

1. Municipal ownership—Sweden.   2. Sweden. Socialiseringsnämnden.
3. Svenska stadsförbundet. 4. Berg-   quist, Karl Gillis Tor, 1889–
jt. au. 5. Ser.
N. Y. P. L.   September 24, 1928

NL 0381105   NN

**JS6251
.S85**

Lindholm, Helge, 1886–1926, ed.
Sveriges landstings tidskrift. årg. 1–
1914–
[Stockholm, 1914–

4NK–45

Lindholm, Idi.
Pitsikirja; aitopitsit ja verkkopitsit.
Helsinki,   Valistus [1947]
89 p.

NL 0381107   DLC-P4 NN

LINDHOLM, IDI.
Virikkeita. Helsinki, Valistus [1953] 15 p.
13 plates. 21x31cm.

1. Handicraft.   t. 1953.

NL 0381108   NN

Lindholm, Inga. Kvinnoprofiler ur de
isländska släktsagorna. Extr. fr. Finsk
tidskrift. Tom. LXXXIII. 1917. pp.
285–307.   IcF7L751

NL 0381109   NIC

VOLUME 334

Lindholm, Johan Fredrik
see
Lindholm, Fredrik, 1861-

Lindholm, John H.
Electronic business machines
see under Appel, Richard W

Lindholm, K.
Müller, Friedrich Max, 1823–1900.
The Schleswig-Holstein question and its place in history, by the Right Hon. Professor Max Müller, and The Danish view of the Slesvig-Holstein question, by Dr. A. D. Jörgensen ... Reprinted from the Nineteenth century of May and of December 1897. With a preface by K. Lindholm—November 1915. London, Spottiswoode & co. ltd. [1916]

NL 0381113　　NN

96.06
L64
Lindholm, Lena.
Bloemen en planten in huis. 3. druk. Zutphen, Thieme [n.d.]
254 p.

1. House plants. 2. Window-gardening. 3. Balcony gardening. I. Lindholm, Folke, joint author. II. Rijks-Ruys, W S ed.

NL 0381114　　DNAL

Lindholm, Lena.
Blommor hemma [av] Lena och Folke Lindholm. [Stockholm] Forum [1955]
245 p. illus. 17 cm. (När-var-hur-serien)

1. House plants. I. Lindholm, Folke, joint author. II. Title.
A 56-1831
Purdue Univ. Library
for Library of Congress　　[1]

NL 0381115　　InLP

Lindholm, Lena.
En bok om rosor [av Lena och Folke Lindholm] Stockholm, Bonnier [1955]
174 p. illus. 24 cm.

1. Roses. I. Lindholm, Folke, joint author. II. Title.
A 55-6857
Purdue Univ. Library
for Library of Congress　　[1]

NL 0381116　　InLP

Lindholm, Lena.
Vägvisare för blomstervänner. [Nyköping, Södermanlands Läns Tidnings Tryckeri, 1953]
28 p.

NL 0381117　　InLP

Lindholm, M S
National old age retirement plan, as a means to Economic recovery. Spokane, n.p. 1934.

NL 0381118　　PPAmSwM Or

Lindholm, M S
National old age retirement plan as a means to economic recovery...2d ed. (Spokane, Wash., 1934)
[7] p. 23 cm

NL 0381119　　DL PPAmSwM

Lindholm, M S.
The unemployment menace; cause and remedy, by M. S. Lindholm. Revised edition. [Spokane, Wash.: M. S. Lindholm, 1932] 4 l. 23cm.

1. Unemployed—U. S., 1929–
N. Y. P. L.　　December 10, 1937

NL 0381120　　NN

HD5724
.Z9
no. 41
Lindholm, M S.
The unemployment menace, cause and remedy. A plan by M.S. Lindholm ... [Spokane, Washington] c1932.
[7] p. 23 cm. [Pamphlets on unemployment in the United States, no. 41]

NL 0381121　　DLC

Lindholm, Mari Fay, 1887-
New York (State) *Public service commission. 1st district. Library.*
Brief list of references on public utilities with especial reference to state supervision. Prepared for the Special libraries association by Mari Fay Lindholm ... [New York] Library, Public service commission, First district 1909.

016.3387
L64r
Lindholm, Mari Fay.
A review of chief sources of material for special library collections. [New York, 1913?]
[7p.]
Presented at the Annual convention of the Special libraries association, Hotel Kaaterskill, June 24-26, 1913

NL 0381123　　IU

Lindholm, Marshall, 1903-
Flyg i natt; en svensk trafikflygares upplevelser under Andra världskriget. [Malmö] Allhems förlag [1952]
124 p. illus. 24 cm.

1. World War, 1939–1945—Personal narratives, Swedish. I. Title.
Full name: Nils Erik Marshall Lindholm.

D811.5.L546　　55–35425 †

NL 0381124　　DLC MnU NN

Lindholm, Matilda Charlotta (Simberg)
see
Simberg, Matilda Charlotta, b. 1819.

Lindholm, Nils Erik Marshall
see
Lindholm, Marshall, 1903-

Lindholm, Oscar.
Forsikringsforeningen i København, 1883–1933, af Oscar Lindholm. København: B. Lunos Boktrykkeri A/S, 1933. 228 p. incl. tables. illus. (ports.) 24½cm.

820887A. 1. Insurance—Assoc.　　and org.—Denmark. I. Title.
N. Y. P. L.　　June 7, 1937

NL 0381127　　NN

Lindholm, P. A.
Gustaf Wasa och Westmanländingen eller sköldemärket. Berättelse från befrielsekriget 1521.
— Stockholm. Lamm. [1890.] 51 pp. [Historiska berättelser. 1.] Sm. 8°.

*D5508 — T.r. — Sweden. Hist. Fict.

NL 0381128　　MB

LINDHOLM, P. A.
Hans Rödskägg och Erik Skeppare, eller, Johan III. och Angermanländingen.
= Stockholm. Lamm. [1890.] 53 pp. [Historiska berättelser 3.] 16°.

NL 0381129　　MB

Lindholm, P A.
Hos Lappbönder. Skildringar, sägner och sagor från södra Lappland. Stockholm, A. Bonnier, [1884].
pp. (4), 159 +.

Folklore–Lapland

NL 0381130　　MH CtY

Lindholm, P A
Västerbottens Län.
Uppsala, J. A. Lindblads förlag, [1926]
358 p. (Hembygdsböckerna, läseböcker för skola och hem)

NL 0381131　　OC1 PPAmSwM

[Lindholm, P A]
Västerbottens län. Skolupplaga.
Uppsala, J.A. Lindblad [1930]
387 p. illus. 20cm. (Hembygdsböckerna; läseböcker för skola och hem)

1. Västerbotten, Sweden.

NL 0381132　　MnU

VOLUME 334

Lindholm, P   T.
Försök till praktisk lärobok i aritmetik, af P. T. Lindholm. Vasa, Minn. [1877]
4 p. l., 128 p. 20½ᵐ.
"Svar till öfnings exempien": p. [117]–128.

1. Arithmetic—1846–1880.

Library of Congress   QA103.L7455   2–27610

NL   0381133   DLC

Lindholm, P. T.
Saaen-album innebraalade...
see under Valline, O.

4D
2449
Lindholm, Pelle.
Hango belägras; bilder från fronterna kring Hangö sommaren och hösten 1941. Albumet redigerat av Pelle Lindholm under medverkan av officerare från Hangöfronten. Helsingfors, Förlagsaktiebolaget Fennia [1942]
159 p.

NL   0381135   DLC-P4 MH

Lindholm, Peter William, 1856–1934.
Beretning om Foreningen "Skolehaven"s 20 aars virksomhed fra 1903–1923, ved P. W. Lindholm ... København, Foreningen "Skolehaven", 1923.
118 p., 1 l. illus. (incl. ports.) diagrs. 23½ᵐ.

1. Agricultural education—Denmark. [1. Denmark—Agriculture—Education] 2. [Forening "Skolehaven"] 3. School gardens.

Agr 23–778

Library, U. S. Dept. of   Agriculture 90F76L

NL   0381136   DNAL

Lindholm, Peter William, 1856–1934.
Kortfattet Vejledning i Skolehavens Anlæg og Ledelse, af P. W. Lindholm. København, Bianco Luno, 1931. 37 p. illus. 23cm.

"Særtryk af Vore Børn, Nr. 11 og 12, 1929 og Nr. 6, 10 og 12, 1930."

1. School gardens—Denmark.
N. Y. P. L.   April 17, 1946

NL   0381137   NN

Lindholm, Peter William, 1856–1934
Skolehaven. Kortfattet vejledning for skolehaveledere. Ved P. W. Lindholm. Trykt som manuskript. København, N. C. Roms forlagsforretning, 1911.
32 p. 20ᵐ.

1. School gardens.

Agr 13–1391

Library, U. S. Dept. of   Agriculture 90L643

NL   0381138   DNAL

Lindholm, Peter William, 1856–1934.
Skolehaven i Opdragelsens Tjeneste, ved P. W. Lindholm ...med Forord af Undervisningsministeriets Konsulent i Skolesager Professor N. A. Larsen.   København: J. H. Schultz Forlag, 1928. 128 p. illus. (incl. plans.) 8°.

1. School gardens and gardening—
N. Y. P. L.   Denmark.   October 19, 1928

NL   0381139   NN

Lindholm, Richard Wadsworth, 1914–
The corporate franchise as a basis of taxation [by] Richard W. Lindholm. Austin, The University of Texas press, 1944.
xviii p., 2 l., [3]–276 p. 23½ cm.
Bibliography: p. 251–264.

1. Corporations—U. S.—Taxation.   I. Title.

HD2753.U6L5   336.274   45–37102 rev

TU TxU CU
NL 0381140   DLC OrU AAP GU NcD ViU PSt PPT OCl OU

ar X
2497
Lindholm, Richard Wadsworth, 1914–
Economic development through deflation; a research paper.   Saigon, Finance Division, USOM, 1955.
18 l.   29cm.

"Unclassified."

1. Deflation (Finance) 2. Economic development. 3. Underdeveloped areas.
I. Title.

NL   0381141   NIC

Lindholm, Richard Wadsworth, 1914–
Introduction to fiscal policy. New York, Pitman Pub. Corp. [1948]
xiii, 285 p. 24 cm.
"Suggested references and additional reading": p. 225–228.

1. Finance. 2. Finance—U. S.

HJ141.L5   336.73   48–9702*

OClW OU MB TU
NL 0381142   DLC PPFRB OrU Or CoU IU PSC PU PPT PSt

Lindholm, Richard Wadsworth, 1914–
Introduction to fiscal policy. 2d ed. New York, Pitman Pub. Corp. [1955]
242 p. illus. 24 cm.
Includes bibliography.

1. Finance, Public. 2. Finance, Public—U. S.

HJ141.L5 1955   336.73   55–13578 ‡

PPT PP PBL DAU NIC IaU CaBVaU MtU OrU WaU
NL 0381143   DLC FU NcRS TU MB MiU OOxM OCl PU-W PSt

Lindholm, Richard Wadsworth, 1914–
Money and banking, an introduction. Ames, Iowa, Littlefield, Adams [1950]
ix, 196 p. diagrs. 21 cm. (Littlefield college outlines, 19)
Bibliography: p. ix.

1. Money—U. S. 2. Banks and banking—U. S.   I. Title.

HG538.L64   332   51–279

NL   0381144   DLC FU ViU OrU TxU OrCS OrU

Lindholm, Richard Wadsworth, 1914–
Money and finance. East Lansing, Michigan State College Press, 1951.
248 p. illus. 22 cm.

1. Finance. 2. Currency question.

HG153.L5   332   51–7513 ‡

NL   0381145   DLC

Lindholm, Richard Wadsworth, 1914–
Principles of money and banking related to national income and fiscal policy [by] Richard W. Lindholm, John J Balles [and] John M. Hunter. [1st ed.] New York, Norton [1954]
673 p. illus. 22 cm.
Includes bibliography.

1. Currency question. 2. Currency question—U. S. 3. Banks and banking. 4. Banks and banking—U. S.

HG221.L547   332   54–1191 ‡

PV TU OClFRB IU MU CaBVaU OrU WaWW
NL 0381146   DLC ScU MB IEN OU TxU PU-W PU OCl OClND

Lindholm, Richard Wadsworth, 1914–
Public finance and fiscal policy; an analysis of government spending, revenue, and debt. New York, Pitman [1950]
xxvii, 732 p. 24 cm.
Includes bibliographies.

1. Finance, Public. 2. Finance, Public—U. S.   I. Title.

HJ141.L52   336.73   50–7641

IU NBuU-L Or OrCS Wa OrU
NL 0381147   DLC PSt PPLas PPT TxU NcU NNUN TU ViU

Lindholm, Richard Wadsworth, 1914–
Public finance of air transportation, a study of taxation and public expenditures in relation to a developing industry. Columbus, Bureau of Business Research, College of Commerce and Administration, Ohio State Univ. [1948]
xvii, 178 p. diagrs. 24 cm.
Bibliography: p. 169–170.

1. Aeronautics, Commercial—Finance. 2. Finance—U. S.
I. Title.

TL552.2.L5   387.713   48–45431 *

CaBVaU
OClJC NN MB MiU ScU NcD WU CaBVa OrU IdU NNC Or WaS
NL 0381148   DLC TxU LU CoU PSt MiEM MiU OClCC OU

Lindholm, Richard Wadsworth, 1914–
Taxation of the trucking industry. Columbus, Ohio, Bureau of Business Research, College of Commerce and Administration, Ohio State University [1951]
141 p. illus. 24 cm.

1. Transportation, Automotive—U. S.—Taxation. 2. Roads—U. S.—Finance. I. Title.

HE5623.L5   388.3   52–8528 ‡

WaU-L TU
MtU CaBVaU TxU MB CaBVa Or OrCS OrP OrU Wa WaS CU
NL 0381149   DLC NcU ViU LU NBuU NcD KMK ICRL CoU IdU

Lindholm, Richard Wadsworth, 1914–
Taxes and public expenditures ... [Cincinnati] °1947.
238 p. diagrs. 28ᵐ.

1. Finance—U. S. 2. Taxation—U. S.   I. Title.
HJ257.L5   336.73   47–23311
                              Brief cataloging

NL   0381150   DLC

VOLUME 334

Lindholm, Stig.

Catechismi förfremielse; studier till catechismusundervisningen i Svenska kyrkan, 1593-1646.   Lund, Hakan Ohlssons Boktryckeri, 1949.
xxxi,269p.   29cm.
Includes bibliography.

I. Catechetics - Lutheran Church.
i. Title.

NL 0381151   MoSCS DLC-P4 MH CtY NNC

Lindholm, Stig.
Konfirmandundervisning; metodiska elementa. Stockholm, Svenska Kyrkans Diakonistyrelses Bokförlag, ₁1954₎
₁117₎p., il., o.

NL 0381152   PPLT

Lindholm, Svante Gottfrid.
Experiences with zoning in Washington, D.C.
see under   District of Columbia. Zoning Commission.

Lindholm, Svante Gottfrid.
Report of survey of the Department of health and the Department of education, city of Atlanta, Georgia
see under   Bureau of municipal research, New York.

LINDHOLM, SWEN   A   , 1852-
Ministerial pension. Why? How? What? [By] S.A.Lindholm. Brief survey; auspices of the Augustana Pension and Aid Fund.   [Des Moines? Ia., 1930?]   46 p. incl. tables. illus. (incl. charts, ports.)   16½cm.

Cover-title.

868219A. 1. Pensions, Clergy—U.S. I. Augustana Pension and Aid Fund.

NL 0381155   NN

LINDHOLM, TAGE.
Dodson & Dids (Tant Sofis miljoner); fars i en akt, av Tage Lindholm.   Stockholm: C.E.Fritzes bokförlags aktiebolag [1935]   36 p.   illus. (plan.)   19½cm. (Amatörteatern. [nr.] 26.)

1. Drama, Swedish. I. Title. II. Ser.

NL 0381156   NN OCl

Lindholm, Valdemar, *1880-*
Bortom storskogen, av Valdemar Lindholm. Stockholm, Nordiska förlaget ₁1912₎
123 p.   16¼ᵐ.
Half-title illustrated in colors.

i. Title.

13-5701

NL 0381157   DLC

Lindholm, Valdemar, *1880-*
Fjället, skogen och myren; tre Norrlandssägner, av Valdemar Lindholm.   Stockholm: A. Bonniers förlag₁, 1930₎.   220 p.   12°.

500711A. 1. Fiction, Swedish.   I. Title. II. Title: Skogen.
III. Title: Myren.
N.Y.P.L.   November 28, 1930

NL 0381158   NN

Lindholm, Valdemar, 1880-

₁Hertzman, *Mrs.* Anna-Mia₎
Lapland legends; tales of an ancient race and its great gods, retold from the Swedish by Leonne de Cambrey ₁pseud.₎   New Haven, Yale university press; London, H. Milford, Oxford university press, 1926.

Lindholm, Valdemar, *1880-*
När Gammelgården såldes, och andra berättelser, af Waldemar Lindholm.   Stockholm: Bokförlaget Minerva ₁1915₎.   187 p.   12°.

Contents. När Gammelgården såldes. Den nya tiden. Per Persas prövningar. Furens saga.

1. Fiction (Swedish). 2. Title.
N.Y.P.L.   December 10, 1915.

NL 0381160   NN

PT9875   Lindholm, Valdemar, 1880-
L576N3   När solen sjunker.   Stockholm, Nordiska förlaget [1912]
Scandi-   268 p.   (Nordiska förlagets elitserie, 1)
navian
Dept.

NL 0381161   CU

PN998   LINDHOLM, VALDEMAR, *1880-*
.L3L7   Sagor från Lappland berättade för barn av Valdemar Lindholm. Med 10 illustrationer av Acke Åslund
Stockholm, Svenska förlaget[1918]
174,[1]p.incl.front.,plates.   23cm.

1.Fairy tales. 2.Folk literature--Lapland.

NL 0381162   ICU

Lindholm, Valdemar, *1880-*
Varg i veum; roman.   Stockholm: Fröléen & Co. ₁1911₎
170 p.   12°.

1. Fiction (Swedish). 2. Title.
N.Y.P.L.   June 8, 1914.

NL 0381163   NN

DL991   LINDHOLM, VALDEMAR, *1880-*
.B7L7   ...Ur Borgsjö sockens krönika. En bok om födelsebygden... Örnsköldsvik,Ågrens boktryckeri,1921.
140 p. illus.(incl.ports.,maps)3 pl. 19½cm.
Title-vignette(seal)

1.Borgsjö,Sweden(parish)--Hist.

NL 0381164   ICU

Lindholm, Valdemar, 1880-
Varulfven. En berättelse fran fjäll och haf. Göteborg, Ahlen & Akerlund, 1909.
93 p.   12°.

NL 0381165   NN

Lindholm, Valdemar, *1880-*
Vildmarkens besegrare; en bok om ett obekant folk i ett obekant land.   Stockholm: Svenska andelsförlaget₁, 1925₎.   159 p.   front., illus., plates, ports.   8°.

Plates printed on both sides.
Illustrated by C. M. Lindquist.

1. Tärna, Sweden. 2. Lapland—   Social life. 3. Lindquist, C. M.,
illustrator.
N.Y.P.L.   March 16, 1926.

NL 0381166   NN

Lindholm, Valdemar, *1881-*
Das einsame Land. Erzählungen. Autorisierte Uebersetzung aus dem Schwedischen von M. Rassow.
— Leipzig. Reclam. [1915.] 212, (1) pp. [Universal-Bibliothek. Nr. 5775, 5776.] 14½ cm., in 8s.
Contents. — Die Sage vom einsamen Lande. — Priester Kouno und der Ansiedler. — Mali-Åsa.

N8919 — T.r. (4) — S.r.c. — Rassow, M., tr.

NL 0381167   MB

Lindholm, Vilhelm Ferdinand Valdemar
see
Lindholm, Ferdinand, *1883-*

Lindholm, W. A.
...Mollusca, bearbeitet von W. Lindholm...   Petrograd, 1919.   10 p.   f°.   (Akad. Nauk, St. Petersburg. Mém. 8. sér., v. 28, no. 10.)

1. Molluscs—Siberia. 2. Ser.
N.Y.P.L.   December 17, 1924

NL 0381169   NN

Lindholm, W. A.
Die mollusken des baikal-sees. Kiel und Berlin, 1909.

NL 0381170   DSI PPAN

Lindholm, Denmark. Statens veterinaere Forsøgsstation for Virussygdomme.
Mund- og klovesyge Virus, Studier over den antigene Variabilitet
see under   Michelsen, Ernfred Bruno, 1907-

TJ
130   Lindholmen-Motala,Aktiebolaget.
.L75   Minnesskrift med anledning av Motala verkstads hundraariga verksamhet,1822-1922, utg.av Aktiebolaget Lindholmen-Motala.
Stockholm, Centraltryckeriet, 1922.
326 p. illus.,ports.,maps (1 fold.col.)
30 cm.

1.Locomotives. 2.Machinery--Trade and manufacture--Sweden. I.Title.

NL 0381172   MiU MH-BA

VOLUME 334

W 6
P3
LINDHOLMER, Björn.
Hur man skall klara sitt magsår.
₍Stockholm₎ Forum ₍1953₎
62 p. illus.
1. Peptic ulcer - Popular works
W6 P3

NL 0381173 DNLM

Lindholz, Joannes
see Lyndholz, Joannes, d. 1535.

Lindhorst, August.
——. Giebt und Nierengries. Das Wesen und die rationelle Behandlung. 3. Aufl. iv, 52 pp. 8°. Grünau, C. M. L. Seeer, 1893.

NL 0381175 DNLM

Lindhorst, August. ,
Gicht, Nierengries und Gelenk-Rheumatismus. Wesen und rationelle Behandlung, von Dr. med. Lindhorst ... Sechste Auflage. Grünau bei Berlin, C. M. L. Seeger, 1893.
86 p. 23½ᵐ.

NL 0381176 ICJ

Lindhorst (August). *Ueber Fremdkörper in den Luftwegen. [Wurtzburg.] 34 pp. 8°. Berlin, G. Schade, [1880].

NL 0381177 DNLM

Film
3499
.5
.791
Lindhorst, Eberhard.
Philipp von Zesen und der Roman der Spätantike. Ein Beitrag zu Theorie und Technik des barocken Romans. Göttingen, Georg-August Universität, 1955.
175 p.

Microfilm (negative) of original in the University of Göttingen Library. 1 reel.
Thesis - Göttingen.

NL 0381178 NjP

Lindhorst, Frank Atkinson.
The minister teaches religion ₍by₎ Frank A. Lindhorst ... New York, Nashville, Abingdon-Cokesbury press ₍1945₎
125 p. 19½ᵐ.
Bibliography at end of each chapter.

1. Religious education. 2. Theology, Pastoral. I. Title.
45-9815
Library of Congress *   BV1471.L54
268

NL 0381179 DLC WaTC KyWAT PPEB

Lindhorst, Frank Atkinson.
Teaching adults. New York, Abingdon-Cokesbury Press ₍1951₎
160 p. 19 cm.

1. Education of adults. I. Title.
LC5219.L5   268.434   51-6772 ‡

NL 0381180 DLC KEmT NN Wa

PN6120
.R4L5
Lindhorst, Frank Atkinson.
"Watchman, tell us of the night," a hymn dramatization for use at Christmas and other seasons, by Frank A. Lindhorst ... [n. p., c1928]
2 p. l., 6 numb. l. 28x21½cm.

Type-written

I. Title.
38M2189

NL 0381181 DLC

Lindhorst, Friedrich.
Pratikum der tierärztlichen Geburtshilfe. Von Dr. med. vet. Friedrich Lindhorst, ... und Dr. med. vet. Fritz Drahn, ... Mit 110 Abbildungen und 1 farbigen Tafel. Berlin, R. Schoetz, 1918.
viii, 176 p. illus., 1 col. pl. 24ᵐ.

NL 0381182 ICJ

Lindhorst, Friedrich.
Praktikum der tierärztlichen geburtshilfe, von ... Friedrich Lindhorst... und ... Fritz Drahn... 2., neubearb. aufl. Berlin, R. Schoetz, 1920.
179 p.

NL 0381183 OU

V
619.007
L644l
LINDHORST, FRIEDRICH.
Praktikum der tierärztlichen geburtshilfe, von Friedrich Lindhorst und Fritz Drahn. 3., wesentlich umgearb. aufl. Berlin, R. Schoetz, 1924.
viii, 211p. illus., col. plate. 24cm.
"Die wichtigsten neueren geburtshilflichen arbeiten": p. 211.

NL 0381184 PU

Lindhorst, Friedrich.
Über die geburtshilfliche entwicklung von kälbern, die im verhältnis zum raum der geburtswege zu gross sind, mit besonderer berücksichtigung der embryotomie ... Berlin, R. Schoetz, 1906.
64 p. illus. 25ᵐ.
Inaug.-diss.—Bern.
"Literatur": p. 63-64.

1. Calves. 2. Obstetrics.
Agr 8-263
Library, U. S. Dept. of   Agriculture 41L642

NL 0381185 DNAL DNLM

Lindhorst, Friedrich, 1907-
... Ueber Resultate von experimentellen Untersuchungen zur Bestimmung des Widerstandskoeffizienten vom Dentin ... Halle, (1930)
Inaug.-Diss. - Halle-Wittenberg.
Lebenslauf.
"Literatur-Verzeichnis": p. 31.

NL 0381186 CtY

Lindhorst, Georg
see Lindhorst, Georg Adolf, 1877-

Lindhorst (Georg Adolf) [1877-]. *Ueber Strangulations-Ileus. 63 pp. 8°. Halle a. S., C. Nietschmann, 1909.

NL 0381188 DNLM ICRL MH

Lindhorst, P   dealer, London, publ.
... Tapestry as needlework... London, Publ. by P. Lindhorst [about 1910]
34 [2] p. illus. 30 cm.

NL 0381189 PPPM

QD319
.L75
Lindhorst, Richard.
Beitraege zur kenntniss des dichlorhydrin's. Freiburg, 1877.
40p
Inaug. diss. Freiburg.

NL 0381190 DLC

Lindhorst, Will L.
A bag of tricks, by Will L. Lindhorst ... illustrated by Tom P. Barrett. Chicago, New York, The Reilly & Lee co. ₍°1931₎
3 p. l., 114 p. illus. 19½ᵐ.

1. Tricks. 2. Conjuring. I. Title.
Library of Congress   GV1547.L68   31-6243
—— Copy 2.
Copyright A 34584   793.8

NL 0381191 DLC TxU ViU OCl

Lindhorst, Will L.
Dick Daring's new bag of tricks, by Will L. Lindhorst ... ₍Chicago, The Reilly & Lee co.₎ °1934₎
64 p. illus. 19ᵐ.
Illustrations on pages ₍2₎ and ₍3₎ of cover.
Advertising matter: p. 63-64.
"Compliments of the Quaker oats company."

1. Tricks. 2. Conjuring. I. Quaker oats company. II. Title.
Library of Congress   GV1547.L685   34-14206
Copyright AA 146724   793.8

NL 0381192 DLC

ZM
791.1
L644e
Lindhorst, Will L.
Exclusive black art secrets, including tricks with apparatus as performed by Chinese, Hindoo and modern magicians. St. Louis, Lindhorst Magic Shop, c1918.
cover-title, ₍6₎p. illus. 15cm.

NL 0381193 TxU

Lindhorst, Will L.
Modern magic; tricks for boys and girls, by Will L. Lindhorst. Chicago, The Reilly & Lee co. ₍°1937₎
₍64₎ p. illus. 19ᵐ.
Illustrations on p. ₍2₎ and ₍3₎ of cover.

1. Tricks. 2. Conjuring. I. Title.
Library of Congress   GV1547.L686   37-31430
—— Copy 2.
Copyright A 111154   793.8

NL 0381194 DLC

VOLUME 334

Lindhorst, Will L.
Tricks and magic; a new bag of tricks, by Will L. Lindhorst ... illustrated by Tom P. Barrett. Chicago, The Reilly & Lee co. [°1934]
3 p. l., 114 p. illus. 20⁰ᵐ.

1. Tricks. 2. Conjuring.   I. Title.
Library of Congress   GV1547.L687   34-22798
———— Copy 2.
Copyright A 74204   [3]   798.8

NL 0381195   DLC TxU PSt MB

Lindhout, Henricus a, d. ca. 1620.
Introductio in physicam indiciariam in qua brevissime sed accurate vera astrologiae fundamenta ... Hamburg, Ohr., 1596.
191 p

NL 0381196   PPC

B156.4
L65   **Lindhout, Henricus a,** d. ca. 1620.
Introdvctio in physicam ivdiciariam. In qva brevissime sed accvrate vera strologiae fvndamenta, & rerum humanarum consensus, cum supe-rioribus atq̃ divinis aperte demonstratur ... Avctore Henrico à Lindhout ... Hambvrgi, Ex officina Binderiana Per Philippum de Ohr, 1597.
[15], 191, [1] p. illus., plate, diagrs., tables. 20cm.

NL 0381197   NNC OkU KU

WZ   LINDHOUT, Henricus a, d. ca. 1620.
240   Introductio in physicam judiciariam. In qua brevissime sed
L745l   accurate vera astrologiae fundamenta, & rerum humanarum con-
1598   sensus, cum superioribus atque divinis aperte demonstratur. Item
in quo vera ac legitima praesagiendi methodus statuitur, & quam
multae lateant in genethliacae [sic] Arabum doctrina vanitates
involutae. Contra calumniatores artis astrologiae, eosque qui
praedictionem penitus nullam ferunt vel ultra fas hominis moliuntur
... Hamburgi, Ex Officina Binderiana per Philippum de Ohr, 1598.
[15], 191, [1] p. illus., plates. 18 cm.
Colophon: ... Impensis Abrahami Kretzeri.

NL 0381198   DNLM

LINDHOUT, Henricus a, d. ca. 1620.
Speculum astrologiae, hoc est in scientiam genethliacam sive physicam iudiciariam intro-ductio. Addita est de astrologiae praestantia et utilitate Gotardi Arthus Dantescani: prae-fatio. Francofurti, apud Wolffg. Richterum, im-pensis Conradi Meulii, 1608.

4 plates, illustr., tables, diagr.

NL 0381199   MH

Lindhult, Henricus Georgius, respondent.
Quid de rebus post mortem futuris...
see under Ahlberger, Haraldus, praeses.

Lindhult, Johan, 1718-1770, respondent.
Linné, Carl von, 1707-1778, *praeses.*
... Dissertatio de materia medica in regno lapideo ... Up-salia, excudit L. M. Höjer [1752]

Lindhult, Johan, 1718-1770.
Schediasma chemicum, resol-vens quaestionem, an et quomque chemia resol-vat corpora naturalia in illas, a quibus fuerunt composita, partes? 18 pp. 4°. *Upsaliae,* [1748].

NL 0381202   DNLM

741.5
L745k   **Lindi.**
Karikaturen-Politik [von] Lindi [pseud.] Bern, Zytglogge-Verlag, 1936.
80p. illus. 25cm.
Lindi, pseud. of Albert Lindegger.

1. Swiss wit and humor, Pictorial.

NL 0381203   IEN

Lindi.
Lindis Papa, 200 lustige Bilder. Zürich, New York, Oprecht [1941]
[47] l. illus. 23 cm.

1. Swiss wit and humor, Pictorial.   I. Title.
NC1659.L5   741.5   48-38827*

NL 0381204   DLC MH NNC

Lindiana. An interesting narrative of the life of Jenny Lind. With a portrait by Linton. Arundel, Sussex, Printed by Mitchell & son; London, Sold by J. Thomas [etc.] 1847.
52 p. incl. front. (port.) 15½ᵐ.

1. Lind-Goldschmidt, Jenny Maria, 1820-1887.
8-4412
Library of Congress   ML420.L7L4

NL 0381205   DLC NN OO MB

Lindicke, Jakob, respondent.
... De cessione legatorum
see under Retz, Johann Friedrich, fl. 1680, praeses.

Lindien, Pehr Henric,   respondent.
Academisk afhandling om gästgifveri och skjutsinrättningen I Sverige...
see under Boëthius, Jacob Edvard, praeses.

Lindig, ———, of Schwerin, Germany.
Entwicklung und gegenwärtiger Zustand des Auswanderungswesens in Mecklenburg.
(In Verein fuer Socialpolitik. Schriften. 52. Pp. 285-349. Leip-zig, 1892.)

E2479 — Mecklenburg, Germany. E

NL 0381208   MB

Lindig, Franz, 1877–
Ueber den einfluss der phasen auf die klangfarbe ... Voorde, Druck von O. Krohn, 1902.
92, [2] p. diagrs. on fold. pl. 23ᵐ.
Inaug.-diss.—Kiel.
Vita.

1. Sound.
9-12371
Library of Congress   QC243.L6

NL 0381209   DLC PU CSt ICRL CtY CU OClW ICJ MH

PT2540   **Lindig, Horst,** 1911–
L5   Der Prosastil Ludwig Tiecks.   [Leipzig]
1937.
139 p. 20ᵐ.
Inaug.-Diss. - Leipzig.
Vita.
Bibliography: p. 139.

1. Tieck, Johann Ludwig, 1773-1853. I.

NL 0381210   CSt

Lindig, Karl Otto.
Ueber den lieferungsgrad textiler Arbeitsmaschinen der jutespinnerei und -weberei.
Inaug. Diss. Dresden, Tech. Hoch.

NL 0381211   ICRL

Lindig, Kurt.
Altsteinzeitliche Funde bei Weimar. Streifzüge durch die Ilmtalkultur. Von Kurt Lindig. Mit 11 Abbildungen und einem Lage-plan. Weimar, F. Fink [1932]
cover-title, 20 p. illus. (incl. plan) 21 cm. (Beiträge zur Geschichte der Stadt Weimar. In Verbindung mit einer Anzahl von Mitarbeitern herausgegeben von F. Fink. Hft. 13. Vorgeschichtliche Beiträge Hft. 1)
Double paging.
Page 20 contains advertisements.

NL 0381212   CtY

Lindig, Kurt.
Altsteinzeitliche Funde bei Weimar; Streifzüge durch die Ilmtalkultur. Weimar, Vimaria Verlag [1932]
65-84 p. illus. (Beiträge zur Geschichte der Stadt Weimar, 13)

NL 0381213   MH

Lindig, Kurt.
Der Altsteinzeitmensch des Ilmtales. Skelettreste aus dem Travertin von Weimar-Ehringsdorf. Von Kurt Lindig. Mit 18 Abbild-ungen und einem Stammbaum. Weimar, F. Fink, 1934.
45 p. illus. 21 cm. (Beiträge zur Geschichte der Stadt Weimar. In Verbindung mit einer Anzahl von Mitarbeitern hrsg. von F. Fink. Hft. 45/47. Vorgeschichtliche Beiträge Hft. 2)
Literatur- und Quellenverzeichnis: p. 45.
1. Man, Prehistoric - Germany. 2. Weimar - Antiq.

NL 0381214   CtY

VOLUME 334

Lindig (Michael). *De peripneumonia vera
.... iv, 48 pp. 12°. Landishuti, J. Thomann,
1804.

NL 0381215   DNLM

Lindig, Paul, 1886–
Proteinkörpertherapie. Von Prof. Dr. Paul Lindig ...
(*In* Biologie und Pathologie des Weibes. Berlin, [etc.], 1924. 27°°.
II. Band, p. [255]–290.)
"Literatur," p. 283–290.

NL 0381216   ICJ

Lindig (Paul) [1886–]. *Die Resorption
von Kalksalzen im Dünndarm. [Jena.] 52
nn. 8°. Berlin, Pass & Garleb, 1912.

NL 0381217   DNLM ICRL

Lindig (Walter) [1895–]. *Ein kasuisti-
scher Beitrag zur Anatomie und Klinik des
Coecumvolvulus. 51 pp., 4 pl. 8°. Leipzig. Sturm & Koppe, 1919.

NL 0381218   DNLM ICRL CtY

NV2   Lindigent, Jacques.
L745   ... Journal d'un juif converti. [Lausanne]
Éditions de l'Église nationale vaudoise[1948]
2p.l., [7]–151p., il. 19cm.

NL 0381219   NNUT CLamB NN

ar W   Lindig's Art Gallery, Lewisburg, Pa.
16199   Souvenir of Lewisburg, Pa. [Lewisburg,
Pa., 19--]
[25] p. illus. 15 x 23cm.

Cover title.

1. Lewisburg, Pa.--Descr.--Views.
2. Bucknell University--Descr.--Views.

NL 0381220   NIC

4BT   Lindijer, Cord Hendrik.
229   Het begrip Sarx bij Paulus.
Assen, Van Gorcum [1952]
239 p.

NL 0381221   DLC-P4 MiU CtY-D NNUT MH-AH

4BX   Lindijer, Gerrit Jacob.
684   Johann Tobias Beck. Assen, Van
Gorcum [1951]
250 p.

NL 0381222   DLC-P4 InGo NcD NNC MH-AH MH InElkB

RBS.   Lindike, August Gottlob.
152103   De morbillis.
Erlangae: Typis Kunstmannianis,
[1796]

NL 0381223   NNNAM DNLM

Lindin, Carl Olof Eric, 1869–
Exhibition of works by C. O. E. Lindin.
The Art Institute of Chicago. March 3 to ... 27,
MDCCCCIV. [Chicago], 1904.
2 l. 8°.

NL 0381224   NN

Lindin, Carl Olof Eric, 1869–
Fallen leaves [by] Carl Eric Lindin. [Woodstock, N. Y.,
The Woodstock press, 1941]
cover-title, [56] p. illus. (incl. port.) 21½°°.
Verse and prose.

I. Title.
41–28228
Library of Congress   PS3523.I 558F3   1941
818.5

NL 0381225   DLC

Lindin, Ester.
see   Lindin, Ester Elisabet, 1890–

Lindin, Ester Elisabet, 1890–
Det är inte lätt att vara barn.   Stockholm,
L. Hökerberg [1941]
165 p. 23 cm.

NL 0381227   PU

Lindin, Ester Elisabet, 1890–
Ta i famn. Stockholm, Hökerberg [1952]
304 p. 22 cm.

I. Title.
A 53–3585
Minnesota. Univ. Libr.
for Library of Congress   [1]

NL 0381228   MnU

PT9875   **Lindin, Ester Elisabet,** 1890–
.L575T16   Tänk, om jag gifter mig med prästen! Roman.
1940   Stockholm, L. Hökerberg [1940]
357 p.

NL 0381229   ICU OC1

Lindin, Ester Elisabet, 1890–
Tre blommiga täcken. Stockholm, Lars
Hökerberg [1946]
356 p. 23cm.

NL 0381230   WU

Lindinger, Fritz.
Manual of the liquor trade.   New York: Trow Directory,
Printing and Bookbinding Co., 1904. 5 p.l., 3-164 p., 1 port.
8°.

1. Alcoholic drinks.--Quotations
Manufacture. 3. Alcoholic drinks.   relating to. 2. Alcoholic drinks.--
N. Y. P. L.   --Popular terms.
June 25, 1913.

NL 0381231   NN

W 4   **LINDINGER, Hans,** 1923–
M96   Zur behandlung der Embolie der Aorta
1950   abdominalis. München, 1950.
42 l.
Inaug.-Diss. - Munich
1. Aorta 2. Embolism

NL 0381232   DNLM

WBI   **LINDINGER, Hermann.**
L745e   Eilsen und seine Heilquellen in
1859   topographischer, physikalisch-chemischer,
therapeutischer, ökonomischer und
socialer Beziehung. Bückeburg, Wolper,
1859.
iv, 135 p. illus.

NL 0381233   DNLM

R   **Lindinger, Johann Simon.**
135.5   De Ebraeorvm vetervm arte medica, de daemone,
.L75   et daemoniacis. Servestae et Levcoreae, Apud
S.G.Zimmermannvm, 1774.
188 p.
Author's name at head of title: Io.Simeon
Lindinger.

1.Medicine, Ancient. 2.Demonology. I.Title.

NL 0381234   MiU CtY-M MH MB DNLM NNJ PU NIC

893   **LINDINGER, Johann Simon.**
L745p   Predigten. Halle, Rengerische Buchhandlung, 1761.
8p.l., 480p. 17cm.

NL 0381235   MH-AH

Lindinger, Johann Simon.
Staat und character d. Athenienser.
Halle im Magdeburgischen, 1766.

NL 0381236   NjP

Lindinger, Karl Hermann Leonhard.
See
Lindinger, Leonhard, 1879–

Lindinger, Leonhard, 1879–
Afrikanische Schildläuse, I. u. II. Mit 24 Abbildungen im
Text. (*In:* Hamburgische wissenschaftliche Anstalten. Ham-
burg, 1909. 4°. Jahrbuch 26, Beiheft 3, p. 13-46.)

1. Cochineal, Africa.
N. Y. P. L.
April 6, 1911.

NL 0381238   NN

Lindinger, Leonhard, 1879–
Afrikanische schildläuse. IV Kanarische
Cocciden; ein beitrag zur fauna der kanarischen
inseln. Hamburg, 1911.
38 p. illus., plates. [3. Beiheft zum
Jahrbuch der hamburgischen wissenschaftlichen
anstalten XXVIII. 1910)
Bound with Himmelbaur, Wolfgang. Zur
kenntnis der Phytophthoreen, and Esmarch,
Ferdinand. Beitrag zur Cyanophyceenflora
unserer Kolonien.

NL 0381239   IU

VOLUME 334

Lindinger, Leonhard i. e. Karl Hermann Leonhard, 1879-
Anatomische und biologische untersuchungen der podalyrieensamen ... Jena, G. Fischer, 1903.
v, 43, [1] p. pl. 23½cm.
Inaug.-diss.—Erlangen.
Lebenslauf.

1. Seeds—Anatomy. 2. Podalyrieae.

Library of Congress   QK701.L74   7-5503

NL 0381240   DLC CU CtY NN

Lindinger, Leonhard, 1879-
Beiträge zur kenntnis von vegetation und flora der Kanarischen inseln, von Leonhard Lindinger; mit 5 tafeln und 2 karten ... Hamburg, Kommissions-verlag L. Friederichsen & co., 1926.
ix, 350 p. v pl., 2 fold. maps. 28½cm. (Added t.-p.: Hamburgische universität. Abhandlungen aus dem gebiet der auslandskunde ... bd. 21. Reihe c. Naturwissenschaften. bd. 8)
"Schriften-verzeichnis": p. 139-141.
CONTENTS.—L. t. Botanische wanderungen und beobachtungen auf der insel Tenerife.—2. t. Flora der Kanarischen inseln; berichtigungen und nachträge zu J. Pitard et L. Proust. Les iles Canaries. Flore de l'archipel. Paris 1909.
1. Botany—Canary Islands. 2. Botany—Teneriffe. 3. Pitard, J. Les iles Canaries.
[Full name: Karl Hermann Leonhard Lindinger]
Library of Congress   QK422.L5   26-16634

NL   DSC 0381241   DLC MH-A CU NIC MiU NNBG OCl ICJ NN   IU

Lindinger, Leonhard, 1879-
Reisestudien auf Tenerife über einige pflanzen der Kanarischen inseln, und bemerkungen über die etwaige einbürgerung dieser pflanzen in Deutsch-Südwestafrika. Von dr. Leonhard Lindinger ... Mit 26 abbildungen im text ... Hamburg, L. Friederichsen & co. (L. & R. Friederichsen) 1911.
ix, 90 p. illus. 28½cm. (Added t.-p.: Abhandlungen des Hamburgischen kolonialinstituts, bd. vi. [Reihe D: Zoologie und botanik, bd. 1])
1. Botany, Economic. 2. Botany—Canary islands. 3. Plant introduction.
[Full name: Karl Hermann Leonhard Lindinger]
13—874
Library of Congress   SB109.L6

NL 0381242   DLC MH-A DNAL MU ICJ PU

Lindinger, Leonhard i. e. Karl Hermann Leonhard, 1879-
Die schildläuse (*Coccidae*) Europas, Nordafrikas und Vorderasiens, einschliesslich der Azoren, der Kanaren und Madeiras, mit anleitung zum sammeln, bestimmen und aufbewahren, von dr. Leonhard Lindinger ... Stuttgart, E. Ulmer, 1912.
8, 388 p. illus. 19cm.
"Abkürzungen der literaturnachweise": p. 351-352.

1. Coccidae.

Agr 13-47
Library of Congress   Agriculture 431.6L,64Sch

NL 0381243   DNAL CoU MtBC NjP PPAN ICJ

Lindinger, Leonhard, 1879-
Die schildlausgattung Leucaspis. [Hamburg, 1906.]
8°. pp. 60. 7 plates.
"2. Beiheft zum Jahrbuch der Hamburgischen wissenschaftlichen anstalten, xxiii, 1906."
"Literaturverzeichnis," pp. 49-54.

NL 0381244   MH-A

Lindinger, Leonhard, 1879-
Die Schildlausgattung Selenaspidus. Mit drei Tafeln und einer Abbildung im Text. (In: Hamburgische wissenschaftliche Anstalten. Hamburg, 1909. 4°. Jahrbuch 26, Beiheft 3, p. 1-12.)

1. Cochineal.
N. Y. P. L.   April 6, 1911.

NL 0381245   NN

Lindinger, Leonhard, 1879-
Die sekundären Adventivwurzeln von Dracaena, und der morphologische Wert der Stigmarien. Mit 24 Abbildungen im Text. (In: Hamburgische wissenschaftliche Anstalten. Hamburg, 1909. 4°. Jahrbuch 26, Beiheft 3, p. 59-88.)

1. Dracaena. 2. Stigmaria.
N. Y. P. L.   April 6, 1911.

NL 0381246   NN

Lindinger, Leonhard i. e. Karl Hermann Leonhard, 1879-
... Die struktur von *Aloë dichotoma* L., mit anschliessenden allgemeinen betrachtungen. Von Leonhard Lindinger. [Hamburg, 1908]
cover-title, p. [211-253] pl. vii-x. 23cm.
At head of title: Überreicht von den botanischen staatsinstituten zu Hamburg.
"Sonderabdruck aus Beihefte zum Botan. centralblatt xxiv (1908) abt. 1."
"Literaturverzeichnis": p. 250-251.

1. Botany, Physiological and structural. 2. Aloe dichotoma.

Agr 10-1762
Library, U. S. Dept. of   Agriculture 463L642

NL 0381247   DNAL

Lindinger, Leonhard, 1879-
Die wirtschaftliche Bedeutung der Baumaloë für Deutsch-Südwestafrika. (In: Hamburgische wissenschaftliche Anstalten. Hamburg, 1909. 4°. Jahrbuch 26, Beiheft 3, p. 47-58, 1 pl.)

1. Agave. Africa (West): German.
N. Y. P. L.   April 6, 1911.

NL 0381248   NN MH-A

Lindinner, Hans Jacob & Compagnie, Zürich
see [Berichthaus, Duchdruckerei, Zürich.

Lindiņš, Rūdolfs, 1887-
...Saimnieciskās krīzes cēloņi un krīzes pagaidu likvidēšana. [Rīgā] "Raiņa klubs," 1934. 94 p. 20cm.

857523A. 1. Crises and panics.
N. Y. P. L.   December 9, 1936

NL 0381250   NN

Lindiri, Romeo,
Il Dio dei vivi; collezione opere moderne grandi scrittori italiana apologisti. [Brescia, Tipografia Queriniana dell'Istituto Artigianelli, 1954]
287 p.

NL 0381251   DCU

Lindisch, Friedrich Alexander Polexius.
Dissertatio inavgvralis medica de seri proflvviis haemorrhagiarvm vices svstinentibvs. Qvam ... pro gradv doctoris ... ervditorvm examini d. x. ivl. MDCCLXV. svbmittet avctor et respondens Frider. Alexander Polexivs Lindisch, Siegena-Nassovicvs. Giessae, ex officina Bravniana [1765]
36 p. 20 x 17cm.

1. Hemorrhage. 2. Leucorrhea.
36-36683
Library of Congress   RC669.L55 1765

NL 0381252   DLC DNLM MnU-B

PC 5399 .04 L7 1888
Lindisch, Friedrich Wilhelm, 1863-1888.
De rebus Olbiopolitarum ... Hallis Saxonum, 1888.
2 p.l., 50 p., 2 l. 19½cm.
Inaug.-diss. - Halle.
Vita.

1. Olbia (Borysthenes)

NL 0381253   MdBJ PU CU ICRL NjP

Lindisfarn Chase
see under   Trollope, Thomas Adolphus, 1810-1892.

Lindisfarne gospels
see Bible. Manuscripts, Anglo-Saxon. N. T. Gospels. Lindisfarne gospels.

Lindius, Johann, respondent.
... De hereditatibvs qvae ab intestato defervntvr
see under   Gaudi, Vincent.

Lindke, Mary R
I need a song. Poems by Mary R. Lindke, Croswell, Mich. Port Huron, Mich., Handcraft print of Clarence M. Burkholder [1945]
59 l.

1. Michigan - Authors   I. T.   2. Port Huron imprints - 1945 - Burkholder, C. M.

NL 0381257   MiD

PT 9773 .I52U4
Lindko, Wilma.
Ula Grip; en berättelse från förra århundradet. Cedar Rapids, Iowa, N. F. Hansen Pub. Co., 1916.
224 p. 18 cm.

NL 0381258   MnHi

Lindknud, Denmark. *Sognerådet.*
Vejvedtægt for Lindknud kommune i Ribe amt. Ribe, Ribe bogtr., 1953.
16 p. illus. 23 cm.
"Foranstående vejvedtægt er stadfæstet af Ribe amtsråd i samme møde den 18. marts 1953."

1. Highway law—Lindknud, Denmark.   I. Title.
56-43849

NL 0381259   DLC MH-L

VOLUME 334

LINDKVIST, E.
Suedana guidlibreto, da E. Lindkvist e E. Sköld.
Upsala, K. W. Appelbergs boktryckeri [1909]   32 p.
14cm.

Film reproduction. Positive.
Cover title.
At head of title: Linguo internaciona di la delegitaro (sistemo Ido).

1. Ido. I. Sköld, E., joint
author. II. Sköld, E. III. Title.

Mrs. Dave H. Morris Collection

NL   0381260   NN

Lindkvist, Erik.
Tio år bland revolutionärer; en bok om Guds
ledning. Stockholm, Nya bokförlag [1937]

NL   0381261   MH

Lindkvist, Erik Harald
see
Lindkvist, Harald, 1881-

---

*Lindkvist, Harald, 1881-
Kärre, Karl, 1885-
Engelsk-svensk ordbok, skolupplaga, av Karl Kärre, Harald
Lindkvist, Ruben Nöjd, Mats Redin under medverkan av
Grenville Grove. Stockholm, P. A. Norstedt & söner [1935]

PD5640   Lindkvist, Harald, 1881-
K8   Kärre, Karl, 1885-   FOR OTHER EDITIONS
[1942   Engelsk-svensk ordbok, skolupplaga, av Karl Kärre, Harald   SEE MAIN ENTRY
           Lindkvist, Ruben Nöjd, Mats Redin under medverkan av Gren-
           ville Grove. 2. uppl., 2. tryckningen. Stockholm, Svenska
           bokförlaget, P. A. Norstedt & söner [1942]

Lindkvist, Harald, 1881-
Middle-English place-names of Scandinavian origin ...
Part I. Upsala, University press, 1912.

2 p. l., lxiii, 226 p., 1 l. 24½ cm.

Inaug.-diss.—Upsala.
Issued also in Uppsala universitets årsskrift, 1911, bd. 1.
Bibliography: p. [v]-xx.

1. Names, Geographical—England. 2. English language—Middle
English (1100–1500)—Etymology. 3. English language—Etymology—
Names. 4. Northmen in Great Britain.

[Full name: Erik Harald Lindkvist]

PE662.L5   13–6649

NL   0381265   DLC MiU OCU OC1 OU IU CU

Lindkvist, Harald, 1881-
Middle-English place-names of Scandinavian origin, by
Harald Lindkvist. Part I. Upsala, University press, 1912.

2 p. l., lxiii, 226 p., 1 l. 24½cm. (Uppsala, universitets årsskrift, 1911,
bd. 1)

Issued also as the author's inaugural dissertation, Uppsala.
Bibliography: p. [v]-xx.

1. Names, Geographical—England. 2. English language—Middle English (1100–1500)—Etymology. 3. English language—Etymology—Names.
4. Scandinavians in Great Britain.

[Full name: Erik Harald Lindkvist]

Library of Congress   A8284.U7 1911 bd.1   13–17190 Revised

NL   0381266   DLC NN NIC PU ICJ

Lindkvist, Harald, 1881-
Minnesskrift af forna lärjungar tillägnad professor Axel
Erdmann på hans sjuttioårsdag den 6 febr. 1913. Uppsala &
Stockholm, Almqvist & Wiksells boktryckeri-a.-b. [1913]

---

*Lindkvist, Harald, 1881-
Rolle, Richard, of Hampole, 1290?-1349.
... Richard Rolle's Meditatio de passione Domini according to ms. Uppsala C. 494 ed. with introduction and
notes by Harald Lindkvist ... Uppsala, Akademiska
bokhandeln; [etc., etc., 1917]

Lindkvist, Harald, 1881-
Some old Scandinavian deposits in middle English records.
(Minnesskrift af forna lärjungar tillägnad Professor Axel Erdmann på hans sjuttioårsdag den 6. Febr., 1913. Uppsala, 1913.
4°. p. 199-219.)

1. English language.—Loan words: Scandinavian. 2. English language (Middle).   guage (Middle).
N. Y. P. L.   January 22, 1914.

NL   0381269   NN

Lindkvist, Karl Gunnar.
Studies on the local sense of the prepositions in, at, on,
and to, in modern English. Lund, C. W. K. Gleerup [1950]

428 p. 24 cm. (Lund studies in English, 20)

Thesis—Lund.
Bibliography: p. [422]-428.

1. English language—Prepositions.   (Series)

PE1335.L5   425.9   51-5779

ViU NIC TxU ODaU OrU CaBVaU PPT
NL   0381270   DLC OOxM NN NcD PU GU NIC MU OrU CU MoU

Lindkvist, Karl Gustav.
Katten; noveller. [Stockholm] LTs förlag [1955]
166 p. 19 cm.

                                              A 56-5141

Minnesota. Univ. Libr.
for Library of Congress   [1]

NL   0381271   MnU

Lindkvist, Karl Gustav.
Klarögd står tystnad; dikter. [Stockholm] LTs förlag
[1953]
58 p. 21 cm.

                                              A 54-2641

Minnesota. Univ. Libr.
for Library of Congress   [1]

NL   0381272   MnU

Lindl, Charlotte, 1911-
... Über einen Fall von gonorrhoischer
Spätarthritis ... München, 1936.
Inaug.-Diss. - München.
Lebenslauf.

NL   0381273   CtY

492.1958   Lindl, Ernest, 1872-1921.
L746b   Die babylonisch-assyrischen Praesens-
           und Praeteritalformen im Grundstamm der
           starken Verba. München, F.Straub,
           1895.
           38p. 24cm.

           Cover-title.
           Inaug.-Diss. - München.
           Vita.
           Includes bibliographical references.

NL   0381274   CLSU OCH

PJ3291   LINDL, ERNEST, 1872-1921.
.L74   Die babylonisch-assyrischen praesens- und praeter-
         italformen im grundstamm der starken verba. Eine
         sprachvergleichende studie, von Ernest Lindl... Mün-
         chen, H. Lukaschik, 1896.
         51, [1]p. 23cm.

         1. Assyro-Babylonian language—Tense.

NL   0381275   ICU DCU-H MH PPDrop PU CtY

Lindl, Ernest, 1872-1921.
Beiträge zur Althbabylonischen Chronologie
und Kulturgeschichte. Habilitations-schrift
der Philosophischen Fakultät... München
vorgelegt von E.I.
               p.32   Leipzig, 1900.

NL   0381276   PPDrop

Lindl, Ernest, 1872-1921.
... Cyrus
   see his Entstehung und blüte der
altorientalischen kulturwelt. Cyrus.

Lindl, Ernest, 1872-1921.
Entstehung und blüte der altorientalischen kulturwelt.
Cyrus, von Ernest Lindl. Mit einer karte und 98 abbil-
dungen. München, Kirchheim, 1903.

2 p. l., 121, [5] p. illus., fold. map. 26½ᶜᵐ. (Added t.-p.: Weltgeschichte
in karakterbildern; hrsg. von Franz Kampers, Sebastian Merkle und Martin
Spahn. 1. abt. Altertum)

1. Cyrus, the Great, king of Persia, d. 529 B. C. 2. Persia—Hist.—Ancient to A. D. 640. 3. Asia, Western—Hist.

Library of Congress   DS71.L74   3—27921

NL   0381278   DLC CLU OU CU NNC CtY MB

BS   Lindl, Ernest, 1872-1921.
744   Die Oktateuchcatene des Prokop von Gaza und die Septuaginta-
L5   forschung. München, G. Franz, 1902.
        viii, 161 p. 25cm.

        1. Procopius, of Gaza, ca. 465-ca. 528. 2. Bible. O.T.
        Greek—Versions—Septuagint. I. Title.

NL   0381279   CBDP

4BS-201   Lindl, Ernest, 1872-1921.
          Die Oktateuchcatene des Prokop von Gaza
          und die Septuagintaforschung. München,
          H. Lukaschik, 1902.
          161 p.

NL   0381280   DLC-P4 NjPT N NBuU MH NNUT ICU

VOLUME 334

Lindl, Ernest, 1872–*1921.*
Das priester- und beamtentum der altbabylonischen kontrakte. Mit einer zusammenstellung sämtlicher kontrakte der I. dynastie von Babylon in regestenform. Ein beitrag zur altbabylonischen kulturgeschichte, von dr. phil. et theol. Ernest Lindl ... Paderborn, F. Schöningh, 1913.
x, 514 p. 24ᶜᵐ. (*Added t.-p.:* Studien zur geschichte und kultur des altertums ... 2. ergänzungsband)

1. Priests, Assyro-Babylonian. 2. Civil service—Babylonia. 3. Babylonia—Comm.
13–16784

Library of Congress   PJ3189.L6

NL 0381281   DLC NjP DDO PPDrop PU OCU OC1 NN MB

Lindl (Franz) [1877–   ]. *Klinische Beobachtungen über Polyneuritis alcoholica.* 32 pp. 2 L 8°. Berlin, O. Francke. 1903.

NL 0381282   DNLM CtY ICRL

Lindl, Ignace.
Leitfaden zur einfachen Erklärung der Apokalypse, besonders für diejenigen, welche sie zu ihrer Erbauung lesen wollen. Von Ignace Lindl.   Berlin, 1826.
18.5 cm.

NL 0381283   CtY

WA
10757
Lindl, Ignas, 1774–1834.
Ein ernstes Wort an unsere Zeit veranlasst durch die Stelle Matth. 12,31.32. oder kurze Abhandlung über die Sünde wider den heiligen Geist. Harrisburg, Pa., G.S. Peters, 1830.
58p.   [Bound with His Der Kern des Christenthums. 1830]

NL 0381284   CtY PSC MH

BV4254   **Lindl, Ignaz,** 1774–1834.
.G3L7   Der kern des Christenthums in predigten, vorgetragen von Ignaz Lindl ... 2. verb. mit noch zwey predigten verm. aufl. Dillingen, F. Rossnagel [1820]
xiv, [15]–140 p. 14½ᶜᵐ.

1. Sermons, German.

NL 0381285   ICU ICRL

WA
10757
Lindl, Ignas, 1774–1834.
Der Kern des Christenthums, nebst einer Abhandlung über die Sünde wider den heiligen Geist, in Predigten vorgetragen. Harrisburg, Pa., G.S. Peters, 1830.
108p.

NL 0381286   CtY PSt MH

Lindlahr, Anna.
The Lindlahr vegetarian cook book and A B C of natural dietetics, by Anna Lindlahr and Henry Lindlahr, M. D. 15th ed., newly rev. and enl. Chicago, The Lindlahr publishing company [1922]
xxvii p., 1 l., 585 p. 20ᶜᵐ. (*Lettered on cover:* Natural therapeutics, vol. III)
"Thoroughly revised and enlarged edition of the Nature cure cook book."—Pref.

1. Vegetarianism. 2. Cookery, American. 3. Diet.   I. Lindlahr, Henry, 1862–1924, joint author. II. Title.
22–11109

Library of Congress   TX392.L5 1922

NL 0381287   DLC LU MoU ICJ

---

ha
TX
392
L5
Lindlahr, Anna.
The Lindlahr vegetarian cook book and ABC of natural dietetics. By Anna Lindlahr and Henry Lindlahr. 18th ed. rev. and enl. Chicago, Lindlahr Publ. Co., 1926.
535p.
Author series: Natural therapeutics, v.3.

1. Vegetarianism. 2. Cookery, American. 3. Diet I. Lindlahr, Henry. 1862– II. Title. III. Series

NL 0381288   NIC WaU

Lindlahr, *Mrs. Anna.*
The nature cure cook book and A B C of natural dietetics, by Mrs. Anna Lindlahr and Henry Lindlahr, M. D. 1st ed.   Chicago, The Nature cure publishing co. [1915]
xii p., 1 l., 469 p. 20½ᶜᵐ.   (*Lettered on cover:* Nature cure series, vol. II)
$2.00

1. Vegetarianism. 2. Cookery, American. 3. Diet.   I. Lindlahr, Henry, 1862–   , joint author. II. Title.
15—2000

Library of Congress   TX392.L5

NL 0381289   DLC UU ICJ

Lindlahr, Anna, and H. Lindlahr.
The nature cure cook book and A B C of natural dietetics, by Mrs. Anna Lindlahr and Henry Lindlahr ...   Chicago: Nature Cure Pub. Co. [1915.]   xii p., 1 l., 469 p.   2. ed.   8°.

On cover: Nature cure series vol. II.

1. Cookery (Dietary and invalid).   2. Vegetarianism. 3. Lindlahr, Henry, 1862–   , jt. au. 4. Title.
N. Y. P. L.   August 15, 1916.

NL 0381290   NN

Lindlahr, *Mrs. Anna.*
The nature cure cook book and A B C of natural dietetics, by Mrs. Anna Lindlahr and Henry Lindlahr, M.D.   Eleventh edition. Chicago, The Nature Cure Publishing Co., [°1918].
xii, [2], 469 p. 20½ᶜᵐ.   (*On back of cover:* Natural therapeutics, vol. 3.)

NL 0381291   ICJ NN

TX
392
.L5
1918
Lindlahr, Anna.
The nature cook book and A B C of natural dietetics, by Mrs. Anna Lindlahr and Henry Lindlahr, M. D. 14th ed. Chicago, The Nature cure publishing co. [1918]
469 p. 21 cm.

1. Vegetarianism. 2. Cookery, American. 3. Diet. I. Lindlahr, Henry, 1862–   joint author. II. Title

NL 0381292   OKentU

Lindlahr, Anna.
One thousand & one vegetarian recipes; the health cook book by Mrs. Henry Lindlahr. 23. ed. rev.   New York: Lindlahr's magazine, 1930. 227 p. 19cm.

183356B. 1. Vegetarianism—   Receipts, menus, etc.
N. Y. P. L.   April 29, 1943

NL 0381293   NN PP

Lindlahr, Mrs. Henry
see Lindlahr, Anna.

Lindlahr, Henry, 1862–*1924.*
... Part I. Acute diseases: their uniform treatment by natural methods. Part II. Mental, emotional and psychic disorders. Extracts from the books of the library of Natural therapeutics, by H. Lindlahr, M. D. Chicago, Lindlahr publishing co. [1918]
2 p. l., 54, 517–522 p. illus. 19½ᶜᵐ. (Natural therapeutics, booklet no. 1)

1. Therapeutics, Physiological.
19–662

Library of Congress   RM702.L65

NL 0381295   DLC DNLM

Lindlahr, Henry, 1862–*1924.*
... Iridiagnosis and other diagnostic methods [by] Henry Lindlahr, M. D. 1st ed. Chicago, The Lindlahr publishing co., 1919.
327 p. front. (col. chart) illus., col. pl. 20½ᶜᵐ. (Natural therapeutics, vol. VI)

1. Diagnosis. 2. Eye.   I. Title.
19–14211

Library of Congress   RC73.5.L65

NL 0381296   DLC DNLM ICJ PPC UU

RC73.5
L5
1919
LINDLAHR, Henry, 1862–1924.
Iridiagnosis and other diagnostic methods. 3d ed. Chicago, Lindlahr, 1919
327p. illus. 21cm. (Natural therapeutics, vol. 6)

1. Diagnosis 2. Eye I. Title

NL 0381297   CtY-M

Lindlahr, Henry, 1862–1924.
Iridiagnosis and other diagnostic methods by Henry Lindlahr, M.D.   5th ed. Chicago, The Lindlahr publishing co., 1922.
327 p. (Natural therapeutics, vol. VI)

NL 0381298   MiU OU

RM700
.L5
Lindlahr, Henry, 1862–1924.
Library of natural therapeutics ...   Chicago, The Lindlahr publishing co., 1918–
3 v.   fronts., illus., col. plates.   20.5 cm.

NL 0381299   DLC

Lindlahr, Henry, 1862–*1924,* joint author.
Lindlahr, *Mrs. Anna.*
The Lindlahr vegetarian cook book and A B C of natural dietetics, by Anna Lindlahr and Henry Lindlahr, M. D. 15th ed., newly rev. and enl. Chicago, The Lindlahr publishing company [°1922]

Lindlahr, Henry, 1862–*1924.*
Natural therapeutics, booklets no. 1 .... By H. Lindlahr, M.D. Chicago, Lindlahr Publishing Co., [°1918].
[4], 54, 517–522 p. illus. 20ᶜᵐ.
No more published.
"Extracts from the books of the Library of natural therapeutics."
Contents.—I. Acute diseases: their uniform treatment by natural methods.—2. Mental, emotional and psychic disorders.—Appendix.

NL 0381301   ICJ ICarbS

VOLUME 334

615.535
L746n Lindlahr, Henry, 1862-1924.
1922 Natural therapeutics. Chicago, Lindlahr
Pub. Co., 1922- ₍c1919₎
v.

Contents.— v.1. Philosophy of natural therapeutics.
4th ed.— v.2. Practice of natural therapeutics. 5th ed.—
v.3. Vegetarian cookbook and A B C of natural dietetics.
15th ed. newly rev. and enl.

1. Naturopathy. 2. Therapeutics, Physiological.
I. Title.

NL 0381302 icarbS

Lindlahr, Henry, 1862-1924.
... Nature cure; philosophy and practice based on the unity of
disease and cure ₍by₎ H. Lindlahr, M. D. 1st ed. Chicago, The
Nature cure publishing co., 1913.
3 p. l., 438 p. front., col. pl., diagr. 20ᵐ. (The nature cure series,
vol. I)

1. Naturopathy. I. Title.
14-887
Library of Congress RM702.L7

NL 0381303 DLC DNLM

Lindlahr, Henry, 1862-1924.
.... Nature cure philosophy and practice based on the unity of
110757 disease and cure. [By] H. Lindlahr, M.D. Fourth edition. Chicago, The Nature Cure Publishing Company, 1914.
[6], 438 p. front. (port.), 1 col. plate. 20½ᶜᵐ. (The nature cure series, vol. I.)

NL 0381304 ICJ

RM Lindlahr, Henry, 1862-1924.
702 Nature cure; philosophy and practice
.L7 based on the unity of disease and cure
1917 [by] H. Lindlahr. 8th ed. Chicago, The
Nature cure publishing co., 1917.
438 p. front., col. pl. (The nature
cure series, vol. I)

#Therapeutics, Physiological.
(A)Nature cure.

NL 0381305 MoU OrU-M

Lindlahr, Henry, 1862-1924.
Nature cure; philosophy and practice based on the unity of
disease and cure, ₍by₎ H. Lindlahr... Chicago: Nature Cure
Pub. Co., 1922. 438 p. chart, front. (port.), pl. 20. ed.
12°.

276452A. 1. Nature cure.
N. Y. P. L. March 28, 1927

NL 0381306 NN

Lindlahr, Henry, 1862-1924.
Nature cure; philosophy and practice based
on the unity of disease and cure ₍by₎ H.
Lindlahr, M.D. 21st ed. Chicago, The Nature
:ure publishing co., 1924.
3 p. l., 438 p. front., col. pl., diagr.
20 cm. (The nature cure series, vol. I)

NL 0381307 CaBVa

Lindlahr, Henry, 1862-1924, joint author.
Lindlahr, Mrs. Anna.
The nature cure cook book and A B C of natural dietetics, by Mrs. Anna Lindlahr and Henry Lindlahr, M. D.
1st ed. Chicago, The Nature cure publishing co. ₍1915₎

Lindlahr, Henry, ed.
Nature cure magazine, devoted to man-building on the
physical, mental and moral planes of being. v. 1-2;
Nov. 1907-Oct. 1909. Chicago, The Nature cure publishing company, 1907-09.

Lindlahr, Henry, 1862-1924.
... Philosophy of natural therapeutics ₍by₎ Henry Lindlahr,
M. D. 1st ed. Chicago, The Lindlahr publishing co., 1918.
ix, 522 p. front. (port.) illus. (incl. forms) col. pl. 20½ᵐ. (Natural
therapeutics, vol. I)

1. Naturopathy.
19-1576
Library of Congress RM700.L5

NL 0381310 DLC DNLM PBa

Lindlahr, Henry, 1862-1924.
.... Philosophy of natural therapeutics, [by] Henry Lindlahr,
131105 M.D. Second edition. Chicago, The Lindlahr Publishing Co.,
1919.
ix, 516, [6] p. front. (port.), illus., diagrs., 1 col. pl. 20½ᵐ. (Natural therapeutics, vol. I.)

NL 0381311 ICJ

Lindlahr, Henry, 1862-1924.
... Philosophy of natural therapeutics ₍by₎
Henry Lindlahr, M. D. 4th ed. Chicago, The
Lindlahr publishing co., 1922 ₍c1919₎
ix, 516p. front. (port.) illus. (incl. forms)
col. pl. 20cm. (Natural therapeutics, vol. I)

1. Naturopathy.

NL 0381312 FMU

Lindlahr, Henry, 1862-1924.
... Practice of natural therapeutics, by Henry Lindlahr, M. D.
1st ed. Chicago, The Lindlahr publishing co., 1919.
4 p. l., 5-470 p. front. (port.) 20½ᵐ. (Library of natural therapeutics,
vol. II)

1. Naturopathy.
19-14210
Library of Congress RM700.L55

NL 0381313 DLC DNLM

Lindlahr, Henry, 1862-1924.
.... Practice of natural therapeutics, by Henry Lindlahr, M.D.
131105 Third edition. Chicago, The Lindlahr Publishing Co., 1920.
[4], 470 p. front., illus., 1 port. 20½ᵐ. (Library of natural therapeutics,
vol. 2.)

NL 0381314 ICJ CoU

Lindlahr, Henry, 1862-1924.
The practice of nature cure ₍by₎ Henry Lindlahr, M. D. 27th
ed., rev. and ed. by Victor H. Lindlahr. New York city, The
Nature cure library, inc. ₍*1931₎
226 p. illus. 20½ᵐ.
Includes advertising matter.

1. Naturopathy. I. Lindlahr, Victor H., 1895- ed. II. Title:
Nature cure.
32-2330
Library of Congress RM702.L7 1931
₍44d1₎ 615.85

NL 0381315 DLC FMU PPLas PP

Lindlahr, Henry, 1862-1924.
The practice of nature cure. 28th ed. Poona ₍M. B. God-
bolay, 1948 ?₎
v, 886 p. illus., ports. 20 cm.
First published 1913 under title: Nature cure.

1. Naturopathy. I. Title: Nature cure.
RM702.L7 1948 615.85 50-19348

NL 0381316 DLC

Lindlahr, Henry, 1862-1924.
... The true nature and source of vitamins, or life elements, by Henry Lindlahr, M. D. Chicago, Ill., The Lindlahr publishing co. ₍*1921₎
57 p. 19½ᵐ. (Natural therapeutics booklets)

1. Vitamines.
21-19588
Library of Congress QP801.V5L5

NL 0381317 DLC

Lindlahr, Victor Hugo, 1895-
Cómo adelgazar comiendo; traducción de Juan Ruiz Alcobre. Ilus. de F. Fábregas. Buenos Aires, Ediciones Cosmos
₍1943₎
262 p. illus. 21 cm.
"Título del original en inglés: 'Eat and reduce.' "

1. Diet. 2. Corpulence. I. Ruiz Alcobre, Juan, tr. II. Title.
RC813.L57 613.2 44-32445 rev*

NL 0381318 DLC

WC Lindlahr, Victor Hugo, 1895-
915.9 Cómo adelgazar comiendo; traducción de
L746e Juan Ruiz Alcobre. Buenos Aires, Ediciones
1947 Cosmos ₍1947₎
270 p. illus.

Translation of Eat and reduce.

1. Obesity - Treatment I. Title

NL 0381319 DNLM

Lindlahr, Victor Hugo, 1895-
Crashing idols. ₍New York₎ 1930.
105, p. 18 cm.

I. Title.
RM702.L73 615.8 30-14473 rev*

NL 0381320 DLC

VOLUME 334

Lindlahr, Victor Hugo, 1895–
Eat—and reduce! New York, Prentice-Hall, 1939.
x, 194 p. illus. 24cm.

1. Diet. 2. Corpulence. I. Title.

RC813.L55   613.2   40–1792 rev*

NL 0381321   DLC

Lindlahr, Victor Hugo, 1895–
Eat—and reduce! Garden City, N. Y., Garden City Pub.
Co. ₁1946₎
x, 194 p. illus. 21 cm.

1. Diet. 2. Corpulence. I. Title.

RC813.L55 1946   613.2   Med 46–77 rev*

NL 0381322   DLC WaE WaSp IaAS ViU

613.2   Lindlahr, Victor Hugo, 1895–
L64e   Eat--and reduce!   New York, *Perm books*
          ₁1948, °1939₎
          240 p. 17 cm.

          "P 7."

          1. Diet. 2. Corpulence. I. Title.

NL 0381323   LU WU

Lindlahr, Victor Hugo, 1895–
Eat to stay young. New York, Journal of Living Pub.
Corp. ₁1952₎
192 p. 20 cm.

1. Diet. 2. Longevity. I. Title.

TX551.L49   613.2   53–3902 ‡

NL 0381324   DLC

Lindlahr, Victor Hugo , 1895– , ed.
Eating for calmer nerves; ed. by Victor H. Lindlahr... New
York, Journal of living pub. corp. ₁1943₎ 24 p. 20cm. (His:
National nutrition society library. no. 15.)

1. Diet. 2. Vitamins, B.
N.Y.P.L.   November 10, 1948

NL 0381325   NN

Lindlahr, Victor Hugo, 1895– ed.
[Food and health guides] no. 1–
see under   National nutrition society.

Lindlahr, Victor Hugo , 1895– , ed.
For women after 40; ed. by Victor H. Lindlahr... New York,
Journal of living pub. corp. ₁1943₎ 40 p. 20cm. (His:
National nutrition society library. no. 21.)

1. Woman—Health and hygiene.   2. Diet.
N.Y.P.L.   November 10, 1948

NL 0381327   NN

Lindlahr, Victor Hugo, 1895–
Guide to balanced diet. Special charter ed. New York,
National Nutrition Society, 1938.
96 p. port. 28 cm.

1. Diet. 2. Cookery, American. I. Title.

TX551.L5   641   38–29565 rev*

NL 0381328   DLC OKentU NN

Lindlahr, Victor Hugo, 1895–
How to win and keep health with foods. New York, National Nutrition Society ₁1942₎
128 p. 27 cm.

1. Diet. 2. Food. I. Title.

RM216.L76   613.2   43–5145 rev*

NL 0381329   DLC OrStbM Wa DNLM

Lindlahr, Victor Hugo, 1895–
Iss und nimm ab! Buenos Aires, Alemann, 1945.
234 ₁1₎ p.

Originally published in English under title:
Eat – and reduce!

NL 0381330   MiD

Lindlahr, Victor Hugo, 1895- ed.
Journal of lifetime living. v. 1-25, no. 9; July 1935-**Mar.**
1960. ₁New York₎

Lindlahr, Victor H**u**g**o** , 1895–
The Lindlahr vitamin cook book, by Victor H. Lindlahr...
New York: Nat. nutrition soc. ₁1941₎ 319 p. illus. 21cm.
"Journal of living subscriber edition."

159004B. 1. Cookery, American.   2. Vitamins. I. National nutrition
society.
N.Y.P.L.   August 30, 1943

NL 0381332   NN ICRL DNLM KMK MiU

Lindlahr, Victor Hugo, 1895–
The Lindlahr vitamin cook book. New York, National
Nutrition Society, °1941.
17 l. 22 x 30 cm. fold. to 22 x 15 cm.
Cover title.

1. Cookery, American. I. Title: Vitamin cook book.

TX715.L758   641.5   43–840 rev*

NL 0381333   DLC CU IaU OU

Lindlahr, Victor Hugo, 1895–
The natural way to health. Special ed. New York, National Nutrition Society, 1939.
255 p. port. 20 cm.
The story of Henry Lindlahr and his Chicago sanitarium.

1. Lindlahr, Henry, 1862–1924. 2. Lindlahr Sanitarium, Chicago.
3. Therapeutics, Physiological. I. Title.

R154.L47L5   615.8   39–33243 rev*

NL 0381334   DLC KMK

Lindlahr, Victor H**u**g**o** , 1895–
An outline of hygiene for women, by Victor H. Lindlahr.
New York: Lindlahr's magazine, 1931.   203 p.   18cm.

190446B. 1. Woman—Health and   hygiene.   March 19, 1943
N.Y.P.L.

NL 0381335   NN

RM702   **Lindlahr, Victor H.,** 1895–   ed.
.L7
1931   **Lindlahr, Henry,** 1862–1924.
          The practice of nature cure ₁by₎ Henry Lindlahr, M. D. 27th
        ed., rev. and ed. by Victor H. Lindlahr. New York city, The
        Nature cure library, inc. ₁°1931₎

Lindlahr, Victor Hugo, 1895–   , ed.
Successful salads; ed. by Victor H. Lindlahr ... New York,
Journal of living pub. corp. ₁1943₎   24 p. 20cm. (His:
National nutrition society library. no. 30)

1. Cookery—Salad.   July 27, 1950
N.Y.P.L.

NL 0381337   NN

RM222   **Lindlahr, Victor Hugo,** 1895–
.2
.J65   **Journal of lifetime living.**
          201 tasty dishes for reducers, including the famous Victor
        H. Lindlahr 7-day reducing diet. New York, 1948.

Lindlahr, Victor Hugo, 1895–
You are what you eat. New York, National Nutrition
Society, 1940.
128 p. diagrs. 27 cm.

1. Diet. 2. Nutrition. I. Title.

TX551.L53   612.39   41–7515 rev*

NL 0381339   DLC WaE OrU OrSaW ScCleU OEac OLaK OU

TX551   **Lindlahr, Victor Hugo,** 1895–
.L53   You are what you eat, by Victor H. Lindlahr ...
1942   New York, National nutrition society, inc.
        ₁1942₎
          128 p. diagrs. 27cm.
          "First published September, 1940."

          1. Diet. 2. Nutrition.   I. National
        nutrition society.   II. Title.

NL 0381340   MB NcRS

TX551   Lindlahr, Victor Hugo, 1895–
L514   You are what you eat, by Victor H. Lindlahr. [New ed.]
1942   New York, National Nutrition Society [c1942]
Agric.   128 p. diagrs.
Library

          1. Diet. 2. Nutrition. I. Title.

NL 0381341   CU

VOLUME 334

389.1
L643Y
1945
Lindlahr, Victor H   1895–
You are what you eat.   New York, Journal
of living publishing corp. [1945]
128 p.

1. Diet. 2. Food. Nutritive value. 3. Nutrition. I. Title.

NL 0381342   DNAL

Lindlahr's magazine
see
Modern living...

Lindlar, Heinrich, ed.
Benjamin Britten
see under title

Lindlar, Heinrich.
... Hans Pfitzners klavierlied. Würzburg-Aumühle, K.
Triltsch, 1940.
vii, 81 p. front. (port.) illus. (music) 23½ᶜᵐ.
Issued also as inaugural dissertation, Cologne.
"Aus dem Pfitzner-schrifttum": p. 76.
"Gesamt-verzeichnis der klavierlieder Hans Pfitzners": p. 77–81.

1. Pfitzner, Hans Erich, 1869–

Library of Congress   ML410.P82L5   41–27524
                                         780.81

NL 0381345   DLC MH NN NIC IU NcU IEN

Lindlar, Herbert, 1909–
Ueber das verhalten der dicarbonsäuren bei
der ureidbildung. ... Zürich, 1939.   40 p.
Inaug. Diss. – Bern, 1939.
Vita.

NL 0381346   ICRL CtY

Lindlar, Jakob.
Die lebensmittelpolitik der stadt
Koeln im mittelalter.   1912.

Diss.

NL 0381347   PU

LINDLAR, Jakob.
Die Lebensmittelpolitik der Stadt Köln im
Mittelalter. Köln: Lempertz 1913. X.

X, 43 S.
Münster, Phil.Diss. v. 21. Febr. 1914.

NL 0381348   MH MiU CtY

Lindlau, Jakob Clemens.
Der gute Hirt Christus; oder Tröstende Betrachtungen auf der Reise zur Ewigkeit. Gebet-Betrachtungs- und Kranken-Buch für katholische
Christen jeden Standes. 2. verb. Aufl.
Augsburg, P. P. Bolling, 1820.
vi, 207 p. front. 18 cm.

NL 0381349   PLatS

Lindlau, Max, 1912–
... Zur Metastasierung der Genitalkarzinome
in die Klavikulargruben ...   Köln, 1938.
Inaug. -Diss. - Köln.
Lebenslauf.
"Schrifttum": p. 29.

NL 0381350   CtY

LINDLEY, A.
Knowledge for infants, or A form of oral instruction. For the use of parents and teachers.
Philadelphia, published by Johnson & Warner, etc.,
1811.

NL 0381351   MH

Lindley, A. L. G.
Design of direct-acting steam winders. [1927?]
55 p. (Association of engineering and ship-
building draughtsmen. Technical section. [Print-
ed pamphlets] 1926/27 [no.1])

NL 0381352   MiD

Lindley, Albert, pseud.
see   Lawsing, Albert Lindley.

Lindley, Alice.
Mundy's child; a romance of everyday life, by Alice Lindley. [London] P. Allan, 1932.
xii, 243, [1] p. incl. front., illus. 19½ᶜᵐ.
Illustrated by Tony Wysard.

I. Title.

Library of Congress   PZ3.L6464Mu   33–5087

NL 0381354   DLC

Lindley, Alice.
Mundy's child, a romance of everyday life, by Alice Lindley.
New York, Dodd, Mead & company, 1933.
x p., 1 l., 231 p. 19ᶜᵐ.

I. Title.

Library of Congress   PZ3.L6464Mu 2   33–4985

NL 0381355   DLC

Lindley, Augustus F.
G170   About the Chincha Islands. (*In* Bates, H. W., ed.
.B32   Illustrated travels. London [1869–] 31¼ᶜᵐ. v. 2 [1870])
         p. 155–160, 174–179)

CA 5–2048 Unrev'd

NL 0381356   DLC

Lindley, Augustus F.
Adamantia. The truth about the South African diamond fields: or, A vindication of the right of the Orange
Free State to that territory, and an analysis of British
diplomacy and aggression which has resulted in its illegal
seizure by the governor of the Cape of Good Hope. By
Captain Augustus F. Lindley ... London, W. H. & L.
Collingridge, 1873.
xiii p., 1 l., 423 p. col. front., maps (part fold.) 23ᶜᵐ.
Frontispiece: arms of Orange Free State.

1. Diamond mines and mining—Africa, South.   I. Title.
                                              16–16907

Library of Congress   DT745.L5

CtY MiU ICJ NN MB
NL 0381357   DLC PU KyLoU WaU NcD MiEM NBuU CU DNLM

Lindley, Augustus F.
After Ophir; or, A search for the South African gold fields.
By Captain Augustus Lindley...   London: Cassell, Petter, and
Galpin [1870]. vii, 312 p. incl. front., illus., plates.   8°.

8917A. 1. Africa (South).—Descrip-   tion and travel, 1800–1900. 2. Title.
N. Y. P. L.   June 28, 1921.

NL 0381358   NN MH NNC MBu PPL CtY

Lindley, Augustus F.
Efg   After Ophir; or, A search for the South
868Lb   African gold fields ... 2d ed. London,
        Paris, and New York, Cassell, Petter, & Galpin
        [187-?]
          vii, [1], 312p. incl. front., illus., plates,
        ports. 22½cm.

NL 0381359   CtY

968.22
L746af   Lindley, Augustus F.
         After Ophir; or, A search for the South
         African gold fields.   London, New York,
         Cassel, Petter, and Galpin [1890]
           vii, 312, 16p. front., illus. 22cm.

1. Africa, South. Descr. & trav. 2. Gold
mines and mining. Africa, South. I. Title.

NL 0381360   IEN

Lindley, Augustus F
A cruise in Chinese waters. Being the log of "The Fortuna"
... By Captain Augustus F. Lindley ... 4th ed. London,
New York [etc.] Cassell, Petter, Galpin & co. [1882]
3 p. l., 256 p. incl. illus., plates, front. 22 x 17½ᶜᵐ.
"The previous editions of this work were published under the title
of 'The log of the Fortuna'."

1. China—Descr. & trav. 2. Voyages and travels.
                                              44–38763
Library of Congress   DS709.L65 1882

NL 0381361   DLC ViU OU MSaE ICN

VOLUME 334

Lindley, Augustus F.
G170   A cruise to Soo-chow. (*In* Bates, H. W., ed. Illus-
.B32   trated travels. London [1869–] 31½ᶜᵐ. v. 2 ([1870])
      p. 79–85)

Library of Congress   CA 5–2047 Unrev'd

NL 0381362   DLC

Lindley, Augustus F.
    The log of the Fortuna: a cruise on Chinese waters. Contain-
ing tales of adventure in foreign climes, by sea and by shore. By
Captain Augustus F. Lindley...   London: Cassell, Petter, and
Galpin [1870?]. 256 p. front., illus. 8°.

24333A. 1. Fiction (Adventure).   2. Title.
N. Y. P. L.   December 20, 1921.

NL 0381363   NN PPL MH CtY NNC MB DN

DS709 **Lindley, Augustus F.**
I59   The log of the Fortuna: a cruise on Chinese
1870   waters; containing tales of adventure in foreign
      climes by sea and by shore. 2d ed. London,
      Cassell, Petter & Galpin [1870]
      256 p. illus.,plates. 22cm.

        Later editions have title: A cruise in
      Chinese waters; being the log of the Fortuna.

        1. China – Descr. & trav. 2. Voyages and
      travels. I. Title.

NL 0381364   CU PU NIC

Lindley, Augustus F.
    A ramble in Peru.
(*In* Bates, H. W., ed. Illustrated travels. London [1869–   ] 31½ᵐ·
v. 2 ([1870]) p. 280–287, 314–319. illus.)

    1. Peru—Descr. & trav.
                                                CA 5–2046 Unrev'd
Library of Congress   G170.B32 vol. 2

NL 0381365   DLC

[Lindley, Augustus F   ]
    ... Ti-ping tien-kwoh; the history of the Ti-ping revo-
lution, including a narrative of the author's personal adventures. By ... Lin-le ... London, Day & son (limited)
1866.
    2 v. front. (fold. facsim.) illus., plates (part col.) port., 2 double maps.
26½ᶜᵐ.
    Paged continuously.
    Caption and author's name in Chinese characters.
    Preface signed: A. F. L.

    1. China—Hist.—Taiping rebellion, 1850–1864.
                                                5–1751
Library of Congress   DS759.L75

      GEU ICN ViU MiU DNW
      MdBP DN OCU MSaE WaU MdBP OC1 InU MB NN ICarbS OO
NL 0381366   DLC OrP OrU WaSp OU IaU UU CU CtY RPB

Rare
BX   [Lindley, Benjamin] d. 1723.
7732   Cerinthus and Ebion: or, The heresie of
F92   tything under the Gospel detected: in some
v.7   observations upon a book entituled, An essay
no.5   concerning the divine right of tythes: by the
        author of the Snake in the grass. Together with
        an essay concerning the first rise of tythes:
        and an essay against their divine right.
        London, Printed by J. Sowle, 1708.
        [16], 48 p. 21cm.
          No. 5 in vol.   lettered: Friends
        pamphlets, VII.
          1. Tithes.   I. Title.

NL 0381367   NIC PHC PU CLU-C

---

626 [Lindley, Benjamin]
    A defence of the book entituled Cerinthus and Ebion:
or, The heresy of tything, under the Gospel detected,
&c. Against the exceptions of an haughty, ignorant
dialogue between (as not for want of the vanity of
self opinion they term themselves) Eubulus and Sophronius, in the pamphlet [by Samuel Parker] call'd
by the proud name of Censura temporum, for the
month of September, 1708. London, Printed and sold
by J. Sowle, 1709.
24 p. 4°.

NL 0381368   MH NIC PU PHC

Lindley, Benjamin.
    The necessity of immediate revelation, towards the
foundation and ground of trve faith, proved; and the Gospel, its true ministers, and their Christian writings, especially R. Barclay's apology, &c. vindicated: in an answer
to the dark attempts of Thomas Bennet, against them;
in his nine first chapters, of his pretended Confutation of
Quakerism. By Benjamin Lindley ... London, Printed
and sold by J. Sowle, 1710.
    6 p. l., 124 p. 20½ᵐ.
                                                4–22468

NL 0381369   DLC MH PPL PHC CtY

Lindley, Benjamin.
    The necessity of immediate revelation, towards
the foundation and ground of true faith proved and
the gospel...
    London, 1713.
    2 v. 8°

NL 0381370   PHC NIC PSC-Hi

---

*EC65   [Lindley, Benjamin, d. 1723]
L6444   The shiboleth of priest-hood, wherein it is
678s   debated and proved by the evidence of Scripture
        and right reason, to be absolutely impossible
        for any unholy man to execute the office of a
        gospel minister ...
        [London] Printed anno Domini 1678.

        2p.l., 18p. 18.5cm.
        Signed at end: Benja. Lindley.

NL 0381371   MH CU PPFr PHC CSmH CtY

---

*Defoe [Lindley, Benjamin] d. 1723.
30   The shiboleth of priest-hood; wherein it is
.678   debated and proved by the evidence of Scripture
.L64Sb and right reason, to be absolutely impossible
        for any unholy man to execute the office of a
        gospel minister ...
        [London] Printed in the year 1701.

        3 p.l., 39 p. 15cm.
        Ex libris (signature): [Abreaham] Shackleton.

NL 0381372   MB

Rare
BX   [Lindley, Benjamin] d. 1723.
7732   The shiboleth of priest-hood. Wherein it
F92   is debated and proved by the evidence of
v.7   Scripture and right reason, to be absolutely
no.4   impossible for any unholy man to execute the
        office of a gospel minister. London,
        Printed and sold by T. Sowle, 1704.
        4, 22, [2] p. 21cm.
        Publisher's catalogue: p. [23]–[24]
        No. 4 in vol. lettered: Friends pamphlets,
VII.
          1. Clergy.   I. Title.

NL 0381373   NIC PHC PSC-Hi

[Lindley, Benjamin]
    Some arguments concerning the rule of faith...
York, 1702.

NL 0381374   PHC

---

*EC65   [Lindley, Benjamin, d. 1723]
L6444   A treatise of election and reprobation; in
700t   vindication of the universal grace and love of
        God to mankind. By B. L.
        London, Printed and sold by T.Sowle, in White-
        Hart-court in Gracious-street, 1700.

        2p.l., 60p. 18.5cm.
        Pages 50–60 contain a reply to George Keith's
        Truth advanced.
        Imperfect: top edges cropped.

NL 0381375   MH PHC PSC-Hi

---

*EC65   [Lindley, Benjamin, d. 1723]
L6444   A treatise of election and reprobation; in
700tb   vindication of the universal grace and love of
        God to mankind. By B. L. The second edition.
        London:Printed and sold by the assigns of J.
        Sowle,in White-Hart-court in Gracious-street;
        and at the Bible,in George-yard,Lombard-street.
        1715.
        96p. 18.5cm.
        Pages 79–96 contain a reply to George Keith's
        Truth advanced.

NL 0381376   MH PHC

Lindley, Mrs. Betty (Grimes) 1902–
    A new deal for youth; the story of the National youth ad-
ministration [by] Betty and Ernest K. Lindley. New York,
The Viking press, 1938.
    xvi, 315 p. plates, diagr. 22ᶜᵐ.
    "First published in July 1938."

    1. U. S. National youth administration.   I. Lindley, Ernest Kidder,
1899–   joint author. II. Title.
                                                38–18002
Library of Congress   HV1431.L5
      Copy 2.
Copyright A 119586   [10–5]   362.70973

      CaBVa WaOB NN
      OrPR OEac OC1 OCLW OU OO WaWW Or WaS OrU WaTC IdU
NL 0381377   DLC OrCS MU NBuU CU OrP MtU IdB WaSp PBm

Lindley, Carl Gustaf
      see
Lindley, Charles, 1865–

Lindley, Charles.
    California code commentaries: by Charles Lindley ... San
Francisco, The author, 1872.
    88, viii p. 23ᵐ.
    Cover-title: Code commentaries. Part I ... : San Francisco, B. F.
Sterett, printer, 1874.
    "Appendix [letter to H. H. Haight and others, dated Jan. 8, 1874]":
viii p.
    No more published?

    1. Law — Codification. [1. Codification — California] 2. Law — Cali-
fornia.   I. Title.
                                                31–34347
Library of Congress

NL 0381379   DLC MH-L

LC1081 **Lindley, Charles.**
.L54   Industrial education. An address on
        the subject, developing a popular plan
        by which industrial colleges shall be
        established in this state to train our
        youths to mechanics, agriculture and
        the leading useful arts. Los Angeles,
        Evening Express steam book and job
        printing house, 1877.
        cover-title,9,[1]p. 22½cm.
        1. Technical education–California.

NL 0381380   NNU-W

VOLUME 334

Lindley, Charles.   FOR OTHER EDITIONS
SEE MAIN ENTRY

California. *Laws, statutes, etc.*
Revised laws of the state of California; in three codes:
Political, Civil and Penal. Penal code ... Commissioners:
Creed Haymond, chairman, John C. Burch, Charles Lindley.
Secretaries: Cameron H. King, Will J. Beatty. Sacramento,
D. W. Gelwicks, state printer, 1870.

Lindley, Charles, 1865–
Frihet :n i fara! Ett varningsord till Sveriges arbetare, av Charles
Lindley...Gunnar Andersson: Hellre krig än slaveri. L. H.
Landén: "Nyordning" och nöd. W. J. Brown: Är Hitler social-
ist? m.m. Stockholm, Trots allt! [1941] 15 p. port. 22cm.

Port. at head of title.

1. World war, 1939–1945—Labor.   2. World war, 1939–1945—Labor
—Sweden.
N. Y. P. L.   June 10, 1949

NL 0381382   NN

HD6759
.L6S9
Lindley, Charles, 1865–
Svenska transportarbetareförbundet.
... Historik ... [Stockholm, A.-b. Arbetarnes tryckeri, 1943–

Lindley, Clara (Hill)
James J. and Mary T. Hill, an unfinished chronicle by
their daughter. New York, North River Press [1948]
135 p. 24 cm.

"For private distribution."

1. Hill, James Jerome, 1838–1916. 2. [Hill, Mary Theresa
(Mehegan) 1846–1921.
HE2754.H5L5   923.873   48–3078*

NL 0381384   DLC CaBViPA

Lindley, Mrs. Clara (Hill) ed.

Caillet, Louis Eugene, 1832–1897.
Some letters of Monsignor Louis E. Caillet and August
N. Chemidlin, 1868–1899, ed. by Clara Hill Lindley. St.
Paul, Printed for private circulation, 1922.

Lindley, Clarence T.
Mound explorations in Jackson County, Iowa. By C. T.
Lindley. [Davenport, Ia., 1877.] 83–84 p. illus. 8°.

Excerpt: Davenport Acad. of Natural Sciences. Proc. v. 2, part 1.

EAMES INDIAN COLLECTION.
1. Mounds, U. S.: Iowa. 2. Jack-   son county, Ia.—Archaeology.
N. Y. P. L.   March 26, 1917.

NL 0381386   NN

Lindley, Curtis Holbrook, 1850–1920.
Reform in our legal procedure. Address
delivered by Curtis H. Lindley, president of
Bar association of San Francisco and California
bar association, before the Commonwealth club
of Santa Clara county, March 7th, 1910.
[San Francisco, The Recorder printing and
publishing co., 1910?]
cover title, 13 p.   (In Legal pamphlets,
v. 28)

NL 0381387   WaU-L

Lindley, Curtis Holbrook, 1850–1920.
A treatise on the American law relating to mines and mineral lands within the public land states and territories and governing the acquisition and enjoyment of mining rights in lands
of the public domain, by Curtis H. Lindley ... San Francisco, Bancroft-Whitney company, 1897.
2 v. 23½cm.

1. Mining law—U. S.   14–6085

PPB DI ViU-L NN
NL 0381388   DLC MtU WaU-L IdU CU NcD NN OO PU-L

Lindley, Curtis Holbrook, 1850–1920.
A treatise on the American law relating to mines and
mineral lands within the public land states and territories and governing the acquisition and enjoyment of
mining rights in lands of the public domain, by Curtis
H. Lindley ... 2d ed. ... San Francisco, Bancroft-Whitney company, 1903.
2 v. 23½cm.

1. Mining law—U. S. [2. Land laws]   3–13384

PU-L PPB ICJ
NL 0381389   DLC MtU CU GU-L CSt OU CaBVaU NcD DI

Lindley, Curtis Holbrook, 1850–1920.
A treatise on the American law relating to mines and
mineral lands within the public land states and territories, and governing the acquisition and enjoyment of
mining rights in lands of the public domain, by Curtis H.
Lindley ... 3d ed. ... San Francisco, Bancroft-Whitney
company, 1914.
3 v. illus. 23½cm. $8.35
Paged continuously.

1. Mining law—U. S. [2. Land laws]   14–4538

GU-L PU-L NcD ViU-L OC1 IdU CaBVaU
NL 0381390   DLC MtU CaBVaU WaU-L MtBuM DS CU-B

F869
S3
.4
L55
Lindley, Curtis Holbrook, 1850–1920.
The value of history to the lawyer. [San Francisco,
Recorder Print. and Pub. Co., 1911]
14 p. 23cm.

"Address delivered before the May First History Club
February 4, 1911."

I. History – Study and teaching.   I. May First History
Club, San Francisco. II. Title.

NL 0381391   CU-B WaU-L

[Lindley, Daniel]
Fys
Z88
L64
Incwadi yezibalo. Ku ya fundiswa ngayo
ukulinganisa ngezibalo. Yona ya balelwa
abafundisi ba semerika. Etekwini,J.Cullingworth,
1856.
140p.,1ℓ. 18cm.

NL 0381392   CtY MH

Lindley, Daniel.

Connecticut. *General assembly. Joint standing committee on agriculture.*
Report of testimony heard by the Joint standing committee on agriculture of the Connecticut Legislature, relative to the disease of cattle now prevalent in Massachusetts ... New Haven, Carrington Hotchkiss, state printers, 1860.

Lindley, Dennis Victor.
Cambridge elementary statistical tables, by D. V. Lindley
and J. C. P. Miller. Cambridge [Eng.] University Press,
1953.
35 p. 28 cm.

1. Statistics—Charts, tables, etc.   I. Miller, Jeffery Charles
Percy, joint author. II. Title.
QA47.L5   311.2083   54–1774 ‡

OrU-M
NcD CtY CU-M DNAL PSt MiU N CoU CaBVaU OrCS IdU
NL 0381394   DLC FU DI PPF NN OU PPD PPTU TxU MB IU

PZ3
.R2818
Ar
Lindley, Denver, 1904–   joint tr.

Remarque, Erich Maria, 1898–
Arch of triumph [by] Erich Maria Remarque, translated from
the German by Walter Sorell and Denver Lindley. New York,
London, D. Appleton-Century company, inc. [1945]

PQ2625
.A95Z53
1943
Lindley, Denver, 1904–   tr.

Maurois, André, 1885–
Call no man happy, by André Maurois; translated from the
French by Denver and Jane Lindley. London, J. Cape [1943]

Lindley, Denver, tr.

Remarque, Erich Maria, 1898–
... Flotsam, translated from the German by Denver Lindley.
Boston, Little, Brown and company, 1941.

PQ2625
.A95Z53
Lindley, Denver, 1904–   tr.

Maurois, André, 1885–
I remember, I remember, by André Maurois, translated
from the French by Denver and Jane Lindley. New York
and London, Harper & brothers [1942]

E178
.M462
Lindley, Denver, 1904–   tr.

Maurois, André, 1885–
The miracle of America, by André Maurois, translated from
the French by Denver and Jane Lindley ... New York and
London, Harper & brothers, 1944.

Lindley, Denver, tr.

Maurois, André, 1885–
Tragedy in France, by André Maurois; translated from the
French by Denver Lindley. New York and London, Harper
& brothers [1940]

Lindley, Denver, 1904–   tr.   FOR OTHER EDITIONS
SEE MAIN ENTRY

Maurois, André, 1885–
... Why France fell; translated from the French by Denver
Lindley. London, John Lane [1941]

VOLUME 334

Lindley, E.C.

[Dunlap, Robert] 1853–
... United States of America vs. Atchison, Topeka & Santa Fe railway company and sixteen other railroad companies. United States of America vs. Union Pacific railroad company and ten other railroad companies. Intermountain rate cases ... Brief and argument on behalf of the appellees. Chicago, Barnard & Miller print [1912]

Lindley, E Marguerite.
Health in the home; a practical work on the promotion and preservation of health, with illustrated prescriptions of Swedish gymnastic exercise for home and club practice, by E. Marguerite Lindley ... New York, The author, 1896.
xii, 414 p. front. (port.) illus. 21cm.

1. Hygiene. 2. Swedish gymnastics. I. Title.

Library of Congress RA776.L74 1-14615

NL 0381402 DLC ICJ NjP CtY-M ODW DNLM PPC

Lindley, E Marguerite.
Health in the home; a practical work on the promotion and preservation of health; with illustrated descriptions of Swedish gymnastic exercise for home and club practice, by E. Marguerite Lindley ... New and rev. ed. Passaic, N. J., The Health-culture co. [c1908]
xiv, 414 p. illus. 18cm.

1. Hygiene. 2. Swedish gymnastics.

Library of Congress RA776.L76 9-12060

NL 0381403 DLC

Lindley, E. Marguerite.
Montpelier. Home of Major-General Henry Knox. [Signed E.M. Lindley] New York, 1886. p. 121-132. illus. 8°.
Frag: Mag. Am. Hist. v. 15, no. 2.

NL 0381404 NN MdBP

Lindley, Elizabeth.
The diary of a book-agent, by Elizabeth Lindley. New York, Broadway publishing co. [c1911]
2 p. l., 3-109 p. 19½cm. $1.00

I. Title.

Library of Congress PZ3.L6465D 12-455

NL 0381405 DLC CLU

Lindley, Elizabeth Valrose
see **Lindley, Valrose.**

Lindley, Ernest Hiram, 1869–1940.
The colleges and the people [by] Ernest Hiram Lindley ...
(*In* National education association of the United States. Addresses and proceedings, 1925. p. 63–68)

1. Universities and colleges—U. S. I. Title.

E 26-285

U. S. Off. of educ. Library for Library of Congress [L13.N4 1925] [a38c1] (370.6273)

NL 0381407 DHEW

Lindley, Ernest Hiram, 1869-1940.
Commemoration of Ernest Hiram Lindley, chancellor, 1920-1939
see under Kansas. University.

Lindley, Ernest Hiram, 1869-1940.

Kansas. University.
Inauguration of Ernest Hiram Lindley as chancellor of the University of Kansas. Lawrence, 1921.

Lindley, Ernest Hiram, 1869-1940.

Bryan, William Lowe, 1860–
On the psychology of learning a life occupation [by] William Lowe Bryan, Ernest Hiram Lindley [and] Noble Harter. Bloomington, Ind., Indiana university [1941]

Lindley, Ernest Hiram 1869-1940.
The revival of personality.
(*In* National education association of the United States. Addresses and proceedings, 1930. p. 115–121)

1. Personality. I. Title.

E 33-159

Library, U. S. Office of Education L13.N212 1930
Library of Congress [L13.N4 1930]

NL 0381411 DHEW

Lindley, Ernest Hiram, 1869-1940.
The revival of personality. (In: Minnesota. Univ. Education College. The changing educational world, 1905–1930. Minneapolis, 1931. 8°. p. 20–28.)

551834A. 1. Personality.
N. Y. P. L. May 12, 1932

NL 0381412 NN

Lindley, Ernest H[iram] 1869-1940.
A study of puzzles with special reference to the psychology of mental adaptation ... [Worcester? Mass.] 1897.
cover-title, [431]-493 p. diagrs. 23½cm.
Thesis (PH. D.)—Clark university.
Reprinted from the American journal of psychology, vol. VIII, no. 4.
Bibliographical footnotes.

6-30035

NL 0381413 DLC OrU CaBVaU OU

BF481 **Lindley,Ernest Hiram,1869-1940.**
.L7 **Ueber arbeit und ruhe. Von Ernest H.Lindley... Leipzig,W.Engelmann,1900.**
cover-title,p.[481]-534. tables. 24cm.

Separat-abdruck aus:Kraepelin,Psychologische arbeiten,III.band,3.heft.

NL 0381414 ICU NjP CtY NNU-W MH

Lindley, Ernest Hiram, 1869-1940.
Ueber Arbeit und Ruhe.
(In Kraepelin. Psychologische Arbeiten. Band 3, pp. 482–534. Leipzig, 1901.)

Aug. 29, 1903
F582 — Rest. — Work. — Psychology. Physiological.

NL 0381415 MB

Lindley, Ernest Kidder, 1899-
Agenda for a second term. [n.p.]
19 p.
Reprint, 1937.

NL 0381416 ViU

Lindley, Ernest Kidder, 1899-

E744
.H43
no. 63 **Higinbotham, William A**
Atomic challenge: Splitting the atom [by] William A. Higinbotham; Harnessing the atom [by] Ernest K. Lindley. [New York, Foreign Policy Assn., 1947]

Lindley, Ernest Kidder, 1899–
Franklin D. Roosevelt; a career in progressive democracy, by Ernest K. Lindley. Indianapolis, The Bobbs-Merrill company [c1931]
379 p. front. (port.) 23cm.
"First edition."

1. Roosevelt, Franklin Delano, 1882–

Library of Congress E748.R75L6 31-28457
——— Copy 2.
Copyright A 46219 923.273

NL 0381418 DLC KEmT CoU OrSaW Or OrP MH NN PPL PSC OCX OU OO OCl MB

Lindley, Ernest Kidder, 1899–
Franklin D. Roosevelt, a career in progressive democracy, by Ernest K. Lindley. New York city, Blue ribbon books, inc. [c1931]
379 p. front. (port.) 21½cm.

1. Roosevelt, Franklin Delano, pres. U. S., 1882–

Library of Congress E807.L565 34-8465
923.173

NL 0381419 DLC OKentU WaTC GU WaU

Lindley, Ernest Kidder, 1899–
Franklin D. Roosevelt; a career in progressive democracy, by Ernest K. Lindley. New York city, Blue ribbon books, inc. [c1934]
3 p. l., 5-366 p. front. (port.) 21½cm.
"Revised edition, June, 1934."

1. Roosevelt, Franklin Delano, pres. U. S., 1882–

Library of Congress E807.L565 1934 34-19478
—— Copy 2.
Copyright A 73392 923.173

NL 0381420 DLC OU TxFTC CLU TU NcRS ViU PHC NN

VOLUME 334

Lindley, Ernest Kidder, 1899–
... Half way with Roosevelt. ₍New York₎ The Viking press, 1936.
x, 426 p. 21½ cm.
"First published in August 1936."

1. U. S.—Pol. & govt.—1933–1945. 2. U. S.—Economic policy. 3. Roosevelt, Franklin Delano, pres. U. S., 1882–1945.   i. Title.
Library of Congress   E806.L54
                                                                        36—18869
                                   ₍a49u1₎   **973.917**

PPD PP NIC WaU MoU MtBC OrPR Or WaS Wa OrU
NL   0381421   DLC OLak OC1h OCU OU OC1 ViU NN MB PU

Lindley, Ernest Kidder, 1899–
... Half way with Roosevelt. Rev. ed. ₍New York₎ The Viking press, 1937.
x, 449 p. 21½ᶜᵐ.
At head of title: Ernest K. Lindley.

1. U. S.—Pol. & govt.—1933—   2. U. S.—Economic policy. 3. Roosevelt, Franklin Delano, pres. U. S., 1882—   i. Title.
Library of Congress   E806.L543
                                                                        37—1821
————— Copy 2.
Copyright A 102513   **973.917**

OOxM OU Ok
NL   0381422   DLC WaS IdU OrP MeB MU ICU NcD TU PPT

D753   **Lindley, Ernest Kidder,** 1899–   joint author.
.D35
Davis, Forrest, 1893–
How war came, an American White paper; from the fall of France to Pearl harbor, by Forrest Davis and Ernest K. Lindley. New York, Simon and Schuster, 1942.

Lindley, Ernest Kidder, 1899–   Joint author.

Davis, Forrest, 1893–
How war came to America, from the fall of France to Pearl harbour, by Forrest Davis and Ernest K. Lindley. London, G. Allen & Unwin ltd ₍1943₎

Lindley, Ernest Kidder, 1899–
National defense and foreign policy.   1940.
By Lindley, E. K. and others.

NL   0381425   OrU

Lindley, Ernest Kidder, 1899–   joint author.

Lindley, Mrs. Betty (Grimes) 1902–
A new deal for youth; the story of the National youth administration ₍by₎ Betty and Ernest K. Lindley. New York, The Viking press, 1938.

Lindley, Ernest Kidder, 1899–
The Roosevelt revolution, first phase, by Ernest K. Lindley. New York, The Viking press, 1933.
viii p., 2 l., 3–328 p. 21ᶜᵐ.

1. U. S.—Pol. & govt.—1933—   2. Roosevelt, Franklin Delano, pres. U. S., 1882—   3. U. S.—Economic policy.   i. Title.
Library of Congress   E806.L56
                                                                        33—27368
————— Copy 2.
                                                                        973.917

IdU OrPR Or WaS CaBVa OrU WaTC
OU OO MiU OCU ODW DL WaE OrP MtU PSC MB NN ViU WaT
NL   0381427   * DLC WaU MoU MeB KEmT NcD TU OOxM OC1

973.917   Lindley, Ernest Kidder, 1899–
L74r   The Roosevelt revolution, first
1934   phase.   London, Gollancz, 1934.
              287p. D.

NL   0381428   IaU

PN4734   **Lindley, Ernest Kidder,** 1899–
.W5
2d   The years of danger; a consideration of
1951   facts, demagoguery and U. S. foreign
              policy. ₍Lawrence, Kan., William Allen
              White Foundation, University of Kansas,
              1951₎
              21 p.   23cm. (William Allen White memorial
              lecture, 2d, 1951)
              Cover title.
              1. U. S.—For. rel.—1945—   I. Title.
              II. Ser.

CoU ScU TxFTC
NL   0381429   ViU CaBVaU NIC NjR CtY NcD AAP TxU FU

Lindley, Ernest R., comp.

Texas. *Legislature. House of representatives.*
Biographical directory of the Texan conventions and congresses, 1832–1845. ₍Huntsville, 1942₎

Lindley, Frances.
Angela Thirkell; an autobiographic sketch

see under

Knopf, firm, publishers, New York.

Lindley, Hon. Sir Francis Oswald, 1872–
A diplomat off duty, by the Honourable Sir Francis Lindley ... Drawings by Ridley Borchgrevink. London, E. Benn limited, 1928.
195, ₍1₎ p. incl. front., illus. 23ᶜᵐ.
CONTENTS.—Where is it? ₍Bird-notes₎—Mount Demavend.—Some experiences in Bulgaria.—Bathing.—The taking of ducks.—Ski-running in Norway.—Tiger-hunting in Korea.—Birds of passage.—Shooting in spring.—About salmon-fishing.—A Philistine fisherman.—Dry-fly fishing and Winchester.
1. Sports. 2. Hunting. 3. Fishing. 4. Demavend, Mount, Persia. i. Title.
Library of Congress   GV165.L5A3
                                                                        28—22684

NL   0381432   DLC CaBViP IEN NN

Lindley, Sir Francis Oswald, 1872–
A diplomat off duty. ₍2d ed.₎ London, E. Benn ₍1947₎
200 p. 22 cm. (The Bouverie library)

1. Sports. 2. Hunting. 3. Fishing. 4. Demavend, Mount, Persia. i. Title. ii. Series.
GV165.L5A3 1947   799   48—1995*

NL   0381433   DLC WaU

Lindley, Sir Francis Oswald, 1872–
Lord Lovat, K. T., K. C. M. G., K. C. V. O., C. B., D. S. O.; a biography by the Rt. Hon. Sir Francis Lindley ... with 34 illustrations. London, Hutchinson & co., ltd. ₍1935₎
2 p. l., 7–319 p. front., plates, ports. 24ᶜᵐ.

1. Lovat, Simon Joseph Fraser, baron, 1871–1933.
                                                                        36—5235
Library of Congress   DA822.L6L5
                                                                        923.241

NL   0381434   DLC CaBViP NIC MiU CLSU NN

Lindley, Sir Francis Oswald, 1872–
The tragedy of Spain, by Sir Francis Lindley ... ₍London, Loxley brothers limited, 1937?₎
11, ₍1₎ p. 24½ᶜᵐ.
"Reprinted from the National review, February, 1937."

1. Spain—Hist.—Civil war, 1936–1939.   i. Title.
                                                                        41—39673
Library of Congress   DP269.L515
                                                                        946.08

NL   0381435   DLC OrU

634.2   **Lindley, George.**
L64g   A guide to the orchard and fruit garden; or, An account of the most valuable fruits cultivated in Great Britain ... Ed. by John Lindley ... 1st American, from the last London ed. ... by Michael Floy.   New York, G. F. Hopkins & son, 1833.
              408p.

NL   0381436   IU MdBP MWA NN

Lindley, George.
A guide to the orchard and fruit garden; or, An account of the most valuable fruits cultivated in Great Britain. By George Lindley ... With additions of all the most valuable fruits cultivated in America ... by Michael Floy ...   A new ed.; with an appendix, describing many American fruits not mentioned in the former ed. New York, J. C. Riker, 1846.
xl, 420 p. fold. col. front., col. pl. 19 cm.

1. Fruit-culture—Gt. Brit. ₍1. Gt. Brit.—Pomology₎ 2. Fruit-culture—U. S. ₍2. U. S.—Pomology₎   i. Floy, Michael, ed.
                                                                        Agr 11—1925
U. S. Nat'l Agr. Libr.   98L64
for Library of Congress   ₍a66d¼₎

NL   0381437   DNAL MBH OU MWA NIC MU

LINDLEY, George.
A guide to the orchard and fruit garden; or an account of the most valuable fruits cultivated in Great Britain. With additions of all the most valuable fruits cultivated in America By Michael Floy. A new ed., with an appendix, describing many American fruits not mentioned in the former ed. N.Y. 1852.

Colored front., colored plate and diagrams.

NL   0381438   MH LU

Lindley, George.
A guide to the orchard and kitchen garden; or, An account of the most valuable fruit and vegetables cultivated in Great Britain: with kalendars of the work required in the orchard and kitchen garden during every month in the year. By George Lindley ... Ed. by John Lindley ... London, Longman, Rees, Orme, Brown and Green, 1831.
1 p. l., ₍vi₎-xxxi, 601, ₍1₎ p. 22ᶜᵐ.
"Abbreviations, and books quoted": p. xxix-xxxi.

1. Fruit-culture—Gt. Brit. 2. Vegetable gardening—Gt. Brit.   i. Lindley, John, 1799–1865, ed.
Library of Congress   SB98.L6
                                                                        11—14693

NL   0381439   DLC MH-A MBH PPHor KyU CU OC1W OU

Lindley, George.
Guide to orchard and kitchen gardens
see also   The fragraria: or Description of the most improved varieties of strawberries and raspberries ...

VOLUME 334

Lindley, George.
*XpfL   A plan of an orchard. Exhibiting at one view, a
.796   select quantity of trees sufficient for planting
.L64P   an acre and an half of land ... with an alphabe-
tical list of above eight hundred species and
varieties, such as are now cultivated in England
... By George Lindley.
Norwich [Eng.]: Printed and sold by Crous,
Stevenson and Matchett. Sold also by Downes,
Yarmouth; Marshall, Lynn; Barker, Dereham; Gedge,
Bury; Bush, Ipswich; Champante and Whitrow, Lon-
don, and all other booksellers. 1796. Price two

[4] p. illus. (plan) 36cm.; in folder 37.5cm.
(fol.)
Title and imprint from endorsed title on p.[4]

NL 0381442   MB

Lindley, Grace.
Protestant Episcopal church in the U. S. A. *National council. Woman's auxiliary. Triennial meeting, Atlantic City,*
1934.
A book of meditations; foreword by Grace Lindley. The
meditations given at the Triennial meeting of the Woman's
auxiliary at Atlantic City, N. J., October, 1934. Milwaukee,
Wis., Morehouse publishing co. [*1935]

[Lindley, Grace]
Studies in the Acts. [New York, Office of the mission-
ary educational secretary, diocese of New York, 1910]
30 p., 1 l. 17¼ᶜᵐ.
Prepared by Grace Lindley.
Supplements the author's Studies in the Gospel of St. Matthew.
Introduction signed: Samuel Thorne, jr., ed. sec. of diocese of New
York.

1. Bible. N. T. Acts—Study.   I. Thorne, Samuel, 1874–   II. Title.
Library of Congress   BS2625.L7
                                              19–7142

NL 0381444   DLC

[Lindley, Grace]
Studies in the Gospel of St. Matthew. [New York,
Board of missions, 190–]
31 p. 17¼ᶜᵐ.
"Prepared by Miss Grace Lindley, assisted by Miss Elizabeth R. Dela-
field."—Pref. note.
"Books for collateral reading": p. 5.

1. Bible. N. T. Matthew—Study.   I. Delafield, Elizabeth Ray, 1872–
II. Title.
Library of Congress   BS2575.L7
                                              19–7143

NL 0381445   DLC

[Lindley, Grace]
Studies in the Gospel revelation. [New York, Office of
the Educational department, Board of missions, 190–]
32 p. 17ᶜᵐ.
Prefatory note signed: Grace Lindley.

1. Bible. N. T. Gospels—Study.   I. Title.
Library of Congress   BS2556.L5
                                              19–16922

NL 0381446   DLC

Lindley, Harlow, 1875–1959, ed.
F486   Cushing, Daniel Lewis, 1764–1815.
.O 526   Captain Cushing in the war of 1812, edited by Harlow
vol. 11   Lindley ... Columbus, O., The Ohio State archaeological and
historical society, 1944.

Lindley, Harlow, 1875–   ed.
The Charity school of Kendal. Edited by Harlow Lindley.
(*In* Ohio state archaeological and historical quarterly. Columbus,
O., 1946. 23½ᶜᵐ. vol. LV, p. 183–188. 1 illus.)

1. Charity school of Kendal.
F486.O51   vol. 55   A 46–6029
Ohio state univ. Library
for Library of Congress

NL 0381448   OU DLC

Lindley, Harlow, 1875–   ed.
Ragan, Allen Edgar, 1897–
Chief Justice Taft, by Allen E. Ragan ... Columbus, O.,
The Ohio state archaeological and historical society, 1938.

Lindley, Harlow, 1875–
Chronology and roster of the Ohio state archaeological and
historical society. By Harlow Lindley.
(*In* Ohio state archaeological and historical quarterly. Columbus,
O., 1945. 23ᶜᵐ. vol. LIV, p. 247–256)

1. Ohio state archaeological and historical society.
                                              A 46–1052
Ohio state univ. Library
for Library of Congress   F486.O51   vol. 54

NL 0381450   OU DLC

Lindley, Harlow, 1875–1959, ed.
Early travelers to Fort Wayne
see under   Fort Wayne. Public Library.

Lindley, Harlow, 1875–
Friends and the Shawnee Indians at Wapakoneta. By Har-
low Lindley.
(*In* Ohio state archaeological and historical quarterly. Columbus,
O., 1945. 23ᶜᵐ. vol. LIV, p. 33–39)

1. Shawnee Indians.   2. Indians of North America—Ohio.   3. Friends,
Society of—Missions.   A 46–1038
Ohio state univ. Library
for Library of Congress   F486.O51   vol. 54

NL 0381452   OU DLC

Lindley, Harlow, 1875–
The government of Indiana, by Harlow Lindley ...
Boston, New York [etc.] Ginn and company [*1909]
110 p. 2 maps. 19ᶜᵐ. $0.50
On cover: Civics of Indiana.
Bibliography: p. 18.

1. Indiana—Pol. & govt.
                                              10–1231
Library of Congress   JK5625.1909.L6

NL 0381453   DLC

Lindley, Harlow, 1875–1959, ed.
History of the Ordinance of 1787 and the old
Northwest Territory
see under   Ohio. Northwest Territory
Celebration Commission.

Lindley, Harlow, 1875–
F491   Wittke, Carl Frederick, 1892–   ed.
.W78   The history of the state of Ohio, edited by Carl Wittke ...
Published under the auspices of the Ohio state archaeological
and historical society ... Publication committee: Harlow Lindley, chairman, Carl Wittke, William T. Utter. [Columbus, O.,
1941–44]

Lindley, Harlow, 1875–   ed.
... Indiana as seen by early travelers
see under   Indiana. Historical Commission.

Lindley, Harlow, 1875–   ed.
Indiana. *Historical commission.*
... The Indiana centennial, 1916; a record of the celebration
of the one hundredth anniversary of Indiana's admission to
statehood, ed. by Harlow Lindley, secretary Indiana Historical
commission. Indianapolis, The Indiana Historical commission, 1919.

Lindley, Harlow, 1875–1959, ed.
Indiana Historical Collections. Indiana as
seen by early travelers
see   Indiana. Historical Commission. Indiana as seen by early travelers.

Lindley, Harlow, 1875–
John Lewis Roth, the first white child born in the Moravian
mission at Gnadenhutten. By Harlow Lindley. [Colum-
bus, O., 1935]
[1], 250–257 p. 23ᶜᵐ.
"Reprinted from the Ohio state archaeological and historical quarterly April 1935."

1. Roth, John Lewis, 1773–1841.   2. Roth, John, 1726–1791.   3. Moravian Indians—Missions.   4. Gnadenhutten, O.
                                              35–12873
Library of Congress   E99.M9L5
                                              970.3

NL 0381459   DLC OFH OClWHi

Lindley, Harlow, 1875–   ed.
The Michigan-Indiana-Ohio museums association, edited by
Harlow Lindley.
(*In* The Ohio state archaeological and historical quarterly. Colum-
bus, O., 1935. 23ᶜᵐ. vol. XLIV, p. 273–289)

1. Michigan-Indiana-Ohio museums association.
                                              37–13775
Library of Congress   F486.O51   vol. 44

NL 0381460   DLC OClWHi OOxM OCl

VOLUME 334

Lindley, Harlow, 1875–   ed.
...... Ohio in the twentieth century, 1900–
1938, planned and compiled by Harlow Lindley ... Columbus,O.,Ohio state archaeological and historical society, 1942.
    xiii,563p. illus.,ports.,maps,tables,
diagr. 23½cm. (Added t.-p.: The history
of the state of Ohio, ed. by Carl Wittke.
cv.6₃)
    "... The work of several contributors."
cf. Editor's introduction.
Bibliographical foot-notes.

NL 0381461   PSt NcD OCU OO

Lindley, Harlow, 1875-1959, ed.
Ohio. State University, *Columbus. College of Medicine.*
    The Ohio State University College of Medicine. Blanchester, Ohio, Brown Pub. Co., 1934–61.

Lindley, Harlow, 1875–
    Possibilities in state historical celebrations, by Harlow
Lindley ... ₍Cedar Rapids? Ia., 1918₎
    cover-title, p. ₍307₎–317. 26ᶜᵐ.
    "Reprinted from the Proceedings of the Mississippi Valley historical
association, vol. IX, pt. II, 1918."

    1. Indiana.   I. Title: State historical celebrations.
                                                    20–22261
    Library of Congress   F527.L74

NL 0381463   DLC OFH OO

Lindley, Harlow, 1875–
    The Quakers in the old Northwest, by Harlow Lindley
... ₍Cedar Rapids, Ia., The Torch press, 1912₎
    15 p. 25ᶜᵐ.
    "Reprinted from the Proceedings of the Mississippi Valley historical
association, volume V."

    1. Friends, Society of. Northwest, Old. 2. Slavery and the church—
Friends, Society of.   I. Title.
                                            CA 25–900 Unrev'd
    Library of Congress   F485.F8L6

NL 0381464   DLC OFH PHC

Lindley, Harlow, 1875-1959.
    Quakers in the old Northwest.   1913.

NL 0381465   NcGuG

Lindley, Harlow, 1875–
    Report on the archives of the state of Indiana, by Harlow
Lindley ...
    ₍In American historical association. Annual report ... for the year
1910. Washington, 1912. 24½ᶜᵐ. p. 315–330)
    Appendix B of the report of the Public archives commission, 1910.

    1. Archives—Indiana.
                                                    C D 17–851
    Library of Congress   Card Div. E172.A60 1910

NL 0381466   DLC NN OFH MiU OCU MB

Lindley, Harlow, 1875–
    A state motto, by Harlow Lindley.
    ₍In Ohio state archaeological and historical quarterly. Columbus,
O., 1944. 23ᶜᵐ. vol. LIII, p. 160–165)
    Based on a letter written by William D. Henkle to William Henry
Smith.

    1. Mottoes.   I. Henkle, William Downs, 1828–1881. II. Title.
Ohio state univ. Library   A 45–4974
for Library of Congress   F486.O51 vol. 53

NL 0381467   OU DLC

Lindley, Harlow, 1875–
    The story of Ohio as told by a museum exhibit, by Harlow
Lindley. ₍Columbus₎ The Ohio state archæological and historical society ₍1932₎
    44 p. illus. (incl. port., maps) 15 x 13ᶜᵐ.
    "Portrayed in a special exhibit of the Ohio state museum."—Fore-
word.

    1. Ohio.   I. Ohio state archæological and historical society. Mu-
seum.
    Library of Congress   F492.L56   33–5252
                                                    917.71

NL 0381468   DLC OU

Lindley, Harlow, 1875–
    Thomas Beals, first Friends minister in Ohio. By Harlow
Lindley.
    ₍In Ohio state archaeological and historical quarterly. Columbus,
O., 1944. 23ᶜᵐ. vol. LIII, p. 55–60)

    1. Beals, Thomas, 1719–1801. 2. Friends, Society of. Ohio.
Ohio state univ. Library   A 45–4971
for Library of Congress   F486.O51 vol. 53

NL 0381469   OU DLC NcGuG PSC-Hi

[LINDLEY,Harlow].
    Western travel,1800–1820. n.p.,[1919?]
    1.8°. pp.(25).
    Without title-page. Caption title.
    "The Mississippi Valley historical review,
volVI,no.2,Sept.1919," pp.[167]–191.
    "This paper was delivered as the presidential
address at the 12th annual meeting of the
Mississippi valley historical association in
St.Louis,May 8,1919."

NL 0381470   MH

Lindley, Harlow, 1875–
    William Clark—the Indian agent, by Harlow Lindley
... ₍Cedar Rapids? Ia., 1909?₎
    cover-title, 13 p. 26ᶜᵐ.
    "Reprinted from the Proceedings of the Mississippi Valley historical
association for the year 1908–1909."

    1. Clark, William, 1770–1838.
                                            CA 25–995 Unrev'd
    Library of Congress   F592.7.C63

NL 0381471   DLC OrHi MB WaU PHC OFH

Lindley, Harold W
    A guide to marine insurance claims with some
answers to questions set in the examinations of
the Chartered insurance institute and Royal
society of arts, by Harold W. Lindley ... and
Sidney J. Saunders ... London, Buckley press
ltd., 1936.
    2 p. l., 282 p. 18½ cm.

    Folded page of text inserted between p. 274
and p. 275.

NL 0381472   NNC

Lindley, Harry.
    "Chick" or Myrtle Ferns... By Harry Lindley.
Peterborough, Ont., Times pub. house, 1893.
40 p. 19cm.

    1. Drama, Canadian. I. Title.

NL 0381473   NN

LINDLEY, HARRY.
    "Chick;" or, Myrtle Ferns, in five acts, re-arranged
from original. Peterborough, Ont., Times pub. house,
1893. 40 p. 19cm.

    Film reproduction. Positive.

    1. Drama, Canadian. I. Title.

NL 0381474   NN

Lindley (J. van) Nursery Co., Pomona, N.C.
    see   Lindley Nurseries, Pomona, N.C.

Lindley, Jacob.
    ... Account of a journey to attend the Indian
treaty, proposed to be held at Sandusky, in the
year 1793, interspersed with various observations,
remarks, and circumstances, that occurred on
this interesting occasion. [Philadelphia, 1832]
    18.5 cm. (Friends' miscellany, v. 2,
no. 2–3)

NL 0381476   CtY

Lindley, Jacob.
    Infant philosophy, containing an analysis of the faculties
of the mind, as discovered in their development, with directions
for the management and training of each in its earliest stages.
By Rev. Jacob Lindley ... Uniontown ₍Pa.₎ Pub. by the author, 1846.
    viii, 344 p. 14ᶜᵐ.

    1. Domestic education.   I. Title.
                                                    6–39638
    Library of Congress   LB1507.L74

NL 0381477   DLC NjP IaU PU OCX

LB1507
.L74   Lindley, Jacob.
1856   Infant philosophy, and parent's assistant;
            containing an analysis of the faculties of the
            mind, as discovered in their development, with
            directions for the management and training of
            each in its earliest stages. Rev., improved,
            and enl. ed.   Louisville, Ky., Cumberland
            Presbyterian Board of Publication, 1856.
                xviii ₍19₎–34 p. 19 cm.

                Imperfect: pages after 342 wanting.

NL 0381478   T

VOLUME 334

M917.3
L74
1892   Lindley, Jacob.
    Journals of Jacob Lindley and Joseph Moore, or
    Quaker accounts of the expedition of 1793 to De-
    troit and vicinity undertaken for the purpose of
    negotiating a general peace with the Indians of
    the Northwestern Territory, and conducted by
    three United States commissioners, accompanied
    by six delegates of Philadelphia Yearly Meeting
    of Friends; being extracts from the Michigan
    Pioneer Collections, vol. XVII, reprinted from
    Friends' Miscellany, vols. II and VI.   Lansing

    R. Smith, Pub. for Ambrose M. Shotwell, Concord,
    Jackson Co., Mich., 1892.
        85p.   24cm.
    On cover: Expedition to Detroit in 1793.
    Stamped on inside cover: Ambrose M. Shotwell,
    Lib'y for Blind, Saginaw W.S., Mich.
        1.Detroit-Hist. 2.Indians of N.A.-Northwest,
    Old. 3.Northwest, Old-Descr. & trav. I.Moore,
    Joseph. II.Shotwell, Ambrose Milton,
    1853-   III.Friends, Society of. IV.Ti-
    tle. V.Expedition to Detroit in 1793.

    NL   0381480   Mi

Lindley, Jacob.
[Severance, Frank Hayward] 1856-1931, ed.
    Narratives of early mission work on the Niagara frontier and
    Buffalo creek.
        (In Buffalo historical society. Publications. Buffalo, 1903. 24cm.
    v. 6, p. [163]-380 incl. facsim. port.)

LINDLEY, J[ames] J., 1822-
    Remarks on the election of speaker, delivered
    in the House of Representatives Jan.11 and 14,
    1856. [Washington, 1856].

    pp. 8.
    Caption-title.
    DLC: YA 5000 J17

    NL   0381482   MH PPL DLC

    Lindley, James J   1822-
        Speech of Mr. Lindley, of Missouri, in the House of
    representatives, June 19, 1856. [Washington, American
    organ, print., 1856]
        8 p.   23cm.
    Caption title.
    In support of Col. Benton and the American party.

        1. Campaign literature, 1856—American.
                                                    10-31068
    Library of Congress   E435.L74

    NL   0381483   MH DLC

PQ2625
.A95Z53
1943   Lindley, Jane Hastings Hickok, joint tr.
    Maurois, André, 1885-
        Call no man happy, by André Maurois; translated from the
    French by Denver and Jane Lindley.   London, J. Cape [1943]

    Lindley, Jane Hastings Hickok, joint tr.
    Maurois, André, 1885-
        I remember, I remember, by André Maurois, translated from
    the French by Denver and Jane Lindley.   New York and Lon-
    don, Harper & brothers [1942]

E178
.M462   Lindley, Jane Hastings Hickok, joint tr.
    Maurois, André, 1885-
        The miracle of America, by André Maurois, translated from
    the French by Denver and Jane Lindley ...   New York and
    London, Harper & brothers, 1944.

BV630
.C35   Lindley, Jeanne (Cammaerts) joint author.
    Cammaerts, Émile.
        Principalities and powers, by Émile Cammaerts and
    Jeanne Lindley. London, Cresset Press, 1947.

Lindley, Jo.
    Three years in Cariboo: by Jo. Lindley, being
    the experiences and observations of a packer,
    what I saw and know of the country; its travelled
    routes, distances, villages, mines, trade and
    prospects. With distances, notes and facts,
    relative to the Salmon River and Nez Perces gold
    fields. By T.R. Olney. San Francisco, Published
    by A. Rosenfield. Towne & Bacon, printers. 1862.

    36 p.   14.2 x 8.7cm.

    On cover: Guide and history of Salmon River &
    Cariboo mining districts, containing valuable
    information, with correct tables of modes and
    prices of travelling; also giving the distances
    from point to point, of all the routes.
    "Vocabulary of the Chinook jargon": p. [32]-36

    NL   0381489   CaBVaU

Lindley, John, 1799-1865.
    [Addition to point out how far substances,
    not chicory, may also be recognized.
    London, 1852]
        13 p. [4 colored plates.   f°.   Lithographed.
        By Lindley, John and Hooker, Sir Joseph
    Dalton.

    NL   0381490   MH-H

610.8
L619m   Lindley, John, 1799-1865.
    Aphorismes de physiologie végétale et de
    botanique, suivis du tableau des alliances des
    plantes, et de l'analyse artificielle des ordres,
    par John Lindley ... Traduits de l'anglais, et
    précédés d'une introduction, par P.-A.Cap ...
    Paris, L.Colas, 1838.
        3 p.l.,180 p.   21 cm.
    With Le Roy, Charles. Mélanges de physique et
    médecine. 1771.
        1.Botany--Physiology. 2.Botany. I.Cap, Paul
    Antoine Gratacap,   called, 1788-1877, tr.
    II.Title.

    NL   0381491   MiU DNLM

QK94
.L5
1838   Lindley, John, 1799-1865.
    Botanik für Damen; oder, Fassliche Einleitung
    in das Studium des natürlichen Systems der
    Pflanzenkunde. Nach der 2. Aufl. aus dem
    Englischen übersetzt. Bonn, Henry und Cohen
    1838.
        xiv, 280 p. 25 col. plates. 24 cm.

    5355 Pritzel. 1202 Nissen.

        1. Botany. i.t.

    NL   0381492   NNBG NN

[Lindley, John] 1799-1865.
    ...Botany ... Published under the superintendence
    of the Society for the diffusion of useful knowledge.
    London, Baldwin and Cradock, 1838.
        iv, 222, [2] p.   illus.   22cm.   (Library of useful knowledge)

        1. Botany.   4-14634

    Library of Congress   QK45.L7.

    NL   0381493   DLC MdBP MH NNBG MB

Lindley, John, 1799-1865.
    Catalogue of North American genera of plants,
    arranged according to the orders of Lindley's
    Introduction to the natural system of botany ...
    New York, Sleight & Robinson, printers, 1831.
        22 p.   23 cm.   [Scientific miscellany, v. 10]

    NL   0381494   CtY MH-A

Lindley, John, 1799-1865.
    Collectanea botanica; or, Figures and botanical illus-
    trations of rare and curious exotic plants. By John
    Lindley ...   London, Printed by R. and A. Taylor, sold
    by J. and A. Arch [etc.] 1821.
        2 p. l., 42 l., 41 col. pl., [4] p.   43 x 29cm.
    Each plate accompanied by leaf with descriptive letterpress (pl. 41 by 2
    leaves)

        1. Botany—Pictorial works.

    Library of Congress   QK98.L74   6-18036†

    NL   0381495   DLC MH-A CU

Lindley, John, 1799-1865.
    Contributions to the orchidology of India.
    No.1. Read January 20, 1857. n.p. [1857]

        170-192 p.   22.5 cm.

    NL   0381496   MH

Lindley, John, 1799-1865.
    Contributions to the orchidology of India.
    No. II. [Read March 4th, 1858]   n.p.

        64 p.   22.5 cm.
    At head of title: Journal of the proceedings
    of the Linnean society of London.

    NL   0381497   MH MBH

Lindley, John, 1799-1865.
    Descriptive botany: or, The art of describing plants correctly in
    scientific language.   For self-instruction, and the use of schools.
    By Professor Lindley, F.R.S. London, Bradbury and Evans,
    1859.
        31, [1] p.   illus.   21½cm.

    NL   0381498   ICJ

Lindley, [John] 1799-1865.
    Descriptive botany; or, The art of describing
    plants correctly in scientific language ...
    London, Bradbury, Agnew, & Co., 1874.
        32 p.   8°.
        8th ed.

    NL   0381499   NN

VOLUME 334

Lindley, John, 1799–1865.
Digitalium monographia; sistens historiam botanicam generis, tabulis omnium specierum hactenus cognitarum illustratam ut plurimum confectis ad icones Ferdinandi Bauer penes Gulielmum Cattley ... Cura Johannis Lindley ... Londini, typis R. et A. Taylor, 1821.
2 p. l., ii, 27, ₍2₎ p. 28 col. pl. 48¼ᶜᵐ.

1. Digitalis.

Agr 10–245

Library, U. S. Dept. of   Agriculture 452.3L64D

NL 0381500   DNAL WU NNBG MU MWelC MBH PPAN PPHor ICJ

Lindley, John.
Edwards's Botanical register: or, Ornamental flower-garden and shrubbery
see under title

QK94
.L48
1833
Lindley, John, 1799–1865.
Einleitung in das natürliche System der Botanik; oder, Systematische Uebersicht der Organisation, natürlichen Verwandtschaften und geographischen Verbreitung des ganzen Pflanzenreichs, nebst Angabe des Nutzens der wichtigsten Arten in der Heilkunde, den Künsten und der Haus- und Feldwirtschaft. Weimar, Verlage des Landes-Industrie-Comptoirs, 1833.
viii, 524 p. 22 cm.

5348 Pritzel.

1. Botany –   Classification. i.t.

NL 0381502   NNBG ICU

580
L746o4
Lindley, John, 1799–1865.
Elements of botany, stuctural, physiological, systematical, and medical; being a 4th ed. of The outline of the first principles of botany ... London, Printed for Taylor and Walton, 1841.
292p. illus.

1. Botany. 2. Botany. Medical.

NL 0381503   IU-M MH MBH KU

QK
49
L55
1847
Lindley, John, 1799–1865.
The elements of botany, structural and physiological; being a fifth edition of the outline of the first principles of botany. With a sketch of the artificial methods of classification, and a glossary of technical terms. London, Bradbury & Evans, 1847.
xii, 142, c p. illus. 23 cm.

"A list of introductions to botany": p. [ix]-x.

1. Botany - Juvenile literature. I. Lindley, John, 1799–1865. An out   line of the first principles of botany.

NL 0381504   ICF NIC CtY OU MH

QK
L746e
1849
LINDLEY, John, 1799–1865.
The elements of botany, structural, physiological, & medical; being a 6th ed. of the outline of the first principles of botany, with a sketch of the artificial methods of classification, and a glossary of technical terms. New ed., with some corrections. London, Bradbury & Evans, 1849.
xii, 142, c p. illus.

NL 0381505   DNLM PPGi MiU MH

Lindley, John.
The elements of botany, structural and physiological: with a sketch of the artificial modes of classification, and a glossary of technical terms. A new edition.
London. Bradbury & Evans. 1861. xii, 142, c pp. Illus. 8°.

E5361 — Botany.   Aug. 11,   1902

NL 0381506   MB PBL OU NjP DNAL

580.3
L644e
Lindley, John, 1799–1865.
Excerpt from Illustrated dictionary of botanical terms ... With introduction by Alice Eastwood. ₍San Francisco₎ 1938.
cover-title, p.319, 347-383, 346. illus., tab.

"Published in Lindley's Introduction to botany in 1848, forming Book III of that ... work."

1. Botany--Dict. I. Eastwood, Alice, 1859-
II. Title: Illustrated dictionary of botanical terms.

NL 0381507   IU NNBG

Lindley, John, 1799–1865, ed.
Moore, Thomas, 1821–1887.
The ferns of Great Britain and Ireland. By Thomas Moore ... Ed. by John Lindley ... Nature-printed by Henry Bradbury. London, Bradbury and Evans, 1855.

QK51
.L5
Lindley, John, 1799–1865.
Fitografia, o de las reglas que deben observarse al describir y denominar plantas. Traducida de la 2. ed. inglesa por J. Enrique Rothe. Tucuman, 1951.
55 p. 24 cm. (Miscelánea. Instituto Miguel Lillo. no. 16)

"Traducción del cuarto libro de ... obra An Introduction to Botany, ed 2ᵃ (1835)"

1. Botany. i. t. ii. s. iii. Rothe, J Enrique,   tr.

NL 0381509   NNBG

Lindley, John, 1799–1865.
Sibthorp, John, 1758–1796.
Flora græca: sive Plantarum rariorum historia, quas in provinciis aut insulis Græciæ legit, investigavit et depingi curavit Johannes Sibthorp ... Characteres omnium, descriptiones et synonyma elaboravit Jacobus Edvardus Smith. Londini, typis Richardi Taylor & socii ₍etc.₎ 1806–40.

Lindley, John, 1799–1865.
Flora medica; a botanical account of all the more important plants used in medicine, in different parts of the world. By John Lindley ... London, Longman, Orme, Brown, Green, and Longmans, 1838.
xiii p., 1 l., 655, ₍1₎ p. 23ᵐ.

1. Botany, Medical. ₍1. Medical botany₎

Agr 3–620

U. S. Dept. of agr.   Library   452.82L64
for Library of Congress   ₍a38e1₎

NL 0381511   MH-A PPAN PPL MBH DNLM T OU MiU ICJ MB NIC TxU KyU   DNAL ICU WaU OKentU CtY OClW ViW NcD

Lindley, John, 1799–1865.
Flower Garden
see his Paxton's flower garden.

Lindley, John, 1799–1865.
... Folia orchidacea. An enumeration of the known species of orchids. By Professor Lindley. ₍Part 1–9₎ London, Published for the author by J. Matthews ₍1852–1859₎

1 v. ??ᵐ. illus., pl. 22ᶜᵐ.
The account of each genus forms a separately-paged section, bearing on the sheets the date of printing.
The sections contained in the first seven parts were alphabetically arranged and issued as "Vol. 1."
Includes "Observations sur la déhiscence du fruit des orchidées. Par Ed. Prillieux", abstracted, or furnished in advance, from that author's paper in the "Bull. Soc. Bot. France", Tom. IV (1857) p. 803–808. cf. British Museum
1. Orchids.   (Natural history) Catalogue.

Library of Congress   QK495.O64L6

5–30196

NL 0381513   DLC MdBP AAP CU MBH MnU MiU ICJ

MICF
584.15
L644f
Lindley, John, 1799–1865.
... Folia orchidacea. An enumeration of the known species of orchids. By Professor Lindley. ₍Part 1–₎ London, Published for the author by J. Matthews ₍1852–₎

IDC Micro-edition.
Microfiche. Tumba, Sweden, International Documentation Center. 1 box (8 cards)

NL 0381514   DLC

Lindley, John, 1799–1865.
The fossil flora of Great Britain; or, Figures and descriptions of the vegetable remains found in a fossil state in this country. By John Lindley ... and William Hutton ... London, J. Ridgway, 1831-3–37.
3 v. illus., 230 (i. e. 231) pl. (9 fold.) incl. fronts. 23ᶜᵐ.

1. Paleobotany--Gt. Brit. i. Hutton, William, 1798–1860, joint author.

6–10114

Library of Congress   QE944.L74

NL 0381515   OU MiU ViU DNLM NIC CU PPAmP OCU ICJ WU MdBP NN KyU   DLC NNBG OC NcD CtY PBL NjP CLSU MnU

Lindley, John, 1799–1865, ed.
Gardeners' Chronicle and gardening illustrated
see under title

Lindley, John, 1799–1865.
The genera and species of orchideous plants. By John Lindley ... London, Treuttel and co., and Ridgways, 1830–35.
4 v. in 1. 22½ cm.
CONTENTS.—pt. I. Malaxideae.—pt. II. Epidendreæ.—pt. III. Vandeæ.—pt. IV. Ophrydeæ.

1. Orchids.

QK495.O64L63   584.15   34—10666

NL 0381517   DLC CLSU

Lindley, John, 1799–1865.
The genera and species of orchidaceous plants. By John Lindley ... London, Ridgways, 1830–40.
xvii, 553 p. 22½ᶜᵐ.

"Orchidaceae. The following are the principal writings upon this order since the revival of natural history by Linnaeus": p. ₍xii₎–xii.

1. Orchidaceae.

Agr 11–690

Library, U. S. Dept. of   Agriculture 452.3L64G

NL 0381518   DNAL NN CtY PPHor MsSM MBH Mi

VOLUME 334

Lindley, John LL. D. 1799-1865.
—— Glossary of botanical terms. London,
1861. 8°.   —2605

NL   0381519   MdBP DP

Lindley, John, 1799-1865.
A glossary of technical terms used in botany. By John
Lindley ... London, Bradbury and Evans, 1848.
1 p. l., (ix)-xii, c p. illus. 22½ᶜᵐ.
"A list of introductions to botany": p. (ix)-x.

1. Botany—Terminology.
                                              5—25750
Library of Congress   QK9.L7

NL   0381520   DLC ViU MH-A

QK10
.L5   Lindley, John, 1799-1865.
1839   Glossology; or, Of the terms used in botany.
       (London, 1839)
       443-544 p. illus. 23 cm.

       Caption title.
       From the author's An introduction to botany.
       3d ed.
       Copy 1 inscribed: E. D. Merrill.

       1. Botany - Terminology. i.t. a. Merrill,
       Elmer Drew, 1876-1956.

NL   0381521   NNBG

QK48 Lindley, John, 1799-1865.
.L7   Grundzüge der anfangsgründe der botanik. Von John
       Lindley ... Aus dem Englischen ... Weimar, Landes-indus-
       trie-comptoir, 1831.
       viii, 116 p. 4 pl. 17½ᶜᵐ.

       1. Botany.

NL   0381522   ICU

Lindley, John, 1799-1865, ed.
Lindley, George.
A guide to the orchard and kitchen garden; or, An account of the most valuable fruit and vegetables cultivated
in Great Britain: with kalendars of the work required in
the orchard and kitchen garden during every month in
the year. By George Lindley ... Ed. by John Lindley ...
London, Longman, Rees, Orme, Brown and Green, 1831.

Lindley, John, 1799-1865.
Loudon, John Claudius, 1783-1843, ed.
Loudon's Hortus britannicus. A catalogue of all the plants
indigenous, cultivated in, or introduced to Britain. Part I.
The Linnean arrangement ... Part II. The Jussieuean ar-
rangement ... A new ed., with supplements including all
the new plants down to March, 1839 ... Ed. by J. C. Loudon
... London, Printed for Longman, Orme, Brown, Green, and
Longmans (1839?)

Lindley, John, 1799-1865, ed. **FOR OTHER EDITIONS
                                SEE MAIN ENTRY**
Cambridge. University. *Botanic garden.*
Hortus cantabrigiensis; or, An accented catalogue of
indigenous and exotic plants cultivated in the Cambridge
botanic garden. By the late James Donn ... Improved
and augm. with references to figures and plants, by Frederick Pursh ... 11th ed., with numerous additions and
corrections, by John Lindley ... London, Printed for C.
and J. Rivington, 1826.

Lindley, John, 1799-1865.
... Illustrated dictionary of botanical terms, by John Lind-
ley ... 1848. With introduction by Alice Eastwood. (San
Francisco, Cal.?) 1938.
cover-title, (2), 347-388, (1) p. illus. 21½ᶜᵐ.
"Published in Lindley's Introduction to botany in 1848, forming
Book III of that valuable work." Reprinted 1938.
Page at end of pamphlet numbered 346.

1. Botany—Dictionaries. 2. Botany—Terminology. I. Eastwood,
Alice, 1859— II. Title.
                                              S 38-74
Smithsonian Inst. Library
for Library of Congress   (3)

NL   0381526   DSI

Lindley, John, 1799-1865.
North of England institute of mining and mechanical engineers, *Newcastle-upon-Tyne.*
Illustrations of fossil plants; being an autotype reproduction of selected drawings. Prepared under the supervision of
the late Dr. Lindley and Mr. W. Hutton, between the years
1835 and 1840, and now for the first time pub. by the North
of England institute of mining and mechanical engineers.
Ed. by G. A. Lebour. London, Longmans and company, 1877.

Lindley, John, 1799-1865.
Bauer, Franz Andreas, 1758-1840.
Illustrations of orchidaceous plants; by Francis Bauer
... with notes and prefatory remarks by John Lindley ...
London, J. Ridgway and sons, 1830-38.

Lindley, John, 1799-1865.
An introduction to botany, by John Lindley ... London, Longman, Rees, Orme, Brown, Green, & Longman,
1832.
xvi, 557, (1) p. illus., vi pl. 22ᶜᵐ.

1. Botany.
                                              Agr 10-28
Library, U. S. Dept. of   Agriculture 452L641In

NL   0381529   DNAL InU MH-A CU KU WaU NNBG PPAN

QK47
.L5   Lindley, John, 1799-1865.
1835
       An introduction to botany. 2d ed., with
       corr. and numerous additions. London,
       Longman, Rees, Orme, Brown, Green, &
       Longman, 1835.
       xiv, 580 p. illus. 22 cm.

       1. Botany.

NL   0381530   ViU DI-GS OU PPAN MiU NjP MH NNBG NWM

580
L644in Lindley, John, 1799-1865.
1839   An introduction to botany. 3rd ed., with
       corrections and numerous additions.
       London, Longman, Orme, Brown, Green, and
       Longmans, 1839.
       xi, 594p. illus., 6 plates 23cm.

       1. Botany.

WU CtY PPF CoGrS
NL   0381531   KU CaBVaU OrPR NjP NjR DI-GS OU NNBG

Lindley, John, 1799-1865.
An introduction to botany. . By John Lindley ... 4th
ed., with corrections and numerous additions ... London, Longman, Brown, Green, and Longmans, 1848.
2 v. illus., vi pl. 22ᶜᵐ.

1. Botany.
                                              4-14975
                                 (30c1)
Library of Congress   QK45.L72

PU-B MB DI-GS ICJ
NL   0381532   DLC NjP MdBP MBH NIC CU NNBG CLSU PU

Lindley, John, 1799-1865.
An introduction to the natural system of botany: or, A systematic view of the organisation, natural affinities, and geographical distribution, of the whole vegetable kingdom; together with the uses of the most important species in medicine,
the arts, and rural or domestic economy. By John Lindley ...
London, Longman, Rees, Orme, Brown, and Green, 1830.
xlviii, 374, (1) p. 23ᶜᵐ.

1. Botany.
U. S. Dept. of agr. Library   452L64 I   Agr 25-345
for Library of Congress   [QK94.L   ]

NL   0381533   DNAL NcD MiU CU NNBG PPL MB ICJ PPPCPh

Lindley, John, 1799-1865.
An introduction to the natural system of botany: or,
A systematic view of the organization, natural affinities,
and geographical distribution of the whole vegetable
kingdom; together with the uses of the most important
species in medicine, the arts, and rural or domestic economy. By John Lindley ... 1st American ed., with an
appendix. By John Torrey ... New York, G. & C. & H.
Carvill, 1831.
lxxix, 392 p. 2 pl. 23ᶜᵐ.
1. Botany. I. Torrey, John, 1796-1873, ed.
                                              5—25371
Library of Congress   QK94.L7

KyU DNLM
PU PPAN ODW OCU OO OU PU NjR NWM MnU-A Wa MBH AU
NL   0381534   DLC NcA-S RP NjP ViU NNBG KU PHC NcU

QK
L746i   LINDLEY, John, 1799-1865.
1829   An introductory lecture delivered in
       the University of London, on Thursday,
       April 30, 1829. London, Taylor, 1829.
       26 p.

NL   0381535   DNLM MH MeB

Lindley, John, 1799-1865.
A key to structural, physiological, and systematic botany, for the use of classes. By John Lindley ... London
Longman, Rees, Orme, Brown, Green, & Longman, 1833.
80 p. 21ᶜᵐ.

1. Botany.
                                              4-34023†
Library of Congress   QK47.L7

NL   0381536   DLC KyU NNBG PPFr CtY PPAN MeB OU

VOLUME 334

Lindley, John, 1799–1865.
A key to structural, physiological, and systematic botany, for the use of classes. By John Lindley, ... With an appendix, containing a catalogue of medicinal plants, most of which may be seen in the garden of the Society of Apothecaries at Chelsea. London, Longman, Orme, Brown, Green, & Longmans, 1839.
[4, 3]–96 p. 21ᶜᵐ.

NL 0381537   ICJ MH

Lindley, John, 1799–1865.
Ladies' botany... 4. ed.   London, n.d.
2 v. in 1.

NL 0381538   NjP

Lindley, John, 1799–1865.
Ladies' botany; or, A familiar introduction to the study of the natural system of botany. By John Lindley ... London, J. Ridgway and sons, 1834–37.
2 v. ɪ. col. pl. (incl. fronts.) 22½ᶜᵐ.

1. Botany.

Library of Congress   QK94.L74   5-25372†

NL 0381539   DLC NNBG

QK94
.L5
1840
Lindley, John, 1799–1865.
Ladies' botany; or, A familiar introduction to the study of the natural system of botany. 2d ed. London, J. Ridgway [184–?]
2 v. 50 col. plates. 23 cm.

Volume 2, copy 2 labeled: Ex libris, Sarah Gildersleeve Fife.

1. Botany.   i.t. ii.t: A familiar introduction to the study of the natural system of botany. a. Fife,   Sarah Gildersleeve

NL 0381540   NNBG CSt NjP WU MH

Lindley, John,
Ladies' botany; or, a familiar introduction to the study of the natural system of botany, illustrated with numerous wood-cuts. New ed. for the use of schools and young persons. Lond., H. G. Bohn, 1841.
424 p

NL 0381541   PU

581
L746l
1847
Lindley, John, 1799–1865.
Ladies' botany; or, A familiar introduction to the study of the natural system of botany. Illustrated with numerous wood-cuts. New ed. for the use of schools and young persons. London, Henry G. Bohn, 1847.
xx, 424p. col. illus. 19cm.

1. Botany. I. Title.

NL 0381542   TxDAM

QK94
.L5
1856
Lindley, John, 1799–1865.
Ladies' botany; or, A familiar introduction to the study of the natural system of botany. London, J. Ridgway [1856]
2 v. 50 col. plates. 23 cm.

"Fifth edition."
5355 Pritzel. 1201 Nissen.

1. Botany. i.t. ii.t: A familiar introduction to the study of the natural system of botany.

NL 0381543   NNBG MH NcD CU MBH

Lindley, John, 1799–1865.
Ladies' botany; or, A familiar introduction to the study of the natural system of botany. By John Lindley ... 6th ed. London, H. G. Bohn, 1865.
2 v. ɪ. col. pl. 22½ᶜᵐ.

1. Botany. ɪ. Title.

Agr 23–662

Library, U. S. Dept. of   Agriculture 452L64L

NL 0381544   DNAL NIC WU ODW OU

Lindley, John, 1799–1865.
Medical and oeconomical botany. By John Lindley ... London, Bradbury & Evans, 1849.
2 p. l., ɪɪɪɪ–iv, 274 p. illus. 23ᶜᵐ. (Half-title: Elements of botany, ɪɪɪ)

1. Botany, Economic. 2. Botany, Medical. ɪ2. Medical botanyɪ

Agr 25–346

Library, U. S. Dept. of   Agriculture 452.82L64M

NL 0381545   DNAL MBH MH-A CU NNBG CtY-M PPC OU

Lindley, John, 1799–1865.
Medical and oeconomical botany. By John Lindley ... 2d ed. London, Bradbury & Evans, 1856.
iv, 274 p. illus. 23ᶜᵐ. (His Elements of botany, ɪɪɪ)

1. Botany, Medical. 2. Botany, Economic.

A 11–2091

Title from Leland Stan-   ford Jr. Univ. Printed by L. C.

NL 0381546   CSt NNBG MiU NjR

Lindley, John, 1799–1865.
Monographie du genre rosier, tr. de l'anglais de m. J. Lindley, avec des notes de m. L. Joffrin, et des changemens importans, suivie d'un appendice sur les roses cultivées dans les jardins de Paris et environs. Par m. de Pronville ... Paris, Audot, 1824.
2 p. l., viii, 182 p. 20½ᶜᵐ.
"Table alphabétique des abréviations": p. ɪiiɪ–viii.

1. Rose. ɪ. Pronville, Auguste de, tr.

Agr 17—663

U. S. Dept. of agr. Library   452.3L64M
for Library of Congress   ɪa41b1ɪ

NL 0381547   DNAL GU MH-A

Lindley, John, 1799–1865.
A natural system of botany; or, A systematic view of the organization, natural affinities, and geographical distribution, of the whole vegetable kingdom; together with the uses of the most important species in medicine, the arts, and rural or domestic economy. By John Lindley ... 2d ed., with numerous additions and corrections, and a complete list of genera, with their synonyms. London, Longman, Rees, Orme, Brown, Green, and Longman, 1836.
xxvi, 526 p. diagrs. 23½ᶜᵐ.
1. Botany.

Agr 4–961

Library, U. S. Dept. of   Agriculture 452L64N.

MWcS PPPCPh OU MiU MB NWM
NL 0381548   DNAL CaBVaU PPFr MBH MH-A ViU NNBG CtY

Lɪɴᴅʟᴇʏ, John. A natural system of botany; or, A systematic view of the organization, natural affinities and geographical distribution of the whole vegetable kingdom. (American journal of science and arts, 1837, xxxii, 292–303.)

NL 0381549   MH-A

Lindley, John, 1799–1865.
Nixus plantarum. Auctore Johanni Lindley ... Londini, apud Ridgway et filios, 1833.
v, ɪ7ɪ–28 p. 22½ᶜᵐ.

1. Botany. Systems.

Agr 5–1080

Library, U. S. Dept. of   Agriculture 452L64Ni

NL 0381550   DNAL NNBG

QK94
L52
1967
Biology
Library
Lindley, John, 1799–1865.
Nixus plantarum. Auctore Johanni Lindley. Londini, Ridgway, 1833. [Ann Arbor, Mich., University Microfilms, 1967]
v. 28 p.

Photocopy (positive)
This work was subsequently incorporated with the author's Outline of the first principles of botany to form his A key to structural, physiological, and systematic botany.

1. Botany – Classification. I. Title.

NL 0381551   CU

QK94
.L515
1834
Lindley, John, 1799–1865.
Nixus plantarum. Die Stämme des Gewächsreiches. Verdeutscht durch C. T. Beilschmied. Mit einer Vorerinnerung von C. G. Nees von Esenbeck. Nürnberg, J. L. Schrag, 1834.
x, 44 p. 24 cm.

5353 Pritzel.

1. Botany – Classification. i.t.

NL 0381552   NNBG

Lindley, John.
——— A notice of some species of Rhododendron inhabiting Borneo. [London. 1848.] 8°. Illustr.
Journal of the Horticultural society of London, 1848, iii, 81–91.

NL 0381553   MH-A

VOLUME 334

SB   Lindley, John, 1799–1865.
408   Notices of certain ornamental plants
L74   lately introduced into England by Professor
Lindley. ₍London, Printed by W. Clowes
& sons. 18––?₎
    14 p. 4 plates. 30 cm.

    1. Plants,   Ornamental. I. Title.

NL   0381554   NIC

Lindley, John.

—— Observations on the natural group of plants called
Pomaceæ. ₍London. 1822.₎ 4°. 4 plates.
Transactions of the Linnean society of London, 1822, xiii, 88–106.

NL   0381555   MH-A

Lindley, John, 1799–1865, tr.

Richard, Louis Claude Marie, 1754–1821.
    Observations on the structure of fruits and seeds; tr. from
the Analyse du fruit of M. Louis-Claude Richard ... with
notes, by John Lindley. London, J. Harding; ₍etc., etc.₎ 1819.

NL   0381556

Lindley, John.

—— Observations upon the effects produced on plants by
the frost which occurred in England in the winter of 1837–8;
abstracted and condensed from the *Horticultural transactions
of London.* ₍New Haven. 1840.₎ 8°.
American journal of science and arts, 1840, xxxix, 18–28.

NL   0381557   MH-A

Lindley, John.

—— On the principal questions at present debated in the
philosophy of botany. 8°. pp. ₍31₎. London, 1833.
*" From the Report of the British association for the advancement of science
for 1833." pp. 27–57.*

NL   0381558   MBH MH-A

Lindley, John, 1799–1865.
    Orchidaceæ Lindenianæ; or, Notes upon a collection of
orchids formed in Colombia and Cuba, by Mr. J. Linden.
By John Lindley ... London, Bradbury and Evans, 1846.
    viii, 28 p. 21½ᶜᵐ.

    1. Orchids—Colombia. 2. Orchids—Cuba. ɪ. Linden, Jean Jules.

    Library of Congress   QK495.O64L7   5–30199†

NL   0381559   DLC CU-B MH

---

fQK495 Lindley, John, 1799–1865.
.O64L7   Orchidaceæ Lindenianæ; or, Notes upon a
collection of orchids formed in Colombia and Cuba,
by Mr. J. Linden. By John Lindley. London,
Bradbury and Evans, 1846.
    viii, 28p. 22cm.

    Photocopy (negative) viii, 28p. on ₍19₎ l.
23 x 34cm.

    1. Orchids—Colombia. 2. Orchids—Cuba.
I. Linden, Jean Jules.

NL   0381560   DLC FMU

NAB   Lindley, John, 1799–1865.
2478   Orchidaceous Plants
L 64   Amsterdam, A. Asher & Co., 1963, Reprint,
London, Ridgways, Piccadilly, 1830–40.

    T.p., Pref., 17 prelim. pp.: Text, Latin
w. sections in English, 553 pp.

    Genera & species of orchidaceous plants;
analysis of organs of fructification;
bibliog. of books on orchids included.

NL   0381561   DDO

V 680
580   Lindley, John, 1799–1865.   Commisit Johannes Lindley.
A p.v.1   Orchidearum sceletos. Commisit Johannes Lindley.
no. 1   Londini, typis R. Taylor, 1826.
    ₍3₎ f., 9–27 p. 3 plates. 21 cm.

    "Amos Eaton, botanical pamphlet" in manuscript on fly-
leaf.

    1. Orchids. I. Eaton, Amos, 1776–1842.

NL   0381562   N MH

Lindley, John, 1799–1865.
    An outline of the first principles of botany. By John
Lindley ... London, Longman and co., 1830.
    viii p., 1 l., 106 p. 4 pl. 14½ᶜᵐ.

    1. Botany—Juvenile and popular literature.

    Library of Congress   QK49.L7   5–25769†

NL   0381563   DLC CU

AC901   Lindley, John, 1799–1865.
.P3   An outline of the first principles of horticulture.   New York, Thorburn, 1836.
    72 p.   (Pamphlets, 19:1)

NL   0381564   DLC

SB
407   Lindley, John, 1799–1865.
.L74   Paxton's flower garden. By Professor
1840   Lindley and Sir Joseph Paxton. London,
Cassell & co., ₍18?–1844₎
    3 v. illus. 108 col pl. 27 cm.
    Plates colored by hand.

    1. Flowers. I. Paxton, Joseph, Sir
1801–1865, Joint author. II. Title

    11–32135

NL   0381565   OKentU

Lindley, John, 1799–1865.
    Paxton's flower garden. By Professor Lindley and
Sir Joseph Paxton. London, Bradbury and Evans,
1850–53.
    3 v. illus., 108 col. pl. 27ᶜᵐ.
    Plates colored by hand.

    1. Flowers. ɪ. Paxton, Sir Joseph, 1801–1865, joint author. ɪɪ. Title.

    Library of Congress   SB407.L74   11–32135

    MiU OU OO WU NN CaBViP MH-A
NL   0381566   DLC DNAL MBH ICU CU NjP NIC WaU PU-B

SB   Lindley, John, 1799–1865.
407   Paxton's flower garden. By Professor Lindley
L5   and Sir Joseph Paxton. Revised by Thomas
1882   Baines ... London, Paris & New York, Cassell,
Petter, Galpin & Co., 1882–1884.

    3 v. in 1. illus., 108 col. plates (incl.
front.). 29 cm.

    1. Flowers. I. Paxton, Sir Joseph, 1801–1865,
joint author. II. Baines, Thomas. III. Title.

NL   0381567   ICF OrP CaBVaU ICJ PPHor NjP WaU PP

Lindley, John, 1799–1865.   ꜰᴏʀ ᴏᴛʜᴇʀ ᴇᴅɪᴛɪᴏɴꜱ
                                       ꜱᴇᴇ ᴍᴀɪɴ ᴇɴᴛʀʏ

Paxton, *Sir* Joseph, 1801–1865.
    A pocket botanical dictionary; comprising the names,
history, and culture of all plants known in Britain; with
a full explanation of technical terms. By Joseph Paxton ... assisted by Professor Lindley ... A new ed. with
supplement, containing all the new plants since its ap-
pearance. London, Bradbury & Evans, 1849.

Lindley, John, 1799–1865.
    Pomologia britannica; or, Figures and descriptions of
the most important varieties of fruit cultivated in Great
Britain. By John Lindley ... London, H. G. Bohn, 1841.
    3 v. 152 col. pl. (partly double) 24ᶜᵐ.
    Binder's title: Lindley's British fruits.

    1. Gt. Brit. Pomology.

                                            Agr 11–692

    Library, U. S. Dept. of   Agriculture 93L64P

    ICJ NN NBu
NL   0381569   DNAL CU WU PPL CSmH MH-A MBH PPAN DLC

₍**Lindley, John**₎ 1799–1865.
    The pomological magazine; or, Figures and descriptions of
the most important varieties of fruit cultivated in Great
Britain. London, J. Ridgway, 1828–39.
    3 v. 152 col. pl. (part double) 25ᶜᵐ.
    Vol. i, 1828; vol. ii, 1839; vol. iii, 1830.
    Reissued in 1841 under the title: Pomologia britannica ... By J. Lind-
ley.

    1. Fruit-culture—Gt. Brit. ₍1. Gt. Brit.—Pomology₎ ɪ. Title.

                                            Agr 20—121

    U. S. Dept. of agr. Library₎   93L64Pm
    for Library of Congress   ₍a41b1₎

NL   0381570   DNAL MBH

Lindley, John.

—— Principes de botanique. Traduits par P. A. Mas-
son-Four. Paris. 1832. 8°. pp. 76. 4 plates.

NL   0381571   MH-A

Lindley, John, 1799–1865.
    Principles of horticulture.

    (*In* U. S. Patent office. Report. Agriculture. 1857, p. 244–256. 23ᶜᵐ.
Washington, 1858)
    Condensed from "A guide to the orchard and kitchen garden," by
John Lindley.

    1. Gardening. ₍1. Horticulture₎

                                           Agr 15–651

    Library, U. S. Dept. of   Agriculture 1Ag84 1857

NL   0381572   DNAL OO OU

VOLUME 334

Lindley, John.
[Report on the best mode of detecting vegetable substances mixed with coffee for the purposes of adulteration.   London, 1852]
8 p.   3 colored plates.   f°.   Lithographed.
By Lindley, John and Hooker, Joseph Dalton.

NL   0381573   MH-A

Lindley, John, 1799-1865.
[Reports on the adulteration of coffee
      see under   Gt. Brit. Board of Inland
Revenue.

Lindley, John, 1799-1865.
   Rosarum monographia; or, A botanical history of roses. To which is added, an appendix, for the use of cultivators ... By John Lindley ... London, Printed for J. Ridgway, 1820.
   2 p. l., lviii-xxxix, 156 p.   19 col. pl. (incl. front.)   24½ᵐ.

1. Rose.

Library of Congress   QK495.R78L7   5-31087†

NL   LU NN MB PBL KyU CU
   0381575   DLC OrP DLC MH-A PPAN MBH PBL WU MH-G

Lindley, John, 1799-1865.
   Rosarum monographia; or, A botanical history of roses to which is added, an appendix, for the use of cultivators, in which the most remarkable garden varieties are systematically arranged ... By John Lindley ... A new ed. London, J. Ridgway, 1830.
   xxxix, 156 p.   19 col. pl.   24½ᵐ.

1. Rose.
                                                Agr 11-693
Library, U. S. Dept. of   Agriculture 452.3L64

NL   0381576   DNAL TxU MiU CU PPHor MiU NN

Lindley, John
   School botany and vegetable physiology; or, The rudiments of botanical science. By John Lindley... A new ed.: with corrections, numerous additions and nearly four hundred illustrations.   London, Bradbury & Evans, 1854.
   182p.   illus.

NL   0381577   MiHM

LINDLEY, John.
School botany, and vegetable physiology. New ed. With corrections, numerous additions,etc. London, 1856.

Illustr. and diagrs.

NL   0381578   MH

Lindley, John
   School botany; descriptive botany, and vegetable physiology; or, the rudiments of botanical science. Ed. 11. Lond. Bradbury, 1866.
   212 p

NL   0381579   PU

---

580   Lindley, John, 1799-1865.
L746s12   School botany, descriptive botany, and vegetable physiology; or, The rudiments of botanical science ... The 12th ed. With corrections, numerous additions, and illustrations.   London, Bradbury, Evans, & co. [1862?]
      212p. illus.

1. Botany.

NL   0381580   IU-M

Lindley, John, 1799-1865.
Skd.85   School botany; or, An explanation of the characters and differences of the principal natural classes and orders of plants belonging to the flora of Europe, in the botanical classification of De Candolle ...
      London, Longman, Orme, Brown, Green, & Longmans, 1839. 18cm.

NL   0381581   CtY MH KyU

Lindley, John, 1799-1865.
   School botany; or, The rudiments of botanical science. By John Lindley ... A new ed.: with numerous alterations and nearly four hundred illustrations. London, Bradbury & Evans, 1849.
   vi p., 1 l., 164 p.   illus.   22ᵐ.

1. Botany.

Library of Congress   QK94.L75   5-25370†

NL   0381582   DLC

[fQL66
.A1v   Lindley, John, 1799-1865.
L5   Sertum orchidaceum: a wreath of the most beautiful orchidaceous flowers, selected by John Lindley. London, J. Ridgway, 1838 [i. e. 1837-41]
      1 v.   49 col. plates.   55 cm.

A revision of Oncidium follows plate 48.
5360 Pritzel. 700 Stafleu. 1205 Nissen.
Copy 1: Ex libris Sarah Gildersleeve Fife. Ex libris Thomas Aloysius Perry.
   1. Orchidaceae – Pictorial works. 2. Orchidaceae. 3. Oncidium. i. t. a. Fife, Sarah Gildersleeve. b.   Perry, Thomas Aloysius.

NL   0381583   NNBG

Lindley, John, 1799-1865.
   Sertum orchidaceum; a wreath of the most beautiful orchidaceous flowers; selected by John Lindley ... London, J. Ridgway and sons, 1838.
   7 p. l., [78] p.   49 col. pl.   56½ᵐ.

Added t-p., engr. in colors. London, 1840.
Issued in 10 fasc. 1837-42.
Plates accompanied by descriptive letterpress (76 p.)

1. Orchids.
                                                5-37275†
Library of Congress   QK495.O64L8

NL   0381584   DLC MdBP MBH NjP CU NIC ViU CSmH

Lindley, John, 1799-1865.
   A sketch of the vegetation of the Swan River colony ... by John Lindley... (In Edwards's botanical register. Appendix to the first twenty-three volumes. London, 1839. 24½ᵐ. lviii p., 1 l. illus., 9 col. pl.)

Subject entries: Swan River colony. Botany.
                                                Agr 3-1118
Library, U. S. Dept. of   Agriculture, no. 450B653.

NL   0381585   DNAL MH-A MBH

Lindley, John, 1799-1865.
   Substances used as food, as exemplified in the great exhibition. iv, 347 pp. 16°. *London, S. Bentley & Co.*, [1851?].

NL   0381586   DNLM PPWa

Lindley, John.
   The symmetry of vegetation; an outline of the principles to be observed in the delineation of plants ...
= London. Chapman & Hall. 1854. 51 pp. Sm. 8°.

F9321 — Vegetation. — Symmetry.

NL   0381587   MB CaBViP

Lindley, John, 1799-1865.
   A synopsis of the British flora; arranged according to the natural orders: containing vasculares, or flowering plants. By John Lindley ... London, Longman, Rees, Orme, Brown, and Green, 1829.
   xii, 360 p., 1 l. 19½ᵐ.

Subject entries: Gt. Brit. Botany.
                                                Agr 3-863
Library, U. S. Dept. of   Agriculture, no. 458L642.

NL   0381588   DNAL MH-A NIC PPAN PWcS

581.942 Lindley, John, 1799-1865.
L746s2   A synopsis of the British flora. 2d ed., with numerous additions, corrections, and improvements. London, Longman, Rees, Orme, Brown, Green, and Longman, 1835.
      376p. 19cm.

1. Botany--Gt. Brit.

NL   0381589   IU-M MH PU-B MH-A CU

LINDLEY, John, 1799-1865.
   Synopsis of British Flora containing vasculares, or flowering plants. London, Joseph Baer & Co., No. 499. 360. 1841.

NL   0381590   MH

QK
306   Lindley, John, 1799-1865.
.L5   A synopsis of the British flora; arranged according to the natural orders: containing vasculares, or flowering plants. 3d ed. London, Longman, Orme, Brown, Green and Longmans, 1841.
      360 p.

1. Botany - Gt. Brit.   I. Title.

NL   0381591   MiEM MiU MH-A

LINDLEY, John.
   A synopsis of the British flora, arranged according to the natural orders, containing vasculares or flowering plants. 3d ed., with numerous additions, corrections, and improvements. London, Longman, Brown, Green, Longman & Roberts, 1859.

NL   0381592   MH MH-A

VOLUME 334

LINDLEY, John.
   Théorie de l'horticulture, ou Essais descriptifs selon les principes de la physiologie sur les principales orations horticoles. [Translated by C.Lemaire.]. Paris, 1481.

   Plates, and other illustr. Lan.2318.41.6

NL 0381593   MH

Lindley, John, 1799-1865.
   Theorie der Gartenkunde; oder, Versuch, die vornehmsten Operationen beim Gartenbau nach physiologischen Grundätzen zu erklären. Uebersetzt mit Anmerkungen von Ludolph Christian Treviranus. Neue Ausg. Erlangen, J.J. Palm und E. Enke, 1850.
   xviii, 424 p.   22 cm.
   1. Plant physiology. 2. Gardening. I. Title. II. Treviranus, Ludolph Christian, 1779-1864, tr. II. Stirm, Th

NL 0381594   NNBG

Lindley, John, 1799-1865.
   The theory and practice of horticulture; or, An attempt to explain the chief operations of gardening upon physiological grounds. Being the 2d ed. of the Theory of horticulture, much enlarged. By John Lindley ... London, Longman, Brown, Green, and Longmans, 1855.
   xvi, 606 p., 1 l. illus., tables (1 fold.) diagrs. 23ᶜᵐ.

   1. Botany—Physiology. 2. Gardening.
                                                45-43779
   Library of Congress   QK711.L745

NL 0381595   DLC PPL MBH NjR MH NNBG PU

Lindley, John, 1799-1865.
   The theory of horticulture; or, An attempt to explain the principal operations of gardening, upon physiological principles. By John Lindley ... London, Longman, Orme, Brown, Green, and Longmans, 1840.
   xvi, 387, t1; p. illus. 22ᶜᵐ.

   1. Botany—Physiology. 2. Gardening.
                                                5—25122
   Library of Congress   QK711.L74

       ViU MB NN
NL 0381596   DLC CaBVaU MBH PPHor CtY NNBG NIC MiU

Lindley, John, 1799-1865.
   The theory of horticulture; or, An attempt to explain the principal operations of gardening upon physiological principles. 1st American ed., with notes, etc., by A. J. Downing and A. Gray. New York, Wiley and Putnam, 1841.
   xxiv, 346 p. illus. 20 cm.

       1. Botany—Physiology. 2. Horticulture. I. Downing, Andrew Jackson, 1815-1852, ed.
       QK711.L742   48-41367*

       T ViU NIC MBH
NL 0381597   DLC OCIW NNBG CU-I MNS MWA ICJ OO MH

Lindley, John, 1799-1865.
   The theory of horticulture; or, An attempt to explain the principal operations of gardening upon physiological principles. By John Lindley ... 2d American ed., with notes, etc. By A. J. Downing. New York, J. Wiley, 1852.
   xx, 364 p. illus. 19ᶜᵐ.

   1. Botany—Physiology. 2. Gardening. I. Downing, Andrew Jackson, 1815-1852, ed.

   Library of Congress   QK711.L744   5-25121†

       ViU
NL 0381598   DLC MBH NNBG CU MU TU NIC MH-A NIC NcU

QK711 Lindley, John, 1799-1865.
.L5   The theory of horticulture; or, An attempt
1859   to explain the principal operations of gardening upon physiological principles. 2d American ed., with notes, etc., by A. J. Downing. New York, Wiley and Halsted, 1859.
          xx, 364 p. illus. 20 cm.

          1. Plant physiology. 2. Gardening. i.t. ii. Downing, Andrew Jackson, 1815-1852.

NL 0381599   NNBG PSt NcD MdBP

QK711 Lindley, John, 1799-1865.
.L5   The theory of horticulture; or, An attempt
1881   to explain the principal operations of gardening upon physiological principles. 2d American ed., with notes, etc., by A. J. Downing. New York, J. Wiley, 1881.
          xx, 364 p. illus. 19 cm.

          1. Plant physiology. 2. Gardening. i.t. ii. Downing, Andrew Jackson, 1815-1852.

NL 0381600   NNBG ViU

Lindley, John, 1799-1865.
   The treasury of botany; a popular dictionary of the vegetable kingdom; with which is incorporated a glossary of botanical terms. Ed. by John Lindley ... and Thomas Moore... New and rev. ed., with supplement...
London, Longmans, Green and co., 1864.
   2 v.

NL 0381601   MiU

Lindley, John, 1799-1865, *ed.*
   The treasury of botany: a popular dictionary of the vegetable kingdom; with which is incorporated a glossary of botanical terms. Ed. by John Lindley ... and Thomas Moore ... Assisted by numerous contributors ... London, Longmans, Green, and co., 1866.
   2 v. illus., 20 pl. (incl. front.) 17ᶜᵐ.
   Paged continuously.

   1. Botany—Dictionaries. I. Moore, Thomas, 1821-1887, joint ed.
                                                5—36427
   Library of Congress   QK7.L74

NL 0381602   DLC CtY PU MH-A PPL NNBG

Lindley, John.

—— and **Moore,** Thomas, *editors.* The treasury of botany; a popular dictionary of the vegetable kingdom, with which is incorporated a glossary of botanical terms. New ed. 2 v. 16°. pp. xx, 1254. il. pl. 20. London, 1870.
   ~~Paged continuously.~~

NL 0381603   MBH WaS NNBG DNLM DLC

Lindley, John, 1799-1865, *ed.*
   The treasury of botany: a popular dictionary of the vegetable kingdom; with which is incorporated a glossary of botanical terms. Ed. by John Lindley ... and Thomas Moore ... Assisted by numerous contributors. Illustrated by numerous woodcuts by Fitch and Branston and steel engravings by Adlard. New ed. New York, W.Wood & company, 1872.
   2 v. illus., 20 pl. (incl. front.) 16½ᶜᵐ.

NL 0381604   ViU PU-B

Lindley, John, 1799-1865, *ed.*
   The treasury of botany: a popular dictionary of the vegetable kingdom; with which is incorporated a glossary of botanical terms. Ed. by John Lindley ... and Thomas Moore ... Assisted by numerous contributors ... New ed. London, Longmans, Green, and co., 1873.
   2 v. illus., 20 pl. (incl. front.) 17½ᶜᵐ.
   Paged continuously.

   1. Botany—Dictionaries. I. Moore, Thomas, 1821-1887, joint ed.
                                                6-1936
   Library of Congress   QK7.L75

NL 0381605   DLC OC1

Lindley, John, 1799-1865, *ed.*
   The treasury of botany: a popular dictionary of the vegetable kingdom; with which is incorporated a glossary of botanical terms. Ed. by John Lindley ... and Thomas Moore ... Assisted by numerous contributors. Illustrated by numerous woodcuts by Fitch and Branston and steel engravings by Adlard. New and rev. ed., with supplement. London, Longmans, Green, and co., 1874.
   2 v. illus., 20 pl. (incl. front.) 16½ᶜᵐ.
   Paged continuously.
   1. Botany—Dictionaries. I. Moore, Thomas, 1821-1887, joint ed.
                                                17-772
   Library of Congress   QK7.L75 1874

NL 0381606   DLC NjP NNBG PPFr

Lindley, John, 1799-1865.
   The treasury of botany; a popular dictionary of the vegetable kingdom; with which is incorporated a glossary of botanical terms. Ed. by John Lindley ... and Thomas Moore ... New and rev. ed., with supplement. London, Longmans, Green and co., 1876.
   2 v. illus., 20 pl. (incl. front.) 17ᶜᵐ.
   Paged continuously.

   1. Botany—Dictionaries. I. Moore, Thomas, 1821-1887, joint author. II. Title.
   U. S. Dept. of agr. Library   452.1L64T   Agr 11—803
   for Library of Congress   [QK7.L   ]
                                   [a45e1]

NL 0381607   DNAL NNBG MoSB CU GU PU-B

QK9   Lindley, John, 1799-1865.
.B5   The treasury of botany; a popular diction-
L5   ary of the vegetable kingdom; with which is
1884   incorporated a glossary of botanical terms. Edited by John Lindley and Thomas Moore, assisted by numerous contributors. New and red. ed., with suppl. London, Longmans, Green, 1884.
          2 v. (xx, 1352 p.) illus. 18 cm.

          1. Botany - Dictionaries. i. Moore, Thomas, 1821-1887. ii.t.

NL 0381608   NNBG MiU MH OC1W

Lindley, John, 1799-1865, *ed.*
   The treasury of botany: a popular dictionary of the vegetable kingdom; with which is incorporated a glossary of botanical terms. Ed. by John Lindley ... and Thomas Moore .. Assisted by numerous contributors. Illustrated by numerous woodcuts by Fitch and Branston and steel engravings by Adlard. New and rev. ed., with supplement. London, Longmans, Green, and co., 1889.   and New Yor!
   2 v. illus., 20 pl. (incl. front.) 16½ᶜᵐ.
   Paged continuously.
   1. Botany—Dictionaries. I. Moore, Thomas, 1821-1887, joint ed. II. Title.

NL 0381609   ViU OrCS MBH OU

VOLUME 334

QK9
.E5
L5
1899

Lindley, John, 1799-1865.
The treasury of botany; a popular dictionary of the vegetable kingdom; with which is incorporated a glossary of botanical terms. Edited by John Lindley and Thomas Moore, assisted by numerous contributors. New impression. London, Longmans, Green, 1899.
2 v. illus. 18 cm.

1. Botany - Dictionaries. i. Moore, Thomas, 1821-1887. ii.t.

NL 0381610   NNBG PPSteph

Lindley, John, 1799-1865.
The vegetable kingdom; or, The structure, classification, and uses of plants, illustrated upon the natural system. By John Lindley ... London, Bradbury and Evans, 1846.
2 p. l., [vi]-lxviii, 908 p. front., illus. 23ᶜᵐ.

1. Botany.

QK94.L76   1846

U. S. Dept. of agr. Library   452L64V
for Library of Congress   [a46b1]†

Agr 26-154

NL 0381611   DNAL MBH NNBG MiU OU Nh ViU PU CLSU DLC

Lindley, John, 1799-1865.
The vegetable kingdom; or, The structure, classification, and uses of plants, illustrated upon the natural system. By John Lindley ... With upwards of five hundred illustrations. 2d ed. with corrections and additional genera. London, Bradbury & Evans, 1847.
lxviii, 911, [1] p. front., illus. 22½ᶜᵐ.

1. Botany.

Library of Congress   QK94.L76

5-29362

NL 0381612   DLC NNBG CtY

Lindley, John, 1799-1865.
The vegetable kingdom; or, The structure, classification, and uses of plants, illustrated upon the natural system. By John Lindley ... 3d ed., with corrections and additional genera. London, Bradbury & Evans, 1853.
2 p. l., [viii]-lxviii, 908 (i. e. 984) p. front., illus. 22½ᶜᵐ.

Extra pages to the number of 76 are intercalated throughout the text, as 11a-11b, 50a-50d, &c.

1. Botany.

Agr 11-804

Library, U. S. Dept. of   Agriculture 452L64V

DNLM NjP DAU ICJ NjR MdBP PPHor
NL 0381613   DNAL KU CU NNBG NcD MiU ODW OCl OU MH-A

Lindley, John, 1799-1865.
The vegetable kingdom; or, The structure, classification, and uses of plants, illustrated upon the natural system. By John Lindley ... 3d ed., with corrections and additional genera. New York, D. Appleton & co., 1853.
2 p. l., [vii]-lxviii, 908 (i. e. 984) p. front., illus. 23.5 cm.

NL 0381614   ViU

[Lindley, John,] 1799-1865.
Vegetable physiology. Published under the superintendence of the Society for the Diffusion of Useful Knowledge... Part 1–
London: Baldwin, Cradock & Joy, 1827–   v.
8°.   (Soc. for the Diffusion of Useful Knowledge. Library of useful knowledge.)

Cover-title.

1. Physiology (Vegetable). 2. Series.
N.Y.P.L.   November 14, 1916.

NL 0381615   NN DLC IU MH Nh

Lindley, John, 1799-1865.
Vegetation of the Swan River Colony. London, J. Ridgeway, 1839.
lviii p. 9 col. plates. 25 cm. (Edwards's botanical register, v. 25, 1839. Appendix)

1. Botany - Australia, Western. I. Title. [II. Series.]

NL 0381616   NIC

Lindley, John, 1799-1865.
—— West African tropical orchids. [London. 1862.] 8°.
123-140.
Journal of the proceedings of the Linnæan society — Botany. 1862. vi.

NL 0381617   MH-A

Lindley, John W., joint author.

Weaver, Samuel Pool, 1882–
Business law, with illustrative cases and problems, by Samuel P. Weaver ... assisted by Nellie M. Catton and John W. Lindley. Boston, New York [etc.] Allyn and Bacon [1926]

Lindley, Joseph.
Memoir of a map of the county of Surrey; from a survey made in the years 1789 and 1790. By Joseph Lindley ... and William Crosley ... London, Printed by G. Bigg, for Lindley and Crosley [1793]
1 p.l., 71 p. 24 cm. [With: Smith, W. An historical account of the expedition against the Ohio Indians.   Philadelphia, 1766]

NL 0381619   OHi

Lindley, Joshua.
Catalogue of fruit trees cultivated and for sale at the North-Carolina Pomological Garden and Nurseries, from 1853 to 1856, by Joshua Lindley.   Raleigh, Star Office, 1853.
18 p. 23cm.

1. N.C.--Fruit culture I. North Carolina Pomological Garden and Nurseries

NL 0381620   NcU

[Lindley, Lafayette W   ] 1841-
History of the people's rights in reference to the militia and the selective draft and how this draft violates the Constitution of the U. S. [Louisville, Ky., Business ptg. co., 1917]
1 p. l, 13 p. 15½ᶜᵐ.
Signed: L. W. Lindley.

1. U. S.—Militia.   i. Title.

Library of Congress   UB343.L6   17-17547

NL 0381621   DLC

Lindley, Lafayette W.   1841-
Review of the tariff and trusts, ...
[Louisville? Ky., c1907]

HF1756
.L6

NL 0381622   DLC

Lindley, Laura.
Our first families. [n.p., °1954]
86 p. illus., ports., map

Cover title.
Bibliography: p. 4.

1. Leelanau Co., Mich. — Biog.
I. T.

NL 0381623   MiD ICN

PN6120
.R4L53   Lindley, Laura.
Ruth, a pageant, by Laura Lindley ...
[n.p., c1934]
15 numb. l.   28cm.

Type-written.

1. Pageants.   2. Ruth--Drama.   I. Title.

NL 0381624   DLC RPB

HV5089
.Z9
no. 117   Lindley, Laura, comp.
State-wide referenda in the United States on the liquor question ... Westerville, Ohio, The American issue publishing company [1930?]
32 p.   [Pamphlets on prohibition in the U.S. No. 117]

NL 0381625   DLC Or

B.5388   Lindley, Laurence.
Memoir of a man of the world. Commonly known as "Tom Nugent, the money lender,"...including notices relative to the dissolution of the Jesuits—money lending—the town—publico-mania—the English bar, &c. &c....London, G. Sidney, 1808.
1 p.l., 72 p. 22 cm.
18

NL 0381626   MH-BA CtY

979.7
L644   Lindley, Lilian.
Boats, bread and meat a century ago, 1850-1950. Centennial ed. [Olympia, Wash., The daily Olympian, 1950?]
72p. illus.,facsims. 20cm.

1. Olympia, Wash.   Hist.
I. Title.

NL 0381627   OrU Wa

JX
4093
L5   Lindley, Mark Frank, 1881-
The acquisition and government of backward territory in international law; being a treatise on the law and practice relating to colonial expansion. London, Longmans, Green, 1926.
391p. 23cm.
Includes bibliography.

1. Territory, National 2. Colonies 3. Native races I. Title II. Title: Backward territory

NL 0381628   WU

VOLUME 334

Lindley, Mark Frank, 1881–
The acquisition and government of backward territory in international law; being a treatise on the law and practice relating to colonial expansion, by M. F. Lindley ... London, New York ₍etc.₎ Longmans, Green and co., ltd., 1926.

xx p., 1 l., 391 p. 22½ᶜᵐ.
Bibliography: p. ₍xv₎–xx.

1. Territory, National. 2. Colonies. 3. Native races. I. **Title.**
II. Title: Backward territory.

Library of Congress   JX4027.L5 ⌐   26–10184

OrPR WaWW
DNW ViU ICJ NN MB NjP PHC MtU MtBC IdU–SB CaBVaU
NL 0381629   DLC KEmT NIC NcD PBm IdU OC1 OCU OU ODW

Lindley, Martha A., tr.

Jeanne, de la Nativité, fl. 1650.
The holy life of Armelle Nicolas, a poor and ignorant servant-maid, commonly known as the "Good Armelle", born 1606, died 1671; translated and revised by Inanda ₍pseud.₎ Philadelphia, G. W. McCalla, 1899.

Lindley, Maybon.
Carillons and cow bells. San Antonio, Press of the Naylor Co. ₍1949₎

55 p. illus. 20 cm.
Poems.

I. Title.

PS3523.I 556C3   811.5   50–6005

NL 0381631   DLC

Lindley, Nathaniel Lindley, baron, 1826–1921, tr.

Thibaut, Anton Friedrich Justus, 1772–1840.
An introduction to the study of jurisprudence; being a translation of the general part of Thibaut's System des Pandekten rechts. With notes and illustrations by Nathaniel Lindley ... London, W. Maxwell; ₍etc., etc.₎ 1855.

Lindley, Nathaniel Lindley, baron, 1828–1921.
Law of Partnership
    see his A treatise on the law of partnership.

Lindley, Nathaniel Lindley, baron, 1828–1921.
A supplement to Lord Lindley's Treatise on the law of partnership. Containing the Limited partnerships act, 1907, with introduction, notes, rules and forms, and an addendum of cases. By T. J. C. Tomlin ... and A. Andrewes Uthwatt ... London, Sweet & Maxwell, limited, 1909.

xx, 92 p. 25½ᶜᵐ.

1. Partnership—Gt. Brit. 2. Limited partnership—Gt. Brit. I. Tomlin, Thomas James Chesshyre, 1867–1935, ed. II. Andrewes-Uthwatt, Augustus, 1879– joint ed.

9–3/068

NL 0381634   DLC PU–L

KN 261 L553

Lindley, Nathaniel Lindley, baron, 1828–1921.
    A treatise on the law of companies, considered as a branch of the law of partnership. 1st–   ed. London, Sweet and Maxwell, 18–
        v.

Law/ Je73 bt

    1. Corporation law – Gt. Brit. 2. Partnership – Gt. Brit. I. Title.

NL 0381635   CaBVaU

Lindley, Nathaniel Lindley, baron, 1828–1921.
A treatise on the law of companies, considered as a branch of the law of partnership. 5th ed. By the Right Honourable Sir Nathaniel Lindley, knt. ... Assisted by Walter B. Lindley ... and William C. Gull ... London, Sweet and Maxwell, limited; Toronto, Carswell & co., 1889.

xvi, ₍v₎–lxiv, 607, ₍1₎, 608–1240 p. 25ᶜᵐ.

——— Supplement ... Containing the Directors liability act, 1890; the Companies (memorandum of association) act, 1890; and the Companies (winding up) act, 1890; and the rules and orders thereunder. With introductions and notes. By the Right Honourable Sir Nathaniel Lindley, knt. ... Assisted by Sir W. Cameron Gull, bart. ... and Walter B. Lindley ... London, Sweet and Maxwell, limited; ₍etc., etc.₎ 1891.

xi, 232 p. 25½ᶜᵐ.

1. Corporation law—Gt. Brit. 2. Partnership—Gt. Brit. I. Lindley, Walter Barry, 1861– II. Gull, Sir William Cameron, bart., 1860–1922.

40–37855 Revised

NL 0381637   DLC WaU–L MH FU PPB OU

Lindley, Nathaniel Lindley, baron, 1828–1921.
A treatise on the law of companies, considered as a branch of the law of partnership, by the Right Honourable Lord Lindley ... 6th ed., by the Honourable Walter B. Lindley ... London, Sweet and Maxwell, limited, 1902.

2 v. 25½ᶜᵐ.
Paged continuously.
"Sixth edition of a portion of the author's Treatise on the law of partnership, including its application to companies."—Pref.

1. Corporation law—Gt. Brit. 2. Partnership—Gt. Brit. I. Lindley, Walter Barry, 1861–

3—20493

NL 0381638   DLC PPB CtY

Lindley, Nathaniel Lindley, baron, 1828–
A treatise on the law of partnership, including its application to joint-stock and other companies. By Nathaniel Lindley ... London, W. Maxwell; ₍etc., etc.₎ 1860.

2 v. 25ᶜᵐ.
Paged continuously.

1. Partnership. 2. Joint-stock companies. 3. Stock companies.

12–39188

NL 0381639   DLC WaU–L IU CaBVaU CtY

Lindley, Nathaniel Lindley, baron, 1828–1921.
A treatise on the law of partnership, including its application to joint-stock and other companies. By Nathaniel Lindley ... Philadelphia, T. & J. W. Johnson & co., 1860.

2 v. 22½ᶜᵐ. (*In* The Law library. Philadelphia. 1860. ₍v. 102₎ Apr./ June, 1860; ₍v. 103; July/Sept. 1860, no. 1₎
Paged continuously.

1. Partnership—Gt. Brit. 2. Stock companies—Gt. Brit. 3. Corporation law—Gt. Brit.
                                          12–39194 Revised
Library of Congress
——— Copy 2.   2 v. in 1. 24ᶜᵐ

NL 0381640   DLC MH GU–L ViU

Lindley, Nathaniel Lindley, baron, 1828–
A treatise on the law of partnership, including its application to companies. 2d ed. By Nathaniel Lindley ... London, W. Maxwell & son; ₍etc., etc.₎ 1867.

2 v. 24½ᶜᵐ.
Paged continuously.

1. Partnership. 2. Joint-stock companies. 3. Stock companies.

12–39195

NL 0381641   DLC OU CtY

Lindley, Nathaniel Lindley, baron, 1828–
A treatise on the law of partnership, including its application to companies. 3d ed. By Nathaniel Lindley ... assisted by Samuel Dickinson ... London, W. Maxwell & son; ₍etc., etc.₎ 1873.

2 v. 24½ᶜᵐ.
Paged continuously.

1. Partnership. 2. Joint-stock companies. 3. Stock companies. I. Dickinson, Samuel, 1840–

12–39196

NL 0381642   DLC OU NN

Lindley, Nathaniel Lindley, baron, 1828–
A treatise on the law of partnership, including its application to companies. 4th ed. By the Honourable Sir Nathaniel Lindley, knt. ... assisted by Samuel Dickinson ... London, W. Maxwell & son; ₍etc., etc.₎ 1878.

2 v. 24½ᶜᵐ.
Paged continuously.

1. Partnership. 2. Joint-stock companies. 3. Stock companies. I. Dickinson, Samuel, 1840–

12–39197

NL 0381643   DLC OU CU CtY MH

Lindley, Nathaniel Lindley, baron, 1828–1921.
A treatise on the law of partnership, including its application to companies. 4th ed. By the Hon. Sir Nathaniel Lindley, knt. ... assisted by Samuel Dickinson ... Edited and annotated by Marshall D. Ewell ... Chicago, Callaghan & company, 1881.

2 v. 24ᶜᵐ.
Paged continuously.

1. Partnership—Gt. Brit. 2. Stock companies—Gt. Brit. 3. Corporation law—Gt. Brit. I. Dickinson, Samuel, 1840–1908, joint author. II. Ewell, Marshall Davis, 1844–1928, ed.

12–39198

Library of Congress

MH OC1W
NL 0381644   DLC OrU WaU–L ICRL NBuU–L PV NcD ViU–L

Lindley, Nathaniel Lindley, baron, 1828–1921.
A treatise on the law of partnership. 5th ed. By the Right Honourable Sir Nathaniel Lindley ... assisted by William C. Gull ... and Walter B. Lindley ... With American notes by Alonzo B. Wentworth ... Boston, C. H. Edson & co., 1888.

2 v. 24½ᶜᵐ. (*Cover-title:* American law series ... vol. I, no. 5; vol. II, no. 7)
Paged continuously.

1. Partnership—Gt. Brit. I. Gull, Sir William Cameron, 2d bart., 1860–1922, joint author. II. Lindley, Hon. Walter Barry, 1861– joint author. III. Wentworth, Alonzo Bond, d. 1894.

Library of Congress   12–36119

NL 0381645   DLC PV NcU–L PV–L TxU OU PPL–L PP NjP

Lindley, Nathaniel Lindley, baron, 1828–1921.
A treatise on the law of partnership; 5th English ed. By the Right Honorable Sir Nathaniel Lindley, knt. ... assisted by William C. Gull ... and Walter B. Lindley ... 2d American ed. Edited and annotated by Marshall D. Ewell ... Chicago, Callaghan and company, 1888.

2 v. 24ᶜᵐ.
Paged continuously.

1. Partnership—Gt. Brit. 2. Partnership—U. S. I. Gull, Sir William Cameron, 2d bart., 1860– joint author. II. Lindley, Hon. Walter Barry, 1861– joint author. III. Ewell, Marshall Davis, 1844–1928, ed.

12–36117

Library of Congress

CoAlC
NL 0381646   DLC MtU WaU–L IdU NcU NcD OU ViU–L OC1W

VOLUME 334

Lindley, Nathaniel Lindley, *baron,* 1828–1921.
A treatise on the law of partnership. By the Right Honorable Sir Nathaniel Lindley ... assisted by William C. Gull ... and Walter B. Lindley ... Reprinted from advance sheets of the 5th English ed. ... with American notes by Stewart Rapalje. Jersey City, F. D. Linn & co., 1888.
2 v. 24ᶜᵐ.
Paged continuously.
On cover: Authorized American edition.
1. Partnership—Gt. Brit. 2. Partnership—U. S.   ɪ. Gull, Sir William Cameron, bart., 1860–1922, joint author.   ɪɪ. Lindley, Walter Barry, 1861–   Joint author.   ɪɪɪ. Rapalje, Stewart.
12–36120

NL 0381647   DLC PV WaU-L MtU

Lindley, Nathaniel Lindley, *baron,* 1828–1921.
A treatise on the law of partnership. From the 5th English ed. By the Right Honourable Sir Nathaniel Lindley, knt. ... assisted by William C. Gull ... and Walter B. Lindley ... With American notes by Chas. Y. Audenried ... Philadelphia, The Blackstone publishing company, 1888.
2 v. 23½ᶜᵐ.   (*On cover:* Text-book series, v. 2, no. 20–21)
Paged continuously.
1. Partnership—Gt. Brit. 2. Partnership—U. S.   ɪ. Gull, Sir William Cameron, bart., 1860–1922, joint author.   ɪɪ. Lindley, Walter Barry, 1861–   joint author.   ɪɪɪ. Audenried, Charles Young, 1863–1930.
12–39199

Library of Congress

NL 0381648   DLC NBuU-L WaU-L NN NjP ViU-L

Lindley, Nathaniel Lindley, *baron,* 1828–1921.
A treatise on the law of partnership. From the 5th English ed. By the Right Honourable Sir Nathaniel Lindley, knt. ... assisted by William C. Gull ... and Walter B. Lindley ... With American notes by Chas. Y. Audenried ... New York and Albany, Banks & brothers, 1891.
2 v. 23½ᶜᵐ.
Paged continuously.
1. Partnership—Gt. Brit. 2. Partnership—U. S.   ɪ. Gull, Sir William Cameron, bart., 1860–1922, joint author.   ɪɪ. Lindley, Walter Barry, 1861–   joint author.   ɪɪɪ. Audenried, Charles Young, 1863–1930.

NL 0381649   DLC MH CaBVaU NIC

Lindley, Nathaniel Lindley, *baron,* 1828–
A treatise on the law of partnership by the Right Honourable Sir Nathaniel Lindley ... 6th ed., by Walter B. Lindley ... with an appendix on the law of Scotland, by J. Campbell Lorimer ... London, Sweet and Maxwell, limited; ₁etc., etc.₎ 1893.
lxii, 939 p. 25½ᶜᵐ.
1. Partnership.   ɪ. Lindley, Walter Barry, 1861–   ed.   ɪɪ. Lorimer, John Campbell.
15–4759

NL 0381650   DLC CaBVaU MH

Lindley, Nathaniel Lindley, baron, 1828–1921.
A treatise on the law of partnership, by the Right Honourable Lord Lindley ... 7th ed., by the Honourable Walter B. Lindley ... and T. J. C. Tomlin ... with an appendix on the law of Scotland by J. Campbell Lorimer ... London, Sweet and Maxwell, limited, 1905.
cxxxiii, 1095p.
1. Partnership—Great Britain. I. Lindley, Walter Barry, 1861–   ed. II. Tomlin, Thomas James Chesshyre, 1867–   ed. III. Lorimer, John Campbell.

NL 0381651   IU CaBVaU

Lindley,Nathaniel Lindley,baron,1828–1921
A treatise on the law of partnership,by the Right Honourable Lord Lindley ... 7th ed.,by the Honourable Walter B.Lindley ... and T.J.C.Tomlin ... With an appendix of the law of Scotland,by J.Campbell Lorimer ... and a supplement containing the Limited partnership act,1907,with introduction,notes,rules,forms,and an addendum of cases. London, Sweet and Maxwell,limited, 1909.
cxxxiii,1095 p.   24½ᶜᵐ.
Bound with this is his: A supplement to Lord Lindley's Tr eatise on the law of partnership ...   1909.

NL 0381652   MiU-L OU

Lindley, Nathaniel Lindley, *baron,* 1828–1921.
A treatise on the law of partnership, by the Right Honourable Lord Lindley ... 8th ed. By the Honourable Walter B. Lindley ... T. J. C. Tomlin ... and A. Andrewes Uthwatt ... with an appendix on the law of Scotland, by J. Campbell Lorimer ... London, Sweet and Maxwell, limited, 1912.
clxi, ₁2₎, 1228 p. 26ᶜᵐ.
1. Partnership—Gt. Brit.   ɪ. Lindley, Walter Barry, 1861–   ed.   ɪɪ. Tomlin, Thomas James Chesshyre Tomlin, baron, 1867–1935, joint ed.   ɪɪɪ. Andrewes-Uthwatt, Augustus, 1879–   joint ed.   ɪv. Lorimer, John Campbell, d. 1922.
12–24525

NL 0381653   DLC NBuU-L PPB CtY

Lindley, Nathaniel Lindley, *baron,* 1828–1921.
A treatise on the law of partnership, by the late the Right Honourable Lord Lindley ... 9th ed., by the Honourable Walter B. Lindley ... assisted by J. S. P. Mellor ... London, Sweet & Maxwell, limited; ₁etc., etc.₎ 1924.
clxxxiv, 1231 p. 25½ᶜᵐ.
The notes on the Scots law by the late Mr. Campbell Lorimer, which have appeared in the last four editions, are omitted in this edition.   *cf.* Pref., p. v.
1. Partnership.   ɪ. Lindley, Walter Barry, 1861–   ed.   ɪɪ. Mellor, John Serocold Paget, 1893–   joint ed.
26–17673

NL 0381654   DLC WaU-L MtU MH PPB CtY ViU-L NcD

Lindley, Nathaniel Lindley, *baron,* 1828–1921.
A treatise on the law of partnership, by the late the Right Honourable Lord Lindley ... 10th ed., by the Honourable Walter B. Lindley ... London, Sweet & Maxwell, limited; Toronto, The Carswell company, ltd.; ₁etc., etc.₎ 1935.
clxx, 1206 p. 25½ᶜᵐ.
1. Partnership—Gt. Brit.   ɪ. Lindley, Walter Barry, 1861–   ed.
36–12003
Library of Congress   ₁2₎   658.11420942

NL 0381655   DLC WaU-L IdU NBuU PU-L CtY ViU-L OU

Lindley, Nathaniel Lindley, *baron,* 1828–1921.
A treatise on the law of partnership. 11th ed. by Henry Salt and Hugh E. Francis, with a foreword by Lord Uthwatt. London, Sweet & Maxwell, 19₍₎.
clx, 1227 p. 26 cm.
Includes legislation.
1. Partnership—Gt. Brit.   ɪ. Gt. Brit. Laws, statutes, etc.
658.1142   51–4303

NL 0381656   WaE WaPS WaS WaSp WaSpG WaT WaTC WaWW MtU-M OrU-L CaBVaU IdB IdPS MtBC MtU Wa OrCS OrP OrU   DLC WaU-L TxU TU Or OrStbM OrSaW OrU-M

Lindley, Percy.
Great Eastern Railway Company's tourist-guide to the Continent
    see under   Great Eastern Railway Company, England.

Lindley, Percy.
Holidays in Belgium. By Percy Lindley.   ₁London? 190–?₎
28 p. incl. col'd plates.   illus.   18cm.
Caption-title.
Cover illustrated in color.
734508. 1. Belgium—Descr. and   trav., 1900–1910. I. Title.
N. Y. P. L.   *Card revised* March 10, 1941

NL 0381658   NN MB

Lindley, Percy, editor.
Holidays in England by the cathedral cities, the Tennyson and Dickens' country, and the homes of the Pilgrim Fathers. Edited by Percy Lindley...   New York ₁191–?₎   97 p. front., illus., map, plates. ob. 32°.
1. England—Description and travel,   1800–1900. 2. Cathedrals, Gt. Br.: England. 3. Title.
N. Y. P. L.   June 30, 1921.

NL 0381659   NN MH MWA MB

ar V 3017
Lindley, Percy, ed.
Holidays in England by the Great Eastern Railway Co.'s "Cathedral route," including the cathedral cities, homes of the Pilgrim Fathers, and Tennyson and Dickens country.   New York ₁1904?₎
62 p. illus., map. 13 x 19 cm.
1. England--Descr. & trav.--Guidebooks. 2. Great Eastern Railway Company, Engl   and. I. Title.

NL 0381660   NIC PP OO

Lindley, Percy, ed.
Holidays in Holland.   Amsterdam, the Helder, and Dead cities of the Zuyder Zee. London, [1883]
20 p.   illus., map.   8°.   [Holiday handbooks.   2]

NL 0381661   MB

Lindley, Percy.
Holidays in north Germany and Scandinavia. Notes on Hamburg and the Hanseatic towns; Rügen and the Baltic coast, Brunswick, the Harz mountains, Hildesheim, Berlin, and the Saxon Switzerland; and a trip in Denmark and southern Norway. Edited by Percy Lindley...   London ₁The author, 189–?₎   92 p. incl. plates.   front. (map), illus.   12 x 19cm.
736935A. 1. Germany—Guidebooks,   189–? 2. Scandinavia—Guidebooks, 189–?
N. Y. P. L.   February 18, 1935

NL 0381662   NN

LINDLEY, Percy, editor.
The Moselle, from the Franco-German battlefields to the Rhine. Lond₁n, [185–?].
pp. 28.   Map and other illus.
(Holiday handbooks, 3.)

NL 0381663   MH

Uxn35 G6 850L
Lindley, Percy.
New holidays in Essex, with rail and walking routes, boating, fishing and shooting notes. London[188–?]
70p.   illus.,map.   12 x 18cm.
"Botanising in South-East Essex, by G.S. Boulger": p.[68]–70.

NL 0381664   CtY PPL

VOLUME 334

LINDLEY, Percy, *ed.*
A trip to the Ardennes : a fortnight in southern Belgium.
Lond. [188–?] 20, (1) pp. Illus. [Holiday handbooks.]

B 6144 B

NL 0381665   MB

LINDLEY, Percy, editor.
Walks in Belgium, cycling, driving, by rail, and
on foot. With some fishing and boating notes,
and a chapter on the French Ardennes. London,
[1895].

1 p.l., [5]–92 p., 1 l. Map, plans, and other
illustr. obl. 32°.

NL 0381666   MH

Lindley, Percy.
Walks in Holland; cycling, boating, by rail, and on foot.
Edited by Percy Lindley ... London [1889].
63, [1] p. front. (fold. map) illus. (incl. maps) pl. 12½ x 18¼ᶜᵐ.

1. Netherlands—Descr. & trav.—Guide-books. I. Title.
                                                                31–17682
Library of Congress   DJ16.L5   914.92

NL 0381667   DLC NN

Rare Book
Room
Eddb
Ar28
887
Lindley, Percy   *ed.*
... Walks in the Ardennes, cycling, driving,
boating, by rail, and on foot. With some
fishing and shooting notes. Edited by Percy
Lindley. London: 125, Fleet street; W.H.Smith &
son, & all booksellers. [1887–88]
1 p.l., [5]–65, [1]p. illus., 16pl. (incl.front.)
fold.map. 12½x18½cm.
On cover: Illustrated by Julian F.Weedon.

NL 0381668   CtY MH

Lindley, Percy.
Walks in the Ardennes... New ed. 1893.

NL 0381669   PP

Lindley, Percy.
The world-war battlefields, ed. by Percy Lindley. London [192–?]
78, [2] p. illus. (part col.) 2 fold. maps. 12 x 18½ᶜᵐ.

Illustrated t.-p.
On cover: The world-war battlefields of Belgium & France.
"Issued by the Great Eastern railway company of England."
"A glimpse of East Anglia": p. 10–31.

1. European war, 1914–1918—Battle-fields. 2. East Anglia—Description
and travel. I. Great Eastern railway company, England. II. Title.
                                                                War 22–100
Library, U. S. Army   War College D525.4.L74 192–

NL 0381670   PCarlA DGU OU IdU Or PPT ODW

Lindley, Percy Elliott, 1895–
Human nature and the church, by Percy Elliott Lindley ...
New York, The Macmillan company, 1932.
7 p. l., 245 p. 19½ᵐ.

1. Church. 2. Theology, Pastoral. 3. Church work. I. Title.
Library of Congress   BV600.L5   32–30777
———— Copy 2.
Copyright A 56548   250

NL 0381671   DLC NcD ViU PCC OO OCl

Lindley, Percy Elliott, 1895–
Rise up and walk. Boston, Chapman & Grimes [1949,
°1948]
167 p. 21 cm.

1. Success. I. Title.
BJ1611.L725   174   49–8672*

NL 0381672   DLC NcD

LINDLEY, ROBERT, 1776–1855.
A duett, for violin and violoncello, composed by
Robert Lindley. London, A. Betts [182–?] 2 parts.

Microfilm.

1. Violin and violoncello.

NL 0381673   NN

M785.72 Lindley, Robert, 1776–1855.
V796   Three duets, for two violoncellos, op. 1.
no.23   London, Monzani & Cimador [1800?]

2 parts. 34cm.

(In: Violoncello duets, no.23)

NL 0381674   NcU

W.C.L. Lindley, Robert, 1776–1855.
M785.72   [Duets, violin & violoncello, op. 12]
L746D
             Three duettos, for a violin & violoncello.
op.12   Op. 12. London, printed for the author, by
          R. Birchall, No. 133, New Bond Street [ca. 1810]
          2 parts. 33 cm.

1. Violin and violoncello music. To 1800.

NL 0381675   NcD

Uncat. **Lindley, Robert,** 1776–1855.
             [Duos, violoncello, op. 1]. Trois duos pour
deux violoncelles ... [op. 1]. Chez Frere, md.
de musique, passage du Saumon, rue Montmarte.
Paris, [c. 1805]. Parts.

NL 0381676   CU

BX7795 Lindley, Ruth Anna (Rutter) 1768–1810.
.L64A3   Account of Ruth Anna Lindley, a minister
of the gospel in the religious Society of
Friends. Philadelphia, Friends' book store
[1893]
35 p.
"Prefatory remarks" signed: W. P. T.

NL 0381677   ICU PHC PSC-Hi OCl NcGU PWcS

Lindley, Samuel Edward, 1915–
The risks of freedom; an introduction to
the philosophy of Karl Jaspers, with
translations. [Ithaca, N. Y.] 1953.
307 l. 27cm.

Thesis (Ph. D.)--Cornell Univ.,
Sept., 1953.

NL 0381678   NIC

Lindley, Thomas.
Authentic narrative of a voyage from the cape of Good Hope
to Brasil, a Portuguese settlement in South America, in 1802,
1803 ... with general sketches of the country, its natural productions, colonial inhabitants, &c ... London, W. Baynes, 1808.
xxxi, 298 p. 22ᵐ.

1. Brazil—Descr. & trav.
                                                      2–6776 Revised
Library of Congress   F2511.L74

NL 0381679   DLC CtY

Ayer
1269
B8
L74
1808
LINDLEY, THOMAS.
Authentic narrative of a voyage from the
Cape of Good Hope to Brasil, a Portuguese settlement in South America, in 1802, 1803; and
terminating in the seizure of a British vessel;
the imprisonment of the author, his wife, and
ship's crew, by the governor's orders, with
general sketches of the country, its natural
productions, colonial inhabitants, &c. ... London, W.Baynes, 1808.
             xxxi, 298p. 19 x 23 cm.
70–373   Xerox copy.

NL 0381680   ICN

Lindley, Thomas.
Narrative of a voyage to Brasil; terminating in the seizure
of a British vessel ... with general sketches of the country,
its natural productions, colonial inhabitants, &c. ... London,
J. Johnson, 1805.
xxxi, [1], 298 p. 21½ᵐ.

1. Brazil—Descr. & trav.
Library of Congress   F2511.L75   2–6777

CtY DCU-IA NN MWA NNH RPJCB MB
NL 0381681   DLC CU MiU-C RPJCB NBu MoSW PPL OCl

G440
T95
Lindley, Thomas.
Reise nach Brasilien und Aufenthalt daselbst
in den Jahren 1802 und 1803. Nebst einer
Beschreibung der Städte und Provinzen Porto-
Seguro und San Salvador. Auszugsweise aus
dem Englischen übers. von T.F. Ehrmann.
Weimar, Im Verlag des F.S. pr. Landes-Industrie-Comptoirs, 1806.
xiv, 168 p. (Bibliothek der neuesten und
wichtigsten Reisebeschreibungen zur Erweiterung der Erdkunde ... hrsg. von M.C. Sprengel,
fortgesetzt von T.F. Ehrmann. Bd.29)

With Turnbull, John. Reise um die Welt.
1806.

NL 0381682   CU IU NN NcD

F
2511
L75
1806
LAC-Z
Lindley, Thomas.
Voyage au Brésil; où l'on Trouve. Tra-
duit de l'anglais par François Soulés.
Paris, Chez Leopold Collin, 1806.
183p. 21cm.

1. Brazil – Descr. & trav. Sp.: Lucuix
Collection.

NL 0381683   TxU DLC RPJCB DCU-IA

VOLUME 334

Lindley, Thomas J.
    Speeches by James S. Barcus
      see under   Barcus, James S.

Lindley, Tinsley.
    The Association game. Portrait.
    (In Fegan. Football, hockey, and lacrosse. Pp. 40–77. London, 1900.)

E3814   Apr. 18,   1902

NL 0381685   MB

Lindley, Valrose.
    ... Easy exit; a thriller for women, in one act ... London, Boston [1946]
    17 p. 19ᶜᵐ. (The Year book press series of plays. General editor: G. W. Bishop)

    I. Title.
                 [Full name: Elizabeth Valrose Lindley]
    PN6120.A5L4815   822.91   47–21312
                                  Brief cataloging

NL 0381686   DLC

Lindley, Valrose
    The open door; a play for women in one act. London, H. F. W. Deane [°1948]
    16 p. (Deane's series of plays)

NL 0381687   MiD

T378.764
A
QbYℓ
    Lindley, Vick.
    The Battalion, 1878–1948; seventy years of student publications at the A & M College of Texas. [College Station, Tex., 1948?]
    7p. illus. 23cm.
    Cover title.
    Reprinted from the January 19–22, 1948, issues of the Battalion.
    1. The Battalion. 2. College and school periodicals. 3. Texas. Agricultural and Mechanical College, College Station.

NL 0381688   TxU MH

Lindley, Vick.
    The flying fleet, consisting of verses by Vick Lindley... Bryan, Tex., 1945. 24 p. 15cm.

    1. World war, 1939–1945—Poetry.   I. Title.
N. Y. P. L.   July 25, 1950

NL 0381689   NN

Lindley, W   B
    Printing and allied machinery
      see under   Gt. Brit. British Intelligence Objectives Sub-committee.

Lindley, W. H.
    see Lindley, Sir William Heerlein, 1853–1917.

Lindley (Walter) [1852–]. 1. Below sea-level; nature's pneumatic cabinet [and] 2. High altitudes in southern California. 6, 6 pp. 8°.
[Los Angeles, 1888.]
1. Repr. from: Med. Rec. N.Y., 1888. xxxiv. 2. Repr. from: South. Calif. Pract., Los Angeles, 1888, ill.

NL 0381692   DNLM MH

Lindley, Walter, 1852–
    California of the south, its physical geography, climate, resources, routes of travel, and health-resorts; being a complete guide-book to southern California, by Walter Lindley, M. D., and J. P. Widney, A. M., M. D. ... New York, D. Appleton and company, 1888.
    viii, 377 p. front., illus., 3 fold. maps. 19½ᶜᵐ.

    1. California, Southern.   I. Widney, Joseph Pomeroy, 1841–   joint author. II. Title.
                                    Rc—905
    Library of Congress   F867.L73

    MBCo CaBViPA DAS
    OC1W OO   OC1W CO OCU OC1 MWA MH I OrHi CaBVa DN
NL 0381693   DLC MdBP NIC NcD KU-M CU TxU DNLM NjP

Lindley, Walter.
    California of the south; its physical geography, climate, mineral springs, resources, routes of travel and health-resorts, being a complete guide-book to southern California, by Walter Lindley, M. D. and J. P. Widney ... With maps and numerous illustrations. 3d ed., rewritten and printed from new plates. New York, D. Appleton and company, 1896.
    xii, 335 p. front., illus., 2 maps (1 fold.) 19½ᶜᵐ.

    1. California, Southern. 2. Pacific states—Climate.   I. Widney, Joseph Pomeroy.
                           F867.L75   Rc–906

    MBCo MH
NL 0381694   DLC MoU CSt CU-I DAS DNLM CaBVaU OC1WHi

Lindley, Walter, 1852–
    California of the south; its physical geography, climate, mineral springs, resources, routes of travel and health-resorts, being a complete guide-book to southern California, by Walter Lindley, M. D. and J. P. Widney... With maps and numerous illustrations. 3d ed., rewritten and printed from new plates. New York, D. Appleton and company, 1896.
    xii, 335 p. front., illus., 2 maps (1 fold.) 19 1/2cm.

NL 0381695   MsU

Lindley, Walter, 1852–
    ... The delinquent child in England, by Walter Lindley ... With appendix. [n. p., 1909?]
    [18] p. 22ᶜᵐ.
    Reprint from the Proceedings of the National conference of charities and correction, 36th session, June, 1909.

    1. Juvenile delinquency—Gt. Brit. 2. Children—Charities, protection, etc.—Gt. Brit.   I. Title.
                                 E 13–98
    U. S. Off. of educ. Library   HV9146.L64
      for Library of Congress   [a41b1]

NL 0381696   DHEW

Lindley, Walter, 1852–
    The delinquent child in England; report of Walter Lindley ... special commissioner. Whittier, Cal., Linotyping and printing by boys of the State school [1909?]
    cover-title, [22] p. 3 pl. (1 col.) 3 port. 24ᶜᵐ.

    1. Juvenile delinquency. 2. Children—Charities, protection, etc.—England.   I. Title.
                                  12–36212
    Library of Congress   HV9146.L6

NL 0381697   DLC ICJ

Lindley, Walter, 1852–
    Dr. John Hall, Shakespeare's son-in-law, by Walter Lindley ... [Los Angeles? 1916.] 4 l. 8°.
    Cover-title.
    "Read before the Los Angeles County Medical Assoc., April 6, 1916."
    Repr.: Medical record. May 21, 1916.

    1. Hall, John, 1575–1635.
N. Y. P. L.   November 19, 1917.

NL 0381698   NN IU NNU-W

Lindley, Walter, 1852.
    What is the state's duty to its unfortunate children?... San Francisco, 1894.
    12p.   YA. 11001

NL 0381699   DLC

Lindley, Walter Barry, 1861–
    A guide to the Probation acts and rules, with special reference to the Somerset combined probation areas order, 1927. Taunton [Eng.] H. G. Mounter, 1927.
    128 p. 22 cm.

    1. Probation—Gt. Brit.   I. Gt. Brit. Laws, statutes, etc.
                                  55–47559 ‡

NL 0381700   DLC MH-L

Lindley, Walter Barry, 1861–
Lindley, Nathaniel Lindley, baron, 1828–1921.
    A treatise on the law of companies, considered as a branch of the law of partnership, by the Right Honourable Lord Lindley ... 6th ed., by the Honourable Walter B. Lindley ... London, Sweet and Maxwell, limited, 1902.

Lindley, Hon. Walter Barry, 1861–   joint author.   FOR OTHER EDITIONS SEE MAIN ENTRY
Lindley, Nathaniel Lindley, baron, 1828–1921.
    A treatise on the law of partnership. 5th ed. By the Right Honourable Sir Nathaniel Lindley ... assisted by William C. Gull ... and Walter B. Lindley ... With American notes by Alonzo B. Wentworth ... Boston, C. H. Edson & co., 1888.

Lindley, W[alter] H[arvey].
    Erläuterungs-Bericht zu den Vorarbeiten u. dem generellen Projekt der Wasserversorgung der Stadt. No. 63300 vom 14 (27) Januar 1903. Crajowa: R. u. I. Samitca, 1903. 2 p.l., 39, vii p., 1 diagr., 1 map. pap. f°. (Crajova, city, Rumania.)

    1. Water supply, Crajova, Rumania.
N. Y. P. L.   July 9, 1912.

NL 0381703   NN

VOLUME 334

Lindley, Will, *pseud.*

    see

Grubbs, William Lindley, 1898–

Lindley, William. A reply to the Bishop of
Lincoln' Pastoral to the Wesleyan Metho-
dists in the diocese of Lincoln. 4th ed.
London, Stock, 18—. 12 p

NL   0381705   PPPD

Lindley, William.
    A reply to the Bishop of Lincoln's pastoral
to the Wesleyan Methodists ... 5th ed.
Beverley, [1873]
    12 p.   8°.   [Bound with the Pastoral, etc.]

NL   0381706   CtY

Lindley, William.
Schlussbericht über die ausgeführten Sielanlagen zur Entwasserung
der Stadt Hamburg nebst Entwurf eines Regulativ's zur Beaus-
sichtigung und Reinhaltung derselben. Veröffentlich auf Versü-
gung der Rath- und Bürger- Deputation.
[Hamburg. Meissner. 1845.]   59 pp. Sm. 4°.
Signed: William Lindley.

                    Nov. 22,   1902
E6198 — Hamburg, Germany. Rath- und Bürger-Deputation. — Hamburg,
Germany. Water sup.

NL   0381707   MB

Lindley, Sir William Heerlein, 1853–1917.
    — Die Anlage von Klärbecken und Riesel-
feldern zur Reinigung der Abflüsse aus den
städtischen Schwemmsielen. Berichte vom 13.
Januar und 17. September 1877. 22 pp., 1 l., 1
map. fol. *Frankfurt a. M., C. Adelmann, 1877.*

NL   0381708   DNLM

Lindley, Sir William Heerlein, 1853–1917.
    Auffindung von Bezugsquellen für die Wasser-
versorgung grösserer Städte auf wissenschaftlicher Grundlage.   München, R. Oldenbourg,
1908.
    67 p.   1 diagr., 9 plans.   8°.
    Repr.: Journal für Gasbeleuchtung und
Wasserversorgung no. 32, 34, 37.
    Ti. fr. cover.

NL   0381709   NN

Lindley, Sir William Heerlein, 1853–1917.
    Barmen-Elberfeld Entwaesserung. Reise-Bericht der zum
Studium der Klärung der Abwässer nach England entsandten
Commission... Elberfeld, im Februar 1902. Im Auftrage der
Commission erstattet von W. H. Lindley... [Elberfeld? 1902.]
    94 p. incl. tables.   f°.

    "Berichtigung zur Denkschrift über die Klärung der Abwässer von Barmen-Elber-
feld vom 14. September 1901," 1 l. preceding t.-p.
    Bibliography, p. 90.

325278.   1. Sewage disposal and   purification—Gt. Br.   I. Bar-
men, Germany. Abwaesser, Commis-   sion zum Studium der Klaerung der.
N. Y. P. L.   April 1, 1931

NL   0381710   NN

K
TD
7
P47
    Lindley, William Heerlein.
        Beschreibung der Entwässerungs-Anlagen
der Stadt Frankfurt am Main, von W. H. Lindley.   Frankfurt am Main, Werk Frankfurt am
Main und seine Bauten, 1886.
    27 p. illus., fold. map. 24cm.

    Cover title.
    "Separat-Abdruck aus dem Werk Frankfurt
am Main und seine Bauten."
    No. 4 in vo   1. lettered: Sewage
disposal, 34.
    1. Frankfu   rt am Main--Sewerage

NL   0381711   NIC MiU

Lindley, Sir William Heerlein, 1853–1917.
    Beschreibung der Frankfurter hafenanlage
    see under   Frankfurt am Main.

627
L74b   Lindley, William   Heerlein, 1853–1917.
    Beschreibung der wasserbauten innerhalb
des stadtgebietes von Frankfurt am Main. Von
stadtbaurath W.H.Lindley. [Frankfurt am
Main],n.pub.,1886.
    cover-title,9 p.   illus.,fold.map. 25½cm
    Separate-abdruck aus dem werk Frankfurt am
Main und seine bauten.

NL   0381713   Mi MiU

[Lindley, Sir William Heerlein,] 1853–1917.
    ...Canalisation de Francfort-sur-Mein.   Francfort-sur-
Mein: C. Adelmann, 1876.   8 p.   4°.

    At head of title: Exposition internationale d'hygiène et de sauvetage de
Bruxelles 1876.
    Text in German and French in parallel columns.
    Signed: W. Lindley.

1. Sewers, Germany: Frankfurt-am-   Main.
N. Y. P. L.   January 31, 1924.

NL   0381714   NN DNLM

Uke25
G2
+896
    Lindley, Sir William Heerlein, 1853–1917.
        Elektricitätswerk Frankfurt a.M. Schluss-
bericht über den Bau des Werkes und über das
erste Betriebsjahr ... Frankfurt am Main,
A.Osterrieth,1896.
    [157]p. front.,illus.,plates,fold.plans,
fold.diagrs.(part col.) 34cm.
    Various pagings.

NL   0381715   CtY

Lindley, Sir William Heerlein, 1853–1917.
    — Entwässerung der Stadt Elberfeld. Gut-
achten im Auftrag des Herrn Oberbürgermeister
Jæger. Frankfurt am Main im September 1882.
28 pp., 2 plans. fol. [*Frankfurt a. M., C. Adelmann,* 1882.]

NL   0381716   DNLM

[Lindley, Sir William Heerlein] 1853–1917.
    Entwässerung der Stadt Hanau; Erläuterungs-Bericht zum
Gesammt-Entwurf vom 20.April 1891, Reg.-Nr.18110. Hanau
Waisenhaus-Buchdruckerei [1891?]

    34 p. 19 cm.

NL   0381717   MH

Lindley, Sir William Heerlein, 1853–1917.
    Entwässerung der Stadt Lodz; Erläuterungsbericht zum
Project Reg.No.92100 vom 28 Oktob.- 10 Nov.1909.
Frankfurt a.M., 1911

    In portfolio with sub-title: Generelles Projekt.
Erläuterungsbericht nebst 5 Anlagen.

NL   0381718   MH

Lindley, Sir William Heerlein, 1853–1917.
    Erläuterungs-Bericht zu dem generallen
Projekt der Kanalistation der Stadt Würzburg,
No. 55876 vom 25. April 1901, von W. H.
Lindley ... Würzburg, Kgl. Universitäts-
druckerei von H. Stürtz [1901]
    v, 37 p., 1 l. fold. tables, fold. diagrs.
33.5 cm.
    1. Sewerage – Würzburg.

NL   0381719   CtY

Lindley, Sir William Heerlein, 1853–1917.
    Exposition internationale d'hygiène et de
sauvetage de Bruxelles, 1876
    see his   ... Canalisation de Francfort-
sur-Mein.

Lindley, Sir William Heerlein, 1853–1917.
    Foreign inquiry. Report on the waterways
of France, Belgium, Germany, and Holland.
London, Wyman & Sons, 1909.
    223 p.   2 maps.   f°.   (Gt. Br. Canals
and Waterways Comm. Reports, v. 6 (Cd. 4841))
    Folded plans and tables included in paging.

NL   0381721   NN

Lindley, Sir William Heerlein, 1853–1917.
    Die Klärbeckenanlage für die Sielwasser von Frankfurt a. M.,
von Stadtbaurath W. H. Lindley...   Braunschweig: F. Vieweg
und Sohn, 1884.   20 p.   diagrs.   8°.
    Repr.: Deutsche Vierteljahrsschrift für öffentliche Gesundheitspflege. Bd. 16,
Heft 4.

1. Sewage.—Disposal, etc., Frank-   furt a. M.
N. Y. P. L.   November 10, 1921.

NL   0381722   NN

Lindley, Sir William Heerlein, 1853–1917.
    Objasnienia zarzutów czynionych przeciw
projektowi wodociąg i kanalizacyi miasta War-
szawy. [Explanation of the projected plan of
sewerage and water-supply for the city of Warsaw.] 29 pp., 8 l., 1 pl., 24, 16 pp. fol. *Warszawa, druk. Magistrata,* 1879.

NL   0381723   DNLM

Lindley, Sir William Heerlein, 1853–1917.
    — Project kanalizatsii i vodosabjenija go-
roda Warszavi, sostavlenii anglijskim ingenerom
v. Lindleem. Perevod s niemetskago. [Pro-
posed plan for sewerage and water-supply of
Warsaw.] xii, 47, 39, 29 pp., 5 l., 5 tab., 3 pl.,
2 ch. fol. *Warszawa, v Gorods. tipog.,* 1879.

NL   0381724   DNLM

VOLUME 334

Lindley, Sir William Heerlein, 1853–1917.
Projekt für das Elektricitäts-Werk der Stadt Warschau. Erläuterungsbericht vom 8. Februar 1898, nebst Anlagen. Various paging. 5 pl. 5 maps. 3 in pocket. 2 tables. F. Frankfurt am Main 1899.
——. Ergänzungs-Projekt (Drehstrom) für das Electricitäts-Werk der Stadt Warschau. Erläuterungsbericht vom 15. October 1898 nebst Anlagen. [2],24 p. F. Frankfurt am Main 1899.

NL 0381725   ICJ MH

Lindley, Sir William Heerlein, 1853–1917.
Projekt kanalizacyi i wodociągu w mieście Warszawie. Przekład z Niemieckiego. [Projected plan of sewerage and water-supply for the city of Warsaw. From the German.] xv,52, 29 pp. 1 l., 6 pl., 1 plan; 2 pl., 32 pp., 5 l., 1 plan. Warszawa, druk. Magistrata, 1879.

NL 0381726   DNLM

Lindley, Sir William Heerlein, 1853–1917.

Gt. Brit. *Royal commission on canals and waterways.*
... Report[s] of the Royal commission appointed to enquire into and to report on the canals and inland navigations of the United Kingdom. Presented to both houses of Parliament by command of His Majesty. London, Printed for H. M. Stationery off., by Wyman & sons, limited, 1906–11.

Lindley, Sir William Heerlein, 1853–1917.
Ueber Reinigung und entwässerung der Städte, besonderers über das Schwemmsielsystem in Frankfurt am Main. Vortrag gehalten auf der XVIII. Jahresversammlung des Vereins von Gas- und Wasserfachmännern Deutschlands in Dresden. München, C. Wolf & Sohn [18--?] 11 p. sq. f°.
Repr.: Journal für Gasbeleuchtung und Wasserversorgung, etc.

NL 0381728   NN

Lindley, Sir William Heerlein, 1853–1917.
Wasserversorgung der Stadt Bukarest; allgemeiner Bericht über die Wasserversorgung der Stadt Bukarest und Vorschläge zu ihrer Verbesserung und Ergänzung. Bukarest, 1905.

NL 0381729   MH

Lindley, Sir William Heerlein, 1853–1917.
Wasserversorgung der Stadt Lodz; Erläuterungsbericht zum Projekt. Reg.No.92050 vom 17./30 Oktober 1909. Frankfurt a.M., 1911.

In portfolio with cover-title: Lodz. Wasserversorgung; Generelles Projekt. Erläuterungsbericht nebst 8 Anlagen.

NL 0381730   MH

Lindley, Sir William Heerlein, 1853–1917.
Welche Erfahrungen sind mit den in den letzten Jahren errichteten Klärvorrichtungen städtischer Abwässer gemacht worden? Referat von Stadtbaurath W. H. Lindley...in der zweiten Sitzung des "Deutschen Vereins für öffentliche Gesundheitspflege" am Freitag, den 14. September 1888... Braunschweig: F. Vieweg und Sohn, 1889.   20 p. incl. diagrs., tables. 8°.
Repr.: Deutsche Vierteljahrsschrift für öffentliche Gesundheitspflege. Bd. 21, Heft 1.

1. Sewage.—Disposal, etc., Frank-   furt a. M.
N. Y. P. L.   June 27, 1921.

NL 0381731   NN NIC

Lindley, Sir William Heerlein, 1853–1917.
Zamiechanija adielannija na project kanalizatcii i vodosnabjenija goroda Warshavi sostavlennii V. Lindleem; i objasnenija po nim zamiechanijam. [Observations on the proposed plan for sewerage and water-supply of Warsaw.] 26, 19, 27, 25, 21, 14, 15, 12 pp., 8 l., 1 pl. fol. Warssawo, v Gorodsk. tipog., 1879.

NL 0381732   DNLM

Lindley (Wm. T.) and company, *Chicago.*
Wm. T. Lindley & co., commission grain and provisions ... Chicago, Cowles & Dunkley, printers, 1881.
16 p. incl. tables. 15 x 7¼ᶜᵐ.
An explanation of the method of doing business on the Chicago Board of trade, with tables giving highest and lowest prices of wheat, corn and oats for each month in the years 1876–1880.

1. Speculation. 2. Chicago. Board of trade.

Library of Congress   HD9009.L5   8-28830 Revised

NL 0381733   DLC

Lindley Cintra, Luis Filipe
see
Cintra, Luis Filipe Lindley.

LINDLEY-JONES, ALAN H.
Boat building materials and methods; a practical guide to the qualities and selection of materials used in boat building, approved methods of working, and the installation of the principal fittings used on small craft, by A.H.Lindley-Jones... London: P.Marshall & Co. Ltd. [1936] 181 p. incl. diagrs., tables. illus. 19cm.

872054A. 1. Boat-building.

NL 0381735   NN MiD

Lindley-Jones, Alan H.
Motor boating for all; a practical handbook on the construction, equipment, and navigation of motor boats and small cruisers, with a section on the conversion of a 30-foot cutter, by A. H. Lindley-Jones. Illustrated by R. Barnard Way. London, P. Marshall & co., ltd. [1933]
151 p. illus., diagrs. 19ᶜᵐ.

1. Motor-boats.   I. Title.

Library of Congress   GV835.L5   33-34549
                                              623.823

NL 0381736   DLC NB N NN WaS

Lindley-Jones, Alan H.
The safety way in motor boating; the elements of seamanship and motor craft management, by A. H. Lindley-Jones. London, Sir I. Pitman & sons, ltd., 1938.
viii, 112 p. illus., diagrs. 19ᶜᵐ.

1. Yachts and yachting. 2. Navigation.   I. Title: Motor boating.

Library of Congress   GV835.L52   38-38688
                                               797.125

NL 0381737   DLC

Lindley-Jones, Walter, 1863–   ed.
The Mercantile year book and directory of exporters in London, Manchester, Liverpool, Birmingham, Glasgow, Bristol, Nottingham, Bradford, Leeds, Huddersfield, Paris, Hamburg, Berlin, Bremen, Amsterdam, Rotterdam, Antwerp, & New York, &c. ... including a walking guide to the shippers of London in street order, a list of importers abroad with their European representatives, and much other information.

London, New York, L. Jones and brother

Lindley-Jones, Walter, 1863–   ed.
The South American importers directory, containing the names of the principal importers, storekeepers, engineers and railway companies in Mexico, Central America, Argentine Republic, Bolivia, Brazil, Chile, Colombia, Ecuador, Paraguay, Peru, Uruguay and Venezuela, showing the class of goods they buy, with notes on the trade of the various countries ... London Lindley Jones & co.

Lindley & Eickhoff.
... Henry F. Emeric, plaintiff, vs. Henry V. Alvarado
see under   Emeric, Henry F
vs. Alvarado, Henry V et al.

The Lindley lectures
see under Kansas. University. Dept. of Philosophy.

The Lindley library; catalogue of books...
see Royal Horticultural Society, London. Library.

Lx12
795my
Lindley Murray examined: or, An address to classical, French, & English teachers, in which several absurdities, contradictions, and grammatical errors in Mr. Murray's Grammar are pointed out; and in which is likewise shown the necessity of "The essentials of English grammar." By a member of the University of Oxford. Oxford, Printed and sold for the author by J.Munday[etc.,etc.]1809.
66,[2]p. 20½cm.

NL 0381743   CtY MH

C630.3
L74c
Lindley Nurseries, Pomona, N.C.
[Catalogue]
Pomona, N.C.
v. illus. 23cm.
Called New Garden Nurseries, 1866-79?; J. Van. Lindley Co., 1880-1925.

NL 0381744   NcU

Cp634
L74h
Lindley Nurseries, Pomona, N.C.
How to plant and cultivate an orchard; fruit the year round. [Greensboro, N.C., 1901]
41 p. illus. 16cm.

1. N.C.--Fruit culture I. Title.

NL 0381745   NcU

VOLUME 334

Lindley on the law of partnership
     see under   Lindley, Nathaniel Lindley,
baron, 1828-1921.

Lindley Training School, Asheville, N.C.
     Report for 1897-'8 and constitution and
by-laws. ₍Asheville, 1898₎
     14 p. 15cm.

     1. N.C.--Children--Charities, protection, etc.

NL   0381747   NcU

Lindlief, William Earl, 1909-   joint author.

Smith, Cyril Stanley.
     ... The equilibrium diagram of the copper-rich copper-silver
alloys, by Cyril Stanley Smith and W. Earl Lindlief ... New
York, American institute of mining and metallurgical engineers, inc., ᶜ1931.

QC100   Lindlief, William Earl, 1909-   joint author.
.L655
no. 447
     Everhart, John Laurence, 1903-
     ... Mechanical properties of metals and alloys, by John L.
Everhart, W. Earl Lindlief, James Kanegis, Pearl G. Weissler,
and Frieda Siegel ... Washington, U. S. Govt. print. off., 1943.

Lindlief, William Earl, 1909-   joint author.

Smith, Cyril Stanley.
     ... A micrographic study of the decomposition of the β phase
in the copper-aluminum system, by Cyril Stanley Smith and
W. Earl Lindlief ... New York, American institute of mining and metallurgical engineers, inc., ᶜ1933.

Lindlin, Christophorus, respondent.
     Disputatio de poenitentia ...
          see under Heerbrand, Jacob, 1521-1600,
praeses.

Lindlof, *Mrs.* Johanna Mariea (Sjoberg) 1872-
     Some presentday issues in education ₍by₎ Mrs. Johanna
Lindlof.
     (*In* National education association of the United States. **Addresses
and proceedings, 1933. p. 334-336**)

     1. Education-₍Economic aspects₎ I. Title.
                                                         E 34-95
     Library, U. S. Office of   Education L13.N212 1933
     Library of Congress   [L13.N4 1933]

NL   0381752   DHEW

Lindlof, Johanna Mariea (Sjoberg) 1872-
          see also

Johanna M. Lindlof camp committee for public school children, *New York.*

Lindlof camp committee for public school children, *New
York*
          see

Johanna M. Lindlof camp committee for public school children, *New York.*

Lindloff, Robert, Ref.: Die Bürgschaftsurkunde nach § 766
B.G.B. unt. bes. Berücks. d. Frage, ob in ihr d. Name
d. Gläubigers enthalten sein muß. [In Maschinenschrift.]
48 S. 4°(2°). — Auszug: Itzehoe [1920]: Pfingsten. 2 Bl. 8°
Marburg, Jur. Diss. v. 29. Jan. 1920 [1921], Ref. Leonhard
[Geb. 13. Dez. 90 Hohenfelde, Kr. Steinburg; Wohnort: Schwarzenbeck i. L.;
Staatsangeh.: Preußen; Vorbildung: G. Neumünster Reife 10; Studium: Heidel-
berg 1, Berlin 3, Kiel 2 S.; Rig. 13. Dez. 19.]   [U 21. 1493

NL   0381755   ICRL

Lindly, John Milton, 1864-
     The history of the Lindley-Lindsley-Linsley families in
America, 1639-1930, by John M. Lindly ... Winfield, Ia.,
1924-
               v. illus. (incl. ports., facsims.) 24ᶜᵐ.

          Vol. 1, ᶜ1930; v. 2, 1924.
          Vol. 2 has title: The history of the Lindley-Lindsley-Linsley families
in America, 1639-1924.

          1. Lindley family. 2. Lindsley family. 3. Linsley family.
                                                              31-10488
          Library of Congress   C871.L746 1924

NL   0381756   DLC PHi ViU

Lindly, Mabel, ed.

     The Nebraska and midwest genealogical record. v. 1-
Jan. 1923-
     Lincoln, Neb. ₍Nebraska genealogical society₎ 1923-

Lindly, Mabel, ed.

     Daughters of the American revolution. *Nebraska.*
          Nebraska state history of the Daughters of the American
     revolution, from June 7, 1894, until February 1, 1929, pub-
     lished by the Nebraska society of the Daughters of the Amer-
     ican revolution ... ₍Lincoln, J. North & co., printers, 1929?₎

Lindman, Alexander, *editor.*
     Turist- och sportutställningen vid Allmänna konst- och industri-
utställningen i Stockholm 1897. En handledning vid studiet af
den materiel och de bilder som här visas från olika idrottsgre-
narne, jemte en allmän öfverblick öfver desammas historia och
utveckling i landet. ... . 88 p. il. O. Stockholm: Svenska
pressbyrån, 1897.
     Text and title-page in Swedish, German, and English.

NL   0381759   ICJ ICRL

948.508   Lindman, Arvid, 1862-1936.
L6447ar   Arbetets politik och ordningens;
          tal i valrörelsen 1932. ₍Stock-
          holm, Egnellska boktr., 1932₎

               204 p.   illus., col. map.
          21cm.

               1. Sweden. Politics and government.
          1905-   I. Title.

NL   0381760   MnU

948.508   Lindman, Arvid, 1862-1939.
L6447e   Ekonomi och politik; sammanfatt-
          ning af tal i valrörelsen 1921.
          2. utökade uppl. Stockholm,
          Tryckeriaktiebolaget Svea, 1921.

               181 p.   20cm.

               1. Sweden. Politics and government.
          1905-   I. Title.

NL   0381761   MnU

Lindman, Arvid, 1862-1936.
     ... Några synpunkter på Sveriges utrikespolitik under
varldskriget; tal af ministern för utrikes ärenden Lindman i
Stockholm den 22 augusti 1917. Stockholm, Aftonbladets
tryckeri, 1917.
     28 p. 21ᶜᵐ.
     At head of title: Medföljer som bilaga till Aftonbladet.

     1. European war, 1914-1918—Sweden. 2. Sweden—For. rel.—1905-
                                    ₍Full name: Salomon Arvid Achates Lindman₎

     Library of Congress   D621.S5L5   19—20169

NL   0381762   DLC

Lindman, Arvid, 1862-1936.
     Samverkan för produktiva uppgifter;
tal i valrörelsen 1928. ₍Stockholm,
Egnellska boktr., 1928₎

     157 p.   21cm.

     1. Sweden. Pol. & govt. 1905-

NL   0381763   MnU

948.508   Lindman, Arvid, 1862-1936.
L6447v   Var svenska väg; urval av tal i
          1934 års valrörelse. ₍Ulricehamn,
          Ulricehamns tidn., 1934₎

               116 p.   illus., col. map.
          21cm.

               1. Sweden. Politics and government.
          1905-   I. Title.

NL   0381764   MnU

TE250   Lindman, Bertram Herman, 1906-
.N3
          National highway users conference.
               Effects of weather and heavy loads on pavements ...
          Washington, D. C., National highway users conference
          ₍1941₎

HE5633   Lindman, Bertram Herman, 1906-
.C2A5
1946   **California.** *Legislature. Joint fact-finding committee on
          highways, streets and bridges.*
               ... A proposed system of highway financing for the state of
          California, submitted to the Joint fact-finding committee on
          highways, streets and bridges, by Bertram H. Lindman. ₍Sac-
          ramento₎ California state printing office, 1946.

VOLUME 334

Lindman, Bertram Herman, 1906–
 Supplemental bond financing for acceleration of the Ohio highway program. [Columbus?] 1951.
 91 p. illus. 23 cm.

 1. Roads—Ohio—Finance.

 HE356.O3L5 388.1 52–62172 ‡

NL 0381767 DLC Or OrP

Lindman, C.

Antevs, Ernst.
 ... Die liassische flora des Hörsandsteins, von Ernst Antevs; mit 6 tafeln und 4 textfiguren; mitgeteilt am 8. januar 1919 durch A. G. Nathorst und C. Lindman. Stockholm, Almquist & Wiksells boktryckeri-a.-b., 1919.

WA **LINDMAN,** Carl Albert, 1860–
qL746d Dödligheten i första lefnadsåret i
1898 sveriges tjugo större städer 1876-95. Stockholm, Nordin & Josephson [1898] 158 p. illus.

NL 0381769 DNLM

Lindman (Carl [Albert]) [1860–]. *Döda-orsakerna och dödligheten i Helsingborg 1876-90. [Causes of death and mortality in Helsingborg, 1876-90.] [Lund.] 106 pp., 2 ch., I diag., 1 map. 4°. *Helsingborg, Schmidt, 1894.*

NL 0381770 DNLM

Lindman, Carl Albert, 1860–
 Sundhets och befolkningsförhållanden i Sveriges städer 1851–1909 af med. D:r Carl Lindman, ... 1–[II]. [Stockholm, A.-b. Nordiska bokhandeln, pref., 1911.]
 2 vol. in 1. 31½ᶜᵐ.
 Contents.— 1. Text. [2], xxxi, [3], 421, [1] p. front.— 2. Tabeller och diagram. 33, 27, [1] p. incl. illus., tables. 1 diagr.

NL 0381771 ICJ ICRL

Lindman, C[arl] A[xel] M[agnus], 1856–1928.
 Beitraege zur Gramineenflora Südamerikas. Stockholm: P. A. Norstedt & Söner, 1900. 52 p., 15 l., 15 pl. illus. f°. (Kongliga Svenska Vetenskaps-Akademien. Handlingar. Ny följd. Bd. 34, no. 6.)

 1. Gramineæ, South America. 2. Grasses, South America.
 N. Y. P. L. December 11, 1911.

NL 0381772 NN LU NcD

Lindman, Carl Axel Magnus, 1856–1928
 ... Beiträge zur Kenntnis der tropisch-amerikanischen Farnflora, von C. A. M. Lindman ... [Stockholm, Kungl. boktryckeriet, 1903]
 p. [187]–275. pl. 7–14 (fold.) 24ᶜᵐ.
 Caption title.
 Excerpt from Arkiv för botanik, bd. 1.

NL 0381773 ICJ MH

QK 495 P17 L74 **Lindman, Carl Axel Magnus,** 1856–1928.
 Beiträge zur Palmenflora Südamerikas. Stockholm, P. A. Norstedt & Söner, 1900.
 42 p. illus., 6 plates. 22 cm.

 At head of title: Bihang till K. Svenska vet.-akad. handlingar. bd. 26, afd. III, no. 5.

 1. Palms – South America. I. Series: Svenska vetenskapsakademien, Stockholm. Bihang. Handlingar. bd. 26, afd. III, no. 5

NL 0381774 NIC MH-A

Lindman, Carl Axel Magnus, 1856–1928.

 Krok, Thorgny Ossian Bolivar Napoleon, 1834–1921.
 Bibliotheca botanica suecana ab antiquissimis temporibus ad finem anni MCMXVII, auctore Th. O. B. N. Krok. Svensk botanisk litteratur från äldsta tider t. o. m. 1918, av Th. O. B. N. Krok. Utg. efter föfattarens död. Uppsala och Stockholm, Almqvist & Wiksells boktryckeri-a.-b. (i distribution) [1925]

QK324 .L53 1905 **Lindman, Carl Axel Magnus,** 1856–1928.
 Bilder ur Nordens flora, på grundvalen af Palmstruchs "Svensk botanik" af C. A. M. Lindman. Stockholm, Wahlström & Widstrand [1905]
 3 v. 519 col. plates. 24 cm.

 1964 ed. published under title: Nordens flora.

 1. Botany – Finland. 2. Botany – Scandinavia 3. Botany – Pictorial works. i.t. ii.t: Nordens flora

NL 0381776 NNBG MH WaU

Lindman, Carl Axel Magnus, 1856–1928
 Bilder ur Nordens flora efter Palmstruch m.fl. Svensk botanik av C. A. M. Lindman. Andra upplagan. Stockholm, Wahlström & Widstrand, [1918–].
 Library has pt. 1+. col. plates. 25ᶜᵐ.
 Cover-title.
 Description of flora of Scandinavia and Finland.

NL 0381777 ICJ

Lindman, Carl Axel Magnus, 1856–1928.
 Bilder ur nordens flora, av C. A. M. Lindman ... 2. och 3. upplagorna. Stockholm, Wahlström & Widstrand [1922–26]
 3 v. 663 col. pl. 24ᶜᵐ.
 Paged continuously.

 1. Botany—Finland. [1. Finland—Botany] 2. Botany—Scandinavia. 2. Scandinavia—Botany]

 Library, U. S. Dept. of Agriculture 459.1L63 Agr 28–1669

NL 0381778 DNAL CU ICJ NNBG

QK324 .L53 1907 **Lindman, Carl Axel Magnus,** 1856–1928.
 Billeder af Nordens flora, med tekst af A. Mentz of C. H. Ostenfeld. København, G. E. C. Gad, 1901–1903[i.e.1907]
 3 v. illus. 24 cm.

 1. Botany - Finland. 2. Botany - Scandinavia. 3. Botany - Pictorial works. i.t. ii.t: Nordens flora.

NL 0381779 NNBG

Lindman, Carl Axel Magnus, 1856–1928.
 ... *Bromeliaceæ* herbarii regnelliani. 1. *Bromelieæ.* Scripsit C. A. M. Lindman. Cum 8 tabulis ... Stockholm, P. A. Norstedt & söner, 1891.
 50 p. VIII double pl. 31ᶜᵐ. (Kongl. svenska vetenskaps-akademiens handlingar. [Ny följd] bd. 24, n:o 8)
 "Index auctorum, quos mihi licuit adire": p. 41–42.

 1. Bromeliaceae. 2. Botany—Brazil.

 Chicago. Univ. Library A 43–183
 for Library of Congress Q64.S85 bd. 24, no. 8
 [2]†

NL 0381780 ICU MH NN DLC

QH44 .L7 **Lindman, Carl Axel Magnus,** 1856–1928.
 Carl von Linné als botanischer forscher und schriftsteller, von C. A. M. Lindman. Jena, G. Fischer, 1908.
 iv, 188 p. 26ᶜᵐ.

 1. Linné, Carl von, 1707–1778. 2. Botany.

NL 0381781 ICU MH-A MdBJ NcRS CSt IU

---

580 L649Yℓi **Lindman, Carl Axel Magnus,** 1856–1928.
 Carl von Linné såsom botanist. Uppsala, Almquist & Wiksells, 1907.
 116p. 26cm. (Carl von Linnés betydelse såsom naturiforskare och läkare. Skildringar utgifna af Kungl. Vetenskapsakademien i anledning af tvåhundraårsdagen af Linnés födelse)

 1. Linné, Carl von, 1707–1778. (Series)

NL 0381782 IU

Lindman, Carl Axel Magnus, 1856–1928.

K. Svenska vetenskapsakademien, Stockholm, ed.
 Carl von Linnés betydelse såsom naturforskare och läkare. Skildringar utgifna af Kungl. vetenskapsakademien i anledning af tvåhundraårsdagen af Linnés födelse. Uppsala, Almqvist & Wiksells boktryckeri-a.-b., 1907.

Lindman, Carl Axel Magnus, 1856–1928.
 De speciebus nonnullis generis Silenes L.
 see his Om några arter af slägtet Silene L.

LINDMAN, Carl Axel Magnus, 1856–1928.
 Einige neue Brasilianische Cyclanthaceen. Stockholm. Wheldon & Co., Cat. 35. 1900.

NL 0381785 MH MH-A

Lindman, Carl Axel Magnus, 1856–1928.
 Einige notizen über Viscum album. [Cassel. 1890.] 8°. pp. 4.
 "Botanisches centralblatt." 1890. xliv. 241–244. "Separatabdruck."

NL 0381786 MH-A

VOLUME 334

Lindman, Carl Axel Magnus, 1856- *1928.*
Illustrerad skol- och exkursionsflora över Sveriges kärlväxter, utgiven av C. A. M. Lindman. Stockholm, P. A. Norstedt & söners förlag ₍1928₎
x, 330 p. illus. 19½ᶜᵐ.

1. Botany—Sweden. ₍1. Sweden—Botany₎

Agr 28-1806

Library, U. S. Dept. of   Agriculture 459.1L63 I

NL 0381787   DNAL MH-G

Lindman, Carl Axel Magnus, 1856-1928.
Leguminosae Austro-Americanae ex itinere Regnelliano primo. Stockholm, P.A. Norstedt & soener, 1898.
61 p. 8°. [Kongl. svenska vet.-akad. handlingar. Bihang. Bd. 24, afd. 3, no. 7]

NL 0381788   MH-A PPAmP

QK31
.15
L582
    Lindman, Carl Axel Magnus, 1856-1928.
    Linné och Goethe. ₍Stockholm, 1909₎
    ₍420₎-435 p. 25 cm. (Nordisk tidskrift för vetenskap, konst & industri, **1909**, häfte 6)

1. Linné, Carl von, 1707-1778. 2. Goethe, Johann Wolfgang von, 1749-1832. i.s.

NL 0381789   NNBG

QK77
.S8
L5
    Lindman, Carl Axel Magnus, 1856-1928.
    A Linnean herbarium in the Natural History Museum in Stockholm. By C. A. M. Lindman. Uppsala, Almqvist & Wiksells boktr., 1907-09.
    2 v. in 1. 21 cm. (Arkiv för botanik, bd.7, no.3; bd.9, no.6)

    Copy 1 inscribed: Dr. N. L. Britton with the compliments of the author.
    Contents. -1. Monandria-Tetrandria. -2. Pentandria.

NL 0381790   NNBG MH-G MH-A

LINDMAN, Carl Axel Magnus.
List of Regnellian Cyperaceae coll. 1894. ib 1900. Stockholm. H.Ulrich,Cat.82.Steglitz bei Berlin.
8. w. 9 pl. (6 M.)

NL 0381791   MH

Lindman, Carl Axel Magnus, 1856- 1928.
—— Några bilder från den sydamerikanska vidmarken El gran chaco. ₍Stockholm. 1899.₎ 8°. Illustr.
"Ur Ymer; tidskrift utgifven af Svenska sällskapet för antropologi och geografi, 1899," xviii, 44-79.

NL 0381792   MH-A

Lindman, Carl Axel Magnus, 1856-1928.
Om drifved och andra af hafsströmmar uppkastade naturföremål vid Norges kuster. Af Carl Lindman ... ₍Göteborg, D. F. Bonniers boktryckeri, 1883₎
105, ₍1₎ p. III pl. 23ᶜᵐ. [Göteborgs kongl. vetenskaps- och vitterhetssamhälles handlingar. Ny ₍i. e. 3.₎ tidsföljd, 18:de häftet. ₍No. 1₎]
Bibliographical foot-notes.

1. Botany—Geographical distribution. 2. Ocean currents—Atlantic ocean. 3. Gulf stream.

Illinois. Univ. Library
for Library of Congress   AS284.G7 föl. 3, hft. 18, no. 1   A 46-2688

NL 0381793   IU MH-A DLC

580.6
S9685a
v.1
no.6
Science
    Lindman, Carl Axel Magnus, 1856-1928.
    Om några arter af slagtet Silene L. Stockholm, I. Marcus, 1891.
    16p. plate. 26cm. (Acta Horti Bergiani. Bd.1, n:o 6)
    Title also in Latin: De speciebus nonnullis generis Silenes L.

I. Series (contents)

NL 0381794   TxDaM NNBG

Lindman, Carl Axel Magnus, *1856-1928*
Om postflorationen och dess betydelse saasom skyddsmedel for fruktanlaget.
Inaug.diss. Upsala, 1884.

NL 0381795   ICRL

Lindman, Carl Axel Magnus, 1856-1928.
... Om postflorationen och dess betydelse såsom skyddsmedel för fruktanlaget. Af C. A. M. Lindman. Med 4 taflor ... Stockholm, P. A. Norstedt & söner, 1884.
81 p. IV pl. 31ᶜᵐ. (Kongl. svenska vetenskaps-akademiens handlingar. ₍Ny följd₎ bd. 21, n:o 4)
Bibliographical foot-notes.

1. Botany—Physiology. I. Title.

Chicago. Univ. Library
for Library of Congress   Q64.S85 bd. 21, no. 4   A 43-142

NL 0381796   ICU MU DLC NN

580.6
S9685a
v.3
no.1B
    Lindman, Carl Axel Magnus, 1856-1928.
    Remarques sur la floraison du genre Silene L. Stockholm, I. Marcus, 1897.
    28p. illus. 26cm. (Acta Horti Bergiani, Bd. 3, n:o 1B)

I. Series (contents)

NL 0381797   TxDaM NNBG

Lindman, Carl Axel Magnus, 1856-
Svensk fanerogamflora, av C. A. M. Lindman. Stockholm, P. A. Norstedt & söners förlag ₍1918₎
viii, 639 p. illus. 22ᶜᵐ.

1. Botany—Sweden. ₍1. Sweden—Botany₎

Agr 20-932

Library, U. S. Dept. or   Agriculture 459.1L642

NL 0381798   DNAL NNBG NIC ICJ MH-A PU-B

QK289
.L56
1926
    Lindman, Carl Axel Magnus, 1856-1928.
    Svensk fanerogamflora, utgiven av C. A. M. Lindman. Andra upplagan. Stockholm, P. A. Norstedt & söners förlag ₍1926₎
    x, 644 p. illus. 22 cm.

1. Botany - Sweden. i.t.

NL 0381799   NNBG MiU PPAN

LINDMAN, Carl Axel Magnus, *1856-1928.*
Ueber die Bromeliaceen-Gattungen Karatas, Nidularium und Regelia. [Stockholm.] Björck & Borgesson, Kat. 60. [1890.]

NL 0381800   MH

LINDMAN,Carl Axel Magnus,1856-*1928*
Die Variationen des Perigons bei Orchis maculata L.Geprüft von V.Wittrock und A.G.Nathorst. Stockholm,P.A.Norstedt & Söner,1897.
pp.15,(1). 21.5 cm. Double table.
"Bihang till K.Svenska vet.-akad.Handlingar, bd.23,afd.III,n: o 1."

NL 0381801   MH PPAmP

Lindman, Carl Axel Magnus, 1856-1928.
A vegetação no Rio Grande do Sul (Brasil austral) pelo prof. dᵣ. C. A. M. Lindman ... Obra publicada em Sueco com subsidio da Real academia das sciencias do fundo Regnelliano. Traducção portugueza por Alberto Löfgren ... Porto Alegre, Typographia da "Livraria universal" de E. Irmãos & cia., 1906.
xiii, 356 p. front. (port.) illus. 2 maps. 22ᶜᵐ.

1. Botany—Brazil. ₍1. Brazil—Botany₎ I. Löfgren, Alberto, 1854-1918. tr. II. ₍Title₎

U. S. Dept. of agr. Library
for Library of Congress   457.2L64V ₍a38d1₎   Agr 7-1722

NL 0381802   DNAL NIC PU

Lindman, Carl Axel Magnus, 1856- *1928.*
Vegetationen i Rio Grande do Sul (Sydbrasilien), af C. A. M. Lindman. Med 69 bilder och 2 kartor. Utgifves med understöd ur Kongl. Vetenskaps akademiens regnellska fonder. Stockholm, Nordin & Josephson. [1900].
x, 239 p. 69 illus., 2 maps. 25½ᶜᵐ.

NL 0381803   ICJ PPAN MH-A NcD PBL

LINDMAN, CARL AXEL MAGNUS, 1856-1928.
Vi och våre blommor, en bok om prydnadsväxterna inne och ute, a v C. A. M. Lindman. Stockholm, Wahlström & Widstrand [1913]
viii, 415 p. col.plates. 28cm.

Issued in parts.

1. Floriculture—Sweden.

NL 0381804   NN

Lindman, Carl Axel Magnus, 1856-1928.
Wie ist die Kollektivart Polugonum Aviculare zu spalten? n.p., n.p. 1912.
v.p. plates. O.

NL 0381805   NcD

VOLUME 334

Lindman, Christian Fredrik, 1816–

Elementarläробok i algebra, enligt de af Kommissionen för granskning af läroböcker i matematik angifna grunder, utarbetad af dr. C. F. Lindman ... Stockholm, P. A. Norstedt & söner, 1875.

3 p.l., 336 p., 2 l. 21ᶜᵐ.

1. Algebra.

NL 0381806 ViU

Lindman, Christian Fredrik, 1816–1901.

... Examen des nouvelles tables d'intégrales définies de m. Bierens de Haan, Amsterdam 1867, par C. F. Lindman ... Stockholm, P. A. Norstedt & söner, 1891.

231 p. 31 cm. (Kongl. svenska vetenskaps-akademiens handlingar. ₍Ny följd₎ bd. 24, n:o 5)

1. Integrals, Definite. 2. Bierens de Haan, David, 1822–1895. Nouvelles tables d'intégrales définies.

Q64.S85 bd. 24, no. 5 A 43—180

Chicago. Univ. Libr.
for Library of Congress ₍57e½₎†

NL 0381807 OCl ICU OrCS OrU LU DLC NcRS InU NNC TU OCU

Phys. Sci.
QA
310
B58
L74+
1944

Lindman, Christian Fredrik, 1816–1901.

Examen des Nouvelles tables d'intégrales définies de M. Bierens de Haan, Amsterdam 1867, par C. F. Lindman. Stockholm, 1891. New York, G. E. Stechert, 1944.

231 p. 28cm. (Kongl. Svenska vetenskaps-akademiens handlingar, bandet 24, no. 5) 3

1. Integrals, Definite. 2. Bierens de Haan, David, 1822–1895. Nouvelles tables d'intégrales définies. I. Title.

NL 0381808 MH-GM OU MiU PPT ViU MiEM NIC NcD CtY FTaSU NNU-W NN CSt OO MiHM

Lindman, Christian Fredrik, 1816–1901.

Observations sur les tables d'intégrales définies de Mr Bierens de Haan. (Amsterdam 1858.) Communiqué à l'Académie roy. des sciences de Suède le 10 Septembre 1884. 268 p. O. (STOCKHOLM. KONGL. SVENSKA VETENSKAPS-AKADEMIEN. Bihang till handlingar. vol. 16, no. 3.) Stockholm 1885.

NL 0381809 ICJ DN-Ob

Lindman, C₍hristian₎ F₍redrik, 1816–1901.

Om de transcendenta funktionerna Z'(ₐ) och Gₐ jemte uträkning af deras värden för flera värden på a. Stockholm: P. A. Norstedt & Söner, 1864. 18 p. f°. (Kongliga Svenska Vetenskaps-Akademien. Handlingar. Ny följd. Bd. 5, no. 2.)

1. Functions (Transcendental).
N. Y. P. L. January 10, 1912.

NL 0381810 NN

Lindman, Christian Fredrik Moritz
see Lindman, Christian Fredrik, 1816–1901.

Lindman, Christianus Fredericus, respondent.
De Bindari dictione disquisitio ...
see under Johansson, Johannes Fredericus praeses.

Lindman, Erick Le Roy, 1909–

The development of an equalized matching formula for the apportionment of state school building aid. Seattle, Univ. of Washington Press, 1948.

19 p. diagrs., tables. 23 cm.

Based on a thesis—Univ. of Washington.
Bibliography: p. 19.

1. School-houses—Washington (State) 2. Public schools—Washington (State)—Finance.

LB3218.W3L5 379.12 A 48–5176*

Washington (State) Univ. Library
for Library of Congress ₍2₎†

NL 0381813 WaPS Or OrCS WaS WaT WATC CU IU MiEM DLC

L111
.A72
no. 274

Lindman, Erick Le Roy, 1909– joint author.

Morphet, Edgar Leroy, 1895–

Public school finance programs of the forty-eight states, prepared by Edgar L. Morphet and Erick L. Lindman. ₍Washington, U. S. Govt. Print. Off., 1950₎

Lindman, Jacob Hendrik.

Zur casuistik seltener herzerkrankungen. Inaug. diss. Giessen, 1880. (Leipzig)

NL 0381815 ICRL DNLM

AS260
.A35

Lindman, Karl Ferdinand, 1874–

Turku, Finland. Akademi (1918–)

Acta. Ser. B: Mathematica et physica. Matematik, naturvetenskaper, teknik. 1.–
Åbo, 1922–

Lindman, Karl Ferdinand, 1874–

... Einige elektrische oszillatoren spezieller form, von dr. Karl F. Lindman ... Åbo, Åbo akademi, 1932.

23 p. diagrs. 25ᶜᵐ. (Acta Academiae aboensis. Mathematica et physica. VI, 13)

1. Oscillators, Electric. 2. Electric waves.

Title from John Crerar A C 33–511
Library of Congress Libr.
[AS262.A35 vol. 6, no. 13]

NL 0381817 ICJ PU OU

Lindman, Karl Ferdinand, 1874–

... Herstellung doppelt brechender körper aus kugelförmigen leitenden bestandteilen, von d:r Karl F. Lindman ... Åbo, Åbo akademi, 1924.

31 p. incl. tables, diagrs. 25ᶜᵐ. (Acta Academiae aboensis. Mathematica et physica. III, 7)

1. Refraction, Double. 2. Stereochemistry.

Title from John Crerar A C 33–487
Library of Congress Libr.
[AS262.A35 vol. 3, no. 7]

NL 0381818 ICJ PU OU

Lindman, Karl Ferdinand, 1874–

Ein Interferometer für elektrische Wellen. Åbo, Åbo akademi, 1944.

20 p. diagrs. 25 cm. (Acta Academiae Aboensis. Mathematica et physica, XIV, 11)

1. Interferometer. 2. Electric waves. (Series: Åbo, Finland. Akademi (1918–) Acta Academiae Aboensis. Mathematica et physica, XIV, 11)
[AS262.A35 vol. 14, no. 11] (067.1) A 48–9711*

Ohio State Univ. Libr.
for Library of Congress ₍2₎

NL 0381819 OU PU

Lindman, Karl Ferdinand, 1874–

... Eine methode und ein apparat zur untersuchung der gleitreibung, von d:r Karl F. Lindman ... Åbo, Åbo akademi, 1924.

27 p. illus., diagrs. 25ᶜᵐ. (Acta Academiae aboensis. Mathematica et physica. III, 8)

1. Friction.

Title from John Crerar A C 33–488
Library of Congress Libr.
[AS262.A35 vol. 3, no. 8]

NL 0381820 ICJ PU OU

Lindman, Karl Ferdinand, 1874–

... Några nya försök rörande elektromagnetiska vågors genom tetraedriska molekylmodeller alstrade rotationspolarisation, av dr. Karl F. Lindman ... Åbo, Åbo akademi, 1925.

22 p. diagrs. 25ᶜᵐ. (Acta Academiae aboensis. Mathematica et physica. IV, 1)

1. Electric waves. 2. Molecules. 3. Photochemistry.

John Crerar library A C 33–491
for Library of Congress [AS262.A35 vol. 4, no. 1]

NL 0381821 ICJ PU DLC OU

Lindman, Karl Ferdinand, 1874–

... Några nya försök rörande ledares av olika form elektriska egensvängningar (mit einer deutschsprachlichen zusammenfassung) von Karl F. Lindman. ₍Åbo₎ Åbo akademi ₍1933₎

41 p. diagrs. 24½ᶜᵐ. (Acta Academiae aboensis. Mathematica et physica. VII, 14)

1. Electric conductors. 2. Oscillators, Electric.

Title from John Crerar A C 33–4458
Library of Congress Libr.
[AS262.A35 vol. 7, no. 14]

NL 0381822 ICJ PU OU

Lindman, Karl Ferdinand, 1874–

... Om en av en asymmetriskt tetraedrisk och av en spiralformig molekylmodell alstrad vridning av de elektromagnetiska vågornas polarisationsplan, av d:r Karl F. Lindman ... Åbo, Åbo akademi, 1923.

68 p. incl. tables, diagrs. 25ᶜᵐ. (Acta Academiae aboensis. Mathematica et physica. III, 4)

1. Molecular theory. 2. Electric waves.

Title from John Crerar A C 33–484
Library of Congress Libr.
[AS262.A35 vol. 3, no. 4]

NL 0381823 ICJ OU PU

Lindman, Karl Ferdinand, 1874–

... Om kvartsens termiska dilatation, af Karl F. Lindman. Helsingfors, Finska litteratursällskapets tryckeri, 1916.

83 p. incl. illus., tables, diagrs. 29 x 23ᶜᵐ. (₍Finska vetenskaps-societeten, Helsingfors₎ Acta Societatis scientiarum fennicae. t. XLVI, n° 5)
Bibliographical foot-notes.

1. Quartz. 2. Expansion of solids.

New York. Public library AC 38–1505
for Library of Congress [Q60.F5 vol. 46, no. 5]
(508)

NL 0381824 NN NIC DLC

Lindman, Karl Ferdinand, 1874–

... Om magnetoelektriska svängningar och vågor, alstrade medelst ring- och spiralformiga oscillatorer (mit einer deutschsprachlichen zusammenfassung) av Karl F. Lindman. ₍Åbo₎ Åbo akademi, 1932.

131 p. 1 illus., diagrs. 24½ᶜᵐ. (Acta Academiae aboensis. Mathematica et physica. VII, 1)
Bibliographical foot-notes.

1. Electric waves. 2. Oscillators, Electric.

Title from John Crerar A C 33–4446
Library of Congress Libr.
[AS262.A35 vol. 7, no. 1]

NL 0381825 ICJ PU OU

VOLUME 334

Lindman, Karl Ferdinand, 1874–
... Om stavformiga elektriska oscillatorers langdkorrektioner (mit einer deutschsprachlichen zusammenfassung) av dr. Karl F. Lindman ... Åbo, Åbo akademi, 1932.
43 p. diagrs. 25ᶜᵐ. (Acta Academiae aboensis. Mathematica et physica. vɪ, 10)

1. Oscillators, Electric. 2. Electric waves.

Title from John Crerar　Libr.　　　　A C 33–509
Library of Congress　[AS262.A35　vol. 6, no. 10]

NL 0381826　ICJ PU OU

Lindman, Karl Ferdinand, 1874–
... Om stavformiga hertz'ska oscillatorers samt rätliniga och ringformiga elektriska resonatorers egensvängningar, av dr. Karl F. Lindman ... ₁Åbo₎ Åbo akademi ₁1929₎
201 p. incl. tables, diagrs. 25ᶜᵐ. (Acta Academiae aboensis. Mathematica et physica. v, 6)
Bibliographical foot-notes.

1. Oscillators, Electric. 2. Electric resonators.

Title from John Crerar　Libr.　　　　A C 33–501
Library of Congress　[AS262.A35　vol. 5, no. 6]

NL 0381827　ICJ OU PU

Lindman, Karl Ferdinand, 1874–
... Om symmetriska och osymmetriska elektriska oscillatorers egensvängningar (mit einer deutschsprachlichen zusammenfassung) av dr. Karl F. Lindman ... ₁Åbo₎ Åbo akademi ₁1931₎
130 p. diagrs. 25ᶜᵐ. (Acta Academiae aboensis. Mathematica et physica. vɪ, 7)

1. Oscillators, Electric. 2. Electric waves.

Title from John Crerar　Libr.　　　　A C 33–506
Library of Congress　[AS262.A35　vol. 6, no. 7]

NL 0381828　ICJ PU OU

Lindman, Karl Ferdinand, 1874–
... Om turmalinens termiska dilatation, af Karl F. Lindman. Helsingfors, Finska litteratursällskapets tryckeri, 1916.
16 p., 1 l. incl. tables, diagrs. 29 x 23ᶜᵐ. (₁Finska vetenskaps-societeten, Helsingfors₎ Acta Societatis scientiarum fennicæ. t. xLvɪ, nᵒ 6)
Bibliographical foot-notes.

1. Tourmaline. 2. Expansion of solids.

　　　　　　　　　　　　AC 38–1506
New York. Public library
for Library of Congress　[Q60.F5　vol. 46, no.6]
　　　　　　　　　　　　　　　　(508)

NL 0381829　NN DLC

Lindman, Karl Ferdinand, 1874–
... Prüfung der grundlagen der theorie der Lippmannschen farbenphotographie durch versuche mit elektrischen wellen, von Karl F. Lindman ... Åbo, Åbo akademi, 1937.
62 p. diagrs. 24½ᶜᵐ. (Acta Academiae aboensis. Mathematica et physica. x, 11)

1. Color photography—Lippmann process.
　　　　　　　　　　　　A C 39–3153
John Crerar library
for Library of Congress　[AS262.A35　vol. 10, no. 11]
　　　　　　　　　　　　　　　　(508)

NL 0381830　ICJ OU PU

Lindman, Karl Ferdinand, 1874–
Rückwirkung reflektierter elektrischer Schwingungen auf den Erreger. Åbo, Åbo akademi, 1941.
19 p. 25 cm. (Acta Academiae Aboensis. Mathematica et physica, xɪɪɪ, 6)

1. Electric waves. 2. Oscillators, Electric. (Series: Åbo, Finland. Akademi (1918–) Acta Academiae Aboensis. Mathematica et physica, xɪɪɪ, 6)
[AS262.A35　vol. 13, no. 6]　　(067.1)　　A 48–9710*

Ohio State Univ. Libr.
for Library of Congress

NL 0381831　OU PU

Lindman, Karl Ferdinand, 1874–
Spektrale Zerlegung einer gedämpften elektrischen Strahlung durch Beugungsversuche. Åbo, Åbo akademi, 1943.
14 p. 25 cm. (Acta Academiae Aboensis. Mathematica et physica, xɪv, 10)
Bibliographical footnotes.

1. Electric waves. ɪ. Title. (Series: Åbo, Finland. Akademi (1918–) Acta Academiae Aboensis. Mathematica et physica, xɪv, 10)
[AS262.A35　vol. 14, no. 10]　(067.1)　　A 48–9695*

Ohio State Univ. Libr.
for Library of Congress　　　　(2)

NL 0381832　OU PU

Lindman, Karl Ferdinand, 1874–
Über die anomale elektrische Dispersion in Wasser im Wellenlängenbereich O, 014–10, 4 cm. Åbo, Åbo akademi, 1947.
39 p. diagrs. 25 cm. (Acta Academiae Aboensis. Mathematica et physica, xv, 9)
Bibliographical footnotes.

1. Electric waves. (Series: Åbo, Finland. Akademi (1918–) Acta Academiae Aboensis. Mathematica et physica, xv, 9)
[AS262.A35　vol. 15, no. 9]　(067.1)　　A 48–9705*

Ohio State Univ. Libr.
for Library of Congress　　　　(2)

NL 0381833　OU PU

Lindman, Karl Ferdinand, 1874–
Über die Brechung freier elektrischer Wellen in Wasser im Wellenlängenbereich 10–55 cm. Åbo, Åbo akademi, 1943.
31 p. diagrs. 25 cm. (Acta Academiae Aboensis. Mathematica et physica, xɪv, 2)

1. Electric waves. 2. Electric resistance. (Series: Åbo, Finland. Akademi (1918–) Acta Academiae Aboensis. Mathematica et physica, xɪv, 2)
[AS262.A35　vol. 14, no. 2]　(067.1)　A 48–9707*

Ohio State Univ. Libr.
for Library of Congress

NL 0381834　OU PU

Lindman, Karl Ferdinand, 1874–
Über die Brechung kurzer elektrischer Wellen in einigen festen Körpern. Åbo, Åbo akademi, 1943.
20 p. diagrs. 25 cm. (Acta Academiae Aboensis. Mathematica et physica, xɪv, 5)

1. Electric waves. 2. Electric resistance. (Series: Åbo, Finland. Akademi (1918–) Acta Academiae Aboensis. Mathematica et physica, xɪv, 5)
[AS262.A35　vol. 14, no. 5]　(067.1)　　A 48–9708*

Ohio State Univ. Libr.
for Library of Congress

NL 0381835　OU PU

Lindman, Karl Ferdinand, 1874–
... Über die doppelbrechung elektrischer wellen im eichenholz, von Karl F. Lindman ... Åbo, Åbo akademi, 1938.
30 p. incl. tables, diagrs. 24½ᶜᵐ. (Acta Academiae aboensis. Mathematica et physica. xɪ, 11)

1. Electric waves. 2. Refraction, Double.

　　　　　　　　　　　　A C 40–360
John Crerar library
for Library of Congress　[AS262.A35　vol. 11, no.11]
　　　　　　　　　　　　　　　　(508)

NL 0381836　ICJ PU OU

Lindman, Karl Ferdinand, 1874–
... Über die durch funkenentladungen erzeugte kurzwellige elektromagnetische strahlung, von Karl F. Lindman ... ₁Helsingfors, 1934₎
80 p. illus., diagrs. 24ᶜᵐ. (Societas scientiarum fennica. Commentationes physico-mathematicae. vɪɪ, 13)
Caption title.
Bibliographical foot-notes.

1. Electric waves.

　　　　　　　　　　　　A C 36–2980
Title from John Crerar　Libr.
Library of Congress　[Q60.F555　vol. 7, no. 13]

NL 0381837　ICJ PU OU ViU

Lindman, Karl Ferdinand, 1874–
Über die Durchlässigkeit des Schellacks und einiger anderen festen Dielektrika für elektrische Schwingungen. Åbo, Åbo akademi, 1943.
13 p. 25 cm. (Acta Academiae Aboensis. Mathematica et physica, xɪv, 6)

1. Dielectrics. 2. Shellac. (Series: Åbo, Finland. Akademi (1918–) Acta Academiae Aboensis. Mathematica et physica, xɪv, 6)
[AS262.A35　vol. 14, no. 6]　(067.1)　　A 48–9712*

Ohio State Univ. Libr.
for Library of Congress

NL 0381838　PU OU

Lindman, Karl Ferdinand, 1874–
Über die Fortpflanzung elektrischer Wellen durch ein Metallrohr und zwischen zwei Metallplatten. Åbo, Åbo akademi, 1942.
39 p. diagrs. 25 cm. (Acta Academiae Aboensis. Mathematica et physica, xɪɪɪ, 8)

1. Electric waves. (Series: Åbo, Finland. Akademi (1918–) Acta Academiae Aboensis. Mathematica et physica, xɪɪɪ, 8)
[AS262.A35　vol. 13, no. 8]　(067.1)　　A 48–9675*

Ohio State Univ. Libr.
for Library of Congress　　　　(2)

NL 0381839　OU PU

Lindman, Karl Ferdinand, 1874–
... Über die fortpflanzungsgeschwindigkeit elektrischer wellen längs dünner metalldrähte und die permeabilität des eisens für Hertzsche schwingungen, von Karl F. Lindman ... Åbo, Åbo akademi, 1938.
50 p. diagrs. 24½ᶜᵐ. (Acta Academiae aboensis. Mathematica et physica. xɪ, 3)

1. Electric waves. 2. Electric conductivity. 3. Wire.

　　　　　　　　　　　　A C 40–352
John Crerar library
for Library of Congress　[AS262.A35　vol. 11, no. 3]
　　　　　　　　　　　　　　　　(508)

NL 0381840　ICJ PU OU

VOLUME 334

Lindman, Karl Ferdinand, 1874–
Über die in der elektromagnetischen Strahlung eines kurzen hertzschen Erregers vorkommenden Wärmewellen. Åbo, Åbo akademi, 1945.

14 p. 25 cm. (Acta Academiae Aboensis. Mathematica et physica. xv, 4)

Bibliographical footnotes.

1. Thermo-electricity. 2. Electric waves. (Series: Åbo, Finland. Akademi (1918–) Acta Academiae Aboensis. Mathematica et physica. xv, 4)

[AS262.A35 vol. 15, no. 4] (067.1) A 48–9713*

Ohio State Univ. Libr.
for Library of Congress

NL 0381841 OU PU

Lindman, Karl Ferdinand, 1874–
... Über die magnetische permeabilität des nickels für Hertzsche elektrische schwingungen, von Karl F. Lindman ... Åbo, Åbo akademi, 1938.

16 p. diagrs. 24½ᶜᵐ. (Acta Academiae aboensis. Mathematica et physica. xi, 8)

1. Electric waves. 2. Electric conductivity. 3. Nickel.

A C 40–357

John Crerar library
for Library of Congress [AS262.A35 vol. 11, no. 8]

(508)

NL 0381842 ICJ PU OU

Lindman, Karl Ferdinand, 1874–
... Über die phasenänderung elektrischer wellen bei reflexion an geteilten metallspiegeln, von Karl F. Lindman ... Åbo, Åbo akademi, 1937.

35 p. diagrs. 24½ᶜᵐ. (Acta Academiae aboensis. Mathematica et physica. x, 12)

1. Electric waves.

A C 39–3154

John Crerar library
for Library of Congress [AS262.A35 vol. 10, no. 12]

(508)

NL 0381843 ICJ PU OU

Lindman, Karl Ferdinand, 1874–
... Über eine bei versuchen mit stehenden elektrischen wellen auftretende erscheinung, von Karl F. Lindman ... Åbo, Åbo akademi, 1937.

46 p. diagrs. 24½ᵐ. (Acta Academiae aboensis. Mathematica et physica. x, 18)

1. Electric waves.

A C 39–3155

John Crerar library
for Library of Congress [AS262.A35 vol. 10, no. 13]

(508)

NL 0381844 ICJ PU OU

Lindman, Karl Ferdinand, 1874–
... Über eine durch ein dreidimensionales resonatorensystem erzeugte interferenz der elektromagnetischen wellen, von d:r Karl F. Lindman ... Åbo, Åbo akademi, 1921.

29 p. diagrs. 25ᵐ. (Acta Academiae aboensis. Mathematica et physica. 1:3)

Bibliographical foot-notes.

1. Electric resonators.

A C 33–471

Title from John Crerar Libr.
Library of Congress [AS262.A35 vol. 1, no. 3]

NL 0381845 ICJ OU PU

Lindman, Karl Ferdinand, 1874–
Über eine durch Stufenreflektoren erzeugte selektive Reflexion elektrischer Wellen. Åbo, Åbo akademi, 1940.

18 p. diagrs. 25 cm. (Acta Academiae Aboensis. Mathematica et physica. xiii, 3)

1. Electric waves. (Series: Åbo, Finland. Akademi (1918–) Acta Academiae Aboensis. Mathematica et physica, xiii, 3)

[AS262.A35 vol. 13, no. 3] (067.1) A 48–9709*

Ohio State Univ. Libr.
for Library of Congress [2]

NL 0381846 OU PU

Lindman, Karl Ferdinand, 1874–
... Über eine von einem resonatorensystem erzeugte selektive dispersion, absorption und reflexion elektromagnetischer wellen, von Karl F. Lindman ... Åbo, Åbo akademi, 1935.

68 p. diagrs. 24½ᶜᵐ. (Acta Academiae aboensis. Mathematica et physica. viii, 11)

Bibliographical foot-notes.

1. Electromagnetic theory. 2. Dispersion.

A C 37–2165

John Crerar library
for Library of Congress [AS262.A35 vol. 8, no. 11]

(067.1)

NL 0381847 ICJ PU OU

Lindman, Karl Ferdinand, 1874–
Über elektrische Wellen an einfachen und an zwei parallelen Metalldrähten (Permeabilität des Eisens und des Nickels) Åbo, Åbo akademi, 1939.

35 p. illus. 25 cm. (Acta Academiae Aboensis. Mathematica et physica. xii, 4)

Bibliographical footnotes.

1. Electric waves. 2. Electric conductivity. 3. Wire. 4. Nickel. 5. Iron. (Series: Åbo, Finland. Akademi (1918–) Acta Academiae Aboensis. Mathematica et physica. xii, 4)

[AS262.A35 vol. 12, no. 4] A 48–7578*

Rochester. Univ. Lib:
for Library of Congress [3]

NL 0381848 NRU PU

Lindman, Karl Ferdinand, 1874–
Ueber stationäre elektrische wellen ... Helsingfors, 1901.

68 p. diagrs. 24½ᶜᵐ.

Thesis—Helsingfors.

1. Electric waves.

Library of Congress QC665.L74 5–26284†

NL 0381849 DLC

Lindman, Karl Ferdinand, 1874–
... Versuche betreffend den übergang von elektrischen wellen zu dunklen wärmewellen, von Karl F. Lindman ... Åbo, Åbo akademi, 1936.

30 p. diagrs. 24½ᶜᵐ. (Acta Academiae aboensis. Mathematica et physica. x, 4)

1. Electric waves. 2. Heat—Radiation and absorption.

A C 39–3146

John Crerar library
for Library of Congress [AS262.A35 vol. 10, no. 4]

(508)

NL 0381850 ICJ PU OU

Lindman, Karl Ferdinand, 1874–
Versuche über die Strömung der Elektrizität in Metallen. Åbo, Åbo akademi, 1942.

16 p. 25 cm. (Acta Academiae Aboensis. Mathematica et physica, xiii, 11)

1. Electric waves. 2. Electric conductivity. (Series: Åbo, Finland. Akademi (1918–) Acta Academiae Aboensis. Mathematica et physica, xiii, 11)

[AS262.A35 vol. 13, no. 11] (067.1) A 48–9706*

Ohio State Univ. Libr.
for Library of Congress [2]

NL 0381851 PU OU

Lindman, Maj.
Dear Little Deer [by] Maj Lindman, author-artist. Chicago, A. Whitman [1953]

unpaged. illus. 26 cm.

ɪ. Title.

PZ10.3.L644De 53–10029 ‡

NL 0381852 DLC Or WaS WaSp OC1 OO PP

Lindman, Maj.
Fire Eye, the story of a boy and his horse. Illus. by the author. Chicago, A. Whitman, 1948.

32 p. illus. (part col.) 21 x 26 cm.

ɪ. Title.

Full name: Maj Jan Lindman

PZ10.3.L644Fi 48–2380*

NL 0381853 DLC Or OrP WaS WaSp

Lindman, Maj.
Flicka, Ricka, Dicka and a little dog. Chicago, A. Whitman, 1946.

[27] p. col. illus. 26 cm.

ɪ. Title.

Full name: Maj Jan Lindman.

PZ7.L659Fk 48–3307*

MiU
NL 0381854 DLC Or WaS WaSp OrP PP PWcS OC1 OO Mi

Lindman, Maj.
Flicka, Ricka, Dicka and the girl next door, by Maj Lindman. Chicago, Ill., A. Whitman & co., 1940.

[27] p. illus. (part col.) 25½ cm.

Illustrated t.-p. and lining-papers in colors.

ɪ. Title.

PZ7.L659Flg 40–10779

NL 0381855 DLC OrP Or PP OC1h OO PPAmSwM WaS WaSp

Lindman, Maj.
Flicka, Ricka, Dicka and the new dotted dresses, by Maj Lindman ... Chicago, A. Whitman & co., 1939.

[26] p. illus. (part col.) 25½ cm.

Illustrated t.-p. and lining-papers in colors.
"Junior press books."

ɪ. Title.

PZ7.L659Fl 39–17419

NL 0381856 DLC OrP Or WaS WaSp PP PWcS

VOLUME 334

Lindman, Maj.
Flicka, Ricka, Dicka and the strawberries, by Maj. Lindman. Chicago, Ill., A. Whitman & company, 1944.
[27] p. col. illus. 25½ x 21ᶜᵐ.

I. Title.
                                        [Full name: Maj Jan Lindman]
Library of Congress   PZ7.L659Flh
                                                    44-3052

NL   0381857   DLC WaS WaSp PP OCl 00

Lindman, Maj.
Flicka, Ricka, Dicka and the three kittens, by Maj Lindman. Chicago, Ill., A. Whitman & co., 1941.
[27] p. illus. (part col.) 25½ x 21 cm.
Illustrated lining-papers in colors.

I. Title.
PZ7.L659Fli
                                                    41-17581

NL   0381858   DLC Or OrCS OrP WaS

Lindman, Maj.
Flicka, Ricka, Dicka and their new friend, by Maj Lindman. Chicago, Ill., A. Whitman & company, 1942.
[27] p. illus. (part col.) 25 x 21 cm.

I. Title.
PZ7.L659Flo
                                                    42-22574

NL   0381859   DLC Or OrP WaS WaSp PWcS MiU

Lindman, Maj.
Flicka, Ricka, Dicka and their new skates. Chicago, A. Whitman [1950]
[27] p. col. illus. 26 cm.

I. Title.
                                        Full name: Maj Jan Lindman.
PZ7.L659Fm
                                                    51-284

NL   0381860   DLC Or OrP WaS WaSp

Lindman, Maj.
Flicka, Ricka, Dicka bake a cake. Chicago, A. Whitman [1955]
unpaged. illus. 26 cm.

I. Title.
PZ10.L76Fl
                                                    55-7571 ‡

NL   0381861   DLC Or OrP Wa WaS WaSp 00 PP OCl

Lindman, Maj , illus.
Donaldson, Lois, 1898–
Greta in Weather land; Maj Lindman painted the pictures; story by Lois Donaldson. Chicago, A. **Whitman** & company, 1932.

Lindman, Maj.
Holiday time. Chicago, Whitman [1952]
unpaged. illus. 26 cm.

I. Title.

PZ7.L659Ho
                                                    52-8929 ‡

NL   0381863   DLC Or OrP WaS WaSp OCl

Lindman, Maj.
Little folks' life of Jesus; stories told by Maj Lindman, illus. by Maj Lindman. Chicago, A. Whitman, 1948.
[28] p. illus. (part col.) 28 cm.
On spine : Life of Jesus.

1. Jesus Christ—Biog.—Juvenile literature.   I. Title.
                                        Full name: Maj Jan Lindman.
BT302.L695   232.9   49-421*

NL   0381864   DLC Or WaS WaSp

Lindman, Maj.
Sailboat time. Chicago, A. Whitman [1951]
unpaged. illus. 26 cm.

I. Title.
                                        Full name: Maj Jan Lindman.
PZ7.L659Sai
                                                    51-14171 ‡

NL   0381865   DLC Or OrP WaS WaSp

Lindman, Maj, illus.
Schnick-Schnack-Schnuck, Bilder von Maj Lindman Jan, Verse von Else Dorn. No pub., n. d.
unp. illus.

I. Dorn, Else.

NL   0381866   MiD

Lindman, Maj.
Snipp, Snapp, Snurr and the big farm, by Maj Lindman. Chicago, Ill., A. Whitman & company, 1946.
[27] p. illus. (part col.) 25 x 20½ᶜᵐ.

I. Title.
                                        [Full name: Maj Jan Lindman]
PZ7.L659Sf
                                                    47-3781

NL   0381867   DLC Or OrP WaS WaSp MiU PP PWcS

Lindman,   Maj.
Snipp, Snapp, Snurr, and the big surprise by Maj Lindman ... Chicago, A. Whitman & co., 1937.
[27] p. col. illus. 25½ x 21½ cm.
Illustrated t.-p. and lining-papers in colors.
"Junior press books."

I. Title.
PZ7.L659Sb
                                                    37-35180

NL   0381868   DLC OrAshS WaS WaSp GU PBa NcD PP

Lindman,   Maj.
Snipp, Snapp, Snurr, and the buttered bread, by Maj Lindman ... Chicago, A. Whitman & co., 1934.
[23] p. illus. (part col.) 25½ cm.
Illustrated t.-p. in colors.
"Junior press books."

I. Title.
                                        Full name: Maj Jan Lindmann.
PZ7.L659Sh
                                                    34-37832

NL   0381869   DLC Or WaS OrP WaSp PWcS PPAp

Lindman, Maj.
Snipp, Snapp, Snurr and the buttered bread.
— New York. Whitman & Co. 1935. (51) pp. Colored plates. Decorated title-page. Illustrated end-papers. [Junior Literary Guild.] 26 cm.
A picture book.
Appended is Snipp, Snapp, Snurr and the red shoes, which is catalogued separately.

D7892 — T.r. — Picture books for children.

NL   0381870   MB

Lindman,   Maj.
Snipp, snapp, Snurr, and the buttered bread. Chicago, Whitman, 1940.

NL   0381871   PP

Lindman, Maj.
Snipp, Snapp, Snurr and the gingerbread [by] Maj Lindman. Chicago, A. Whitman & company, 1932.
[23] p. col. illus. 25ᶜᵐ.
"Printed in Germany."

I. Title.
                                        [Full name: Maj Jan Lindman]
Library of Congress   PZ7.L659Sn
                                                    33-5986

NL   0381872   DLC Or OrLgE

Lindman, Maj.
Snipp, Snapp, Snurr and the gingerbread [by] Maj Lindman. Chicago, Ill., A. Whitman & company, 1936.
[23] p. illus. (part col.) 25 cm.
Illustrated lining-papers.

I. Title.
                                        Full name: Maj Jan Lindman.
PZ7.L659Sn 4
                                                    36-32643

NL   0381873   DLC WaS OrLgE GU

Lindman, Maj.
Snipp, Snapp, Snurr and the magic horse [by] Maj Lindman. [Chicago] The Junior literary guild and Albert Whitman & company, 1933.
[47] p. col. illus. 24 cm.
"Printed in Bavaria."
On cover : Snipp, Snapp, Snurr, the magic horse and the gingerbread.
Contains also the author's Snipp, Snapp, Snurr and the gingerbread.

I. Title.   II. Title: Snipp, Snapp, Snurr and the gingerbread.
III. Title: Snipp, Snapp, Snurr, the magic horse and the gingerbread.
[PZ7.L659   ]   398.2   A 33-2245
Providence. Public Libr.
for Library of Congress   [a61n10]

NL   0381874   RP WaS WaSp Or

VOLUME 334

Lindman, Maj
 Snipp, Snapp, Snurr and the magic horse.
Chicago, Whitman, 1939.

NL 0381875 PP

PZ
7
.L7484   Lindman, Maj.
1944   Snip, Snapp, Snurr and the magic horse. Chicago,
       A. Whitman, 1944 ₍c1935₎
       ₍23₎ p.   col. illus.   25 cm.

NL 0381876   MiU PBa RP

Lindman, Maj.
 Snipp, Snapp, Snurr, and the red shoes ₍by₎ Maj Lindman
... Chicago, Albert Whitman and company, 1932.
 ₍24₎ p. illus. 26 x 21 cm.
 Printed in Germany.
 Foreword by Alice Dagliesh.

      I. Title.
                          398.2   A 32—2696
 Jones Library, Amherst,   Mass.
 for Library of Congress   ₍a61r35j5₎

      OrAshS OrPS
NL 0381877   MAJ Or WaS WaSp PWcS PP MB CaBVaU MtBC

J
PZ7
.L659Snr   Lindman, Maj.
       Snipp, Snapp, Snurr and the red shoes.
       Chicago, Albert Whitman ₍c1936₎
       1 v.   illus.   26 cm.

NL 0381878   AAP MiU MoU NbU OrCS PP PPT

PZ 7
.L 67 87   LINDMAN, MAJ
       Snipp, Snapp, Snurr and the red shoes.
       Eau Claire, Wisc., E. M. Hale ₍1936₎
       ₍unp₎ illus.

       Spec. ed. publ. by arrgt. with A. Whitman.
       Bound with her Snipp, Snapp, Snurr, and
       the yellow sled.

NL 0381879   InU

Lindman, Maj
 Snipp, Snapp, Snurr, and the red shoes...
Cleveland, O., Cleveland chapter American Red
cross, 1942.
 9 p.

NL 0381880   OCl

PZ
7
.L7488   Lindman, Maj.
1943   Snipp, Snapp, Snurr, and the red shoes. Chicago,
       A. Whitman, 1943 ₍c1936₎
       ₍27₎ p.   col. illus.   26 cm.

NL 0381881   MiU

Lindman, Maj.
 Snipp, snapp, snurr, and the red shoes ₍by₎
Maj Lindman.   Chicago, Illinois, Albert
Whitman & company, 1947 ₍c1936₎
 ₍27₎ p.   col. illus.   25.5 cm.

NL 0381882   00

Lindman, Maj.
 Snipp, Snapp, Snurr, and the yellow sled, by Maj Lind-
man ... Chicago, A. Whitman & co., 1936.
 ₍27₎ p. illus. (part col.) 25½ cm.
 Lining-papers illustrated in colors.
 "Junior press books."

      I. Title.

PZ7.L659Sny   36—27391

NL 0381883   DLC Or WaSp WaS MB PBa

Lindman, Maj
 Snipp, Snapp, Snurr, en lustig saga för de
minsta. Bonnier, n. d.
 10 ℓ. illus. (col.)

 Cover title.

NL 0381884   MiD PP

Lindman, Maj.
 Snipp, Snapp, Snurr learn to swim. Chicago, A. Whitman ₍1954₎
 unpaged. illus. 26 cm.

      I. Title.

PZ7.L659Sp   54—9945 ‡

NL 0381885   DLC MtBC Or WaS WaSp OCl 00 00xM PP

Lindman, Maj.
 Snowboot, son of Fire Eye; illustrated by the author.
Chicago, Whitman ₍1950₎
 26 p. col. illus. 21 x 26 cm.

      I. Title.

PZ10.3.L644Sn   50—8391

NL 0381886   DLC Or OrP WaS WaSp

Lindman, Salomon Arvid Achates

see

Lindman, Arvid, 1862- 1936.

Lindman, Sven Olof Gustav, 1910–
 Diskussionen om häradskommuner i Finland under åder-
tonhundratalets sista årtionden. Åbo, Åbo akademi, 1942.
 43 p. 24 cm. (Acta Academiae Aboensis. Humaniora, XIV, 8)
 Bibliographical footnotes.

      1. Local government—Finland.   I. Title.   (Series: Åbo, Fin-
 land. Akademi (1918–   ) Acta Academiae Aboensis. Humaniora, XIV, 8)
      [AS262.A3 vol. 14, no. 8]   A 57—4920
 Columbia Univ.   Libraries
 for Library of Congress   ₍2₎

NL 0381888   NNC NIC MU OU CtY ICU

Lindman, Sven Olof Gustav, 1910–
 De homogena partiregeringarna i Finland 1926–1928.
Åbo, Åbo akademi, 1940–41.
 2 v. 24 cm. (Acta Academiae Aboensis. Humaniora, XIV, 1–2)
 Bibliographical footnotes.
 CONTENTS.—1. Det socialdemokratiska regeringsexperimentet, 1926–
 1927.—2. Den första agrarregeringen, 1927–1928.

      1. Finland—Pol. & govt.—1917–   I. Title. II. Title: Det social-
 demokratiska regeringsexperimentet, 1926–1927. III. Title: Den första
 agrarregeringen, 1927–1928.   (Series: Åbo, Finland. Akademi
 (1918–   ) Acta Academiae Aboensis. Humaniora, XIV, 1–2)
      [AS262.A3 vol. 14, no. 1–2]   A 57–4919
 Columbia Univ.   Libraries
 for Library of Congress   ₍2₎

NL 0381889   NNC NIC MU OU CtY

Lindman, Sven Olof Gustav, 1910–
 Johan Jacob Nordström. Hans samhällssyn och politiska
personlighet. ₍Åbo, Åbo akademi, 1948–
 v. ports. 24 cm. (Acta Academiae Aboensis. Humaniora,
 XVI, 2)
 Bibliography : v. 1, p. ₍11₎–13.
 CONTENTS.—v. 1. Tiden intill 1854.

      1. Nordström, Johan Jacob, 1801–1874. (Series: Åbo, Finland.
 Akademi (1918–   ) Acta Academiae Aboensis. Humaniora, XVI, 2)
      [AS262.A3 vol. 16, no. 2]   A 59–8183
 Columbia Univ.   Libraries
 for Library of Congress   ₍2₎

NL 0381890   NNC NIC MU CU ICU NN

A42a
25   Lindman, Sven Olof Gustav, 1910–
19   Notes on the presidential elections in
       Finland. Åbo, Åbo Akademi, 1951.
       17p. tables. 25cm. (Acta Academiae
       Aboensis, Humaniora 19:2)

NL 0381891   CtY NIC MU

Lindman, Sven Olof Gustav, 1910–
 ...Parlamentarismens införande i Finlands statsförfattning,
av Sven Lindman.   Uppsala ₍etc.₎ Almqvist & Wiksells boktryckeri-a.-b. (i distribution) ₍1935₎ 85 p. 23½cm. (Skrifter
utgivna av Statsvetenskapliga föreningen i Uppsala. 5.)
 "Käll- och litteraturförteckning," p. ₍83₎–85.

      1. Finland—Govt. 2. Ministerial   responsibility—Finland. I. Ser.
 N. Y. P. L.   March 15, 1940

NL 0381892   NN MnU MH CtY

Lindman, Sven Olof Gustav, 1910–
 Statsskick och förvaltning i Finland, en översikt. Helsingfors, Söderström ₍1941₎
 161 p. 23 cm. (Medborgarens handbok, n:o 2)

      1. Finland—Pol. & govt.   I. Title.   (Series)

JN6710.L5   51–53488

NL 0381893   DLC

Lindman, Sven, 1910–
 Statsskick och förvaltning i Finland; en översikt, av Sven Lindman... 2. uppl. Helsingfors, Söderström & c:o ₍1949₎ 139 p.
21cm.

      1. Finland—Govt.

NL 0381894   NN MnU

VOLUME 334

Lindman, Sven Olof Gustav, 1910–
Studier över parlamentarismens tillämpning i Finland 1919–1926, med särskild hänsyn till regeringsbildningens problem, av Sven Lindman ... ₍Åbo, Åbo tidnings och tryckeri aktiebolag, 1937₎

382 p., 1 l. 24½ cm.

Akademisk avhandling—Åbo.
Published also as Acta Academiae Aboensis. Humaniora XII:1.
"Källförteckning": p. ₍377₎–382.

1. Finland—Pol. & govt.—1917–   2. Representative government and representation.   I. Title: Parlamentarismens tillämpning i Finland 1919–1926.

DK459.L5 1937   947.1   37–38666 rev

NL   0381895   DLC IEN MU CU

Lindman, Sven Olof Gustav, 1910–
... Studier över parlamentarismens tillämpning i Finland 1919–1926, med särskild hänsyn till regeringsbildningens problem, av Sven Lindman ... Åbo, Åbo akademi, 1937.

3 p. l., ₍9₎–382 p., 1 l. 24½ᵐᵐ. (Acta Academiae aboensis. Humaniora XII:1)

Issued also as thesis, Åbo.
"Källförteckning": p. ₍377₎–382.

1. Finland—Pol. & govt.—1917–   2. Representative government and representation.   I. Title: Parlamentarismens tillämpning i Finland 1919–1926.

[AS262.A3 vol. 12, no. 1]   (067.1)   A C 39–2106 rev

Princeton univ. Library
for Library of Congress   ₍r47c2₎

NL   0381896   NjP PU PBm OC1 OU NIC

JN6719   **Lindman, Sven Olof Gustav,** 1910–   joint
.A5S97   author.
Wikman, Karl Robert Villehad, 1886–
Svenska Finlands folkting, 1919–1920, en orientering av K. Rob. V. Wikman ... och Sven Lindman ... Åbo, Förlaget Bro ₍1941₎

NA   **Lindman, V**
⁵693   Muistoonpanoja Turun tuomiokirkosta; ja sen mui-
L6½m   naismuistoista. Helsinki, 1890.
1890   103 p.

1. Turku. Tuomiokirkko. 2. Churches – Finland.

NL   0381898   CLU

Lindman, Volmar, 1861–
Aftonskymning; dikter. Helsingfors ₍Mercators tryckeri₎ 1937.
31 p.

NL   0381899   WaU

Lindman, Volmar, 1861–
Dikter i urval, 1878–1903. Helsingfors, Huvudstadsbladets Nya Tryckeri, 1903–
111 p.

NL   0381900   WaU

Lindman, Volmar, 1861–
Efterskörd; dikter. Helsingfors ₍Mercators tryckeri₎ 1937.
40 p.

NL   0381901   WaU

Lindman, Volmar, 1861–
De sista; dikter (tolfte samlingen) Helsingfors ₍Mercators tryckeri₎ 1936.
46 p.

NL   0381902   WaU

Lindman, Volmar, 1861–
Valda dikter, 1878–1913. Helsingfors ₍Huvudstadsbladets Nya Tryckeri₎ 1913.
239 p.

NL   0381903   WaU

Lindman, W   E
Wisdom in homes. Hollywood, Calif. ₍1951₎
96 p. illus., plans. 28 cm.
"An International Correspondents publication."

1. Architecture, Domestic—Designs and plans. 2. Architecture, Domestic—U. S. I. Title.

NA7127.L63   728.6084   51–1662

NL   0381904   DLC WaSp NN

Lindmann, J
Ueber subcutane knotenbildung bei acutem gelenkrheumatismus ... Leipzig und Berlin, G. Thieme, 1888.
17 p. 24 cm. [Heidelberg. Universität. Dissertation. v. 2, no. 18]
Inaug.-diss. - Heidelberg.

NL   0381905   CU DNLM PPC

Lindmann (Karl August) [1882–   ]. *KIi-
nische und experimentelle Beiträge zur phar-
makologischen Beeinflussung der Blutviscosi-
tät. 2 pp., 2 ch. 8°. Marburg, J. Hamel, 1908.

NL   0381906   DNLM CtY ICRL

Lindmann, Werner.
Die haftung des luftschiffers nach geltendem reichs-
recht.
Inaug. diss. Erlangen, 1914.
Bibl.

NL   0381907   ICRL

832.08   **Lindmann, Wilhelm,** 1828–1879, ed.
L64   Bibliothek deutscher Classiker für Schule und Haus; mit Lebensbeschreibungen, Einleitungen und Anmerkungen herausgegeben... Freiburg im Breisgau, Herder, 1868–71.
5v fronts (ports) 18cm

Contents: 1. Goethe. 2. Schiller. 3. Les-
sing. Die Göttinger; Bürger, Höty, v.Stolberg, Voss, Claudius. Jean Paul. Herder. 4. Goethe's Prosa. Klopstock. Romantiker. 5. Schwäbische Dichter. W. Müller. Chamisso. Lehr und Gedanken-Dichter. Oester-   reicher.

NL   0381908   MnCS

Lindmar, Theodor: Die Beteiligung der Arbeitnehmer an Gewinn
und Kapital wirtschaftlicher Unternehmungen. [Maschinenschrift]
IX, 96, 39 S. S. 4°. — Auszug: Halle a. S. 1924.
Halle, R.- u. staatswiss. Diss. v. 28. März 1924.   [U 24. 4117

NL   0381909   ICRL

Lindmark, Algot, 1888–
Ingvar Fryle; roman av Algot Lindmark.   **Uppsala:** J. A. Lindblad ₍1923₎. 214 p. 12°.

NL   0381910   NN

4JN   **Lindmark, Gunnar.**
Swed.-   Sveriges Riksdag 1924. [Fotograferingen
20   utförd av Wolfenstein
147 p.

NL   0381911   DLC-P4

Lindmark, Gustavus Fr. , respondent.
De caussis contemtae nostra aetate...
    see under   Juringius, Carolus Axel, 1771–1832 praeses.

---

*
PS646   **Lindmark, John.**
.F5
.L55V5   The vigilant farmers, a Western tale; and
1832   The magic stone, an Eastern tale. New-York: Published by the Author, 1832.
70 p. front. 18½cm.
Card with "Christmas Greetings from Seven Gables Bookshop" laid in.
Wright 1673.

I. Title. II. Title: The magic stone.

NL   0381913   ViU CtY

FILM   **Lindmark, John**
4274   The vigilant farmers, a western tale; and
PR   The magic stone, an eastern tale ... New
v.1   York, The author, 1832.
reel   70 p. front., plate. (Wright American
L5   fiction, v.1, 1774–1850, no.1673, Research Publications Microfilm, Reel L–5)

I. Title. II. Title: The magic stone.

NL   0381914   CU

Lindmark, John, *perfumer.*
John Lindmark's perfumery and jewelry store, no. 88 Chatham street, New York. New York, Printed by W. B. & T. Smith, 1842.
19 p. fold. front., plates (part fold.) 13ᵐ.

                            44–22266
Library of Congress   HD9999.T6L5

NL   0381915   DLC

Lindmark (Olavus)
De triturandi modo apud Orientales. Upsaliae, 1774.
10 pp. 4°.

NL   0381916   NN

VOLUME 334

Lindmark, Ralph, 1909–
Poems, by Ralph Lindmark. New York, H. Harrison
[*1938]
61 p. 21½ᶜᵐ.

38–17938

Library of Congress   PS3523.I 56P6 1938
———— Copy 2.
Copyright A 119419   811.5

NL 0381917   DLC OU

TA 4   **Lindmark, Tore Gustaf Emanuel.**
I46   The flame radiation in water-cooled boiler
no.66   furnaces. By Tore Lindmark and Henrik Edenholm...
Stockholm, Svenska bokhandelscentralen a.-b., 1927.
46 p. incl. illus., diagrs. 24cm.
(Ingeniörsvetenskapsakademiens Handlingar nr 66)

NL 0381918   OU

Lindmark, Tore Gustaf Emanuel, 1872–

Stockholm. Tekniska högskolan.
... Skrifter utg. med anledning av Kungl. tekniska högskolans 100-års jubileum 1927. Stockholm [Centraltryckeriet]
1927.

Lindmark, Wiktor
Solstickan. Lucia-tabla i en avdelning.
Skollersta, Goransons Forlag, 1936.
4 p

NL 0381920   PPAmSwM

Lindmeyer, Bernhard, editor.
Neue fragmente des mittelniederländischen
gedichtes Karel ende Elegast.
see under Karel ende Elegast.

Lindmeyr, Bernhard.
Der Wortschatz in Luthers, Emsers und Ecks Übersetzung
des Neuen Testamentes. Ein Beitrag zur Geschichte der neu-
hochdeutschen Schriftsprache. Strassburg: K. J. Trübner, 1899.
2 p.l., 106 p., 1 l. 8°.

Dissertation, Munich.

1. Bible.—New testament: Trans-   lations, Germany. 2. German
language—History, 16th century.   3. Luther, Martin. 4. Emser.
Hieronymus. 5. Eck, Johann von.
N. Y. P. L.   March 25, 1911.

NL 0381922   NN NNU-W CU CLU ViU NcU MH PU PPeSchw

Lindner,
Hamburgs christliche liebesthätigkeit. Ein wegweiser durch
die anstalten und vereine der inneren mission und milden
stiftungen in Hamburg, von pastor Lindner ... Hamburg,
K. Grädener, 1887.
iv, 140 p. 17½ᶜᵐ.

1. Inner missions. 2. Missions—Hamburg.   I. Title.
39–5947
Library of Congress   BV2955.H3L5

NL 0381923   DLC

Lindner, Dr.
Waldmorgen...
see under Becker, Reinhold, 1842–

Lindner, A. L., pseud.

see

Fleck, Wilhelmine, 1864–

Lindner (A. M.). *Postoperative leukocytosis
and eosinophilia. [Marquette University
School of Medicine.] 10 pp. 4°. Milwaukee.
1924–25.
[Typewritten.]

NL 0381926   DNLM

Lindner, Adalbert, 1860–
Max Reger; ein Bild seines Jugendlebens und künstlerischen
Werdens, von Adalbert Lindner. Stuttgart: J. Engelhorns
Nachf., 1922. 329 p. illus. (facsim., music), plates, ports.
23cm.

"Zeittafel zu Max Regers Leben und Schaffen," p. 307–321.
"Nachweis der Quellen und Übersicht über die Regerliteratur," p. 323–324.

652091A.   1. Reger, Max,   CARNEGIE CORPORATION OF NEW YORK.
N. Y. P. L.   1873–1916.
September 19, 1933

MiU ICarbS KMK MH
NL 0381927   NN CaBVaU MiD ICU PU-FA CU MB NcD NIC

Lindner, Adalbert, 1860–
Max Reger; ein bild seines jugendlebens und künstlerischen
werdens, von Adalbert Lindner. [2. aufl., 4. bis 6. tausend]
Stuttgart, J. Engelhorns nachf., 1923.
324 p. front., illus. (music) pl., ports. 23ᶜᵐ.
"Nachweis der quellen und übersicht über die Regerliteratur": p. [313]–
318.

1. Reger, Max, 1873–1916.
26–16849
Library of Congress   ML410.R25L6
[a40b1]   927.8

NL 0381928   DLC NcU PP TxU

Lindner, Adalbert, 1860–
Max Reger; ein bild seines jugendlebens und künstlerischen
werdens, von Adalbert Lindner. 3., erweiterte und ergänzte
aufl. Regensburg, G. Bosse [1938]
452 p. illus. (music) plates, ports., facsims. [part fold., incl. music]
19ᶜᵐ. (Added t.-p.: Deutsche musikbücherei, begründet und hrsg. von
Gustav Bosse. [Neuausg.] bd. 27)
"Zeittafel zu Max Regers leben und schaffen": p. 390–427. "Nachweis
der quellen und übersicht über die Regerliteratur": p. 428–440.

1. Reger, Max, 1873–1916.
Library of Congress   ML410.R25L6 1938   39–23933
Copyright A—Foreign   43664
927.8

NL 0381929   DLC GU NN

WG   **Lindner, Adolf,** 1849–
29555   Experimentelle Prüfung der von Clarke
und Schneider für den Serpentin aufgestellten
Constitutionsformel. Breslau, 1893.
35 p. illus.

Inaug.-Diss. - Breslau.

NL 0381930   CtY CU ICRL OCl PU

Lindner (Adolf) [1861–   ]. *Ueber Nieren-
affectionen als Complication der Lebercirrhose.
52 pp., 1 l. 8°. Breslau. T. Schatzky, 1886.

NL 0381931   DNLM

Lindner, Agathe, 1892–
see Lindner-Welk, Agathe, 1892–

Lindner, Albert, 1831–1888
Bemerkungen ueber symbolische kunst im
drama mit besonderer Beruecksichtigung
Shakespeare's
[i]n Deutsche Shakespeare gesellschaft. Jahrbuch. 1865– v2

NL 0381933   PU

Lindner, Albert, 1831–1888.
Die bluthochzeit; ein geschichtliches
trauerspiel in 4 acten. Officielle ausgabe nach
dem scenarium des herzogl. Sachsen-Meiningen'schen
hoftheaters bearbeitet.
Leipzig, Conrad, n.d.
86 p.

NL 0381934   OClW

Lindner, Albert, 1831–1888.
Die bluthochzeit; oder, Die Bartholomäusnacht. Ein trauerspiel in vier akten, von Albert Lindner. 3. aufl. Leipzig, J. J.
Weber, 1890.
3 p. l., [8]–148 p. 18ᶜᵐ.

1. St. Bartholomew's day, Massacre of, 1572—Drama.   I. Title.
44–46666
Library of Congress   PT2424.L4B5 1890

NL 0381935   DLC NN TNJ

Lindner, Albert, 1831–1888.
Brutus und Collatinus. Trauerspiel, von Albert
Lindner. Berlin, G. Reimer, 1866.
xiv, 109 p. 19½ᶜᵐ.

I. Title.
G–1448
Library of Congress   PT2424.L4B7 1866

NL 0381936   DLC NjP

PT 2424   **Lindner, Albert,** 1831–1888.
L4   Brutus und Collatinus; Trauerspiel.
B7   Leipzig, J. J. Weber, 1872.
1872:1   134 p. 18 cm.
On spine: Dramen.
Bound with the author's Marino Falieri.
Leipzig, 1875; and his Der Reformator.
Leipzig, 1883; and his Die Bluthochzeit.
Leipzig, 1890.

NL 0381937   CaBVaU

VOLUME 334

Lindner, Albert, 1831–1888.
Catharina the Second, a tragedy in five acts by Albert Lindner. As performed by Mlle. Fanny Janauschek, and her company
of German artists, at the Academy of Music, New York, and at
the principal theaters of the United States of America. New
York: F. Janaus[c]hek [186–?]. 43 p. 8°.

On cover: Classic dramas as performed by Fanny Janauschek.
German and English in parallel columns.

1. Drama (German). 2. Catharine   II, empress of Russia, 1729–96.—
Drama. 3. Title.
N. Y. P. L.   November 19, 1920.

NL   0381938   NN MH

LINDNER, Albert, 1831–1888.
Cothurnus Sophocleus. Berolini, 1860.

sm. 8°.

NL   0381939   MH CtY PU

Lindner, Albert, 1831–1888.
Dante Alighieri; dramatisches gedicht in
3 abtheilungen. Jena, 1855.
118 p.

NL   0381940   PBm

LINDNER, Albert, 1831–1888.
Don Juan d'Austria. Ein geschichtliches Trauerspiel.
Berlin. Stilke. 1875. (7), 115 pp. 16°.

NL   0381941   MB

Lindner, Albert. 1831–1888.
Geschichten und Gestalten.
Leipzig. Reclam. [1877.] 308 pp. [Universal-Bibliothek. 861–
863.] 14½ cm., in 8s.
Contents. — Vogeltobies. — Wie man Taugenichtse bessert. — Im Bann
der Sinne. — Der Componist. — Die Brüder.

H2177 — T.r.

NL   0381942   MB MH

Lindner, Albert, 1831–1888.
Der Hund des Aubri. Ein Zeit-Bild in 3 Acten.
Berlin, A. Paul & Co., 1869.
1 p.l., 59 p. 12°.

NL   0381943   NN

Lindner, Albert, 1831–1888.
Katharina die Zweite,... Berlin, 1868.

NL   0381944   NjP

Lindner, Albert, 1831–1888.
Katharina die Zweite. Ein Trauerspiel.
Berlin, Georg Reimer, 1868.
130p.

Microcard edition.

NL   0381945   ICRL

PT 2424
L4
B7
1872:2
Lindner, Albert, 1831–1888.
Marino Falieri; Trauerspiel in 4
Akten. Leipzig, J. J. Weber, 1875.
143 p. 18 cm.
Bound with the author's Brutus und
Collatinus. Leipzig, 1872.
On spine: Dramen.

NL   0381946   CaBVaU NjP

Lindner, Albert, 1831–1888.
Das Rätsel der Frauenseele. Berlin, 1882.

NL   0381947   NjP

PT 2424
L4
B7
1872:3
Lindner, Albert, 1831–1888.
Der Reformator: dramatische Dich-
tung in 3 Teilen. 2., veränderte
Aufl. Leipzig, J. J. Weber, 1883.
112 p. 18 cm.
Bound with the author's Brutus und
Collatinus. Leipzig, 1872.
On spine: Dramen.

NL   0381948   CaBVaU NjP

[Lindner, Albert] 1831–1888.
Der Schwan vom Avon! Schauspiel in 5 Aufzügen. [Anon.]
Berlin. Paul & Co. 1863. (2), 141 pp. 19½ cm., in 8s.

L4384 — Shakespeare, William. Fiction, drama, etc., relating to him. — Anon.
ref. made.

NL   0381949   MB

PR
2935
.L75
Lindner, Albert, 1831–1888.
Der Schwann vom Avon. Culturbilder aus alt-
England. Von Albert Lindner. Berlin, R. Hanow,
1881
viii,182 p. 18½ cm.

1.Shakespeare in fiction,drama,poetry,etc. I.Title.

NL   0381950   MiU MB PU-F NcU

Lindner, Albert, 1831–1888.
Stauf und Welf,... Jena, 1867.

NL   0381951   NjP

Lindner, Albert 1831–1888.
William Shakspeare. Ein Schauspiel in drei Abtheilungen.
[Rudolstadt. 1864.] (1), 122 pp. 16 cm., in 8s.
Shakespeare, Queen Elizabeth, and the Earl of Southampton are among
the characters.

K2667 — Shakespeare, William. Fiction relating to him.

NL   0381952   MB

Lindner, Albert, 1831–1888.
Zwei Frauen. Ein Trauerspiel in 4 Aufzügen.
Berlin, R. Bell, 1870.
2 p.l., 59 p. 12°.

NL   0381953   NN

Lindner, Alfred.
... Was der flieger und der flugmotoren-monteur vom stand-
motor wissen müssen! Von Alfred Lindner; mit 10 abbildungen im text. Berlin, R. C. Schmidt & co., 1918.
118 p. illus., diagrs. 17ᵐ. (Flugtechnische bibliothek bd. 7)

1. Aeroplanes—Motors.

Library of Congress	TL701.L5	31–18474
———— Copy 2.	[2]	629.13

NL   0381954   DLC NN

LINDNER, Alfred, 1879–
Die vertretungsmacht des vorstands der
aktiengesellschaft. Leipzig, 1905.

41+(1) p.
Inaug.-diss. - Leipzig.

NL   0381955   MH-L ICRL

1886–
Lindner, Alfred, Ref.: Berechtigt eine vom Konkursverwalter
ausgestellte Prozessvollmacht zur Vertretung des Gemein-
schuldners auch nach Beendigung des Konkurses? [In
Maschinenschrift.] IV, 64 S. 4°(2°). — Auszug: Berlin 1921.
2 Bl. 8°
Breslau, R- u. staatswiss. Diss. v. 2. Mai 1921, Ref. Fischer
[Geb. 6. Febr. 86 Glatz; Wohnort: Königshain b. Glatz; Staatsangeh.: Preußen;
Vorbildung: G. Neiße Reife 06; Studium: Freiburg I, Marburg 3, Breslau
4 S.; Rig. 8. Juli 20.]   [U 21. 297

NL   0381956   ICRL

Lindner, Alois.
...Abenteuerfahrten eines revolutionären Arbeiters. Berlin: Neuer deutscher Verlag[, 1924]. 54 p. illus. 16°.

175008A. 1. No subject. 2. Title.
N. Y. P. L.   April 22, 1925.

NL   0381957   NN

(V)
DD233
G373
v.3:5
Lindner, Alois, defendant.
Die Attentate im Bayerischen Landtag; der
Prozess gegen Alois Lindner und Genossen
vor dem Volksgericht München. München,
G. Birk [1920?]
91 p. 22cm. ([German pamphlets on the
Revolution of 1918 and subsequent events,
v.3:5])

1. Trials (Political crimes and offenses)
- Bavaria. 2. Bavaria. Landtag. 3. Bavaria
Hist. - Revolution   1918–1919. I. Munich.
Volksgericht.   II. Title.

NL   0381958   CSt-H

LINDNER, Alois Franz, 1900–
Beiträge zu den veränderungen von kohlehy-
draten, besonders von monosen und biosen, unter
einwirkung verdünnter alkalien. Inaug.-diss.
München, druck der Salesianischen Offizin, [1927]

pp.[83]+. Tables.
"Lebenslauf",at end.

NL   0381959   MH-C CtY DNLM

Lindner, Alwin, 1906–
Die auslegung der verfügungen von todes wegen.
... Marburg, 1933. 76 p.
Inaug. Diss. - Marburg, 1933.
Lebenslauf.

NL   0381960   ICRL

VOLUME 334

*
M1
.S444 **Lindner, Anton**
v.68
no. 28   Give me thy hand, from Gems of German songs
With English translation. ₜPriceₗ 25 cts.
nett. Baltimore, F. D. Benteen; New Orleans,
W. T. Mayo ₜᶜ1851ₗ Pl. no. 2136.
5 p. 31cm. ₜSheet music collection, v. 68, no.
28ₗ
Gillingham.

1. Songs with piano. I. Title.

NL   0381961   ViU

₍Lindner, Anton, 1874-1915₎
Die Barrisons; ein Kunsttraum. Zum Kapitel:
Zeitsatire. ₍Von₎ Pierre d'Aubecq ₍pseud.₎ Aus dem
Manuskript übersetzt und eingeleitet von Anton Lindner.
Berlin, Schuster & Loeffler, 1897

140 p.   illus.
Illus. by T.T.Heine

NL   0381962   MH PP

Lindner, Arthur, 1871–
Die Basler Galluspforte und andere romanische
bildwerke der Schweiz.
Inaug. Diss. Basel, 1899

NL   0381963   ICRL

Lindner, Arthur, 1871–
... Die Basler Galluspforte und andere romanische
bildwerke der Schweiz. Von dr. Arthur Lindner. Mit
xxv textillustrationen und x tafeln. Strassburg, J. H. E.
Heitz, 1899.
116 p.   illus. ₁x (i. e. 10) pl. 24½ᶜᵐ. (Studien zur deutschen kunstgeschichte, 17. hft.)
Bibliographical foot-notes.

1. Sculpture, Romanesque. 2. Sculpture—Switzerland. 3. Basel. Cathedral.
11–13931
Library of Congress   NB843.L5

NL   0381964   DLC CSt CLU IaU CtY PU NcU MB

FILM
X67   **Lindner,Arthur,**1871–
v.17   Die Basler Galluspforte und andere romanische
Bildwerke der Schweiz. Von Dr.Arthur Lindner.
Mit XXV Textillustrationen und X Tafeln.
Strassburg, J.H.E.Heitz, 1899.
116 p.   illus.,IX (i.e.10) pl.   25 cm.
(Studien zur deutschen Kunstgeschichte,17.
Hft.)
Bibliographical foot-notes.
Microfilm copy (positive)
1.Sculpture,Romanesque. 2.Sculpture—
Switzerland. 3.Basel. Cathedral.

NL   0381965   MiU CtY

Lindner, Arthur, 1871–
Der Breslauer Froissart, von Arthur Lindner; festschrift des Vereins für geschichte der bildenden künste
zu Breslau, zum fünfzigjährigen jubiläum verfasst im
auftrage des vereins; mit 50 lichtdrucktafeln und 22 textabbildungen. Berlin, Kommissions-verlag von Meisen-
bach, Riffarth & cᵒ, 1912.
3 p. l., 77 p., 1 l.   illus., 50 pl. (5 col.)   36½ᶜᵐ.
Bibliography included in "Anmerkungen."
1. Froissart, Jean, 1338-1410? 2. Illumination of books and manuscripts—
Specimens, reproductions, etc.   ɪ. Verein für geschichte der bildenden
künste zu Breslau. ₁ɪₗ Breslau. Stadtbibliothek. ɪɪɪ. Title.

Library of Congress   ND3399.F7L5   13—16635

NL   0381966   DLC NcD CU-S IaU OU OCl NN MH IU PPMoI

Lindner, Arthur, 1871–
Danzig, von Arthur Lindner. Leipzig, E. A. Seemann,
1903.
3 p. l., 114 p.   illus.   24½ᶜᵐ.   (Half-title: Berühmte kunststätten, nr. 19)

1. Danzig—Descr.   2. Art—Danzig.
6—38348

Library of Congress   N6886.D2L5

NL   0381967   DLC OU NcU MdBJ NN MB

LINDNER,Arthur,1871–
Danzig. 2e.verbesserte aufl. Leipzig,E.U.
Seemann,1913.

Ports.and other illustr.
Half-title: Berühmte kunststätten,19.

NL   0381968   MH NjP PU OCl IdU

Lindner, Arthur, 1871–
Der dom zu Köln und seine kunstschätze; 50 tafeln mit text
von dr. Arthur Lindner und einem vorwort von M. C. Nieuwbarn ... Haarlem ₍etc.₎ H. Kleinmann & co. ₍1905₎
2 p. l., III, ₍1₎ p., 1 l., v, 50 p.   illus., 50 pl. (part fold., 10 col.; incl.
plan)   43ᶜᵐ.
In portfolio.
Title within ornamental border.
"Verzeichnis einer reihe der wichtigsten schriften über den Kölner
dom": p. III–v.
1. Cologne. Cathedral.   2. Art objects—Cologne.   ɪ. Nieuwbarn,
M. C. ɪɪ. Title.

Library of Congress   NA5586.C7L5   10—27278

NL   0381969   DLC MiU

Lindner, Arthur, 1871–
Festschrift der Handwerkskammer zu Danzig
see under Danzig. Handwerkskammer.

NC1020
.C6   **Lindner, Arthur,** 1871–   ed.
fol.
Cologne. Wallraf-Richartz-Museum.
Handzeichnungen alter meister im besitze des Museum
Wallraf-Richartz zu Köln am Rhein; 25 lichtdruck-tafeln
mit text, hrsg. von dr. Arthur Lindner. Köln am Rhein,
W. Abels ₍1907₎

N5301
.K6   **Lindner, Arthur,** 1871–   joint author.
folio
Kisa, Anton Carel, 1857–
Der kunstschatz. Die geschichte der kunst in ihren meister-
werken; ein buch der erhebung und des genusses, mit erläutern-
dem text von dr. A. Kisa ... dr. A. Lindner ... und dr. E.
Renard ... Berlin & Stuttgart, W. Spemann ₍1907₎

Lindner (August)ᵗ. ₜ₌ₜDₓₑ therapeutische Anwendung des Paraldehyds. ₜStrasburg.₎ 26
pp., 1 s. f. 8°. ₜKassel, Weber u. Weidemeyer, 1884. ₎

NL   0381973   DNLM ICRL MH

Lindner (August)ᵗ. ₜUeber einen Fall von
Scrophulose. 19 pp. 8°. *Würzburg, C. W. Becker,*
1867.

NL   0381974   DNLM

LINDNER, AUGUST, 1820–1878, ed.
Altitalienische Canzonetten und Arien für Gesang
mit Pianoforte eingerichtet von August Lindner, op.40.
Offenbach a/M., J. André ₍pref. 1875₎ Pl. no.11895.
15 p.   35cm.

Microfilm.
For voice and piano; Italian and German words.

CONTENTS.--Chi d'amor spaventa il fuoco.--Apri le luci amanti.--
Dio Cupido, che mai sarà?--Occhi belli.--Parte il piè.--Spirti rei.

1. Songs, Italian--Collections, 17th-18th cent.

NL   0381976   NN

LINDNER, AUGUST, 1820–1878, ed.
Altitalienische Canzonetten und Arien für Gesang
mit Pianoforte eingerichtet von August Lindner. Op.40.
Offenbach a/M., J. André; New York, G. Schirmer
₍pref. 1875₎ Pl. no. 12374.   1 v.   35cm.

Microfilm.
Heft 2.
For voice and piano. Italian and German words.

1. Songs, Italian--Collections.

NL   0381977   NN

M
1017   **Lindner, August,** 1820–1878.
L644c34   ₍Concerto, violoncello, op.34; E minor;
1857   arr.₎
Concert, E moll für Violoncell mit Begl.
des Orchesters oder des Pianoforte, op.34.
Leipzig, C. F. W. Siegel ₍ca.1857₎ Pl.no.
1788.
score (35 p.) and part.

1. Concertos (Violoncello) - Solo with
piano.

NL   0381978   CLU MH

Lindner, August, 1820–1878, arr.
Drei Sonaten nach Instrumental-Konzerten
see under Händel, Georg Friedrich,
1685–1759.

Lindner, August, 1820–1878.
₍Lieder, op. 5. Abschied₎

Give me thy hand, from Gems of German songs. With
English translation. Published by F. D. Benteen Baltimore.
W. T. Mayo New Orleans. ₍ᶜ1851₎ Pl. no. 2136.
5 p.   34 cm.
English and German words.

1. Songs (Medium voice) with piano. 2. Songs, German.   ɪ. Title.
M1.A13L   M 55–1871 rev
ca. 1835–65₎   Copy 2.   No. 12 in a vol. with binder's title: Songs. ₍v. p.,
M1.A15   vol. 91, no. 12

NL   0381980   DLC

M236
.C   **Lindner, August,** 1820–1878, ed.

Corelli, Arcangelo, 1653–1713.
₍Sonata, violin & continuo, op. 5, no. 8, E minor; arr.₎

Sonata, in D minor, for cello (or viola) and piano. ₍Ed-
ited by A. Lindner₎ New York, International Music Co.
₍1944₎ Pl. no. 662.

VOLUME 334

Lindner, August, 1848–
Die aufhebung der klöster in Deutschtirol, 1782–1787; ein beitrag zur geschichte Kaiser Joseph's II. Innsbruck, Wagner, 1886.
pp. (1), 485.
"Aus der Zeitschrift des Ferdinandeums."

Joseph II, emperor of   Germany|Monasteries–Tyrol

NL 0381982   MH

Lindner, August, 1848–
Die schriftsteller und die um wissenschaft und kunst verdienten mitglieder des Benediktinerordens im heutigen königreich Bayern vom jahre 1750 bis zur gegenwart. Von August Lindner ... Regensburg, Druck von G. J. Manz, in commission der M. Hueber'schen buchhandlung in Schrobenhausen, 1880.
2 v. in 1. 24ᶜᵐ.
"Quellen": v. 1, p. 1–13.
—— Nachträge zum I. und II. bande. Regensburg, G. J. Manz, 1884.
89, (2), p. 24ᶜᵐ.
Subject entries: Benedic-   tines in Bavaria—Bio-bibl.

                         3–7513–3** Cancel
Library of Congress, no.   Z7840.B3L5.

NL 0381983   DLC ICJ

Lindner, B., respondent.
Sacra Christianorum veterum in castris
see under   Kalinsky, Johann Gottlieb,
fl. 1715–1749, praeses.

Lindner, Benedikt, 1902–
Die erkenntnislehre des Thomas von Strassburg; nach den quellen dargestellt von dr. p. Benedikt Lindner ... Münster i. W., Aschendorff, 1930.
x, 141 p. 24ᶜᵐ. (*Added t.-p.:* Beiträge zur geschichte der philosophie und theologie des mittelalters ... bd. xxvII. hft. 4/5)
"Literaturverzeichnis": p. (135)–137.

1. Thomas of Strassburg, d. 1357. 2. Knowledge, Theory of.
                                 31–922
Library of Congress   B720.B4 bd. 27, hft. 4/5
                       (109) [189.4] 121

     MoU
NL 0381985   DLC CtY–D NcU PU MiU OU OCU OCl ICN NNUT

Lindner, Benedikt, 1902–
Prolegomena zu Thomas von Strassburg ... Würzburg, 1930.
Pamphlet
Inaug.-Diss. - Würzburg.
"Die 'Prolegomena zu Thomas von Strassburg' bilden einen Teil der "Erkenntnislehre des Thomas von Strassburg', die, vom gleichen Autor verfasst, in den 'Beiträgen zur Geschichte der Philosophie des Mittelalters' ... erschienen ist."
Lebenslauf.
"Literaturverzeichnis": p. [v]–vii.

NL 0381986   CtY MH ICRL

Lindner, Benedikt Max
see   Lindner, Benedikt, 1902–

Lindner, Benjamin, comp.
Das Nutzbareste aus denen gesamten (erbaulichen) Schriften des seligen Herrn D. Martini Luther.
         see under   Luther, Martin,
1483–1546.

Lindner, Bernhard
Beiträge zur untersuchung von kranen ...
Halle a. S., 1909.   62 p.
Inaug. Diss. -Techn. Hochsch. Braunschweig, 1909.

NL 0381989   ICRL DBS

Lindner, Berthold, 1908–
Über die insulin-resistenz bei diabetes-mellitus. ... 23 p.
Inaug. Diss. - Berlin, [1934]
Lebenslauf.
Bibliography.

NL 0381990   CtY

Lindner, Bruno, 1853–1930.
Altindische nominalbildung. Nach den Samhitâs dargestellt von Bruno Lindner ... Jena, H. Costenoble, 1878.
2 p. l., iii p., 1 l., (7)–167, (1) p. 22ᶜᵐ.

1. Vedic language—Word formation.
                  (*Full name:* Wilhelm Bruno Lindner)
                          11—23962
Library of Congress   PK261.L5

   TxU
NL 0381991   DLC ICU CU CtY PU OCl OClW MH NN NjP

Lindner, Bruno, 1853– 1930.
Die dîkshâ oder weihe für das somaopfer ... Leipzig, Druck von Pöschel & Trepte, 1878.
47, (1) p. 22½ᶜᵐ.
Habilitationsschrift—Leipzig.

1. Soma. 2. Rites and ceremonies—India. I. Title.
              (*Full name:* Wilhelm Bruno Lindner)
                          32–11953
Library of Congress   BL1215.S6L5   294

NL 0381992   DLC CtY ICRL

PK3021
.K3
1887
Lindner, Bruno, 1853–1930, ed.
Kauṣîtakibrâhmaṇa.
Das Kaushitaki Brâhmana. Hrsg. und übers. von B. Lindner. I. Text. Jena, H. Costenoble, 1887.

1853–1930.
Lindner, Bruno, Ueber eine handschrift des ersten buchs der Maitrâyani-Samhitâ. 1 p. (Deutsch. morg. gesells. Zeits. v. 39, 1885, p. 103.)

NL 0381994   MdBP

Lindner, Carlo.
Una gloria degli uomini cattolici: Armando Crotti. Reggio nell'Emilia (Uomini di Azione cattolica) 1952.
32 p. port. 25 cm.

1. Crotti, Armando, 1906–1947. I. Title.
                               A 54–6089
Catholic Univ. of   America. Library
for Library of Congress   (1)

NL 0381995   DCU DLC

Lindner, Carlo.
La Madonna della Ghiara. Reggio Emilia, Società editrice Age (1954)
269 p. plates 24 cm.

"Opere citate in questo lavoro o consultate per la sua preparazione": p. (231)–244.

1. Reggio Emilia. Madonna della Ghiara (Shrine)

NL 0381996   DCU

Lindner, Carlo
Nostri preti. Reggio Emilia, Age Editrice, 1950.
330 p.

NL 0381997   DCU

Lindner, Caspar Gottlieb
see   Lindner, Kaspar Gottlieb.

Lindner, Christian Albert.
See
Lindner, Albert, 1831–1888.

Lindner, Christian Friedrich, respondent.
... De singvlari cavsa exheredandi liberos in dvcatv magdebvrgico
see under   Wildvogel, Christian, 1644–1728, praeses.

Lindner (Christianus Theophilus). *De erroribus in potulentia commissis.* 22 pp. 4°. *Erfordia, typ. J. H. Groschii,* (1713).

NL 0382002   DNLM

Lindner, Clarence Richard, 1890–
Private Lindner's letters, censored and uncensored; letters, anecdotes, sketches, by Private Clarence R. Lindner during world war; selection and arrangement by his wife, Gladys Dudley Lindner. (San Francisco, ᶜ1939)
5 p. l., 13–126 p. illus. 29ᶜᵐ.

1. European war, 1914–1918—Personal narratives, American. I. Lindner, Mrs. Gladys Dudley, ed. II. Title.

Library of Congress   D570.9.L48   40–10405
—— Copy 2.
Copyright   (2)   940.48173

NL 0382003   DLC

Lindner, Clementine.
Aus Frau Musikas reich; zehn skizzen, von Clementine Lindner. Berlin, C. F. Vieweg, g. m. b. h., 1908 (1907)
83 p. 17½ᶜᵐ.

CONTENTS.—Vor grauen zeiten.—Übers jahr.—Auf der wanderschaft.—Träume.—Notenkinder.—Ein gestrenger herr.—Seine schule.—Im kloster.—Klein sykopus.—Liebeskunde.—Zuletzt.

                             7–35644
Library of Congress   (Copyright 1907 Res. no. 1221)

NL 0382004   DLC

VOLUME 334

Lindner, Conrad, 1868-
  Eine neue Methode der Unterbindung der
A. subclavia unter dem Schlüsselbein (und der
Ausräumung der Achselhöhle) Leipzig, 1904.
  16 p.
  Inaug. - Diss. - Leipzig.
  Bibl.

NL 0382005   ICRL CtY

Lindner, Constantin. Christoph. Guil., 1778-1808.
——. Commentatio anatomica de cornea. 26 pp.
8°. *Dorpat, lit. M. G. Grenzii,* 1806.

NL 0382006   DNLM

---

de Lindner (Constantin. Christoph. Guil.)
[1778-1808.] *De cornea ejusque obscurationi-
bus.   20 pp.   8°. *Dorpat, lit. M. G. Grenzii,* 1804.

NL 0382007   DNLM

3A
544   LINDNER, CORNELIUS.
  Gründliche Anleitung zum nützlichen Gebrauche der Erd- u. Himmels-Kugeln, den An-
fängern, in Erlernung der Geographie und Astronomie, zum Besten: andern Liebhabern aber
dieser ... Wissenschafften, zu weiterer Auf-
munterung und Belustigung, auf eine leichte
Art deutlich ausgefertiget ... von M. Cornelius Lindner.   Nürnberg, Bey P.C.Monath,1726.
  [15]ℓ.,296p.   6 plates. 18cm.

NL 0382008   ICN

Lindner, Curt 1891-
  Die zahnaerztlichen lehren des Galenos.
  Inaug. Diss. Berlin, 1920
  Bibl.

NL 0382009   ICRL CtY

Lindner, Cyrilla P.   ed.
  Chinese theatres in America
    see under Federal Theatre Project. San
Francisco.

Lindner, Cyrilla P.
  Los pastores; the story of the mission play
    see under Federal Theatre Project. San
Francisco.

Lindner (Daniel). De tilia. 7 l. 4°. *Lipsia,*
stanno C. Michaelis, [1683].

NL 0382012   DNLM

Lindner, Daniel Gottlieb
  Monita et vota suprema quibus juvenes ornatis-
simos, Joannem Henricum nec non Eliam Ernestum
Wieseleros, ad academiae subsellia iter parantes.
Luneburgi,1747.

NL 0382013   CtY

JX4521   LINDNER,DAVID, 1604-1644.
.L75   De bellorum justitia, quae ex interdictione na-
scitur,exercitatio ad 1.hostes.XXIV. D.De captiv.et
postlim... Altdorffi,typis G.Hagen[1659]
  [28]p. 19½x15½cm.
  Diss.--Altdorf.

  1.War. 2.Ulpianus,Domitius.

NL 0382014   ICU

Lindner, David, 1604-1644, praeses
  ... De casuum fortuitorum periculo,
ratione dominii, ac possessionis, ut
& qvatenus possessor fructus restitu-
ere necesse habeat? ... [Lipsiae]
G. Ritzsch [1639]
  [64] p. 19cm.
  Diss. - Leipzig (Christian Schürer,
respondent)

NL 0382015   MH-L

Lindner, David, 1604-1644, praeses
  ... De casibus fortuitis in genere ...
[Lipsiae] G. Ritzsch [1638]
  [27] p. 19cm.
  Diss. - Leipzig (Rudolph Putscher,
respondent)

NL 0382016   MH-L

Lindner, David, 1604-1644
  ... Continens explanationem substan-
tialium, naturalium, et accidentalium
omnium eorum negotiorum, quae in arte
juris, tàm in ultimis voluntatibus, pro-
cessu judiciario, & aliis, consideranda
veniunt ... proponit David Lindener ...
[Lipsiae] Typis Ritzschianis [1633]
  [56] p. 19cm.
  Diss. - Leipzig.

NL 0382017   MH-L

491.05   Lindner, David Jonathan
L74v   Vergleichende grammatik der
lateinischen, italienischen, spanischen,
portugiesischen, franzosischen und
englischen sprache, in bezug auf den
mechanismus und die eigenthumlich-
keiten dieser sprachen unter einander.
Nach der zweiten ausgabe der von Blon-
din hrsg. Grammaire polyglotte bearbeitet. Orthoepie, orthographie und
etymologie. Leipzig, Baumgartner.
1827.
  312p. O.

NL 0382018   IaU ViU PU MH NN

833.91 Lindner, Dolf
L74f   Der Feuerreiter, roman um das leben
Hugo Wolfs. Biberach, Koehler [1950]
303p.

  1. Wolf, Hugo, 1860-1903--Fiction. I. Title

NL 0382019   ICarbS NN OC1

ML410
.S93L5
        Lindner, Dolf.
  Richard Strauss/Joseph Gregor: Die Liebe der Danae;
Herkunft, Inhalt und Gestaltung eines Opernwerkes. Mit
einem Vorwort von Clemens Krauss. Wien, Österreichi-
scher Diana Verlag [1952]
  67 p. illus., port., music. 19 cm.

  1. Strauss, Richard, 1864-1949. Die Liebe der Danae. 2. Gregor,
Joseph, 1888-   Die Liebe der Danae.

                                              A 52-8680
Oregon. Univ. Libr.
  for Library of Congress   [1]

NL 0382020   OrU NIC NN DLC

Lindner, Dominikus, 1889-
  Die allgemeinen fastendispensen in den jeweils bayerischen
gebieten seit dem ausgang des mittelalters; ein beitrag zur
geschichte des kirchlichen dispensationswesens und dispensa-
tionsrechtes, von dr. Dominikus Lindner ... München, J.
Kösel & F. Pustet, 1935.
  xiv, 211 p. 24½ᶜᵐ. (Added t.-p.: Münchener studien zur historischen
theologie, hrsg. ... von professor G. Pfeilschifter ... hft. 13)
  "Quellen und schrifttum": p. [ix]-xiv.

  1. Fasting—Dispensations. 2. Bavaria—Church history. I. Title.
                                              35-10333
Library of Congress   BX1939.D6L5
                                 [2]   248

NL 0382021   DLC CBPac MoSC

Lindner, Dominikus, 1889-
  Die anstellung der hilfspriester; eine kirchenrechtsge-
schichtliche untersuchung, von dr. Dominikus Lindner.
[München] J. Kösel & F. Pustet, komm.-ges.], 1924.
  viii, 157 p. 24½ᶜᵐ. (Added t.-p.: Münchener studien zur historischen
theologie ... hft. 3)
  "Quellen und öfter wiederkehrende literatur": p. [146]-150.

  1. Catholic church—Clergy. 2. Catholic church—Hist. 3. Canon law.
I. Title.
                                              26-16745
Library of Congress   BX1912.L5

NL 0382022   DLC CtY

Lindner, Dominikus, 1889-
  Die gesetzliche verwandtschaft als
ehehindernis im abendlaendischen kirchenrecht
des mittelalters. 1919
  dissertation

NL 0382023   PU

Lindner, Dominikus, 1889-
  ... Die gesetzliche verwandtschaft als ehehindernis im abend-
ländischen kirchenrecht des mittelalters. Von dr. Dominikus
Lindner. Paderborn, F. Schöningh, 1920.
  90 p. 23½ᶜᵐ. (Görres-gesellschaft zur pflege der wissenschaft im katholischen Deutschland. Veröffentlichungen der Sektion für rechts- und sozialwissenschaft. 36. hft.)
  "Verzeichnis der öfter wiederkehrenden literatur": p. 9.

  1. Sponsors (Canon law) 2. Marriage (Canon law) 3. Adoption (Canon
law)   I. Title.
                                              35-37558

NL 0382024   DLC MH NN

CQC   Lindner, Dominikus, 1889-
.L64   Die lehre vom privileg nach Gratian und den
glossatoren des Corpus iuris canonici, von dr.
theol. Dominikus Lindner ... Regensburg, Alfred
Coppenrath, 1917.
  127, [1] p. 19cm.
  "Quellenverzeichnis mit angabe der benützten
handschriften und ausgaben": p.5-6.

  1. Canon law. 2. Gratianus. Decretum.
3. Catholic church. Corpus juris canonici.
I. Title: Privileg, Die lehre vom

NL 0382025   WU PU

VOLUME 334

Lindner, Dominikus, 1889–
Die Lehre von der Inkorporation in ihrer geschichtlichen
Entwicklung. München, M. Hueber, 1951.
94 p. 24 cm.

1. Church property (Canon law) 2. ₍Incorporation (Canon law)₎

Catholic Univ. of   America. Library   A 53–5469
for Library of Congress ₍⅜₎

NL 0382026   DCU

K 571   Lindner, Dominikus, 1889–
P4L74   Der usus matrimonii; eine untersuchung über seine sittliche
Bewertung in der katholischen Moraltheologie alter und neuer Zeit.
München, Kösel & Pustet, 1929.
244 p. 20cm.

1. Marriage (Canon law)

NL 0382027   CLL OrStbM MH MH-L

Lindner, Eberhard.
Zur Kenntnis der Eier der Limoniidae (Diptera, Tipuli-
formia).
(*In* Berlin. Universität. Zoologisches Museum. Mitteilungen.
Berlin. 24 cm. 34. Bd., Heft 1 (1958) p. ₍118₎–₍133₎ illus.)

Lindner, Edwin, comp.

Wagner, Richard, 1813–1883.
Richard Wagner über Parsifal; aussprüche des meisters
über sein werk, aus seinen briefen und schriften sowie
anderen werken zusammengestellt und mit erläuternden
anmerkungen versehen, von dr. Edwin Lindner ... Leipzig, Breitkopf & Härtel, 1913.

Lindner, Edwin, comp.

Wagner, Richard, 1813–1883.
Richard Wagner über "Tannhäuser"; aussprüche des
meisters über sein werk, aus seinen briefen und schriften
sowie anderen werken zusammengestellt und mit erläuternden anmerkungen versehen, von dr. Edwin Lindner ...
Leipzig, Breitkopf & Härtel, 1914.

Lindner, Edwin, comp.

Wagner, Richard, 1813–1883.
Richard Wagner über Tristan und Isolde; aussprüche
des meisters über sein werk, aus seinen briefen und
schriften zusammengestellt und mit erläuternden anmerkungen versehen, von dr. Edwin Lindner ... Leipzig,
Breitkopf & Härtel, 1912.

Lindner, Edwin, 1896–
Die therapie der retroflexio uteri...
Inaug. Diss. Jena, 1896 (Grossroehrsdorf)

NL 0382031   ICRL

Lindner, Elisabeth
So hat jede Frau Erfolg [by] E. und C. Lindner. Wien,
Bücher des Lebens [1952]

200 p.

NL 0382032   MH

Lindner, Elise
Untersuchungen über die ätiologie der
osteomyelitis der kiefer an hand von kranken-
geschichten aus dem zahnärztlichen Institut und
der chirurgischen Poliklinik München.
Diss. 1931.

NL 0382033   PPWI

Lindner, Elizaveta Borisovna, joint ed.

PG2643   **Polak, G**   **F**   *ed.*
.G5P6   Немецко-русский словарь; под ред. Г. Полак и Е. Линд-
нер. Методическая ред. Э. Ризель. Около 22000 слов с
приложением грамматических таблиц. Москва, Гос.
изд-во иностранных и национальных словарей, 1941.

Lindner, Elizaveta Borisovna, joint ed.

PG3892   **Polak, G**   **F**   *ed.*
.P57   Німецько-український словник. ₍Перекладено з ро-
1955   сійського вид. шкільного німецько-російського словника
Г. Полак і Е. Ліндер₎ Під ред. І. В. Шаровольського.
Близько 25 000 слів. Вид. 2. Київ, Радянська школа, 1955.

Lindner, Elli.
... El derecho arancelario español; defensa de la producción
y nacionalismo económico en España bajo tres regímenes:
hasta la postguerra, durante la dictadura y con la república.
Barcelona, Bosch, 1934.
187 p., 1 l. diagrs. (part fold.) 22ᶜᵐ.
"Este trabajo está escrito en alemán y en español."—p. 9.
"Bibliografía": p. ₍175₎–181.

1. Spain—Commercial policy. 2. Tariff—Spain.   I. Title.

      35–12977
Library of Congress   HF1569.L5
      ₍2₎   337.0946

NL 0382036   DLC

Lindner, Elli.
...Etude sur les conseils économiques dans les
differents pays du monde ...
see under   League of Nations. Economic
Committee.

Lindner, Elli, joint author.

Hauff, Lilly.
Der Lette-verein in der geschichte der frauenbewegung, von
dr. Lilly Hauff ... unter mitarbeit von dr. Elli Lindner. Berlin, J. Jastrow, 1928.

Lindner, Elli.
JX1975   **League of nations.** *Economic committee.*
.A25   ... Review of the economic councils in the different coun-
1932.   tries of the world, prepared for the Economic committee by
п.B.10   Dr. Elli Lindner. Geneva, League of nations. 1932.

Lindner, Elli.
Die wirtschaftsräte in Europa; ein beitrag zur frage der
schaffung einer europäischen wirtschaftsunion, von dr. E.
Lindner. Berlin, E. S. Mittler & sohn, 1931.
55 p. fold. tab. 23½ᶜᵐ.
"Literatur": p. 54.

1. Industry and state—Europe. 2. Europe—Econ. condit.—1918–
I. Title.
      31–11399
Library of Congress   HD3616.E831,5
      ₍2₎   338.094

NL 0382040   DLC NN

Lindner, Erich.
Beitrag zur Klärung des Systems Blei-Zink-Kadmium-
Zinn unter Berücksichtigung der Eignung seiner Legierun-
gen für Lotzwecke. Berlin, Verlag Technik, 1952.
98 p. illus., diagrs. (3 in pocket) 21 cm. (Wissenschaftliche
Berichte, Bd. 55)
Bibliography: p. 98.

1. Lead-zinc-cadmium-tin alloys. 2. Solder and soldering.
I. Title. (Series)

TA490.L45   64-57605

NL 0382041   DLC

Lindner, Erich Walter
see   Lindner, Walter, 1878–

Lindner, Ernő, 1826–1902.
Kempelen Farkas és viszonylasai a nyelvtudoma
nyhoz.
Pesten, Eggenberg, F. M. Akad. Konyvarusnal, 1870.
325–480 p.

NL 0382043   OC1

Lindner, Ernst.
Beitraege zur kenntnis der divertikel œs
duodenum und ileum. (Auszug)
Inaug. diss. Kiel, 1925.

NL 0382044   ICRL CtY

Lindner, Ernst.
... Die familie Stockmann, von Ernst Lindner. London,
New York ₍etc.₎ T. Nelson and sons, ltd., 1939.
65 p. illus. 16¼ᶜᵐ. (Supplementary German readers: set A, grade I)
"First published 1939."

1. German language—Chrestomathies and readers.   I. Title.

      42–33296
Library of Congress   PF3115.L6

NL 0382045   DLC

Lindner, Ernst
Fran Finlands frihetskrig. Stockholm, P. A.
Norstedt & soner (1920)
231 p. 23cm.

NL 0382046   DNW

PT1205   **Lindner, Ernst,** 1826–1902.
.H9L7   Fartblihndijer Zépserscher liederposchen ... en verflitzten
jong und verschëmten jongfier vor die brost gestocken, von
Lëndners Ernst von Käisenmark. 2. verb. und verm. aufl.
mit angehängtem glossar. Budapest, C. Grill; ₍etc., etc.₎
1879.
vii, 168 p. 17ᶜᵐ.

1. Folk-songs, German—Hungary—Zips. 2. German language—Dialects—Zips.

NL 0382047   ICU

Bonaparte
Collection   Lindner, Ernst,   1826–1902.
No. 9822
Fliegende blätter in Zipser mundart...
1. und 2.lieferung... Wien,1864.

NL 0382048   ICN

VOLUME 334

Lindner, Ernst, 1879–
Die poetische personifikation in den jugendschauspielen Calderon's. Ein beitrag zu studien über stil und sprache des dichters. Von dr. Ernst Lindner. Leipzig, A. Deichert, 1904.

3 p. l., (v)-x, 150 p. 23¼ᶜᵐ. (Added t.-p.: Münchener beiträge zur romanischen und englischen philologie. Hrsg. von H. Breymann und J. Schick. xxxiI)

Issued in part as the author's inaugural dissertation, München, 1904. "Benützte literatur": p. (vij)-x.

1. Calderón de la Barca, Pedro, 1600–1681. 2. Personification in literature.

Library of Congress   PB13.M8 (ol. 32.   5–3398

OCl OU ViU MB NN
NL 0382049   DLC PBm MH CU CtY NjP CU MiDW OU OCU MiU

Lindner, Ernst, 1880–
Ein beitrag zur kenntnis der meralgia paraesthetica...
Inaug. Diss. Leipzig, 1906.   35 p.
Bibl.

NL 0382050   ICRL

Lindner, Ernst, 1886–
Ulcus corneae rodens und rosacea...
Inaug. diss. Rostock, 1913.
Bibl.

NL 0382051   ICRL MBCo

W 4
F82   **LINDNER, Ernst,** 1918–
1944   Verlauf und Prognose der arteriellen Hypertonie, unter besonderer Berücksichtigung der Blutdruck- und Augenhintergrundsveränderungen. Frankfurt, Wagner, 1944.
30 p.
Cover title.
Inaug.–Diss.–Frankfurt.
1. Blood pressure - High

NL 0382052   DNLM

Lindner, Ernst Fischer-
see Fischer-Lindner, Ernst, 1874–

Lindner, Ernst Friedrich Theodor
see
Lindner, Theodor, 1843–1919.

Lindner, Ernst Otto Timotheus, 1820–1867.
Arthur Schopenhauer. Von ihm. Über ihn. Ein wort der vertheidigung von Ernst Otto Lindner ...
see under Schopenhauer, Arthur, 1788–1860.

Lindner, Ernst Otto Timotheus, 1820–1867.
De relatione quae inter Spinozae cogitata metaphysica et Cartesii doctrinam intercedit... Auctor E. Otto Lindner... Vratislaviae: Typis Fritzianis (1844?)   31 p.   21½cm.

Dissertation — Breslau, 1844.
Vita.
Bibliographical footnotes.

1. Spinoza, Benedictus de, 1632–1650.   1677. 2. Descartes, René, 1596–
N. Y. P. L.   Card revised
                                March 10, 1941

NL 0382056   NN NNC

Lindner, Ernst Otto (Timotheus) 1820–1867.
Die erste stehende deutsche oper. Dargestellt von Ernst Otto Lindner ... Mit achtzehn musikalischen beilagen enthaltend neun bisher ungedruckte compositionen von Reinhard Keiser in partitur und im clavierauszug. Berlin, Schlesinger'sche buch- und musikhandlung, 1855.

2 v. 21ᶜᵐ (v. 2: 33½ x 26¼ᶜᵐ)
Title of v. 2: 9 compositionen aus den jahren 1700–1734; ouverture, 7 opernarien und duett, von Reinhard Keiser. Band II 1700 D' E. O. Lindner Die erste stehende deutsche oper. (Full score and piano-forte arrangement, the latter by Wilhelm Rust)
"Verzeichnis der auf der Hamburger opernbühne aufgeführten musikalischen werke": v. 1, p. (168)–200.
Subjectentries: Opera—   Germany—Hamburg.
                                        3–29455

Library of Congress, no.   ML3072.8.L74.

NL 0382057   DLC CtY MH NcRS NIC CoU PPL OCIW

Lindner, Ernst Otto Timotheus, 1820–1867.
Geschichte des deutschen liedes im xvIII. jahrhundert. Von Ernst Otto Lindner. Nachgelassenes werk. Hrsg. von Ludwig Erk. Mit LXXXIII musikalischen beilagen. Leipzig, Breitkopf und Härtel, 1871.

xvi, 144 p., 1 l., 167 p. illus. (music) 26½ᶜᵐ.
"Notenbeilagen": 167 pages at end.

1. German ballads and songs—Hist. & crit. 2. Ballads, German. 3. Songs, German—Hist. & crit. I. Erk, Ludwig Christian, 1807–1883. ed.
                                        3–6000
Library of Congress   ML2829.3.L74
                        (35d1)

MiU
NL 0382058   DLC CtY NcU IU OO NIC PSt NjR InU NN MB

ML
410   Lindner, Ernst Otto Timotheus, 1820–1867.
.M55   Meyerbeer's Prophet als Kunstwerk. Berlin,
L75   R.Gaertner, 1850.
40 p.

1.Meyerbeer,Giacomo,1791–1864. Le prophète.

NL 0382059   MiU

LINDNER, ERNST OTTO TIMOTHEUS, 1820–1867.
Meyerbeer's Prophet als Kunstwerk. Berlin, R. Gaertner, 1850. 40 p.

Microfilm (master negative)

NL 0382060   NN

Lindner, Ernst Otto Timotheus, 1820–1867.
Zur tonkunst. Abhandlungen von Ernst Otto Lindner. Berlin, I. Guttentag, 1864.

4 p. l., 378 p. fold. pl. (music) 22¼ cm.
CONTENTS.—Die entstehung der oper.—Ritter Vittorio Loreto.—Gay's Bettleroper.—Biedermann und Bach.—Johann Sebastian Bach's werke.—Ueber künstlerische weltanschauung.—Anhang: Nachträge zur geschichte der ersten stehenden deutschen oper. Zwei recitative aus R. Keiser's Siegendem David.

1. Opera—Hist. & crit. 2. Loreto, Vittorio, 3. Gay, John, 1685–1732. The beggar's opera. 4. Bach, Johann Sebastian, 1685–1750. 5. Music—Philosophy and aesthetics. 6. Opera—Hamburg.

ML60.L46   780.4   3–29447

NL 0382061   DLC CtY MH GU NcRS MH NIC ViU

Lindner (Erwin) (1875–   ). *Ein Fall von Endotheliom der Dura mater mit Metastase in der Harnblase. (Munich.) 21 pp. 8°. *Wien & Leipzig, W. Braumüller, 1902.
*Repr. from: Ztschr. f. Heilk., Berl., 1902, n. F., iii, patthol. Anat., 118–138.

NL 0382062   DNLM

QL531   **Lindner, Erwin,** 1888–
L5   Blepharoceridae und Deuterophlebiidae. Stuttgart, E.
v. 2   Schweizerbart (E. Nägele) 1930.
Biology   36 p. illus., plates. (His Die Fliegen der palaearktischen
Library   Region. Bd. 2)

Includes bibliographies.

1. Blephaoceridae. 2. Deuterophlebiidae.

NL 0382063   CU

Lindner, Erwin, 1888–
... Die fliegen der palaearktischen region ... Stuttgart, E. Schweizerbart, 1924.

v. illus., plates (part col., part fold.) 27¼ᶜᵐ.

1. Diptera. 2. Insects—Palearctic regions. (2. Palearctic regions—Entomology)
                                        Agr 25–221
Library, U. S. Dept. of   Agriculture 428L642

InU NBuU
NL 0382064   DNAL PSt CoU CU KU GU TxU NcRS MU MiU ICJ

(ucu)
QL531   **Lindner, Erwin,** 1888–   ed.
L5   Die Fliegen der palaearktischen Region. Stuttgart, E. Schweizerbart, 1930–
v. illus., plates (part col., part fold.) 27cm.

Includes bibliographies.

1. Diptera. 2. Insects - Palearctic regions. I. Title.
Contents.

NL 0382065   OrCS PPAmE CU MnU IU OU MiU ICU

QL531   **Lindner, Erwin,** 1888–
L5   Handbuch. Stuttgart, E. Schweizerbart,
introd.   1949.
Biology   xii,422 p. illus.,28 col.plates. (His
Lib.   Die Fliegen der palaearktischen Region. Bd.1.
(Introd.))

Bibliography: p.402–409.

1. Diptera.

NL 0382066   CU

QL531   Lindner, Erwin, 1888–
L5   Phryneidae (Anisopodidae, Rhyphidae). Petauristidae
v.1   (Trichoceridae) Stuttgart, E. Schweizerbart, 1930.
Biology   22 p. illus., plates. (His Die Fliegen der palaerktischen
Library   Region. Bd. 1a-b)

Includes bibliographies.

1. Phryneidae. 2. Petauristidae.

NL 0382067   CU

Lindner, Erwin, 1888–
... Rhagionidae (leptidae) von Erwin Lindner... Stuttgart, E. Schweizerbart'sche verlagsbuchhandlung (E. Nägele) g.m.b.h., 1925.
1 p.l., 49 p. 2 pl. (1 col. fold.)   26 cm.
(On cover: Erwin Lindner: Die fliegen der palaearktischen region. lief. 1–3 (v. 20))
Plates accompanied by leaves with descriptive letterpress.
Issued in parts, 1924–25.
1. Leptidae. I. Title.

NL 0382068   CU

Lindner, Erwin, 1888–
... Stratiomyiidae, von Erwin Lindner ... Stuttgart, E. Schweizerbart'sche verlagsbuchhandlung (E. Nägele) 1938.
2 p.l., 218 p. illus., VII pl. 27 cm.
(On cover: Erwin Lindner. Die fliegen der palaearktischen region. lief. 104, 108, 110, 114, 116 (v.) 18)
Plates accompanied by leaves with descriptive letterpress.
Issued in parts, 1936–38.
1. Stratiomyidae.

NL 0382069   CU

VOLUME 334

Lindner, Erwin, 1888–
Stratiomyiiden (*Diptera*) von den kleinen Sundainseln. (Ergebnisse der Sunda-expedition Rensch.) Von dr. E. Lindner ... (Mit einer abbildung.)
(*In* Mitteilungen aus dem Zoologischen museum in Berlin. Berlin, 1937. 23½ᶜᵐ. 22. bd., 2. hft., p. ₍265₎–267. illus.)

1. ₍Stratiomyidae₎ 2. Diptera—Sunda islands.
A C 38–1199
Ohio state univ. Library
for Library of Congress   [QL1.B38   bd. 22, hft. 2]
₍2₎   (590.82)

NL 0382070   OU

QL531   Lindner, Erwin, 1888–
L5   Thaumaleidae (Orphnephilidae) Stuttgart, E. Schweizerbart
v.3   (E. Nägele) 1930.
Biology   16 p.   illus., plates.   (His Die Fliegen der palaearktischen
Library   Region. Bd. 3)

Bibliography: p. 15.

1. Thaumaleidae.

NL 0382071   CU

Lindner, Erwin, 1888–
Über die Spermatogenese von Schistosomum haematobium Bilh. [Bilharzia haematobia Cobb] mit besonderer Berücksichtigung der Geschlechtschromosonmen. Mit 1 Fig. im Text. Leipzig & Berlin, W. Engelmann 1914.
516–538 S.   8°.
Mit Tafeln in: Archiv f. Zellforschung. Bd 12.
Inaug.-diss. — Munich.

NL 0382072   CtY ICRL PU MiU

Lindner, Erwin, 1888–
Zoo-Safari; Bericht der Deutschen Zoologischen Ost-afrika-Expedition 1951/52 (Gruppe Stuttgart) Stuttgart, E. Schweizerbart, 1954 ₍i. e. 1953₎
ix, 189 p.   illus., group ports., fold. col. map. 25 cm.
Bibliography: p. 189.

1. Zoology—Africa, East. 2. Africa, East—Descr. & trav. I. Deutsche Zoologische Ostafrika-Expedition, 1951–1952. II. Title.

QL5.L5   54–20837

NL 0382073   DLC MsU ICU InLP MB

Lindner, Erwin, 1909–
Zur Reform der deutschen Ehescheidungsgesetz-gebung unter Berücksichtigung der ausländischen Rechte ... Emsdetten, 1934.
Inaug.-Diss. - Köln.

NL 0382074   CtY

Lindner, Eugen, 1858–1915.
Ramiro; romantische Oper in vier Acten. Text von Th. Herrmann u. v. Componisten. Musik von Eugen Lindner. Clavierauszug mit Text.   Leipzig ₍ca. 1885₎ 193 p.   ob. 4°.

Vocal score. German words.
First performed in 1885.
Photolithograph.

109670A. 1. Operas.—Piano and   JUILLIARD FOUNDATION FUND.
musician. 3. Title.   voice. 2. Herrmann, Theodor,
N. Y. P. L.   December 10, 1923.

NL 0382075   NN

Lindner, F   G
... Abhandlung des ... dr. Lindner De Lvcio Cestio Pio ...   Züllichau, 1858.
2 p.l., ₍3₎–17 p.   25 cm.
"Jahresbericht der Steinbart'schen erziehungs-und unterrichts-anstalten bei Züllichau".
1. Cestius Pius, Lucius.

NL 0382076   CU

Lindner, F   G
... De Arellio Fusco commentatio. Scripsit F.G. Lindner ...   Breslau, 1862.
23 p.   25 cm.
Programm - Gymnasium zu St. Maria Magdalena, Breslau.
1. Fuscus, Arellius.

NL 0382077   CU

Lindner, F   G
De Gaio Albvcio Silo commentatio, scripsit F.G. Lindner ... [Vratislaviae, typis Grassii, Barthii et socii (W. Friedrich), 1861]
18 p.   28 cm.
Programm - Gymnasium ad aedem St. Mariae Magdalenae, Breslau. (Celebrating 50th anniversary of the University of Breslau)
1. Silus, Caius Albucius. Latin.

NL 0382078   CU PU NjP PBm

Lindner, F   G
... De Junio Gallione commentatio; vom ... F.G. Lindner.   Hirschberg, 1868.
14 p.   24 cm.
Programm - Gymnasium, Hirschberg.
1. Gallio, Junius.

NL 0382079   CU NjP PU

Lindner, F.G.
Griechische syntax.   Breslau, 1862.

NL 0382080   NjP

WG   Lindner, Felix
33949   Beiträge zur Kenntnis der Phenmorpholin-derivate. Rostock, 1902.
34 p.

Inaug.-Diss. - Rostock.

NL 0382081   CtY MH

Lindner, Felix, 1849–1917.
The alliteration in Chaucer's Canterbury tales.
(*In* Chaucer Society. Publications. Essays on Chaucer ... Part 3, pp. 197–226. London. [1876])

H2088 — Alliteration. — Chaucer, Geoffrey.

NL 0382082   MB OU NcD PU-F

Lindner, Felix, 1849–1917.
Die Chansen de Roland und die alten-glische epik. n.t.p.   n.p., ₍1892₎

NL 0382083   PU

[Lindner, *Felix*] 1849–1917.
Ein französisches calendarium aus dem anfang des XV. jahrh.   n.p., [1875]

NL 0382084   NjP

441.5   **Lindner, Felix,** 1849–1917.
L64g   Grundriss der laut- und flexions-analyse der neufranzösischen schriftsprache. Oppeln, 1881.
109p.

NL 0382085   IU

Lindner, Felix, 1849–1917.
Henry Fieldings dramatische werke; litterarische studie. Leipzig, etc., C. A. Koch, 1895.
pp. 185 +.

Fielding‖Mol. catal.‖

NL 0382086   MH CtY KU MBU OkU MB NjP

PR3328   Lindner, Felix, 1849–1917, ed.
.B5A7
1904   **Buckingham, George Villiers,** 2d duke of, 1628–1687.
... The rehearsal, first acted 7. December 1671, published 1672; mit einleitung hrsg. von Felix Lindner. Heidelberg, C. Winter, 1904.

Lindner, Felix, 1849–1917.
Ein roman von Geoffrey Drage. 3 pp. (*Eng. studien*, v. 14, 1890, p. 452.)—Englische uebersetzung des Romans von der Rose. 10 pp. (*Eng. studien*, v. 11, 1888, p. 163.)—The Tale of Gamelyn. 44 pp. (*Eng. studien*, v. 2, 1879, pp. 94, 321.)—Bemerkungen zu Thackeray's Lectures on the Engl. humorists. 1 p. (*Eng. studien*, v. 10, 1887, p. 337.)

NL 0382088   MdBP

Lindner, Felix, 1849–1917, ed.

Fielding, Henry, 1707–1754.
... Fielding's Tom Thumb; mit einleitung herausgegeben von Felix Lindner.   Berlin, E. Felber, 1899.

Lindner, Felix, 1849–1917.
Ueber das präfix a im englischen ... von dr. F. Lindner. Jena, E. Frommann, 1873.
25 p.   19½ᶜᵐ.
Habilitationsschrift—Jena.

1. English language—Suffixes and prefixes.

NL 0382090   ViU IU RPB OC1 NcD

Lindner, Felix, 1849–1917.
Ueber die beziehungen des Ortnit zu Huon de Bordeaux ... Rostock, Univ.-buchdr. von Adler's erben, 1872.
45 p.   21½ᶜᵐ.
Inaug.-diss.—Rostock.

1. Ortnit. 2. Huon de Bordeaux. 3. Literature, Comparative—French and German. 4. Literature, Comparative—German and French.
16–24065
Library of Congress   PT1629.O8L5

NL 0382091   DLC CU OC1

PN687   **Lindner, Felix,** 1849–1917.
O18L7   Zur geschichte der Oberonsage. Vortrag zur feier des geburtstages Sr. Königlichen Hoheit des grossherzogs Friedrich Franz IV. am 9. april 1902 gehalten von dr. Felix Lindner ... Rostock i. M., H. Warkentien, 1902.
18 p.   23ᶜᵐ.
Bibliographical foot-notes.

NL 0382092   ICU MH MB CU OC1

VOLUME 334

⌐Lindner, Ferdinand¬
Die Corps der deutschen Hochschulen nebst einer eingehenden Darstellung studentischer Verhältnisse. Anhang: Die modernen Burschenschaften. Leipzig, T. Lissner, 1870.
⌐2¬ ⌐v¬–viii, 150, ⌐1¬ p. 22ᶜᵐ.

NL 0382093 ICJ

Lindner, Ferdinand, 1906–
Ueber die thermische zersetzung von merkaptanen in gegenwart von katalysatoren. ... Inaug. Diss. – Würzburg. [1934]
Lebenslauf.

NL 0382094 ICRL CtY

Lindner, Franz, joint ed.
Jehle, Josef, ed.
Der schriftenverkehr der gemeinden; ein führer durch die gesamte verwaltungsarbeit der mittelbaren gemeinden, hrsg. von J. Jehle ... ⌐und¬ F. Lindner ... München, Bayerischer kommunalschriften-verlag gmbh., 1923–

Lindner, Franz, 1885–
Ueber hydrops foetus... 1913.
Inaug. diss. – München.

NL 0382096 MiU

¡1892–¡
Lindner, Franz¡ Ueber die Verantwortlichkeit bei Rechtspflichtverletzungen [Auszug: Amtspflichtverletzungen] der Grundbuchbeamten. [In Maschinenschrift.] 59 S. 4°(2°). —
Auszug: Breslau 1920: Lampner & Schmidt. 2 Bl. 8°
Breslau, R– u. staatswiss. Diss. v. 5. März 1921, Ref. Rehme
[Geb. 17. Okt. 92 Breslau; Wohnort: Breslau; Staatsangeh.: Preußen; Vorbildung: Johannis-G. Breslau Reife 11; Studium: Phil. Breslau 1, München 1, Breslau 1, Jur. Breslau 8 S.; Rig. 14. Mai 20.] [U 21. 20S]

NL 0382097 ICRL

Lindner, Franz ¡Martin Wilhelm¡ 1852–
Die zusammenkunft kaiser Friedrich III. mit Karl dem Kühnen von Burgund im jahre 1473 zu Trier ... Cöslin, Gedruckt bei C. G. Hendess ⌐1876¬
2 p. l., 96 p., 1 l. 21ᶜᵐ.
Inaug.-dis.—Griefswald.
Vita.

1. Holy Roman empire—Hist.—Frederick III, 1440–1493. 2. Germany—Hist.—Frederick III, 1440–1493. 3. Burgundy—Hist.
4–29187

Library of Congress DD173.5.L74

NL 0382098 DLC

Lindner, Fred V.
... Der segelflug. Von dr. Fred V. Lindner ... Prag, Im eigenen verlage des vereines; Reichenberg, Vertriebsstelle: Verlagsbuchhandlung gebrüder Stiepel ges. m. b. h. ⌐1932¬
cover-title, 40 p. illus. (incl. port.) 22ᶜᵐ. (Sammlung gemeinnütziger vorträge. Herausgegeben vom Deutschen vereine zur verbreitung gemeinnütziger kenntnisse in Prag ... nr. 635/636)
"Schrifttum": p. 27–28.

1. Gliders (Aeronautics) I. Title.

Library of Congress TL760.L5 32–32683
⌐2¬ 629.13333

NL 0382099 DLC

Lindner, Friedrich
... De poena temere litigantium, & de officio iudicis. Respondente Friderico Lindnero ... ⌐n.p.,n.d.¬
⌐8¬ p. 18½ᶜᵐ.
Caption title.
At head of title: Dispvtat. XXXVI.
Praeses unnamed.

NL 0382100 MH-L

Lindner, Friedrich
GB638 Die preussische Wüste einst und jetzt.
.49 Bilder von den Kurischen Nehrung. Anhang:
L56 Vollständiges Verzeichnis aller bis zum Frühjahr 1898 auf der Nehrung beobachteten Vogelarten. Osterwieck/Harz, A.W. Zickfeldt ⌐cover 1898¬
72 p. illus.,maps.

1. Kurische Nehrung, Ger. 2. Birds – Germany – Kurische Nehrung.

NL 0382101 CU

Lindner, Friedrich, Dr.
Die unehelichen geburten als sozialphänomen. Eine studie zur statistik der bevölkerungsbewegung im königreiche Bayern ... Naumburg a. S., Lippert & co., 1899.
2 p. l., 68 p. 8°.
Inaug.-diss.—Würzburg.
Pub. in enlarged form in 1900 as part VII of Wirtschafts- und verwaltungsstudien mit besonderer berücksichtigung Bayerns.

Library of Congress 1-G-2565

NL 0382102 DLC CtY

Lindner, Friedrich, Dr.
Die unehelichen Geburten als Sozialphänomen. Ein Beitrag zur Statistik der Bevölkerungsbewegung im Königreiche Bayern, von Dr. Friedrich Lindner. Mit 2 Karten. Leipzig, A. Deichert'sche Verlagsbuchhandlung Nachf., 1900.
x, 238 p. 2 fold. maps. 23½ᶜᵐ. (In Wirtschafts- und Verwaltungsstudien mit besonderer Berücksichtigung Bayerns, VII.)
"Litteratur," p. [ix]–x.

NL 0382103 ICJ CtY NjP ICU MB

Lindner, Friedrich, Dr.
Der Wohnungsaufsichtsdienst in Bayern. Handbuch mit Zusammenstellung der einschlägigen Vorschriften von F. Lindner, ... München, Mames & Müller, 1909.
16o p. 18⁴ᶜᵐ.
"Literaturverzeichnis," p. 160.

NL 0382104 ICJ ICRL

Lindner, Friedrich, ca.1540–1597, comp.
Bicinia sacra, ex variis autoribus in usum iuventutis scholasticae collecta: quibus adjuncta est compendiaria in artem canendi introductio:... Noribergae, Gerlach, 1591
1 pt. (vox inferior)
Microfilm (positive)
Original in British Museum, London
Title page also in German

NL 0382105 MH-I

M Lindner,Friedrich,1540 (ca.)-1597,ed.
2081 Continuatio Cantionvm sacrarvm qvatvor,qvinqve,
.L75 sex,septem,octo et plvrivm vocvm,de festis praecipvis anni,a praestantissimis Italiae mvsicis nuperrimè concinnatarum. Qvarvm qvaedam in Italia separatim editae sunt,quaedam verò planè novae,nec usquam typis excusae. At nunc,in usum scholarum & ecclesiarum germanicarum,in unum corpus redactae,studio & opera Friderici Lindneri ... Noribergae, In officina typographica C.Gerlachiae, 1588.
6 parts in slip-case. 18 x 24 cm.
Continuation of his collection: Sacrae cantiones. Noribergae,1585.

Title pages of cantus,quinta vox,and altus parts supplied in facsim. Sexta vox part has additional t.p.in facsim.
Sign.l of cantus part supplied from another copy.
Imperfect: sign.l₃ of cantus part partly torn away and crudely restored,affecting text. Some vols.water-damaged along lower edge.
1.Part-songs, Sacred--To 1800.

NL 0382107 MiU NRU-Mus

Vault
M Lindner, Friedrich, 1540 (ca) - 1597, comp
1490 Corollarivm cantionvm sacrarvm qvinqve,
L747C sex, septem, octo, et plvrivm vocvm, de festis praecipvis anni. Quarum quaedam antea à praestantissimis nostrae aetatis musicis, in Italia separatim editae sunt, quaedam vero nuperrimè concinnatae... at nunc in unum quasi corpus reductae studio & opera Friderici Lindneri &c. Noribergae: C. Gerlach, 1590. 6 pts. (in box). 17 x 21 1/2 cm.

Separate parts: Cantus, Tenor, Altus, Bassus, 5th voice, 6th voice.
On each title-page a woodcut of the printer's mark.

NL 0382109 NRU-Mus

Zg16 Lindner, Friedrich, 1540 (ca.)-1597, comp.
A13 ... Gemma mvsicalis; selectissimas varii
588 stili cantiones (vvlgo italis madrigali et napolitane dicvntvr) qvatvor, qvinqve, sex et plvrivm vocvm continens: Quae ex diversis praestantissimorum musicorum libellis, in Italia excusis, decerptae, & in gratium untriusq musicae studiosorum, uni quasi corpori insertae & in lucem editae sunt, studio & opera Friderici Lindneri ... Liber primvs. Noribergae, Imprimebatur in officina typographica Catharinae Gerlachiae, 1588.
[119]p. 16x21cm.
Initials.
Signatures: aa-pp⁴.
At head of title: Alto.
Words in Italian.
Includes songs by A.Gabrielli, Orlando di Lasso,L.Marentio, G. da Palestrina, and others.

NL 0382111 CtY

Micro
Film Lindner, Friedrich, 1540(ca.)-1597, comp.
D144 ... Gemma mvsicalis; selectissima varii stili canreel tiones (vvlgo italis madrigali et napolitane dicvn-
1 tur) qvatvor, qvinqve, sex et plvrivm vocvm conti-
no.12 nens: Quae ex diversis praestantissimorum musicorum libellis, in Italia excusis, decerptae, & in gratium untriusq musicae studiosorum, uni quasi corpori insertae & in lucem editae sunt, studio & opera Friderici Lindneri ... Liber primvs. Noribergae, Imprimebatur in officina typographica Catharinae Gerlachiae, 1588.
1reel 35mm.
Signatures: aa-pp4.
Second volume appeared in 1589.
(German Baroque Literature, reel 1, No. 12)

Research Publications, New Haven, Conn., 1970.
"Index included"
Microfilm (positive)
Collation of the original: [119]p.

NL 0382113 PSt CU

FILM Lindner, Friedrich, 1540(ca.)-1597.
M783.22 Missae qvinqve, qvinis vocibvs, a diversis et
1644m aetatis nostrae praestantissimis mvsicis compositae: ac in usum ecclesiae Dei nuperrimè editae, studio & opera Friderici Lindneri. Noribergae, Officina typographica Gerlachia, 1590.
Microfilm copy (positive) made in 1963 of the original in the Eastman School of Music, Rochester, N.Y.
Collation of the original as determined from the film: 5 parts (vocal)
Parts: cantvs, quinta vox, tenor, bassus, altus.

NL 0382115 IU

Lindner, Friedrich, 1864–
Grundstein zur Ornis des Fallsteingebiestes ... [Gera-Untermhaus, 1900]
Inaug.-Diss. - Leipzig.
Lebenslauf.
"Separatabdruck aus Jahrg. XXVI, der Ornith. Monatschrift."

NL 0382116 CtY ICRL PU

VOLUME 334

Lindner, Friedrich, 1901-
... Geschwülste im Wurmfortsatz ...
Köslin, 1933.
Inaug.-Diss. - Berlin.
Lebenslauf.
"Literatur": p. 37-38.

NL 0382117   CtY

Lindner, Friedrich, 1909-
Die infektiosität des krebses. ... Erlangen,
1935.   22 p.
Inaug. Diss. - Erlangen, 1935.
Lebenslauf.
Bibliography.

NL 0382118   CtY ICRL

Lindner, Friedrich Christoph Gerhard
see   Lindner, Gerhard, 1878-

Lindner, Friedrich Georg Ludwig 1772-1845
see   Lindner, Friedrich Ludwig, 1772-1845.

943.07
L644F   ₍LINDNER, Friedrich Ludwig₎ 1772-1845.
Considérations politiques sur l'état
actuel de l'Allemagne; ouvrage attribué
au professeur Fischer, et saisi au-dela
du Rhin; traduction nouvelle, avec des
notes et des remarques de mm. Bignon,
De Pradt, Régnault-Warin, Schoeffer,
Thérémin, etc.   Paris, Chez Corréard,
1821.
234 ₍i.e. 323₎p.   22cm.
Page 333 wrongly numbered 224.
Crown stamped in gold on cover, with
monogram M.L.

Translated by Georg Bernhard Depping.-
cf. Bib. nat. Cat. gen.
Translation of: Manuscript aus Süd-
deutschland.
1. Germany. History. 1789-1815. 2.
German confederation, 1815-1866. 3.
Europe. Politics. 1789-1815. I. Depping,
Georg Bernhard, 1784-1853, tr. II.Fischer
Christian August, 1771-1829, "
attributed   auth. III. Title.

NL 0382122   MnU NcD

1885   Lindner, Friedrich Ludwig, 1772-1845.
Dissertatio inavgvralis medica, sistens
prodromvm censvrae de natvra febris doctrinae.
Jenae, litteris Goepferdtii, [1797]
20 p.   8°.   *Toner Collection*

NL 0382123   DLC OClW-H DNLM PPC NNNAM

Lindner, Friedrich Ludwig, 1772-1845.
Geheime Papiere.   Stuttgart, Franckh,
1824.
According to Allgem. deut. biog., v. 18,
p. 704 Lindner was not the author of these
papers, but they are generally ascribed to him.

NL 0382124   MH

Lindner, Friedrich Ludwig, 1772-1845.
Gemälde der europäischen Türkei. Ein
Beitrag zur Länder- und Völkerkunde. Hrsg.
von F.L. Lindner ...   Weimar, im Verlage
des Geographischen Instituts, 1813.
vi, 581., 2 maps, 1 plan, 11 pl.   12°.

NL 0382125   NN

₍Lindner, Friedrich Ludwig₎ 1772-1845.
Manuscript aus Süd-Deutschland. Hrsg. von
George Erichson₎ London, J. Griphi, 1820.
222 p.   21 cm.
1. Rhine, Confederation of the, 1806-1813.
2. Germany - Hist. - 1806-1815. I. Title.

NL 0382126   MH DLC-P4

JN
3295
.L75   Lindner,Friedrich Ludwig,1772-1845.
1821   Manuscript aus Süd-Deutschland ... Hrsg.von
George Erichson ₍pseud.₎ 2.aufl. London ₍i.e.
Stuttgart₎ Bei James Griphi, 1821.
xviii,₍19₎-276 p.   17cm.

Formerly attributed to Christian August Fischer.

1.Europe--Politics--1789-1900. 2.Germany--Pol.& govt.
--1789-1900. I.Fischer,Christian August,1771-1829,sup-
posed author. II.   Title. III.Title: Süd-
Deutschland.

NL 0382127   MiU KyU

WA
27070   Lindner, Friedrich Ludwig, 1772-1845.
Neueste Kunde von Asien. 3. Bd. Süd- und
Ost-Asien. Weimar, Im Verlage des Landes-
Industrie-Comptoirs, 1812.
vi, 585 p. illus. 20 cm. (His Neueste
Länder- und Völkerkunde, Bd. 12)

1. East (Far East) 2. Asia, Southeastern.
I. Lindner, Friedrich Ludwig, 1772-1845. Neueste Länder- und   Völkerkunde, Bd. 12.

NL 0382128   CtY

PA4005
.4
.L75   Lindner, Friedrich Ludwig, 1772-1845.
Skythien und die Skythen des Herodot, und
seine Ausleger, nebst Beschreibung des heutigen
Zustandes jener Länder. Stuttgart, E. Schweizerbart, 1841.
x, 239 p. maps.

1. Herodotus. 2. Scythians.

NL 0382129   ICU CU NIC

LINDNER Friedrich Wilhelm.
Andeutungen zur zweckmassigen einrichtung
eines evang.-protest.missions-seminariums
mitgetheilt. Leipz.,1831.

NL 0382130   MH-AH

BV823
.L74   LINDNER,FRIEDRICH WILHELM,1779-1864.
Die lehre vom abendmahle nach der Schrift. Ein exe-
getisch-historisch-dogmatischer versuch; nebst kritik
aller vom anfange der kirche bis auf die neueste zeit
darüber öffentlich bekannt gemachter lehrmeinungen,der
protestantischen kirche zur prüfung überreicht, von
Friedrich Wilhelm Lindner... Leipzig,C.H.Reclam,1831.
[2],xxviii,507,[1]p. 21½cm.

1.Lord's supper.

NL 0382131   ICU MH

₍Lindner, Friedrich Wilhelm₎ 1779-1864.
Mac-Benac, er lebet im sohne, oder Das positive der
freimaurerei. Zum gedächtniss der durch Luther wie-
dererkämpften evangelischen freiheit ... ₍n. p.₎ 1818.
viii, 96 p. 20¼⁺.

1. Freemasons.

9-27905†

Library of Congress   HS475.L7

NL 0382132   DLC NIC

HS
475
L74
1819   Lindner, Friedrich Wilhelm, 1799-1864.
Mac-Benac, er lebet im Sohne, oder:
Das Positive der Freimaurerei. Zum
Gedächtniss der durch Luther wiederer-
kämpsten evangelischen Freiheit. 3.
verbesserte und stark vermehrte Aufl.
Leipzig, C. H. Reclam, 1819.
xvi,278 p. 21cm.

1. Freemasons. I. Title.

NL 0382133   NIC

PT5810
A1
1781
v.7   Lindner, Friedrich Wilhelm, 1779-1864.
Mac-Benac; of, Het stellige der vrijmetselary.
Naar den 3. druk uit het Hoogduitsch vertaald
₍door Willem Bilderdijk₎ Leyden, L. Herdingh,
1820.
xiv,260 p. 22cm. ₍With Bilderdijk, Willem.
Werken. 1781. v.7₎

1. Freemasons. I. Bilderdijk, Willem, 1756-
1831, tr. II. Title.

NL 0382134   CU

QH45
.L74   LINDNER,FRIEDRICH WILHELM,1779-1864.
Malerische naturgeschichte der drei reiche,für schule
und haus. Mit besonderer beziehung auf das practische
leben bearb.von F.W.Lindner;unter mitwirkung von dr.
Fr.H.A.Lachmann ... Braunschweig,Oehme & Müller,
1840.
[3],iv,476,iv p. 28 pl.(part col.) 29cm.
Illustrated t.-p.

1.Natural history.

NL 0382135   ICU

Book
Collection   Lindner, Friedrich Wilhelm, 1779-1864, comp.
Music   Musikalischer Jugendfreund; oder, Instructive
K27   Sammlung von Gesängen für die Jugend gebildeter
z811   Stände, sowohl für Schulen und Institute, als
auch für den häuslichen Kreis geeignet ...
Leipzig,Auf Kosten des Herausgebers₍1811-12₎
3v. 18x22cm.
Vol.1, 2.Ausg.; dedication dated, 1811.
With piano accompaniment.
Musical settings by Reichardt of Goethe poems.
1. Hft: Gott (aus dem Faust); Wer darf ihn
nennen? - Meeresstille; Tiefe Stille herrscht

im Wasser. - Mailied; Wie herrlich leuchtet. -
Warnung; Wecke den Amor nicht auf [composer
not named] - Wahre Liebe; Das ist die wahre
Liebe. - 3.Hft.: Zum neuen Jahr; Zwischen
dem alten. - Aus Göthens Lila; Wir helfen
gerne.

NL 0382137   CtY

-VM
1994
L 74m   LINDNER, FRIEDRICH WILHELM, 1779-1864, comp.
Musikalischer jugendfreund; oder, Instructive
sammlung von gesängen für die jugend gebildeter
stände... Leipzig,F.C.W.Vogel₍pref.1812-14₎
3v.in 1. 18½x22½cm.

Vol.1, 3. durchaus verbesserte und stark vermehrte auflage ₍pref. 1814₎; v.2, 2. verbesserte
und stark vermehrte auflage ₍pref. 1814₎; v.3, 2.
unveränderte auflage ₍pref. 1812₎

NL 0382138   ICN PV

VOLUME 334

LINDNER, FRIEDRICH WILHELM, 1779-1864.
Musikalischer Jugendfreund; oder, Instructive
Sammlung von Gesängen für die Jugend gebildeter
Stände, sowohl für Schülen und Institute, als auch für
die häuslichen Kreis geeignet. Vierte verbesserte
Aufl. Leipzig, F. C. W. Vogel [1814-17; Heft 1:1817]
2 v. in 1. 18 x 23cm.
Heft 2: Zweite verbesserte und stark vermehrte Aufl.
For 1-4 voices, principally with piano acc.
1. Children's music--Songs. German. I. Title.

NL 0382139 NN

Lindner, Friedrich Wilhelm, 1779-1864.
Das Nothwendigste und Wissenswertheste
aus dem Gesammtgebiete der Tonkunst ...
Leipz., 1840.
8°.

NL 0382140 CtY

B2948
.L74 Lindner, Friedrich Ludwig, 1772-1845.
Der von Hegel'scher philosophie durch-
drungene Schuster-geselle; oder, Der absolute stiefel. Drama in zwei auftritten,
von Fr. Ludw. Lindner. Stuttgart, E.
Schweizerbart, 1844.
47p. 17½cm.

1. Hegel, Georg Wilhelm Friedrich, 1770-
1831. I. Title: Der schuster-geselle;
oder, Der absolute stiefel.

NL 0382141 NNU-W

330.921
B98
Lindner, Fritz
Charles de Butré, ein französischer physio-
krat des 18. Jahrhundert an einem deutschen
fürstenhofe; ein beitrag zur geschichte der
physiokratie. Bern, Scheitlin, Spring, 1906.
85 p.
Thesis, Bern.
"Literatur": p. [84]-85.

NL 0382142 NNC ICRL

Lindner, Fritz.

Dreesen, Walter.
Hundert tage auf Bali, beschrieben und gezeichnet von Wal-
ter Dreesen, photographiert von Fritz Lindner. Hamburg,
Broschek & co. [1937]

Lindner, Fritz
Ueber den tabakbau im Gebiet der
Matakaleute.
(Berichte u. Land u. Forstwirths.
in Deutsch-Ostafrika. II. 1904)

NL 0382144 PPAN

Lindner, Fritz.
Zur kenntnis einiger natürlicher Porphyrine.
München, 1926.
Inaug. - Diss. - Technische Hochschule,
Munich.

NL 0382145 ICRL

Lindner, Fritz, Ph.D., Würzburg.
Das eiserne tor im voelkerrecht. Eine
studie zum Donaurecht. Würzburg, 1926. 65p.
Inaug.-diss. - Würzburg.
Bibl.

NL 0382146 ICRL CtY MH

Lindner, Fritz, 1886-
Studien über das iridium ... Bamberg, W. Gärtners
buchdr., 1909.
37, [1] p. illus. 22cm.
Inaug.-diss.--Erlangen.
Lebenslauf.

1. Iridium.
G S 12-354
Library, U. S. Geol. survey

NL 0382147 DI-GS CtY ICRL NIC NN

Lindner, Fritz, 1911-
Über die in der ehewahl zum ausdruck kommende
affinität bei geisteskranken und psychopathen.
... Gunzenhausen, 1937. 40 p.
Inaug. Diss. - Erlangen, 1937.
Lebenslauf.
Literaturverzeichnis.

NL 0382148 CtY

Lindner, Georg
Der Schutz des wahlrechtes im geltenden straf-
gesetzbuch und im entwurf von 1927.
Inaug. Diss. Erlangen, 1930.
Bibl.

NL 0382149 CtY DLC ICRL

Lindner, Georg, 1859-
Dampfhammer-diagramme. Von prof. Georg Lindner.
(In Mitteilungen über forschungsarbeiten auf dem gebiete des in-
genieurwesens ... Berlin, 1902. 26½cm. hft. 4, p. [21]-34 incl. diagrs.)

1. [Steam-hammers]
P O 28-70
Library, U. S. Patent Office TA3.F732

NL 0382150 DP

Lindner, Georg, 1859-
Maschinenelemente von Georg Lindner. Stuttgart, Deutsche
Verlags-Anstalt, 1910.
[8], 294 p. incl. tables, 807 diagr. 27cm.

NL 0382151 ICJ NN

Lindner, Georg, 1859-
Spinnerei und Weberei. Karlsruhe: F. Gutsch [1913].
vi p., 1 l., 264 p. obl. 8°.

1. Spinning. 2. Weaving.
N. Y. P. L. May 7, 1914.

NL 0382152 NN

Lindner, Georg, 1859-
Spinnerei und Weberei von Georg Lindner, ... Karlsruhe
und Leipzig, F. Gutsch, [1914].
vi, [2], 264 p. 275 illus. 21 x 27cm.

NL 0382153 ICJ

Lindner, Georg, 1859-
Wanddruck in silos und schachtöfen. Von Georg Lindner
(In Mitteilungen über forschungsarbeiten auf dem gebiete des in-
genieurwesens ... Berlin, 1912. 26½cm. hft. 124, p. 1-32. diagrs.)
Bibliographical foot-notes.

1. Ensilage. 2. Furnaces.
P O 28-268
Library, U. S. Patent Office TA3.F732

NL 0382154 DP

Lindner, Georg, 1859-
L671 P703
Zeichnungen zu den Vorträgen über mechanische Technologie.
Giesserei und Schmiede. Gezeichnet von Wilhelm Eberle. 39 pl.
sq.Q. Karlsruhe i. B.: J. Linck, 1897.
Text never published.
No title-page. Title taken from inside cover.

NL 0382155 ICJ ICRL

Lindner, Georg, 1859-
L621.9 P903
Zeichnungen zu den Vorträgen über mechanische Technologie.
Werkzeugmaschinen. Gezeichnet von Otto Stahl. 39 pl. sq.Q.
Karlsruhe i. B.: J. Linck, 1899-1900.
Text never published.
No title-page. Title taken from inside cover.

NL 0382156 ICJ

1883-
Lindner, Georg, Rechtsprakt.: Grundzüge des kirchlichen
Umlagenrechts nach dem geltenden Rechte im rechts-
rheinischen Bayern und dem Entwurf einer Kirchengemeinde-
ordnung. Würzburg 1909:Fränkische Gesellschaftsdr. 43 S. 8°
Würzburg, Jur. Diss. v. 6. Mai 1909, Ref. Meurer
[Geb. 28. Sept. 83 Marktsteinach; Wohnort: Schweinfurt; Staatsangeh.:
Bayern; Vorbildung: Gymn. Schweinfurt Reife Juli 03; Studium: Würzburg
8 S.; Rig. 27. Jan. 09.] [U 09. 4066]

NL 0382157 ICRL MH-L CtY

Lindner, Georg, 1925-
Die abgrenzung zwischen enteignung
und eigentumsbindung im bereich des
heutigen bau- und bodenrechts ...
[Frankfurt a.M., 1955]
112 p., 1 l. 21cm.
Inaug.-diss. - Frankfurt a.M.
"Lebenslauf."
Bibliographical footnotes.

NL 0382158 MH-L

Lindner, George J
Stray leaves gathered here and there. By
George J. Lindner. Nashville, Hearld job
office, 1891.
136 p. 18.5 cm.

NL 0382159 NcD RPB

Lindner, George J, writer on religion
The church and the synagogue, by George J.
Lindner. Second edition...Cincinnati, the Sixth
street printing works, 1894. YA 27065
94 p. 17 1/2 cm.

NL 0382160 DLC

Lindner, George J., writer on religion.
Modern Judaism and the church; a review of
the history of Israel since the beginning
of the Christian era. Their religion of to-day,
including modern attacks on Christianity, by
Geo. J. Lindner. Washington, D.C., Frank B.
Clarkson, 1891.

NL 0382161 GEU NN OCH CtY

VOLUME 334

Lindner (Georgius Christophorus). * Diss. exhibens febrim petechialem. 1 p. l., 28 pp. sm.
°. [Erfurt, typ. J. H. Groschii 1719]

NL 0382162   DNLM

Lindner, Gerda, 1906–
Zur frage der konservativen behandlung oder
operation der chronisch entzündlichen adnexe ...
Breslau, 1936.
Inaug. Diss. – Breslau, 1936.
Lebenslauf.

NL 0382163   CtY MiU

QU   Lindner, Gerhard
25   Klinisch-chemische Untersuchungs-
L747k   methoden. Wolfenbüttel, Wolfen-
1948   bütteler Verlagsanstalt, 1948.
        74 p. (Bücher der Medizin)

        1. Biochemistry – Laboratory manuals
        Series

NL 0382164   DNLM

Lindner, Gerhard, 1879–
Die henker und ihre gesellen in der altfranzösischen
mirakel- und mysteriendichtung. (XIII.–XVI. jahrhundert) ... Greifswald, Hans Adler, buchdruckerei, 1902.
81, [2] p. 22 cm.
Inaug.-diss.—Greifswald.
Lebenslauf.

Library of Congress   5–22876†

NL 0382165   DLC NjP CU PU MiU

LINDNER, Gerhard, 1889–
Über die gasbewegung in dikotylen holzgewäch-
sen und die chemische zusammensetzung der
durchgesogenen luft in ihrer abhängigkeit von
physikalischen und physiologischen faktoren.
Inaug.-Diss. Breslau, R.Nischkowsky, 1916.
Illustr.
"Lebenslauf", p.following title-page.

NL 0382166   MH ICRL

Lindner, Gerhard, 1911–
Die Entwicklung der deutschen Getreidewirtschaft und ihr
Einbau in den Reichsnährstand... von Gerhard Lindner...
Seesen a. Harz: W. Flentje [1937?]   viii, 70 p.   21cm.

Inaugural-Dissertation — Frankfurt a. M., 1937.
Lebenslauf.
"Literaturverzeichnis," p. vi-viii.

1. Grain—Trade and stat.—
N. Y. P. L.   Germany.   July 9, 1940

NL 0382167   NN

Lindner, Gerhard i. e. Friedrich Christoph Gerhard,
1878–
Die abhängigkeit der specifischen wärme fester körper
von der temperatur ... Erlangen, Buchdruckerei von
Junge & sohn, 1903.
27, [1] p. fold. pl. 22 cm.
Inaug.-diss.—Erlangen.
Lebenslauf.

1. Specific heat.

Library of Congress   QC295.L74   5–27193†

NL 0382168   DLC CtY CU NN

Lindner, Gertrud Hildegard
   see Lindner, Hildegard, 1869–

Lindner, Gisela Michels-
   see
Michels-Lindner, Gisela.

Lindner, Gladys Dudley, comp.
Marcel Proust; reviews and estimates in English, compiled
by Gladys Dudley Lindner. Stanford University, Calif., Stanford university press [1942]
xviii, 314 p. 24½ cm.

1. Proust, Marcel, 1871–1922.
                                            43–253
Library of Congress   PQ2631.R63Z69
                                 [7]   843.91

WaSpG WaT WaTC WaWW
IdPI MtU MtBC OrCS OrPR OrU Wa WaE WaPS WaS WaSp
OC1 OO Or OrStbM OrSaW OrU-M MtBuM CaBVaU IdB IdU
NL 0382171   DLC TxU ICU CU MB NcC NcD PP PSC NN OU

Lindner,   Gladys Dudley, ed.

Lindner, Clarence Richard, 1890–
Private Lindner's letters, censored and uncensored; letters,
anecdotes, sketches, by Private Clarence R. Lindner during
world war; selection and arrangement by his wife, Gladys
Dudley Lindner. [San Francisco, °1939]

FLGZ   Lindner, Gottfried.
148   ... De cautione de non offendendo ... Basileae,
no.9   J. Bertsch [1688]
        [32]p. 20cm.
        (Foreign law pamphlet collection, v.148, no.9)

        Inaug.-disp. – Basel.

NL 0382173   CtY-L MH-L

W 4   LINDNER, Gottfried, 1910–
M31   Eugenische Gesetzgebung und
1938   moralischer Schwachsinn anhand einer
        hessischen Sippe. Bochum, Pöppinghaus,
        1938.
        38 p.
        Cover title.
        Inaug.-Diss. – Marburg.
        1. Psychopathic personality

NL 0382174   DNLM

R629.1092 Lindner (Gottfried) AG
L644g   Gottfried Lindner A. G., Ammendorf bei
            Halle/Saale [1823–1923] Berlin, Ecksteins
            Biographischer Verlag [1923]
            68 [1] p. illus.

            1. Carriages

NL 0382175   MiD

Adelmann
QM   Lindner, Gottlob Emanuel, 1734–1818.
421   Specimen inaugurale medicum De lymphati-
A99   corum systemate... Halae ad Salam, Typis
1788   Michaelis, 1787.
        86 p. 21cm.

        Diss.--Halle.
        Bound with: Azzoguidi, Germano. Obser-
        vationes ad uteri constructionem pertinen-
        tes. Lugduni Batavorum, 1788.

        1.Lymphatics.

NL 0382176   NIC DNLM

Lindner, Günter, 1905–
Inwieweit ergeben sich rechtsbeziehungen bei
geschäftlichen unterredungen? Quakenbrück
i. Hann., 1935.
Inaug. Diss. – Göttingen, 1935.
Lebenslauf.
Literaturverzeichnis.

NL 0382177   ICRL

Lindner, Gustaf Vincent.
Newspaper library manual. Adapted for use in newspaper
offices and schools of journalism. [New York: the author,
1912.] 1 p.l., 5–42 p.   8°.
With autograph of author.

1. Libraries (Newspaper).
N. Y. P. L.   February 17, 1913.

NL 0382178   NN MB

Lindner, Gustaf Vincent.
Newspaper library manual, adapted for use in newspaper offices and schools of journalism, by Gustaf V.
Lindner ... New York, The Progressive age publishing
co., °1912.
1 p. l., 5–42 p. 21 cm. $1.00

1. Newspaper office libraries.
Library of Congress   Z675.N4L6   13–1136

NL 0382179   DLC NjP WaS PP MoU OC1 MiU ICJ

LINDNER, Gustav.
Aus dem naturgarten der kindersprache, ein
beitrag zur kindlichen sprach- und geistesentwickelung in den ersten vier lebensjahren.
Leipzig,T.Grieben,1898.

NL 0382180   MH CtY PU IEN

PA6451 Lindner, Gustav.
.L35L5   De M. Porcio Latrone commentatio. Dissertati
        ...
        Vratislaviae [1855]
        52p.   21 1/2 cm.

NL 0382181   DLC PU NjP

Lindner, Gustav.
Das feuer; eine cultu.rhistorische studie.
Bruenn, Rohrer, 1881
231 p

NL 0382182   PU

4M-   Lindner, Gustav.
137   Frühling der Liebe. Spring of love. Walzer.
        Berlin, Musikverlag Rema [c1935]
        piano-conductor score (8 p.) and parts.

NL 0382183   DLC-P4

Lindner, Gustav, of Hirschberg.
... Kritische bemerkungen zum text einiger
schulschriftsteller ... vom direktor dr. Lindner.
Hirschberg, Druck von P. Oertel, 1886.
11 p.   26 cm.
Programm - Königliches gymnasium,
Hirschberg.

NL 0382184   CU NjP

Lindner, Gustav Adolf, 1828–1887.
Allgemeine erziehungslehre. Ed. 6.
Wien, Pichler, 1886.
168 p

NL 0382185   PU

VOLUME 334

Lindner, Gustav Adolf, 1828–1887.
Allgemeine erziehungslehre. Von schulrat dr. G. A. Lindner ... 7. verb. aufl. Für deutsche lehrer- und lehrerinnenbildungsanstalten nach dem gegenwärtigen stande der wissenschaft neu bearb von dr. Gustav Fröhlich ... Leipzig und Wien, A. Pichlers witwe & sohn, 1890.
viii, 211, ₍3₎ p. diagrs. 21ᶜᵐ.

1. Teaching. I. Fröhlich, Gustav, ed.

E 11—368

U. S. Off. of educ. Library
for Library of Congress
LB1025.L62
₍a41b1₎

NL 0382186 DHEW

Lindner, Gustav Adolf, *1828–1887*.
Allgemeine Erziehungslehre. Von Schulrat Dr. G. A. Lindner, ... Dreizehnte Auflage. Von Dr. Theodor Tupetz, ... Unveränderter Abdruck der mit hohem k. k. Ministerial-Erlass vom 8. Juli 1903, Z. 22060, zum Unterrichtsgebrauche an Lehrer- und Lehrerinnen-Bildungsanstalten zulässig erklärten 12. Auflage. ... Wien, A. Pichlers Witwe & Sohn, 1905.
₍2₎, 166 p. 21ᶜᵐ.

NL 0382187 ICJ

Lindner, Gustav Adolf, 1828–1887.
Allgemeine erziehungslehre. Von schulrat dr. G. A. Lindner ... 15. aufl. Von dr. Theodor Tupetz ... Wien, A. Pilchers witwe & sohn, 1908.
1 p. l., 166 p. 20½ᶜᵐ.
Unveränderter abdruck mit dem hohem k. k. Ministerial-erlass vom 8. juli 1903, z. 22060, zum unterrichtsgebrauche an lehrer- und lehrerinnenbildungsanstalten zulässig erklärten 12. aufl.

1. Teaching. I. Tupetz, Theodor, 1852–

E 10–1816

Library, U. S. Bur. of Education LB1025.L64

NL 0382188 DHEW

Lindner, Gustav Adolf, 1828–1887.
Allgemeine unterrichtslehre. Lehrtext zum gebrauche an den bildungs-anstalten für lehrer und lehrerinnen. Von schulrath dr. G. A. Lindner. 4. durchgesehene aufl. ... Wien, A. Pichler's witwe & sohn, 1882.
3 p. l., 111 p. double diagr. 20½ᶜᵐ.

1. Teaching.

E 10–2633

Library, U. S. Bur. of Education LB1025.L59

NL 0382189 DHEW

Lindner, Gustav Adolf, 1828–1887.
Allgemeine unterrichtslehre. Von schulrat dr. G. A. Lindner ... 7. verb. und verm. aufl. Für deutsche lehrer- und lehrerinnen-bildungsanstalten nach dem gegenwärtigen stande der wissenschaft neu bearb. von dr. Gustav Fröhlich ... Leipzig und Wien, A. Pichler's witwe & sohn, 1891.
x, 146 p. diagrs. 20ᶜᵐ.

1. Teaching. I. Fröhlich, Gustav, ed.

E 10–2489

Library, U. S. Bur. of Education LB1025.L6

NL 0382190 DHEW

LB675
.N5L5
Lindner, Gustav Adolf, 1828–1887.
August Hermann Niemeyer. Grundsätze der erziehung und des unterrichtes. Mit einer einleitung: August Hermann Niemeyer, sein leben und wirken. Geordnet... von dr. G. A. Lindner... Wien, A. Pichler's Witwe & Sohn, 1877–1878.
2v. in 1. 21cm. (Added t.-p.: Pädagogische klassiker. bd.4-5)
Contents.- bd.1. Erziehungslehre.- bd.2. Unterrichtslehre.

1. Niemeyer, August Hermann, 1754–1828.

NL 0382191 NNU-W

Lindner, Gustav Adolf, 1828–1887.
Eine cardinalfrage der schulpädagogik. Von dr. G. Lindner ... Langensalza, H. Beyer, 1875.
20 p. 19¼ᶜᵐ.
Separatabdruck aus dem Jahrbuch des Vereins für wissenschaftliche pädagogik, VII. jahrgang.

1. Teaching. I. Title.

E 12–735

Library, U. S. Bur. of Education LB775.L638

NL 0382192 DHEW

QA
135
.L727
Lindner, Gustav Adolf, 1828–1887.
Contar en estampas. Numeros fundamentales 1 à 10, por el doctor G. A. Lindner. Arreglado al español y al uso de las escuelas nacionales primarias, por el profesor J. Manuel Guillé. México, Impr. y litografía de J. V. Villada, 1880.
12 p. 10 pl.(part col.) 22ᶜᵐ.

1. Arithmetic—Study and teaching. I. Guillé, J. Manuel.

NL 0382193 MiU

LINDNER, Gustav Adolf, 1828–1887.
Einleitung in das Studium der Philosophie. Mit Rücksicht auf das Bedürfniss der Gymnasien entworfen. Wien, 1866.

sm.8°.

NL 0382194 MH

Lindner, Gustav Adolf, 1828–1887.
Encyklopädisches handbuch der erziehungskunde mit besonderer berücksichtigung des volksschulwesens ... Von schulrath dr. Gustav Ad. Lindner ... Wien & Leipzig, A. Pichler's witwe & sohn, 1884.
1 p. l., v, 1039 p. illus. (incl. ports., tables) fold. maps, diagrs. 23½ᶜᵐ.

1. Education—Dictionaries. ₍1. Education—Encyclopedias₎

E 17–558

Library, U. S. Bur. of Education LB15.L635

NL 0382195 DHEW MH MiU

Lindner, Gustav Adolf, 1828–1887.
Encyklopädisches handbuch der erziehungskunde mit besonderer berücksichtigung des volksschulwesens ... Von schulrath dr. Gustav Ad. Lindner ... Mit ca. 100 porträts, diagrammen, tabellen, karten u. dgl. 4. stereotyp-aufl. Wien & Leipzig, A. Pichler's witwe & sohn, 1891.
1 p. l., v, ₍1₎, 1039 p. illus. (incl. ports., tables) fold. maps, diagrs. 23½ᶜᵐ.

1. Education—Encyclopedias.

E 10–1439

Library, U. S. Bur. of Education LB15.L64

NL 0382196 DHEW PU OClW ICJ

BJ
107
P6L74
Lindner, Gustav Adolf, 1828–1887.
Die Erziehung zur pietas im alten Rom; ein Beitrag zur Geschichte der Erziehung im Altertum. Leipzig, O. Schmidt, 1890.
27 p. 23cm.

Diss.—Leipzig.

1. Ethics, Roman. 2. Moral education.

NL 0382197 NIC NjP ICRL

Lindner, Gustav Adolf, 1828–1887.
Grundriss der pädagogik als wissenschaft. Im anschluss an die entwickelungslehre und die sociologie. Verfasst von dr. Gustav A. Lindner ... Aus dessen literarischem nachlasse hrsg. von professor Karl Domin. Wien u. Leipzig, A. Pichler's witwe & sohn, 1889.
2 p. l., III-IV, ₍2₎, 153 p. 21ᶜᵐ.

1. Education. I. Domin, Karl, ed.

E 10—2490

U. S. Off. of educ. Library
for Library of Congress
LB775.L64
₍a41b1₎

NL 0382198 DHEW

306
L75
Lindner, Gustav Adolf, 1828–1887.
Ideen zur psychologie der gesellschaft, als grundlage der socialwissenschaft. Von Dr. Gustav Adolph Lindner. Wien, C. Gerold's sohn, 1871.
viii, 366 p., 1 ℓ. 22 cm.

NL 0382199 MiU MH

LINDNER, G₍ustav₎ A₍dolf₎, 1828–1887.
Leerboek der empirische zielkunde, herzien door Dr. Fröhlich, naar het Hoogduitsch door F. C. J. de Ridder. Zutphen, 1895.

Diagrams.

NL 0382200 MH

B
49
.505
LINDNER, GUSTAV ADOLF, 1828–1887.
Lehrbuch der allgemeinen logik. Für höhere bildungsanstalten. Mit benützung der 7. auflage des Lehrbuches der formalen logik von G. A. Lindner, verfasst von G. A. Lindner und Anton v. Leclair... 5. gekürzte auflage. Wien, K. Geraldssohn, 1911.
140p.

"Durch hohen ministerial-erlass vom 18. August 1911, Z. 35.768, zum unterrichtsgebrauche an gymnasien mit deutscher unterrichtssprache allgemein zugelassen."

NL 0382201 ICN

LINDNER, G₍ustav₎ A₍dolf₎, 1828–1887.
Lehrbuch der allgemeinen logik, für höhere bildungsanstalten. Verfasst von G. A. Lindner und Anton v. Leclair. 6ᵉ (doppel-) Aufl. Wien, C. Gerold's sohn, 1914.

NL 0382202 MH

B
5
.505
LINDNER, GUSTAV ADOLF, 1828–1887.
Lehrbuch der empirischen psychologie. Für den gebrauch an höheren lehranstalten. Mit benützung von G. A. Lindners Lehrbuch der empir. psychologie, verfasst von G. A. Lindner und Franz Lukas. 3. gekürzte auflage besorgt von Anton von Leclair... Wien, K. Geralds sohn, 1909.
144p.

"Durch hohen ministerial-erlass vom 2. september 1909, Z. 24.709, zum lehrgebrauche an mittelschulen mit deutscher unterrichtssprache allgemein zugelassen."

NL 0382203 ICN

LINDNER Gustav Adolf, 1828–1887.
Lehrbuch der empirischen Psychologie als inductiver Wissenschaft. 3e durchgesehene Aufl. Wien, 1872.

sm.8°.

NL 0382204 MH

VOLUME 334

Lindner, Gustav Adolf.
  Lehrbuch der empirischen Psychologie als
inductiver Wissenschaft .. 5te. Aufl.
Wien, 1877.
  8°.

NL 0382205 CtY

Lindner, Gustav Adolf, 1828-1887.
  Lehrbuch der empirischen psychologie als inductiver wissenschaft, für
den gebrauch an höheren lehranstalten
und zum selbstunterrichte… 6.neuer-
dings durchgesehene…aufl. Wien, Gerold,
1880.
  215 p. illus. 21 ᶜᵐ.

  1.Psychology.

NL 0382206 NjP NNU-W

150   Lindner, Gustav Adolf, 1828-1887
L6417   Lehrbuch der empirischen psychologie
      als inductiver wissenschaft. Für den
      gebrauch an höheren lehranstalten und
      zum selbstunterrichte. 7. unveränderte
      aufl.   Wien, 1883.
      248p.

NL 0382207 IU

LINDNER,Gust[av] Ad[olf],1828-1887.
  Lehrbuch der empirischen psychologie als
inductiver wissenschaft. 9e unveränderte aufl.
Wien,C.Gerold's sohn,1889.

NL 0382208 MH

150   Lindner, Gustav Adolf, 1828-1887.
L64110 Lehrbuch der empirischen psychologie
      als inductiver wissenschaft … nach
      dem gegenwärtigen stande der wissen-
      schaft neu bearb. und ergänzt von dr.
      Gustav Fröhlich. 10. verb. und verm.
      aufl. Wien, 1891.
      269p.

NL 0382209 IU

Lindner, Gustav Adolf, 1828-1887
  Lehrbuch der formalen logik; für den
gebrauch an höheren lehranstalten und zum
selbstunterricht. 2d ed. enl. Wien, Gerold's
sohn, 1867
  258 p

NL 0382210 PP

Lindner, Gustav Adolf, 1828-1887.
  Lehrbuch der formalen logik. Für höhere bildungs-
anstalten. Von schulrath dr. Gust. Ad. Lindner. 6. rev.
aufl. Wien, C. Gerold's sohn, 1885.
  viii, 158 p. diagr. 20½ᶜᵐ.

  1. Logic.   I. Title.

                            17-30316
  Library of Congress   BC114.L5 1885

NL 0382211 DLC

LINDNER,Gustav Adolf,1828-1887.
  Lyckans problem. Öfversättning af G.
Swederus. Stockholm,F.G.Berg,1869.

  Diagrs.

NL 0382212 MH

Lindner, Gustav Adolf, 1828-1887.
  Manual of empirical psychology as an inductive science.
A text-book for high schools and colleges. By Dr. **Gustav
Adolf Lindner** … Authorized translation by Chas. De
Garmo … Boston, D. C. Heath & company, 1889.
  xiii, 274 p. diagrs. 19 cm.

  1. Psychology.   I. De Garmo, Charles, 1849-1934, tr.

                                              E 9—1200
  U. S. Office of Education. /   Library BF133.L6D3
  for Library of Congress   BF131.L6

                 NIC
NL 0382213 DHEW OC1 OC1W OCU MH MB PU PHC DLC KEmT

Lindner, Gustav Adolf, 1828-1887.
  Manual of empirical psychology as an inductive science.
A text-book for high-schools and colleges. Authorized
translation by Chas. De Garmo. Boston, D.C.Heath & co.,
1890.

  xiii, 274 p. diagrs. 19 cm.

NL 0382214 MH PU PSC NjP ViU

Lindner, Gustav Adolf, 1828-1887.
  Manual of empirical psychology as an inductive
science; a textbook for high schools and
colleges. Authorized translation by Chas. De-
Garmo. Boston, D.C.Heath & co., 1894.

NL 0382215 MH KMK

Lindner, Gustav Adolf, 1828-1887.
  … Myšlenky k psychologii společnosti jako základ společen-
ské vědy. O utajených představách. Přeložil a úvodní stu-
dií opatřil Josef Král. V Praze, Nákladem České akademie
věd a umění, 1929.
  3 p. l., [ii]-clxxxiv p., 1 l., 258 p., 1 l. 24½ᶜᵐ. (Added t.-p.: Filosofická bibliotéka … Rada I. číslo 8)
  "Gustav Adolf Lindner. Život a filosofie. Napsal Josef Král":
clxxxiv p.
  First published under title: Ideen zur psychologie der gesellschaft
als grundlage der sozialwissenschaft. Wien, 1871.

  1. Social psychology.   I. Král, Josef, 1882-   tr.

  Library of Congress   HM251.L48
                                              31-29754
                  [2]

NL 0382216 DLC ICU MoU

Lindner, Gustav Adolf, 1828-1887.
  Die pädagogische hochschule. Von dr. G. A. Lindner.
Wien, A. Hölder, 1874.
  44 p. 23ᶜᵐ.

  1. Teachers—Training—Universities and colleges. 2. Teachers—Training—Germany.
                                              E 11-1692

  Library, U. S. Bur. of   Education LB1738.L64

NL 0382217 DHEW

LINDNER,Gustav Adolf,1828-1887.
  Das problem des Glücks; psychologische unter-
suchungen über die menschliche glückseligkeit.
Wien,C.Gerold's sohn,1868.

NL 0382218 MH

LINDNER,Gustav Adolf,1828-1887.
  Das rechnen in bildern. Zahlenraum I bis
X. Wien,1875.

  (Atlas of 10 plates f°.)
  Imperfect: lacks text.

NL 0382219 MH

PT2482   Lindner, Gustav Adolf, 1828-1887.
.S4   … Schiller als aesthetiker, von dr.
v.2   G. A. Lindner… Cilli, E. Jeretin,
      1868.
      33p. 23cm. (On cover: Schiller
      pamphlets. [v.2,no.5.])
      "Programm des k.k. Gymnasiums zu
      Cilli… 1868."

      1. Schiller, Johann Christoph Fried-
rich von, 1759-1805.

NL 0382220 NNU-W NjP

Lindner, Gustav Adolf, 1828-1887.
  Záhada štěstí; psychologická zkoumání o lidské blaže-
nosti. Přel. Josef Král. V Praze, Nákl. České akademie
věd a umění, 1931.
  vi, 154 p. port., 7 diagrs. 25 cm. (Filosofická bibliotéka. Řada
I, čís. 9)

  1. Psychology.   I. Title. (Series)

  BF41.L512   [4]-42771

NL 0382221 DLC ICU MH MoU NN

Slavic   Lindner, Gustav Adolf [1828-1887]
Coll.   Život Jana Amosa Komenského; učitelům
420.91   podává Josef K. Nejedlý. Praha, František
G4   A. Urbánek, 1878.
L558   72 p. 23 cm.

      English translation of title: Jan Amos
Komensky's life; adapted for teachers and
translated from German to Czech by J. K.
Nejedlý.   rw

NL 0382222 IEdS

Lindner, Gustav Vincent
  see Lindner, Gustaf Vincent.

Lindner (Gustavus Adolphus) [1820-]. *De
iridis membranæque Descemeti inflammatione.*
29 pp., 1 l. 8°. *Berolini, typ. Nietackianis,* [1842].

NL 0382224 DNLM PPC

Lindner, Gusztáv, 1836-
  Az Altenberger féle codex…
  see under Codex Altenberger.

RC   Lindner, H
89   Pastoralmedizin. Briefe an einen jungen Pfarrer. 3. Aufl.
L5   Berlin, M. Warneck, 1903.
1903   180 p. illus. 22cm.

      1. Pastoral medicine.   I. Title.

NL 0382226 CBPac

VOLUME 334

LINDNER, Hanns [Heinrich Leopold].
Die durchbrechung des publizitätsprinzips
für die übertragung dinglicher rechte an
beweglichen sachen durch zulassung des consti-
tum possessorium, ihre notwendigkeit und ihre
gefahren. Borna-Leipzig, 1913.

8+61+[3] p.
Insug.-diss. - Heidelberg.

NL 0382227   MH-L

Lindner, Hans.
Hydraulische Pressanlagen für die Kunstharzverarbei-
tung. Berlin, J. Springer, 1940.
62 p. illus., diagrs. 23 cm. (Werkstattbücher für Betriebsbeamte,
Konstrukteure und Facharbeiter, Heft 82)

1. Plastics—Molding. 2. Hydraulic presses.   I. Title.
(Series)
TP986.A2L47   57-52285

NL 0382228   DLC NN IaAS MCM

Lindner, Hans.
Hydraulische pressanlagen für die kunst-
harzverarbeitung. 2.Aufl. Berlin, Springer,
1951.
60 p.   ill.   O.
Werkstattbücher #82.

NL 0382229   PPF

Lindner, Hans, 1886—
        Untersuchungen über gefärbte Bunsen-
flammen. Borna-Leipzig 1911: Noske.   58 S. 8°
Leipzig, Phil. Diss. v. 25. Nov. 1911, Ref. Beckmann, Hantzsch
[Geb. 14. Sept. 86 Lehesten; Wohnort: Leipzig; Staatsangeh.: Sachsen; Vor-
bildung: König-Albert-Gymn. Leipzig Reife O. 05; Studium: Leipzig 9 S.;
Rig. 27. Okt. 11.]   [U 12. 1303]

NL 0382230   ICRL CtY MH PU OCU

Lindner, Hans, 1902-
Studien ueber vliesszummensetzung und rendement an
ausstellungstieren der wuerttembergischen schafrasse.
Probeschur der DLG.- Ausstellung zu Breslau 1926.
Inaug. diss. Halle, 1928.
Bibl.

NL 0382231   ICRL CtY MiU MH

LINDNER, Hans Georg, 1900-
Gewichtsverlegung und ausnutzung des reibungs-
gewichtes bei elektrischen lokomotiven mit
einzelachsantrieb. Diss. [Osterwieck-Harz, A.W.
Zickfeldt, 1930.]

1.8°. pp. (4), 25+ Diagrs.
"Diese arbeit erschien als Heft 333 der
Forschungsarbeiten auf dem Gebiete des inge-
nieurwesens." Inaug.-diss. - Technische Hochschule, Berlin.
"Lebenslauf", at end.

NL 0382232   MH ICRL

Lindner, Hans Joachim
Fertigungskosten, (insbesondere brandkosten-
verrechnung) und fertigungsvorbereitung bei der
hartporzellan- herstellung für elektrotechnische
zwecke. ... Würzburg, 1936.
Inaug. Diss. - Techn. Hochschule München, 1936.
Schrifttum.

NL 0382233   ICRL

LINDNER, Hans Joachim, 1912-
Die Biologie der Frakturheilung.
Eisfeld i. Thür., Beck, 1938.
51 p.
Cover title.
Inaug.-Diss. - Marburg.
1. Fractures - Healing

NL 0382234   DNLM

Lindner, Hans Julius, 1886-
    see Lindner, Hans, 1886-

Lindner, Harold, 1923-
An analysis of the psychological characteristics of a se-
lected group of imprisoned sexual offenders. [College Park,
Md.] 1951.
x, 216 l. illus., tables. 28 cm.
Thesis—University of Maryland.
Typescript (carbon copy)
Vita.
"Selected bibliography": leaves 132–134.

1. Sex crimes. 2. Criminal psychology.   I. Title. II. Title: Psychological characteristics of a selected group of imprisoned sexual
offenders.
HQ71.L53   A 52-4792
Maryland. Univ. Libr.
for Library of Congress   [3]†

NL 0382236   MdU DLC

Film   Lindner, Harold, 1923-
1288   An analysis of the psychological chara-
cteristics of a selected group of imprisoned
sexual offenders. [College Park] 1951.
x, 216L.   illus., tables.
Thesis--University of Maryland.
Vita.
Bibliography: L. 132-134.
Microfilm (negative) of typescript.
College Park, University of Maryland, [n.d.]

NL 0382237   NSyU

Lindner, Hedda.
Die frau im schwarzen schleier, die geschichte eines ver-
dachts, von Hedda Lindner. Berlin, Rot-blau verlag [*1932]
2 p. l., 9-279. [1] p., 1 l. 20cm.

I. Title.
Library of Congress   PT2623.I 62F7 1932   33-10255
Copyright A—Foreign   18539
                                [2]   833.91

NL 0382238   DLC

Lindner, Hedda.
Glück auf Madeira.   Berlin: Ullstein [cop. 1934]   245 p.
16°.

I. Title.
N. Y. P. L.   August 29, 1935

NL 0382239   NN

Lindner, Heinrich.
Karl der Zwölfte vor Friedrichshall
see under title [supplement]

Lindner, Heinrich August, d. 1787.
Lindnersche Ahnentafel-Sammlung. Hrsg. von
Oswald Spohr. Leipzig, Degener, Inh. O. Spohr,
1933-[35] 1 v., 218 tables. 38cm.

Band 1 and Tafeln 121A-1698a (Incomplete).
Issued in 19 parts (Lieferungen), 1930-35.
Facsimile reproductions of the author's holo-

graphic tables.
Includes lists of contents for parts as original-
ly issued.
No more published?
Contents.—Bd. 1. 240 Ahnentafeln des deutschen
Adels.
1. Nobility—Germany. I. Spohr, Oswald, 1888-
ed.

NL 0382242   NN

Lindner, Heinrich August, d. 1787.
Lindnersche Stammtafel-Sammlung. [Leipzig,
Degener, Inh. O. Spohr, 1930-33?] 1 v., 7 pts.
38cm.

Band 1-2, Lieferung 1-[7]
Issued in 17 parts.
Title from list of contents.

Imperfect: Vol. 2, pt. 3 lacks chart 42a.
Facsimile reproductions of the author's halo-
graphic charts.

1. Nobility--Germany. I. Spohr, Oswald, 1888-
ed.

NL 0382244   NN

Lindner, Helmut.
Atome bauen die welt, eine anschauliche chemie, von Helmut
Lindner, mit 5 tafeln und 123 abbildungen. Stuttgart, Franckh
[1942]
82 p. incl. illus., tables, diagrs. 26cm.
"7.-12. tausend."
"Schrifttumsnachweis": p. 80.

1. Chemistry, Physical and theoretical.   I. Title.
QD453.L62   541   A F 46-892
Illinois. Univ. Library
for Library of Congress   [4]†

NL 0382245   IU TxU MH CtY LU NcD NjP TxU DLC ViU

Lindner, Helmut.
Elektro-Aufgaben; Übungsaufgaben zu den Grundlagen
der Elektrotechnik (mit Lösungen) Leipzig, Fachbuchverlag, 1954-
v. diagrs. 23 cm.
CONTENTS.-T. 1. Gleichstrom.—

1. Electric engineering—Examinations, questions, etc.   I. Title.
TK169.L55   56-37068 :

NL 0382246   DLC

Lindner, Helmut.
Lehrbuch der Physik für Techniker und Ingenieure.
Leipzig, Fachbuchverlag, 1953-
3 v. illus., ports., diagrs. 24 cm.
Includes various editions of some volumes.
CONTENTS.—Bd. 1. Mechanik der festen Körper, Flüssigkeiten und
Gase.—Bd. 2. Wärmelehre, Akustik, Optik.—Bd. 3. Elektrizitätslehre
und Atomphysik.

1. Physics.   I. Title.
QC23.L614   61-45436 rev

NL 0382247   DLC InLP ICU

Lindner, Henricus Gustavus
Nonnulla de hepate et bile evertebratorum.
Dissert. Inaug. phys. chem. 1844
Berolini.

NL 0382248   PPAN

Lindner, Herbert.
Die eiszeiten und der eiszeitliche mensch im südlichen
Oberschlesien. Mit 33 tafeln, 5 bildern im text und einer über-
sichtstabelle. Von Herbert Lindner, Ratibor. Gleiwitz, Ober-
schlesische volksstimme Gmbh., 1938?
64 p., 1 l. incl. illus., tab. xxIII pl. on 17 l. 22½cm. (On cover:
Jahresberichte, 1937, der Geologischen vereinigung Oberschlesiens [1.
teil]; hrsg. von professor Gustav Eisenreich, Gleiwitz)

"Benutztes schrifttum": p. 62-64.
1. Glacial epoch. 2. Man, Prehistoric—Silesia, [Upper]   I. Title.
                                              G S 40-307
U. S. Geol. survey. Library   353(530) L64e
for Library of Congress   [GN774.G7   ]

NL 0382249   DI-GS

VOLUME 334

Egleston
D621.9
L644
  Lindner, Herbert
    Vom Lindner gewindeschleifen und lehren-
bohren. Berlin-Wittenau [1942]
    276 p. illus., diagrs., tables. (Druck-
schrift no. 133)

    1. Screw-cutting machines. 2. Drilling
and boring machines.

NL 0382250   NNC

Lindner, Herbert, *of Saxony.*
    Sachsen, Land und Volk; Querschnitt durch das Werden
und Schaffen eines Grenzlandgaues. [16. Aufl.] Dresden,
Nationalsozialistischer Verlag für den Gau Sachsen [1937]
    127 p. illus., port. 30 cm.

    1. Saxony—Descr. & trav.   I. Title.
DD801.S34L58 1937   49–44657*

NL 0382251   DLC

Lindner, Herbert, 1902–
    Die aufhebung der ehelichen gemeinschaft nach
dem buergerlichen gesetzbuch.
    Inaug. diss. Breslau, 1928.
    Bibl.

NL 0382252   DLC

3459 Lindner, Herbert, 1903–
.1
.791   Hugo von Hofmannsthals "Jedermann"
und seine vorgänger... Leipzig, 1928.
    125 p. 22½ cm.

    Inaug.-diss. - Leipzig.
    Lebenslauf.
    "Literatur": p.125.

    1.Hofmannsthal,Hugo Hofmann,edler von,
1874–1929. Jedermann.

NL 0382253   NjP CtY ICRL NN InU IU NNC MH

W 4 LINDNER, Hermann
M96   Über die Indikation zur operativen
1951   Behandlung bei Hochdruck und die
Erfolge. [München] 1951.
    [55] l.
    Inaug.-Diss. - Munich.
    1. Blood pressure - High - Treatment

NL 0382254   DNLM

RD540 LINDNER,HERMANN,1852–
.L74   Die chirurgie des magens und ihre indikationen,ein-
schliesslich diagnostik. 12 vorlesungen für praktische
ärzte von dr.H.Lindner...und dr.L.Kuttner... Berlin,
O.Enslin,1898.
    [7],312 p. illus. 22½cm.

    1.Stomach--Surgery.

NL 0382255   ICU DNLM IU-M PPC ICRL ICJ MoSU

Lindner (H[ermann]) [1852–]. Ueber
Abscessblutungen grösserer Gefässtämme. 4
pp. 8°. [Berlin, J. Sittenfeld, 1887.]
    Repr. from: Deutsche med. Wchnschr., Leipz. u. Berl.,
1887, xiii.

NL 0382256   DNLM

Lindner, Hermann, 1852–
    Ueber Bauchdeckenbrüche. 39 pp. 8°.
    Berlin, Fischer, 1892.
    Forms 49. Hft. of: Berl. Klinik.

NL 0382257   DNLM

Lindner (H.) Ueber die allgemeinen Grundsätze
für die chirurgische Behandlung bösartiger Geschwülste.
    In: Sammi. klin. Vortr., Leipz., 1881, No. 196 (Chir., No.
60, 1615–1636).

NL 0382258   DNLM OClW-H

Lindner, Hermann, 1852–
    Ueber Gefässnaht. 15 pp. 8°. *Berlin,*
Fischer, 1898.
    Forms 118. Hft. 1898, of: Berl. Klin.

NL 0382259   DNLM

Lindner, Hermann, 1876–
    Zur kasuistik der temporaeren resektion der äusseren
orbitalwand nach Kroenlein.
    Inaug. diss. Giessen, 1902.
    Bibl.

NL 0382260   ICRL MH

Lindner, Hildegard, 1869–
    Kasuistischer beitrag zur myxodemfrage ...
Halle, a. S., C.A. Kaemmerer & co., 1904.
    Cover-title, 32 p. plate.
    Inaug. - Diss. - Friedrichs-Universität
Halle-Wittenberg.
    Lebenslauf.
    "Litteraturverzeichnis": p. [30]

NL 0382261   MiDW ICRL

Lindner, Hubert: Beiträge zur Spondylitis tuberculosa. [Maschinen-
schrift.] 35 S. 4°. - Auszug: Breslau 1924: 'Merkur'. 2 Bl. 8°
Breslau, Med. Diss. v. 17. Okt. 1924 [1925]   [U 25. 961

NL 0382262   ICRL

Lindner, Hugo, 1863–1925, ed.

Batovcův almanach; politický kalendář Republiky československé ... Zákony, rady, pokyny, statistika, schematismus, adresář.
V Praze, Tiskem a nákladem F. B. Batovce

NL 0382264   CoU WaU

PT2623 Lindner, Hugo Gabriel, 1890–
I 63B58   Der blühende Eros; Roman. Leipzig, W.
Borngräber [n.d.]
    436 p. 19cm.

NL 0382264   CoU WaU

Lindner, Hugo Gabriel, 1890–
    Das karrenphänomen, von dr. Hugo Gabriel Lindner ... mit
14 tabellen, 26 abbildungen im text und auf tafeln und 1
diagramm. Gotha, J. Perthes, 1930.
    83, [1] p. incl. illus., tables. 4 pl. fold. diagr. 27½cm. (Ergänzungs-
heft nr. 208 zu "Petermanns mitteilungen")

    "Literaturangaben": p. 80–83.

    1. Kar formation.   I. Title.
                            30–33209
  Library of Congress   G1.P44 no. 208
                 [2]   (910.8) 551.8

NL 0382265   DLC MoU IaU ViU TxU MiU OCU OU

Lindner, Hermann, 1852–
    Ueber Bauchdeckenbrüche. 39 pp. 8°.

Lindner, Hugo Gabriel. 1890–
    Waldläufer Silberhorn, Geschichte einer Jugendfreund-
schaft. Nürnberg, Sebaldus-Verlag [1955–
    v. illus. 20 cm.

    I. Title.
PZ33.L485   56–33079 ‡

NL 0382266   DLC IU

Lindner, Ilse, 1902–
    Durch glykokollbehandlung hervorgerufene reaktive
gewebsprozesse bei meerschweinchen.
    Inaug. diss. Greifswald, 1928
    Bibl.

NL 0382267   ICRL MiU CtY

Lindner, Ilse, 1910–
    Beiträge zur klinik der bronchial- und
trachealfremdkörper. ... 1934. 19 p.
    Inaug. Diss. - Rostock, 1934.
    Lebenslauf.

NL 0382268   CtY

Lindner, J   T
    Wanderungen durch die interessantesten Gegenden
des sächsischen Obererzgebirges; ein Beitrag zur
speciellern Kenntniss desselben, seines Volkslebens,
der Gewerbsarten, Sitten und Gebräuche. Annaberg,
Rudolph und Dieterici, 1848

    58, 56, 20 p. illus.

NL 0382269   MH

Lindner (Jacob). *De furunculo Aleppensi.* 16
pp. 8°. *Monachii, F. S. Hübschmann,* 1834.

NL 0382270   DNLM

Lindner, Jerzy
    Elektryk-instalator; podręcznik dla instala-
torów ... Solingen, 1947.
    256 p. illus.

NL 0382271   MiD

Lindner, Joannes Christianus.
    De cinnabaris inertia medica. Francof.
ad Viadr., typ. P. Schwartzii, [1743]
    24 p., 1 l. 4°.
    Also, in: Cartheuser (J.F.) Diss. non. select.
Phys.-Chym. ac med. 12°. Francof. ad Viadr.,
1775, 1–27.

NL 0382272   DNLM

Lindner, Joannes Christianus.
    De oleis destillatis empyreumaticis. Francof.
ad Viadr., typ. M. Hubneri, [1744]
    18 p., 1 l. 4°.

NL 0382273   DNLM

Lindner, Joannes Christianus.
    De usu aquae calcis vivae interno. Francof.
ad Viadr., typ. P. Swartzii, [1743]
    16 p. 4°.

NL 0382274   DNLM

Lindner, Joannes Christianus.
    *De vero universe medicinae principio.
Halae Magdeb., typ. C.A. Zeitleri, [1715]
    28 p. 4°.

NL 0382275   DNLM

VOLUME 334

Lindner (Joannes Fridericus). *De hydrome-
tra.* vi, 7–80 pp. 8°. *Solisbaci, apud Seidelium,*
1822.

NL 0382276   DNLM

Lindner (Joannes [Gustavus] Carolus) [1796–
]. *De variis pupillae artificialis confor-
mandae methodis hucusque jamjam laudatis.*
vi, 7–48 pp. 12°. *Vratislaviae, typ. Kupferianis,*
[1891].

NL 0382277   DNLM

X
672
.504
   LINDNER, JOHANN.
     Fodina lingvae latinae, in quâ cmneo
omnium vocabulorum significationes erutae,
autorum classicorum exemplis illustratae ...
Editio tertia, auctior et correctior.
Lipsiae, Sumptibus J.F. Gleditschii et M.G.
Wiedmanni, 1692.
     1v.(various pagings) 17cm.

     Title vignette.
     Title at head of text: Viridarum latinae
linguae.

NL 0382278   ICN

Lindner, Johann. *Monk of Pirna.* 1450–1530.
Excerpta Saxonica, Misnica, et Thuringiaca ex Ono-
mastico autographo. 23 pp. (Mencke, J. B. Script.
rer. Germanic. v. 2, p. 1447.)

NL 0382279   MdBP

X
975
.507
   LINDNER, JOHANN GOTTHELF, 1729–1776.
     Ganz besonderer und merkwürdiger Brief an
die Herren Herren hohen unbekannten obern Gold-
und Rosenkreuzer, alten Systems in Deutschland
und anderen Ländern. [Cleve, 1820]
     16p. 17cm.

     "Was written in 1768 but was not issued in
print until 1816."—Gardner, Bibl. Rosicruciana.

NL 0382280   ICN

---

*GC7
L6444
767l
   Lindner, Johann Gotthelf, 1729–1776.
     Lehrbuch der schönen Wissenschaften,
insonderheit der Prose und Poesie, von Johann
Gotthelf Lindner ...
     Königsberg und Leipzig, bey Johann Jacob
Kanter, 1767–68.
     2v. in 1. 17cm.

NL 0382281   MH

   Lindner, Johann Gottlieb, 1726–1811, ed.
     Apologia pro Christianis
       see under   Athenagoras, 2d cent.

---

ar V
1110
   Lindner, Johann Gottlieb, 1726–1811.
     Curae posteriores in Athenagorae
Deprecationem pro Christianis.
Longosalissae, I. C. Martini, 1775.
     24 p. 18cm.

     Bound with Athenagoras, 2d cent.
Deprecatio pro Christianis. 1774.

     1. Athenagoras, 2d cent. Deprecatio
pro Christianis.

NL 0382283   NIC ICU

   Lindner, Johann Gottlieb, 1726–1811.

Cyprianus, *Saint, bp. of Carthage.*
     ... S. Thascii Cæcilii Cypriani episcopi carthaginensis et
martyris Opera omnia ad Stephani Baluzii editionem expressa,
et præcipuis Martini Routhii, Felli, Pamelii, Rigaltii lectionibus et notis instructa, variisque aucta opusculis, recentius in
lucem editis. Præmittuntur patrum minorum qui sæculo tertio a Tertulliano ad Cyprianum in ecclesia latina floruere
scripta quæ supersunt accurante et denuo recognoscente J.-P.
Migne ... Parisiis, apud Garnier fratres et J.-P. Migne suc-
cessores, 1886.

   Lindner, Johann Wilhelm Sigismund, 1783–1831.

Hamberger, Georg Christoph, 1726–1773.
     Das gelehrte Teutschland; oder, Lexikon der jetzt lebenden
teutschen schriftsteller. Angefangen von Georg Christoph
Hamberger ... Fortgesetzt von Johann Georg Meusel ... 5.
durchaus verm. und verb. ausg. Lemgo, Meyersche buchhandlung, 1796–1834.

   Lindner, Johann Wilhelm Sigismund, 1783–1931.

Rassmann, Christian Friedrich, 1772–1831.
     ... Kurzgefasstes lexicon deutscher pseudonymer schriftstel-
ler, von der ältern bis auf die jüngste zeit aus allen fächern der
wissenschaften. Mit einer vorrede über die sitte der literarischen verkappung, von J. W. S. Lindner. Leipzig, W.
Nauck, 1830.

W 4
L68
1940
   LINDNER, Johannes
     Heimwee, een phathopsychologisch
[sic] onderzoek. Amsterdam, Paris,
1940.
     189 p.
     Proefschrift - Leyden.
     Summary in Dutch and English.
     1. Emotions

NL 0382287   DNLM

BF575
.N6L7
   Lindner, Johannes
     Heimwee; een pathopsychologisch Onderzoek.
Amsterdam, 1941.
     189 p.

     Proefschrift--Leyden.

     1. Nostalgia.

NL 0382288   ICU

   Lindner, Johannes, de Grunau
     Ueber bromnitrophenole, ...
     Inaug. diss. Tübingen, 1885. (Elberfeld)

NL 0382289   ICRL

1885–
Lindner, Johannes, Referendar: Das beschränkte Akzept
Art. 22 der allgemeinen deutschen Wechselordnung.
Leipzig: Wigand 1909. 85 S. 8°
Leipzig, Jur. Diss. v. 23. Dez. 1909
[Geb. 27. Dez. 85 Siegmar; Wohnort: Leipzig; Staatsangeh.: Sachsen; Vor-
bildung: Gymn. Chemnitz Reife O. 05; Studium: Freiburg i. B. 1, Leipzig
7 S.; Rig. 27. Jan. 09.]   [U 10. 2785]

NL 0382290   ICRL

LINDNER, Johannes, 1891–
     Über den Einfluss günstiger Temperaturen
auf gefrorene Schimmelpilze. Leipzig: Borntraeger 1914. 52 p.

     Leipzig, Phil. Diss.

NL 0382291   MH-Z CtY ICRL OCU

834L644
Og
   Lindner, Johannes, 1896–
     Gott, erde, mensch, gedichte   Berlin, E.
Fleischel & co., 1920.
     79p.

NL 0382292   IU

634.9
L644s3
   Lindner, John.
     Skogen. [3. omarb. uppl.], Stockholm,
Scoutförlaget [1955]
     207p. illus. 19cm. (I markerna)

     1. Forests and forestry.

NL 0382293   OkU OrCS

   Lindner, Josef, 1880–
     Die konstitution des benzols. Entwurf zur
stereochemie der aromatischen verbindungen ...
von dr. J. Lindner ... Berlin, R. Friedländer &
sohn, 1913.
     24 p. diagrs. 25 cm.
     1. Benzene. 2. Stereochemistry.

NL 0382294   CU NjP

Lindner, Josef, 1880–
     Mikro-massanalytische bestimmung des kohlenstoffes und
wasserstoffes mit grundlegender behandlung der fehlerquellen
in der elementaranalyse, mit 56 haupt-
und nebenabbildungen und 8 tabellen. Berlin, Verlag Chemie,
g. m. b. h., 1935.
     vii, 374 p. illus., diagrs. 23½ᶜᵐ.
     "Einschlägige werke und abhandlungen": p. 13–14.
     1. Volumetric analysis. 2. Carbon. 3. Hydrogen. 4. Microchemistry.
I. Title.

Library of Congress	QD111.L5	35–31953
Copyright A—Foreign	20427	
	[2]	545.5

NL 0382295   DLC NN CU CtY PSC OU MH WU

Lindner, Josef, 1880–
     Mikro-massanalytische bestimmung des kohlenstoffes und
wasserstoffes mit grundlegender behandlung der fehlerquellen
in der elementaranalyse, von Josef Lindner ... mit 56 haupt-
und nebenabbildungen und 8 tabellen. Berlin, Verlag Chemie,
g. m. b. h., 1935. [Ann Arbor, Michigan, Lithoprinted by
Edwards brothers, 1944]
     vii, 374 p. illus., diagrs. 22ᶜᵐ.
     "Einschlägige werke und abhandlungen": p. 13–14.

NL 0382296   ViU ICJ PU-Sc OO

Lindner, Josef, 1880–
     Über den zeitlichen Verlauf des Zerfalles der Malonsäure in Kohlen-
säure und Essigsäure. Diagram. Chart.
     (In Kaiserliche Akademie der Wissenschaften, Vienna. Sitzungs-
berichte. Mathematisch-naturwissenschaftliche Klasse. Band 116.
Halbband 2, Abteilung 2B, pp. 945–951. Wien. 1907.)

     H13 — Chemical physics. — Malonic acid.

NL 0382297   MB

LINDNER, Josef, 1895–
     Über verbindungen mit trichromi-formiato-
(propionato)-fluoro-komplexen. Wurzburg,
C.J. Becker, 1929.

     Inaugural-dissertation - Würzburg.
     "Lebenslauf", at end.

NL 0382298   MH-C ICRL CtY

VOLUME 334

Lindner, Joseph Leicht, 1909–
Hydrothermal experiments with alkali sulphide solutions ... by Joseph Leicht Lindner ... ₍Urbana, Ill., 1939₎
cover-title, p. 537–560. 23½ᵐ.
Thesis (PH. D.)—University of Minnesota, 1937.
Vita.
Caption title: Action of alkali sulphide solutions on minerals at elevated temperatures. ₍By₎ J. L. Lindner and John W. Gruner.
"Reprinted from Economic geology, vol. xxxiv, no. 5, August, 1939."
Bibliographical foot-notes.

1. Sulphides. 2. Mineralogy. 3. Thermochemistry.   I. Gruner, John Walter, 1890–   joint author.
Library of Congress   QD181.S1L53 1937
Univ. of Minnesota Libr.   40–30865
——— Copy 2.   ₍2₎   546.22

NL 0382299   MnU DLC

Lindner (Josephus). *De diabete. 24 pp. 8°.
₍ Monachii, lit. Hübschmannianis, 1810.

NL 0382300   DNLM

Lindner, Julius: Verletzung des Namensrechtes durch Namensgebrauch im Sinne des § 12 BGB. und Namensänderung. ₍Maschinenschrift.₎ IV, 89 S. 4°. — Auszug: Marburg 1923: Friedrich. 2 Bl. 8°
Marburg, Jur. Diss. v. 9. Nov. 1923   [U 23. 8814

NL 0382301   ICRL

Lindner, K   F.
Die privatforstwirtschaft in ihrem wesen, sein und werden. Von K. F. Lindner ... Forstwirtschaftstechnische und andere, die privatforstbetriebe betreffende betrachtungen auf psychologischer grundlage. Eine denkschrift für waldbesitzer, forstleute und volkswirte ... Hannover, M. & H. Schaper, 1928.
xix, 246 p. diagrs. 24½ᵐ.

1. Forests and forestry. ₍1. Forest management₎
                                        Agr 29–819
Library, U. S. Dept. of   Agriculture 99.55L64

NL 0382302   DNAL MH-A WaU MiU

Lindner, Kaete: Ergebnisse der histologischen Untersuchung der Menstruationsabgänge. ₍Maschinenschrift.₎ 54 S. 4°. — Auszug: Breslau 1921: Schatzky. 2 Bl. 8°
Breslau, Med. Diss. v. 10. Jan. 1922   [U 22. 1475

NL 0382303   ICRL

Lindner, Käte, 1872–
Die das Leben meistern, Roman aus Südtirol. Reutlingen, Ensslin ₍1929₎

NL 0382304   PPG

Lindner, Kaete, 1872–
Glueck ohne Ruh. Roman. Reutlingen, Ensslin ₍1929₎
284 p

NL 0382305   PPG

Lindner, Käte, 1872–
Zur schönen königin; roman. Bad Rothenfelde, Holzwarth, [c1924]

NL 0382306   WaSp

Lindner, Karl, 1890–
Geschichte der Allgäuer Milchwirtschaft; 100 Jahre Allgäuer Milch im Dienste der Ernährung. Hrsg. vom Milchwirtschaftlichen Verein im Allgäu und in dessen Auftrag bearb. von Karl Lindner. Kempten, 1955.
582 p. illus. 30 cm.

1. Milk trade—Allgäu. 2. Dairying—Allgäu.   I. Title.

HD9282.G3A44   62–27673 ‡

NL 0382307   DLC DNAL

Lindner, Karl, 1890–
Musik der Millionen, soziale Dichtungen von Tilly Lindner [pseud.] Regensburg, J. Kösel & F. Pustet, 1920.
55 p. port.

NL 0382308   NjP

Lindner, Karl, 1909–
Verletzung der dingpflicht. ... 1935.   40 p.
Inaug. Diss. - Erlangen, 1935.
Lebenslauf.
Bibliography.

NL 0382309   ICRL

Lindner, Karl David, 1883–
Die bestimmung des astigmatismus durch die schattenprobe mit cylindergläsern, von prof. dr. K. Lindner ... Mit 83 zum teil farbigen abbildungen im text. Berlin, S. Karger, 1927.
iv p., 1 l., 111 p. illus., diagrs. 26ᵐ.

1. Astigmatism. 2. Skiascopy. 3. Lenses.
Library of Congress   RE932.L5   27–14306

NL 0382310   DLC ICJ PPC

WW
100
L747L
1952
LINDNER, Karl David, 1883–
Lehrbuch der Augenheilkunde. Wien, Urban & Schwarzenberg, 1952.
xii, 380 p. illus.
1. Eye - Diseases

NL 0382311   DNLM InU PU-Med DeS PU

617.7
L74s
Lindner, Karl David, 1883–
A series of five lectures given at Chicago, Ill., on April 3,9,10,11,12, 1935, before the Chicago ophthalmological society and at Northwestern university medical school. Chicago ₍n. pub., 1935₎
cover-title, 72 l. Q.
Autographic reproduction of typewritten copy.
Maud Fairbairn, reporter.

Contents: 1. Degeneration of the vitreous in relation to glaucoma and retinal detachment.- 2. Retinal detachment.- 3. Trachoma.- 4. Pathology underlying fundus diseases.- 5. Bacteriology of the eye.

NL 0382313   IaU

Lindner, Karl Gunnar, 1901–

Hünefeld, Ehrenfried Günther, *freiherr* von, 1892–1929.
Mein Ostasienflug; der erste weltflug Berlin–Tokio, von E. G. freiherr v. Hünefeld † Vollendet und herausgegeben von Alexander Roechling auf grund von Hünefelds aufzeichnungen und berichten von K. G. Lindner, mit 36 abbildungen. Berlin, Union deutsche verlagsgesellschaft ₍ᶜ1929₎

Lindner, Karl Heinz
Marktordnung u. Marktpolizei.
Inaug. Diss. Breslau, 1929

NL 0382315   DLC

Lindner (Kaspar Gottlieb). *De noxis ex remediis domesticis incongrue applicatis. 3 p. l., 28 pp. sm. 4°. Halæ Magdeb., lit. C. Henckelii, ₍1729₎.

NL 0382316   DNLM

Zg17
L64
743
Lindner, Kaspar Gottlieb
D. Caspar Gottlieb Lindners ... Deutsche Gedichte und Uebersetzungen, mit vielen poetisch- und historischen Anmerkungen, auch alten und höchst seltenen schriftlichen Urkunden versehen. Erste Sammlung. Bresslau, und Leipzig, Verlegts Daniel Pietsch, 1743.
11p.*l.*, 591p. front. 20cm.
Translations include poems by Johann Fechner, Pancras Geier, Valentin Kleinwaechter, and Henricus Closius; Latin and German text on opposite pages.

NL 0382317   CtY NjP CU

FILM
4333
PT
Reel
596
Lindner, Kaspar Gottlieb
D. Caspar Gottlieb Lindners...Deutsche Gedichte und Übersetzungen, mit vielen poetisch- und historischen Anmerkungen, auch alten und höchst seltenen schriftlichen Urkunden versehen. Erste Sammlung. Bresslau, und Leipzig, Verlegts Daniel Pietsch, 1743.
11p.*l.*, 591p. front. 20cm.
Translations include poems by Johann Fechner, Pancras Geier, Valentin Kleinwächter, and Henricus Closius; Latin and German text on opposite pages.
(German Baroque Literature, No.1670, reel No. 596, Research Publications, Inc.)

NL 0382318   CU

Lindner, Kaspar Gottlieb, tr.
D. Kaspar Gottlieb Lindners ... Deutsche Übersetzungen der unvergleichlichen lateinischen Gedichte M. Johann Fechners.
see under   Fechner, Johann, 1604?- 1686.
[Supplement]

Lindner, Kaspar Gottlieb, tr.
M. Joh. Fechneri Aureum carmen de Hortis Hesperidum
see under   Fechner, Johann, 1604?-1686.
[Supplement]

PT1756
.L7
Lindner, Kaspar Gottlieb.
Umständliche nachricht von des weltberühmten Schlesiers, Martin Opitz von Boberfeld, leben, tode und schriften, nebst einigen alten und neuen lobgedichten auf ihn ... Hrsg. von d. Kaspar Gottlieb Lindnern ... Hirschberg, I. Krahn, 1740–41.
2 v. 17ᵐ.
"Christophori Coleri lateinische lobrede auf Martin Opitzen" (followed by German translation) p. ₍35₎–238.

NL 0382321   ICU RPB WU CLU NNC CtY

FILM
4333
PT
Reel
57
Lindner, Kaspar Gottlieb, ed.
Umständliche Nachricht von des weltberühmten Schlesiers, Martin Opitz von Boberfeld, Leben, Tode und Schriften, nebst einigen alten und neuen Lobgedichten auf ihn. Erster₍-Anderer₎ Theil. Herausgegeben von D. Kaspar Gottlieb Lindnern... Hirschberg, druckts und verlegts Immanuel Krahn, 1740–41.
2v. in 1. fold. front. (coat-of-arms) 18cm.
"Von Opitzes gedruckten Schriften": v.2., p.[1]–68.
(German Baroque Literature, No.237a, reel No. 57 Research Publications, Inc.)
Microfilm.

NL 0382322   CU

[Lindner, Kaspar Gottliedb] ed.
Vergnügte und unvergnügte reisen auf das weltberuffene schelsische Riesen-gebirge, welche von 1696 bis 1737 ... von allerhand liebhabern angesteller worden sind ... und mit einigen bekannten und unbekañten historien von dem abentheurlichen Rieben-zahl vergesellschaftet ... Hirschberg, D. Krahn, 1736.
2 v. in 1. illus., fold. pl. 21 cm.
Title in red and black.
1. Riesengebirge - Descr. & trav. I. Title.

NL 0382323   CU CU-W

VOLUME 334

FILM
4333
PT
Reel
596

[Lindner, Kaspar Gottlieb] , ed
Vergnügte und unvergnügte Reisen auf das welt-
beruffne schlesische Riesen-Gebirge, welche von
1696. biss 1737. ... von allerhand Liebhabern ange-
stellet worden sind, die sich...in die...Schnee-
koppen-Bücher...eingeschrieben haben...herausgege-
ben, und mit einigen bekannten und unbekannten Historien von dem abentheurlichen Rieben-Zahl verge-
sellschafftet...Hirschberg, druckt und verlegts
Dietrich Krahn, 1736.
20p.ℓ.,350., 1ℓ.,97,[3]p. illus., fold.plate.
22x17cm.

"Bekannte und unbekannte Historien von...Rieben-
Zahl...von Praetorio, Schwencken, und andern ge-
wehrten Scribenten" has special half-title and
separate paging.
(German Baroque Literature, No.1671, reel No. 596,
Research Publications, Inc.)
Microfilm.

NL 0382325   CU CtY

Lindner, Konrad.
Die zeitliche verteilung der handarbeit in der land-
gutswirtschaft. illus., 6 pl.
Landw. jahrb. bd. 38, p. 421-532.   Berlin, 1909.

1. Agricultural labor. 2. Division of labor.
Agr 9-2474
Library, U. S. Dept. of   Agriculture

NL 0382326   DNAL

Lindner, Konrad, 1868-
see Lindner, Conrad, 1868-

1893-
Lindner, Kurt, Arzt: Cystische Neubildungen im Nasenvorhof.
Ihr Vorkommen u. ihre Entstehung. Aus d. Kl. f. Hals-,
Nasen- u. Ohrenkrankh. d. Univ. Breslau. [In Maschinen-
schrift.] 38 S. 4°(2°). — Auszug: Breslau 1921. 2 Bl. 8°
Breslau, Med. Diss. v. 10. Febr. 1921, Ref. Hinsberg
[Geb. 22. Jan. 93 Breslau; Wohnort: Breslau; Staatsangeh.: Preußen; Vor-
bildung: Friedrichs-G. Breslau Reife 13; Studium: München 1, Breslau 2,
Berlin 6, Leipzig 2, Breslau 3 S.; Coll. 19. Juli 20; Approb. 10. Aug. 20.]
[U 21. 2996]

NL 0382328   ICRL

Lindner, Kurt, 1899-
Textilhilfsmittel und Waschrohstoffe, von Kurt Lindner
unter Mitwirkung von M. Kehren ₍et al.₎, Stuttgart, Wissenschaftliche Verlagsgesellschaft, 1954.
xxiv, 976 p. illus. 24 cm.
Bibliography : p. ₍908₎-946.

1. Textile chemistry.   I. Title.

TS1449.L5
54-24454 rev

NL 0382329   DLC NBC

SK21
L5

Lindner, Kurt, 1906-
La chasse préhistorique, traduit de l'Allemand par le Dr George Montandon ...   Paris,
Payot, 1941.
480 p. illus.,plates. 22cm. (Bibliothèque
scientifique)

"Bibliographie": p.₍469₎-476.

1. Hunting.   I. Montandon, George, 1879-
tr.

NL 0382330   CU

GN
799
H8L5

Lindner, Kurt, 1906-
La chasse préhistorique. Paris, Payot,
1950.
480 p. illus., plates. (Bibliothèque
scientifique)

Bibliography: p. ₍469₎-476.

1. Hunting, Primitive. I. Title.

NL 0382331   ICIU CtY

Lindner, Kurt, 1906-   ed. & tr.
De arte bersandi; ein Traktat des 13. Jahrhunderts ...
see under Guicennans, 13th cent.

LINDNER, KURT, 1906-
Die deutsche Habichtslehre; das Beizbüchlein und
seine Quellen, eingeleitet und hrsg. von Kurt Lindner.
V Berlin, W. de Gruyter, 1955.   275 p. 21cm. (Quellen
und Studien zur Geschichte der Jagd. 2)

"300 Exemplare gedruckt." Nr. 169.

1. Hunting--Germany.   I. Series. II. Title: Das
Beizbüchlein.

NL 0382333   NN CaBVaU NIC NcD OU MH

Lindner, Kurt, 1906-
Geschichte des deutschen weidwerks, von Kurt Lindner ...
Berlin und Leipzig, Walter de Gruyter & co., 1937-
v. illus., plates. 25½cm.
Contains bibliographies.
CONTENTS.—I. Die Jagd der vorzeit.

1. Hunting—Germany.
A C 38-2566
Columbia univ. Library
for Library of Congress   ₍2₎

NL 0382334   NNC CaBVaU MH CtY PBm OCl ICU NN

Lindner, Kurt, 1906-
Die Jagd der Vorzeit. Berlin, De Gruyter,
1937
vi, 435 p. illus. (His Geschichte des deutschen
Weidwerks, 1)

NL 0382335   MH

Lindner, Kurt, 1906-
Die Jagd im frühen Mittelalter. Berlin, De Gruyter,
1940.
477 p. illus. (His Geschichte des deutschen
Weidwerks, 2)

NL 0382336   MH CoFS NNM CtY MnU

SK
21
.L75

Lindner, Kurt, 1906-   ed.
Quellen und Studien zur Geschichte der Jagd.
₍Berlin, W.de Gruyter, 1954-
v. illus.

1.Hunting--Hist. I.Title.

NL 0382337   MiU

Nb10
J41e
v.20

Lindner, Kurt, 1906-
Die Realkreditversorgung der mittleren und
kleinen Industrie nach der Währungserneuerung,
von Dr.Kurt Lindner. Jena, G.Fischer,1929.
x,142p. 24½cm (Abhandlungen des wirtschafts-
wissenschaftlichen Seminars zu Jena,20.Band,
4.Heft.)
Published also as Inaug.-diss. - Jena.
"Literatur," p.₍140₎-142.

NL 0382338   CtY CU MH ICRL PU ICJ MiU

W 4
M96
1950

LINDNER, Kurt, 1921-
Ein Beitrag zum Problem der
Thorotrastschädigung. ₍München₎ 1950.
26 ℓ. illus.
Inaug.-Diss. - Munich.
1. Radiography - Contrast media

NL 0382339   DNLM

701
G373
v.1

LINDNER, Kurt Joachim
Die evangelisch-lutherische Landeskirche
in Sachsen und ihre Landessynode nach der
Verfassung vom 29. Mai 1922. Borna-Leipzig,
Robert Noske, 1929.
viii, 82p. 22cm.

No. 2 in bound volume of church law
pamphlets.
Dissertation - Leipzig.

NL 0382340   MH-AH DLC

Lindner, Lina.
...Neues Kochbuch; 1400 der besten Kochvorschriften, erst-
mals mit Angabe des Vitamin- und Kaloriengehalts und einer
praktischen Aufstellung der Zutaten; neu durchgesehen von
Hanna Supp... 113. Auflage.   Stuttgart: Franck'sche Ver-
lagshandlung₍, 1932₎.   514 p.   illus., 8 col'd pl.   23½cm.

Some pages blank for "Kochrezepte aus eigener Erfahrung."

647070A. 1. Cookery, German.   I. Supp, Hanna, editor.
N. Y. P. L.   June 9, 1933

NL 0382341   NN

Lindner, László.
Sakkmezők népe közt.   Kecskemét [Magyar
Sakkvilág] 1947.
142, [1] p. port.

NL 0382342   OCl

Lindner (Ludovicus Hermannus). *De septi
narium restitutione chirurgica. 20 pp. 4°. Lipsia, typ. G. Staritzii. ₍1844₎.*

NL 0382343   DNLM

NA
6166
.L75

Lindner, Ludwig.
Alte volkstümliche grabmäler aus Norddeutschland.
Eine auswahl ... Text von dr.Ludwig Lindner. El-
berfeld, A.Schöpp [1922]
[4] p.   45 pl.   28 cm.
In portfolio.

NL 0382344   MiU PP CtY NN ViU NBuG

ND588
.G78L7

Lindner, Ludwig.
Ruf aus der Stille; ein Grünewald-Buch. Wuppertal,
Abendland-Verlag, 1949.
247 p. mounted col. illus., 16 plates. 22 cm.
"Literatur": p. 241-248.

1. Grünewald, Mathias, 16th cent.   I. Title.

ND588.G7L5   927   50-16961

NL 0382345   DLC ICU

---

ar W
53075
no.12

Lindner, Ludwig, gynecologist.
Ueber Prolapsus Uteri bei Nulliparen.
Kaiserslautern, H. Kayser, 1896.
34 p. 22cm.

Inaug.-Diss.--Erlangen.

NL 0382346   NIC DNLM ICRL

Lindner, Ludwig, 1772-1845.

See

Lindner, Friedrich Ludwig, 1772-1845.

VOLUME 334

Lindner, Ludwig, 1884-
　　Das bürgerliche Recht der Reichsstadt
Regensburg ... von Ludwig Lindner ...
Regensburg, R. Neuhaus, 1908.

　　3 p.l., 71 p.　22cm.
　　Inaug.-diss. - Erlangen.
　　"Literatur": p.1-2.

NL　0382348　　MH-L NIC MH NN ICRL

---

ar W　　Lindner, Ludwig, 1888-
54392　　　　Ein Fall von Tuberkulose der platten
no.7　　Schädelknochen mit Kompression des Gehirns
　　durch tuberkulöse Granulationen.　Erlangen,
　　Druck von E. T. Jacob, 1913.
　　　　21 p.　22cm.

　　　　Inaug.-Diss.--Erlangen.

NL　0382349　　NIC DNLM CtY ICRL

Lindner, Ludwig Max Friedrich
　　see　Lindner, Max, 1863-

Lindner, Manfred.
　　Über die seelischen Abläufe in Lebensgefahr; eine psychologische Untersuchung des Ertrinkungsvorganges.　[Er-
langen] 1944.
　　55 p.　21 cm.
　　Inaug.-Diss.—Erlangen.
　　Bibliography: p. 53-55.

　　1. Drowning—Psychological aspects.

　　BF789.D7L5　　　　　　　　　　51-53466

NL　0382351　　DLC NIC CtY CtY-M

W 4　　LINDNER, Manfred
E69　　　　Über die Verstehbarkeit des Geistes-
1944　　kranken; Versuch einer theoretischen
　　Orientierung des Verstehensproblems
　　in der Psychiatrie.　[Erlangen] 1944.
　　　　60 p.
　　　　Inaug.-Diss. - Erlangen.
　　　　1. Communication 2. Mental disorders

NL　0382352　　DNLM

QD466　　Lindner, Manfred, 1919-
L5　　　　Nuclear reactions in antimony with high
　　energy particles.　[Berkeley, Calif., 1948.
　　[2], 71 l. diagrs., tables.
　　　　Thesis (Ph.D.) - Univ. of California, Sept.
1948.
　　Bibliography: p.70-71.

　　1. Antimony. 2. Isotopes.

NL　0382353　　CU

Lindner, Maria: Heimstaetten.
　　— Auszug: o. O. u. J.　2 Bl.　8°
　　Bonn, Phil. Diss. v. 9. März 1923 [1924]　　　　[U 24. 1305

NL　0382354　　ICRL

Lindner, Marie Margarete, 1910-
　　... Beobachtungen über Arthrosis deformans
am Kiefergelenk und ihre chirurgische Behandlung
nach dem Material der Eppendorfer Klinik ...
[Hamburg] 1934.
　　Inaug.-Diss. - Hamburg.
　　Lebenslauf.
　　"Literatur-Verzeichnis": p. 15.

NL　0382355　　CtY

LINDNER, Martin, 1900-
　　Die kredittheorie von Henry Dunning Macleod.
Görlitz, A.-G. Görlitzer nachrichten und anzeiger,
1929.

　　Inaugural-dissertation - Freiburg im Breisgau.
　　"Lebenslauf", p.107.

NL　0382356　　MH CtY MiU PU ICRL

Lindner, Max.
　　Der Blitzschutz.　Praktische Anleitung zur Projektierung, Herstellung und Prüfung von Gebäude-Blitzableitern jeder Art auf
Grund der neueren Anschauungen über das Wesen der Blitzent-
ladungen. iv, [4], 176 p. 142 il. D. Leipzig: O. Leiner, 1901.

NL　0382357　　ICJ

HQ　　LINDNER, Max
L747g　　　　Goldenes Buch für Eheleute; ein
1911　　Buch über Ehefragen.　Dresden,
　　Rudolph [1911]
　　　　126 p. illus.

NL　0382358　　DNLM

PA　　LINDNER, Max
2092　　　　Das Latinum des Dentisten, mit einer
L747L　　Einführung in die griechische Sprache.
1950　　München, Pflaum, 1950.
　　　　228 p.
　　　　1. Greek language - Medical & scientific
　　Greek 2. Latin language - Grammar
　　3. Latin language - Medical & scientific
　　Latin

NL　0382359　　DNLM

Lindner, Max, engineer
　　Die elektricität im dienste von gewerbe
und industrie.　Von Max Lindner ...　Leipzig,
G. Knapp, 1883.
　　29 p. incl. tables.　22cm.

　　1. Electric apparatus and appliances.

Library, U.S. Patent Office.　　TK148.L747

NL　0382360　　DP

Lindner, Max, engineer
　　Leitfaden der praktischen haustelegraphie. Das
wissenswertheste aus dem gebiete der haustelegraphie, insbesondere die herstellung, unterhaltung und
reparatur elektrischer telegraphen-einrichtungen.
Für mechaniker, uhrmacher, schlosser und verwandte
berufszweige bearbeitet von Max Lindner...　Halle
a.S., W. Knapp, 1889.
　　ivp., 1 l., 72p. illus.　21 1/2cm.

　　1. Electric bells.　　2. Telephone.

Library, U.S. Patent Office.　　TK7109.L747

NL　0382361　　DP

Lindner, Max, engineer
　　Leitfaden der praktischen Haustelegraphie.　Das Wissenswertheste aus dem Gebiete der Haustelegraphie, insbesondere die
Herstellung, Unterhaltung und Reparatur elektrischer Haustelegra-
phen, Fernsprech- und Sprachrohr-Anlagen.　Für Mechaniker,
Uhrmacher, Schlosser und verwandte Berufszweige.　Zweite vermehrte und verbesserte Auflage.　vi. [2], 90 p. 153 il. O.　Halle
a. S.: W. Knapp, 1900.

NL　0382362　　ICJ

Lindner, Max, engineer
　　Schaltungsbuch für Schwachstrom-Anlagen.　179 Schaltungs-
und Stromverlaufsskizzen mit erläuterndem Text für Hauustele-
graphen- und Signalanlagen, Fernsprechanlagen, Wasserstands-
melde-, Sicherheits-, Feuermelde- und Kontrollanlagen, elektrische
Uhren und Elementbeleuchtung.　Nebst einem Anhang mit
Tabellen.　Zusammengestellt von Max Lindner, ...　Fünfte,
vermehrte und verbesserte Auflage.　Leipzig, Hachmeister &
Thal, 1905.
　　xii, 234 p. 146 diagrs. 184cm.

NL　0382363　　ICJ

Lindner, Max, engineer
　　Die Technik des Blitzableiters.　Anleitung zur Herstellung
und Prüfung von Blitzableiteranlagen auf Gebäuden jeder Art für
Architekten, Baubeamte und Gewerbetreibende, die sich mit
Anlegung und Prüfung von Blitzableitern beschäftigen.　Hrsg.
von Max Lindner...　Weimar: B. F. Voigt, 1892.　viii, 82 p.
illus.　8°.　(Neuer Schauplatz der Künste und Handwerke
... Bd. 32.)

1. Lightning conductors. 2. Series.
N. Y. P. L.　　　　　　　　　　September 20, 1924

NL　0382364　　NN DAS

Lindner, Max, father
　　see his name in religion　　　　Lindner,
　　　　Benedikt.

WBC　　LINDNER, Max, 1863-
L747t　　　　Thure Brandt'sche Massage und
1904　　Gymnastik sowie Wasserbehandlung und
　　Pflege bei weiblichen Unterleibszuständen;
　　Handbuch für Ausübende der physikalisch-
　　diätetischen Heilweise, besonders auch
　　für Masseure und Masseusen.　Dresden,
　　Pierson, 1904.
　　　　200 p. illus.

NL　0382366　　DNLM PPC

QD319　　Lindner, Max, 1863-
.L76　　　　Ueber die einwirkung von chlor auf dimethyl-
　　kohlensaeureester und untersuchung von vier
　　chlorsubstitutionsproducten desselben.
　　Heidelberg, 1894.
　　　　42p.
　　　　Inaug. diss.　Erlangen.

NL　0382367　　DLC DNLM PU

HD660　　Lindner, Max, 1900-
H2L747　　　　Die bodenpolitik der stadt Halle (Saale) von
　　1870 bis zum frühjahr 1933 ...　Halle (Saale) E.
　　Klinz buchdruck-werkstätten, 1937.

　　　　190 p., 1 l. incl. tables.　23cm.
　　　　Inaug.-diss. - Halle.
　　　　Lebenslauf.
　　　　"Quellen": p. 189-190.

　　　　1. Real property - Halle. 2. Land - Taxation
　　- Halle. 3. Halle　　　　- Public works. I. Title.

NL　0382368　　CSt-H MiU CtY

LINDNER, Max Willy.
　　Kakao und Kakaoerzeugnisse.　Berlin, A. W. Hayn's
Erben, 1953.　152 p. illus. 22cm. (Grundlagen und Fortschritte
der Lebensmitteluntersuchung, Bd. 1)

　　Bibliography, p. 142-146.

　　1. Chocolate and cocoa as food.　　I. Series.

NL　0382369　　NN InLP

VOLUME 334

LINDNER, Max Willy.
Warenkunde und Untersuchung von Kaffee, Kaffee-
Ersatz- und- Zusatzstoffen. Berlin, A.W. Hayn's
Erben, 1955. 156 p. illus., map. 22cm. (Grundlagen und
Fortschritte der Lebensmitteluntersuchung. Bd.3)

Bibliography, p. 143-151.

1. Coffee. I. Series.

NL 0382370   NN DNLM NIC ICJ

SH234
C39
1954t
no.13
Lindner, Milton Jerome, 1908–
Crecimiento, mortalidad y pesca excesiva.
[n.p.] Organización de las Naciones Unidas para
la Agricultura y la Alimentación [1954?]
[1], 33 l. diagrs., tables. 33 cm.
(Centro Latinoamericano de Capacitación Pesquera,
2d, México, 1954. Textos. T–13)
At head of title: ... Textos: Biología.
Bibliography: l. [.] –33.

1. Fishes – Growth. 2. Fishes – Mortality. 3. Fisheries. I. Title.   (Series)

NL 0382371   DI

Lindner, Milton Jerome, 1908–
Estimation of growth rate in animals by marking experi-
ments. Washington, U. S. Govt. Print. Off., 1953.
65–69 p. diagrs. 27 cm. (U. S. Fish and Wildlife Service.
Fishery bulletin, 78)
"From Fishery bulletin of the Fish and Wildlife Service, volume
54."
"Literature cited": p. 68.

1. Growth. 2. Graphic methods.   (Series)

SH11.A25 no. 78   591.134   53–63331

NL 0382372   DLC PP DI

SH11
.C27
no. 25
Lindner, Milton Jerome, 1908–

California. State fisheries laboratory.
... Fishing areas along the California coast for the sardine
(*Sardina caerulea*), by the California state fisheries labora-
tory ... [Sacramento, California state print. off., 1930]

Lindner, Milton Jerome, 1908–   joint author

Weymouth, Frank Walter, 1884–
... Preliminary report on the life history of the common
shrimp *Penaeus setiferus* (*Linn.*) by F. W. Weymouth, Milton J. Lindner and W. W. Anderson ... Washington, U. S.
Govt. print. off., 1933.

Lindner, Milton Jerome, 1908–   joint author.

Johnson, Fred Francis, 1898–
... Shrimp industry of the south Atlantic and Gulf states,
with notes on other domestic and foreign areas, by Fred F.
Johnson and Milton J. Lindner. Washington, U. S. Govt.
print. off., 1934.

HD9464
87L5
Lindner, Milton Jerome, 1908–
Survey of markets for fishery products in
South America – 1950, by Milton J. Lindner
and Robert O. Smith. [Washington? 1950].
63 l. tables (part fold.) 27 cm.
Typewritten (carbon copy).

1. Fish trade – Latin America. 2. Market
surveys – Latin America. I. Smith, Robert
Otto, 1903–   , jt. auth. I. Title.

NL 0382376   DI

Lindner, Oscar Eduard, 1847–
Über *Echinococcus* der leber ... Leipzig, Druck von
C. G. Naumann [1869]
14, [2] p. 21cm.
Inaug.-diss—Leipzig.
Vita.

1. Liver, Hydatids of.

Library of Congress   RC242.L74   6–22567†

NL 0382377   DLC DNLM ICRL

Lindner, Otto
Teophrastus Paracelsus als bekaempfer des
Pabstthums. Mitgetheilt und seinem freunde
Johannes Ronge gewidmet. Lpz., Koehler, 1845.
31 p

NL 0382378   PU

1886–
Lindner, Otto] Über Trypsinkaseinpepton. Weida i.Th. 1910:
Thomas & Hubert. 76 S. 8°
Leipzig, Phil. Diss. v. 14. Juni 1910, Ref. Beckmann, Hantzsch
[Geb. 20. März 86 Fichtelberg; Wohnort: Fichtelberg; Staatsangeh.: Bayern;
Vorbildung: Gewerbeakad. Chemnitz Reife 06; Studium: Aachen Techn.
Hochsch. 2, Leipzig 5 S.; Rig. 10. Mai 10.]   [U 10. 3184]

NL 0382379   ICRL CtY OCU PU

Lindner, Paul.
Ueber begrenzte ableitungen mit komplexem
zeiger. Cöslin, 1890.

NL 0382380   NjP

Lindner, Paul, 1861–
Alkohol in der natur; eine naturwissenschaftliche vorlesung
für die alkoholgegner, von professor dr. Paul Lindner ...
Hannover, Norddeutsches druck- und verlagshaus [1927]
27 p. 21cm.
"Nach einem auf der 89. versammlung der 'Gesellschaft deutscher
naturforscher und aerzte' in Düsseldorf 1926 gehaltenen vortrag."

1. Alcohol.

Library of Congress   HV5037.L5   27–13630
                            34050

NL 0382381   DLC

Lindner, Paul, 1861–
Anwendung der photographie bei hefeuntersuchungen. Von
P. Lindner ...
(*In* Abderhalden, Emil, ed. Handbuch der biologischen arbeits-
methoden ... Berlin, 1920–   25cm. abt. XII, Leistungen der
niederen organismenwelt. t. 1 (1925) p. [285]–288. illus.)

1. Yeast.
                                        A C 36–4067
Title from Ohio State   Univ.
Library of Congress   [QH324.A3 1920 abt. 12, t. 1]
                        [2]   (574.072)

NL 0382382   OU

Lindner, Paul, 1861–
Atlas der mikroskopischen grundlagen der gärungskunde mit besonderer berücksichtigung der biologischen
betriebskontrolle. Von professor dr. Paul Lindner ...
111 tafeln mit 418 einzelbildern. Berlin, P. Parey, 1903.
9 p., 1 l. 111 pl. 24½cm.

1. Micro-organisms in fermentation. 2. Yeast. 3. Bacteria.

Library of Congress   TP515.L74   3–26424

NL 0382383   DLC DNLM ICJ ICRL

Lindner, Paul, 1861–
Atlas der mikroskopischen Grundlagen der Gärungskunde mit besonderer Berücksichtigung der biologischen Betriebskontrolle,
von Dr. Paul Lindner, ... Zweite, vermehrte Auflage. 168
Tafeln mit 578 Einzelbildern. Berlin, P. Parey, 1910.
27 p. 168 pl. 24½cm.

NL 0382384   ICJ CU

Lindner, Paul, 1861–
Atlas der mikroskopischen grundlagen der gärungskunde
mit besonderer berücksichtigung der biologischen betriebskontrolle, von professor dr. Paul Lindner ... 3., neubearb.
aufl. ... Berlin, P. Parey, 1927–28.
2 v. 322 pl. 24½cm.

1. Fermentation. 2. Yeast. 3. Bacteria.

Library of Congress   QR151.L7 1927   29–13273

NL 0382385   DLC CtY

LINDNER, Paul, 1861–
Beitrage zur naturgeschichte der alkoholischen Garung. Berlin, Franken, 1920.

28 pp. Illus. 26 cm.

NL 0382386   MBCo

Lindner, Paul, 1861–   joint author

Euler-Chelpin, Hans Karl August Simon von, 1873–
Chemie der hefe und der alkoholischen gärung, von dr. Hans
Euler ... und dr. Paul Lindner ... Mit 2 kunstdrucktafeln und
zahlreichen textabbildungen. Leipzig, Akademische verlagsgesellschaft m. b. h., 1915.

QP501
.C4
Lindner, Paul, 1861–   ed.

Chemie der Zelle und Gewebe. Bd. 1–13, Heft 2; 1912–
Sept. 1926. Leipzig, Gebrüder Borntraeger.

Q
162
L74
Lindner, Paul, 1861–
Entdeckte Verborgenheiten aus dem
Alltagsgetriebe des Mikrokosmos. Berlin,
P. Parey, 1923.
291 p. illus. 25 cm.

1. Science. 2. Micro-organisms.
I. Title.

NL 0382389   NIC ICRL NcD PPEC

Lindner, Paul, 1861–
Methoden der bestimmung der hefezellvermehrung. Von P.
Lindner ...
(*In* Abderhalden, Emil, ed. Handbuch der biologischen arbeits-
methoden ... Berlin, 1920–   25cm. abt. XII, Leistungen der
niederen organismenwelt. t. 1 (1925) p. [275]–284. illus., diagrs.)
Bibliographical foot-notes.

1. Yeast.
                                        A C 36–4066
Title from Ohio State   Univ.
Library of Congress   [QH324.A3 1920 abt. 12, t. 1]
                        [2]   (574.072)

NL 0382390   OU

VOLUME 334

Lindner, Paul, 1861–
Methoden zur sichtbarmachung von fett in hefen und in zellen höherer pflanzen. Von P. Lindner ...

(*In* Abderhalden, Emil, ed. Handbuch der biologischen arbeitsmethoden ... Berlin, 1920– 25^{cm}. abt. XII. Leistungen der niederen organismenwelt. t. 1 (1925) p. ₍289₎–294. illus.)

1. Yeast. 2. Fat.
Title from Ohio State   Univ.   A C 36–4068
Library of Congress   [QH324.A3 1920 abt. 12, t. 1]
                                    ₍2₎   (574.072)

NL 0382391   UU

Lindner, Paul, 1861–
Mikroskopische Betriebskontrolle in den Gärungsgewerben, mit einer Einführung in die Hefenreinkultur, Infektionslehre und Hefenkunde, für Studierende und Praktiker, bearbeitet von Dr. Paul Lindner ... Berlin, P. Parey, 1895.

ix, 278, 3 p. illus., plates, tables, diagrs. 25^{cm}.

NL 0382392   ICJ PU MH InU

Lindner, Paul, 1861–
Mikroskopische Betriebskontrolle in den Gärungsgewerben mit einer Einführung in die Hefenreinkultur, Infektionslehre und Hefenkunde. .... Zweite, neubearbeitete Auflage. x,365 p. 156 il. 4 pl. 2 tables. Q. Berlin: P. Parey, 1898.

NL 0382393   ICJ

Lindner, Paul, 1861–
Mikroskopische Betriebskontrolle in den Gärungsgewerben mit einer Einführung in die technische Biologie, Hefenreinkultur und Infektionslehre. Für Studierende und Praktiker bearbeitet. Dritte, neubearbeitete Auflage. xii,468 p. 229 il. 4 pl. 2 tables. O. Berlin: P. Parey, 1901.

NL 0382394   ICJ PPF MH

Lindner, Paul, 1861–
Mikroskopische betriebskontrolle in den gärungsgewerben, mit einer einführung in die technische biologie, hefenreinkultur und infektionslehre. Für studierende und praktiker bearb. von prof. dr. Paul Lindner ... 4. neubearb. aufl. Mit 257 textabbildungen und 4 tafeln. Berlin, P. Parey, 1905.

viii, 521 p. illus., iv pl., 2 tab. 24½^{cm}.

1. Yeast. 2. Fermentation. 3. Brewing. 4. Microscope and microscopy.

Library of Congress   QR151.L74   5–18764

NL 0382395   DLC NIC ICJ

Lindner, Paul, 1861–
Mikroskopische betriebskontrolle in den gärungsgewerben mit einer einführung in die technische biologie, hefenreinkultur und infektionslehre. Für studierende und praktiker bearb. von prof. dr. Paul Lindner ... 5. neubearb. aufl. ... Berlin, P. Parey, 1909.

viii, 574 p. illus., iv pl., 11 double tab. 24½^{cm}.

1. Yeast. 2. Fermentation. 3. Brewing. 4. Microscope and microscopy.
U. S. Dept. of agr. Library   390L64M   Agr 9–2806
for Library of Congress   ₍a38b1₎

NL 0382396   DNAL CU ICJ MH

Lindner, Paul, 1861–
Mikroskopische und biologische betriebskontrolle in den gärungsgewerben mit besonderer berücksichtigung der brauerei, zugleich eine einführung in die technische biologie, hefenreinkultur, infektionslehre und allgemeine gärungskunde, für technische biologen, chemiker, mediziner, studierende und praktiker, bearbeitet von prof. dr. Paul Lindner ... 6., neubearb. aufl. Mit 324 textabbildungen. Berlin, P. Parey, 1930.

xvi, 692 p. illus., tables (2 fold.) diagrs. 24^{cm}. (*Half-title:* Pareys bücherei für chemische technologie ... 5. bd.)

1. Yeast. 2. Fermentation. 3. Brewing. 1. Title.
                                                         P O 31–4
Library, U. S. Patent   Office QR151.L94 1930

NL 0382397   DP IU ICJ

Lindner, Paul, 1861–
Landolt, Hans Heinrich, 1831–1910.
The optical rotating power of organic substances and its practical applications, by Doctor Hans Landolt ... assisted by Dr. O. Schönrock, Dr. P. Lindner, Dr. F. Schütt, Dr. L. Berndt, and Dr. T. Posner. 2d ed. Authorized English translation with additions by Dr. John H. Long ... Easton, Pa., The Chemical publishing co., 1902.

Lindner, Paul, 1861–
Landolt, Hans Heinrich, 1831–1910.
Das optische drehungsvermögen organischer substanzen und dessen praktische anwendungen, bearb. von dr. H. Landolt ... unter mitwirkung von dr. O. Schönrock, dr. P. Lindner, dr. F. Schütt, dr. L. Berndt, dr. T. Posner. 2. gänzlich umgearb. aufl. ... Braunschweig, F. Vieweg und sohn, 1898.

Lindner, Paul, 1861–
Photographie ohne kamera, von prof. dr. Paul Lindner ... Berlin, Union deutsche verlagsgesellschaft, 1920.

2 p. L, ₍7₎–58, ₍2₎ p. 16 pl., diagr., plan. 20^{cm}. (Photographische bibliothek, bd. 29)

Plates printed on both sides of the leaf.

1. Photography. 1. Title.
                                                         Agr 21–111
Library, U. S. Dept. of   Agriculture 332L64

NL 0382400   DNAL ICJ

P589.95
O802
Lindner, Paul, 1861–
Die Sarcina-Organismen der Gährungs-Gewerbe ... von Paul Lindner ... Berlin, Gebr. Unger, 1888.

59 p. diagrs. 19^{cm}.
Inaug.-Diss.—Berlin. Universität.

NL 0382401   ICJ MH ICRL

589.2
L646s
Lindner, Paul, 1861–
Schimmelbildung und Verhütung. Berlin, Verlag der "Tageszeitung für Brauerei", 1904.
47p. illus. 21cm.

"Volkstümlicher Vortrag, gehalten am 13. Oktober 1905 auf der Oktobertagung der Versuchs- und Lehranstalt für Brauerei in Berlin."

1. Molds (Botany) 2. Fungi.

NL 0382402   TxU

Lindner, Paul, 1861–
Eine stichprobe aus dem gebiet der momentmikrophotographie. illus.
Landw. jahrb. bd. 38, suppl. 5, p. 337–339.   Berlin, 1909.

1. Microphotography.
                                                         Agr 9–1957
Library, U. S. Dept. of   Agriculture

NL 0382403   DNAL NN

Lindner, Paul, 1861–
Über die mutationen bei hefen und schimmelpilzen. Von P. Lindner ...

(*In* Abderhalden, Emil, ed. Handbuch der biologischen arbeitsmethoden ... Berlin, 1920– 25^{cm}. abt. XII. Leistungen der niederen organismenwelt. t. 1 (1925) p. ₍295₎–298. illus.)

Bibliographical foot-notes.

1. Yeast. 2. Hyphomycetes.
                                                         A C 36–4069
Title from Ohio State   Univ.
Library of Congress   [QH324.A3 1920 abt. 12, t. 1]
                                    ₍2₎   (574.072)

NL 0382404   OU

Lindner, Paul, 1885–
Beitrag zur kasuistik ueber die akute eitrige osteomyelitis der patella.
Inaug. Diss.   Rostock, 1918
Bibl.

NL 0382405   ICRL CtY

Lindner, Paul, 1920–
Die Posten der Rechnungsabgrenzung in der DM-Eröffnungsbilanz (steuerrichtliche ₍sic₎ Untersuchung) München, 1951.
iv, 71 l. 30 cm.
Typescript (carbon copy)
Inaug.-Diss.—Munich.
Vita.
Bibliography: leaves iii–iv.
1. Accounting—Law—Germany (Federal Republic, 1949–   ) 2. Revalorization of debts—Germany (Federal Republic, 1949–   ) 3. Tax accounting—Germany (Federal Republic, 1949–   ) 4. Financial statements. 1. Title.

                                                         56–15112

NL 0382406   DLC

Lindner, Pirminius August, 1848–1912.
Die Äbte und Mönche der Benediktiner-Abtei Tegernsee ...
          see his   Familia S. Quirini in Tegernsee.

BX2618
T44L5
Lindner, *Pirminius August,* 1848–1912.
Familia S. Quirini in Tegernsee. Die Äbte und Mönche der Benediktiner-Abtei Tegernsee, von den ältesten Zeiten bis zu ihrem Aussterben (1861) und ihr literarischer Nachlass. München, Verlag des Histor. Vereins von Oberbayern, in Kommission bei G. Franz, 1897–98.
2 v. in 1.

"Sonderabdruck aus dem 50. Bande des Oberbayerischen Archives des Historischen Vereines von Oberbayern."

1. Tegernsee, Ger. (Benedictine abbey) – Hist.

NL 0382408   CU KAS

LINDNER, *Pirminius August,* 1848–1912.
Fünf Professbücher süddeutscher Benediktiner-Abteien: Beiträge zu einem Monasticon-benedictum Germaniae. Kempton, Commissions-Verlag von J. Kösel, 1909.
5 v. in 1. 28cm.

Includes bibliographies; also includes biographies and lists of works of the members of the monasteries.
CONTENTS.—1. Wessobrunn.—2. Weingarten.—3. Zwiefalten.—

4. Benediktbeuern.—5. Petershausen.

1. Wessobrunn, Bavaria (Benedictine abbey). 2. Weingarten, Germany, Würtemberg (Benedictine abbey). 3. Zwiefalten, Germany (Benedictine abbey). 4. Benediktbeuern,   Germany (Benedictine abbey). 5. Petershausen, Constance,   Germany (Benedictine abbey). 6. Benedictines—Germany.

NL 0382410   NN InStme CtY

VOLUME 334

Lindner, Pirminius August, 1848-1912.
Gallia Benedictina; oder, Uebersicht der
am Beginne des XVIII. Jahrhunderts bis zum
Ausbruche der französichen Revolution (1789)
in Frankreich noch bestandenen Männer- und
Frauen- Abteien des Benediktiner-Ordens.
Kampten und München, J. Koesel, 1909.
vii,62p. 29cm.

NL 0382411   InStme

Lindner, Pirminius August, 1848-1912.
Monasticon episcopatus Augustani antiqui.
Verzeichnisse aller Aebte, Pröpste und Aeb-
tissen der Klöster der alten Diözese Augsburg.
Bregens, J. N. Teutsch, 1913.
17hp. 30cm.
With this is bound: Lindner, P. Monasticon
metropolis Salzburgensis antiquae. Supplementum. Bregens, 1913.

NL 0382412   InStme

LINDNER, PIRMINIUS August, 1848-1912.
Monasticon metropolis Salzburgensis antiquae. Verzeichnisse aller
Aebte und Pröpste der Klöster der alten Kirchenprovinz Salzburg.
Salzburg, Druck von A. Pustet, Kommissionsverlag der J. Kösel'sche
Buchhandlung, Kempten, 1908.   xiii, 554, 48 p.   30cm.
Issued in 2 parts. Pt. 1 has special t. -p. with imprint: Kempten,
J. Kösel, 1907.
Includes bibliographies.
—— Supplementum. Verzeichnisse der Aebte und Pröpste der
Klöster der jetzigen Erzdiözese Wien, nebst Nachträgen und Berichtigungen
Bregens, 1913.
Bound with above.
Includes bibliographies.
1. Monasteries — Austria —   Salzburg.

NL 0382413   NN KAS InStme MH

Lindner, Pirminius August, 1848-1912.

Oberbayerisches archiv für vaterländische geschichte. Herausgegeben von dem Historischen vereine von Oberbayern.
1.—   bd. München, 1839-

Lindner, Pirminius August, 1848-1912.
Professbuch der Benediktiner-Abtei St. Peter
in Salzburg (1419-1856). Salzburg, Buchdruckerei
Ringlschwendtner & Rathmayr, 1906.
328 p.   24 cm.

1. Salzburg, Austria. St. Peter (Benedictine
abbey) - Registers. I. Title.
BX7082.A55L5

NL 0382415   KAS MH

Lindner, Pirminius August, 1848-1912.
Die schriftsteller und die um wissenschaft
und kunst verdienten mitglieder des Benediktiner-
Ordens im heutigen Königreich Bayern vom jahre
1750 bis zur gegenwart... Regensburg, G. Manz,
1880.
2v in 1 23 1/2cm

NL 0382416   MnCS

Lindner, Richard.
Die landeshypothekar-institute und die landwirtschaft-
liche entschuldung. Von dr. Richard Lindner ... Aus
dem böhmischen übersetzt vom verfasser. Prag, Selbstverlag, in kommission der buchhandlung Fr. Řivnáč,
1907.
63, [1] p. 24cm.

1. Agricultural credit—Bohemia. 2. Mortgage banks—Bohemia. I. Title.

Library of Congress   HG2051.A9B7   15-9801

NL 0382417   DLC

HJ2687
L747
Lindner, Richard P
Steuern, steuern .... herr reichsfinanz-
minister? Es gibt auch andere wege; vorschläge
zum umbau der steuer- und finanzpolitik
Deutschlands, von Richard P. Lindner.   Berlin
[Druck: Deutscher schriftenverlag] 1930.
12 p.   22½cm.

1.Taxation - Germany. 2.European war, 1914-
1918 - Reparations. 3.Finance - Germany.
I.Title.

NL 0382418   CSt-H MH CtY

4HJ
23
Lindner, Richard P
Wider Schacht, finanzhistorische
Aufklärungen.

NL 0382419   DLC-P4

Lindner, Robert, Ritter von.
Das Eingreifen der Götter in die Handlung der
Ilias.   Böhm, 1882.
Programm - Gymnasium Landskron im Böhm.
Lacks t.-p.

NL 0382420   CtY

Lindner, Robert Clement, 1913-
... Factors affecting regeneration of the horseradish root ...
by Robert C. Lindner ... [Lancaster, Pa.,1940]
1 p. l., p. 161-181. illus., diagrs. 26cm.
Thesis (PH. D.)—University of Chicago, 1939.
"Contributions from the Hull botanical laboratory no. 513."
"Private edition, distributed by the University of Chicago libraries,
Chicago, Illinois."
"Reprinted from Plant physiology, vol. 15, January, 1940."
"Literature cited" : 180-181.
1. Regeneration (Botany) 2. Roots (Botany) 3. Horse-radish.
Library of Congress   QK840.L56 1940   40-35975
Univ. of Chicago Libr.
—— Copy 2.   [2]   581.1657

NL 0382421   ICU DLC

HV6080
.S36
Lindner, Robert Mitchell, 1914-   joint ed.

Seliger, Robert Victor, 1900-   ed.
Contemporary criminal hygiene, a sourcebook edited by Rob-
ert V. Seliger, M. D., Edwin J. Lukas, LL. B. [and] Robert M.
Lindner, PH. D. [Baltimore] Oakridge press, 1946.

NL 0382425   DLC KEmT CSt LU DNLM NN FMU OOxM OU OCl
PP ICJ DAU GU NBuU OClW-H CaBVaU IdPI Wa

Lindner, Robert Mitchell, 1914-   ed.
Explorations in psychoanalysis; essays in honor of Theodor Reik, on the occasion of his sixty-fifth birthday, May
12, 1953. Robert Lindner, editor; Clement Staff, associate
editor. Advisory editorial committee: Gisela Schwaetzer-
Barinbaum [and others] New York, Julian Press [1953]
xiii, 308 p. Illus., port. 25 cm.
Includes bibliographies. "Bibliography of Theodor Reik (1911-
1952) compiled and annotated by Henry Walter Brann": p. 289-296.
CONTENTS.—Theodor Reik, by J. C. Gustin.—General and theoretical problems: Within the pleasure principle, by J. Nydes. Good gifts
to share, by R. P. Berkeley. Thought control and confession compul-
sion, by J. A. M. Meerloo. Psychodynamics and cognition, by E.
Frenkel-Brunswick.—Special studies: On symbolism and the genesis
of ornamentation, by A. Garma. Recall and distortion of legendary
material in the course of psychoanalysis, by M. S. Bergmann. Dame
Holle, dream and folk tale, by G. Roheim.—Literature and art: Reik
and the interpretation of literature, by A. B. Feldman. The reader
and the writer, by B. K. Ephron. On artistic production, by F. J.
Hacker. The psychoanalyst looks at contemporary art, by F. Alexander.—Clinical and therapeutic studies: Psychological distance as
a factor in the treatment of a schizophrenic patient, by M. Wexler.
Psychoanalytic notes on the paranoid personality, by C. F. Sulzberger.
False confessions, by M. Frym. The psychodynamics of gambling,
by R. Lindner.—Technique and training: Training the third ear, by
M. Grotjahn. On current trends in psychoanalytic training, by R.
Ekstein. Wir Schueler Riek's, by E. Frankel. Background and aims
of the National Psychological Association for Psychoanalysis, by G.
Schwaetzer-Barinbaum.

1. Reik, Theodor, 1888-   2. Psychoanalysis—Addresses, essays,
lectures. I. Title.
BF173.R44L5   131.3404   54-340

WM
460
L747:
1954
Lindner, Robert Mitchell, 1914-
The fifty-minute hour, a collection of
true psychoanalytic tales. Introd. by Max
Lerner. New York, Bantam Books [c1954]
xiii, 207 p.

1. Psychoanalysis - Cases, clinical reports,
statistics. 2. Psychiatry - Cases, clinical
reports, statistics. I. Title.

NL 0382426   WaU KMK MtBC IEG

Lindner, Robert Mitchell, 1914-
The fifty-minute hour: a collection of true psychoanalytic
tales. Introd. by Max Lerner. New York, Rinehart [1955,
°1954]
296 p. 21 cm.

1. Psychoanalysis—Cases, clinical reports, statistics.   I. Title.

RC501.L5   *616.89   54—9863 ‡

PSC NcC TxU NN ViU TU NcD OCl MoU OCU OClW MiU DNLM
OrAshS CaBVa WaS AU CoU PPD PSt OClW OOxM OU PP PPL
NL 0382427   DLC IdU NBuC Wa IdPI WaTC OrP Or CaBViP

Lindner, Robert Mitchell, 1914-
A functional study of emotion.
[Ithaca, N. Y.] 1938.
59 l. illus. 28cm.

Thesis (Ph. D.)--Cornell University,
August, 1938.

1. Emotion.

NL 0382428   NIC

Lindner, Robert Mitchell, 1914-   ed.
Handbook of correctional psychology, edited by Robert M.
Lindner, PH. D. and Robert V. Seliger, M. D. New York, Philo-
sophical library [1947]
8 p. l., 691 p. diagrs. 22cm.
Includes bibliographies.
1. Crime and criminals. 2. Criminal psychology. 3. Psychiatry. I.
Seliger, Robert Victor, 1900-   joint ed. II. Title: Correctional psy-
chology.
HV6080.L64   364.34   47-4509

MsSM NcD TxU ICU PSt CU
NL 0382429   DLC CaBVaU OrCS OrU CaBVa Wa CtY-M NcU

BF1400
.L748
Lindner, Robert Mitchell, 1914-
The jet-propelled couch, and other true
psychoanalytic tales. Introd. by Max Lerner.
London, Secker & Warburg, 1955.
272 p.

1. Psychoanalysis—Cases, clinical reports,
statistics. I. Title.

NL 0382430   ICU

Lindner, Robert Mitchell, 1914-
Prescription for rebellion. New York, Rinehart [1952]
305 p. 22 cm.
Includes bibliography.

1. Psychoanalysis. I. Title.

BF173.L53   131.34   52-8743 ‡

OrPR MtU OrU Or Wa WaS OrCS WaT OrP WaTC
NcD OU PSC WaU DNLM MiU KEmT AU CaBVa OrPS CaBViP
NL 0382431   DLC MU PSt PPT MB TxU NN ViU TU OOxM OClW

VOLUME 334

BF 173 L53 1953
Lindner, Robert Mitchell, 1914–
Prescription for rebellion. London,
V. Gollancz, 1953.
305p. 21cm.

Includes bibliography.

1. Psychoanalysis. I. Title.

NL 0382432   MU MH

Lindner, Robert Mitchell, 1914–
Rebel without a cause; the story of a criminal psychopath, by Robert M. Lindner. Introd. by Sheldon Glueck and Eleanor Glueck. New York, Grove Press ₍c1944₎
xvi, 335 p. 18cm. (An Evergreen black cat book, BC-124)

Bibliography: p. 323-327.

1. Criminal psychology. 2. Personality, Disorders of. 3. Psychoanalysis. 4. Hypnotism. I. Title. II.   Title: The story of a criminal psycho   path.

NL 0382433   GU IaU NjP NcU MB NBuU WaU

Lindner, Robert Mitchell, 1914–
Rebel without a cause; the hypnoanalysis of a criminal psychopath, by Robert M. Lindner ... Introduction by Sheldon Glueck ... and Eleanor T. Glueck ... New York, Grune & Stratton, 1944.
xiii, 296 p. 23 cm.
Bibliography: p. 290-292.

1. Psychoanalysis. 2. Hypnotism. 3. Personality, Disorders of. 4. Criminal psychology.   I. Title.   II. Title: Hypnoanalysis of a criminal psychopath.

RC602.L513   131.34   S G 44—211
U. S. Armed Forces   Medical Libr.
for Library of Congress   ₍a56₎²₂₎†

OrPS
WaSpG WaT WaTC WaWW OrStbM OrSaW OrU-M MtBuM Or MtBC MtU OrCS OrP OrPR OrU Wa WaE WaPS WaS WaSp OU NcGU NcD NcRS MiU ViU DLC CaBVaU IdB IdPI IdU
NL 0382434   DNLM NcU PSt MoU ScU PHC PPT OC1W OC1

Lindner, Robert Mitchell, 1914–
Rebel without a cause; the hypnoanalysis of a criminal psychopath. Intro. by Sheldon Glueck and Eleanor Glueck. London, Research Books, 1945.
xii, 259p. 23cm.

Includes bibliography.

1. Psychoanalysis. 2. Hypnotism. 3. Personality, Disorders of. 4. Criminal psychology. I. Title. II.   Title: Hypnoanalysis of a criminal psycho-'   path.

NL 0382436   MtU NcU

Lindner, Robert Mitchell, 1914–1956
Stone walls and men ₍by₎ Robert M. Lindner ... New York, Odyssey press ₍1946₎
x p., 1 l., 496 p. 21 cm.
"First edition."

1. Crime and criminals. 2. Prisons.   I. Title.

HV6025.L5   364   46—898

ViU WaU-L
CLSU IdU Or OrCS PP PU PPT PBL NcD NcGU ViU-L MsSM WaWW CtY MtU OrPS Wa MiU AU CaBVa CaBVaU
NL 0382437   DLC OrP CU-I OrSaW CU OrU NBuU WaT

Lindner, Rose E
The everyday business of one man's family, by Rose E. Lindner. [Los Angeles, Calif., Kellaway-Ide Company, c1939]
2 v.   forms.   28 cm.
Cover-title.
Cop. 2, 2 v. in 1.
1. Business education – Problems, exercises, etc. I. Title.

NL 0382438   CU OrU

Lindner, Rudolf.
Der erste Sprachunterricht Taubstummer auf Grund statistischer, experimenteller und psychologischer Untersuchungen. (Pädagogisch-psychologische Arbeiten. Leipzig, 1910.   4°. ₍Bd. 1,₎ p. 17-87, 2 pl.)
Leipziger Lehrerverein. Institut für experimentelle Pädagogik und Psychologie.   Veröffentlichungen. Bd. 1.
Bibliography, p. 86.

I. Deaf.—Education.
N. Y. P. L.   August 19, 1913.

NL 0382439   NN

Lindner, Rudolf, ed.
Das taubstumme kind in vergleichen mit vollsinnigen schulkindern... (In Pädagogisch-psychologische arbeiten... 1925. bd. 14)

NL 0382440   OU

Lindner, Rudolf.
Untersuchungen über die Lautsprache und ihre Anwendung auf die Pädagogik. ₍Leipzig, A. Hahn, 1916₎
142 p. illus. 26 cm. (Pädagogisch-psychologische Arbeiten; Veröffentlichungen des Instituts für Experimentelle Pädagogik u. Psychologie des Leipziger Lehrervereins, 7. Bd.)

1. Speech—Study and teaching.   (Series: Pädagogisch-psychologische Arbeiten, 7. Bd.)
LB1051.A2P3 Bd. 7   51—48128

NL 0382441   DLC OU

QD341 .A8L75
Lindner, Rudolf, 1866–
Ueber zwei isomere benzylderivate des nitroso-b-benzylhydroxylamins.
Leipzig, 1893.
38p.
Inaug. diss. Leipzig.

NL 0382442   DLC

Lindner, Rudolf, 1890–
Zur geschichte der therapie der hernia inguinalis der haustiere.
Inaug. diss. Leipzig, 1914. [Dresden]
Bibl.

NL 0382443   ICRL

Lindner, Rudolf Oskar, 1888–
... Über die genickbeule und ihre behandlung ... Dresden, V. Protze, 1912.
39 p.   23¼ᶜᵐ.
Inaug.-diss.—Leipzig.
Lebenslauf.
"Literaturverzeichnis": p. 37–38.

1. ₍Poll-evil₎
Agr 14–1612
Library, U. S. Dept. of   Agriculture   41L645

NL 0382444   DNAL ICRL CtY

Lindner (8.) Studien über Malthusianismus.
44 pp., 1 tab.   8°.   Wien, W. Braumüller, 1890.
Repr. from: Wien. med. Bl., 1889, xii.

NL 0382445   DNLM

Lindner, Theodor, 1843–1919.
Der angebliche Ursprung der Vemegerichte aus der Inquisition. Eine Antwort an Friedrich Thudichum. Paderborn, F. Schöningh, 1890.
81 p.   24 cm.

1. Thudichum, Friedrich Wolfgang Karl von, 1831–1913. Femgericht und Inquisition. 2. Fehmic courts.   I. Title.
Full name: Ernst Friedrich Theodor Lindner.

52–57596 ‡

NL 0382446   DLC MH NN

Lindner, Theodor, 1843–1919.
Anno ɪɪ. der heilige, erzbischof von Köln, 1056–1075. Von dr. Theodor Lindner ... Leipzig, Duncker und Humblot, 1869.
1 p. l., 117, ₍1₎ p.   23ᶜᵐ.

1. Anno, Saint, abp. of Cologne, d. 1075.
₍Full name: Ernst Friedrich Theodor Lindner₎
33–10351
Library of Congress   BX4700.A5L5   922.243

NL 0382447   DLC CU MH OC1W

BX830 .L7
Lindner, Theodor, ₁₈₄₃–₁₉₁₉.
1064
De Concilio mantuano ... Berolini, typis expressit P. Schantze ₍1865₎
33 p.   21¼ᵐ.
Inaug.-diss.—Berlin.
Vita.

1. Mantua, Council of, 1064.

NL 0382448   ICU ICRL NjP NjNbS DLC

LINDNER, Theodor, 1843–1919.
De Santo Annone archiepiscopo Coloniensi, pare prior: usque ad annum 1062. Dissertatio. Vratislaviae, typis A. Neumanni, 1868.

pp.(1),31+.

NL 0382449   MH

Lindner, Theodor, 1843–1919.
Deutsche geschichte unter den Habsburgern und Luxemburgern (1273-1437) von Theodor Lindner ... Stuttgart, J.G. Cotta, 1890-93.
2 v.   26ᶜᵐ.   (Added t.-p.: Bibliothek deutscher geschichte ... hrsg. von H. v. Zwiedineck-Südenhorst ₍5. t.₎)

CONTENTS.—1.bd. Von Rudolf von Habsburg bis zu Ludwig dem Baiern.—2.bd. Von Karl IV. bis zu Sigmund. Die allgemeinen zustände.

1. Germany—Hist.—1273-1517. 2. Holy Roman empire—1273-1517.

NIC InU PPL OO OC1 OU MWelC ICN
NL 0382450   MiU MH DDO CSmH CaBVaU ICU MnCS CtY PU CU

Lindner, Theodor, 1843-1919.
Die deutsche Hanse. Ihre geschichte und bedeutung. Für das deutsche volk dargestellt von Theodor Lindner ... Leipzig, F. Hirt & sohn, 1899.
215 p.   front., illus., ports., fold. map.   23ᶜᵐ.

1. Hanseatic league.

NL 0382451   MH CtY NjP MoU ICN NN NcD

Lindner, Theodor, 1843-1919.
Die deutsche Hanse. Ihre geschichte und bedeutung. Für das deutsche volk dargestellt von Theodor Lindner... 2. aufl.   Leipzig, F. Hirt & sohn, 1901.
192p.   incl.front.,illus.,ports.,maps (1 fold.)facsims.   23ᶜᵐ.

Illustrated lining papers.

NL 0382452   KU OO OU MU

VOLUME 334

Lindner, Theodor, 1843-1919.
Die deutsche Hanse. Ihre Geschichte und Bedeutung. Für das deutsche Volk dargestellt von Theodor Lindner, ... Mit Titelbild, 72 Abbildungen im Text und einer Karte in Farbendruck. Dritte Auflage. .... Leipzig, F. Hirt & Sohn, 1902.
192 p. incl. front. (port.), illus., 1 fold. map. 23cm.

NL 0382453   ICJ

DD801
H2L7
1911
Lindner, Theodor, 1843-1919.
Die deutsche Hanse, ihre Geschichte und Bedeutung, für das deutsche Volk dargestellt. 4. Aufl. Leipzig, F. Hirt & sohn, 1911.
192 p. incl. front., illus. (incl. ports., facsims.) fold. map.

1. Hanseatic league.

NL 0382454   CU GU MiU IU OClJC MH MB

Lindner, Theodor, 1843-1919.
Die deutschen königswahlen und die entstehung des kurfürstenthums, von Theodor Lindner. Leipzig, Dyk, 1893.
xii, 234 p. 24cm.

1. Germany—Kings and rulers—Succession. 2. Holy Roman empire—Constitutional history. 3. Electors (Kurfürsten) 1. Title.
(Full name: Ernst Friedrich Theodor Lindner)

Library of Congress   JN3250.C83L5   41-39257

NL 0382455   DLC MH ICU NjP CtY CU CaBVaU

Lindner, Theodor, 1843-1919.
Die fabel von der bestattung Karls des Grossen. Aachen, verlag der Cremerschen buchhandlung, 1893.
pp. (3), 82.

Charlemagne||AcS 186068   HCL 24-870

NL 0382456   MH CU NIC OCU

DD167
.L7
LINDNER, THEODOR, 1843-1919.
Geschichte des deutschen reiches vom ende des vierzehnten jahrhunderts bis zur reformation. Von dr. Theodor Lindner... 1.abth.:Geschichte des deutschen reiches unter könig Wenzel. 1.-2.bd. Braunschweig, C.A.Schwetschke und sohn (M.Bruhn) 1875-80.
2 v. 22cm.
No more published.

1.Germany--Hist.--Wenzel, 1378-1400.

NL 0382457   ICU ICN MH NIC CU MdBP MiU CtY

Lindner, Theodor, 1843-1919.
Geschichte des deutschen volkes. Von Theodor Lindner ... Stuttgart, J. G. Cotta'sche buchhandlung, nachfolger, 1894.
2 v. in 1. 22½cm.
CONTENTS.—1. bd. Bis zum Augsburger religionsfrieden.—2. bd. Vom Augsburger religionsfrieden bis zur gründung des neuen reichs.

1. Germany—Hist.

NL 0382458   ICU OCl MiU NjP PPG RP OClW OO NN PV

Lindner, Theodor, 1843-1919.
Geschichtsphilosophie. Einleitung zu einer Weltgeschichte seit der Völkerwanderung. Stuttgart. Cotta. 1901. xii, 206 pp. 8°.

N1221 — History. Philosophy.

NL 0382459   MB MH NjP NNF OCH OCl ICN NBuU

D
16
.8
L74
1904
Lindner, Theodor, 1843-1919.
Geschichtsphilosophie; das Wesen der Geschichtlichen Entwickelung. Einleitung zu einer Weltgeschichte seit der Völkerwanderung. 2. erweiterte und umgearbeitete Aufl. Stuttgart und Berlin, Cotta, 1904.
xii, 241 p. 22cm.

1. History--Philosophy. 2. World history.

NL 0382460   NIC IU NN

LINDNER, Theodor, 1843-1919.
Geschichtsphilosophie: das wesen der geschichtlichen entwicklung; einleitung zu einer weltgeschichte seit der völkerwanderung. 3te auf. Berlin, Stuttgart, 1912.

NL 0382461   MH-L

901
L747g
1921
Lindner, Theodor, 1843-1919.
Geschichtsphilosophie, das Wesen der geschichtlichen Entwicklung; Einleitung zu einer Weltgeschichte. [4.Aufl.] Stuttgart, J.G.Cotta, 1921.
viii, 220p. 21cm.

Bibliographical footnotes.

1. History - Philosophy.

NL 0382462   CLSU CaBVaU UU NcU NcD

Lindner, Theodor, 1843-1919.
Der hergang bei den deutschen königswahlen, von Theodor Lindner. Weimar, H. Böhlaus nachfolger, 1899.
2 p. l., 70 p. 22cm.
Bibliographical foot-notes.

1. Electors (Kurfürsten) 2. Holy Roman empire—Kings and rulers. I. Title.
(Full name: Ernst Friedrich Theodor Lindner)   43-32834

Library of Congress   JN3250.C83L52

NL 0382463   DLC CtY MH

Lindner, Theodor, 1843-1919.
Historiens filosofi; den historiska utvecklingens vasen, af Theodor Lindner... Af författaren genomsedd och omarb. uppl. Bemyndigad öfversättning, af O.H.D. Stockholm, H. Geber [1908]

4 p. l., 268, [4] p. 21cm.

Translation of: Geschichtsphilosophie.
1. History. Philosophy. I. Dumrath, Oscar Heinrich, 1844-   tr. II. Title.

NL 0382464   MnU

Lindner, Theodor, 1843-1919.
Kaiser Heinrich IV. Berlin, C. Habel, 1881.
pp. 40. (Sammlung gemeinverständlicher wissenschaft. vorträge, xvi, 374.)

Heinrich IV, emperor   of Germany||CB 1: 149|A

NL 0382465   MH CtY NIC MdBP

Lindner, Theodor, 1843-1919.
Der krieg gegen Frankreich und die einigung Deutschlands. Zur 25jährigen wiederkehr der gedenktage von 1870/71. Von Th. Lindner ... Mit zwanzig vollbildern, zahlreichen abbildungen im text und fünf karten-tafeln. Berlin, A. Asher & co., 1895.
4 p. l., 163, [1] p. front., illus., plates, ports., maps (1 fold.) 31cm.

1. Franco-German war, 1870-1871.
(Full name: Ernst Friedrich Theodor Lindner)

Library of Congress   DC290.L74   G-8 Revised

MiU
NL 0382466   DLC WaS MdBJ CtY CU CLSU IaU NBuU NN PPL

---

q943.08
L64k
Lindner, Theodor, 1843-1919.
Der krieg gegen Frankreich und die einigung Deutschlands. Zur 25 jährigenwiederkehr der gedenktage von 1870/71. Berlin, 1912.
163p. front. illus., plates, ports., fold. maps (part col.)

NL 0382467   IU

Lindner, Theodor, 1843-1919.
Die sogenannten schenkungen Pippins, Karls des Grossen, und Ottos I. an die päpste. Stuttgart, J. G. Cotta, 1896.
pp. 99.

Papacy–Relations with secular powers||A

NL 0382468   MH CU MCM OO

Lindner, Theodor, 1843-1919.
... Urkunden der Luxemburger periode. Ausgewählt und erklärt von Theodor Lindner.
(In Sybel, Heinrich i. e. C. L. H. von, ed. Kaiserurkunden in abbildungen ... Berlin, 1880-91. 27½cm. 2 p. l., p. [89]-108. and atlas. 62 x 85cm. lfg. 5: taf. 1-24)

1. Germany — Hist. — 1273-1517 — Sources. 2. Holy Roman empire — Hist.—1273-1517—Sources.
(Full name: Ernst Friedrich Theodor Lindner)

Library of Congress   CD135.S96   7-3424 Revised

NL 0382469   DLC

LINDNER, Theodor, 1843-1919.
Das urkundenwesen Karls IV und seiner nachfolger, 1346-1437. Stuttgart, J.G.Cotta, 1882.

NL 0382470   MH NjP ICU DDO ICN

Lindner, Theodor, 1843-1919.
Die Veme. [A history of the secret tribunals of Westphalia.] Münster, etc., F. Schöningh, 1888.
pp. xxiv, 668.

Fehmic courts||AcS 186075

NL 0382471   MH CtY NIC OClW MWelC MdBP

K
347
.54
LINDNER, THEODOR, 1843-1919.
Die Veme... Neue ausgabe. Paderborn, F. Schöningh, 1896.
xxiv, 668p.

Bibliographical foot-notes.
Contents.—1. buch. Die freigrafschaften und die freistühle.—2. buch. Die rechtsquellen.—3. buch. Die freigerichte.—4. buch. Uebergang und entwicklung.—5. buch. Die gerichtsverfahren.

NL 0382472   ICN MH RPB NcU MdBP MiU-L NjP

VOLUME 334

Lindner, Theodor, 1843-1919.
... Veme und inquisition. Halis,
formis Gebauero-Schwetschkeianis,
1893.

13 p. 30½cm.

Programm - Wittenberg.

NL 0382473   MH-L NNJ MH

Lindner, Theodor, 1843- *1919*.
Weltgeschichte der letzten hundert Jahre (1815-1914)...
Von Theodor Lindner...   Stuttgart: J. G. Cotta, 1914-16.
2 v.   8°.

"Literatur-Angaben," at end of each volume.
Contents: Bd. 1. Geschichte Europas bis zum Beginn der neuesten Zeit.
Bd. 2. Geschichte Europas und der aussereuropäischen Staaten bis zum Beginn des
Weltkrieges.

1. History (Modern), 19th century.   2. History (Modern), 19th century.
—Bibliography.
N.Y.P.L.   April 27, 1920.

NL 0382474   NN NjP GASC

Lindner, Theodor, 1843-1919
Weltgeschichte, in zehn Bänden...
Stuttgart und Berlin, Cotta, 1902-1920.
10 v.

NL 0382475   OCl

D
102
L742

Lindner, Theodor, 1843-1919.
Weltgeschichte in zehn Bänden.
ːStuttgart und Berlin, Cotta, 1920-21.
10 v. port. 23 cm.

Includes bibliographical references.
Contents:- 1.Bd. Altertum.- 2.Bd. Der
Ursprung der byzantinischen, islamischen,
abendländisch-christlichen, chinesischen
und indischen Kultur.- 3.Bd. Niedergang
der islamischen und der byzantinischen
Kultur. Bildung der europäischen Staaten.

- 4.Bd. Vom dreizehnten
Jahrhundert bis zum ende der Konzile. Die
abendländisch-christliche Kultur. Anfänge
einer neuen Zeit.- 5.Bd. Der Stillstand
des Orients und das Aufsteigen Europas.
Die deutsche Reformation.- 6.Bd. Die Kämpfe
um die Reformation. Der Übergang in die
heutige Zeit.- 7.Bd. Das neue europäische
Staatensystem. Absolutismus und
Merkantilismus. Die geistige Befreiung
und die Aufklärung. Asien und Afrika.

- 8.Bd. Amerika. Europa
bis zum Beginn der französischen Revolution.
Die Revolution und die Republik. Napoleon.-
9.Bd. Das europäische Geistesleben zu
anfang des neunzehnten Jahrhunderts. Europa
bis zur Julirevolution 1830. Europa von der
Julirevolution bis zur Februarrevolution.
Revolution und Reaktion. Der Übergang in
unserer Zeit 1848-1859.- 10.Bd. Die Zeit
Bismarcks. Die aussereuropäischen Staaten.
Die letzten Jahrzehnte des alten Europa.
Der Ursprung des Weltkrieges bis zu den
Kriegser-   klärungen.
        1. World   history. I. Title.,

NL 0382478   LU

Lindner, Theodor, 1843-1919.
Weltgeschichte seit der völkerwanderung, von Theodor
Lindner ... Stuttgart und Berlin, Cotta, 1901-16.
9 v. 22½ cm.

"Literatur-angabe" at end of each volume.
CONTENTS.—1. bd. Der ursprung der byzantinischen, islamischen,
abendländisch-christlichen, chinesischen und indischen kultur. 1901.—
2. bd. Niedergang der islamischen und der byzantinischen kultur.
Bildung der europäischen staaten. 1902.—3. bd. Vom dreizehnten
jahrhundert bis zum ende der konzile. Die abendländisch-christliche
kultur. Anfänge einer neuen zeit. 1908.—4. bd. Die deutsche reformation.
Orients und das aufsteigen Europas. Die deutsche reformation.
1905.—5. bd. Die kämpfe um die reformation. Der übergang in die
heutige zeit. 1907.—6. bd. Das neue europäische staatensystem. Ab-

solutismus und merkantilismus. Die geistige befreiung und die aufklärung. Asien und Afrika. 1909.—7. bd. Amerika. Europa bis zum
beginn der französischen revolution. Die revolution und die republik.
Napoleon. 1910.—8. bd. Das europäische geistesleben zu anfang des
neunzehnten jahrhunderts. Europa bis zur julirevolution 1830. Europa von der julirevolution bis zur februarrevolution. Revolution und
reaktion. Der übergang zu unserer zeit 1848-1859. 1914.—9. bd. Die
zeit Bismarcks. Die aussereuropäischen staaten. Die letzten jahrzehnte des alten Europa. Der ursprung des weltkrieges bis zu den
kriegserklärungen. 1916.
  1. History, Universal.   I. Title.
                              ːFull name: Ernst Friedrich Theodor Lindnerː

Library of Congress   D102.L74

                                              6—4887

NL 0382480   DLC IU MB MH NjP OO ViU NN

Lindner, Theodor, 1843- *1919*.
Die Weltlage Europas seit den Befreiungskriegen. Vortrag
gehalten in der Gehe-Stiftung zu Dresden am 14. März 1914
von...ːTheodorː Lindner... (Gehe-Stiftung zu Dresden. Vorträge. Leipzig, 1914. 8°. Bd. 6, p. 113-139.)

1. World politics.
N.Y.P.L.   October 20, 1914.

NL 0382481   NN CU

Lindner, Theodor, 1843-1919.
Zur fabel von der bestattung Karls des Grossen.
Eine entgegnung von Theodor Lindner.   Aachen,
H. Kaatzer, 1896.
1 p.l., 12 p.   24 cm.
"Sonderabdruck aus band XVIII der Zeitschrift
des Aachener geschichtsvereins."
1. Charlemagne, 742-814.

NL 0382482   CU

Lindner, Theodore Gotthilfe, 1906-
The psychological necessity of St. Paul's
conversion ... 1949.
Thesis (PH.D.) - Ohio state university,
1949.

NL 0382483   OU

Lindner, Therese.
Was mache ich meinen Eltern zu Weihnachten. [Von] Therese
Lindner, Emma Carp, Annemarie Pallat Hartleben.
Leipzig. Teubner. 1912. (2), 22 pp. Plates. [Handarbeit für
Knaben und Mädchen. 10.] 21 cm., in 8s.
Some of the plates are colored.

K1884 — Christmas gifts. — Carp, Emma, jt. auth. — Pallat-Hartleben, Annemarie, jt. auth. — S.r.c.

NL 0382484   MB

Lindner, Tilly, pseud.
see Lindner, Karl, 1890-

WM
90
L747h
1951

LINDNER, Torsten
Helhetssyn på människan; kropp och
själ i nutida medicin. Stockholm,
Kooperativa förbundets bokförlag, 1951.
159 p.
1. Psychosomatic medicine

NL 0382486   DNLM NN ICRL

4BV
851

Lindner, Torsten.
Psykologiska gåtor i Helander
-affären.   Stockholm, Nutids förlag
ː1955ː
100 p.

NL 0382487   DLC-P4 MH

Lindner, Vera Borisovna.
Практическая фонетика немецкого языка; пособие для
учителей средней школы. Изд. 2., испр. Москва, Гос.
учебно-педагог. изд-во, 1955.
171 p. illus. 23 cm.

1. German language—Phonetics.   I. Title.
                          Title transliterated: Prakticheskaía
                          fonetika nemeskogo íazyka.

PF3135.L5 1955   56-36847 ‡

NL 0382488   DLC

Lindner, Walter.
Waldkraiburg; vom Bunker zur Siedlung. Die vier-
jährige Geschichte einer Industriesiedlung von Heimatver-
triebenen in Oberbayern. München, Verlag "Christ Unter-
wegs" ː1950ː
123 p. illus., fold. map. 22 cm.

1. Waldkraiburg, Ger.

DD901.W24L5   51-32417

NL 0382489   DLC MH

Lindner, Walter, writer on real estate
                          FOR OTHER EDITIONS
                          SEE MAIN ENTRY
Hardy, Edward Rochie, 1862-
Insurance, by Edward R. Hardy ... with the collaboration
of Fred W. Field ... Real estate, by Walter Lindner ... with
the collaboration of Alfred Bicknell ... New York, Alexander
Hamilton institute ː1918ː

Lindner, Walter, writer on real estate
                          FOR OTHER EDITIONS
                          SEE MAIN ENTRY
Insurance and real estate. Part I: Fire insurance, by
Edward R. Hardy ... rev. by Fred W. Field ... Part II:
Real estate, by Walter Lindner ... rev. by E. W. Wright
... New York, Alexander Hamilton institute ː1914ː

Lindner, Walter, and Alfred Bicknell, of Toronto.
Real estate.
(In Hardy, Edward Rochie, and Frederick William Field. In-
surance. Pp. 177-359. New York. [1917. Alexander Hamilton
Institute, New York. Modern business. Vol. 18.])

L7057 — Real property. — Jt. auth.

NL 0382492   MB OCl

Lindner (Walter) [1878-]. *Subcutane Dauerdrainage bei einem Fall von Hy-
drocephalus internus. 29 pp., 1 l. 8°.
Leipzig, B. Georgi, 1908.
ːFull name: Erich Walter Lindnerː

NL 0382493   DNLM CtY ICRL MH

W 4
296
1948

Lindner, Walter, 1919-
Die Quantitative Blutalkoholbestimmung
bei verkehrsunfällen seit 1926 mit besonderer Berücksichtigung der Fussgänger.
Winterthur, Lüthi, 1948.
29 p. illus.

Inaug.-Diss. - Zürich.
Bibliography: p. 28.

NL 0382494   DNLM

Lindner (Walther) [1874-]. *Beitrag zur
Lehre von den Fremdkörpern im Respirations-
tractus. 66 pp., 1 l. 8°. Göttingen, W. F. Kaest-
ner, 1901.

NL 0382495   DNLM

833G55
BL64

Lindner, Werner.
Goethe; ein bildheft zu seinem leben und wirken,
bearb. von dr. W. Lindner und dr. W. Spohr.
Berlin-Tempelhof, Universum-verlagsanstalt g.m.b.
h.ː1932ː
64p. incl.plates, ports., facsims.

1. Goethe, Johann Wolfgang von, 1749-1832. I.
Spohr, Wilhelm, 1868-

NL 0382496   IU CtY

VOLUME 334

Lindner, Werner.
  Handwerk tut not! Fördert das handwerk.
Das büchlein für alle! Herausgeber: Reichsverband des deutschen handwerks und Deutscher
handwerks- und gewerbekammertag.
Bearbeitet von W. Lindner. Zeichn. von Wilh.
Petersen ... [Berlin-Tempelhof, Druck und
verlag H.A. Braun & co.,] 1931.
  64 p. illus. 16 cm.
  1. Handicraft. I. Reichsverband des deutschen
handwerks. II. Deutscher handwerks- und gewerbekammertag.

NL 0382497   CU

Lindner, Werner.
  Mehrfachfunkenaufnahmen von explosionsvorgaengen
nach der Toeplerschen schlierenmethode.
Inaug. diss. Tech. Hoch. Dresden, (1930) (Berlin)
18 p.

NL 0382498   ICRL

Lindner, Werner: Vorkommen von Talgdrüsen in der Wangenschleimhaut. [Maschinenschrift.] 31 S. m. Abb. 4°. — Auszug: Breslau
1922: Bresl. Genoss.-Buchdr. 2 Bl. 8°
Breslau, Med. Diss. v. 15. Juli 1922
                                   [U 22. 1476

NL 0382499   ICRL

Lindner, Werner: Zähne und Kiefer in forensischer Beziehung. [Maschinenschrift.] 36 S. m. Taf. 4°. — Auszug: Halle (Saale) 1922:
Karras, Kröber & Nietschmann. 4 S. 8°
Halle, Med. Diss. v. 6. Juli 1922 [1923]
                                   [U 23. 5024

NL 0382500   ICRL

Lindner, Werner, architect.
  Die bäuerliche Wohnkultur.   Dresden, 1912.
      Inaug. - Diss. - Technische Hochschule,
Dresden.

NL 0382501   ICRL

q728   Lindner, Werner, architect,
L64b   Die bäuerliche wohnkultur in der provinz Westfalen und
ihren nördlichen grenzgebieten ... Berlin, 1912.
    92 p.
    Reprint from his Beiträge zur geschichte des westfälischen bauernstandes.

    1. Germany—Architecture. 2. Architecture, Domestic.

NL 0382502   IU

725.4   Lindner, Werner, architect.
L38   Bauten der Technik, ihre Form und Wirkung;
Werkanlagen. Berlin, E. Wasmuth [c1927]
    232 p. illus.

    1. Industrial buildings.
    I. Title.

NL 0382503   CaOTP MiD DCU PP IEN NjP

Lindner, Werner, architect
  Denkmäler für unsere Krieger. von Dr. Werner Lindner...
München: G. D. W. Callwey [1915]. 22 p., 1 l., 8 pl. 8°.
(Duererbund. Flugschrift. [no.] 139.)
    Cover-title.
    Plates printed on both sides.

    1. Military parks, cemeteries and   monuments, Germany. 2. European
war, 1914–   . 3. Title. 4. Series.
N. Y. P. L.   April 7, 1917.

NL 0382504   NN

DD20   Lindner, Werner, architect
.B6
  Block, Max Paul, ed.
    Deutsche heimat, bilder aus stadt u. land ... herausgegeben
von M. Paul Block u. Werner Lindner. Berlin, Deutsche buchgemeinschaft g. m. b. h. [1926–27]

323.354   Lindner, Werner, architect, ed.
qL747   Das Dorf, seine Pflege und Gestaltung, bearb. von Werner
Lindner, Erich Kulke, Franz Gutsmiedl in Verbindung mit
Wilhelm Grebe [et. al.] München, D. W. Callwey [Vorwort
1938]
    234 p. illus., map, plans. 30 cm. (Die landschaftlichen
Grundlagen des deutschen Bauschaffens; Buchreihe der
Arbeitsgemeinschaft Heimat und Haus, 1. Bd.)

    I. Villages. Germany. 2. Architecture. Domestic. Germany.
3. Farm buildings.   Germany. I. Title. (Series)

NL 0382506   N OClSA

Lindner, Werner, architect, ed.
  ... Das dorf, seine pflege und gestaltung, bearbeitet von
Werner Lindner, Erich Kulke [und] Franz Gutsmiedl, in verbindung mit Herbert Frank, Wilhelm Grebe, Heinrich Hartmann [u. a.] ... 2., verb. aufl. München, G. D. W. Callwey
[1940]
    237 p. illus. incl. maps, plans] 30cm. (Half-title: Die Landschaftlichen grundlagen des deutschen bauschaffens; buchreihe der Arbeitsgemeinschaft Heimat und haus. 1. bd.)
    Series title in part at head of t.-p.
    1. Villages—Germany. 2. Architecture, Domestic—Germany. 3. Farm
buildings—Germany.   I. Kulke, Erich, 1908–   joint ed. II. Gutsmiedl, Franz, 1901–   joint ed. III. Title.

    NA8204.L5 1940   323.354   46–31163 rev

NL 0382507   DLC CtY NNC CtY

Lindner, Werner, architect, ed.
  ... Das dorf, seine pflege und gestaltung, bearbeitet von Werner Lindner, Erich Kulke [und] Franz Gutsmiedl, in verbindung mit Herbert Frank, Wilhelm Grebe, Heinrich Hartmann
[u. a.] ... 3., verb. aufl. München, G. D. W. Callwey [1943]
    258 p., 2 l. illus. (incl. maps, plans) 30cm. (Half-title: Die Landschaftlichen grundlagen des deutschen bauschaffens; buchreihe der Arbeitsgemeinschaft Heimat und haus. 1. bd.)
    Series title in part at head of t.-p.
    "Schriftenverzeichnis für das ländliche bauwesen": p. 256.
    1. Villages — Germany. 2. Architecture, Domestic — Germany. 3.
Farm buildings—Germany.   I. Kulke, Erich, 1908–   joint ed. II.
Gutsmiedl, Franz, 1901–   joint ed. III. Title.

    NA8204.L5 1943   47–34594

NL 0382508   DLC NN OrU IU MH

Avery

Lindner, Werner, architect.
  Ehrenmale; grundsätze und beispiele ihrer
gestaltung, bearbeitet von Werner Lindner,
mit darstellungen von Fritz Hille. Kassel,
Bärenreiter-verlag, 1952.
    55 p. illus. 21cm. (Friedhof und denkmal.
1)

    1. Sepulchral monuments.

NL 0382509   NNC

LINDNER, WERNER, architect.
HEIMAT UND NATUR. HRSG. VOM DEUTSCHEN BUND
HEIMATSCHUTZ UND VON DER STAATLICHEN STELLE FUER
NATURDENKMALPFLEGE IN PREUSSEN. BERLIN, VERLAG DER
DEUTSCHEN SCHUELERBIBLIOTHEK.
                                   64p.

NL 0382510   MH NN CtY

Lindner, Werner, architect.
  Der Heimatschutz im neuen Reich. Leipzig, E. A. Seemann [1934]
    79 p. 21 cm. (Schriften zur deutschen Lebensicht)

    1. Cities and towns—Planning—Germany. 2. Architecture—Germany.   I. Title.

    NA9199.L49   51–45293

NL 0382511   DLC NNC MH

Lindner, Werner, architect.
  ... Die Ingenieurbauten in ihrer guten Gestaltung; hrsg. und
bearbeitet von Dr.-Ing. Werner Lindner in Verbindung mit Architekt Georg Steinmetz. Berlin: E. Wasmuth A.-G. [, 1923].
206 p. incl. plans, plates. sq. 4°.
    At head of title: Deutscher Bund Heimatschutz und Deutscher Werkbund, in
Gemeinschaft mit dem Verein deutscher Ingenieure und der Deutschen Gesellschaft
für Bauingenieurwesen.
    Most of the plates are printed on both sides.

196871A. 1. Building. 2. Engineer-   ing 3. Steinmetz, Georg, 1882–
N.Y.P.L.   jt. au. 4. Bund Heimatschutz.   5. Deutscher Werkbund.
                                              December 14, 1925

    NIC
NL 0382512   NN CtY CU IU NjP DLC-P4 MnU OClW FU CLSU

Lindner, Werner, architect.
  Das Land an der Ruhr
      see under Deutscher Bund Heimatschutz.

Lindner, Werner, architect
  ... Mark Brandenburg; Text & Bildersammlung von Werner
Lindner...   München: Delphin Verlag], pref. 1924]. 31 p.
illus. (map, plan), 43 pl. 4°. (Deutsche Volkskunst. Bd. 2.)
    Plates printed on both sides.

206981A. 1. Art, Peasant—Germany.   2. Architecture—Germany—Brandenburg. 3. Art, German. 4. Ser.
N. Y. L.   November 6, 1925

NL 0382514   NN WaU OC1 OOxM PPCS

Lindner, Werner, architect.
  Mark Brandenburg, Text & Bildersammlung. Mit 245
Bildern. Weimar, Verlag Böhlau [1941?]
    31 p. illus., plates, map. 26 cm. (Deutsche Volkskunst, Bd. 2)

    1. Folk art—Brandenburg. 2. Architecture, Domestic—Brandenburg.   (Series)
    NK952.B7L5   49–58238 •

NL 0382515   DLC

Lindner, Werner, architect.
  Mauerwerk, hrsg. vom Deutschen Bund Heimatschutz
in Verbindung mit dem Deutschen Handwerksinstitut. Gesammelt und bearb. von Werner Lindner und Friedrich
Tamms. [3., verb. Aufl.] Berlin, A. Metzner [1938]
    132 p. illus., plates. 31 cm.
    Bibliography: p. 132.

    1. Walls.   I. Tamms, Friedrich, joint author. II. Title.

    NA2940.L5 1938   729.31   50–50248

NL 0382516   DLC NIC

Lindner, Werner, architect
  Das niedersächsische bauernhaus in Deutschland und
Holland; ein beitrag zu seiner erkundung, von Werner
Lindner ... Hannover, E. Geibel, 1912.
    4 p. l., 195 p. illus. (incl. plans) 32½°. (Added t.-p.: Beiträge zur
heimatkunde des regierungsbezirks stade. bd. III)
    "Verzeichnis der angeführten bücher und schriften": p. 191-192.
    "Verzeichnis der mit abbildungen vertretenen niederländischen künstler": p. 193-194.
    1. Architecture, Domestic. 2. Architecture—Germany. 3. Architecture—Holland.

NL 0382517   MiU CU MH NN NNC IU

NA1068   Lindner, Werner, architect, joint ed.
.S35
  Schulte-Frohlinde, Julius, ed.
    ... Der osten, bearbeitet von Julius Schulte-Frohlinde, Walter Kratz ... und Werner Lindner ... München, G. D. W. Callwey [1940]

VOLUME 334

Lindner, Werner, *architect.*
Reihengrab und Gräberfeld in ihrer Gestaltung, bearb. von Werner Lindner ₁et al.₎ Kassel, Bärenreiter-Verlag, 1955.
88 p. illus. 21 cm. (Friedhof und Denkmal, 4. Heft)

1. Sepulchral monuments—Germany. ɪ. Title. (Series)

NB1870.L5   56-33304

NL 0382519   DLC

Lindner, Werner, architect.
Schoene Brunnen in Deutschland; in Verbindung mit dem deutschen Bunde Heimatschutz, von Werner Lindner. ₁Berlin: E. Wasmuth A. G., cop. 1920.₎   303 p.   illus.   f°.   (West-faelischer Heimatbund. Veröffentlichung. Folge 1, ₁Nr.₎ 5.)
Bibliography, p. 299.

396954A. 1. Fountains—Germany.   2. Ser.
N. Y. P. L.   May 31, 1929

NL 0382520   NN MH MB OC1 PPTU MiD IU

Lindner, Werner, *architect.*
Die stadt, ihre pflege und gestaltung; bearbeitet von Werner Lindner und Erich Böckler. München, G. D. W. Callwey ₁1939₎
288 p. illus. (incl. maps, plans, facsims.) diagrs. 30ᶜᵐ. (Half-title: Die Landschaftlichen grundlagen des deutschen bauschaffens; buchreihe der Arbeitsgemeinschaft Heimat und haus ... Herausgeber: der Reichsorganisationsleiter der NSDAP. ɪɪ. bd.)

1. Cities and towns—Planning—Germany. 2. Cities and towns—Civic improvement. 3. Architecture, Domestic—Germany. ɪ. Böckler, Erich. ɪɪ. Title.
NA9199.L5   A F 47-2890
Harvard univ. Library
for Library of Congress   ₍2₎†

NL 0382521   MH OrU CU PU ICU NN DLC NNC

Lindner, Werner, *architect*

Technische kulturdenkmale, im auftrag der Agricola-gesellschaft beim Deutschen museum herausgegeben von Conrad Matschoss und Werner Lindner, unter mitarbeit von August Hertwig, Hans v. u. zu Loewenstein, Otto Petersen und Carl Schiffner. München, F. Bruckmann, a. g., 1932.

G
157
.L56
   Lindner, Werner, *architect*
   Vom Reisen und Wandern in alter und neuer Zeit. Berlin, Furche Verlag, 1921.
143 p. illus. 22 cm.

1. Travel. I. Title.

NL 0382523   TNJ

TA3
.V515
hft. 363
   Lindner, Werner, dr.-ing.
   Langen, Arnold, 1876–
   ... Die Diesellokomotive mit unmittelbaren antrieb, von dr. Arnold Langen ... Untersuchungen über den spülvorgang an zweitaktmaschinen, von dr.-ing. W. Lindner ... Mit 67 abbildungen und einer zahlentafel. Berlin, VDI-verlag g. m. b. h., 1933.

Lindner, Werner, dr.-ing
Entzündung und verbrennung von gas- und brennstoffdampfgemischen, von dr.-ing. W. Lindner, mit 35 abbildungen. Berlin, VDI-verlag g. m. b. h., 1931.
viii, 85 p. illus. diagrs. 22ᶜᵐ.

"Die vorliegende schrift stellt einen erweiterten abdruck eines im dezember 1929 im Dresdener bezirksverein des Vereines deutscher ingenieure vom verfasser gehaltenen vortrages dar."—Vorwort.
"Literaturverzeichnis": p. 81–85.

1. Combustion. 2. Gases. ɪ. Title.   32–7646 Revised 2
Library of Congress   QD516.L5
                      ₁r44c2₎
                           541.39

NL 0382525   DLC NN CtY

HS3325
.G3L5
1955
   Lindner, Werner, *writer on trade unions.*
   Grundlagen der Arbeit der Pionierorganisation Ernst Thälmann. Berlin, Volk und Wissen, 1955.
229 p. illus. 21 cm.

At head of title: Deutsches Pädagogisches Zentralinstitut.
Bibliographical footnotes.

1. Pionierorganisation "Ernst Thälmann."

                          A 56-3620
Wisconsin. Univ. Libr.
for Library of Congress   ₍3₎

NL 0382526   WU DLC

Lindner, Werner, 1910–
   ... Die chirurgische Behandlung tuberkulöser Lymphdrüsen im Mesenterium, Mesocolon und Retroperitoneum. Nachuntersuchungen zu diesem Thema und besondere Berücksichtigung der Differential-diagnose zur Appendicitis und zu Harnsystemerkrankungen ... [Leipzig, 1934]
   Inaug.-Diss. - Leipzig.
   Lebenslauf.
   "Literatur": p. 37–44.

NL 0382527   CtY

PITN
014
.589
   Lindner, Werner Rudolf, 1910–
   Die strafe im völkerrecht... ₁Frankfurt a.W.?₎ 1934.
   13,48 p.   21 ᶜᵐ.

   Inaug.-diss. - Frankfurt am Main.
   Lebenslauf.
   "Verzeichnis der benutzten schriften": p. ix–xiii.

   1. International law and relations.

NL 0382528   NjP CtY

₍BR60
.L74
   Lindner, Wilhelm Bruno, 1814–1876.
   Bibliotheca patrum ecclesiasticorum selectissima. Ad optimarum editionum fidem recudi... Lipsiae, 1857–
     v. 17½ᶜᵐ.
   Each vol has also special t.-p.
   With fasc. I is bound₁Muncker, Franz Johann Kaspar Lavater... Stuttgart, 1883.

NL 0382529   ICU PU CU

Lindner, Wilhelm Bruno, 1814–1876.
   De Joviniano et Vigilantio purioris doctrinae quarto et quinto saeculo antesignanis. Accedunt nonnulla de Synodo Gangrensi ... Lipsiae, Ex officina C. Tauchnitii [1839?]
   4 p.l., [3]–68 p., 1 l.   18 cm.
   Diss.-Leipzig.
   Contains bibliographies.
   1. Jovinian, d.ca. 410. 2. Vigilantius, fl. ca. 400. 3. Gangra, Council of, ca. 340. 4. Heresy.

NL 0382530   CU

911
L747ℓe
1848
   LINDNER, Wilhelm Bruno, 1814–1876.
   Lehrbuch der christlichen Kirchengeschichte mit besonderer Beruecksichtigung der dogmatischen Entwicklung von W. Bruno Lindner. Leipzig, E.B. Schwickert, 1848–1854.
     2v. 22cm.

   Format varies: Cop.1 is 1 v.
   Contents: v.1. 1.Abt. Geschichte der alten Kirche.- 2.Abt. Geschichte der

   Kirche der mittleren Zeit.- v.2.3.Abt. 1.u.2. Haelftes. Geschichte der Kirche der neuren Zeit.

NL 0382532   MH-AH CtY NjPT PPLT

Pamph.
v.483
   LINDNER, Wilhelm Bruno, 1814–1876
   Symbolae ad historiam theologiae mysticae; de Macario. Dissertatio historico-theologica ... die XXI mens. Novembris MDCCCXLVI ... defendet Guil. Bruno Lindner. Lipsiae, ex officina Caroli Tauchnitii [1846]
     92p. 21cm.

NL 0382533   MH-AH NjNbS

Lindner, Wilhelm Bruno, 1853–1930
   see under   Lindner, Bruno, 1853–1930.

1883 –
Lindner, Wilhelm Eduard, Das Zollgesetz von 1818 und Handel und Industrie am Niederrhein. Trier 1911: Lintz. 112 S. 8° ¶(Aus: Westdeutsche Zeitschrift f. Gesch. u. Kunst. Jg. 30, H. 2/3.)
Bonn, Phil. Diss. v. 20. Dez. 1911, Ref. Wygodzinski
[Geb. 13. Okt. 83 München; Wohnort: Augsburg; Staatsangeh.: Bayern; Vorbildung: Gymn. Freising Reife Juli 02; Studium: München 2, Cöln Handelshochsch. 3, Bonn 4 S.; Rig. 17. Mai 11.]   [U 12.499

NL 0382535   ICRL PU MH CtY

Lindner, Willj.
   Das künftige landesstrafrecht. Kallmünz, 1931. Inaug. Diss. Erlangen, 1931.   VII, 66 p.
   Bibl.

NL 0382536   ICRL

M2003
.H112L5
   Lindner, Willi, 1891–   Das Lied von der Mutter.
   Haas, Joseph, 1879–
   Das Lied von der Mutter. Piano-vocal score. German₎

   Das Lied von der Mutter; ein Oratorium nach Worten von Willi Lindner für Sopran- und Bariton-Solo, gemischten Chor, Kinder-, Frauen- und Männerchor mit Orchester. Op. 91. Klavierauszug. Mainz, B. Schott's Söhne ₁*1939₎

M2000
.H112L5
   Lindner, Willi, 1891–   Das Lied von der Mutter.
   Haas, Joseph, 1879–
   ₁Das Lied von der Mutter. German₎

   Das Lied von der Mutter; ein Oratorium nach Worten von Willi Lindner für Sopran- und Bariton-Solo, gemischten Chor, Kinder-, Frauen- und Männerchor mit Orchester. Op. 91. Partitur. Mainz, B. Schott's Söhne ₁*1939₎

M1531
.H2Z8
   Lindner, Willi, 1891–   Zum Lob der Arbeit.
   Haas, Joseph, 1879–
   ₁Zum Lob der Arbeit. German₎

   Zum Lob der Arbeit; Kantate für ein- bis dreistimmigen Jugendchor mit Streichorchester und Orgel (oder nur mit zwei- bzw. vierhändiger Klavierbegleitung) Nach Worten von Willi Lindner. Op. 81, Nr. 4. Partitur (zugleich Orgelbzw. Klavierstimme) Mainz, B. Schott's Söhne ₁*1941₎

W 4
M961
1951
   LINDNER, Willibald, 1923–
   Sublimatverdünnungsreihe und ihr Einfluss auf Serum. ₁München, 1951₎
     29 ℓ.
   Inaug.-Diss. - Munich.
   1. Takata-Ara test

NL 0382540   DNLM

VOLUME 334

Lindner, Wolfgang, 1904-
Untersuchungen ueber den vitamin-B-gehalt
verschiedener brotgebaecke.
Inaug. diss.   Leipzig, 1927 (Luoka i. Thuer.)
Bibl.

NL 0382541   ICRL

4Z
92   Lindner, Wolfgang Richard.
Gegenwart, deutscher Literaturführer.
[1. Aufl.] Leipzig, W.R. Lindner [1934]
67 p.

NL 0382542   DLC-P4

Lindner, Wolfram.
Berechnung, Eigenschaften und Herstellung von Kegel-
schraubgetrieben mit Palloidverzahnung. Berlin, VDI-
Verlag, 1943.
37 p. illus. 21 cm.

1. Gearing, Bevel. I. Title.

TJ193.L5   63-57258

NL 0382543   DLC

Lindner, Wolfram.
... Fräsmaschinen, Schleifmaschinen und
Verzahnmaschinen. 9. neubearbeitete auflage,
von dr. -ing. Wolfram Lindner, Remscheid, mit
171 abbildungen. Leipzig, Dr. M. Jänecke,
1943.
180 p.

Spangebende formung der metalle in maschinen-
fabriken, durch werkzeuge und werkzeugmaschinen

NL 0382544   NNE NjP IU TxHR InLP CoU

TJ184
.S33
Lindner, Wolfram.

Schiebel, Adalbert, 1872-1931.
Zahnräder. 4., völlig neubearb. Aufl. von W. Lindner.
Berlin, Springer, 1954-

LINDNER CORPORATION, New York.
York's national theatre list... New York City, N.Y.:
The Lindner Corporation[, 1933?]. 222 l. 33cm.

Reproduced from typewritten copy.

693987A. 1. Stage—Directories—U.S. I. Title.

NL 0382546   NN

LINDNER-VERLAG, publisher.
Die Förderung des Kleinwohnungsbaues mit
Bildern aus der in der Provinz Pommern geleis-
teten Arbeit. Herausgegeben vom Lindner-Verlag,
Düsseldorf, unter Mitwirkung der Pommerschen
Heimstätte G.m.b.H., Gemeinnützigen Wohnungs-
Fürsorgegesellschaft und Bauberatungsstelle für
die Provinz Pommern. Düsseldorf, Lindner-Verlag,
[1927?].

28 x 22 cm. pp.92. Plans and other illustr.

NL 0382547   MH

Lindo,
United Secular and Separate Religious
Education. - Education in Holland.
Birmingham, 1872.
10 p. 8°. [In College Pamphlets, v. 1729]

NL 0382548   CtY

Lindo, Abigail, 1803-1848.
A Hebrew and English and English and Hebrew dictionary with roots and abbreviations. London, Printed by S.
Meldola, 1846.
iv, 359 p. port. 22 cm.

1. Hebrew language—Dictionaries—English. 2. English language—
Dictionaries—Hebrew.

PJ4833.L6   48-30208*

NL 0382549   DLC IEN NcRS MH

Lindo, Abigail, 1803-1849.
A Hebrew and English, and English and Hebrew
vocabulary; also Hebrew and English dialogues,
intended for the use of those who may wish to
learn the holy language.
London, E. Justins & Son, 1837.
165 p.

NL 0382550   OCH

[Lindo, Abigail] 1803-1848.
...A Hebrew and English vocabulary; from a selection of the
daily prayers; intended for the use of schools and young beginners.
By a lady. Revised by Sabato Morais...   London: S. Solomon,
1848. 109 p. nar. 12°.

2445A. 1. Hebrew language—Dic-   SCHIFF COLLECTION.
Sabato, 1823-97, editor.   tionaries (English). 2. Morais,
N. Y. P. L.   June 30, 1921.

NL 0382551   NN OCH

PJ4845
.L5
1878
Hebraic
Sect.   [Lindo, Abigail] 1803-1848.
מאיר עין בני הנעורים A Hebrew and English vocabulary;
from a selection of the daily prayers, intended for the use
of schools and young beginners, by a lady. Rev. by Sabato
Morais and under the sanction of David Meldola. London,
P. Vallentine, 1879.
109 p. 19 cm.

1. Hebrew language—Glossaries, vocabularies, etc.   I. Morais,
Sabato, 1823-1897, ed. II. Title. III. Title: A Hebrew and English
vocabulary.   Title transliterated: Me'ir 'en bene ha-ne'urim.

PJ4845.L5 1878   52-59330

NL 0382552   DLC

347.7
L7471   Lindo, Abraham Alexandre.
The injurious tendency of the modifying of
our navigation laws, made manifest; and the
consequent necessity for revising the concession
made in favor of the navigation of other nations,
clearly proved... in communications addressed to
His Majesty's ministers, and principally to the
Right Hon. William Huskisson, when president of
the Board of Trade. London, S. Low, 1828.
xx,216p. 21cm.

NL 0382553   IEN PU MH NN NNC NjP ICU

Lindo, Abraham Alexandre.
... To the directors of the Colonial bank,
and of the Royal mail steam packet company.
[n.p., 1840?].
74 p. 19½ cm.
Caption title.
A letter dated 16th March,1840,and signed by A.A.Lindo,
claiming that his work in effecting the organization of
the Colonial bank and the Royal mail steam packet company entitles him to an appointment with one or the other.
Accompanied by papers in support of his contention,one
of which has special t.-p.: Letter to the proprietors
and mortgagees of estates in the island of Jamaica,on
promoting immigration   into that colony.
1.Jamaica—Comm.—H*   HG2844.L75

NL 0382554   MiU

---

ar V
7629   Lindo, Abraham Alexandre.
An argumentative statement with accompanying documents to show that the agricultural and commercial prosperity of
Jamaica will be most effectually promoted
through the combined efforts and influence
of the mercantile and planting interests.
Kingston, A. D. Y. Henriques, [18--]
xxxviii p. 20cm.

Cover title.

NL 0382555   NIC

Lindo, Abraham Alexandre
Discourse on the Passover festival, London, 30th
Mar., Westminster, 5th Apr. 1839. London, 1839.
8°

NL 0382556   NN

Lindo, Abraham Alexandre.
Dr. Underhill's testimony on the wrongs of the Negro in Jamaica
examined in a letter to the editor of "The Times."
London. Wilson. 1866. 32 pp. 8°.

G8545 — Underhill, Edward Bean. — Jamaica. Soc. sci. — Negro.

NL 0382557   MB

Lindo, Abraham Alexandre.
A retrospect of the past, as connected with
and preparatory to a faithful exposition intended
to be given to the divine will and dispensation
disclosed in the sacred books received as authority
by Jews. Cincinnati, Robinson & Jones, 1848.
49 p. 8°.

NL 0382558   PHi PPDrop OCH

Lindo, Abraham Alexandre.
A word in season from an Israelite to his brethren.   London: the author, 1839. 1 p.l., 14 p. 8°.   (no. 1.)

1. Jews in Gt. Br.: Eng.: London.
N. Y. P. L.   January 6, 1912.

NL 0382559   NN

Lindo, Algernon H.
... The art of accompanying, by Algernon H. Lindo.
New York, Boston [etc.] G. Schirmer [1916]
1 p. l., v-xii, 109 p. illus. (music) 21½ᶜᵐ.

1. Musical accompaniment. I. Title.
Library of Congress   MT68.L48   16—18771

CoU NcD
WU PPCI PBa OO OCl ODW OU NN MB CU WaU KMK InU UU
NL 0382560   DLC WaTC CaBVa Or OrCS WaSp OrP WaT IdU

VOLUME 334

Lindo, Algernon H.
　Aural tests for examinations, specially written for teachers and students preparing for examinations, by Algernon H. Lindo ... London, Phillips & Page; Boston, The Boston music co.; ₍etc., etc.₎ ʻ1923.
　　32 p. illus. (music) 22ᶜᵐ.

　　1. Ear training. 2. Music—Instruction and study. 3. Music—Examinations, questions, etc. I. Title.

　　Library of Congress　　　MT9.L56　　　　24-2170

　NL 0382561　　DLC

Lindo, Algernon H.
　Pedalling in pianoforte music, by Algernon H. Lindo ... London, K. Paul, Trench, Trubner & co., ltd.; New York, E. P. Dutton & co., 1922.
　　12, 185 p. illus. (music) 19ᶜᵐ. (*Half-title:* The musician's bookshelf ₍6₎)

　　1. Pianoforte—Instruction and study. I. Title.

　　Library of Congress　　　MT227.L67　　　22—21334

　NL 0382562　　DLC WaS MiU NIC WU PP OO OCl MiU NN

MT
220　**Lindo, Algernon H.**
L55　　Pianoforte study; hints for teachers & students. London, Augener ₍1900?₎
P52　　79 p. music. 22 cm. (Augener's edition, no. 10122)
1900

　　1. Piano - Instruction and study. I. Title. II. Series.

　NL 0382563　　CaBVaU

Lindo, Algernon H.
　Thyra. Operetta-cantata in one act for female voices. ⁄ Libretto by Ernest Pertwee. Music by Algernon H. Lindo. [Accomp. for pianoforte.]
　London. Willcocks & Co. [1884?] 59 pp. L. 8°.

　　　　　　　Mar. 21,
　E3389 — Cantatas (Female voices). — Pertwee, Ernest.

　NL 0382564　　MB

Lindo, Algernon H.
　... A treatise on modulation, with typical examples from well-known works, by Algernon H. Lindo ... London ₍etc.₎ Bosworth & co.; New York, T. B. Harms co., ʻ1913.
　　1 p. l., 75 p. 30½ᶜᵐ. (*On cover:* Bosworth edition, no. 860)

　　1. Modulation.

　　　　　　　　　　　　　　　14-12085
　　Library of Congress　　　MT52.L57

　NL 0382565　　DLC NN

Lindo, Archie.
　Bronze; short stories, articles, a poem and a play ... Mandeville, Jamaica, College press, 1944.
　　80p. front. (port.) O.

　NL 0382566　　CaBViP

Lindo, Archie.
　My heart was singing; poems and short stories, by Archie Lindo. Mandeville, Jamaica, B. W. I., College press, 1945.
　　60 p.　22cm.

　NL 0382567　　NN

Lindo, Elias Hiam, d. 1865, ed. and tr.

Manasseh ben Joseph ben Israel, 1604–1657.
　The Bible conciliator or Rabbi Manasseh ben Israel; a reconcilement of the apparent contradictions in Holy Scripture. To which are added explanatory notes, and biographical notices of the quoted authorities. By E. H. Lindo ... Glasgow, M. L. Oppenheim & co., 1902–

Lindo, Elias Hiam, *d.* 1865.
　The history of the Jews of Spain and Portugal, from the earliest times to their final expulsion from those kingdoms, and their subsequent dispersion; with complete translations of all the laws made respecting them during their long establishment in the Iberian peninsula. By E. H. Lindo ... London, Longman, Brown, Green & Longmans, 1848.
　　xiv, 384 p. 2 pl. (incl. front.) fold. facsim. 22½ᶜᵐ.

　　1. Jews in Spain. 2. Jews in Portugal.

　　Library of Congress　　　DS135.S7L7　　　5—6380

　　　CLU MiU OCH ICN NN MdBP　　　CtHC NjNbS
　NL 0382569　　DLC DAU OrP CU NcU MoSW ICU PP PU PPL NcD

Bg19p　**Lindo, Elias Hiam,** *d.* 1865.
838ℓ　　A Jewish calendar for sixty-four years, detailing the new moons, festivals, and fasts ... To which are added tables for continuing the calendar to A.M. 6000 - 2240 C.AE., and a chronological table, forming a summary of Jewish history from the Flood to the present time. With various other useful tables; by E.H. Lindo ... London, Printed by L.Thompson, to be had of the author₍etc.₎1838.
　　vi,[2],iv,[5]-134p.,1ℓ.　24½cm.
　　With autograph of Sir Moses Montefiore on inside of front cover.

DN-Ob
　NL 0382570　　CtY NcU　　WU MdBP PPDrop OClW OCH NN

Lindo, F.
　Revenge: or, The robber of Guatemala. By F. Lindo ... Cincinnati, Robinson & Jones, 1848.
　　104 p. 24ᶜᵐ.

　　Library of Congress　　　PZ3.L647R　　　7-16049†

　NL 0382571　　DLC N

FILM　**Lindo, F**
4274　　Revenge: or, The robber of Guatemala.
PR　　Cincinnati, Robinson & Jones, 1848.
v.1　　104 p.　(Wright American fiction, v.1, 1774-1850, no.1674, Research Publications Microfilm, Reel L-5)
reel
L5

　NL 0382572　　CU

822　**Lindo, Frank.**
L63d　　The dentist, a farcical duologue. London, New York, S. French ₍1873?₎
　　10p. 19cm. (French's acting edition ₍no.₎ 2236)

　NL 0382573　　IU

Lindo, Frank.
　The dentist. A farcical duologue. London: S. French, Ltd. ₍190-?₎　10 p.　12°.　(French's acting ed. of plays. v. 150 ₍no. 1₎.)

　1. Drama (English). 2. Title.
　N. Y. P. L.　　　　　　　　　October 21, 1913.

　NL 0382574　　NN

Lindo, Hugo, *ed.*
　Antología del cuento moderno centroamericano. ₍San Salvador₎ Universidad Autónoma de El Salvador, 1949–
　　v. illus. 25 cm. (Biblioteca universitaria, v. 13)
　　Biographical sketches.
　　Contents.—t. 1. Los nacidos en el siglo XIX, del maestro Gavidia a Salarrué.

　　1. Short stories, Central American. I. Title.

　　PQ7085.L5　　　　60-29806

　NL 0382575　　DLC CU NN TxU PSt

Lindo, Hugo.
　Clavelia. San Salvador [Editorial diario La prensa] 1936.
　　116 p.　19 cm.
　　On cover: Publicaciones de la Biblioteca nacional de El Salvador.
　　Poems.

　NL 0382576　　MH

Lindo, Hugo.
　El divorcio en El Salvador (historia legislativa, jurisprudencia, anotaciones críticas) ₍San Salvador₎ Univ. Autónoma de El Salvador, 1948.
　　223 p. 23 cm. (Biblioteca universitaria, v. 6)
　　Tesis—Univ. Autónoma de El Salvador.

　　1. Divorce—Salvador. I. Title. (Series: Biblioteca universitaria. San Salvador, v. 6)

　　　　　　　　　　　　　49-22268*

　NL 0382577　　DLC ICU LU TxU CU FU LNT-MA

tPQ7539　**Lindo, Hugo**
L5G8　　Guaro y champaña (relatos). San Salvador, El Salvador, 1947.
　　139 p. 14cm.

　　With author's autograph.

　NL 0382578　　CU NN NjP KU NNC

Lindo, Hugo.
　Guaro y Champaña. ₍Cuentos₎ Ilus. de Camilo Minero. San Salvador, Ministerio de Cultura, Departamento Editorial ₍1955₎
　　151 p. illus. (Colección Contemporáneos, 2)

　　I. Title. II. Title: Champaña.

　　PQ7539.L5G8　　　　56-37236 ‡

　　　KU MU WaU KyU MiU
　NL 0382579　　DLC CtY CU NN TxU IU IaU AAP LU DPU MB TU

PQ7539
.L5L5　**Lindo, Hugo.**
　　Libro de horas; poesías. Premio centroamérica, no. "15 de Septiembre" 1947. Guatemala, C. A., Editorial "El Libro de Guatemala", 1948.
　　146, [5] p. 21cm.

　　　CU InU MU CLSU
　NL 0382580　　MB CaBVaU LU NcU OCl MWelC RPB MH TxU NcU

VOLUME 334

Lindo, Hugo.
Libro de horas, poema. 2. ed. San Salvador, Editorial Ahora, 1950.
148 p. 20 cm. (Biblioteca universitaria, v. 19)

I. Title.

PQ7539.L5L5 1950

55–41499 ‡

CLSU PBL PSt
NL 0382581   DLC FU IU NN IaU KMK LU MH MNU-W CtY CU

Lindo, Hugo.
Poema eucarístico, y otros. San Salvador, 1943.
xi, 77 p. 22 cm.

I. Title.

PQ7539.L5P6   861.6   48–32647*

NL 0382582   DLC DPU KU

Lindo, Hugo.
Sinfonía del límite. ¡Edición dirigida por Trigueros de León; ilus. de Marquet Lichet¡ San Salvador, Ministerio de Cultura, Dirección General de Bellas Artes, 1953.
148 p. illus. 22 cm.
Poems.

I. Title.

PQ7539.L5S5   54–25999 ‡

NL 0382583   DLC CU KU IU TxU NN DPU PSt

Lindo, Hugo.
... Los tres regalos del "guegue," leyenda nicaragüense; ilustraciones de Mario Torrealba. ¡Santiago de Chile¡ Zig-zag ¡1940¡
¡29¡ p. col. illus. 16 x 18ᶜᵐ. ¡Cuentos ilustrados para niños; directora: Henriette Morvan¡

I. Title.

Library of Congress   43–1720
PZ74.1.L5

NL 0382584   DLC MiD

Lindo, J   A.
Description of a trip to Niigata, along the Shinshiu-road and back by the Mikuni pass. By J. A. Lindo.
(*In Asiatic society of Japan. Transactions. Yokohama ¡etc.¡ 1883. 23ᶜᵐ. v. 3, pt. 1, p. 52–80)*
"Reprint of the first edition, published in 1875, edited by the secretaries ¡of the society¡"

1. Japan—Description and travel.

A C 38–3138
Chicago. Univ. Library   AS552.A83   vol. 3
for Library of Congress   [AS552.Y8   vol. 3, pt. 1]
¡4¡   (068.52)

NL 0382585   ICU NcD OU DLC

Lindo, J. A.
On some Japanese woods. (In Asiatic society of Japan. 1876. v. 4, p. 50–54)

NL 0382586   OU MH-A

Lindo, J   A.
On some Japanese woods. By J. A. Lindo ...
(*In Asiatic society of Japan. Transactions. Tōkyō, 1888. 23ᶜᵐ. v. 4, p. 50–54)*
"Reprint of the original edition ¡of 1876¡ edited by the council ¡of the society¡"

1. Trees—Japan. 2. Wood.

A C 38–3153
Chicago. Univ. Library   AS552.A83   vol. 4
for Library of Congress   [AS552.Y8   vol. 4]
¡4¡   (068.52)

NL 0382587   ICU NcD DLC

Lindo, João Amoroso.
Paulo, apaixonado! Novella de amor, humorismo; pequena critica aos costumes politicos, epoca–1928, scenario–Copacabana, por João Amoroso Lindo. Rio de Janeiro, Civilização brasileira editora, 1932.
175 p. 18¼ᶜᵐ.

I. Title.

Library of Congress   PQ9697.L55P3   33–24813
¡2¡   869.3

NL 0382588   DLC

¡**Lindo, Juan**¡ Al publico. ¡Comayagua, Impr. del Progreso, 1850¡/¡3¡p. 32cm. (Central American miscellaneous documents. 50)

NL 0382589   CU-B

¡**Lindo, Mark Prager**¡ 1819–1877.
Volledige werken van den ouden Heer Smits ¡pseud.¡ uitg. door zijn vriend Mulder ... 2. goedkoope uitg. Schiedam, H. A. M. Roelants, 1882–83.
5 v. 20ᶜᵐ.
CONTENTS.—deel 1. Levensschets. Brieven en uitboezemingen. Losse schetsen in en om Parijs, in den zomer van 1852. Familie van ons. Beden om hulp.—deel 2. Clementine. Le saltimbanque. Uittreksels uit het dagboek en nadere levensberichten van wijlen den Heer Janus Snor.—deel 3–4. Uit den Nederlandschen spectator.—deel 5. Verspreide stukken.

I. Mulder, Lodewijk, 1822–   ed.

D–356
Library of Congress   PT5854.L6 1882

NL 0382590   DLC

839.31
L645a   **Lindo, Mark Prager, 1819–1879.**
Afdrukken van indrukken, met talryke houten andere sneden, door den ouden Heer Smits en zijn vriend [Lodewijk] Mulder. Arnhem, D.A. Thieme [1854]
ii, 292p. illus. 25cm.

1075886   I. Mulder, Lodewijk, 1822–1907, joint author. II. Title.

NL 0382591   TxU

PT5854
L6   **Lindo, Mark Prager, 1819–1877.**
1877   Kompleete werken van den ouden Heer Smits, uitg. door zijn vriend Mulder. 's Gravenhage, D. A. Thieme, 1877–79.
5 v.

Contents.– 1. Brieven en uitboezemingen. Losse schetsen in en om Parijs, in den zomer van 1852. Familie van ons. Beden om hulp.– 2–4. Uit den Nederlandschen Spectator.– 5. Verspreide stukken.

NL 0382592   CU

Lindo, Mark Prager, 1819–1877, ed.
De Nederlandsche spectator. 1856–29. Feb. 1908. Arnhem, D. A. Thieme; ¡etc., etc.¡ 1856–1908.

Lindo, Mark Prager, 1819–1877, tr.
Wie niet sterk is moet slim zijn, of Een avond vol vergissingen
see under   Goldsmith, Oliver, 1728–1774.

Lindo, William Cleaver
Plans and estimates for the proposed boat course on the Olentangy River by ... Columbus, Ohio state university, 1896.
2–9, x numb. 1.
Thesis (C.E.) – Ohio state university.

NL 0382595   OU

Lindo et Zelaya, Juan.
Propositiones De Iure Naturali, Ac Regio Castellae, Et Indiarum. Defendendae A.D. Joanne Lindo et Zelaya Sub disciplina D.D. Iosephi Mariae Alvarez Iuris Civ. Profes. Guatemalae M.DCCC.IX.   Apud Arevalo.
1 p.l., 37 p. 4°. engr.

NL 0382596   RPJCB

Lindo-Webb, James.
Condensed English tourist guide to Palma and other places of interest in Majorca. Palma, Impr. F. Soler.

NL 0382597   NN

Lindo Z   , Erasmo Carías
see
Carías Lindo Z   , Erasmo.

Lindö, K
Hevi-teny amy ny filazantsara nosoratany li'oka. Antananarivo, Den Norske Mission, 1894.

NL 0382599   MH

W 4   **LINDOE, Robert**
L68   Dissertatio medica inauguralis de melancholia ... Lugduni
1792   Batavorum, Haak, 1792.
L 2   29 p. 25 cm.
    Diss. - Leyden.

NL 0382600   DNLM

Slavery
E   **Lindoe, Robert.**
441   Observations upon slavery; setting forth, that to hold the principle of slavery is to deny Christ. London, J. Hatchard, 1824.
M46
v.23   34 p. 23cm.
no.4
    No. 4 in a vol. lettered: Pamphlets on slavery, 4.
    May anti-slavery pamphlets, v. 23.

    1. Slavery.   2. Slavery in the Bible.

NL 0382601   NIC NNC CtY PPL OClWHi

VOLUME 334

Lindoft, Hazel Madelin.
Hearts for adoption! A comedy-drama in three acts, by Hazel Madelin Lindoft ... New York, N. Y., Los Angeles, Calif., S. French; London, S. French, ltd.; ₁etc., etc.₎ °1938.
89, ₁1₎ p. diagr. 18½ᵐ.

I. Title.   38-37805

Library of Congress   PS3523.I565H4 1938
———— Copy 2.
Copyright D pub. 60150   ₁2₎   812.5

NL   0382602   DLC

Lindolf, Alfred
Moses Mendelssohn. Schauspiel in einem Akt. Hannover, Helwing, 1874.
28 p.

NL   0382603   OCH

Lindolf, Alfred.
Vatels Geheimniss. Lustspiel in einem Akt. Hannover, Schluter, 1874.
35 p.   8°.

NL   0382604   NN

Lindolf, Alfred.
Nitetis. Dramatisches Gedicht in fünf Akten. Mit freier Benutzung eines Romans des Georg Ebers. Hannover, T. Mierzinsky, 1873.
103 p.   12°.

NL   0382605   NN

Lindolfo Rocha ₁por₎ Aloísio de Carvalho Filho ₁et al. Rio de Janeiro₎ Ministério da Educação e Saúde, Serviço de Documentação ₁1953₎
52 p. 22 cm.

1. Rocha, Lindolfo Jacinto, 1862-1911. I. Carvalho, Aloysio de, ed.
PQ9697.R6235Z75   56-21330 ‡

NL   0382606   DLC DPU DS IU NIC TxU CU KU

Lindon, B
Love & loyalty. 1795. (Larpent collection. Ms. #1074) New York, ₁1954.₎
(In Three centuries of drama: English, Larpent collection)

Microprint.

I. Title. II. Larpent collection. Ms. #1074.

NL   0382607   MoU

Herbarium
Lindon, Edward Francis, 1848-
Flora of Bournemouth including the Isle of Purbeck, being an account of the flowering plants, ferns, &c. of the country within a twelve-mile radius of the centre of Bournemouth. Bournemouth, H.G. Commin ₁1900₎
viii, 290p. front.(fold. map) 19cm.

1. Botany--England--Bournemouth.

NL   0382608   TxDaM

Lindon, Frances (Brawne) 1800-1865.
Keats   Letters from Fanny Brawne to Fanny Keats.
*EC8   [Norwood,Mass.? 189-?]
K2262   93ℓ.   24cm.,in case 25.5cm.
YBf890ℓ   Contains rough proofs of 21 letters dated 19 Sep. 1820 to 1824, trimmed and mounted on 54 leaves; a leaf containing a layout for a sample page; original typewritten copies of 11 additional letters, on 20 leaves; carbon copies of 9 letters of the latter group, on 17 leaves. The title is taken from the caption to the

proof sheets (leaf 2); a ms. t.-p. precedes (leaf 1): Copies of original letters of Fanny Brawne to Fanny Keats 1820-24.
Prepared by Fred Holland Day from the original letters, in his possession, for an edition that was never published (see the pref. to H. E. Rollins and S. M. Parrish: Keats and the Bostonians (1951)). The letters as part of his Keats collection, were bequeathed by Day to the Keats memorial   house, Hampstead, Eng. Unbound; in   half morocco case.

NL   0382610   MH

Lindon, *Mrs.* **Frances (Brawne)** 1800-1865.
Letters of Fanny Brawne to Fanny Keats ⟨1820-1824⟩ edited with a biographical introduction by Fred Edgcumbe ... with a foreword by Maurice Buxton Forman. London, Oxford university press, H. Milford, 1936.
xxvii, 77, ₁1₎ p. front., illus., ports., fold. facsim. 19½ᵐ.

1. Llanos Gutiérrez, Frances Mary (Keats) 1803-1889. I. Edgcumbe, Fred, ed. II. Title.
                                                37-1962

Library of Congress   PR4836.A65 1936
Copyright A ad int. 22372   ₁5₎   920.7

CSmH
NL   0382611   DLC KEmT OrP OrPR MH CtY PWcT PBm OCU ViU

Lindon, Frances (Brawne) 1800-1865.
Letters of Fanny Brawne to Fanny Keats, 1820-1824; edited with biographical introduction by Fred Edgcumbe ... with a preface by Maurice Buxton Forman. New York, Oxford university press, 1937.
xxix, 103 p. front., illus., ports., fold. facsim. 21½ cm.

1. Llanos Gutiérrez, Frances Mary (Keats) 1803-1889. I. Edgcumbe, Fred, ed. II. Title.
PR4836.A65 1937   920.7   37—3789

PSC PHC PIm MH MoU NcD IEN MiU TU MeB
WaSp OrCS ViU PU MiU OU ODW OO OC1 NN WaU MB PPL PPT
NL   0382612   DLC OrSaW CaBVaU NB OrU WaTC Or WaWW WaS

Lindon, Mrs. Frances (Brawne) 1800-1865
Letters of Fanny Brawne to Fanny Keats (1820-1824) edited with a biographical introduction by Fred Edgcumbe... with a foreword by M. B. Forman.
London, Oxford university press, ₁1939₎
77 p.

NL   0382613   OC1W DCU

Lindon, Frances (Brawne) 1800-1865.
Keats   ... Nickel List and his merry men or Germany
*EC8   in the 17th century. By Fanny Brawne.
K2262   [Edinburgh] 1942.
YBf942ℓ   [81]-91p. 23cm.,in folder 24cm.
Offprint from Blackwood's magazine, vol.251, no.1516, Feb. 1942.
Caption title.
Original blue wrappers, in cloth folder.
Inscribed: For Harvard College Library. One of six copies of "Nickel List" printed off for

me before the publication of the February 1942 issue of "Blackwood's Magazine." M. Buxton Forman.
Laid in is an engraved portrait of Fanny Brawne.

NL   0382615   MH

BS1604   **Lindon, Jérôme,** 1925-   *tr.*
.F7L5   **Bible.** *O. T. Jonah. French. 1955. Lindon.*
Jonas; le livre de Jonas, traduit par Jérôme Lindon. ₁Paris₎ Éditions de Minuit ₁1955₎

---

812   **Lindon, Patrick C**
L644d   Dr. Baxter's servants. Farce, in one act, by Patrick C. Lindon. To which is added a description of the costumes, cast of the characters ... Clyde, O., Ames' publishing co., c1898.
7p.   (On cover: Ames' series of standard and minor drama. no.407)

NL   0382617   IU CLSU NN RPB PU

Lindon, Raymond.
Étretat; son histoire, ses légendes. ₁Paris₎ Éditions de minuit ₁1949₎
227, ₁21₎ p. illus. (part fold.) 19 cm.
Bibliography: p. ₁229₎-₁233₎

1. Étretat, France.
                                                A 52-5530
New York. Public Libr.
for Library of Congress   ₁1₎

NL   0382618   NN

Lindon, Raymond.
... Histoire de la Haute cour de justice en France. Paris, Éditions universelles ₁1945₎
128 p. 18½ᵐ.

1. France. Haute cour de justice.
                                                46-16528

NL   0382619   DLC MH CLU

Lindon, Raymond.
Histoire savoureuse deu parc à huitres d'Etretat. ₁Paris₎ Éditions du Minuit ₁1955₎ 59 p. 19cm.

1. Oyster culture--France--   Étretat.

NL   0382620   NN

Lindon-Howard, Percy
    see   Howard, Percy Lindon-

Lindon Smith, Corinna
    see
Smith, Corinna Haven (Putnam) (1876-   )

Lindonk, J. Van, joint author.

Tuymelaar, C   T.
Pseudoniemen uit nederlandsche en vreemde literatuur, verzameld door C. T. Tuymelaar en J. van Lindonk. Assen, Uitgave Born n. v. ₁1939₎

VOLUME 334

Lindop, Audrey Erskine, 1920–
The bandit and the priest. Pocket Books, c1953.

Original title: The singer not the song.

NL 0382624   WaE

Lindop, Audrey Erskine, 1920–
Details of Jeremy Stretton. London, Heinemann [1955]
276 p. 19 cm.

American ed. (New York, Appleton-Century-Crofts) has title: The outer ring.

I. Title: The outer ring. II. Title.

PZ3.L6474De   823.91   55–30419 ‡

NL 0382625   DLC CaBVa LU MH

Lindop, Audrey Erskine, 1920–
Fortune my foe, by Audrey Lindop. New York and London, Harper & brothers [1947]
4 p. l., 311 p. 21½ cm.

"First [American] edition."
"This story is published in England under the title of In me, my enemy."

I. Title.

PZ3.L6474Fo   47–1579 rev

NL 0382626   DLC ViU PP WaSp WaE OrP CaBVa

Lindop, Audrey Erskine, 1920–
Out of the whirlwind. London, Heinemann [1951]
480 p. 19 cm.

I. Title.

PZ3.L6474Ou   51–39005 rev ‡

NL 0382627   DLC CaBVa WaE WaS

Lindop, Audrey Erskine, 1920–
Out of the whirlwind. New York, Appleton-Century-Crofts [1952, °1951]
414 p. 22 cm.

I. Title.

PZ3.L6474Ou 2   52–8831 rev ‡

NL 0382628   DLC ViU

Lindop, Audrey Erskine, 1920–
The outer ring. New York, Appleton-Century-Crofts [1955]
308 p. 21 cm.

London ed. (Heinemann) has title: Details of Jeremy Stretton.

I. Title.

PZ3.L6474Ov   55–5439 ‡

NL 0382629   DLC Or WaT ViU OOxM OCU PP

Lindop, Audrey Erskine, 1920–
The singer not the song. London, Heinemann [1953]
367 p. 21 cm.

I. Title.

PZ3.L6474Si   53–25384 ‡

WaS WaSp WaSpG WaT WaTC WaWW
IdB IdPI IdU MtBC MtU OrCS OrP OrPR OrU Wa WaE WaPS
NL 0382630   DLC MH Or OrStbM OrSaW OrU-M MtU-M CaBVaU

Lindop, Audrey Erskine, 1920–
The singer not the song. New York, Appleton-Century-Crofts [1953]
371 p. 21 cm.

I. Title.

PZ3.L6474Si 2   52—14029 ‡

~~Library of Congress~~   [90m1]

FTaSU WaSpG
WaS WaSp WaE CLSU Or OrU OrP CoU OrStbM OrU WaT TNJ
NL 0382631   DLC IdB FU OCl PPCCH OOxM PP OU OO NN TxU

PR6023
.I58S5 **Lindop, Audrey Erskine,** 1920–
1954   The singer not the song. London, Reprint Society [1954]
351 p. 19cm.

NL 0382632   ViU

Lindop, Audrey Erskine, 1920–
Soldiers' daughters never cry, a novel. [New York] Simon and Schuster, 1948.
310 p. 21 cm.

I. Title.

PZ3.L6474So   48–3949 rev*

NL 0382633   DLC Mi

Lindop, Audrey Erskine, 1920–
Soldiers' daughters never cry, by Audrey Erskine Lindop. Melbourne [etc.] W. Heinemann [1949] 313 p. 19cm.

524955B. I. Title.
N. Y. P. L.   December 4, 1950

NL 0382634   NN

Lindop, Audrey Erskine, 1920–
The tall headlines. London, Heinemann [1950]
326 p. 19 cm.

I. Title.

PZ3.L6474Tal   50–30862 rev

NL 0382635   DLC

Lindop, Audrey Erskine, 1920–
The tall headlines. New York, Macmillan, 1950.
326 p. 19 cm.

I. Title.

PZ3.L6474Tal 2   50–9821 rev

NL 0382636   DLC IdB WaE WaS

FILM
2330   Lindop, Boyd Edwin.

The university and radio education: opportunities and their acceptance. Los Angeles, University of California, 1953.

Microfilm copy (positive)
Collation of the original: vi, 313 l.
Thesis—University of Los Angeles.
Bibliography: leaves 265–281.

1. Radio in education. I. Title.

NL 0382637   ViU

Lindop, Kenneth James Hulme, 1898–
Burma. *Settlement dept.*
Report on the settlement operations in the cadastrally surveyed portion of the Myitkyina district. Season 1926–28. By K. J. H. Lindop ... Rangoon, Superintendent, government printing and stationery, Burma, 1929.

Lindor and Adelaide, a moral tale
see under Sayer, Edward.

Lindor; or Early engagements; a novel
see under Selden, Catharine.

PQ
1947   Lindor, ou Les excès de l'amour. Lettres.
A1L64   Londres, Vente, 1772.
183 p.

NL 0382641   CLU

Lindores Abbey.
The chartularies of Balmerino and Lindores
see under Balmerino Abbey.

Lindores abbey.
Chartulary of the abbey of Lindores, 1195–1479; ed. from the original manuscript at Caprington castle, Kilmarnock, with translation and abstracts of the charters, illustrative notes, and appendices, by the Right Rev. John Dowden ... Edinborough, Printed by T. and A. Constable for the Scottish history society, 1903.
xcv, 351, [1] p. 4 pl., 3 facsim. 23cm. (Half-title: Publications of the Scottish history society, vol. XLII)
Latin, with English translation.
The Introduction contains a history of the abbey, and a biography of the founder, David, earl of Huntingdon.
1. Huntingdon, David, earl of, 1144?–1219. I. Dowden, John, bp. of Edinburgh, 1840– ed.
                                                    4–3

Library of Congress   DA750.S25 vol. 42

ViU MH MB NN
NL 0382643   DLC PPPD WaSpG InStme CBBD MoU MiU OCU OCl

LINDORES   Abbey.
Liber Sancte Marie de Lundoris. [Edited by W.B.D.D. Turnbull.] Edinburgi, 1841.

Plate.
(In BALMERINO, Scotland – Abbey. The chartularies of Balmerino and Lindores.)

NL 0382644   MH

Lindorf, Heinrich, 1907–
Technische Temperaturmessungen. Essen, W. Girardet [1952]
168 p. illus. 22 cm. (Fachbücher für Ingenieure)

1. Thermometers and thermometry. I. Title.

QC271.L52   52–39345 ‡

NL 0382645   DLC PU-Math CU NN IU OU

VOLUME 334

Lindorf, Paul.
... Die notwendigkeit einer reform unserer notenschreibweise und ein weg dazu. Görlitz-Biesnitz, Druck und auftragsweise verlegt durch Druckerei und verlagsanstalt Hans Kretschmer ₍1937₎

15 p. illus. (music) 21ᶜᵐ.

1. Musical notation.

39–23034

Library of Congress   ML432.A2L5

₍2₎   781.21

NL   0382646   DLC NN

Lindorf and Caroline; or, The danger of credulity... see under [Naubert, Christiane Benedicte Eugenie (Hebenstreit) Holderieder] 1756–1819.

Lindorfer, Joseph, ed.
M2152
.L55O3   **Catholic Church.   Liturgy and ritual.**
Officium des katholischen Chorregenten. Mit Bemerkungen über sonstige kirchendienstliche Verrichtungen von Joseph Lindorfer. Sallach.

Lindorfer, Robert Karl.
The influence of hormonal alterations and avitaminosis D on swine influenza virus infection in mice. Ann Arbor, University Microfilms ₍1955₎
(₍University Microfilms, Ann Arbor, Mich.₎ Publication no. 13,367)
Microfilm copy of typescript. Positive.
Collation of the original: iv, 57 l. tables.
Thesis—University of Minnesota.
Abstracted in Dissertation abstracts, v. 15 (1955) no. 10, p. 1700.
Bibliography: leaves 47–57.

1. Virus diseases. 2. Vitamins. 3. Hormones, Sex.

Microfilm AC–1 no. 13,367   Mic 55–302

Minnesota. Univ. Libr.
for Library of Congress   ₍1₎†

NL   0382649   MnU DLC

Lindorff, Theodore Julius.
Carnelian and white. Words by K. L. Roberts. ₍Ithaca₎ Cornell University Glee Banjo & Mandolin Clubs ₍°1906₎
5 p. 35 cm.
For piano, with interlinear words.

1. Cornell University—Songs and music. ɪ. Title.

M1959.C6L   M 57–127

NL   0382650   DLC

Lindorff, Theodore Julius.
Fight for Cornell. Words by K. L. Roberts. ₍Ithaca₎ Cornell University Glee Banjo and Mandolin Clubs ₍°1907₎
7 p. 35 cm.

1. Cornell University—Songs and music. 2. Football—Songs and music. ɪ. Title.

M1959.C6L   M 57–115

NL   0382651   DLC

M1508   **Lindorff, Theodore Julius**
L5   ₍Three queens. Selections₎
Musical selections from the comic opera Three queens. Book by John Clarke; music by T. J. Lindorff. Interpolation by Lewis B. Franklin. ₍Flushing, N. Y.?, N. p.₎ 1908₎

22p. 27½cm.

I. Title: Three queens.
II. ₍Clarke,   John.

NL   0382652   NBuG

Lindorff, Theodore Julius.
Panatela; a political comic opera in three acts, written for the Cornell Masque./ Book and lyrics by Kenneth L. Roberts... Romeyn Berry...music by T. J. Lindorff...H. C. Schuyler... H. E. Childs... ₍Ithaca₎ Cornell Masque, cop. 1907. 54 p. f°.

English words.
Vocal score.

1. Operettas.—Piano and voice.   2. Operas (Comic). 3. Schuyler, Hender Clarke. 4. Childs, Hamilton   Eugene. 5. Roberts, Kenneth Lewis.
6. Berry, Romevn. 7. Title.
N. Y. P 1   December 3, 1917.

NL   0382653   NN NBuG OC1 NjP

785.6   **Lindorff-Larsen, Eilert.**
L32c   Concerto for saxofon og piano, for Eb saxophone and piano.   København, Wilhelm Hansen ₍°1954₎
score (15 p.) and part. 31 cm.   (Wilhelm Hansen Edition, Nr. 3969)
DLC: M1353.L

1. Concertos (Saxophone)—Solo with piano.

NL   0382654   LU DLC

Lindorm, Bo, 1914–   comp.
DL867   **Lindorm, Erik, 1889–1941,** *comp.*
.L5   Gustaf v och hans tid ... en bokfilm. Stockholm, Wahlström & Widstrand ₍1936–

Lindorm, Bo, 1914–
TL720
.9   **Aerotransport, Aktiebolaget.**
.A35A53   På säkra vingar, 20 års lufttrafik, 1924/1944. Stockholm, Ab Aerotransport ₍1944₎

Lindorm, Erik, 1889–1941.
Bekännelser. ₍Dikter₎ Stockholm, Bonnier ₍1922₎
76 p.

NL   0382657   WaU

Lindorm, Erik, 1889–1941, *comp.*
... Carl xiv Johan–Carl xv och deras tid, 1810–1872, en bokfilm av Erik Lindorm. Stockholm, Wahlström & Widstrand ₍1942₎
480 p. illus. (incl. ports., map, facsims., music) 30ᶜᵐ.
At head of title: Ny svensk historia.
"Offsettryck."
"Under överinseende av: Riksbibliotekarie Oscar Wieselgren."

1. Sweden—Hist.—1814–1905—Pictorial works. 2. Sweden—Hist.—1814–1905—Sources. 3. Sweden—Soc. life & cust.

46–33978

Library of Congress   DL809.L5

₍2₎   948.07

NL   0382658   DLC WaU

Lindorm, Erik, 1899–1941.
Dikter. Stockholm, A.Bonnier, 1946.
298p. 20cm.

NL   0382659   CtY MnU MH CU NN NNC CLU

Lindorm, Erik, 1889–1941.
Domedagar. ₍Dikter₎ Stockholm, Bonnier ₍1920₎
70 p.

NL   0382660   WaU MH

NL   0382661   NN WU

DL650
.L5   **Lindorm, Erik, 1889–1941.**
Ett folk på marsch. En bokfilm. Stockholm, Bonnier, 19₎
v.   illus. 29 cm. (*His* Ny svensk historia)
Bonniers folkbibliotek.
Contents.—
5. 1947–1950, av Per-Erik Lindorm. 57.— skr (S 67–23)

1. Sweden—Hist. ɪ. Lindorm, Per Erik. ɪɪ. Title.

DL650.L5   67–97693

NL   0382662   DLC

Lindorm, Erik, 1889–1941.
Från Delaware till Garbo; en bokfilm till Delawarejubiléet 1938, redigerad av Erik Lindorm.   Stockholm: Åhlén & Åkerlund ₍1937₎ 61 p. illus. (incl. facsims.), mounted col'd plates, ports. (1 col'd, mounted.) 39½cm.

938702A. 1. Swedes in the U. S.   I. Title.   June 28, 1938
N. Y. P. L.

NL   0382663   NN OrP IdU CU MnHi MnU PP OC1

Lindorm, Erik, 1889–1941, *comp.*
Gustaf v och hans tid ... en bokfilm.   Stockholm, Wahlström & Widstrand ₍1936–47₎
4 v. illus., ports., facsims. 30 cm. (*His* Ny svensk historia)
Vol. ₍4₎ by Bo Lindorm and Per-Erik Lindorm.
Contents.—₍1₎ 1907–1918.—₍2₎ 1919–1927.—₍3₎ 1928–1938.—₍4₎ 1938–1947.

1. Sweden — Hist. — Gustavus v, 1907–1950 — Pictorial works. 2. Sweden—Hist.—Gustavus v, 1907–1950—Sources. 3. Gustaf v, King of Sweden, 1858–1950. 4. Sweden—Soc. life & cust. ɪ. Lindorm, Bo, 1914–   comp. ɪɪ. Lindorm, Per Erik, comp. ɪɪɪ. Title.

DL867.L5   948.5   41–13472 rev*

NL   0382664   DLC MnU NN WaU MH

948.5   **Lindorm, Erik, 1889–1941, comp.**
L6451m   Med kungen för fosterlandet; en bokfilm, 1858–1933. Stockholm, Bonnier ₍1933₎
95 p. illus.

NL   0382665   WaU PPAmSwM

VOLUME 334

948.507
fL645m
LINDORM, Erik, 1889-1941, comp.
Med kungen för fosterlandet; en bokfilm, 1858-1933... Stockholm, Albert
Bonniers förlag (1934)
95, (1) p. illus. (incl. ports.,
facsims.) 36cm.
Portrait of King Gustaf V on cover.
Consists of photographic reproductions of selected issues of various
newspapers published in Sweden 1858-
1933.
1. Gustaf V, King of Sweden, 1858-
2. Sweden. Hist Gxv
1814-1905. 3. Sweden. History.1905-
I. Title.

NL 0382666   MnU

Lindorm, Erik, 1889-1941
Mellan himmel och jord, av Erik Lindorm. Stockholm, A.
Bonnier (1924)
209, (2) p. 19½ᵐ.

I. Title.

33-21982
Library of Congress   PT9875.L63M4 1924   839.746

NL 0382667   DLC MnU WU

Lindorm, Erik, 1889-1941.
Min värld, av Erik Lindorm. Stockholm: A. Bonnier (1918)
61 p. 19cm.

212360B. 1. Poetry, Swedish.   I. Title.
N.Y.P.L.   April 16, 1943

NL 0382668   NN MH WaU

Lindorm, Erik, 1889-1941.
Moloch; lustspel i tre akter, av Erik Lindorm. Stockholm:
A. Bonniers förlag (1926). 107 p. 12°.

1. Drama, Swedish. 2. Title.
N.Y.P.L.   November 15, 1927

NL 0382669   NN CU

Lindorm, Erik, 1889-1941.
Ny svensk historia... En bokfilm av Erik Lindorm. Stock-
holm, Wahlström & Widstrand (1938-43) 5 v. illus. 30cm.
Vols. 1-2, 4. uppl.
After the death of Erik Lindorm the work was continued by his collaborators Olle
Hilding and Bo Lindorm.—cf. Pref., v. 5.
CONTENTS.—bd. 1) Oscar II och hans tid. (1941)—bd. 2-4) Gustaf V och hans
tid, 1907-1938. (1938-43)—bd. 5) Carl XIV Johan — Carl XV och deras tid, 1810-
1872. (1942)
—— Another issue
Vol. 1. (1934); v. 2, 2. uppl. (1937)

399479-83B. 1. Sweden—Hist., 1814-   . I. Hilding, Olle. II. Lindorm, Bo. III. Title.   June 25, 1947
N.Y.P.L.

NL 0382670   NN OC1

Lindorm, Erik, 1889-
Oscar II och hans tid; en bokfilm, av
Erik Lindorm. Stockholm: Wahlström & Widstrand (1934)
2 v. illus. (incl. facsims., ports.) 30½cm. (His Ny svensk
historia)
Paged continuously.

777610-11A. 1. Sweden—Hist.—   Oscar II, 1872-1907.
N.Y.P.L.   November 8, 1935

NL 0382671   NN MnU MH CtY

Lindorm, Erik, 1889-   comp.
... Oscar II och hans tid; en bokfilm, av Erik Lindorm. 2.
upplagan. Stockholm, Wahlström & Widstrand (1936)
509 p., 1 l. illus. (incl. ports., facsims., music) 30½ᵐ. (His Ny
svensk historia)
Colored portrait on cover.
Issued in 2 parts.

1. Sweden—Hist.—Oscar II, 1872-1907—Pictorial works. 2. Sweden—
Hist.—Oscar II, 1872-1907—Sources. 3. Oscar II, king of Sweden, 1829-
1907. 4. Sweden—Soc. life & cust.   I. Title.
41-39872
Library of Congress   DL852.L5 1936
(2)   948.5

NL 0382672   DLC PPAmSwM WaU

DL852
L5   Lindorm, Erik, 1889-1941, comp.
1943   ... Oscar II och hans tid; en bokfilm, av Erik Lindorm. 5.
upplagan. Stockholm, Wahlström & Widstrand c1943)
500 p. 1 l. illus. (incl. ports., facsims., music) 30½ᵐ. (His Ny
svensk historia)
Colored portrait on cover.

NL 0382673   CU

Lindorm, Erik, 1889-1941.
...På marsch; nya dikter. Stockholm: A. Bonnier (1934)
124 p. 24cm.

786591A. 1. Poetry, Swedish.   I. Title.
N.Y.P.L.   November 14, 1935

NL 0382674   NN ICU

LINDORM, Erik, 1889-1941.
På villovägar och andra kåserier.
1922.
Contents: På villovägar: Ceders
salonger. Maxim. "Orfeus i underjor-
den". Folies Caprices. Cecils. Fem
"frön". Gröna Lunds tivoli. Birger-
jarlsgatan nattetid. Farser för dagen
Utan telefon. Bellman privatim.

NL 0382675   WaS

Lindorm, Erik, 1889-1941.
Personligt ovett. Stockholm, Bonnier
c1932)
238 p.

NL 0382676   WaU MnU

PT   Lindorm, Erik, 1889-1941
+9875   Revyn 1928. Stockholm, A. Bonnier
+L63   (1928)
R4   71p. illus. (part col.) 31cm.

NL 0382677   WU

Lindorm, Erik, 1889-1941.
Rötmånad; komedi i tre akter, av Erik Lindorm. Stockholm: A. Bonniers förlag (1928). 119 p. 12°.

1. Drama, Swedish. 2. Title.
N.Y.P.L.   September 11, 1928

NL 0382678   NN CU MH

Lindorm, Erik, 1889-1941, comp.
Selma Lagerlöf: en bokfilm. Regissör: Erik Lindorm.
Stockholm, Albert Bonniers förlag (1933)
111 p. incl. illus. (incl. ports., plan, facsims.) geneal. tab. 29½ᵐ.
"Till andre bibliotekarien d: r Nils Afzelius frambär jag ett tack för
att han ställt ett stort Selma Lagerlöf-material till förfogande. Och så
tackar jag min medhjälpare herr Olle Hilding, för oförtröttad flit."
A few selections from Selma Lagerlöf are included in this collection
of literary and pictorial material in her honor.
"Selma Lagerlöfs samlade skrifter": p. 109.

1. Lagerlöf, Selma Ottiliana Lovisa, 1858-   I. *Afzelius, Nils,
1894-   II. Hilding, Olle.
A C 34-2363
Title from N. Y. Pub.   Libr. Printed by L. C.

NL 0382679   NN OC1 MnU WU WaU

Lindorm, Erik, 1889-1941.
Svenska kärleksdikter; et urval av
Erik Lindorm. Stockholm, A. Bonnier
(1926)
155 p. 20cm.
1. Swedish poetry. Collections. I.
Title.

NL 0382680   MnU

Lindorm, Erik, 1889-1941.
Tal till mitt hjärta. Stockholm, Vanadis
c1912)
62 p.

NL 0382681   WaU

Lindorm, Erik, 1889-1941.
Tal til mitt hjärta. 2ª uppl. Stockholm,
A. Bonnier, [1915]
64+ p.
Poems.

NL 0382682   MH

Lindorm, Erik, 1889-1941.
...Tal till mitt hjärta. Min värld. Stockholm: A. Bonnier
(1935) 141 p. 24cm.

834299A. 1. Poetry, Swedish.   I. Title. II. Title: Min värld.
N.Y.P.L.   August 12, 1936

NL 0382683   NN

Lindorm, Erik, 1889-1941.
Uppslagsbok för alla.
(Stockholm) Ahlen & Akerlunds förlag, Albert
Bonnier, c1939)
2 v.

NL 0382684   OC1

Lindorm, Erik, 1889-1941.
...Valda dikter. Stockholm: A. Bonniers förlag (1925).
194 p. 8°.

1. Poetry, Swedish.
N.Y.P.L.   July 14, 1926

NL 0382685   NN WaU ICU MH OC1

Lindorm, Per Erik, ed.
Bilen går vidare. 50 år med KAK i motorismens tjänst;
en bokfilm. (Stockholm, Kunglinga Automobil klubben,
1953)
78 p. illus., ports. 30 cm.

1. Automobile industry and trade—Sweden. 2. Kungliga Automobil
klubben.   I. Title.
TL89.L5   54-20353

NL 0382686   DLC NN

DL650   Lindorm, Per Erik.
.L5
Lindorm, Erik, 1889-1941.
Ett folk på marsch. En bokfilm. Stockholm, Bonnier,
19

VOLUME 334

Lindorm, Per Erik, comp.

DL867
.L5

Lindorm, Erik, 1889–1941, comp.
Gustaf v och hans tid ... en bokfilm. Stockholm, Wahlström & Widstrand [1936–47]

Lindorm, Per Erik.
Kärleksöden i Norden under tusen år; en antologi. Stockholm, Sohlman [1949]
447 p. illus. 22 cm.
Bibliography: p. 445–447.

1. Swedish literature (Selections: Extracts, etc.) 2. Love.
I. Title.
PT9555.L53   839.5082   50–32443

NL 0382689   DLC NN WaU IEN

Lindorm, Per Erik.
Stockholm genom sju sekler; från Birger Jarl till Gustav
vi Adolf. En bokfilm. [Stockholm] Sohlman [1951]
511 p. illus., ports., maps. 30 cm.

1. Stockholm—Hist.—Sources. 2. Stockholm in literature.
DL976.L5   52–24877

NL 0382690   DLC MnU NN

Lindorm, Per Erik, comp.
Svensk humor under 100 år, en kavalkad i ord och bild.
Stockholm, L. Hökerberg [1948]
543 p. illus. 25 cm.

1. Swedish wit and humor.   I. Title.
                 A 49–2947*
Illinois. Univ. Library
for Library of Congress   [1]

NL 0382691   IU ICU

Lindorm, Per Erik.
Vårt kristna arv; från Ansgar till våra dagar, en bokfilm.
[Stockholm?], Svensk bokfilm [1952]
511 p. illus., ports., facsims. 31 cm.

1. Sweden—Church history—Sources. 2. Svenska kyrkan.—Hist.—
Sources.   I. Title.
BR1012.L5   A 53–2842
Minnesota. Univ. Libr.
for Library of Congress   [3]†

NL 0382692   MnU DLC

DL976
.F59

Lindorm, Per Erik.
Fog, Ebbe.
Det vackra Stockholm. Beautiful Stockholm. Original-
litografier av Ebbe Fog; text av Per-Erik Lindorm. Stockholm, E. Holm [195–]

Lindorme, C. A. F.
On immortality; concluded philosophically from manifold relations. New York: Fowler & Wells Co., [189–?] 41. 16°.

1. Immortality.
N. Y. P. L.   July 14, 1911.

NL 0382694   NN

Lindorme, C. A. F.
Scientific basis of eclecticism in medicine. Read before the
National Eclectic Medical Association at its annual meeting at
Topeka, Kansas, June 20th, 1883. n. p., 1884. 20 p. 8°.
With bibliographical footnotes. Title from cover.

1. Medicine (Eclectic).
N. Y. P. L.   August 19, 1912.

NL 0382695   NN ICRL MH

Lindoro Elateo, *Arcadian name of* **Lorenzo Magalotti**
   see
Magalotti, Lorenzo, conte, 1637–1712.

Lindorp, Michael Caspar.
Der Römischer Keisserlichen, auch zu
Hungern und Böhmen Königl. Majest.
   see under   Holy Roman Empire.
Sovereigns, etc. 1619–1637 (Ferdinand II)

[Supplement]

Lindos. Fouilles et recherches 1902–1914.
   see under   Blinkenberg, Christian
Sørensen, 1863–

CB19
.C76

Lindou, Leslie Dae, joint author.

Cross, Neal.
The search for personal freedom; a text for a unified course
in the humanities, by Neal M. Cross and Leslie Dae Lindou.
Dubuque, Iowa, W. C. Brown Co. [1950]

Lindov, G., pseud.
   see
Leiteizen, Gavriil Davidovich, 1877–1919.

Lindovius, Johannes.
Rubram Jesu Christi chlamydem exponent præses Caspar
Sagittarius et respondens Johannes Lindovius. Jenæ, exprimebat
J. J. Bauhofer, 1672.
   sm. 4°. pp. (40).
Præses: Caspar Sagittarius.

Jesus Christ‖Sagittarius‖AcS 24776

NL 0382701   MH

Lindow, Carl Warning.
The copper content of plant and animal foods.
By C. W. Lindow, C. A. Elvehjem, and W. H.
Peterson. [Baltimore, 1929]
   cover-title, p. 465–471.
"Reprinted from the Journal of biological
chemistry, vol. LXXXII, no. 2, May, 1929."

NL 0382702   DLC

Lindow, Carl Warning.
The determination of copper in biological
materials. By C.A. Elvehjem and C. W. Lindow.
[Baltimore, 1929]
   cover-title, p. 435–443.
"Reprinted from the Journal of biological
chemistry, vol. LXXXI, no. 2, February, 1929."

NL 0382703   DLC

Lindow, Carl Warning.
The manganese content of plant and animal
materials. By C. W. Lindow and W. H. Peterson.
[Baltimore, 1927]
   cover-title, p. 169–175.
University of Wisconsin, 1929, Ph.D.
Thesis note stamped on cover.
"Reprinted from the Journal of biological
chemistry, vol. LXXV, no. 1, October, 1927."

NL 0382704   DLC

Lindow, Carl Warning.
Variations in the manganese content of certain
vegetables. [By] W. H. Peterson and C. W. Lindow.
[Baltimore, 1928]
   p. 149–153.
"Reprinted from Soil science, vol. XXVI, no.
2, August, 1928."

NL 0382705   DLC

Lindow, Conrad, 1888–
Die bedeutung der gewerbtchen sozialpolitik in der
brandenburg-preussischen merkantilzeit, insbesondere
auf dem gebiete des bergbaues und der eisen-industrie.
Inaug. diss. Giessen, 1928.
Bibl.

NL 0382706   ICRL MH CtY MiU

N4010
.M5
1946

Lindow, Cora E., 1887–
Michigan. State library, *Lansing.*
Pictures, presented by the Michigan state library. Lansing
[1946]

Lindow, Erich.
Freiherr Marschall von Bieberstein als botschafter in Kon-
stantinopel, 1897–1912, von Erich Lindow. Danzig, A. W.
Kafemann g.m.b.h., 1934.
215 p. 21½ᵐ.
Issued also in part as inaugural dissertation, Danzig.
"Literatur": p. 197–199.

1. Marschall von Bieberstein, Adolf Hermann, freiherr, 1842–1912. 2.
Turkey—Hist.—1878–1909. 3. Turkey—Hist.—Muhammad v, 1909–1918.
4. Europe—Politics—1871–
Library of Congress   DD219.M3L5   39–5917
                                 [2]   949.6

NL 0382708   DLC CtY NcD NN MH

1892–

Lindow, Hans; Zur Kasuistik der akuten Pankreatitis und
ihrer operativen Behandlung. [In Maschinenschrift.] 26 S.
4°(2°). — Auszug: Marburg 1920: Hamel. 5 S. 8°
Marburg, Med. Diss. v. 30. Juli 1920 [1921], Ref. Läwen
[Geb. 16. Juli 92 Charlottenburg; Wohnort: Marburg; Staatsangeh.: Preußen;
Vorbildung: Luisen-G. Berlin Reife 12; Studium: Berlin KWAk. 8, Marburg
3 S.; Coll. 12. Mai 20; Approb. 6. Mai 20.]   [U 21. 5009

NL 0382709   DLC ICRL

Lindow, Harald.
Kongefærden til Grønland 1921. København, Munksgaard, 1948.
111 p. illus., map. 25 cm. (Det Grønlandske selskabs skrifter,
16)

1. Christian x, King of Denmark, 1870–1947. 2. Greenland—Descr.
& trav. I. Title.   (Series: Grønlandske selskab, Copenhagen.
Skrifter, 16)
DL255.L5   50–25344

NL 0382710   DLC MH

VOLUME 334

Case
MS
5A
24
LINDOW, JOHN, 1729-1806.
₍Sermons. n.p., 1775-79₎
1 v.(unpaged) 26cm.
Manuscript in ink. Made-up volume of
fair copies, with numerous insertions on
papers of smaller size; all apparently
autograph, written at various times.
Of the 12 sermons listed on inside of
front cover, only nos. 3-6, 9, and 11 are
present.

NL 0382711   ICN

Lindow, *Mrs.* Laura (Lapham) 1884–   *comp.*
Chronological art chart of 2,250 painters, compiled by Laura
Lapham-Lindow ... ₍and₎ G. E. Kaltenbach ... ₍Milwaukee,
Broadway press₎ °1936.
51 p. 30 x 23ᶜᵐ.
"Partial list of references used": p. 50.

1. Painters.   I. Kaltenbach, Gustave Emile, joint comp. II. Title.
III. Title: Art chart of 2,250 painters.
36-20890
Library of Congress   ND55.L5
——— Copy 2.
Copyright AA 213500   ₍2₎   759.084

      NcC OCU OO ViU
NL 0382712   DLC OrCS Or IdB TU PP IU KEmT CSmH OCl MB

Lindow, Martin Paul Johannes, 1880–
Die Anwendung der Differentialrechnung auf das technische
Zeichnen, von Dr. Martin Lindow ... Jena, H. W. Schmidt,
1910.
iv, 88 p. diagrs. 21ᶜᵐ.

NL 0382713   ICJ

Lindow, Martin Paul Johannes, 1880–
...Differential- und integralrechnung, mit berücksichtigung der praktischen anwendung in der technik, von dr.
Martin Lindow ... Mit 42 figuren im text. Leipzig, B. G.
Teubner, 1913.
vii, 111, ₍1₎ p. diagrs. 18½ᶜᵐ. (Aus natur und geisteswelt ... 387.
bdchn.) M. 1.25

1. Calculus.
Library of Congress   QA303.L6   13-23451

NL 0382714   DLC MB

Lindow, Martin Paul Johannes, 1880–
...Differentialgleichungen unter Berücksichtigung der prak-
tischen Anwendung in der Technik mit zahlreichen Beispielen und
Aufgaben versehen, von Dr. Martin Lindow ... Leipzig: B. G.
Teubner, 1921. 106 p. diagrs. 16°. (Aus Natur und
Geisteswelt. Bd. 589.)

1. Equations (Differential). 2. Series.
N. Y. P. L.   July 1, 1924

NL 0382715   NN NcD MH NjP MiU IU

G
517.07
L643d2
Lindow, Martin Paul Johannes, 1880–
... Differentialrechnung unter berücksichtigung der praktischen anwendung in der technik mit
zahlreichen beispielen und aufgaben versehen ...
2. aufl. Mit 45 figuren im text und 161 aufgaben.
Leipzig und Berlin, B. G. Teubner, 1918.
xi, 96 ₍1₎ p. diagrs. (At head of tit[l]e:
Aus natur und geisteswelt ... bd. 387)

Advertising on lining-papers.

NL 0382716   WaPS

QA304
.L5
1919
Lindow, Martin Paul Johannes, 1880–
... Differentialrechnung, unter berücksichtigung der praktischen anwendung in der technik mit zahlreichen beispielen
und aufgaben versehen, von dr. Martin Lindow ... 3. aufl., 11.-
15. tausend. Mit 45 figuren im text und 161 aufgaben. Leipzig
und Berlin, B. G. Teubner, 1919.
vi, 100, ₍1₎ p. diagrs. 18½ᶜᵐ. (Aus natur und geisteswelt; sammlung
wissenschaftlich-gemeinverständlicher darstellungen. 387. bdchen.)

1. Calculus, Differential.

43-44153
Library of Congress   QA304.L5 1919
₍2₎   517.2

NL 0382717   DLC NjP NcD

517
L64d4
Lindow, Martin.
... Differentialrechnung unter berücksichtigung der praktischen anwendung in
der technik mit zahlreichen beispielen
und aufgaben versehen. 4.aufl.
Leipzig, 1922.
102p. diagrs. (Aus natur und geisteswelt; sammlung wissenschaftlich-gemeinverständlicher darstellungen. 387.bd.)

NL 0382718   IU

Lindow, Martin Paul Johannes, 1880–
... Differentialrechnung, unter berücksichtigung der praktischen anwendung in der technik mit zahlreichen beispielen
und aufgaben, von dr. Martin Lindow ... 5. aufl. Mit 50
figuren im text und 161 aufgaben. Leipzig und Berlin, B. G.
Teubner ₍1933₎
vi, 102 p., 1 l. diagrs. 18½ᶜᵐ. (Mathematisch-physikalische bibliothek, reihe II ... 2)

1. Calculus, Differential.

34-6564
Library of Congress   QA304.L5 1933
₍2₎   517.2

NL 0382719   DLC NcRS

Lindow, Martin Paul Johannes, 1880–
Differentialrechnung unter Berücksichtigung der physikalisch-technischen Anwendungen mit zahlreichen Beispielen
und Aufgaben. 7. Aufl. Leipzig, B. G. Teubner, 1949.
120 p. diagrs. 19 cm. (Mathematisch-physikalische Bibliothek,
Reihe II, 2)

1. Calculus, Differential.   (Series: Mathematische Bibliothek)

QA304.L5 1949   517.2   50-20292

NL 0382720   DLC OU

Lindow, Martin Paul Johannes, 1880–
... Gewöhnliche differentialgleichungen, unter berücksichtigung der physikalisch-technischen anwendungen mit zahlreichen beispielen und aufgaben, von dr. Martin Lindow ...
2. aufl., mit 39 figuren im text, 45 beispielen und 160 aufgaben. Leipzig und Berlin, B. G. Teubner, 1933.
vi, 121 p. diagrs. 18½ᶜᵐ. (Mathematisch-physikalische bibliothek ...
reihe II ... 4)

1. Differential equations.

34-836
Library of Congress   QA372.L75 1933
₍2₎   517.38

NL 0382721   DLC CU OU

Lindow, Martin Paul Johannes, 1880–
Gewöhnliche Differentialgleichungen unter
Berücksichtigung der physikalisch -technischen
Anwendungen, mit zahlreichen Biespielen und
Aufgaben. 3. Aufl. Leipzig, Teubner, 1948.
120 p. illus. 19 cm. (Mathematisch-
physikalische Bibliothek. Reihe 2, [bd.] 4)

NL 0382722   OU

Lindow, Martin Paul Johannes, 1880–
Gewöhnliche differentialgleichungen unter
berücksichtigung der physikalisch-technischen
anwendungen mit zahlreichen beispielen und
aufgaben. 4. aufl. Leipzig, B.G. Teubner,
1950.
120 p. diagrs. 20 cm. (Mathematisch-
physikalische bibliothek. Reihe 2: Abrisse aus
dem gebiete der mathematik und der exakten
naturwissenschaften, 4)
"Lösungen": p. 98-117.

NL 0382723   PU

Lindow, Martin Paul Johannes, 1880–
Integralrechnung ... 2. aufl. Lpz. 1919.
(Aus natur und geisteswelt. 673. bd.)

NL 0382724   NjP

Math.
517.3
L747I
3.Aufl
Lindow, Martin Paul Johannes, 1880–
Integralrechnung, unter berücksichtigung der praktischen anwendung in der technik mit zahlreichen beispielen
und aufgaben versehen, von dr. Martin Lindow ... 3. aufl., 11.-
15. tausend. Mit 43 figuren im text und 200 Aufgaben.
Leipzig, B. G. Teubner, 1922.
102 p. diagrs. 18½ᶜᵐ. (Aus natur und geisteswelt; sammlung
wissenschaftlich-gemeinverständlicher darstellungen. 673. Bd.)

1. Calculus, Integral.

NL 0382725   NcD

Lindow, Martin Paul Johannes, 1880–
... Integralrechnung, unter berücksichtigung der physikalisch-technischen anwendungen mit zahlreichen beispiele und
aufgaben, von dr. Martin Lindow ... 4. aufl. Mit 43 figuren
im text, 61 beispielen und 200 aufgaben. Leipzig und Berlin,
B. G. Teubner, 1933.
102 p. diagrs. 18½ᶜᵐ. (Mathematisch-physikalische bibliothek,
reihe II ... 3)

1. Calculus, Integral.

34-6565
Library of Congress   QA308.L5 1933
₍2₎   517.3

NL 0382726   DLC CU

Lindow, Martin Paul Johannes, 1880–
Integralrechnung unter Berücksichtigung der physikalisch-technischen Anwendungen mit zahlreichen Beispielen
und Aufgaben. 6. Aufl. Leipzig, B. G. Teubner, 1949.
112 p. diagrs. 19 cm. (Mathematisch-physikalische Bibliothek,
Reihe II, 3)

1. Calculus, Integral.   (Series: Mathematische Bibliothek)

QA308.L5 1949   517.3   50-20295

NL 0382727   DLC OU

Lindow, Martin Paul Johannes, 1880–
Die nullstellen des allgemeinen integrals der differentialgleichung für die zugeordneten kugelfunktionen ... ₍von₎ Martin Lindow ... Halle a. S., Hofbuchdr. von C. A. Kaemmerer
& co., 1902.
65, ₍1₎ p., 1 l. diagr. 22½ᶜᵐ.
Inaug.-diss.—Halle.
Lebenslauf.

1. Spherical harmonics. 2. Differential equations.
5-31336
Library of Congress   QA406.L74
₍a39b1₎

NL 0382728   DLC CtY CU NjP

Lindow, Martin Paul Johannes, 1880–
Numerische infinitesimal-rechnung, von dr. Martin Lindow
... Mit 17 figuren. Berlin und Bonn, F. Dümmler, 1928.
viii, 176 p. diagrs. 24½ᶜᵐ.

1. Calculus. 2. Interpolation. 3. Differential equations.   I. Title.

28-27736
Library of Congress   QA303.L65

      NN DBS NjP
NL 0382729   DLC CU NBuU NcD CtY PBm PPT OClW MiU DN-Ob₎

VOLUME 334

439.1
L64n
Lindow, Max.
     ... Niederdeutsch als evangelische
kirchensprache im 16. und 17. jahrhundert ... Greifswald, 1926.
     96p.

     Inaug.-diss.--Griefswald.
     Lebenslauf.
     "Benutzte literatur": p.[5]-8.

NL 0382730   IU CtY MiU ICRL PU

Lindow, Max, 1875–
     Herzenbauer; eine lustige Dorfkomödie in 1 Aufzug, von Max Lindow. Mühlhausen i. Thür.: G. Danner [1936] 36 p. 19½cm. [Der heitere Einakter]

904505A. 1. Drama, German.   I. Title.
N. Y. P. L.   October 8, 1937

NL 0382731   NN

Lindow, Max, 1875–
     Hüter der Scholle; Bauernkomödie in 4 Aufzügen, von Max Lindow... Mühlhausen i. Thür.: G. Danner [1938] 52 p. 20cm. [Heimatspiele. Nr. 12]

1. Drama, German. I. Title.
N. Y. P. L.   August 23, 1940

NL 0382732   NN

Lindow, Max, 1875–
     Sieg auf der ganzen Linie. Lustspiel in einem Aufzuge, von Max Lindow... Mühlhausen i. Thür.: G. Danner [1938] 31 p. 20cm. (Der heitere Einakter. 10.)

1. Drama, German. I. Title.
N. Y. P. L.   August 23, 1940

NL 0382733   NN

Lindow, Max, 1875–
     Soldat bleibt Soldat; ein lustiges Soldatenstück in 1 Akt, von Max Lindow   Mühlhausen i. Thür.: G. Danner [1937] 40 p. 20cm. ([Der] h[eitere] E[inakter] 4.)

1. Drama, German. I. Title.
N. Y. P. L.   October 10, 1938

NL 0382734   NN CtY

Lindow, Max, 1875–
     Die Urlauber; ein froher Einakter für Soldaten und die es gewesen sind, von Max Lindow   Mühlhausen i. Thür.: G. Danner [1937] 40 p. 20cm. ([Der] h[eitere] E[inakter] 3.)

1. Drama, German. I. Title.
N. Y. P. L.   October 10, 1938

NL 0382735   NN

Lindow, Otto, 1900–
     Die entwicklung der chemischen holzverkohlungsindustrie Deutschlands. Auszug.
     Inaug. diss. Giessen, 1928

NL 0382736   ICRL

Lindow, Walter: Spektralphotometrische Untersuchungen an der Glimmentladung. Greifswald 1925: Hartmann. 40 S. 8°
Greifswald, Phil. Diss. v. 23. Nov. 1925   [U 25.8910

NL 0382737   ICRL MiU CtY

Lindow, Wilhelmine, 1905–
     Verblutungstod nach spontanem cervixriss von der geburt des kindes. 1930.
     Inaug. diss. - Universitat zu Berlin.

NL 0382738   OU ICRL CtY

Lindows børn
     see under   [Christiansen, Arne Einar] 1861–1939.

Lindpaintner (Peter Paul) [1889–]. *Ueber Schwangerschaften im vorgerückten Lebensalter.* 25 pp. 8°. Marburg, J. Hamel, 1916.

NL 0382740   DNLM ICRL CtY

Lindpaintner (Julius). *Ueber die Gefahren bei Operationen am Halse.* 24 pp. 8°. München, F. Straub, 1873.

NL 0382741   DNLM

Lindpaintner, Peter Joseph von.
     Aglaé, l'élève de l'Amour. Ballet anacréontique en 1 acte de Philippe Taglioni. Composé ... par P. Lindpaintner. [Partition pour piano.]
     Mannheim. Heckel. [183–?] 67 pp. L. 8°, obl.

Mar. 21,   1902
E3389 — T.r. — Ballet music.

NL 0382742   MB

Lindpaintner, Peter Joseph von, 1791–1856
     Am Grabe. [Männerchor.]
     (In Das Rütli. Pp. 108–111. St. Gallen, 1873.)

Mar. 21,   1902
E3389 — T.r. — Part songs.

NL 0382743   MB

Lindpaintner, Peter Joseph von, 1791–1856.
     Arien und Gesänge aus: Die Genueserin, grosse romantische Oper in drei Akten, von C. P. Berger. Musik von P. Lindpaintner ... Breslau: Grass, Barth und Comp.[, ca. 1838.] 39 p. 12°.

     Libretto. German words.

1. Drama, German. 2. Title: Die Genueserin.
N. Y. P. L.   December 21, 1927

NL 0382744   NN

Lindpaintner, Peter Joseph von, 1791–1856.
     Bajaderen-Gesang. [Für S. A. mit Klavierbegleitung.]
     [N. p. 183–?] [1] p. F°.
     There is no title-page.

F6681 — T.r. — Duets. Vocal.

NL 0382745   MB

Lindpaintner, Peter Joseph von, 1791–1856.
     [Sie stand auf ihres Schlosses Zinnen.] Ballade aus der Oper, Die sicilianische Vesper, von Heribert Rau. Musick von P. Lindpaintner. [Für eine Singstimme [S.] mit Begleitung des Pianoforte.]
     [N. t. p. 184–?] 2 pp. F°.

F6682 — T.r. — Songs. With music.

NL 0382746   MB

M
782.1
L645b
Lindpaintner, Peter Joseph von, 1791–1856.
     [Der Bergkönig. Piano-vocal score. German]
     Der Bergkönig; romantische Oper in 3 Aufzügen. Vollständiger vom Componisten verfertigter Clavier-Auszug. Mannheim, F. Heckel [182–]
     score (122 p.) 23 x 33cm.

     · 1. Operas - Vocal scores with piano.
I. T.

NL 0382747   MiDW

Lindpaintner, Peter Joseph von, 1791–1856.
     Der Bergkönig. Romantische Oper in 3 Aufzügen. Vollständiger Clavier-Auszug.
     Mannheim. Heckel. [183–?] [1], 122 pp. L. 8°, obl.

Mar. 21,   1902
E3389 — T.r. — Operas.

NL 0382748   MB ICN

Lindpaintner, Peter Joseph von, 1791–1856.
     Der blinde Gärtner, oder die blühende Aloe. Liederspiel von A. v. Kotzebue, in Musik gesetzt ... von Peter Lindpaintner. Klavierauszug.
     Leipzig. Breitkopf & Härtel. [182–?] 55 pp. L. 8°, obl.

Mar. 21,   1902
F3389 — Kotzebue, August Friedrich Ferdinand von. — Operas.

NL 0382749   MB

Lindpaintner, Peter Joseph von, 1791–1856.
     [Concertinos. Horn. F min. Arr. for horn & pf.]
     Concertino pour le cor avec accompagn' de l'orchestre ou de piano, composé par P. Lindpaintner... Leipsic: Breitkopf & Härtel [1837] Publ. pl. no. 5598. 2 parts in 1 v. 34cm.

     Score (15 p.) and horn part.

CARNEGIE CORP. OF NEW YORK.
1. Concertos—Horn—Piano acc.
N. Y. P. L.   April 26, 1937

NL 0382750   NN

Lindpaintner, Peter Joseph von, 1791–1856.
     [Concerto, flute, op. 28, E major]
     Concerto pour la flûte, avec accompagnement de grand orchestre. Oeuv. 28. Leipzig, Breitkopf & Härtel [1821]. Pl. no. 3383.
     parts. 34 cm.

     1. Concertos (Flute)—Parts.
ML30.4c no.2534 Miller   68–125568

NL 0382751   DLC

VM
33
L 74d
LINDPAINTNER, PETER JOSEPH VON, 1791–1856.
     Danina; oder, Joko, der brasilianische affe. Idealisches ballet in 4 acten von Ph. Taglioni, in musik gesetzt von Lindpaintner. Vollständiger von seinem schüler Ludwig Schunke verfertigter clavier-auszug. Mannheim, F. Heckel [18--] 95p. 26½x33cm.

     Illustrated t.-p., engraved.

NL 0382752   ICN NN

LINDPAINTNER, PETER JOSEPH VON, 1791–1856.
[DANINA]
     Danina; oder Jocho, der brasilianische Affe. Grosses pantomimisches Ballet in 4 Akten, von Taglioni. In Musik gesetzt von Lindpaintner. [182–?] score (1 v., various pagings)

     Film reproduction of manuscript in the Kongelige bibliotek, Copenhagen. Positive.

Continued in next column

VOLUME 334

Continued from preceding column

For orchestra, with superlinear instructions for dancing.

1. Ballets (Orchestra). I. Taglioni, Filippo, 1777-1871. Danina.

NL 0382754   NN

LINDPAINTNER, PETER JOSEPH VON, 1791-1856.
[DANINA]
Danina; oder Joko, der brazilianische Affe; grosses pantomimisches Ballet in 4 Akten von Taglioni, in Musik gesetzt von Lindpaintner. [182-?] score (1 v. (unpaged))

Holograph (?) in ink, of the orchestra score of acts 1-2.

1. Autographs (Music)--Lindpaintner, P. 2. Ballets (Orchestra).
I. Taglioni, Filippo, 1777-1871. Danina. II. Title. III. Title: Joko der brazilianische Affe.

NL 0382755   NN

Lindpaintner, Peter Joseph von, 1791-1856.
Danina, oder Joko, der brasilianische Affe, Ballet in 4 Acten von Ph. Taglioni. Clavier-Auszug.
[Wien? 182-?] (1), 95 pp. L. 8°, obl.

E3389 — T.r. — Ballet music.   Mar. 21,   190-

NL 0382756   MB

Lindpaintner, Peter Joseph von, 1791-1856.
Danina; oder, Joko, der brasilische Affe.
For scenario see under Taglioni, Filippo, 1777-1871.

Lindpaintner, Peter Joseph von, 1791-1856.
Demophoon, eine grosse heroische Oper in drei Aufzügen, nach dem französichen des Desriaux.

Metrisch bearbeitet van Castelli. Musik von P. Lindpaintner.   München, 1811.

NL 0382758   NN

Lindpaintner, Peter Joseph von, 1791-1856.

Deutscher Heldensinn. Dargestellt in verschiedenen Gedichten von J. Sendtner, in Musik gesetzt mit Clavier oder Guitarre Begleitung von Peter Lindpaintner. München, J. Sidlers'chen Haupt-Steindruck-Niederlage [18—]
13, 11, 17 p.   26 x 34 cm.
For voice and piano or guitar.

1. Songs (Medium voice) with piano.   I. Title.

M1621.L   62-50989/M

NL 0382759   DLC

Lindpaintner, P[eter Joseph] von, 1791-1856.
Die Fahnenwacht (Standard Watch). Gedicht von F. Löwe. Favorit-Lied des berühmten Sängers J.B. Pischek. In Musik gesetzt von P. von Lindpaintner – [Song with piano acc.] [German text, and English version by Th's Oliphant.] n. p. n. d.
7 p.   f°.

NL 0382760   NN

Lindpaintner, Peter Joseph von, 1791-1856.
[Die Fahnenwacht. Op. 114]
[Die Fahnenwacht, von] P. v. Lindpaintner. Op. 114. [Hamburg: Schuberth & Co., ca. 1848] Publ. pl. no. 1000. 15 p. 35½cm.

Full score: high voice with orchestra. German words cued in.
Title-page wanting; title from Pazdirek, Franz. Universal-Handbuch der Musik-literatur aller Zeit und Völker. v. 17.
First line: Der Sänger hält im Feld die Fahnenwacht.

1. Songs, with orchestra. 2. Songs,   German.
N. Y. P. L   April 14, 1937

NL 0382761   NN

Lindpaintner, Peter Joseph von, 1791-1856.
Frauenlob. [Männerchor.]
(In Fink. Die deutsche Liedertafel. P. 153. Altona, 1863.)

E3390 — T.r. — Part songs.   Mar. 21,   1902

NL 0382762   MB

M1503   Lindpaintner, Peter Joseph von, 1791-1856.
L497G4   [Die Genueserin. Piano-vocal score. German]
1840   Die Genneserinn; grosse romantische Oper in zwei Aufzügen.
Case   Gedichtet von J. [sic] P. Berger. In Musik gesetzt von P.
X   Lindpaintner. Vollständiger Clavier-Auszug. Wien, T. Haslinger [184-?] Pl. no. T. H. 7720.
287 p.

Cover title.
Originally published in this edition 1839; reissued.
The overture arr. for piano, 4 hands.

I. Berger, Carl Philipp. II. Title.

NL 0382763   CU MB

MS
VM   LINDPAINTNER, PETER JOSEPH VON, 1791-1856.
1530.3   Die glocke. Gedicht von Fr. Schiller. Musik
L 74g   zur declamation von Lindpaintner. Op.80.
[n.p.,n.d.]
2v. 27½-34½cm.(v.2,34½cm.)

Manuscript copy by an unknown hand.
Music to Schiller's Das lied von der glocke.
Contents.—[v.1] Score.—[v.2] Parts.

NL 0382764   ICN

VM   LINDPAINTNER, PETER JOSEPH VON, 1791-1856.
1533.3   Die glocke. Gedicht von Friedrich v.Schiller,
L 74g   mit musik zur declamation von P.von Lindpaintner.
Für pianoforte zu vier händen vom componisten eingerichtet. Opus 80...   London,Schott & co. [18--]
43p. 35cm.

Plate no.: 13490.

NL 0382765   ICN MH

Lindpaintner, Peter Joseph von, 1791-1856.
„Herr Gott, dich loben wir," nach Klopstock, in Musik gesetzt. [Partitur.]
Leipzig. Breitkopf & Härtel. [182-?] 92 pp. L. 8°, obl.

E3390 — Klopstock, Friedrich Gottlieb. — Cantatas.   Mar. 21,   1902

NL 0382766   MB

Lindpaintner, Peter Joseph von, 1791-1856.
Huldigung. [Männerchor.]
(In Fink. Die deutsche Liedertafel. Pp. 171, 172. Altona, 1863.)

E3390 — T.r. — Part songs.   Mar. 21,   1902

NL 0382767   MB

Lindpaintner, Peter Joseph von, 1791-1856.
Leiden und Freuden. [Männerchor.]
(In Eidgenoessischer Saengerverein. Männerchöre für das IIte ... Sängerfest. Pp. 20, 21. Bern, 1864.)

E3390 — T.r. — Part songs.   Mar. 21,   1902

NL 0382768   MB

VM   LINDPAINTNER, PETER JOSEPH VON, 1791-1856.
1503   [Lichtenstein. Piano-vocal score. German]
L 74L   Lichtenstein, grosse Oper in 5 Acten. Text nach W.Hauff von Franz Dingelstedt, in Musik gesetzt von Peter von Lindpaintner. Vollständiger Clavierauszug vom Componisten. Hamburg, Schuberth & C.[1845?]
score(276p.) illus. 34cm.

Presented at Stuttgart in 1845 and Aug. 24, 1846.

NL 0382769   ICN MB CU MH

Lindpaintner, Peter Joseph, 1791-1856.
Lichtenstein
For libretti see under Dingelstedt, Franz, freiherr von, 1814-1881.

Lindpaintner, Peter Joseph von, 1791-1856.
[In eines treuen Volkes Mitte.] Lied gesungen bei der Eröffnungs-feyer des Königlichen Theaters zu Canstatt, den 29ten May, 1840. [Für eine Singstimme mit Begleitung des Pianoforte.]
[N. t. p. 184-?] (1) p. F°.

F6682 — T.r. — Songs. With music.

NL 0382771   MB

Lindpaintner, Peter Joseph von, 1791-1856.
Lieder des Schmerzes. Auf dem Thurme. Gedicht von Dräxler-Manfred. [Für eine Singstimme mit Begleitung des Pianoforte.]
[N. p. 184-?] 4 pp. F°.
There is no title-page.

F6688 — Songs. With music. — T.r.

NL 0382772   MB

VM   LINDPAINTNER, PETER JOSEPH VON, 1791-1856.
1503   [Die Macht des Liedes. Piano-vocal score.
L 74m   German] Die Macht des Liedes, komische Oper in drei Akten mit Tanz, von I.F.Castelli. Vollständiger Klavierauszug vom Componisten. Leipzig,F.Hofmeister[1837]
204p. 27x36cm.

Plate no.: 2186.
First produced at Stuttgart, 1836.

NL 0382773   ICN MB

Lindpaintner, Peter Joseph von, 1791-1856.
Missa solemnis, C moll, für vier Solo- und Chor-Stimmen mit Orchester-Begleitung. Op. 110. [Partitur.]
Stuttgart. Allgemeine Musikhandlung. [186-?] 163 pp. F°.

E3386 — Masses.

NL 0382774   MB

Lindpaintner, Peter Joseph von, 1791-1856.
[Der Vampyr.] Ouverture zur Oper: Der Vampyr für grosses Orchester. Op. 70. Partitur.
Leipzig. Peters. [183-?] 63 pp. L. 8°.

E3386 — Overture.

NL 0382775   MB

VOLUME 334

Lindpaintner, Peter Joseph von, *1791-1856*.
  [Ouverture . . . Partitur.]
  Manuscript. [185-?] (29) ff. F°.

E3391 — Manuscripts in this Library. — Overtures.

NL 0382776   MB

M207
.S38U4
  Lindpaintner, Peter Joseph von, 1791-1856.
  Ouvertures à 4 mains.

  Schubert, Franz Peter, 1797-1828.
    [Overtures. Selections; arr.]

    Schubert, Spohr, Lindpaintner, ouvertures à 4 mains.
    [Leipzig, C. F. Peters, 18— Pl. no. 5293.

Lindpaintner, Peter Joseph von, *1791-1856*.
  Die Pflegkinder. Operette in 1 Act von K. Thienemann, in Musik gesetzt und im vollständigen Klavierauszug gebracht von P. Lindpaintner.
  Leipzig. Hofmeister. [183-?] 81 pp. L.8°, obl.

E3391 — Thienemann, Carl. — Operas.

NL 0382778   MB

---

*
M1
.S444   Lindpainter, Peter Joseph von, 1791-1856.
v.112
no. 47 . Roland the brave; the companion song to the
     Standard bearer [n. p., 18—?]
       [53]-56 p. 34cm. [Sheet music collection,
       v. 112, no. 47]
       Caption title
       "Musical bouquet, [no. 254]"
       Bottom of p. [53] cut off.

       1. Songs with piano. I. Title.

NL 0382779   ViU

---

eVM   LINDPAINTNER, PETER JOSEPH VON, 1791-1856.
1613
L 747r   [Roland] Roland (Seitenstück zur Fahnen-
     wacht) gedichtet von Feodor Löwe. Romanze für
     eine Singstimme mit Orchester- oder Piano-
     Begleitung. Partitur-Ausgabe.   Hamburg,
     Schuberth[184—?]
       score(15p.) 35cm.

       Words not included in the score; printed
     only as text on p.[2]
     Version for solo voice and orchestra.

NL 0382780   ICN

Lindpaintner, Peter Joseph von, *1791-1856*.
  Roland . . . Romanze für eine Singstimme [T.] mit Orchester-Begleitung.
  Hamburg. Schuberth & Co. [186-?] 15 pp. F°.

       Mar. 21,   190*
E3391 — T. r. — Songs. With music.

NL 0382781   MB

Lindpaintner, Peter Joseph von, *1791-1856*.
  [Combien j'ai douce souvenance.] Romanze aus der Oper, Die Gewalt des Liedes von Castelli, Musik von Lindpaintner. [Für eine Singstimme, mit Begleitung des Pianoforte.]
  [N. t. p. 183-?] (1) p. F°, obl.

F6682 — T.r. — Songs. With music.

NL 0382782   MB

Lindpaintner, Peter Joseph von, *1791-1856*.
  [Die Dame an dem Fenster.] Romanze aus der Oper, Die sicilianische Vesper. [Für eine Singstimme, T., mit Begleitung des Pianoforte.]
  [N. p. 184-?] (2) pp. F°.
  There is no title-page.

F6742 — T.r. — Songs. With music.

NL 0382783   MB

Lindpaintner, Peter Joseph von, *1791-1856*.
  [Qualen der Liebe.] Romanze aus der Oper, Die sicilianische Vesper von Heribert Rau, mit Musick v. P. Lindpaintner. [Für eine Singstimme, T., mit Begleitung des Pianoforte.]
  [N. t. p. 184-?] (1) p. F°.

F6682 — T.r. — Songs. With music.

NL 0382784   MB

Lindpaintner, Peter Joseph von, *1791-1856*.
  Der Rose. Aus der Oper, Die Gewalt des Liedes. Text von Castelli, Musik von Lindpaintner. [Für eine Singstimme mit Begleitung des Pianoforte.]
  [N. t. p. 183-?] (2) pp. F°, obl.

F6682 — T.r. — Songs. With music.

NL 0382785   MB

Lindpaintner, Peter Joseph von, *1791-1856*.
  Schlummerlied. [S. S. T. B. B. mit Begleitung von Flöte, Clarinett und Hörnern.]
  [N. t. p. 183-?] (4) pp. F°.

F6682 — Part songs. — T.r.

NL 0382786   MB

Lindpaintner, Peter Joseph von, 1791-1856.
  2nde Concertante, op. 44, flute, oboe, clarinet, horn and bassoon (with pianoforte accompaniment)
  [Boston?, 190-?]
  32 p. 38 cm.
  A skeleton piano-conductor score in manuscript. The printed parts may be found on another call-number.
  1. Symphonies. 2. Manuscripts in this Library. Music. 3. Orchestra. Music.

NL 0382787   MB

Lindpaintner, Peter Joseph von, 1791-1856.
  Seconde sinfonie concertante, pour flute hautbois, clarinette, cor et basson avec accompagnement de grand orchestre composée... par P. Lindpaintner ... Oeuvre 44. Mayence, B. Schott, fils [184-?]
  21 parts. 34.5 cm.
  The t.-p. is bound in with the part of the flaute principale.
  A skeleton piano-conductor score in manuscript may be found on another call-number.
  1. Symphonies. 2. Orchestra. Music.

NL 0382788   MB

Lindpaintner, Peter Joseph von, *1791-1856*.
  Sehnsucht nach der Schweiz. [Männerchr.]
  (In Das Rütli. Pp. 129-131. St. Gallen, 1873.)

       Mar. 21,   1902
E3391 — T.r. — Part songs.

NL 0382789   MB

Lindpaintner, Peter Joseph von, *1791-1856*.
  Die sicilianische Vesper. Grosse heroische Oper in 4 Acten von Heribert Rau, in Musik gesetzt von Peter Lindpaintner. Vollständiger Clavier-Auszug.
  = Mainz. Schott. [1843?] 10, 211 p. F°.

       Mar. 21,   190-
E3391 — Rau, Heribert. — Operas.

NL 0382790   MB

Lindpainter, Peter Joseph, 1791-1856.
  Die sicilianische Vesper, grosse heroische Oper in 4 Acten von Heribert Rau, in Musik gesetzt von Peter Lindpainter. 113.tes Werk. Vollständiger Clavier-Auszug vom Componisten. Mit unterlegtem italienischem Texte v. Wilhelm Häser ... Mainz [etc.] B. Schott's Söhnen [1844]
  2 p.l., 10, 6-211 p.   34.5 cm.
  Publ. no. 7781.
  Libretto, German text only, 10 p. at beginning.

  First performance, Stuttgart, May 10, 1843.
  Lithographed t.-p.: music printed from the plates.

NL 0382792   CtY

LINDPAINTNER, PETER JOSEPH VON, 1791-1856.
  [ZEPHIR UND ROSE. SELECTIONS. ARR. FOR PIANO 4 HDS.]
  Six pièces favorites du ballet Zephir et Rose, pour le piano-forte à quatre mains, par P. Lindpaintner. Op. 75. Leipzig. C.F. Peters [ca.1830] Pl. no. 2129. 29 p. 33 x 25cm.

     For piano, 4 hands.
     CONTENTS.--Ouverture.--Andante.--Rondoletto.--Romanza.--Scherzo.--Allegretto.--   Romanza e rondo.
     1. Ballets (Piano, 4 hands)--   Suites etc. 2. Piano, 4 hands
     --Arr.

NL 0382793   NN

Lindpaintner, Peter Joseph von, *1791-1856*.
  Solo- und Chor-Gesänge aus den Psalmen von Benedetto Marcello (1723) nach G. A. Giustiniani's Dichtung in's Deutsche übertragen von Carl Grüneisen; bearbeitet und instrumentirt von P. Lindpaintner Partitur und Clavier-Auszug.
  Stuttgart, G. A. Zumsteeg, by Metzler, 19—?
  3-95 p.

NL 0382794   OCH

LINDPAINTNER, Peter Joseph von, *1791-1856*.
  The standard bearer. Arranged as a piano solo by Ferd. Beyer.
  New York. Hall. [183-?] 9 pp. F°.

NL 0382795   MB

Lindpaintner, Peter Joseph von, *1791-1856*.
  The standard watch. Die Fahnen Wacht. [Song, A. or Bar. Accomp. for pianoforte.]
  Boston. Ditson & Co. 1859. 5 pp. [Germania.] F°.

G4038 — T.r. — Songs. With music.

NL 0382796   MB

Lindpaintner, Peter Joseph von, 1791-1856.
  Trois grands trios pour violon, alto et violoncelle... par P.Lindpaintner, oeuvre 52.
  Leipzig, F.Kistner, n.d. 3v. 36cm.
  Publ.no. 184.

NL 0382797   CU PU

VOLUME 334

M
1503
L74V2++

Lindpaintner, Peter Joseph von, 1791-1856.
₍Der Vampyr. Piano-vocal score. German &
Italian₎

Der Vampyr; romantische Oper in 3 Akten von
Cesar Heigel. Vollständiger Klavierauszug vom
Komponisten. 72. Werk.   Leipzig, C.F.
Peters ₍18--₎ Pl. no. 2016, 2029.
1 v. (various pagings) 25 x 33cm.

1. Operas--Vocal scores with piano. I.
Heigel, César   Max, b.ca.1783. Der
Vampyr. II. T   itle.

NL 0382798 NIC

VM
1503
L 74v

LINDPAINTNER, PETER JOSEPH VON, 1791-1856.
₍Der Vampyr. Piano-vocal score. German and
Italian. Op.72₎ Der Vampyr, romantische Oper
in 3 Akten von Cesar Heigel in Musik gesetzt von
P. Lindpaintner. Vollständiger Klavierauszug vom
Komponisten. 72ᵗᵉˢ Werk.   Leipzig, C.F. Peters
₍1829?₎
score(117,75,28p.) 27x33cm.

Presented at Turin 1829.
Overture arranged for piano duet.

NL 0382799 ICN PBL CtY CU WaU MH MB

LINDPAINTNER, Peter Joseph von, 1791-1856.
24 Psalmen nach verschiedenen Dichtungen. Solo- und Chor-Gesänge
mit Orchester- oder Pianoforte-Begleitung, in Musik gesetzt ... von P.
Lindpaintner. No. 1-8. Partitur und Clavierauszug.
Braunschweig. Meyer. [185-?] 8 parts in 1 v. F°.
Contents. — 1. Gott behüte alle Frommen. 2. Du bist der Weg, die Wahrheit und
das Leben. 3. O Herr mein Gott dein ist das Reich. 4. Guter Hirte, Trost der Armen.
5. Morgenstern und Abendstern. 6. Heil und Trost ist uns erschienen. 7. Seraphine
steigen nieder. 8. Von himmlischer Klarheit herrlich umstrahlet.

NL 0382800 MB

Lindpaintner, Peter Joseph von, 1791-1856.
The warrior bard, or the standard bearer. [Song, A. or Bar. Piano-
forte accomp.]
Boston. Russell & Tolman. 1847. 5 pp. F°.

G3982 — T.r. — Songs. With music.

NL 0382801 MB MH

Lindpaintner, Peter Joseph von, 1791-1856.
Wehmuthsträne. 1834. [2] p. 22 x 32.5 cm.

Holograph in ink, signed. Caption title.
At end: Stuttgart im April 1834. P. J.
Lindpaintner, K. Würt. Hofkapellmeister. For
4-part male voices, unaccompanied. First
line: Thräne die dem Aug' entquillt.
Albrecht census no. 1064. Formerly owned by
Joseph Muller.

1. Choruses, Secular (Men's voices, 4
parts), Unaccompanied. 2. Music -
Manuscripts. (TITLE)

NL 0382803 NN

Lindpaintner, Peter Joseph von, 1791-1856.
The widow of Nain, (Der Jüngling von Nain, Gedicht von Carl
Grüneisen). Oratorio, for voices and piano, composed by P. von
Lindpaintner, the English version by Desmond Ryan... Op. 155
... London: Wessel & C°. ₍ca. 1853.₎ Publ. pl. nos. W. & C°.
n°. 8040-8052. 14 nos. in 1 v. f°.

Added t.-p.
English and German.
Vocal score.

1. Oratorios.—Piano and voice.   2. Grueneisen, Carl von, 1802-78.
3. Ryan, Desmond Lumley, 1851-88,   translator. 4. Title. 5. Title:
Der Jüngling von Nain.   March 31, 1919.
N.Y.P.L.

NL 0382804 NN

Lindpaintner, Peter Joseph von, 1791-1856.
Zwölf deutsche Liedlein für eine Singstime [S. o. T.], mit Begleitung
des Klaviers, gesetzt.
[N. p. 183-?] 4 ff. F°.
Contents. — Meine Mutter. — Lebewohl. — Treue Liebe. — Minnelied. —
Verspäteter Frühling. — Der Baum im Odenwald. — Rosmarin. — Wiegen-
liedchen. — Grabesblumen. — Mutterklage. — Schlaf nur ein. — Der
schwere Traum.
There is no title-page.

F6683 — T.r. — Songs. With music.

NL 0382805 MB

Lindquest, Calvert Bernard, 1914-
How to tell if your ads will sell ... ₍Chicago, Helpful
Press, 1950₎
97 p. illus. 28 cm. (Millionaire's manual series)
Bibliography: p. 97.

1. Advertising. I. Title.

HF5823.L69   659.13   50-4446

NL 0382806 DLC CaBVa OrU WaS TxU

BT
985
L56

Lindquist, A   G
Antikrist, eller det kommande verldstyrannen;
en kort afhandling öfver bibelns utsagor om
denne mystiske person, hans namn, karaktär,
egenskaper, tiden under hvilken han skall
uppträda, hans verk och gerningar samt hans
förskräckliga slut och ändalykt. Chicago,
Chicago-Bladets förlag, 1901.
120 p.

NL 0382807 WaU MnHi

BX
8049.5
.B92K23
.L5

Lindquist, Albert William, 1873-1944.
Minnen af Kansas-konferensens femtio-års-
fest. Tvenne tal af Albert W. Lindquist och
G. A. Dorf ... Rock Island, Ill., Augustana
Book Concerns tryckeri ₍1920₎
32 p. illus. 20 cm.

1. Evangelical Lutheran Augustana Synod
of North America. Kansas Conference. I. Dorf,
Gustav Alfred, 1871-1943. II. Title.

NL 0382808 MnHi PPAmSwM

PL6048
.F6

Lindquist, Alice, joint author.

Forsberg, Vivian.
Tagabili vocabulary ₍by₎ Vivian Forsberg and Alice Lindquist. Manila, Published by the Summer Institute of Linguistics in cooperation with the Bureau of Public Schools
and the Institute of National Language of the Department
of Education, 1955.

Lindquist, Arthur William, 1903-
... Notes on the habits of certain coprophagous beetles and
methods of rearing them. By Arthur W. Lindquist ...
₍Washington, U. S. Govt. print. off.₎ 1935.
10 p. illus. 23ᵐ. (U. S. Dept. of agriculture. Circular no. 351)
Contribution from Bureau of entomology and plant quarantine.

1. ₍Dung beetles₎   I. Title : Coprophagous beetles.

                                                    Agr 35-210
Library, U. S. Dept. of   Agriculture 1Ag84C no. 351
Library of Congress   [S21.A47 no. 351]

NL 0382810 DNAL WaWW PPComm OU OCl

Lindquist, Axel
Foerskjutningar i foerhaallandet mellan
grammatiskt och psykologiskt subjekt...
Inaug. diss. Lund, 1912 (Leipzig)

NL 0382811 ICRL PU

Lindquist, Axel, tr.
Varthan hör Elsass-Lothringen...
see under [Lienhard, Friedrich] 1865-1929.

Lindquist, Berger
see Lundquist, Berger.

99.45
L64

₍Lindquist, Bertil, 1904-
Bättre frö för framtidens tallskogar.
Stockholm, Svenska skogsvårdsföreningen
₍1943₎
11 p.

NL 0382814 DNAL

Lindquist, Bertil, 1904-
Dalby Söderskog, en skånsk lövskog i forntid och nutid.
Mit einer deutschen Zusammenfassung. Stockholm, Karto-
grafiska institutet, 1938.
₍2₎, 1, 3-273 p. illus., maps. 27 cm. (Acta phytogeographica suecica
edidit Svenska växtgeografiska sällskapet, 10)
"Citerad litteratur": p. ₍254₎-258.

1. Forests and forestry—Sweden—Scania.   I. Title. II. Series:
Svenska växtgeografiska sällskapet, Uppsala. Acta phytogeographica
suecica, 10.
                          Full name: Sven Bertil Gunvald Lindquist.

SD212.S35L5   634.909486   47-41574*

NL 0382815 DLC DSI NNBG MoU PU DI

99.45
L64g

Lindquist, Bertil, 1904-
Elitträdens betydelse för våra tallskogars
framtida virkesproduktion. Stockholm,
Svenska skogsvårdsföreningens förlag ₍1942₎
44 p.

1. Pine. Growth. 2. Pine. Seed.

NL 0382816 DNAL

Mann
SD
399
.5
L74a

Lindquist, Bertil, 1904-
Forstgenetik in der schwedischen
Waldbaupraxis.   Radebeul und Berlin,
Neumann ₍c1951₎
167 p. illus. 21 cm.

1. Forests and forestry - Sweden.
2. Afforestation - Sweden. 3. Genetics.
I. Title.

NL 0382817 NIC

SD399.5
L747
1954

Lindquist, Bertil, 1904-
Forstgenetik in der schwedischen Wald-
baupraxis. Autorisierte Ubersetzung durch
Jürgen Räder-Roitzch und Ingrid Pein, hrsg.
und mit einen Schlusswort versehen von Ernst
Rohmeder. 2., überarb. Aufl. Radebeul,
Neumann ₍1954₎
155 p. illus., map. 25cm.

1. Forests and forestry - Sweden. 2.
Forest reproduc-   tion. I. Title.
         Full name: Sven Bertil Gunwald
                                    Lindquist.

NL 0382818 GU IdU CtY NcD DNAL

VOLUME 334

Lindquist, Bertil, 1904–
Genetics in Swedish forestry practice. Stockholm, Svenska Skogsvårdsforeningens forlag; Waltham, Mass., Cronica Botanica Co. ₁1948₎
173 p. illus., maps. 22 cm.
Bibliography: p. 169–173.

1. Forests and forestry—Sweden. 2. Afforestation—Sweden. 3. Genetics.   I. Title.
Full name: Sven Bertil Gunvald Lindquist.
A 51–431

Duke Univ. Library
for Library of Congress   ₁3₎

NL 0382819   PSt PPUNA MiHM MB CaBVaU MtU OrU OrCS IdPI WaSpG
NcD MsSM CU ICU ICJ NNC TU LU NN NIC PPAN

XA
.C645
bd.14
no.7
Lindquist, Bertil, 1904–
The main varieties of Picea abies (L.) Karst. in Europe, with a contribution to the theory of a forest vegetation in Scandinavia during the last Pleistocene glaciation. Uppsala, Almqvist & Wiksells boktr., 1948.
₁249₎–342 p. illus. 27 cm. (Acta Horti Bergiani, bd.14, no.7)

Cover title.
Bibliography: p. 335–342.

1. Picea abies – Europe. 2. Pinaceae. 3. Paleobotany – ’leistocene. i.t. ii.s.

NL 0382820   NNBG TxDaM

QK
495
.U5L5
Lindquist, Bertil, 1904–
Om den vildväxande skogsalmens raser och deras utbredning i nordvästeuropa. Uppsala, Almqvist & Wiksells boktr., 1932.
56 p. illus. (Acta phytogeographica Suecica, 4)

English summary.

#Elm.
#Trees--Europe.

NL 0382821   MoU DCU DLC-P4 NNBG PU-B NcD ICU NNC

Lindquist, Bertil, *1904*–
Den skandinaviska bokskogens biologi, The ecology of the Scandinavian beech-woods ... av Bertil Lindquist ... ₁Stockholm, Centraltryckeriet, 1931₎
2 p. l., p. ₁179₎–532 incl. illus., tables, diagrs. fold. map (in pocket) 24½ᵐ.
Akademisk avhandling—Uppsala.
"Särtryck ur Svenska skogsvårdsföreningens tidskrift, häfte 3, 1931."
"Summary": p. 486–520.
"Litteraturförteckning": p. 521–532.
1. Beech. 2. Forests and forestry—Scandinavia.
34–33924
Library of Congress   SD397.B4L5 1931   634.9725

NL 0382822   DLC CtY ICRL MH-A ICU MnU

Lindquist, Bertil, 1904–
Den skogliga rasforskningen och praktiken. Stockholm, Svenska skogsvårdsföreningens förlag, 1946.
176 p. illus., maps, diagrs. 22cm.

1. Forests and forestry - Sweden. 2. Trees - Sweden.

NL 0382823   CU OrCS

Lindquist, Bertil, 1904–
Studien über die Stammrindentypen der Gattung *Betula* L. Uppsala, Almqvist & Wiksell, 1946.
92–132 p. illus. 28 cm. (Acta Horti Bergiani, bd. 14, n:o 4)
Cover title.
Bibliography: p. 131–132.
1. Birch. 2. Bark.   (Series: Svenska vetenskapsacademien, Stockholm. Trädgård Bergielund. Acta Horti Bergiani, bd. 14, n:o 4)
Full name: Sven Bertil Gunvald Lindquist.
QK495.B56L5   583.978   51–19793

NL 0382824   DLC NNBG

99.35
L64
Lindquist, Bertil, 1904–
Den svenska tallen; en rasstudie i bild, av Bertil Lindquist... Stockholm, Svenska skogsvårdsföreningens förlag ₁1938₎
83 p. illus. 23½cm.

1. Pine. 2. Sweden. Forestry.

NL 0382825   DNAL NNBG NN

Lindquist, Bertil, 1904–
... Timmesöbjerg, en biologisk studie i bokskogen på Möens klint, av B. Lindquist. Med 19 tavler ... København, Levin & Munksgaard, E. Munksgaard, 1938.
59 p. incl. tables. xix pl. (incl. 2 diagr., 1 fold.) on 11 l. 26½ᵐ. (D. Kgl. danske vidensk₁abernes₎ selsk₁abs₎ skrifter. Naturv₁idensk.₎ og math₁em.₎ afd., 9. række, vii, 4)
Series title in French at head of title.
Summary also in German.
"Litteratur": p. 58–59.
1. Beech. 2. Soils. 3. Forests and forestry—Denmark—Möen.
₁Full name: Sven Bertil Gunvald Lindquist₎
A 40–1832
John Crerar library
for Library of Congress   [AS281.D223 9. række, vii, 4]
₁2₎   (508)

NL 0382826   ICJ ICU OU

Lindquist, Bertil, 1917–
Effect of vitamin D on the metabolism of radiocalcium in rachitic rats. ₁Translated by L. James Brown₎ Lund, 1952.
82 p. illus. 25 cm.
Akademisk avhandling—Lund.
Extra t. p., with thesis statement, inserted.
"This work also appears as supplementum to Acta paediatrica."
Bibliography: p. ₁80₎–82.
1. Vitamin D in the body 2. Rickets.   I Title
Full name: Karl Bertil Johan Lindquist.
QP801.V5L525 1952   55–16350 rev

NL 0382827   DLC

Lindquist, Bertil, 1917–
Effect of vitamin D on the metabolism of radiocalcium in rachitic rats. Lund, 1952.
82 p. plate, diagrs. 24 cm. (Acta pædiatrica. Supplementum 86)
At head of title: From the Pediatric Clinic ... and the Pharmacologic Institute ... of the University of Lund, Sweden.
Issued also as thesis, Lund.
"References": p. ₁80₎–82.
1. Calcium in the body. 2. Rickets. 3. Vitamin therapy. (Series)
Full name: Karl Bertil Johan Lindquist.
A 55–3021
John Crerar Library
for Library of Congress   ₁2₎

NL 0382828   DNLM MoU ViU PPT-M

Lindquist, C. R., ed.
Air cadets of America.
... Handbook ... copyright ... ₁by₎ C. R. Lindquist. ₁Philadelphia₎ °1932.

NL 0382830   DNAL

Lindquist, Carl Adolf, d. 1904.
Beskrifning öfirr svinpasten pa uppdrag af kongl. medicinalstyrelsen. 1888.
29 p.

NL 0382830   DNAL

Lindquist, Carl Sigurd
see
Lindquist, Sigurd, 1895–

Lindquist, Cyril Albin
see
Director, Cyr Vita.

Lindquist, David, 1905–
Acta Dioecesis Holmiensis; till belysning av kyrko- och församlingsstyrelsen i Stockholm. Lund, C. W. K. Gleerup ₁1947₎
158 p. 26 cm. (Lunds universitets årsskrift, n. f., avd. 1, bd. 44, nr. 2)
"Bilagor" (documents): p. ₁115₎–148.
"Zusammenfassung": p. ₁149₎–158.
Bibliographical footnotes.
1. Stockholm—Church history. 2. Stockholms stads konsistorium.   I. Stockholm (Diocese)   II. Title. (Series: Lund. Universitet. Acta Universitatis Lundensis, n. s. Lunds universitets årsskrift, n. f., avd. 1, bd. 44, nr. 2)
AS284.L8   bd. 44, nr. 2   A 51–2972
Chicago. Univ. Libr.
for Library of Congress   ₁2₎†

NL 0382833   ICU TxU PU DLC

Lindquist, David, 1905–
... Första-mässan i S₁tockholm; en liturgihistorisk studie... Stockholm, Svenska kyrkans diakonistyrelses bokförlag ₁1945₎
210 p., 23ᵐ. (Samlingar och studier till Svenska kyrkans historia. 12)

"Tryckt med bidrag ur Längmanska Kulturfonden."
Summary in German.
Bibliographical footnotes.

NL 0382834   NjPT CtY ICU MoSCS

Lindquist, David, 1905– ed.
Härnösands stift i ord och bild
see under title

Lindquist, David, 1905–
Hovförsamlingens liturgiska tradition, 1614–1693. Lund, C. W. K. Gleerup ₁1944₎
51 p. 25 cm. (Lunds universitets årsskrift, n. f., avd. 1, bd. 41, nr. 1)
Bibliographical footnotes.
1. Svenska kyrkan. Liturgy and ritual. 2. Sweden—Church history.   I. Title. (Series: Lund. Universitet. Acta Universitatis Lundensis, n. s. Lunds universitets årsskrift, n. f., avd. 1, bd. 41, nr. 7)
Full name: Gunnar David Lindquist.
AS284.L8   n. f., avd. 1, bd. 41, nr. 1   A 48–4413*
Chicago. Univ. Libr.
for Library of Congress   ₁2₎†

NL 0382836   ICU NcU TxU NIC PU DLC

Lindquist, David, 1905–
Nattvarden i svenskt kultliv; en liturgihistorisk studie. Lund, C. W. K. Gleerup ₁1947₎
187 p. 25 cm. (Lunds universitets årsskrift, n. f., avd. 1, bd. 43, nr. 7)
Bibliographical footnotes.
1. Lord's Supper. 2. Sweden—Church history.   I. Title.   II. Series: Lund. Universitet. Acta Universitatis Lundensis, n. s. Lunds universitets årsskrift, n. f., avd. 1, bd. 43, nr. 7.
Full name: Gunnar David Lindquist.
[AS284.L8   n. f., avd. 1, bd. 43, nr. 7]   A 48–3965*
(378.485)
Chicago. Univ. Libr.
for Library of Congress   ₁1₎

NL 0382837   ICU TxU NIC PU NcU

4BV
517
Lindquist, David, 1905–
Stockholms liturgiska tradition; högmässa och bigudstjänster. Stockholm, Svenska kyrkans diakonistyrelses bokförlag [1951]
388 p.

NL 0382838   DLC-P4

Lindquist, David, 1905–
Studier i den svenska andaktslitteraturen under stormaktstidevarvet, med särskild hänsyn till bön-, tröste- och nattvardsböcker. Stockholm, Svenska kyrkans diakonistyrelses bokförlag ₁1939₎
xliii, 444 p. facsims. 22 cm.
Akademisk avhandling—Lund.
Extra t. p., with thesis statement, inserted.
Bibliography: p. ₁xiii₎–xliii.
1. Devotional literature—Hist. & crit. 2. Devotional literature—Bibl.   I. Title.
Full name: Gunnar David Lindquist.
BV4818.L5   55–46006

NL 0382839   DLC MH NjP MnU ICU CtY-D CtY

VOLUME 334

Lindquist, David L.
Recent developments of electric skip hoists and bell hoists for blast furnaces, by David L. Lindquist. ₍Pittsburgh?₎ 1918. p. 29-85. diagr. 8°.

Cover-title.
At head of title: Association of Iron & Steel Electrical Engineers.
Repr.: Assoc. of Iron and Steel Electrical Engineers. Proc. 1918.

1. Hoisting and conveying machinery (Electric). 2. Furnaces (Blast). 3. Association of Iron and Steel Electrical Engineers.
N. Y. P. L. August 21, 1918.

NL 0382840 NN

Lindquist, Emory Kempton, 1908–
Smoky Valley people; a history of Lindsborg, Kansas. Lindsborg, Bethany College, 1953.

269 p. illus. 24 cm.

Includes bibliography.

1. Lindsborg, Kan. 2. Bethany College, Lindsborg, Kan. 3. Swedes in Kansas. I. Title.

F689.L7L5 978.155 53–13457 ‡

NL 0382841 DLC CtY-D KEmT

Lindquist, Emory Kempton, 1908–
Smoky Valley people; a history of Lindsborg, Kansas. Lindsborg, Bethany College, 1953.

x, 269 p. illus., ports. 24 cm. (Augustana Historical Society publications, v. 13)

Bibliography : p. 257-265.

1. Lindsborg, Kan. 2. Bethany College. Lindsborg, Kan. 3. Swedes in Kansas. I. Title. (Series: Augustana Historical Society, Rock Island, Ill. Publications, v. 13)

F536.A96 vol. 13 978.155 55–1517

NL 0382842 DLC MnHi KMK CLU PU PPLT

Lindquist, Erik
Ueber die einwirkung von salpetersaeure auf komponenten des buchenholzes. (Auszug)
Inaug. diss. Berlin tech. hoch. 1927.

NL 0382843 ICRL

Lindquist, Erik Gustaf Werner, 1893–
...Formler för beräkning av medelhastigheten i öppna ledningar, av Löjtnant Erik Lindquist. ₍Stockholm, 1926.₎ p. 513-580. incl. diagrs., plan, tables. pl. 4°.

Cover-title.
Repr.: Kungliga väg- och vattenbyggnadskårens 75-årsskrift
Bibliography, p. 538-539.

486065A. 1. Water—Flow of.
N. Y. P. L. July 21, 1930

NL 0382844 NN

Lindquist, Erik Gustaf Werner, 1893–
On velocity formulas for open channels and pipes, by Erik G. W. Lindquist ... Stockholm, Generalstabens litografiska anstalts förlag ₍1934₎

62 p. tables, diagrs. (part fold.) 24ᶜᵐ. (Ingeniörsvetenskapsakademiens handlingar. nr. 130)

"Special report presented at the World power conference sectional meeting 1933."
Includes summaries in French and German.

1. Hydraulics. I. Title.

Title from Iowa State College A C 34–4413
Library of Congress [TA4.I 43 no. 130]

NL 0382845 IaAS PPAmP OU OCl

HN29 **Lindquist, Everet Franklin.**
L5 Achievement tests in the social studies ₍by₎ E. F. Lindquist and H. R. Anderson. Reprinted from "The Educational record" for April, 1933. Washington, D. C., American council on education ₍1933?₎

cover-title, 61p. 22½cm. in 23cm.

NL 0382846 NBuG PPPL

LB1775 **Lindquist, Everet Franklin.**
.I6 **Iowa.** *State board of educational examiners.*
1928-29 ... A census of the public school teaching personnel of Iowa for the school year 1928-29. Prepared by E. T. Peterson, PH. D., E. F. Lindquist, PH. D., M. P. Price, PH. D., H. A. Jeep, PH. D. Issued by the Board of educational examiners, Agnes Samuelson, president. Des Moines, Published by the state of Iowa ₍1932₎

~~**Lindquist, Everet Franklin, joint ed.**~~

Hawkes, Herbert Edwin, 1872– *ed.*
The construction and use of achievement examinations; a manual for secondary school teachers, prepared under the auspices of a committee of the American council on education ... Editors: Herbert E. Hawkes, E. F. Lindquist, C. R. Mann. Boston, New York ₍etc.₎ Houghton Mifflin company ₍ᶜ1936₎

Lindquist, Everet Franklin, 1901– joint author
Cooperative American history test.
see under Anderson, Howard Richmond, 1898–

Lindquist, Everet Franklin, 1901– joint author
Cooperative ancient history test.
see under Anderson, Howard Richmond, 1898–

Lindquist, Everet Franklin, 1901– joint author
Cooperative English history test.
see under Anderson, Howard Richmond, 1898–

Lindquist, Everet Franklin, 1901– joint author
Cooperative medieval history test.
see under Anderson, Howard Richmond, 1898–

Lindquist, Everet Franklin, 1901– joint author
Cooperative modern European history test.
see under Anderson, Howard Richmond, 1898–

Lindquist, Everet Franklin, 1901– joint author
Cooperative world history test.
see under Anderson, Howard Richmond, 1898–

Lindquist, Everet Franklin, 1901–
Design and analysis of experiments in psychology and education. Boston, Houghton Mifflin ₍1953₎

393 p. illus. 25 cm.

1. Psychology—Methodology. I. Title.

BF39.L5 150.72 53–9156 ‡
Library of Congress

OrU WaSp WaT WaTC WaWW Or OrPS OrAshS MtBuM
PHC MtBC CaBVaU IdB IdPI IdU MtU OrCS OrP OrPR
PPTU Wa OrStbM OrSaW OrU-M PSC OCU TxU MiU MsU
WaPS WaE WaU OO OClW OU PBm PP ViU PSt PBL MB
NL 0382855 DLC WaS MoU TxDaS NjR MsSM DPU KEmT

Lindquist, Everet Franklin, 1901– *ed.*
Educational measurement. With chapters by Gordon V. Anderson ₍and others₎ Washington, American Council on Education ₍1951₎

xix, 819 p. illus. 25 cm.

Includes bibliographies.

1. Educational tests and measurements. I. American Council on Education. II. Title.

LB3051.L5 371.26 51–9853

Or IdU OrPS Wa WaS MB OrAshS MtU MtBuM CaBViP
OrPS CaBVa IdPI MtBC OrCS OrU WaTC CaBVaU WaT
WaSp OrSaW NcU MiHM NN TU ViU TxU CtY MsSM WU
NL 0382856 DLC KEmT NSyU AU MiU MH-M WaWW OrPR

Lindquist, Everet Franklin.
Fall testing program for Iowa high schools ₍by₎ E. F. Lindquist, director. ₍Iowa City, The University, 1942₎

36 p. incl. form. 23¼ᶜᵐ. (On cover: University of Iowa publication. ₍New series, no. 1242. April 11, 1942₎)

1. Mental tests. I. Title.

LB1131.L56 42–20081
Library of Congress ₍2₎ 371.26

NL 0382857 DLC

Lindquist, Everet Franklin, 1901–
A first course in statistics, their use and interpretation in education and psychology. Boston, Houghton Mifflin ₍1938₎

xi, 226 p. diagrs., tables. 22 cm.

———— Study manual. Boston, Houghton Mifflin ₍ᶜ1938₎

120 p. 28 cm.

Folded "correlation chart" inserted.

1. Statistics. 2. Statistics—Graphic methods. 3. Education—Stat.

HA29.L8 311 38–10182 rev

NIC
CaBVaU KEmT MU TU PP PSC OClW OU ViU NN OCU OCl OO
NL 0382858 DLC MtU IdPI IdU Or OrCS OrU WaS WaWW MB

Lindquist, Everet Franklin.
A first course in statistics, their use and interpretation in education and psychology ₍by₎ E. F. Lindquist ... Rev. ed. Boston, New York ₍etc.₎ Houghton Mifflin company ₍1942₎

xi p., 1 l., 242 p. tables (1 fold.) diagrs. 22ᶜᵐ.
HA29.L8 1942

———— Study manual ... (Rev. ed.) ... ₍Iowa City, Ia.₎ University printing service, State university of Iowa, 1941₎

1 p. l., 78 numb. l. incl. tables. 28ᶜᵐ.
Reproduced from type-written copy.

1. Statistics. 2. Statistics—Graphic methods. 3. Education—Stat.

Library of Congress HA29.L8 1942 Manual 42–5875
₍10₎ 311

MtBC
MsSM MB OrU-M OrU WaWW MtU OrPS OrPR OrStbM IdPI
OCl OCU OU ViU NIC NBuU KMK KEmT MoU DAU GU ScU
NL 0382859 DLC CU TU PCM PU NcGU PSC PSt NcC OClW

Lindquist, Everet Franklin, 1901–
The form of the American history examination of the cooperative test service ₍by₎ E. F. Lindquist. Washington, D. C. 1931.
20 p. O.
Reprinted from "The educational record" for October, 1931.

NL 0382860 NcD

Lindquist, Everet Franklin.
Instructors manual and key for Study manual for A first course in statistics, rev. ed. ... Boston, Houghton Mifflin ₍c1942₎
3 p. l., 49 p. 22 cm.

NL 0382861 RPB

VOLUME 334

371.26   Lindquist, Everet Franklin.
L6451   ... The Iowa every-pupil achievement
  testing program.   Iowa City, Published
  by the University [1933]
   22p.   (On cover: Bulletin of the
  State university of Iowa. New series,
  no.716)

   At head of title: The State university
  of Iowa, Iowa City.
   "Contains announcements for the sixth
  annual contests."

NL   0382862   IU

[Lindquist, Everet Franklin] 1901–
  The Iowa tests of educational development: how to use the
  test results; a manual for teachers and counselors. Chicago,
  Science Research Associates, ‘1949.
   66 p. illus. 22 cm.

   1. Iowa tests of educational development.   I. Title.

   LB1131.L49   56–46447 ‡

NL   0382863   DLC

Mann
LB   [Lindquist, Everet Franklin] 1901–
1131   The Iowa tests of educational development:
L73   how to use the test results; a manual for
1953   teachers and counselors. 4th revision,
  1953 ed. Chicago, Science Research Associates, c1953.
   64 p. illus. 21 cm.

    1. Iowa tes   ts of educational develop-
  ment.

NL   0382864   NIC

LB1573   Lindquist, Everet Franklin, 1901–   joint
.B55   author.
  Blommers, Paul J   1910–
   Rate of comprehension of reading: its measurement and its
  relation to comprehension, by Paul J. Blommers ... Baltimore,
  Warwick & York, inc. [1944]

Lindquist, Everet Franklin, joint author.
       (1901–

Anderson, Howard Richmond, 1898–
  ... Selected test items in American government, by Howard
  R. Anderson ... and E. F. Lindquist ... Cambridge, Mass., The
  National council for the social studies [‘1939]

E178   Lindquist, Everet Franklin, joint author.
.25   FOR OTHER EDITIONS
.A33   Anderson, Howard Richmond, 1898–   SEE MAIN ENTRY
1947   Selected test items in American history, by Howard R. Anderson and E. F. Lindquist, rev. by Harry D. Berg. Washington, 1947.

Lindquist, Everet Franklin, joint author.

Anderson, Howard Richmond, 1898–
  ... Selected test items in economics, by Howard R. Anderson ... and E. F. Lindquist ... Cambridge, Mass., The National
  council for the social studies [‘1939]

D21   Lindquist, Everet Franklin, 1901–   joint
.A53   author.   FOR OTHER EDITIONS
1947   Anderson, Howard Richmond, 1898–   SEE MAIN ENTRY
  ... Selected test items in world history, by Howard R. An-
  derson ... and E. F. Lindquist ... revised by Frederick H.
  Stutz ... Washington, 1947.

Lindquist, Everet Franklin.
  Statistical analysis in educational research [by] E. F. Lindquist ... [Iowa City, Ia.] ‘1939.
   3 p. l., 166 numb. l., 5 l. incl. tables, diagrs. 27½ᶜᵐ.

   1. Statistics.   2. Education—Stat.   I. Title.
              40–8837
   Library of Congress   LB2846.L5 1939
      ——— Copy 2.
   Copyright A 131159   [2]   270.78

NL   0382870   DLC

Lindquist, Everett Franklin, 1901–
  Statistical analysis in educational research [by] E. F. Lindquist ... Boston, New York [etc] Houghton Mifflin company
  [‘1940]
   xi p., 1 l., 266 p. incl. tables, diagrs. 22½ cm.

   1. Statistics.   2. Education—Stat.   I. Title.
   Library of Congress   LB2846.L5 1940   40—8838
          [a49v1]   370.78

  OrCS CaBVaU IdU OrP OrU-M OrLgE OrStbM
  OC1W OC1 ICJ CU MB WU-M KEmT OrPR Or MtU OrU OrMonO
NL   0382871   DLC IEG WaTC NcD NcRS TU PPTU PSC OU OCU

Lindquist, Everet Franklin, 1901–   joint
       author.
HA29   Paden, Donald W
.P25   Statistics for economics and business [by] Donald W.
  Paden [and] E. F. Lindquist. 1st ed. New York, McGraw-
  Hill, 1951.

Lindquist, Everet Franklin.
  Study manual for A first course in statistics [by] E. F. Lindquist ... Boston, New York [etc.] Houghton Mifflin company
  [‘1938]
   3 p. l., 120, [2] p. 28ᶜᵐ.
   Folded "correlation chart" laid in.

   1. Statistics.
              39–13190
   Library of Congress   HA29.L8 Manual
   Copyright AA 262852   [3]   311

NL   0382873   DLC IdU-SB OrCS CU OU OC1W ICU ViU PHC

HA   Lindquist, Everet Franklin, 1901–
941L   Study manual for a first course in statistics.
  Rev. ed. New York, Houghton Mifflin[1941]
  117p. 28cm.

   1. Statistics. I. Title.

NL   0382874   CtY-M MtU CU

Lindquist, Everet Franklin.
  ... Study manual in elementary statistics, by Everett F.
  Lindquist ... and George D. Stoddard ... New York, Lon-
  don [etc.] Longmans, Green and co., 1929.
   vii p., 1 l., 109 p. diagrs. 27½ᶜᵐ. (Longmans' education series)
   "References": p. 3.

   1. Statistics.   I. Stoddard, George Dinsmore, 1897–   joint author.
              29–25928
   Library of Congress   HA29.L83

  OCX OU MH MB
NL   0382875   DLC OrAshS CaBVaU IdU CU NcD PU-Penn PPTU

Lindquist, Everet Franklin, joint author.

Peterson, Elmer Theodore, 1896–
  ... Teacher supply and demand in Iowa, by E. T. Peterson,
  E. F. Lindquist, H. A. Jeep and M. P. Price. Iowa City,
  The University [1932]

Lindquist, Everet Franklin.

Iowa. *State board of educational examiners.*
  ... Teachers of the public elementary and secondary schools
  of Iowa; a summary. Board of educational examiners.
  Agnes Samuelson, president. Des Moines, The State of Iowa
  [‘1931]

Lindquist, Everet Franklin.
  ... Testing in the social studies, by Everet F. Lindquist ...
  Howard R. Anderson ... [and] Edgar B. Wesley ... Iowa City,
  The University [1933]
   24 p. 23½ᶜᵐ. (University of Iowa extension bulletin ... no. 310.
  February 15, 1933)
   At head of title: ... Aids for history teachers, by the Department of
  history. xiv.

   1. History—[Tests and scales]   I. Anderson, Howard Richmond,
  1898–   joint author. II. Wesley, Edgar Bruce, joint author. III. Title.
  IV. Title: Aids for history teachers.   E 33–1350
   Library, U. S. Office of   Education LB1581.I 7 no. 14

NL   0382878   DHEW PU PPTU

Lindquist, Everet Franklin, 1901–
  What good is high school? By E. F. Lindquist, Lauren
  A. Van Dyke and John R. Yale. Chicago, Science Research
  Associates, 1948.
   43 p. illus. 22 cm. (Life adjustment booklet)
   Bibliography: p. [8] of cover.
   ——— Instructor's guide. By E. F. Lindquist, Lauren
  A. Van Dyke, and John R. Yale. [Chicago, Science Re-
  search Associates, ‘1948]
   11, [1] p. illus. 22 cm.
   Bibliography: page at end.
          LB1609.L47 Guide
   1. Education, Secondary.   I. Van Dyke, Lauren Andrew, 1906–
  joint author.   II. Yale,   John R., joint author. III. Title.
   LB1609.L47   373   49–1485*

NL   0382879   DLC Mi AAP Or MtU CaBViP

Lindquist, Everet Franklin, 1901–
  What good is high school? By E. F. Lindquist, Lauren
  A. Van Dyke and John R. Yale. Chicago, Science Research
  Associates [1951]

NL   0382880   IdPS

Lindquist, Frank Eugene, 1907–
  Dielectric constants of aqueous solutions of
  certain amino acids, by Frank Eugene Lindquist ...
  [Berkeley, Calif., 1937]
   2 p. l., 66 numb. l., 52 l. incl. mounted diagrs.
  29 cm.
   Thesis (Ph. D.) - Univ. of California, May 1937.
   "References": p. 64–66.

   1. Dielectrics.   2. Amino acids.

NL   0382881   CU

Lindquist, Gösta.
  The healing of skin defects; an experimental study on
  the white rat. Stockholm, 1946.
   163 p. illus. 24 cm.
   At head of title: From the Histological Dept. and the Surgical
  Clinic of the University of Uppsala, Sweden.
   Inaug. diss.—Uppsala.
   Extra t. p., with thesis statement (inserted) and cover, have im-
  print: Uppsala, Almqvist & Wiksells boktr., 1946.
   Tr. by Greenville Grove.
   "Also published as Supplementum 107 to Acta chirurgica scandi-
  navica, vol. xciv."
   Bibliography: p. [159]–163.
   1. Skin—Wounds and injuries.

   RL801.L5 1946   617.14   50–21573

NL   0382882   DLC

VOLUME 334

Lindquist, Gösta.
The healing of skin defects; an experimental study on the white rat. Stockholm, 1946.

163 p. illus. 24 cm. (Acta chirurgica Scandinavica, suppl. 107)

Issued also as thesis, Uppsala.
Bibliography: p. ₍159₎–163.

1. Wounds—Treatment. (Series)

A 49–7887*

John Crerar Library
for Library of Congress ₍3₎

NL 0382883 ICJ ViU MoU

Lindquist, Gunnar David
see **Lindquist, David,** 1905–

Lindquist, Gustavus Elmer Emanuel, 1886–
Bland Nordamerikas indianer, bilder ur indianernas utvecklingshistoria intill våra dagar, av G. E. E. Lindquist ... med förord av fil. d:r Karl Fries. Uppsala, J. A. Lindblad ₍1926₎

238 p. incl. front., illus. 21ᶜᵐ.

Music: p. 117, 156.

1. Indians of North America. I. Title.

28–4533

Library of Congress E77.L73

NL 0382885 DLC CLSU OO NN

Lindquist, Gustavus Elmer Emanuel, 1886–
A handbook for missionary workers among the American Indians, by G. E. E. Lindquist ... New York, Home missions council and Council of women for home missions ₍1932₎

87 p. 23ᶜᵐ.

Material for this handbook was gathered by a small committee appointed by the Joint committee on Indian work of the Home missions council and Council of women for home missions. *cf.* Foreword.
Bibliography: p. 83–87.

1. Indians of North America—Missions. I. Home missions council. II. Council of women for home missions. III. Title. IV. Title: Missionary workers among the American Indians, A handbook for.

32–28956

Library of Congress E98.M6L73
———— Copy 2.
Copyright A 55393 ₍3₎

NL 0382886 DLC UU DI MH-P OO

Lindquist, Gustavus Elmer Emanuel, 1886–
The Indian in American life, by G. E. E. Lindquist, with the collaboration of Erna Gunther, John H. Holst, and Flora Warren Seymour; foreword by Mark A. Dawber. New York, Friendship press ₍1944₎

xi, 180 p. maps (1 fold.) 18½ᶜᵐ.

"References" at end of each chapter. "A selected reading list": p. ₍168₎–173.

1. Indians of North America—Culture. 2. Indians of North America—Missions. 3. Indians of North America—Government relations. I. Gunther, Erna, 1896– II. Holst, John Henry, 1873– III. Seymour, Flora Warren (Smith) 1888– IV. Title.

44–3204

Library of Congress E98.C9L56
₍20₎ 970.6

CaBVaU
KyWAT FTaSU NIC NcC PPLT PWcS OLak OC1 OO WaWW
NL 0382887 DLC IdPI CaBViP WaS Wa Or MSohG OrP MtU

E95
.L6
Lindquist, Gustavus Elmer Emanuel, 1886–
Indian treaty making. [Oklahoma City, Okla., 1949?]

416–448 p. 23cm.

Cover title.
Reprinted from the Chronicles of Oklahoma, v. 26, no. 4.

1. Indians of North America—Treaties. 2. Indians of North America—Government relations. I. Title.

NL 0382888 MB PSt WaWW

Lindquist, Gustavus Elmer Emanuel, 1886–
Indians in transition; a study of Protestant missions to Indians in the United States, by G. E. E. Lindquist, with the collaboration of E. Russell Carter. Foreword by L George Nace. New York, Division of Home Missions, National Council of Churches of Christ in the U. S. A., 1951.

120 p. maps. 23 cm.

1. Indians of North America—Missions. I. Title.

E98.M6L733 970.6266 51–4466

NL 0382889 DLC DI NN WHi

Lindquist, Gustavus Elmer Emanuel, 1886–
Indians in urban centers; a manual for city pastors, religious education directors, church social workers and directors of social agencies. By G. E. E. Lindquist... Lawrence, Kan., Home missions council of North America, 1948. 23 p. 22cm.

1. Indians, N. A.—Culture. 2. Indians, N. A.—Missions. I. Home missions council of North America. N. Y. P. L. April 1 , 1950

NL 0382890 NN

LINDQUIST, GUSTAVUS ELMER EMANUEL, 1886–
Indians of Minnesota; a survey of social and religious conditions among tribes in transition... New York, Division of home missions, National council of Churches of Christ in the U. S. A., 1952. 29 p. 22cm.

1. Indians, N. A.—Reg. areas—Minnesota—Missions. 2. Indians, N. A.—Tribes—Chippewa. I. National council of the churches of Christ in the United States of America. Home missions, ⁄Division of.

NL 0382891 NN WaTC WaU PPAmSwM

Lindquist, Gustavus Elmer Emmanuel, 1886–
New trails for old; a handbook for missionary workers among the American Indians. Rev. 1951. New York, National council of the churches of Christ in the U.S.A. Division of home missions [1952] 82 p. illus. 23cm.

Bibliography, p. 66–82.

1. Missionaries—Education and training. 2. Indians, American—Missions. I. National council of the churches of Christ in the United States of America. Home Missions, Division of.

NL 0382892 NN NjP DI NcD

Lindquist, Gustavus Elmer Emanuel
Indians of North Carolina.

(In His Red man in the U.S. ₍c.1923.₎)

NL 0382893 NcU

Lindquist, Gustavus Elmer Emanuel, 1886–
The Jesus road and the red man, by G. E. E. Lindquist ... New York, Chicago ₍etc.₎ Fleming H. Revell company ₍1929₎ 155 p. 19½ᶜᵐ.

I. Title.

Library of Congress E98.M6L74 29–24168
———— Copy 2.

NL 0382894 DLC MH DI NcD

Lindquist, Gustavus Elmer Emanuel, 1886–
The red man in the United States; an intimate study of the social, economic and religious life of the American Indian, made under the direction of G. E. E. Lindquist, with a foreword by Honorable Charles H. Burke ... New York, George H. Doran company ₍1923₎

xxviii, p. 1 l., 29–461 p. front., illus, plates, ports. maps. 22½ cm.

"The Committee on social and religious surveys ... is responsible for this publication."
"Bibliography on the American Indian": p. 442–447.

1. Indians of North America. 2. Indians of North America—Missions. I. Institute of social and religious research. II. Title.

E77.L74 23–10398 8

Or OrStbM MSohG Wa WaE MtBuM
WaSp WaSpG CaBVaU IdB IdPS WaWW WaT WaTC OrSaW
OOxM OClW OC1 MiU OO OU ICJ WaU MB NcD DI
OrU-M CoU TxU KyLx IdU MtU MtBC OrU PSC PHC PU
NL 0382895 DLC DSI MeB NIC PPPrHi OrCS OrPB

Lindquist, H D
Some factors related to the time of dissipation of fog or stratus at Seattle

see under

U.S. Weather Bureau.

Lindquist, H D
A study of summertime stratus & fog in western Washington.

see under

U.S. Weather Bureau.

Lindquist, Hans.
En praktisk handbok om inköp. ₍Stockholm₎ Forum ₍1955₎ 283p.

NL 0382898 NNU-W NNU

Lindquist, Harry, 1905–
Program för en lyckodag. Stockholm, Harrier ₍1946₎ 192 p. 19 cm.

1. Success. I. Title.

BF637.S8L5 63–37849 ‡

NL 0382899 DLC

Lindquist, Harry Gotfred, 1905– joint author.

Mueller, William Samuel, 1901–
... Some factors affecting the properties of whipping cream and the quality of the finished product, by W. S. Mueller, M. J. Mack and H. G. Lindquist ... Amherst, Mass., Massachusetts state college, 1936.

Lindquist, Harry L., ed.

The Collectors' journal ... v. 1–
Jan. 1909–
Chicago, Lindquist and Lauritzen, 1909–

Lindquist, Harry L., ed.

The Stamp specialist. v. 1– Nov. 1939–
New York, N. Y., H. L. Lindquist ₍1939₎

Lindquist, Harry L., ed.

Stamps; a weekly magazine of philately. v. 1–
Sept. 17, 1932–
₍New York, etc.₎ H. L. Lindquist ₍1932₎

Lindquist, Hjalmar, tr.

PL248
.A3A97
Adivar, Halide Edib, 1885–
Eldskjortan; roman från världskriget, av Halidé Edib; auktoriserad översättning från osman-turkiskan av Hjalmar Lindquist; med förord av författarinnan, inledning och förklaringar av översättaren samt författarinnans porträtt. Stockholm, P. A. Norstedt & söners ₍1928₎

VOLUME 334

Lindquist, Ida Pauline, 1878–
The value of lip reading for the hard-of-hearing adult.
(*In* National education association of the United States. Addresses and proceedings, 1928. p. 446–448)

1. Deaf and dumb. ₁1. Deafness₁

E 31–140

Library, U. S. Office of   Education L13.N212 1928

NL 0382905   DHEW OU

Lindquist, Ivar, 1895–
... A propos d'une inscription de la fin de la période mycénienne, par Ivar Lindquist. Lund, C. W. K. Gleerups förlag, 1931.
1 p. l., 18 p. illus. 23½ᶜᵐ. (K. Humanistiska vetenskapssamfundets i Lund. Årsberättelse 1930–1931, 11)
Running title: Inscription mycénienne.

1. Inscriptions, Greek—Asine. 2. Asine, Greece—Antiq. ι. Title: Inscription mycénienne.
₁Full name: Ivar Artur Lindquist₁
Cincinnati. Univ. Libr.   A 41–3924
for Library of Congress   [AS284.L85 1930/1931]
₂₂₁   (068.485)

NL 0382906   OCU IaU

Lindquist, Ivar, *1895–*
Galdrar de Gamla germanska trollsångernas stil undersökt i samband med en Svensk runinskrift från folkvandringstiden. ...
Göteborg, 1923.   193 p.
Inaug. Diss. - Göteborgs, 1923.

NL 0382907   ICRL

Lindquist, Ivar,   1895–
Galdrar, de gamla germanska trollsångernas stil undersökt i samband med en svensk runinskrift från folkvandringstiden, av Ivar Lundquist.   Göteborg: Elanders boktryckeri Aktiebolag, 1923. viii, 193 p. 8°. (Göteborgs högskola. Årsskrift. bd. 29, nr. 1.)

1. Runes, Magic—Sweden.   ⁷ Magic, German.
N.Y.P.L.   October 28, 1926

NL 0382908   NN NRU RPB NIC CU

Lindquist, Ivar, 1895–
... Der gott Lobbonus, von Ivar Lindquist. Lund, C. W. K. Gleerups förlag, 1933.
1 p. L., 11 p. 23½ᶜᵐ. (K. Humanistiska vetenskapssamfundets i Lund. Årsberättelse 1932–1933, vi)

1. Germanic languages—Etymology—Names. 2. Mythology, Germanic. ι. Title. ιι. Title: Lobbonus, Der gott.
₁Full name: Ivar Artur Lindquist₁
A C 40–1342
Cincinnati. Univ. Libr. AS284.L85 1932–1933, 6
for Library of Congress   [AS284.L85 1932/1933, 6]
₂₂₁   (068.485)

NL 0382909   OCU

AS284
.L85
1937/38

Lindquist, Ivar, 1895–   ed.
Agrell, Sigurd, 1881–1937.
Die Herkunft der runenschrift. Von S. Agrell.
(*In* K. Humanistiska vetenskapssamfundet i Lund.   Årsberättelse 1937–1938. Lund, 1938. 23½ᶜᵐ. p. 65–117. illus.)

893.6   Lindquist, Ivar, 1895-   ed.
.L64n   Norröna lovkväden från 800- och 900-talen ...
Lund, C. W. K. Gleerup [1929-
v.   (Added t.-p.: Nordisk filologi; undersök-, ningar och handböcker, utgivna av Ivar Lindquist och Jöran Sahlgren. bd.2)

NL 0382911   IU CU CSt NRU NIC MnU

PT7244
.K57

Lindquist, Ivar, 1895–   joint ed.
Kock, Ernst Albin, 1864–1943, *ed.*
Den norsk-isländska skaldediktningen ₁utg. av Elisabeth Kock och Ivar Lindquist₁ Lund, C. W. K. Gleerup ₁1946–49₁

PD5773
L5

Lindquist, Ivar, 1895-
Olåst låst i åldre Västgötalagen. Lund, Gleerup [1941]
40 p. (Nordisk filologi; undersökningar och handböcker, bd. 3)

1. Swedish language - Old Swedish. 2. Västgötalagen.

NL 0382913   CU

Lindquist, Ivar. Ordstudier och tolk-
ningar i Havamal. (Studier i nord. filol.
IX. bd. 1. 1918.) 8°. pp. 17. IcA45S49

NL 0382914   NIC

DL3
.N6
bd. 7
1948

Lindquist, Ivar, 1895–
Janzén, Assar Götrik, 1904–   *ed.*
Personnamn. Stockholm. Bonnier ₁1948₁

DL3
.N6
bd. 7

Lindquist, Ivar, 1895–
Janzén, Assar Götrik, 1904–   *ed.*
Personnavne. Stockholm, A. Bonnier ₁1947₁

Lindquist, Ivar, 1895–
Religiösa runtexter ... av Ivar Lindquist. Lund, H. Ohlssons boktryckeri, 1932–
v. illus. (plan) plates, facsim. 25ᶜᵐ. (Added t.-p.: Skrifter utg. av Vetenskaps-societeten i Lund. Publications of the New society of letters at Lund. 15
English summary: v. 1, p. ₁106₁–111.

1. Inscriptions, Runic. 2. Sweden—Antiq. 3. Amulets. ι. Title.
₁Full name: Ivar Artur Lindquist₁
35–11851
Library of Congress   PD2014.L45
₂₂₁   439.617

NL 0382917   DLC PU AU NcU TxU NcD

Lindquist, Ivar, 1895–
— En skinnhandskrift från Flatey som beskriver Rökstensrunor. *In* Minnesskrift utg. av Filologiska Samfundet i Göteborg. Göteborg, 1920. pp. 114–121.   IcA31G321

NL 0382918   NIC

Lindquist, Ivar.
— Till två små dikter i Havamal.
In Ver sacrum. Göteborg, 1917. pp. 126–135.   IcF33B719

NL 0382919   NIC

Lindquist, Ivar, 1895–
Västgötalagens litterära bilagor, medeltida svensk småberättelsekonst på poesi och prosa, av Ivar Lindquist. Lund, H. Ohlssons boktryckeri, 1941.
106, ₁1₁ p. 23½ᶜᵐ. (Added t.-p.: Skrifter utgivna av Vetenskaps-societeten i Lund. Publications of the New society of letters at Lund. 26)
Imprint on cover and added t.-p.: Lund, C. W. K. Gleerup.

1. Swedish literature—Old Swedish. 2. Swedish language—Old Swedish—Texts. 3. Sweden—Hist.—Sources. 4. Sweden—Hist.—To 1397. ι. Title.
₁Full name: Ivar Artur Lindquist₁
43–1448
Library of Congress   PT9552.L5
₃₁   839.7

NL 0382920   DLC AU TxU CaBVaU NcD

Z720
.H59C3

Lindquist, Jennie Dorothea, *1899–*
Caroline M. Hewins, her book: containing A mid-century child and her books, by Caroline M. Hewins ₁and₁ Caroline M. Hewins and books for children, by Jennie D. Lindquist. Boston, Horn Book, 1954.

Lindquist, Jennie Dorothea, 1899–
The golden name day. Pictures by Garth Williams. ₁New York₁ Harper ₁1955₁
247 p. illus. 21 cm.

ι. Title.

PZ7.L6592Go   55—8823 ↑

OrCS OrAshS OrMonO OrU
NcD OU WaS KU AAP MiU FU MB NBuU WaSp N OrP OrPS Or
NL 0382922   DLC ViU MiU OOxM OC1 TU OCU PP NcGU CU IU

Lindquist, John.
Framställning af Torbern Bergmans Fysiska geografi. I ... af John Lindquist ... Stockholm: G. Lindströms boktryckeri, 1900. 110 p. 8°.
Dissertation, Upsala, 1900.
Bibliography, p. ₁109₁–110.

532293A. 1. Bergman, Torbern   Olof, 1735–1784. 2. Geography,
Physical.   June 22, 1931
N.Y.P.L

NL 0382923   NN PU ICRL

657
L64a

Lindquist, John A
Accounting problems of today. [Paper read at₁ second Accountants' Graduate Study Conference, Univ. of Michigan. ₁Ann Arbor₁ 1949.
21ℓ. 28cm.

Cover title.
Errata leaves inserted.

1. Accounting. I. Accountants' Graduate Study Conference. 2d, University of Michigan, 1949. II. Title.

NL 0382924   IU MiU

Lindquist, John Maurits
see   Lindquist, John.

---

ar W
34383

Lindquist, Joseph Alexander.
Comparison, item by item, of the tariff of 1883; the tariff as left by the Mills Bill; the ₁McKinley₁ tariff of 1890, giving tariff according to each, and ad valorem equivalents of specific duties. New York, Reform Committee of the Reform Club, 1890. ₁501₁–552 p. 24cm.

Detached from Tariff reform, v.3, no.16.

NL 0382926   NIC RPB OO

VOLUME 334

QK627
.P97
L5
Lindquist, Juan Carlos.
Las especies de Puccinias, parásitas de Malváceas en la República Argentina. La Plata, 1945.
[17]-33 p. illus. 23 cm. (Notas del Museo de la Plata, t. 10. Botánica, no. 47)

"Trabajo realizado en el Instituto de Botánica C. Spegazzini del Museo de La Plata." Bibliographical footnotes.

1. Puccinia. 2. Malvaceae - Diseases and pests. i.t. ii.s.

NL 0382927 NNBG

QK621
.P45
L5
Lindquist, Juan Carlos.
Muerte de manzanos ocasionada por "Phytophthora cactorum." Buenos Aires, Coni, 1938.
[195]-199 p. illus. 27 cm.

"De la Revista de la Facultad de Agronomía de la Plata (tercera época) tomo XXI (1936)."

1. Phytophthora cactorum. 2. Pyrus malus - Diseases and pests. 3. Peronosporaceae. i.t.

NL 0382928 NNBG

QK621
.P45
L515
Lindquist, Juan Carlos.
Una nueva especie del género "Peronospora," "Peronospora convolvuli" Lindquist, nov. sp. La Plata, 1946.
[29]-31 p. illus. 27 cm.

"De la Revista de la Facultad de Agronomía de La Plata (tercera época) tomo XXVI, entrega 1ª (1946)."

1. Peronospora convolvuli. 2. Peronosporaceae. i.t.

NL 0382929 NNBG

QK627
.P97
L515
Lindquist, Juan Carlos.
Puccinia tessariae y Uromyces tessariae. La Plata, 1948.
[35]-58 p. 1 plate. 23 cm. (Notas del Museo de la Plata, t. 13. Botánica, no. 58)

1. Puccinia tessariae. 2. Uromyces tessariae. 3. Tessaria - Diseases and pests. i.s.

NL 0382930 NNBG

QK627
.R3
L5
Lindquist, Juan Carlos.
Tres especies, nuevas e críticas, de Ravenelias argentinas. La Plata, El Sol [1946]
[298]-302 p. illus. 24 cm.
"Apartado del Boletín de la Sociedad Argentina de Botánica, Vol. I Nº 4 ... Noviembre 1946."

1. Ravenelia - Argentine Republic. 2. Ravenelia spegazziniana. 3. Ravenelia chacoensis. 4. Ravenelia imperspicua. i.t.

NL 0382931 NNBG

Lindquist, Karl Sigurd
see Lindquist, Sigurd, 1895-

Lindquist, L. W.
A study of short wave receiving antennae Thesis, 1934.

NL 0382933 OClW

Lindquist, Lilly, joint author.
Bovee, Arthur Gibbon, 1882-
Une aventure en français, by Arthur Gibbon Bovee ... and Lilly Lindquist ... New York, Chicago, Harcourt, Brace and company, 1934-

---

LT
PC2111
.L725
Lindquist, Lilly.
French for daily use. Columbus, C. E. Merrill, 1946.
84 p. illus. (Skilltext for beginning French)

NL 0382935 ICU

Lindquist, Lilly.
General language; English and its foreign relations [by] Lilly Lindquist ... New York, H. Holt and company [*1940]
xiii, 398 p. illus. (incl. maps) 20½ᵐ.
Includes songs with music.
"Part two, A sampling of languages": p. [255]-385.
"Books to read" at end of most of the chapters.

1. Language and languages. 2. English language. i. Title.

Library of Congress   P124.L5   40-4832
—— Copy 2.
Copyright A 136491   [3]   407

NL 0382936 DLC OrCS WaU PU PP OCU

Lindquist, Lilly.
General language; English and its foreign relations [by] Lilly Lindquist [and] Clarence Wachner. Rev. ed. New York, Holt [1952]
433 p. illus. 21 cm.

1. Language and languages. 2. English language. i. Wachner, Clarence, joint author. ii. Title.

P124.L5 1952   407   52-4906 ‡

NL 0382937 DLC CLU CoU KEmT

LINDQUIST, LILLY.
A laboratory course in general language. Books 1-2. [New York] H. Holt [c1929] 2 v. in 1. maps. 25cm.

1. Language--Hist.
words and phrases.   2. English language--Foreign

NL 0382938 NN PPT MH

P121
.L5
Lindquist, Lilly
Manual and key for a laboratory course in general language...
N. Y., [c1929]
1 pam. 4°

NL 0382939 DLC

Lindquist, Lilly, ed.
Dumas, Alexandre, 1802-1870.
Les trois mousquetaires, par Alexandre Dumas, edited for school use by Lilly Lindquist ... illustrated by Clarence Rowe and Leon D'Emo. New York, Cincinnati [etc.] American book company [*1931]

Lindquist, Martin G.
Plans for funeral homes; elevations—floor plans, salesroom layouts and analytical discussions, by Martin G. Lindquist. Prepared for Joint conference on business procedure. [Cincinnati, Printed by the C. J. Krehbiel co., *1931]
cover-title, 40 p. illus. (incl. plans) 28ᵐ.

1. Architecture—Designs and plans. 2. Undertakers and undertaking. i. Joint conference on business procedure. ii. Title: Funeral homes, Plans for.

Library of Congress   NA6115.L5   31-23903
—— Copy 2.
Copyright A 42245   [3]   726.8

NL 0382941 DLC MB

Lindquist, Maude Lucille, 1906-
Community life in Minnesota, by Maude L. Lindquist ... and James W. Clark ... New York, Boston [etc.] C. Scribner's sons [*1933]
xvi, 319 p. incl. front., illus., maps. 20ᵐ.
"A class library": p. 310-311; Bibliography at end of each chapter.

1. Minnesota—Hist. 2. Minnesota—Pol. & govt. 3. Minnesota—Econ. condit. i. Clark, James Westfall, 1893- joint author. ii. Title.

Library of Congress   F606.L67   33-25058
Copyright A 65196   [5]   977.6

NL 0382942 DLC OCl

Lindquist, Maude Lucille, 1906-
Community life in Minnesota, by Maude L. Lindquist ... and James W. Clark ... New York, Chicago [etc.] C. Scribner's sons [*1936]
xvi, 323 p. incl. front., illus. 19½ᵐ.
Maps on lining-papers.
"A class library": p. 313-314; Bibliography at end of each chapter.

1. Minnesota—Hist. 2. Minnesota—Pol. & govt. 3. Minnesota—Econ. condit. i. Clark, James Westfall, 1893- joint author. ii. Title.

Library of Congress   F606.L67 1936   36-13991
—— Copy 2.
Copyright A 96207   [5]   977.6

NL 0382943 DLC

Lindquist, Maude Lucille, 1906-   comp.
Early days and ways in the old Northwest, by Maude L. Lindquist ... and James W. Clark ... New York, Chicago [etc.] C. Scribner's sons [*1937]
x p., 1 l., 295 p. col. front. 20ᵐ.
Selections from primary and secondary sources on the beginnings of Minnesota. cf. Foreword.

1. Minnesota—Hist. i. Clark, James Westfall, 1893- joint comp. ii. Title.

Library of Congress   F606.L675   37-6331
—— Copy 2.
Copyright A 105437   [5]   977.6

NL 0382944 DLC OClW IdB

Microfilm
Lindquist, Maude Lucille, 1906-
Efforts toward Lutheran union in the United States to 1860. [Minneapolis, Minn.] 1949.
468 p.
Thesis--University of Minnesota.
Microfilm (negative) Minneapolis, Minn., University of Minnesota, 1 reel. 35mm.
Filmed with Mauelshagen, C. The effect of German immigration upon the Lutheran Church in America, 1820-1870. 1935.

1. Lutheran Church in the U.S.--Hist. 2. Christian union--Lutheran Church. I. Title.

NL 0382945 CBPL

Lindquist, Maude Lucille, 1906-
Minnesota, the story of a great state; a textbook for Minnesota schools, sixth grade, by Maude L. Lindquist and James W. Clark. New York, Scribner [1950]
viii, 420, ix-xxviii p. illus., ports. 22 cm.
Includes bibliographies.

1. Minnesota—Hist. i. Clark, James Westfall, 1893- joint author.

F606.L677   977.6   50-2862

NL 0382946 DLC Or NN

F9
.L74
[Lindquist, Maude Lucille] 1906-
New England summer tour guide. [Duluth] University of Minnesota, Duluth Branch [1955?]
cover-title, 82 p. maps. 28cm.

NL 0382947 MnHi

H83
.F75
1945
Lindquist, Maude Lucille, 1906-   joint author.
FOR OTHER EDITIONS SEE MAIN ENTRY
Freeland, George Earl, 1886-
... Social studies for Minnesota. 7th-[8th] year. [By] George Earl Freeland ... and contributing editor, James Truslow Adams ... and James W. Clark and Maude L. Lindquist ... New York, Chicago [etc.] C. Scribner's sons [1945]

VOLUME 334

Lindquist, Nils, 1901–
... Studien über die cutane capillarresistenz im kindesalter, von Nils Lindquist ... Lund, H. Ohlssons buchdruckerei, 1937.
167 p. incl. tables, diagrs. 24ᶜᵐ. (Acta pædiatrica. vol. xx, supplementum II)
At head of title: Aus der Pädiatrischen universitätsklinik zu Lund. Akademisk avhandling—Lund.
Translated by Fru Maria Grönwall. *cf.* Vorwort.
Summary also in English.
"Literaturverzeichnis": p. [159]–167.
1. Capillaries. I. Grönwall, Fru Maria, tr. II. Title: Capillarresistenz im kindesalter.
[*Full name*: Nils Gunnar Ingevald Lindquist]
A C 38–3789
John Crerar library
for Library of Congress   [4]

NL 0382949   ICJ MoU ViU

Lindquist, Nils Gustaf, 1906–
Deklarationshandbok för löntagaren, av Nils G. Lindquist och Dag Helmers. Stockholm, Wahlström & Widstrand [1953]
69p.
(Wahlström & Widstrands deklarationshandböcker)

NL 0382950   NNU

Lindquist, Nils Gustaf, 1906–
Konjunkturskatten, av Nils G. Lindquist och Sven Crabo. Stockholm, Wahlström & Widstrand [1952]
100 p. 24 cm. (Svenskt affärsbibliotek)

1. Excess profits tax—Sweden. I. Crabo, Sven, joint author. II. Title.
54–31452 ‡

NL 0382951   DLC

Lindquist, Nils Gustaf, 1906–
De nya bestämmelserna om beskattning av realisationsvinst, goodwill och ackumulerad inkomst, av Nils G. Lindquist och Dag Helmers. Stockholm, Wahlström & Widstrand [1952]
74 p. 23 cm. (Wahlström & Widstrands deklarationshandböcker)

1. Capital gains tax—Sweden. 2. Income tax—Sweden—Law. I. Helmers, Dag, joint author. II. Title.
57–44960

NL 0382952   DLC MH-L NNU-W

Lindquist, Olaus, respondent
Fant, Erik Mikael, 1754–1817, *praeses.*
... Dissertatio historica de religionis in Svecia controversiis quibusdam recentioribus ... Upsaliæ, litteris viduæ direct. J. Edman [1792]

Lindquist, Orville Alvin.
Common fallacies regarding United States history. Richmond, Dietz Press, 1948.
99 p. 23 cm.
Bibliographical footnotes.

1. U. S.—Hist.—Errors, inventions, etc. I. Title.
E179.L6   973.0883   48–3411*

NL 0382954   DLC Mi ViU CaBVa MiU NBuC

Lindquist, Orville Alvin.
Untruths about animals; a cyclopedia of animal fallacies. Richmond, Dietz Press, 1950.
117 p. 24 cm.
Bibliography: p. 111–117.

1. Animals, Habits and behavior of. 2. Zoology—Dictionaries. I. Title.
QL50.L55   591.5   51–1783

NL 0382955   DLC NcU CaBVa MB

Lindquist, Orville Alvin, 1873–
Alone [by] Orville A. Lindquist. [Boston, New York, The Arthur P. Schmidt co., c1923]
5 p. 32 cm.

NL 0382956   00

Lindquist, Orville Alvin, arr.
Chorale. Gedankenvoll ich wandere
    see under   Grieg, Edvard Hagerup, 1843–1907.

Lindquist, Orville Alvin.
Finger action. 35 exercises for pianoforte for developing uniform strength of all the fingers. Boston, A. P. Schmidt, c1931.
29 p. 31 cm. (Schmidt's educational series, no. 421)

NL 0382958   00 OrP

Lindquist, Orville, Alvin, arr.
Nocturne ...
    see under   Grieg, Edvard Hagerup, 1843–1907.

Lindquist, Orville Alvin, 1873 –
One hundred exercises for the weak fingers. Boston, O. Ditson [c1914]
30 p. 31 cm. (Ditson edition no. 195)
For piano.

NL 0382960   00

Lindquist, Orville Alvin, arr.
Peasant's song, op. 65, no. 2
    see under   Grieg, Edvard Hagerup, 1843–1907.

L786.3
L7472p
Lindquist, Orville Alvin, 1873–
Precision studies, for the development of finger control, for piano forte. Boston, A.P.Schmidt, 1926.
score(22p.) 31cm. (Schmidt's educational series, no.349)

1. Piano. Studies and exercises. I. Title.

NL 0382962   IEN 00

M786.3
L747t
Music
lib.
Lindquist, Orville Alvin, 1873–
Technical variants on Hanon's exercises for pianoforte. Boston, The Arthur P. Schmidt Co., c1929.
29p. 32cm. (Schmidt's Educational Series, no.395)

1. Piano - Studies and exercises. I. Hanon, Charles Louis, 1820–1900. Le pianiste-virtuose. II. Title.

NL 0382963   NcU IU OrP

Lindquist, Orville Alvin, 1873 –
12 velocity studies in unison for pianoforte. Boston, A. P. Schmidt, c1927.
13 p. 31 cm. (Schmidt's educational series, no. 368)

NL 0382964   00

Lindquist, Orville Alvin, 1873–
Whole-tone scale finger technics. Twenty-five [i. e. Twenty-six] exercises on the pianoforte. New York, G. Schirmer [c1924]
29 p. 31 cm. (Schirmer's library of musical classics, vol. 161)
Text in English and Spanish, translation into Spanish by Maria Paz Gainsborg.

NL 0382965   00 OrP

027.67
L747r
Lindquist, Raymond Charles, 1905–
The reading of prisoners. [Chicago? 1935?]
15 l. incl. forms.
Caption title.
Mimeographed.
"Study made ... in 1934-35 for the American library association, and under the direction of the School of library service at Columbia university."
1. Prison libraries. I. American library association. II. Columbia university—School of library service. III. Title.

NL 0382966   IU NNC

Lindquist, Raymond Charles, comp., 1905–
... A reference list of important war legislation and regulations thereunder, compiled by Raymond C. Lindquist ... [New York, The Law library association of Greater New York, 1942]
15 numb. l. 28 x 21½ᶜᵐ.
Caption title.
At head of title: Legist supplement 2. February, 1942.
Reproduced from type-written copy.
1. World war, 1939– —Law and legislation—U. S.—Bibl. I. The Legist. Supplement. II. Title: War legislation and regulations thereunder.
42–14427
Library of Congress   Z6207.W8L56
[2]   016.9405373

NL 0382967   DLC

Lindquist, Raymond Charles, 1905–
What the public library system can do for you. By Raymond C. Lindquist, secretary and librarian, New Jersey Public library commission. [Trenton, 1945] 2 l. illus. 31cm.
"Reprinted from New Jersey municipalities, March and April, 1945."
1. No subject. I. New Jersey. Public library commission.
N. Y. P. L.   November 22, 1946

NL 0382968   NNC

Lindquist, Robert.
Planning and budgeting a bank's advertising program ... New Brunswick [Financial advertisers association?] 1945.
ix, 132 p. incl. charts, tables, forms.
"Submitted in partial fulfillment of the requirements of The Graduate school of banking conducted by the American bankers association at Rutgers university."
"Bibliography": p.128–132.

NL 0382969   MH-BA IU MiDW TxU CU

308t
L7469
Lindquist, Robert Henry
The relative rate of isomerization of isotopically substituted cyclopropane. [Berkeley, 1955]
iii, 52 ℓ. diagrs., tables.
Thesis (Ph. D. in Chemistry) - Univ. of California, Sept. 1955.
Bibliography: leaves 50–52.
1. Chemical reaction, Rate of. 2. Isomerism. 3. Cyclopropane.

NL 0382970   CU

Lindquist, Robert Jerome, 1902–
Approach to electrotherapeutics, by R. Jerome Lindquist. Los Angeles, The Ward Ritchie press, 1939.
3 p. l., 117 p. diagrs. 23 cm.
1. Electrotherapeutics.
39—31738
Library of Congress   RM871.L74
[a49c½]   615.84

NL 0382971   DLC CtY-M CaBVaU

VOLUME 334

Lindquist, Robert Jerome
RM871 Approach to electrotherapy. Los Angeles, 1948.
948ℓ vii, 139p. illus. 23cm.
Bibliography: p. 131-132.

1. Physical medicine - Electrotherapy. I. Title.
(stamp 1, I)

NL 0382972 CtY-M

Y378.7M66
qODL6456 Lindquist, Robert Marion.
Studies in the fields of benz(f)iso-
quinolines and of benz(h)isoquinolines.
[Minneapolis] 1950.

v, 85 ℓ. 29 cm.

Thesis (Ph.D.) - Univ. of Minnesota,
1951.
Bibliography: leaves 84-85.

1.Isoquinoline.

NL 0382973 MnU

Lindquist, Roy Carl, 1898-
... Efficient methods of retailing meat. By Roy C. Lindquist ... Washington ¡Govt. print. off.¡ 1925.
ii, 44 p. illus. 23ᶜᵐ. (U. S. Dept. of agriculture. Miscellaneous circular no. 54)

Contribution from Bureau of agricultural economics in cooperation with
Bureau of business research, Northwestern university.

1. Meat—(Marketing)
Agr 25-1444
Library, U. S. Dept. of
Agriculture 1Ag86Cm no. 54

NL 0382974 DNAL WaS PP OO OU OCl MB

Lindquist, Roy Carl, 1898-
338.156
T003
A study of sales, margins, expenses and profits in a group of
Chicago meat markets for the year 1929, prepared for "Meat
merchandising" by Roy C. Lindquist ... Chicago ¡1930¡
¡16¡ p. incl. tables. 21ᶜᵐ.

Unpaged.

NL 0382975 ICJ DNAL

Lindquist, Ruben Alvin
see Lundquist, Ruben Alvin.

Lindquist, Rudolph Daniel, 1888-
National education association of the United States. Dept.
of supervisors and directors of instruction.
Effective instructional leadership; a study of the problem of
integration; the sixth yearbook of the Department of supervisors and directors of instruction of the National education
association, by a committee of the department, Rudolph D.
Lindquist, chairman. New York, Bureau of publications,
Teachers college, Columbia university, 1933.

LD 7501 Lindquist, Rudolph Daniel, 1888-
C7 L5 Report on contributions of the University
School at Ohio State University, Columbus,
Ohio, by Rudolph D. Lindquist ¡and¡ Laura
Zirbes. ¡Columbus, Ohio State University¡
1933.
18 l. 28 cm.

NL 0382978 OU

Lindquist, Rudolph Daniel, 1888-
The secondary-school principal as a supervisor ¡by¡ Rudolph
D. Lindquist.

(*In* National education association of the United States. **Addresses
and proceedings.** 1931. p. 583-585)

1. School management and organization. ¡1. School supervision—
Secondary schools¡ I. Title.

E 33-561
Library, U. S. Office of
Library of Congress
Education L13.N212 1931
[L13.N4 1931]

NL 0382979 DNAL

Lindquist, Rudolph Daniel, 1888-
The university school at Ohio state university:
an evaluation of its program of education for
children and youth, by Rudolph Daniel Lindquist ...
[Berkeley, Calif., 1937]
2 p.l., vii numb. l., , 1 l., 395 numb. l. tables.
29 cm.
Thesis (D. Educ.) - Univ. of California, May 1937.
Bibliography: p. 391-395.

NL 0382980 CU

M(055) Lindquist, Rune.
0684h Ionospheric effects of solar flares.
nr.95 Göteborg, Elands Boktryckeri Aktiebolag, 1950.
11 p. illus., diagrs., tables. 25cm.
(Gothenburg, Sweden. Chalmers Tekniska Högskolas. Handlingar. Nr.95)

At head of title: Transactions of Chalmers
University of Technology, Gothenburg, Sweden.
Preliminary reports nos.2 and 3.
Reports from the Research Laboratory of
Electronics, no 13.

NL 0382981 DAS

Lindquist, Rune.
Polar blackouts recorded at the Kiruna observatory.
Göteborg, Elander, 1951. 24 [2] p. illus.
25cm. (Chalmers tekniska högskola, Gothenburg.
Handlingar. nr. 103)

"Reports from the Research laboratory of
electronics. no. 16."
Bibliography, p. [25]

1. Radio—Transmitters and transmission. 2. Radio—
transmitters and transmission, 1951. I. Ser.
II. Chalmers tekniska högskola, Gothenburg.
Institutionen för elektronik.

NL 0382983 NN

LINDQUIST, RUNE.
... A 16 kW panoramic ionospheric recorder, by Rune Lindquist...
Göteborg, Elander, 1951. 40 p. illus, 25cm. (Chalmers tekniska
högskola, Gothenburg. Handlingar. nr. 109)

"Reports from the Research laboratory of electronics. no. 23."
"References," p. [4I]

1. Electronics—Apparatus and supplies. 2. Electricity, Atmospheric.
I. Ser.

NL 0382984 NN

HV742 Lindquist, Ruth.
.N8L5 Families receiving aid to dependent
children in North Carolina, by Ruth
Lindquist and Margaret Woodson. Raleigh,
North Carolina State Board of Public
Welfare, 1949.
vii,67p. diagrs.,tables,forms. 23cm.
(North Carolina. State Board of
Public Welfare. Information bulletin
no.14)

NL 0382985 NNU-W ScU

Lindquist, Ruth.
Families receiving general assistance in North
Carolina, by Ruth Lindquist and Margaret Woodson.
North Carolina, State Board of Public welfare, 1948.
110 p.

NL 0382986 PU-PSW

Lindquist, Ruth.
The family in the present social order; a study of needs of
American families, by Ruth Lindquist, written and published
with the coöperation of the American home economics association. Chapel Hill, The University of North Carolina press,
1931.
xiii, 241 p. diagrs. 22ᶜᵐ. ¡The University of North Carolina. Social study series¡
Thesis (PH. D.)—University of North Carolina, 1931.
Without thesis note.
"Selected bibliography": p. 232-236.
1. Family. 2. Marriage—U. S. 3. U. S.—Soc. condit. 4. Domestic
economy—U. S. 5. Social problems. I. American home economics
association. II. Title.

Library of Congress HQ535.L5 31-14395 Revised
——— Copy 2.
Copyright A 38536 ¡r35y2¡ 392.3

ICJ MB CaBVaU
OrU CU NcD NcU PPD PPT MiU OCU OU OO OClW WaU OCl
NL 0382987 DLC NBuU NN KMK MtBC ICRL UU OrP Or OrSaW

Lindquist, Ruth. The family in the present
social order.
Morgan, Winona Louise.
The family meets the depression; a study of a group of
highly selected families, by Winona L. Morgan ... Minneapolis, The University of Minnesota press, 1939.

Lindquist, Ruth, joint author.
Wood, Mildred Weigley.
Managing the home, by Mildred Weigley Wood ... Ruth
Lindquist ... and Lucy A. Studley ... Boston, New York
¡etc.¡ Houghton Mifflin company ¡°1932¡

301.42 Lindquist, Ruth.
L645f Marriage and family life of officers and
airmen in a strategic air command wing; an
exploratory study. ¡Chapel Hill, Institute
for Research in Social Science, University of
North Carolina¡ 1952.
v, 111ℓ.
"Air Force Base Project, Technical report
no.5."
"Sponsored by Human Resources Research In-
stitute, U.S. Air Force."
Photocopy. Alexandra, Va., Defense
Documentation Center, n.d. 26cm.
"AD-491 621."

NL 0382990 IU

HV1468
.N8L5 Lindquist, Ruth.
Needs of persons 60 years of age
and over, and services rendered by
the Department of Public Welfare in
Warren County, North Carolina, by
Ruth Lindquist and Lora P. Wilkie.
¡Raleigh¡ North Carolina State Board
of Public Welfare, Research and
Statistical Service, 1950.
xi,60p. diagr.,tables,form. 28cm.
(Research publication no.1)

NL 0382991 NNU-W

Lindquist, Ruth.
A study of home management in its relation to child development, by Ruth Lindquist. Omicron nu and Phi upsilon
omicron cooperating with the Committee on child development and parental education of the American home economics
association. ¡Pittsburg, Kan., °1929¡
x, 120 p. 23ᶜᵐ.
Cover-title: The Candle of Phi upsilon omicron, vol. xv, no. 1, and
Omicron nu magazine of Omicron nu, vol. IX, no. 2. Joint issue, Fall
1929.
1. Domestic economy. 2. Family. 3. Children—Care and hygiene.
4. Children—Management. I. American home economics association.
II. Omicron nu. III. Phi upsilon omicron. IV. Title: Home management
in its relation to child development. V. Title: The Candle.

Library of Congress TX145.L5 30-13455
——— Copy 2.
Copyright A 22739 ¡5¡ 640

NL 0382992 DLC IU

VOLUME 334

640
L64u   Lindquist, Ruth.
        Using and sharing our hours.   Chapel Hill,
        N.C., 1946.
        50p. illus., forms.

        Lithoprinted by Edwards brothers, inc., Ann
        Arbor, Michigan, 1946.

        1. Leisure. 2. Home making. I. Title.

NL 0382993   IU NcU

Cp362.6
L74w   Lindquist, Ruth.
        "We closed our county home," by Ruth Lind-
        quist and Lora P. Wilkie.   Raleigh, N.C.
        State Board of Public Welfare, 1949.
        10 p. 28cm.

        1. Warren Co., N.C.--Charities   2. N.C.--
        Almshouses

NL 0382994   NcU

Lindquist, Sigurd.
        Manikeismens religionshistoriska ställning I. Några
    orienterande synpunkter i fråga om dess förhållande till
    den historiska miljön ... Uppsala, Almqvist & Wiksells
    boktryckeri, 1921.
        vi, 132 p. 24½ᵐ.
    Akademisk avhandling—Uppsala.
    "Ur Uppsala universitets årsskrift 1921."
    Contents.—Källkritiska synpunkter.—Det religiösa systemets ställning.

        1. Manichaeism.   I. Title.

    Library of Congress   BT1410.L5   22–25641

NL 0382995   DLC CBPL ICU PU

Lindquist, Sigurd, 1895–
        Die methoden des yoga ... von Sigurd Lindquist. Lund,
    H. Ohlssons buchdruckerei, 1932.
        4 p. l., 233 p. 25ᵐ.
    Inaug.-diss.—Uppsala.
    Extra t.-p., with thesis note in full, inserted.
    "Literaturverzeichnis": p. ₍217₎–224.

        1. Yoga.
                            ₍Full name: Carl Sigurd Lindquist₎
                                               35–29534
    Library of Congress   B132.Y6L5 1932   181.4

NL 0382996   DLC CtY ICRL NN PPDrop PU NjP

Lindquist, Sigurd, 1895–
        ... Siddhi und abhiññā; eine studie über die klassischen wun-
    der des yoga, von Sigurd Lindquist. Uppsala, A.-b. Lunde-
    quistska bokhandeln ₍1935₎
        98 p., 1 l. 24½ᵐ. (Uppsala universitets årsskrift 1935: 2)
    Series title also in French.
    "Ins deutsche übersetzt von dr. D. Schultz."
    "Literaturverzeichnis": p. ₍95₎–98.

        1. Yoga.   I. Schultz, D.   II. Title.
                            ₍Full name: Carl Sigurd Lindquist₎
                                               A C 38–1354
    Minnesota. Univ. Library
        for Library of Congress   [AS284.U7 1935]
                                       ₍4₎   (378.485)

NL 0382997   MnU PU DLC MoU NPurMC

BF199   Lindquist, Stanley Elmer, 1917–
        Stimulation deafness: a study of temporary and
    permanent hearing losses resulting from exposure
    to noise and to blast impulses. 1949.
        92 l.

        Typewritten.
        Thesis—Univ. of Chicago.

        1. Hearing. 2. Noises. 3. Deafness.

NL 0382998   ICU DNLM

Lindquist, Sven Bertil Gunvald
    see Lindquist, Bertil, 1904–

Lindquist, Ted, illus.
        The Twenty-third Psalm: Ted Shawn in his
    dance version of the Twenty-third Psalm.
    [n. p. , 1943?]
            see under   Bible. O. T. Psalms.
    XXIII. English. 1943.

Lindquist, Theodore, 1875–
        Grade school arithmetic; unification &
        correlation of arithmetic.   Emporia, State
        normal school, 1916.

NL 0383001   PU

Lindquist, Theodore, 1875–
        Junior high school mathematics
    by Theodore Lindquist ... New York, Chicago ₍etc.₎ C. Scrib-
    ner's sons ₍1920–
        v. illus., diagrs. 19ᵐ.

        1. Mathematics.

    Library of Congress   QA39.L5   20–3725

NL 0383002   DLC KEmT CU PU MiU ViU

Lindquist, Theodore, 1875–
        Junior high school mathematics, one book course, by Theodore
    Lindquist...   New York: C. Scribner's Sons₍, 1924₎. x, 361 p.
    incl. diagrs., tables. illus. 12°.

    180774A. 1. Mathematics—Text-   books, 1924.   June 11, 1925

NL 0383003   NN MH

Lindquist, Theodore, 1875–
        ... Mathematics for freshmen students of engineering
    ... by Theodore Lindquist. ₍Ann Arbor, The Ann Arbor
    press, printers₎ 1911.
        2 p. l., iiii–ix, 135 p. diagrs. 24ᵐ.
    Thesis (PH. D.)—University of Chicago, 1911.
    Vita.
    Bibliography: p. ₍131₎–135.

        1. Mathematics—Study and teaching.

    Library of Congress   QA11.L7   14–3575
    Univ. of Chicago Libr.   ₍s21c2₎

            MiU ICJ IU NN
NL 0383004   ICU DLC PU NjP CoU KEmT CU NIC PPAmP OO

Lindquist, Theodore.
        Mathematics, the project instrument.
    ₍*In* National education association of the United States. Addresses
    and proceedings, 1921. p. 435–437₎

        1. Project method in teaching. ₍1. Project work₎ 2. Mathematics—
    ₍Study and₎ teaching.   I. Title.

                                               E 22–139
    U. S. Off. of educ. Library
        for Library of Congress   ₍a41d1₎

NL 0383005   DHEW OO OU

Lindquist, Theodore, 1875–
        Modern arithmetic methods and problems, by Theodore
    Lindquist ... ed. by George W. Myers ... Chicago, New York,
    Scott, Foresman and company ₍ᶜ1917₎
        xvi, 300 p. fold. tab., diagrs. 20ᵐ. $1.00
    Contains bibliographies.

        1. Arithmetic—Study and teaching.   I. Myers, George William,
    1864–

    Library of Congress   QA135.L7   17–30592

PPT
NL 0383006   DLC MtU Or OOxM MiU OCl OU ICJ MB PWcT

Lindquist, Willis.
        Burma boy. Pictures by Nicholas Mordvinoff. New York,
    Whittlesey House ₍1953₎
        93 p. illus. 22 cm.

        1. Elephants—Legends and stories.   I. Title.

    PZ10.3.L645Bu 2   53–8017 ‡

                    WaS
    GU IdPI Or OrAshS OrCS OrLgE OrMonO OrP OrPS WaSp
NL 0383007   DLC MoU MiU OCl PSt PPT PPi PP OO FU MsSM

Lindqvist, Åke.
        Politiska förbindelser mellan Sverige och Danmark, 1648–
    1655, av Åke Lindqvist. Lund, Håkan Ohlssons boktryckeri,
    1944.
        303 p. diagrs. 24ᵐ.
    "Källor och litteratur": p. ₍9₎–16.

        1. Denmark—For. rel.—Sweden. 2. Sweden—For. rel.—Denmark. 3.
    Denmark—Hist.—Frederick III, 1648–1670. 4. Sweden—Hist.—Christina,
    1632–1654. I. Title.

                                               46–17496
    Library of Congress   DL191.5.L5

NL 0383008   DLC CtY ICU NjP NN

Lindqvist, Adolf Natanael.
    See
Lindqvist, Natan, 1882–

Lindqvist, Arne, joint author.
        Elektroteknik för bilar

        see under

    Jonsson, Åke.

Lindqvist, Axel Fritiof Axelsson, 1872–   ed.

    Grob, Johann, 1643–1697.
        ... Epigramme, nebst einer auswahl aus seinen übrig en-
    gedichten ₍1₎; herausgegeben und eingeleitet von Axel Lind-
    qvist. Leipzig, K. W. Hiersemann, 1929.

Lindqvist, Axel Martin, 1882–
        Dansk-svensk ordlista. 4. omarb. uppl.
    Lund, Gleerup ₍1947₎
        89 p. (Skrifter utgivna av Moders-
    målslärarnas förening, nr.24)

NL 0383012   CU

VOLUME 334

Lindqvist, Axel Martin, 1882–
Deutsche Vergangenheit und Gegenwart 1770–1930; Gestalten, Ideen, Werke, mit Anmerkungen und verbindendem Texte; herausgegeben von Axel Lindqvist...und Hans Pollak... Stockholm: P. A. Norstedt & söners forlag₁, 1930₁. 296 p. 8°.

524912A. 1. German literature— Collections. I. Pollak, Hans Wolfgang.
May 27, 1931

NL 0383013 NN

Lindqvist, Axel Martin, 1882–
Deutsches Kultur- und Gesellschaftsleben im Spiegel der Sprache. ₁Aus dem Schwedischen übers. von Karl Witthalm₁ Wiesbaden, O. Harrassowitz, 1955.
172 p. 23 cm.
"Erschien in 1. Auflage 1942 ... unter dem Titel 'I språkets spegel. Glimtar ur tyskt kultur- och samhällsliv' und wurde vom Verfasser für die vorliegende deutsche Ausgabe (zugleich 2. Auflage) umgearbeitet und bedeutend erweitert."
"Berichtigung": slip inserted.
1. German language—Words—Hist. 2. German language — Semantics. I. Title.
A 57–6202
Rochester. Univ. Libr. PF3585
for Library of Congress

NL 0383014 FTaSU PPT WaU KyU ICU ViU OU OCU NcU TxU CtY MoU NRU CU MH VtMiM IU NBC IaU NIC MiU NcD TU

PT1101
.L5
vol. 273 Lindqvist, Axel Martin, 1882– ed.
Grob, Johann, 1643–1697.
... Epigramme, nebst einer auswahl aus seinen übrig engedichten ₁!₁; herausgegeben und eingeleitet von Axel Lindqvist. Leipzig, K. W. Hiersemann, 1929.

Lindqvist, Axel Martin, 1882–
Förskjutningar i förhållandet mellan grammatiskt och psykologiskt subjekt i svenskan. Lund, Gleerup ₁1912₁
xiv, 170 p. 25 cm. (Lunds universitets årsskrift, n. f., afd. 1, bd. 8, nr. 2)
"Bibliografi": p. ₁ix₁–xiv.
1. Swedish language—Verb. (Series: Lund. Universitet. Acta Universitatis Lundensia, n. s. Lunds universitets årsskrift, n. f., afd. 1, bd. 8, nr. 2)
AS284.L8 bd. 8, nr. 2 A 50–3277
Chicago. Univ. Libr.
for Library of Congress †

NL 0383016 ICU ViU NN DLC

Lindqvist, Axel Martin, 1882–
I språkets spegel; glimtar ur tyskt kulturoch samhällsliv. Stockholm, Svenska bokförlaget, A. Bonnier [1942]
150 p. 21 cm.

NL 0383017 PU

Lindqvist, Axel Martin, 1882–
Joachim Rachels satyrische Gedichte. Zur Textkritik und Interpretation. Von Axel Lindqvist. (In: Germanica. Halle an der Saale, 1925. p. ₁583–₁590. 8°.)

1. Rachel, Joachim, 1618–1669.
November 24, 1926

NL 0383018 NN

PA
3405
896
no.30 Lindqvist, Axel Martin, 1882–
Latinet och tyskan, av Axel Lindqvist.
Lund, C.W.K. Gleerup ₁1945₁
20 p. 20cm. (Skrifter utg. av Svenska Klassikerförbundet, nr.30)

1. Latin language--Grammar, Comparative-- German. 2. German language--Grammar, Comparative--Latin. I. Title.

NL 0383019 NIC PU

Lindqvist, Axel Martin, 1882–
Mannen, kvinnan och språket, jämte andra essayer. Stockholm, C. E. Fritzes bokförlag ₁1945₁
223 p. 21 cm.

1. Swedish language—Addresses, essays, lectures. I. Title.
PD5027.L5 50–34776

NL 0383020 DLC PU

439.708
L6450
1952 Lindqvist, Axel Martin, 1882–
Ordets makt och namnets tjusning: språkliga studier. Lund, C.W.G. Gleerup ₁1952₁
190p. 20cm. (Göteborgs Högskola forskningar och föreläsningar)

Bibliography: p. 187–190.

1. Swedish language. Addresses, essays, lectures. 2. Language and languages. Addresses, essays, lectures. 3. Names. Addresses, essays, lectures. I. Title.

NL 0383021 KU DLC-P4 CU ICU

PT1375
.D4
bd. 31 Lindqvist, Axel Martin, 1882– ed.
Konrad, *von Helmsdorf, 14th cent.*
... Der spiegel des menschlichen heils aus der St. Gallener handschrift, herausgegeben von Axel Lindqvist. Mit einer tafel in lichtdruck. Berlin, Weidmann, 1924.

Lindqvist, Axel Martin, 1882–
Det tyska 1600-talsepigrammets motiv och tendenser; några konturer. Göteborg, Elanders boktr., 1949.
62 p. 25 cm. (Göteborgs högskolas årsskrift 55, 1949: 1)
Bibliography included in "Noter" (p. ₁60–₁62)

1. Epigrams, German. (Series: Gothenburg, Sweden. Högskolan. Acta Universitatis Gotoburgensis. Göteborgs högskolas årsskrift, 55, 1949: 1)
AS284.G6 vol. 55, no. 1 A 51–4493
Michigan. Univ. Libr.
for Library of Congress †

NL 0383023 MiU DSI PU ViU DLC

Lindqvist, Axel Martin, 1882–
... Urg. dazan-, daza- in wörten des typus ahd. siohtags, mnd. rikedage, an. skildagi. bezw. mhd. irretac, von Axel Lindqvist. Lund, C. W. K. Gleerup; ₁etc., etc.₁, 1918₁
1 p. l., 45 p. 25ᶜᵐ. (Lunds universitets årsskrift. n. f., avd. 1, bd. 14, nr. 25)

1. Germanic languages—Word formation.
A 28–673
Chicago. Univ. Library AS284.L96 n.f., avd. 1, bd. 14²
for Library of Congress [AS284.L8 n. f., avd. 1, bd. 14]

NL 0383024 ICU MoU NIC NN ViU

Lindqvist, E.
Führer durch Helsingfors, herausgegeben von E. Lindqvist. Helsingfors, 1921.
cover-title, 24 p. fold. plan. 24 x 14 cm.
1. Helsingfors - Descr. - Guide-books.

NL 0383025 CU

Lindqvist, Ebba, *1908–*
Fiskläge; dikter av Ebba Lindqvist. Stockholm: A. Bonnier ₁1939₁ 96 p. 24cm. *CU*

82525B. 1. Poetry, Swedish. I. Title.
October 28, 1940

NL 0383026 NN MH MnU WaU CU

Lindqvist, Ebba
Jord och rymd, dikter. Stockholm, A. Bonnier ₁1931₁
67 p.

NL 0383027 CU

Lindqvist, Ebba, *1908–*
Labyrint; dikter. Stockholm, Bonnier ₁1949₁
56 p. 24 cm.

I. Title.
A 50–5914
Minnesota. Univ. Libr.
for Library of Congress

NL 0383028 MnU NN WU

Lindqvist, Ebba, *1908–*
Lava, dikter. Stockholm, A. Bonnier ₁1933₁
65 p.

NL 0383029 CU

Lindqvist, Ebba, *1908–*
Liv, dikter. Stockholm, A. Bonnier ₁1934₁
62 p.

NL 0383030 CU

Lindqvist, Ebba, *1908–*
Lyrisk dagbok. Stockholm, A. Bonnier ₁1937₁
48 p.

NL 0383031 CU

Lindqvist, Ebba, *1908–*
Manhattan, och andra dikter. Stockholm, A. Bonnier ₁1943₁
80 p. 23cm.

Contents.- En dikt om Karlson.- På Nordsjön.- Historien om en urna.- Manhattan.- Natt.

NL 0383032 MnU

VOLUME 334

Lindqvist, Ebba.
Rod klanning; dikter.   Stockholm,
A. Bonnier ₁1941₎

84 p.   23cm.

NL 0383033   MnU CU

Lindqvist, Ebba, *1908-*
Sången om Fedra. ₁Dikter₎ Stockholm, Bonnier ₁1952₎
83 p. 24 cm.

I. Title.

A 53-3953

Minnesota. Univ. Libr.
for Library of Congress

NL 0383034   MnU WaU MH

D   Lindqvist, Eric
811.5   I ofredens Berlin; intryck och upplevelser
.L549   som utrikeskorrespondent.   Stockholm, Tidens
förlag, 1942.
192 p.   20 cm.

1. World War, 1939-1945 - Personal narratives, Swedish   2. World War, 1939-1945 -
Germany   I.   Title.

NL 0383035   WU MH

Lindqvist, Eric.
I ofredens Berlin; intryck och upplevelser som utrikeskorrespondent. 2. uppl. Stockholm, Tidens förlag, 1942.
192 p. 20 cm.

1. World War, 1939-1945—Personal narratives, Swedish. 2. World
War, 1939-1945—Germany.   I. Title.

D811.5.L549   1942   62-57386 ‡

NL 0383036   DLC

Lindqvist, Eric.
... Kan Tyskland hålla ut? Stockholm, Tidens förlag, 1944.
2 p. L., 7-188, ₁1₎ p., 1 l. 20ᶜᵐ.

1. World war, 1939-1945—Personal narratives, Swedish. 2. Journal-
ists—Correspondence, reminiscences, etc.   I. Title.
S D 44-24
U. S. Dept. of state. Libr.
for Library of Congress   D811.5.L55
₍a45c1₎†   940.548

NL 0383037   DS DLC

Lindqvist, Erik Vilhelm, *1895-*
... Ueber die aborte in Malmö 1897-1928; eine statistisch-
medizinisch-soziale studie, von Erik Lindqvist ... Helsingfors, 1931.
324 p. tables (part fold.) diagrs. 24½ᶜᵐ. (Half-title: Supplementum
ad Acta obstetricia et gynaecologica scandinavica. vol. XII, suppl. 1)
At head of title: Aus der Obstetrisch-gynäkologischen und der chirurgischen abteilung des Malmöer allgemeinen krankenhauses.
Summary also in English and French.
"Autorenverzeichnis": p. ₍317₎-324.

1. Abortion. 2. Malmö, Sweden—Statistics, Medical.
A C 34-1026
Title from John Crerar   Libr.   Printed by L. C.

NL 0383038   ICJ DCU MoU PPC MiU OU

Lindqvist, Gregor.   6213.65
Quelques observations sur le développement des désinences du
présent de l'indicatif de la première conjugaison latine dans les
langues romanes. Thèse. Upsala, Almqvist & Wiksell, 1898.
pp. (4), 159 +.

Romance languages-Verb‖AcS 186076

NL 0383039   MH PU ICRL CtY

₍Lindqvist, Gustaf₎ 1872-
Bara en hundracka, samt andra berättelser ₍av₎
Mari Mihi ₍pseud.₎ Stockholm, A. Bonnier
₍1912₎
128 p.

NL 0383040   CU

₍Lindqvist, Gustaf₎ 1872-
Från Donau till Save, av Mari Mihi ₍pseud.₎ Stockholm, A. Bonnier ₍1916₎
84 p., 1 l. front. (port.) 18¼ᶜᵐ. ₍Från kriget, IV₎
CONTENTS.—På väg till Donaumonarkien.—Bland fångar och flyktin-
gar.—Greven med järnnäven.—Mellan drabbningarna.—I det erövrade Belgrad.—Freden—och därefter!

1. European war, 1914-   —Austria.   I. Title.
₍Full name: Karl Gustaf Oskar Eugen Lindqvist₎
20-23564
Library of Congress   D512.L5

NL 0383041   DLC MH

₍Lindqvist, Gustaf₎ 1872-
De gamle herrarne; en herrgårds-
roman av Mari Mihi ₍pseud.₎ Stockholm, Åhlen & Åkerlunds förlags a.-b.
₍1917₎

377 p.   20 cm.

"Tredje upplagan."

NL 0383042   MnU NjP

Lindqvist, Gustaf, 1872-

De gamle herrarne, en herrgårds-
roman... Stockholm, Åhlén ₍1917₎
377 p.   19½ᶜᵐ.

"6. uppl."

NL 0383043   NjP

Lindqvist, Gustaf, *1872-*   4909b.433
Hjärtan och hjältar. Berättelser [Af] Mari Mihi [pseud.]. 7:e-
10:e tusendet.
— Stockholm. Bonnier. [1909.] 228, (1) pp. [De bäste böckerna.]
18 cm., in 8s.

K217 — T.r. — S.r. — Sweden. Lang. Works in Swedish.

NL 0383044   MB

Lindqvist, Gustaf, *1872-*
Junkern utan land, och andra berättelser
af Mari Mihi ₍pseud.₎ Stockholm, Bonnier
₍1907₎
243 p.

NL 0383045   WaU

₍Lindqvist, Gustaf,₎ 1872-
Signy; roman ur Stockholms sällskapslif, af Mari Mihi
₍pseud.₎   Göteborg: Åhlén & Åkerlunds förlag, 1911.   224 p.
12°.

1. Fiction, Swedish. 2. Title.
August 20, 1927

NL 0383046   NN WaSp

₍Lindqvist, Gustaf,₎ 1872-
Stigmannens bok ₍av₎ Mari Mihi ₍pseud.₎
Göteborg, Åhlen & Åkerlund ₍c1913₎
159 p.

NL 0383047   CU WaU

Lindqvist, Gustaf, 1872-
Studentens lyckliga dar, minnen fran
nittiotalets uppsala.
Stockholm, Bonniers ₍1911₎

Mari Mihi, pseud.

NL 0383048   WaSp

Lindqvist, Gustaf, 1872-

Världens vildaste vågspel, och andra berättelser, av Mari
Mihi.   Stockholm: Åhlén & Åkerlund ₍1919₎.   166 p.   12°.

Contents.: Slatin den oförvägne. Licht in den Fenstern für den schwedischen
Hussaren. Le brave général och gymnasisten. Svenskund. Krigets förfall. Världens vildaste vågspel.

1. Swedish literature.—Misc.   2. European war, 1914-   . 3. Title.
April 27, 1920.

NL 0383049   NN

Lindqvist, Ingeborg Wilcke-
see Wilcke-Lindqvist, Ingeborg.

Lindqvist, Ingvar.
Some new aspects of the polymolybdates.
Presented to the Royal society of sciences of Upsala,
September 29, 1950. Uppsala, Almqvist & Wiksell,
1950.
22 p.   diagrs.   29 cm. (Nova acta Regiae
societatis scientiarum Upsaliensis, ser. 4, v. 15,
no. 1)
Inaug. - diss. - Uppsala.
Added title-page with thesis note inserted.
References: p. 21-22.

NL 0383051   PU-Sc CaBVaU

Lindqvist, John.
Uppslagsbok foer svenska musiklandeln ...
see under title

Lindqvist, Josef L   ed.
Samlande gärning

see under

Samlande gärning.

VOLUME 334

WA
32
GS8
L7r
1948
LINDQVIST, K   H
    Rättsfall av intresse för hälso-
vårdsnämnderna, avgjorda i regerings-
rätten åren 1941-1945. ₁Stockholm₁
Hygienisk revy, 1948.
    31 p.
    Cover title.
    Issued as supplement to Hygienisk revy.
    1. Public health - Laws & legislation -
Sweden
    I. Hygienisk revy. Supplement

  NL 0383054   DNLM

WA
675
L747v
1948
LINDQVIST, K   H
    Vatten och avlopp, av K. H. Lindqvist
och Gösta Vahlne. Stockholm,
Landskommunernas förbunds förlag
₁1948₁
    xvi, 139 p. illus.
    1. Water supply   I. Vahlne, Gösta,
1913-

  NL 0383055   DNLM

Lindqvist, Kajsa
    Scandinavian ₍knitting₎ Boston, Mass., Plays,
inc. ₍c1946-48₎
    3 v. in 1. illus.

    Contents.-v.1. Sweaters.-v.2. Snow sets.-v.3.
Mittens.

  NL 0383056   Wa

q746
L645S
LINDQVIST, Kajsa.
    Scandinavian snow sets; caps, mittens,
gloves, after-ski boots, slipper socks.
    Boston. Plays, inc. c1947. 17p.
illus.

  NL 0383057   WaS

Lindquist, Kajsa.
  Scandinavian sweaters; with titles in English and Swedish, by
Kajsa Lindquist and Natalie Hebert. Boston, Plays, inc. ₁1946₁
30 p. illus. 28cm.

    1. Knitting and crocheting.   I. Hebert, Natalie, jt. au.
                                           January 3, 1951

  NL 0383058   NN WaS

Lindqvist, Karl Gustaf Oskar Eugen.
  See
Lindqvist, Gustaf, 1872-

LINDQVIST, LARS ERIC.
    Ur litteraturen om Jönköping. [Jönköping, 1953]
27 p. illus., ports. 21cm.

    Cover title.
    "Särtryck ur Gudmundsgillets årsbok 1953."
    Bibliography, p. 27.

    1. Jönköping, Sweden, in literature.

  NL 0383060   NN

Lindqvist, Märta, *1888-1940*
  Ansgarskapellet på Björkö; historik och beskrivning på uppdrag
av Kapellstiftelsen Ansgars minne. 3. uppl. Stockholm, Svenska
kyrkans diakonistyrelses bokförlag ₁1950₁ 32 p. illus., group
port., map (p. ₁4₁ of cover). 19cm.

  1. Chapels—Sweden—Björko,   I. Kapellstiftelsen Ansgars minne,
Stockholm.

  NL 0383061   NN

Lindqvist, Märta, *1888-1940.*
  Hos filmstjärnor i U. S. A.; snapshots från New York och
Hollywood, av Märta Lindqvist ... Stockholm, H. Geber
₁1924₁
  149 p. plates, ports. 19½ᶜᵐ.

    "Föreliggande skildringar av amerikanska filmpersonligheter—inklu-
sive den svenske filmregissören Victor Sjöström—ha under våren 1924
publicerats i Svenska dagbladet i form av resebrev från tidningens till
Amerika utsända medarbetare."—Förord.

    1. Moving-pictures—Biog. 2. Hollywood, Calif.   I. Title.

                                       37-20825

  Library of Congress   ᵂPN1998.A2L5
                                          927.92

  NL 0383062   DLC

CT
1323
L645m
Lindqvist, Märta, 1888-
    Människor. Stockholm, Skoglund [1938]
    358 p. ports.

    1. Sweden - Biog. I. Title.

  NL 0383063   CLU

LINDQVIST, MÄRTA, *1888-1940.*
  Palestinska dagar, av Märta Lindqvist (Quelqu'une).
Stockholm, Skoglund [1931] 205 p. illus.,map. 23cm.

    1₁ Palestine--Descr. and trav., 1914-

  NL 0383064   NN

Lindqvist, Margit, 1890-
  Från Bretagne till Sahara. Helsingfors, Söderström
₁1954₁
  244 p. illus. 22 cm.

    1. France—Descr. & trav.—1945—   2. Sardinia—Descr. & trav.
  3. Corsica—Descr. & trav. 4. Tunis—Descr. & trav.   I. Title.

  D974.L5   57-30858 ‡

  NL 0383065   DLC NN

Lindqvist, Margit, 1890-
  Vi kastar loss. Helsingfors, Söderström ₁1946₁
  188 p. 23 cm.

    1. Voyages and travels.   I. Title.

  G463.L62   53-28708 ‡

  NL 0383066   DLC

LINDQVIST, NATAN, *1882-*
  En Bellmanstolkning och en dialektal ljudutveckling.
  (IN: Thors, Carl-Eric, ed. Studier tillägnade Rolf Pipping den 1 juni
1949. Helsingfors, 1949. 24cm. p. 62-77)

    1. Bellman, Carl Michael, 1740-1795. Fredmans epistlar. 2. Swedish
language--Words--Indiv. --   Klinga.

  NL 0383067   NN

439.73
L648
LINDQVIST, NATAN, 1882-
    Bibelsvenskans medeltida ursprung.
Uppsala,Appelbergs boktr. a.-b.,1929.
96p. 23½cm.

    Reprinted from Nysvenska studier;tidskrift
för svensk stil-och språkforskning,arg.8,1928.

  NL 0383068   PU

PD5576
.L68
Lindqvist, Natan, 1882-
    Björka-Säby ortnamn ... Stockholm, Svenska
kyrkans diakonistyrelses förlag ₁1926₁-
    v. illus., map. (Half-title: Björka-Sä-
by i monografier)
    "Öfriga källor och vetenskapliga arbeten":
v.1, p.14-21.

    1. Names, Geographical--Sweden--Östergötland.
  2. Swedish language--Etymology--Names.

  NL 0383069   ICU PU MH

Lindqvist, Natan, 1822-
  En isländsk svartkonstbok från 1500-talet
    see under [Galdrabok]

Lindqvist, Natan, 1882-
  Stort och smått i språkets spegel, av Natan Lindqvist. Uppsala: Almqvist & Wiksells förlag₁ 1927₁ 97 p. 8°.

    1. Swedish language.   October 13, 1928

  NL 0383071   NN NIC PU

Lindqvist, Natan, 1882-
  Studier över reformationstidens bibelsvenska; språket i Nya
Testamentet 1526 i belysning av de svenska reformatorernas
språk ... av Natan Lindqvist ... Stockholm, I. Hæggströms
boktryckeriaktiebolag, 1918.
    1 p. l., 200, ʷ97, 30 p. VIII facsim. on 4 l. 22½ᶜᵐ.
    Akademisk avhandling—Uppsala.
    At head of caption title: Del 20. Antikvarisk tidskrift för Sverige.
nr. 7.
    Running title: Reformationstidens bibelsvenska.
    1. Swedish language—Hist. 2. Swedish language—Phonology. 3.
Bible. N. T. Swedish—Versions. 4. Bible. Swedish—Versions—N. T.
  I. Title: Reformationstidens bibelsvenska.

                                  ₁Full name: Adolf Natanael Lindqvist₁

  Library of Congress   PD5075.L5   22-2184
                             ₁37b₁₁

  NL 0383072   DLC IU PU ICU CU CtY

Lindqvist, Natan, 1882-   , ed.
  Studier till en svensk dialektgeografisk atlas
    see under title

VOLUME 334

Lindqvist, Natan, 1882–
Sydväst-Sverige, i språkgeografisk belysning. Lund, C. Bloms boktr. ¡Stockholm, Natur och kultur i distribution¡ 1947.
2 v. 25 cm. (Skrifter utg. genom Landsmålsarkivet i Lund, 2)
CONTENTS.—1. Text.—2. Kartor.

1. Swedish language—Dialects.   I. Title.   (Series: Lund: Landsmålsarkivet. Skrifter, 2)
Full name: Adolf Natanael Lindqvist.
PD5832.L5   52–34069

NL 0383074   DLC WaU TxU CU ICU MnU MdBJ

Lindqvist, Olof V
Blast hole diamond drilling ¡by¡ Olof V. Lindqvist ... New York, N. Y., J. K. Smit & sons, inc., °1944.
1 p. l., ¡5¡–54 p., 3 l. incl. 2 pl., diagrs. 23ᶜᵐ.
Bibliographical foot-notes.

1. Boring. 2. Boring machinery.   I. Title.   II. Title: Diamond drilling.
Library of Congress   TN279.L5   44–9562
                                                622.23

NL 0383075   DLC OrP Or MtBuM DI NcC PPD OCU NcD NNC

Lindqvist, Otto Magnus, respondent.
De praecipuis philosophorum recentioris ...
see under Ahlander, Johannes August, praeses.

Lindqvist, Rafael, editor and translator, 1867–
Finsk lyrik; ett urval dikter från den finska konstpoesins uppspirande till dess nuvarande blomstring. Svensk tolkning av Rafael Lindqvist. Helsingfors: Blinkfyrens förlag¡ 1926–32¡.
2 v. in 1. illus. (ports.) 18cm.
Includes short biographical notes.

667649A. 1. Poetry, Finnish.   I. Title.   October 5, 1933

NL 0383077   NN CLU

Lindqvist, Rafael, 1867–
Rim och rapp, af Sepia ¡pseud.¡
Helsingfors, A. B. Fyren, 1907.
v. illus.

NL 0383078   WaU

Lindqvist, Rafael, 1867–
Sprakfåle och pegas; ny samling rim och rapp. Helsingfors, Söderström ¡1941¡
272 p. illus. 20 cm.

No. 256 of 300 numbered copies.

NL 0383079   NcD

Lindqvist, Rafael, ed. and tr., 1867–
Under röd himmel, nyryska dikter i urval. 2. uppl. Stockholm, Bonnier ¡1947¡
372 p. 22 cm.

1. Russian poetry—Translations into Swedish. 2. Swedish poetry—Translations from Russian.   I. Title.
PG3238.S8L5 1947   50–32950

NL 0383080   DLC

Lindqvist, Rafael, 1867–   comp.
Ur Rysslands sång. I –   dikter öfver- satta från originalspråket af Rafael Lindqvist. Helsingfors, Aktiebolaget Helios, 1904.
1 v. ports. 19 cm.

NL 0383081   CU

Lindqvist, Ragnar
A treatise on reliable predictions of water conditions ... Stockholm, 1932.   184 p.
Inaug. Diss. –Stockholm, 1932.
Bibliography.

NL 0383082   ICRL NcD NN CtY

Lindqvist, Silas Gustaf Erik, 1874–
Studier öfver resultaten af radikaloperationer för bråck vid Kirurgiska kliniken i Uppsala ¹/₉ 1888 ³¹/₁₂ 1904 ... Uppsala, Akademiska boktryckeriet, E. Berling, 1908.
3 p. l., 368, 135, ¡2¡ p. incl. tables. 23ᶜᵐ.
Akademisk afhandling—Upsala.
"Tabell-bilagor": 135 p. at end.
"Litteraturförteckning": p. 357–365.

1. Hernia.   9–9175
Library of Congress   RD621.L6

NL 0383083   DLC DNLM

Lindqvist, Sune, 1887–   ed.
Montelius, Oscar, 1843–1921.
Die älteren kulturperioden im Orient und in Europa, von Oscar Montelius. Stockholm. 1903–1923.

LINDQVIST, SUNE, 1887–
Bildstenarna i fornsalen. (IN: Gotländskt arkiv. Lund. 24cm. ¡bd. 14¡ (1942) p. 16–24. illus.)

1. Sculpture, Rock--Sweden   --Gotland (Island).

NL 0383085   NN

Lindqvist, Sune, 1887–
Björkö. 3. uppl. Stockholm, Wahlström & Widstrand, 1933.
32 p. illus. 19 cm. (Svenska fornminnesplatser, vägledningar utg. genom Kungl. Vitt. hist. och antikvitets akademien, n:o 2)
Map on cover.

1. Birka, Sweden.   (Series: Vitterhets-, historie- och antikvitets-akademien, Stockholm. Svenska fornminnesplatser, n:o 2)
DL991.B6L5 1933   63–57283

NL 0383086   DLC CU MH

Lindqvist, Sune, 1887–
GN799 .C5P6
Post, Lennart von, 1884–
Bronsåldersmanteln från Gerumsberget i Västergötland, av Lennart von Post, Emelie von Walterstorff ¡och¡ Sune Lindqvist. Mit deutscher Übersetzung. Utg. med bidrag ur Oscar Montelius fond. ¡Stockholm, Akademiens förlag, 1924–25¡

Lindqvist, Sune, 1887–
Från Nerikes sten- och bronsålder, af Sune Lindqvist ... ¡Örebro¡ Örebro dagblads tryckeri ¡1912¡
cover-title, 103 p. illus., 2 fold. maps. 23ᶜᵐ.
"Särtryck ur Meddelanden från Föreningen Örebro läns museum. v. år 1912."

1. Sweden—Antiq. 2. Stone age—Sweden—Nerike. 3. Bronze age—Sweden—Nerike.
                                                23–1970
Library of Congress   GN826.S8L5

NL 0383088   DLC

Lindqvist, Sune, 1887–
Gamla Uppsala fornminnen. Stockholm, Wahlström & Widstrands förlag, 1929.
75 p. plan. illus., 18.5 cm.
"Svenska fornminnesplatser, 13."
Plan on back paper cover.

NL 0383089   MH

Lindqvist, Sune, 1887–
Gotlands Bildsteine. Gesammelt und untersucht von Gabriel Gustafson und Fredrik Nordin, mit Zeichnungen von Olof Sörling, Photographien von Harald Faith-Ell. Nach erneuter Durchsicht und Ergänzung des Materials hrsg. von Sune Lindqvist. Stockholm ¡Kungl. Vitterhets- historie- och antikvitets-akademien¡ Wahlström & Widstrand i distribution, 1941–42.
2 v. illus., plates, ports. maps. 31 cm.
At head of title: Kungl. Vitterhets-, historie- och antikvitets-akademien.
Bibliography: v. 2, p. 11.
1. Monuments—Sweden. 2. Sculpture—Gotland. 3. Gotland—Antiq., historie- och antikvitets-
NB1622.G6L5   731.76   50–47136
Library of Congress

DDO NbU CSt MoU NcD OrU
NL 0383090   DLC NN OC1MA WaU PBm MnU InU IU MH CtY

BR133 **Lindqvist, Sune.**
.S5L7 Den helige Eskils biskopsdöme. Några arkeologiska vittnesbörd om den kristna kyrkans första organisation inom mellersta Sverige... Stockholm, I. Hæggströms boktryckeri aktiebolag, 1915.
¡3¡, 174, ¡1¡ p. illus. (incl. maps, plans) 23ᶜᵐ.
Akademisk afhandling—Upsala.
"Del. 22. Antikvarisk tidskrift för Sverige. nr. 1."
Bibliographical foot-notes.

1. Christian antiquities—Sweden. 2. Sweden—Church history.

NL 0383091   ICU MH PU ICRL CtY

Lindqvist, Sune, 1887–
... En hjälm från Valsgärde, av Sune Lindqvist. Uppsala, Almqvist & Wiksells boktryckeri-a.-b., 1931.
21 p. illus. 8 pl. on 4 l. 25ᶜᵐ. (Uppsala universitets årsskrift. 1931. Program 3)

1. Helmets. 2. Sweden—Antiquities.   I. Title.
                                                A C 34–4241
Title from Univ. of Minn.
Library of Congress   [AS284.U7 1931]

NL 0383092   MnU PPAmP PU MoU MiU

VOLUME 334

Lindqvist, Sune, 1887–
Ramsundsbron vid Sigurdsristningen och en
storbondesläkt från missionstiden. In Fornvännen.
LX. årg. 1914. p. 204–230, 290–293, figs.

NL 0383093 NIC

Lindqvist, Sune, 1887–
De svenska holkyxorna från bronsåldern, af Sune
Lindqvist. ₍Stockholm, 1913₎
p. ₍79₎–90. illus. 29ᶜᵐ.
Caption title.
"Särtryck ur Opuscula archaeologica Oscari Montelio septuagenario
dicata. Stockholm, 1913."

1. Bronze age—Sweden. 2. Axes. ɪ. Title.
22–9917
Library of Congress GN778.S2L5

NL 0383094 DLC

Lindqvist, Sune, 1887–
Svenskarna i heden tid, av Sune Lindqvist. Stockholm, A.
Bonnier ₍1935₎
264 p. illus. (incl. maps) 19½ᶜᵐ. ₍Orientering i aktuella ämnen, un-
der redaktion av Knut Tynell₎
"Litteraturanvisningar": p. 252–261.

1. Sweden—Antiq. ɪ. Title.
41–32655
Library of Congress DL621.L5
013.485

NL 0383095 DLC NNMM IU NIC CU CtY NN NjP MnU

GN826
.S8L53
Lindqvist, Sune, 1887–
Svenskt forntidsliv. Stockholm, A. Bonnier ₍1944₎
302 p. illus., maps. 19 cm. (Orientering i aktuella ämnen)
"Litteraturanvisningar": p. 295–300.

1. Sweden—Antiq. ɪ. Title. (Series)
A 48–4233*
Harvard Univ. Library
for Library of Congress

NL 0383096 MH KU MnU ICU CtY PPAmSwM DLC

Lindqvist, Sune, 1887–

Fåhræus, Robin, 1888–
... Tal vid Uppsala universitets fest den 13 december 1930
till högtidlighållande av trehundraårsminnet av Olof Rudbeck
d.ä:s födelse, av Robin Fåhræus, Rutger Sernander och Sune
Lindqvist. Uppsala, Almqvist & Wiksells boktryckeri-a.-b.,
1930.

Lindqvist, Sune, 1887–
...Uppsala högar och Ottarshögen, av Sune Lindqvist; with
an English summary. Stockholm: Wahlström & Widstrand,
1936. xii, 363 p. illus., 25 pl. (incl. plans) on 18 l. 29½cm.
(Kungl. vitterhets historie och antikvitets akademien. ₍Arkeo-
logiska monografier. 23.)
Includes a discussion of the Ynglinga saga and text and discussion of the Ynglinga
tal.
"Summary," p. ₍327₎–353.
"Litteratur," p. ₍355₎–363.

906468A. 1. Mounds—Sweden— Uppsala. 2. Ynglinga saga. I. Þjo-
ðólfr hvinverski. II. Ser.
November 30, 1937

NL 0383098 NN MdBJ WU RPB CU DLC-P4 NIC MH NjP CtY

Lindqvist, Sune, 1887–
Vår svenska guldålder. Uppsala, J. A. Lindblad ₍1945₎
143 p. illus. 22 cm. (Konst och kultur)

1. Sweden—Antiq. 2. Goldsmithing—Sweden. ɪ. Title.
(Series)
DL621.L53
51–19493

NL 0383099 DLC WaU MnU ICU PPAmSwM CU MH

Lindqvist, Sune, 1887–
...Vendelkulturens ålder och ursprung, av Sune Lindqvist.
Stockholm: Akademiens förlag, 1926. 202 p. incl. plans, tables.
illus. 8°. (Kungliga vitterhets- historie- och antikvitets aka-
demien, Stockholm. Handlingar. Del 36¹.)
Bibliography, p. 199–202.

1. Wends—Hist. 2. Art, Wendish. 3. Ser.
October 21, 1926

NL 0383100 NN OO CtY NcD NNU CU MnU PU NIC

Lindqvist, Sven, 1932–
Ett förslag. ₍Uppsatser och anteckningar₎ Stockholm,
Bonnier ₍1955₎
161 p. 18 cm.

ɪ. Title.
PT9875.L632F6
55–35846 ‡

NL 0383101 DLC MnU

Lindqvist, Torsten, 1906–
Studien über das vitamin A beim menschen, von Torsten
Lindqvist ... Uppsala, Appelbergs boktryckeriaktiebolag,
1938.
xii, 262, 52 p. incl. 1 illus., tables, 2 diagr. 23½ᶜᵐ. (On cover: Acta
medica scandinavica. Supplementum xcvii)
Thesis—Uppsala. Without thesis note.
"Literaturverzeichnis": p. ₍252₎–262.

1. Vitamins. 2. Deficiency diseases.
₍Full name: Johan Torsten Lindqvist₎
John Crerar library A C 39–2761
for Library of Congress

NL 0383102 ICJ DNLM PU CtY CU IU ViU

Lindrath, Hermann, 1896–
Das arbeitsrecht des kaufmännischen angestellten in frage
und antwort, von dr. Hermann Lindrath. Halberstadt, H.
Meyer, 1926.
111 p. 17½ᶜᵐ.

1. Labor laws and legislation—Germany. ɪ. Title.
Library of Congress HD7887.L5
33589
27–19539

NL 0383103 DLC

Lindrath, Hermann: Die bergrechtliche Gewerkschaft und Aktiengesellschaft als Unternehmungsformen im Bergbau. [Maschinen-
schrift.] 152 S. u. Tab. 4°. — Auszug: (Eisleben) 1922: (Eder).
4 S. 8°
Halle, R.- u. staatswiss. Diss. v. 2. Juli 1923 [U 23. 4870

NL 0383104 ICRL

Lindrath, Hermann
... Nachtrag, steuerwesen, von dr
Hermann Lindrath ... München, F. E. Nachf,
₍194–?₎
103 p
Die Gemeindeverwaltungs-und sparkassenschule,
band 6 a)

NL 0383105 MiU CoD NcU CU NjP IU MH-BA

Lindrath, Hermann, 1896–
Steuerwesen. Norddeutsche ausgabe. München,
F. Eher nachf. ₍1936₎
299 p. (Die gemeindeverwaltungs- und sparkassenschule, bd. 6)

1. Taxation - Germany - Law.

NL 0383106 NNC

Lindrath, Hermann, 1896–
Steuerwesen. Norddeutsche Ausg. München, F. Eher
Nachf. ₍1936–38₎
2 v. 22 cm. (Die Gemeindeverwaltungs- und Sparkassenschule,
Bd. 6–6a)
Vol. 2: Nachtrag.
——— Ergänzungsheft für Baden. Das badische
Steuerwesen. München, F. Eher Nachf. ₍1938₎
67 p. 22 cm. (Die Gemeindeverwaltungs- und Sparkassenschule,
Bd. 6b)
"Unter mitwirkung verschiedener Beamten verfasst von Mini-
sterialrat Dr. Bund und Dr. Jäkle."—p. ₍7₎
HJ2687.L5 Suppl.
1. Taxation—Germany. ɪ. Bund, Alfred. ɪɪ. Jäkle, Eduard,
1887– (Series)
HJ2687.L5 A F 48–910 rev*
Harvard Univ. Library
for Library of Congress ₍r40b1₎†

NL 0383107 MH NNC NN NcU NjP CU ICU CtY CoD DLC

Lindridge, George
Collection of psalm and hymn tunes, with
chants and services, arranged for the organ or
pianoforte... Second ed., erv. Hastings n.a.

NL 0383108 PPL

PZ
2.1
L645m
[Lindridge, James] supposed author.
The merry wives of London. A romance of
metropolitan life, by the author of the "Socialist girl," etc., etc. London, Printed
for the bookseller's [1850?]
208 p. illus.

Issued in 26 penny numbers, the first
published Sept. 16, 1850.

NL 0383109 CLU MH

Lindridge, James, ed.
Tales of shipwrecks and adventures at sea...together with
celebrated voyages, amusing tales, tough yarns, and interesting
anecdotes. Illustrated...by Landells and others. Ed. by James
Lindridge. London, W. M. Clark, 1846. ix, 948 p. illus.
25cm.

Issued in 60 nos.

285799B. 1. Sea life. 2. Ship- wrecks.
February 14, 1945

NL 0383110 NN OrU

Lindroos, Carolus, 1874–
Quaestiones platonicae...
Inaug. diss. Helsingfros, 1891

NL 0383111 ICRL NjP

VOLUME 334

Lindros, John.

Svenska Cypernexpeditionen, 1927-1931.
The Swedish Cyprus expedition; finds and results of the excavations in Cyprus, 1927-1931 ... by Einar Gjerstad, John Lindros, Erik Sjöqvist ₍and₎ Alfred Westholm. Stockholm, The Swedish Cyprus expedition ₍1934-

---

LINDROTH, A.F.
[STUDIES, VIOLIN]
Fem studier för violin-solo, komponerade af A.F. Lindroth. Stockholm, A. Hirsch [187-?] Pl. no. 1671.
19 p. 33cm.

1. Violin--Studies and exer-   cises.

NL 0383113   NN

Lindroth, Anders Arne
see Lindroth, Arne, 1910-

Lindroth, Andreas Bernhard, respondent.

QH9
.T6
no.186-
188
Thunberg, Karl Peter, 1743-1828, *praeses.*
De nutritione plantarum ... Upsaliæ, excudebant Regiæ academiæ typographi ₍1819₎

Lindroth, Arne, *1910-*
Die assoziationen der marinen weichböden. Eine kritik auf grund von untersuchungen im Gullmars-fjord, Westschweden. Von Arne Lindroth ... (Mit 5 textfiguren.)
(*In* Uppsala. Universitet. Zoologiska bidrag från Uppsala. Uppsala ₍etc.₎ 1934-35₎ 25½ᶜᵐ. v. 15, p. ₍333₎-₍369₎ illus.)
"Literaturangaben": p. ₍364₎-366.
"Verzeichnis der erwähnten tierarten mit autorennamen": p. ₍367₎-368.

1. Marine fauna. 2. Deep-sea deposits. I. Title. A C 40-2692
Notre Dame univ. Library
for Library of Congress   [QL1.U7 vol. 15]
                               (590.82)

NL 0383116   InNd

Lindroth, Arne.
Die biologische Bedeutung des "Hämoglobins" (Erythrocruorins) der Wirbellosen.
(*In* Ergebnisse der Biologie. Berlin. 24 cm. Bd. 19 (1943) p. ₍324₎-374. diagrs.)
"Literaturverzeichnis": p. 370-374.

1. Hemoglobin. 2. Invertebrates. 3. Oxidation, Physiological.
I. Title.
                        Full name: Anders Arne Lindroth.
QH302.E7 Bd. 19   A 52-2091
New York. St. Coll. of   Agr., Cornell Univ. Library
for Library of Congress   †

NL 0383117   NIC DLC

SH349
L5
Lindroth, Arne, *1910-*
Laxbeståndets fluktuationer i de Norrländska Elvarna. Stockholm, Centraltryckeriet, 1950.
[97]-224 p. double map, diagrs., tables.
21 cm. (Svenska Vattenkraftföreningen. Publikationer 415 (1950:5))
English summary.
Bibliography: p. [141]-144.

1. Salmon - Baltic region. 2. Salmon-fisheries - Baltic region. 3. Fish populations. 4. Salmon - Sweden. I. Title.   (Series)

NL 0383118   DI

Lindroth, Arne, *1910-*
Studien über die respiratorischen mechanismen von *Nereis virens* Sars. Von Arne Lindroth ... Mit 3 tafeln und 48 figuren im text.
(*In* Uppsala. Universitet. Zoologiska bidrag från Uppsala. Uppsala ₍etc.₎ 1938₎ 25½ᶜᵐ. v. 17, p. ₍367₎-497. illus. 3 pl. (part col.) diagrs.)
"Literaturverzeichnis": p. ₍490₎-495.

1. Nereis virens. 2. Respiratory organs—Worms.
                                A C 40-2698
Notre Dame univ. Library
for Library of Congress   [QL1.U7 vol. 17]
                               (590.82)

NL 0383119   InNd NcD CtY MH ICRL

QL638
E7
L5
Biological
Sciences
Library
Lindroth, Arne, *1910-*
... Zur biologie der befruchtung und entwicklung beim hecht. Gäddans befruktnings- och utvecklingsbiologi samt gäddklöckning i glas ... Stockholm ₍I. Haeggström₎ 1946.
173 p. incl. illus., plates, diagrs. 24 cm. (Sweden--Kungl. lantbruksstyrelsen. Meddelanden fran Statens undersöknings- och försöksanstalt för sötvattensfisket N:r.24.)
Series title also in German.
Text in German and Swedish.
"Literaturverzeichnis": p.₍159₎-165

NL 0383120   RPB CtY ViU ICU PPAN

Lindroth, Augustinus Hjalmar Johannes

see

Lindroth, Hjalmar, 1893-

Lindroth, Carl Hildebrand, *1905-*
Bidrag till kännedomen om coleopterfaunan i övre Norrlands kustland, faunistiska, ekologiska och djurgeografiska studier, av Carl H. Lindroth och Thure Palm. Göteborg, Elanders boktr., 1934.
127 p. illus., map. 26 cm. (Göteborgs kungl. vetenskaps- och vitterhets-samhälles handlingar, 5. följden, ser. B, bd. 4, n:o 3)
Meddelanden från Göteborgs musei Zoologiska avdelning, 64.
"Inlämnad den 12 februari 1934."

1. Beetles—Sweden—Norrland. I. Palm, Thure Wilhelm, 1894- joint author. (Series: Göteborgs kungl. vetenskaps- och vitterhetssamhälle. Handlingar, 5. följden, ser. B, bd. 4, no. 3. Series: Gothenburg, Sweden. Museum. Zoologiska avdelningen, 64.)
AS284.G7 föl. 5,   ser. B, bd. 4, no. 3   A 48-8517*
Illinois. Univ. Libr.
for Library of Congress   †

NL 0383122   IU NcU CtY AAP DLC

QL461
O6
suppl.
v. 12
Entomol.
Library
Lindroth, Carl Hildebrand, 1905-
The carabid beetles of Newfoundland, including the French islands St. Pierre and Miquelon. Lund, Entomologiska sälliskapet [1955]
160 p. illus., plates, maps. (Opuscula entomologica, suppl. 12)
Bibliography: p. [150]-156.

1. Carabidae. 2. Beetles - Newfoundland.

NL 0383123   CU IdU CtY-KS AAP ICU GU

Lindroth, Carl Hildebrand, 1905-
... Die fennoskandischen *Carabidæ*, eine tiergeographische studie, von Carl H. Lindroth ... Göteborg, Elanders boktryckeri aktiebolag, 1945-
v. maps. 25ᶜᵐ. (Göteborgs kungl. vetenskaps- och vitterhets-samhälles Handlingar. 6. följden, ser. B, bd. 4, n:o 1-
Meddelanden från Göteborgs musei zoologiska avdelning. 100-
"Mitgeteilt am 11. september 1944."
"Literatur": v. 1, p. ₍677₎-696.
CONTENTS.--I. Spezieller teil.--II. Die karten.

1. Carabidae. 2. Beetles—Scandinavia. 3. Beetles—Finland. 4. Beetles—Finland. 4. Beetles—Lapland. 5. Beetles—Karelia.
                                     A 46-4944 DLC
Illinois. Univ. Library
for Library of Congress   AS284.G7 föl. 6, ser. B, bd. 4, no. 1-
         †   (068.485)   595.762

NL 0383124   IU CU CtY DLC

Lindroth, Carl Hildebrand, 1905-
Handledning för insektsamlare. Stockholm, Entomologiska Föreningen, 1949.
66p. illus. (Svensk insektfauna)

NL 0383125   InLPU

Lindroth, Carl Hildebrand, 1905-
Die insektenfauna Islands und ihre probleme ... von Carl H. Lindroth ... mit einem beitrag von M. Goetghebuer. Uppsala, Almqvist & Wiksells boktryckeri-a.-b., 1931.
1 p. l., p. ₍105₎-599 incl. illus. (incl. maps) plates. 25½ᶜᵐ.
Inaug.-diss.--Uppsala.
"Sonderabdruck aus Zoologiska bidrag från Uppsala. Band 13."
Includes bibliographies.

1. Insects—Iceland. I. Goetghebuer, Maurice. 36-29145
Library of Congress   QL591.I 4L5 1931
                                   595.709491

NL 0383126   DLC AAP ICU PU-Z MnU

Lindroth, Carl Hildebrand, 1905-
Die insektenfauna Islands und ihre probleme. Von Carl H. Lindroth. (Mit einem beitrag von M. Goetghebuer.)
(*In* Uppsala. Universitet. Zoologiska bidrag från Uppsala. Uppsala ₍etc.₎ 1930-31₎ 25½ᶜᵐ. v. 13, p. ₍105₎-599. illus.)
Issued also as the author's thesis, Uppsala.
"Verzeichnis der zum allgemeinen teil benutzten literatur": p. 572-578.
"Literatur zu der karte fig. 41": p. ₍579₎

1. Insects—Iceland. I. Goetghebuer, Maurice. A C 40-2684
Notre Dame univ. Library
for Library of Congress   [QL1.U7 vol. 13]
                               (590.82)

NL 0383127   InNd DSI

Lindroth, Carl Hildebrand, 1905-
Interglacial insect remains from Sweden. Stockholm, P. A. Norstedt, 1948.
29 p. illus., maps, 2 plates. 24 cm. (Sveriges geologiska undersökning. Ser. C, Avhandlingar och uppsatser, n:o 492. Årsbok 42 (1948) n:o 1)
"Literature": p. 28-29.

1. Insects, Fossil. 2. Paleontology—Sweden. I. Title. (Series: Sweden. Geologiska undersökningen. Ser. C. Avhandlingar och uppsatser, n:o 492. Arsbok 42 (1948) n:o 1)
QE282.A3   Ser. C, no. 492   565.76   G S 49-58*
U. S. Geol. Survey. Libr.
for Library of Congress   †

NL 0383128   DI-GS CU DLC

AS284
.G7
föl. 5,
ser. B.
Lindroth, Carl Hildebrand, 1905-
Isländische Spinnentiere. Göteborg, Elanders boktr. 1932.

VOLUME 334

Lindroth, Carl Hildebrand, 1905–
Random notes on North American Carabidae (Coleopt.)
Cambridge, The Museum, 1954.

₁117₁–161 p. illus. 24 cm. (Bulletin of the Museum of Comparative Zoology at Harvard College, v. 111, no. 3)
Bibliography: p. 159–161.

1. Beetles—North America. 2. Carabidae. (Series: Harvard University. Museum of Comparative Zoölogy. Bulletin, v. 111, no. 3)

QL1.H3   vol. 111, no. 3   A 55–1573

Harvard Univ. Library
for Library of Congress   †

NL   0383130   MH DI DLC

Lindroth, Carl Hildebrand, 1905–
A revision of *Diachila* Motsch. and *Blethisa* Bon., with remarks on *Elaphrus* larvae (Col. Carabidae) Lund, C. W. K. Gleerup ₁1954₁
28 p. illus. maps. 26 cm. (Lunds universitets årsskrift. n. f., avd. 2, bd. 50, nr. 2)
Kungl. Fysiografiska sällskapets handlingar, n. f., bd. 65, nr. 2.
Bibliography: p. ₁27₁–28.
1. Carabidae. (Series: Lund. Universitet. Acta Universitatis Lundensis, n. s. Lunds universitets årsskrift, n. f., avd. 2, bd. 50, nr. 2. Series: Fysiografiska sällskapet i Lund. Acta. Handlingar, n. f., bd. 65, nr. 2)
[AS284.L82 bd. 50, nr. 2]   A 57–200

Chicago. Univ. Libr.
for Library of Congress

NL   0383131   ICU

Lindroth, Carl Hildebrand, 1905–   , ed.
Svenska djur.
see under title

Lindroth, Carl Hildebrand, 1905–
Timotjvecklaren (Tortrix paleana ₁B.₁) ett skadedjur pa vallar, av Carl H. Lindroth...
Stockholm, O. L. Svanbacks boktryckeri, 1932.
32 p. (Meddelande nr 423 fran K. Landtbruksakademien. Centralanstalten for forsoksvasendet pa jordbruksomradet. Lanthruksentomologiska avdelningen nr 66)

NL   0383133   OU

Lindroth, Carl Hildebrand, 1905–
Våra skalbaggar, och hur man känner igen dem; illustrerad fickbok ... 2. upplagan.
Stockholm, Albert Bonniers förlag ₁1946₁
3 v. in 1. illus., plates (part col.) 18 cm.
v. 3 1st ed., c1945.
CONTENTS.–Del. 1. Markens och vattnets skalbaggar jordlöpare, vattenbaggar och kortvingar, Del.2. De växtätande skalbaggarna långhorningar, bladbaggar, vivlar och barkborrar. - Del. 3. Knäppare,

Nyckelpigor, Bladhorningar och många andra.

1. Beetles.   I. Title.

NL   0383135   DSI

Lindroth, Carl Hildebrand, 1905–
Zur Land-Evertebratenfauna Islands. Göteborg, Elanders boktr., 1928–29.
2 v. illus. 26 cm. (Göteborgs kungl. vetenskaps- och vitterhets-samhälles handlingar, 5. följden, ser. B, bd. 1, n:o 4, 6)
Meddelanden från Göteborgs musei Zoologiska avdelning, 48–49.
"Literatur": v. 2, p. 34.
1. Invertebrates—Iceland. (Series: Göteborgs kungl. vetenskaps-och vitterhets-samhälle. Handlingar, 5. följden, ser. B, bd. 1, no. 4, etc. Series: Gothenburg, Sweden. Museum. Zoologiska avdelningen. Meddelanden, 48–49)
AS284.G7 föl. 5, ser. B, bd. 1, no. 4, 6   A 49–2843*

Illinois. Univ. Library
for Library of Congress   †

NL   0383136   IU NcU CtY NIC DLC

Lindroth, Gustaf T 1883–
Geologiska och petrografiska studier inom den järnmalmsförande formationen omkring Ramhäll ... av G. T. Lindroth ... Stockholm, Kungl. boktryckeriet. P. A. Norstedt & söner, 1916.
iv, 149, ₁1₁ p. illus., 2 fold. maps, fold. profile. 24ᶜᵐ.
Akademisk avhandling—Stockholms högskola.
"Särtryck ur Sv. geol. unders. årsbok 1915."
"Litteraturförteckning": p. ₁148₁–149.

1. Geology—Sweden—Ramhäll. 2. Petrology—Sweden—Ramhäll. I. Title.

Library of Congress   QE282.L5 1916   38–35804
                                          554.87

NL   0383137   DLC ICRL CtY OU

Lindroth, Gustaf T.
... Geologiska och petrografiska studier inom den järnmalmsförande formationen omkring Ramhäll, av G. T. Lindroth. Stockholm, Kungl. boktryckeriet. P. A. Norstedt & söner, 1916.
iv, 149, ₁1₁ p. illus., 3 fold. maps, diagrs. 25ᶜᵐ. (Sweden₁ Sveriges geologiska undersökning. ser. c. Avhandlingar och uppsatser. n:o 266. Årsbok 9 (1915) : n:o 2)
"Litteraturförteckning": p. ₁148₁–149.

1. Geology—Sweden. 2. Petrology—Sweden.
                                          G S 19–125
Library, U. S. Geological Survey (583) D 1915 no.266

NL   0383138   DI-GS

QE282
.A3
ser. Ca
no. 35

Lindroth, Gustaf T., 1883–

Geijer, Per Adolf, 1886–
... De mellansvenska järnmalmernas geologi, av Per Geijer och Nils H. Magnusson. Med 56 tavlor. Stockholm, P. A. Norstedt & söner, 1944.

Lindroth, Hjalmar , 1878–
Aktuella språkfrågor; utkast och inlägg av Hjalmar Lindroth. Stockholm: H. Gerbers förlag₁, 1928₁. 180 p. 12°.

408916A. 1. Swedish language.   April 22, 1929
N. Y. P. L.

NL   0383140   NN CtY PU CU WaU NIC ICU IaU

Lindroth, Hjalmar , 1878–
Bidrag till Rökstensinskriftens tolkning. ₁Helsingfors, 1911.₁ 16 p. 8°. (Svenska Litteratursällskapet i Finland. Skrifter. ₁v.₁ 95, ₁no.₁ 8.)
Signed by Hjalmar Lindroth.
Pipping, H. Studier i nordisk filologi. Band 2, ₁no.₁ 8.

1. Runic inscriptions, Sweden: Rök.   September 1, 1915.

NL   0383141   NN NIC

DL971
G6L54
Scandi-
navian
Dept.

Lindroth, Hjalmar, 1878–
Bohusläns härads- och sockennamn. Göteborg, Elanders boktr., 1918.
115 p. illus. (Skrifter utgivna av Institutet för ortnamns-och dialektforskning vid Göteborgs Högskola. 1)

Includes bibliography.

1. Names, Geographical - Bohuslän.

NL   0383142   CU CtY MnU

Lindroth, Hjalmar, 1878–
Dulgadråp. En språklig-rättshistorisk undersökning. Av Hjalmar Lindroth. ₁Helsingfors, 1912.₁ 9 p. 8°. (Svenska Litteratursällskapet i Finland. Skrifter. ₁v.₁ 103, ₁no.₁ 6.)
Pipping, H. Studier i nordisk filologi. Band 3, ₁no.₁ 6.

1. Law (Norse). 2. Norse language.   September 8, 1915.

NL   0383143   NN

Lindroth, Hjalmar, *1878–*
Ett gammalt svenskt skällsord. (Festskrift til H. F. Feilberg... København, 1911. 8°. p. 265-272.)

1. Swedish language.   April 23, 1912.

NL   0383144   NN

Lindroth, Hjalmar, 1878–
En gensaga. (Studier i nordisk filologi.
IV. Nr. 4. Helsingfors, 1913)
p. 2. 8°.
Treats of the Rök stone. A reply to Nordenstreng.

NL   0383145   NIC

Lindroth, Hjalmar, *1878 –*
Från Island
see under title

Lindroth, Hjalmar, 1878–
Iceland, a land of contrasts, by Hjalmar Lindroth, translated from the Swedish by Adolph B. Benson. Princeton, Princeton university press; New York, American Scandinavian foundation, 1937.
viii, 3 l., ₁3₁–234 p. front. illus. (map) plates. 23½ᶜᵐ.
"The original Swedish publication, Island: motsatsernas ö, appeared in Stockholm in 1930 ... An attempt has been made in the American edition to bring the essential facts and figures up to date, whenever possible. The author has also made several other changes ... in the original text."—Translator's pref.
Bibliography: p. ₁225₁–228.
1. Iceland—Civilization. I. Benson, Adolph Burnett, 1881– tr. II. American-Scandinavian foundation, New York.
₁Full name: Hjalmar Axel Lindroth₁
                                          37–31219
Library of Congress   DL326.L55
——— Copy 2.
Copyright A 110784   914.91

OKentU WaSp OrU OrMonO WaS
PPAmSwM WaU FTaSU Wa CaBVa OrCS Or MtU TNJ DAM OrP
NL   0383147   DLC FMU PU PBm OC1W OU OO OC1 NIC NN MB

AS284
.G6
vol. 47

Lindroth, Hjalmar, 1878–
Gothenburg, Sweden. Högskolan.
Inbjudning till Göteborgs högskolas femtioårsfest med filosofie doktorspromotion den 11 oktober 1941 utfärdad av rektor och promotor ... Göteborg, Elanders boktryckeri aktiebolag, 1941.

DL326
.I54
1930

Lindroth, Hjalmar, 1878–
Island, motsatsernas ö. Stockholm, H. Gebers Förlag ₁1930₁
xi, 240 p. illus. 24cm.
Bibliography: p. ₁238₁–240.

1. Iceland—Civilization. I. Title.
Full name: Hjalmar Axel Lindroth.

NL   0383149   ViU TxU PPAmSwM NN NIC IEN CtY CU

VOLUME 334

Lindroth, Hjalmar, 1878–
J. Th. Bureus, den svenska grammatikens fader, utarbetad af Hjalmar Lindroth ... Lund, Berlingska boktryckeriet, 1911–12.
4 p. l., 328 p., 1 l. 22½ᶜᵐ. (Half-title: Samlingar utg. af Svenska fornskrift-sällskapet. (hft. 140–141;)

1. Bure, Johan, 1568–1652. 2. Swedish language—Grammar. 3. Runes.
[Full name: Hjalmar Axel Lindroth]
31–17411

Library of Congress   PT9550.B8 vol. XL

NL 0383150   DLC TxU NN CtY MnU OU MH NIC

Lindroth, Hjalmar, 1878–
Kust- och skärgårdsnamnen i Göteborgs och Bohus län. Göteborg, Elanders boktr., 1922–
v. fold. map. 21cm. (Skrifter utg. av Institutet för ortnamns- och dialektforskning vid Göteborgs högskola. 3–)

1. Names, Geographical in Sweden. Gothenburg and Bohus.

NL 0383151   MnU

Lindroth, Hjalmar, 1878–
Namnforskningar bland västkustens öar och skär. Stockholm, Bonnier (1921)

75 p. 20cm. (Populärt vetenskapliga föreläsningar vid Göteborgs högskola. Ny följd. 19)

1. Names, Geographical in Sweden.

NL 0383152   MnU CtY NIC

Lindroth, Hjalmar, 1878–
En nordisk gudagestalt i ny belysning genom ortnamn.
(Antikvarisk tidskrift för Sverige. Del 20. Nr. 3. 1919.) 8°. pp. 76.
IcA45B20
Deals with the goddess Skaði.

NL 0383153   NIC

Lindroth, Hjalmar, 1878–
De nordiska ortnamnen på -rum, språklig och bebyggelsehistorisk undersökning, av Hjalmar Lindroth. Göteborg, W. Zachrissons boktryckeri a.-b., 1916.
148, (1) p. II maps (1 fold.) 25½ᶜᵐ. (Göteborgs kungl. vetenskaps- och vitterhets-samhälles handlingar. 4. följden, 18. häftet.)
Bibliography included in "En del förkortningar" (p. 148)

1. Names, Geographical—Scandinavia. 2. Scandinavian languages—Etymology—Names. 3. Linguistic geography.
[Full name: Hjalmar Axel Lindroth]
A 45–5666
Illinois. Univ. Library
for Library of Congress   AS284.G7 föl. 4, hft. 18
†

NL 0383154   IU MnU TxU NcU PU DLC ICU

Lindroth, Hjalmar, 1878–
De nordiska systerspråken. Stockholm, Bokförlaget Natur och kultur (1942)

63, (2) p. 20cm.

"Litteraturförteckning": p. (65)

1. Scandinavian languages. I. Title.

NL 0383155   MnU PU CU ICU NNC MH WaU

Lindroth, Hjalmar, 1878–
... Ölands folkmål, av Hjalmar Lindroth ... Göteborg, Wettergren & Kirber, 1926–
v. fold. map. 25 cm. (Göteborgs högskolas årsskrift. (XXXI; 1925: 1; LI, 1945: 1
Vol. 2 has imprint: Göteborg, Elanders boktryckeri aktiebolag.
CONTENTS.—I. Inledningar, källöversikt, vokaler i starkton.—II. Öländskan på 1600- och 1700-talen.

1. Swedish language—Dialects—Öland.
[Full name: Hjalmar Axel Lindroth]
AS284.G6 vol. 31, no. 1   A 46–2021 rev

Michigan. Univ. Libr.
for Library of Congress   (r48d1;†

NL 0383156   MiU TxU DSI NcD ViU NNC NN DLC

Lindroth, Hjalmar, 1878–
Om adjektivering af particip. En studie inom nusvensk betydelselära ... af Hjalmar Lindroth ... Lund, H. Ohlssons boktryckeri, 1906.
4 p. l., 176 p. 25ᶜᵐ.
Akademisk afhandling—Lund.

1. Swedish language—Semantics. 2. Swedish language—Participle.
[Full name: Hjalmar Axel Lindroth]
6–46565 Revised
Library of Congress   PD5290.L7

NL 0383157   DLC CU MH CtY

Lindroth, Hjalmar, 1878–
—— Om lämlarna i Gisle Surssons saga.
In Minnesskrift utg. av Filologiska Samfundet i Göteborg. Göteborg, 1925, pp. 62–70.
IcA31G322

NL 0383158   NIC

Lindroth, Hjalmar, 1878–
... En omdebatterad önamnsgrupp ...; [Stockholm, Cederquists graf. a. - b., 1914?]
cover-title, [125] - 202 p. II fold. maps. 23 cm.
"Ur Fornvännen 1914."
"Rättelser" slip attached to p. [125]
Includes names of country estates.
"Några förkortningar" (containing bibliography) p. 202. Bibliographical foot-notes
1. Names, Geographical - Scandinavia.
2. Scandinavian languages - Etymology - Names.

NL 0383159   CU

Lindroth, Hjalmar, 1878–
... De reflexiva pronomina; ett stycke tillämpad språkteori, av Hjalmar Lindroth. Göteborg, Elanders boktryckeri aktiebolag, 1941.
72 p. 25ᶜᵐ. (Göteborgs högskolas årsskrift XLVII, 1941: 17)
Summary in German.

1. Scandinavian languages—Pronoun. 2. Language and languages.
[Full name: Hjalmar Axel Lindroth]
A 46–5059
Michigan. Univ. Library
for Library of Congress   AS284.G6 vol. 47, no. 17
†

NL 0383160   MiU TxU DSI ViU DLC

PT9710   Lindroth, Hjalmar, 1878–
H485   Stiernhielms Hercules, en diktmonografi.
Lund, C.W.K. Gleerup (1913)
vi,350 p.

"Dikten": p.4–17.

1. Stiernhielm, Georg, 1598–1672./ Hercules.
I. Stiernhielm, Georg, 1598–1672./ Hercules.

NL 0383161   CU MnU

Lindroth, Hjalmar, 1878–
Studier i svensk etymologi och ordhistoria, av Hjalmar Lindroth. [n. p., 19--?]
56 p. 29 cm.
Extract from an unidentified collection.
Paged also: 1 p. l., [123] - 176.
1. Swedish language - Etymology.
(Full name: Hjalmar Axel Lindroth)

NL 0383162   CU

Lindroth, Hjalmar, 1878–
Studier över de nordiska dikterna om runornas namn. In Ark. f. nord. Fil. XXIX. bd. 1913. p. 256–295.
Indledning; - A. De västnord. rundikterna (1. Översikt av det nya materialet; 2. Den norska dikten; 3. De isländska þrideilurna; 4. De västnord. rundikternas litt. hist.) To be continued.
See also Leffler, L. F. Det evigt grönsk. trädet. 1914.

NL 0383163   NIC

Lindroth, Hjalmar, 1878–
... Studier över ortnamnen på - lösa ...
[Stockholm, Cederquists graf. a. - b., 1915?]
cover-title, 52 p. II fold. maps. 24 cm.
"Ur Fornvännen 1915."
Bibliographical foot-notes.
1. Names, Geographical - Scandinavia.
2. Scandinavian languages - Etymology - Names.

NL 0383164   CU

Pamphlet
P   Lindroth, Hjalmar, 1878–
503   Svensk språkhistoria. För gymnasier och självstudium. 2. uppl. Stockholm, A. Bonnier (1935)
47 p. 20cm.

1. Swedish language--Hist. I. Title.

NL 0383165   NIC

PD5075   Lindroth, Hjalmar, 1878–
L5   Svensk språkhistoria för gymnasier och
1950   självstudium. 3. uppl. Stockholm, Svenska bokförlaget, A. Bonnier (1950)
47 p.

1. Swedish language - Hist.

NL 0383166   CU MnU NNC

Lindroth, Hjalmar, 1878–
Tron och vetandets gräns; kritiska synpunkter på den moderna Upsala-filosofien. Upsala, J.A. Lindblad (1933)

142 p. 20cm.

1. Hägerström, Axel Anders Theodor, 1868–1939.

NL 0383167   MnU NcD

VOLUME 334

Lindroth, Hjalmar, 1878–
DL606 · Våra ortnamn och vad de lära oss, av Hj.
L5 · Lindroth. Stockholm, Bokförlaget Natur
Stack · och kultur ₍1923₎
183 p. 19cm. (Natur och kultur, 25)
Bibliography: p.161-171.

1. Names, Geographical – Scandinavia.
2. Scandinavian languages – Etymology
– Names. I. Title.

NL 0383168 CSt NIC CU

Lindroth, Hjalmar , 1878–
...Våra ortnamn och vad de lära oss, av Hj. Lindroth...
Stockholm: Bokförlaget Natur och kultur₍, 1931₎. 184 p.
2. ed. 12°. (Natur och kultur. ₍bd.₎ 25.)

555273A. 1. Geography—Names— Sweden.
November 18, 1931

NL 0383169 NN ICU

Lindroth, Hjalmar, 1878–
Yggdrasils "barr" och eviga grönska. En replik.
In Ark. f. nord. Fil. XXX. Bd. 1914. p. 218-226.
A reply to Leffler.

NL 0383170 NIC

Lindroth, Hjalmar, 1878–
Ytterligare till Rökstenens huarfurniualtumanurþi.
(Studier i nordisk filologi. III. bd. Nr. 7.
Helsingfors, 1912.)
p. 4. 8°.

NL 0383171 NIC

Lindroth, Hjalmar, 1878–
Zur urnordischen Runeninschrift des sog. Rösteines in Bohuslän. Von Hjalmar Lindroth. (In: Germanica. Halle an
der Saale, 1925. p. ₍212–₎222. 8°.)

Bibliographical footnotes.

1. Runic inscriptions—Sweden— Bohuslän.
N.Y.P.L. November 24, 1926

NL 0383172 NN

Lindroth, Hjalmar, 1893–
Den apostoliska trosbekännelsen; till frågan
om dess upprinnelse, dess ursprungliga innebörd
och dess bestående betydelse. Stockholm, Svenska
kyrkans diakonistyrelses bokförlag ₍1933₎
312 p. 21 cm.

Bibliographical footnotes.

NL 0383173 CtY-D

Lindroth, Hjalmar, 1893– , ed.
En bok om kyrkans ämbete. ₍Uppsala,
Almqvist & Wiksells boktryckeri, 1951₎
309 p., 25ᵃ.

NL 0383174 NjPT

Lindroth, Hjalmar, 1893–
... Försoningen; en dogmhistorisk och systematisk undersökning, av Hjalmar Lindroth. Uppsala, A.-b. Lundequistska
bokhandeln ₍1935₎
xi, ₍1₎, 371 p. 24½ᶜᵐ. (Uppsala universitets årsskrift 1935: 8)
Series title also in French.
"Förkortningar": p. ₍xi₎; bibliographical foot-notes.

1. Atonement. I. Title.
₍Full name: Augustinus Hjalmar Johannes Lindroth₎
A C 38-1359

Minnesota. Univ. Library
for Library of Congress [AS284.U7 1935]

(378.485)

NL 0383175 MnU IEG MoU PU DLC

Lindroth, Hjalmar, 1893–
... Katolsk och evangelisk kristendomssyn; en typologisk
studie, av Hjalmar Lindroth ... Uppsala, A.-b. Lundequistska
bokhandeln ₍1933₎
viii, 255 p. 24½ᶜᵐ. (Uppsala universitets årsskrift 1933. Teologi. 4)

1. Theology, Doctrinal. I. Title.
₍Full name: Augustinus Hjalmar Johannes Lindroth₎
A C 38-1340

Minnesota. Univ. Library
for Library of Congress [AS284.U7 1933]

(378.485)

NL 0383176 MnU MoU IEG PU DLC

Lindroth, Hjalmar , ed. & tr., 1893–
Konkordieformeln i svensk översättning,
med inledning och kommentar
see under Lutheran Church. [Formula of
concord. Swedish]

Lindroth, Hjalmar, 1893–
Lutherrenässansen i nyare svensk teologi ...
Stockholm, Svenska Kyrkans Diakonistyrelses
Bokförlag [1941]
120 p. 20 cm.
1. Luther, Martin. Theology. 2. Religious
thought. Sweden. 20th century

NL 0383178 NcD PPLT CtY-D

Lindroth, Hjalmar, 1893– ed.
922.448
L747N Nordisk kristendom; kristna gestalter
från de nordiska länderna, av Martin Lindström ₍och andra₎ ... Stockholm, Natur och
Kultur ₍1944₎
206 p. 22 cm.

"Ordförklaringar" inserted after t. p.
1. Lutheran Church. Biography. 2.
Lutherans in Scandinavia. I. Title.

NL 0383179 NcD

BT
30
S8 Lindroth, Hjalmar, 1893–
L5 Recent theological research in Sweden:
a Luther renaissance. Tr. by Gustav Carlberg.
Taofongshan, Hongkong, Lutheran Theological
Seminary, 1950.
143p.
Previously pub. in the form of articles in
Ny kyrklig tidskrift under the title Four
decades of Swedish Luther research. 1941 ed.
96974 R has title: The Luther renaissance in recent

Swedish theology.
Translation of Lutherrenässansen i nyare
svensk teologi.
Bibliographical references.

NL 0383181 MoSCS ICU

B3096 Lindroth, Hjalmar, 1893–
.L74 Schleiermachers religionsbegrepp. Förutsättningar och
konsekvenser. I. ... Uppsala, Appelbergs boktryckeri, 1926.
xiii, ₍2₎, 277, ₍1₎ p. 24½ᶜᵐ.
Akademisk afhandling—Uppsala.
"Källor och litteratur": p. ₍vii₎-xiii.

1. Schleiermacher, Friedrich Ernst Daniel, 1768-1834.

NL 0383182 ICU MH IU MiU PU CtY ICRL

Lindroth, Hjalmar, 1893–
... Schleiermachers religionsbegrepp. Förutsättningar och
konsekvenser ... Av Hjalmar Lindroth. Uppsala, A.-b.
Lundequistska bokhandeln ₍1926–30₎
2 v. 24½ᶜᵐ. (Uppsala universitets årsskrift. 1926. Teologi 1; 1930.
Teologi 1)
Part i issued also as author's thesis, Uppsala, 1926.
"Källor och litteratur": v. 1, p. ₍vii₎-xiii; "Schleiermachers skrifter 1
kronologisk uppställning": v. 2, p. ₍xi₎-xxii.
"Rättelser": 1 leaf at end of v. 1.
1. Schleiermacher, Friedrich Ernst Daniel, 1768-1834.
₍Full name: Augustinus Hjalmar Johannes Lindroth₎
A C 34-4234

Title from Univ. of Minn.
Library of Congress [AS284.U7 1930]

NL 0383183 MnU PU IEG MoU

Lindroth, Hjalmar, 1893–
Tankar om kyrkan och sakramenten, av
Hjalmar Lindroth. Stockholm, Svenska kyrkans
diakonistyrelses bokförlag ₍1948₎
307, ₍1₎ p. 21.5cm.

NL 0383184 NNUT ICU

Lindroth, Hjalmar, 1893–
Verkligheten och vetenskapen; en
inblick i Axel Hägerströms filosofi,
av A. Hjalmar J. Lindroth. Uppsala,
Lindblad ₍1929₎
68 p. 20cm.

1. Hägerström, Axel Anders Theodor,
1868-1939.

NL 0383185 MnU

Lindroth, Hjalmar Axel
see Lindroth, Hjalmar, 1878–

QH7 Lindroth, Johan Ivar.
.F5H4 Die umbelliferen-uredineen. Von J. Ivar Lindroth ...
v. 22 Helsingfors, 1902.
no. 1 ₍2₎, 223, ₍1₎ p. pl. 23½ᶜᵐ. (Acta Societatis pro fauna et flora fennica, 22,
no 1)
"Verzeichnis der citierten litteratur und exsiccatenwerke": p. ₍205₎-215.

QK627 —— —— Another copy.
.A1L7 Added t.-p. with dissertation note, Helsingfors.

1. Uredineae.

NL 0383187 ICU ICRL

Lindroth (Johann₍es₎ Freder₍icus₎).
*De civilibus turbis foederati Belgii sub domu Auriaca
juniori₍ [Parts 1-3.] Upsaliae, 1812. 3 pts. 4°.
In: BTE p. 9.

By Johannes Fredericus Lindroth, E.J.Grönlund and
C. G. Embring.

NL 0383188 NN

VOLUME 334

Lindroth, K   Ingeborg Carlsson-
see
Carlsson-Lindroth, K   Ingeborg.

Lindroth, Kristen.
Reflection of electromagnetic waves from thin metal strips (passive antennas) Göteborg, Elanders boktr.; ₍H. Lindståhls bokhandel i distribution, Stockholm₎ 1955.
60 p. illus. 25 cm. (Transactions of the Royal Institute of Technology, Stockholm, Sweden, nr. 91)

1. Radar confusion reflectors.   I. Title.

UG630.L52   56–469 ‡

NL 0383190   DLC MoU NcD

Lindroth, Ludvig
Gammalt och nytt Frans-Roms kristna katakomber. Stockholm, Svenska Kyrkans Diakonistyrelses, c1924.
191 p

NL 0383191   PPAmSwM

Lindroth, Ludvig
Trachiniarum Sophoclis versus 1-224,...
Inaug. diss. Upsala, 1869.

NL 0383192   ICRL

Lindroth, Saimi
Taamottu; romaani Lapin suuren luonnon keskeltä. Jyväskylä, Gummerus [1948]
124 p.

NL 0383193   MH

Lindroth, Sten.
Charles Darwin. ₍Stockholm₎ Lindfors ₍1946₎
176, ₍1₎ p. port. 21 cm.
Bibliography : p. ₍177₎

1. Darwin, Charles Robert, 1809–1882.

QH31.D2L5   52–38837

NL 0383194   DLC NNBG NN

Lindroth, Sten.
Christopher Polhem och Stora Kopparberget; ett bidrag till bergsmekanikens historia. Uppsala, Almqvist & Wiksells boktr., 1951.
233 p. illus. (part fold.) ports., maps, facsims. 30 cm. (Skrifter utg. av Stora Kopparbergs bergslags aktiebolag)
Summary in German.
Bibliography: p. 215–219.

1. Polhem, Christopher, 1661–1751. 2. Stora Kopparbergs bergslags. 3. Mining engineering—Hist.   (Series: Stora Kopparbergs bergslags aktiebolag. Skrifter)

TN445.S8L5   54–33795

NL 0383195   DLC ICU NN MnU ICJ WU CU MH

Z
675.M4
L747e
1946

Lindroth, Sten.
Erik Wallers bibliotek. [Stockholm, 1946]
58 p. illus., plate
1. Bibliography of Medicine 2. Science - bibl.
3. Waller, Erik, 1875-1955. I. Title

NL 0383196   MH DNLM

Lindroth, Sten.
Gruvbrytning och kopparhantering vid Stora Kopparberget intill 1800-talets början. Mit deutscher Zusammenfassung. Uppsala, Almqvist & Wiksells boktr., 1955.
2 v. illus., plates (part col.) ports., maps, diagrs., facsims. 29 cm. (Skrifter utg. av Stora Kopparbergs bergslags aktiebolag)
Bibliography : v. 2, p. 392–405.
CONTENTS.—1. Gruvan och gruvbrytningen. 2. Kopparhanteringen.

1. Stora Kopparbergs bergslags aktiebolag.   2. Copper mines and mining. 3. Copper—Metallurgy.   I. Title.   (Series: Stora Kopparbergs bergslags aktiebolag. Skrifter)

TN445.S8L53   56–20387

NL 0383197   DLC ICJ MnU MH CtY CU NN

Lindroth, Sten.
Paracelsismen i Sverige till 1600-talets mitt. Uppsala, Almqvist & Wiksells boktr., 1943.
540 p. 25 cm. (Lychnos-bibliotek; studier och källskrifter, 7)
Akademisk avhandling—Uppsala.
Extra t. p., with thesis statement, inserted.
Bibliography : p. 506–531.

1. Paracelsus, 1493–1541.   I. Title.

BF1598.P2L55   56–53052

NL 0383198   DLC PU NcU PSt TxU CtY ICU DNLM NN MH MnU

Lindroth, Sten, *ed.*
Swedish men of science, 1650–1950. ₍Translated from the Swedish by Burnett Anderson₎ Stockholm, Swedish Institute, 1952.
295 p. 23 cm.

1. Scientists, Swedish.   I. Title.

Q127.S85L5   925   53—16761 ‡

OrCS MB ICU NN ICJ MH MnU NNC CtY TxU PBL PPT
NL 0383199   DLC ScU CaBVaU PSt PU DNLM OU OrU NcU TU

Lindrum, Horace.
Billiards and snooker for amateurs, by Horace Lindrum... With a chapter by Melbourne Inman.   London, Sir I. Pitman & sons, 1948. xvii, 119 p. illus. 19cm. (Games and recreations series)
"First published in 1937 as one of the Penguin books... Reissued...thoroughly revised and rearranged."

504499B. 1. Billiards.   January 18, 1950

NL 0383200   NN CaBVaU

Lindrum, Horace
Billiards and snooker for amateurs. With a chapter by Melbourne Inman. London, I.Pitman ₍1955₎
xvii,119p. illus. 19cm. (Pitman's games and recreations series)

NL 0383201   PSt

Lindrum, Karl Hermann Willi
see   Lindrum, Willi, 1884-

4HV–108   **Lindrum, L**
Zehn Lehrproben zur Alkoholfrage, ein Handbuch für Lehrer zum Gebrauch bei der Alkoholbelehrung durch die Schule.   Hamburg, Verlag: Deutschland Grossloge II des Internationalen Guttemplerordens [Vorwort 1908]
75 p.

NL 0383203   DLC-P4

LINDRUM, WALTER.
Billiards. London, Methuen [1952] vii, 149 p. illus. 20cm.

1. Billiards.

NL 0383204   NN

1884-₎
Lindrum, W₍illi₎ Die Beziehungen zwischen Oberflächen- und Tiefenwirkung harter Röntgenstrahlen ohne und mit Benutzung von Filtern. Halle a. S. 1912: John. 36 S., 1 Taf. 8°
Halle, Phil. Diss. v. 10. Juni 1912, Ref. Dorn
[Geb. 2. Mai 84 Goslar; Wohnort: Bergen a. Rügen; Staatsangeh.: Preußen; Vorbildung: Realgymn. Goslar Reife O. 04; Studium: Tübingen 1, Berlin 3, Göttingen 1, Halle 5 S.; Rig. 6. März 12.]   [U 12. 1974

NL 0383205   ICRL MiU MH DBS PU CtY

4PH
Est.
47

Lindsaar, Peeter
Kodukūla; lihtsaid lugusid ja laaste. [   ] Eesti Kirjanike Kooperatiiv [1954]
303 p.

NL 0383206   DLC-P4 C NN

Lindsaar, Peeter.
Neptuun ilmus laevale; reisukirjeldus. ₍n. p., 1951₎
200 p. illus. 20 cm.
Published in Australia.

1. Voyages and travels—1950-   I. Title.

G464.L5   54–22747 ‡

NL 0383207   DLC NN ICN

Lindsaar, Peeter.
Vana hobune. ₍Illustratsioonid valmistanud Eduard Rüga.₎Sydney ₎ 1950.
112 p. illus. 23 cm.

I. Title.

PH665.L5V3   54–17845 ‡

NL 0383208   DLC ICN

---

*
M1
.S444
v.11
no.24

Lindsay,
Come unto me. ₍Words by W. H. Bellamy₎ New York, S. T. Gordon & Son, 13 East 14th St., near 5th Avenue ₍not after 1894₎ Pl. no. 6602 - 5.
7 p.   35cm. (Gems of sacred songs. 2d ser.)
₍Sheet music collection, v. 11, no.24₎

1. Sacred songs (Medium voice) with piano. I. Bellamy, W   H   . II. Title.

NL 0383209   ViU

VOLUME 334

Lindsay, Lady
    see   Argyll, Anna (Mackenzie) Campbell,
countess of, 1621-1707.
    and
Lindsay, Caroline Blanche Elizabeth (Fitzroy)
    Lady, d. 1912

Lindsay, lord
    see   Crawford, James Ludovic Lindsay,
26th earl of, 1847-1913.
    and
Lindsay, Sir Coutts, bart., 1824-1913.

Lindsay, A.A.
    see   Lindsay, Arthur Adolphus.

Lindsay, A. D.
    see
Lindsay, Alexander Dunlop, Baron Lindsay of
Birker, 1879-1952.

Lindsay, Mrs. A.D.
    see   Lindsay, Mrs. Erica V.

Lindsay, A.M.
    see   Lindsay, Alexander Martin, 1844-1906.

Lindsay, A.W.C.
    see   Crawford, Alexander William Lindsay,
25th earl of, 1812-1880.

E   Lindsay, Mrs. Adelaide Ela (Towle)
7   1855-
.T 658   Some of the descendants of Philip
Towle of Hampton, N.H... [Boston,1889]

    Inserted: Manuscript genealogical
charts and blank pages for notes.
    Caption title.
    "Reprinted from the New England his-
torical and genealogical register for
October 1889."

NL 0383217 ICN MWA

Lindsay, Ailsa.
    Time—please! By Ailsa Lindsay. London, Joiner & Steele
[1932]
    2 p. l., 248 p. 19ᶜᵐ.

ɪ. Title.

Library of Congress   PZ3.L6476Ti

                           33-14726

NL 0383218 DLC

Lindsay (Alexander). On the Amphioxus lar
ceolatus. 3 pp. 8°. [*London*, 1857.]
Repr. from: Ann. & Mag. Nat. Hist., Lond., 1857, xx.

NL 0383219 DNLM

British
Tracts
1641
L64
    [Lindsay, Alexander] bp. of Dunkeld.
    The recantation, and hvmble svbmission of
two ancient prelates, of the kingdome of
Scotland: subscribed by their own hands; and
sent to the Generall Assemblie. As also, The
act of the said Assemblie, condemning
episcopacy and other abuses which are contrary
to the word of God, and the laws of this church
and kingdome. [London?]1641.
    1p. l., 6p. 19cm.

NL 0383220 CtY NNUT-Mc MdBP MH

Lindsay, Alexander, 1808?-1864.
    The drunkard's doom, by Rev. Alexander Lindsay... [New
York: Amer. Temperance Union, 186-?] 4 p. 12°.

    Caption-title.
    In: VTZ p. v. 131, no. 14.

1. Temperance.—Addresses, essays, lectures. 2. Title.
                                 December 19, 1918.

NL 0383221 NN

WV10
L747
    Lindsay, Alexander, 1808-1864.
    Espoused to Christ: papers by the late Rev.
Alexander Lindsay ... Ed.by Alexander Macleod
... Edinburgh,A.Elliot[186-?]
    160p. 17cm.

NL 0383222 NNUT

    Lindsay, Alexander Bertram, 1872-   tr.
Semenov, Vladimïr Ivanovich, 1867-1910.
    The battle of Tsu-shima between the Japanese and Russian
fleets, fought on 27th May 1905, by Captain Vladimir Seme-
noff (one of the survivors) translated by Captain A. B. Lindsay ... with a preface by Sir George Sydenham Clarke ...
London, John Murray, 1906.

DS517
.K8
    Lindsay, Alexander Bertram, 1872-   tr.
Kuropatkin, Aleksei Nikolaevich, 1848-1925.
    The Russian army and the Japanese war, being historical
and critical comments on the military policy and power of
Russia and on the campaign in the Far East, by General Kuro-
patkin. Translated by Captain A. B. Lindsay ... Edited by
Major E. D. Swinton ... London, J. Murray, 1909.

    Lindsay, Alexander Bertram, 1872-   tr.
Nozhin, E K.
    The truth about Port Arthur, by Monsieur E. K.
Nojine ... tr. and abridged by Captain A. B. Lindsay ...
ed. by Major E. D. Swinton ... London, J. Murray, 1908.

Lindsay, Alexander Dunlop, *Baron Lindsay of Birker,*
1879-1952.
    The background and issues of the war, by H. A. L. Fisher,
A. D. Lindsay ... [and others] Oxford, The Clarendon press,
1940.

Lindsay, Alexander Dunlop, Baron Lindsay of
    Birker, 1879-1952.   3567-750
Benedict Spinoza.
    (*In* Hearnshaw, Fossey J. C., editor, 1869- . The social & political
ideas of some great thinkers of the sixteenth and seventeenth
centuries. Pp. 204-220. London. [1926.])
    Bibliography, p. 220.

D8595 — Spinoza, Benedict de, 1632-1677.

NL 0383227 MB OU

Lindsay, Alexander Dunlop, Baron Lindsay of
    Birker, 1879-1952.
    The Christian college in India ...
        see under   Commission on Christian higher
education in India.

Lindsay, Alexander Dunlop, Baron Lindsay of
    Birker, 1879-1952.
    Christianity and economics, by A. D. Lindsay ... Lon-
don, Macmillan and co., limited, 1933.
    vii, 177 p. 19½ cm.

    Lectures originally delivered in Oxford in 1930 under the auspices
of the Henry Scott Holland memorial trust. *cf.* Pref.

1. Christianity and economics.

BR115.E3L5   261   34-6592 rev
    Library of Congress   [r47h1]

PHC PSC MB MdBJ NN CSaT ScU MiU TxU NBuU
NL 0383229 DLC IdU OrU CaBVa WaTC CaBVaU KMK UU NcD

Lindsay, Alexander Dunlop, 1879-
    Christianity and economics, by A. D. Lindsay...
London, Macmillan and co., limited, 1934.
    vii, 177 p.

NL 0383230 OO PCC ODW OrU CtY

BR479
.C4
    Lindsay, Alexander Dunlop, 1879-
    Christianity and the present moral unrest. New York, Ox-
ford university press, 1927.

    Lindsay, Alexander Dunlop, 1879-   ed.
Kant, Immanuel, 1724-1804.
    Critique of pure reason, by Immanuel Kant; translated by
J. M. D. Meiklejohn. London & Toronto, J. M. Dent & sons,
ltd.; New York, E. P. Dutton & co., inc. [1934]

Lindsay, Alexander Dunlop, *Baron Lindsay of Birker,* 1879-
    1952.
    The churches and democracy. [2d ed.] London, Epworth
Press [1934]
    87 p. 21 cm. (The Social service lecture, 1934)
    "Published for the Social service lecture trust."

1. Christianity and politics. 2. Democracy. ɪ. Title. (Series:
The Beckly social service lecture, 1934)

BR115.P7L47 1934a   261   35-15609

NL 0383233 DLC KMK CtY NN

VOLUME 334

Lindsay, Alexander Dunlop, *Baron Lindsay of Birker,* 1879-
1952.
... The essentials of democracy, by A. D. Lindsay ...
Philadelphia, University of Pennsylvania press, 1929.
82 p., 1 l. 19 cm. (William J. Cooper Foundation lectures, 1929)
Printed in Great Britain.

1. Democracy.   I. Title.   (Series: Swarthmore College,
Swarthmore, Pa. William J. Cooper Foundation lectures, 1929)

JC423.L55 1929   321.4   30-15395

    OC1W ODW MiU
    OKentU PSt DAU IEG WU TNJ NIC CtY NcD IU OU OC1 OO
NL 0383234   DLC MH-L MB NN WaU PP PSC PHC ViU IdU MH

Lindsay, Alexander Dunlop, Baron Lindsay of Birker,
1879-1952.
... The essentials of democracy, by A. D. Lindsay ... London, Oxford university press, H. Milford, 1930.
82 p., 1 l. 19 cm. (William J. Cooper foundation lectures)
"Second impression April 1930."

1. Democracy. I. Title.

JC423.L55 1930   321.4   30-19870 rev

NL 0383235   DLC PU TxU OrU

JC423   LINDSAY, Alexander Dunlop, 1879-
.L748   The essentials of democracy, by A.D.
1935   Lindsay. 2d ed. Oxford, Clarendon Press
        [1935]
        74 p. (William J. Cooper Foundation
        lectures)

        1.Democracy. I.Title. Ser.: Swarthmore
        College, Swarthmore, Pa. William J. Cooper
        Foundation lectures [1929]

    ICU
NL 0383236   MCM DAU OrPR CaBVa WaU AAP NNC-L IEdS NcU

JC   Lindsay, Alexander Dunlop, Baron Lindsay of Birker
423   1879-1952.
L55   The essentials of democracy, by A. D.
1945   Lindsay. 2d ed. London, Oxford University
        Press [1945]
        74 p. 19 cm. (William J. Cooper
        Foundation lectures)

        "Third impression (Reset)"

        1. Democracy. I. Title.

NL 0383237   NBuU

SX27   Lindsay, Alexander Dunlop, 1879-
L74   ... The essentials of democracy, by A.D.
E   Lindsay ... 2d ed. London, New York [etc.]
        G.Cumberlege,Oxford university press [1948]
        3p.l.,74p. 19cm. (William J. Cooper
        foundation lectures)

NL 0383238   NNUT TU CtY

LINDSAY, Alexander Dunlop, 1879-1952.
The essentials of democracy. Second
edition. London; New York;Toronto,
Geoffrey Cumberlege, Oxford University
Press [1951]
74p. 19.cm. (William J. Cooper
Foundation Lectures)
[Fifth printing of 2nd edition,1935]

NL 0383239   MH-AH CtY-D

JC   Lindsay, Alexander Dunlop, 1879-1952.
423   ... El estado democrático moderno; version
.L5   española de Vicente Herrero.   México, Fondo
       de cultura económica [1945]
       414 p.   20.5 cm.   (Half-title: Sección de
       obras de ciencia política [del Fondo de cultura
       económica])
       "Primera edición en español, 1945."

NL 0383240   DPU

Lindsay, Alexander Dunlop, 1879-

Plato.
Five dialogues [of] Plato. London, J. M. Dent & sons, ltd.;
New York, E. P. Dutton & co.. inc. [1936]

Lindsay, Alexander Dunlop.   2829-37
German philosophy.
(In German culture ... Pp. 35-63. New York. 1915.)

K6486 — Germany. Philosophy.

NL 0383242   MB

Lindsay, Alexander Dunlop
The good and the clever, by A. D. Lindsay, c. n. e. ... Cambridge [Eng.] The University press, 1945.
27, [1] p. 18½ cm. (The Founders' memorial lecture, Girton college,
1945)

1. Good and evil.   I. Title.
                                                 A 46-4722 rev
Harvard univ. Library
for Library of Congress   [r47g2]

NL 0383243   MH OO CtY IU NNC DLC NIC

Lindsay, Alexander Dunlop, Baron Lindsay of
Birker, 1879-
... General will and common mind.
London, 1928.
29 p.   18 cm.   (University college of
South Wales and Monmouthshire. University terminal
lecture, January, 1928.)

NL 0383244   RPB

Lindsay, Alexander Dunlop, baron Lindsay of
Birker, 1879-1952.
The government of Oxford
see under Oxford. University.

LINDSAY, Alexander Dunlop, 1879-
The historical Socrates and the Platonic form
of the good. (Readership lectures for the year
1930) ... [Calcutta] Published by the University of Calcutta, 1932.
2 p. L., 33 p.

NL 0383246   WaU IaU CtY

Lindsay, Alexander Dunlop
I believe in democracy; addresses broadcast in the B. B. C.
empire programme on Mondays from May 20th to June 24th
1940, by A. D. Lindsay ... London, New York [etc.] Oxford
university press, 1940.
3 p. l., 63, [1] p. 18½ cm.

1. Democracy. 2. World war, 1939-1945—Addresses, sermons, etc.
I. Title.
JC433.L47   321.8   A 41-626
Harvard univ. Library
for Library of Congress   [r47e1]†

NL 0383247   MH OrCS PSC PBm NN OU DLC

Lindsay, Alexander Dunlop, 1879-
The international crisis...
see under title

Lindsay, Alexander Dunlop, Baron Lindsay of
Birker, 1879-1952.
Kant, by A. D. Lindsay ... London, E. Benn limited [1934]
x, 316 p. 22 cm. (Half-title: Leaders of philosophy)

1. Kant, Immanuel, 1724-1804.

B2798.L66   193.2   34-40489 rev

    MoSU NcD PHC PPT OO OC1W OCU NN WU TxU IEdS KU
NL 0383249   DLC NIC OU TNJ MH-AH OrU CaBVaU OrPR IaAS

Lindsay, Alexander Dunlop, 1879-

Kant. London, Oxford University Press
[1936]

x, 316 p. 23cm. (Leaders of philosophy)

First published 1934.

NL 0383250   WaSpG CaBVaU CtY

Lindsay, Alexander Dunlop
Karl Marx's Capital; an introductory essay, by A. D.
Lindsay ... London, Oxford university press, H. Milford,
1925.
128 p. front. (port.) 19 cm. (On cover: The World's manuals)

1. Marx, Karl, 1818-1883. Das kapital. 2. Value.

HB501.M37L5 192   26-26615 rev

    CaBVaU OrCS
    OC1W OCX OOxM OU NN MB ICJ NjP FMU TxDaM Or WaTC
NL 0383251   DLC FU TNJ WU CU OrPS OrU NcD TU PSC PU

Lindsay, Alexander Dunlop
Karl Marx's Capital; an introductory essay, by A. D. Lindsay ... London, Oxford university press, H. Milford [1931]
128 p. front. (port.) 19 cm. (On cover: The World's manuals)
"First published 1925; reprinted 1931."

NL 0383252   ViU

Lindsay, Alexander Dunlop, Baron Lindsay of Birker,
1879-1952.
Karl Marx's capital.
Ox. Univ. Press, 1935.

NL 0383253   OCX

Lindsay, Alexander Dunlop, Baron Lindsay of
Birker, 1879-1952.
Karl Marx's Capital; an introductory essay, by A. D.
Lindsay ... London, Oxford university press, H. Milford
[1937]
128 p. front. (port.) 19 cm. (On cover: The World's manuals)
"First published 1925; reprinted 1931, 1937."

1. Marx, Karl, 1818-1883. Das kapital. 2. Value.

HB501.M37L5 1937   335.41'1   38-2009 rev 2

NL 0383254   DLC TxU OrPS

VOLUME 334

Lindsay, Alexander Dunlop, Baron, Lindsay, of
Birker, 1879-1952.
Karl Marx's Capital; an introductory essay, by
A. D. Lindsay ...   London, Oxford university press,
H. Milford [1947]
128 p.   front. (port.) 19 cm.   (On cover:
The World's manuals)
"First published 1925; reprinted 1931. 1937."

NL   0383255   MiU

HB
501
M37L5
1969
Lindsay, Alexander Dunlop.
Karl Marx's Capital; an introductory essay,
by A. D. Lindsay. London, Oxford university
press, 1947.
128 p. 19 cm.
Photoreproduction. Ann Arbor, Mich., University Microfilms, 1969. 18 cm. On double
leaves.
1. Marx, Karl, 1818-1883. Das Kapital. 2.
Value. I. Title.   fo

NL   0383256   IEdS WaT MiU

Lindsay, Alexander Dunlop, 1879-   ed.

Hobbes, Thomas, 1588-1679.
Leviathan, by Thomas Hobbes. London, J. M. Dent & sons.
ltd.; New York, E. P. Dutton & co. [1914?]

4JC-205 Lindsay, Alexander Dunlop, Baron Lindsay of
Birker, 1879-1952.
Macht, Freiheit und Wissenschaft.
[Übersetzung besorgte Gertrud Herding. München]
Nymphenburger Verlagshandlung, 1949.
86 p.

NL   0383258   DLC-P4

Lindsay, Alexander Dunlop, Baron Lindsay of
Birker, 1879-1952.
The modern democratic state ... by A. D. Lindsay ... London, New York [etc.] Oxford university press, 1943.
v. 19 cm.
"Issued under the auspices of the Royal institute of international
affairs."

1. Democracy. 2. State, The.   I. Royal institute of international
affairs. II. Title.

JC423.L56   321.8   A 43—1642
Harvard Univ. Library
for Library of Congress   [a49e1]†

WaS WaWW Or
PPD PP NcD OC1JC IEG TU WU DLC CaBViP MtBC OrPR OrU
NL   0383259   MH MiU TxU MB CaBVaU OO ODW OC1W OU OC1

Lindsay, Alexander Dunlop, Baron Lindsay of
Birker, 1879-1952.
The modern democratic state; with a pref. by W. Y. Elliott.
[1st American ed.] New York, Oxford Univ. Press, 1947-
v. 19 cm.
"Issued under the auspices of the Royal Institute of International
Affairs."

1. State, The. 2. Democracy.   I. Title.

JC423.L562   321.8   47-31174*

CU IdU OrCS WaSpG WaTC
NL   0383260   DLC MtU MB ICA ICU ViU TxU KEmT TNJ NcU

JC423
L554
Lindsay, Alexander Dunlop, Baron Lindsay of
Birker, 1879-1952.
The modern democratic state, by A.D. Lindsay.   Vol. L.
London, New York. Oxford University Press [1951]
286 p.

"Issued under the auspices of the Royal Institute of International
Affairs."
First printed 1943; reprinted.
No more published.

NL   0383261   CU

321.8
L645m
1955
Lindsay, Alexander Dunlop, Baron Lindsay of
Birker, 1879-1952.
The modern democratic state.   Oxford Univ.
Press [1955]
2p.l., 286p. 19cm.
"First printed 1943."
"Issued under the auspices of the Royal Insti-
tute of International Affairs."

1. State, The. 2. Democracy. I. Title. II.
Royal Institute of International Affairs.

NL   0383262   TxU IEdS

Lindsay, Alexander Dunlop Lindsay, baron, 1879-
The moral teachings of Jesus; an examination of the Ser-
mon on the Mount, by A. D. Lindsay ... London, Hodder &
Stoughton, limited [1937]
v. 7-185, [1] p. 19 cm.
"Six addresses ... given in Balliol college chapel."—Introd.

1. Sermon on the Mount. 2. Jesus Christ—Ethics.   I. Title.

BT380.L53 1937   226.2   37-14088 rev

NL   0383263   DLC CaBVa TU PSC PHC FTaSU NIC

Lindsay, Alexander Dunlop Lindsay, baron, 1879-
The moral teaching of Jesus; an examination of the Ser-
mon on the Mount, by A. D. Lindsay ... New York and
London, Harper & brothers, 1937.
v. 7-185, [1] p. 19½ cm.
"Six addresses ... given in Balliol college chapel."—Introd.
"First edition."

1. Sermon on the Mount. 2. Jesus Christ—Ethics.   I. Title.

BT380.L53 1937a   226.2   38-465 rev

NL   0383264   DLC WaTC PPEB NcD ODW WU PP1PT

Lindsay, Alexander Dunlop Lindsay, baron,
1879-
The nature of religious truth; sermons
preached in Balliol college chapel.
London, Hodder and Stoughton [1927]
ix, 221 p.   20cm.

CU NIC
NL   0383265   NN MH MiU PSt PSC CU NNC PSt CBBD CaBVaU

CD
L635
N
Cutter
Lindsay, Alexander Dunlop, Baron, Lindsay of
Birker, 1879-1952
The nature of religious truth; sermons
preached in Balliol college chapel, by A. D.
Lindsay ... Garden City, New York, by Doubleday,
Doran & company, inc., 1928.
ix, 221 p. 20cm.

NL   0383266   WU NbFC OO IEG

LINDSAY, Alexander Dunlop, 1879-
Our duty to God and to the state. London,
Lutterworth Press, [1940].

pp. 43.

NL   0383267   MH-AH

Lindsay, Alexander Dunlop, 1879-
Pacifism as a principle and pacifism as a dogma ... by A. D.
Lindsay ... London: Student Christian movement press [1939]
46 p.   18½cm.   (Burge memorial trust. Burge memorial
lectures. 1939.)
"Second edition."

1. War and peace, 1914-   I. Ser.

December 20, 1940

NL   0383268   NN PHC MH CtY NjP PSC

JX1963
.L74
LINDSAY, ALEXANDER DUNLOP, 1879-
Pacifism as a principle and pacifism as a
dogma, being the Burge memorial lecture for the
year 1939. [2d ed.] London, Student Christian
movement press [1939] 47p.

NL   0383269   InU

Lindsay, Alexander Dunlop, Baron Lindsay of
Birker, 1879-1952.
The philosophy of Bergson, by A. D. Lindsay ... [Lon-
don] J. M. Dent & sons, ltd., 1911.
ix, 247, [1] p. 20½ cm.
"The substance of lectures ... delivered at Balliol as Jowett lecturer."—Pref.

1. Bergson, Henri Louis, 1859-1941.

B2430.B43L5   48-40841 rev

ViU CaBVaU CaBVa FMU MsSM CBBD CSaT ICMcC TU
WU CtY OO OC1 OCU OU MiU CtMW NNC LU NN ICJ NNUT
NL   0383270   DLC PPEB NcGU IdU NIC KyU OkU NcD OKentU

Lindsay, Alexander Dunlop, 1879-
The philosophy of Bergson, by A. D. Lindsay ... [London]
Hodder & Stoughton.; New York, Geo. H.
Doran company, [1911]
ix, 247, [1] p. 20½ cm.
"The book contains the substance of lectures ... delivered at Balliol as
Jowett lecturer."—Pref.

NL   0383271   WaTC OrP

Lindsay, Alexander Dunlop.
The philosophy of Bergson.   3608.240
— [London.] Hodder & Stoughton. [1912.] ix, 247, (1) pp. 20
cm., in 8s.

H7971 — Bergson, Henri Louis, 1859-

NL   0383272   MB

193
K13YLind
Lindsay, Alexander Dunlop.
The philosophy of Immanuel Kant, by A. D. Lindsay
... London [etc.] T. C. & E. C. Jack; New York, Dodge
publishing co. [1913]
89, [1] p. front. (port.) 16½ᶜᵐ. (Half-title: The people's books)

NL   0383273   IU OCX CU MB MH

Lindsay, Alexander Dunlop
The philosophy of Immanuel Kant, by A. D. Lindsay ...
London [etc.] T. C. & E. C. Jack; New York, Dodge publish-
ing co. [1914]
89, [1] p. front. (port.) 16½ cm.   (Half-title: The people's books)
On cover: The philosophy of Kant.
Bibliography : p. [90]

1. Kant, Immanuel, 1724-1804.

A 15-299 rev

Enoch Pratt free library
for Library of Congress   [r47d1]

ViU CtHC IEN
NL   0383274   MdBP OrStbM IdU CaBVa CaBVaU WaS WU OkFG

VOLUME 334

B2797
.L7
LINDSAY, ALEXANDER DUNLOP, 1879-
The philosophy of Immanuel Kant, by A.D. Lindsay..
London and Edinburgh, T.C.& E.C. Jack [etc.] 1919.
126 p. incl. front. (port.) 16½cm. (Half-title: The
People's books)
Bibliography: p.126.

1. Kant, Immanuel, 1724-1804.

OCU OU ODW
NL 0383275   ICU MiU LU ViU CU NcRS MH CU PHC PSC MiU

BR479
.P7
Lindsay, Alexander Dunlop, 1879-

The **Predicament** of the church; contemporary essays, **by**
A. D. Lindsay [and others] ... London and Redhill, Lutterworth press [1944]

Lindsay, Alexander Dunlop, Baron Lindsay of
Birker, 1879-1952.
The principle of private property.   (In: Property, its duties
and rights, historically, philosophically, and religiously regarded.
London, 1913.   8°.   p. 65-81.)

1. Property (Private).   April 7, 1914.

NL 0383277   NN MB

Lindsay, Alexander Dunlop, Baron Lindsay of
Birker, 1879-1952.
Religion, science, and society in the modern world [by]
Alexander D. Lindsay ... New Haven, Yale university
press; London, H. Milford, Oxford university press, 1943.
vi p., 1 l., 73 p. 21 cm. (Half-title: The Terry lectures)

1. Civilization, Modern. 2. Religion and science—1900-
3. Sociology, Christian.   I. Title.

HM101.L5   261.7   A 43-1290 rev
Yale Univ. Library
for Library of Congress   [r47d²4]†

DLC IdU CaBVaU OrU WaS WaT WaWW OrCS MiU NIC
NL 0383278   CtY OC1FC OC1 OCU ODW PBm PU CU WU LU OrU

Lindsay, Alexander Dunlop, 1879-
Religion, science, and society in the modern world [by] Alexander D. Lindsay ... New Haven, Yale university press; London, H. Milford, Oxford university press [1944]
vi p., 1 l., 73 p. 21ᶜᵐ. (Half-title: The Terry lectures)   [v.19]

"Second printing, August, 1944."

NL 0383279   ViU NcD CLSU

JS3166
1947
Lindsay, Alexander Dunlop, Baron Lindsay of Birker, 1879-1952.
Gt. Brit. Inter-Departmental Committee on Expenses of
Members of Local Authorities.
Report. London, H. M. Stationery Off. [1947]

Lindsay, Alexander Dunlop, 1879-   tr.

Plato.
The Republic of Plato. London, J. M. Dent & sons, ltd.;
New York, E. P. Dutton & co. inc. [1935]

HM276
.L5
Lindsay, Alexander Dunlop, *Baron Lindsay of Birker*, 1879-
1952.
Toleration and democracy. London, Oxford University
Press, H. Milford, 1942.
17 p. 19 cm. (The Lucien Wolf memorial lecture, 1941)

1. Toleration. 2. Democracy.   I. Title.   (Series)

HM276.L5   261.7   A 42-2161
Harvard Univ. Library
for Library of Congress   [r69e2]†

NL 0383282   MH DLC MiU

Lindsay, Alexander Dunlop, *baron Lindsay of Birker*, 1879-
1952.
The two moralities; our duty to God and to society, by
A. D. Lindsay ... With an introduction by His Grace the
Lord Archbishop of York. London, Eyre & Spottiswoode,
1940.
vii p., 1 l., 110, [1] p. 22 cm. (On cover: The Archbishop of
York's Lent book, 1940)
"First published, January 1940."

1. Ethics. 2. Christian ethics.   I. Title.
                                                   A 43-2122
Harvard Univ. Library
for Library of Congress   [r60e2]

CLU WU KU TNJ-R CU NNC CaBVaU
NL 0383283   MH PSC CtY NIC NBuU ICMcC TNJ TU UU CSaT

Q25
L748
Lindsay, Alexander Dunlop, 1879-
The two moralities; our duty to God and to
society, by Lord Lindsay ... with an introduction by William Temple, late archbishop
of Canterbury. London, Eyre & Spottiswoode,
1948.
vii, 9-94p. 19cm.

NL 0383284   NNUT PSt ICU IaU InU

Lindsay, Alexander Dunlop, *Baron Lindsay of Birker*, 1879- [1952]
... War against war, by A. D. Lindsay. 3d impression ...
London, New York [etc.] Oxford university press, H. Milford [1914]
22 p. 18½ cm. (Oxford pamphlets, 1914. [No. 16])

1. War. 2. International relations.   I. Title.

D509.08 no. 16b   15-4950 rev

CaBViP WU NIC CaBVaU TxU WaS
NL 0383285   DLC DNW MB OU OO MiU PPT PU LCA MB OrU NN

Lindsay, Alexander Hynd-
see
Hynd-Lindsay, Alexander, 1870-

Lindsay, Alexander Johnston, 1896-

Collins, Clem Wetzell, 1883-
C. P. A. review; a manual for colleges and schools and for
accountants preparing for the C. P. A. examination, by Clem
Wetzell Collins ... and special collaborators: Frank C. On-
stott ... Alexander J. Lindsay ... Ralph J. Cummings ... Theodore J. Witting ... New York, J. Wiley & sons, inc.; London, Chapman & Hall, limited, 1927.

Lindsay, Alexander Martin, 1844-1906.
A gold standard without a gold coinage, in England
and India, a step towards an international monetary system ... by A. M. Lindsay ... Edinburgh, D. Douglas,
1879.
72 p. 20½ᶜᵐ.
"Reprinted, with additions, from the Calcutta review of October 1878."

1. Currency question—India. 2. Currency question—Gt. Brit.   I. Title.

                                                   17-11193
Library of Congress   HG1234.L5

NL 0383288   DLC ICU CtY

Lindsay, Alexander Martin, 1844-1906.   332.42 P804
How to fix sterling exchange: a well-tried, safe and economical
method. By A. M. Lindsay, ... Calcutta, Thacker, Spink
& Co.; London, W. Thacker & Co., 1898.
xxiii, 116 p. 24½ᶜᵐ.
"The proposals contained in these pages were first made by me in 1876. They appeared in the Calcutta review of Oct. 1878 and July 1885, and in the Bankers' magazine
of Aug. and Sept. 1892; also in letters to the Times, Economist, Statist, and Indian
papers. They were published in pamphlet form in 1892 under the title of Ricardo's exchange remedy." — Pref.

NL 0383289   ICJ MH-BS NNC ICU IEN CtY

[Lindsay, Alexander Martin] 1844-1906.
A plan for maintaining the rupee currency at a
fixed value relatively to sterling. To the editor of
the "Pioneer." Akyab, 1877.
[3] p. 33 cm.
Caption title.
Signed: A. M. Lindsay.

NL 0383290   CtY

HG
1238
L74
Lindsay, Alexander Martin, 1844-1906.
Ricardo's exchange remedy: a proposal to
regulate the Indian currency by making it
expand and contract automatically at fixed
sterling rates, with the aid of the silver
clause of the Bank act. London, Effingham
Wilson, 1892.
ii, 36 p. 22cm.

1. Money—India. 2. Richardo, David,
1772-1823.

NL 0383291   NIC OC1WHi NjP CtY

Lindsay, Alexander Martin, 1844-1906.
A uniform currency for the British empire and in-
ternational currency system. [Akyab, 1878]
[2] p. 33 cm.
Caption title.
Signed: A. M. Lindsay.

NL 0383292   CtY

Lindsay, Alexander William Crawford, *25th earl of*
Crawford
see
Crawford, Alexander William Crawford Lindsay, *25th*
earl of, 1812-1880.

Lindsay, Lady Alice Frances
see
Houblon, Lady Alice Frances (Lindsay) Archer,
1849

Lindsay, Alva F., comp.   1871-
St. Joseph, *Mo. Ordinances, etc.*
Revised ordinances of the city of St. Joseph, Missouri; em-
bracing all general ordinances in force and effect January 1,
1925, together with all statutes of the state of Missouri in effect
at time of compilation applicable to said city ... Compiled by
Alva F. Lindsay under supervision of L. C. Gabbert ... St.
Joseph, Mo., Combe printing co., 1925.

VOLUME 334

Lindsay, *Mrs.* **Amelia H.**
Lindsay's simplified shorthand, by Amelia H. Lindsay. ₍Pittsburgh? 1904₎
28 p. 22 x 17½ᶜᵐ.
Third and later editions issued as joint work of Hugh P. Lindsay and Amelia H. Lindsay.

1. Shorthand.

Library of Congress   Z56.L73   11—29466

NL 0383296   DLC

Lindsay, *Mrs.* **Amelia H.**
Lindsay's simplified shorthand ... by Amelia H. Lindsay ... ₍2d ed.₎ Pittsburgh, Pa., Colonial printing and lithographing company, 1904.
54 p. 22ᶜᵐ.
Third and later editions issued as joint work of Hugh P. Lindsay and Amelia H. Lindsay.

1. Shorthand.

      11—29465
Library of Congress   Z56.L74 1904 a

NL 0383297   DLC

Lindsay, *Mrs.* **Amelia H., joint author.**
      FOR OTHER EDITIONS
      SEE MAIN ENTRY
Lindsay, Hugh P.
Lindsay's simplified shorthand; a system of shorthand writing without shading, by which the vowel and diphthongal sounds are expressed by the inclinations of consonant strokes, embodying simplicity—rapidity—legibility. By Hugh P. Lindsay and Amelia H. Lindsay. 6th ed. Pittsburgh, Pa., The Lindsay publishing company ₍ᶜ1907₎

Lindsay, Ann.
The theatre. London, Bodley Head ₍1948₎
64 p. 19 cm. (New developments, no. 5)

1. Theater—Gt. Brit.   ɪ. Title.   (Series)

PN2595.L5   792   49–48352*

NL 0383299   DLC NcU MH InU OClJC TxU QN WaS CaBVa

Lindsay, Anna (Mackenzie), countess of Balcarres.
   See
Argyll, Anna (Mackenzie) Campbell, countess of, 1621–1707.

LINDSAY, ANNA ROBERTSON (BROWN) 1864–*1948*
Culture and reform, by Anna Robertson Brown... Fifth thousand. New York [etc.] T.Y. Crowell & Co. [cop. 1896]
32 p. 18½cm.

1. Sociology, 1860–1900. 2. Culture.

NL 0383301   NN OClW MWelC MiU OCl PU PP PPL

Lindsay, *Mrs.* **Anna Robertson (Brown) 1864–**
Giving what we have, by Anna Robertson Brown Lindsay ... New York, Boston, T. Y. Crowell & company ₍ᶜ1897₎
32 p. 18½ᶜᵐ.

1. Conduct of life.   ɪ. Title.

Library of Congress   BJ1595.L6   13–9996

NL 0383302   DLC WaWW PU OO

Lindsay, *Mrs.* **Anna Robertson (Brown) 1864–**
Gloria Christi; an outline study of missions and social progress, by Anna Robertson Brown Lindsay ... New York, London, The Macmillan company, 1907.
vii, 290 p. 18½ᶜᵐ.   (On verso of half-title: United study of missions)
"Published for the Central committee on the United study of missions."
Bibliography: p. 285–290.

Library of Congress   7–21541

NL 0383303   DLC PPWe NcD

Lindsay, *Mrs.* **Anna Robertson (Brown) 1864–**
Gloria Christi; an outline study of missions and social progress, by Anna Robertson Brown Lindsay ... New York, The Macmillan company; London, Macmillan & co., ltd., 1907.
ix, 302 p. 19½ᶜᵐ.   (On verso of half-title: United study of missions)
Bibliography: p. 285–290.

1. Missions, Foreign.   ɪ. Title.

Library of Congress   BV2060.L7 1907   7—24265

     PSC OO ODW OCl MB
NL 0383304   DLC MH-AH OrP ICRL PPPrHi IEG NjNbS PP

266   **Lindsay, Anna Robertson (Brown) 1864–**
L64g   Gloria Christi; an outline study of missions and social progress.   New York, Macmillan, 1908.
     ix, 302 p.   (United study of missions)
     "Published for the Central committee on the United study of missions."
     Bibliography: p. 285–290.

     1. Missions. I. Title.

NL 0383305   KEmT WaS

Lindsay, Anna Robertson (Brown) 1864–
The spiritual care of a child, by Anna Robertson Brown Lindsay ... New York, T. Y. Crowell & company ₍1907₎
32 p. 18½ᶜᵐ.

1. Religious education.   ɪ. Title.

      7–31179
Library of Congress   BV1475.L5

NL 0383306   DLC PU OO ICJ

Lindsay, *Mrs.* **Anna Robertson (Brown) 1864–**
The suburban child, by Anna Robinson ₍!₎ Brown Lindsay, PH. D. ₍Worcester? 1910₎
7 p. 23ᶜᵐ.
Caption title.
"An address given before the Child conference for research and welfare held at Clark university, July, 1909, and reprinted from the Pedagogical seminary, Dec., 1909, vol. XVI, no. 4."

1. Children—Care.

      E 10–1225
Library, U. S. Bur. of   Education LB1119.L64

NL 0383307   DHEW

BT771   **Lindsay, Mrs. Anna Robertson (Brown)**
.L74   The victory of our faith. New York,
1894   Thomas Y. Crowell [1894]
in: 34p. 19cm.
GTS

     1. Faith. I. Title.

NL 0383308   IEG NNUT PU CU ViU OCl OO

Lindsay, Anna Robertson (Brown) 1864–1948.
The warrior spirit in the republic of God, by Anna Robertson Brown Lindsay ... New York, London, The Macmillan company, 1906.
3 p. l., v–vii p., 1 l., 217, ₍1₎ p. 19½ cm.
"'The warrior spirit in the republic of God' was published in 1903 under the title of 'The warriors.'"—Foreword.

1. Civilization, Christian.   ɪ. Title.
BR115.C5L52 1906   6–42942

NL 0383309   DLC PU MB

Lindsay, *Mrs.* **Anna Robertson Brown**
The warrior spirit in the republic of God.
N.Y., Macmillan, 1908, ᶜ1903.

NL 0383310   PPGi

Lindsay, Anna Robertson (Brown) 1864–1948.
The warriors, by Anna Robertson Brown Lindsay ... New York, T. Y. Crowell and co., 1903.
vi p., 1 l., 217, ₍1₎ p. 19½ cm.
CONTENTS.—Chords of awakening: the higher conquest.—Prelude: the call of Jesus.—Processional: the church of God.—The world-march: of kings; of prelates and evangelists; of sages; of traders; of workers.

1. Civilization, Christian.   ɪ. Title.
BR115.C5L52   3–16392

NL 0383311   DLC NIC ViU TU MH-AH PP OO OCl

Lindsay, Anna Robertson (Brown) 1864–1948.
What good does wishing do? By Anna Robertson Brown Lindsay ... New York and Boston, T. Y. Crowell & co. ₍1898₎
32 p. 18½ cm.

ɪ. Title.
BJ1595.L7   98—2092

NL 0383312   DLC PU OrU

Lindsay, *Mrs.* **Anna Robertson (Brown) 1864–**
What is worth while? By Anna Robertson Brown, PH. D. New York, Boston, T. Y. Crowell & company ₍1893₎
32 p. 18½ᶜᵐ.
"A paper read before the Philadelphia branch of the Association of collegiate alumnæ."

1. Conduct of life.   ɪ. Title.

Library of Congress   BJ1595.L65   13—9998

     MiU OrCS OrU NjP TxU OKentU NcU NIC
NL 0383313   DLC Or NcD NcC ViU PSC MH PU NN OO OCl

Lindsay, *Mrs.* **Anna Robertson (Brown) 1864–**
What is worth while? By Anna Robertson Brown ... 75th thousand. New York, Boston, T. Y. Crowell & company ₍1897₎
32 p. 18½ᶜᵐ. ₍What is worth while series₎
"A paper read before the Philadelphia branch of the Association of collegiate alumnæ."

1. Conduct of life.   ɪ. Title.

      37–6430
Library of Congress   BJ1595.L65 1897₎
      170

NL 0383314   DLC NNC LU ViU PV

VOLUME 334

Lindsay, Mrs. Anna Robertson (Brown) 1864–
What is worth while? N. Y. Crowell,
c1920.
31 p.

NL 0383315 NcC

Lindsay, Mrs. Anna Robertson (Brown) 1864–*1948*.
What is worth while? and Working with giant power,
by Anna R. Brown Lindsay ... New York, Thomas Y.
Crowell company ₁1924₁
48 p. front. (port.) 18½ᶜᵐ.

1. Conduct of life.   i. Title.   ii. Title: Working with giant power.

Library of Congress   BJ1595.L65 1924   24-24078

NL 0383316 DLC

PQ2211
.C24A7
1955

Lindsay, Anna Suzanne (O'Dwyer) 1764–1820.

Constant de Rebecque, Henri Benjamin, 1767–1830.
Adolphe; anecdote trouvée dans les papiers d'un inconnu.
Texte établi, avec introd., bibliographie, variantes, notes et,
en appendice: des extraits de la correspondance de Benjamin
Constant avec Anna Lindsay, Lettre sur Julie, De Madame
de Staël et de ses ouvrages, par Jacques-Henri Bornecque.
Paris, Garnier, frères ₁1955₁

Lindsay, Anna Suzanne (O'Dwyer) 1764–1820.
Correspondance de Benjamin Constant et d'Anna
Lindsay
see under   Constant de Rebecque, Henri
Benjamin, 1767–1830.

Lindsay, Mme. Anna Suzanne (O'Dwyer) 1764–
1820.

Constant de Rebecque, Henri Benjamin, 1767–1830.
L'inconnue d'Adolphe. Correspondance de Benjamin Constant et d'Anna Lindsay, publiée par la baronne Constant de
Rebecque. Préface de Fernand Baldensperger. Avec dix
gravures hors texte. Paris, Plon ₁1933₁

---

p1926
LI4162f

Harris
Collection

Lindsay, Anne
First-rate programs for Christmas.
Recitations, songs, monologs, drills, exercises, plays, complete programs, etc.
... Chicago, The Dramatic publishing
company, ₍c1947₎
138p. 19 cm.

NL 0383320 RPB Or

Lindsay, Anne W
Group work recording, principles and practices. New
York, Woman's Press ₁1952₁
146 p. 23 cm.
Includes bibliography.

1. Social group work.   i. Title.

HV45.L53   *361.4 361.8   52-8010 ‡

PBm OrU OrU–M WaOB
NL 0383321 DLC CaBVaU IdU Wa MtU UU TU CU TxU NN OO

Toner

Lindsay, Archibald.
Dissertatio inauguralis, de plantarum incrementi causis.
Quam ... ex auctoritate ... d. Gulielmi Robertson ... Academiæ
edinburgenæ præfecti ... pro gradu doctoratus ... eruditorum
examini subjicit Archibaldus Lindsay. Britannus ... Ad diem
12. septembris ₁1781₁ ... Edinburgi, apud Balfour et Smellie,
academiae typographos, M,DCC,LXXXI.
43 p. 20½ᶜᵐ.

1. Growth (Plants)   37-85551

Library of Congress   QK781.L75

NL 0383322 DLC DNLM

Lindsay, Archibald Dunlop
see
Lindsay, Alexander Dunlop, *Baron Lindsay of Birker*,
1879–1952.

E185
.8
.A84

Lindsay, Arnett Grant, 1897–

Association for the study of Negro life and history, inc.
The Negro as a business man, by J. H. Harmon, jr., Arnett
G. Lindsay, and Carter G. Woodson. Washington, D. C.,
The Association for the study of Negro life and history, inc.
₁°1929₁

ND2092
.H45A4
Rare bk.
coll.

Lindsay, Sir Arthur, 1874–

Heysen, Hans, 1877–
The art of Hans Heysen. Special number of Art in Aus-
tralia, edited by Sydney Ure Smith, Bertram Stevens and C.
Lloyd Jones. Sydney, Angus & Robertson, ltd., 1920.

Lindsay, Arthur Adolphus.
The chemistry, electricity and psychology of love...by A. A.
Lindsay...   Detroit, Mich.: A. A. Lindsay Pub. Co., cop. 1916.
42 p. 8°.

1. Love.   January 5, 1918.

NL 0383326 NN

Lindsay, Arthur Adolphus.
Daily life psychology ... by A. A. Lindsay ... Detroit
Mich., A. A. Lindsay publishing company ₁1915₁
1 p. l., ₅–99, ₍1₎ p. front. (mounted port.) plates. 23ᶜᵐ. $1.00

1. New thought.   i. Title.   15-19848

Library of Congress   BF636.L5

NL 0383327 DLC

Lindsay, Arthur Adolphus
Daily life psychology...by A. A. Lindsay...
Rev. & enl. Detroit, Mich. A. A. Lindsay
publishing company ₍°1917₎
1 p. l., ₍5₎–132 p. front. (mounted port.)
plates.

NL 0383328 MiD–B MH

Lindsay, Arthur Adolphus.
Daily life psychology; health, happiness, success ₁by₁ Dr.
A. A. Lindsay ... Detroit, Mich., Wm. E. Dale printing co.;
₁New York, Detroit, The author₁ °1944–45.
2 v. fronts. (ports.) 1 illus. 22ᶜᵐ.

1. New thought.   i. Title.   44-52092 Revised

Library of Congress   BF636.L512
        ₍r46c2₎   131.324

NL 0383329 DLC

Lindsay, Arthur Adolphus.
The life ideal, scientific prayer ... by A. A. Lindsay,
M. D. Detroit, Mich., A. A. Lindsay publishing co. ₍°1918₎
1 p. l., ₍7₎–94 p. 15½ᶜᵐ.

1. New thought. 2. Prayer. 3. Mental healing.   i. Title.

Library of Congress   BF636.L52   18-6303

NL 0383330 DLC MiD

Lindsay, Arthur Adolphus.
Life's high way and how to travel it, by A. A. Lindsay
... New York city, A. A. Lindsay publishing co., °1926.
2 p. l., 138 p. 23½ᶜᵐ.

1. Therapeutics, Suggestive.   i. Title.

Library of Congress   RM921.L5   26-17262

NL 0383331 DLC

Lindsay, Arthur Adolphus.
Living the life, and The valley of the ideal...by A. A. Lindsay...   Detroit. Mich.: A. A. Lindsay Pub. Co. ₍cop. 1915.₁
27 p. 8°.

1. Ideals. 2. Title. 3. Title: The   valley of the ideal.

        March 23, 1918.

NL 0383332 NN

Lindsay, Arthur Adolphus.
Mind the builder, "The new psychology" continued;
the relationship of the designer and the builder. The
treatise with formulas for body building or physical culture, mind building or mental culture, character building
or soul culture, by A. A. Lindsay ... Portland, Or., Lindsay publishing company, 1908.
3 p. l., 111–208 p. incl. front. (port.) 17ᶜᵐ.

1. Character. 2. Self-culture.   i. Title.

Library of Congress   BF639.L72   9-3057

NL 0383333 DLC ICJ NN

Lindsay, Arthur Adolphus.
Mind the builder, Soul-culture, by A. A. Lindsay ...
₍10th ed.₁ Detroit, Mich., Lindsay publishing company
₍°1913₁
5 p. l., 15–183 p. incl. plates. mounted port. 23½ᶜᵐ. $1.50

1. New thought.   i. Title.

Library of Congress   BF639.L73   13-12885

NL 0383334 DLC WaS

VOLUME 334

Lindsay, Arthur Adolphus, ed.

Mind the builder magazine; exponent of the new psychology ... v. 1–
Oct. 1910–
Seattle, Wash. [etc.], Lindsay publishing co.] 1910–

BF638
.M698   **Lindsay,** Arthur Adolphus, ed.
Mind the builder magazine. v. 1–
New York [A. A. Lindsay, 1938–

Lindsay, Arthur Adolphus.
Mind the transformer; the new psychology complete, by A. A. Lindsay ... Seattle, Wash., Lindsay publishing company [1911]
2 p. l., 9–154 p. front. (port.) plates. 17½ᶜᵐ. $0.75

1. Mental healing. 2. New thought.

Library of Congress   BF1156.P9L6   11–910

NL 0383337   DLC ICJ

Lindsay, Arthur Adolphus.
Mind the transformer; the new psychology complete, by A. A. Lindsay ... 7th ed. Los Angeles, Lindsay publishing company [1911]
2 p. l., 9–220 p. front. (port.) 16½ᶜᵐ. $1.00

1. Mental healing. 2. New thought. I. Title.

Library of Congress   BF1156.P9L63   12–1336 Revised

NL 0383338   DLC

Lindsay, Arthur Adolphus.
Mind the transformer; the new psychology complete, by A. A. Lindsay ... Detroit, Mich., Lindsay publishing company [1913]
3 p. l., 11–215 p. port. 17ᶜᵐ. $1.00
Cover-title: The new psychology complete.

1. Mental healing. 2. New thought. I. Title.

Library of Congress   BF1156.P9L63 1913   13–12531

NL 0383339   DLC

Lindsay, Arthur Adolphus.
The new psychology complete, and Mind the builder, by A. A. Lindsay ... Detroit, Mich., A. A. Lindsay publishing company [1915]
3 p. l., 9–235, [1] p. front. (port.) plates. 25ᶜᵐ. $2.50
"Twelfth edition, revised."

1. Mental healing. 2. New thought. I. Title. II. Title: Mind the builder.

                                15–19847

Library of Congress   BF636.L54

NL 0383340   DLC

Lindsay, Arthur Adolphus.
New psychology complete, Mind the builder, and Scientific man building (three books in one) by A. A. Lindsay ... New York city, Lindsay publishing company [1922]
vii p., 1 l., 11–443 p. incl. front. (port.) 23½ᶜᵐ.
"Thirteenth edition, revised."

1. Mental healing. 2. New thought. I. Title. II. Title: Mind the builder. III. Title: Scientific man building.

Library of Congress   BF636.L54 1922   22–23127

NL 0383341   DLC CtY TU DNLM PP

Lindsay, Arthur Adolphus.
New psychology complete ... by A. A. Lindsay, M. D. [Detroit, A. A. Lindsay publishing company, 1946–47]
2 v. fronts. (ports.) 22ᶜᵐ.
Cover-title.
Each volume has special t.-p.
Paged continuously.
CONTENTS.—I. New psychology complete and mind the builder.—II. New psychology complete and scientific man building.

1. Mental healing. 2. New thought. I. Title. II. Title: Mind the builder. III. Title: Scientific man building.

BF636.L55   131.324   47–2078

NL 0383342   DLC

Lindsay, Arthur Adolphus.
New psychology handbook; healing and culture, by A. A. Lindsay ... Detroit, Mich.: A. A. Lindsay Pub. Co. [cop. 1913.]
3 p. l., (1)10–96 p. 8°.

1. New thought and mental healing.

                                December 21, 1917.

NL 0383343   NN MiD-B

Lindsay, Arthur Adolphus.
The new psychology, its basic principles and practical formulas, by A. A. Lindsay ... Portland, Or., E. & A. Lindsay [1908]
2 p. l., 9–99 p. front. (port.) 25½ᶜᵐ.

                                8–7160

NL 0383344   DLC ICRL ICJ

Lindsay, Arthur Adolphus.
The new psychology pearls; essays, by A. A. Lindsay ... San Francisco, Cal.: A. A. Lindsay Pub. Co. [cop. 1914.] 2 p.l., 9–219 p. [4. ed.] 16°.

1. Psychology.—Essays and misc.   2. Title.

                                December 18, 1917.

NL 0383345   NN MiD

Lindsay, Arthur Adolphus.
New psychology pearls, by A. A. Lindsay ... [8th ed.] Detroit, Mich., A. A. Lindsay publishing co. [1919]
2 p. l., [9]–93 p. port. 22½ᶜᵐ.

1. New thought. I. Title.

                                19–1275

Library of Congress   BF639.L738 1919

NL 0383346   DLC DNLM

Lindsay, Arthur Adolphus.
New psychology question book, by A. A. Lindsay, M. D. 1500 questions on four of the author's psychology books: "The new psychology complete," "Mind the builder—soul culture," "New psychology handbook of healing and culture," "New psychology pearls" ... Detroit, Mich., Lindsay publishing co. [1914]
94 p. 20 x 10ᶜᵐ. $0.50

1. New thought. 2. Mental healing. I. Title.

                                14–5071

Library of Congress   BF645.L5

NL 0383347   DLC

Lindsay, Arthur Adolphus
Pure, precious, priceless ... Seattle, Wash., Lindsay publishing company, c1910.
36 p.

NL 0383348   Wa

Lindsay, Arthur Adolphus.
Scientific man building through thought force, by A. A. Lindsay ... Detroit, Mich., A. A. Lindsay publishing company [1916]
2 p. l., [9]–204 p., 1 l. 23½ᶜᵐ. $2.00

1. New thought. I. Title.

                                16–23601

Library of Congress   BF639.L735

NL 0383349   DLC ICJ

Lindsay, Arthur Adolphus.
Scientific prayer — The silence ... by A. A. Lindsay ... Detroit, Mich.: A. A. Lindsay Pub. Co. [cop. 1915.] 1 p.l., (1)6–29 p. 8°.

1. Prayer. 2. Silence.

                                March 19, 1918.

NL 0383350   NN

Lindsay, Arthur Adolphus.
Soul-culture (practical psychology), scientific prayer (religious suggestion), religion (attitude toward spirit), theology (conception of supreme power and intelligence) by A. A. Lindsay ... Seattle, c1909.
62 p. 15 cm.

NL 0383351   CU

Lindsay, Arthur Adolphus.
The tyranny of love; and its sequel, Love the liberator, by A. A. Lindsay ... Seattle, Wash.: Lindsay Pub. Co., cop. 1910.
28 p. illus. (incl. port.) 32°.

1. Love. 2. Title.

                                February 26, 1918.

NL 0383352   NN

Lindsay, Arthur Adolphus.
The valley of the ideal, by A. A. Lindsay ... Detroit, Mich., Lindsay publishing company, [1913.
45 p. 23½ᶜᵐ. $0.25

1. New thought. 2. Mental healing. I. Title.

                                13–12530

Library of Congress   BF639.L74

NL 0383353   DLC

VOLUME 334

Lindsay, Arthur Adolphus.
The wayside and the goal; or, The gospel of liberation...by A. A. Lindsay... Detroit, Mich.: A. A. Lindsay Pub. Co. cop. 1917. 181. 8°.

1. Conduct of life. 2. Future life.   3. Title.
                                                            March 21, 1918.

NL 0383354   NN

Lindsay, Miss B.   d. 1917.
Animal life. (Stories of the universe)
N.Y. Review of Reviews corp. [c1902]

NL 0383355   WaE

590
L645a
1909
Lindsay, Miss B   d. 1917.
Animal life. With forty-seven illus. New York, Review of Reviews Co., 1909 [c1902]
196p. illus. 16cm. (Stories of the universe)

The library of useful stories.

1. Zoology. I. Title.

NL 0383356   TxU MtHi IU CtY KAS PBa NcU

Lindsay, Miss B   d. 1917.
Animal life. New York, Review of Reviews Co., 1910.
196 p. illus. 16cm. (Stories of the universe)

1. Zoology. I. Title.

NL 0383357   ViU WaPS CU NcC

QL49 **Lindsay, Miss B.**
.L75   ... Animal life, by B. Lindsay, with forty-seven illustrations. New York, Review of reviews company, 1911.
196 p. incl. front., illus., tables. 16ᵐᵐ. (Stories of the universe)

1. Zoology—Juvenile and popular literature.

NL 0383358   ICU MH

Lindsay, Miss B.   d. 1917
590.2 P501
An introduction to the study of zoology. xix,356 p. 124 il. 1 pl. D. [Introductory science text-books.] London: Swan Sonnenschein & Co., 1895.
"The use of books", p. 309-325.

NL 0383359   ICJ PP CU OCU MeWaC NjR OU

Lindsay, Miss B   d. 1917.
The story of animal life, by B. Lindsay. With forty-seven illustrations. New York, D. Appleton and company, 1902.
196 p. front., illus. 15½ᵐᵐ. [The library of useful stories]

1. Zoology. I. Title.
                                            2—14675
Library of Congress   QL49.L74

NL 0383360   DLC Or PPL PPM PP OC1W OC1 OU ICJ NN MB

Lindsay, Miss B   d. 1917.   2259a.234
The story of animal life.
New York. McClure, Phillips & Co. 1904. 196 pp. Illus. Plate. Table. [Library of valuable knowledge.] 18½ cm., in 8s.

M5360 — T.r. — S.r. — Zoology.

NL 0383361   MB NcC PPWI MH

Lindsay, Miss B   d. 1917.
The story of animal life. New York: [D. Appleton and Co.] 1912. 196 p. diagr., illus. 12°. (Library of valuable knowledge.)

1. Zoology. 2. Series. 3. Title.
                                            September 18, 1924

NL 0383362   NN MH OOxM

Lindsay, Miss B.   d. 1911.
The story of animal life, by B. Lindsay; with forty-seven illustrations. New York, 1915.
196 p. front., illus. 19ᵐᵐ. (Lettered on cover: Library of valuable knowledge)

1. Zoology. I. Title.

Library of Congress   QL49.L74 1915   16-2029

NL 0383363   DLC PPPM

Lindsay, Barbara.
Fun at my house; illustrated by Jane Brookhart March. [1st ed.] New York, Aladdin Books [1955]
unpaged. Illus. 22 cm.

I. Title.

PZ7.L6597Fu   55–10126 ‡

NL 0383364   DLC OC1 PP WaS Or OrLgE

Lindsay, Barbara.
The toy show surprise. Illustrated by Doug Anderson. New York, Sterling Pub. Co. [1955]
unpaged. illus. 22 cm.

I. Title.

PZ7.L6597To   55–10370 ‡

NL 0383365   DLC Or PP

Lindsay, Batterman. Abandoned: a tale of the plains. 8 pp. [Atlant. Monthly, v. 78, 1896, p. 533.]

NL 0383366   MdBP

Lindsay, Batterman *i. e.* **Annie Batterman.**
Derelicts of destiny. New York [etc.] London, The Neely co. [1900]
1 p. l., 7-76 pp. 12°.
CONTENTS.—Abandoned.—My great aunt's wedding.—An aboriginal episode.—Kweish-Elite: the proud slave.—The vanishing city of Tamalpais.—Squaw Charley.
Copyright by Batterman Lindsay, Seattle, Wash. Class A, XXc, no. 16232, Sept. 5, 1901; 2 copies rec'd Nov. 8, 1901.
                                            1-23046—M 4 Oct. 24

NL 0383367   DLC CU WaS

LINDSAY, Batterman,
Derelicts of destiny; being a few short annals of a vanishing people; limited ed. re-arranged by Harry S. Stuff. Seattle, Ivy press, 1901.
76 p.

NL 0383368   WaU

[Lindsay, Beckett (Weigall)]
Through darkest Pondelayo
see under   Lindsay, Joan (Weigall)

Pam   **Lindsay, Bertha**
68-1407   INDUSTRIES AND INVENTIONS OF THE SHAKERS SHAKER MUSIC, A BRIEF HISTORY. [By] Sister Bertha Lindsay [and] Sister Lillian Phelps. Canterbury, New Hampshire, Canterbury Shakers. [n.d.]
[15] p.

Cover title.

NL 0383370   WHi

Lindsay, Blanche Elizabeth, Lady, 1844-
see   Lindsay, Caroline Blanche Elizabeth (Fitzroy) 1844-1912.

Lindsay, C   H   Forbes-
see   Forbes-Lindsay, Charles Harcourt Ainslie, 1860-

Lindsay, C   Seton.
Negotiable bond policy. [By] C. Seton Lindsay. New York, 1895.
cover-title, 29 p. 15 x 11½ᵐᵐ.

1. Insurance, Life—Plans.
                                            8-8211†
Library of Congress   HG8816.L6
                             (Copyright 1895: 23088)

NL 0383373   DLC

QL
676
.L54
Lindsay, Caroline Blanche Elizabeth (Fitzroy), lady, 1844-1912.
About robins; facts and songs, legends. Collected and illustrated by Lady Lindsay. London, Frederick Warne & Co. [188-?]
111 p. illus. 28 cm.

NL 0383374   OKentU

Lindsay, Caroline Blanche Elizabeth (Fitzroy), lady, d. 1912.
About robins. Songs, facts, & legends, collected & illustrated by Lady Lindsay. London [etc.] G. Routledge & sons [1889] 111, [4] p. incl. facsim. (music), plates (part col'd). col'd front., illus. (part col'd.) 28½cm.

Illustrated t.-p.
Includes music.
With autograph of author.

85031B. 1. Robin. 2. Birds in   poetry.
                                            November 18, 1940

NL 0383375   NN

VOLUME 334

LINDSAY, CAROLINE BLANCHE ELIZABETH (FITZROY),
lady, d.1912.
The apostle of the Ardennes, by Lady Lindsay. London:
Kegan Paul, Trench, Trubner & Co., Ltd., 1899. 161 p.
17½cm.

639589A. 1. Poetry, English. I. Title.

NL 0383376 NN MiU NcU CaBVaU

PR 10
S L5
1899
A7
Lindsay, Caroline Blanche Elizabeth Fitzroy,
Lady.
The art of poetry with regard to women
writers... [Hatchards, 1899]
14 p.

NL 0383377 CaBVaU

PR4934
.L6435
1891
Lindsay, Caroline Blanche Elizabeth (Fitzroy)
lady, d.1912.
Bertha's earl, a novel. London, R. Bentley,
1891.
3 v.

NL 0383378 ICU NcU CU

3828
.48
.324
Lindsay, Lady Caroline Blanche Elizabeth
A Christmas posy of carols, songs... by
Lady Lindsay. London, Kegan, 1902
114 p. 18 cm

NL 0383379 NjP NIC MB CaBVaU CtY PU MH

Lindsay, Caroline Blanche Elizabeth (Fitzroy) lady.
Dora's defiance. By Lady Lindsay ...
(*In* Lippincott's monthly magazine. Philadelphia, 1894. 23½ᵐ. vol. 54.
p. ₍5771-649₎)

Library of Congress   7-16048†* Cancel
——Copy 2, de-   tached.
Library of Congress   PZ3.L649D₍

NL 0383380 DLC NN

Lindsay, Caroline Blanche Elizabeth (Fitzroy) *lady.*
The flower seller, and other poems, by Lady Lindsay.
London, New York ₍etc.₎ Longmans, Green, and co., 1896.
viii, 187, ₍1₎ p. 20ᶜᵐ.

Library of Congress   8-4297

NL 0383381 DLC NBuG MiU MB NNC

Lindsay,, Caroline Blanche Elizabeth (Fitzroy)
lady.
From a Venetian balcony and other poems of
Venice and the near lands, by Lady Lindsay. Pen
sketches by Clara Montalba. London, Kegan,
Trench, Trubner and co., ₍td., 1903.
66p. illus. 17.5cm.

T.p. in red and black with ornamental border.
Plates with guardsheets.
"This edition on Japanese vellum is limited
to 100 copies for England and America."

Continued in next column

Continued from preceding column

Half title inscribed: "With kind regards."
Full vellum; gilt lettering.
Pages uncut.

I. Montalba, Clara, illus. II. Title.

NL 0383383 WyU NNC MH MB CU-S CaBVaU

PR 10
S L5
1908
Lindsay, Caroline Blanche Elizabeth Fitzroy,
Lady.
From a Venetian calle. K. Paul, Trench,
Trübner, 1908.
63 p.

NL 0383384 CaBVaU

Lindsay, Caroline Blanche Elizabeth, Lady.   *P.83.527.5
Godfrey's quest. A fantastic poem.
= London. Kegan Paul, Trench, Trübner & Co., Ltd. 1905. 127,
(1) pp. Sm.8°.

NL 0383385 MB MH CaBVaU

Lindsay, Caroline Blanche Elizabeth (Fitzroy)
lady,
The king's last vigil, and other poems.
London, K. Paul, Trench, Trübner, 1894.
viii, 202 p. 16½cm.

NL 0383386 NNC

LINDSAY,₍Caroline Blanche Elizabeth (Fitzroy)₎
lady.
The king's last vigil and other poems.
2d ed. London, K. Paul, Trench, Trübner & Co.,
ltd., 1805.

NL 0383387 MH PPL

Lindsay, Caroline Blanche Elizabeth, Lady.
The King's Last Vigil, and other Poems.
London [1897]
60 p. 8°. [In "Poems" 81]

NL 0383388 CtY

PR4889
L4K5
Lindsay, Caroline Blanche Elizabeth (Fitzroy)
lady.
The king's last vigil and other poems.
London, "Review of reviews" ₍1900?₎

60p. 18cm. (The penny poets. LXII)

NL 0383389 NBuG

821
L844
Lindsay, Caroline Blanche Elizabeth (Fitzroy)
lady, d.1912.
Lyrics and other poems. London, K. Paul,
Trench, Trübner, 1890.
xii, 169p. 16cm.

NL 0383390 IU CtY

Lindsay, Caroline Blanche Elizabeth (Fitzroy) lady.
Lyrics, and other poems. [2d ed.]
London, 1890.
16.5 cm.

NL 0383391 CtY

Lindsay, Caroline Blanche Elizabeth (Fitzroy) lady, d.
1912.
Original plays ₍by₎ B. L. ₍London, Privately printed
for the author by Bradbury, Agnew, & co., n. d.₎
1 p. l., 20, 14, 18, 24 p. 18ᶜᵐ.
Binder's title: no general title-page; each play has separate paging; per-
haps a made-up copy.
The author's autograph presentation copy to F. Locker.
Book-plate: Frederick Locker.
CONTENTS.—Three girls. A comedietta, in one act. 1875.—Runa. A sketch.
₍n. d.₎—A weak plot. A comedietta, in one act. ₍n. d.₎—Forget-me-not. A
play, in two short acts. ₍n. d.₎
I. Title: Three girls. II. Title: Runa. III. Title: A weak plot. IV. Title:
Forget-me-not.

NL 0383392 MiU

AC-L
W357L
L645p
Lindsay, Caroline Blanche Elizabeth (Fitzroy)
Lady.
Poems, by Lady Lindsay. London, K. Paul,
Trench, Trübner, 1907.
viii, 215p. 16cm. (Dryden library)
Author's autograph presentation copy to
Arthur Waugh, Nov. 1907.
From the library of Evelyn Waugh.

NL 0383393 TxU CaBVaU

Ip
1645
907P
Lindsay, Caroline Blanche Elizabeth (Fitzroy)
lady.
Poems of love and death, by Lady Lindsay.
London, K. Paul, Trench, Trübner, 1907.
154p. 17cm.

NL 0383394 CtY NNC MH MB

PR
4889
.L3P7
Lindsay, Caroline Blanche Elizabeth (Fitzroy)
Lady.
The prayer of St. Scholastica and other
poems, by Lady Lindsey. London, K. Paul,
Trench, Trübner, 1900.
166 p. 18cm.

NL 0383395 KyLoU ScU CtY CaBVaU

LINDSAY, CAROLINE BLANCHE ELIZABETH (FITZROY),
lady, d.1912.
The prayer of St Scholastica, and other poems, by Lady
Lindsay. Boston: Small, Maynard & Co., 1901. 166 p.
17½cm.

558331A. 1. Poetry, English. I. Title.

NL 0383396 NN

Lindsay, Caroline Blanche Elizabeth, Lady.   *P.83.527.3
The prayer of St. Scholastica and other poems. 2d edition.
= London. Kegan Paul, Trench, Trübner & Co., Ltd. 1901. 167
pp. Sm.8°.

NL 0383397 MB

VOLUME 334

LINDSAY, [Caroline Blanche Elizabeth (Fitzroy)]
lady.
The prayer of St.Scholastica and other
poems. 3d ed. London,K.Paul,Trench,Trübner
& Co.,ltd.,1901.

NL 0383398   MH

Wordsworth
CT   Lindsay, Caroline Blanche Elizabeth
788   (Fitzroy) lady, 1844-1912.
G48   Some recollections of Miss Margaret
L74   Gillies. [London, 1887]
              265-274 p. 22cm.

              Extract from Temple bar, v. 81,
            Oct. 1887.
              Miss Gillies was a friend of the
            Wordsworths and painted both the poet
            and his wife.
              Healey 1138.
              1. Gillies.   Margaret, 1803-1887.
            I. Temple bar,   v. 81, Oct. 1887.

NL 0383399   NIC

Lindsay, Caroline Blanche Elizabeth
(Fitzroy) Lady, 1844-1912.
A string of beads. Verses for children.
By Lady Lindsay. London, A. and C. Black,
1892.
ixp.,1ℓ., 96p.

First edition.

NL 0383400   ScU CaBVaU

Lindsay, Catherine, 1924–
... The country of the young. New York, Reynal & Hitch-
cock [1946]
4 p. l., 11-220 p. 19½ᶜᵐ.
At head of title: A novel by Catherine Lindsay.

  I. Title.
  Library of Congress   PZ3.L6492Co   46-6842

NL 0383401   DLC

Lindsay, Celeste Dunbar.
Quality house, by Celeste Dunbar Lindsay. New York, The
Dial press [1935]
3 p. l., 280 p. 19½ᶜᵐ.

  I. Title.
  Library of Congress   PZ3.L6493Qu   35-38318

NL 0383402   DLC NcD

Lindsay, Celeste Dunbar.
Red dusk, by Celeste Dunbar Lindsay. New York, L. Mac
Veagh, The Dial press, 1932.
3 p. l., 3-310 p. 19½ᶜᵐ.

  I. Title.
  Library of Congress   PZ3.L6493Re   32-5038

NL 0383403   DLC

Lindsay, Charles, called earl of Crawford and
Lindsay
    see Crawford, Charles, b. 1752.

Lindsay, Charles, of Toronto
    see Lindsey, Charles, 1820-1908.

Lindsay, Charles, 1895-1931.
The Big Horn basin, by Charles Lindsay ... [Lincoln?
Neb., 1932]
274 p. illus., maps (part fold.) 23ᶜᵐ.
Thesis (PH. D.)—University of Nebraska, 1930.
Issued also as University of Nebraska, University studies, v. 28-29.
Bibliography: p. 261-274.

  1. Big Horn river. 2. Wyoming—Hist.   I. Title.
                                                        32-24275
  Library of Congress   F767.B4L6
                             [a36d1]   978.7

       AU CoD OU OrU MtBC WaTC
NL 0383406   DLC IdU MtU MU NIC NcU PU PBm CU MB MH IU

Lindsay, Charles, 1895-1931.
... The Big Horn basin, by Charles Lindsay. Lincoln, Neb.
[1932]
cover-title, 4 p. l., 7-274 p. illus., maps (part fold.) 23ᶜᵐ. (University studies, pub. by the University of Nebraska. vol. xxviii-xxix)
Issued also as thesis (PH. D.) University of Nebraska.
Bibliography: p. 261-274.

  1. Big Horn river. 2. Wyoming—Hist.   I. Title.
                                            32-27720
  Library of Congress   AS36.N2 vol. 28/29
                                            (082) 978.7

       OCU ViU OU MH MtHi
NL 0383407   DLC OrPR PSt WaU PPT NIC OO OClW OCl MiU

LINDSAY,Charles Fowler, 1879–
The conductivities of some double salts
as compared with the conductivities of mixtures of their constituents. n.p.,1901.

NL 0383408   MH-C

Lindsay, Charles Fowler, 1879–

Jones, Harry Clary, 1865-1916.
Conductivity and viscosity in mixed solvents. A study of
the conductivity and viscosity of solutions of certain electrolytes in water, methyl alcohol, ethyl alcohol, and acetone; and
in binary mixtures of these solvents. By Harry C. Jones ...
and C. F. Lindsay, C. G. Carroll, H. P. Bassett, E. C. Bingham, C. A. Rouiller, L. McMaster, W. R. Veazey. Washington, D. C., Carnegie institution of Washington, 1907.

Lindsay, Charles Fowler, 1879–
A study of the conductivity of certain salts in water,
methyl, ethyl, and propyl alcohols, and mixtures of these
solvents ... Easton, Pa., The Chemical publishing co.,
1902.
55, [1] p. diagrs. 23ᶜᵐ.
Thesis (PH. D.)—Johns Hopkins university.
Biography.
From the American chemical journal, v. 28.

  1. Electrolytes, Conductivity of.
                                                        8-1564
  Library of Congress   QD565.L7

NL 0383410   DLC MiU NIC NjP MB NN

Lindsay, Charles Harcourt Ainslie Forbes-.
    See
Forbes-Lindsay, Charles Harcourt Ainslie, 1860–

Lindsay, Charles Monfort, 1861–   ed.
The Negotiable instruments law of Kentucky. Annotated
by Charles M. Lindsay ... Louisville, Geo. G. Fetter company, 1904.
xvi, 174 p. 23ᶜᵐ.

  1. Negotiable instruments—Kentucky.   I. Kentucky. Laws, statutes, etc.   4-25128
  Library of Congress

NL 0383412   DLC

[Lindsay, Clara A   ] 1844-1909.
In life's sweet afternoon; rhymes of the quiet hour, by
C. A. L. Philadelphia, Printed for the author by G. W.
Jacobs & co. [1909]
2 p. l., 203 p. 18½ᶜᵐ.

                                                        9-31453

NL 0383413   DLC

Lindsay, Clara A., 1844-1909.
Memories of gentle life. Phila., priv. print.,
1882.
68 p.

NL 0383414   PPPrHi

Lindsay, Clarence M[ansfield]
Breakfast for two. A farce in one act.
Phil., 1926.
14 p. 19 cm.

NL 0383415   RPB

FILM Lindsay, Crawford Bernard, 1905–

        The Cornell University special collection
     on slavery; American publications through
     1840. Ithaca, N. Y., 1949.

        Microfilm copy (negative)
        Collation of the original as determined
     from the film: 728 numb. ℓ.
        Thesis—Cornell University.
        Vita.
        Includes bibliography.
        1. Slavery in   the U. S. Bibliography.
     I. Cornell   University. Library

NL 0383416   NcD NIC ICN

Lindsay, Clarence Mansfield, comp.
Cavalier poets. New York [etc.] The Abbey press [1901]
v, xiii-xv, 15-138 p. ports. 19½ᶜᵐ.
CONTENTS.—Colonel Richard Lovelace.—Sidney Godolphin.—Sir William
Davenant.—Alexander Broome.—James Graham, marquis of Montrose.—
Sir Roger L'Estrange.—Sir John Suckling.—Thomas Carew.—William
Chamberlayne.—Sir Edward Sherburne.—James Shirley.—Sir John Den-
ham.—Sir Richard Fanshawe.—John Cleiveland.

  1. English poetry—Early modern (to 1700)   I. Title.
                                                        1-25563
  Library of Congress   PR1209.L45

NL 0383417   DLC GU NcD NN

VOLUME 334

Lindsay, Clarence M[ansfield]
False colors. A comedy in one act.   Phil.,
1926.
16 p.   18 cm.

NL   0383418   RPB

Lindsay, Clarence Mansfield
p1901
L7484C1   The Lindsay book; plays and exercises for
Harris   special occasions for the elementary grades, by
Collections   Clarence M. Lindsay ... Evanston, Ill ., Row,
Peterson, c1949.
49p.   21 cm.

NL   0383419   RPB

LINDSAY, Clarence Mansfield.
Looking for more, or Turn about is fair
play; a farce in one act.   Boston, W.H. Baker
& co., [cop. 1909].

pp. 21.

NL   0383420   MH OC1 RPB NN PU

Lindsay, Clarence Mansfield.
What happened, a sketch in one act.   Boston,
Baker, n.d.
7 p.

NL   0383421   PU

Lindsay, Colin, 3d earl of Balcarres.
See
Balcarres, Colin Lindsay, 3d earl of, 1654?-1722.

Lindsay, *Hon.* Colin, 1755-1795.
Extracts from Colonel Tempelhoffe's History of the
seven years war: his remarks on General Lloyd: on the
subsistence of armies; and on the march of convoys. Also
a treatise on winter posts [by K. F. Lindenau] To
which is added a narrative of events at St. Lucie and Gibraltar, and of John duke of Marlborough's march to the
Danube, with the causes and consequences of that measure ... By the Honourable Colin Lindsay ... London,
T. Cadell, 1793.
2 v. fold. pl. 3 fold. maps. 22ᶜᵐ.

Paged continuously.
Half-title: A military miscellany.

1. Military art and science. 2. Seven years' war, 1756-1763. 3. Lloyd
Henry, 1720?-1783. 4. Military posts. 5. St. Lucia—Hist. 6. Gibraltar—
Siege, 1779-1783. 7. Marlborough, John Churchill, duke of, 1650-1722.
8. Gt. Brit.—Hist.—1688-1722. I. Tempelhof, Georg Friedrich von, 1737-
1807. Geschichte des siebenjährigen krieges. II. Lindenau, Karl Friedrich
von, 1742-1817. Über winterpostirungen. III. Title.

14-16332

Library of Congress   U19.L74

NL   0383424   DLC InU MdBP NN MdAN MiU-C

Lindsay, *Hon.* Colin, 1755-1795.

Crawford, Alexander William Crawford Lindsay, *25th earl
of,* 1812-1880.
Lives of the Lindsays: or, A memoir of the houses of Crawford and Balcarres, by Lord Lindsay. To which are added,
extracts from the official correspondence of Alexander sixth
earl of Balcarres, during the Maroon war; together with personal narratives by his brothers, the Hon. Robert, Colin,
James, John, and Hugh Lindsay; and by his sister, Lady
Anne Barnard. 2d ed. London, J. Murray, 1858.

Lindsay, *Hon.* Colin, 1755-1795.
Narrative of the occupation and defence of the island St.
Lucie, MDCCLXXIX. By the Hon. Colin Lindsay ...
(*In* Crawford, Alexander W. C. Lindsay, 25th earl of. Lives of
the Lindsays. London, 1849. 22ᶜᵐ. v. 3, p. [329]-356)

1. St. Lucia—Hist.
8—22925
Library of Congress   DA758.3.L8C7   vol. 3

NL   0383426   DLC MdBP

Lindsay, *Hon.* Colin, 1755-1795.
Some account of the assault on Gibraltar in 1782; in a
letter to the Earl of Balcarres. By the Hon. Colin Lindsay ...
(*In* Crawford, Alexander W. C. Lindsay, 25th earl of. Lives of the Lindsays. London, 1849. 22ᶜᵐ. v. 3, p. [357]-368)

1. Gibraltar—Hist.—Siege, 1779-1783.
8—30543
Library of Congress   DA758.3.L7

NL   0383427   DLC

BR759
.A1P13   Lindsay, Hon. Colin, 1819-1892.
no. 14   Church Union, Scotland. Address delivered
by the Hon. Colin Lindsay at the first annual
in: meeting, held at Aberdeen, on the 22d October,
SWTS   1867. With the proceedings of the meeting.
Aberdeen, A. Brown, 1868.
15p. 21cm. (Pamphlets [no. 14])

1. Church union—Scotland. I. Church union,
Scotland.

NL   0383428   IEG

Lindsay, Hon. Colin. 1819-1892.   3526.10
De ecclesia et cathedra: or, the Empire-Church of Jesus Christ. An
epistle.
London. Longmans, Green & Co. 1877. 2 v. Folded tables. 22
cm., in 8s.

H7205 — Roman Catholic Church. Doctr. and contr. — T.r. (2).

NL   0383429   MB IMunS

1623
Lindsay, Hon. Colin, 1819-1892.
Defence of the orthodox party in the Church
of England, a letter to his grace, the Duke of
Manchester, in reply to a circular and report,
issued by his grace as president of the National
Club ... London, Joseph Masters, 1851.
40 p.
Bound with 1608.
1. London, National Club

NL   0383430   TxDaM CtY MH

Lindsay, *Hon.* Colin, 1819-
The evidence for the papacy, as derived from the
Holy Scriptures and from primitive antiquity.
London, Longmans, 1870.
lxv, (1), 339 p.   8°.

NL   0383431   MB OrStbM PLatS

Lindsay, *Hon.* Colin, 1819-1892.
Mary queen of Scots and her marriage with Bothwell.
Seven letters to "The Tablet," revised, with a preface & notes,
and a supplement. By the Hon. Colin Lindsay ... London,
Burns & Oates; [etc., etc.] 1883.
viii, 94 p. 18½ᶜᵐ.

1. Mary Stuart, queen of the Scots, 1542-1587. 2. Bothwell, James
Hepburn, 4th earl of, 1536?-1578.
3—32659
Library of Congress   DA787.A3L7

NL   0383432   DLC CaBVaU FTaSU CtY OC1

LINDSAY, Colin, 1819-
The ornaments of the church not catholic
only, but scriptural. A lecture delivered at
Brighton and Liverpool. London, etc., 1866.

pp. 30.

NL   0383433   MH

LINDSAY, *Hon.* Colin, *1819-*
The ritual law of the Church of England.
(Shipley's church and the world. Vol. 2, pp. 434-471. L
1867.)

NL   0383434   MB

△
BR83
.705   Lindsay, Hon. Colin, 1819-1892.
Union and Unity; an address to the members
of the English Church Union, and others, on
the Constitution, organisation, and objects of
the Union... London, J. Masters, 1860.
27 p. 20 cm.

NL   0383435   MB

Lilly
Library
PR 4889   LINDSAY, Sir COUTTS, bart., 1824-1913
.L 5 A7   Alfred, a drama. By Sir Coutts Lindsay,
bart. London, Longmans, Brown, Green, and
Longmans, 1845.
144 p. 17.5 cm.

First edition.
Copy 1, in the original green embossed
cloth, has publisher's catalogue at end,
dated February, 1846. 32 p.
Copy 2 in full polished calf. Both are
author's in-   scribed presentation
copies;

NL   0383436   InU IU CSmH MH

Lindsay, *Sir* Coutts, *bart.,* 1824-1913.
Boadicea: a tragedy. By Sir Coutts Lindsay, bart. ...
London, Printed by W. Clowes and sons, 1857.
2 p. l., 83, [1] p. 24½ᶜᵐ.

I. Title.
24-31460
Library of Congress   PR4889.L4B6

NL   0383437   DLC InU ViU MH

VOLUME 334

Lilly
PR 4889
.L 5 E3
LINDSAY,Sir COUTTS,bart.,1824-1913
Edward the Black Prince. A tragedy. By
Sir Coutts Lindsay ... London, Longman,
Brown, Green, and Longmans, 1846.
218 p. 17 cm.

First edition.
Author's inscribed presentation copy.
At end: publisher's catalogue, dated
May, 1846. 32 p.
Bound in green embossed cloth.

NL 0383438   InU ICU CSmH

Lindsay, Sir Coutts, Bart., 1826-1913.
The Grosvenor Gallery; Sir Coutts Lindsay,
Bart., proprietor and director
see under title

Lindsay, Sir Coutts
Sketches of the history of Christian art.
By Lord Lindsay. London, J. Murray, 1847.
3 v. 23cm.

NL 0383440   MiAlbC IEG NjP MH PU-FA CtY

N
2830
L74
1886
Lindsay, Sir Coutts, bart., 1824-1913.
Sketches of the history of Christian art.
2d ed. New York, C. Scribner's Sons, 1886.
2 v. 21cm.

1. Christian art and symbolism.

NL 0383441   NIC

Lindsay, Crawford, tr.

F1054
.5
.Q3G14
Gagnon, Ernest, 1834-1915.
... Le palais législatif de Québec (Government buildings in
Quebec) Québec, C. Darveau, imprimeur, 1897.

Lindsay, D   R
Survey of common barberry (Berberis vulgaris
L.) in southwestern Ontario, 1951
see under ___ Canada. Division of Botany
and Plant Pathology.

Lindsay, Dan.
The mating cry, by Frank Daniels ₍pseud.₎ Cover painting by Barye Phillips. New York, Fawcett Publications
₍1954, *1955₎
173 p. 19 cm. (Gold medal book, 449)

I. Title.

PZ4.L748Mat   55-24552 ‡

NL 0383444   DLC

Lindsay, Daniel *Curtis, ed.*

Carrier engineering corporation.
Drying and processing of materials by means of conditioned
air; a treatise for manufacturers, engineers and students—an
illustrated discussion of the many interesting problems in-
volved in the drying and processing of numerous familiar
materials, under controlled conditions of temperature, humid-
ity and air movement. Based on investigations by the research
department of Carrier engineering corporation; edited by
D. C. Lindsay ... Newark, N. J., Carrier engineering corporation ₍*1929₎

Lindsay, Daniel Curtis, joint author.

QC304
.C34
Carrier, Willis Haviland, 1876—
The temperatures of evaporation of water into air; an experi-
mental determination of the laws governing the deviation of
the actual temperature of evaporation from the theoretical, by
W. H. Carrier ... and Daniel C. Lindsay. New York, The
American society of mechanical engineers ₍1924₎

•NC
1115
L645d
Lindsay, Daryl, 1890-
"Digger" book. [Melbourne, D. Lindsay and
D. Dillon, c1919]
[2]ℓ.,15 plates.

Cover title.

1. European War, 1914-1918 - Pictorial
works. I. Title

NL 0383447   CLU NN CaBVaU

Lindsay, Daryl, 1890-   joint author.

₍Lindsay, Joan (Weigall)₎
The story of the Red cross. ₍Melbourne₎ Australian Red
cross society ₍1941?₎

Lindsay,David,defendant
The tryal and condemnation of David Lindsay,a
Scotch gent,late secretary to the Earl of Melford,
for high treason,upon the statute made in the
ninth year of the late King William the IIId,for
returning from France without license under the
privy-seal of England. At the Queen's-Bench-Bar
at Westminster,the 24th of April,1704. With all
the learned arguments of Council on both sides.
Before the right honourable the Lord Chief Justice Holt ... London, Printed for Isaac Cleave,
1704.
24 p. 33cm.
No.2 in a volume   lettered: Tryals &c.

NL 0383449   MiU-L N MB DFo CtY MH-L NN InU

WILLIAM
ANDREWS
CLARK
MEMORIAL
LIBRARY
Lindsay, David,   defendant.
The tryal and condemnation of David Lindsay,
a Scotch gent ... for high treason, upon the
statute made in the ninth year of ... King Wil-
liam the IIId, for returning from France with-
out license under the privy-seal of England.
At the Queen's Bench-bar at Westminster, the
24th of April, 1704. With all the learned
arguments of council on both sides ... Dublin,
Reprinted, 1704.
40 p. 20cm.

NL 0383450   CLU-C

BV4380
.L75
LINDSAY,DAVID,merchant,New York.
The claims of pastors of churches,and preachers of
the gospel,for maintenance: considered in the light
of Holy Scripture. By David Lindsay... New York,
Printed by C.McGowan,1843.
iv,165 p. 19cm.

1.Clergy--Salaries,pensions,etc.

NL 0383451   ICU

STC
15658
Lindsay, Sir David, fl. 1490-1555.
The warkis of ... Schir Dauid Lyndesay ...
Newly correctit, and vindicate from the former
errouris quhairwith thay war befoir corruptit:
and augmentit with sindrie warkis quhilk was
not befoir imprentit ... Newlie imprentit be
Iohne Scot, at the expensis of Henrie Charteris,
1568.
Colophon: Newlie and correctlie imprentit at
Edinburgh ...

✠⁴, A-B⁴, C-F⁸, G⁴, H-Q⁸, R², ₍2d₎A-₍2d₎B⁸,

₍2d₎C⁶, ₍2d₎D-₍2d₎F⁸, ₍2d₎G⁴, ₍2d₎H², ₍2d₎I-₍2d₎L⁸.
(R2 and ₍2d₎H2, probably blanks, lacking.) 4to.
The outer corners of the first 4 leaves are
frayed and repaired with missing text supplied in
facsimile. ₍2d₎L7 torn affecting text.
See Dickson and Edmond, *Annals of Scottish
Printing*, v. 1, pp. 177-179.
Pearson-Roxburghe-Heber-Britwell Court-
Harmsworth copy.

NL 0383453   DFo

FILM
Lindsay,Sir David,fl.1490-1555.
The warkis of ... Schir Dauic Lyndesay ...
Newly correctit,and vindicate from the former
errouris ... and augmentit with sindrie warkis
quhilk was not befoir imprentit ... Newlie
imprentit be Iohne Scot,at the expensis of Henrie Charteris ... M.D.LXVIII.
Colophon: Newlie and correctlie imprentit at Edinburgh,be Johne Scot. At the expensis of Henrie Charteris ... 1568 ...
University microfilms no.15900 (case 44,carton 263)
Short-title catalogue no.15658.

NL 0383454   MiU

FILM
Lindsay,Sir David,fl.1490-1555.
The warkis of ... Schir Dauic Lyndesay ...
Newly correctit ... and augmentit with sindrie
warkis quhilk was not befoir imprentit ...
₍Edinburgh, J.Ros, 1580?₎

Lower half of t.p.torn off; imprint supplied from
Short-title catalogue.
University microfilms no.16337 (case 79,carton 474)
Short-title catalogue no.15661.

NL 0383455   MiU

FILM
Lindsay,Sir David,fl.1490-1555.
The warkis of ... Schir Dauid Lyndesay ...
Newly correctit ... and augmentit with sindrie
warkis quhilk was not befoir imprentit ...
Imprentit at Edinburgh be Johne Scot at the
expensis of Henrie Charteris ... M.D.LXXX.

University microfilms no.16335 (case 79,carton 474)
Short-title catalogue no.15659.

NL 0383456   MiU

Rare Book
Room
If
L99
a597
Lindsay, Sir David, fl.1490-1555.
The warkis of the famous & vvorthie
knicht, Sir Dauid Lindsay of the Mont,
alias Lyoun ... Newlie correctit ...
Imprentit at Edinburgh be Henri Charteris.
1597.
[336]p. 18cm.
Edition with caption on B₁ recto "Ane
prologue" (cf. The Library, 4th ser., vol.10
p.31)
Signatures: A-X⁸.
Imperfect: some foot-lines bled.

NL 0383457   CtY

VOLUME 334

Lindsay, Sir David, 1490-1555.
The workes of the famovs and worthie Knight
Sir David Lyndesay,... Newly corrected and
vindicate from the formers errours wherewith they
were corrupted, and augmented with Sundrie workes
neuer before imprinted. Iob 7. ... Edinbvrgh,
Printed by Andro Hart, ... 1614.
sm. 8 vo.   Red morocco by Mercier

NL 0383458   CSmH

FILM

Lindsay, Sir David, fl.1490-1555.
Workes. Newly corr.and vindicate from the
former errours wherewith they were corrupted, and
augm.with sundrie workes neuer before imprinted.
Edinbvrgh, Printed by A.Hart, 1614.
Date on t.p.mutilated by ownership stamp.
Duplicate sig.R bound in place of sig.P which
is lacking.
Short-title catalogue no.15666 (carton 807)
Microfilm.

NL 0383459   MiU

STC   Lindsay, Sir David, fl. 1490-1555.
15667.2   The workes of ... Sir David Lindesay ... Newly
corrected and vindicate from the former errours,
wherewith they were corrupted: and augmented with
sundrie workes ... Printed at Edinburgh, by
Andro Hart, 1619.
*⁴, A-X⁸. (*1-4, A4-5, T1 and U5-X8 lacking.)
8vo.
Title, imprint and completion of collation taken
from The works ... edited by Douglas Hamer (1931-
1936), v. 4, p. 81.
Hume family   library copy.

NL 0383460   DFo

STC   Lindsay, Sir David, fl. 1490-1555.
15668   The workes of ... Sir Dauid Lindesay... Truelie
corrected, and vindicated from the former errours,
and now justly printed according to the author's
true copie ... Aberdene, Imprinted by Edward Raban,
for David Melvill, 1628.
A-X⁸. (A5 and H5 repaired affecting text.) 8vo.
See J. F. K. Johnstone and Robertson, Bibl.
Aberdonensis, v. 1, p. 241.
Crawford library-Harmsworth copy.

NL 0383461   DFo CSmH

Lindsay, Sir David, 1490-1555.
The workes of the famovs and worthy Knight,
Sir David Lindesay ... Newlie corrected and
vindicate from the former errours wherewith they
were corrupted: and augmented with Sundrie workes,
& c. ... Edinbvrgh, by [the heirs of Andro Hart,
1634]
sm. 8 vo.   Green morocco by Rivière
Imprint cut into.
Britwell sale, March 1923, no. 419.

NL 0383462   CSmH

FILM

Lindsay, Sir David, fl.1490-1555.
Workes. Newlie corr.and vindicate from the
former errours wherewith they were corrupted: and
augm.with sundrie workes,&c. Edinbvrgh, Printed
by A.Hart, 1634.
Short-title catalogue no.15670 (carton 807)
Microfilm.

NL 0383463   MiU

Lindsay, Sir David
Works ... newly corrected ...   Glasgow, 1636

NL 0383464   RPB

Lindsay, Sir David, fl. 1490-1555.
The Workes of the famous and worthie knight
Sr. David Lindsay of the Mount, alias, Lyon,
king at armes. Newly corrected and vindicate
from the former errours wherewith they were
corrupted: and augmented with sundry works, &c.
Edinburgh, Printed by Gideon Lithgovv, 1648.
[307] p. 15cm.
Signatures: A-T8, U2.
Signature A3 marked A2.
Printed in black letter.
Bookplate of the Hon. Archibald Campbell, 1708.
Book label of   the Earl of Minto's library

NL 0383465   MB CSmH DFo

Af   Lindsay, Sir David, fl. 1490-1555.
L645Aw   The works of the famous and worthy knight, Sir
1656   David Lindesay of the Mount, alias Lyon, King of
Stark   Armes. Newly corrected and vindicate from the
Lib'y   former errors wherewith they were corrupted: And
augmented with sundry works, &c.   Glasgow, Printed
by R. Sanders, 1656.
264,[3]p.   12½cm.

Wing L.2314.
First published in 1648.
Armorial bookplate of Iohn Marques of Tweeddale.

NL 0383466   TxU

Lindsay, Sir David, 1490-1555.
The works.   Glasgow, R. Sanders
1665.   8vo.

NL 0383467   MWiW-C

Lindsay, Sir David, 1490-1555.
Works. ..   Edinburgh, Andrew Anderson, 1670.
sm. 12 mo.   blank morocco, gilt edges.   R. B.
Stewart's copy, with his book-plate.

NL 0383468   CSmH

Lindsay, Sir David, fl.1490-1555.

The works of the famous and worthy knight,
Sir David Lindsay of the Mount ... Newly
corrected and vindicate from the former er-
WILLIAM   rours wherewith they were corrupted: and aug-
ANDREWS   mented with sundry works, &c. ... Glasgow,
CLARK   Printed by Robert Sanders ... 1683.
MEMORIAL   254,[2] p. 13ᵐ.
LIBRARY
Signatures: A-K¹², L8 (sig.E incorrectly
bound in preceding sig.D)

Pages 97-120 incorrectly bound in preced-
ing p.73.
Title within ornamental border.   Black
letter.
From the library of C. K. Ogden.
Bound in old calf, rebacked.

NL 0383470   CLU-C CtY CSmH

Case   LINDSAY, Sir DAVID, fl.1490-1555.
-Y   The works of the famous and worthy knight,
185   Sir David Lindesay of the Mount, alias Lyon,
.L 64   king of armes. Newly corr. and augm. with sun-
dry works, &c.   Glasgow, R. Sanders, 1696.
264p.   12cm.
STC II L 2320.
Poetry.
Imperfect: closely trimmed.
Errors in paging.
Bound by J. Ramage & Co.

NL 0383471   ICN CSmH MH

PR2296 Lindsay, *Sir* David, 1490-1555.
.L6   The works of the famous and worthy knight, Sir
1712   Lindsay of the Mount ... Newly cor. and vindicate from
the former errors wherewith they were corrupted: and augm.
with sundry works, &c. ...   Glasgow, Printed by R. Sanders, 1712.
296 p. 12ᵐᵒ.

NL 0383472   ICU NjP

Lindsay, Sir David, fl. 1490-1555.
The works of the famous and worthy knight,
David Linsay of the Mount, alias Lyon, king of
arms. Newly corrected and vindicated from the
former errors wherewit they were corrupted and
augmented with sundry worls,&c... Belfast, J.
Blow, 1714.

NL 0383473   PU

Lindsay, Sir David.   12435.19
Works. Newly corrected and augmented with sundry works &c.
Glasgow, J. Hall, 1754.
24°. pp. 287.

NL 0383474   MH

Lindsay, Sir David.   12435.20
Works; corrected and amended, with new additions. Edinburgh, P. Williamson and C. Elliot, 1776-77.
2 vol.
Vol. 2 has title-page: The additional poems of Sir David Lindsay, 1777.

NL 0383475   MH CSmH OrU MdBP ScU IU PPL TxU

Lindsay, *Sir* David, *fl.* 1490-1555.
... Sir David Lyndesay's Works ...   London, Pub. for the
Early English text society, by N. Trübner & co., 1865-71.
5 pts. in 1 v. 22½ cm. [Early English text society. Original series,
no. 11, 19, 35, 37, 47]
No more published.
No general t.-p.: cover-title, pts. 3-5, as above.
Parts 1, 3-5 have special title-pages [reproductions of original
titles] ; pt. 2 has half-title: The poems of Sir David Lindesay.
Paged continuously.
Parts 1-4 edited by F. Hall ; pt. 5 by J. A. H. Murray.

"A sketch of Scottish poetry up to the time of Sir David Lyndesay,
with an outline of his works, by John Nichol" (p. ix-liv) prefixed as
preface. (Published with pt. 5)
Henry Charteris's preface to 1568 ed. of Lindsay's Works, with reproduction of original t.-p.: 13ᵃ p. appended.
CONTENTS.—pt. 1. The Monarche and other poems. 1865-66.—
pt. 3. The Historie of ane nobil and wailyeand sqyver, William Meldrum, 1868.—pt. 4. Ane Satyre of the thrie Estaitis. 1869.—pt. 5. The
minor poems of Lyndesay. 1871.

1. Scottish poetry—Hist. & crit. I. Hall, Fitzedward, 1825-1901,
ed. II. Murray, Sir James Augustus Henry, 1837-1915, ed. III. Nichol,
John, 1833-1894.

PR1119.A2 no.   11, 19, 35, 37, 47   24—2866

MB OC1 OU OCU MiU OO PV PHC NNC GU KMK CaBVaU
NL 0383477   DLC TxU NcRS NNC MB PU NcGW KEmT ViU NcU

Lindsay, *Sir* David, *fl.* 1490-1555.
The works of Sir David Lindsay of the Mount, 1490-1555;
edited by Douglas Hamer ...   Edinburgh and London, Printed
for the Society by W. Blackwood & sons ltd., 1931-36.
4 v. facsims. 23ᵐᵒ. (Half-title: The Scottish text society. [Publica-
tions. 3d ser. 1-2, 6, 8])

"The bibliographical notes prefixed to the poems are summarised
from the editor's article, The bibliography of Sir David Lindsay (1490-
1555), published in the Library (Transactions of the Bibliographical
society), June 1929, vol. x, pp. 1-42, and from a full monograph and
bibliography of Sir David Lindsay to be published by the London
bibliographical society."—Note, v. 1.

CONTENTS.—v. 1. Text of the poems.—v. 2. Ane satyre of the thrie
estaitis, versions I-III.—v. 3. Notes to the poems.—v. 4. Introduction.
Bibliography (p. [1]-122) Notes to Ane satyre. Appendices and indexes.
Glossary.

1. Lindsay, Sir David, fl. 1490-1555—Bibl. I. Hamer, Douglas, ed.
31-15675 Revised

Library of Congress   PR8633.S4 3d ser., no. 1-2, 6, 8
(820.82) 821.26

ScU
NL 0383479   DLC CaBVaU MB OC1 OOxM MB ViU OU OCU OC1W

VOLUME 334

[Lindsay, Sir David] 1490-1555.
   The complaynte and testament of a Popiniay which lyeth sore wounded and maye not dye, tyll euery man hathe herd what he sayth: Wherfore gentyll readers haste you y he were oute of his payne.   Colophon: Imprynted at London ... by Iohn Byddell. ... M.D. xxxviii. ... [1538]
      sm. 4 to   Blue morocco

NL 0383480   CSmH

FILM
   Lindsay,Sir David,fl.1490-1555.
      The complaynte and testament of a popiniay ... ⌈Colophon: Jmptynted at London ... by John Byddell ... M.D.xxxviii ... ⌉
         At end: Here endes The complaynt, & testament of the kynge of Scottes papinpo,compiled by Dauid Lyndesay ... and finysshed the.xiiij.day of Decembre ... 1530.
         In verse.
         University microfilms no.1848 (case 51,carton 301)
         Short-title catalogue no.15671.

NL 0383481   MiU

STC   Lindsay, Sir David, fl. 1490-1555.
15672   Ane dialog betuix Experience and ane Courteour. Off the miserabyll estait of the world ... deuidit in foure partis ... And imprentit at the command and expensis off Doctor Machabeus, in Copmahouin ... ⌈St. Andrews, John Scot, 1554⌉

      ⌈A⌉⁴, B⁴, C-F⁸, G⁴, H-Q⁸, R². (⌈A⌉1 and R2, probably blanks, lacking.)   8vo.
      See Dickson and Edmons, Annals of Scottish Printing, v. 1, pp. 182-187.

NL 0383482   DFo CSmH

FILM
   Lindsay,Sir David,fl.1490-1555.
      Ane dialog betuix experience and ane courteour,off the miserabyll estait of the warld. Compylit be Schir Dauid Lyndesay ... And is deuidit in foure partis ... And jmptentit at the conmand and expensis off Doctor Machabevs jn Copmahouin ⌈i.e.St.Andrews, J.Scot, 1554⌉
         Running title: The first ⌈secvnd,thrid,fovrt⌉ bvke of the monarche.
         University microfilms no.15901 (case 44,carton 263)
         Short-title catalogue no.15672.

         I.Title: A dialogue betweene experience and a courtier.

NL 0383483   MiU

STC   Lindsay, Sir David, fl. 1490-1555.
15673   Ane dialog betuix Experience and ane Courteour. Off the miserabill estait of the warld ... Ane imprentit at the command, and expenses of Maister Samuel Iascuy, in Paris ⌈Rouen? J. Petit?⌉ 1558.

      Pt.1: ⌈A⌉⁴, B-E⁴, F⁸, G¹², H-Q⁸, R⁴.   Pt.2: ⌈A⌉⁴, B-F⁴.   Pt.3: ⌈A⌉⁴, B-F⁴, G². Pt.4: ⌈A⌉⁴, B⁴.
      (Pts. 3-4 misbd. before pts. 1-2.   Pt.1: ⌈A⌉1, t-p, defective; F4-5, G9-10 and I3 lacking; O7-8 are cancels; G12 bd. before G11 and gathering H bd. before gathering G.   Pt.3: G1-2 bd. after pt.4.

      Pt.4: B1-4 lacking.)   4to.
      Contents: 1) "Ane dialog." 2) "Heir follows the testament and complaynt of our souuerane lordis Papyngo." 3) "Heir follows the dreme of Shir Dauid Lindsay" which includes "The deploratioun of the deyth of Quene Magdalene." 4) "Heir follows the tragedie of the ... Cardinal." Each part has a separate title-page.
      See The works... edited by Douglas Hamer (1931-1936), v. 4, p. 26.
         Harmsworth copy.

NL 0383485   DFo CSmH

FILM   Lindsay,Sir David,fl.1490-1555.
                       Ane dialog betuix experience and ane courteour. Off the miserabill estait of the warld. Compilit be Sychir Dauid Lyndesay of ye Mont knycht alias, Lyone kyng of armes. And is diuidit in foure partis. Is efter followis, &c. And imprentit at the command, and expenses of Maister Sammuel Iascuy. In Paris ⌈i.e.Rouen? J.Petit?⌉ 1558.
                       Running title: The first ⌈-fourt⌉ bvke of the monarche.
                       Contains also " ... The testament and complaynt

of Our Souuerane Lordis papyngo. Kyng Iames the Fyft," " ... The dreme of Shir Dauid Lindsay," and " ... The tragedie of the vnqhyle,Maister ... Reuerende Fader Dauid," each with special t.p.
                    Short-title catalogue no.15673 (carton 995)
                    Microfilm.

NL 0383487   MiU

FILM
         Lindsay,Sir David,fl.1490-1555.
            Ane dialog betuix experience and ane courteour. Off the miserabill estait of the warld. Compilit be Schir Dauid Lyndesay ... And is deuidit in foure partis ... And jmptentit at the command, and expenses of Maister Sammuel Jascuy. In Paris ⌈i.e.Rouen?, J.Petit?⌉ 1558.
               Running title: The first ⌈secund,thrid,fourt⌉ buke of the monarche.
               Contains also "... The dreme of Shir Dauid Lindsay", "... The tragedie of ... Fader Dauid","... The testament and complaynt of Our souuerane Lordis Papyngo,Kyng James the fyft",each with special t.p.
               University microfilms no.15903 (case 44,carton 263)
               Short-title catalogue no.15674.
               I.Title: A dia-   logue betweene experience and a courtier.

NL 0383488   MiU

STC   Lindsay, Sir David, fl. 1490-1555.
15675   Ane dialog betuix experience and ane courteour, off the miserabyll estait of the warld ... deuidit in foure partis ... Imprentit at the command and expensis of Doctor Nachabeus. In Copmanhouin ... ⌈Edinburgh, John Scot, 1559⌉

      ⌈A⌉⁴, B⁴, C-F⁸, G⁴, H-Q⁸, R², S⁸, ⌈2d⌉A-⌈2d⌉G⁸. (⌈A⌉1 and R2, probably blanks, lacking. Two duplicates each of S3 and S6 bd. in at the end.)   4to.
      Contents: 1) "Ane dialog" 2) "Heir follouis the tragedie, of the ... Cardinall" 3) "Heir follouis

the testament, and complaynt of our souerane lordis Papyngo" 4) "Heir follouis the dreme, of Schir Dauid Lyndesay" and 5) "Heir beginnis the complaynt of Schir Dauid Lindesay."
      See Dickson and Edmond Annals of Scottish printing, v. 1, pp. 187-196.
      T. F. Dibdin-York Minster library copy.

NL 0383490   DFo

Lindsay, Sir David, fl.1490-1555.
   ⊄ A Dialogue between Experience and a Courtier, of the miserable estate of the worlde, first compiled in the Schottishe tongue, by syr Dauid Lyndsey Knight, (a man of great learning and science) nowe newly corrected, and made perfit Englishe, pleasaunt & profitable for al estates, but chiefly for Gentlemen, and such as are in authoritie. ⊄ Hereunto are anexid certaine other pithy pieces of woorkes, inuented by the said Knight, as shal largely appeare in the table

after folowing. (∴) Anno. 1566.   [Colophon: ⊄ Imprinted at London by Thomas Purfoote, and William Pickering. An. 1566]
   4 p.l.,154 numb.l. illus. 19ᵐ.

   First London edition.
   Signatures: ⊬ ⁴, A-T⁸, U².
   Leaves 34, 40, 80 incorrectly numbered 39, 33, 70, respectively.
   Title within triple line border. Initials.

   Black letter.
   In verse.
   Running title: The first [-fourth] boke of the Monarche.
   Armorial book-plate of Baron Bolland.
   Bound in red morocco, decorated with gold and blind tooling, gilt edges, by H. Faulkner.
   Cf. Hoe, Robert. Catalogue of books by English authors ... before the year 1700. New York, 1903-05.   v.5, p.324-326.

NL 0383493   CLU-C MH CSmH DFo

Lindsay, Sir David, fl. 1490-1555.
If   A dialogue betweene experience and a
L99   courtier, of the miserable state of the
575   worlde. Compiled in the Scottish tung by Syr Dauid Lindsey Knight ... first turned and made perfect Englishe: and now the seconde time corrected ... Imprinted at London in Paules churchyarde by Thomas Purfoote. Anno Domini.1575.
         4p.ℓ.,140[i.e.148]numb.ℓ.   19cm.
         Signatures: ⊤(ij.))⁴A-S⁸T4.
         In verse.

NL 0383494   CtY DFo ICN MiU CSmH

Lindsay, Sir David, 1490-1555.
   A Dialogue betweene Experience and a Courtier, of the miserable state of the Worlde. Compiled in the Scottish tung by Syr Dauid Lindsey Knight... First turned and made perfect Englishe: And now the seconde time corrected and amended according to the first Copie... Herevnto also are annexed certain other workes inuented by the saide Knight... London, Jmprinted by Thomas Purfoote, 1581.   4 p.l., 140 ⌈i. e. 148⌉ f.   20cm. (4°.)

      STC 15678. Huntington check-list, 1919, p. 257.
      Numerous errors in foliation.
      Running title: The first-fourth, Booke of the Monarche.
      Included are The tragedy of David Beton, The dreame, and other shorter poems.
      Imperfect: several leaves at beginning and end mutilated and repaired.
      With autographs of Richard, Symon and William Stockwooll, Thomas Eliazar and Thomas Smyth.
      With leather label of Herschel V. Jones.

NL 0383496   NN CtY MiU ICN CSmH WU MWiW-C DFo

PR   Lindsay, Sir David, fl.1490-1555.
2296   Dialogus eller en Samtale imellom Forfarenhed
L6   oc en Hofftienere om Verdens elendige vaesen,
A13   oc begribis vdi fire Bøger om Monarchier ...
D3   Nu nylige transfererit aff Skotske Maal paa
1591   Latine ved Anders Robertson ... oc siden aff
Cage   Latine paa Danske Rijm ved Jacob Mattssøn ... Prentet i Kiøbenhaffn, 1591.
             Colophon: ... Aff Hans Stockelman ...
             ⌈16⌉ 210 l.):(⁴, (:)⁴, ⊿⁴, A-z⁴, a-z⁴, 3A-3G⁴, 3H² ():(, title-page, damaged and repaired, affec-   ting text) 4to.

NL 0383497   DFo

Lindsay, Sir David, fl. 1490-ca. 1555.
   Fac simile of an ancient heraldic manuscript, emblazoned by Sir David Lyndsay of the Mount. Lyon king of armes 1542. Ed. by David Laing ... Edinburgh, W. Paterson, 1878.
   2 p.l., 21 p., 133 col. pl. (incl. coats of arms) 36½ᵐ.
      Title-page and plates illuminated.
      "The small paper impression, crown folio, limited to two hundred and fifty copies of which this is no. 2 ... Five copies extra on small paper for presentation."
      "First edition issued in 1822."
      1. Heraldry—Scotland. i. Laing, David, 1793-1878, ed. ii. Paterson, William, publisher, Edinburgh. iii. Title.
                                                          20-23963
      Library of Congress   CR1659.L5

NL 0383498   DLC NBuU MH CtY PP OU

Lindsay, Sir David, 1490-1555.
   Heir followis the Tragedie of the vnqhyle Maister Reuerende Fader Dauid, ... Compylit be Schir Dauid Lyndesay, ... And Imprentit at the command, and expenses of Maister Samuel Iascuy in Paris, 1558.
      sm. 4 to   Green morocco by Lewis

NL 0383499   CSmH

Lindsay, Sir David, 1490-1555.
   The historie of a noble valiant sqvyer VVilliam Meldrvm, ... Compyled by sir David Lindesay ... The testament of the said William Meldrum ... Compyled alswa be Sir David Lindesay, & c. ... Edinbvrgh, for Richard Lawson, 1610.
      sm. 4 to
      Bound and probably issued with his: VVorks. 1610.

NL 0383500   CSmH

VOLUME 334

Micro-
film
PR
72

Lindsay,Sir David,fl.1490-1555.
The historie of a noble and valiant sqvyer
VVilliam Meldrvm,vmquhile laird of Cleish and
Binnes. Compyled be Sir David Lindesay... The
testament of the said William Meldrum squyer.
Compyled alswa be Sir David Lindesay... Edin-
bvrgh,Printed for R.Lawson,1610.

In verse.
Negative;original in the Henry E.Huntington
library,San Marino,Calif.

NL   0383501   ICU

FILM

Lindsay,Sir David,fl.1490-1555.
The historie of ane nobil and wailzeand
squyer,William Meldrum ... Compylit be Sir David
Lyndesay ... The testament of the said Williame
Meldrvm ... compylit alswa be Sir Dauid Lynde-
say ... Imprentit at Edinburgh be Henrie
Charteris ... M.D.XCIIII ...
Running title: The Sqvyer of the Bynnis.
In verse.
University microfilms no.15906 (case 68,carton 405)
Short-title catalogue no.15679.

1.Meldrum,William,fl.1506-1550.

NL   0383502   MiU MH

LINDSAY,Sir David.
The historie of one nobil and wailzland
squyer,William Mildrum,etc. Edinburgh,H.
Charteris,1594. [Reprinted.]

pp.(2),321-374.   12435.22 .7

NL   0383503   MH ViU DFo PHC

LINDSAY, Sir DAVID, 1490-1555.
The historie of ane nobil and wails eand sqvyer,
William Meldrum. London, N. Trübner, 1868.
321-374 p. 22cm. (HIS: Works. pt. 3)

Micro-opaque. 2 cards. 7.5 x 12.5cm.
Early English text society. Original series. no. 35.

NL   0383504   NN CSmH MdBP

Lindsay, Sir David, fl 1490-1555.
—— Minor poems. Ed. by J. A. H. Murray.
London, 1871. 8°. (Early Eng. Text Soc.
No. 47.)
2125

NL   0383505   MdBP ODW

220.8
L47

Lindsay, Sir David, fl. 1490-1555.
The monarche, and other poems. pt.I,II.
1365-66. (Early English text society. Publications. Original series. v.19, #11,19)

NL   0383506   OrU MdBP UO

Lyndesay, David, fl 1490-1555
The Monarche and other poems of Sir ... Edited
by Fitzedward Hall, John Small and J.H. Murray.
London, N. Trubner & co., 1868-1871
5 parts.

NL   0383507   PPDrop

---

*PR2296
.L6M7

Lindsay, Sir David, fl. 1490-1555.
The Monarche and other poems of Sir David
Lyndesay. Edited by John Small ... Part I.
⟨2d ed., rev., 1883.⟩ London, Pub. for the
Early English text society, by N. Trübner & co.,
1865 [i.e. 1883]
3 p. l., 126 p. 23cm. (Half-title: Early
English text society. Original series. [Re-

I. Small, John. II. Title.

*PR2296.L6M7

NL   0383509   MB

Lindsay, Sir David, fl. 1490-1555.
Ane pleasant satyre of the thrie estaitis, in commenda-
tion of vertue, and vituperation of vice; a play, maid be
Sir David Lindesay. Edinburgh, 1802.
xvi, 142 p., 1 l. 20cm.
Edited by James Sibbald; 50 copies printed.
Running title: The parliament of correction.

I. Sibbald, James, 1745-1803, ed. II. Title. III. Title: The parliament
of correction.
25-3593

Library of Congress   PR2659.L5A7

NL   0383510   DLC MH

Lindsay, Sir David, fl. 1490-1555.
Poems, selected and ed. by Maurice Lindsay. ⟨Edin-
burgh⟩ Pub. for the Saltire Society by Oliver and Boyd,
1948.
76, ⟨2⟩ p. 19 cm. (The Saltire classics)
"Shortened bibliography": p. ⟨77⟩

I. Lindsay, J. Maurice, 1918-   ed. (Series: Saltire Society.
The Saltire classics)
PR2296.L6A6 1948   821.26   48-28103*

NL   0383511   TxU MiU FTaSU CaBVaU
DLC NBuU CoU PU NN OU CU ViU ICU PU DFo

Lindsay, Sir David, fl. 1490-1555.
The poetical works of Sir David Lyndsay of the Mount,
Lion king at arms, under James v. A new ed., cor. and
enl.: with a life of the author; prefatory dissertations;
and an appropriate glossary. By George Chalmers ...
London, Longman, Hurst, Rees, and Orme; ⟨etc., etc.⟩
1806.
3 v. illus. 19½cm.

I. Chalmers, George, 1742-1825.
17-21200

Library of Congress   PR2296.L6 ⟨1806

CoU PSC NN
NL   0383512   DLC CaBVaU MeB MdBP NN NjP CtY NcD NcU

PR2296 Lindsay, Sir David, 1490-1555.
.L6A15   The poetical works of Sir David Lyndsay of the Mount,
Lyon king of arms. A new ed. carefully rev. ... Edinburgh,
W. Paterson, 1871.
2 v. 18cm. (Early Scottish poets)
Title vignette.
Preface signed: David Laing.

NcRS ICN RPB NNU MH MB ScU
NL   0383513   ICU NBuG KyU MH OrU WaWW OCU OClW NcD TU

Lindsay, Sir David, fl. 1490-1555.
The poetical works of Sir David Lyndsay, with memoir,
notes and glossary by David Laing ... Edinburgh, W. Paterson, 1879.
3 v. illus., facsims. (1 fold.) 21cm.
Includes reproductions of original title-pages.
"Limited to four hundred and eighty-five copies ... No. 391."

I. Laing, David, 1793-1878, ed.
45-50825

Library of Congress   PR2296.L6 1879

NcGU PSt ICN IU
NL   0383514   DLC CaBVaU MiU OO NcD CtY PSt PBm NIC

Lindsay, Sir David, fl. 1490-1555.
Satire of the three estates [by] David
Lindesay. Edinburgh, 1602.
(In Three centuries of drama: English,
1512-1641)

Microprint.

NL   0383515   MoU

822.2
L748s
1949

Lindsay, Sir David, fl. 1490-1555.
The satire of the three estates. The acting
text prepared by Robert Kemp for Tyrone Guthrie's production at the Edinburgh Festival,
1949. Edinburgh, Scots Review [1949]
vii,59p. 22cm.

I. Kemp, Robert, 1879-   ed. II. Title.

NL   0383516   IEN CSt MH CaBVaU

822
L645a
1951

Lindsay, Sir David, 1490-1555.
The satire of the three estates. Edinburgh
Festival version by Robert Kemp. With an introd.
by Tyrone Guthrie. London, W. Heinemann [1951]
xviii, 61p. 22cm. (The Drama library)

Original title: Ane pleasant satyre of the thrie
estaitis.

I. Kemp, Robert, ed. II. Title.

WU
NL   0383517   TxU CaBVaU IU InU NBuG CU MiD MiU NNC WaS

STC
15681

Lindsay, Sir David, fl. 1490-1555.
Ane satyre of the thrie estaits, in commendation
of vertew and vituperation of vyce ... At
Edinburgh, Printed be Robert Charteris, 1602.
Colophon.
⟨A⟩¹, B-V⁴. 4to.
Harmsworth copy.

NL   0383518   DFo CSmH

AW
1
R475:
1278

Lindsay,Sir David,fl.1490-1555.
Ane satyre of the thrie estaits,in commendation of
vertew and vituperation of vyce. Maid be Sir Dauid
Lindesay ... Edinburgh, Printed be R.Charteris, 1602.
In verse.
Imperfect? sig.A,except t.p.,lacking.

CaBVaU Microfilm of original in the Huntington Library.
Ann Arbor,Mich., University Microfilms, 1972. (Early English books,1475-1640,reel 1278)

Micro/ STC no.15681.
mr73   Microfilm.
jme

NL   0383519   MiU

VOLUME 334

MP
2
Lindsay
Lindsay, Sir David, fl. 1490-1555.
Ane satyre of the thrie estaits, in
commendation of vertew and vituperation of
vyce.   Edinburgh, Printed by Robert Charteris,
1602.
154p.

Micro-opaque.   New York, Readex Microprint,
1953. 2 cards. 25 x 15cm. (Wells, H. W.,
ed. Three centuries of drama: English)

NL 0383520   FMU MoU

Lindsay, Sir David. Circa 1495-1567.
— Ane satyre of the thrie estaits, in commendation of vertew and vituperation of
vyce. Ed. by F. Hall. London, 1869. 8°.
(*Early Eng. Text Soc.* No. 37.)   2125

NL 0383521   MdBP ODW CaBVaU

Lindsay, *Sir David, fl.* 1490-1555.
Ane satyre of the thrie estaits. Edited by James Kinsley,
with a critical introd. by Agnes Mure Mackenzie and a foreword by Ivor Brown. London, Cassell [1954]
286 p. 22 cm.

I. Kinsley, James, ed. II. Title.
A 55—3949

Temple Univ. Library   PR2659
for Library of Congress   [a57c2]

MH MoSU TU OU IaU TNJ IdU CaBVaU CU-I
NL 0383522   PPT LU CtY PU PLF OClJC TxU IU NN ICU CU

Lindsay, Sir David, fl. 1490-1555.

Pinkerton, John, 1758-1826, ed.
Scotish poems, reprinted from scarce editions ... with three
pieces before unpublished. Collected by John Pinkerton ...
London, J. Nichols, 1792.

Af
L645
6—m   [Lindsay, Sir David] fl. 1490-1555.
Rare   [Six leaves of "The monarche" from an
Books   unidentified early edition. n.p., n.d.]
Col   [6]ℓ. illus. 18cm. in envelope in folder
23cm.

Folios numbered 24, 41-42, 92-93, and 104.

NL 0383524   TxU

FILM
Lindsay, Sir David, 1490-1555.
The tragical death of Dauid Beatō bishoppe of
sainct Andrewes in Scotland: whereunto is ioyned
the martyrdom of maister George Wyseharte gentleman, for whose sake the aforesayed bishoppe
was not longe after slayne ... [London, 1548?]
Film reproduction, position 3.
Colophon: Imprinted at London, by John Day, and William
Seres ...
Edited with an address to the reader by Roberte Bur-
rant.
University microfilms no.1849 (case 18, carton 106)
Short-title catalogue no.15683.
1. Beaton, David,   cardinal, abp. of St. Andrews, 1494-1546.   2. Wishart, George, 1513?-
1546. I. Bur-   rant, Robert, fl. 1553, ed.

NL 0383525   MiU

STC
15684   Lindsay, David, 1566?-1627.
The godly mans iourney to Heauen: containing ten
seuerall treatises. Viz. 1. An heauenly chariot
the first part. 2. An heauenly chariot the second
part. 3. The blessed chariots man [etc.] ...
London, Printed by R. F. for Robert Bird, 1625.

A-2Q⁸. (A1, blank, and 2Q8, probably blank,
lacking; A2, t-p, backed; Y1 is a cancel.) 8vo.
A much augmented edition of the work first published in 1622 under the title "An heauenly
chariot ..." Cf. J. F. K. Johnstone and Robertson,

Bibl. Aberdonensis, v. 1, p. 224.
Y1, a cancel, is a separate title-page for the
last eight treatises.
Harmsworth copy.

NL 0383527   DFo

STC
15654   Lindsay, David, 1566?-1627.
An heauenly chariot, layde open for transporting
the new-borne babes of God, from time infected
with sin, towards that aeternitie in the which
dwelleth righteousnesse ... Imprinted at
Sainct-Andrewes, by Edward Raban, 1622.

A-K⁴. 4to.
See J. F. K. Johnstone and Robertson, Bibl.
Aberdonensis, v. 1, pp. 205-206.
Harmsworth copy.

The imprint date, which has been tampered with,
is taken from The works ... edited by Douglas
Hamer (1931-1936), v. 4, p. 57.
R. F. S. Colvill-Harmsworth copy.

lger Library

NL 0383529   DFo

[Lindsay, David, *bp. of Edinburgh,* d.1641?
De potestate principis aphorismi. [*Colophon:* Edinbvrgi,
excudebat Thomas Finlason, augustiss. regiæ maj[t]. typogra-
phus. 1617]
7 l. front. (port.) 23¼ᶜᵐ.
Caption title.
"Photostat facsimile [positive] reproduced from the copy in the Henry
E. Huntington library."
Collation of original on the basis of the facsimile: 1 p.l., [6] p.
Original preceded by a leaf on the recto of which is a portrait of
King James I, and on the verso, a dedicatory epistle to the same signed
David Linde. *cf.* Brit. mus. Catalogue.
1. Prerogative, Royal—Gt. Brit. 2. Aphorisms and apothegms.
I. Title.

Library of Congress   JN354.L5   42-46376

NL 0383530   DLC CSmH ICN

FILM
Lindsay, David, Bp. of Edinburgh, d.1641?
De potestate principis aphorismi. [Edinbvrgi,
Excudebat T. Finlason, 1617]
Caption title.
Short-title catalogue no.15655 (carton 806)

1. Prerogative, Royal—Gt. Brit. 2. Aphorisms and
apothegms. I. Title.

NL 0383531   MiU

STC
15656   Lindsay, David, bp. of Edinburgh, d. 1641?
The reasons of a pastors resolution, touching
the reuerend receiuing of the holy communion ...
London, Printed by George Purslowe, for Ralph
Rounthwaite, 1619.

A-M⁸, N⁴. 8vo.
The running title reads "Resolutions for
kneeling."
See J. F. K. Johnstone and Robertson, Bibl.
Aberdonensis, v. 1, p. 185.

NL 0383532   DFo

FILM
S-6   Lindsay, David, Bp. of Edinburgh, d.1641?
reel   The reasons of a pastors resolution, touching
1209   the reuerend receiuing of the Holy Communion:
Written by Dauid Lindesay ... London, Printed
by G. Pvrslowe for R. Rovnthwaite, 1619.
Short-title catalogue no.15656 (carton 1209)

1. Church of Scotland—Ceremonies and practices.
2. Lord's Supper—Church of Scotland. 3. Posture
in worship. I. Title.

NL 0383533   MiU DFo

Lindsay, David, bp. of Edinburgh, d. 1641?
A Trve Narration Of All The Passages Of The Proceedings In
the generall Assembly of the Church of Scotland, Holden at Perth
the 25. of August, Anno Dom. 1618. Wherein is set downe the
Copy of his Maiesties Letters to the said Assembly: Together
with a iust defence of the Articles therein concluded, against a
seditious Pamphlet. By D[r]. Lyndesay... London, Printed
by William Stansby for Ralph Rounthwait, 1621. 14 p.l., 136,
152, 125 p., 1 l. 19cm. (4°.)

STC 15657.   Union theological seminary: McAlpin collection, v. 1, p. 332.
Last leaf blank.
A reply to David Calderwood's Perth Assembly.
Imperfect: t-p. and prelim. l. 5 and 9 mutilated.
With autographs of W[m] Henderson and John Leslie.

327059B. 1. Church of Scotland.   General assembly, 1618. 2. Church
history—Gt. Br.—Scotland, 17th cent.   3. Calderwood, David, 1575-1650.
Perth Assembly.
January 15, 1946

NNUT-Mc
NL 0383535   NN PPL CSmH MdBP NLC NcGU CtY MH ICU

FILM
Lindsay, David, Bp. of Edinburgh, d.1641?
A trve narration of all the passages of the
proceedings in the generall assembly of the
Church of Scotland, holden at Perth the 25. of
August, anno Dom. 1618. Wherein is set downe the
copy of His Maiesties letters to the said
assembly: together with a iust defence of the
articles therein concluded, against a seditious
pamphlet. London, Printed by W. Stansby for R.
Rounthwait, 1621.
Short-title catalogue no.15657 (carton 806)
1. Church of   Scotland—Doctrinal and
controversial   works.

NL 0383536   MiU

Lindsay, David, 1856-1922.
Explorations through Arnheim's land. np [1884?]
21 p. map

NL 0383537   MH

Lindsay, David, 1856-
Journal of the Elder Exploring Expedition, 1891.
[Comprising the final report and journal of D. Lindsay
and the journal of L.A. Wells. Adelaide, 1893]
78 p. 2 maps

NL 0383538   MH

Lindsay, D[avid] *1856-1922*
Journal of the Elder scientific exploring expedition,
1891-2. Under command of D. Lindsay. Equipped
solely at the cost of Sir Thomas Elder, G. C. M. G., for the
purpose of completing the exploration of Australia, and
placed under the control of the Royal geographical society of Australasia—South Australian branch. With
maps. Adelaide, C. E. Bristow, government printer, 1893.
207 p. *and* portfolio of 2 fold. maps. 21ᶜᵐ.
Portfolio lettered: Maps to accompany the Journal of the Elder scientific exploring expedition, 1891-2.
"Vocabularies of words and phrases, with translations ... By L. A.
Wells": p. [193]-207.
1. Australia—Disc. & explor. 2. Scientific expeditions. I. Elder scientific exploring expedition,   1891-1892. II. Elder, Sir Thomas,
1818-   III. Wells, L. A.   IV. Royal geographical society of Australasia. South Australian   branch, Adelaide.
6-19821

Library of Congress   DU390.E3

NL 0383539   DLC PPAN NN ICJ

VOLUME 334

Lindsay, David, *1876–1945.*
Adventures of Monsieur de Mailly, by David Lindsay ... London & New York, A. Melrose, ltd., 1926.
319 p. 19½ᵐ.

ɪ. Title.
27–1590 Revised
Library of Congress   PZ3.L6495Ad

NL 0383540 DLC

Lindsay, David, *1876–*
A blade for sale; the adventures of Monsieur de Mailly, by David Lindsay ... New York, R. M. McBride & company, 1927.
319 p. 20ᵐ.

ɪ. Title.
27–4318 Revised
Library of Congress   PZ3.L6495Bl

NL 0383541 DLC PP

Lindsay, David, *1876–1945.*
The haunted woman, by ... London, V. Gollancz
ltd., 1947 ₍c1945₎
176 p.
"First published 1922, re-issued 1947"

NL 0383542 PU MH CoU ICarbS

823.91
L748s Lindsay, David, 1876–1945.
       Sphinx.   London, John Long ₍c1923₎
       318p.

NL 0383543 ICarbS

PR
6023   Lindsay, David, 1876–1945.
I58115   Sphinx. London, J. Long, 1923.
S6   318 p. 21 cm.
1923a   Photocopy.

NL 0383544 CaBVaU

Lindsay, David, *1876–*
A voyage to Arcturus, by David Lindsay. London, Methuen & co., ltd. ₍1920₎
3 p. l., 303, ₍1₎ p. 19½ᵐ.

ɪ. Title.
21–8416 Revised
Library of Congress   PZ3.L6495Vo

NL 0383545 DLC WaSp CaBVa WU WaSp MnU

Lindsay, David, *1876–1945.*
A voyage to Arcturus, by David Lindsay, with a note by E. H. Visiak. London, V. Gollancz ltd, 1946.
248 p. 19ᵐ. ₍The Connoisseur's library of strange fiction₎
"First published in 1920; re-issued 1946."

ɪ. Title.
PZ3.L6495Vo 3   47–15092

NL 0383546 DLC CaQMM IaU

336.24   Lindsay, David A
L6451i   Items of gross income. ₍1954 revenue
         code ed. New York₎ Practising Law
         Institute, ᶜ1955.
            60 p. (New York (City) Practising Law
         Institute. Fundamentals of Federal taxa-
         tion)

         1. Income tax – U. S.   I. Title
         II. Series

NL 0383547 MiD ViU NNC PPT NcU NcD-L WaU-L

Lindsay, David Alexander Edward, *27th earl of Crawford.*
See
Crawford, David Alexander Edward Lindsay, 27th earl of, 1871–

Lindsay, David Alexander Robert, *28th earl of Crawford*
see
Crawford, David Alexander Robert Lindsay, 28th earl of, 1900–

Lindsay, David Moore, 1862–
Adventures of Monsieur de Mailly
see Lindsay, David, 1876–1945.

Lindsay, David Moore, *1862–*
Camp fire reminiscences; or, Tales of hunting and fishing in Canada and the West, by David Moore Lindsay ... Boston, D. Estes & company ₍ᶜ1912₎
x, 11–233 p. front., plates. 21½ᵐ.
CONTENTS.—Introduction.—Sport in Quebec.—Mule deer shooting.—Duck shooting on Bear River swamps.—A trip to Chamberlain Basin, Idaho.—A cruise on Great Salt Lake.—Goat shooting in Montana.—Goat shooting in Catalina.—Shooting in Wyoming.—Fishing in Idaho.

1. Hunting—U. S. 2. Hunting—Canada. 3. Fishing—U. S.   ɪ. Title.
12—22151
Library of Congress   SK41.L6

CaOTP OKentU WaS CaBViP IdU
NL 0383551 DLC CaBVaU Or PP ViU ICJ NN MB WaS ICRL

Lindsay, David Moore, *1862–*
A voyage to the Arctic in the whaler Aurora, by David Moore Lindsay ... Boston, D. Estes & company ₍ᶜ1911₎
3 p. l., v–ix, 11–223 p. front., illus., plates, ports. 21½ᵐ. $2.00

1. Arctic regions. 2. Aurora (Ship) 3. Whaling.   ɪ. Title.
11—20639
Library of Congress   G720.L6

OC1 ICJ MB NN WaU IC ICN OrP Wa
NL 0383552 DLC MiD WaSp CaBVaU WaS CaBViP OU AU MiU

823.9
L7481w Lindsay, David T
        Wings over Africa.   London, J.Hamilton
        [1936]
        255p. plates. 19cm. ("Ace" series)

NL 0383553 IEN

Lindsay, Donald.
A portrait of Britain between the exhibitions, 1851–1951, by Donald Lindsay and E. S. Washington. Illustrated by R. S. Sherriffs. Oxford, Clarendon Press, 1952.
321 p. illus. 21 cm.

1. Gt. Brit.—Hist.—19th cent. 2. Gt. Brit.—Hist.—20th cent. 3. Gt. Brit.—Civilization.   ɪ. Title.
DA550.L5   942.08   52–8389 †

CaBVaU OrPS WaSpG
NL 0383554 DLC ICU NcU NN OU PPT CoU KU WU CaBViP

Lindsay, Donald.
A portrait of Britain from peril to pre-eminence, 1688–1851, by Donald Lindsay and E. S. Washington. Illustrated by R. S. Sherriffs. Oxford, Clarendon Press, 1954.
336 p. illus. 20 cm. (The Oxford introduction to British history)

1. Gt. Brit.—Hist.—18th cent. 2. Gt. Brit.—Hist.—19th cent.   ɪ. Washington, Edward Stuart, joint author.
DA480.L5   55–4111 †

CtY NN MiD MB IEN LU
NL 0383555 DLC DAU CSt OEac PP IEN CLSU MH NNU-W ViU

Lindsay, Dorothy E.
... Report upon a study of the diet of the labouring classes in the city of Glasgow carried out during 1911–1912, under the auspices of the corporation of the city, by Dorothy E. Lindsay ... with an introduction by D. Noël Paton ... ₍Glasgow₎ 1913.
97, ₍3₎ p. 25ᵐ.
At head of title: Physiological department, University of Glasgow.

1. Dietary studies.   ɪ. Glasgow—University—Physiological dept.
Agr 14–147
Library, U. S. Dept. of   Agriculture 389.1L64

NL 0383556 DNAL CtY WU ICJ NN

Lindsay, Douglas Marshall.
Civilian first aid for war wounded; the Ministry of health pamphlet "First aid in brief" explained in simple terms for A. R. P. workers and the man in the street. By Douglas Lindsay ... Illustrated by H. D. Harding ... Croydon, H. R. Grubb, ltd. ₍1940₎
2 p. l., 90, ₍2₎ p. illus. 17½ᵐ.
"First impression, August 17th, 1940 ... Third impression, August 31st, 1940."
Two blank pages for "Memoranda" at end.
1. First aid in illness and injury.   ɪ. Title.
41–7808
Library of Congress   RC87.L6 1940 b
                            614.8

NL 0383557 DLC CtY NN

W
900   LINDSAY, Douglas Marshall
L748t   Trauma and compensation in obstetric
1928   and gynaecological cases. Edinburgh,
        Hodge, 1928.
           172 p.
           1. Gynecology - Jurisprudence
        2. Insurance - Liability

NL 0383558 DNLM PPC

Lindsay, Edward.
Law relating to probates & administrations as connected with the practice of the Courts of probate, with appendix of some of the Prerogative court rules still in force. By Edward Lindsay ... Dublin, W. Leckie, 1858.
viii, 171, ₍1₎ p. geneal. tab. 23ᵐ.

1. Wills—Ireland. 2. Probate law and practice—Ireland. 3. Ireland. Court of probate.   ɪ. Ireland. Prerogative court.   ɪɪ. Title.
31–34350

NL 0383559 DLC

VOLUME 334

Lindsay, Edward Reginald, 1876–   ed.

DA750
.S25
3d ser.,
vol. 23,
etc.

Vatican. Archivio valicano.
Calendar of Scottish supplications to Rome, edited by E. R. Lindsay and A. I. Cameron. Edinburgh, Printed at the University Press by T. and A. Constable, for the Scottish History Society, 1934–

Lindsay, Edward Yager, 1888–
... An etymological study of ten thousand words in Thorndike's Teacher's word book, by Edward Y. Lindsay ... ₍Bloomington, Ind., 1925₎
115 p. 22½ᵐ. (Indiana university studies. vol. XII, study no. 65. March, 1925)
"Because of the lack of sufficient funds to print this study in its complete form, it was found necessary ... to omit entirely the English list and to transliterate all Greek words."—p. 3.
1. English language—Foreign words and phrases—Latin. 2. English language—Foreign words and phrases—Greek. 3. Latin language—Study and teaching.   I. Thorndike, Edward Lee, 1874–   The teacher's word book.   II. Title.
25—27322
Library of Congress   AS36.I 4   vol. XII, no. 65

OCl MiU OU ViU
NL 0383561   DLC OrMonO WaTC OrU PHC PU IdU OClW OO

BV2552
.A248M6L7   Lindsay, Effie Grout.
Fifty eventful years, 1883-1933. ₍Minneapolis₎ Methodist Episcopal Church. Woman's Foreign Missionary Society, Minneapolis Branch. n.d.
96 p. ports., illus. 23 cm.

1. Methodist Episcopal Church. Woman's Foreign Missionary Society. Minneapolis Branch--Hist. I. Title.

NL 0383562   IEG

---

*BV2550   Lindsay, Effie Grout.
.M6L6   Missionaries of the Minneapolis branch of the Woman's foreign missionary society of the Methodist Episcopal church. ₍Minneapolis, Murphy-Travis co.₎ 1904.
82 p.   illus.   21cm.

NL 0383563   MnHi

LINDSAY, Effingham.
Le grand -duché de Bade. Traduit de l'anglais par M. Évariste-Arnauld Desmoulins. Paris T. Boulé, 1838.

pp.24..   Ger 10498.38

NL 0383564   MH

Lindsay, Elisabeth Conner.
Religion
see under   American Association of University Women. Springfield, Ill. branch.

Lindsay, Elizabeth, 1896–
Inventory of the Lindsayana Collection in Springfield, Illinois
see under   Lincoln library, Springfield, Ill.

HQ766
.L75   LINDSAY, Mrs. ERICA V   (STORR)
Birth control and human integrity, by E. V. Lindsay (Mrs. A. D. Lindsay) and A. D. Lindsay ... With a foreword by W. B. Selbie... London, Independent press [1929]
95 p. 18½cm.

1. Birth control.

NL 0383567   ICU NN

Lindsay, Erica V
Losing religion to find it ₍by₎ E. Lindsay ... London, J. M. Dent and sons, ltd. ₍1935₎
xii, 271, ₍1₎ p. 20ᵐ.
"First published, 1935."

1. Christianity—Apologetic works—20th cent. 2. Free will and determinism. 3. Philosophy and religion.   I. Title.
36–732
Library of Congress   BT1101.L53
239

NL 0383568   DLC OC1

LINDSAY, ERICA V. (STORR).
Those obstinate questionings; an essay on birth control, by E. V. Lindsay. With a foreword by A. D. Lindsay. London: Independent Press, Ltd. [, 1931.] 72 p. 12°.

639761A. 1. Birth control.

NL 0383569   NN

Lindsay, *Sir* Ernest Daryl
see
Lindsay, *Sir* Daryl, 1890–

Lindsay, Ernest Earl.
College and university administration, by E. E. Lindsay ... and E. O. Holland ... New York, The Macmillan company, 1930.
xv, 666 p. incl. diagrs., forms. 20½ᵐ.
"Selected references" at end of each chapter.

1. Universities and colleges—U. S.—Administration.   I. Holland, Ernest Otto, 1874–   joint author. II. Title.
30–19738
Library of Congress   LB2341.L5
Copyright A 26346   378.1

FMU PPLas NcD ViU MB MiHM MtBC IdU
NL 0383571   DLC NN OC1JC WaTC OrPR Or IdU-SB CaBVaU

Lindsay, Ernest Earl.
Problems in school administration, with emphasis on fiscal and personnel phases, by E. E. Lindsay ... with an introduction by William F. Russell ... New York, The Macmillan company, 1928.
xxiv p., 1 l., 544 p. illus., diagrs. 20½ cm. ₍American teachers college series₎
"Selected references" at end of each chapter.

1. Education—U. S.—Finance. 2. School management and organization.
28—8719
Library of Congress   LB2825.L5

MH NN ViU CaBVaU Wa
NL 0383572   DLC ICRL KEmT WaTC Or NcD PU PSC PPT ICJ

C
W276Eℓ   Lindsay, Ernest Earl.
The State College of Washington, a land-grant college. New York ₍1940?₎
43p. illus. 27cm.

"Reprinted from 'Americana,' vol. XXXIV, No. 2, April, 1940."

1. Washington. State College, Pullman.

NL 0383573   IU WaPS WaTC WaSpG WaSp WaS Wa

LINDSAY, ETHEL,   comp.
The children's treasury of verse. ₍2d ed.₎ Partridge ₍1933₎
320 p.

NL 0383574   Or:

Lindsay, Ethel.
The life and adventures of Robinson Crusoe see Defoe, Daniel, 1661?-1731. Robinson Crusoe. Miscellaneous editions. [1928]

₍Lindsay, Evelyn M
Eighty two old and new adventures in woodcraft. ₍St. Paul, St. Croix publications, 1944₎
1 v. illus., diagrs. 24 x 36ᵐ.
Cover-title.
Reproduced from type-written copy.
Foreword signed: John Marvin Sloyd ₍pseud.₎

1. Woodwork.   I. Title.
45–12492
Library of Congress   TT185.L5
680

NL 0383576   DLC

Lindsay, Flora Alice, 1861–
A glimpse of love; or, The doctor's wooing, by Flora A. Lindsay ... Seattle, Wash., and Portland, Ore., Lindsay publishing company, ᶜ1910.
1 p. l., 7-150 p. port. 17 x 13ᵐ.

Library of Congress   PZ3.L6497G   10–11359

NL 0383577   DLC

Lindsay, Forbes
see   Forbes-Lindsay, Charles Harcourt Ainslie, 1860–

1.9609
Ad2   **Lindsay, Francis C**
Address given at the 1951 annual meeting of the Oregon Soil Conservation District Association, Salem, Oregon, November 8, 1951. ₍n. p., 1952?₎
12 p.

1. Soil conservation. U.S. 2. Soil conservation districts. I. U.S. Soil Conservation Service. Pacific Coast Region.

NL 0383579   DNAL

VOLUME 334

56.7
L643   **Lindsay, Francis C**
          Soil conservation.   [n.p.] 1952.
          7 p.

          1. Soil conservation. Addresses, essays,
    lectures.

NL   0383580   DNAL

Lindsay, Frank B
    Teaching today's youth
          see under   National Congress of Parents and
    Teachers. California Branch.

Lindsay, Frank Whiteman, 1909–
    Dramatic parody by marionettes in eighteenth century Paris
    [by] Frank W. Lindsay.   New York, King's crown press, 1946.

    3 p. l., 185 p.   23ᶜᵐ.

    Thesis (PH. D.)—Columbia university, 1945.
    Without thesis note.
    Bibliographical references included in "Notes" (p. [170]–180) Bibli-
    ography: p. [181]–185.

    1. Puppet plays.   2. Parody.   3. French drama—18th cent.—Hist. &
    crit.   4. Theater—France—Hist.   I. Title.
                                                                A 46—3007
    Columbia univ. Libraries
          for Library of Congress   PN1978.F8L5
    ——— Copy 2. Thesis   note on label mounted on t.-p. Vita
    on label mounted on verso.   of p. 185.
                                                        †   791.5

          WaT WaTC WaWW CaBVaU IdB IdPI IdU MtBC MtU OrCS OrP
          OrSaW OrStbM PU Or WaU Wa WaE WaPS WaS WaSp WaSpG
NL   0383582   NNC DLC Mi NcU ViU ICU IU MiD MtBuM OrU-M

Lindsay, Frederic Nye, 1866–
    Kerubim in Semitic religion and art ... [New York?]
    1912.

    40 p.   23ᶜᵐ.
    Thesis (PH. D.)—Columbia university.
    Life.

    1. Cherubim.   I. Title.
                                                                A 12—803

    Title from Columbia Univ.   Printed by L. C.

NL   0383583   NNC CtY-D CU

Lindsay, Frederic Nye, 1866–
    Philosophy of mind; an essay in the
    vindication of the realty of mind as the
    basis of mental consciousness. n.p., n.p.,
    n.d.
          16 p.

    Bound 7th with six other pamphlets with
    Binder's title "Essays in metaphysics".

NL   0383584   OClW

Lindsay, Frederic William, 1903–
    The outlaws. With pen and ink sketches by
    Florence Lindsay.   [Quesnel, B.C., The Author,
    1933]
          64 p.   illus., ports. 24cm.

    "1st Printing."

NL   0383585   CaBViPA

Lindsay, George.
    A brief introduction to astronomy, by way of question
    and answer; with a few useful problems on both globes
    ... By Geo. Lindsay ...   2d ed. greatly impr. and ex-
    tended.   Edinburgh, Sold by W. Whyte & co.; [etc.,
    etc.] 1831.

    112 p.   17½ᶜᵐ.

    Subject entries: Astronomy, Juvenile and popular.
                                                        8–20656†

    Library of Congress, no.   QB46.L74.

NL   0383586   DLC

American
Tracts   **Lindsay, George**
1822   Essays on the human mind, as connected
L645   with a future state of existence and the
               revelations of Providence ... No. I.
               New-York, Printed by J. Seymour, 1822.
               69 p.   20½ cm.

               Imperfect: p. 17–18 mutilated.
               Correction in ms. on p. [3]

NL   0383587   CtY ICRL

Lindsay, George.
    An explanation of the mechanism and uses of a
    general portable microscope, first invented and
    made in the year 1728 ...   [London, 1742]
    Caption title.

NL   0383588   CtY

Lindsay, George A.
    The annual rainfall and temperature of the United States.
    (Academy of Science of St. Louis. Transactions. [St. Louis,]
    1912.   8°.   v. 21, p. 71–78, 1 diagr.)

    1. Rainfall, U. S.   2. Temperature,   U. S.
                                                October 7, 1912

NL   0383589   NN

Lindsay, George Allan, 1879–   tr.

Siegbahn, Manne, 1886–
    The spectroscopy of X-rays, by Manne Siegbahn ... trans-
    lated with the author's additions by George A. Lindsay ...
    London, Oxford university press, H. Milford, 1925.

Lindsay, George Allan, 1879–
    A study of the longitudinal vibration of wires, by
    George A. Lindsay ...   Lancaster, Pa., Press of the New
    era printing company [1914]

    1 p. l., p. 397–438.   pl. I, diagrs.   25½ᶜᵐ.

    Thesis (PH. D.)—University of Michigan, 1913.
    "Reprinted from the Physical review, n. s., vol. III., no. 6, June, 1914."

    1. Vibration.

    Library of Congress   QA935.L5   14–14495
    Univ. of Michigan Libr.

NL   0383591   MiU OU OO NIC DLC

580.92   **Lindsay, George Edmund.**
L748   Notes concerning the botanical explorers and
          exploration of Lower California, Mexico. A
          paper prepared for Biology 199, Stanford Univer-
          sity, Winter quarter, 1955.   [Stanford, Calif.,
          1955]
               106, [7] l.   illus.,ports.,2 fold.maps. 28ᶜᵐ.
               Typewritten (carbon copy)
               "A botanical bibliography for Lower California"
          [prepared by Mrs. Ethel Bailey Higgins]:l.82–106

               1.Botanists.2.California,Lower - Descr.3.Scien-
          tific expeditions.   4.Botany - California,
          Lower - Bibl. I.   Higgins,Ethel(Bailey)

NL   0383592   CSt UU CU-B

QL138   **Lindsay, George Edmund.**
L5   The Sefton Foundation - Stanford University
1952a   Expedition to the Gulf of California, 1952.
          [n.p.] Reprinted by the Belvedere Scientific
          Fund [195-?]
               98 l. maps. 28ᶜᵐ.
               Cover title.
               The J.W. Sefton Foundation of San Diego
          furnished their research ship the "Orca"; the
          scientific personnel (except one) were from
          Stanford University. 23 of the 26 collecting
          stops were made in the Gulf.
               1.Sefton-Stanford Gulf Expedition, 1952.
          2.California, Gulf of. 3.Orca (Ship)

NL   0383593   CSt UU

331   **Lindsay, George F**
L64a   An analysis in an endeavor to help solve the
          problem of "low cost housing for the lower in-
          come group" by recognizing and not ignoring cer-
          tain basic and controlling facts ... Made at the
          request of Frederick E. Weyerhaeuser, December
          10,1937.   [St. Paul? 1937]
               80 numb.l.
               Caption title.
               Mimeographed.
               1. Labor and laboring classes--Dwellings. 2.
          Housing--U.S.

NL   0383594   IU DNAL NNC MnHi PPBMR NN

Lindsay, George F., d. 1857, defendant.

Bready, J   Hall.
    The defence of George F. Lindsay, asst. qr. master of the
    Marine corps, delivered before a marine general court martial,
    at the Marine barracks, Washington city, on the 8th day of
    December, A. D. 1841, upon charges furnished the Navy depart-
    ment by Alexander G. Gordon of the U. S. navy.   [By] J. Hall
    Bready ... Philadelphia, J. C. Clark, printer, 1842.

Lindsay, George LeRoy, joint comp.

Gartlan, George Hugh, comp.   FOR OTHER EDITIONS
                                       SEE MAIN ENTRY

    Assembly songs for intermediate grades, selected and ar-
    ranged by George H. Gartlan ... George L. Lindsay ... [and]
    Fowler Smith ... New York, Philadelphia, Hinds, Hayden &
    Eldredge, inc. [*1937]

M1420   **Lindsay, George Le Roy,** 1888–   joint comp.
.W
    Weaver, Richard L   arr.

    Concertmaster orchestra album, transcribed by Richard L.
    Weaver, selected by George P. Spangler [and] George L.
    Lindsay. New York, Mills Music, [*1948.

VOLUME 334

MT825
.S54   Lindsay, George LeRoy, 1888–   joint author.

Shaw, William Warren, 1866–
Educational vocal technique in song and speech, for classes and individuals, by W. Warren Shaw ... Adapted for use in schools and colleges. In collaboration with George L. Lindsay ... Philadelphia, Theodore Presser co., ʿ1936.

Lindsay, George Le Roy, 1888–   joint ed.

McConathy, Osbourne, 1875–   ed.
Music, the universal language, edited by Osbourne McConathy ... Russell V. Morgan ... ₍and₎ George L. Lindsay ... Alfred Howell, art editor ... New York, Chicago ₍etc.₎ Silver Burdett company ₍ʿ1941₎

Lindsay, George Le Roy, 1888–
Recognition of music education in the public schools—A necessity.
(*In* National education association of the United States. **Addresses and proceedings,** 1927. p. 492–494)

1. Music—Instruction ₍and study₎   i. Title: Music education in th public schools.

Library, U. S. Bur. of   Education   E 28-283

NL 0383600   DHEW

Lindsay, George Le Roy, 1888–
Songs of culture for children; words and music by George Le Roy Lindsay ... and M. Jaffe ... New York, N. Y., Mills music, inc. ₍1945₎
cover-title, 24 p. 30½ᶜᵐ.
With piano accompaniment.

1. Children's songs.   i. Jaffe, Moe, 1901–   joint composer.
ii. Title.   46–18694
Library of Congress   M1998.L72S6

NL 0383601   DLC

Lindsay, George M.
College and private school directory of the United States. ₍v. 1₎–
Chicago, Educational bureau incorporated ₍1907–

Lindsay, George Mackintosh, 1880–
La guerra en los frentes civil y militar. México, Ediciones Minerva, 1943.
156 p.   20 cm.
"Título del original inglés The war on the civil and military fronts. Versión cestellana de O. Durán d'Ocon."
1. Military art and science - Addresses, essays, lectures. 2. Tanks (Military science) 3. Mechanization. Military. 4. Gt. Brit. - Civilian defense. I. Durán d'Ocon, O., tr. II. Title.

NL 0383603   CSt-H DPU

Lindsay, George Mackintosh, 1880–
... The war on the civil and military fronts, by Major-General G. M. Lindsay ... Cambridge ₍Eng.₎ The University press, 1942.
xii, 112 p. 19ᶜᵐ.
At head of title: The Lees Knowles lectures on military history for 1942.

1. Military art and science—Addresses, essays, lectures. 2. Tanks (Military science) 3. Mechanization, Military. 4. Gt. Brit.—Civilian defense. i. Lees Knowles lectures, 1942. ii. Title.
42–18600
Library of Congress   U17.L5 1942
355.04

NL 0383604   DLC NIC WaS

Lindsay, George Mackintosh, 1880–
... The war on the civil and military fronts, by Major-General G. M. Lindsay ... Cambridge ₍Eng.₎, The University press, New York, The Macmillan company, 1942.
xii, 112 p. 19¼ᶜᵐ.
At head of title: The Lees Knowles lectures on military history for 1942.
"First printing."
1. Military art and science—Addresses, essays, lectures. 2. Tanks (Military science) 3. Mechanization, Military. 4. Gt. Brit.—Civilian defense. i. Lees Knowles lectures, 1942. ii. Title.
42–21112
Library of Congress   U17.L5 1942 a
355.04

NL 0383605   DLC WaE MtU PU NcC NcD FTaSU OU OCl

HS1510
R34L5   Lindsay, George W. 1826–1904
Official history of the Improved Order of Red Men, compiled under authority from the Great Council of the United States by past Great Incohonees George W. Lindsay of Maryland, Charles C. Conley of Pennsylvania, Charles H. Litchman of Massachusetts. Edited by Charles H. Litchman. Boston, Fraternity Publishing Co, 1893.
623 p. illus., plates, ports. 24cm.

1. Improved Order of Red Men. I. Conley, Charles C   II. Litchman, Charles H

NL 0383607   CoU

Lindsay, Gertrude Ann.
Psychology of the hand, by Gertrude Ann Lindsay ... Detroit, Mich., A. A. Lindsay publishing company, ʿ1919.
2 p. l., ₍9₎–92 p. incl. illus., plates. port. 23½ᶜᵐ. $1.50

1. Palmistry. i. Title.
19–1276
Library of Congress   BF921.L5

NL 0383608   DLC Or

Lindsay, Gertrude Ann, comp
Thought chimes, pure, precious, priceless; psychology symposium by Gertrude Lindsay ...   Detroit, Mich.: A. A. Lindsay, cop. 1914.   20 l., front. 8°.

1. Aphorisms. 2. Title.
February 16, 1914

NL 0383609   NN

Lindsay, Gertrude Ann, comp.
Thought chimes, by Gertrude Ann Lindsay ... Detroit, Mich., A. A. Lindsay publishing co. ₍ʿ1919₎
2 p. l., ₍7₎–73 p. 15ᶜᵐ. $1.00

i. Title.
19–1745
Library of Congress   PN6331.L46

NL 0383610   DLC

Lindsay, Gertrude Ann.
Your hand interpreter and your character, health, vocation; scientific, by Gertrude Ann Lindsay ... New York city, A. A. Lindsay publishing company, ʿ1926.
1 p. l., 7–239 p. front. (port.) illus. 24ᶜᵐ.

1. Palmistry. i. Title.
26–11729
Library of Congress   BF921.L52

NL 0383611   DLC OKentU

Lindsay, Gordon, comp.
Amazing discoveries in the words of Jesus. Shreveport, La., Voice of Healing Pub. Co., ʿ1951.
119 p. 31 cm.

1. Jesus Christ—Words. 2. Bible. N. T. Gospels—Indexes, Topical. i. Title.   *Full name: James Gordon Lindsay.*
BT306.L54   232.9   52–18344 ‡

NL 0383612   DLC

4RZ-
5001   Lindsay, Gordon.
Bible days are here again ...   Shreveport, La. [1949]
190 p.

NL 0383613   DLC-P4 CLamB

Lindsay, Gordon.
The blueprints of God ... by Rev. Gordon Lindsay. Portland, Ore., Cosbys—printers, ʿ1940.
v. illus., diagrs. (part double) 19½ᶜᵐ.

1. Bible—Prophecies—Chronology. i. Title.
40–14696
Library of Congress   BS649.C5L5
———— Copy 2.
Copyright   220.1

NL 0383614   DLC Or

Lindsay, Gordon.
The life of John Alexander Dowie, whose trials, tragedies, and triumphs are the most fascinating object lesson of Christian history. ₍Shreveport, La.₎ Voice of Healing Pub. Co. ₍ʿ1951₎
275 p. illus. 20 cm.

1. Dowie, John Alexander, 1847–1907.   *Full name: James Gordon Lindsay.*
BX7430.D7L5   922.89   52–18343 ‡

NL 0383615   DLC

Lindsay, Gordon
The mystery of the flying saucers in the light of the Bible. Dallas, Voice of Healing Publishing Co. [1953]
94 p.

NL 0383616   CLamB

Lindsay, Gordon, ed.
BV3785
.C556A3   Coe, Jack, 1918–
The story of Jack Coe; from pup tent to world's largest gospel tent, prepared and edited by Gordon Lindsay ₍in collaboration with Jack Coe. Shreveport₎ La.₎ ʿ1951.

VOLUME 334

220.15
L645
Lindsay, Gordon.
Strange facts about Adolph Hitler.
Portland, Ore., The Anglo-Saxon Christian
Association, c1942.
38p. 22cm. (The Blueprints of God series)

1. World War, 1939-1945. Prophecies.
2. Bible. Prophecies. I. Title.
II. Series.

NL 0383618 OrU

Sem
236.294
Is7
L64t
Lindsay, Gordon
Thunder over Palestine; or, The Holy Land
in prophecy. [No imprint]
123 p. illus.

1. Palestine--Prophecies. I. Title.

NL 0383619 CLamB

Lindsay, Gordon.
William Branham; a man sent from God, by Gordon
Lindsay in collaboration with William Branham. Jeffersonville, Ind., W. Branham [1950]
216 p. illus., ports. 21 cm.

1. Branham, William, 1909-   *Full name: James Gordon Lindsay.*

BR1716.B7L5   922   51-17099

NL 0383620 DLC

Lindsay, Gordon.
World evangelization now by healing and miracles.
[Shreveport, La., 1951]
169 p. illus. 21 cm.

1. Faith-cure. 2. Evangelistic work. I. Title.
Full name: James Gordon Lindsay.

BR115.H4L47   265.8   52-18342 ‡

NL 0383621 DLC

Lindsay, Gordon, *writer on international relations.*
Legal status of aliens resident in Canada, introduction, by
Gordon Lindsay and D. R. Michener. The legal status in British
Columbia of residents of Oriental race and their descendants, by
H. F. Angus... [Montreal] The Canadian Institute of Internat.
Affairs [1931], 16 p. 24cm.

"Prepared for the fourth bi-annual conference of the Institute of Pacific Relations
to be held at Hangchow from October 18th – November 3rd, 1931."
Bibliographical footnotes.

788715A. 1. Aliens--Jurisp.—   Canada. 2. Orientals—Canada—
British Columbia. I. Michener, D. R.,   jt. au. II. Angus, H. F. The
legal status in British Columbia of   residents of Oriental race.
III. Canadian Institute of International   Affairs. IV. Institute of Pacific
Relations.

                                            December 20, 1935

NL 0383622 NN RPB MiU-L

Lindsay, Guy A
The Great Lakes - St. Lawrence deep waterway...
see under Canada. Dept. of Transport.

Lindsay, H   A
see Lindsay, Harold Arthur, 1900-

Lindsay, H
330.9945
L748I
The industrial resources of Victoria with
practical suggestions on agriculture,
employment of labor, water supply, &c., &c.,
by H. Lill Lindsay. Melbourne, G. Robertson,
1856.
88 p. 23 cm.
Photocopy. Melbourne, National Library of
Australia [1968?] double leaves.
1. Victoria, Australia. Econ. condit.
2. Agriculture. Econ. aspects. Australia.
Victoria. 3.   Natural resources.
Victoria. I.   Title.

NL 0383625 NcD

Lindsay, H. Lill.
Industrial resources of Victoria.
Melb., 1878.
88 p.

NL 0383626 CSt

Lindsay, Harlow.
Vincennes first capitol of Indiana territory
by Harlow Lindsay in cooperative school bulletin
May, 1928. p. 8-9   21. 3 cm.

NL 0383627 MiU-C

823
L64495a **Lindsay, Harold Arthur, 1900-**
The Arnhem treasure.   Adelaide, Waninga Press
[1952]
172p. 19cm.

NL 0383628 TxU

Lindsay, Harold Arthur, 1900-
The bushman's handbook; a practical guide for finding
water, snaring game, catching fish, camping and general
bushcraft. Sydney, Angus and Robertson, 1948.
xi, 158 p. illus. 19 cm.

1. Outdoor life. I. Title.

SK602.A8L5   796.54   48-23657 rev*

NL 0383629 DLC TxU NN

Lindsay, Harold Arthur, 1900-
The bushman's handbook; a practical guide for finding water, snaring game, catching fish, camping
and general bushcraft... Sydney [etc.] Angus and
Robertson [1951] vii,159 p. illus. 18cm.
2. ed.

1. Outdoor life.

NL 0383630 NN

Lindsay, Harold Arthur, 1900-
Living monuments; a practical guide to conservation.
Sydney, Commonwealth Office of Education [1949?]
27 p. illus. 24 cm. (Platypus pamphlets, no. 1)
Cover title.

1. Wild life, Conservation of—Australia. 2. Plants, Protection of—
Australia. I. Title. (Series)

QH77.A8L55   *333.78 799   53-20565 rev

NL 0383631 DLC DNAL

Lindsay, Harriet Sarah (Loyd) Loyd-   baroness
Wantage
see Wantage, Harriet Sarah (Loyd) Loyd-
Lindsay, baroness, 1837-1920.

Lindsay, Harry.
The cark of coin, by Harry Lindsay ...   New York,
London [etc.] F. H. Revell company [1903]
338 p. 20ᶜᵐ.
                                            3-21014

NL 0383633 DLC

Div.S. Lindsay, Harry
823.91 Gypsy Roy, a story of early Methodism,
L748G   by Harry Lindsay [pseud.] London, C. H.
Kelly, 1904.
viii, 312 p. illus. 20 cm.
Full name: Harry Lindsay Hudson.

1. Methodism. Fiction. I. Title.

NL 0383634 NcD

Lindsay, Harry.   *4578.491
The Jacobite. A romance of the Conspiracy of the Forty. A new
edition.
— London. Chatto & Windus. 1899. xi, 338 pp. 19 cm., in 8s.
The conspiracy of 1696 against William III.

K3404 — T.r. — Great Britain. Hist. Fict. William III., 1689–1702.

NL 0383635 MB

Lindsay, Harry.   *4578.492
Judah Pyecroft, Puritan: a romance of the Restoration.
— London. Chatto & Windus. 1902. ix, 345 pp. 19 cm., in 8s.

L1432 — T.r. — Great Britain. Hist. Fict. Charles II., 1660–1685.

NL 0383636 MB

PZ3
.H3673
Me
Lindsay, Harry.
Methodist idylls, by Harry Lindsay [pseud.]
... London, James Bowden, 1897.
6 p. l., [15]-395 p. 19cm.
"First edition, August, 1897. Reprinted
September, 1897."
CONTENTS.—Aaron Priestley's stewardship.—
Do unto others.—The mellowing of Jesse
Stallard.—Removing old landmarks.—The making

of a minister.—Ned Thornbury's love story.—
A member o' th' boörd.—John Oakey's Christmas
box.—The backslider.—The Woodleigh poet.—
Lingerers overlong.

NL 0383638 MB GEU RPB NcD IEG

Lindsay, Harry.
Methodist idylls. 4th ed. London,
Charles H. Kelly [c1920?]
395 p. 20 cm.

NL 0383639 KyWAT

VOLUME 334

823
H85r
Lindsay, Harry.
   Rhoda Roberts, a Welsh mining story, by Harry
Lindsay [pseud.] London, Chatto & Windus, 1895.
439p. 20cm. (The Piccadilly novels)

NL 0383640   IU CLU MGM

Lindsay, *Sir* Harry Alexander Fanshawe, 1881–   *ed.*
   ... British commonwealth objectives. Published in conjunc-
tion with the Royal society of arts. London, M. Joseph ltd.
[1946]
   288 p. illus. (map) 19ᵐ.
   At head of title: Edited by Sir Harry Lindsay.
   "First published 1946."
   CONTENTS.—Foreword, by Sir Harry Lindsay.—Empire relations, by
Viscount Bennett.—Empire raw materials and post-war reconstruction,
by F. L. McDougall.—Capital and colonies, by Lord Hailey.—The pro-
jection of Great Britain on the colonial empire, by Sir Angus Gillan.—
An Oriental cultural centre (in London) by F. H. Andrews.—Canada's

new north, by Charles Camsell.—Scientific aspects of Australia's industrial development, by G. B. Gresford.—Scientific collaboration between
the United Kingdom and New Zealand in war and peace, by A. L. Poole
and I. E. Coop.—Industrial development in the Union of South Africa,
by A. P. van der Post.—Recent labour legislation in India, by Sir Frank
Noyce.—Partnership in Nigeria, by Sir Bernard Bourdillon.—Educational
problems of East and West Africa, by H. M. Grace.

   1. Great Britain. 2. Gt. Brit.—Colonies.   I. Royal society of arts,
London. II. Title.

   Library of Congress   DA11.L5   46–4295

                                              325.342

NL 0383642   DLC CaBVaU IaU ICU ViU NNC

Lindsay, Harry Alexander Fanshawe, 1881–
   ..."Economic rapprochements." Note presented...
   see under   League of Nations. Economic
Committee.

JX1975
.A25
1927.
II.39
Lindsay, Sir Harry Alexander Fanshawe, 1881–
   **Preparatory Committee for the International Economic
Conference.**
      International Economic Conference (Geneva, May 1927)
Documentation. Agriculture and the international economic
crisis. Memorandum by M. Jules Gautier, Dr. Andreas
Hermes and Mr. H. A. F. Lindsay, members of the Sub-
committee on Agricultural Questions of the Preparatory
Committee for the International Economic Conference. Ge-
neva, 1927.

Lindsay, Sir Harry Alexander Fanshawe, 1881–
   Report on lac and shellac. By H. A. F. Lindsay
and C. M. Harlow.   Allahabad, Pioneer press,
1921.
   x, 162 p. 4 plates. diagrs. (part fold)
26 cm. (The Indian forest records, vol.
VIII, part 1)

NL 0383645   PU CU MiD

Lindsay, Harry Clay, 1861–   joint comp.
Nebraska. *Laws, statutes, etc.*
   Compiled statutes of the state of Nebraska, 1922, comprising all the statutory law of a general character in
force July 1, 1922, comp. by Clinton Orrin Bunn, under
the supervision of Harry C. Lindsay, Henry P. Stoddart
and Clarence A. Davis, commissioners. Pub. by the state
of Nebraska. Columbia, Mo., E. W. Stephens publishing
company, 1922.

Lindsay, Harry Clay, 1861–   reporter.
Nebraska. *Supreme court.*
   Reports of cases in the Supreme court of Nebraska ...
v. [1]–   ; [1860]–
Lincoln, Neb., Claflin printing company; [etc., etc.] 1871–19

Lindsay, Harry Clay, 1861–   reporter.
Nebraska. *Supreme court.*
   Reports of cases in the Supreme court of Nebraska. January
and September terms, 1901–January term, 1904. ⟨Unofficial⟩
... Lincoln, Neb., State journal company, 1903–05.

LINDSAY, HECTOR, 1859–
   Jungle Lindsay; the life and adventures of Hector Lindsay.
London: S. Low, Marston & Co., Ltd. [1936] v, 282 p.
plates. 23cm.

   832749A. 1. Vagrants and vagrancy. 2. African tribes—Fan.
I. Title.

NL 0383649   NN IEN CU

Lindsay, Hector, 1859–
   Jungle Lindsay; the life and adventures of Hector Lindsay.
London, S. Low, Marston & co., ltd. [1937]
   v, 282 p. plates. 23ᶜᵐ.

   1. Adventure and adventurers.   I. Title.   37–38303
   Library of Congress   G530.L65
                                            910.4

NL 0383650   DLC KU FTaSU

[LINDSAY, Henry].
   An essay upon I Corinth. 1.21. against the
infidelity of the age, etc. Edin., 1736.
      pp. 64.   Tr. 214. (6)

NL 0383651   MH

Lindsay, Henry.
   The glory and stability of the city of
God, in a sermon preached in the High
church, Edinburgh, before His Majesty's
High commissioner to the General assembly
of the Church of Scotland, May the 11th,
1735...   Edinburgh, Printed by Alexander
Alison for John Traill, 1735.
      22 p., 18ᶜ⁸.

NL 0383652   NjPT

Lindsay, Henry L.
   Railway communication from Dublin to the North
of Ireland. Armagh, J. M'Watters, 1845.
   iv, [5]–24 p. 19.5 cm.

NL 0383653   MH-BA

Lindsay, Henry Lill.
South Africa. *Unemployment commission.*
   ... Interim report of the Unemployment commission.
March, 1921 ... Cape Town, Cape times limited, govern-
ment printers, 1921.

Lindsay, Henry Lill
South Africa. *Unemployment commission.*
   ... Report of the Unemployment commission ... Cape
Town, Cape times limited, government printers, 1922.

Lindsay, Hierome, *pseud.*
   see
Meade, Julian, 1865–

[Lindsay, Howard] 1889–
   Anything goes.   [New York? 1936]   [137] f.   35½cm.
   Various paging.
   Reproduced from typewritten copy.
   Scenario adapted from their musical comedy with the same title.

   828935A. 1. Moving picture plays—   Texts and outlines. I. Crouse, Russel, 1893–   , jt. au. II. Paramount   Pictures Corporation. III. Title.
N. Y. P. L.   July 30, 1936

NL 0383657   NN

Lindsay, Howard, 1889–
   Call me madam...
   see under   Berlin, Irving, 1888–

Lindsay, Howard, 1889–
   Clarence Day's "Life with father" made into a play, by Howard
Lindsay and Russel Crouse.   [New York, 1939]   48, 45, 29 f.
29cm.
   Prompt-book; typewritten.
   First New York production at the Empire theatre, Nov. 8, 1939.

   66754B. 1. Drama, American.   2. Prompt-books. I. Crouse, Russel,
1893–   , jt. au. II. Day, Clarence   Shepard, 1874–1935. Life with
father. III. Title: Life with father.
                                              September 25, 1940

NL 0383659   NN

Lindsay, Howard, 1889–
   Clarence Day's Life with father, made into a play by Howard
Lindsay and Russel Crouse; with an introduction by Brooks
Atkinson.   New York, A. A. Knopf, 1940.
   xii p., 4 p. l., 3–208 p., 1 l. front., plates. 21½ᵐ.
   "First edition."
   With cast of characters as produced by Oscar Serlin at the Empire
theatre, New York, Nov. 8, 1939.

   I. Crouse, Russel, 1893–   joint author. II. *Day, Clarence, 1874–
1935. Life with father. III. Title: Life with father.
                                              40–27161
   Library of Congress   PS3507.A858L55
   Copyright D pub. 69028   812.5

MtBC Or OrSaW
OO OCU OU PJA ViU CaBVa IdPI OrCS WaE WaT WaSp OrU
CaBVaU OC1CS OrP OrPR PPLas WaS PBm PU NN OC1W OC1
NL 0383660   DLC WaU PPT KMK MeB CaOTP CoU MiU ViU IdB

Lindsay, Howard, 1889–
   Clarence Day's Life with father, made into a play in three
acts by Howard Lindsay and Russel Crouse. Acting ed.,
with notes to the stage directors by the authors. [New York]
Dramatists Play Service [1948]
   109 p. 19 cm.

   I. Crouse, Russel, 1893–   joint author. II. Day, Clarence, 1874–
1935. Life with father. III. Title: Life with father.
   PS3507.A858L55 1948 812.5   49–4847*

NN GU MiD
NL 0383661   DLC Or LU OrAshS WaT NcU CLSU WU MoU ViU

VOLUME 334

Lindsay, Howard, 1889–
Clarence Day's Life with father and Life with mother, made into plays by Howard Lindsay and Russel Crouse. With an introd. by Brooks Atkinson. ₁1st combined ed.₎ New York, Knopf, 1953.

208, 240 p. illus. 22 cm.

I. Crouse, Russel, 1893– joint author. II. Day, Clarence, 1874–1935. Life with father. III. Day, Clarence, 1874–1935. Life with mother. IV. Title: Life with father and Life with mother.

[PS3507]   812.5   53—6848 ‡/CD

Printed for Card Div.
Library of Congress   ₁a66q2₎

NL 0383662   MB IU OC1 NcGW PBL OOxM NcC GU PP OrP
OrAshS

Lindsay, Howard, 1889–
Clarence Day's Life with mother, made into a play by Howard Lindsay and Russel Crouse. ₁1st ed.₎ New York, A. A. Knopf, 1949.

240 p. illus. 22 cm.

I. Crouse, Russel, 1893– joint author. II. Day, Clarence, 1874–1935. Life with mother. III. Title: Life with mother.
PS3507.A858L67 1949 812.5   49–10536*

NL 0383663   DLC TU MB OEac PHC Or CaBVa MnU FMU OrP
Wa WaS WaSp WaT WaSpG

Lindsay, Howard, 1889–
Clarence Day's Life with mother, made into a play in three acts by Howard Lindsay and Russel Crouse. Acting ed., with notes to the stage director by the authors. ₁New York₎ Dramatists Play Service ₁1950₎

112 p. 19 cm.

I. Crouse, Russel, 1893– joint author. II. Day, Clarence, 1874–1935. Life with mother. III. Title: Life with mother.
PS3507.A858L67 1950   812.5   50–12828

NL 0383664   DLC NcU OrPS ViU WaS CaBVa CaBVaU

812
L645tm
1949r
Lindsay, Howard, 1889–
Clarence Day's Life with mother, made into a play by Howard Lindsay and Russel Crouse. New York, A.A. Knopf, 1951 [c1949] 7p.ℓ.,240p.,1ℓ. illus. 22cm.

"Second printing, November 1951."

I. Crouse, Russel, 1893– Joint author. II. Day, Clarence, 1874–1935. Life with mother. III. Title: Life with mother.

NL 0383665   TxU

Lindsay, Howard, 1889–
The Great Sebastians, a play in three acts by Howard Lindsay and Russel Crouse. New York ₁1955₎

1 v. (various pagings) 30 cm.

Typescript (carbon copy)

I. Crouse, Russel, 1893– joint author. II. Title.
PS3523.I 575G7 1955   812.5   56–18398

NL 0383666   DLC RPB NN

Lindsay, Howard, 1889–
Life with mother; a comedy...by Howard Lindsay and Russel Crouse. (In: The best plays of 1948–49. New York, 1949. p. 207–237)

Caption-title.
In story form with extracts from the dialogue.

511292B. 1. Drama, American.   I. Crouse, Russel, 1893– , jt. au.
II. Title.
                                                January 3, 1950

NL 0383667   NN

p1926
L7485pr
1954
Lindsay, Howard, 1889–
The Prescott proposals, play in three acts, by Howard Lindsay and Russel Crouse. ₁New York₎ Dramatists Play Service ₁c1954₎ 80 p. illus. 20 cm.

NL 0383668   RPB NN MiD MtU LU

Lindsay, Howard, 1889–
The Prescott proposals, by Howard Lindsay and Russel Crouse. New York, Random House ₁1954₎

168 p. illus. 21 cm. (A Random House play)

I. Crouse, Russel, 1893– joint author. II. Title.
PS3523.I 575P7   812.5   54–7469 ‡

OrU-M NN ViU MB PSt CaBVa Or OrU
MtBC MtU OrCS OrP OrPR OrSaW MsSM NIC OU GU IU KMK
WaTC WaWW WaSp WaS WaPS WaE Wa CaBVaU IdB IdPI IdU
PPT PP NcRS NcWil OC1 MtBuM OrLgE OrMonO OrPS WaT
NL 0383669   DLC OrStbM CoU TU NcGW TxU OO OOxM OC1JC

Lindsay, Howard, 1889–
Remains to be seen; comedy in three acts, by Howard Lindsay and Russel Crouse. Acting ed. ₁New York₎ Dramatists Play Service ₁c1951₎

94 p. illus. 19 cm.

I. Crouse, Russel, 1893– joint author. II. Title.
PS3523.I 575R42   812.5   52–14382 ‡

NL 0383670   DLC TxU NN NIC Wa

Lindsay, Howard, 1889–
Remains to be seen, by Howard Lindsay and Russell Crouse. New York, Random House ₁1951₎

185 p. illus. 21 cm.

A play.

I. Title.
PS3523.I 575R4   812.5   51–14538 ‡

NIC WaSp CaBVa WaS CaBVaU IdPI WaSpG OrPS WaWW WaT
NL 0383671   DLC Or OrP NN MH NcU ViU NSyU MeB MiU GU

Promptbook; includes cast, scene plots.
Dramatized from Edward Hope Coffey's novel.
Produced by Bill Butler at the Paul Bunyan festival, at Bemidji, Minn., 1951.
1. Drama, American. 2. Drama–   Promptbooks and typescripts.
I. Coffey, Edward Hope,   1896– . She loves me not.
II. Title.

NL 0383672   NN

LINDSAY, HOWARD.
She loves me not; dramatized from Edward Hope's [pseud.] novel by Howard Lindsay... [New York, N.Y., 1933.] [124] f. diagr., plans. 28cm.

Various paging.
Reproduced from typewritten copy.
Prompt-book.
"Presented...November 20, 1933, at the Forty-Sixth St. Theatre, N.Y."

711846A. 1.Drama, American.   2. Prompt-books. I. Coffey, Edward Hope, 1896– :   She loves me not. II. Title.

NL 0383673   NN

LINDSAY, HOWARD, 1889–
She loves me not; dramatized from Edward Hope's novel by Howard Lindsay. [New York, Hart stenographic bureau, 1933?] 59, 54 l. 28cm.

Typescript.
Includes original cast.
Includes costume, light and property plots, and ground plans.
Produced at the Forty-Sixth Street theatre, New York, Nov. 20, 1933.

1. Drama, American.   I. Coffey, Edward Hope, 1896– She loves me not.   II. Title.

NL 0383674   NN

Lindsay, Howard, 1889–
She loves me not; a comedy in two acts; dramatized from Edward Hope's novel, by Howard Lindsay ... New York, N. Y., Los Angeles, Calif., S. French, inc.; London, S. French, ltd.; ₁etc., etc.,₎ c1935.

145, ₁3₎ p. plates. diagrs. 19ᶜᵐ. (On cover: French's standard library edition)

I. Coffey, Edward Hope, 1896– She loves me not. II. Title.

Library of Congress   PS3523.I 575S5 1935
                                            cA 36–28 Unrev'd

Copyright D pub. 40792   812.5

NL 0383675   DLC CU PSC

Lindsay, Howard, 1889–   joint author.

Runyon, Damon, 1880–
A slight case of murder; comedy in two acts, by Damon Runyon and Howard Lindsay. ₁New York₎ Dramatists play service, inc. ₁c1940₎

College
Library
810
L748
tS.2
Lindsay, Howard, 1889–
State of the union; comedy in three acts, by Howard Lindsay and Russel Crouse. Acting ed. ₁New York₎ Dramatists Play Service ₁1946₎ 101p. plans. 20cm.

₁I.Crouse, Russel. 1893– joint author. ₁II.Title.

NL 0383677   CLSU WU MtU

Lindsay, Howard, 1889–
State of the union, a comedy by Howard Lindsay and Russel Crouse, with a foreword by Thomas L. Stokes. New York, Random house ₁1946₎

xii, 226 p. front., plates. 21ᶜᵐ.

"First printing."

I. Crouse, Russel, 1893–   II. Title.
                                            46–3010
Library of Congress   PS3523.I 575S65 1946
                                            812.5

OC1W OCU OO OC1
WaWW WaSp IdU WaT LU OU ViU KU MiU NcRS NcC NN PU
CaBVa ViU NN MtU Or OrP OrSaW OrPS OrU Wa WaE WaS
NL 0383678   DLC NIC CaBVaU NcD MtBC FTaSU CoU IdB

Lindsay, Howard, 1889–
"Strip for action," by Howard Lindsay and Russel Crouse. ₁New York, 1942₎ 2, 51, 51 f. 29cm.

Typescript.
In two acts.
Produced at the National theatre, New York, Sept. 30, 1942.

209953B. 1. Drama, American.   I. Crouse, Russel, 1893– , jt. au.
II. Title.
                                            October 5, 1943

NL 0383679   NN

VOLUME 334

Lindsay, Howard, 1889–
  Strip for action ₍by₎ Howard Lindsay & Russel Crouse. New York, Random house ₍1943₎
  6 p. l., 3–250 p. front., plates. 21ᵐ.
  A play.
  "First printing."

  ɪ. Crouse, Russel, 1893– joint author. ɪɪ. Title.
                                                  43–1669
  Library of Congress   PS3523.I 575S7
                                                      812.5

              TU NBuU PSt NcWil NcC OU OC1 CaBVa CaBVaU IdU OrP
NL 0383680   DLC NIC NcD MiU NSyU ScU WaU WaSp CoU KMK

LINDSAY, HOWARD, 1889–
  Tall story; a comedy in three acts, by Howard Lindsay and Russel Crouse. Suggested by "The homecoming game" by Howard Nemerov. [New York, A. Meyerson, 195–] 55, 43, 32 l. 30cm.

  Typescript.

  1. Drama, American. 2. Drama--Promptbooks and typescripts.
  I. Crouse, Russel, 1893–   joint author. II. Nemerov,
  Howard. The homecoming   game. III. Title.

NL 0383681   NN

Lindsay, Howard, 1889–
  Tommy; a comedy in three acts, by Howard Lindsay and Bertrand Robinson ... New York, S. French; London, S. French, ltd., ᶜ1928.
  140, ₍1₎ p. diagr. 19ᵐ. (*On cover:* French's standard library edition)

  ɪ. Robinson, Bertrand, joint author. ɪɪ. Title.

  Library of Congress   PS3523.I 575T6 1928   28–3210

         MsSM OC1
NL 0383682   DLC OrP CaBVaU OrCS OrCS IdU OU PPLas LU

Lindsay, Howard, 1889–
  Your uncle Dudley, by Howard Lindsay and Bertrand Robinson. [New York, Century play co., 1929]
  1 v. (various pagings) plan. 30cm.

  Typescript.
  Prompt-book; includes ground plan, property plot and electrical plot.
  Produced at the Cort theatre, New York, November 18, 1929.

  1. Drama, American. 2. Prompt-books. I. Robinson, Bertrand, joint author. II. Title.

NL 0383684   NN

Lindsay, Howard, 1889–
  Your Uncle Dudley, by Howard Lindsay and Bertrand Robinson ... New York, N. Y., Los Angeles, Calif., S. French, inc.; London, S. French, ltd., ᶜ1930.
  2 p. l., 3–135, ₍1₎ p. pl., diagr. 19ᵐ. (*On cover:* French's standard library edition)

  ɪ. Robinson, Bertrand, joint author. ɪɪ. Title.
                                                  30–24718
  Library of Congress   PS3523.I 575Y6 1930
  Copyright D pub. 273   812.5

NL 0383685   DLC OrCS Or CaOTP MeB NcU ICU MsSM OC1

Lindsay, *Hon.* Hugh, 1765–1844.
  An adventure in China, in a letter to the Lady Anne Barnard. By the Hon. Hugh Lindsay.
  (*In* Crawford, Alexander W. C. Lindsay, 25th earl of. Lives of the Lindsays. London, 1849. 22ᵐ. v. 3, p. ₍477₎–486)

                                                  8–22923

  Library of Congress   DA758.3.L8C7

NL 0383686   DLC MdBP

Lindsay, Hon Hugh, 1765–1844.
  Crawford, Alexander William Crawford Lindsay, *25th earl of,* 1812–1880.
    Lives of the Lindsays: or, A memoir of the houses of Crawford and Balcarres, by Lord Lindsay. To which are added, extracts from the official correspondence of Alexander sixth earl of Balcarres, during the Maroon war: together with personal narratives by his brothers, the Hon. Robert, Colin, James, John, and Hugh Lindsay; and by his sister, Lady Anne Barnard. 2d ed. London, J. Murray, 1858.

Lindsay, Hugh, b. 1804.
  History of the life, travels and incidents of Col. Hugh Lindsay, the celebrated comedian, for a period of thirty-seven years. Written by himself. Philadelphia, 1859. 96 p. illus. 18cm.

NL 0383688   NN

LINDSAY, Hugh, 1804–
  History of the life, travels and incidents of Col. Hugh Lindsay, the celebrated comedian, for a period of thirty-seven years. Written by himself. Macungie, Pa., O.P.Knauss, 1883.

  pp.60.

NL 0383689   MH

thesis
QP
L557
  Lindsay, Hugh Alexander, 1926–
    Serum esterases of man in health and disease. Toronto, 1955.
      xv, 161 leaves. diagrs., tables.

    Thesis – University of Toronto.
    Bibliography: leaves ₍155₎–161.

    1. Esteras 2. Serum 3. Man I. Toronto. University. Theses (Ph.D.) II. Title

NL 0383690   CaOTU

DS
646
.38
B7
L5
  Lindsay, Hugh Hamilton, 1802–1881.
    The Eastern Archipelago Company and Sir James Brooke, by H.H.Lindsay. Honolulu, Reproduced by Pacific Scientific Information Center, Bernice P.Bishop Museum, ₍n.d.₎
      9 l.
      Cover title.

    1.Brooke,Sir James,Rajah of Sarawak,1803–1868. 2.Sarawak--History. I.Title.

NL 0383691   NSyU NIC

Asia
DS646.38
.B7L55
  Lindsay, Hugh Hamilton, 1802–1881.
    The Eastern Archipelago Company and Sir James Brooke. ₍London, 1853₎
      14 p. (on double leaves)

    Photographic copy of pamphlet in the National Central Library.

    1. Brooke, Sir James, rajah of Sarawak, 1803–1868. 2. Eastern Archipelago Company. I. Ti-   tle.

NL 0383692   HU

LINDSAY, H₍ugh₎ Hamilton,1802–1881.
  Is the war with China a just one? London, J.Ridgway,1840.

  pp.40.

NL 0383693   NN MSaE

4DA
453
  Lindsay, Hugh Hamilton, 1802–1881.
    Is the war with China just one? 2d ed. London, J. Ridgway, 1840.
      40 p.

NL 0383694   DLC-P4 NIC MH

Lindsay, H₍ugh₎ Hamilton, 1802–1881.
  Letter to the Right Honourable Viscount Palmerston, on British relations with China. 2. ed. London: Saunders & Otley, 1835.
    1 p.l., 19 p. 8°.

NL 0383695   NN

Lindsay, Hugh Hamilton, 1802–1881.
  Letter to the Right Honourable Viscount Palmerston on British relations with China. By H. Hamilton Lindsay ... London, Saunders and Otley, 1836.
    1 p. l., 19 p. 20¼ᵐ.

  1. China—For. rel.—Gt. Brit. 2. Palmerston, Henry John Temple, 3d viscount, 1784–1865. 3. Gt. Brit.—For. rel.—China.
                                                  6—46462
  Library of Congress   DS740.5.G5L7

NL 0383696   DLC NcD PBm MSaE MH-BA NIC CtY NN

Lindsay, Hugh Hamilton, 1802–1881.
  Letter to Viscount Palmerston, on the British relations with China. 3rd. ed. London, 1836.

NL 0383697   PPL

[LINDSAY,Hugh Hamilton,1802–1881].
  Remarks on occurrences in China since the opium seizure in March 1839 to the latest date. By a resident i n China. London, Sherwood,Gilbert,and Piper,1840.

NL 0383698   MH MSaE CtY

VOLUME 334

HF
3508
.C5
L75

Lindsay, Hugh Hamilton, 1802–1881.
Report of proceedings on a voyage to the northern ports of China in the ship Lord Amherst.   London, B. Fellowes,   1833.
296 p. 23 cm.

NL 0383699   MiU T NN MH PPAN ICN CU

Lindsay, Hugh Hamilton, 1802–1881.
Report of proceedings on a voyage to the northern ports of China in the ship Lord Amherst. 2d ed. London, B. Fellowes, 1834.
296 p. 23 cm.

1. Gt. Brit.—Comm.—China.   2. China—Comm.—Gt. Brit.   3. China—Descr. & trav.   I. Title.
HF3508.C5L5 1834   50–49953

NL 0383700   DLC MSaE ICN MnU CtY NIC CtY-D CU

Lindsay, Hugh Hamilton, *1802–1881.*
[————]   The rupture with China and its causes, including the opium question and other important details; in a letter to Lord Viscount Palmerston. By a resident in China.   London, 1840.   60 p. 8°.

NL 0383701   MSaE MH

Lindsay, Hugh P.
Lindsay's simplified shorthand; a system without shading, in which the vowels are expressed by the inclination of the stems to a real or an imaginary horizontal line, by Hugh P. Lindsay and Amelia H. Lindsay ...   [3d ed.]   Pittsburg, Pa., Dermitt printing co., 1905.
3 p. l., 5–59 p. 23ᶜᵐ.

1. Shorthand.   I. Lindsay, Mrs. Amelia H., joint author.
Library of Congress   Z56.L74 1905
5–19569

NL 0383702   DLC

Lindsay, Hugh P.
Lindsay's simplified shorthand. 4th ed.   A system of writing without shading, in which the vowel and diphthongal sounds are expressed by the inclinations of lines called strokes to a real or an imaginary horizontal line ...   By Hugh P. Lindsay and Amelia H. Lindsay.   Pittsburg, Pa. [ᶜ1906]
2 p. l., 3–66 p.   18½ x 14½ᶜᵐ.

1. Shorthand.   I. Lindsay, Amelia H., joint author.
6–8139
Library of Congress   Z56.L734   (Copyright A 139411)

NL 0383703   DLC

Lindsay, Hugh P.
Lindsay's simplified shorthand. 5th ed.   A system of writing without shading in which the vowel and diphthongal sounds are expressed by the inclinations of lines called strokes to a real or an imaginary horizontal line ...   By Hugh P. Lindsay and Amelia H. Lindsay.   Pittsburgh, Pa. [ᶜ1906]
2 p. l., [3]–64, x p.   19½ x 15ᶜᵐ.

1. Shorthand.   I. Lindsay, Amelia H., joint author.
6–37629
Library of Congress   Z56.L735   (Copyright A 155548)

NL 0383704   DLC

Lindsay, Hugh P.
Lindsay's simplified shorthand; a system of shorthand writing without shading, by which the vowel and diphthongal sounds are expressed by the inclinations of consonant strokes, embodying simplicity—rapidity—legibility. By Hugh P. Lindsay and Amelia H. Lindsay. 6th ed. Pittsburgh, Pa. The Lindsay publishing company [ᶜ1907]
v, 3–151 p. illus. 20ᶜᵐ.

1. Shorthand.   I. Lindsay, Mrs. Amelia H., joint author.

Library of Congress   Z56.L74 1907
7–27007

NL 0383705   DLC ICJ

428
L643

Lindsay, I   S
An olfactometer for examining the effect of vapors on adult mosquitoes.   Ralston, 1955.
7 l.   (Canada. Suffield Experimental Station, Ralston. Suffield technical paper no. 76)

1. Olfactometer. 2. Smell. Insects. 3. Culicidae. Extermination. I. Canada. Suffield Experimental Station, Ralston. Entomology Section. II. Canada. Suffield Experimental   Station, Ralston. Suffield technical   paper no. 76.

NL 0383706   DNAL

Lindsay, Ian Gordon.
The cathedrals of Scotland, by Ian Gordon Lindsay; foreword by Sir George Douglas, bart.   London [etc.] W. & R. Chambers, limited, 1926.
256 p. incl. front., plates, ports., double map, plans. 19½ᶜᵐ.

1. Cathedrals—Scotland.
Library of Congress   NA5472.L5
27–578

OClh OCl MB NN
NL 0383707   DLC WaS CaBVa CaBViP GU CaBVaU KyLxCB CtY

Lindsay, Ian Gordon.
Georgian Edinburgh.   Edinburgh, Oliver and Boyd [1948]
55 p. illus., fold. maps. 23 cm.

1. Edinburgh—Descr. 2. Edinburgh—Historic houses, etc. 3. Cities and towns—Planning—Edinburgh.   I. Title.
DA890.E3L5   724.14207   49–872*

NL 0383708   DLC MB ICU CtY OOxM CU KU WaS CaBVa

Lindsay, Ian Gordon.

Old Edinburgh, 1939. Edinburgh, London, Pub. under the auspices of the Cockburn association, by Oliver and Boyd, 1939.

Lindsay, Ian Gordon.
Old Edinburgh, 1947
see under title

DA890
.G5C3

Lindsay, Ian Gordon, joint author.
Cant, Ronald Gordon.
Old Glasgow; a description of old buildings, illus. with photos., plans and a map, by Ronald G. Cant and Ian G. Lindsay.   Edinburgh, Oliver and Boyd, 1947.

Lindsay, Ian Gordon.
The Scottish tradition in burgh architecture. [Edinburgh] Pub. for the Saltire Society [by] T. Nelson [1948]
8 p., 20 plates. 19 cm. (Saltire Society. Scottish tradition series)

1. Architecture—Scotland. 2. Cities and towns—Planning—Scotland.   I. Title.   (Series)
NA972.L5   720.941   48–10454*

NL 0383712   DLC DSI

E185
.8
L54
SOCIAL
SCIENCE

Lindsay, Inabel Burns, 1900–
The participation of Negroes in the establishment of welfare services, 1865–1900, with special reference to the District of Columbia, Maryland, and Virginia. Pittsburgh, 1952.
xi, 243 ℓ.

Thesis - University of Pittsburgh.
Photocopy.
Includes bibliography.

1. Negroes as social workers. 2. Negroes - Social conditions - To 1964. 3. Freedmen. I. Title.

NL 0383713   CU DHU

Lindsay, J   J   1871–
Inside the prison; or, In chains and stripes. Weldon, Harrell's Printing House, 1913.
34 p. port. 16cm.

1. N.C.—Temperance—Addresses, essays, lectures 2. N.C.—Prisons

NL 0383714   NcU

Lindsay, J. O.
The eldership.   A sermon ... Due West, S.C., Due West Telescope press., 1859.
pamph.

NL 0383715   PPPrHi

[Lindsay, J   R   ]
... Some ideas, by Harry Hinton [pseud.] as published in the National economist ... Washington, D. C., The National economist publishing co., 1891.
127 p. front. 18ᵐᵐ. (Library of National economist extras. v. 1. February, 1891. no. 2)
No more published?

1. Social problems—Miscellanea. 2. U. S.—Pol. & govt.   I. Title.
16–10550
Library of Congress   HN64.L52

NL 0383716   DLC

Lindsay, J   T.
French exiles of Louisiana. By J. T. Lindsay ... New York, W. B. Smith & co. [ᶜ1881]
240 p. incl. front., 3 pl. 20ᶜᵐ.
An historical novel dealing with the Napoleonic wars, the Murat family and the life of French exiles in Louisiana.

1. French in Louisiana.
5–37654
Library of Congress   F380.F8L6

NL 0383717   DLC CaBViPA MeB CU MH ICN OClW

VOLUME 334

Lindsay, Jack, 1900–
Adam of a new world, by Jack Lindsay ... London, I. Nicholson & Watson, limited, 1936.
393 p. 20½ᶜᵐ.
Running title: The triumphant beast.

1. Bruno, Giordano, 1548–1600—Fiction.   ɪ. Title.
                                                              37–5114
Library of Congress   PZ3.L651Ad

NL   0383718   DLC IaU

Lindsay, Jack, 1900–
The anatomy of spirit; an inquiry into the origins of religious emotion, by Jack Lindsay. London, Methuen & co., ltd. ₍1937₎
vii, 182, ₍2₎ p. 19ᶜᵐ.
"First published in 1937."
"The core of this book is an attempt to fuse the basic ideas of Marx and Freud."—p. v.
"Dialectical materialism ... enables us ... to see precisely how far mind can affect conditions."—p. 6.
1. Materialism. 2. Philosophy and religion. 3. Religion, Primitive. 4. Marx, Karl, 1818–1883. 5. Freud, Sigmund, 1856–   ɪ. Title.   ɪɪ. Title: Dialectical materialism.

Library of Congress   BL51.L48   38–38085
                                                            201

NL   0383719   DLC LU TNJ CtY TxU OCU

PR1225
.C27
Lindsay, Jack, 1900–   joint ed.

Carpenter, Maurice, ed.
... Anthology; new lyrical ballads ₍by₎ Maurice Carpenter, Jack Lindsay, Honor Arundel. ₍London₎ Editions Poetry London, PL ₍1945₎

Lindsay, Jack, 1900–   ed.
Anvil; life & the arts, a miscellany. London, Meridian Books, 1947–
v. 18 cm.

ɪ. Title.

AC5.L73   808.8   49–18109*

NL   0383721   DLC NN

Lindsay, Jack, 1900–
... The barriers are down; a tale of the collapse of a civilisation, by Jack Lindsay. London, V. Gollancz ltd, 1945.
280 p. 19ᶜᵐ.

1. Huns—Fiction. 2. Rome—Hist.—Empire, 284–476—Fiction.
ɪ. Title.
                                                              A 46–2744
Yale univ. Library
for Library of Congress

NL   0383722   CtY IaU NcD TxU MH

Lindsay, Jack.
The battle for production ₍by₎ Jack Lindsay ... ₍Sydney₎, The Worker trustees, 1942₎
cover-title, 15, ₍1₎ p. 21ᶜᵐ.

1. World war, 1939–   —Economic aspects—Australia. 2. Labor and laboring classes—Australia.   ɪ. Title.
                                                              A 44–1379
New York. Public library
for Library of Congress

NL   0383723   NN

823
L6451b
Lindsay, Jack, 1900–
Betrayed spring; a novel of the British way. London, Bodley Head ₍1953₎
413p. 21cm.

NL   0383724   TxU MH CaBVa

Lindsay, Jack, 1900–
Betrayed spring; a novel of the British way. Moscow, Foreign Languages Publishing House, 1955.
606 p. front. (port.)

NL   0383725   NNC NjP MH

823
L6451be
Lindsay, Jack, 1900–
Beyond terror; a novel of the Battle of Crete. London, A. Dakers ₍1943₎
311p. 19cm.

1. World War, 1939–1945 – Campaigns – Crete – Fiction. I. Title.

NL   0383726   TxU KMK IEN

Lindsay, Jack, 1900–
Brief light; a novel of Catullus, by Jack Lindsay ... London, Methuen & co., ltd. ₍1939₎
x, 354, ₍2₎ p. 19ᶜᵐ.
"First published in 1939."

1. Catullus in fiction, drama, poetry, etc.   ɪ. Title.
                                                              40–2197
Library of Congress   PZ3.L651Br

NL   0383727   DLC IaU

Lindsay, Jack, 1900–
... British achievement in art and music, by Jack Lindsay ... London, The Pilot press ltd ₍1945₎
36 p. illus. (part col., incl. ports.) 31½ᶜᵐ. (Achievement books; general editor: Noel Carrington)
Text on p. ₍2₎ and ₍3₎ of cover.

1. World war, 1939–1945—Art and the war. 2. World war, 1939–1945—Music and the war. 3. World war, 1939–1945—Gt. Brit.   ɪ. Title.
                                                              45–10183
Library of Congress   D810.E8L5
                                                            940.53187

NL   0383728   DLC

Lindsay, Jack, 1900–
Byzantium into Europe; the story of Byzantium as the first Europe (326–1204 ᴀ. ᴅ.) and its further contribution till 1453 ᴀ. ᴅ. London, Bodley Head ₍1952₎
485 p. illus, maps. 22 cm.
Bibliography: p. 474–476.

1. Byzantine Empire—Hist.   ɪ. Title.
DF552.L52   949.5   53–1241

TxU ViU InU MB
CaBViP OrPR CaOTP MoU LU CtY-D NSyU FMU CoU MU ICMcC OOxM OU FU DDO PU PPPD MsSM GU FTaSU AU KMK CaBVa
NL   0383729   DLC OCU OO TU NN MH CtY NNC IaU NcU NcD

Lindsay, Jack, 1900–
Cæsar is dead, by Jack Lindsay. London, I. Nicholson & Watson, limited, 1934.
366 p., 1 l. illus. (map) 22½ᶜᵐ.
"First edition."

1. Rome—Hist.—Republic, ʙ. c. 265–30—Fiction.   ɪ. Title.
                                                              34–41984
Library of Congress   PZ3.L651Cae

NL   0383730   DLC TxU IaU

Lindsay, Jack, 1900–
Catalog of an exhibition of drawings and prints of Poland by Paul Hogarth
    see under   A. I. A. Gallery. London.

Lindsay, Jack, 1900–
Charles Dickens; a biographical and critical study. London, Dakers ₍1950₎
459 p. 23 cm.

1. Dickens, Charles—Biog.

PR4581.L5   928.2   50–13629

NcU IU NIC TxU OCU OClW CaBVaU IdPI
NL   0383732   DLC KMK IaU MiU ICU OCl MH MiD CtY ICU

Lindsay, Jack, 1900–
Charles Dickens; a biographical and critical study.   New York, Philosophical Library ₍1950₎
459 p. 23 cm.

1. Dickens, Charles—Biog.

PR4581.L5 1950a   928.2   50–9420

MeB NcU OrSaW OrCS IdU OrU MtU WaS
NL   0383733   DLC GU TU MH ViU MB TxU KMK KyU TNJ-P MoU

Lindsay, Jack, 1900–
Civil War in England. London, F. Muller ₍1954₎
365 p. illus. 21 cm.

1. Gt. Brit.—Hist.—Civil War, 1642–1649.   ɪ. Title.

DA415.L5   942.062   54–2555 ‡

CaBViP
NL   0383734   DLC WaU TxU NN PP OCl MB IEN OrU OrCS

Lindsay, Jack, 1900–
Clue of darkness. London, A. Dakers ₍1949₎
82 p. 19 cm.
Poem-sequence on the legend of Theseus.

1. Theseus—Poetry.   ɪ. Title.

PR6023.I 5814C55   821.91   50–24520

NL   0383735   DLC NN IEN TxU WU NBC

PZ
3
.L651
Co
Lindsay, Jack, 1900–
Come home at last.   London, I. Nicholson & Watson ₍1936₎
383 p. 20 cm.

NL   0383736   WU

VOLUME 334

Lindsay, Jack, 1900–   tr.

Petronius Arbiter.
The complete works of Gaius Petronius done into English by Jack Lindsay, with one hundred illustrations by Norman Lindsay; comprising the Satyricon and poems. London, Fanfrolico press ₁1927₎

Lindsay, Jack, 1900–
Cressida's first lover; a tale of ancient Greece, by Jack Lindsay. London, John Lane ₁1931₎
3 p. l., 312 p. 19ᶜᵐ.

1. Cressida.   I. Title.
Library of Congress   PZ3.L651Cr
32–12127

NL   0383738   DLC

Lindsay, Jack, 1900–
Cressida's first lover, a tale of ancient Greece, by Jack Lindsay. New York, R. Long & R. R. Smith, inc., 1932.
3 p. l., 288 p. 20½ᶜᵐ.

I. Title.
Library of Congress   PZ3.L651Cr 2
32–16444

NL   0383739   DLC TxU ViU

Lindsay, Jack, 1900–
Delighted earth
    see under   Herrick, Robert, 1591–1674.

Lindsay, Jack, 1900–
Despoiling Venus, by Jack Lindsay. London, I. Nicholson & Watson, 1935.
359, ₁1₎ p. 19ᶜᵐ.

1. Clodia—Fiction. 2. Caelius Rufus, Marcus—Fiction.   I. Title.
Library of Congress   PZ3.L651De
35–38583

NL   0383741   DLC TxU

Lindsay, Jack, 1900–
Dionysos, Nietzsche contra Nietzsche; an essay in lyrical philosophy, by Jack Lindsay; with reproductions from works by Peter-Paul Rubens and Norman Lindsay, Titian and Turner, Francesco Goya and William Blake and the Hellenes, and a foreword by R. L. Hall ... London, The Fanfrolico press ₁1928₎
xi, 243 p. plates, diagrs. 26½ᶜᵐ.
Title vignette.
"This edition is limited to 500 copies. No. 153."
1. Nietzsche, Friedrich Wilhelm, 1844–1900.   I. Title.
A 40–502

Northwestern univ. Libr.   L193N67Z
for Library of Congress

NL   0383742   IEN MH WU IaU KMK NcU CU–S MnU TxU NN CtY

PZ
3
.L651
Do
Lindsay, Jack, 1900–
The Dons sight Devon; a story of the defeat of the invincible Armada. Illus. by E. Boye Uden. London, New York, Oxford University Press ₁1941₎
287 p.   illus.   20 cm.

NL   0383743   WU

823.91
L748D
Lindsay, Jack, 1900–
The Dons sight Devon; a story of the defeat of the invincible armada. Illus. by E. Boye Uden. ₁London₎ Oxford University Press ₁1951₎
287 p. illus. 19 cm.

"First printed 1941."

NL   0383744   NcD

₁Lindsay, Jack₎ 1900–
End of Cornwall, by Richard Preston. New York, The Vanguard press ₁1938₎
414 p. 19½ᶜᵐ.
"Printed in Great Britain."

I. Title.
40–8315

Library of Congress   PZ3.P9283En

NL   0383745   DLC PSt

Lindsay, Jack, 1900–
England, my England. ₁London₎ Fore publications, ltd. ₁1939₎

64 p.   18.5 cm.
"Key books, 2."
Cover: A pageant of the English people.

NL   0383746   MH CtY KyLoU

△
PR
9599
L33 F38
1923
Lindsay, Jack, 1900–
Fauns and ladies. With 3 original woodcuts by Norman Lindsay. [Sydney, J. T. Kirtley, 1923]
61 p.   mounted illus.
Signed by the author.
Limited to 210 copies.   No. 96.

NL   0383747   CaBVaU

Lindsay, Jack, 1900–
Fires in Smithfield, a novel of Mary Tudor's reign.   London, Bodley Head [1950]
458p. 20cm.

1. Gt. Brit. Hist. Mary I, 1553–1558. Fiction.   I. Title.

NL   0383748   IEN TxU MH NcD WU

Lindsay, Jack, 1900–
En fremmed vender hjem. ₁Til norsk ved Egil Meidell Hopp₎ Oslo, Bergendahl ₁1947₎
295 p. 21 cm.
"Originalens titel: Hullo stranger."

I. Title.

PR6023.I 5814H86
50–24420

NL   0383749   DLC

Lindsay, Jack, 1900–   tr.

Apuleius *Madaurensis.*
The golden ass, by Apuleius, translated by Jack Lindsay, illustrated by Percival Goodman. New York, The Limited editions club, 1932.

823.91
Lindsay, Jack, 1900–   ed.
A handbook of freedom; a record of English democracy through twelve centuries, chosen by Jack Lindsay and Edgell Rickword. New York, International publishers ₁1939₎
xxiii, 408 p. 19ᶜᵐ.
Verse and prose.
Printed in Great Britain.
"First published 1939."

1. Liberty. 2. English literature (Selections: Extracts, etc.) 3. Gt. Brit.—Soc. condit.   I. *Rickword, Edgell, 1898–   joint ed. II. Title.   III. Title: English democracy through twelve centuries.
40–2772

Library of Congress   DA26.L5
942

NL   0383751   DLC NIC NN LU

Lindsay, Jack, 1900–
... Hannibaal takes a hand. London, A. Dakers limited ₁1941₎
319 p. 19ᶜᵐ.
"First published June 1941. Reprinted July 1941."

1. Hannibal, B. C. 247–183—Fiction.   I. Title.
A 42–1105

New York. Public library
for Library of Congress

NL   0383752   NN OClW OO OCU ICU

LFanfrolico
Li
Lindsay, Jack, 1900–
Helen comes of age, three plays.   London, Fanfrolico Press, 1927.
221p. 27cm.

500 signed copies. No. 83.
Contents.– Helen comes of age.– Ragnhild.– Bussy d'Ambrose.

CaBVaU TxHU
NL   0383753   IEN TxU NBuG NNC PU IaU InU NcU CtU CoU

822
L645lh
Lindsay, Jack, 1900–
Hereward, a play. With music by John Gough. ₁London₎ Fanfrolico Press ₁1929?₎
114 ₁39₎ p.

Incidental music: 37 pages at end.

1. Hereward, fl.1071 – Drama. I. Gough, John. II. Title.

NL   0383754   WaU MH NN CtU ICarbS TxU WU

Z825L645
qOHo
Lindsay, Jack, 1900–
A homage to Sappho made by Norman and Jack Lindsay. ₁London, Fanfrolico Press₎ 1928.

64 p.   illus.   29 cm.

Text by Jack Lindsay; illustrations by Norman Lindsay.
Limited to 70 copies. No. 22. Signed by the author.
I. Sappho.   II. Lindsay, Norman, 1879–   III. Title:

NL   0383755   MnU CaBVaU

VOLUME 334

Lindsay, Jack, 1900–
    Hullo stranger, by Jack Lindsay.   London, A. Dakers [1945]
214 p.   20cm.

NL 0383756   NN WU

Lindsay, Jack, 1900–   tr.
    I am a Roman; translations from the Latin by Jack Lindsay.
London, E. Mathews & Marrot ltd., 1934.
    255, [1] p. 20½ᶜᵐ.

    1. Latin literature—Translations into English. 2. English literature—
Translations from Latin. I. Title.
                                                            35–19124
    Library of Congress   PA6163.L5
                                                            870.822

NL 0383757   DLC CaBViP PU WU TxU OC1

701
L6451   Lindsay, Jack, 1900–   ed.
    Inspiration; an anthology of utterances by crea-
tive minds defining the creative act and its lyrical basis in life.   London, Fanfrolico Press,
1928.
    124p. illus.,plates. 23cm.

    "The edition is limited to seven hundred and
twenty-five copies of which this is no.204."

    1. Creation (Literary, artistic, etc.)

NL 0383758   TxU OKentU WU OU ViU NN

Lindsay, Jack, 1900–
    Into action; the battle of Dieppe, a poem by Jack Lindsay.
London, A. Dakers, limited [1942]
    60 p. 18½ᶜᵐ.

    Cover-title: Into action; Dieppe, a poem of the commandos.

    1. Dieppe raid, 1942—Poetry. I. Title.
                                                            43–5150
    Library of Congress   PR6023.I 5814 I 5
                                                            821.91

NL 0383759   DLC TxU InU IaU

Lindsay, Jack, 1900–
    John Bunyan, maker of myths, by Jack Lindsay; with 2
illustrations. London, Methuen [1937]
    xiii p., 1 l., 270, [2] p. 2 port. (incl. front.) 22½ᶜᵐ.
    "Sources": p. 264–265.

    1. Bunyan, John, 1628–1688.
                                                            38–2919
    Library of Congress   PR3331.L5 1937
    Copyright A ad int. 23350   928.2

        OO CaOTP TNJ CU–S CoU FTaSU
NL 0383760   DLC CaBVaU OrU TU PU NcD CtY IaU OCU OU

Lindsay, Jack, 1900–
    Last days with Cleopatra, by Jack Lindsay. London, I.
Nicholson & Watson, limited, 1935.
    347, [1] p. 22ᶜᵐ.
    Third volume of a trilogy, the first and second volumes being "Rome
for sale" and "Caesar is dead".

    1. Cleopatra, queen of Egypt, d. B. c. 30—Fiction. 2. Antonius, Mar-
cus, B. c. 83?–30—Fiction. I. Title.
                                                            35–10322
    Library of Congress   PZ3.L651Las

NL 0383761   DLC TxU WU

Lindsay, Jack, 1900–
    Light in Italy, by Jack Lindsay. London, V. Gollancz ltd,
1941.
    277 p. 19ᶜᵐ.

    I. Title.   A 42–1106

New York. Public library
for Library of Congress

NL 0383762   NN ICU

AP4
.L447   Lindsay, Jack, 1900–   ed.

    The London Aphrodite: a miscellany of poems, stories, and
essays by various hands eminent or rebellious. Published in
six sections between August 1928 and June 1929. London,
The Fanfrolico press [1928–29]

Lindsay, Jack, 1900–
    Lost birthright, by Jack Lindsay. London, Methuen & co.,
ltd. [1939]
    ix, 582, [2] p. 20ᶜᵐ.
    "First published in 1939."

    I. Title.   39–17649

    Library of Congress   PZ3.L651Lo

NL 0383764   DLC WU NcD

Lindsay, Jack, 1900–   ed.
    Loving Mad Tom. Bedlamite verses of the XVI and XVII
centuries, with five illustrations by Norman Lindsay; foreword by Robert Graves, the texts edited with notes by Jack
Lindsay, musical transcriptions by Peter Warlock [pseud.]
London, The Fanfrolico press [1927]
    5 p. l., 9–110 p., 1 l. Illus., pl. 29ᶜᵐ.

    "Limited to 375 copies, of which this is no. 93."
    "The musicks" : p. [55–60]

    1. English ballads and songs. 2. Insanity in literature. I. Graves,
Robert, 1895–   II. *Lindsay, Norman, 1879–   Illus. III. Title.

    Library of Congress   PR1205.L5   30–11444

        MB PU CtY NBuU WU CSt CU–B
NL 0383765   DLC CaBVaU NBuG NBu CtY–M CU–S IU TxU PSC

Lindsay, Jack, 1900–
    Marc Antony, his world and his contemporaries, by Jack
Lindsay. London, G. Routledge & sons, ltd., 1936.
    xii, 329, [1] p. front., plates, ports. 22ᶜᵐ.
    "Note on sources": p. 321–323.

    1. Antonius, Marcus, B. c. 83?–30. 2. Rome—Hist.—Republic, B. c.
265–30.   37–10488
    Library of Congress   DG260.A6L5
                                                            923.13'

NL 0383766   DLC PSt PU WU PV NcD OC1W OCU NN

Lindsay, Jack, 1900–   2944.72
    Marc Antony: his world and his contemporaries.
— New York. E. P. Dutton & Co. 1937. xii, 329, (1) pp. Portraits.
Plates. 22 cm., in 8s.
Note on sources, pp. 321–323.

E2990 — T.r. — Antonius, Marcus, 83–30 B.C. — Rome. Hist. Republic.

        PHC
NL 0383767   NN ViU NcRS MB KEmT OKentU WaE OU OO PSC

Lindsay, Jack, 1900–
    Marion Faliero.   London, Fanfrolico Press,
1927.
    104p. 26cm.

    A play.
    450 copies. No.22, signed by the author.

NL 0383768   IEN NcU CtU MiDW CU–A NN MH MdBP CaBVaU

Lindsay, Jack, 1900–
    Marxism and contemporary science; or, The fullness of
life. London, D. Dobson [1949]
    261 p. 22 cm.
    Bibliography: p. 248–257.

    1. Socialism. 2. Science. I. Title. II. Title: The fullness of life.

    HX541.L5   335.4   50–731

        MU CU MiU LU TNJ
NL 0383769   DLC NNUN NcU NcD MH IEN ViU ICU OU IU KU

Lindsay, Jack, 1900–   tr.
    Medieval Latin poets, by Jack Lindsay. London, E.
Mathews & Marrot, ltd., 1934.
    274, [1] p. 20½ᶜᵐ.

    1. Latin poetry, Medieval and modern—Translations into English.
2. English poetry—Translations from Latin. I. Title.

    Library of Congress   PA8164.L5   34–40686
                                                            879.10822

NL 0383770   DLC MB NN IU CU TxU CtY NcGW OCX OC1

Lindsay, Jack, 1900–
    Men of Forty-eight, by Jack Lindsay.   London, Methuen &
co. [1948] viii, 448 p. 20cm.

    506229B. 1. France—Hist.—Revo-   lution of 1848—Fiction. 2. Chartism
    —Fiction. I. Title.   April 17, 1950

NL 0383771   NN WU MH

PR2284
.N4
1927
Rare Bk
Coll   Harington, Sir John, 1560–1612.
    The metamorphosis of Aiax, a new discourse of a stale
subiect by Sir John Harington, with An anatomie of the
metamorpho-sed Aiax; reprinted from the original editions,
edited by Peter Warlock [pseud.], and Jack Lindsay. London [Fanfrolico press [1927]

823.9
L7491mo   Lindsay, Jack, 1900–
    The moment of choice, a novel of the
British way. London, Bodley Head [1955]
    335p. 20cm.

NL 0383773   IEN TxU WU PU

Lindsay, Jack, 1900–
    Mulk Raj Anand; a critical essay. Bombay, H. Kitabs [1948]
35, [1] p. 19cm.
    "A brief bibliography of the works of Mulk Raj Anand," p. [36]

    1. Anand, Mulk Raj, 1905–

NL 0383774   NN

VOLUME 334

Lindsay, Jack, 1900–
 Opowieść o roku 1649. ₍Tłumaczyła z jęz.
angielskiego Krystyna Tarnowska. Redaktor:
Anna Przedpełska. Warszawa₎ Czytelnik, 1951.
 621 p.

 I. Tarnowska, Krystyna   tr.

NL 0383775   NNC

Lindsay, Jack, 1900–
 Paintings and drawings by Leslie Hurry
        see under   Hurry, Leslie, 1909–

Lindsay, Jack, 1900–   ed.

Eliot, John, *fl.* 1593.
 The parlement of pratlers, a series of Elizabethan dialogues
and monologues illustrating daily life and the conduct of a
gentleman on the grand tour, extracted from Ortho-epia gal-
lica, a book on the correct pronunciation of the French language written by Iohn Eliot, and published in the year 1593.
London, The Fanfrolico press, 1928.

W821   Lindsay, Jack, 1900–
L7485p   The passionate neatherd. A lyric sequence.
 ₍With two decorations by Norman Lindsay₎
 London, Fanfrolico Press ₍1930₎
 63p. illus. 23cm.

 1 of 50 signed copies on Japanese vellum.
This is no.34.

NL 0383778   NcU MU MH LU CLU

823.91   Lindsay, Jack, 1900–
L748P   The passionate pastoral; an 18th century
 escapade. London, the Bodley Head ₍1951₎
 324 p. 21 cm.

NL 0383779   NcD WU CtU IEN MH

821
L6453p   Lindsay, Jack, 1900–
 Peace is our answer. Linocuts by Noel Counihan
and poems by Jack Lindsay. With further prefatory
poems by Paul Eluard, Pablo Neruda, Louis Aragon,
and a foreword by J.G. Crowther. London, Collets
Holdings ₍1950₎
 ₍37₎p. illus. 22cm.

 I. Counihan, Noel, 1913–   illus. II. Title.

NL 0383780   TxU CLSU IEN MH

Lindsay, Jack, 1900–
 ... Perspective for poetry ₍by₎ Jack Lindsay. ₍London₎
Fore publications ltd., 1944.
 30, ₍1₎ p. 21¼ᵐ. (Key essays, no. 1)
 Bibliographical references in "Notes" (p. 30–₍31₎)

 1. English poetry—20th cent.—Hist. & crit.   I. Title.

 Harvard univ. Library   A 46–663
 for Library of Congress   PR604.L7

                                                                821.9109
                        †

NL 0383781   MH ICU MtU IEN FMU NN CtY DLC

Lindsay, Jack, 1900–

Blake, William, 1757–1827.
 Poetical sketches, by William Blake; with an essay on
Blake's metric by Jack Lindsay. London, The Scholartis
press, 1927.

Lindsay, Jack, 1900–
 Poetry in Australia, 1923.
    see under title

PZ   Lindsay, Jack, 1900–
3   Rebels of the goldfields. With illus. by
.L651   George Scott. London, Lawrence & Wishart
Rb   ₍1936₎
 264 p. illus. 19 cm.

NL 0383784   WU

Lindsay, Jack, 1900–
 A restrospect of the Fanfrolic Press, with
a list of Fanfrolico Press books. [n.p., n.d.]

NL 0383785   WU

823.9
L7491r   Lindsay, Jack, 1900–
 Rising tide, a novel of the British
 way. London, Bodley Head [1953]
 272p. 21cm.

NL 0383786   IEN NBuU MH

Lindsay, Jack, 1900–
 Rome for sale, by Jack Lindsay; foreword by Colin Still.
London, E. Mathews and Marrot, limited, 1934.
 xv, 437 p. illus. (map) 22½ᶜᵐ.
 "An account in fictional form of the Catiline conspiracy in Rome."—
Foreword.
 "First edition."

 1. Catilina, Lucius Sergius, B. C. 108 (ca.)–62—Fiction. 2. Rome—
Hist.—Republic—Conspiracy of Catilina, B. C. 65–62—Fiction.   I. Title.

 Library of Congress   PZ3.L651Ro
                                                            34–8057

NL 0383787   DLC TxU OO

Lindsay, Jack, 1900–
 Rome for sale, by Jack Lindsay. New York and London,
Harper & brothers, 1934.
 vii p., 1 l., 416 p. 21¼ᶜᵐ.
 "First edition."

 1. Catilina, Lucius Sergius, B. C. 108 (ca.)–62—Fiction. 2. Rome—
Hist.—Republic—Conspiracy of Catilina, B. C. 65–62—Fiction.   I. Title.

 Library of Congress   PZ3.L651Ro 2
                                                            34–17654

NL 0383788   DLC OrU PPT PP OEac MB

Lindsay, Jack, 1900–
 The Romans, by Jack Lindsay. Illustrated by Pearl Binder
... London, A. & C. Black, ltd., 1935.
 96 p. incl. front. illus. (incl. map) 19ᶜᵐ. (The how-&-why series, ed.
by Gerald Bullett. ₍no. 17₎)

 1. Rome—Hist. 2. Rome—Civilization.   I. Binder, Pearl, illus.

 Library of Congress   DG210.L7
                                                            35–29195

                                                                937

NL 0383789   DLC NIC OO OCU

Lindsay, Jack, 1900–
 Rumanian summer; a view of the Rumanian People's Republic, by Jack Lindsay, with the collaboration of Maurice
Cornforth. London, Lawrence & Wishart, 1953.
 152 p. illus. 23 cm.

 1. Communism — Rumania. 2. Reconstruction (1939–   ) — Rumania.   I. Title.

 DR267.L53   949.8   53–26630 ‡
                          ₍54b2₎

     NcU OC1 NBuU
NL 0383790   DLC CaBVaU CaBViP IaU CoU NcGW NcD MU MH

Lindsay, Jack, 1900–
 Second front, poems by Jack Lindsay. London, A. Dakers
limited ₍1944₎
 49 p. 18½ᵐ.
 "First published 1944."

 1. World war, 1939–   —Poetry.   I. Title.
                                                            44–6219
 Library of Congress   PR6023.I 5814S4

                                                                821.91

NL 0383791   DLC TxU ICarbS

Lindsay, Jack, 1900–
 A short history of culture, by Jack Lindsay. London, V.
Gollancz ltd., 1939.
 408 p. illus. 22½ᵐ.
 Bibliographical references in "Acknowledgments" (p. ₍390₎–394)

 1. Culture. 2. Civilization—Hist.   I. Title.
                                                            39–20055
 Library of Congress   CB63.L5 1939
 Copyright A ad int. 25256   901

NL 0383792   DLC OC1FC CtY CU

Lindsay, Jack, 1900–
 1649; a novel of a year, by Jack Lindsay. London, Methuen ₍1938₎
 xi p., 1 l., 562 p. 22½ᵐ.
 "First published in 1938."

 1. Gt. Brit.—Hist.—Commonwealth and protectorate, 1649–1660—Fiction.   I. Title.
                                                            38–16692
 Library of Congress   PZ3.L651S1

     CLU
NL 0383793   DLC WaU NcU IEdS CtY NRU TxU IaU LU NIC

Lindsay, Jack, 1900–
 Song of a falling world; culture during the break-up of
the Roman Empire (A. D. 350–600) London, A. Dakers
₍1948₎
 308 p. 22 cm.
 "Notes" (bibliographical) : p. 286–308.

 1. Latin poetry (Collections) 2. Latin poetry—Hist. & crit.
I. Title.
 PA6051.L5   879.109   50–1015

     MH NcD CtY ICU TxU MtU IdB OrU IdPI OrPR
     PPDrop NN IEN NcU OCU CU NNU NN CaQMM MBAt ICN CU
NL 0383794   DLC KyLxT NbU INS FU MiU InStme InU PU

Dubloon
Li   Lindsay, Jack, 1900–
 Spanish main & taverns. With decora-
tions by F. Finley. ₍Sidney, Australia?
Printed at the Dubloon Press for the₎
Panurgean Society [1924; i.e. 1924?]
 ₍23₎p. illus. 25cm.

 Poems.

NL 0383795   IEN

VOLUME 334

Lindsay, Jack, 1900–
Storm at sea. Wood-engravings by John Farleigh. London, 1935.
75 p. illus. 25 cm. (Golden Cockerel series of first editions by contemporary authors, no. 10)
"Limited to 250 copies, of which this is number 232. ₍Signed₎ Jack Lindsay."

ɪ. Farleigh, John, 1900–   Illus. ɪɪ. Title.

PR6023.I 5814S8   47–43989*

NL 0383796   DLC IaU MiU WU MH NN ICN PSC NBuG CU-A

Lindsay, Jack, 1900–
The stormy violence, by Jack Lindsay. London, A. Dakers limited ₍1941₎
277 p. 18¼ᵐ.
"Published December 1941. Reprinted December 1941."

ɪ. Title.

                                          A 42–4678

New York. Public library
for Library of Congress

NL 0383797   NN

Lindsay, Jack, 1900–
The subtle knot [novel] London, A. Dakers 1947₎
264p. 19cm.

NL 0383798   IEN TxU MH NN

PR6023   Lindsay, Jack, 1900–
I5383S94   Sue Verney. London, Nicholson, 1937.
              416p. 19cm.

NL 0383799   IaU

Lindsay, Jack, 1900–
Three letters to Nikolai Tikhonov. London, Fore Publications, 1950.
24 p. 16 cm. (Key poets, 7)

ɪ. Title.
PR6023.I 5814T48 1950   821.91   51–29581

NL 0383800   DLC TxU CoU CU MiU NN ICU MH IEN

Lindsay, Jack, 1900–
Time to live ₍a novel₎ London, A. Dakers ₍1946₎
270 p. 19 cm.

ɪ. Title.
                                          A 48–2728*

Harvard Univ. Library
for Library of Congress

NL 0383801   MH INS WU NcD TxU CtY PU IaU CaBVaU

PZ   Lindsay, Jack, 1900–
3   The triumphant beast. London, I.
L651   Nicholson, 1936.
Tr   393p. 21cm.

NL 0383802   WU

Lindsay, Jack, 1900–
The wanderings of Wenamen, 1115–1114 B.C. Based on the report made by that ambassador from Upper Egypt of his travels through Egypt, Palestine, Syria, and Cyprus on a mission for cedar from the Lebanon mountains. London, Ivor Nicholson & Watson, 1936

346 p. map
A novel

NL 0383803   MH

Lindsay, Jack, 1900–
We shall return; a novel of Dunkirk and the French campaign, by Jack Lindsay. London, A. Dakers limited ₍1942₎
320 p. 19ᵐ.
"First published November 1942."

1. World war, 1939–   —Fiction. ɪ. Title.   A 43–2083

Harvard univ. Library
for Library of Congress

NL 0383804   MH TxU CaBVa

821
L6453w   Lindsay, Jack, 1900–
          Who are the English? [London, 193–]
          7p. 23cm. (A Left review pamphlet)

A poem.

NL 0383805   TxU

828
B581ZL   Lindsay, Jack, 1900–
          William Blake; creative will and the poetic
          image, by Jack Lindsay. London, Fanfrolico
          press, 1927.
          [2]55[1]p. illus. 20cm.

1. Blake, William, 1757-1827.₎

          MiU TxU GU KU FMU CU-S KMK WaU NBuU
NL 0383806   LU MiU NNU-W IU ICN NjP MH CtY NN CLU-C

Lindsay, Jack, 1900–
William Blake; creative will and the poetic image, by Jack Lindsay... London: Fanfrolico Press, 1929.   3 p.l., 89(1) p.
2. ed., enl.   8°.
Printed by Morrison and Gibb, Ltd., London and Edinburgh.
Contents: Thistles and old men. Los and Crizen. Enitharmon. Vala. The creative will. The colour-image and the future. William Blake. Notes.

449391A. 1. Blake, William, 1757-1827.   *December 28, 1929*

NL 0383807   NN CU-S CtU MeB CoU NRU OC1 OCU OU IU

HD   Lindsay, Jack
6220   Women in the workshops, by Jack Lindsay,
Z6N37ℓ   research officer, Labor Council of N.S.W.
            [Sydney, 1942?]
            16 p.

1. Woman – Employment – New South Wales.
2. Discrimination in employment – New South Wales. I. Title.

NL 0383808   CLU NN

Lindsay, Jack, 1900–
A world ahead; journal of a soviet journey. London, Fore Publications ₍1950₎
164 p. illus. 19 cm. (A Key book)

1. Russia—Descr. & trav.—1945–   2. Russia—Intellectual life.
ɪ. Title. (Series: Key books (London))

DK28.L5   914.7   51–540

NL 0383809   DLC MH

Lindsay, James.   616.991 R303
.... Gout, its ætiology, pathology and treatment, by James
115178 Lindsay, ... London, [The Joint Committee of] H. Frowde [and] Hodder & Stoughton, 1913.
xii, 212 p. xii pl. 18¼ᶜᵐ.   (*Half-title:* Oxford medical publications.)
Series title also at head of t.-p.

NL 0383810   ICJ PPJef DNLM

Lindsay, James, D. D.
A sermon occasioned by the death of Joseph Towers, delivered at Newington-Green, June 2d, 1799. To which is added the oration delivered at his interment by Thomas Jervis. London, Printed for J. Johnson, 1799.

NL 0383811   MH CtY

Lindsay, James, D. D.
A sermon preached at Monkwell Street Meeting-house, October 16th, 1796, on the occasion of the death of Dr. James Fordyce. London, Printed for J. Johnson, 1797.
iv, 66 p.   ₍Bound with: Milton, John. Comus. 1777₎

"List of ... Dr. Fordyce's works": p.₍67₎

NL 0383812   CU CtY MH

---

871   LINDSAY, James, D. D.
F987sc   A sermon preached at St. Thomas's, for
1781   the benefit of the charity-school, in
         Gravel-Lane, Southwark. London, printed
         by H. Goldney, 1788.
         24p. 22cm.

         No. 4 in a volume with binder's title
         Sermons for the school/Gravel Lane.

NL 0383813   MH-AH

Lindsay, James, D. D.
A sermon preached at the meeting-house, Salters Hall, Cannon-Street, on the 8th of August, 1813, on the death of the Rev. Hugh Worthington, in the fortieth year of his ministry in that place; with explanatory notes. London, J. Johnson and Co., 1813.
32p.

NL 0383814   ICRL

Lindsay, James, D. D.
Sermon preached at the ordination of Rev. James Lindsay
        see under Hunter, Henry, 1741-1802.

VOLUME 334

Lindsay, James, 1852–1923.
Autobiography of Rev. James Lindsay, D. D. Edinburgh and London, W. Blackwood and sons, 1924.
vi p., 1 l, 166 p., 1 l. front. (port.) 19ᶜᵐ.
Preface signed: Margaret D. Lindsay.
Bibliography: p. 88–137.

1. Lindsay, Mrs. Margaret D. (Cook) ed.

Library of Congress   B1646.L64A3   25–1268

NL   0383816   DLC CtY NN NjP

arV   **Lindsay, James,** 1852–1923.
6490   A critical essay on European literature.
Edinburgh, W. Blackwood, 1913.
57 p. 19cm.

"The following essay appeared, in substance, in two numbers of a London quarterly ..." cf. Prefatory note.

1. Europe—Literature—Hist. & crit.

NL   0383817   NIC MB

B1646 **Lindsay, James,** 1852–1923.
.L75A3   Essays, literary and philosophical, by James Lindsay ...
1896   Edinburgh and London, W. Blackwood and sons, 1896.
xiii, 166 p. 19½ᵐ.
CONTENTS.—The mind of Dante.—The philosophy of 'Faust'.—The philosophy of Tennyson.—Emerson as a thinker.

1. Philosophy—Addresses, essays, lectures.   2. Literature—Addresses, essays, lectures.

NL   0383818   ICU DLC ScU

Lindsay, James, 1852–
The fundamental problems of metaphysics, by James Lindsay ... Edinburgh [etc.] W. Blackwood & sons, 1910.
xii, 135 p. 19½ᵐ.
With bibliographies.

1. Philosophy.

                                            A 11–1312
Title from Harvard Univ.   Printed by L. C.

NL   0383819   MH PU PBm LU CtY NIC OO OC1W ICJ NjP

Lindsay, James, 1852–
Great philosophical problems, by James Lindsay ... Edinburgh and London, W. Blackwood and sons, 1922.
vi p., 1 l, 281 p. 19ᶜᵐ.
Supplements the author's Philosophical system of theistic idealism (Edinburgh and London, Blackwood, 1917)
CONTENTS.—The greatest problem in value.—The ethical value of individuality.—The character of cognitive acts.—Rationalism and voluntarism.—The ontological consciousness.—Philosophy and faith.—The unity of God and man.—The ethics of some modern world-theories.—The phenomenology of pain.—Index of authors and subjects.

1. Philosophy—Addresses, essays, lectures.   1. Title.

Library of Congress   B1646.L63G7 1922
                                            23–9931

NL   0383820   DLC PSC PBm TxU OO

Y   LINDSAY, JAMES, 1852–1923.
145   Literary essays... Edinburgh,W.Blackwood
L 65   and sons,1912.
64p.

Contents.—Was Goethe a philosopher?—The poetry of Lowell.—Hamlet as thinker.—Milton on the nativity.—On biographical literature.

NL   0383821   ICN

Lindsay, James, 1852–   Edinburgh, 1896.
The mind of Dante.

NL   0383822   NIC

K51   Lindsay, James, 1852–1923.
901L   Momenta of life; essays ethical, historical, and religious. By James Lindsay ... London, Elliot Stock,1901.
4p.l.,146p. 19½cm
Reprinted from various periodicals.

1.Ethics – Addresses, essays, lectures.
2.Religion – Addresses, essays, lectures.

NL   0383823   CtY

B1646   Lindsay, James, 1852–1923.
L62B5   New essays, literary and philosophical.
Edinburgh and London, W. Blackwood, 1896.
xiii, 166 p. 19cm.

1. Philosophy – Addresses, essays, lectures.   2. Literature – Addresses, essays, lectures.

NL   0383824   CoU

Lindsay, James, 1852–1923.
New essays, literary and philosophical, by James Lindsay ... Edinburgh and London, W. Blackwood and sons, 1912.
xvi, 184 p. 19 cm.

1. Philosophy – Addresses, essays, lectures.   2. Literature – Addresses, essays, lectures.

                                            A 13—1651
Leland Stanford Jr.   Univ.
for Library of Congress   [a66c¼]

NL   0383825   CSt PBm OO

Lindsay, James, 1852–1923.
A philosophical system of theistic idealism, by James Lindsay ... Edinburgh and London, W. Blackwood and sons, 1917.
xi p., 1 l, 530 p. 22½ᶜᵐ.

1. Idealism.   2. Theism.

Library of Congress   B823.L6
                                            18—552

       MdBJ MiU OO OC1W
NL   0383826   DLC MBU–T PBm PHC PPPD NcD NIC NjP CU MB

C   LINDSAY, JAMES, d. 1923.
537   The progressiveness of modern Christian
.5   thought... Edinburgh,W.Blackwood and sons, 1892.
xix,182p.

NL   0383827   ICN CtY MH NRCR PPAmP PHC

Lindsay, James, 1852–1923.
The psychology of belief. By James Lindsay ... Edinburgh and London, W. Blackwood & sons, 1910.
xi, 71 p. 19½ᵐ.
"Bibliographical note": p. [68]

1. Belief.
                                            A 11–824
Title from Newberry Libr.   Printed by L. C.

NL   0383828   ICN NjP NIC OO OC1W NN

Lindsay, James, 1852–1923.
Recent advances in theistic philosophy of religion, by James Lindsay ... Edinburgh and London, W. Blackwood and sons, 1897.
lvi, 547 p. 23ᵐ.

1. Religion—Philosophy.   2. Theism.

Library of Congress   BL51.L5   5—32830

       NNUT ICN
NL   0383829   DLC CU TxU IEG NIC CtY NjNbS OO OC1W NN

Lindsay, James, 1852–1923.
Seven theistic philosophers; an historico-critical study, by James Lindsay ... Edinburgh and London, W. Blackwood & sons, 1920.
vi p., 1 l. 137, [1] p. 19½ᵐ.
CONTENTS.—Immanuel Hermann Fichte.—Christian Hermann Weisse.—Karl Philipp Fischer.—Heinrich Moritz Chalybäus.—Franz Hoffmann.—Hermann Ulrici.—Friedrich Adolf Trendelenburg.—Conclusion.

1. Theism.   2. Philosophers, German.   1. Title.

Library of Congress   B2741.L5   22–15315

NL   0383830   DLC CtY OO MiU CU NjP

Lindsay, James, 1852–1923.
The significance of the Old Testament for modern theology..... Edinburgh, Blackwood, 1896.
63 p.   19 cm.

NL   0383831   CtY

Lindsay, James, 1852–1923.
Studies in European philosophy, by James Lindsay ... Edinburgh and London, W. Blackwood and sons, 1909.
xxi, 370 p.   22½ cm.

1. Philosophy—Hist.

B823.L7   10—8431

       NjP ICJ MH NN
NL   0383832   DLC LU PBm PHC PPLT NcD OO NIC OC1 OCU

Lindsay, James, 1852–1923.
The teaching function of the modern pulpit.
Edinburgh, Blackwood, 1897.
60 p.   18.5 cm.

NL   0383833   CtY

VOLUME 334

Lindsay, James Alexander, 1856–*1931.*
Among the thinkers; leaves from my note-books, by James Alexander Lindsay...   London: H. K. Lewis & Co., Ltd., 1931.
ix, 197 p.   12°.

537258A. 1. Quotations. I. Title.
July 22, 1931

NL 0383834   NN

WF
330
L748C
1887

Lindsay, James Alexander, *1856–*
The climatic treatment of consumption; a contribution to medical climatology.
London & New York, Macmillan, 1887.
xii, 228 p.   20 cm.

1. Climate. 2. Tuberculosis, Pulmonary – therapy. I. Title.

NL 0383835   WU-M MiD-W DNLM PPC MiU DNLM

WF
L748L
1904

LINDSAY, James Alexander
Lectures chiefly clinical and practical on diseases of the lungs and the heart.
London, Baillière, Tindall and Cox, 1904.
viii, 447 p.
2d ed. has title: Lectures on diseases of the lungs.

NL 0383836   DNLM IU-M PPHa ICJ CaBVaU

Lindsay, James Alexander, 1856–1931.
Lectures, chiefly clinical and practical on diseases of the lungs and the heart. New York, W. Wood, 1904.
447p.

NL 0383837   ICRL IU-M

WF
L748L
1906

LINDSAY, James Alexander
Lectures on diseases of the lungs.
2d ed., enl. and rewritten.   London, Baillière, Tindall and Cox, 1906.
ix, 509 p.
1st ed. has title: Lectures chiefly clinical and practical on diseases of the lungs and the heart.

NL 0383838   DNLM

Lindsay, James Alexander.
Medical axioms, aphorisms, and clinical memoranda; by James Alexander Lindsay ... London, H. K. Lewis & co., ltd., 1923.
viii, 192 p.   19½ᶜᵐ.
"Authorities quoted in this work": p. 187–188.

1. Maxims, (Medical) I. Title.
Library, U. S. Surgeon-   General's Office   S G 23–77

NL 0383839   DNLM CaBVaU WU-M

616.04
L645

Lindsay, James Alexander, 1856–1931.
Medical axioms, aphorisms, and clinical memoranda, by James Alexander Lindsay ... New York, P. B. Hoeber, 1924.
xi, 194 p.   19ᶜᵐ.
Printed in Great Britain, 1923.

NL 0383840   ICJ

19th
cent
RC311.3
C4L55
1892

LINDSAY, James Alexander, 1856–*1931.*
Traitement climatérique de la phtisie pulmonaire; contribution de climatologie médicale, par James Alex. Lindsay. Traduit et annoté par F. Lalesque. Paris, O. Doin, 1891 [cover 1892]
244p.   23cm.
acc. no. ACK   cat. ` LC ˉ SG ```

1. Tuberculosis 2. Physical medicine – Climatotherapy 3. Climatology, Medical
I. Title ACK

NL 0383841   CtY-M DNLM

Lindsay, James Armour, 1897–
Annual and semi-annual promotion, with special reference to the elementary school, by James Armour Lindsay ... Published with the approval of Professor Paul R. Mort, sponsor. New York city, Teachers college, Columbia university, 1933.
vii, 171 p.   23ᶜᵐ.
Vita.
Thesis (PH. D.)—Columbia university, 1933.
Published also as Teachers college, Columbia university, Contributions to education, no. 570.
"General bibliography": p. 161–170; "Bibliography for chapter IX": p. 155–158.
1. Grading and marking (Students) 2. School management and organization. 3. Education of children. I. Title. II. Title: Promotion, Annual and semi-annual.
33–30737
Library of Congress   LB3063.L5 1933
Columbia Univ. Libr.
371.28

NL 0383842   NNC DLC

Lindsay, James Armour, 1897–
Annual and semi-annual promotion, with special reference to the elementary school, by J. Armour Lindsay ... Published with the approval of Professor Paul R. Mort, sponsor. New York city, Teachers college, Columbia university, 1933.
vii, 170 p.   23½ᶜᵐ.   (Teachers college, Columbia university. Contributions to education, no. 570)
Issued also as thesis (PH. D.) Columbia university.
"General bibliography": p. 161–170; "Bibliography for chapter IX": p. 155–158.
1. Grading and marking (Students) 2. School management and organization. 3. Education of children. I. Title. II. Title: Promotion, Annual and semi-annual.
Library of Congress   LB3063.L5 1933 a
___ViU —Copy 2.   LB5.C8 no. 570
33–30736
371.28
Copyright A 65282

NcD PU PWcT NcU OC1W OO OC1 OCU OU MiU ViU
NL 0383843   DLC NNC KEmT PSt MtU OrU MB CaBVaU OrP

QB
52
L55
1858

Lindsay, James Bowman, *1799–1862.*
The chrono-astrolabe: containing a full set of Astronomic tables, with rules and examples for the calculation of eclipses and other celestial phenomena; comprising also plane and spherical trigonometry, and the most copious list of ancient eclipses ever published; connected with these, the dates of ancient events   are exactly determined,   and the authenticity

of Hebrew, Greek, Roman, and Chinese writings is demonstrated. Dundee, Middleton, Chalmers, Shaw, & Stephen, 1858.
152, xxxvi p.   22 cm.

1. Astronomy – Tables, etc. I. Title.

NL 0383845   CaBVaU ICJ RPB

Lindsay, James Bowman, 1799–1862, ed.
Pentecontaglossal Paternoster; or, The Lord's Prayer in fifty languages ...
see under Lord's Prayer. Polyglot.

Lindsay, James Bowman, 1799–1862.
Treatise on the Mode and Subjects of Baptism. Dundee, 1861.
48 p. + pl.   8°.   [In "College Pamphlets" v. 1996]

NL 0383847   CtY

Lindsay, James Donald, 1899–
The Joule-Thomson coefficient and the effect of pressure on the thermal properties of hydrocarbons, by J. D. Lindsay ... Ann Arbor, Mich., 1935.
cover-title, p. 817–820.   diagrs.   30ᶜᵐ.
Thesis (PH. D.)—University of Michigan, 1934.
Caption title: Thermal properties of hydrocarbons under pressure.
II (by) James D. Lindsay and George Granger Brown.
"Reprinted from Industrial and engineering chemistry, vol. 27 ... July, 1935."
"Literature cited": p. 820.
1. Hydrocarbons. 2. Pentane. 3. Benzene. 4. Thermodynamics.
I. Brown, George Granger, 1896– joint author. II. Title. III. Title: Thermal properties of hydrocarbons under pressure.
36–5527
Library of Congress   QC318.L5 1934
Univ. of Michigan Libr.
536.7

NL 0383848   MiU ViU OCU OU DLC

Lindsay, James Gordon
see Lindsay, Gordon.

Lindsay, James Howard, editor.
The London Scottish in the Great war, edited by Lt. Col. J. H. Lindsay ... with a foreword by Field-Marshal Earl Haig ... London: Regimental Headquarters, 1925.   xvi, 425 p. incl. tables. facsims., front., maps, plates, ports.   8°.

225317A. 1. Army, British—Regimental histories—London Regiment
—14th (County of London) Batt.   (London Scottish). 2. European
war, 1914–1918—Regimental histories —Gt. Br.—Inf.—London Regiment
—14th (County of London) Batt.   (London Scottish).
N. Y. P. L.
March 6, 1926

NL 0383850   NN MH NjP MiU

Lindsay, James Hubert, 1862–1933.
[Biographical sketch of John Sergeant Wise, with selections from his writings, by J. H. Lindsay]   3169
(In Alderman, E. A. Library of Southern literature. 1909. v. 13. p. 5937–5956)

NL 0383851   Vi

Lindsay, James Hubert, 1862–
A greenhorn in Europe, by James H. Lindsay. Philadelphia, Dorrance and company [°1929]
125 p.   19½ᵐ.

1. Europe—Descr. & trav. I. Title.
Library of Congress   D921.L55
29–6164

NL 0383852   DLC ViU

Lindsay, James Hubert, 1862–1933.
The McCue murder; complete story of the crime and the famous trial of the ex-mayor of Charlottesville, Virginia ... Charlottesville, Va., The Progress publishing company [1904]
1 p. l., [5]–192 p. incl. illus., ports., plan.   23½ᵐ.
By James H Lindsay and John S. Patton.
"Personal sketches": p. 179–186.

1. McCue, James Samuel, 1861–1905. 2. McCue, Mrs. Fannie McNutt (Crawford) d. 1904. I. Patton, John Skelton, 1857– joint author.
15–28110
Library of Congress   HV6534.C38A6 1904 e

NL 0383853   DLC NcD ViU

VOLUME 334

Lindsay, James Hubert, 1862-1931

Virginia. *Constitutional convention, 1901-1902.*
Report of the proceedings and debates of the Constitutional convention, state of Virginia. Held in the city of Richmond June 12, 1901, to June 26, 1902 ... Richmond, Va., The Hermitage press, 1906.

Lindsay, James Ludovic, 26th earl of Crawford.
See
Crawford, James Ludovic Lindsay, 26th earl, 1847-1913.

Lindsay, James Martin.
Thomas Mann. Oxford, Blackwell, 1954.
137 p. illus. 23 cm. (Modern language studies)
Includes bibliographies.

1. Mann, Thomas, 1875-

PT2625.A44Z744   55-3252 rev ‡

OrCS MoSU MiU PPD NIC CU OC1 NNC PSC PP PBL NcC NcGW
TU WaS ICU MH OrU MB ICN OrPR CtY OrMonO NcU MiU PHC
NL 0383856   DLC CaBVaU PU KU TxU OCU IEN ViU NN NbU

Lindsay, Hon. James Stair, d. 1783.

Crawford, Alexander William Crawford Lindsay, *25th earl of, 1812-1880.*
Lives of the Lindsays; or, A memoir of the houses of Crawford and Balcarres, by Lord Lindsay. To which are added, extracts from the official correspondence of Alexander sixth earl of Balcarres, during the Maroon war; together with personal narratives by his brothers, the Hon. Robert, Colin, James, John, and Hugh Lindsay; and by his sister, Lady Anne Barnard. 2d ed. London, J. Murray, 1858.

Lindsay, *Hon.* **James Stair,** *d. 1783.*
Two narratives of the proceedings of the British army under General Sir Hector Monro and Colonel Baillie, and of the battle of Conjeveram, September 10, 1780, in which the division under Colonel Baillie was either cut to pieces or taken prisoners; by the Hon. James and John Lindsay, 73rd Highlanders.
(In Crawford, Alexander W. C. Lindsay, 25th earl of. Lives of the Lindsays ... London, 1849. 22ᶜᵐ. v. 3, p. ₍227₎-260)
1. India—Hist.—British occupation, 1765-   2. Ḥaidar Shāh, called Ḥaidar 'Alī, Khān Bahādur, nawab of Mysore, ca. 1702-1782.   I. Lindsay, Hon. John, 1762-1826.

8-23792

Library of Congress   DA758.3.L8C7

NL 0383858   DLC MdBP

Lindsay, Jane, *pseud.*
see
Lindsay, *Mrs.* **Mary (McDowell)** 1903-

Lindsay, Jean Olivia, *comp.*
A Cambridge scrapbook. Foreword by Dame Myra Curtis. Cambridge ₍Eng.₎ Heffer, 1955.
147 p. 19 cm.

1. Cambridge. University.   I. Title.

LF128.L5   378.42   55-4975 ‡

NL 0383860   DLC PBL MH NN CU

Lindsay, Jean Olivia.
The early history of science; a short handlist. ₍London₎ Published for the Historical Association by G. Philip, 1950.
68 p. 18 cm. (Helps for students of history, no. 52)

1. Science—Hist.—Bibl.   I. Title.   (Series)

Z7405.H6L5   016.509   51-18625

NL 0383861   DLC NN OrCS OU WaU CU WU NcU CLSU PSt IaU

Lindsay, Jean Olivia, ed.
The history of science; origins and results of the scientific revolution, a symposium ...
see under title

Film   Lindsay, Jean Stirling, 1891-
N1192   A survey of the town-country and court-country themes in non-dramatic Elizabethan literature. ₍Ithaca, N. Y.₎ 1943.
214 l. 27cm.

Thesis (Ph. D.)--Cornell University, Jan., 1943.
Microfilm (negative) Ithaca, N.Y., Photo Science, Cornell University, 1964. 1 reel. 35mm.

NL 0383863   NIC

Lindsay, Jessie,
Manual of modern cookery, by Jessie Lindsay...and V. H. Mottram... London: Univ. of London Press, Ltd., 1927.
316 p. incl. tables. illus. 12°.

308767A. 1. Cookery. 2. Mottram,   Vernon Henry, 1882- ₍jt. au.
                                      June 30, 1927

NL 0383864   NN

Lindsay, Jessie,
Manual of modern cookery, by Jessie Lindsay...and V. H. Mottram... London: Univ. of London Press, Ltd., 1930.
316 p. incl. tables. new ed., rev. 12°.

529623A. 1. Cookery. I. Mottram,   Vernon Henry, 1882- , jt. au.
                                      July 11, 1931

NL 0383865   NN

Lindsay, Jessie.
Manual of modern cookery, by Jessie Lindsay ... and V. H. Mottram ... 3d and rev. ed. London, University of London press, ltd., 1936.
316 p., 1 l. 20ᶜᵐ.
Blank page for "Notes" (p. ₍317₎)

1. Cookery, English.   I. Mottram, Vernon Henry, 1882-   joint author.
Library of Congress   TX717.L5 1936   38-7883
                                          641.5

NL 0383866   DLC OrCS NN

Lindsay, Jessie.
Manual of modern cookery. [9th ed.] London, University of London press, ltd. [1947]
318 p.

NL 0383867   MiEM

TX   Lindsay, Jessie
717   Manual of modern cookery, by Jessie Lindsay..
L5   and V.H. Mottram... London, University of
1948   London press, ltd., 1948.
     316 p.

COOKERY, ENGLISH
Mottram, Vernon Henry, 1882-
Manual of modern cookery

NL 0383868   KMK

Lindsay, Jessie,
Modern cookery for schools, by Jessie Lindsay...and Helen Tress... London: Univ. of London Press, Ltd., 1934. 171 p. incl. tables. 20cm.
"This book is an abridged edition of the Manual of modern cookery, with some additional recipes and other matter suitable for schools and colleges."

731395A. 1. Cookery, English.   I. Tress, Helen M., jt. au.
                                       October 8, 1934

NL 0383869   NN

Lindsay, Jessie.
What every cook should know, by Jessie Lindsay ... and Helen M. Tress ... With an introduction by Professor V. H. Mottram ... London, Nisbet and co. ltd. ₍1932₎
168 p. 20ᶜᵐ.

1. Cookery.   I. Tress, Helen M., joint author.   II. Title.
Library of Congress   TX651.L5   33-12408
                                          641.5

NL 0383870   DLC NN

₍**Lindsay, Joan (Weigall)**₎
The story of the Red cross. ₍Melbourne₎ Australian Red cross society ₍1941?₎
₍106₎ p. illus. (part col.; incl. ports., facsims.) 28 x 22½ᶜᵐ.
"Written and compiled by Joan and Daryl Lindsay."—p. ₍1₎
Illustrated lining-papers.

1. Red cross.   I. Lindsay, Daryl, 1890-   joint author.   II. Red cross. Australia. Australian Red cross society.
Library of Congress   UH535.L5   42-19246
                                          361.506

NL 0383871   DLC OC1W

LINDSAY, JOAN (WEIGALL)
Through darkest Pondelayo; an account of the adventures of two English ladies on a cannibal island, by Serena Livingstone-Stanley [pseud.] Edited by Rev. Barnaby Whitecorn D.D. London, Chatto & Windus, 1936. vii, 200 p. illus. 22cm.

1. Satire, English. I. Title.

NL 0383872   NN IEN

---

4   **Lindsay, John**
Music
3012   Fare well; intermezzo. Berlin, R. Birnbach, c1914.
     parts.

Title changed by label to Kriegers Abschied, Farewell.

NL 0383873   DLC-P4

VOLUME 334

Lindsay, John, D. D.
   see   Lindsay, John Summerfield, 1842-1903.

Lindsay, John, *Rev.*
   The Scripture doctrine, history and laws,
relating to oaths and vows, leagues and cove-
nants; set forth in a full and clear light ...
London, T. Gardner [etc.] 1761.
   viii,153p.

   Includes bibliographical references.

NL 0383875   GEU

311 LINDSAY, JOHN, *Rev.*
   Sermon preached at the funeral of His Excellency Sir Basil Keith,
Governor of Jamaica, in the parish church St. Catherine and town of
St. Jago de la Vega, June 16, 1777. London, 1780.

NL 0383876   MChB

Lindsay, John, *Rev.*
   A voyage to the coast of Africa, in 1758. Containing a succinct account of the expedition to, and the taking of the island of Goree, by a squadron commanded by
the Honourable Augustus Keppel. Illus. with copper-
plates. By the Reverend Mr. John Lindsay ... London, S. Paterson [etc.] 1759.
   4 p. l., 110 p. 9 fold. pl. (incl. 2 fold. maps, fold. plan) 24°ᵐ.

   1. Goree.   2. Senegal—Descr. & trav.

   Library of Congress   DT549.L74
                                            5-14407†

NL 0383877   DLC CU NN

Lindsay, John, *carding master.*
   Practice in cotton-carding. A complete manual for the
card room of the cotton mill ... By John Lindsay, carding-
master. Philadelphia, The Textile record, 1888.
   142 p. 18°ᵐ. (*On cover:* Textile record hand-book, no. 4)

   1. Cotton carding.

   Library of Congress   TS1578.L7
                                            8—37830

NL 0383878   DLC PPT PPF ICJ

Lindsay, John, *dramatist.*
   Emma, a play in three acts (adapted from Jane Austen's
famous novel) by John Lindsay and Ronald Russell. London,
S. French limited [°1943]
   74 p. pl., diagr. 21¼°ᵐ. (*On cover:* French's acting edition. No. 215)

   I. Russell, Ronald, dramatist, joint author. II. Austen, Jane, 1775-
1817. Emma. III. Title.
   Library of Congress   PR4034.E52L5
                                            44—13109
                                   [822.91] 823.74

NL 0383879   DLC

Lindsay, John, *Fellow of Dulwich College.*
   English grammar, for the use of national
and other elementary schools. By the Rev.
John Lindsay ...; London, J. G. F. & J.
Rivington, 1842.
   88 p. 14.5 cm.

   1. English language - Grammar - 1800-1870.

NL 0383880   NNC NNU-W

Lindsay, John, *lord* Menmuir
   see
   Menmuir, John Lindsay, *lord*, 1552-1598.

Lindsay, John, New York.
   Specimens of printing types.   New York [186-]   46 l.
ob. 8°.

   Title from cover.

   1. Type.—Specimens.   April 24, 1913.

NL 0383882   NN

Lindsay, John, *New York.*   L655.24 N1
   [Specimens of printing types. By John Lindsay, New York.
100580 New York, J. Lindsay, 1871?]
   45 leaves. 24 x 29½ cm.
   Binder's title.

NL 0383883   ICJ

Lindsay, John, of St. Mary's Hall, Oxford.
   see   Lindsay, John, 1686-1768.

Lindsay, John, *surgeon.*
   De calore
   see   Lindsay, John, fl. 1732.

Lindsay, John, *surgeon of Jamaica.*
   An account of the *Quassia polygama*, and of the *Cinchona brachycarpa.*
   (*In* Royal society of Edinburgh. Transactions. Edinburgh, 1794. 28°ᵐ.
v. 3, pt. 2, I, p. 205-214)

                                   CA 5—329 Unrev'd
   Library of Congress   Q41.E2 vol. 3

NL 0383886   DLC MH-A

LINDSAY, Sir John, Town clerk of Glasgow.
   Glasgow, its municipal undertakings and
enterprises; lecture, November, 1921. Glasgow,
R. Anderson, printer, [1921].

   pp. 72. Port. and plates.
   Many of the plates are printed on both sides.
                                   Br 9887.27.12.10

NL 0383887   MH

[Lindsay, John, 1686-1768]
18th   A brief history of England, both in church and
cent. state; by way of question and answer: faithfully
       extracted from the most authentic histories
       and records. London: Printed for the author, 1748.
          8p. l., 376p., 16l. 20cm.

   1. England - History. I. Title: A brief
history of England.

NL 0383888   CtY-M ICN

Lindsay, John, 1686-1768.
   A critical and practical commentary on the
New Testament of Our Lord and Saviour Jesus
Christ ... London, 1740
      see under Bible. N.T. English. 1740.
Authorized.

Lindsay, John, 1686-1768.
   The evangelical history of our Lord
Jesus Christ ...
      see under Bible. N.T. Gospels. English.
Harmonies. 1757.

[LINDSAY, John, *1686-1768.*
   The grand and important question about the
church, and parochial communion, debated, in a
dialogue between a country gentleman, and his
neighbour. London, 1756.

   pp. (2), 2-.   Tr. 550. (4.)

NL 0383891   MH NN

RARE BOOK
DEPT.   [Lindsay, John] 1686-1768.
ˣXDefoe   A short history of the regal succession; and
.717   the rights of the several kings recorded in the
.L64S   Holy Scriptures. With a postscript occasion'd
         by Mr. Whiston's new book of Scripture politicks
         ...
            London: Printed for the author; and sold by J.
         Morphew near Stationers-Hall. 1717. Price 6d.
            48p. 20cm. (8vo)
            Stitched & untrimmed, as issued.

NL 0383892   MB

[Lindsay, John] 1686-1768.
   The short history of the regal succession, and
the rights of the several Kings recorded in the Holy
Scriptures ... dedicated to ... the true sons of the
Church of England. By a Presbyter of the same
church. [i. e. J. Lindsay] London. The author
[1719]
   16 p. l., 120 p. 8°.
   3. ed.

NL 0383893   NN

[LINDSAY, John, *1686-1768*
   The short history of the regal succession,
and the rights of the several kings recorded
in the Holy Scriptures. 3d ed. London, [17?0]

                                   Tr. 550. (6.)

NL 0383894   MH

Rare   Lindsay, John, Rev., of St. Mary Hall, Oxford,
book   1686-1768.
coll.   The short history of the regal succession
BS635   and the rights of the several kings recorded
.A2   in the holy scriptures. Enl. and improved in
L5   a 2d ed. ... By a presbyter of the same church
1731   London, Printed for the author [1731?].
            120p. 20cm.

            Dedication signed: J. L.

            1. Bible - History of Biblical events. I.
         Title.

NL 0383895   NcU NjPT

VOLUME 334

.Augustan
JN 357
.L 7
⌐LINDSAY, JOHN₎1686-1768
The short history of the regal succession;
and the rights of the several kings recorded in
the Holy Scriptures; enlarg'd and improv'd
in a fourth edition ... dedicated to all the
true sons of the Church of England. By a
priest of the same church ... London,
Printed for the author,1731.
lviii, ⌐2₎,269 p.

Dedication signed:John Lindsay.

NL 0383896 InU

511.8
L645b
LINDSAY, John, 1731-
The British practical gauging; or Trader
& officer's instructor. Edinburgh, Printed
for the author by T. Gliber, 1801.
xviii, 367, ⌐1₎ p. front. (port.)
diagrs., tables, 5 fold. plates.

1. Gaging. 2. Weights and measures -
Scotland. I. Title. II. Title: Trader
& officer's instructor.

NL 0383897 WaU

Lindsay, Sir John, 1737-1788
Letters of Sr. I. Lindsay to Secretary of
state, 1771 & between Nabob & govr. of Fort St.
Geo. 1750 to 1770.
[4],160p.

Manuscript.
An account of Lindsay's secret mission from
the Secretary of state and his investigations of
the negotiations of the previous 20 years.

NL 0383898 OC1

Lindsay, Hon. John, 1762-1826.
Journal of an imprisonment in Seringapatam, during
the years 1781, 1782, 1783, and part of 1780 and 1784, by
the Hon. John Lindsay ...

(In Crawford, Alexander W. C. Lindsay, 25th earl of. Lives of the Lindsays. London, 1849. 22^cm. v. 3, p. ⌐261₎-328)

8-22926

Library of Congress DA758.3.L8C7

NL 0383899 DLC MdBP

Lindsay, Hon. John, 1762-1826.

**Crawford, Alexander William Crawford Lindsay, *25th earl
of,* 1812-1880.**
Lives of the Lindsays: or, A memoir of the houses of Crawford and Balcarres, by Lord Lindsay. To which are added,
extracts from the official correspondence of Alexander sixth
earl of Balcarres, during the Maroon war: together with personal narratives by his brothers, the Hon. Robert, Colin,
James, John, and Hugh Lindsay; and by his sister, Lady
Anne Barnard. 2d ed. London, J. Murray, 1858.

Lindsay, Hon. John, 1762-1826.

Lindsay, *Hon.* James Stair, *d.* 1788.
Two narratives of the proceedings of the British army under
General Sir Hector Monro and Colonel Baillie, and of the
battle of Conjeveram, September 10, 1780, in which the division under Colonel Baillie was either cut to pieces or taken
prisoners; by the Hon. James and John Lindsay, 73rd Highlanders.

(In Crawford, Alexander W. C. Lindsay, 25th earl of. Lives of the
Lindsays ... London, 1849. 22^cm. v. 3, p. ⌐227₎-260)

Kress
Room
Lindsay, John, 1789-1870.
Notices of remarkable medieval coins,
mostly unpublished ... Cork, Printed by
J.Crowe [etc., etc.] 1849.
10 p. 3 plates. 26.5 cm.

1.Coins. I.Title.

NL 0383902 MH-BA MB NjP PBL

Lindsay, John, 1789-1870.
Notices of remarkable Greek, Roman, and
Anglo Saxon, and other medieval coins, in the
cabinet of the author, mostly unpublished,
with engravings ... Cork, Printed by P.J.Crowe,
1860.
1 p.l., 12 p. 3 pl. 26 cm.

Author's presentation copy.
Bound with his A view of the coinage of
Ireland. 1839.

NL 0383903 MH-BA PP IEN

Lindsay, John, 1789-1870.
Some observations on an ancient talisman
brought from Syria, and supposed to be the
work of the Chaldaeans, with engravings ...
Cork, Printed by J.Crowe, 1855.
5 p. pl. 26 cm.

Bound with his A view of the coinage of
Ireland. 1839.

NL 0383904 MH-BA PPDrop NN CU OC1 OCU

Lindsay, John, 1789-1870.
A view of the coinage of Ireland, from the invasion of the
Danes to the reign of George IV.; with some account of the
ring money; also, copious tables, lists, and descriptions of
Hiberno-Danish and Irish coins; and an account of some of
the principal hoards or parcels of coins, discovered in Ireland. Illustrated with engravings of upwards of one hundred
and fifty unpublished coins. By John Lindsay ... Cork,
Printed by L. H. Bolster, 1839.
2 p. l., iv, 143, ⌐1₎ p. 14 pl., 8 tab. 27½^cm.

1. Numismatics—Ireland.

Library of Congress CJ2555.L6
11—5267

NL 0383905 DLC ViU PV CSt TxU MH-BA CtY OC1 ICJ NN

Lindsay, John, 1789-1870.
A view of the coinage of Scotland, with copious tables, lists,
descriptions, and extracts from acts of Parliament; and an account of numerous hoards or parcels of coins discovered in
Scotland, and of Scottish coins found in Ireland. Illustrated
with upwards of 350 engravings of Scottish coins, a large number of them unpublished. By John Lindsay ... Cork, Printed by Messrs. Bolster, 1845.
vii, 291, ⌐1₎ p. 18 pl. (part col.) 28½^cm.

—— A supplement to the coinage of Scotland, with lists, descriptions, and extracts, from acts of Parliament, and an account of several hoards or parcels of coins discovered in Scotland, illustrated with three plates of unpublished coins. By
John Lindsay ... Cork, Printed by P. J. Crowe, 1859.
vii, 64, ⌐4₎ p. 3 pl. (part col.) 27½^cm.

1. Numismatics—Scotland. 2. Coinage—Scotland. I. Title.

Library of Congress CJ2526.L6
11—5298-9

NL 0383907 DLC MdBP MH-BA OCU ICJ NN

LINDSAY,John,1789-1870.
A view of the coinage of Scotland.
A second supplement to the coinage of
Scotland,with lists,descriptions,extracts
from sale catalogues,etc. Cork,printed by
P.J.Crowe,1868.

4°. pp.(2),vi,48+. 2 plates.

NL 0383908 MH MH-BA

Lindsay, John, 1789-1870.
A view of the coinage of the Heptarchy; to which is
added a list of unpublished mints and moneyers of the
chief or sole monarchs, from Egbert to Harold II. Also,
copious tables, lists, and descriptions; with an account of
some of the principal hoards or parcels of Anglo-Saxon
coins which have been discovered. Illustrated with numerous engravings of unpublished coins. By John Lindsay ... Cork, Printed by Messrs. Bolster, 1842.
viii, 135, ⌐1₎ p. 6 pl. 28½^cm.

1. Numismatics—Gt. Brit. 2. Coins, Anglo-Saxon.

11—5170

Library of Congress CJ2491.L6

NL 0383909 DLC CtY MH-BA DSI NN ICJ MB OCU

Lindsay, John, 1789-1870.
A view of the history and coinage of the Parthians, with
descriptive catalogues and tables, illustrated with a complete
set of engravings of coins, a large number of them unpublished.
By John Lindsay ... Cork, Printed by J. Crowe, 1852.
vii, 250 p., 1 l. 12 pl. 28 x 22^cm.

Page 250 erroneously numbered 50.

1. Numismatics—Parthia. 2. Parthia—Hist.

Library of Congress CJ692.L7
10—27951

NL 0383910 DLC CtY TxU CU ICU OCU OC1 NN

Lindsay, Sir John, 1860-   joint author.

Renwick, Robert, 1841-1920.
History of Glasgow, by Robert Renwick ... and Sir John
Lindsay ... Glasgow, Maclehose, Jackson & co., 1921-34.

Lindsay, John, 1864-
Amazing experiences of a judge; with an autobiography and
tribute to Marcus Daly, by John Lindsay. Philadelphia, Dorrance and company ⌐*1939₎.
117 p. 20^cm.

1. Lawyers—Correspondence, reminiscences, etc. 2. Butte, Mont.—
Hist. 3. Copper mines and mining—Montana—Butte. 4. Daly, Marcus,
1841-1900. I. Title.

Library of Congress
39-30086

NL 0383912 DLC CoU MtBuM MtU MtHi MtBC

Lindsay, John Douglas, 1865-
The Court of Star Chamber, its origin and
history ... [Boston] M.B. Brown Co. [1895?]
77 p. 8°.
Repr.: Green Bag, 1894-95.

NL 0383913 NN

Lindsay, John Douglas, 1865-
Mothers' pension laws and kindred legislation, by John D.
Lindsay... ⌐New York, 1916.₎ 78 p. 8°.
Cover-title.

1. Pensions (Widows and orphans),   U. S.
March 28, 1923.

NL 0383914 NN

Lindsay, John M.
Decennial indexes to the services of heirs in
Scotland,

see under

Scotland. Chancery Office.

VOLUME 334

Lindsay, John Maurice, 1918–
The advancing days; first poems.   [Glasgow]
Priv. print., 1940.
15p. 17cm.

NL   0383916   IEN

821.91
L645a9   Lindsay, John Maurice, 1918–
At the wood's edge.   Edinburgh, Serif
Books ₁1950₎
52p. 20cm.

Poems.

NL   0383917   KU MH NN MU

Lindsay, John Maurice, 1918–
The enemies of love; poems, 1941–1945. Glasgow, W. Mac-
Lellan, 1946.
50 p.   24 cm.   (Poetry Scotland series, 8)

I. Title.   (Series)

PR6023.I 58144E5   821.91   A 47–1160 rev*

Harvard Univ.   Library
for Library of Congress   †

NL   0383918   MH PU FU MiU DLC

Lindsay, John Maurice, 1918–
Hurlygush; poems in Scots. Illus. by Susan Yorke, with
an introd. by Hugh MacDiarmid. Edinburgh, Serif Books
₁1948₎
99 p. illus. 22 cm.

I. Title.

PR6023.I 58144H8   821.91   49–24729*

NL   0383919   DLC CaBVaU NN MH LU MiU

Lindsay, John Maurice, 1918–
The Lowlands of Scotland. London, R. Hale ₁1953–56₎
2 v. illus. 23 cm. (The County books series)
CONTENTS.—₁1₎ Glasgow and the North.—₁2₎ Edinburgh and the
South.

1. Scotland—Descr. & trav.   I. Title.

DA866.L5   914.13   54–3177 rev ‡

CtY PPP MB
NL   0383920   DLC CaBVa NN IU MiU OU OCl TxU PP CU NN

Lindsay, John Maurice, 1918–   ed.
Modern Scottish poetry; an anthology of the Scottish
renaissance, 1920–1945. London, Faber and Faber ₁1946₎
145 p. 20 cm.

1. Scottish poetry (Collections) 2. English poetry—Scottish authors.   I. Title.

PR8651.L5   821.91082   46–21950 rev*

NcD TU TxU MB NNC NIC WaS PU
NL   0383921   DLC CaBVaU MtU CtY CaBVa FTaSU TU MiU WaU

Lindsay, John Maurice, 1918–
No crown for laughter; poems. ₁1st ed.₎ London,
Fortune Press ₁1943₎
40 p. 20 cm.

I. Title.

PR6023.I 58144N6   821.91   A 44–2272 rev*

Harvard Univ.   Library
for Library of Congress   ₁r49d1₎†

NL   0383922   MH LU ICU DLC CaBVaU

Lindsay, John Maurice, 1918–   ed.
No Scottish twilight; new Scottish short stories, ed. by
Maurice Lindsay and Fred Urquhart. ₁Glasgow₎ W. Mac-
lellan ₁1947₎
167 p. 19 cm.
CONTENTS.—Jenny Stalry's hat, by Margaret Hamilton.—Fever, by
William Montgomerie.—Boxing match, by Maurice Lindsay.—Sailor's
wooing, by Thomas Henderson.—Bohemia is never far, by Alexander
Reid.—Thirst, by D. K. Haynes.—The hunting of Ian Og, by Naomi
Mitchison.—The bitter tree, by Morley Jamieson.—Peepshow, by J. F.
Hendry.—I'll join the Merchant Navy, by Fred Urquhart.—I did not
like Sunday, by Peter Jamieson.—The renegade, by Edward Gaitens.—
The cat, by Robert McLellan.—Griselda, by Coleman Milton.
1. Scottish fiction (Collections)   I. Urquhart, Fred, 1912–
joint ed. II. Title.

A 49–3036*

New York. Public Libr.
for Library of Congress

NL   0383923   NN OOxM WU NcD MiU MH

PR
6023
I58144   Lindsay, John Maurice, 1918–
934   Ode for St. Andrew's night and other
poems. Edinburgh, New Alliance Publications
[1951]
31p. 19cm.

Author's autographed copy.

NL   0383924   MU CaBVaU IEN

Lindsay, John Maurice, 1918–
Perhaps to-morrow. Oxford, Printed at the Shakespeare
Head Press and sold by B. Blackwell, 1941.
40 p. 20 cm.
Poems.

I. Title.

PR6023.I 58144P4   821.91   42–9271 rev*

NL   0383925   DLC IEN

Lindsay, *John Maurice, 1918–*   *,ed*
A pocket guide to Scottish culture.   Glasgow,
Maclellan [1947]

52 p. illus.

NL   0383926   MH

PR2296
.L6A6   Lindsay, *John Maurice,* 1918–   ed.
1948   Lindsay, *Sir David, fl.* 1490–1555.
Poems, selected and ed. by Maurice Lindsay. ₁Edin-
burgh₎ Pub. for the Saltire Society by Oliver and Boyd,
1948.

PR8658
.P6   Lindsay, *John* Maurice, 1918–   ed.
Poetry—Scotland. no. 1–
Glasgow, W. Maclellan ₁1943–

821.91
L645p   Lindsay, John Maurice, 1918–
1942   Predicament; thirteen poems.   Oxford,
The Alden Press, 1942.
16p. 20cm.

"This edition is limited to 200
numbered copies, of which this is number
22."

NL   0383929   KU MH

Lindsay, John Maurice, 1918–
Robert Burns, the man, his work, the legend. London,
MacGibbon & Kee, 1954.
291 p. illus. 22 cm.

1. Burns, Robert, 1759–1796.

PR4331.L5   928.2   55—19961 ‡

CaBVa CaBVaU ScClEA N ScU NcGW
PPT PLF CtY OU IEN TU NcU IaU InStme WaSpG OrU CoU
NL   0383930   DLC OrP CU MH ICU TxU NN MB PSt OO OCl PU

Lindsay, John Maurice, 1918–   ed.
Sailing to-morrow's seas; an anthology of new poems, by
Henry Treece ₁and others₎ Ed. by Maurice Lindsay, with
an introd. by Tambimuttu. London, Fortune Press ₁1944₎
46, ₁1₎ p. 20 cm.
"Biographical notes": p. 45–₁47₎

1. English poetry—20th cent.   I. Treece, Henry, 1912–
II. Title.

PR1225.L5   821.91082   44–8780 rev 2*

NL   0383931   DLC IEN NNC

820.991
L645s   Lindsay, John Maurice, 1918–
1948   The Scottish renaissance.   Edinburgh,
Serif books ₁1948₎
28p. 23cm.

1. English literature. 20th cent. Hist.
and crit. 2. English literature. Scottish
authors. Hist.   and crit. 3. Scottish
literature. Hist.   and crit. I. Title.

NL   0383932   KU LU MH MA WU

PR
6023
.I 5813   Lindsay, John   Maurice, 1918–
A6   Selected poems. Edinburgh, Published for
1947   the Saltire Society ₁by₎ Oliver and Boyd,
1947.
21, ₁3₎p. 16.5cm. (Saltire modern
poets)

NL   0383933   ScU MH CaBVaU NN MH LU WU InU IEN

Lindsay, John Maurice, 1918–   ed.
Selected poems of Alexander Gray
see under   Gray, Sir Alexander, 1882–

Lindsay, John Maurice, 1918–
Thomas Mann
see under   Lindsay, James Martin.

VOLUME 334

WV
258
L748m
1947

LINDSAY, John Ralston, 1898-
Ménière's disease; differential
diagnosis and treatment. A manual
prepared for the use of graduates in
medicine. ₍n. p.₎ American Academy of
Ophthalmology and Otolaryngology, 1947.
30 p.   illus.   (American Academy of
Ophthalmology and Otolaryngology,
Omaha.   Home study course.)
1. Vertigo - Aural   Series

NL 0383936   DNLM OrU-M ICU

Lindsay, John Randolph, 1894-
Shelley's life as reflected in Alatsor, The revolt of Islam, and
Rosalind and Helen ... by John Randolph Lindsay. ₍Ithaca,
N. Y.₎ 1936.
₍3₎ p. 23ᶜᵐ.

Abstract of thesis (PH. D.)—Cornell university. 1936.

1. Shelley, Percy Bysshe, 1792-1822.

Library of Congress   PR5438.L47 1936   37-1171
Cornell Univ. Libr.   821.77

NL 0383937   NIC DLC OU

Lindsay, John Robert
The location of oil refining in the United States

Thesis - Harvard, 1955

NL 0383938   MH

Lindsay, John Robert

F3590r

Film
Copy

The location of oil refining in the
United States.   Cambridge, Mass., 1954.

Microfilm copy--Negative, of typescript.
Collation as determined from film: vi,
403 ℓ.
Thesis--Harvard University.
Abstract.
Bibliography: ℓ. 398-403.

NL 0383939   RPB

MF338.21 Lindsay, John Robert.
L645   The location of oil refining in the
United States.   Cambridge, Mass., 1954.
v1,403ℓ.

Microfilm (positive)
Thesis- Harvard University.
Bibliography: ℓ.398-403.

1. Petroleum.   Refining.   I. Title.

NL 0383940   OrU

Lindsay, John Seymour.
Iron & brass implements of the English and American
home ₍by₎ J. Seymour Lindsay.   Illustrated by the author.
With an introd. by Ralph Edwards.   Boston, Medici Society
₍1927₎
xi, 211 p.   illus., plates.   29 cm.

First published in England in 1927 under title: Iron & brass implements of the English house.

1. Art metal-work, English.   2. Art metal-work, American.   3. Implements, utensils, etc.—England.   4. Implements, utensils, etc.—U. S.
I. Title.

₍NK6443.L₎   A 29-212 rev

Providence.   Public Libr
for Library of Congress   ₍r65d₎₎

MB DSI OC1W MWA MiDA OrP MiU
NL 0383941   RP OC1 OrCS WaS FU OC1 PP PPD PPPM NcGW

Lindsay, John Seymour.
Iron & brass implements of the English house ₍by₎ J. Seymour Lindsay.   Illustrated by the author.   With an introd.
by Ralph Edwards.   London, Boston, Medici Society ₍1927₎
xi, 211 (4, e. 79 p., 132 numb. l.) p.   illus., plates.   29 cm.

The plates included in paging are numbered as leaves (13-48, 67-
97, 120-161, 172-178, 185-193, 200-206)

1. Art metal-work, English.   2. Implements, utensils, etc.—England.
I. Title.

NK6443.L5   1927   28-10946 rev

NL 0383942   DLC NN ViU Vi ICU PPT IdB WaE

Lindsay, John Shanks, 1840-
The Mormons and the theatre; or, The history of theatricals
in Utah; with reminiscences and comments, humorous and
critical, by John S. Lindsay.   Salt Lake City, Utah ₍Century
printing₎ 1905.
178 p.   front. (port.)   19½ᶜᵐ.

1. Theater—Utah—Hist.   I. Title.

Library of Congress   PN2275.W81L5   5—36934

NL 0383943   DLC IdB CtY UU NN

Lindsay, John S₍hanks₎, 1840-
The true American citizen.   An address delivered before the
Association of the Oldest Inhabitants of the District of Columbia,
in Washington City, July 4th, 1887.   Washington: W. H. Moore,
1887.   12 p.   8°.

1. Citizenship, U. S.   2. Patriotism.   U. S.

November 18, 1912.

NL 0383944   NN

LINDSAY, John Summerfield, 1842-
Christian citizenship; a sermon delivered
at the commencement of the University of the
South, Tennessee, July 28, 1895.   n.p., n.d.

Pamphlet.
(University of the South papers.   Series B.
no. 81.)

NL 0383945   MH CSmH

Lindsay, John S₍ummerfield₎ 1842-1903.
Hamilton parish. 1730-1876.   An anniversary discourse, delivered by the rector, Rev. John S. Lindsay, in
St. James' church, Warrenton, Va., on the eighth Sunday
after Trinity, August 6th, 1876.   Baltimore, Printing
house of Sherwood & co., 1876.
15 p.   23½ᶜᵐ.

Subject entries: 1. Hamilton parish, Va.—Hist.   2. Warrenton, Va. St.
James' church.

Library of Congress, no.   E232.H2L7.   3-5934

NL 0383946   DLC Vi MWA

Lindsay, John Summerfield, 1842-1903
Know ye not that there is a prince and a
great man fallen this day in Israel.   A sermon
on the death of the Rt. Rev. Phillips Brooks...
preached in St. Paul's church, Boston, Septuage-
sima, 1893...   Boston, Damrell & Upham, 1893.
22 p.

NL 0383947   MiD-B MH Nh NNG MB

Lindsay, John Summerfield, 1842-   7551.209
The open door.   A sermon preached . . . November 2, 1902.
= ₍Boston.₎ 1902.   10 pp.   8°.
A discussion of the work and the difficulties of St. Paul's Church, Boston.

E8116 — Boston. Churches. St. Paul's Church.

NL 0383948   MB

Lindsay, John Summerfield, 1842-1903.
A sermon on the death of Phillips Brooks
see his   Know ye not that there is a prince ...

LINDSAY, JOHN WESLEY, 1820-1912.
The English language.   By Rev. J. W. Lindsay...   [New
York, 1861]   255-266 p.   22cm.

"From the Methodist quarterly review, April, 1861."

1. English language—Hist.

NL 0383950   NN

Lindsay, John William, 1875-
The life of a non-professional missionary, by J. W. Lindsay.
London, New York city ₍etc.₎ World dominion press ₍1931₎
21 p.   24½ᶜᵐ.
"Reprinted from World dominion."

1. Missions, Medical.   2. Missions—Paraguay.   I. Title.

Library of Congress   R722.L46   37-21739
                                            ₍266₎ 278.9

NL 0383951   DLC CtY CtY-D

Lindsay, John William, 1875-   tr.

Bible.   N. T. Guarani.   1913.   Lindsay.
Tûpã Ñandeyára ñeẽ Ñandeyára Jesu Cristo.   Recocue ja
remimboecue rejeguare umi evangelio marangatú cuera ja umi
apóstoles rembiapocue ja remimboecue rejeguare.   London,
British and foreign Bible society, 1913.

L⁺ndsay, Joseph Alexander.
The climatic treatment of comsumption...
London, 1887.

NL 0383953   PPL

Wordsworth
PR
5881
S53

Lindsay, Julian Ira.
A note on the marginalia.

(In The Huntington Library quarterly.   San
Marino, Calif.   24cm.   v, 1 (1937) p. 95-99)

Healey 1566.

1. Shearer, Edna Aston.   Wordsworth and
Coleridge margi   nalia ...   I. The
Huntington Li   brary quarterly.   v. 1,
no. 1.

NL 0383954   NIC

VOLUME 334

Lindsay, Julian Ira.
Tradition looks forward; the University of Vermont: a history, 1791–1904. Burlington ₍University of Vermont and State Agricultural College₎ 1954.
285 p. illus. 24 cm.

1. Vermont. University. I. Title.

LD5633.L5   378.743   54–13022 ‡

NL 0383955   DLC PSt NN TxU TU PU

Lᴉɴᴅsᴀʏ, Kᴀᴛᴇ.
Some comparison of methods for the analysis of cotton seed meal, submitted . . 1918. 4 p. *Manuscript.*

NL 0383956   ScU

LINDSAY, KATE.
Five monologue sketches: Three for tea, Shakespeare rehearsed, Flat to let, Great occasion, Shopping and art.   Manchester, A. Heywood [1947]
16 p.   19cm.   (White house community dramas, no. [Cm]10)

1. Monologues, English.   I. Series.

NL 0383957   NN

Lindsay, Katherine.
The manuscripts of the Silvae of Statius. 1914.

NL 0383958   CU

Lindsay, Kathleen.
Lady Make-believe, by Kathleen Lindsay. London, H. Jenkins limited ₍1941₎
284 p. 19¼ᵐ.
"A Herbert Jenkins' book."
"First printing 1941."

I. Title.
41–26423
Library of Congress   PZ3.L6515Lad

NL 0383959   DLC

Lindsay, Kathleen
Wright Coll.   'Neath the southern cross. London, H.Jenkins
Iq   [19—]
L643   312p. 17cm.
920

NL 0383960   CtY

Lindsay, Kathleen.
The splendour falls; a Cromwellian romance. London, Hutchinson, 1952.
248 p.

NL 0383961   PPL

Lindsay, Kathleen.
Unbroken barriers, by Kathleen Lindsay. London, H. Jenkins limited ₍1940₎
255 p. 19ᵐ.
"First printing 1940."

I. Title.
40–33589
Library of Congress   PZ3.L6515Un

NL 0383962   DLC

Lindsay, Keith.
A modern Rasselas, by Keith Lindsay. London, New York, F. T. Neely ₍ᵗ1899₎
1 p. l., ₍5₎–310 p. 19½ᵐ.

I. Title.
99–951 Revised
Library of Congress   PZ3.L652M

NL 0383963   DLC

HJ5797   Lindsay, Kenneth, 1897–
.M3
McAllister, Gilbert, *ed.*
The book crisis, by Sir Hugh Walpole, J. B. Priestley, Geoffrey Faber ₍and others₎ ... with an introduction by the editor, Gilbert McAllister. London, Faber and Faber, limited, for the National committee for the defence of books ₍1940₎

Lindsay, Kenneth, 1897–
La educación inglesa ₍por₎ Kenneth Lindsay; con 8 láminas en colores y 18 ilustraciones en negro. ₍Buenos Aires₎ Espasa Calpe argentina, s. a. ₍1944?₎
47, ₍1₎ p. illus. (incl. facsim.) col. plates, ports. (part col.) 23ᵐ. (*Half-title:* La Gran Bretaña pictórica)
"Impreso en la Gran Bretaña."

1. Education—England.   I. Title.
46–39492
Library of Congress   LA631.L558
370.942

NL 0383965   DLC NcU

Lindsay, Kenneth, *1847–*
Eldorado, an agricultural settlement; a brief history of its origin and development, by Kenneth Lindsay.   ₍Birmingham, Eng.₎ Printed by the Kynoch Press ₍1931₎   59 p. incl. map, plan, plates.   23½cm.

790158A. 1. Eldorado, Argentine   Republic. 2. Land settlement—
Argentine Republic—Misiones.   November 29, 1935

NL 0383966   NN NIC

Lindsay, Kenneth, 1897–
English education ₍by₎ Kenneth Lindsay, with 8 plates in colour and 18 illustrations in black & white. London, W. Collins, 1941.
47, ₍1₎ p. illus., col. plates, col. ports. 23½ᵐ. (*Half-title:* Britain in pictures)

1. Education—England.   I. Title.
42–16193
Library of Congress   LA631.L55
370.942

OU OCl OClW
NL 0383967   DLC OrPR OrSaW OrStbM CaBViP IEN ViU FMU

Lindsay, Kenneth, *1897–*
Social progress and educational waste; being a study of the "free-place" and scholarship system, by Kenneth Lindsay ... with an introduction by Viscount Haldane. London, G. Routledge & sons, ltd., 1926.
vii, 215 p. illus. (map) 22½ᵐ. (*Half-title:* Studies in economics and political science ... no. 88 in the series of monographs by writers connected with the London school of economics and political science)

1. Education—Gt. Brit. 2. Scholarships—Gt. Brit.   I. Title.
27–321
Library of Congress   LA635.L5

NL 0383968   DLC CaBVaU PU NIC OCl OO ICJ IU

Lindsay, Kenneth, *1897–*
The young worker, by Kenneth Lindsay.   London: I. L. P. Publ. Dept.₎ 1925?₎   7 p.   8°.

₁. Child labor—Gt. Br.
February 17, 1927

NL 0383969   NN

Lindsay, Kenneth Clement
see   Lindsay, Kenneth Clement Eriksen, 1919–

FILM   Lindsay, Kenneth Clement Eriksen, 1919–
4034   An examination of the fundamental theories
MAIN   of Wassily Kandinsky.   [Madison, Wis.] 1951.
244ℓ.   illus.,port.

Thesis – University of Wisconsin.
Bibliography: leaves 227–244.
Microfilm (negative) 1 reel. 35mm.

1. Kandinsky, Wassily, 1866–1944. I. Title.

NL 0383971   TxU MH CU InU

Microfilm   Lindsay, Mlle. L., *tr.*
21101
DT   White, Arthur Silva, 1859–1932.
... Le développement de l'Afrique; traduit de l'anglais sur la 2ᵉ éd. par le dʳ E. Verrier ... mᵐᵉ L. Lindsay ... avec quatorze cartes gravées et coloriées par m. F-G. Ravenstein (Londres) et une quinzième carte sur la valeur des terres africaines par m. A. Silva White. Bruxelles, C. Muquardt, 1894.

LINDSAY, LEWIS F., *ed.*
Hymn-songs for use in the Sunday school, young people's meeting, the church and home. Selected by Lewis F. Lindsay and Jas. N. Clemmer. Musical editors: John R. Sweney and Wm. J. Kirkpatrick. Philadelphia, J J. Hood, c1895.   close score(223 p.)
20cm.

1. Hymns, Sunday school. I. Clemmer, James N., joint editor.
II. Lindsay, Lewis F.   III. Clemmer, James N.

NL 0383973   NN NNUT

Lindsay, Lilian.
A short history of dentistry, by Lilian Lindsay. London, J. Bale, sons and Danielsson, ltd., 1933.
88 p. 1 illus. (music) 18¼ᵐ. (*Half-title:* Short history series)

1. Dentistry—Hist.
34—2478
Library of Congress   RK29.L6
₍a44c1₎   617.609

NcD-MC KU-M
NL 0383974   DLC DNLM PU-D PPD NcD OClW OCl OU MiU

VOLUME 334

Lindsay, Lilian, tr.

Fauchard, Pierre, 1678–1761.
The surgeon dentist; or, Treatise on the teeth. In which is seen the means used to keep them clean and healthy, of beautifying them, of repairing their loss and remedies for their diseases and those of the gums and for accidents which may befall the other parts in their vicinity. With observations and reflexions on several special cases. Tr. from the 2d ed., 1746, by Lilian Lindsay. London, Butterworth, 1946.

1. Modernism (Art) 2. Painting—Hist. I. Title.
43–16798
Library of Congress N6400.L5
701.16

NL 0383976 DLC

Lindsay, *Sir* Lionel Arthur, 1874–
Addled art, by Lionel Lindsay ... Sydney, London, Angus and Robertson ltd, 1942.
xvi, 65, [1] p. plates. 24½ᵐ.

1. Modernism (Art) 2. Painting—Hist. I. Title.
43–16798
Library of Congress N6400.L5
701.16

NL 0383976 DLC

Lindsay, *Sir* Lionel Arthur, 1874–
Addled art, by Lionel Lindsay ... London, Hollis and Carter ltd. [1946]
xiii, 15–65, [1] p. plates. 25ᵐ.
"First published in England, 1946."

1. Modernism (Art) 2. Painting—Hist. I. Title.
N6490.L5 1946
701.16
47–15530

NL 0383977 DLC CtY PSt IEN

Lindsay, Sir Lionel Arthur, 1874–
ND2092
.H45A4
Heysen, Hans, 1877–
The art of Hans Heysen. Special number of Art in Australia, edited by Sydney Ure Smith, Bertram Stevens and C. Lloyd Jones. Sydney, Angus & Robertson, ltd., 1920.

Arthur,
Lindsay, Lionel, 1874–
Arthur Streeton's Australian work.
(*In* Streeton, Arthur, 1867– The art of Arthur Streeton. Pp. 5–16. Sydney. 1919.)

M5712 — Streeton, Arthur, 1867–

NL 0383979 MB

Lindsay, Lionel Arthur, 1874–
Australian art.
(*In* Society of Artists, Sydney. The exhibition of Australian art in London, 1923. Pp. (9–17). London. 1923.)

N611 — Australia. F.a.

NL 0383980 MB

Arthur,
Lindsay, Lionel, 1874–
Australian etchings
see under Art in Australia.

Lindsay, *Sir* Lionel Arthur, 1874–
A book of woodcuts, drawn on wood and engraved by Lionel Lindsay. Sydney, N. S. W., Art in Australia limited; London, Constable & co., ltd., 1922.
3 p. l., [2] p., 2 l. col. mounted front., mounted illus., 19 mounted pl. 27ᵐ.
"This edition is limited to 200 copies, of which 175 are for sale in Australia. The remaining 25 copies are reserved for a London edition." Initial.

1. Wood-engravings. I. Art in Australia.
23–7681 Revised
Library of Congress NE1217.L49A4
[r43c2]

NL 0383982 DLC

Arthur,
Lindsay, Lionel, 1874–
Charles Keene, the artists' artist.
— London. Colnaghi & Co. 1934. (8), 15, (1) pp. 55 plates. Portrait. 32 cm.
No. 88 of an edition of 130 copies.

E131 — Drawings. Colls. — Keene, Charles Samuel, 1823–1891.

NL 0383983 MB

Lindsay, *Sir* Lionel Arthur, 1874–
Conrad Martens, the man and his art, by Lionel Lindsay ... Sydney, Australia, Angus & Robertson ltd., 1920.
6 p. l., 32, [1] p. front. (mounted col. port.) illus., LX pl. (part col. mounted) double facsim. 26ᵐ.

1. Martens, Conrad, 1801–1878.
43–40074
Library of Congress ND1942.M35L5

NL 0383984 DLC CaBVaU PP NN PSt CU

LINDSAY, *Sir* Lionel Arthur, 1874–
Etchings & drypoints of Spain & Australia, April–May, 1927. Lond., P.& D.Colnaghi, [1927.] Pl. 0.

NL 0383985 MoS MH

Lindsay, *Sir* Lionel Arthur, 1874–
Etchings and drypoints. [1st ed. Sydney, U. Smith, 1949]
48 p. illus. 20 cm. (Ure Smith miniature series, 2)

NE2210.L54A44
767.2
50–34861

NL 0383986 DLC CaBVaU PSt

NC1260
.L52
Rare bk.
coll.
Lindsay, *Sir* Lionel Arthur, 1874–
Lindsay, Norman, 1879–
The pen drawings of Norman Lindsay. Special number of Art in Australia, edited by Sydney Ure Smith & Bertram Stevens. Sydney, Angus & Robertson ltd, 1918.

Lindsay, Lionel Arthur, 1874–
Pictures of horses and English life
see under Munnings, Alfred James, 1878–

Arthur,
Lindsay, Lionel, 1874–
Twenty-one woodcuts; drawn, engraved & printed, by Lionel Lindsay. Sydney: Meryon Press, 1924. 4 l. front., 20 pl. 4°.

391837A. 1. Wood-engravings, Australian.
December 31, 1928

NL 0383989 NN

ND2089
.H48
folio
Lindsay, Sir Lionel Arthur, 1874–
Heysen, Hans, 1877–
Watercolours and drawings. Text by Sir Lionel Lindsay and James S. MacDonald. [Sydney] Legend Press [1952?]

BX1423 Lindsay, Lionel St. George, 1849–
.Q35 Le centenaire de l'Archevêché de
1919L Quebec, 1819–1919, par Monseigneur L.S.
G. Lindsay ... Quebec, l'Action sociale catholique, 1919.
16 p. 23cm.
"Extrait de la Semaine religieuse de Quebec."
Bibliographical footnotes.

NL 0383991 MnHi MH

LINDSAY, Lionel St. George, 1849–
Louis Liénard de Beaujeu; premier docteur en théologie de la Nouvelle-France. Québec, imp.de la compagnie de l'"Événement ",1907.
pp.29.
"Extrait de la Nouvelle-France."

NL 0383992 MH

Lindsay, Lionel St. George, 1849–
Notre-Dame de la Jeune-Lorette en la Nouvelle France; étude historique, par l'abbé Lionel Saint-George Lindsay... Montréal, La Cie de publication de la Revue canadienne, 1900 [i. e. 1901] 319 p. illus. 26cm.
Colophon dated 1901.
"Les chants des Hurons," including musical examples, p. 261–264.
Bibliographical footnotes.

586785B. 1. Indians, N. A.—Tribes —Huron—Missions. 2. Indian
Lorette, Que.—Hist.
N. Y. P. L. February 14, 1952

NL 0383993 NN CaBVaU CaOTU NRU CtY MH MB MiU

Lindsay, Lionel Saint George, 1849–
Pèlerinages d'outre-mer: Lourdes, Assise, La Salette, Le Mont Saint-Michel, Le Mont-Cassin, etc. Québec, N.S.Hardy, 1890.
227 p. 22.5 cm.

NL 0383994 MH

VOLUME 334

Lindsay, Lionel St. George, 1849–
Un precurseur de la Trappé du Canada; Dom
Urbain Guillet.

(Nouvelle France. Quebec, 1911-18. v. 10, p. 417-428;
453-463, 541-552; v. 13, p. 369-374, 456-464; v. 14,
p. 121-130, 370-376; v. 15, p. 134-137, 207-215;
v. 16, p. 227-233, 274-276; v. 17, p. 184-189,
219-228.

NL 0383995   NN

Lindsay, Lionel St. George, 1849–
Le premier concile plénier de Quebec
(10 septembre -1er novembre 1909) Travaux
préparatoires. Séances sclennelles. Fêtes
religieuses et civiques. Allocutions.   Québec:
Imp. de "L'événement", 1910.
vii, 305 (1) p. 9 pl., 3 port.   4°.

NL 0383996   NN

Lindsay, M.
...The bridge. ₍By₎ Lindsay...   New York: F. Blume₍,
n. d.₎.   Publ. pl. no. 272.   5 p.   f°.

English words; music for 1 voice with piano acc.
Words by Longfellow.
At head of title: Lyric sparks; a collection of songs & ballads...

1. Songs, American. 2. Longfellow,   Henry Wadsworth, 1807–1882.
3. Title.
N. Y. P. L.   October 28, 1926

NL 0384001   NN

Lindsay, M.
The bridge. "I stood on the bridge at midnight." [Song, with
pianoforte accompaniment.]   Written by H. W. Longfellow.
Music composed by Miss M. Lindsay [Mrs. M. Bliss].
Boston. Ditson & Co. ₍185-?₎ 5 pp. Decorated cover. 36 cm.

NL 0384002   MB

Lindsay, M.
The bridge; written by H. W. Longfellow. Composed by
Miss M. Lindsay. ₍Chicago: Published by Root & Cady, 67
Washington Street. 186-?₎
5 p. 34 cm. (The Vocalist's companion, a selection of beautiful
ballads, arranged with piano accompaniment, by various authors)
Caption title.

1. Songs (Medium voice) with piano.   ᴵ. Title.

M1621.L   52–55800

NL 0384003   DLC

Lindsay, M
The bridge. Words by H.W.Longfellow. Music by
Miss M.Lindsay. ₍n.p., 1861?₎
5 p.   34.5cm.
Caption title.
On title page: "Favorite songs of the period."
Dichter and Shapiro. Early American sheet music,
N.Y.,1941,p.159, lists another ed.of this work,
printed at Boston in 1861.
1.Vocal music.I.t.II.Longfellow,Henry Wadsworth,
1807–1882.

NL 0384004   MiU-C

Lindsay, M.
The bridge; written by H. W. Longfellow. Composed by
Miss M. Lindsay. ₍Chicago, Root & Cady, ⁰1869₎
5 p. 34 cm. (Songs and cavatinas, 2)

1. Songs (Medium voice) with piano.   ᴵ. Title.

M1621.L   52–55797

NL 0384005   DLC

Lindsay, M
The bridge. Words by H. W. Longfellow. Music by Miss
M. Lindsay. ₍Chicago?₎ 1882.
5 p. 28 cm.
"Musical supplement to The Inter ocean, no. 56."

1. Songs (Medium voice) with piano.   ᴵ. Inter-ocean (Chicago)
Supplement. ᴵᴵ. Title.

M1621.L   M 54–309

NL 0384006   DLC

Lindsay, M
Every inch a king; or, The adventures of Rex
and his friends. Trans. into the language of
"humans" by Mrs. J. Worthington Bliss. Illus.
by Harrison Weir. London and Sydney, Griffith
Farran Okeden & Welsh [18--?]
160, 47, [1] p. illus. 19 cm.

Publisher's catalog: 47, [1] p. at end.

NL 0384007   NjP

Lindsay, M
Hymn of the Moravian nuns of Bethlehem (U. S.), at the conse-
cration of Pulaski's banner. [With accompaniment for piano-
forte.] Words by H. W. Longfellow, Esq. Music by Miss M.
Lindsay [Mrs. M. Bliss].
London. Cocks & Co. [184-?] ₍ᴵ₎, 7 pp. 34½ cm.
The title on the cover is Pulaski.

NL 0384008   MB

Lindsay, M.
Too late, too late! Poetry by Tennyson,
music by Miss M. Lindsay. Boston, Published
by Oliver Ditson & co.;N.York,Firth Pond & co.
[etc.,etc.,18--?] Publ.no. 21084.
5p. 35½cm.
Engraved t.-p.
For one voice, with piano accompaniment.
Begin: Late, late, so late!

NL 0384009   CtY MB

Lindsay, M
Unto Thee, O Lord, will I lift up my soul. Anthem. [Accomp. for
organ.]
[London. Cccks & Co. ₍185-?₎ 4 pp. [Chorister's handbook.] L. 8°.

Mar. 21,   19c2
E₃₃₉₂ — T.r. — Church music. Anthems, &c.

NL 0384010   MB

Lindsay, Mrs. M   A
Memoir of Miss Elizabeth McQuerns, by
Mrs. M. A. Lindsay. Due West, S. C., Associate
Reformed Presbyterian Print., 1887.
23 p. 23 cm.

1. McQuerns, Elizabeth, 1802-1886.
ᴵ. Title.

NL 0384011   NcD

Lindsay, Mabel M.
Anni Domini, a gospel study ...   Lond.
Methuen₍1909₎.
2v. maps, O.

NL 0384012   CaBViP

Lindsay, Mrs. Margaret D. (Cook) ed.
Lindsay, James, 1852-1923.
Autobiography of Rev. James Lindsay, D. D. Edin-
burgh and London, W. Blackwood and sons, 1924.

Lindsay, Margaret Isabella.
The Lindsays of America. A genealogical narrative,
and family record beginning with the family of the earliest settler in the mother state, Virginia, and including in
an appendix all the Lindsays of America. By Margaret
Isabella Lindsay ... Albany, N. Y., J. Munsell's sons,
1889.
xv, ₍1₎, 275 p., 1 l. plates, fold. geneal. tables. 21½ᶜᵐ.
Blank pages at end: Family record and additions.

1. Lindsey family (David Lindsay, d. 1667) 2. Lindsey family.

Library of Congress   CS71.L753 1889   9—11621

NL 0384014   DLC Vi MWA ViU MH NcU

Lindsay, Mrs. Margaret Julia (Brown)
₍Brown. Mrs. Charlotte (Cowdrey), 1872–
The New Jersey Browns. Allied families: Freeman, Moores,
Skinner, Brittain, Dunham. Lewis, Pain (Payne), Edgar,
Harned, Anderson, Crane, Munn, Ayer, Putnam, Albertus,
Aldridge. Milwaukee, Wis., 1931.

Lindsay, Margaret (Lindsay) countess of
Crawford
see
Crawford, Margaret (Lindsay) Lindsay, countess of
1824-1909

Lindsay, Marian, tr.
Perroy, Louis, 1858–
The ascent of Calvary, by Père Louis Perroy; authorized
translation from the French by Marian Lindsay, with in-
troduction by Most Rev. John J. Glennon ... New York,
P. J. Kenedy & sons ₍1922₎

Lindsay, Marian, tr.
Laveille, E.
The life of Father de Smet, s. ᴶ. (1801–1873) by E. Laveille,
s. ᴶ., authorized translation by Marian Lindsay, introduction
by Charles Coppens ... New York, P. J. Kenedy & sons, 1915.

VOLUME 334

Lindsay, Marian, tr.

Melegari, Dora.

Makers of sorrow and makers of joy ... by Dora Melegari; authorized translation from the original French by Marian Lindsay. New York and London, Funk & Wagnalls company, 1910.

BX2183
.P42

Lindsay, Marian, tr.

Petit, Adolphe, 1822–1914.

My bark; a souvenir of retreats given by the Rev. P. Adolphe Petit, s. j.; translated from the French by Marian Lindsay. St. Louis, Mo. ₍etc.₎ B. Herder, 1914.

Lindsay, Martin.

History of 7th Armoured Division, June 1943–July 1945
see under Gt. Brit. Army. 7th Armoured Division.

Lindsay, Martin, 1905–
The epic of Captain Scott, by Martin Lindsay ... New York, G. P. Putnam's sons, 1934.

3 p. l., 9–178 p. incl. front. (port.) illus. fold. map. 19½ᶜᵐ. (*Half-title:* "Great occasions")

"Bibliographical note": p. 173.

1. Scott, Robert Falcon, 1868–1912. 2. Antarctic regions. 3. Scientific expeditions. 4. British Antarctic ("Terra Nova") expedition, 1910–1913. 5. Terra Nova (Ship) 6. Discovery (Ship) 7. South pole. i. Title.

₍Full name: Martin Alexander Lindsay₎

Library of Congress — G875.S35L5
—— Copy 2.
Copyright A 69263 ₍r39k2₎ 34–2248 Revised

923.942

DN ViU NN CaBVa
NL 0384022 DLC IdU–SB Or WaS OCl OClh MB PP PPG

Lindsay, Martin, 1905–
The epic of Captain Scott. Lond. Falcon press[1948].
124p. front.(port.)l illus.plates,D.

NL 0384023 CaBViP RPJCB

Lindsay, Martin, 1905–
The House of Commons. London, Collins, 1947.

47, ₍1₎ p. illus. (part col.) 23 cm. (Britain in pictures)

The British people in pictures.
"Short bibliography": p. ₍48₎

1. Gt. Brit. Parliament. House of Commons. i. Title. (Series. Series : The British people in pictures.)

Full name: Martin Alexander Lindsay.

JN673.L5 328.42 48–20708*
₍2₎

RPB OU PU ViU NN IEN IdPI MtU OrStbM
NL 0384024 DLC CaBViP CaBVa GU IU TxU CLSU TU MH

Lindsay, Martin, 1905–
Shall we reform 'the Lords'? London, Falcon Press ₍1948₎

71 p. 19 cm. ₍Forum books₎
Bibliography: p. 71.

1. Gt. Brit. Parliament. House of Lords. i. Title.
Full name: Martin Alexander Lindsay.

JN623 1948.L5 328.42 49–15283*

NL 0384025 DLC PSt ICU MH ViU IaU CtY

Lindsay, Martin, 1905–
Sledge; the British trans-Greenland expedition, 1934, by Martin Lindsay ... with 5 maps, 48 half-tone plates, and numerous line illustrations. London ₍etc.₎ Cassell and company, ltd. ₍1935₎

xl, 342 p. front., illus. (incl. maps) plates (1 fold.) ports., diagr. 24ᶜᵐ.

1. British trans-Greenland expedition, 1934. 2. Greenland—Disc. & explor. i. Title.

₍Full name: Martin Alexander Lindsay₎

Library of Congress G743.L48 1935 36–3940
—— Copy 2.
Copyright A ad int. 21024 ₍5₎ 919.8

CaBVaU
NL 0384026 DLC IU CaOTP AMAU PP MiU OCl NN OrU

Lindsay, Martin, 1905–
Sledge; the British trans-Greenland expedition, 1934, by Martin Lindsay. Harmondsworth, Middlesex, Eng., Penguin books limited ₍1939₎

viii, 9–247 p. illus. (incl. maps) plates, ports. 18ᶜᵐ. (*On cover:* Penguin books. 193)

"First published 1935; published in Penguin books 1939."
"In this edition... I have cut out all extraneous material ... I have omitted Andrew Croft's account of his Greenland winter."—Pref. to the Penguin edition.

1. British trans-Greenland expedition, 1934. 2. Greenland—Disc. & explor. i. Title.

₍Full name: Martin Alexander Lindsay₎

Library of Congress G743.L48 1939 41–20295
₍2₎ 919.8

NL 0384027 DLC

Lindsay, Martin, 1905–
So few got through; the personal diary of Lieut.-Col. Martin Lindsay, d. s. o., m., who served with the Gordon Highlanders in the 51st Highland division from July, 1944, to May, 1945, by Martin Lindsay. London, Collins, 1946.

287 p. illus. (incl. maps) 20½ᶜᵐ.

1. World war, 1939–1945—Regimental histories—Gt. Brit.—Gordon Highlanders. 2. World war, 1939–1945—Personal narratives, English. 3. World war, 1939–1945—Campaigns—Western. 4. Gt. Brit. Army. Gordon Highlanders. i. Title.

₍Full name: Martin Alexander Lindsay₎

Library of Congress D760.G6L5 46–6824
₍a3₎ 940.542

NL 0384028 DLC MB KU

Lindsay, Martin, 1905–
Those Greenland days, by Martin Lindsay ... with illustrations and maps. Edinburg and London, W. Blackwood & sons, ltd., 1932.

xii, 256 p. plates, ports., maps. 22 cm.

1. British Arctic air-route expedition, 1930–1931. 2. Greenland—Descr. & trav. i. Title.

G743.L5 919.8 32–34797

NL 0384029 DLC KU MB NN DAL CaOTP DAS MiU

Lindsay, Martin, 1905–
Three got through; memoirs of an Arctic explorer. London, Falcon Press ₍1946₎

262 p. plates, maps. 19 cm.

1. Greenland. 2. British Trans-Greenland Expedition, 1934. 3. British Arctic Air-Route Expedition, 1930–1931. i. Title.

Full name: Martin Alexander Lindsay.

G743.L52 919.8 47–26688*

NL 0384030 DLC FTaSU KU GU CaBVa

MT67
.L74

LINDSAY, MARTIN, 1915–
Teach yourself songwriting. London, English Universities Press ₍1955₎
164 p. music. (Teach yourself books)

1. Music, Popular (Songs, etc.)—Writing and publishing. I. tc.

NL 0384031 InU NN OCl CaBVa CaBViP NcU

Lindsay, Martin Alexander

see

Lindsay, Martin, 1905–

F2235
.3
.L9
1947

Lindsay, Mary H., tr.

Ludwig, Emil, 1881–
Bolivar, the life of an idealist. ₍Tr. by Mary H. Lindsay₎ London, W. H. Allen ₍1947₎

Lindsay, Mary H., tr.

Selinko, Annemarie.
... Everything will be better to-morrow; a novel: translated from the German by Mary H. Lindsay. London, Secker and Warburg ₍1939₎

DT115
.L82
1947

Lindsay, Mary H., tr.

FOR OTHER EDITIONS
SEE MAIN ENTRY

Ludwig, Emil, 1881–
The Nile; the life-story of a river. Tr. by Mary H. Lindsay. ₍Reprint ed.₎ Garden City, N. Y., Garden City Pub. Co. ₍1947, *1937₎

Lindsay, Mary H., tr.

Selinko, Annemarie.
Tomorrow is another day, a novel by Anne Marie Selinko; translated by Mary H. Lindsay. New York, Alliance book corporation, Longmans, Green and co., 1939.

₍Lindsay, Mary (McDowell)₎ 1903–
Kurrajong, by Jane Lindsay ₍pseud.₎ Sydney, London, Angus and Robertson ltd., 1945.

3 p. l., 249, ₍1₎ p. 18¾ᶜᵐ.

i. Title.

Library of Congress PZ3.L6529Ku 46–1440

NL 0384037 DLC CaBVaU NcU

₍Lindsay, *Mrs.* Mary (McDowell)₎ 1903–
Sweet virgin, by Jane Lindsay ₍pseud.₎ London, T. Butterworth, limited ₍1931₎

351 p. 19¾ᶜᵐ.

i. Title.

Library of Congress PZ3.L65298w 31–13488

NL 0384038 DLC

VOLUME 334

₍Lindsay, *Mrs.* Mary (McDowell)₎ 1903–
Trip no further, by Jane Lindsay ₍pseud.₎ London, T. Butterworth limited ₍1930₎
316 p. 19½ᶜᵐ.

I. Title.

30–12530

Library of Congress   PZ3.L6529Tr

NL 0384039   DLC

₍Lindsay, *Mrs.* Mary (McDowell)₎ 1903–
Wear the green willow, by Jane Lindsay ₍pseud.₎ London, T. Butterworth, ltd. ₍1935₎
3 p. l., 9–285 p. 19½ᶜᵐ.

I. Title.

35–23316

Library of Congress   PZ3.L6529We

NL 0384040   DLC

Lindsay, Mrs. Mary (Rodgers) 1901– comp.
FOR OTHER EDITIONS
SEE MAIN ENTRY
U. S. *National youth administration, New York (City)*
Directory of youth organizations. Compiled by Mary Rodgers Lindsay, director of information and research, assisted by Simon Uhrman of the Research department. Rev. and enl. ed., 1940. New York city, Federal security agency, National youth administration for New York city ₍1940₎

HF5549 Lindsay, Mary (Rodgers) 1901–
.P45
Personnel club of New York.
Pioneering in personnel, a history of the Personnel club of New York ₍by₎ Mary Rodgers Lindsay ₍chairman of₎ the Publicity committee of the Personnel club. New York city. The Personnel club of New York, 1943.

Lindsay, Mary (Rodgers) 1901–
Report on proposed occupational study of New York City Board of education. **Rev.** May 6, 1941. ₍1941₎
117 l. tables, forms. 37ᶜᵐ.

1. New York (City) Vocational survey commission. 2. Labor and laboring classes – New York (City). 3. Occupations – New York (City)

NL 0384043   NNC

Lindsay, *Mrs.* Mary (Rodgers) 1901–
Youth gets its chance, by Mary Rodgers Lindsay, assistant director in charge of research. A study of N. Y. A. workers in New York city—their characteristics, use of income and attitudes toward their jobs. ₍New York₎ National youth administration for New York city, 1938.
viii, 213 numb. l. incl. tables, forms. 28ᶜᵐ.
Loose-leaf.
Mimeographed.

1. Youth. 2. Unemployed—New York (City)   I. U. S. National youth administration, New York (City)   II. Title.

E 40—627

U. S. Off. of educ. Library   HV1437.N7L3
for Library of Congress   ₍40c2₎

NL 0384044   DHEW WaS NN OU PPT CU CSt NPV NIC   OO

Lindsay, Matthew.
Security, an address given to the Rotary club, Glasgow, by Matthew Lindsay ... Glasgow, Jackson, son & co. ltd. ₍1942₎
15, ₍1₎ p. 18¾ᶜᵐ.

1. Insurance, State and compulsory—Gt. Brit.   I. Title.

43–11415

Library of Congress   HD7168.L55
₍2₎   331.2544

NL 0384045   DLC NN

Lindsay, Matthew.
The span of life. Glasgow, W. MacLellan ₍1948₎
81 p. 19 cm.

1. Old age.   I. Title.

HQ1061.L5   179   49–24189*

NL 0384046   DLC

Stefansson
F
931   LINDSAY, MATTHEW J
.Y9L5   Yukon and Klondyke gold fields of Alaska; containing three authentic maps, the Yukon mining laws, and other miscellaneous information of general interest, compiled by Matthew J. Lindsay. San Francisco, ₍Goodall, Perkins & co. 1897₎
48 p. illus. maps. 24 cm.

In portfolio.

1. Klondike   gold fields. I. Title.

NL 0384047   NhD

Lindsay, Mattie Virginia Sarah

See

₍Lomax, Virginia₎

Lindsay, Maud McKnight, 1874– *1941*
The amazing adventures of Ali, by Maud Lindsay; illustrated by W. M. Berger. Boston, Lothrop, Lee & Shepard co. ₍*1931₎
166 p. col. front., col. plates. 20¼ᶜᵐ.

I. Title.

31–31936

Library of Congress   PZ7.L66Am

NL 0384049   DLC OC1 OC1h WaSp MB

Lindsay, Maud McKnight, 1874–
Annemin yeni masallari, yazan Maud Lindsay, nakleden Mutia Sabri ... İstanbul, Devlet matbaasi, 1929.
3 p. l., 3–47 p. illus. 19½ᶜᵐ.

I. Sabri, Mutia, tr.   II. Title.

40–24595

Library of Congress   PZ90.T8L55

NL 0384050   DLC

Lindsay, Maud McKnight, 1874–
Bobby and the big road, by Maud Lindsay, illustrated by Florence Liley Young. Boston, Lothrop, Lee & Shepard co. ₍*1920₎
112 p. col. front., 1 illus. (music) col. plates. 18½ x 16¼ᶜᵐ.

I. Title.

20–26565

Library of Congress   PZ7.L66Bo

NL 0384051   DLC PBa PP PWcS MB

Lindsay, Maud McKnight, 1874–
The choosing book, by Maud Lindsay, illustrated by Florence Liley Young. Boston, Lothrop, Lee & Shepard co. ₍*1928₎
5 p. l., 13–177 p. col. front., illus., col. plates. 18½ᶜᵐ.

I. Title.

28–22730

Library of Congress   PZ8.L645Ch
₍3₎

NL 0384052   DLC CoU WaSp PP Or OO OC1 ODW MB

Lindsay, Maud McKnight, 1874–
Christmas plays ... Boston, Chicago, The Pilgrim press ₍*1927₎
26 p. 19ᶜᵐ.
Includes music.
CONTENTS.—The first Christmas morning, by Maud Lindsay.—What child is this? By Martha Race.—Frankincense, by Louise L. G. Cummings.

1. Christmas plays.   I. Race, Martha. What child is this?   II. Cummings, Louise L. G. Frankincense.   III. Title.   IV. Title: The first Christmas morning.

Library of Congress   PN6120.C5L483   40–23623
Copyright A 1014438   ₍2₎   812.5082

NL 0384053   DLC RPB

Lindsay, Maud McKnight, 1874–
Fun on Children's street, by Maud Lindsay; illustrations by Marion Downer. Boston, New York, Lothrop, Lee & Shepard co. ₍*1941₎
124 p. illus. (part col.; incl. music) 23½ x 18½ᶜᵐ.
Illustrated lining-papers in color.

1. Games. 2. Amusements.   I. Title.

41–7953

Library of Congress   GV1203.L54
——— Copy 2.   ₍5₎   793

NL 0384054   DLC WaSp

Lindsay, Maud McKnight, 1874–
The harper's song ₍a song₎
In– her– The story-teller ... Boston, ₍c1915₎
p. 42. 18 cm.

NL 0384055   RPB

Lindsay, Maud McKnight, 1874–
Jock Barefoot, by Maud Lindsay; pictured by Jane Linton. Boston, New York, Lothrop, Lee and Shepard company, 1939.
x, 13–177 p. col. front., illus. 22¾ᶜᵐ.

I. Title.

39–25439

Library of Congress   PZ7.L66Jd

NL 0384056   DLC WaSp Or OC1

VOLUME 334

Lindsay, Maud McKnight, 1874–1941.
The joyous guests, by Maud Lindsay and Emilie Poulsson, illustrated by W. M. Berger. Boston, Lothrop, Lee & Shepard co. ₁1921₁
206 p. col. front., col. plates. 23 cm.
Illustrated lining-papers.

ɪ. Poulsson, Emilie, 1853–1939, joint author. ɪɪ. Title.
21—21201
Library of Congress   PZ7.L66J

NL 0384057   DLC CoU OC1 Or PP OC1h OO NN

Lindsay, Maud McKnight, 1874–
The joyous travelers, by Maud Lindsay and Emilie Poulsson, illustrated by W. M. Berger. Boston, Lothrop, Lee & Shepard co. ₁1919₁
157 p. col. front., illus. (incl. music) 22¼ᶜᵐ.
Illustrated t.-p. and lining-papers.

ɪ. Poulsson, Emilie i. e. Anne Emilie, 1853–   joint author. ɪɪ. Title.
Library of Congress   PZ7.L66Jo   19—9661

NL 0384058   DLC CoU WaSp Or OrP OC1 MB NN

Lindsay, Maud *McKnight*, *1874–*
The joyous travellers... by ... & Emil
Poulsson. London., Harrap, 1925.
206 p.

NL 0384059   PP

Lindsay, Maud McKnight, 1874–
Little Missy, by Maud Lindsay; illustrated by Florence Liley Young. Boston, Lee & Shepard co. ₁1922₁
188 p. col. front., col. plates. 18¼ x 16¼ᶜᵐ.
Illustrated lining-papers.

ɪ. Title.
Library of Congress   PZ7.L66Li   22—23714
₍s25h2₎

NL 0384060   DLC OLak OC1 PBa PPT Or OrP CoU

Lindsay, Maud McKnight, 1874–
More mother stories, by Maud Lindsay; illustrated by F. C. Sanborn and Mrs. Fanny Railton ... Springfield, Mass., Milton Bradley company, 1905.
183 p. front., 19 pl. 19ᶜᵐ.

ɪ. Title.
Library of Congress   PZ7.L66Mo   6—37

NL 0384061   DLC OO MB WaS Or Wa OrP MiU CoU

Lindsay, Maud (McKnight) 1874–
More mother stories. Illustrated by F.C.
Sanborn and Mrs. Fanny Railton. Springfield
Mass., M.Bradley co., 1906.

NL 0384062   MH

Lindsay, Maud McKnight, 1874–
More mother stories. Illustrated by F.C.
Sanborn and Mrs. Fanny Railton. Springfield,
Mass., M.Bradley co., 1908.

NL 0384063   MH

Lindsay, Maud McKnight, 1874–
More mother stories. Illustrated by F.C.
Sanborn and Mrs. Fanny Railton. Springfield,
Mass., Milton Bradley co., 1914.

NL 0384064   MH OLak

372.2   Lindsay, Maud McKnight, 1874–
More mother stories   Springfield,
Mass. Milton Bradley co.c1929.

NL 0384065   NcC

Lindsay, Maud McKnight, 1874–
Mother stories, by Maud Lindsay; illustrated by Sarah Noble-Ives ... Springfield, Mass., M. Bradley company, 1900.
4 p. l., 182 p. plates. 19ᶜᵐ.

ɪ. Title.
1—30112
Library of Congress   PZ7.L66M
Copyright 1900 A 29149   ₍a35d1₎   901

NL 0384066   DLC PPT PP MiU Wa MtBC Or AU

Lindsay, Maud *McKnight*, *1874–*
Mother stories. Illustrated by Sarah Noble-Ives. 3d edition.
— Springfield, Mass. Milton Bradley Co. 1902. (7), 182 pp. Plates.
12°.

E8965 — T.r. — Kindergarten.   1903
May 12,

NL 0384067   MB

Lindsay, Maud McKnight, 1874–
Mother stories. Illustrated by Sarah Noble-
Ives. 8th ed. Springfield, Milton Bradley co.,
1907.

NL 0384068   MH PPPL

Lindsay, Maud McKnight, 1874–
Mother stories. Illustrated by Sarah Noble-
Ives. 10th ed. Springfield, Mass., M.Bradley
co., 1909.

NL 0384069   MH NRCR

Lindsay, Maud McKnight, 1874–
Mother stories, by Maud Lindsay; illustrated by
Sarah Noble-Ives.
Springfield, Mass., M. Bradley company, 1915.
4 p. l., 182 p. plates.

NL 0384070   CaOTP

Lindsay, Maud McKnight, 1874–
Mother stories, by Maud Lindsay; illustrated by Sarah
Noble-Ives ... Springfield, Mass., M. Bradley company,
1919.
4 p. l., 182 p. plates. 19

NL 0384071   ICU NRAB

Lindsay, Maud McKnight, *1874–*
Mother stories. Illustrated by Sarah Noble-Ives.
Springfield, Mass. Milton Bradley Co. 1920. (7), 182 pp
Plates. 19 cm.
Several copies of various editions.
Stories for mothers to tell their children.

M8380 — T.r. — Story-telling. — Ives, Sarah Noble-, illus.

NL 0384072   MB

Lindsay, Maud McKnight, *1874–*
Mother stories; illustrated by Sarah Noble-
Ives, ...Springfield, Mass. Bradley, 1927.
27th.ed.
182 p.

NL 0384073   PPT

Lindsay, Maud McKnight, 1874–
Mother stories, by Maud Lindsay; illustrated by Sarah
Noble-Ives ... *Springfield, Mass., M. Bradley company,
1928.
4 p. l., 182 p. plates. 19ᶜᵐ.
*28 ed.

NL 0384074   DLC

Lindsay, Maud McKnight, 1874–1941.
Mother stories and More mother stories, by Maud Lindsay, illustrated by Gertrude H. Howe. New York, The Platt & Munk co., inc. ₁1947₁
4 p. l., 13–188 p. col. front., illus. 25¼ᵐ.

ɪ. Title.
PZ7.L66Mop   47–18107

NL 0384075   DLC WaS Or

Lindsay, Maud McKnight, 1874–
Posey and the peddler, by Maud Lindsay; illustrated by Ellis Credle. New York, Boston, Lothrop, Lee and Shepard company, 1938.
x p., 1 l., 11–186 p. incl. front., illus. 20¼ᶜᵐ.

ɪ. Title.
38–19252
Library of Congress   PZ7.L66Po

NL 0384076   DLC Or OEac OC1

₍Lindsay, Maud McKnight₎ 1874–
The quest for the nightingale ₁a poem₁
In- her- The story-teller ... Boston, ₁c1915₁
p. 90. 18 cm.

NL 0384077   RPB

VOLUME 334

Lindsay, Maud McKnight, 1874–
Silverfoot, by Maud Lindsay; illustrated by Florence Liley Young. Boston, Lothrop, Lee & Shepard co. [1924]
223 p. col. front., col. plates. 18½ᶜᵐ.

ɪ. Title.

Library of Congress   PZ7.L66Si

25–26025

NL 0384078   DLC OC1h OO

Lindsay, Maud McKnight, 1874–
The song that traveled [a song]
In- her- The story-teller ... Boston, [c1915]
p. 89.   18 cm.

NL 0384079   RPB

Lindsay, Maud McKnight, 1874–
Songs for Alabama, by Maud Lindsay ...
[Sheffield, Ala?] The blue pencil club of Muscle Shoals district [n. d.]

NL 0384080   AU

Lindsay, Maud McKnight, 1874–1941.
A story garden for little children, by Maud Lindsay; illustrated by Florence Liley Young. Boston, Lothrop, Lee & Shepard co. [1913]
1 p. l., vii p., 2 l., 91 p.   front., illus., 19 pl.   18½ cm.
Illustrated t.-p. and lining-papers.

ɪ. Title.

A 13—1956

Springfield, Mass. City   Library
for Library of Congress   [a4901]

NL 0384081   MSC WaSp CoU PP PJA MB NN ViU OrP

Lindsay, Maud McKnight, 1874–
The story-teller, by Maud Lindsay, illustrated by Florence Liley Young. Boston, Lothrop, Lee and Shepard co. [1915]
117 p.   col. front., col. plates.   18½ᶜᵐ.
Illus. t.-p. and lining-papers.

ɪ. Title.

15–25349

Library of Congress   PZ7.L66St

NL 0384082   DLC CoU Or OrP PCC PPPL NcC AU NN MB

Lindsay, Maud McKnight, 1874–
The storyland tree, by Maud Lindsay; illustrated by Kayren Draper and Mimi Clare Hill. Boston, Lothrop, Lee & Shepard co. [1933]

159 p. incl. illus., plates. col. front. 18½ᶜᵐ.
ɪ. Title.

33–24194

Library of Congress   PZ7.L66Su

NL 0384083   DLC Or OrLgE OrAshS

Lindsay, Maud McKnight, 1874– *1941.*
The toy shop, by Maud Lindsay; illustrated by Florence Liley Young. Boston, Lothrop, Lee & Shepard co. [1926]
158 p. incl. illus., plates. col. front. 18½ᶜᵐ.

ɪ. Title.

26–16364

Library of Congress   PZ7.L66To

NL 0384084   DLC PJA MB OrAshS

Lindsay, Maurice
see **Lindsay, John Maurice**, 1918–

Lindsay, Maurice Monroe, 1886–
Corporate organization and accounts, by Maurice M. Lindsay, c. ᴘ. ᴀ. Boston, Mass., The Bentley school of accounting and finance [1935]
24, 25A–25B, 25–194 p. incl. forms.   27ᶜᵐ.

1. Corporations—Accounting. 2. Corporations—U. S. 3. Corporations—Forms, blanks, etc. ɪ. Title.
36–5087

Library of Congress   HF5686.C7L5
———— Copy 2.
Copyright A 88768   [3]   658.1145

NL 0384086   DLC

Lindsay, Maurice Monroe, 1886–
Holding companies and consolidation statements, by Maurice M. Lindsay, c. ᴘ. ᴀ. Boston, The Bentley school of accounting and finance [1939]
199 (i. e. 215) p. incl. 16 tab. (13 fold.) 26ᶜᵐ.
Each table numbered as a leaf.

1. Holding companies—Accounting. 2. Financial statements.
39–23023

Library of Congress   HF5686.H6L5
———— Copy 2.
Copyright A 133300   [2]   658.162

NL 0384087   DLC MtU PU MB

HF5686
.H6L5
1947   **Lindsay, Maurice Monroe**, 1886–
Holding companies and consolidation statements. Boston, Bentley School of Accounting and Finance [c1947]
218 p.   27cm.

1. Holding companies—Accounting.
2. Financial statements.

NL 0384088   MB

Lindsay, Maurice Monroe, 1886–
Mergers, consolidations and holding companies, by Maurice M. Lindsay, c. ᴘ. ᴀ. Boston, Mass., The Bentley school of accounting and finance [1936]
138 p. incl. tables. 27ᶜᵐ.

1. Industry—Organization, control, etc. 2. Corporations. 3. Holding companies. ɪ. Title.
36–21672

Library of Congress   HF5686.C7L52
———— Copy 2.
Copyright A 98729   [3]   658.16

NL 0384089   DLC

Lindsay, Maurice Monroe, 1886–
Probate accounting, by Maurice M. Lindsay, c. ᴘ. ᴀ. Boston, Mass., The Bentley school of accounting and finance [1936]
3 p. l., 5–145 p. incl. forms. 27ᶜᵐ.
"Includes sufficient law to make the accounting clear in the settlement of estates in Massachusetts."—Introd.

1. Probate law and practice — Massachusetts.   2. Accounting.
ɪ. Title.
36–29861

Library of Congress
———— Copy 2.
Copyright A 99535   [2]   347.6

NL 0384090   DLC

Lindsay, Mayne.
The whirligig, by Mayne Lindsay ... New York [etc.] Longmans, Green and co., 1901.
4 p. l., 285 p. 19ᶜᵐ.
A novel.

Mar. 28, 1901–42

Library of Congress   PZ3.L653W   Copyright

NL 0384091   DLC NN MB

Lindsay, Meta R.
Learning to live as friends of Jesus
see under title

Lindsay, Michael, *baron Lindsay of Birker,* 1909–
China and the cold war; a study in international politics. [Carlton] Melbourne University Press [1955]
286 p. 22 cm.

1. China—For. rel.—1949–   2. Communism—China.   ɪ. Title.
Full name: Michael Francis Morris Lindsay, *baron Lindsay of Birker.*

DS777.55.L46   327.51   55–1680 ‡

OKentU IEN Or OrP IdU IdPI CaBVaU WaT NNC
IEN PHC OC1W OC1 WaE OrU OrPR OOxM MiU OO OU PU
CtY CU IU NN TxU ViU NcD PPT PP DeU PLF LU TU PBL
NL 0384093   DLC AAP NIC NBuU WaSpG HU WaS MH IaU MB

LINDSAY, MICHAEL, *baron Lindsay of Birker,* 1909–
China and the West. Canberra, Australian national university, 1953. 28 p. 22cm. (George Ernest Morrison lecture in ethnology, 15)
Bibliography, p. 28.

1. China—Relations, General, with Europe. 2. Europe—Relations, General, with China. ɪ. Series.

NL 0384094   NN MH HU

Lindsay, Michael, *baron Lindsay of Birker,* 1909–
The military prospects in a Chinese civil war. [London, 1946]

14 numb. l.

NL 0384095   MH

VOLUME 334

Lindsay, Michael. *baron Lindsay of Birker,* 1909–
North China front. With a pref. by Lord Listowel. ₍London, China Campaign Committee, 1944?₎
23 ₍ plates, port. 20 cm.
Cover title.
Originally published in the March and April 1944 issues of Amerasia.

1 World War, 1939–1945—China. 2. Communism—China.
I. Title.
Full name: Michael Francis Morris Lindsay, *baron Lindsay of Birker.*

DS777.53.L57   951.042   49–38525 rev*

NL 0384096   DLC CU CtY IaU TxU NcD

Lindsay, Michael, *baron Lindsay of Birker, 1909–*
Notes on educational problems in communist China, 1941–47, with supplements on developments in 1948 and 1949 by Marion Menzies, William Paget, and S. B. Thomas. New York, International Secretariat, Institute of Pacific Relations, 1950.
iii, 194 p. 28 cm.

1. Education—China.

LA1131.L5   370.951   50–7573

NN ICU N PU NNUN CaBVa
NL 0384097   DLC TxU MiU CSt-H NIC CU ViU NNC TxU MH

Lindsay, Michael, *baron Lindsay of Birker,* 1909–
Scientific method and international affairs. ₍Melbourne₎ Australian Institute of International Affairs ₍1955₎
31 p. 21 cm. (Roy Milne memorial lecture, 6)

1. International relations—Research.   I. Title.
Full name: Michael Francis Morris Lindsay, *baron Lindsay of Birker.*

JX1311.L5   59–44625 ‡

NL 0384098   DLC NN NNC-L MH-L NIC

Lindsay, Nicholas Vachel, 1879–1931.
Abraham Lincoln walks at midnight (in Springfield, Illinois)
see under   George, Earl Robert, 1924–

M1555
.S

Lindsay, Nicholas Vachel, 1879–1931.
Siegmeister, Elie, 1909–

... Abraham Lincoln walks at midnight; poem by Vachel Lindsay. New York, Arrow music press, inc. ₍c1939₎

Lindsay, Nicholas Vachel, 1879–
Adventures while preaching the gospel of beauty ₍by₎ Nicholas Vachel Lindsay. New York, M. Kennerley, 1914.
186 p. 19¼ᵐ.

I. Title.
14–30915
₍Library of Congress   PS3523.I 58A65 1914
₍27j2₎

ICarbS PWcS
OC1W MB NcRS PPD NcD MoSW TU OC1U MH OOxM TxU ICU
NL 0384100   DLC OrCS OrP OrPR Or WaS NN NjP MiU OC1

Lindsay, Nicholas Vachel, 1879–1931.
Adventures while preaching the gospel of beauty ₍by₎ Vachel Lindsay. New York, Macmillan, 1916 ₍c1914₎
186 p. 20 cm.

I. Title.

PS3523.I 58A65 1916   68–127115

LU
NL 0384101   DLC ViU MdBJ IU OO ViU RPB MB MH CLSU

Lindsay, Nicholas Vachel, 1879–1931.
Adventures while preaching the gospel of beauty ₍by₎ Vachel Lindsay. New York, The Macmillan company, 1921.
5 p. l., 9–186 p. 19½ᵐ.

I. Title.   1. Mennonites in Kansas.
23–26570
Library of Congress   PS3523.I 58A65 1921

NL 0384102   DLC PPT MtBC OB1C KMK KU CoU CLSU

Lindsay, Nicholas Vachel, 1879–1931.
The art of the moving picture, by Vachel Lindsay ... New York, The Macmillan company, 1915.
viii p., 1 l., 289 p. 19¼ᵐ.

1. Moving-pictures.   I. Title.
15–26851
Library of Congress   PN1994.L5
₍a3811₎

WaT AU NcU WaE MtU
MiU OC1ND ODW NN MB IdU NcD OrPR Or FU MoSU ICU
NL 0384103   DLC MH SPt TU CLSU PSC PBa PU OO OC1

Lindsay, Nicholas Vachel, 1879–1931.
The art of the moving picture ... being the 1922 revision of the book first issued in 1915 ... by Vachel Lindsay ... New York, The Macmillan company, 1922.
xliii, 289 p. 19¼ᵐ.

1. Moving-pictures.   I. Title.
22–8068
Library of Congress   PN1994.L5 1922

CaOTP MsU NIC KMK NSyU
NL 0384104   DLC WaS WaTC OOxM MB OC1 CLSU InU PPT

Lindsay, Nicholas Vachel, 1879–1931.
"The Babbitt Jambouree"; eight poems. [Notre Dame, Ind., 1926]
7–17p. 24cm.

Detached from Pan; Poetry and youth, April, 1926, v.2, no.3.
Contains manuscript notes by author.

NL 0384105   IEN

Lindsay, Nocholas Vachel, 1879–1931.
Babylon. A drawing, design and rhyme inscribed to Carl Sandburg. Memphis, Printed by the author, 1923.
broadside. illus. 82x29cm.

I. Sandburg, Carl, 1878–   II. Title.

NL 0384106   NNC RPB IEN InU

Lindsay, Nicholas Vachel, 1879–1931.
Ballad of the Arizona sheriff [a ballad never before published]
From- The News Review, March 2, 1931.
Clipping mounted

NL 0384107   RPB

Lindsay, Nicholas Vachel, 1879–1931.
Banquet given...
see under
Abraham Lincoln association, Springfield, Ill.

Lindsay, Nicholas Vachel, 1879–1931.
Billboards and galleons.   (Inscribed to Stephen Graham)
In- The New Republic, Wed. Sept. 10, 1924.
p. 46–47.   31 cm.

NL 0384109   RPB

PS3523
f.I4A59A2
Modern
poetry

Lindsay, Nicholas Vachel, 1879–1931.
Broadsides. ₍Springfield, Ill., etc., 190 - pieces in portfolio (36cm.) illus.
Partial contents.—The Ezekiel chant. 1930.—The gospel of beauty. ₍1912?₎—Proclamation of the gospel of beauty. ₍n.d.₎—The kind of a visit I like to make. ₍n.d.₎—A letter for your wicked private ear only. ₍With autographed inscription₎ n.d.₎—A map of the universe issued in 1909. ₍Copy no.287₎ signed₎ 1924.—Our little new cave-man. 1927.—The village improvement parade. 1910.—War bulletin number three. ₍With   autographed inscription₎ 1909.

NL 0384110   ICU

Lindsay, Nicholas Vachel, 1879–1931.
The candle in the cabin; a weaving together of script and singing, by Vachel Lindsay.   New York, London, D. Appleton and company, 1926.
x p., 1 l., 130, ₍1₎ p.   illus. 23ᵐ.
Poems.

I. Title.
26–21496
Library of Congress   PS3523.I 58C3 1926

MoU NSyu MsU TNJ NBuU
CSmH NN ViU PU MtU WaS WaT OrCS Or IdU CaBVaU FU
NL 0384111   DLC NBu WaU TxU PRosC NcU MH OU OC1 MB

Lindsay, Nicholas Vachel, 1879–
The Chinese nightingale, and other poems, by Vachel Lindsay ... New York, The Macmillan company, 1917.
x, 127 p. 19¼ᵐ. $1.25
Reprinted in part from various periodicals.

17–25832
Library of Congress   PS3523.I 58C5 1917
— — Copy 2.
Copyright A 476465   ₍27j2₎

NSyU   MB NcU CU MiU
WaSp IdB WaT OrPR Or WaS OrStbM CaBVaU MU NIC MH TxU
NL 0384112   DLC TU IEN MoSW CoU OrP NcD OO OC1 MiU NN

---

*AC9
I6455
917cb

Lindsay, Nicholas Vachel, 1879–1931.
The Chinese nightingale, and other poems, by Vachel Lindsay ...
New York, The Macmillan company, 1918.   All rights reserved
x, 127p.   19.5cm.
Original decorated yellow cloth; advts. (₍6₎p.) at end.
Inscribed: My most fraternal and affectionate greeting to Josephine Peabody Marks this month of February 1919. Nicholas Vachel Lindsay.
Cambridge   Massachusetts.

NL 0384113   MH NjP RPB ODW PP

VOLUME 334

Lindsay, Nicholas Vachel, 1879–1931.
   The Chinese nightingale, and other poems, by Vachel
Lindsay ... New York, The Macmillan company, 1919.
   x, 127 p. 19½ cm.
   Reprinted in part from various periodicals.

NL 0384114   CU-I OC1 MoSW

PS3523   Lindsay, Nicholas Vachel, 1879-1931.
.I58   The Chinese nightingale, and other poems.
C5   New York, Macmillan, 1920 [°1917]
          127 p. 19cm.

NL 0384115   OrCS

811.5   **Lindsay, Nicholas Vachel,** 1879-1931.
L64   **The Chinese nightingale and other poems.**
Oc   **New York, Macmillan, 1922.**
1922   127p. 20cm.

NL 0384116   KU NBuU ViU MoU

Lindsay, Nicholas Vachel, 1879–1931.
   The Chinese nightingale, and other poems, by Vachel
Lindsay ... New York, The Macmillan company, 1926
[°1917]   x, 127 p. 19½ cm.
   Reprinted in part from various periodicals.

NL 0384117   OrPS CaOTP PPT OrPS

PS3523   **Lindsay, Nicholas Vachel,** 1879-1931.
.I 58C5   **The Chinese nightingale, and other**
1930   **poems. New York, Macmillan, 1930.**
       x, 127 p. 19cm.
       Reprinted in part from various
       periodicals.

NL 0384118   MB PP

Lindsay, Nicholas Vachel, 1879–1931.
   The Chinese nightingale ... musical setting
   see under   Greene, Flora Thomson.

Lilly
PS 3523   LINDSAY *Nicholas Vachel, 1879-1931.*
.I 58 Z95   [Christmas greeting for the year 1933,
      from Nicholas, Susan and Elizabeth, children
      and widow of Vachel Lindsay. Oakland, Calif.]
      Mills College, 1933.
      1 card. 10.5 by 13.5 cm.

      Contains a four line quotation from
      Vachel Lindsay's The golden book of Spring-
      field.

NL 0384120   InU

Lindsay, Nicholas Vachel, 1879–1931.
   Collected poems, by Vachel Lindsay. New York, The Macmillan company, 1923.
   xv p., 1 l., 390 p. 20½ᶜᵐ.

Library of Congress   PS3523.I 58A17 1923

      IaU InU NcD NSyU WU MeB ViU
      Or WaS OC1 NjP NN MB OOxM NjP WaU KyLx CoU CSt MsU
NL 0384121   DLC CaBVaU OrU OrCS CaBVa WaWW IdB WaSp

Lindsay, Nicholas Vachel, 1879–
   Collected poems, by Vachel Lindsay. Rev. and illustrated
ed. New York, The Macmillan company, 1925.
   5 p. l., ix-lxii p., 1 l., 464 p. illus., plates. 20½ᶜᵐ.
   Illustrated lining-papers.
   "Of this illustrated edition ... three hundred fifty copies have been
printed, of which this is number 345."

                           25—10046
Library of Congress   PS3523.I 58A17 1925

      OrMonO IdU TxU WaE PU CaBVa OrP MtU
      OrCS OrAshS WaS WaSp OrU OrPR MiU WU KU KyLxCB Wa
      NcRS ViU PP NcC KEmT PBa NcD OC1h OC1W MiU OCU MB
NL 0384122   DLC IEN NSyU MeB KMK OU NSyU NBuC WaU

Lindsay, Nicholas Vachel, 1879-1931.
   Collected poems, ... Rev. and illustrated ed.
New York, 1926.
   5 p., l., ix-lxiip., 1 l., 464 p. illus.,
plates. 21 cm.
   Illustrated lining-papers.

NL 0384123   RPB

Lindsay, Nicholas Vachel, 1879-1931.
   Collected poems by ... rev. and
illustrated ed. New York, The Macmillan
company, 1927 [c1925]
   5 p. l., ix-ixii p., 1 l., 464 p.

NL 0384124   OO OU

Lindsay, Nicholas Vachel, 1879–
   Collected poems by ... Rev. and
illustrated ed. New York, The Macmillan
company, 1929.

NL 0384125   OC1 CaBVaU MtBC

Lindsay, Nicholas Vachel, 1879-1931.
   Collected poems. Revised ed., with illustrations by the author. New York, Macmillan co.,
1930.

     1xii, 464 p. plates, illus. 20.5 cm.
   "Published May 1923. Rev. and illus. ed. pub.
June 1925. Reprinted ... April 1930."

NL 0384126   MH PU

Lindsay, Nicholas Vachel, 1879-1931.
   Collected poems by ... Rev. ed. Illustrated.
New York, The Macmillan company, 1931.
   464 p. illus.

NL 0384127   OU

Lindsay, Nicholas Vachel, 1879–1931.
   Collected poems, by Vachel Lindsay. Rev. ed.
with illustrations by the author. New York,
The Macmillan company, 1941.
   6p.l.,ix-lxii p.,l.,464p. front.,illus.,
plates. 20½cm.

NL 0384128   MoU OC1W PSt PHC

Lindsay, Nicholas Vachel, 1879–1931.
   Collected poems, by Vachel Lindsay.
Rev. ed. with illustrations by the
author. New York, The Macmillan company,
1946[c1925]
   1xiip.,1l.,464p. front.,illus. 20cm.

   Illustrated end-papers.

NL 0384129   PSt Vi

Lindsay, Nicholas Vachel, 1879– [1931]
   The Congo, and other poems; by Vachel Lindsay, with
an introduction by Harriet Monroe. New York, The
Macmillan company, 1914.
   xv, 159 p. 20ᶜᵐ.
   Reprinted in part from various periodicals.

   ɪ. Title.

Library of Congress   PS3523.I 58C6 1914   14—17118

      MB MH TxU WU MU FU NcU LU MiU NcGU CoU ViU IEN MeB
      OrCS OrStbM OCX OC1 OO OC1W MiU PPM PP PBm ViU OCU
NL 0384130   DLC TxU NjP NN NSyU IEN OrP Or IdB WaE

LINDSAY, NICHOLAS VACHEL, 1879-1931.
   The Congo, and other poems, by Vachel Lindsay.
With an introd. by Harriet Monroe. New York,
Macmillan, 1915. xv, 159 p. 20cm.

   I. Monroe, Harriet, 1860-1936. II. Title.
   i. subs. for 1914 ed.

NL 0384131   NN OrPR OU IEdS

Lindsay, Nicholas Vachel, 1879-1931.
   The Congo, and other poems; by Vachel Lindsay, with an
introduction by Harriet Monroe. New York, The Macmillan
company, 1916.
   xv, 159 p. 20 cm.
   Reprinted in part from various periodicals.
   Contains manuscript poem signed by the
author.

NL 0384132   NjP MtU

PS   Lindsay, Nicholas Vachel.
3523   The Congo, and other poems; by Vachel
I58   Lindsay, with an introduction by Harriet
C6   Monroe. New York, The Macmillan co., 1918.
1918   159 p.

NL 0384133   KMK RPB

PS3523
.I 58C6   **Lindsay, Nicholas Vachel,** 1879-1931.
1919   **The Congo, and other poems; with an introd.**
      by Harriet Monroe. New York, Macmillan, 1919.
      xv, 159 p. 20 cm.
      Reprinted in part from various periodicals.

NL 0384134   MB CaBVaU MH ViU

VOLUME 334

Lindsay, Nicholas Vachel, 1879-1931

1901
L7493c The Congo, and other poems; by Vachel Lind-
1920 say, with an introd. by Harriet Monroe. New
York, Macmillan Co., 1920.
xv, 159 p. 20 cm.

Reprinted in part from various periodicals.
Author's autographed presentation copy.

NL 0384135   RPB OrSaW

Lindsay, [Nicholas] Vachel.
The Congo, and other poems; with an introduction by Harriet
Monroe. New York: The Macmillan Co., 1922. 159 p. 12°.

NL 0384136   NN MtBC ODW MoU WU ViU TxU NN

811.5 Lindsay, Nicholas Vachel, 1879-1931.
L64 The Congo, and other poems. With an
9co introduction by Harriet Monroe. New
1924 York, Macmillan, 1924.
159p. 20cm.

NL 0384137   KU

Y Lindsay, Nicholas Vachel,   1879-
285
L 6423   The Congo, and other poems... With
an introduction by Harriet Monroe...
N.Y.1928.   D.

Reprinted in part from various
periodicals.

NL 0384138   ICN OOxM

PS3523 Lindsay, Nicholas Vachel, 1879-1931.
.I4C8 The Congo. Illus. by Alexander King. Mount
1931 Vernon [N.Y.] Printed at the press of W. E.
Modern Rudge, 1931.
poetry [13] p. (on double leaves) illus. (Linweave
limited editions, 1931)

NL 0384139   ICU IEN

Lindsay, Nicholas Vachel, 1879- 1931.
The Congo, and other poems; by Vachel Lindsay, with an
introduction by Harriet Monroe...New York, The Macmillan
company, 1933.
xv,167 p. 20cm.
Reprinted in part from various periodicals.
"Reissued January, 1933."

NL 0384140   ViU NBuU OrU Mi ICU

M1532 Lindsay, Nicholas Vachel, 1879-1931.
.B47C6
Bergh, Arthur, 1882-
[The Congo; arranged]

... The Congo [by] Arthur Bergh. [Op. 25] Arr. by Maynard Klein. (Choral fantasy for mixed voices and instruments) ... Philadelphia, Oliver Ditson company, Theodore
Presser co., distributors [1941]

M1621 Lindsay, Nicholas Vachel, 1879-1931.
.W
Wolfe, Jacques, 1896-
[The Congo]

The Congo; for voice and piano, poem by Vachel Lindsay.
Medium low voice. New York, C. Fischer [1948]

4PS Lindsay, Nicholas Vachel, 1879-1931.
382 Congo; un estudio de la raza negra.
[Traducción, prólogo y notas de Horacio
Jorge Becco.   ]
Cuadernos del Unicornio [1950]
29 p.

NL 0384143   DLC-P4

---

*AC9 [Lindsay, Nicholas Vachel, 1879-1931]
I6455 The cup of paint.
B931e [New York,1905]

broadside. 24x15cm.,in case 26cm.
Printed on red paper cut in the shape of a
cup; mounted on black cardboard.
Signed in autograph: Nicholas Vachel Lindsay
1905.
Inscribed: Nicholas Vachel Lindsay 1905.
Number 25. This is the first edition of this
poetical toy.
In a case   lettered: Vachel Lindsay.
Ephemera.

NL 0384144   MH

---

*AC9 [Lindsay, Nicholas Vachel, 1879-1931]
I6455 The dance of unskilled labor.
B931e [Springfield,Ill.,1908]
folder ([4]p.) 11.5cm.,in case 26cm.
Illus. on t.-p.
Signed on p.[3]: Nicholas Vachel Lindsay,
lecturer. H. N. Hansen, secretary.
Includes Lindsay's poem "I saw in a vision the
dance of unskilled labor" on p.[2]; advertising
his lecture "The Italian", the seventh in the
series on the "Composite citizenship of Spring-
field."
Unbound, as   issued; in a case lettered:
Vachel Lindsay.   Ephemera.

NL 0384145   MH RPB CtY

Lindsay, Nicholas Vachel, 1879-
The Daniel jazz and other poems, by Vachel Lindsay.
London, G. Bell & sons, 1920.
4 p. L, 94 p, 1 l. 19¼ᵐ.

I. Title.

Library of Congress   PS3523.I 58D3 1920   21-11550

RPB
NL 0384146   DLC MB NN NcD MU MsU CU-S NcU CtY IaU

Lindsay, Nicholas Vachel, 1879-1931.
The Daniel jazz and other poems by Vachel
Lindsay, with a foreword by Louis Untermeyer.
New York, Editions for the Armed Services,
Inc. [1931]
223 p.

NL 0384147   NBuU ViU

Lindsay, Nicholas Vachel, 1879-1931
The Daniel jazz and other poems, by
Vachel Lindsay. With a foreword by Louis Un-
termeyer. New York, Editions for the Armed
Services, Inc. [194-?]
223 p. 10 x 14 cm.   (No. 901)

"Published by arrangement with the
Macmillan Company, New York."

NL 0384148   RPB

Lindsay, Nicholas Vachel, 1879-
Daniel; Vachel Lindsay's poem, with musical
score
see under   Enders, Harvey.

Lindsay, Nicholas Vachel, 1879-1931.
Doctor Mohawk; inscribed to Ridley Wills.   [New York,
1923] p. 40. 32cm.
Signed: Vachel Lindsay.
In verse.
Excerpt: The New republic. Dec. 5, 1923.
With the author's ms. corrections and notes.

NL 0384150   NN

---

*pAB9 . Lindsay, Nicholas Vachel, 1879-1931.
I6455 Drink for sale.
909d [Springfield,Ill.,1909]
broadside. 35x16cm.
Signed: Nicholas Vachel Lindsay, rhymer and
designer.
With illustration by the author.
"Distributed at the Anti-saloon lecture by
Nicholas Vachel Lindsay at the Lavinia beach
reading room, Thursday, July 29, 1909. Springfield, Illinois."

NL 0384151   MH RPB

Lindsay, Nicholas Vachel, 1879-
Every soul is a circus, by Vachel Lindsay; decorations by
the author and George M. Richards. New York, The Macmillan company, 1929.
xxxii, 120 p. illus. 24ᵐ.
Poems.

I. Title.   29-23338

Library of Congress   PS3523.I 58E8 1929

CaBVa WaT IdU WaSp Or WaS CaBVau OrCS
PU PBm PP OClW OCl OCU OU ViU MB NN NcD OrP IdB OrU
NL 0384152   DLC MH RPB KU NSyU CoU TxU NcD OU MiU

Lindsay, Nicholas Vachel, 1879-1931.
The eyes of Queen Esther, and how they
conquered King Ahasuerus. Written for the
Phi Beta Kappa Society of Philadelphia, and
read at their meeting Dec. 8, 1917.
From- Contemporary Verse, April 1918.
23 cm. p. 49-51.

NL 0384153   RPB

---

810 Lindsay, Nicholas Vachel, 1879-1931.
L749 The Ezekial chant. [Springfield,
tEZ Ill., 1930]
Broadside. 1 mounted illus. 28 x
22cm.

Ex libris Hamlin Garland.
In a case.

NL 0384154   CLSU CtY

VOLUME 334

Lindsay, Nicholas Vachel, 1879–1931.
　The flower-fed buffaloes, by Vachel Lindsay.　[n. p., 1925?]
broadside.　33 x 23cm.

"From 'The Saturday review of literature' [v. 1, no. 32, March 7, 1925. p. 573.]"
Illustrated border signed: McAfee.

52R0360.　1. Bison, American—　　　　　Poetry.　I. Title.

NL　0384155　　NN

---

*AC9
L6455
B931e
　[Lindsay, Nicholas Vachel, 1879–1931]
　For the miners of Ridgely.
　[Springfield, Ill., 1909?]
　　folder ([3] p.)　18.5cm., in case 26cm.
　　An announcement of "Practical talks for miners
by Nicholas Vachel Lindsay" and his series of
English lessons, both to be given at Ridgely
mission.
　　Unbound; in a case lettered: Vachel Lindsay.
Ephemera.

NL　0384156　　MH

Lindsay, Nicholas Vachel, 1879–1931.
　The forest ranger's honeymoon.　[Chicago,
1926]
　　8p.　21cm.

　Detached from Poetry, a magazine of verse,
Chicago, 1926, v.28, no.1.

NL　0384157　　IEN

Lindsay, Nicholas Vachel, 1879–1931.
　From four letters [to Stephen Graham]　London,
1933.
　　p. 272–275　illus.　25 cm.
　　Letters in the Poetry quarterly, vol. 1, no. 5
(new series no. 2) Winter, 1933.

NL　0384158　　RPB

---

*AC9
L6455
B931e
　Lindsay, Nicholas Vachel, 1879–1931.
　"The future of Springfield". Illustrated.
The last of the series of ten lectures on
"Composite citizenship", Wednesday Dec. 16,
Y. M. C. A. building, Nicholas Vachel Lindsay,
speaker ...
　[Springfield, Ill., 1908]
　　folder ([4] p.)　14.5cm., in case 26cm.
　　Advertising the lecture, and containing (p.
[2]-[3]) Lindsay's poem: On the building of
Springfield.
　　Unbound, as　　　　　issued; in a case lettered
Vachel Lindsay.　　　　　Ephemera.

NL　0384159　　MH

Lindsay, Nicholas Vachel, 1879–1931.
　General William Booth enters into Heaven, and other poems,
by Nicholas Vachel Lindsay.　New York, M. Kennerley, 1913.
　　4 p. l., 119 p.　19½ᶜᵐ.

　1. Booth, William, 1829–1912.　I. Title.
　　　　　　　　　　　　　　　　　　　　　　14—184
　Library of Congress　　　PS3523.I 58G4 1913

MiU MB TxU MoU CoU NSyU ICU
OO OOxM OC1 MB TxU NjP PU MH PSt OU WU IEN TU NjP
NL　0384160　　DLC WaS IdU NcRS OrP WaT FU IU ViU NN

---

*AC9
L6455
913gb
　Lindsay, Nicholas Vachel, 1879–1931.
　General William Booth enters into heaven, and
other poems, by Nicholas Vachel Lindsay.
　New York, Mitchell Kennerley, 1915.

　　4 p. l., 119 p.　19.5cm.
　　Publisher's monogram on t.-p.
　　Original maroon cloth.
　　Inscribed: To Peter Clark Macfarlane – with
the very good wishes of Vachel Lindsay, 603
South 9th, Springfield, Ill. ...
　　With the author's profuse annotations through-
out.

NL　0384161　　MH NcD PPFr PPD ICN NcD OrPR

Lindsay, Nicholas Vachel, 1879–1931.
　General William Booth enters into Heaven, and other poems,
by Vachel Lindsay.　New York, The Macmillan company,
1916.
　　5 p. l., 119 p.　19½ᶜᵐ.
　　First published in 1913.

　1. Booth, William, 1829–1912.　I. Title.
　　　　　　　　　　　　　　　　　　　　　　A 16–804
　The Booklist
　　for Library of Congress　　　[PS3523.I 58G　　]

MiU ODW OCU OrCS OrStbM
NL　0384162　　NN TxU ICU NIC MsSM MB ViU OU MU TxD MB

PR 10
V3 N5
1919
　Lindsay, Nicholas Vachel, 1879–1931.
　General William Booth enters heaven,
and other poems.　With an introd. by Robert
Nichols.　Chatto & Windus, 1919.
　　119 p.

NL　0384163　　CaBVaU

PS
3523
.I58G
1919
　Lindsay, Nicholas Vachel, 1879–1931.
　General William Booth enters into Heaven,
and other poems, by Vachel Lindsay.
New York, The Macmillan Company, 1919 [c1913]
　　5 p. l., 119 p.　20 cm.
　　First published in 1913.

　1. Booth, William, 1829–1912.　I. Title.

NL　0384164　　NBuU CaBVaU NNC WU NjP CtY RPB TxU IU

Lindsay, Nicholas Vachel, 1879–1931.
　General William Booth enters into Heaven, and other
poems, by Vachel Lindsay.　New York, The Macmillan company, 1921.
　　5 p. l., 119 p.　19½ᶜᵐ.
　　First published in 1913.

NL　0384165　　ViU OU

Lindsay, Nicholas Vachel, 1879–1931.
　General William Booth enters into heaven
　　see also　Ives, Charles Edward, 1874–
1954.
　　General Booth's entrance into heaven ...[song]

Lindsay, Nicholas Vachel, 1879–1931.
　General William Booth enters into heaven.
The poem　[a score]
　　see under　James, Philip, 1890–

[Lindsay, Nicholas Vachel] 1879–1931.
　God help us to be brave.　A poem concerning the
twenty-six representative citizens of the world from
Rameses II. to Roosevelt.　[New York, G. Becker,
190?]
　　4 l.　8°.

NL　0384168　　NN

Lindsay, Nicholas Vachel, 1879–1931.
　Going-to-the-stars, by Vachel Lindsay ...　New York, London, D. Appleton and company, 1926.
　　viii, [2], 102 p.　illus.　23ᶜᵐ.
　　Poems.

　I. Title.　　　　　　　　　　　　　　　　26—11986
　Library of Congress　　　PS3523.I 58G44 1926

MsU CoU LU NBu KU
ViU OrP WaSp Or IdU WaTC OrCS KMK NcRS MB NSyU MoU
NL　0384169　　DLC TU MB MH PBm PU NN OC1W OC1 OU OCU

Lindsay, Nicholas Vachel, 1879–1931.
　Going-to-the-sun, by Vachel Lindsay ...　New York, Lon-
don, D. Appleton and company, 1923.
　　viii, 1 l., 101 p.　illus.　23ᶜᵐ.
　　Poems.
　　"This book is a sequel and a reply to a book by Stephen Graham, ex-
plorer-poet, and Vernon Hill, artist" [Tramping with a poet in the
Rockies]

　　　　　　　　　　　　　　　　　　　　　　23—4731
　Library of Congress　　　PS3523.I 58G45 1923

DLC WU TxU WaS MoU NSyU OC MsU OU CoU NcU
NjP CSmH MB ViU MiU OCU OC1 OC1W PPL PP PU MH NcD
NL　0384170　　DLC OrP MtU WaSp IdB WaWW Or OrSaW NN

Lindsay, Nicholas Vachel, 1879–1931.
　Going-to-the-sun, by Vachel Lindsay... New
York, London, D. Appleton and company, 1926.
　　viii p., 1 l., 101 p.　illus.　25cm.
　　Poems.
　　"This book is a sequel and a reply to a book by
Stephen Graham, explorer-poet, and Vernon Hill,
artist" [Tramping with a poet in the Rockies]

NL　0384171　　ViU MoU MtHi

Lindsay, Nicholas Vachel, 1879–
　The golden book of Springfield, by Vachel Lindsay ...
being the review of a book that will appear in the autumn
of the year 2018, and an extended description of Springfield, Illinois, in that year.　New York, The Macmillan
company, 1920.
　　2 p. l., iii–iv, 329 p.　19½ᶜᵐ.

　I. Title.　　　　　　　　　　　　　　　20—19074
　Library of Congress　　　PS3523.I 58G47 1920

CaBVaU CoU FU OrU NIC MU MoU IEN NSyU OrU
ODW OU NjP ViU NN MB WaT WaTC OrP IdB WaS WaSp IdU
NL　0384172　　DLC MH TNJ NcRS PSC PPL NcD OC1W OC1

Za
Za1
+C1
　Lindsay, Nicholas Vachel, 1879–1931.
　"The golden whales of California." By Vachel
Lindsay.　[Chicago, 1919]
　　broadside.　41x24½cm.
　　"Reprinted from the Wednesday book page of
the Chicago daily news of May 21, 1919 ..."

NL　0384173　　CtY

VOLUME 334

Lindsay, Nicholas Vachel, 1879–1931.
The golden whales of California and other rhymes in the American language, by Vachel Lindsay. New York, The Macmillan company, 1920.
xx, 181 p. 19½ cm.
Reprinted in part from various periodicals.

I. Title.

PS3523.I 58G5 1920   20—2832

NBuU NSyU FU MiU
WaE Wa OrStbM MH MB WU NcD OU OC1 ODW OCU ViU NN
NL 0384174   DLC Or OrPR WaSp IdB IdU WaT MtU OrP

810
L749
tG08
Lindsay, Nicholas Vachel, 1879–1931.
The gospel of beauty; being the new "creed of a beggar" by that vain and foolish mendicant Nicholas Vachel Lindsay. Printed for his personal friends in his home village ... Springfield, Ill. [author] 1912.
Broadside. 19 x 23cm.

In a case.

NL 0384175   CLSU CtY MH RPB IEN WU

Nicholas
Lindsay, ∧ Vachel, 1879–1931.
Greetings from Vachel, Elizabeth, Susan, and Nicholas Lindsay, Dec. 25, 1929; [a Christmas card. n.p., 1929]
[1]ℓ. illus. 11x14cm.

NL 0384176   IEN InU

Lindsay, Nicholas Vachel, 1879–
A handy guide for beggars, especially those of the poetic fraternity; being sundry explorations, made while afoot and penniless in Florida, Georgia, North Carolina, Tennessee, Kentucky, New Jersey, and Pennsylvania. These adventures convey and illustrate the rules of beggary for poets and some others. By Vachel Lindsay ... [New York, Boston, etc.] The Macmillan company, 1916.
xi, 205 p. 19½ᵐ. $1.25

I. Title.

Library of Congress   PS3523.I 58H3 1916
16—23558

NN MB NSyU AU TU NcRS Wa WaE OrP WaT
Or OrPR IdB   PBm PSC PU OC1W OO MiU OC1 OCU ViU
NL 0384177   DLC NjP MH NN MsU ScU WU CoU TxU CU MU

Lindsay, Nicholas Vachel, 1879–1931.
A handy guide for beggars, especially those of the poetic fraternity; being sundry explorations, made while afoot and penniless in Florida, Georgia, North Carolina, Tennessee, Kentucky, New Jersey, and Pennsylvania. These adventures convey and illustrate the rules of beggary for poets and some others. By Vachel Lindsay ... [New York, Boston, etc.] The Macmillan company, 1920 ᵨc1916ᵩ
xi, 205p. 20cm.

Author's autograph presentation copy.

NL 0384178   IU NcU WaTC WaSp

AC-L
L646ha
1923
Lindsay, Nicholas Vachel, 1879–1931.
A handy guide for beggars, especially those of the poetic fraternity; being sundry explorations, made while afoot and penniless in Florida, Georgia, North Carolina, Tennessee, Kentucky, New Jersey, and Pennsylvania. These adventures convey and illustrate the rules of beggary for poets and some others. By Vachel Lindsay ... [New York, Boston, etc.] The Macmillan company, 1923.
xi, 205p.   19½cm.

Continued in next column

Continued from preceding column

With autograph of Robert Hunter Paterson.
Autograph presentation copy to J.W.B.[?] from C. & G[?] Hutchins, 1929.
Florence Hamilton Collection.

I. Title. A.F.: Paterson, Robert Hunter.
A.F.: Hamilton, Florence.

NL 0384180   TxU NSyU

Lindsay, Nicholas Vachel, 1879–1931.
A handy guide for beggars, especially those of the poetic fraternity; being sundry explorations, made while afoot and penniless in Florida, Georgia, North Carolina, Tennessee, Kentucky, New Jersey, and Pennsylvania. These adventures convey and illustrate the rules of beggary for poets and some others. By Vachel Lindsay ... [New York, Boston, etc.] The Macmillan company, 1930.
xi, 205 p. 19½ᵐ.

NL 0384181   ViU OU

LINDSAY, Nicolas Vachel, 1879–1931.
The heroes of time; a poem illustrating the position of Abraham Lincoln among the dominating personalities of history. n.p., [19–?].

pp.(12).
Without title-page. Caption title.
Paper cover designed by the author.

NL 0384182   MH

Case
3A
402
[LINDSAY, NICHOLAS VACHEL] 1879–1931.
The heroes of time... [Springfield, Ill., Published by the educational department of the Young men's christian association, 1908?]
8p. 16cm.

"Written in praise of Abraham Lincoln...in commemoration of the one hundredth anniversary of the birth of Abraham Lincoln."
Cf. Johnson, Merle, American first editions, p.316.

NL 0384183   ICN MH

Lindsay, Nicholas Vachel, 1879–1931.
The heroes of time; a poem illustrating the position of Abraham Lincoln among the dominating personalities of history. By Nicholas Vachel Lindsay. [Springfield? Ill., 1910] 6 l. 21cm.

Caption-title.
In original illustrated covers (dated 1910 and signed: Nicholas Vachel Lindsay, rhymer and designer), with cover-title: A memorial of Lincoln, called The heroes of time.
Author's presentation copy.

612285B. 1. Lincoln, Abraham, 16th   pres. U.S.—Poetry. I. Title.
II. Title: A memorial of Lincoln,   called The heroes of time.
NN

NL 0384184   NN MB RPB

Lindsay, Nicholas Vachel, 1879–1931.
I Know All This When Gipsy Fiddles Cry, by Vachel Lindsay. San Francisco, By Paul Elder & Company, 1922.
Sheet, 12 x 9 1-2 inches, folded to 9 x 4 inches.
Authors auograph on title.

NL 0384185   CSmH IEN

Lindsay, Nicholas Vachel, 1879–1931.
The Illinois city. The Illinois village, and The Illinois farmer. A triad of poems... [New York, M. Kennerley, 1915]
14 p. 16ᶜᵐ.
On cover: Community poems for Illinois.
"Reprinted from a collection published under the title 'General William Booth enters into Heaven and other poems'."

NL 0384186   NjP ICU

Lindsay, Nicholas Vachel, 1879–1931.
[Improvised drawings, made from the words "Amy Lowell", with verses referring to the drawings]
2 drawings, and 3 leaves of manuscript on yellow glazed paper.
Made at Miss Lowell's home.
Each drawing and poem has inscription signed by the author, and date: April 15, 1922.

NL 0384187   MH

Lindsay, Nicholas Vachel, 1879–1931.
In praise of Johnny Appleseed, by Vachel Lindsay. [New York, American fruit growers, 192–?] 8 l. 26cm.
Caption-title, l. 4ª.
Preceded by "The Rodin of American poetry (an editorial by Mr. Glenn Frank in The Century for August, 1921)," l. 3ª–4ª.
In verse.

612292B. I. Chapman, John, 1774–   1845–Poetry. I. Frank, Glenn,
1887–1940. II. Title.

NL 0384188   NN

Lindsay, Nicholas Vachel, 1879–1931.
Inventory of the Lindsayana collection in Springfield, Ill., December 23, 1949
see under   Lincoln library, Springfield, Ill.

Nicholas
[Lindsay, ∧ Vachel] 1879–1931.
John Brown [and other poems. n.p., n.d.]
[8]p. (in columns) 24x22cm. fold. to 24x11cm.

NL 0384190   IEN

Lindsay, Nicholas Vachel, 1879–1931.
Johnny Appleseed and other poems, by Vachel Lindsay; illustrated by George Richards. New York, The Macmillan company, 1928.
ix p., 2 l., 3–144 p., 1 l. incl. illus., plates. col. front., col. plates 19½ cm. [The Macmillan children's classics]

I. Title.

PS3523.I 58J6 1928   28—30471

WaS OrU OrP OrLgE WU MoU NcU NvU
NL 0384191   DLC PWcS NN TNDC GU OO OC1 OOxM ViU Or

PS
3523
I58
J6
1930
Lindsay, Nicholas Vachel, 1879–1931.
Johnny Appleseed and other poems. Illustrated by George Richards. [New edition]
New York, Macmillan [1930, c1928]
ix, 144 p. illus. 20 cm.

I. Richards, George, illus. II. Title.

NL 0384192   NBuC MoU CLU MU NcC OrCS

VOLUME 334

Lindsay, Nicholas Vachel, 1879-1931.
Johnny Appleseed and other poems, by ...,
illustrated by George Richards. New York, The
Macmillan company, 1941.
144 p.
"Published...1928...New ed. 1930. Reprinted
... 1941."

NL 0384193   PSC

PS   Lindsay, Nicholas Vachel, 1879-1931.
3523   Johnny Appleseed and other poems, by
.I58   Vachel Lindsay; illustrated by George
J6   Richards.   New York, The Macmillan
1950   company, 1950 ₍°1930₎
ix, 144p. illus.,plates. 20cm.
(The Macmillan children's classics)

NL 0384194   KU

---

*pAB9   Lindsay, Nicholas Vachel, 1879-1931.
L6455   The kind of a visit I like to make, by Vachel
919k   Lindsay.
Springfield,Illinois,[1919]

broadside. 35.5x24cm.
Inscribed: not for publication. (Nicholas)
Vachel Lindsay May 2, 1919. Springfield
Illinois.

NL 0384195   MH

Lindsay, Nicholas Vachel, 1879-1931.
The last song of Lucifer. [New York, 1908
[12]p. 14cm.

Caption title.
1st ed.

NL 0384196   IEN NN MH CtY RPB InU

LINDSAY,₍Nicholas₎ Vachel,1879-1931.
A letter about my four programmes for com-
mittees in correspondence. ₍Springfield,Ill.,
Jefferson Printing Co.,1910.₎

4°. pp.65+. Illustr.₍by the author₎.
Contents: i.The letter.- ii.The hierogylphics.
Presentation copy to Amy Lowell,with inscrip-
tion.

NL 0384197   MH

Lindsay, Nicholas Vachel, 1879-1931.
A letter about my four programmes, for committees in correspondence, by Vachel Lindsay ... ₍Springfield, Ill., The
Jeffersons printing co., 1916₎
65 p., 1 l. Illus. 26½ x 21ᶜᵐ.

The programmes are: The gospel of beauty. A talk on The art of the
moving picture. An evening of higher vaudeville, and orthodox verse as
well. The Chinese nightingale, and dramas for impromptu actors.

ɪ. Title.
                                                        44-29616
Library of Congress   PS3523.I58L4

NL 0384198   DLC MH NN NjP

Za   Lindsay, Nicholas Vachel, 1879-1931.
L645   A letter for your wicked private ear
+1   only. [Springfield, Ill., 1912?]
broadside. 28 x 22 cm.

Reissued as a pamphlet, 28 p., 1921, and
with revisions, as The kind of visit I like
to make.

NL 0384199   CtY

LINDSAY, NICHOLAS VACHEL, 1879-1931
A letter for your wicked private ear
only. Springfield, Ill., V. Lindsay,
₍1920₎
1l.   21 1/2 by 28 cm.

Author's autographed presentation
copy to Frederic Melcher.

NL 0384200   InU

---

*AC9   [Lindsay, Nicholas Vachel, 1879-1931]
L6455   A letter for your wicked private ear only.
B931e   [Springfield,Ill.,1921]
26p. 16cm.,in case 26cm.
Caption title; signed and dated at end:
Vachel Lindsay, 603 South Fifth, Springfield,
Illinois. January 1, 1921.
Unbound, as issued; in a case lettered:
Vachel Lindsay. Ephemera.
With author's markings, and autograph note
below caption: page 8 and page 24.

Another copy. 16cm.,bd.to 24cm.
No.1 in a volume labelled: Pamphlets by
Vachel Lindsay.
Inscribed: This is what I am sending to people
who ask me to come and speak for them. See page
24.

NL 0384202   MH TxU RPB NjP

Lindsay, Nicholas Vachel, 1879-1931.
A letter of Vachel Lindsay on the "movies." ₍n. p.₎ Priv.
print., 1945.
1 p. l., facsim. (₍5₎ p.), 1 p. 36 x 27ᶜᵐ.
Facsimile of a manuscript letter to Paul Powell, dated July 24, 1916.
"25 copies."

1. Moving-pictures.   ɪ. Powell, Paul.

PS3523.I58Z52   47-23191

NL 0384203   DLC IEN CtY CLSU NN

Lindsay, Nicholas Vachel, 1879-1931.
Letter to Mr. William Stanley Braithwaite signed
and dated July 31, 1916. (Manuscript)
Mounted in binder.

NL 0384204   RPB

MS   Lindsay, Nicholas Vachel, 1879-1931.
B   Letters, 1914-1929.
L749£1   2v.(103£.) transcripts (handwritten and
typewritten) 29cm.

Copies made by Edith Kellogg from originals
in the Springfield, Illinois, Public Library.
Poet. Letters to Mrs. William Vaughan Moody,
from her first invitation to call upon her in
Chicago (April, 1914) until June 18, 1929, when
he invited her to visit him in Springfield.

NL 0384205   IU

Lindsay, Nicholas Vachel, 1879-1931.
Letters of Nicholas Vachel Lindsay to A. Joseph Armstrong,
edited by A. Joseph Armstrong. Waco ₍Tex.₎ Baylor university press ₍°1940₎
xiv, 121 p. ports. 23½ᶜᵐ. (On cover: The Baylor bulletin, Baylor
university, Waco, Tex., v. 43, no. 3)
Half-title: Baylor university literary publications.

ɪ. Armstrong, A. Joseph, 1873–   ɪɪ. Title.
                                                        41-9003
Library of Congress   PS3523.I58Z53
                                      ₍6₎   928.1

        ODW MtU OrCS IdU
NL 0384206   DLC NIC TU PPT PU OrSaW WaTC OCU OU OC1

LINDSAY,Nicholas Vachel,1879-1931.
[Letters to Arthur Davison Ficke,1911-1918,
with his A memorial to Booker T.Washington].

Manuscript and typewritten.

NL 0384207   MH

PS3523   Lindsay, Nicholas Vachel, 1879-1931.
.I4L72   Litany of Washington Street, a fantasy.
1927   ₍n.p., 1927₎
Modern   9 p.
Poetry   "Of this brochure fifty-five copies have
been printed for private distribution by the
author. This is number 19."

NL 0384208   ICU

Lindsay, Nicholas Vachel, 1879–
The litany of Washington street ₍by₎ Vachel Lindsay. New
York, The Macmillan company, 1929.
xii p., 1 l., 121 p. incl. front., illus., plates, ports. 24ᶜᵐ.
Illustrated lining-papers.
"This is a work of the imagination ... These orations and litanies
are held together by quotations from Walt Whitman."—Prologue.

ɪ. Title.
Library of Congress   PS3523.I58L5 1929   29-7625

        MoU MsSM CoU MB TxU
        ViU NN MWA MB TU NcD OrP MtU OrPR WaS Or IdU-SB
NL 0384209   DLC CoU KMK MsU NSyU MH OO OU OC1 MiU

Lindsay, Nicholas Vachel, 1879-1931.
The litany of Washington street ₍by₎ Vachel Lindsay.
New York, The Macmillan company, 1932 [1929]
xii p., 1 l., 121 p. incl. front., illus., plates, ports. 24ᶜᵐ.
Illustrated lining-papers.
"This is a work of the imagination ... These orations and litanies
are held together by quotations from Walt Whitman."—Prologue.

NL 0384210   NcRS ODW OCU ViU PSC IdU

Lindsay, Nicholas Vachel, 1879-1931.
PS3205   Whitman, Walt, 1819-1892.
.G4G4   Manhattan and Illinois. Amerikanische Lyrik von Walt
Whitman und Vachel Lindsay. Eingeleitet und übertragen
von Max Geilinger. Herrliberg-Zürich, Bühl-Verlag ₍1947₎

ZZa   Lindsay, Nicholas Vachel, 1879-1931.
Zal   A map of the universe issued in 1909...
C1   Spokane, 1924.
broadside. illus. 87 x 71 cm. 2 copies.
"First edition of this poster - 500 copies."

In manuscript on both copies: " Frontispiece of the new collected poems - eight times
enlarged into a poster ... N. V. L."

NL 0384212   CtY

Lindsay, Nicholas Vachel, 1879-1931.
A map of the universe issued in 1909; this map is one
beginning of the golden book of Springfield. ₍2d ed. Spokane, 1926₎
Broadside. illus. 71 x 86 cm.

ɪ. Title.
PS3523.I58M3 1926   61-57439

NL 0384213   DLC CLSU NjP NRU CtY OrCS MdBP NjP MB

VOLUME 334

Lindsay, Nicholas Vachel, 1879–1931.
A memorial of Lincoln called The heroes of time. ₍n. p.,
n. d.₎
₍16₎ p. illus. 21 cm.
Poem.

1. Lincoln, Abraham, Pres. U. S.—Poetry. ɪ. Title. ɪɪ. Title:
The heroes of time.
PS3523.I 58M4   59–31063

NL 0384214   DLC IaU

PS3523   Lindsay, Nicholas Vachel, 1879–1931.
.I4H55   A memorial of Lincoln, called The heroes of
1910   time. ₍A poem illustrating the position of
Modern   Abraham Lincoln among the dominating personali-
poetry   ties of history. Springfield, Ill.₎ 1910.
            ₍16₎ p.

1. Lincoln, Abraham, pres. U.S.—Poetry.

NL 0384215   ICU IU IaU IEN MH

Micro-   Lindsay, Nicholas Vachel, 1879–1931.
film   ₍Miscellaneous publications₎
PS
26   Negative; originals in the University of
            Chicago library.

NL 0384216   ICU

Lindsay, Nicholas Vachel, 1879–1931.
The moon-worms. (What the hyena said.)   Springfield, Ill.
₍1910₎   broadside.   illus.   54 x 25cm.
Illustration signed: N. V. L. 1910.
In verse.
Author's autographed presentation copy.

NL 0384217   NN

[LINDSAY, Nicholas Vachel, 1879–1931.
On the building of Springfield. [Springfield,
Ill.?, 1908].

sq.24°. pp.(4).
Without title-page. Caption title.
A poem advertising his tenth and last lecture
in the series "Composite citizenship ₍of Spring-
field₎" entitled "The future of Springfield."

NL 0384218   MH InU

Lindsay, Nicholas Vachel, 1879–1931
Za   On the building of Springfield. ₍n.p.,
L645   1931?₎
+1   folder (3 ₗ.) incl. front. (port.),
       illus. 22 cm.

Caption title.
Text printed on outside of a single sheet
folded twice.

NL 0384219   CtY

Lindsay, Nicholas Vachel, 1879–1931
ZZa   ... Our little new cave-man: Nicholas Cave
Zal   Lindsay born September 16, 1927, Spokane.
.1   [Spokane, 1927]
      broadside. 49 x 21 cm. folded to 28 x 21cm.
      At head of title: Vachel Lindsay.

1. Lindsay, Nicholas Cave, 1927–

NL 0384220   CtY

---

810   Lindsay, Nicholas Vachel, 1879–1931.
L749   The person who gets this package is asked to
tP   denounce loudly to his neighbors any ideas in
       the prose or the verse he does not like ...
       Springfield, Ill., author [1910?]
       Broadside. 15 x 10cm.

Packing slip, apparently mailed out with the
first edition of the Village magazine.
Ex libris Hamlin Garland; in a case.

NL 0384221   CLSU

---

q811   Lindsay, Nicholas Vachel.
L64p   Poems, cartoons, advertisements and mis-
       cellaneous material.   [Springfield, Ill.
       1905–15]
       15 pieces, illus.

NL 0384222   IU

Za   [Lindsay, Nicholas Vachel] 1879–1931.
L645   Proclamation of the gospel of beauty.
+1   [Springfield, 1912]
      broadside 24 x 19 cm.

NL 0384223   CtY

Lindsay, Nicholas Vachel, 1879–1931.
Rhymes to be traded for bread, being new verses by Nicholas
Vachel Lindsay, Springfield, Illinois, June 1912. Printed expressly as a substitute for money. This book is to be used in
exchange for the necessities of life on a tramp-journey from the
author's home town, through the West and back ... ₍Spring-
field? 1912?₎
₍16₎ p. 23½ᵐ.
Caption title.

ɪ. Title.   44–31489 Revised
Library of Congress   PS3523.I 58R5

         CLSU
NL 0384224   DLC MsU CoU NSyU IEN NIC MH RPB NjP NN

Spec.
PS 3501   Lindsay, Nicholas Vachel, 1879–1931.
I 5   Rigamarole, rigamarole, by Vachel Lindsay.
P 6   New York, Random House, 1929.
1929a   ₍4₎ p. 26 cm. (The Poetry quartos)
no. 8   "475 copies for Random House."

          Paper wrappers; in a case with Prelude,
       by C. Aiken ₍and others₎

          CoU HU
NL 0384225   MoSW CSmH MH CSt NcU ScU NIC ICarbS OkU

Lindsay, Nicholas Vachel, 1879–1931.
Za   The Sangamon County peace advocate. Number
L645   one. By Nicholas Vachel Lindsay. Springfield,
+1   Ill., 1909.
       broadside 22 x 31 cm.
       Nine poems.
       At head of title in manuscript: "Please read
       it once more. N. V. L. "

NL 0384226   CtY RPB CLSU

Lindsay, Nicholas Vachel, 1879–1931.
[Scrapbook of Lindsay material: newspaper
clippings, broadsides, programmes, notices, etc.]
n. p., n. d.
     port.   29 cm.
     Contains an autographed photo of the poet.

NL 0384227   RPB

Lindsay, Nicholas Vachel, 1879–1931.
Selected poems of Vachel Lindsay, edited with an introduction by Hazelton Spencer ... New York, The Macmillan
company, 1931.
     xviii p., 1 l., 226 p. incl. front. 19 cm. (The modern readers' se-
ries)

ɪ. Spencer, Hazelton, 1893–   ed.
PS3523.I 58A6 1931   811.5   31–3164

     PPD PWcS NcD OOxM
NL 0384228   DLC OC1 OCU OU MB NN CU GU WaWW IdB PP

LINDSAY, NICHOLAS VACHEL, 1879–1931.
Selected poems of Vachel Lindsay. New York: The
Macmillan Co., 1936. viii, 226 p. 19cm.

850085A. 1. Poetry, American.

NL 0384229   NN ViU ICU

Lindsay, Nicholas Vachel, 1879–1931.
So keep going to the sun. So keep going to the sun! A draw-
ing, design and rhyme inscribed to Carl Sandburg. Memphis,
Tenn., 1923. broadside. 83 x 29cm.
     At head of title: ₍illustration, with caption₎ Babylon, Babylon, Babylon, Babylon.
     Signed: Vachel Lindsay.
     Facsimile reproduction of author's drawing and holograph text.
     "Originally appeared in Christopher Morley's Bowling Green column in the New
York Evening Post... Now, several months later, it is printed in Memphis, Tennessee
... in anticipation of Carl Sandburg's ... recital ... Nov. 17, 1923."
     Appears in his collected poems with title: Babylon, Babylon, Babylon the great.

NL 0384230   NN CtY

₍Lindsay, Nicholas Vachel₎ 1879–1931.
The soul of the city receives the gift of the Holy Spirit.
₍Springfield, Ill., 1913?₎   10 l. illus. 25cm.
     "Postscript" signed: Nicholas Vachel Lindsay, rhymer and designer.
     "Printed by the designer expressly for gratuitous distribution in Springfield, Illinois."
     With illustrations signed by the author and dated 1913.
     In verse.

NL 0384231   NN ICN NjP PU IaU MH CtY IEN IHi RPB

---

810   Lindsay, Nicholas Vachel, 1879–1931.
L749   The Spring harbinger. Nicholas Vachel
tSP   Lindsay, rhymer and designer. Springfield,
       Ill. [1910]
       ₍19₎ p. illus. 16 x 9 cm.

       Humorous drawings and verse.
       Pamphlet.
       Ex libris Hamlin Garland.
       In a case.

NL 0384232   CLSU RPB

Lindsay, Nicholas Vachel, 1879–1931.
*AC9   These ten lectures by Nicholas Vachel Lindsay
.L6455   for men only will be given Wednesdays at eight
B931e   in the evening, beginning October 14, in the
         Y. M. C. A. building free to members and their
         friends ... Young men's Christian association,
         Henry N. Hansen, general secretary.
         [Springfield, Ill., 1908]
         [12] p. illus. 16.5cm., in case 26cm.
         Announcement of the series of lectures on
         "Composite citizenship of Springfield"; illus-
         trated by Lind-   say.
         Unbound,   wire-stitched, as issued;
         in case lettered: Vachel Lindsay. Ephemera.

NL 0384233   MH

VOLUME 334

---

*AC9
L6455
B931e

Lindsay, Nicholas Vachel, 1879-1931.
To the sweet singer of Israel. A poem by
Nicholas Vachel Lindsay.
[Springfield,Ill.,1908]
folder ([4]p.) 15cm.,in case 26cm.
Advertising his sixth lecture in the series
"Composite citizenship of Springfield."
Unbound, as issued; in a case lettered:
Vachel Lindsay. Ephemera.

NL 0384234   MH IEN RPB

---

*pAB9
L6455
911t

Lindsay, Nicholas Vachel, 1879-1931.
... To the United States Senate. Revelation
16: verses 16 through 19. (Armageddon.)
[Springfield,Ill.,1911]
broadside. 33.5x18.5cm.
At head: The following verses were written on
the evening of March the first, nineteen hundred
and eleven, and printed next morning in the
Illinois state register. They celebrate the
arrival of the news that the United States
Senate had declared the election of William

Lorimer good and valid, by a vote of forty-six
to forty.
Signed: Nicholas Vachel Lindsay, 603 South
Fifth street. Springfield, Illinois.

NL 0384236   MH InU RPB

Lindsay, Nicholas Vachel, 1879–
The tramp's excuse, and other poems by Nicholas Vachel
Lindsay. [Springfield, Ill., 1909.] 84 l. 8°.

Cover-title.
Leaves printed on one side only.
Autograph letter of author and newspaper clipping relating to book, inserted.

I. Poetry, American. 2. Title.
N. Y. P. L.   January 12, 1926

NL 0384237   NN TxU IEN NNC NjP MH NRU CU

Lindsay, Nicholas Vachel, 1879-1931.
The tree of laughing bells [by] Nicholas Vachel Lindsay.
[Springfield? Ill.] 1905.   4 l.   17cm.

In original illustrated pink covers, with cover-title.
With the author's ms. correction on l. 2ᵇ.
Author's autographed presentation copy to Katharine Lee Bates, 1917.

NL 0384238   NN IU RPB CtY MH IEN NTRS

Lindsay, Nicholas Vachel, 1879-1931.
The trial of the dead Cleopatra.
In- The American Mercury, Aug. 1924.
26 cm.   p. 411-418.

NL 0384239   RPB

Lindsay, Nicholas Vachel, 1879-1931.
United States bards and Scotch reviewers.
From- The Landmark, Oct. 1929.
22 cm.   p. 599-609.

NL 0384239-1   RPB

Lindsay, Nicholas Vachel, 1879-1931.
Und Simson soll über euch kommen; zwei
Negerpredigten von Hyazinth Lehmann. Bear-
beitung nach dem Amerikanischen des Vachel
Lindsay. [Berlin-Wilmersdorf, A.R. Meyer]
1921.
8p.   22cm.   (2. Privatdruck des Klubs
Kartoffelsalat)

I. Lehmann, Hyazinth, tr.   II. Title.

NL 0384240   IEN

Am
Li

Lindsay, Nicholas Vachel
Under Spokane's brocaded sun.   Spokane, Spokane art association, 1929.
illus.

"This print is one of a limited number
of reproductions made from the original
design by Vachel Lindsay, purchased by his
friends and placed in the Spokane public
museum, May 1929. Movement sponsored by the
Spokane art association".

NL 0384241   WaSp

Am
Li

Lindsay, Nicholas Vachel, 1879-1931.
Vachel Lindsay on "The Santa Fe trail,"
by A. L. Bader.   [Durham, N.C., 1948?]
[360]-362p.   25cm.

"Reprinted from American Literature,
vol. 19, no.4, January, 1948."

1. Lindsay, Nicholas Vachel, 1879-1931.
The Santa Fe trail.   I. Bader, Arno Lehman.

NL 0384242   IEN

Z4
L645
+1

Lindsay, Nicholas Vachel, 1879-1931.
The village improvement parade. Nicholas
Vachel Lindsay. [n.p.] 1910.
broadside in 3 sheets. illus.   24 x 40 cm.
3 copies.
In manuscript on copy 1: "These are originals. This is the exact form in which I
carried 'The Village Improvement Parade'
into Kansas in 1912 ..."

NL 0384243   CtY

---

q811
L64v

Lindsay, Nicholas Vachel, 1879-1931.
The village improvement parade; souvenir programme of recital by Mr. and Mrs. Vachel Lindsay,
at the First Christian church, October 13, 1930.
[New York? 1930?]
[10]p. illus.

"Of this edition one thousand are printed and
signed by Mr. and Mrs. Vachel Lindsay. [This is
no.] 563."

NL 0384244   IU ICU NIC CLSU

[Lindsay, Nicholas Vachel] 1879-1931.
The village magazine. [Springfield, Ill., 1910]

cover-title. [75] p. illus.   29 x 23½ cm.

Written and illustrated by Vachel Lindsay.
Reissued, with additions, as second imprint, 1920; third imprint,
1925; fourth imprint, 1925.

I. Title.

PS3523.I58V5 1910   12-23631 rev 2

NL 0384245   DLC MiEM IaU RPB NN MiU NjP NN

[Lindsay, Nicholas Vachel,] 1879–
The village magazine. [Springfield, Ill.: Jeffersons Prtg.
Co., 1920.] 128 p. incl. illus., plates. [2. ed.]   f°.

Cover-title.
Plates printed on both sides.

i. American literature.—Misc.   2. Drawings (U. S.). 3. Title.
N. Y. P. L.   December 13, 1922.

NL 0384246   NN OC1 MH TxU ICU ViU RPB NjP

Lindsay, Nicholas Vachel, 1879-1931.
The village magazine. Fourth imprint. Written and illustrated by Vachel Lindsay. [Springfield, Ill., Jeffersons printing company, 1925.]

1 p. l., x, 109 p. illus.   31½ x 24ᶜᵐ.

First published in 1910; re-issued, with additions, as second imprint,
1920; third imprint, 1925; fourth imprint, 1925.

i. Title.   45-45081

Library of Congress   PS3523.I58V5 1925

CLSU ICU RPB NRU 1CN IEN TxU MsU
NL 0384247   DLC OC1 WaS CaBViP WaSp ICU IU NN CtY

---

f810
L749
tVIR

Lindsay, Nicholas Vachel, 1879-1931.
The Virginians are coming again.
Springfield, Ill. [1928]
Broadside. illus.   49 x 22cm.

"From the American Mercury, July,
1928.
No.27, autographed by the author.
Ex libris Hamlin Garland; in a
case.

NL 0384248   CLSU

---

f810
L749
tW

Lindsay, Nicholas Vachel, 1879-1931.
War bulletin, Number 1 [3, and 5]
The Sangamon County Peace advocate, Number 1.
Springfield, Ill. [author] 1909.
c15p. 31cm.

The War bulletins are leaflets of 4 or 6 pp.; the Peace
advocate is a broadside.
Bound together in a folder by the author for Hamlin
Garland, with one marginal note in the author's hand.
War bulletin no.2 and War bulletin no. 4, "The tramp's
excuse," are not included.
Ex libris Hamlin Garland.
In a case.

I. Title: War bulletin.   II. Title: The
Sangamon County Peace advocate.

NL 0384250   CLSU MH NN RPB NjP IEN

Lindsay, Nicholas Vachel, 1879-1931.
"We who are playing tonight" [Poem in facsimile]
2 ed. n.p. 1905.
[4] p.   1 pl. (mount)   14 cm.
Inscribed on front cover by author: "second
edition, fifteen copies. No. 5"

NL 0384251   RPB

---

*AC9
L6455
B931e

[Lindsay, Nicholas Vachel, 1879-1931]
We who are playing to-night.
[New York, 1905]
folder (2l. incl. pl.)   16cm., in case 26cm.
Caption title.
Plate designed by the author.
Printed in green ink.
Inscribed on recto of l. [1]: [?No.] 449.
[Third edition May 22, 1905. Nicholas Vachel
Lindsay.
Unbound; in a case lettered: Vachel Lindsay.
Ephemera.

NL 0384252   MH RPB

VOLUME 334

Lindsay, Nicholas Vachel, 1879–1931.
The wedding of the rose and the lotus. A poem written on the near-completion of the Panama canal, showing how the genius of the West, here typified by the rose, and the genius of the East, here typified by the lotus, are to be merged and mingled in one. Nicholas Vachel Lindsay, rhymer and designer. Springfield, Ill. ₁1912?₎ folder (₃₎ p.) illus. 28cm.

Signed by the author and dated: 1912.

467219B. 1. Canals, Interoceanic—   America—Panama—Poetry.
I. Title.
N. Y. P. L.   January 31, 1949

NL 0384253   NN NRU ICN MH CtY NjP

Lindsay, Nicholas Vachel, 1879–1931.
*AB9   The wedding of the rose and the lotus. A poem
L6455   written on the completion of the Panama canal
912wb   ... [by] Nicholas Vachel Lindsay.
         [Washington,D.C.? 1915]
         broadside. 33x21.5cm.
         Dated at end: California day. Feb. 20, 1915.
         Printed within ornamental border designed by
         H. F. Clark.
         In this ed., the 1st stanza has been revised.
         Inscribed: To Professor Bliss Perry ... Nicho-
         las Vachel Lind-   say - March 4, 1915.

NL 0384254   MH TxU NNC

---

q811   Lindsay, Nicholas Vachel, 1879–1931.
L64w   What grandpa mouse said. ₁Springfield, Ill.,
1909   1909₎
           1ℓ.
           Original autograph poem within colored ornamen-
         tal border and with colored illustration hinged
         above poem, so as to cover it, designed and made
         by the author; on verso: autograph note signed
         "Nicholas Vachel Lindsay - August 5,1909. Spring-
         field, Ill." and concluding with "Picture and poem
         for Mrs. Haegler".
           Accompanied by photographic reproduction of the
         poem with border   and of the note on verso
         (2ℓ.)

NL 0384255   IU

Lindsay, Nicholas Vachel, 1879–1931.
     What it means to be a poet in America.
     Article from the Saturday Evening Post
November 13, 1926. 35 cm. p. 12–

NL 0384256   RPB

Lindsay, Nicholas Vachel, 1879–1931.
*pAB9   When the stuffed prophets quarrel, by Vachel
L6455   Lindsay. Written for the Illinois state
924w   teachers' association, Friday morning, April 4,
         1924.
           [St.Louis?, 1924]
           broadside. 96.5x30.5cm.
           "Two hundred copies printed and type dis-
         tributed."
           With ms. corrections & additions by the author.
           Inscribed: My dear Squire:—This "poem" I
         read aloud to 3000 teachers in East St. Louis
         the same day I   wrote and printed it.
         Nicholas Vachel Lin[dsay].
           Imperfect: slightly mutilated; silked
         at folds.

NL 0384257   MH MiU-C MoSW NjP

Lindsay, Nigel.
     The America's cup, a short account of its origin and the various challenges which have been made for it since 1870, by Nigel Lindsay ... with an introduction by Colonel the Rt. Hon. R. G. Sharman-Crawford ... London, Heath, Cranton limited, 1930.
     187 p. front., plates, maps (1 fold.) 22ᶜᵐ.
     Bibliography: p. ₁1₎

     1. Yacht racing.   I. Title.

     Library of Congress   GV829.L5   31–2690
                               ₁3₎   797.14

NL 0384258   DLC PU CtY AU NN

Lindsay, Norman, 1879–1969.
     Age of consent, by Norman Lindsay; with illustrations by the author. New York, Toronto, Farrar & Rinehart, inc. ₁ᶜ1938₎
     4 p. l., 3–302 p. illus. 19½ᶜᵐ.

     I. Title.

     Library of Congress   PZ3.L6533Ag   ₍Full name: Norman Alfred William Lindsay₎
                                            38–16536

NL 0384259   DLC AAP ICU NcD CoU NcU OKentU

Lindsay, Norman, 1879–
     Age of consent. L, Laurie [1951]

     241 p.

NL 0384260   MH

Lindsay, Norman, 1879–
Typ   The bookplates of Norman Lindsay, by F. C. V.
975   Lane.
44.524   Adelaide,The Wakefield press,1944.
           1p.ℓ.,7–25,[6]p. mounted front.,mounted
         illus. 22cm.,in folder 23cm.
           Title vignette in red.
           "This, the fourth publication of The Wake-
         field press, has been printed at The Hassell
         press, Adelaide, in Caslon Old Face type on
         wove antique book paper during the month of
         November, 1944.   Limited to three hundred

and seventy-five copies numbered 1–375 for sale, and twenty-five copies lettered A–Y for presentation. Copy no.356."
     "A checklist of the bookplates of Norman Lindsay": p.17–19.
     "Bibliography": p.23–25.
     Original printed cream wrappers; in cloth folder.

NL 0384262   MH IaU

Lindsay, Norman, 1879–
     The cautious amorist, by Norman Lindsay; illustrated by the author. New York, Farrar & Rinehart, incorporated ₁ᶜ1932₎
     3 p. l., 3–300 p. incl. illus., plates. 20ᶜᵐ.

     I. Title.

     Library of Congress   PZ3.L6533Cau   ₍Full name: Norman Alfred William Lindsay₎
                                            32–32261

NL 0384263   DLC CaBVaU AU

PR   Lindsay, Norman, 1879–
9599   The cautious amorist. Illustrated by
L74C3   the author. London, T.W. Laurie ₁1934₎
           251 p. illus. 19 cm.

NL 0384264   NIC TxU

Lindsay, Norman, 1879–
823.91   The cautious amorist. Illustrated by
L749CU   the author. London, T. Werner Laurie
         ₁1935₎
             251 p. illus. 20 cm.

     First published 1934.

NL 0384265   NcD

Lindsay, Norman, 1879–
     The cautious amorist, by Norman Lindsay; illus. by the author. New York, Grayson Publishers ₁1947,c1932₎
     300 p. illus.

NL 0384266   CU NcU CoU

PR   Lindsay, Norman, 1879-1969.
6023   The cautious amorist. Illustrated by
I5815C3 author. London, T.W. Laurie ₁1949₎
1934   250 p. illus. 19 cm.

     "First published April 1934...Reprinted
March 1949."

NL 0384267   LU

PE1625   Lindsay, Norman, 1879–   illus.
.S7   FOR OTHER EDITIONS
1945 a   **Petronius Arbiter.**   SEE MAIN ENTRY
           The complete works of Gaius Petronius, done into English by Jack Lindsay, with one hundred illustrations by Norman Lindsay. Comprising The Satyricon, and poems. New York, Willey book company, 1944.

Lindsay, Norman, 1879–
     The cousin from Fiji, by Norman Lindsay. Sydney, London, Angus and Robertson ltd, 1945.
     2 p. l., 261, ₁1₎ p. 22ᶜᵐ.

     I. Title.

     Library of Congress   PZ3.L6533Co   ₍Full name: Norman Alfred William Lindsay₎
                                            45–10705

NL 0384269   DLC CaBVaU CSt LU TxU CtY CU-S NcU

Lindsay, Norman, 1879–
     Cousin from Fiji, by Norman Lindsay. New York, Random house ₁1946₎
     2 p. l., 3–286 p. 20½ᶜᵐ.
     "First ₁American₎ printing."

     I. Title.

     Library of Congress   PZ3.L6533Co 2   ₍Full name: Norman Alfred William Lindsay₎
                                              46–2494

NL 0384270   DLC MB OU WaSp WaS CaBVa NNC NcD

BD431   Lindsay, Norman, 1879–
L54   Creative effort; an essay in affirmation.   Sydney, Published
         for the author by Art in Australia, 1920.
           293 p.

           120 copies printed.

           1. Life.   I. Title.

NL 0384271   CU TxU

Lindsay, Norman, 1879–
     Creative effort; an essay in affirmation, by Norman Lindsay ... ₁London:₎ C. Palmer₁, 1924₎. vii, 292 p. 1. ed. 8°.

     171812A. 1. Life. 2. Morality.   3. Title.
     N. Y. P. L.   April 6, 1925

NL 0384272   NN MH WU TxDaM-P IaU NcU IEN TxU CaBVaU

Lindsay, Norman, 1879–
823.91
L7¹·B   A curate in Bohemia. With 37 illus. by
         the author. Sydney, N. S. W. Bookstall Co.,
         1915 ₁c1913₎
             192 p. illus. 22 cm.

NL 0384273   NcD

VOLUME 334

Lindsay, Norman, 1879–
A curate in Bohemia by Norman Lindsay ...
Sydney, N.S·W. Bookstall Co., 1932.
4 p.l. 169 p. 19 cm.

NL 0384274 NcU

Lindsay, Norman, 1879–
A curate in Bohemia, by Norman Lindsay ... illustrated by
the author. London, T. Werner Laurie, ltd. [1937]
vii, 248 p. illus. 19ᶜᵐ.

ɪ. Title.
[Full name: Norman Alfred William Lindsay]
38-101
Library of Congress PZ3.L6533Cu

NL 0384275 DLC NIC

*Lindsay, Norman, 1879– illus.
Donne, John, 1573–1631.
... A defence of women for their inconstancy & their paintings, made by Jack Donne & printed now with five decorations
by Norman Lindsay. London, Fanfrolico press [1930]

Lindsay, Norman, 1879–
Dust or polish? Sydney, Angus and Robertson [1950]
205 p. 23 cm.

ɪ. Title.
Full name: Norman Alfred William Lindsay.
PZ3.L6533Du 50-38096

NL 0384277 DLC TxU MH IaU CU NcU CaBVaU

ND1105
.G7L5
Lindsay, Norman, 1879–
Gruner, Elioth, 1882–1939.
Elioth Gruner: twenty-four reproductions in colour from
original oil paintings. Foreword by Norman Lindsay.
Sydney, Shepherd Press [1947]

Lindsay, Norman, 1879–
The etchings of Norman Lindsay. London, Constable & co.
ltd., 1927.
3 p. l., xLv pl., [3] p. 38½ᶜᵐ.
Each plate accompanied by leaf with descriptive letterpress.
"Limited to 129 copies of which 120 are for sale. No. 18. [Signed
Norman Lindsay]."
"Chronology of the published etchings of Norman Lindsay (1918-
1925)": [3] p. at end.
[Full name: Norman Alfred William Lindsay]
43-18744
Library of Congress NE2210.L55A4

NL 0384279 DLC CtY

Lindsay, Norman, 1879–
Every mother's son [by] Norman Lindsay. New York, Cos-
mopolitan book corporation, 1930.
4 p. l., 352 p. 19¾ᶜᵐ.

ɪ. Title.
[Full name: Norman Alfred William Lindsay]
30-23199
Library of Congress PZ3.L6533Ev

NL 0384280 DLC WU NBuU CaBVaU ViU PPM PSt IdU-SB

Lindsay, Norman, 1879–
The flyaway highway, by Norman Lindsay. Sydney, Australia: Angus & Robertson ltd., 1936. 120 p. illus. 24½cm.

911777A. 1. Juvenile literature· Fiction, Australian. I. Title.
N.Y.P.L. October 19, 1937

NL 0384281 NN CLU IaU NcU

PZ3
.D55
Gr
35
Lindsay, Norman, 1879– illus.
Dickens, Charles, 1812–1870.
Great expectations, with 46 illus. by Norman Lindsay.
Sydney, Shepherd Press. 1947.

Lindsay, Norman, 1879–
Halfway to anywhere, by Norman Lindsay. Sydney [etc.]
Angus and Robertson, 1947. 227 p. illus. 22cm.
Sequel to his: Saturdee.

IaU
NL 0384283 NN CaBVaU CU TxU WU NcU PSt CtY MH LU

Lindsay, Norman, 1879–
A homage to Sappho made by Norman and Jack
Lindsay
see under Lindsay, Jack, 1900–

Spec.
PR 6023
I 5815
H 9
1928
4°
Lindsay, Norman, 1879–
Hyperborea; two fantastic travel essays
[written and decorated] by Norman Lindsay...
London, Fanfrolico Press [1928]
27 p. illus. 30 cm.
"Edition limited to seven hundred and
twenty five copies, MCMXXVIII. This is number
291."
Contents.–On man and hyperborean.–The
conspiracy of tailors.–Some pictures and the
hyperborean landscape.
Mendle col-   lection.

TxU CaBVaU
NL 0384285 MoSW KU TxU IEN CU-A ICN IdU NcU WU MiU

Lindsay, Norman, 1879– illus.
The inns of Greece & Rome
see under Firebaugh, W   C

*Lindsay, Norman, 1879– illus.
Lindsay, Jack, 1900– ed.
Loving Mad Tom, Bedlamite verses of the xvi and xvii
centuries, with five illustrations by Norman Lindsay; fore-
word by Robert Graves, the texts edited with notes by Jack
Lindsay, musical transcriptions by Peter Warlock [pseud.]
London, The Fanfrolico press [1927]

Lindsay, Norman, 1879– illus.
Aristophanes.
Lysistrata, translated from the Greek of Aristophanes; illus-
trations by Norman Lindsay ... Cleveland, O., New York,
N. Y., The World publishing company [1942]

Lindsay, Norman, 1879–
Madam Life's lovers; a human narrative embodying a philoso-
phy of the artist in dialogue form. With a gravure by the author.
By Norman Lindsay. London: The Fanfrolico Press[, 1929].
vii p., 1 l., 11–188 p., 1 l. front. 4°.
Printed by Neill and Co., Ltd., Edinburgh.

MH NcU CU-S
NL 0384289 NN ICarbS IEN IaU TxU WU ICarbS CaBVaU

PR
6023
.I 5815
M3
1918
Lindsay, Norman, 1879– 1969.
The magic pudding; being the adventures of Bunyip Blue-
gum and his friends Bill Barnacle & Sam Sawnoff, by Norman
Lindsay; illustrations by the author. Sydney, Angus &
Robertson [1918]
171 p. illus.

NL 0384290 INS

Lindsay, Norman.
The magic pudding; being the adventures of Bunyip Bluegum
and his friends Bill Barnacle & Sam Sawnoff. Sydney: Angus
& Robertson Ltd. [1930] 171 p. illus. sq. 8°.

NL 0384291 NN NcU

Lindsay, Norman, 1879–
The magic pudding; being the adventures of Bunyip Blue-
gum and his friends Bill Barnacle & Sam Sawnoff, by Norman
Lindsay; illustrations by the author. New York, Farrar &
Rinehart, incorporated [1936?]
[150] p. illus. 23ᶜᵐ.

NL 0384292 TxU

Lindsay, Norman, 1879–
The magic pudding; being the adventures of Bunyip Blue-
gum and his friends Bill Barnacle & Sam Sawnoff, by Norman
Lindsay; illustrations by the author. New York, Farrar &
Rinehart, incorporated [1936]
[150] p. illus. 23ᶜᵐ.

ɪ. Title.
[Full name: Norman Alfred William Lindsay]
36-35619
Library of Congress PZ8.L67Mag

NL 0384293 DLC NIC WaS NN OEac OLak OCl

823
L645m
1938
Lindsay, Norman, 1879–
The magic pudding: being the adventures of Bunyip
Bluegum and his friends Bill Barnacle & Sam Sawnoff.
Sydney, Angus & Robertson [1938]
[172]p. illus. 25cm.

NL 0384294 TxU

823.91
L6449m
1954
Lindsay, Norman, 1879–
The magic pudding, being the adventures of
Bunyip Bluegum and his friends Bill Barnacle
& Sam Sawnoff. Sydney, Angus & Robertson
[1954]
171p. illus. 24cm.

NL 0384295 KU CaBVaU IaU

PR6023
.I 5815
M5
Lindsay, Norman, 1879–
Miracles by arrangement. London, Faber and
Faber [1932]
336p. 19cm.

NL 0384296 NcU TxU PP

VOLUME 334

Lindsay, Norman, 1879–
Mr. Gresham and Olympus, by Norman Lindsay. New York, Farrar & Rinehart, incorporated ₁*1932₎
3 p. l., 3–313 p. 19½ᶜᵐ.

ɪ. Title.
₍Full name: Norman Alfred William Lindsay₎

Library of Congress   PZ3.L6533Mr   32–5297

NL 0384297   DLC LU ViU NcU MH TxU

Lindsay, Norman, 1879–
Norman Lindsay water colour book. Eighteen reproductions in colour from original watercolours, with an appreciation of the medium by Norman Lindsay, and a biographical survey of the artist's life and work by Godfrey Blunden. Sydney, The Springwood press, 1939.
4 p. l., 57, ₁1₎ p., 1 l. incl. 18 mounted col. pl. (incl. front.) 32 x 25½ᶜᵐ.
L. C. copy imperfect: pl. 17 wanting.
ɪ. Blunden, Godfrey.
₍Full name: Norman Alfred William Lindsay₎

Library of Congress   ND2002.L5B5   46–31167
                             ₍2₎   751.42

NL 0384298   DLC NN PP

PR6023 Lindsay, Norman, 1875–
.I 5815   Norman Lindsay's book. Ed. by Harold Burston
N67   Sydney, New South Wales Bookstall Co.,1912–15.
        2v. in 1. illus.

        Issued in case.

NL 0384299   NcU

Lindsay, Norman, 1879–
Paintings in oil ₁by₎ Norman Lindsay. Fourteen reproductions in colour from the original oil paintings, and 16 half-tone plates reproduced in black and white; with essays by Douglas Stewart and Norman Lindsay. Sydney, Australia, The Shepherd press ₁1945₎
₍36₎ p., 3 l. illus., 30 pl. (part mounted col.) 33ᶜᵐ.
Colored plates accompanied by guard sheets with descriptive letterpress.
ɪ. Stewart, Douglas Alexander, 1913–
₍Full name: Norman Alfred William Lindsay₎

                                    A 46–2705
New York. Public library
for Library of Congress   ₍2₎

NL 0384300   NN CtY

Lindsay, Norman, 1879–
Pan in the parlour, by Norman Lindsay; illustrated by the author. New York, Farrar & Rinehart, incorporated ₁*1933₎
4 p. l., 3–346 p. illus. 19½ᶜᵐ.

ɪ. Title.
₍Full name: Norman Alfred William Lindsay₎

Library of Congress   PZ3.L6533Pan   33–30001

NL 0384301   DLC ViU NIC PSt CaBVaU IdPI

PZ   Lindsay, Norman, 1879–
3   Pan in the parlour. Illustrated by the
.L6533   author. London, T. W. Laurie ₁1934₎
Pan   346 p. illus. 19 cm.

NL 0384302   WU NcD NcU

Lindsay, Norman, 1879–
Pan in the parlour. Illustrated by the author.
London, Laurie ₁1939₎

254 p. illus.

NL 0384303   MH

Lindsay, Norman, 1879–
The pen drawings of Norman Lindsay. Special number of Art in Australia, edited by Sydney Ure Smith & Bertram Stevens. Sydney, Angus & Robertson ltd, 1918.
₍15₎ p., LVI mounted pl., 1 l. 2 mounted port. (incl. front.) 40 x 30½ᶜᵐ.
"35 copies ... printed ... No. 17. ₍Signed₎ Norman Lindsay."
"Norman Lindsay. By Julian Ashton": p. ₍8₎–₍10₎ "Norman Lindsay: his inspiration and technique. By Lionel Lindsay": p. ₍11₎–₍15₎
ɪ. Smith, Sydney Ure, 1887– ed. ɪɪ. Stevens, Bertram, 1872–1922, joint ed. ɪɪɪ. Art in Australia. ɪᴠ. Ashton, Julian Rossi, 1851– ᴠ. Lindsay, Sir Lionel Arthur, 1874–
₍Full name: Norman Alfred William Lindsay₎

                                    44–24790
Library of Congress   NC1260.L52
                             ₍2₎   741.91

NL 0384304   DLC NcU

Zeta   Lindsay, Norman, 1879–
JJ18   Pen drawings. Sydney,A.McQuitty, 1924.
L645   [12]p. 12 plates. 42cm.
924   No.18 of an ed. of 500 copies signed by the
         artist.

NL 0384305   CtY

Lindsay, Norman, 1879–
Norman Lindsay's pen drawings. Sydney, Art in Australia limited ₁1931₎
₍8₎ p., 64 (i. e. 62) pl. (incl. front. (port.)) on 31 l. 29½ x 23ᶜᵐ.
"Many of the illustrations ... appeared in the Pen drawings of Norman Lindsay, published by Angus & Robertson in 1918."

                   ₍Full name: Norman Alfred William Lindsay₎
                                    43–22546
Library of Congress   NC1260.L5
                             ₍2₎   741.91

NL 0384306   DLC ICN NN

Lindsay, Norman, 1879–
Redheap, by Norman Lindsay. London, Faber & Faber limited ₁1930₎
317, ₍1₎ p. 19½ᶜᵐ.

ɪ. Title.
₍Full name: Norman Alfred William Lindsay₎

Library of Congress   PZ3.L6533Re   30–15217
                             .₃

CaBVaU
NL 0384307   DLC IaU CtY IU LU NcD NIC TxU CaBVa

LINDSAY, NORMAN, 1879–
"Saturdee," by Norman Lindsay. Sydney: The Endeavour Press[, 1933]. 259 p. 19cm.

727135A. 1. Juvenile literature—Fiction, Australian.
I. Title.

NL 0384308   NN NcU CtY

PR6023 Lindsay, Norman, 1879–
I55S37   Saturdee. Illustrated by the author.
         London, T.Werner Laurie ₑ1936₎
         vii,277p. illus. 19cm.

NL 0384309   IaU

Lindsay, Norman, 1879–
"Saturdee," by Norman Lindsay ... illustrated by the author.
London, T. W. Laurie ltd ₁1939₎
vii, ₍1₎, 277 p. illus. 19ᶜᵐ.
"First published ... 1936; reprinted March 1939."

ɪ. Title.
₍Full name: Norman Alfred William Lindsay₎

                                    43–42358
Library of Congress   PZ7.L6605Sat

NL 0384310   DLC AAP LU PU CU PSt NNC

PA6558 Lindsay, Norman, 1879–   illus.
.E5F5
Rare bk. Petronius Arbiter.
Coll.   The Satyricon of Petronius Arbiter. Complete and unexpurgated translation by W. C. Firebaugh, in which are incorporated the forgeries of Nodot and Marchena, and the readings introduced into the text by De Salas. Illustrations by Norman Lindsay ... New York, Published for private circulation only by Boni and Liveright, 1922.

Lindsay, Norman, 1879–
[Watercolours and etchings] Sydney, Art in Australia, 1930.

64 p. 39 plates. 25 cm.

Norman Lindsay number of Art in Australia, 3d ser., no. 35, Dec. 1930.

1. Artists, Australian. I. Art in Australia. II. Title.

NL 0384312   CaBVaU

7555   Lindsáy, Onopre
L64   Hácia la casa propria, sana, alegre y barata. Exposición de medios prácticos para mejorar la vivienda de los empleados de oficina. ₍Valparaíso, 1923₎
         49 p. 23cm.

NL 0384313   NNC

         Lindsáy, Onopre
312.0983   El problema fundamental: la repoblación
L749P   de Chile y los E. U. de Sudamérica ₍por₎ O. Lindsáy. ₍Valparaíso, Chile, 1926?₎
         xvi, 94 p. 23 cm.

         1. Chile. Population. 2. Latin America. Population. I. Title.

NL 0384314   NcD

Lindsay, Orrin.
Orrin Lindsay's plan of aerial navigation see under Riddell, John Leonard, 1807–1867.

VOLUME 334

Lindsay, Owen, *d.* 1875? *defendant.*
The Baldwinsville homicide. Verbatim report of the trial of Owen Linsday, for the murder of Francis A. Colvin, containing the testimony in full; opening and closing speeches of counsel; charge to the jury, &c. printed from the minutes of the official reporters. Also, accurate likenesses of Lindsay, Colvin and Vader, engraved from photographs recently taken. Published by Tinsley & Morgan, official stenographers of the Supreme court. Syracuse, N. Y., Truair, Smith & co., printers, 1875.
268 p. plates, ports. 22½ᶜᵐ.
Trial at a Court of oyer and terminer in and for Onondaga county, New York, starting January 26th, 1875.—*cf.* p. 6.
1. Colvin, Francis A., d. 1873. I. Tinsley, Charles G., reporter. II. Morgan, Fred J., 1851— reporter. III. New York (State) Court of oyer and terminer (Onondaga co.) IV. Title.
Library of Congress   41-32897

NL 0384316   DLC MnU-L ICU IU

Lindsay, Mrs. Patricia (Robertson)
Recollections of a royal parish, by Patricia Lindsay. With illustrations. London, J. Murray, 1902.
x p., 1 l., 133 p., 1 l. front., pl., port. 20ᶜᵐ.
1. Crathie and Braemar, Scotland (Parish) 2. Victoria, queen of Gt. Brit. and Ireland, 1819-1901. 3. Balmoral castle. I. Title.
                                                3—7832
Library of Congress   DA890.C89L7

NL 0384317   DLC PPL MB

Lindsay, Patrick, *d.* 1753.
The interest of Scotland considered, with regard to its police in imploying of the poor, its agriculture, its trade, its manufactures, and fisheries ... Edinburgh, Printed by R. Fleming and company, 1733.
5 p. l., xxxv, [10], 229 p.   17.5 cm.
1. Scotland—Economic conditions. 2. Scotland—Industries. 3. Fisheries—Scotland.
                                        A 17-1971 Revised
Title from Harvard   Univ. Printed by L. C.

CLU-C ViU RPJCB KU ViU NNC
NL 0384318   MH-BA RPB NN MU NcD CtY CaBVaU CU OkU

Lindsay, Patrick, *d.* 1753.
The interest of Scotland considered, with regard to its police in imploying of the poor, its agriculture, its trade, its manufactures, and fisheries ... London, Printed for T. Woodward [etc.] 1736.
8 p. l., xxxv, 256 p. 20¾ᶜᵐ.
1. Scotland—Economic conditions. 2. Scotland—Industries. 3. Fisheries—Scotland.
                                        A 18-1405 Revised 2
Title from Harvard   Univ. Printed by L. C.

NL 0384319   MH ICJ NNC FMU MH-BA NIC MoU MdBJ

[Lindsay, Patrick] *d.* 1753.
Reasons for encouraging the linnen manufacture of Scotland, and other parts of Great-Britain. Humbly submitted to Parliament, by the author of The interest of Scotland consider'd, &c. London, Printed for J. Peele, 1735.
63 p. 21 cm.
1. Linen—Scotland. 2. Linen—Gt. Brit. I. The interest of Scotland consider'd, Author of. II. Title.
HD9930.S32L55   72-202511

NL 0384320   DLC InU NNC CSmH ICU NcD MH-BA

[Lindsay, Patrick] *d.* 1753.
Reasons for encouraging the linnen manufacture of Scotland, and other parts of Great-Britain. Humbly submitted to Parliament. By the author of The interest of Scotland consider'd, &c. London, J. Peele [etc., etc.] 1738.   63 p.   19cm.
1. Textile trade and statistics—   Gt. Br.—Scotland, 1738. I. Title.
N. Y. P. L.   June 29, 1945

NL 0384321   NN

Lindsay, Perry, *pseud.*
see **Gaddis, Peggy,** 1896-

Lindsay, Philip, 1906-
All that glitters, by Philip Lindsay.   London, S. Low [1949]
402 p.   19cm.
Author's autographed presentation copy to Ralph Straus.

NL 0384323   NN MH TxU

Lindsay, Philip, 1906-
An artist in love. New York, Roy Publishers [1954?]
280 p. 19 cm.
1. Lawrence, Sir Thomas, 1769-1830—Fiction. 2. Siddons, Sarah (Kemble) 1755-1831—Fiction. 3. Siddons, Sarah Martha, 1775-1803—Fiction. 4. Siddons, Maria, 1779-1798—Fiction. I. Title.
[PZ3]   54-10476 ‡
Printed for U. S. Q. B. R.
by Library of Congress   [7]

NL 0384324   TxU OC1 NN

AC-L
L647be   **Lindsay, Philip,** 1906-
1950   Beauty or the beast.   London, S. Low [1950]
            264p. 19cm.
            Author's autograph presentation copy to John Gawsworth [i.e. Terence Ian Fytton Armstrong] 1950.
            Bookplate of Phil Lindsay.
            I. Title. A.F.: Armstrong, Terence Ian Fytton Armstrong, 1912-

NL 0384325   TxU

Lindsay, Philip, 1906-
The bells of Rye, a novel by Philip Lindsay. London, I. Nicholson & Watson, limited, 1937.
428 p. 19ᵐᵐ.
I. Title.
                                            38-2966
Library of Congress   PZ3.L6534Be

NL 0384326   DLC

Lindsay, Philip, 1906-
... Bride for a buccaneer. London, Hutchinson & co., ltd. [1938]
vii, 9-352 p. 19ᵐᵐ.
I. Title.
                                            38-16696
Library of Congress   PZ3.L6534Br
                            [3]

NL 0384327   DLC KyLoU WU TxU

AC-L
L647br   **Lindsay, Philip,** 1906-
1955   Bride for a buccaneer. 50th thousand.
            London, New York, Hutchinson [1955]
            304p. 19cm. (Arrow book, 283II)
            Pictorial paper wrapper.
            Mounted on half title page: British Museum book request of Philip Lindsay. Bookplate of Phil Lindsay.

NL 0384328   TxU DLC

Lindsay, Philip, 1906-
Crowned king of England; the coronation of King George VI in history and tradition, by Philip Lindsay. London, Ivor Nicholson & Watson, ltd., 1937.
287, [1] p. front., plates, ports. 22ᵐᵐ.
Bibliography: p. 279-282.
1. Coronations—Gt. Brit. 2. George VI, king of Gt. Brit., 1895- —Coronation.
                                            A 40-3617
Yale univ. Library
for Library of Congress   [2]

NL 0384329   CtY NN CU TxU

PR 6023 LINDSAY, PHILIP, 1906-
.I 54 C8   The counterfeit lady, a novel.   London, Hutchinson [1955]
            336 p.

NL 0384330   InU WU

Lindsay, Philip, 1906-
The devil and King John, a novel by Philip Lindsay. 10th thousand ... London, New York [etc.] Hutchinson & co., ltd. [1943]
v, 6-223, [1] p. 19ᵐᵐ.
1. John, king of England, 1167?-1216—Fiction. I. Title.
                                            44-369
Library of Congress   PZ3.L6534De

NL 0384331   DLC TxU

AC-L
L647E𝓁   **Lindsay, Philip,** 1906-
1948   Dr. Johnson awakes.   [London, 1948]
            p.47-49. 22cm.
            Detached from the Literary digest (London) winter 1948.
            "Condensed from John O'London's."
            1. Johnson, Samuel, 1709-1784 - Fiction. I. Title.

NL 0384332   TxU

AC-L
L647thTSWs
1950   **Lindsay, Philip,** 1906-
            En drottning spelas ut, roman. Till svenska av Sten Söderberg. Stockholm, C.E. Fritzes [c1950]
            487p. 24cm.
            Translation of There is no escape.
            Check order form signed by Philip Lindsay mounted on half title page.
            Bookplate of Phil Lindsay.
            1. Dudley, Lady Jane, known as Lady Jane Grey, 1537-1554 - Fiction. I. Söderberg, Sten Valdemar, 1908-   tr. II. Title.

NL 0384333   TxU

VOLUME 334

Lindsay, Philip, 1906–
The duke is served; a novel, by Philip Lindsay. London,
I. Nicholson and Watson, limited, 1936.
447, ₁1₁ p. 19¾ᶜᵐ.
Illustrated lining-paper.

I. Title.

36–19097

Library of Congress   PZ3.L6534Du

NL   0384334   DLC WU

Lindsay, Philip, 1906–
The fall of the axe, a novel by Philip Lindsay. London and
Melbourne, Hutchinson & co., ltd. ₁1940₁
xi p., 13–416 p. 19ᶜᵐ.

1. Cenci, Beatrice, 1577–1599—Fiction. 2. Cenci, Francesco, 1549–
1598—Fiction. I. Title.

Library of Congress   PZ3.L6534Fa   41–1977

NL   0384335   DLC

Lindsay, Philip, 1906–
For King or Parliament. London, Evans Bros., 1949.
204 p. ports. 23 cm.
Bibliography: p. ₁203₁–204.
CONTENTS.—George Villiers, first duke of Buckingham, 1592–1628.—
Thomas Wentworth, earl of Strafford, 1593–1641.—John Hampden,
1594–1643.—Richard Lovelace, 1618–58.

1. Buckingham, George Villiers, 1st duke of, 1592–1628. 2. Strafford,
Thomas Wentworth, 1st earl of, 1593–1641. 3. Hampden, John, 1594–
1643. 4. Lovelace, Richard, 1618–1658.   I. Title.

DA396.A1L55   942.06   50–21506

CaBViP
NL   0384336   DLC CU–I MH TxU DFo CoU TxU NcU LU

Lindsay, Philip, 1906–
The gentle knight, a novel by Philip Lindsay. London, New
York ₁etc.₁ Hutchinson & co., ltd. ₁1942₁
ix (i. e. xi), 13–206, ₁1₁ p. 19ᶜᵐ.
The story, woven around the Roman de la Rose, presents the charac-
ters of Chaucer and his Canterbury pilgrims. cf. p. vi.

1. Chaucer, Geoffrey—Fiction.   I. Title.

43–5794

Library of Congress   PZ3.L6534Gc

NL   0384337   DLC TxU

Lindsay, Philip, 1906–
Gentleman Harry retires; a novel, by Philip Lindsay. London, I. Nicholson & Watson, 1937.
412 p. 19ᶜᵐ.

I. Title.

37–18657

Library of Congress   PZ3.L6534Ge

NL   0384338   DLC

Lindsay, Philip, 1906–
Gentleman Harry retires; a novel, by Philip
Lindsay.   London, John Langdon [1948]
304p.   19cm.

"First published 1937. Reprinted 1948."

I. Title. A.F.: Rasdall, E.H. A.F.: Fair-
banks, Douglas, Jr. A.F.: Armstrong, Terence
Ian Fytton, 1912–   A.F.: Armstrong,
Estelle.

NL   0384339   TxU WU DLC

Lindsay, Philip, 1906–
The great buccaneer, being the life, death and extraordi-
nary adventures of Sir Henry Morgan, buccaneer and Lieutenant Governor of Jamaica. London, New York, P. Nevill
₁1950₁
305 p. illus., ports. 22 cm.
Bibliography: p. 293–294.

1. Morgan, Sir Henry, 1635?–1688.   I. Title.

F2161.M8448 1950   [923.41] 923.242   50–58253

NL   0384340   DLC AU MiU MH CaBVa CaBViP OrU CaBVaU

Lindsay, Philip, 1906–
The great buccaneer; being the life, death, and extraor-
dinary adventures of Sir Henry Morgan, buccaneer and
Lieutenant Governor of Jamaica. New York, W. Funk
₁1951₁
305 p. 21 cm.
Bibliography: p. 293–294.

1. Morgan, Sir Henry, 1635?–1688.   I. Title.
F2161.M8448 1951   [923.41] 923.242   51–3835

NL   0384341   DLC KyLx ScU TxU TNJ ViU OrP WaT WaS

Lindsay, Philip, 1906–
Hampton Court, a history, with illus. by Denis Duffield.
London, Meridian Books, 1948.
282 p. illus. 22 cm.
Bibliography: p. 282.

1. Hampton Court. 2. Gt. Brit.—Kings and rulers.

DA690.H2L55   942.19   49–1747*

NL   0384342   DLC CU–S CtY ICU NNC NN

Lindsay, Philip, 1906–
The haunted man; a portrait of Edgar Allan Poe. London, Hutchinson ₁1953₁
256 p. illus. 22 cm.

1. Poe, Edgar Allan, 1809–1849.   I. Title.

PS2631.L49   928.1   54–2812 ‡

MB MH CU NIC NN IU FTaSU CoU TxU MU OKentU IaU
NL   0384343   DLC NBuU MiU PSt PPT IEN OU OO TU TxU

Lindsay, Philip, 1906–
The haunted man; a portrait of Edgar Allan Poe. New
York, Philosophical Library ₁1954₁
256 p. illus. 22 cm.

1. Poe, Edgar Allan, 1809–1849.   I. Title.

[PQ2631]   928.1   54–11394 ‡
Printed for U. S. Q. B. R.
by Library of Congress   ₁12₁

CaBVa KEmT OKentU UU FTaSU
NL   0384344   OOxM ViU OCl PP NcD ODW PIm FMU Or OrCS

Lindsay, Philip, 1906–
He rides in triumph; a novel by Philip Lindsay. London,
New York ₁etc.₁ Hutchinson & co., ltd. ₁1945₁
280 p. 19 cm.

I. Title.

A 47–5658

Harvard univ. Library
for Library of Congress   ₁1₁

NL   0384345   MH

Lindsay, Philip, 1906–
He rides in triumph; a novel.   London,
Bouverie House ₌1946₌
280p.   19cm.

"Universal Book Club Edition."

NL   0384346   IaU WU

Lindsay, Philip, 1906–
Heart of a king; a novel, by Philip Lindsay.
London [etc.] Hutchinson & co. [1946] 256 p.
19cm.

568205B. 1. Henry VIII, king of England, 1491–1547—
Fiction. I. Title.

NL   0384347   NN

Lindsay, Philip, 1906–
Heart of a king, a novel. London, New York,
Hutchinson [1948]
256p.   19cm.
Author's autograph presentation copy to
John Gawsworth [i.e. Terence Ian Fytton Arm-
strong] with ms. note, '48. Bookplate of Phil
Lindsay.
1. Henry VII, King of England, 1491–1547 –
Fiction. I. Title. A.F.: Armstrong, Terence
Ian Fytton, 1912–   A.F.: Lindsay, Philip,
1906–

NL   0384348   TxU

Lindsay, Philip, 1906–
Heart of a king; a novel.   ₌1949₌

NL   0384349   CaBVa

Lindsay, Philip, 1906–
Here comes the king, by Philip Lindsay. Boston, Little,
Brown, and company, 1933.
x, 342 p. 21¼ᶜᵐ.

1. Catharine Howard, queen consort of Henry VIII, d. 1542—Fiction.
I. Title.

Library of Congress   PZ3.L6534He 2   33–21273

NL   0384350   DLC OCl CaBVa PPL CaBVaU NN IEN FMU

VOLUME 334

Lindsay, Philip, 1906–
Here comes the king, by Philip Lindsay. London, I. Nicholson & Watson, ltd., 1933.
352 p. 19ᶜᵐ.
"First published in 1933; reprinted July 1933."

1. Catharine Howard, queen consort of Henry VIII, d. 1542—Fiction.
I. Title.

Library of Congress   PZ3.L6534He

33–21932

NL 0384351   DLC

Lindsay, Philip, 1906–
Here comes the king, by Philip Lindsay. London, I. Nicholson & Watson, 1934.   352 p.   19cm.
"First edition, July, 1933...Cheap edition, October, 1935."

322379B. 1. Catharine Howard, queen·   consort of Henry VIII, king of
N. Y. P. L.   England, d. 1542—Fiction. I. Title.
                                                        December 17, 1945

NL 0384352   NN TxU

Lindsay, Philip, 1906–
I'd live the same life over; being the progress, or rather the circumgyration, of Philip Lindsay. London and Melbourne, Hutchinson & co., ltd. ₁1941₎
285, ₁1₎ p. 24ᶜᵐ.

I. Title.   A 41–8397

Harvard univ. Library
  for Library of Congress   PR6023.I 5817A3 1941
                                ₁2₎   928.2

NL 0384353   MH DLC IdU

Lindsay, Philip, 1906–
The Iron Duke, by Philip Lindsay; this novel is based on the original film story by H. M. Harwood, a Gaumont-British picture with George Arliss as the Duke of Wellington. London, The Queensway press ₁1934₎
2 p. l., 9–312 p. front., plates. 20ᶜᵐ.

1. Wellington, Arthur Wellesley, 1st duke of, 1769–1852—Fiction.
I. Harwood, Harold Marsh, 1874–   II. Title.

Library of Congress   PZ3.L6534 Ir

35–2812

NL 0384354   DLC TxU

PR6023
I5817
1955
Lindsay, Philip, 1906–
The Iron Duke, by Philip Lindsay; this novel is based on the original film story by H.M. Harwood, a Gaumont-British picture with George Arliss as the Duke of Wellington. Sydney, Angus and Robertson, 1935.
250p. illus. 19cm.

NL 0384355   IaU TxU

Lindsay, Philip, 1906–
Jack laughs at locksmiths; a novel, by Philip Lindsay. London [etc.] Hutchinson & co. [1943]
263 p. 19cm.

568512B. 1. Sheppard,   Jack, 1702–1724—
Fiction. I. Title.

NL 0384356   NN

Lindsay, Philip, 1906–
King Henry v; a chronicle, by Philip Lindsay. London, I. Nicholson & Watson, ltd., 1934.
388 p. front., plates, ports. 22ᶜᵐ.
"Acknowledgements": p. 361–364.

1. Henry v, king of England, 1387–1422. 2. France—Hist.—Charles VI, 1380–1422.

Library of Congress   DA256.L5 1934   35–2788
Copyright A ad int. 19373   ₁5₎   923.142

NL 0384357   DLC TxU OU OrU CaBViP OU NN OO OCl

Lindsay, Philip, 1906–
King Richard III; a chronicle, by Philip Lindsay. London, I. Nicholson & Watson, ltd., 1933.
362, ₁2₎ p. front., ports. 22½ᶜᵐ.
"First edition September 1933."
American edition (New York, R. M. McBride & company) has title: The tragic king, Richard III.
"Acknowledgements" containing bibliography: p. 343–345.
"Errata for King Richard III—a chronicle" in the author's On some bones in Westminster abbey (London, 1934) p. 53–54.

1. Richard III, king of England, 1452–1485. 2. Gt. Brit.—Hist.—Lancaster and York, 1399–1485.

Library of Congress   DA260.L6 1933   34–255
Copyright A nd int. 18416   ₁a37c1₎   923.142

NL 0384358   DLC TxU MU CaBVaU PV WaSpG OCl

Lindsay, Philip, 1906–
Kings of merry England from Eadward the Confessor, 1042–1066, to Richard the Third, 1483–1485, by Philip Lindsay. London, I. Nicholson & Watson, ltd., 1936.
617 p. front., plates, ports. 23½ᶜᵐ.

1. Gt. Brit.—Kings and rulers. I. Title.   36–12522

Library of Congress   DA28.1.L48 1936
                                                923.142

NL 0384359   DLC TxU GU IU CaBViP PU NN

Lindsay, Philip, 1906–
The knights at bay, by Philip Lindsay ... Oxford, B. Blackwell ₁1933₎
viii, 9–190 p. incl. plates. col. front. 20½ᶜᵐ. (Tales of action. no. 1)

1. Malta—Siege, 1565—Fiction. 2. Malta, Knights of—Fiction.
I. Title.

Library of Congress   PZ7.L661Kn

33–32595

NL 0384360   DLC WaSp

Lindsay, Philip, 1906–
... The knights at bay; illustrated by Oscar Ogg. New York, Loring & Mussey ₁'1935₎
viii p. 1 l., 11–222, ₁1₎ p. incl. illus., plates, map. 21½ᶜᵐ. (Tales of action. no. 1)

1. Malta—Siege, 1565—Fiction. 2. Malta, Knights of—Fiction.
I. Title.

Library of Congress   PZ7.L661Kn 2

35–6537

NL 0384361   DLC PP PJA OrP OLak OO

Lindsay, Philip, 1906–
The last of the Irish R. M.s. London, Cassell ₁1951₎
208 p. 22 cm.

1. George IV, King of Great Britain, 1762–1830.
DA538.A1L5 1951   923.142   52–34602 ‡

NL 0384362   DLC

Lindsay, Philip, 1906–
The little wench, by Philip Lindsay. London, I. Nicholson and Watson, limited, 1935.
483 p. 19ᶜᵐ.
Illustrated lining-papers.

1. Gueneverc, Queen. 2. Lancelot. I. Title.

Library of Congress   PZ3.L6534Li

35–8476

NL 0384363   DLC CaBVaU PP NN

Lindsay, Philip, 1906–
London bridge is falling ₁by₎ Philip Lindsay. Boston, Little, Brown, and company, 1934.
xiv, 389 p. 21½ᶜᵐ.
Illustrated t.-p. and lining-papers.

1. Cade's rebellion, 1450—Fiction. I. Title.   34–19488
Library of Congress   PZ3.L6534Lo

NN OCl OU OCU
NL 0384364   DLC NIC IdU Or CaBVa PSC PPL PP WaE

Lindsay, Philip, 1906–
London bridge is falling, a novel, by Philip Lindsay. London, I. Nicholson & Watson, ltd., 1934.
447, ₁1₎ p. 19ᶜᵐ.
Illustrated lining-papers.
"First edition."

1. Cade's rebellion, 1450—Fiction. I. Title.

Library of Congress   PZ3.L6534Lo 2   34–20027

NL 0384365   DLC TxU

Lindsay, Philip, 1906–
The loves of Florizel. ₁London₎ Hutchinson, 1951.
208 p. 22 cm.

1. George IV, King of Great Britain, 1762–1830.
DA538.A1L5 1951   923.142   52–34602 rev ‡

NL 0384366   DLC OrU NN MH

AC-L
L647love **Lindsay, Philip,** 1906–
1949   The loves of my lord admiral, a novel. London, New York, Hutchinson [1949]
        400p. port. 21cm.
        Author's autograph presentation copy to John Gawsworth [i.e. Terence Ian Fytton Armstrong] June '49.
        Bookplate of Phil Lindsay.
        1. Seymour, Thomas Seymour, baron, 1508?–1549 – Fiction. I. Title. A.F.: Armstrong, Terence Ian Fytton, 1912–

NL 0384367   TxU

Lindsay, Philip, 1906–
The loves of My Lord Admiral; a novel, by Philip Lindsay. London ₁etc.₎ Hutchinson & co. ₁1950?₎   400 p. port. 21cm.

596992B. 1. Seymour of Sudeley,   Thomas Seymour, baron, 1508?–1549
—Fiction. I. Title.
N. Y. P. L.   December 13, 1951

NL 0384368   NN

VOLUME 334

AC-L
L647me
1952
Lindsay, Philip, 1906–
The merry mistress, a novel.   London,
Hutchinson [1952]
304p. 19cm.

Author's autograph presentation copy to
E.H. Rasdall.

1. Shore, Jane, d. 1527? - Fiction. I.
Title. A.F.: Rasdall, E.H.

NL 0384369   TxU DLC

Lindsay, Philip, 1906–
The merry mistress, a novel. New York, Roy [1953]
304p. 19 cm.

1. Shore, Jane, d. 1527?–Fiction. I. Title.

A 55–868

Wisconsin. Univ. Libr.
for Library of Congress   [2]

NL 0384370   WU TxU NcU OOxM N

Lindsay, Philip, 1906–
A mirror for ruffians, by Philip Lindsay. New York, For-
tuny's [1939]
382 p. plates. 22ᶜᵐ.

A reworking of the fundamental idea of the author's earlier book,
Ruffians' hall, but so different that it is practically a new work. *cf.*
p. 11–12.
"First published 1939."

1. Adventure and adventurers. I. Title.

40–33622

Library of Congress   CT105.L5
[2]   920.02

OU OCU IdU WaS
NL 0384371   DLC Vi TxU CU-S PrU OrU NcGU CU NcU

Lindsay, Philip, 1906–
Morgan in Jamaica; being an account biographical and informative of the latter
days of Sir Henry Morgan ... written by
Philip Lindsay ... with a poem panegyr-
ical by Mr. Jack Lindsay and some portraits
by Mr. Raymond Lindsay and published by
the Fanfrolico press.   London, MCMXXX.
[40] p. illus.,port. 28cm.
Title on two leaves.
Unpaged.
Colophon: "... Typography by J. Lindsay

handset in Weiss antiqua. Reproductions
by collographic method. The fourth book
printed by the Fanfrolico press. 450
signed copies of which this is no.81.
[signed] Philip Lindsay. Composition
and machining by W. J. Hatton."

1.Morgan,Sir Henry,1635?–1688. I.Lind-
say,Jack. II.Lindsay,Raymond. III.Fan-
frolico press, London.   IV. Title.

NL 0384373   NNU-W FU MH CtY NN MChB

Lindsay, Philip, 1906–
... The nutbrown maid. London, Hutchinson & co., ltd
[1939]
2 p. l., vii–xvi p., 1 l., 19–382 p. 19ᶜᵐ.
"Based on the famous mediæval ballade 'The nut-browne maide'."

1. The nut-brown maid.

39—10378

Library of Congress   PZ3.L6534Nu

NL 0384374   DLC OCl

AC-L
L647nu
1954
Lindsay, Philip, 1906–
The nutbrown maid.   Toronto, Harlequin
Books [1954]
287p. 17cm.

Based on the famous mediaeval ballad The
nut-brown maid.
British Museum book request of Philip Lindsay mounted on half title page. Bookplate of
Phil Lindsay.

I. The nut-brown maid. II. Title.

NL 0384375   TxU DLC

Lindsay, Philip, 1906–
On some bones in Westminster abbey; a defence of King
Richard III, by Philip Lindsay. London, I. Nicholson & Wat-
son, ltd., 1934.
54 p. front. (port.) 22½ᶜᵐ.
"On some recent investigations regarding the fate of the princes
in the Tower."—p. 9.
"Errata for King Richard III—a chronicle": p. 53–54.

1. Richard III, king of England, 1452–1485. I. Title.

35–18090

Library of Congress   DA260.L63
[3]   942.046

NL 0384376   DLC TxU NN ICN

Lindsay, Philip, 1906–
One dagger for two; a novel, by Philip Lindsay...
London [etc.] Cassell and co. [1932] 311 p.
19cm.

NL 0384377   NN WU TxU

AC-L
L647one
1952
Lindsay, Philip, 1906–
One dagger for two, a novel.   [London]
Published and distributed by the "News of the
World" by arrangement with Cassell [1952]
246p. 17cm. (Pocket book, B64)
Pictorial paper wrapper.
"First published 1932 ... First Pocket book
edition 1952."
Canceled check from Philip Lindsay to Percy
Ide mounted on half title page.
Bookplate of Phil Lindsay.

NL 0384378   TxU

Lindsay, Philip, 1906–
Panama is burning, by Philip Lindsay. London [etc.] Cassell
and company, limited [1932]
5 p. l., 308 p. 19½ᶜᵐ.

1. Buccaneers. 2. Morgan, Sir Henry, 1635?–1688—Fiction. I. Title.

32–13941

Library of Congress   PZ3.L6534Pan 2

NL 0384379   DLC TxU

Lindsay, Philip, 1906–
Panama is burning, by Philip Lindsay. New York, Farrar &
Rinehart, incorporated [*1932]
4 p. l., 3–346 p. 20ᶜᵐ.

1. Buccaneers. 2. Morgan, Sir Henry, 1635?–1688—Fiction.
I. Title.

32–13939

Library of Congress   PZ3.L6534Pan

NL 0384380   DLC PPM PSt TxU FMU

Lindsay, Philip, 1906–
The Peasants' Revolt, 1381, by Philip Lindsay and Reg
Groves. London, New York, Hutchinson [1950]
184 p. plates. 24 cm.
Bibliography: p. 177–178.

1. Tyler's Insurrection, 1381. I. Groves, Reginald, 1908–
joint author. II. Title.

DA235.L5   942.038   51–2656

FMU CaBVaU CaBViP OrU MtU WaS
NL 0384381   DLC InRenS TU ViU NIC MH NNC OClW OCU NN

PZ
3
.L6534
Pi
Lindsay, Philip, 1906–195
A piece for candlelight; a novel.   London,
Hutchinson [1953]
303 p. 19cm.

1. Robinson, Mary (Darby) 1758–1800 - Fiction
I. Title

NL 0384382   WU

Lindsay, Philip, 1906–
Pudding lane [by] Philip Lindsay. London and Melbourne,
Hutchinson & co., ltd. [1940]
xii, 13–516 p. 19ᶜᵐ.

1. Plague—London, 1665—Fiction. 2. London—Fire, 1666—Fiction.
I. Title.

40–9863

Library of Congress   PZ3.L6534Pu

NL 0384383   DLC

AC-L
L647qu
1934
Lindsay, Philip, 1906–
Queen Christina.   London, Reader's Library
Pub. Co. [1934]
250p. 18cm.
"Copyright edition."
Author's autograph presentation copy to
John Gawsworth [i.e. Terence Ian Fytton Arm-
strong]
Bookplate of Phil Lindsay.
1. Kristina, Queen of Sweden, 1626–1689.
A.F.: Armstrong,   Terence Ian Fytton,
1912–

NL 0384384   TxU NN

PZ
3
.L6534
Que
Lindsay, Philip, 1906–1958
Queen Honeypot.   London, S. Low [1951]
342 p. 19cm.

1. Mary Stuart, Queen of the Scots, 1542–
1587 - Fiction I. Title

NL 0384385   WU

Lindsay, Philip, 1906–
The Queenmaker; a portrait of John Dudley, viscount
Lisle, earl of Warwick and duke of Northumberland, 1502–
1553. London, Williams & Norgate, 1951.
208 p. ports. 22 cm.
Bibliography: p. 205.

1. Northumberland, John Dudley, 1st duke of, 1502–1553. I. Title.

DA345.1.N6L5   923.242   51–8521

NL 0384386   DLC NN NIC MH OrU CaBViP LU

VOLUME 334

Lindsay, Philip, 1906–
The queen's confession; a novel, by Philip Lindsay.   London
[etc.] Hutchinson & co. [1947]   352 p.   19cm.

NL   0384387   NN CLSU TxU

Lindsay, Philip, 1906–
The rake's progress.   New York, Sheridan House [1950]
320 p.   21 cm.

I. Title.

PZ3.L6534Rak   50–9396

NL   0384388   DLC PP Or IdU

Lindsay, Philip, 1906–
Ruffians' hall, by Philip Lindsay.   London, D. Harmsworth
[1931]
223 p.   ports.   22½cm.
Contents.—Morgan in Jamaica.—Hildebrand at Salerno.—Columbus
at sea.—The Prince Regent [George IV] at home.—Bligh in New South
Wales.—Edward Kelly dead.—Walker in Nicaragua.—Postscript.

1. Adventure and adventurers.   I. Title.

Library of Congress   G525.L65   33–8241
                               [2]   910.4

NL   0384389   DLC FTaSU KU FU TxU CtY

Lindsay, Philip, 1906–
The secret of Henry the Eighth.   London, Meridian
Books [1953]
188 p.   illus.   22 cm.

1. Henry VIII, King of England, 1491–1547.   I. Title.

DA332.L5   923.142   53–32023 ‡

NL   0384390   DLC LU OCl NNC MB MiD MH NIC

AC-L
L647sh   Lindsay, Philip, 1906–
1952   The shadow of the red barn, a novel.   Lon-
              don, Hutchinson [1952]
              319p.   19cm.
              Author's autograph presentation copy to
              John Gawsworth [i.e. Terence Ian Fytton Arm-
              strong]
              Bookplate of Phil Lindsay.
              I. Title.   A.F.: Armstrong, Terence Ian
              Fytton, 1912–

NL   0384391   TxU WU MH

Lindsay, Philip, 1906–
Sir Rusty Sword; a novel. [Cheap ed.] London, Hutchinson [1951]
205 p.

NL   0384392   MH

AC-L
L647G1   Lindsay, Philip, 1906–
1946   A stepson of London.   [London, 1946?]
              p.18-19.   22cm.

              Detached from the Literary digest (London)
              1946[?]

NL   0384393   TxU

PR
6023   Lindsay, Philip, 1906–
I415S8   The swell yokel [a novel]   London,
              Hutchinson [1955]
              364 p.   21cm.

NL   0384394   NIC TxU WU

Lindsay, Philip, 1906–
There is no escape; a novel, by Philip Lindsay.   London [etc.]
Hutchinson & co. [1950]   367 p.   21cm.

567436B.   1. Grey, Lady Jane, 1537–   1554—Fiction. I. Title.
N. Y. P. L.   December 13, 1951

NL   0384395   NN

Lindsay, Philip, 1906–
The tragic king, Richard III, by Philip Lindsay.   New York,
R. M. McBride & company, 1934.
xxxii, 320 p. incl. geneal. tab. front., plates, ports. 22½cm.
Illustrated lining-papers.
London edition (I. Nicholson & Watson, ltd.) has title: King
Richard III.
"Acknowledgments" containing bibliography: p. 305–307.

1. Richard III, king of England, 1452–1485. 2. Gt. Brit.—Hist.—
Lancaster and York, 1399–1485.   I. Title.
Library of Congress   DA260.L6 1934
                                                      34–20197
—— Copy 2.
Copyright A 73449   [5-5]   923.142

WaT IdPI
NL   0384396   DLC KyLx NN MB TNJ AAP IaAS OCU OCl MtU

Lindsay, Philip, 1906–
Whither shall I wander? A novel, by Philip Lindsay.   London [etc.] Hutchinson & co. [1947]   400 p.   19cm.

NL   0384397   NN TxU WU

Lindsay, R. H., ed.

Cristisone, Sir John, 16th cent.
    ... Protocol book of Sir John Cristisone, 1518–1551. Ed
ited by R. H. Lindsay ... Edinburgh, Printed for the So
ciety by J. Skinner & company, ltd., 1930.

Lindsay, Mrs. Rachel Tupper (Easterbrooks)
joint tr.
Holst, Helge, 1871–
The atom and the Bohr theory of its structure; an elementary presentation, by H. A. Kramers ... and Helge Holst ...
with a foreword by Sir Ernest Rutherford ... London [etc.]
Gyldendal, 1923.

LINDSAY, Ralph.
    Etymology of Southwark.   3d ed. London,
Smith, Elder, and co., 1839.

    pp.24.   Plates.

NL   0384400   MH

Lindsay, Richard
Registration and election laws of the city
of Detroit... Detroit, Mich., Houghton-
Jacobson ptg. co., 1913.
66 p.

NL   0384401   MiD-B

WCF
L749e   LINDSAY, Robert
1895   An essay on malaria and its conse-
              quences.   London, Lewis, 1895.
              116 p.

NL   0384402   DNLM CU PPC

Lindsay, Robert, supposed author.
A letter from a friend to the Right Honourable.
[Dublin, Printed in the year 1724]
see under title

Lindsay, Robert.
Reminiscences of the cruise of the United States flag ship
Lancaster. Written in rhyme ... By Robert Lindsay. New
York, The author, 1887.
83 p. front. 17½cm.

1. Lancaster (Training ship)   I. Title.

Library of Congress   PS2246.L56   28–4762

NL   0384404   DLC CSmH CtY

Lindsay, Robert, 1532?–1578?
The Cronicles of Scotland, by Robert Lindsay, of Pitscottie.
Published from several old manuscripts ... Edinburgh,
Printed by G. Ramsay and co., for A. Constable and co.; [etc.,
etc.] 1814.
2 v. 22cm.
Edited by Sir J. G. Dalyell.
First published 1728 under title: The history of Scotland.
Closes with the reign of James VI.

1. Scotland—Hist.—15th century. 2. Scotland—Hist.—16th century.
I. Dalyell, Sir John Graham, 6th bart., 1775–1851, ed.
                                                      3–29488 Revised
Library of Congress   DA783.5.L72

NL   0384405   DLC MdBP CaBVaU NjP OC

Lindsay, Robert, 1532?–1578?
The historie and cronicles of Scotland, from the slauch-
ter of King James the First to the ane thousande fyve
hundreith thrie scoir fyftein zeir; written and collected
by Robert Lindesay of Pitscottie, being a continuation of
the translation of the chronicles written by Hector Boece,
and translated by John Bellenden; now first published
from two of the oldest manuscripts, one bequeathed by
Dr. David Laing to the University of Edinburgh, and the
other in the library of John Scott of Halkshill, c. b.; ed.

by Æ. J. G. Mackay ... Edinburgh and London, Printed
for the Society by W. Blackwood and sons, 1899–1911.
3 v. 22cm. (Half-title: Scottish text society. Pitscottie's Chronicles)
The Introduction contains a biographical sketch of Lindsay, and a list of
the mss. and printed editions of this work.

1. Scotland—Hist.—To 1603. I. Mackay, Æneas James George, 1839–
1911, ed. II. Title: Pitscottie's Chronicles.

                                                      12–20390
Library of Congress   DA779.L75

ViU OClW NIC CtY WU CaBVaU AAP PU
NL   0384407   DLC NN NjP OrU CaBVaU OrPR ScU FMU MiU

VOLUME 334

Lindsay, Robert, *1532?- 1578.*
The history of Scotland; from 21 February, 1436. to March, 1565. In which are contained accounts of many remarkable passages altogether differing from our other historians; and many facts are related, either concealed by some, or omitted by others. ₍By Robert Lindesay of Pitscottie. Done from the most authentick and most correct manuscripts. To which is added a continuation, by another hand, till August, 1604. Edinburgh, Baskett and company, 1728.

xviii, 239 p. 29ᶜᵐ.
Dedication signed: Robert Freebairn.

1. Scotland—Hist.—15th cent. 2. Scotland—Hist.—16th cent. I. Freebairn, Robert, ed.

NL 0384409   MiU MnU OrU InU ICN IU NN

Lindsay, Robert, 1532?–1578?
The history of Scotland, from February 21. 1436, to March 1565; in which are contained, accounts of many remarkable passages, altogether differing from our other historians; and many facts are related, either concealed or omitted by others. By Robert Lindsay of Pitscottie. To which is added, a continuation by another hand, till August 1604. The 3d ed., carefully compared and rev. by the 1st ed. With a compleat index ... Edinburgh, C. Elliot ; ₍etc., etc.₎ 1778.
2 p. l., xvi, 11, ₍3₎–367, 55 p. 18ᶜᵐ.
With the dedication of the first edition (1728) signed by Robert Freebairn, editor of that edition.

1. Scotland—Hist.—15th cent. 2. Scotland—Hist.—16th cent.
3–29487 Revised
Library of Congress   DA783.5.L7

NL 0384410   DLC FMU PHi PPL OrP

Lindsay, *Hon. Robert,* 1754–1836.
Anecdotes of an Indian life, by the Hon. John Lindsay.
(*In* Crawford, Alexander W. C. Lindsay, 25th earl of. Lives of the Lindsays. London, 1849. 22ᶜᵐ. v. 3, p. 147–226)

8–22927
Library of Congress   DA758.3.L8C7

NL 0384411   DLC MdBP

Lindsay, *Hon. Robert,* 1754–1836.

Crawford, Alexander William Crawford Lindsay, *25th earl of,* 1812–1880.
Lives of the Lindsays; or, A memoir of the houses of Crawford and Balcarres, by Lord Lindsay. To which are added, extracts from the official correspondence of Alexander sixth earl of Balcarres, during the Maroon war; together with personal narratives by his brothers, the Hon. Robert, Colin, James, John, and Hugh Lindsay; and by his sister, Lady Anne Barnard. 2d ed. London, J. Murray, 1858.

QC225
.S85

Lindsay, Robert Bruce, 1900–   joint author.

Stewart, George Walter, 1876–
Acoustics; a text on theory and applications, by George Walter Stewart ... and Robert Bruce Lindsay ... New York, D. Van Nostrand company, inc., 1930.

[Lindsay, Robert Bruce] 1900–
Advanced acoustics. ₍experiments₎ ₍Providence? 1942₎
58, 8, ₍22₎ numb. l. diagrs. 28 cm.
Course given at Brown university, summer 1942.
Mimeographed.
Includes bibliographies.

NL 0384414   RPB

Lindsay, Robert Bruce, 1900–   tr.

Holst, Helge, 1871–
The atom and the Bohr theory of its structure; an elementary presentation, by H. A. Kramers ... and Helge Holst ... with a foreword by Sir Ernest Rutherford ... London ₍etc.₎ Gyldendal, 1923.

Lindsay, Robert Bruce, 1900–
... Biographical memoir of Carl Barus, 1856–1935, by R. B. Lindsay. Presented to the academy at the autumn meeting, 1941.
(*In* National academy of sciences, Washington, D. C. Biographical memoirs. City of Washington, 1943. 23 cm. Vol. xxii, 9th memoir, 1 p. l., p. 171–213. front. (port.))
Issued also separately.
Bibliography : p. 196–213.
———— Separate.
Cover-title, dated 1943.
1. Barus, Carl, 1856–1935.   QC16.B3L5
Q141.N2 vol. 22, 9th memoir   925.3   44—2312

NL 0384416   DLC CU

Lindsay, Robert Bruce, 1900–
Concepts and methods of theoretical physics. New York, Van Nostrand ₍1951₎
515 p. 22 cm.

1. Mathematical physics.   I. Title.
QC20.L5   530.151   51–12767 ‡

NL 0384417   DLC WaW WaSp WaT WaE Wa OrU OrPR MtBC
NcD NIC ViU TxU NN MB MiHM CU Or OrStbM WaSpG WaTC MtU OrCS OrP CaBVaU IdB IdPI IdU MiU ICU CoU NBuC

Lindsay, Robert Bruce, 1900–
Foundations of physics, by Robert Bruce Lindsay ... and Henry Margenau ... New York, J. Wiley & sons, inc.; London, Chapman & Hall, limited, 1936.
xiii p., 1 l., 537 p. diagrs. 23½ᶜᵐ. $4.50

1. Physics—Philosophy.   I. Margenau, Henry, 1901–   joint author.
II. Title.
36–3805
Library of Congress   QC6.L42
———— Copy 2.
Copyright A 91199   ₍5₎   530.1

NL 0384418   DLC KEmT DAU ViU CU OrCS OrPR NcD NcRS
WaWW CaBVaU MtBuM OrAshS TU NIC OO MiU OU OCU OCl ViU NN MB IdU MtBC OrPR Or

---

Lindsay, Robert Bruce, 1900–
Foundations of physics, by Robert Bruce Lindsay ... and Henry Margenau ... * New York, J. Wiley & sons, inc.; London, Chapman & Hall, limited,₍1944₎
xi p., 1 l., 508p. diagrs. 2 ᶜᵐ.
*1st ed., 2d printing.
"Second printing, March, 1944."

NL 0384419   ViU PSt

Lindsay, Robert Bruce, 1900–
Foundations of physics, by Robert Bruce Lindsay ... and Henry Margenau ... New York, J. Wiley & sons, inc.; London, Chapman & Hall, limited ₍1947₎
xi p., 1 l., 537 p. diagrs. 23½ᶜᵐ.

NL 0384420   ICJ

Lindsay, Robert Bruce, 1900–
General physics for students of science, by Robert Bruce Lindsay ... New York, J. Wiley & sons, inc.; London, Chapman & Hall, limited, 1939.
3 p. l., v–xiv, 512 p. illus., diagrs. 23½ᶜᵐ. $3.00

1. Physics.
39–30740
Library of Congress   QC21.L47
———— Copy 2.
Copyright A 132864   ₍3₎   530

NL 0384421   DLC PPT

Lindsay, Robert Bruce, 1900–
General physics for students of science, by Robert Bruce Lindsay ... New York, J. Wiley & sons, inc.; London, Chapman & Hall, limited, 1940.
3 p. l., v–xiv, 534 p. illus., diagrs. 23½ᶜᵐ. $3.75

1. Physics.
40–6104
Library of Congress   QC21.L47 1940
———— Copy 2.
Copyright A 136652   ₍3₎   530

NL 0384422   DLC TxU TU PBm PSC PHC OCU OU OO ViU DAS
MiHM PU NcD NcRS CU OrPR WaWW MtU OrCS

Lindsay, Robert Bruce, 1900–
General physics for students of science. New York, Wiley ₍1947₎
xiv, 534 p. illus.

NL 0384423   MH

Lindsay, Robert Bruce, 1900–
Introduction to physical statistics, by Robert Bruce Lindsay ... New York, J. Wiley & sons, inc.; London, Chapman & Hall, limited, 1941.
ix, 306 p. diagrs. 23½ᶜᵐ.

1. Mathematical physics. 2. Physics—Methodology.   I. Title.
II. Title : Physical statistics.
41–22044
Library of Congress   QC175.L5
₍a45q1₎   530.151

NL 0384424   DLC CLSU ScCleU CoU KEmT MiU CU CaBVaU
WaWW OrCS OrPR MtU OrU MtBC IdPI WaS OrPS NIC TU PBm PSC PPD ICJ OClW OCU OU ViU NcD NcRS

Lindsay, Robert Bruce, 1900–
Introduction to physical statistics, by Robert Bruce Lindsay ... New York, J. Wiley & sons, inc.; London, Chapman & Hall, limited, 1941. ₍i.e. 1947₎
ix, 306 p. diagrs. 23½ᶜᵐ.

NL 0384425   ViU

Lindsay, Robert Bruce.
On the atomic models of the alkali metals, by Robert Bruce Lindsay. Boston, 1924. p. 191–236. diagrs., tables. 8°.
(Massachusetts Institute of Technology. Rogers Laboratory of Physics. Contributions. Ser. 2, no. 20.)
Repr.: Jour. of mathematics and physics. v. 3, no. 4.

1. Atoms—Models. 2. Metals,   Alkaline.
N. Y. P. L.
January 7, 1925

NL 0384426   NN NNC OU

VOLUME 334

Lindsay, Robert Bruce, 1900–
Physical mechanics; an intermediate text for students of the physical sciences, by Robert Bruce Lindsay ... New York, D. Van Nostrand company, inc., 1933.

3 p. l., iii–x, 436 p. illus., diagrs. 22ᶜᵐ. (*Half-title:* University physics series)

1. Mechanics.   I. Title.
Library of Congress   QA807.L5   33–16087
———— Copy 2.
Copyright A 62996   ₍₃₎   531

OrCS
OO OCU ODW PCM NcRS NcD WaWW MtBC OrPR CaBVaU OrU
NL 0384427   DLC KEmT CU ICJ NIC OC1JC TU TxU OU DNAL

Lindsay, Robert Bruce, 1900–
Physical mechanics; an intermediate text for students of the physical sciences. 2d ed. New York, Van Nostrand ₍1950₎

x, 451 p. illus. 23 cm. (University physics series)

1. Mechanics.   I. Title.
QA807.L5 1950   531   50–8406

CoU CU NcD OrU OrCS IdPI OrPS
NL 0384428   DLC PU PP PSt NIC MiHM TxU OC1 NNC ICU

Lindsay, Robert Bruce, 1900–
Student's handbook of elementary physics ₍by₎ Robert Bruce Lindsay ... New York, N. Y., The Dryden press ₍1943₎

1 p. l., v–xv, 270 p., 1 l., 271–382 p.   diagrs.   21½ᶜᵐ.

"Answers to selected problems": p. 370–371.
"Bibliography of suggested reading for general physics": p. 299–306.

1. Physics.   2. Physics—Dictionaries.
          43–12543
Library of Congress   QC21.L48
          ₍4₎   530

OC1ND ViU CaBVaU WaT
NL 0384429   DLC CU NcD PRosC PPG PSt PWcS TU TxU OU

QC223
.R262
1945
Lindsay, Robert Bruce, 1900–
Rayleigh, John William Strutt, *baron*, 1842–1919.
The theory of sound, by John William Strutt, baron Rayleigh ... with a historical introduction by Robert Bruce Lindsay ... 2d ed. rev. and enl. New York, Dover publications, 1945.

Lindsay, Robert Burns, 1824–1902
see also **Alabama.** *Governor, 1870–1872* (*Lindsay*)

Lindsay, Robert Howard, 1910–
Fowl murder, the mystery of between the lines, by R. Howard Lindsay. Boston, Little, Brown and company, 1941.

5 p. l., 3–285 p.   19½ᶜᵐ.
"First edition."

I. Title.
Library of Congress   PZ3.L65345Fo
          41–18897

NL 0384432   DLC OEac

Lindsay, Robert James Loyd-, baron Wantage
s ee
Wantage, Robert James Loyd-Lindsay, baron, 1832–1901

Beinecke
Library
Zc52
899₊4i
Lindsay, Robert L
Digest and history of the Beales-Royuella land grant and Mexican concession, dated March 14, 1832, and partly located in Oklahoma Territory, Texas, Colorado and New Mexico. A concise statement of the law and the facts relating to this grant ... Kansas City, Mo., 1899.
cover-title, 20 p.   fold.map.   22 cm.

1. Beales, John Charles
2. Royuela, José Manuel   3. Land grants
– Texas.   4. Dienst, Alex, 1870–1938 –
Autograph.   I. Title (1)

NL 0384435   CtY

Lindsay, Robert M.
Catalogue for the most part, the Fine Art portion of the library of the late James L. Claghorn.
see under   Claghorn, James L.

Lindsay, Robert M.
Illustrated list of engravings, etchings and fine art prints. Season of 1899–1900. Phila., ₍1899₎
91 p.

NL 0384437   PHi

Lindsay, Robert M.
March 1893. Print exhibition. The wonders of engraving. Phila., 1893.
28 p.

NL 0384438   PHi

LINDSAY, Robert M.
Some etchings and books. [A catalogue.] Philadelphia,[1884].
pp.71.
Engraved cover serves as title-page.

NL 0384439   MH DLC

Lindsay, Robert M.
Some etchings, engravings and books [Catalogue].
[Phila., ? 1885]

NE70
.L5

NL 0384440   DLC ICN

Lindsay, Robert Strathern.
A history of the Mason Lodge of Holyrood House (St. Luke's), No. 44 holding of the Grand Lodge of Scotland with roll of members, 1734–1934, by Robert Strathern Lindsay... Edinburgh: Printed by T. and A. Constable Ltd., at the Univ. Press, 1935. 2 v.   front., plates, ports.   29cm.

Paged continuously.
No. 58 of 500 copies printed.
Map in pocket, v. 1.
Bibliography, v. 1, p. ₍xvii₎–xx.

36225–6A.   1. Freemasons. Edin-   burgh. Lodge of Holyroodhouse
(St. Luke's) No. 44.
N. Y. P. L.   July 31, 1936

NL 0384441   NN

Lindsay, R₍onald₎ C₍harles₎.
United States. Report on immigration into the United States. London: Harrison and Sons, 1906.   29 p., 1 l.   8°.   (Great Britain.   Foreign Office.   Diplomatic and consular reports.   Miscellaneous series.   no. 655.)

₍   Emigration, etc₎, U. S., 1905.
N. Y. P. L.   January 8, 1913.

NL 0384442   NN

Lindsay, R₍onald₎ C₍harles₎.
United States. Report on liquor traffic legislation of the United States.   London: Harrison and Sons, 1907.   111(1) p 8°.   (Great Britain. Foreign Office. Diplomatic and consular reports. Miscellaneous series. no. 657.)

1. Alcoholic drinks.—Jurisprudence,   U. S., 1906.
N. Y. P. L.   January 4, 1913.

NL 0384443   NN

Lindsay, Ruth Hutchinson.
The chromosomes of some dioecious angiosperms ₍by₎ Ruth H. Lindsay ... ₍Brooklyn, N. Y., 1930₎

cover-title, ₍1₎, 152–174 p. pl. IX–XI. 25½ᶜᵐ.
Thesis (PH. D.)—University of Wisconsin, 1929.
Thesis note stamped on cover.
Running title: Dioecism.
"Reprinted from American journal of botany, vol. XVII, no. 2 ... February, 1930."
"Literature cited": p. 170–173.

1. Chromosomes. 2. Angiospermae.   I. Title: Dioecism.
          31–5385
Library of Congress   QH605.L55 1929
Univ. of Wisconsin Libr.   ₍2₎   581.16

NL 0384444   WU DLC

Lindsay, S   B
Studies in Acts, by S. B. Lindsay.
Buffalo, 1924.
iv, ₍3₎–99p.
"Studies ... originally published in the Lookout."

1. Bible. N. T. Acts - Commentaries.
I. Title.

NL 0384445   TNDC

Lindsay, Samuel McCune, 1869–₍1960₎, ed.

Academy of political science, *New York.*
... American foreign trade relations, a series of addresses and papers presented at the annual meeting of the Academy of political science in the city of New York, December 9–10, 1921; ed. by Samuel McCune Lindsay. ₍New York₎ The Academy of political science, Columbia university, 1921.

VOLUME 334

Lindsay, Samuel McCune.
Child labor a national problem. n. t.-p. ₍New York, 1906.₎ 6 p. 8°. (Child Labor Committee. Pamphlets. no. 30.)

Repr.: Amer. Acad. of Political and Social Science. Annals. v. 27, no. 2.

1. Labor (Child). U. S.
N. Y. P. L. March 3, 1914.

NL 0384447 NN MH OO Or

Lindsay, Samuel McCune.
Child labor and the public schools. n. t.-p. ₍New York, 1907.₎ 6 p. 8°. (Child Labor Committee. Pamphlets. no. 52.)

Repr.: Amer. Acad. of Political and Social Science. Annals. v. 29, no. 1.

1. Labor (Child). U. S.
N. Y. P. L. March 2, 1914.

NL 0384448 NN RPB MB

LINDSAY, Samuel McCune.
Child labor legislation. [Albany.] [1905]

NL 0384449 MH

Lindsay, Samuel McCune, 1869–
Civic club of Philadelphia. *Dept. of social science.*
Civic club digest of the educational and charitable institutions and societies in Philadelphia. Comp. by a committee of the social science section of the Civic club. With an introduction on social aspects of Philadelphia relief work. By Samuel McCune Lindsay. Philadelphia ₍G. H. Buchanan and company₎ 1895.

LINDSAY, Samuel McCune.
Constitution making in New York; the revised constitution proposed by the convention. [New York?, 1915].

f°. pp.(4).
"Reprinted from The Survey, September 25, 1915"

NL 0384451 MH

Lindsay, Samuel McCune, 1869–   tr.

Italy. *Constitution.*
... Constitution of the kingdom of Italy. Translated and supplied with an historical introduction and notes by S. M. Lindsay, ph. d., and Leo S. Rowe ... Philadelphia. American academy of political and social science, 1894.

Lindsay, Samuel McCune, 1869–
Economic aspects of the so-called emergency housing legislation of 1920 in New York state and the alleged housing shortage in New York City, by Samuel McCune Lindsay... ₍New York? 1921?₎ iii, 113 p. incl. diagr., tables. 8°.

Cover-title.
Includes: How to meet the housing situation, by Henry R. Brigham, p. 104–113.
Bibliographical footnotes.

1. Habitations—U. S.—New York.   2. New York (city)—Habitations.
3. Rent—Jurisp.—U. S.—New York,   1920–1924. 4. Brigham, Henry Randolph, 1880–
N. Y. P. L. August 13, 1926

NL 0384453 NN NNC

Lindsay, Samuel McCune, 1869–1959.
Henry Rogers Seager, 1870–1930, by Samuel McCune Lindsay ... ₍New York, 1930?₎
cover-title, ₍428₎–431 p. port. 27cm.

"Reprinted from the Columbia University quarterly, December, 1930."

1. Seager, Henry Rogers, 1870–1930.

NL 0384454 NNC

Lindsay, Samuel McCune.
How to make child labor legislation more effective. ₍New York,₎ 1913. 12 p. 8°. (Child Labor Committee. Pamphlet no. 197.)

Repr.: Child Labor Bull. v. 2, no. 1.

1. Labor (Child).—Jurisprudence,   U. S.
N. Y. P. L. September 27, 1913.

NL 0384455 NN OrU

Lindsay, Samuel McCune.
Inauguration of the American school system in Porto Rico.
(In United States. Bureau of Education. Report of the Commissioner for 1905. Vol. I, pp. 293–344. Washington. 1907.)

G5763 — Porto Rico. Educ. — Americans in Porto Rico.

NL 0384456 MB

Lindsay, Samuel McCune, 1869–
... Inauguration of the American school system in Porto Rico. By Samuel McCune Lindsay, ph. d. Washington, Govt. print. off., 1907.

cover-title, p. 293–344. 22ᶜᵐ.

At head of title: Advance sheets. United States Bureau of education. Chapter from the Report of the commissioner of education for 1905. Chapter xv.

1. Education—Porto Rico.
E 15–2666

Library, U. S. Bur. of   Education LA501.L64

NL 0384457 DHEW

Lindsay, Samuel McCune, 1869–   joint ed.

National conference on international problems and relations, *Briarcliff Manor, N. Y., 1926.*
... International problems and relations; a series of addresses and papers presented at the National conference on international problems and relations, held under the auspices of the Carnegie endowment for international peace with the cooperation of the Academy of political science in the city of New York, at Briarcliff lodge, May 10–14, 1926, edited by James Thomson Shotwell, Samuel McCune Lindsay and Parker Thomas Moon. ₍New York₎ The Academy of political science, Columbia university, 1926.

341.6 Lindsay, Samuel McCune, 1869–
L641   Labor and world peace ... ₍Washington, D.C., 1936₎
8p.

"Reprinted from April issue, 1936, American federationist."

1. International labor organization. 2. Peace.
I. Title.

NL 0384459 IU DL

Lindsay, Samuel McCune, 1869–
... The league of nations covenant, the new international obligations of the United States under the proposed covenant of the league of nations; a series of addresses and papers presented at the national conference held under the auspices of the Academy of political science in the city of New York, June 5, 1919; ed. by Samuel McCune Lindsay. New York, The Academy of political science, Columbia university, 1919.
vi, 154 p. 22½ᵐ. (Proceedings of the Academy of political science in the city of New York. vol. VIII ... no. 3)

Contents.—Preface.—The relation of the covenant to recent international cooperation, by D. W. Morrow.—The potentialities and significance of the league of nations covenant, by K. Pittman.—The objections to the league of nations covenant, by G. W. Pepper.—Proportional representation in the league of nations, by A. K. Kuhn.—The league of nations covenant, by H. C. Pell, jr.—International labor standards and their possible enforcement in the United States, by G. W. Wickersham.—The mandatory system under the covenant of the league of nations, by A. H. Snow.—International labor legislation and how it can be enforced in the United States, by A. I. Elkus.—International labor standards and legislation, by J. B. Andrews.—The power of the United States under the Constitution to enter into labor treaties, by J. P. Chamberlain.—The enforcement of international labor standards relating to child labor, by W. H. Swift.—Some international financial obligations of the United States and one way of meeting them, by W. P. Malburn.—The absorption of foreign obligations by savings bank and trustee investors, by M. W. Harrison.—The new national processes and organs required for adopting and effectuating the covenant, by A. H. Snow.—Appendix: Covenant for the league of nations showing the preliminary reported draft and the covenant as finally adopted at the plenary session, by K. Pittman.

1. League of nations.   I. Title.
19–27598
Library of Congress   JX1975.L73
——— Copy 2.   H31.A4 vol. VIII, no. 3
Copyright B 449202   ₍10₎

OCU OU ODa ICJ MB
NL 0384462 DLC NBuU MoU WaU-L MtBC WaS NcD MiU OC1

Lindsay, Samuel McCune.
The minimum wage as a legislative proposal in the United States. n. t.-p. ₍Philadelphia, 1913.₎ 43–53 p. 8°.

Repr.: Amer. Acad. of Political and Social Science. Annals. no. 725.

1. Wages (Minimum), U. S.
N. Y. P. L. January 22, 1914.

NL 0384463 NN

Lindsay, Samuel McCune, 1869–   ed.
Academy of political science, *New York.*
... The money problem; a series of addresses and papers presented at the semi-annual meeting of the Academy of political science in the city of New York, November, 1922, edited by Samuel McCune Lindsay and Parker Thomas Moon. ₍New York₎ The Academy of political science. Columbia university, 1923.

Lindsay, Samuel McCune, 1869–   joint ed.

Academy of political science, *New York.*
... National expenditures and public economy; a series of addresses and papers presented at the semi-annual meeting of the Academy of political science in the city of New York, May 23, 1921, ed. by Frederick A. Cleveland and Samuel McCune Lindsay. ₍New York₎ The Academy of political science, Columbia university, 1921.

Lindsay, Samuel McCune, 1869–
Die preisbewegung der edelmetalle seit 1850 verglichen mit der der andern metalle, unter besonderer berücksichtigung der produktions- und konsumtionsverhältnisse. Von Dr Samuel McCune Lindsay ... Jena, G. Fischer, 1893.
xiii, 218, ₍2₎ p. 24ᶜᵐ. (Added t.-p.: Sammlung nationalökonomischer und statistischer abhandlungen des staatswissenschaftlichen seminars zu Halle a. d./S. ... 7. bd. 3. hft.)

1. Precious metals.

Library of Congress   HG279.L73   1-G-1010

NL 0384466 DLC MiEM PU CtY NcU CU OU

VOLUME 334

Lindsay, Samuel McCune, 1869–
The public charities of Porto Rico.

(*In* The annals of the American academy of political and social science. Philadelphia, 1904. vol. XXIII, no. 3, p. 502–513)

1. Charities—Puerto Rico. 2. Anemia.   I. title.   C D 17—211

Library of Congress.   Card div.   H1.A4 vol. 23, no. 3

NL 0384467   DLC NN OrCS OrU CaBVaU NcD ICJ

Lindsay, Samuel McCune, 1869–
Railway employees in the United States.
U. S. *Bureau of labor.* Bulletin.   No. 37, Nov. 1901.

Lindsay, Samuel McCune, 1869–
Recollections of Theodore Roosevelt by Samuel McCune Lindsay ...
49 l.   29cm.

Reproduction of typescript, with corrections in ink.
Dated: Winter Park, Florida, April, 1955.
Revised, August, 1955.

NL 0384469   NNC

Lindsay, Samuel McCune, 1869–
Report on railway labor in the United States. Prepared under the direction of the Industrial Commission by Samuel McCune Lindsay ... ₁Washington? 1901?₎ p. 709–1135.   8°.

1. Railways—Employees, U. S.   2. United States. Industrial Commission.
N. Y. P. L.   October 9, 1925

NL 0384470   NN

Lindsay, Samuel McCune, 1869–

U. S. *Industrial commission.*
Reports of the Industrial commission on labor organizations, labor disputes, and arbitration ₁by Charles E. Edgerton and E. Dana Durand₎ and on railway labor ... ₁by Samuel McCune Lindsay₎ Washington, Govt. print. off., 1901.

Lindsay, Samuel McCune.
Services of the International labor office to legislative projects. 1933.

NL 0384472   PU

Lindsay, Samuel McCune.
Social aspects of Philadelphia relief-work
Philadelphia, 1896

NL 0384473   DL

Lindsay, Samuel McCune, 1869–
Social work at the Krupp foundries ...

(*In* The annals of the American academy of political and social science. Philadelphia, 1893. vol. III, no. 3, p. 330–362 incl. tables)
Signed : Samuel M. Lindsay.

1. Krupp'sche gustahlfabrik, Essen. 2. Welfare work in industry.
I. Title.
H1.A4   vol. 3, no. 3   (306.273)   C D 16—61

CaBVaU
NL 0384474   DLC OrU OrCS WaS PPT ICJ NcD CtY MH

Lindsay, Samuel McCune, 1869–
... Social work at the Krupp foundries. By Samuel M. Lindsay. A paper submitted to the American academy of political and social science. Philadelphia, American academy of political and social science; ₁etc., etc., 1893₎

cover-title, ₁1₎, ₁74₎–106 p.   23 cm.   (Publications of the American academy of political and social science. no. 72)

1. Krupp'sche gusstahlfabrik, Essen. 2. Welfare work in industry.
I. Title.
HD7459.K9L5   331.7672   35–22582

NL 0384475   DLC

Lindsay, Samuel McCune, 1869–
Some economic aspects of the recent emergency housing legislation in New York, memorandum report on a fact finding inquiry prepared for the Law committee of the Real estate board in the city of New York, by a small staff of investigators under the direction of Samuel McCune Lindsay ... ₁New York₎ The Law committee, Real estate board in the city of New York, 1923.

3 p. l., viii, 120 p., 4 numb. l. diagrs. 26½ᵐᵐ.
Questionnaire, 1 leaf, inserted.
1. Housing—New York (City)   I. Real estate board of New York.
Law committee. II. Title.
24–19313
Library of Congress   HD7304.N5L5

NL 0384476   DLC DL

Lindsay, Samuel McCune, 1869–
Ndv26   Some economic aspects of the recent emergency
N5   housing legislation in New York. Memorandum report
+923Lb   on a fact-finding inquiry prepared for the Law
         Committee of the Real Estate Board in the city of
         New York by a small staff of investigators under
         the direction of Samuel McCune Lindsay ...
         ₁New York₎ The Ballou Press, 1924.
         ₁6₎, viii, 137p. incl. tables, diagrs.   27ᶜᵐ
         "A revised edition of the Memorandum report which

first appeared in connection with the hearings
of the Bureau of Housing and Regional Planning
of New York State, held in the middle of
October, 1923." – Pref. note.
Questionnaire inserted between p. 34 and 35.

NL 0384478   CtY MH

Lindsay, Samuel McCune, 1869–
The study and teaching of sociology. The annual meeting of 1898.

(*In* The annals of the American academy of political and social science. Philadelphia, 1898. vol. XII, no. 1, p. 1–48)

1. Sociology—Study and teaching.
C D 17–1
Library of Congress   Card Div. H1.A4

NL 0384479   DL OrCS OrU WaS ICJ CaBVaU

Lindsay, Samuel McCune, 1869–
The study and teaching of sociology; report of the annual meeting of the academy in 1898. Philadelphia, American Academy of Political and Social Science ₁1898₎

48 p.   23 cm.   (Publications of the American Academy of Political and Social Science, no. 231)
Cover title.
Reprinted from the Annals of the American Academy of Political and Social Science, v. 12, no. 1.

1. Sociology—Study and teaching.   (Series: American Academy of Political and Social Science, Philadelphia. Publications, no. 231)

HM45.L5   48–38807*

NL 0384480   DLC MB ICJ NcD-L NN

Lindsay, Samuel McCune, 1869–   **joint author.**   FOR OTHER EDITIONS SEE MAIN ENTRY
Willoughby, William Franklin, 1867–
The system of financial administration of Great Britain; a report, by William F. Willoughby ... Westel W. Willoughby ... ₁and₎ Samuel McCune Lindsay ... introduction by A. Lawrence Lowell ... Washington, D. C., The Brookings institution, 1929.

Lindsay, Samuel McCune, 1869–

Small, Albion Woodbury, 1854–
... A "unit" in sociology.

(*In* The annals of the American academy of political and social science. Philadelphia, 1899. vol. XIII, no. 1, p. 81–89)

Lindsay, Samuel McCune, 1869–
The unit of investigation or of consideration in sociology.

(*In* The annals of the American academy of political and social science. Philadelphia, 1898. vol. XII, no. 2, p. 214–228)

1. Sociology.   I. Title.
C D 17–7
Library of Congress (Card ₋ivision)   H1.A4

NL 0384483   DLC ICJ NcD-L CaBVaU OrU OrCS WaS NN MH

Lindsay, Samuel McCune, 1869– 1960.
Speirs, Frederic William, 1867 or 8–1905.
... Vacant-lot cultivation by Frederic W. Speirs, Samuel McCune Lindsay, and Franklin B. Kirkbride ... New York, The Charities review ₁1898₎

Lindsay, Samuel McCune, 1869– 1960, ed.
Labor reconstruction conference, *New York*, 1918.
... War labor policies and reconstruction; a series of addresses and papers presented at the Labor reconstruction conference held under the auspices of the Academy of political science in the city of New York, December 6–7, 1918, ed. by Samuel McCune Lindsay. New York, The Academy of political science, Columbia university, ₍1919.

Lindsay, Samuel Stewart, 1856–
The decimal plate and sheet glass calculator, containing more than 28,000 superficial areas, expressed in feet and decimals of a foot with concise examples for readily ascertaining the contents of any number of lights of whatever size. Compiled and published by Samuel S. Lindsay ... Pittsburgh, Pa., ₍1925.
3 p. l., 95 p.   25½ᵐ.

1. Glass trade—Tables and ready-reckoners.   I. Title.
25–17826 Revised
Library of Congress   HF5716.G4L8

NL 0384486   DLC

VOLUME 334

Lindsay, Samuel Stewart, 1856–   *comp.*
The plate and sheet glass calculator. Containing above 28,000 superficial areas, with concise examples for readily ascertaining the contents of any number of lights of whatever dimensions. Comp. by Samuel S. Lindsay ... Pittsburgh, Pa., The Pittsburgh plate glass company 1900.
7, ₍94₎ p. 26 x 14½ᶜᵐ.

1. Glass trade—Tables and ready-reckoners.

Library of Congress   HF5716.G4L7   0–6930 Revised

NL 0384487   DLC

Lindsay, Samuel Stewart, 1856–   *comp.*
The plate and sheet glass calculator. Containing above 28,000 superficial areas, with concise examples for readily ascertaining the contents of any number of lights of whatever size. Comp. by Samuel S. Lindsay ... Pittsburgh, The Pittsburgh plate glass company, 1905.
7, ₍94₎ p. 26 x 15ᶜᵐ.

1. Glass trade—Tables and ready-reckoners.

Library of Congress   TP860.L7   5—17967

NL 0384488   DLC ICJ MB

Lindsay, Samuel Stewart, 1856–   *comp.*
The plate and sheet glass calculator, containing about 28,000 superficial areas, with concise examples for readily ascertaining the contents of any number of lights of whatever size. Comp. and copyrighted by Samuel S. Lindsay. Pittsburgh, Pa., The Pittsburgh plate glass company, 1920.
₍101₎ p. 26ᵐᵐ.

1. Glass trade—Tables and ready-reckoners.   I. Title.

Library of Congress   TP860.L7 1920   20–14366

NL 0384489   DLC

Lindsay, Lady Sarah.
A few choice recipes collected by Lady Sarah Lindsay.   London, Richard Bently & Son, 1883.
vi, 234 p.   17 cm.

NL 0384490   DLC MH

BX5067 **Lindsay, Sydenham Bagg.**
.L74   The Church of England and the Reformation. Ilfracombe ₍Eng.₎ A. H. Stockwell ₍1954₎
38 p.
"A lecture delivered in the Diocesan College, Montreal, on 10th March, 1954."

1. Church of England—Hist. 2. Reformation—England.

NL 0384491   ICU NjPT MH

₍Lindsay, Thales.₎   622.09788 M400
Suggestions upon the purchase and sale of lode mining property in Colorado, and the tunnel claim. 24 p. O. ₍New York 1864.₎

NL 0384492   ICJ

FILM   **Lindsay, Thomas.**
M788.5107 The elements of flute-playing according to the
L645e   present advanced state of the art — A brief essay on style and expression has been added and a copious exposition is given of the harmonics, the shake — double-tonguing, phrasing, &c., the whole being illustrated by a variety of popular national and operatic melodies.   London, Cramer, Addison and Beale ₍1828–30₎

Microfilm copy (negative) made in 1964 by

the British Museum Photographic Service, London.
Collation of the original as determined from the film: 2v. in ₁(150p.) illus.
Each part with special t.p. has imprint: London, T. Lindsay.
1. Flute—Instruction and study. 2. Flute—Studies and exercises. I. Title.

NL 0384494   IU CtY

Lindsay, Thomas.
Jiujutsu ... The old Samurai art of fighting without weapons. By Rev. T. Lindsay and J. Kano ...
(*In* Asiatic society of Japan. Transactions. Yokohama, 1889. 23ᶜᵐ. v. 16, pt. 2, p. 192–205)
First word of title also in Japanese.

1. Jiu-Jitsu.   I. Kano, Jigoro, 1860–   joint author.
A C 38–3318

Chicago. Univ. Library   AS552.A83 vol. 16
for Library of Congress   [AS552.Y8 vol. 16]
₍1₎   (068.52)

NL 0384495   ICU NcD OU DLC MH

Lindsay, Thomas, 1854–1901, ed.

Royal astronomical society of Canada.
Transactions ... 1890/91–1905. Toronto ₍1891₎–1906.

Lindsay, Thomas Bond, 1853–1909.
Easy Latin lessons, by Thomas B. Lindsay ... and George W. Rollins ... Boston, Allyn and Bacon, 1890.
viii, 374 p. 18¼ᶜᵐ.

1. Latin language—Composition and exercises.   I. Rollins, George W., joint author.

Library of Congress   PA2087.L74   10—23386

NL 0384497   DLC PV OO OCl MiU ViU MH

Lindsay, Thomas Bond, 1853–1909.
Easy Latin lessons, by Thomas B. Lindsay and George W. Rollins. Boston, Allyn and Bacon, 1891.

NL 0384498   MH

Lindsay, Thomas Bond, 1853–1909.
Easy Latin lessons, by Thomas B. Lindsay and George W. Rollins. Boston, Allyn and Bacon, 1894.

NL 0384499   MH

Lindsay, Thomas Bond, 1853–1909.
Easy Latin lessons, by Thomas B. Lindsay and George W. Rollins. Boston, Allyn and Bacon, 1895.

NL 0384500   MH

Lindsay, Thomas Bond, 1853–1909, ed.

Nepos, Cornelius.
The lives of Cornelius Nepos, with notes, exercises, and vocabulary; edited by Thomas B. Lindsay ... ₍2d ed.₎ New York, Cincinnati ₍etc.₎ American book company ₍ᶜ1895₎

Lindsay, Thomas Bond, 1853–1909, ed.

Juvenalis, Decimus Junius.
... The Satires of Juvenal, edited by Thomas B. Lindsay... New York, Cincinnati ₍etc.₎ American book company ₍1890₎

Lindsay, Thomas Bond, 1853–1909.
... Sight slips in Latin. Prepared by T. B. Lindsay ... ₍Boston, New York ₍etc.₎ Leach, Shewell, & Sanborn₎ ᶜ1889.
4 no. in 1 v. 19½ᶜᵐ.
Caption title.
CONTENTS.— no. 1. For beginners.— no. 2. For students in Nepos or Cæsar.— no. 3. For students in Vergil or Ovid.— no. 4. For students in Cicero.

1. Latin language—Composition and exercises.

Library of Congress   PA2087.L744   10–23385†

NL 0384503   DLC

Lindsay, Thomas Fanshawe, 1910–
Dictionary of the English and Italian languages, English-Italian and Italian-English, containing words in common use and a wide range of technical terms, together with useful appendices. Rev. ₍and enl.₎ New York, Harper ₍1948?₎
550 p. 11 cm. (Harper pocket series)

1. English language—Dictionaries—Italian. 2. Italian language—Dictionaries—English.

PC1640.L46 1948   453.2   52–40784 rev ‡

NL 0384504   DLC Or

Lindsay, Thomas Fanshawe, 1910–
... The Holy Rule for laymen, with an introduction by His Eminence the Cardinal Archbishop of Westminster. London, Burns Oates, 1947.
xii, 160 p. 17 cm.

1. Benedictus, Saint, Abbot of Monte Cassino. Regula - Commentaries. I. Title.

NL 0384505   PLatS OrStbM KAS MnCS

Lindsay, Thomas Fanshawe, 1910–   tr.
Dalbiez, Roland.
Psychoanalytical method and the doctrine of Freud, by Roland Dalbiez ... With an introduction by E. B. Strauss ... Translated from the French by T. F. Lindsay. London, New York ₍etc.₎ Longmans, Green and co. ₍1941₎

271.1 Lindsay, Thomas Fanshawe, 1910–
B43we   Saint Benedict, his life and work.   London, Burns, Oates ₍1949₎
196p. 23cm.

NL 0384507   IU TU

VOLUME 334

Lindsay, Thomas Fanshawe, 1910–
Saint Benedict, his life and work. London, Burns, Oates [1950]
198 p. 23 cm.

1. Benedictus, Saint, Abbot of Monte Cassino.

BX4700.B3L5   922.245   50-9293 rev

MH NNC IEN NIC MiD
LU WaSpG Wa OrU OrSaW MB CtY-D PPT OO PP NRCR ICMcC
NL 0384508   DLC LU KyU KyLxCB NN NcD TxU ICU OC1JC

Lindsay, Thomas Harold.
Gems from the Thomas H. Lindsay collection. [Long Beach, Calif.] °1944.
19, [1] p. illus. (incl. ports., facsim.) 21½ᶜᵐ.
Cover-title: Amusement hall of fame, 1566 to 1942; the Thomas H. Lindsay collection.

1. Theater—Hist.   I. Title: Amusement hall of fame, 1566 to 1942.
45–16407

Library of Congress   PN2181.L5
[3]   792.09

NL 0384509   DLC

Lindsay, Thomas Martin.
Sherwood Rangers. London, Burrup, Mathieson, 1952.
182 p. illus. 25 cm.

1. World War, 1939-1945—Regimental histories—Gt. Brit.—Nottinghamshire Sherwood Rangers. Yeomanry. 2. Gt. Brit. Army. Nottinghamshire Sherwood Rangers. Yeomanry.

D760.N7L5   940.542   53-32782 ‡

NL 0384510   DLC NN

Lindsay, Thomas Martin, 1843-1914, *ed.*
The Acts of the Apostles... Edinburgh
[pref. 1884-85]
see under Bible. N. T. Acts.
English. 1884?-85?

Lindsay, Thomas Martin, 1843-1914.
Acts of the apostles, chapters XIII-XXVIII...
London, Blackie [188-] (Commentaries for Bible-classes...)
see under Bible. N. T. Acts. XIII-XXVIII.
English. 188- .

Lindsay, Thomas M[artin], 1843-1914.
The church and the ministry in the early centuries. New York: George H. Doran Co. [19—?] 398 p. 12°. (The Cunningham lectures.)

1. Church history. 2. Ministers (of the gospel). 3. Priesthood (Catholic). 4. Series.
N.Y.P.L.   December 1, 1924

NL 0384513   NN PPWe MBtS

Lindsay, Thomas Martin, 1843-1914.
The church and the ministry in the early centuries. The eighteenth series of the Cunningham lectures. By Thomas M. Lindsay ... London, Hodder and Stoughton, 1902.
xxii, 398 p. 23 cm.
CONTENTS.— The New Testament conception of the church of Christ.—A Christian church in apostolic times.—The prophetic ministry of the primitive church.—The church of the first century—creating its ministry.—The churches of the second and third centuries—changing their ministry.—The fall of the prophetic ministry and the conservative revolt.—Ministry changing to priesthood.—The Roman state religion and its effects on the organization of the church.—Appendix. Sketch of the history of modern controversy about the office-bearers in the primitive Christian churches.—Indexes: References to contemporary authorities, canonical and non-canonical. Names and subjects.
1. Church polity.   Early church. 2. Clergy—Hist.
BR155.L7   3—7869

NjNbS PBm ViU
NL 0384514   DLC CLSU OrSaW OrStbM NcD PCC CtY-D PU

BR   Lindsay, Thomas Martin, 1843-1914.
155   Church and the ministry in the
L7   early centuries. The eighteenth
1903   series of the Cunningham lectures.
           2. ed. London,Hodder and Stoughton,
           1903,
           398p. 23cm.

           1. Church polity - Early church.
           2. Clergy - History. I. Title.

NL 0384515   MU OC1 OO PHC PPLT WaWW

Lindsay, Thomas Martin, 1843-1914.
The church and the ministry in the early centuries.
The eighteenth series of the Cunningham letures. By
Thomas M. Lindsay ... 4th ed.   London, Hodder
and Stoughton, 1910.
xxii, 398 p.   23 cm.

NL 0384516   CtY

LINDSAY,Thomas Martin,1843-
College addresses; and sermons preached on
various occasions,by the late Thomas Martin
Lindsay... Glasgow,James Maclehose and sons,
1915.

viii,236 p. 20 cm.

NL 0384517   MH-AH NcD NRCR

Lindsay, Thomas Martin, 1843-1914, ed.
Golden thoughts from the Imitation of Christ
see under Imitatio Christi. English.
Selections.

Lindsay, Thomas Martin, 1843-1914, ed.
The Gospel according to St. Luke ...
Edinburgh, Clark (also New York, Scribner) [1887?]
see under Bible. N. T. Luke. English.
1887?

Lindsay, Thomas Martin, 1843-1914.
The gospel according to St. Mark...
Edinburgh [1883]
see under Bible. N. T. Mark.
English. 1883.

Lindsay, Thomas Martin, 1843-1914.
Gospel of St. Mark ... London, Blackie, 1883.
(Commentaries for Bible-classes ...)
see under Bible. N. T. Mark. English.
1883.

Lindsay, Thomas Martin, 1843-1914.
... A history of the reformation, by Thomas M. Lindsay ...
New York, C. Scribner's sons, 1906-07.
2 v. 21ᶜᵐ. (*Half-title:* The International theological library. Ed. by C. A. Briggs ... and ... S. D. F. Salmond)
Series title also at head of t.-p.
Map in pocket (v. 2)
Bibliographical foot-notes.
CONTENTS.—I. The reformation in Germany from its beginning to the religious peace of Augsburg.—II. The reformation in Switzerland, France, the Netherlands, Scotland and England, the Anabaptists and Socinian movements, the counter-reformation.

1. Reformation. 2. Counter-reformation. 3. Socinianism. 4. Anabaptists.
6—23686

Library of Congress   BR305.L5
[42a2]

MB PPWe OrSaW
ODW OU ViU NNUT PPEB OB1C KyU KyWAT CaBVa IdU NN Or
NL 0384522   NcD TU NjNbS PCC PSC PPLT OC1W OO OCU MiU

BR   Lindsay, Thomas Martin, 1843-
305   A history of the reformation, by Thomas
L5   M. Lindsay. 2d ed. Edinburgh, T. & T.
1908   Clark [1907-08.
           2v. 21cm. (International Theological
           Library)

           Includes bibliography.

           1. Reformation

NL 0384523   WU OrPR FTaSU

IR6   Lindsay, Thomas Martin, 1843-1914.
L645h   A history of the reformation. 2d ed.
1908   Edinburgh, T. & T. Clark, 1908-09 [v. 1, 1909]
           2 v. map (in pocket) 22 cm. (International
           theological library)

           Vol. 2 "reprinted April 1914."
           Bibliographical footnotes.
           Contents.- v. 1. The reformation in Germany
           from its beginning to the religious peace of

           Augsburg.- v. 2. The reformation in Switzerland,
           France, the Netherlands, Scotland and England,
           the Anabaptist and Socinian movements, the
           counter-reformation.

NL 0384525   CtY-D

Lindsay, Thomas M[artin], 1843-1914.
A history of the reformation. New York: Charles Scribner's Sons, 1910. 2 v. 2. ed. 8°. (International theological library.)
Map in pocket of v. 2.
v. I. The reformation in Germany from its beginning to the religious peace of Ausburg.
v. 2. The reformation in Switzerland, France, the Netherlands, Scotland, and England; the Anabaptist and Socinian movements, the counter-reformation.

NL 0384526   NN KEmT OU MH ICN OC1W CU ICN PPGi

Lindsay, Thomas Martin, 1843-1914.
... A history of the reformation, by Thomas M. Lindsay
2d ed. New York, C. Scribner's sons, 1912.
2 v. 21 cm. (*Half-title:* The International theological library. Ed. by C. A. Briggs ... and ... S. D. F. Salmond)
Series title also at head of t.-p.
Map in pocket (v. 2)
Bibliographical foot-notes.
CONTENTS.—I. The reformation in Germany from its beginning to the religious peace of Augsburg.—II. The reformation in Switzerland, France, the Netherlands, Scotland and England, the Anabaptists and Socinian movements, the counter-reformation.

NL 0384527   ViU NjPT

Lindsay, Thomas Martin, 1843-1914.
— A history of the Reformation...
3d ed.   N.Y., C. Scribner's sons, 1914.
v., 21ᶜᵐ. (International theological library)

Contents: 1. The Reformation in Germany from its beginning to the religious peace of Augsburg.

NL 0384528   NjPT

VOLUME 334

Lindsay, Thomas Martin, 1843-1914.
History of the reformation.   New York, 1916.
2 v.

NL   0384529   NjP

Lindsay, Thomas M. 1843-1914. History of the Reformation. N. Y. 1917. 2v.
Contents: Reformation in Germany from its beginning to the religious peace of Augsburg. — v. 2. Reformation in Switzerland, France, the Netherlands, Scotland and England, the Anabaptist and Socinian movements, the counter-Reformation.

NL   0384530   MBrZ OC1W

Lindsay, Thomas Martin, 1843-1914.
A history of the reformation. I, The reformation in Germany from its beginning to the religious peace of Augsburg, by ... New York, Scribner, 1922.
528 p.

NL   0384531   PPRETS PPPD NcC

Lindsay, Thomas Martin, 1843-1914.
... A history of the reformation, by Thomas M. Lindsay ... Second edition. Edinburgh, T. & T. Clark [1933-34]

BR305
L7

2 v. 21 1/2 cm. (Half-title: The international theological library. Edited by C. A. Briggs ... and ... S. D. F. Salmond)
Vol. 1, "First edition, April 1906 ... reprinted April 1933." Vol. 2, "First edition, March 1907 ... reprinted, October 1934."
Series title also at head of t.-p.
Map in pocket   (v. 2)

Bibliographical footnotes.
Contents.—I. The reformation in Germany from its beginning to the religious peace of Augsburg.
—II. The reformation in Switzerland, France, the Netherlands, Scotland and England, the Anabaptist and Socinian movements, the counter-reformation.

1. Reformation. 2. Counter-reformation. 3. Socinianism. 4. Anabaptists.

NL   0384533   CSmH PPDrop

LINDSAY, Thomas Martin, 1843-1914.
A history of the reformation. [Vol.] I. New York, C. Scribner's Sons, 1936.

21 cm.
Half-title: The international theological library.
Contents: I. The reformation in Germany from its beginning to the religious peace of Augsburg.

NL   0384534   MH

BR305
.L786

Lindsay, Thomas Martin, 1843-1914.
A history of the Reformation. New York, C. Scribner's Sons, 1950-
v. (The international theological library)
Pref. dated March, 1906.
Contents.—v.1. The Reformation in Germany from its beginning to the religious peace of Augsburg.

NL   0384535   ICU

Lindsay, Thomas Martin, 1843-1914, ed.
The imitation of Christ. Selected ...
see under   Imitatio Christi. English.
Selections.

Lindsay, Thomas Martin, 1843-1914.
Letters of Principal T. M. Lindsay to Janet Ross. London [etc.] Constable & company, ltd., 1923.
x, 266 p. front. (port.) 22ᶜᵐ.

1. Ross, Mrs. Janet Anne (Duff-Gordon) 1842-   ed. II. Title.

Library of Congress   PR4889.L42Z52   24-7346

NL   0384537   DLC MH-AH OC1W CtY MB

Lindsay, Thomas Martin, 1843-1914.
... Luther and the German reformation, by Thomas M. Lindsay ...   Edinburgh, T. & T. Clark [1900]
xii, 300 p.   29 cm.   (The world's epoch-makers. [xv])
"Chronological summary of the history of the reformation": p. 267-291.
"A list of some of the books read or consulted for this volume": p. 293-296.

NL   0384538   NcGU NcD PSt

Lindsay, Thomas Martin, 1843-1914.
... Luther and the German reformation, by Thomas M. Lindsay ... New York, C. Scribner's sons, 1900.
xii, 300 p. 29ᵐᵐ. (The world's epoch-makers. [xv])
"Chronological summary of the history of the reformation": p. 267-291.
"A list of some of the books read or consulted for this volume": p. 293-296.

1. Luther, Martin, 1483-1546. 2. Reformation—Germany—Hist.

Library of Congress   BR325.L48   2-12314

NL   0384539   DLC NjNbS MB OC1 ViU OCU MH NjPT CtY-D
KEmT KMK NIC WaTC OrP OrCS CaBVaU CLSU RPB

Lindsay, Thomas Martin, 1843-1914.
... Luther and the German reformation, by Thomas M. Lindsay ...   Edinburgh, T. & T. Clark, 1908.
xii, 300 p.   29 cm.   (The world's epoch-makers. [xv])
"Chronological summary of the history of the reformation": p. 267-291.
"A list of some of the books read or consulted for this volume": p. 293-296.

NL   0384540   OC1W CtY PU

Lindsay, Thomas Martin, 1843-1914.
...Luther and the German reformation, by ... Edinburgh, Clark, 1912.
300 p.

NL   0384541   PSC

Lindsay, Thomas Martin, 1843-1914.
Luther and the German Reformation. Edinburgh, 1913.

NL   0384542   MBrZ OO OU PPLT

Lindsay, Thomas Martin, 1843-1914.
... Luther and the German reformation, by Thomas M. Lindsay ...   Edinburgh, Clark [1925]
300 p.

NL   0384543   NcRS

Lindsay, Thomas Martin, 1843-1914, ed.
The New Testament ... arranged in the order in which its parts came ... London, Dent [and/or] New York, Dutton (Everyman's library)
see under   Bible. N. T. English. 1906. Authorized.   (also 1907, 1911, 1917, 1920, 1928, 1933 (title just "The New Testament"))

370.941   Lindsay, Thomas Martin, 1843-1914.
L64n   Notes on education in Scotland in early days. [Glasgow, 1883]
p.[13]-48.   (Glasgow archaeological society. Transactions [n.s., v.1] no.2-3)

Caption title.
Detached copy.

NL   0384545   IU

Lindsay, Thomas Martin, 1843-1914, ed.
"Odd minutes" with the Imitation of Christ
see under   Imitatio Christi. English.
Selections.

Lindsay, Thomas Martin, 1843-1914.
... Our foreign missions ...   Edinburgh [etc.] 1899.
cover-title, 24 p.   illus.   20 cm.
At head of title: The young people's Free church day, 1899.

NL   0384547   CtY

X282
S86r
v.116

Lindsay, Thomas Martin, 1843-1914.
An Oxford bookseller in 1520.
(In Stirling's and Glasgow public library. Report for the hundred-and-sixteenth year. Glasgow, 1907. 22cm. p.8-14)

1. Dorne, John. 2. Booksellers and bookselling 3. Oxford. University. Corpus Christi college. Library. Mss.131.

NL   0384548   CtY

Lindsay, Thomas Martin, 1843-1914.
The reformation. Edinburgh, T. & T. Clark, 1882.
pp. x, 214. (Handbooks for Bible classes [and private students].)

NL   0384549   MH OO MtBC CtY PCC

Sem
270.7
L64r
2

Lindsay, Thomas Martin, 1843-1914.
The Reformation. 2d ed. Edinburgh, T. & T. Clark [Pref. 1883]

x, 214 p. (Handbooks for Bible classes and private students)

NL   0384550   CLamB PHC TxFTC TxDaM NjNbS CLSU MH

VOLUME 334

BR305 **Lindsay, Thomas Martin,** 1843–1914.
.L8   The reformation. By T. M. Lindsay ... 5th thousand.
         Edinburgh, T. & T. Clark ₍1883₎
         x, 214 p. 18¾ᵉᵐ. (*Added t.-p.:* Hand-books for Bible classes)
         2d ed.
         "Chronological summary": p. 195–209.

         1. Reformation—Hist.

NL 0384551   ICU ICN CtY OClW

Lindsay, Thomas M₍artin₎, 1843–1914. The reformation. [2d
ed.] 7th thousand. Edinburgh. [1883.] sm. 8°.
(HANDBOOKS for Bible classes and private students.)

NL 0384552   MH

Lindsay, Thomas Martin, 1843–1914.
The Reformation. Edinburgh, 1913.

NL 0384553   MBrZ

Lindsay, Thomas Martin, 1843–1914.
The Reformation by ... Edinburgh, Clark, 1929.
214 p.
(Handbooks for Bible classes and private
students...)

NL 0384554   PJB

Lindsay, Thomas Martin, 1843–1914.
Religious life in Scotland
see under title

Lindsay, Thomas Martin, 1843–1914.
Revivals. London, Griffiths, 1909.
41p. (Essays for the Times. no.29)

         1. Revivals.

NL 0384556   TxFTC

Lindsay, Thomas Martin, 1843–1914, tr.

Ueberweg, Friedrich, 1826–1871.
      System of logic and history of logical doctrines. By Dr.
Friedrich Ueberweg ...   Tr. from the German, with notes
and appendices, by Thomas M. Lindsay ...   London, Longmans, Green, and co., 1871.

Lindsay, Thomas Martin, 1843–1914.
      The triumph of Christianity.   (In: Cambridge medieval
history. Cambridge, 1911. 8°. v. 1, p. 87–117.)
      Bibliography, p. 636–641.

NL 0384558   NN OU

Lindsay, Thomas Martin, 1843–1914.
      William of Occam and his connexion with the
reformation.
      43 p.

NL 0384559   PPPD

245.09   **Lindsay, Thomas** Somerville Reeves, 1854–
L749C   The church's song; a companion to the
         Irish church hymnal ... Dublin, Published by
         the Association for promoting Christian know-
         ledge, 1908.
             viii, 227 p. 19 cm.

             1. Church of Ireland. Hymns. 2. Hymns.
         History and criticism. I. Title.

NL 0384560   NcD

BV310   Lindsay, Thomas Somerville Reeves, 1854–
.L74   The church's song. A companion to the
1920   Church Hymnal. By T.S. Lindsay and others.
         2d ed. Dublin, Association for Promoting
         Christian Knowledge, 1920.
             231p. 19cm.

             1. Hymns—History and criticism. I. The
         Church Hymnal. II. Title.

NL 0384561   IEG

Lindsay, Thomas Somerville Reeves, 1854–
      ... Plant names, by T. S. Lindsay ... London, The
Sheldon press; New York ₍etc.₎ The Macmillan co., 1923.
      vii, 93 p. 19ᶜᵐ. (Nature lover's series)

         1. Botany—Nomenclature.   I. Title.

      Library of Congress   QK96.L75   23–16669

      WaS MiU CU MBH
NL 0384562   DLC OCl MiU CaBViP OrCS PPHor OrP Or

---

*BX5590   **Lindsay, Thomas Somerville Reeves,** 1854–
.L5   Some archbishops of Dublin. Dublin, Church
         of Ireland Print. and Pub. Co., 1928.
             104 p. illus., ports. 19 cm.

             1. Bishops—Ireland—Dublin. 2. Church of
         Ireland—Clergy.   I. Title.

NL 0384563   MB IEG

Lindsay, Tullye Borden (Olds)
      Provision for continuity through the selection of curriculum
units; an evaluation of one aspect of progressive elementary
school practice ... by Tullye Borden Lindsay ... ₍New Haven?
1943₎
      111 p. incl. tables. 23ᶜᵐ.
      Thesis (PH. D.)—Yale university, 1938.
      "Selected bibliography": p. 107–111.

         1. Education of children. 2. Education—Curricula.   I. Title.
      Yale univ. Library   A 43–1291
        for Library of Congress   LB1570.L56
                                       ₍3₎†   372

NL 0384564   CtY PU–Penn TxU OOxM DLC

Lindsay, Vachel
      see
Lindsay, Nicholas Vachel, 1879–1931.

Lindsay, Vincent.
      Leave it to grandma, a comedy by Vincent Lindsay.   Franklin,
O. ₍etc.₎ Eldridge ₍1947₎   81 p.   19cm.   (An Eldridge 3-act
play)

NL 0384566   NN

PN6111B
.L54S5   Lindsay, Vincent.

             Sixteen is spring, a comedy in three acts.
         Franklin, Ohio, Eldridge Entertainment House
         ₍1949₎
             71 p. diagr. 19cm. (An Eldridge 3–act
         play)

NL 0384567   ViU

DC162   **Lindsay, W.**
.S8
         Sutherland, George Granville Leveson Gower, *1st duke of,*
         1758–1833.
             The despatches of Earl Gower, English ambassador at
         Paris from June 1790 to August 1792, to which are added the
         despatches of Mr. Lindsay and Mr. Monro, and the diary of
         Viscount Palmerston in France during July and August
         1791, now published for the first time. Edited for the Syn-
         dics of the University Press by Oscar Browning. Cam-
         bridge, University Press, 1885.

Lindsay, W. M.
      Catalogue of the Youths' Free Library, Brooklyn
Institute ...
      see under   Brooklyn Institute of Arts and
Sciences. Youths' Free Library.

Lindsay, W. R.

Godshall, Ammon B
      Edible, poisonous and medicinal fruits of Central America,
by Ammon B. Godshall ... The Panama canal, March 20, 1942.
Technical assistance by: W. R. Lindsay & M. F. Ward ...
₍Balboa? 1942₎

Ba23   Lindsay, Wallace Martin, 1858–1937.
1   The abbreviation-symbols of ergo, igitur ...
1912l   [Leipzig, O. Harrassowitz, 1912]

             Signed: W.M.Lindsay.
             "Separatabdruck aus dem Zentralblatt für
         Bibliothekswesen ..."

NL 0384571   CtY

Lindsay, Wallace Martin, 1858–
      The ancient editions of Martial, with collations of the
Berlin & Edinburgh mss., by W. M. Lindsay ... Oxford,
J. Parker and co., 1903.
      2 p. l., 120 p. 21½ᶜᵐ. (*On cover:* St. Andrews university. Publications,
no. II)

         1. Martialis, Marcus Valerius—Manuscripts.

                                                    3–16174
      Library of Congress   Z8551.5.L74

      MH MB
NL 0384572   DLC CU NN NIC PHC PU NcD MiU OCU OClW

VOLUME 334

Lindsay, Wallace Martin, 1858–
The ancient editions of Plautus. By W. M. Lindsay ... Oxford, J. Parker and co., 1904.

2 p. l., 152 p. 21½ᶜᵐ. (*On cover:* St. Andrews university. Publications, no. III)

CONTENTS.—Preliminary.—Plautus-citations in Varro.—Plautus-citations in Verrius Flaccus. — Plautus-citations in Nonius Marcellus. — Other evidence.—The Ambrosian and Palatine archetypes.—Conclusion.

1. Plautus, Titus Maccius—Manuscripts.   I. Title.

4—14902

Library of Congress   Z8697.L55

MB OC1W
NL 0384573   DLC CaBVaU OU NcU NIC PU PBm CU MiU NN

Lindsay, Wallace Martin, 1858–1937.
... Ancient lore in medieval Latin glossaries. By Professor W. M. Lindsay and H. J. Thomson. London, New York [etc.] H. Milford, Oxford university press [1921]

xii, 185 p. 21½ᶜᵐ. (St. Andrews university publications, no. XIII)

CONTENTS.—Preface.—The Festus-glosses of the Abolita glossary.—Fragments of ancient scholia preserved in Latin glossaries (Virgil scholia in the Abstrusa glossary)—Notes on Virgil-glosses (by H. J. Thomson)

1. Latin language—Glossaries, vocabularies, etc. 2. Festus, Sextus Pompeius. 3. Vergilius Marco, Publius. I. Thomson, Henry John, joint author. II. Title. III. Title: Abolita glossary. IV. Title: Abstrusa glossary.

Library of Congress   PA2359.L47   23—7015

NL 0384574   DLC PU OC1W OCU OU MB MiU CU TU

Lindsay, Wallace Martin.
Anthologie latine, I, xxvi.
(In Mélanges Boissier. Pp. 361–364. Paris, 1903.)
Relates to the authorship of the poem Rure morans quid agam.

F3666 — Anthologia Latina.

NL 0384575   MB

Lindsay, Wallace Martin, 1853–   joint ed.
Arma
     see under   Arma glossarium.

[Lindsay, Wallace Martin] 1858–
... The Bobbio scriptorium: its early minuscule abbreviations. [Leipzig, O. Harrassowitz] 1909.
p. [293]–306. 23½cm.
"Separatabdruck aus dem Zentralblatt für Bibliothekswesen ..." XXVI. Jahrg., 7. Hft., Juli 1909.
Caption title.

1. Bobbio, Italy (Benedictine monastery)
2. Abbreviations, Latin

NL 0384577   CtY

Lindsay, Wallace Martin, 1858–   ed.

Plautus, Titus Maccius.
The Captivi of Plautus; ed. with introduction, apparatus criticus, and commentary. by W. M. Lindsay ... London, Methuen & co., 1900.

Lindsay, W[allace] M[artin], 1858–
The codex Turnebi of Plautus. [A reproduction of a marginal collation derived from the lost codex Turnebi.] Oxford, Clarendon press, 1898.
pp. (7), 1–24, (146), 25–59.
pp. (146) are facsimile plates.

Plautus–Text|Manu   scripts (c)–Latin–Plautus|Plautus. 1898|

NL 0384579   MH ICU NcD ViU CtY OU OC1W MB NjP MiU

Lindsay, Wallace Martin, 1858–1937.
Contractions in early Latin minuscule mss., by W. M. Lindsay ... Oxford, J. Parker and co., 1908.

1 p. l., 54 p. 21½ cm. (*On cover:* St. Andrews university publications, no. v)

1. Abbreviations, Latin.

8—16462

Library of Congress   Z111.L55

NL 0384580   DLC NjP MiU OCU NN MB IaU NcD

Lindsay, Wallace Martin, 1858–
... The Corpus, Épinal, Erfurt and Leyden glossaries, by W. M. Lindsay ... London, New York [etc.] Oxford university press [1921]

viii, 121, [1] p. 22ᶜᵐ. (Publications of the Philological society, VIII)

1. Corpus glossary. 2. Épinal glossary. 3. Erfurt glossaries. 4. Leyden glossary. 5. Latin language—Glossography. 6. Anglo-Saxon language—Glossography.

24–4367

Library of Congress   PA2359.L5

OC1W OU ViU IU ICU NjP
NL 0384581   DLC CaBVaU OrU CU WU DDO PBm LU NIC MiU

Gnp50   [Lindsay, Wallace Martin] 1858.
+ay897   ... Discovery of a collation of the lost
         'Codex Turnebi' of Plautus ... [London, D. Nutt] 1897.
         2 v. in 1. 27cm.
         Caption title.
         From the Classical review, vol. XI, p. [177]–180, 246–250.

1. Plautus, Titus Maccius. Manuscripts.

NL 0384582   CtY

Lindsay, Wallace Martin, 1858–1937.
Early Irish minuscule script. By W. M. Lindsay ... Oxford, J. Parker and co., 1910.

2 p. l., 74 p., 1 l. XII facsim. (7 fold.) 24½ᶜᵐ. (*On cover:* St. Andrews university. Publications, no. VI)

1. Paleography, Irish. 2. Manuscripts, Latin—Facsimiles. I. Title. II. Title: Irish minuscule script.

10—16321

Library of Congress   Z115 Ir.L75

NIC NcD
NL 0384583   DLC KU TxU PU PBm OU MiU OCU MH NN MB

Lindsay, Wallace Martin, 1858–1937.
Early Latin verse, by W. M. Lindsay ... Oxford, The Clarendon press, 1922.

ix p., 1 l., 372 p. 23 cm.

"Plautus and Menander": p. [11]–112.
Bibliography: p. 359–365.

1. Latin language—Metrics and rhythmics. 2. Plautus, Titus Maccius. 3. Menander, of Athens. 4. Latin language, Preclassical to ca. 100 B. C. I. Title.

PA2329.L5   23—8438

PBm PU DAU
NL 0384584   DLC TNJ CU CtY ViU OO OU MiU OCU OC1W

Lindsay, Wallace Martin, 1858–
Early Welsh script, by W. M. Lindsay ... Oxford, J. Parker and co., 1912.

2 p. l., 64 p. XVII facsim. (14 fold.) 25ᶜᵐ. (*On cover:* St. Andrews university. Publications, no. x)

1. Paleography, Welsh. 2. Manuscripts, Latin—Facsimiles.

13–6550

Library of Congress   Z115 W.L5

NL 0384585   DLC TxU MiU OCU NN MB MH KU OCU CU NIC

Lindsay, Wallace Martin, 1858–1937, ed.
Glossarium Ansileubi; sive Librum glossarum ... see under   Ansileubus.

Lindsay, Wallace Martin, 1858–1937.
... Handbook of Latin inscriptions, illustrating the history of language, by W. M. Lindsay ... Boston, Allyn and Bacon, 1897.

v, 134 p. 17½ᶜᵐ. (Allyn and Bacon's college Latin series)

1. Inscriptions, Latin.

12—36190

Library of Congress   PA6111.A7A25 1897

OrU CaBVaU OC1W OO OC1 MiU OCU CU TU NcU NjP PBa
NL 0384587   DLC MB ViU NNC PU PSC PPT ICU IdU Or

PA   **Lindsay, Wallace Martin,** 1858–1937.
658.5.   Introduction à la critique des textes
L514   latins, basée sur le texte de Plaute... Traduit
          par J.P. Waltzing. Paris, Klincksieck, 1893.
          viii, 170p 18cm (Nouvelle collection à
          l'usage des classes. xxiv)

          "Bibliographie": p. [vii]–viii.

          1. Latin literature. Criticism, Textual.
          2. Plautus, Titus Maccius. Criticism and
          interpretatio[n]

NL 0384588   MnCS

Lindsay, Wallace Martin, 1858–
An introduction to Latin textual emendation, based on the text of Plautus, by W. M. Lindsay ... London, Macmillan and co., ltd.; New York, The Macmillan co., 1896.

xii, 131 p. 17½ᶜᵐ.

Bibliography: p. xi–xii.

1. Latin literature—Criticism, Textual. 2. Plautus, Titus Maccius—Criticism and interpretation.

1–18584

Library of Congress   PA6585.L5

OO MH WaWW IdPI OrU NNJ CU NIC CLSU FTaSU CSt
NL 0384589   DLC NjP PBL ViU PBm PV PU OU OO OCU ODW

Lindsay, Wallace Martin, 1858–   ed.

Isidorus, *Saint, bp. of Seville,* d. 636.
Isidori Hispalensis episcopi *Etymologiarum* sive Originvm libri xx; recognovit brevivqve adnotatione critica instrvxit W. M. Lindsay ... Oxonii, e typographeo Clarendoniano [1911]

---

871   Lindsay, Wallace Martin.
P5.V1.Gt Jahresbericht über Plautus 1895–1905
(1906)   (1906)   [Leipzig, 1906]
          [116]–282p.

          From Jahresbericht für altertums-
          wissenschaft. Bd. CXXX. (1906. II)
          Tr. from English by A. Tesch.

NL 0384591   IU

VOLUME 334

Lindsay, Wallace Martin, 1858–1937.
Jahresbericht über Plautus 1907–1911. Von W. M. Lindsay

...

(In Jahresbericht über die fortschritte der klassischen altertums-
wissenschaft ... 1914. Leipzig, 1914. 22ᶜᵐ. 167. bd. (42. jahrg., 2. abt.)
p. ₍1₎–58)

1. Plautus, Titus Maccius—Bibl.

                               A 42–2581
Rochester. Univ. Library
for Library of Congress   [PA3.J3 bd. 167]
                       ₍2₎   (880.5)

NL 0384592   NRU NcD

PA8360
J8A7
1922
Lindsay, Wallace Martin, 1858–1937, ed.

Julianus, *Saint, bp. of Toledo, d.* 690.
Julian of Toledo 'De vitiis et figuris,' by Professor W. M.
Lindsay. London, New York ₍etc.₎ Pub. for St. Andrews
university by H. Milford, Oxford university press, 1922.

Lindsay, Wallace Martin, 1858–1937.
The Laon az-type.
(In Revue des bibliothèques. Paris. 1914. 25ᶜᵐ. v. 24. p. ₍15₎–27.
2 facsim.)
Signed: W. M. Lindsay.

1. Paleography, Latin.   ɪ. Title.

Title from Cleveland   Pub. Libr.   A C 34–1283
Library of Congress   [Z671.R45 vol. 24]

NL 0384594   OCl

Lindsay, Wallace Martin, 1858–1937.

Die lateinische sprache; ihre laute,
stämme und flexionen in sprachgeschicht-
licher darstellung... Vom verfasser geneh-
migte und durchgesehene übersetzung von
Hans Nohl. Leipzig, Hirzel, 1897.
xvi, 747 p. 22½ ᶜᵐ·

1. Latin language–Grammar, Historical.
I. Nohl, Hans, tr.

NL 0384595   NjP ODW MH IU MnCS NIC

Lindsay, Wallace Martin, 1858–1937.
The Latin language; an historical account of Latin sounds,
stems and flexions, by W. M. Lindsay ... Oxford, Clarendon
press, 1894.
xxviii, 650, ₍1₎ p. 23ᶜᵐ·
Bibliography: p. ₍xxvi₎–xxviii.

1. Latin language—Grammar. Historical.

                                 10–31887
Library of Congress   PA2071.L6

OrPR WaWW CaBVaU
ViU PPL NcU OClW OO OCl OCU MiU OU OCU CtY MtU IdU
NL 0384596   DLC NBuU NjP NIC MU MB CU PBm PSC PHC

Lindsay, Wallace Martin, 1858–1937, ed.
The Liebaert collection of photographs from
Latin mss.
    see under   Liebaert, Paul, d. 1915.

Lindsay, Wallace Martin, 1858–   ed.

Martialis, Marcus Valerius.
M. Val. Martialis Epigrammata; recognovit brevique adnotatione critica instrvxit W. M. Lindsay ... Oxonii, e typographeo Clarendoniano ₍1902₎

Lindsay, Wallace Martin, 1858–   ed.

Nonius Marcellus.
Nonii Marcelli De compendiosa doctrina libros xx, Onionsi-
anis copiis vsvs, edidit Wallace M. Lindsay ... Lipsiae, in
aedibvs B. G. Tevbneri, 1903.

Lindsay, Wallace Martin, 1858–1937.
Nonius Marcellus' dictionary of Republican Latin. By
W. M. Lindsay ... Oxford, J. Parker and co., 1901.
1 p. l., 120 p. 21½ cm. *(On cover:* St. Andrews university publications, no. 1)

                             8—27351
Library of Congress   PA6518.N6L5

      ICU NcD
NL 0384600   DLC NcU OO MiU OClW MH NN MB IU NjP PU

Lindsay, W₍allace₎ M₍artin₎ 1858–1937.
The notae juris of Vat. Reg. 886.
(In: **Mélanges offerts à M. Emile Chatelain** ...
Paris, 1910. 4°. p. 155–162)

NL 0384601   NN

Lindsay, Wallace Martin, 1858–
Notae latinae; an account of abbreviation in Latin mss.
of the early minuscule period (c. 700–850) by W. M. Lindsay ... Cambridge, University press, 1915.
xxiv, 500 p. 22½ᶜᵐ·
"List of mss. used": p. ₍444₎–494.

ɪ. Abbreviations, Latin.   ɪ. Title.

                             16–9299
Library of Congress   Z111.L56

    MiU OU OCU NN MB MdBJ NjP PPT OrU
NL 0384602   DLC MiDW LU DDO PBm PHC PSC ViU OClWHi

Lindsay, Wallace Martin, 1858–1937. *Notae latinae.*

Bains, Doris.
A supplement to Notae latinae (abbreviations in Latin mss.
of 850 to 1050 A. D.) by Doris Bains ... with a foreword by
W. M. Lindsay ... Cambridge ₍Eng.₎ The University press,
1936.

Lindsay, Wallace Martin, 1858–
The old script of Corbie, its abbreviation symbols (with
two photographs of Montpellier, Bibl. univ., 69, in natural
size)
(In Revue des bibliothèques. Paris, 1912. 25ᶜᵐ. v. 22, p. ₍405₎–429.
2 facsim.)
Signed: W. M. Lindsay.

1. Paleography, Latin. 2. Abbreviations, Latin.   ɪ. Montpellier,
France. Université. Bibliothèque. Mss. 69. ɪɪ. Title.
                               A C 34–1268
Title from Cleveland Pub   Libr.
Library of Congress   [Z671.R45 vol. 22]

NL 0384604   OCl MiU CtY

Lindsay, Wallace Martin, 1858–1937, ed.

Terentius Afer, Publius.
P. Terenti Afri Comoediae; recognovervnt breviqve adno-
tatione critica instrvxervnt Robert Kauer Vindobonensis,
Wallace M. Lindsay Sanctandreanvs. Oxonii, e Typographeo
Clarendoniano, 1926.

Lindsay, Wallace Martin, 1858–1937, ed.

... Palaeographia latina. pt. ɪ–   London, New
York ₍etc.₎ Pub. for St. Andrews university by H. Milford, Oxford university press, 1922–

Lindsay, W₍allace₎ M₍artin₎ 1858–
The Palatine text of Plautus. Oxford, etc., J. Parker and Co.
1896.
pp. 20.

Plautus–Text‖

NL 0384607   MH MB NIC CU

Lindsay, Wallace Martin, 1858–
Plavti codicis senonensis lectiones. Scripsit W. M. Lindsay.
(In Philologus ... Supplementband. Leipzig, 1899. 22ᶜᵐ. vɪɪ,
p. ₍117₎–132)
Gives the readings of T, *i. e.* Codex Turnebi or Fragmenta senonen-
sia, a fragmentary manuscript, now lost, used by Adrien Turnèbe,
which belonged to the Benedictine monastery of St. Colombe at Sens
in central France, as deduced from references in Turnèbe's Adversaria,
books ɪ–xxx, Paris, 1564–73, from Denis Lambin's edition of Plautus,
1577, and from manuscript marginalia in the Gryphius edition of Plautus, 1540, now preserved, with shelf mark Linc. 8° D 105, in the Bodleian library, Oxford. *cf.* p. ₍119₎ and the author's The Codex Turnebi
of Plautus, Oxford, 1898, his edition of the Captivi of Plautus, London,
1900, and the Classical review, London, 1899, v. 13, p. 222–224, 254–265.
    1. Plautus, Titus Mac-   cius. Mss. (Cod. Turnebi)
                               A C 35–199
Title from Illinois Univ
Library of Congress   [PA3.P55 vɪɪ]

NL 0384608   IU OCU MiU OClW CU

Lindsay, Wallace Martin, 1858–   ed.

Festus, Sextus Pompeius.
Sexti Pompei Festi De verborum significatu quae supersunt
cum Pauli epitome; Thewrewkianis copiis usus edidit Wallace
M. Lindsay. Lipsiae, in aedibus B. G. Teubneri, 1913.

Lindsay, W₍allace₎ M₍artin₎, 1858–
A short historical Latin grammar. Oxford, Clarendon Press,
1895.
pp. xii, 201 +. (Clarendon press series.)

    OWorP CSt CU
NL 0384610   MH CtY OCU OO ICU MB NjP MdBJ ViU CU

Lindsay, Wallace Martin, 1858–1937.
A short historical Latin grammar, by W. M. Lindsay ...
2d ed. Oxford, The Clarendon press, 1915.
xii, 224 p. 19½ᶜᵐ·

1. Latin language—Grammar, Historical.
                                 A 16–324
Williams college. Library
for Library of Congress   PA2071.L65
                      ₍a49e1₎

PBm ICU OClW
CtY MdBJ DLC IU ViU MiU OU OCU OO OCX ODW PU PSC
NL 0384611   MWiW PPCCH CaBVaU NcD MtU IdU CU DDO

VOLUME 334

Lindsay, Wallace Martin, 1858–
A short historical Latin grammar. [2d ed.]
Oxford, Clarendon Press [1937]

xii, 224 p.

NL 0384612   MH

Lindsay, Wallace Martin, 1858–
Syntax of Plautus. By W. M. Lindsay ... Oxford,
J. Parker and co., 1907.

iv, 138 p., 1 l. 21½ᶜᵐ. (On cover: St. Andrews university publications,
no. IV)

7–29203* Cancel

ViU MB NN
NL 0384613   DLC PJB CU AU NBuU PU PBm OClW OO MiU

Lindsay, Wallace Martin, 1858–1937.
Syntax of Plautus, by W. M. Lindsay ... Oxford 1907,
reprint 1936. New York, G. E. Stechert & co. [1936]

iv, 138 p. 22½ cm.

1. Plautus, Titus Maccius. 2. Latin language—Syntax.
                                                37—24313
Library of Congress   PA6905.L5 1936
                       [a49d1½]   872.3

CaBVaU OrPR
NL 0384614   DLC CSt TxU OCU DCU CtY OU OCl MtU OrU

Lindsay, Wallace Martin, 1858–1937, ed.

Plautus, Titus Maccius.
T. Macci Plavti Comoediae; recognovit brevique adnotatione
critica instrvxit W. M. Lindsay ... Oxonii, e Typographeo
Clarendoniano [pref. 1903]

Lindsay, Wallace Martin, 1858–1937.
Varia Plautina.
(In Harvard studies in classical philology.
Vol. 9, p. 126–132.   Boston, 1898)

NL 0384616   MB

Lindsay, Walter.
Port and other bins; being a collection of verses, stories,
and letters, by Walter Lindsay; illustrated with cartoons
drawn by the author and photographs taken by J. Howard
Fell. Philadelphia [Printed by Wm. F. Fell co.] 1928.

121 p., 1 l. front., illus., plates (incl. music) 21½ᶜᵐ.

"Collected and edited by J. Howard Fell."
"A private edition of 207 copies, all of which are autographed by
the author." This copy not autographed.

I. Fell, J. Howard, ed. II. Title.
                                                29–6493
Library of Congress   PS3523.I 583P6 1928

NL 0384617   DLC NN

Lindsay, Walter.
This wooden pig went with Dora, by Walter Lindsay; with
pictures by James Reid. New York, R. M. McBride & company, 1930.

4 p. l., 78 p. col. front., illus., col. plates. 23½ᶜᵐ.

I. Title.
                                                30–29569
Library of Congress   PZ8.9.L645Th

NL 0384618   DLC

Lindsay, Walter, pseud.

    see   Annandale, Robert Burns, 1889–

Lindsay, Walter, 1870–
Poems of the eighty-ninth class, Central high school of
Philadelphia, by Walter Lindsay ... Philadelphia, The class,
1938.

100 p. 21½ᶜᵐ.

1. Philadelphia. Central high school. Class of 1888. I. Title.
                                                39–2896
Library of Congress   PS591.S3L5
————— Copy 2.
Copyright A 125300   [2]   811.50822

NL 0384620   DLC PU PP PHi

Lindsay, Walter M.
Poems; by Walter M. Lindsay ... New-York, D. Appleton
& company, 1856.

196, [1] p. 18½ᶜᵐ.

                                                28–11503
Library of Congress   PS2246.L57

NL 0384621   DLC NBuG MB ICU CU WU NN MiU OO MdBP

Lindsay, Walter Manville, 1867–1907.
The jurisdiction of the Probate court, the execution and
proof of wills, and the statutes of descent and distribution, in
Massachusetts, including the appointment of administrators,
executors, guardians, and trustees, their duties and obligations.
By Walter M. Lindsay ...   Boston, Mass., Manville publishing
co., 1896.

98, [2] p. 17ᶜᵐ.

1. Probate law and practice—Massachusetts. 2. Massachusetts. Probate courts. 3. Inheritance and succession—Massachusetts. [3. Succession and descent—Massachusetts] 4. Executors and administrators—
Massachusetts. I. Title.
                                                31–34355

NL 0384622   DLC

Lindsay, Walter M[anville] 1867–1907.
The land forces of the United States. Elements of
military authority, organization and administration. By
Walter M. Lindsay ... Published by authority of Gen.
William Stopford ... Boston, Wright & Potter printing
co., state printers, 1905.

vi, [2], 134 p. 14½ᶜᵐ.

1. Military law—U. S.   5–32441

Library of Congress   UB500   1905   (Copyright A 123610)

NL 0384623   DLC DNW NcU OO ICJ NN

Lindsay, William.
.... Maize and maize oil. [New York City, 1880?]

10 p. 19½ x 15ᶜᵐ.
Caption title.
At head of title: For private circulation only.
Signed: Wm. Lindsay.

NL 0384624   ICJ

Lindsay, William, M.A., ed.

Law

Gt. Brit. Laws, statutes, etc.
The Finance act, 1948, by William Lindsay. London,
Butterworth, 1948.

Lindsay, William, of New York.
Tables for computing the weight of cattle, sheep, hogs
&c. by measurement. By William Lindsay ... N[ew]
Y[ork] Printed for the author by Liddle and son, 1838.

19 p. illus. 18ᶜᵐ.

1. Meat trade—Tables and ready-reckoners.

                                                7–16888†
Library of Congress   HF5716.C2L7

NL 0384626   DLC

Lindsay, William, 18th earl of Crawford, d. 1698
see Crawford, William Lindsay, 18th earl of, d. 1698.

Lindsay, William, 1802–1866, tr.

Olshausen, Hermann, 1796–1839.
Commentary on the Gospels: adapted expressly for preachers and students. By Hermann Olshausen ... Translated
from the German, with additional notes, by the Rev. H. B.
Creak ... To which is prefixed the same author's Proof of
the genuineness of the writings of the New Testament. Translated from the German, with notes, by David Fosdick, jr. ...
Edinburgh, T. and T. Clark; New York, J. Wiley; [etc., etc.]
1848–55.

Lindsay, William, 1802–1866.
Inquiry into the Christian law, as to the relationships which
bar marriage. By William Lindsay ... Glasgow, M. Ogle
and son; London, Hamilton, Adams, and co.; [etc., etc.] 1855

ix, 230 p. 18ᶜᵐ.
Errata slip inserted.

1. Marriage. 2. Consanguinity. I. Title. II. Title: Christian law
as to the relationships which bar marriage.

                                                37–17718
Library of Congress   HQ1026.L5
                       [2]   173.1

NL 0384629   DLC

BM   Lindsay, William, 1802–1866.
521   Inquiry into the Christian law as to
P5.4   the relationships which bar marriage.
       Second ed. London, J. Nisbet, 1871.
         xii, 226 p.   17 cm.
         Bd. with Pirie, James. School manual
       of the law of Moses. London, 1880.

         1. Marriage (Jewish law) I. Title
       II. Title: Christian law as to the
       relationships which bar marriage.

NL 0384630   OCH

BS3776 **Lindsay, William,** 1802–1866.
.L74   Lectures on the Epistle to the Hebrews. By the late
       William Lindsay ... Philadelphia, Smith, English, and co.,
       1867.

         2 v. 22½ᶜᵐ.
       "Preface" signed: George Brooks.

         1. Bible. N. T. Hebrews—Commentaries.

NL 0384631   ICU CSaT NjNbS PPL PCC OO MH

VOLUME 334

LINDSAY, William, *1802-1866*.
The miracles of scripture defended from the assaults of modern scepticism, the lecture delivered at the opening of the United presbyterian theological hall session 1850. Edinburgh, Oliphant, 1850.

pp. 36.   17.5 cm.

NL 0384632   MH-AH

Lindsay, [William], 1802-1866.

Taylor, James, 1813-1892.
The pictorial history of Scotland, from the Roman invasion to the close of the Jacobite rebellion. A. D. 79-1746. By James Taylor, D. D., assisted by Professor Lindsay, D. D., Professor Eadie ... John Anderson, D. D., George Macdonald ... and other contributors ... Illustrated with engravings on steel. London and New York. J. S. Virtue, 1859.

Lindsay, William, 1821-
Some notes: personal and public. Aberdeen [Scot.] W. & W. Lindsay, 1898.
iii, 328 p.   port.

NL 0384634   MiD

1835 - 1909.
Lindsay, William, Address [before Virginia state bar association] of Hon. William Lindsay, of Kentucky. The man and the corporation.   3172
(In Virginia state bar association. 20 report, 1908.   p. 202-232)

NL 0384635   Vi

Lindsay, William, 1835-1909.
An address on the character and services of John Marshall, as chief justice of the Supreme court of the United States; delivered at Springfield, Illinois, before the Supreme court of that state, on the 5th day of February, 1901. By William Lindsay. [n. p.] Law reporter print. [1901]
cover-title, 31 p.   23½ᶜᵐ.   (*In* Dillon, J. F., comp. Centenary and memorial addresses and proceedings ... on Marshall day, 1901. [New York, 190-]   27½ᶜᵐ.   v. 4)

1. Marshall, John, 1755-1835.   CA 15-1070 Unrev'd

Library of Congress   E302.6.M4D57 vol. 4

NL 0384636   DLC MdBP MH

Lindsay, William, 1835-1909.
... Bonds or greenbacks?
see under title

Lindsay, William, *1835-1909.*
The influence of corporations on political life.   (Amer. Acad. of Political and Social Science. Annals.   Philadelphia. 1900. 8°.   Suppl. [Corporations and public welfare.] May, 1900, p. 77-104.)

1. Corporations, U. S.
N. Y. P. L.   August 4, 1913.

NL 0384638   NN OCl OU

Lindsay, William, 1835- *1909.*
Power of the United States to acquire and govern foreign territory. The annual address before the American bar association ... August 28, 1899. By William Lindsay ... [n. p., 1899]
cover-title, 31 p.   23½ᶜᵐ.

1. U. S.—Colonial question.
                                              1-18579

Library of Congress   JV568.1899.L5

NL 0384639   DLC PU-L MWA MdBP

Lindsay, William, 1835- *1909.*
The relations of the general government with the states composing the federal Union.   The annual address before the New York state bar association at Albany, N. Y., January 17, 1905, by William Lindsay. [Albany, 1905]
cover-title, 23 p.   23½ᶜᵐ.

1. U. S.—Pol. & govt.—Addresses, essays, lectures. 2. State rights.
                                              9-23694†

Library of Congress   JK325.L7

NL 0384640   DLC

Lindsay, William, *1835- 1909.*
A uniform system of bankruptcy. Speech... April 5, 1897.
Wash., 1897.

YA5000   (Congressional speeches, by author)
J 17

NL 0384641   DLC

Lindsay, William Alexander, 1846-*1927,* ed.

Inchaffray abbey.
Charters, bulls and other documents relating to the abbey of Inchaffray, chiefly from the originals in the charter chest of the Earl of Kinnoull; ed. by William Alexander Lindsay ... John Dowden ... bishop of Edinburgh, John Maitland Thomson ... Edinburgh, Printed by T. and A. Constable for the Scottish history society, 1908.

Lindsay, William Alexander.
The evidence to the truth of Christianity supplied by prophecy
(In Credentials of Christianity. Pp. 41-83. London. 1876.)

NL 0384643   MB

Lindsay, William Alexander, 1846-   ed.

Brenan, Gerald, 1872-1906.
A history of the house of Percy from the earliest times down to the present century, by Gerald Brenan; ed. by W. A. Lindsay ... London, Freemantle & co., 1902.

Lindsay, William Alexander, 1846-
The O'Briens. London and Aylesbury, Hazell, Watson, and Viney, 1876.
16 p.

NL 0384645   OClWHi

Lindsay, W[illiam] A[lexander] 1846-
Pedigree of the house of Stewart. N. B.—This pedigree, founded upon the accounts printed in Wood's edition of Douglas' peerage and other printed books (with some corrections and additions), was compiled for the Stewart exhibition, by W. A. Lindsay ... London and Bungay, R. Clay and sons, limited [1889]
geneal. tab.   col. coat of arms.   66 x 130ᶜᵐ fold. to 24 x 19½ᶜᵐ.

1. Stuart, House of.
                                              6-45683

NL 0384646   DLC OCl

Lindsay, William Alexander, 1846-
Pedigree of the royal house of Guelph, dukes of Brunswick, kings of Great Britain and Ireland, and of Hanover, proceeding from the house of D'Este.   Founded principally on "L'art de vérifier les dates," with a few modern notes.   By William Alexander Lindsay.   London and Bungay, R. Clay and sons, limited, 1891.
geneal. tab.   71 x 124ᶜᵐ fold. to 25 x 22ᶜᵐ.

1. Guelf, House of.
                                              6—45682

Library of Congress   CS418.L5

NL 0384647   DLC ICN OCl

DA111   **Lindsay, William Alexander,** 1846-
.L74   The royal household, by W. A. Lindsay ... London, K. Paul, Trench, Trübner & co., 1898.
xvi, 273 p.   28x22½ᶜᵐ.
"This edition is strictly limited to 750 copies."
The Ceremonials are reprinted from the Supplements to the London gazette for the respective dates.   *cf.* p. xiv.
CONTENTS.—Succession to offices.—Biographical notes.—Ceremonials.

1. Gt. Brit.—Royal household, 1837-1901. 2. Gt. Brit.—Peerage.

NL 0384648   ICU MB NN MdBP CSmH OCl OrP RPB

Lindsay, William Alexander, 1846-1927.
Yorkshire charters from the Lindsay collection
see under title

Lindsay, William Bell, 1889-   ed.
Coleman, William Henry, 1888-
The Coleman spelling vocabulary and how it was obtained [by] W. B. Lindsay. Chicago, Hall & McCreary company [1932]

ML87   Lindsay, William Bell, 1895-
.P73
Portraits of great composers, with biographical sketches. Chicago, Hall & McCreary Co. [1936-

Lindsay, William Birkhead, 1858-*1922,* ed.
Eliot, Charles William, 1834-1926.
The compendious manual of qualitative chemical analysis of C. W. Eliot and F. H. Storer, as revised by W. R. Nichols. 16th ed.   Newly revised by W. B. Lindsay ... New York, D. Van Nostrand company, 1892.

Lindsay, William Birkhead, 1858-1922, joint author.
Storer, Francis Humphreys, 1832-1914.
An elementary manual of chemistry; by F. H. Storer and W. B. Lindsay ... Being a revision and rewriting of Professor W. R. Nichols's abridgment of Eliot and Storer's Manual. New York, Cincinnati [etc.] American book company [1894]

VOLUME 334

Lindsay, William C.
Sketch of New Boston, N.H. including the Presbyterian Church. n.p. 1909.
pamph.

NL 0384654   PPPrHi

Lindsay, William C.
Sketch of the Presbyterian Church, Bedford, N.H., 1898.
pamph.

NL 0384655   PPPrHi

929.2 Lindsay,William David.
qB334   Batson family genealogy,revised to
May 1,1949. ₍Comp.by William D.Lindsay
and Sam W.Batson₎ ₍Milwaukee,Wis.,
1949₎
unp. geneal.charts. 29cm.

1.Batson family. 2.Genealogy. Batson family. I.Batson,Samuel Waite, jt.au.

NL 0384656   N WHi MnHi

Lindsay, W₍illiam₎ Fraser.
The film and composition. Glasgow, Scottish Educational Film Association, 1949.

vii, 16 p. 25 cm. (Scottish Educational Film Association. Research publication no. 4)
Bibliographical footnotes.

1. Moving-pictures in education. I. Title. (Series)
LB1044.A2S35 no. 4   371.33523   51–37521

NL 0384657   DLC NN CtY

Lindsay, William Lauder, 1829–1880.
Annual medical reports
see under   Perth, Scotland. James Murray's royal asylum.

Lindsay, W₍illiam₎ Lauder, 1829–1880.
... The auriferous quartzites of Scotland. By W. Lauder Lindsay ... ₍Perth? 1875₎
11 p. 21ᶜᵐ.
"From the 'Scottish naturalist' of April, 1875."

1. Gold mines and mining—Scotland.

Library of Congress   TN425.G7L5   6–19279†

NL 0384659   DLC

Lindsay, W₍illiam₎ Lauder, 1829–1880.
Botanical notes of a visit to Schleswig-Holstein, in August, 1850. By W. Lauder Lindsay ... Read before the Botanical society of Edinburgh, 9th Jan., 1851. ⟨From the North British agriculturist⟩. Edinburgh, Printed at the North British agriculturist office, 1851.
12 p. 19ᶜᵐ.

1. Botany—Schleswig-Holstein.

Library of Congress   QK314.L72   5–25569†

NL 0384660   DLC DNLM

Lindsay, W₍illiam₎ Lauder, 1829–1880.
Contributions to New Zealand botany, by W. Lauder Lindsay ... London and Edinburgh, Williams & Norgate, 1868.
102 p. 4 col. pl. 28½ x 22ᶜᵐ.
"Bibliography": p. ₍89₎–91.
Plant collections made in Otago.

1. Botany—New Zealand—Otago.

Library of Congress   QK447.L7   5–29363†

NL 0384661   DLC MH–A MiU NN

Lindsay, William Lauder, 1829–1880.
Contributions to the natural history of Iceland, Greenland, and other Arctic or northern countries, by W. Lauder Lindsay ... ₍n. p., 187–?₎
5, ₍1₎ p. 22½ᶜᵐ.
A list of titles.

1. Natural history—Arctic regions—Bibl.

Library of Congress   Z8506.3.L6   CA 7—3321 Unrev'd

NL 0384662   DLC

Lindsay, W₍illiam₎ Lauder, 1829–1880.
The development and reform of the higher education in Scotland: a series of papers by W. Lauder Lindsay ... ₍Perth? 1874₎
₍78₎ p. 17¾ᶜᵐ.
Various paging.
"The Perth academy" wanting.
Reprinted from the Perthshire Constitutional, 1872–74.

CONTENTS.—1. The education of girls.—2. The modern Fair maid of Perth.—3. The Perth academy.—4. Botany as a branch of female education.—5. University development and reform.

1. Education of women—Scotland. 2. Universities and colleges.

Library of Congress   LA657.L75   6–20010†

NL 0384663   DLC

Lindsay, W₍illiam₎ Lauder, 1829–1880.
Enumeration of micro-lichens parasitic on other lichens. By W. Lauder Lindsay ... ₍London, 1869₎
36 p. 22ᶜᵐ.
Caption title.
Reprinted from the Quarterly journal of microscopical science, 1869, vol. IX, p. 49–57, 135–146, 342–358.

1. Lichens. 2. Parasitic plants.

Library of Congress   QK583.L74   5–25129†

NL 0384664   DLC

Lindsay (W₍illiam₎ Lauder) ₍1829–80₎. Experiments on the communicability of cholera to the lower animals. 48 pp. 8°. *Edinburgh, Mill & Co.,* 1854.
[*Also, in:* P., v. 590.]
Repr. from: Edinb. M. & S. J., 1854, lxxxi.   c.

NL 0384665   DNLM

Lindsay, William Lauder, 1829–1880.
Experiments on the dyeing properties of lichens. By W. Lauder Lindsay ... Edinburgh, Printed by Neill and company, 1855.
26 p. 22½ᶜᵐ.
"From the Edinburgh philosophical journal, new series, for July 1855."

1. Dye plants. 2. Lichens.

Library of Congress   SB285.L74   12–10436

NL 0384666   DLC

Lindsay, W₍illiam₎ Lauder, 1829–1880.
The flora of Iceland. By W. Lauder Lindsay ... Edinburgh, Printed by Neill and company, 1861.
40 p. 21½ᶜᵐ.
From the Edinburgh new philosophical journal, new series, for July, 1861.
"Enumeration ... of ... publications containing lists of the plants of Iceland": p. 39–40.

1. Botany—Iceland.

Library of Congress   QK275.L74   5–20317†

NL 0384667   DLC NIC

Lindsay, William Lauder, 1829–1880.
General history of the Murray royal institution ⟨for the insane,⟩ Perth: from its establishment in 1827 to the end of the first half-century of its existence in 1877. By W. Lauder Lindsay ... Perth, 1878.
1 p. l., 24, 25, ₍1₎ p. front., illus. 26 x 21ᶜᵐ.
No. 37 and 38 of "Excelsior: the Murray royal institution literary gazette," January, 1877, and January, 1878, with addition of t.-p. and frontispiece.

1. Perth, Scotland. James Murray's royal asylum. I. Excelsior.

Library of Congress   RC503.P46   9–30916†

NL 0384668   DLC NIC NN NjP

₍Lindsay, William Lauder₎ 1829–1880.
General index to memoirs on the spermogones and pycnides of the I. Higher lichens ⟨filamentous, fruticulose, and foliaceous species⟩: published in vol. XXII., pt. I, of the Transactions of the Royal society of Edinburgh: 1859 ... II. Lower lichens ⟨crustaceous species⟩: published in vol. XXVIII., pt. II., of the Transactions of the Linnean society of London: 1872 ... ₍Edinburgh, 1874₎
49 p. 28ᶜᵐ.
Added half-title: Memoirs on the spermogones and pycnides of lichens ...

1. Lichens. 2. Reproduction.

Library of Congress   QK581.L75   5–37735†

NL 0384669   DLC

Lindsay, W₍illiam₎ Lauder, 1829–80.
——. The histology of the blood in the insane. 18 pp. 8°. *[Perth,* 1854.] [*Also, in:* P., v. 590.]

NL 0384670   DNLM

Lindsay, William Lauder, 1829–1880.
... The lichen-flora of Greenland, with remarks on the lichens of other Arctic regions. By W. Lauder Lindsay ... ⟨Reprinted ... from the Transactions of the Botanical society of Edinburgh, vol. x., p. 32–65. Read January 14, 1869⟩ ₍London, 1875₎
₍1₎, 284–311 p. 21½ cm.
Caption title.
Label on half-title: Reprint from the Admiralty manual of the natural history of Greenland: prepared for the use of the Arctic expedition of 1875.

1. Lichens—Greenland.

Library of Congress   QK597.L6   5—25111

NL 0384671   DLC CtY

Lindsay, William Lauder, 1829–1880.
... Insanity in the lower animals. By W. Lauder Lindsay ... ₍London, 1871₎
37 p. 21½ cm.
Caption title.
From British and foreign medico-chirurgical review, 1871.

1. Animal intelligence. 2. Animals, Habits and behavior of.
I. Title.

QL785.L74   CA 9–2737 Unrev'd

NL 0384672   DLC

VOLUME 334

Lindsay, William Lauder, 1829–1880.
∴ Memoir on the spermogones and pycnides of crustaceous lichens. By W. Lauder Lindsay ... ₁London, 1872₁
₁189₁–318 p. 8 col. pl. 30ᶜᵐ.
Caption title.
"Extracted from the 'Transactions of the Linnean society of London.' vol. XXVIII."

1. Plants—Reproduction. 2. Lichens.   5–37740

Library of Congress   QK581.L75

NL 0384673   DLC MH
―――

Lindsay, William Lauder, 1829–1880.
Memoir on the spermogones and pycnides of filamentous, fruticulose, and foliaceous lichens.
(*In* Royal society of Edinburgh. Transactions. Edinburgh, 1861. 28ᶜᵐ. v. 22, p. 101–303)

CA 5–245 Unrev'd
Library of Congress   Q41.E2 vol. 22

NL 0384674   DLC MiU NIC
―――

Lindsay, W. William Lauder, 1829–80.
―――. Memoranda anent pensions to asylum physicians. March 17, 1879. 3 pp. fol. [London, 1879.]

NL 0384675   DNLM
―――

Lindsay, William Lauder, 1829–1880.
Mind in the lower animals in health and disease, by W. Lauder Lindsay ... London, C. K. Paul & co., 1879.
2 v. 23ᶜᵐ.
CONTENTS.—v. 1. Mind in health.—v. 2. Mind in disease.

1. Animal intelligence. 2. Insanity. I. Title.
6–26717
Library of Congress   QL751.L74

MdBP NcD CLSU
NL 0384676   DLC DNLM MH ViU OC1W OCU CtY OrP CU

Lindsay, William Lauder, 1829–1880.
Mind in the lower animals, in health and disease, by W. Lauder Lindsay ... New York, D. Appleton and company, 1880.
2 v. 22½ᶜᵐ.
CONTENTS.—vol. I. Mind in health.—vol. II. Mind in disease.

1. Animal intelligence. 2. Insanity. I. Title.   E 16–127
Library, U. S. Office of   Education QL785.L6
Library of Congress   QL785.L76 1880

OrCS PSt
NL 0384677   DHEW AAP NIC TU CU NjP DI–GS ICJ NN AU

Lindsay, W. William Lauder, 1829–1880.
Monograph of the genus *Abrothallus* (De Notaris and Tulasne emend.) By W. Lauder Lindsay ... (Read before section D. of the meeting of the British association, at Cheltenham, in August, 1856.) ₁London, 1857₁
37, ₁4₁ p. 2 col. pl. 22½ᶜᵐ.
Caption title.
Each plate accompanied by leaf of descriptive letterpress.
From the Quarterly journal of microscopical science. 1857. v. 5, p. 26–63.

1. Abrothallus.
5–25126†
Library of Congress   QK585.A16L

NL 0384678   DLC

Lindsay, William Lauder, 1829–1880.
New Zealand plants. [London, 1878]
Broadside.
"From the Gardeners' chronicle, 1878"
new ser. x, 79.

NL 0384679   MH–A
―――

Lindsay, W. William Lauder, 1829–1880.
Observations on lichenicolous micro-parasites. By W. Lauder Lindsay ... ₁London, 1871₁
28–42 p. 22½ᶜᵐ.
Caption title.
"Reprinted from the Quarterly journal of microscopical science." 1871, new series, vol. XI.

1. Lichens. 2. Parasitic plants.

Library of Congress   QK583.L745   5–25127†

NL 0384680   DLC
―――

Lindsay, William Lauder, 1829–1880.
Observations on new lichenicolous micro-fungi.
Royal society of Edinburgh. Transactions. Edinburgh, 1869. 28ᶜᵐ.
v. 25, p. 513–555.   Q41.E2 vol. 25
―――― From the Transactions of the Royal society of Edinburgh, vol. xxv. Edinburgh, Printed for the Society, 1869.
1 p. l., 513–555 p. pl. xxiii–xxiv (col.) 27½ᶜᵐ.
1. Fungi. 2. Lichens.
CA 5–580–1 Unrev'd
Library of Congress   QK583.L748

NL 0384681   DLC NcD
―――

Lindsay, William Lauder, 1829–1880.
Observations on new lichens and fungi collected in Otago, New Zealand.
Royal society of Edinburgh. Transactions. Edinburgh, 1867. 28ᶜᵐ.
v. 24, p. 407–456.   Q41.E2 vol. 24
―――― From the Transactions of the Royal society of Edinburgh, vol. xxiv. Edinburgh, Printed for the Society, 1866.
1 p. l., 407–456 p. pl. xxix–xxx (col.) 28ᶜᵐ.
1. Lichens—New Zealand. 2. Fungi—New Zealand.
CA 5–578–9 Unrev'd
Library of Congress   QK593.N56L7

NL 0384682   DLC
―――

Lindsay, William Lauder, 1829–1880.
... Observations on New-Zealand lichens. By W. Lauder Lindsay ... Read June 7, 1866. ₁London, 1866₁
₁493₁–560 p. 4 col. pl. 29½ᶜᵐ.
Caption title.
From the Transactions of the Linnean society, vol. xxv.

1. Lichens—New Zealand.   5–24929
Library of Congress   QK593.L6

NL 0384683   DLC
―――

Lindsay, W. William Lauder, 1829–1880.
... Observations on the lichens collected by Dr. Robert Brown ... in West Greenland in 1867. By W. Lauder Lindsay ... Read February 4th, 1869. ₁London, 1869₁
₁305₁–368 p. 5 col. pl. 29½ᶜᵐ.
Caption title.
Extracted from the Transactions of the Linnean society of London, vol. XXVII.

1. Lichens—Greenland.   5–24930†
Library of Congress   QK595.L7

NL 0384684   DLC

Lindsay, W. William Lauder, 1829–1880.
... On *Arthonia melaspermella.* By W. Lauder Lindsay ... ₁London, 1867₁
₁1₁, ₁268₁–286 p. pl. 21½ᶜᵐ.
Extracted from the Linnean society's Journal.—Botany, vol. IX.

1. Arthonia melaspermella.

Library of Congress   QK583.L749   5–25128†

NL 0384685   DLC MBH
―――

Lindsay, W. William Lauder, 1829–1880.
... On chemical reaction as a specific character in lichens. By W. Lauder Lindsay ... ₁London, 1868₁
₁1₁, ₁36₁–63 p. 22ᶜᵐ.
Extracted from the Linnean society's Journal.—Botany, vol. XI.

1. Lichens. 2. Plants, Chemical analysis of.

Library of Congress   QK583.L75   5–36029†

NL 0384686   DLC
―――

Lindsay (W. William Lauder) 1824–1880.
On insanity and lunatic asylums in Norway. 51 pp.
London: Savill & Edwards, 1858. 8°.
Repr.: *Psychological Journal.*
In: *C. p. v. 418.

NL 0384687   NN
―――

Lindsay, W. William Lauder, 1829–1880.
On polymorphism in the fructification of lichens. By W. Lauder Lindsay ... ₁London, 1868₁
13 p. 22½ᶜᵐ.
Caption title.
From the Quarterly journal of microscopical science. 1868. vol. VIII, p. 1–13.

1. Reproduction. 2. Lichens.

Library of Congress   QK581.L76   5–37738†

NL 0384688   DLC
―――

Lindsay, William Lauder, 1829–1880.
On the eruption, in May 1860, of the Kötlugjá volcano, Iceland. By W. Lauder Lindsay ... Edinburgh, Printed by Neill and company, 1861.
52 p. map. 23ᶜᵐ.
"From the Edinburgh new philosophical journal, new series, for January, 1861."

1. Katla, Iceland (Volcano)
12–6914
Library of Congress   QE523.K7L7

NL 0384689   DLC NIC
―――

Lindsay, William Lauder, 1829–1880.
... On the present uses of lichens as dye-stuffs. By W. Lauder Lindsay ... ₁London₁ 1867.
11, 141–144 p. 22ᶜᵐ.
Caption title.
"From the Report of the British association for the advancement of science for 1867."

1. Dye plants. 2. Lichens.
12–9832
Library of Congress   SB285.L76

NL 0384690   DLC

VOLUME 334

Lindsay, W[illiam] Lauder, 1829–1880.
On the *Protophyta* of Iceland. By W. Lauder Lindsay ... [n. p., 1867]
7 p. 22^{cm}.
Caption title.
Reprinted from the Quarterly journal of microscopical science, vol. VII, 1867, p. 197–203.

1. Botany—Iceland.

Library of Congress   QK275.L745   5–20316†

NL 0384691   DLC

Lindsay, W[illiam] Lauder, 1829–1880.
On the *Protophyta* of New Zealand. By W. Lauder Lindsay ... [London, 1867]
16 p. 22^{cm}.
Caption title.
From the Quarterly journal of microscopical science, 1867. New series, v. 7, p. 97–112.

1. Protophyta. 2. Botany—New Zealand.

Library of Congress   QK577.N56L   5–37257†

NL 0384692   DLC OU

Lindsay, W[illiam] Lauder, 1829–1880.
On the structure of *Lecidea lugubris* (Sommf.) By W. Lauder Lindsay ... [London, 1857]
9, [2] p. col. pl. 22½^{cm}.
Caption title.
Plate accompanied by two pages of descriptive letter press.
From the Quarterly journal of microscopical science, 1857. v. 5, p. 177–185.

1. Lecidea lugubris. 2. Botany—Anatomy.

Library of Congress   QK581.L765   5–24832†

NL 0384693   DLC NN

Lindsay, William Lauder, 1829–1880.
On the Tertiary coals of New Zealand.
(*In* Royal society of Edinburgh. Transactions. Edinburgh, 1867. 28^{cm}. v. 24, p. 167–174)
    Q41.E2 vol. 24
——— From the Transactions of the Royal society of Edinburgh, vol. xxiv. Edinburgh, Printed for the Society, 1865.
1 p. l., 167–171, [3] p. 28^{cm}.

1. Coal—New Zealand.

Library of Congress   QE691.L74   CA 5—582–3 Unrev'd

NL 0384694   DLC

Lindsay, William Lauder, 1829–1880.
... On the toot-poison of New Zealand. By W. Lauder Lindsay ... [Cambridge. Eng., 1862]
3 p. 22^{cm}.
Caption title.
Extracted from the Proceedings of section D (Botany and Zoology) of the British association at Cambridge. Oct. 1862.

1. Coriaria.

Library of Congress   RA1242.C8L7   CA 7–4666 Unrev'd

NL 0384695   DLC

Lindsay, William Lauder, 1829–1880.
On the transmission of diseases between man and the lower animals. Edinburgh [A. Jack, 1858]. 16 p. 8°.
Repr.: Edinburgh veterinary review and Annals of comparative pathology. July, 1858. With bibliographical footnotes.

1. Diseases.—Transmission.
N. Y. P. L.   August 16, 1912.

NL 0384696   NN

LINDSAY, William Lauder, 1829–1880.
The Physiology and Pathology of Mind in the Lower Animals. Edinburgh, 1871.
pp.19.

NL 0384697   MH

Lindsay, W[illiam] Lauder, 1829–1880.
The place and power of natural history in colonisation with special reference to Otago (New Zealand). By W. Lauder Lindsay ... Edinburgh, Printed by Neill and company, 1863.
36 p. 22^{cm}.
From the Edinburgh new philosophical journal for April and July 1863.

1. Natural history—New Zealand.

Library of Congress   QH21.N5L7   5–42228†

NL 0384698   DLC

Lindsay, William Lauder, 1829–1880.
A popular history of British lichens ... By W. Lauder Lindsay ... London, L. Reeve, 1856.
xxxii, 352 p. xxii col. pl. (incl. front.) 17^{cm}.
Bibliographies at end of chapters.

1. Lichens—Gt. Brit.

Library of Congress   QK589.L75   5–25132

NL 0384699   MdBP ViU ICJ MiU OOxM CU NjP NN DLC DNLM MBH CaBVaU PU-B PPAN NcD CtY

LINDSAY, William Lauder.
Public water-supply: with special reference to Perth. [Perth.] 1876. 3 pt. in 1 v. Sm. 8°.

NL 0384700   MB

Lindsay, William Lauder, 1829–1880.
Public water-supply: with special reference to the requirements of Perth. By W. Lauder Lindsay ... being an address delivered to the Perthshire society of natural science on 3d February, 1876. Perth, Scotland, 1876.
11 p. 18½^{cm}.
"Reprinted from the Perthshire constitutional and journal, Monday, February 7, 1876."

1. Perth, Scotland—Water-supply.

Library of Congress   TD264.P4L7   7–27146†

NL 0384701   DLC

[Lindsay, William Lauder] 1829–1880.
Recent gold discoveries in Scotland. [Perth, Scotland, 1874]
15 p. 18^{cm}.
Caption title.
Published anonymously.
"Reprinted from Perthshire Constitutional, Feb. 18, 1874."

1. Gold mines and mining—Scotland.

Library of Congress   TN425.G7L52   6–19278†

NL 0384702   DLC

Lindsay, W[illiam] Lauder, 1829–1880.
Recent publications on insanity and its treatment by W. Lauder Lindsay ... [Perth, 1872]
8 p. 22^{cm}.
A list of Lindsay's contributions.

1. Insanity—Bibl.

Library of Congress   Z8506.3.L8   1–14441 Additions

NL 0384703   DLC

Linsay, William Lauder, 1829–1880.
——. Statement on behalf of Mr. Jón Árnason.
3 l. 4°. Perth, 1878. [P., v. 1296.]

NL 0384704   DNLM

Lindsay, William Lauder, 1829–1880.
Syllabus of lectures on substitutes for paper-material. By W. Lauder Lindsay. [Perth, Christie & Tainsh, printers, 186-]
7 p. 22^{cm}.
Caption title.

1. Paper making and trade. 2. Fibers.

Library of Congress   TS1109.L74   9–713†

NL 0384705   DLC NIC

Lindsay, William Lauder, 1829–1880.
Tables illustrative of the practice of British hospitals for the insane, as regards the superannuation of all classes of officers and servants: by W. Lauder Lindsay ... London, J. & A. Churchill, 1875.
120 p., 1 l. 22^{cm}.

1. Insane hospitals—Gt. Brit.

Library of Congress   RC495.L6   9–1731†

NL 0384706   DLC CtY-M DNLM MH NN

Lindsay, William Lauder, 1829–1880.
The theory and practice of non-restraint in the treatment of the insane: by W. Lauder Lindsay ... Edinburgh, Oliver and Boyd, 1878.
25 p. 23^{cm}.
Reprinted from the Edinburgh medical journal for April and June, 1878.

1. Insane—Care and treatment.

Library of Congress   RC439.L74   7–18670†

NL 0384707   DLC DNLM

VOLUME 334

Lindsay, William Lauder, 1829–1880.
  The University of Otago, New Zealand: as a college for the people. By W. Lauder Lindsay ... ₍Perth? 1875₎
  32 p. 21½ᶜᵐ.

  1. Dunedin, New Zealand. University of Otago.

  Library of Congress   LG741.O82L5   7-280921

  NL 0384708   DLC CtY NN NjP

Lindsay, William Lindsay, *2d earl of*
  see Crawford, William Lindsay, *18th earl of*, d. 1698.

Lindsay, William Schaw, 1816–1877.
  Confirmation of Admiralty mismanagement ... with reply to the charges of Sir Charles Wood ... in a letter to Samuel Morley ...   London, 1855.
  68 p.
  No. 12 of a volume of pamphlets.

  NL 0384710   NjP PU

Lindsay, William Schaw, 1816–1877.
  Confirmation of Admiralty mismanagement ... with reply to the charges of Sir Charles Wood ... in a letter to Samuel Morley ...   London, 1855.
  68 p.
  No. 12 of a volume of pamphlets.

  NL 0384710   NjP PU

Lindsay, William Schaw, 1816–1877.
  History of merchant shipping and ancient commerce. By W. S. Lindsay ... London, S. Low, Marston, Low, and Searle, 1874–76.
  4 v. illus., plates, fold. maps, fold. tab. 23ᶜᵐ.
  Vol. 4 deals with steam navigation.

  1. Commerce—Hist. 2. Shipping—Hist. 3. Steam-navigation—Hist.

  Library of Congress   HF352.L75   5–41460

  CtY MH NIC OrPS PPL ICJ NN CtNICG NjP NBuU MeB
  NL 0384711   DLC MH MB NN OCU MiU OU OCl DN MdBP CU

HF   Lindsay, William Schaw, 1816–1377.
352   History of merchant shipping and ancient
L75   commerce. By W. S. Lindsay ... London,
1874   Sampson Low, Marston, Low, and Searle,
Rare   1874–83.
Book   4 v. illus., plates, fold. maps, fold.
        tab. 23cm.
        Vol. 4 deals with steam navigation.
        Imprint varies slightly.

        1. Commerce - Hist. 2. Shipping - Hist.
        3. Steam navigation - Hist.

  NL 0384712   ViW

Lindsay, William Schaw.
¹⁷⁴⁸⁸ History of merchant shipping from 1816–1874. 2 vol. il. pl.
  maps, tables. O. London: Sampson Low, Marston & Co.
  [188–].
    Originally published as: History of merchant shipping and ancient commerce, vol. 3–4. 1874–1876.

  NL 0384713   ICJ

Lindsay, William Schaw, 1816–1877.
  Letter to Lord John Russell, on belligerent rights, with reference to merchant shipping; and the reply thereto.   London, [1863]
    6 p.   F.
  "Presented to the House of commons by command of Her Majesty, in pursuance of their address dated March 14, 1860".
  Bound with Great Britain--Parliament. Correspondence relating to the civil war in the U.S. 1863

  NL 0384714   RPB

Lindsay, William Schaw, 1816–1877.
  Letters on the navigation laws: (reprinted from the Morning herald) addressed to the Right Hon. Lord John Russell, First lord of the Treasury, &c. containing, a review of the measure of Mr. Labouchere ... London, Smith, Elder, and co., 1849.
  52 p.   21.5 cm.

    1. Commercial law - Gt.Brit. 2. Gt.Brit. - Commercial policy.

  NL 0384715   MH-BA ICU

LINDSAY, William Schaw, 1816–1877.
  Manning the royal navy & mercantile marine; also belligerent and neutral rights in the event of war. London, 1877.

    Front.

  NL 0384716   MH MH-L CtY

VM   Lindsay, William Schaw, 1816–1877.
16   On ancient galleys, and their mode of propulsion.
.L75   London, Taylor, 1871.
           46 p.   illus.

           1. Galleys.

  NL 0384717   MiU

Lindsay, William Schaw, 1816–1877.
  Our merchant shipping. Lond., 1853.

  NL 0384718   DN

Lindsay, W₍illiam₎ S₍chaw₎ 1816–1877.
  Our merchant shipping: its present state considered. By W. S. Lindsay ... London, Longman and co.; ₍etc., etc.₎ 1860.
  xiii p., 1 l., 317 p. incl. tables. 18½ᶜᵐ.

  1. Shipping bounties and subsidies - Gt. Brit. 2. Merchant marine—Gt. Brit.

  Library of Congress   HE743.G7L7   5–19430

  NL 0384719   DLC MH CtY MeB OkU

Lindsay, William Schaw, 1816–1877.
  Our navigation and mercantile marine laws considered with a view to their general revision and consolidation; also, an enquiry into the principal maritime institutions. By W. S. Lindsay. London, Longman, Brown, Green, and Longmans, 1852.
  xii, 280 p. fold. tab. 22ᶜᵐ.

  1. Maritime law—Gt. Brit. 2. Merchant marine—Gt. Brit.
  I. Title.

                                                     31–32485

  NL 0384720   DLC MB NcU ICU

KG7   Lindsay, William Schaw, 1816–1877
L5   Our navigation and mercantile marine laws
         considered with a view to their revision and
         consolidation; also, an enquiry into the
         principal maritime institutions, by W. S.
         Lindsay. 2d ed., condensed and carefully
         rev. London, Longman, Brown, Green and
         Longmans, 1853.
           xii, 198 p. 23 cm.

  NL 0384721   MeB

[LINDSAY, William Schaw]. 1816–1877.
  Recollections of a sailor. Pt. I. London, 1876.

    I. Cruise of the "Arethusa, 1876."

  NL 0384722   MH

347.7   Lindsay, William Schaw, 1816–1877.
L645r   Remarks on the law of partnership and
         limited liability, by W. S. Lindsay and
         Richard Cobden. London, Effingham
         Wilson, 1856.
           28 p.

           1. Limited liability. I. Cobden,
         Richard, 1804–1865. II. Title.

  NL 0384723   WaU

Lindsay (W₍illiam₎ S₍chaw₎) 1816–1877.
  Second series. Practical letters on the navigation laws: addressed to... Lord John Russell...containing a review of the measure introduced by Mr. Labouchere for their overthrow. Glasgow: *Acting Committee of Merchants*... 1849. 2 p. l., 5–27 pp. 8°.
  In: *C p v. 1183.

  NL 0384724   NN

Lindsay, Winifred Frederick.
  Outlines of general and surgical nursing, by Winifred Frederick Lindsay ... Loma Linda, Cal., The College press, 1912.
  4 p. l., 114, ₍2₎ p. 23ᶜᵐ. $1.00
  Interleaved.

  1. Nurses and nursing.

  Library of Congress   RT51.L6   12–12881

  NL 0384725   DLC ICJ DNLM ICRL

VOLUME 334

Lindsay-Bucknall, Hamilton.
A search for fortune; the autobiography of a younger son, a narrative of travel and adventure, by Hamilton Lindsay-Bucknall ... With numerous illustrations by P. W. Barlow, jun. ... London, Daldy, Isbister & co., 1878. xxiv, 452 p. illus. 22cm.

286852B. 1. Voyages and travels,   1850-   I. Title.
N. Y. P. L.   December 12, 1944

NL 0384726   NN NBuG MH

Lindsay of Birker, Alexander Dunlop Lindsay, *Baron*
see
Lindsay, Alexander Dunlop, *Baron, Lindsay of Birker,* 1879-1952.

Lindsay of Birker, Michael Francis Morris Lindsay, *baron*
see
Lindsay, Michael, *baron Lindsay of Birker,* 1909-

F869
L4L4   Lindsay, Calif.   Chamber of Commerce.
A camera trip through Lindsay in California's garden of the sun.   [Lindsay? Calif., 192-]
[18] p.(chiefly illus.) 14cm.

Cover title.

1. Lindsay, Calif. - Descr.   I. Title.

NL 0384729   CU-B

F
5547
L48L5   Lindsay, Ont.   Old Home Week Committee
Lindsay past and present, 1827-1924;
souvenir of Old Home Week, June 28th-July 5th. [Lindsay] 1924.
[82] p. illus., ports.

Cover title.

1. Lindsay, Ont. - History   I. Title

NL 0384730   CaOTU CtY

Lindsay & Blakiston,   Philadelphia, *publishers.*
Catalogue of medical, dental and scientific books published by Lindsay & Blakeston, Philadelphia, and for sale ... by George S. Blanchard & co. ... [Philadelphia, 1867].
29, [3] p.

NL 0384731   OClWHi

Z
973.56
J152Bt   Lindsay & Blakiston, firm, publishers, Philadelphia.
Life of Jackson. With illus. [by] Gilbert & Gihon. Philadelphia, Lindsay & Blakiston [pref. 1845]
viii, 9-185p. 7 plates. 18½cm. (Biographical school series)

Illustrated title-page.

1. Jackson, Andrew, pres. U.S., 1767-1845. I. Title. II. Series.

NL 0384732   TxU

016.61
L645   LINDSAY & BLAKISTON, Philadelphia.
Lindsay & Blakiston's Catalogue of works on the practice of medicine, surgery, anatomy, physiology, midwifery, diseases of children, chemistry, materia medica, dental surgery and medicine, pharmacy, hygiene, the microscope, anaesthesia, &c. &c. &c., and medical, dental and pharmaceutical journals.   Philadelphia [1852?]

[36] p.   22cm.

1. Catalogs,   Booksellers' of Phila
delphia.   2. Medi
Bibliography.   cine.   Catalogs.

NL 0384733   MnU

Lindsay & Blakiston, Philadelphia, publishers.
Medical and literary circular.   Published annually for gratuitous circulation.   Phil., 1846.
22 p.   1 l.   23.5 cm.

NL 0384734   NNNAM

Lindsay & Blakiston, Philadelphia, publishers.
Poetical and prose illustrations of celebrated American painters
see under   Sartain, John, 1808-1897, ed.

FOR OTHER EDITIONS
SEE MAIN ENTRY
Lindsay & Blakiston, Philadelphia, pub.
The stranger's guide in Philadelphia to all public buildings, places of amusement, commercial, benevolent, and religious institutions, and churches, principal hotels, &c. ... including Laurel Hill, Woodlands, Monument, Odd-fellows', and Glenwood cemeteries ... Philadelphia, Lindsay & Blakiston, 1866.

Lindsay and Blakiston, Philadelphia, pub.
The young American's picture gallery ... Philadelphia, Lindsay & Blakiston [1856].

Lindsay auto parts company, appellee.

Law

Winton motor carriage company, *appellant.*
... The Winton motor carriage company, appellant, *vs.* Lindsay auto parts company, appellee.   No. 284.   Equity.   Appeal from United States District court, Northern district of Ohio, Eastern division.   Transcript of record.   Thurston & Kwis ... Frederick P. Fish, esq., and J. L. Stackpole, esq. ... [and others,] attorneys for appellant.   Karl Fenning ... Charles Martindale ... Melville W. Church ... attorneys for appellee. [Cleveland, The Gates legal pub. co., 1915]

F902
.LI   Lindsay Brothers, firm, Milwaukee.
Binder twine appropriation. [Milwaukee, Wis. 1909?]
[12] p.   16 x 19 cm.

1. Wisconsin - Convict labor.
I. Title.

NL 0384739   WHi

QD172
R2L7   Lindsay Chemical Company.
Cerium, rare earth and thorium chemicals. West Chicago, Ill. [1955]
1 v. (unpaged)   illus., diagrs., tables.
29 cm.
Cover title.

1. Earths, Rare. 2. Cerium. 3. Thorium.

NL 0384740   DI

Lindsay collegiate institute. *Library.*
Catalogue of the books in the library of the Lindsay collegiate institute.   Lindsay, S. Hughes, printer, 1895.
cover-title, 22 numb. l. 19ᵐᵐ.

E 12-736

Library, U. S. Bur. of   Education Z881.L64

NL 0384741   DHEW

LINDSAY Crawford, class of 1919 at the Phillips Exeter Academy, class of 1923 at Harvard Engineering School. [New York, Wynkoop Hallenbeck Crawford Co., printers], 1922.

Port.
"Printed in connection with the establishment at Harvard University of the Lindsay Crawford memorial scholarship, Feb.1,1922".

NL 0384742   MH

Lindsay family association of America.
Annual report. 1st-
1904-
[Boston?] 1904-
nos. in v. 23ᵐ.
Report for 1904 issued without title.

1. Lindsay family.

6-16039 Revised 2
Library of Congress   CS71.L753 1904

NL 0384743   DLC NbHi MWA MB

Lindsay gazette.
Golden anniversary edition, Lindsay gazette ... Oct. 19, 1951. Lindsay, Tulare county, Calif., 1951.
1 v (unpaged) illus.,ports.,maps. 56x44cm.

Caption title.
Includes a reproduction of "the reading matter contained in volume 1, number 1, of the Lindsay gazette, published 50 years ago."

NL 0384744   CU-B

Lindsay irrigation company, plaintiff-respondent.
... Lindsay irrigation company, plaintiff and respondent, *vs.* William Mehrtens et al., defendant. Transcript on appeal taken by defendants Dale and Cross. W. B. Wallace, attorney for defendant Dale. Wm. W. Cross, in propria persona ... Visalia, Calif., Tulare county times power print [1891].
cover-title,141 p. 25cm.

At head of title: No. ____ in the Supreme court of the state of California.

NL 0384745   CU-B

Lindsay laboratories.   Everything for the sick. [Fulton, Morrill pr.]n.d. [16]p. illus. Cover title.

NL 0384746   NBLiHi

VOLUME 334

Lindsay past and present, 1827-1924.
   see under   Lindsay, Ont. Old Home Week
Committee.

Lindsay-Strathmore land development directory, Tulare
county, California ...
   Lindsay, Calif., Hall & Burr, distributors, ˢ19
   v. maps, plans. 23½ᶜᵐ.
Compiler: 1929—   H. S. Drake.

   1. Tulare co., Calif.—Direct. 2. Lindsay, Calif.—Direct. 3. Strath-
more, Calif.—Direct. 4. Fruit-culture—California—Tulare co.   I.
Drake, H. S., comp.
   Library of Congress   SB359.L5   31-21219
   ——— 2d set.
   Copyright   ₍2₎   634.0979486

NL   0384748   DLC CU-B

Wing   **Lindsay type foundry, New York.**
Z   Specimen book, printing types, orna-
404   ments, borders.   New York[1903]
.514

NL   0384749   ICN

Lindsay type foundry, *New York.*
   Specimens of printing types made by the Lindsay type
foundry ... New York. ₍New York, 1886?₎
   cover-title, 74 l. illus. 24 x 29½ᶜᵐ.
   Printed on one side of leaf only.

   1. Type and type-founding. 2. Printing—Specimens.
                                                         9-7352
   Library of Congress   Z250.L65

NL   0384750   DLC MWA ICN

L250   **Lindsay type foundry, New York.**
L655   Specimens of printing types made by the
1887   Lindsay type foundry ... New York.   [New York,
       1887?]
          cover-title, 87 l.   illus.   24 x 30 cm.

NL   0384751   DLC

L250   **Lindsay type foundry, New York.**
L655   Specimens of printing types made by the Lindsay
1890   type foundry ... New York. [New York, 1890?]
          cover-title, 103 p.   illus.   24 x 30 cm.

NL   0384752   DLC

Lindsay's international register of wire, rod and strip.
   Wolverhampton, Eng., Lindsay's Wire Publications ₍etc.₎
   v. 25 cm.
   "Incorporating 'Rod and strip annual' and 'Heat treatment re-
view.'"
   Title varies: Wire reference year book and directory.

   1. Wire—Yearbooks. 2. Metal-work—Yearbooks. 3. Metal trade—
Yearbooks.
   TS203.L5   671.84058   55-23712 rev ‡

NL   0384753   DLC

Lindsborg, Kan. Bethany church.
   Lindsborg; bidrag till svenskarnas och den lutherska kyrkans
historia i Smoky Hill river dalen; samlade på uppdrag af
Bethania-församlingen i Lindsborg, Kansas, för fyrtio-års-
festen af Alfred Bergin. Lindsborg, Bethania-församlingen
₍ˢ1909₎
   368 p. incl. front., illus., ports., map. double pl. 27ᶜᵐ.
   Advertising matter: p. 349-368.

   1. Lindsborg, Kan. 2. Swedes in Kansas. 3. Lutheran church in
Kansas.   I. Bergin, Alfred, comp.
                                                         9-14464
   Library of Congress   F689.L7L7

NL   0384754   DLC OrU NN PPAmSwM

Lindsborg, Kan. Bethany church.
   Lindsborg efter femtio år; bidrag till vår lutherska kyr-
kas och svenskarnas historia i Kansas och Sydvästern;
samlade på uppdrag af Bethania-församlingen för half-
sekelfesten 1919, af Alfred Bergin. Lindsborg, Bethania-församlingen ₍1919₎
   239 p. incl. front., illus. (incl. ports.) 27ᶜᵐ.

   1. Lindsborg, Kan. 2. Swedes in Kansas. 3. Lutheran church in Kansas.   I. Bergin, Alfred, 1866- comp. II. Title.
                                                         19-11607
   Library of Congress   F689.L7L76

NL   0384755   DLC PPAmSwM NdU KMK ICN

Lindsborg, Kan. Bethany College
   see   Bethany College, Lindsborg, Kansas.

FKB   The Lindsborg news-record. v.1-   1881-
H1   Lindsborg, Kan., ₍Bethany Publishing Co.₎
55   v illus. 62cm. weekly
L645
      Title varies; 1881-1886, Smoky Valley news.
      1887-1911, Lindsborg news.
      Consolidated in 1912 with Lindsborg record.

NL   0384757   KU

Lindschoten, Jan Huygen von
   see   Linschoten, Jan Huygen Van.

Linschotten, Joan Hugo van

see

Linschoten, Jan Huygen van.

Lindsell, Arthur James Gurney, 1880-
   joint author.
Atchison, George Turnour, 1877-
   The why and wherefore of bridge, by G. T. Atchison and
A. J. G. Lindsell. London, New York ₍etc.₎ Longmans,
Green, and co., 1905.

1926   **Lindsell, Gerald Charles Huntingdon,** 1883-
LI4116g   The grey geese.   Toronto, W. H. Apted,
       c1931.
          18 p. 18 cm.

   Poems.

   1. Canadian poetry. I. Title.

NL   0384761   RPB

Lindsell, Harold, 1913-
   Abundantly above, by Harold Lindsell. Grand Rapids,
Mich., Wm. B. Eerdmans publishing company, 1944.
   150 p. 20ᵐ.

   I. Title.
                                                         44-4187
   Library of Congress   PZ3.L65347Ab

NL   0384762   DLC

LD3907   **Lindsell, Harold,** 1913-
.G7   The Chilean-American controversy of
1942   1891-1892...   ₍New York₎ 1942.
.L47   2p.l., iv,231 typewritten leaves.
       29cm.
          Thesis (Ph.D.) - New York university,
       Graduate school, 1942.
          Bibliography: p.221-231.

NL   0384763   NNU-W

Lindsell, Harold, 1913-
   The Chilean-American controversy of 1891-1892 ₍by₎ Harold
Lindsell ...   New York, New York university, 1943.
   14 p. 23ᵐ.
   Abridgment of thesis (PH. D.)—New York university, 1942.

   1. Chile—Hist.—Revolution, 1891. 2. Chile—For. rel.—U. S. 3. U. S.—
For. rel.—Chile.   I. Title.   A 43-1085
   New York univ. Libraries
     for Library of Congress   E183.8.C4L56
                                 ₍3₎†   327.73860983

NL   0384764   NNU NcD OrU NNC DLC

Lindsell, Harold, 1913-
   A Christian philosophy of missions. Wheaton, Ill., Van
Kampen Press ₍1949₎
   238 p. 20 cm.

   1. Missions—Theory.   I. Title.
   BV2060.L72   266.01   50-862

NL   0384765   DLC PPEB PPWe NcD

Lindsell, Harold, 1913-
   A handbook of Christian truth, by Harold Lindsell and
Charles J. Woodbridge. Westwood, N. J., F. H. Revell Co.
₍1953₎
   351 p. 21 cm.

   1. Theology, Doctrinal.   I. Woodbridge, Charles Jahleel, 1902-
joint author. II. Title.
   BT75.L55   230   53-9083 ‡

NL   0384766   DLC WaS OO PPEB PPWe TNJ-R

Lindsell, Harold, 1913-
   Missionary principles and practice. ₍Westwood, N. J.₎
Revell ₍1955₎
   384 p. 21 cm.
   Includes bibliography.

   I. Title.
   BV2060.L74   266   55-7636

   PPLT WaT MBtS
NL   0384767   DLC KyLxCB KyWAT Wa TxU NcD PP PPWe

VOLUME 334

Lindsell, Harold, 1913–
Park Street prophet, a life of Harold John Ockenga.
Wheaton, Ill., Van Kampen Press ₁1951₎
175 p. illus., ports. 20 cm.

1. Ockenga, Harold John, 1905–   2. National Association of
Evangelicals for United Action.   ɪ. Title.

BX7260.O3L5   922.573   51–10787

NL 0384768   DLC MB

4PS-
5029
Lindsell, Harold, 1913–
The thing appointed.   Wheaton, Ill., Van
Kampen Press [1949]
143 p.

NL 0384769   DLC-P4

LINDSELL, R   A
A short history of Queen Victoria's own Madras sappers & miners, during
World war II, 1939–1945; compiled from war diaries and unit histories,
completed up to December, 1947.   [Bangalore, pref. 1947]
iv, 148 p.   illus., ports., fold. col., maps.   22cm.

1. World war, 1939–1945—Regt. hist. —India.

NL 0384770   NN

Sir
Lindsell, Wilfrid Gordon, 1884–
A. & Q.; or, Military administration in war, by Lieut.-Col.
W. G. Lindsell...   Aldershot₍, Eng.₎ Gale & Polden, Ltd.₍,
1928.₎   vii, 195 p. incl. tables.   plans.   8°.

382602A.   1. Military administration
N. Y. P. 1.   —Gt. Br.
                                                December 3, 1928

NL 0384771   NN CaOTP CSt

Lindsell, Wilfred Gordon.
A. & Q., or Military administration in war, by
... W. G. Lindsell ...   *2d* ed.   Aldershot [etc.]
Gale & Polden, ltd.   [1929]
vii, 195 p.   tables (part fold.) diagrs. (part
fold.)   22 cm.
1. Military administration.   2. Gt. Brit.-Army.
ɪ. Title.   ɪɪ. Title: Military administration in war.

NL 0384772   CU

UB 145
L55
1933
Lindsell, Sir Wilfrid Gordon, 1884–
A. & Q.; or, Military administration in
war. 3d ed. Aldershot, Gale & Polden,
1933.
197 p. illus.

1. Military administration. I. Title.

NL 0384773   CaBVaU

UA649
L75
1923
Lindsell, Wilfrid Gordon.
Military organization and administration,
by W. G. Lindsell. 2d ed.   Aldershot, Gale
& Polden ₍1923₎
xii, 241 p.   19cm.

NL 0384774   CSt

Lindsell, Wilfrid Gordon, 1884–
Military organization and administration.   By Major W. G.
Lindsell ...   4th ed.   Aldershot, Gale & Polden, ltd. ₍1925₎
xiv, 273 p., incl. charts, diagrs.   19ᶜᵐ.

1. Gt. Brit.—Army.   2. Military administration.   ₍2. Administration—
Gt. Brit.—Army₎   ɪ. Title.
                                                           War 26—12
U. S. Army war coll.   Libr.   UA649.L75   1925
for Library of Congress   ₍a42c1₎

NL 0384775   DNW

Lindsell, Wilfrid Gordon
Military organization and administration.
5th ed.   Aldershot, Gale & Polden, ltd.
(1926)
270 p.   19 cm.

NL 0384776   DNW

Lindsell, Wilfrid Gordon, 1884–
Military organization and administration, by Lieut.-General
W. G. Lindsell ...   Covering the ground included in the syllabus of the following examinations and courses of instruction in
matters pertaining to administration and interior economy in
the army: staff college entrance examination, promotion examinations for lieutenants and captains, courses for cadets at
Woolwich and Sandhurst ...   Twenty-second edition.
Aldershot, London ₍etc.₎ Gale & Polden, Ltd. ₍1940₎
xiv, 282 p.   diagrs. (1 fold.)   19ᶜᵐ.

NL 0384777   ICJ

Lindsell, Wilfrid Gordon, 1884–
Military organization and administration, by Lieut.-General Sir
W. G. Lindsell...   25. ed.   Aldershot ₍etc., etc.₎ Gale & Polden
₍1941₎   xiv, 282 p.   illus.   19cm.
"List of official publications..." p. 265–270.

₌84656B.   1. Military administration   —Gt. Br.   I. Gale & Polden ltd.
N. Y. P. 1.   August 25, 1950

NL 0384778   NN

Lindsell, *Sir* Wilfrid Gordon, 1884–
Military organization and administration, by Lieut.-General
Sir W. G. Lindsell ...   Covering the ground included in the
syllabus of the following examinations and courses of instruction in matters pertaining to administration and interior economy in the army:—staff college entrance examination, promotion examinations for lieutenants and captains, courses for
cadets at Woolwich and Sandhurst.   Illustrated with diagrams.
26th ed.   Aldershot, London ₍etc.₎ Gale & Polden ltd. ₍1943₎
xiv, 282 p. incl. tables.   diagrs. (1 fold.)   19ᶜᵐ.

1. Gt. Brit.—Army.   2. Military administration.   ɪ. Title.
                                                           A 43–2969
Harvard univ.   Library
for Library of Congress   ₍2₎

NL 0384779   MH CtY

Lindsell, *Sir* Wilfrid Gordon, 1884–
Military organization and administration. 28th rev. and
enl. ed. by H. C. Boyce.   Aldershot ₍Eng.₎ Gale & Polden,
1953.
xvii, 311 p.   illus.   19 cm.
First published in 1923.   The 27th ed., published in 1948, was
thoroughly revised and in large part rewritten by H. B. Benoy.

1. Gt. Brit. Army —Organization.   2. Military administration.
ɪ. Benoy, James Francis, 1894–   ɪɪ. Boyce, Harry Carlisle, 1902–
ɪɪɪ. Title.
UA649.L5   1953   355   54–16336

NL 0384780   DLC NN

Law
Lindsell, William Harry Barber, 1848–1898,
joint author.
Clerk, John Frederic, 1848–1931.
Clerk & Lindsell on torts. 11th ed. ₍Under the general
editorship of John Burke and Peter Allsop. Editors: A. L.
Armitage and others₎ London, Sweet & Maxwell, 1954.

Lindsell, William Harry Barber, 1848–1898.
joint author.
Clerk, John Frederic, 1848–
The law of torts, by J. F. Clerk ... and W. H. B. Lindsell
... 8th ed., by W. A. Macfarlane and G. W. Wrangham ...
London, Sweet & Maxwell, limited; Toronto, The Carswell
company, limited; ₍etc., etc.₎ 1929.

Lindsen, J. F. A.
Catalogue de tableaux modernes et aquarelles formant les
collections J. F. A. Lindsen à Utrecht, J. K....à Amsterdam et
autres provenances.   Vente à Amsterdam le 12 mai 1908...
₍Amsterdam: F. Muller & Cie., 1908.₎   2 p.l., 49 p.   4°.

1. Paintings (Dutch and Flemish   —Collections (Private). K....,
J.
N. Y. P. L.   October 28, 1915.

NL 0384783   NN

Lindseth, Linnie (Currin) 1890–
Josephine Walkley and Josephine Currin,
her story.   ₍Hillsboro, Ore.₎ H.W. Currin,
1952.
21⌐.   port.   30cm.

With this bound her The Van Curen family.
1952.

1. Currin, Josephine Walkley, 1863–
Bound with.

NL 0384784   OrU CaBViPA

Lindseth, Linnie (Currin) 1890–
The Van Curen family; the descendants of
Jacob Van Curen and his wife, Maria Amanda,
who crossed the plains to Oregon in 1865.
Hillsboro, Ore., H.W. Currin, 1952.
7⌐.   30cm.

Bound with her Josephine Walkley and
Josephine Currin, her story.   1952.

1. Van Curen family.   Bound with.

NL 0384785   OrU

Lindsey,   colonel.
A true and faithful narrative of Oliver Cromwell's
compact with the devil for seven years
see under title

Lindsey,   pseud. ₍?₎
Rechtshandel der drey Könige
see   Goudar, Ange, 1720–1791, supposed
author.

Lindsey, A.L.
Biographical sketch of Thomas R. Lee, Esq, with
a sermon preached at his funeral.   New York, 1860.
(pam)

NL 0384788   PPPrHi

VOLUME 334

ar X   Lindsey, A   V
452   British pioneers in coffee. Santos,
1954.
4 l. 30cm.

Caption title.
Typewritten.

1. British in Brazil. 2. Coffee.

NL 0384789   NIC

Lindsey, Adrian Herve, 1897–
... Relation between egg quality and price, by Adrian H. Lindsey and Hubert W. Yount ... Amherst, Mass., 1982.
22 p. tables. 23ᶜᵐ. (Massachusetts. Agricultural experiment station, 1888–   Bulletin no. 282)

1. Eggs—Marketing.   I. Yount, Hubert William, 1900–   joint author. II. Title.
Title from Mass. State   College   A 32-2697
Library of Congress   [873.I94 no. 282]

NL 0384790   MU

Lindsey, Adrien Herve, 1897–
... Shipping Massachusetts apples to out-of-state markets, by A. H. Lindsey and A. A. Brown ... Amherst, Mass., 1933.
p. [2]–27. map. tables. 23ᶜᵐ. (Massachusetts. Agricultural experiment station, 1888–   Bulletin no. 299)

1. Apple—Marketing.   I. Brown, Alfred Alexander, 1908–   joint author. II. Title.
Title from Mass. State   College   A 34-117
Library of Congress   [873.E35 no. 299]

NL 0384791   MU

Lindsey, Albert J   1905–
Lifted to heaven; a functional approach to the great Biblical doctrines of the Christian faith. Cleveland, Union Gospel Press [1948]
144 p. 20 cm.

1. Theology, Doctrinal—Popular works.   I. Title.
BT77.L5   230   48-17477*

NL 0384792   DLC CBPac

Lindsey, Albert J   1905–
The prophetic pulpit. Berne, Ind., Berne Witness Co. [1954]
118 p. 21 cm.

1. Bible—Prophecies.   I. Title.
BS647.L485   *220.15   54-37433 ‡

NL 0384793   DLC WaT

Lindsey, Alice, d. 1940.
With these, by Alice Lindsey. Dallas, Tex., The Kaleidograph press [1941]
xi, 13-62 p. 20ᶜᵐ.
Poems.

I. Title.   42-4071
Library of Congress   PS3523.I584W5 1941
[2]   811.5

NL 0384794   DLC

Lindsey, Alice Miller Hall (Mrs. E.A. Lindsey)

Dorris, *Mrs.* Mary C   (Currey) 1850–
The Hermitage, home of General Andrew Jackson, seventh president of U. S. A., near Nashville, Tennessee, under management of the Ladies' Hermitage association; originally compiled by Mrs. Mary C. Dorris, revised June 1, 1931, by Mrs. Edward A. Lindsey, regent; Mrs. Paul DeWitt, secretary. [Nashville, 1931]

Lindsey, *Mrs.* Alliene Lizzie (Harris) [1861–]
Light upon a pilgrim's way; poems, by Alliene L. Lindsey. [Chicago, Printed by Mathews typesetting co., 1914]
vii p., 1 l., 140, [10] p. incl. front. (port.) 19½ᶜᵐ. $1.50
10 blank pages at end for "Album."

I. Title.
Library of Congress   PS3523.I585L5 1914   14-8770

NL 0384796   DLC

Lindsey, Alma James.
Merchandising vs. muddling; contains a merchandise mark-up table which saves mental effort and serves you with accurate information on margins of profit, by A. J. Lindsey. Salt Lake City, Utah, ©1927.
3 p. l., [5]–99 p. illus., diagrs. 18ᶜᵐ.

1. Grocery trade.   I. Title.   27-9157
Library of Congress   HD9321.6.L5

NL 0384797   DLC

Lindsey, Almont, 1906–
The Pullman strike, the story of a unique experiment and of a great labor upheaval, by Almont Lindsey ... Chicago, Ill., The University of Chicago press [1942]
xi, 385 p. plates, ports. 23½ cm.
Bibliography: p. 364–370.

1. Chicago strike, 1894.
HD5325.R12 1894.C54   331.892899   42—50022

WaS Or WaTC OrU OrCS KyU
OO OU OCl NcD NcRS OrPR MtU NmU WaSpG MsSM MU CU
NL 0384798   DLC MiU ViU-L PU PPT MiHM TU OC1W OCU

309.7731   Lindsey, Almont, 1906–
L64t   The town of Pullman as a social experiment ...
Urbana, Ill. [1936]
310 numb.l. incl.map.

Thesis (Ph.D.)--University of Illinois, 1936.
Typewritten (carbon copy)
Vita.
Bibliography: leaves 302-308.

——— ——— Thesis copy.

NL 0384799   IU

Lindsey, Almont, 1906–
The town of Pullman as a social experiment, by Almont Lindsey ... Urbana, Ill., 1936.
14 p., 1 l. 23½ᶜᵐ.
Abstract of thesis (PH. D.)—University of Illinois, 1936.
Vita.
"Sources": p. 13–14.

1. Pullman, Ill.   36-16527
Library of Congress   HD7544.P9L5 1936
Univ. of Illinois Libr.
——— Copy 2   [2]   309.17731

NL 0384800   IU DLC PU

Thesis   Lindsey, Alton Anthony, 1907–
1937   The floral anatomy and morphology of the
L752   Gentianaceae. [Ithaca, N. Y.] 1937.
96 l. illus. 27 cm.

Thesis (Ph. D.) - Cornell Univ., June 1937.

1. Flowers - Anatomy. 2. Flowers - Morphology. 3. Gentianaceae. I. Title.

NL 0384801   NIC

Lindsey, Alva J.
...The Merrillville white pine (Pinus-strobus) bog, Lake County, Indiana [by]...
[Indianapolis, Butler university 1932.
dover title, p. 167–178 table diagrs.
O.
(Butler university. Botanical studies.
Vol. 2, paper no. 14)

Issued in one cover with nos. 15–16.
"Literatur cited": p. 176.

NL 0384802   OO OU

Lindsey, Alva J.
...Preliminary fossil pollenanalysis of the Merrillville white pine bog [by]...
[Indianapolis, Butler university] 1932.

Cover-title, p. 179–182 diagr. O.

(Butler university. Botanical studies. vol. 2. paper no. 15)
Issued in one cover with nos. 14, 16.
"Literature cited": p. 182.

NL 0384803   OO OU

Lindsey, Alva J. The trees of Indiana in their local and general distribution according to physiographic divisions. Maps. (In *Butler university botanical studies*, 1932, ii, 93–124.)
"Literature cited," p. 124.
"Contribution no. 30 from the botany laboratory of Butler university."

NL 0384804   MH-A OO OU

Lindsey, Mrs. Ann (Kennedy)
see
McGinty, Mrs. Ann (Kennedy)

Lindsey, Arthur Ward, 1894–
The Cornell university entomological expedition to South America of 1919–1920. Scientific results. no. II. Hesperioidea by A. W. Lindsey. [Granville,] O.
71–113 p.   pl. XXV–XXX

"Reprinted from Denison university bulletin, Journal of the scientific laboratories, vol. XXI, March, 1925."

NL 0384806   OU

Lindsey, Arthur Ward, 1894–
... Echinoderms and insects from the Antilles. Iowa City, The University [1926]

VOLUME 334

Lindsey, Arthur Ward, 1894–
... The *Hesperioidea* of America north of Mexico; a generic revision and synopsis of the species, by Arthur Ward Lindsey, PH. D. Iowa City, The University ₁1921₎
114 p. illus., II pl. (incl. front.) 24ᶜᵐ. (University of Iowa studies in natural history ... vol. IX, no. 2 ₍ᵢ. ₑ. no. 4₎)
On cover: University of Iowa studies. 1st ser., no. 43. Feb. 15, 1921.
The author's doctoral dissertation, University of Iowa, 1919, but not published as a thesis.
Bibliography: p. ₁111₎–114.

1. Hesperioidea. 2. Butterflies—North America.

Library of Congress   QH1.I 58 vol. IX, no. 4   21–27021

MB ViU OrU
NL 0384808   DLC OU WaS PU PPAmP OU OO OCU MiU OC1

QL 561
H5 L5
1931a
Lindsey, Arthur Ward, 1894–
The Hesperioidia of North America, by A. W. Lindsey, E. L. Bell and R. C. Williams, Jr. Granville, Ohio, 1931.
142 p. illus. 26 cm. (Denison University bulletin, vol. 31, no. 2. Journal of the scientific laboratories, vol. 26, article 1)
Cover title.

NL 0384809   OU NIC

Lindsey, Arthur Ward, 1894–
A preliminary revision of Hesperia, by ... ₍Granville, O., 1942₎
cover-title, 50, ₍2₎ p. VIpl.
"Reprinted from Denison university bulletin, Journal of the scientific laboratiries, vol. XXXVII, April, 1942."

NL 0384810   OU

Lindsey, Arthur Ward, 1894–
Principles of organic evolution. St. Louis, Mosby, 1952.
375 p. illus. 26 cm.

1. Evolution. I. Title : Organic evolution.

QH366.L46   575   52–10812

MtBC IdU OrCS WaT OrPS CU
NL 0384811   DLC PU OC1Ur PV TxU ViU MB OU DNLM DNAL

Lindsey, Arthur Ward, 1894–
The problems of evolution, by Arthur Ward Lindsey ... New York, The Macmillan company, 1931.
xiii, 236 p. 19½ᶜᵐ.
Bibliographical foot-notes.

1. Evolution.
Library of Congress   QH366.L47   31–7220
———— Copy 2.
Copyright A 34740   ₍5₎   575

ICJ NN WaTC MtU WaSp OrPR MtBC MBCo NIC MsSM
NL 0384812   DLC CU PU PSC NcD OC1W OO OO OC1 DNLM

Lindsey, Arthur Ward, 1894–
The science of animal life, by Arthur Ward Lindsey ... New York, Harcourt, Brace and company ₍1937₎
xi, 656 p. illus., diagrs. 22ᶜᵐ.
"One hundred books on biology": p. 613–620.

1. Zoology. I. Title.
Library of Congress   QL47.L7   37–2666
———— Copy 2.
Copyright A 103289   ₍5₎   590

NN ViU OrMonO OrCS
NL 0384813   DLC TU OKentU CU MtU DNLM NcU OO ODW OU

Lindsey, Arthur Ward, 1894–
Textbook of evolution and genetics, by Arthur Ward Lindsey ... New York, The Macmillan company, 1929.
xii p., 1 l., 459 p. illus., diagrs. 22½ᶜᵐ.
"References" at end of most of the chapters.

1. Evolution. 2. Heredity.
Library of Congress   QH366.L5   29–3302

OU MiU NN ViU OrPR NcD
NL 0384814   DLC OKentU CU MtU ICU PSC PHC PP OCX OU

Lindsey, Arthur Ward, 1894–
A textbook of genetics, by Arthur Ward Lindsey ... New York, The Macmillan company, 1932.
xvi p., 1 l., 354 p. illus. diagrs. 22½ᶜᵐ.
"References" at end of each chapter.

1. Heredity. 2. Breeding.
Library of Congress   QH431.L425   32–14531
———— Copy 2.
Copyright A 51490   575.1

OCX ViU NcD
NL 0384815   DLC CU MtU OrCS OrMonO OC1 MtBC IdU OU

Lindsey, Ben.
Irish lace: its origin and history... Dublin, Hodges, Figgis and co., 1886. 33 p. illus., map. 18cm.

1. Lace and lace making—Ireland.

NL 0384816   NN

Lindsey, Benjamin Barr, 1869–1943.
Address at the grave of Luther Burbank. Girard, Kan., Haldeman-Julius Publications ₍1926₎
32 p. 13 cm. (Little blue book no. 724)

1. Burbank, Luther, 1849–1926.

SB63.B9L5   [925.8] 926.3   53–48078 ‡

NL 0384817   DLC MeB

Lindsey, Benjamin Barr, 1869–1943.
An address on the delinquent child delivered at the First National Conference on Race Betterment at the Battle Creek Sanitarium, January 8, 9, 10, 11, and 12, 1914. ₍n. p., 1914₎
12 p. 23 cm.

1. Juvenile delinquency. I. Title : The delinquent child.

HV9069.L5   52–59165 ‡

NL 0384818   DLC

Lindsey, Benjamin Barr, 1869–1943.
An answer to the critics of The companionate marriage. ₍n. p., ⁰1929₎
xxi p. 21 cm.
"'Foreword' ... reprinted from the Star edition of The companionate marriage, by Ben. B. Lindsey and Wainwright Evans."

1. Marriage, Companionate. I. Lindsey, Benjamin Barr, 1869–1943. The companionate marriage. II. Title.

HQ803.L5255   52–59166 ‡

NL 0384819   DLC NN NcD

Lindsey, Benjamin Barr, 1869–
Bad boys and girls. Plate.
(In Uplift Publishing Company, Philadelphia. The uplift book of child culture. Pp. 131–141. Philadelphia. [1913.])

NL 0384820   MB

Lindsey, Benjamin Barr, 1869–1943.
The beast, by Judge Ben B. Lindsey ... and Harvey J. O'Higgins ... New York, Doubleday, Page & company, 1910.
xiv, 340 p. front. 20½ cm.

1. Corruption (in politics)—Colorado. 2. Juvenile courts—Colorado. I. O'Higgins, Harvey Jerrold, 1876–1929, joint author. II. Title.

HV6308.L5   10—10595
Library of Congress   ₍a5604₎

OrU Wa MtU
OC1W OO OC1 ICJ MB NN ViU NcC WaT WaTC WaSp Or WaS
NL 0384821   DLC DAU FMU NcU KEmT CoU PSC PJA OOxM

324.788
L64b
1911
Lindsey, Benjamin Barr, 1869–
The beast, by Judge Ben B. Lindsey ... and Harvey J. O'Higgins ... Garden City, N.Y., Doubleday, Page & company, 1911.
340p. front.

1. Corruption (in politics) 2. Juvenile courts I. O'Higgins, Harvey Jerrold, 1876– joint author.

NL 0384822   IU MH NjP

Lindsey, Benjamin Barr, 1869–1943.
... Die bestie, Denver chronik. Leipzig, F. Meiner ₍1944₎
2 p. l., 7–287 p. ports. 21½ᶜᵐ.
At head of title: Ben B. Lindsey.
"Die amerikanische buchausgabe erschien erstmalig im april 1910 unter dem titel 'The beast,' by Judge Ben B. Lindsey and Harvey J. O'Higgins. Die deutsche übersetzung stammt von Ilse Hecht, das nachwort von Elisabeth Noelle."

1. Corruption (in politics) 2. Juvenile courts—Colorado. I. O'Higgins, Harvey Jerrold, 1876–1929, joint author. II. *Hecht, Ilse, 1907– tr. III. Title.
HV6308.L514   A F 46–1158
Columbia univ. Libraries
for Library of Congress   ₍4₎†

NL 0384823   NNC CoDU NN NcD DLC TNJ

Lindsey, Benjamin Barr, 1869–1913.
A Campaign for childhood
see under title

Lindsey, Benjamin Barr, 1869–
The child and the community.
(In National education association of the United States. Journal of proceedings and addresses, 1909. p. 737–743)

1. Children—Care. 2. Juvenile delinquency.

E 10–726
Library, U. S. Bur. of   Education

NL 0384825   DHEW OU

Lindsey, Benjamin Barr, 1869–1943.
Child labor legislation and methods of enforcement in the Western States; address delivered at first annual meeting of the National Child Labor Committee, New York City, February 14–16, 1905 ... New York, National Child Labor Committee ₍1905₎
8 p. 23 cm.
"Reprinted from the Proceedings as published by the American Academy of Political and Social Science, Philadelphia, in The annals of the Academy, vol. XXV, no. 3, May, 1905."

1. Children—Employment—The West. I. Title.

52–59434 ‡

NL 0384826   DLC

VOLUME 334

LINDSEY, BENJAMIN BARR, 1869-1943.
The child, the movie, and censorship. New York,
Motion picture producers & distributors of America
[1926?] 15 p. 23cm.

Film reproduction. Negative.

1. Moving pictures--Censorship--U.S. 2. Moving pictures and children.
3. Censorship--Cinema--U.S. I. Motion picture association of America,
inc.

NL 0384827 NN

Lindsey, Benjamin Barr, 1869-
Childhood and morality.

(*In* National education association of the United States. Journal of proceedings and addresses, 1909. p. 146-157)

1. Education and crime. 2. Moral education.

E 10-614

Library, U.S. Bur. of Education

NL 0384828 DHEW OU

Lindsey, Benjamin Barr, 1869-1943.
Children and the movies; address. [n. p., 1921]
[8] p. 23 cm.

1. Moving-pictures and children. I. Title.

PN1995.9.C5L5   *792.93 791.4   52-59061 ‡

NL 0384829 DLC

Lindsey, Benjamin Barr, 1869-
... Children and the movies, address by Judge
Ben B. Lindsey ... [Albany, N. Y. S. Lib., 1924]
7 l. 27 cm.
At head of title: New York (State) library.
Legislative reference section.
On cover: Public affairs information service.
Type-written.
1. Moral education. 2. Moving-pictures.
I. New York (State) Library. Legislative
reference section.

NL 0384830 CU

Lindsey, Benjamin Barr, 1869-   joint author.

Markham, Edwin, 1852-
Children in bondage; a complete and careful presentation
of the anxious problem of child labor—its causes, its crimes,
and its cure, by Edwin Markham, Benjamin B. Lindsey, and
George Creel, with an introduction by Owen R. Lovejoy ..
New York, Hearst's international library co., 1914.

Lindsey, Benjamin Barr, 1869-1943.
The companionate marriage, by Judge Ben B. Lindsey &
Wainwright Evans. New York, Boni & Liveright, 1927.
xvi, 396 p. 21¼ cm.

1. Marriage, Companionate. 2. Sexual ethics. I. Evans, Wainwright, joint author. II. Title.

Library of Congress   HQ803.L5 1927   27—22775
[a48v2.1]

CaBVaU WaTC OrCS IdB Or MtBC MtU OrMonO Wa OrPR
CtY-M PV ViU OCl NN OClW OO MiU NcU CU ViU NcD WaS
NL 0384832 DLC OFH OU AAP ViU OClW IEG NBuU GU CoU

HQ
803
.L5
Lindsey, Benjamin Barr, 1869-
The companionate marriage, by Ben B. Lindsey & Wainwright Evans. New York, Brentano's [1928]
xvi, 396 p.

1. Marriage, Companionate. 2. Sexual ethics.
I. Evans, Wainwright. II. Title.

NL 0384833 DAU NcGU OU

LINDSEY, BENJAMIN BARR, 1869-
...The companionate marriage, by Judge Ben B. Lindsey
and Wainwright Evans. Garden City, New York: Garden City
Pub. Co., Inc. [cop. 1929] xxxiv, 396 p. 21cm. (Star
book.)

804871A. 1. Marriage, Companionate. I. Evans, Wainwright,
jt.au.

ICN MH
NL 0384834   NN NcD MsU MoU IU MiDW-M NIC CtY PP ViU

Lindsey, Benjamin Barr, 1869-1943.
"Companionate" marriage; address. [n. p., 1927]
23 p. 23 cm.

1. Marriage, Companionate. I. Title.

HQ803.L5253   52-59167 ‡

NL 0384835 DLC ViU

Lindsey, Benjamin Barr, 1869-1943.
The constructive work I have undertaken in the United
States. Leipzig, Elbemühl-Verlag, 1931.
9 p. 23 cm.
"Extract of the Report of the 4th Congress of the World League
for Sexual Reform, Vienna (Austria) 1930."

1. Domestic relations—Colorado. 2. Domestic relations—U. S.—
States. I. Title.

*301.42 392   53-51911 ‡

NL 0384836 DLC

Lindsey, Benjamin Barr, 1869-1943.
The dangerous life [by] Ben B. Lindsey and Rube Borough. New York, H. Liveright, inc. [*1931]
xiv, 450 p. 21¼ cm.
Autobiography of Judge Lindsey.

1. Denver. Juvenile court of the city and county of Denver. 2.
Child welfare—Denver. I. *Borough, Rube, 1883- joint
author. II. Title.
HV9094.D4L48   923.473   31—8649

NIC OCl NN CU OU MB 1dU WaU-L OrP OrU
NL 0384837   DLC PSC PP OClh MiU MsU ViU IEN GU MH-L

Lindsey, Benjamin Barr, 1869-
Debate between Judge Ben Lindsey and G. C. Brewer on
"Companionate marriage". Auditorium, city of Memphis,
April 2, 1928. Cincinnati, O., The Christian leader corporation [*1928]
52 p. 19½ᶜᵐ.

1. Marriage. 2. Sexual ethics. I. Brewer, Grover Cleveland, 1884-
II. Title: Companionate marriage.   28-13988
Library of Congress   HQ734.L57

NL 0384838 DLC

Lindsey, Benjamin Barr, 1869-
The doughboy's religion and other aspects of our day,
by Ben B. Lindsey and Harvey O'Higgins. New York
and London, Harper & brothers [1920]
7 p. l., 89, [1] p. 19¼ᶜᵐ.

1. European war, 1914- —Religious aspects. 2. European war, 1914-
I. O'Higgins, Harvey Jerrold, 1876- joint author. II. Title.

Library of Congress   PS3523.I 587D6 1920   20—1683

NL 0384839   DLC ODW OCl NN MsU Or WaSpG NN MB

Lindsey, Benjamin Barr, 1869-1943.
Das gefährliche Leben; aus dem Amerikanischen übersetzt
von Rudolf Nutt. Stuttgart: Deutsche Verlags-Anstalt, 1931.
305 p. 8°.

Translation of The dangerous life.

1. Title. 2. Lindsey, Benjamin Barr   3. Juvenile delinquency. 4. Borough, Rube, jt. au.
N. Y. P. L.   December 7, 1931

NL 0384840 NN

JK1911 Lindsey, Benjamin Barr, 1869-
.C6D5   How it works in Colorado. ...
[Warren, O., 1909]

By B. Lindsey and Mrs. Sarah Platt Decker.

NL 0384841 DLC

---

ar W   Lindsey, Benjamin Barr, 1869-1943.
31841   If I were a woman. New York, National
v.8   American Woman Suffrage Association [1912]
8 p. 23cm.

"Reprinted by courtesy of 'The Housekeeper'.
No. 11 in a vol. lettered: Woman. Pamphlets
VIII.

1. Woman--Suffrage--U.S.

NL 0384842 NIC

Lindsey, Benjamin Barr, 1869-1943.
Judge Ben B. Lindsey on the child, the movie, and censorship. [Address] New York, Motion Picture Producers &
Distributors of America [n. p., 1926]
15 p. 23 cm.

1. Moving-pictures and children. 2. Moving-pictures—Censorship.

PN1995.9.C5L52   *792.93 791.4   52-59205

NL 0384843 DLC

Lindsey, Benjamin Barr, 1869-1943.
Judge Lindsey on suffrage. Warren, Ohio
[1906?]
2 pl. 16°. (National American Woman
Suffrage Association. Political equality series.
v. 1. no. 5)

NL 0384844 NN

Lindsey, Benjamin Barr, 1869-1943.
Justice for parent and child without cost. [n. p., 192-?]
12 p. 23 cm.

1. Juvenile courts—Colorado. 2. Legal aid—Colorado. I. Title.

53-47676 ‡

NL 0384845 DLC

VOLUME 334

Lindsey, Benjamin Barr, 1869–
₍Juvenile court and companionate marriage pamphlets.
Girard, Kan., 1927.₎   8 pams. in 1 v.   8°.

401918A.   1. Marriage.   2. Criminals,
—Censorship.   4. Criminal law—Pro-
Klan.
N. Y. P. L.
Juvenile—Courts.   3. Moving pictures
cedure.   5. Knights of the Ku Klux
May 21, 1929

NL   0384846   NN

₍**Lindsey, Benjamin Barr**₎ 1869–1943.
Juvenile court laws, etc. ₍By the Judge of the Denver
Juvenile Court. Denver₎ Juvenile Improvement Association
of Denver ₍19—₎
48 p. 23 cm.

1. Juvenile courts—U. S.

364.524   52–68593 ‡

NL   0384847   DLC

Lindsey, Benjamin Barr, 1869–1943, comp.
The juvenile court laws of the state of Colorado
see under   Colorado. Laws, statutes, etc.

Lindsey, Benjamin Barr, 1869–1943.
The juvenile court of the future. The trial of criminal
cases and adult probation in the Chancery Court. ₍New
York, 1925₎
27 p. 23 cm.
"Reprinted from 'The development of juvenile courts and probation,' Proceedings of the National Probation Association ... 1925."

1. Juvenile courts.   I. Title.

HV9088.L5   52–59164 ‡

NL   0384849   DLC

Lindsey, Benjamin Barr, 1869–
340.92   Een leven vol gevaren, door Ben B. Lindsey en
L752La   Rube Borough; vertaling van E. A. Voogd-Pull.
Amsterdam, H. Meulenhoff ₍19 ₎

441 p. 23ᶜᵐ.

Translation of the autobiography of Judge
Lindsey, The dangerous life.

1.Denver. Juvenile court of the city and county
of Denver. 2.Children - Charities, protection,
etc. - Denver.   I.   borough, Rube, 1883-
II.Voogd-Pull; E   A   tr. III.Title.

NL   0384850   CSt

Lindsey, Benjamin Barr, 1869–1943.
... El matrimonio de compañía. Versión española de R.
Cansinos-Assens. Madrid, M. Aguilar, 1930.
419 p., 1 l. 20½ᶜᵐ. (On cover: Biblioteca de ideas y estudios con-
temporáneos)
At head of title: Ben B. Lindsey y Wainwright Evans.

1. Marriage, Companionate. 2. Sexual ethics.   I. Evans, Wainwright,
joint author.   II. Cansinos Assens, Rafael, 1883–   tr.   III. Title.
44–17427
Library of Congress   HQ803.L525
₍2₎   173.1

NL   0384851   DLC

JK1911
.C6C7
Lindsey, Benjamin Barr, 1869–1943, joint author.

Creel, George, 1876–
Measuring up equal suffrage, by George Creel and Ben B.
Lindsey. New York, National American Woman Suffrage
Association ₍19—₎

Lindsey, Benjamin Barr, 1869–1943.
Milk for babies; an address. ₍n. p., 1916₎
23 p. 16 cm.

1. Child welfare.   I. Title.

HV715.L5   53–47689 ‡

NL   0384853   DLC

Law   **Lindsey, Benjamin Barr**, 1869–1943.

₍Miscellaneous pamphlets, reports, addresses, etc., by Benjamin Barr Lindsey, and material relating to his work as judge
of the Juvenile Court of Denver and of the Superior Court
of Los Angeles, including Court laws and reports, petitions,
campaign literature, etc. v. p., 1902–43₎

Lindsey, Benjamin Barr, 1869–
Moral training.
(In National education association of the United States. Journal of pro-
ceedings and addresses, 1909. p. 940–945)

1. Moral education.
E 10–763
Library, U. S. Bur. of   Education

NL   0384855   DHEW

Lindsey, Benjamin Barr, 1869–1943.
My fight with the Ku Klux Klan. ₍n. p., 1925₎
8 p. illus. 31 cm.
"Reprinted from Survey graphic for June, 1925."

1. Ku-Klux Klan (1915–   )   I. Title.

HS2330.K63L5   53–48887 ‡

NL   0384856   DLC

Lindsey, Benjamin Barr, 1869–1943.
The new Probate law; an address before the Colorado Bar
Association at its annual meeting at Colorado Springs, July 1
and 2, 1903. To the address is added the key, prepared by
Junius Henderson, comparing old and new sections of the
Probate law. ₍n. p., 1903₎
26 p. 23 cm.

1. Probate law and practice—Colorado.

52–59123 ‡

NL   0384857   DLC NN

Lindsey, Benjamin Barr, 1869–1943.
A pamphlet containing a list and explanation of bills concerning women and children now pending in the nineteenth
General Assembly. ₍Denver, 1913₎
18 p. 23 cm.

1. Woman—Legal status, laws, etc.—Colorado. 2. Children—
Law—Colorado.   I. Title: Bills concerning women and children.

52–59138 ‡

NL   0384858   DLC

Lindsey, Benjamin Barr, 1869–1943.
A pamphlet containing arguments in favor of the Mothers
compensation act, being an act to amend an act, concerning
dependent and neglected children and permitting keeping
such children in family homes, and for workhouses for men
convicted of non-support. To be submitted to the legal
voters of the State of Colorado for their approval or rejection at the regular general election to be held on the fifth
day of November, 1912. ₍n. p., 1912₎
₍8₎ p. 23 cm.

1. Colorado. Laws, statutes, etc. Mothers' compensation act.

53–55702 ‡

NL   0384859   DLC

Lindsey, Benjamin Barr, 1869–
The parenthood of the state.
(In National education association of the United States. Addresses and
proceedings, 1921. p. 42–54)

1. Education and state—U. S.   I. Title.

Library, U. S. Bur. of   Education   E 22–50

NL   0384860   DHEW

Law   **Lindsey, Benjamin Barr**, 1869–1943.

Sandoval, Adelaide C   petitioner.
The people of the State of Colorado, ex rel. Manuel Cruz,
by Adelaide C. Sandoval, his next friend, petitioner, v.
Clarence J. Morley, Judge of the fifth division of the District Court, Second Judicial District, city and county of
Denver, Colorado, respondent. Petition for a writ of prohibition. Petition for rehearing in the above entitled cause.
Also statement by Ben B. Lindsey concerning the facts in
said cause. Denver, Eastwood Print. Co. ₍1924?₎

Lindsey, Benjamin Barr, 1869–1943.
The people, the schools and the playgrounds; a pamphlet
containing arguments in favor of the School and social
center amendment. An amendment to section 7 of Article xx
of the Constitution, providing for the wider use and control
of the public schools by the people. To be submitted to the
legal voters of the State of Colorado for their approval or
rejection at the regular general election to be held on the
fifth day of November, 1912. Compiled and issued by Ben
B. Lindsey and W. H. Malone. ₍n. p., 1912₎
₍8₎ p. 22 cm.
1. Community centers.   I. Malone, W. H., joint author.
II. Title.

LC223.L5   54–45825 ‡

NL   0384862   DLC

Lindsey, Benjamin Barr, 1869–1943.
The political crisis in Denver; an address delivered at
Trinity Church, Thursday evening, March 24, 1904. ₍Den-
ver, 1904₎
11 p. 20 cm.

1. Denver—Pol. & govt. 2. Corruption (in politics)—Denver.
I. Title.

F784.D4L5   53–47038 ‡

NL   0384863   DLC

Lindsey, Benjamin Barr, 1869–1943.
Probation and the criminal law. ₍Denver, 1901?₎
20 p. 23 cm.

1. Probation—Colorado.   I. Title.

52–59137 ‡

NL   0384864   DLC DL

VOLUME 334

Lindsey, Benjamin Barr, 1869–

Denver. *Juvenile court of the city and county of Denver.*
The problem of the children and how the state of Colorado cares for them. A report of the Juvenile court of Denver 1904. ₍Denver, The Merchants publishing co., 1904₎

Lindsey, Benjamin Barr, 1869–
... Public playgrounds and juvenile delinquency, by Judge Ben B. Lindsey ... ₍New York, 1908₎
₍4₎ p. 25ᶜᵐ. ₍Russell Sage foundation. Dept. of child hygiene. Pamphlet, no. 21₎
Caption title.
Reprinted from the Independent, New York, August 20, 1908.

1. Playgrounds. 2. Juvenile delinquency.

E 10–1608

Library, U. S. Bur. of   Education LB3517.L64

NL 0384866   DHEW

Lindsey, Benjamin Barr, 1869–1943.
Recent progress of the juvenile court movement; a report of the chairman of the Committee on Juvenile Courts and Probation. Columbus, F. J. Heer, 1905.
20 p. 23 cm.

1. Juvenile courts—U. S.   ı. Title.

53–54250 †

NL 0384867   DLC NN

Lindsey, Benjamin Barr, 1869–1943.
The reformation of juvenile delinquents through the juvenile court. Read before the National Conference of Charities and Correction at its thirtieth meeting, in Atlanta, Ga. ₍n. p.₎ Press of F. G. Heer, 1903.
27 p. 23 cm.

1. Juvenile delinquency—Denver. 2. Juvenile courts—Denver. ı. Title.

HV9094.D4L49   53–47688 †

NL 0384868   DLC KyU NN

Lindsey, Benjamin Barr, 1869–
Reply to anti-suffragists at a meeting held under the auspices of the Equal Franchise Society in the Assembly Chamber, Albany, N. Y., February 24, 1911. New York, Equal Franchise Society ₍1911?₎
33 p. 15 cm.

1. Woman—Suffrage—U. S.

JK1901.L48   53–47160 †

NL 0384869   DLC

Lindsey, Benjamin Barr, 1869–1943.
Report of Hon. Ben. B. Lindsey ... chairman of Committee on Juvenile Courts, before the International Congress on the Welfare of the Child, held under the auspices of the Mothers' Congress at Washington, D. C., April 22 to 27, 1914. ₍Denver, 1914₎
19 p. 24 cm.

1. Juvenile courts.

53–55701 †

NL 0384870   DLC NN IU

Lindsey, Benjamin Barr, 1869–1943.
Restore the people's rights! Democracy, not revolution. A pamphlet containing arguments in favor of the initiated bill providing for an appeal to the people from decisions of the courts declaring laws unconstitutional. An amendment to section 1 of Article vɪ of the Constitution of the State of Colorado to be submitted to the legal voters of the State of Colorado for their approval or rejection at the regular general election to be held on the fifth day of November, 1912. Compiled and issued by Ben B. Lindsey and W. H. Malone. ₍n. p., 1912₎

16 p. 22 cm.

1. Judicial review—Colorado. 2. Referendum—Colorado. ı. Malone, W. H., joint author. ɪɪ. Title.

53–36356 †

NL 0384872   DLC

Lindsey, Benjamin Barr, 1869–1943.
The revolt of modern youth, by Judge Ben B. Lindsey and Wainwright Evans. New York, Boni & Liveright, 1925.
vii p., 1 L, 11–364 p. 21½ᶜᵐ.

1. Juvenile delinquency. 2. Sexual ethics. 3. Denver. Juvenile court of the city and county of Denver. ı. Evans, Wainwright. ɪɪ. Title.

25—23190

Library of Congress   HV9094.D4L5

MtU CaBVaU IdB OrPR Or OrSaW IdU WaS WaSpG CaBVa WaSp PBm OO OU NN ViU CU RP PPFr NcD-MC ICRL MH TxU WaTC
NL 0384873   DLC NN MB ICJ OCl ODW OCU NcD TxU PCC MU

HV9094
.D4L5
1928

Lindsey, Benjamin Barr.
₍The revolt of modern youth by Judge Ben B. Lindsey and Wainwright Evans. New York, Garden City Publishing Co., ₍1928₎
364p. 21cm. (A Star book)

1. Juvenile delinquency. 2. Sexual ethics. 3. Denver. Juvenile Court of the City and County of Denver. I. Evans, Wainwright. II. Title.

NL 0384874   AAP

Lindsey, Benjamin Barr, 1869–1943.
The revolt of modern youth, by Ben B. Lindsey and Wainwright Evans. Garden City, N. Y., Garden City Pub. Co. ₍1930₎
vii, xii, 11–364 p. 21cm. (A Star book)

1. Juvenile delinquency. 2. Sexual ethics. 3. Denver. Juvenile Court of the City and County of Denver. I. Evans, Wainwright, jt. author. II. Title.

NL 0384875   ViU MH

Lindsey, Benjamin Barr, 1869–
The revolt of modern youth, by Judge Ben B. Lindsey and Wainright Evans. London, J. Lane, The Bodley head ltd. ₍1932₎
vii, xiip., 1L., 11–364p. 22cm. (The international library of psychology and sexology)

NL 0384876   PSt

Lindsey, Benjamin Barr, 1869–1943.
Die Revolution der modernen Jugend, von Ben B. Lindsey und Wainwright Evans. Deutsche Übersetzung und Bearbeitung von Toni Harten-Hoencke und Friedrich Schönemann. Stuttgart, Deutsche Verlags-Anstalt, 1927.
258 p. front. (port.) 21 cm.

1. Juvenile delinquency. 2. Sexual ethics. 3. Denver. Juvenile Court of the City and County of Denver. ıı. Schönemann, Toni (Hoencke) 1872–   ed. and tr. ɪɪı. Title.

HV9094.D4L53   A F 48–2623*

Columbia Univ.
for Library of Congress   Libraries ₍1₎†

NL 0384877   NNC NIC CaBVaU DLC

Lindsey, Benjamin Barr, 1869–1943.
... די רעוואלוציע פֿון דער מאָדערנער יוגנט. ייִדיש—פֿועה ראקאוסקא. וואַרשע, פֿאַרלאַג י. א. צוקער, 1930.
₍Warsaw₎
301 p. 20½ᵐ.
At head of title: ריכטער בען ב. לינדזי
Translation of The revolt of modern youth.

1. Juvenile delinquency. 2. Sexual ethics. 3. Denver. Juvenile court of the city and county of Denver. ı. Rakowski, Puah, 1865–   tr. *Title transliterated:* Di revolutsie fun der moderner yugnt.

A 45–894

New York. Public library
for Library of Congress   ₍2₎

NL 0384878   NN OCl

Lindsey, Benjamin Barr, 1869–1943.
The rule of plutocracy in Colorado; a retrospect and a warning. Denver, Hicks Print. House ₍1908₎
68 p. 21 cm.

1. Colorado—Pol. & govt. 2. Corruption (in politics)—Colorado. ı. Title.

F781.L5   53–47037 †

NL 0384879   DLC NN

Lindsey, Benjamin Barr, 1869–1943.
A secret political league, who and what it is, its anonymous circulars exposed and court cases involving the sex problem frankly discussed. ₍Denver, 1912?₎
92 p. 23 cm.

1. Sex crimes—Denver. 2. Juvenile courts—Denver.

HQ72.U53C645   53–47686 †

NL 0384880   DLC DL CU OO NN

Lindsey, Benjamin Barr, 1869–1943.
Statement in support of House bill 143 by Hon. Wm. H. Andrew, of Denver, to provide for a State Bureau of Child and Animal Protection ... ₍Denver? 1900?₎
12 p. 23 cm.

1. Colorado. State Bureau of Child and Animal Protection. 2. Child welfare—Colorado.

HV742.C6L5   60–56635 †

NL 0384881   DLC

Lindsey, Benjamin Barr, 1869–1943.
A statement to the friends of the Juvenile Court of Denver. ₍Denver, 1913₎
₍4₎ p. 28 cm.

1. Juvenile courts—Denver.

HV9094.D4L55   53–47691 †

NL 0384882   DLC

VOLUME 334

Lindsey, Benjamin Barr, 1869–

The uplift book of child culture ... Ed. by the Uplift publishing company editorial staff ... Philadelphia, Pa., Uplift publishing company [*1913]

Lindsey, Benjamin Barr, 1869–1943.
What a Democratic judge says about the Democratic Fire and Police Board. Judge Lindsey says: Dens of vice and iniquity are protected by the Fire and Police Board. Terrible arraignment by a Democratic judge of Democratic officials for being under the spell of dive-keepers. Demands that the children of the city be saved from the wine room and the gambling hell. [n. p., 19—?]

4 p. 21 cm.

1. Denver. Fire and Police Board. 2. Crime and criminals—Colorado—Denver.

HV6795.D4L5   53–53924 ‡

NL 0384884   DLC

Lindsey, Benjamin James, 1843–   comp.

Marblehead historical society.
Old Marblehead sea captains and the ships in which they sailed ... comp. and pub. for the benefit of the Marblehead historical society by Benjamin J. Lindsey, treasurer. [Marblehead, Mass.] 1915.

Lindsey, Bessie M
Lore of our land pictured in glass. [n. p.] 1948–
v. Illus. 24 cm.

1. Glassware—U. S. 2. Glassware—Collectors and collecting. I. Title.

NK5112.L53   748.8   48–3817*
Library of Congress

Wa WaE MtHi CaBViP
NCorniC OFH NcGU PHC PJA WaE WaS WaT Or IdB IdU MtU
NL 0384886   DLC MB CtY DLC KyHi Wa PHi IU TxU MdBP

Lindsey, Casimir Charles, 1923–
... Variation in anal fin ray count of the redside shiner, Richardsonius balteatus (Richardson)
N. p., Canadian journal of zoology, 1953.
p. [211]–225, tables, diagrs.   O.

NL 0384887   CaBViP

Lindsey, Charles, 1820–1908.
... Catalogue of the ... historical library of Charles Lindsey, F. R. S. C., of Toronto, Canada ... C. F. Libbie & co., auctioneers ... Boston, Mass. [Boston. 1895]

cover-title, 90 p. 24cm.

At head of title: Auction sale ... March 7th and 8th. 1895.
1,386 entries.

13–7047
Library of Congress   Z997.L74

NL 0384888   DLC NN

Lindsey, Charles, 1820–1908.
The clergy reserves: their history and present position, showing the systematic attempts that have been made to establish in connection with the state, a dominant church in Canada. With a full account of the rectories. Also an appendix containing Dr. Rolph's speech on the clergy reserves, delivered in 1836. By Charles Lindsay [sic] Toronto, North Amer. press, 1851. 59, xv p. 23cm.

296073B. 1. Church property—Canada.   I. Rolph, John, 1793–1870.
N. Y. P. L.   May 22. 1945

NL 0384889   NN CU NIC CaNSWA MnU CaOTP MH

Lindsey, Charles, 1820–1908.
An investigation of the unsettled boundaries of Ontario. By Charles Lindsey. Toronto, Printed by Hunter, Rose & co., 1873.

2 p. l., 250 p. 3 fold. maps. 22½cm.

"An enquiry which has for its object to trace out the western and the northern boundaries of Ontario."

1. Ontario—Bound.

14–14062
Library of Congress   F1059.B7l 7

MB CtY CaBVa CaBVaU CaBViPA
NL 0384890   DLC NBuU-L CaOTP LU CaOTU CLSU CU ICJ NN

Lindsey, Charles, 1820–1908.
The life and times of Wm. Lyon Mackenzie. With an account of the Canadian rebellion of 1837, and the subsequent frontier disturbances, chiefly from unpublished documents. By Charles Lindsey ... Philadelphia, J. W. Bradley, 1862.

2 v. in 1. fronts., plates, port. 23cm.

Vol. 2 has imprint: Toronto, C. W., P. R. Randall, 1862.

1. Mackenzie, William Lyon, 1795–1861. 2. Canada—Hist.—Rebellion, 1837–1838.

4–36343
Library of Congress   F1032.M15

CaBVa CaBVaU
NL 0384891   DLC PV CU OClWHi MiU OU OO MnHi OKentU

Lindsey, Charles, 1820–1908.
The life and times of Wm. Lyon Mackenzie. With an account of the Canadian rebellion of 1837, and the subsequent frontier disturbances, chiefly from unpublished documents. By Charles Lindsey ... Toronto, C. W., P. R. Randall, 1862.

2 v. fronts., plates, port., facsims. 22cm.

1. Mackenzie, William Lyon, 1795–1861. 2. Canada—Hist.—Rebellion, 1837–1838.

12–12545
Library of Congress   F1032.L152

InU CaOTP CaNSWA
MdBP MtU INS CtY PPT IaU MdBP OU OOxM NcU NBuHi TxU
NL 0384892   DLC CaBVaU CaBVa DSI ICN NN MH MiU-C

Lindsey, Charles, 1820–1908.
The life and times of Wm. Lyon Mackenzie. With an account of the Canadian rebellion of 1837 ...
Toronto. Pike. 1863. 2 v. in I. Portraits. Plates. Facsimile. 8°.

NL 0384893   MB NcU CSmH

Lindsey, Charles, 1820–1908.
Life and times of Wm. Lyon Mackenzie; with an account of the Canadian rebellion of 1837 & the subsequent frontier disturbances; chiefly from unpublished documents. Toronto, Randall, 1864.
2v.

NL 0384894   PU

Lindsey, Charles, 1820–1908.
The prairies of the western states: their advantages and their drawbacks. By Charles Lindsey. Toronto, Printed at the 'Leader' & 'Patriot' steam-press, 1860.

100 p. 17½cm.

1. Northwest, Old—Descr. & trav. 2. Mississippi Valley—Descr. & trav. I. Title.

18–23428
Library of Congress   F484.3.L75

NL 0384895   DLC IHi CaBVaU IU

Lindsey, Charles (1820–1908)
Prohibitory liquor laws: their practical operation in the United States. The subject discussed as a question of state policy & legislation, with suggestions for the suppression of tippling houses.
32p.   Toronto, MacLear, 1855.

NL 0384896   CaOTU

Lindsey, Charles, 1820–1908.
Rome in Canada. The ultramontane struggle for supremacy over the civil authority. By Charles Lindsey. Toronto, Lovell brothers, 1877.

4 p. l., [3]–398 p. 21½cm.

1. Catholic church in Canada. 2. Church and state in Canada.

9–25842
Library of Congress   F1035.C3L7

CtY MWA NN OU OrP CaBVa CaBVaU
NL 0384897   DLC NBuU NcU ICRL NcD WaU CaNSWA PPL CU

Lindsey, Charles, 1820–1908.
Rome in Canada. The ultramontane struggle for supremacy over the civil power. By Charles Lindsey.   Toronto: Williamson & Co., 1889.   5 p.l., xxxviii, (1)4–398 p.   [2. ed.]   8°.

1. Catholic question, Canada.   2. Church and state, Canada.
3. Title.
N. Y. P. L.   July 22. 1918.

NL 0384898   NN MtHi PPPD TxDaM-P NRU CaOTU TxU OO

Lindsey, Charles, 1820–1908.
... William Lyon Mackenzie, by Charles Lindsey; ed., with numerous additions, by G. G. S. Lindsey. Ed. de luxe. Toronto, Morang & co., limited, 1908.

xviii, 542 p. incl. front. (port.) 24cm. (The makers of Canada)

"This edition is limited to four hundred signed and numbered sets, of which this is number 196 [signed] George N. Morang."

First edition, Philadelphia and Toronto, 1862, published under title: The life and times of William Lyon Mackenzie ...

1. Mackenzie, William Lyon, 1795–1861. 2. Canada—Hist.—Rebellion, 1837–1838. I. Lindsey, George Goldwin Smith, 1860–   ed.

9–839
Library of Congress   F1032.M154

MH OCl
NL 0384899   DLC NIC OrU CaBVaU WaTC PP PPL MiU-C

971
M289
v.11

Lindsey, Charles, 1820–1908.
... William Lyon Mackenzie, by Charles Lindsey; ed., with numerous additions, by G.G.S. Lindsey. Parkman ed.   Toronto, Morang & co., 1909.
4p.l., ix-xviii, 542p. incl. front.(port.) 22cm.   (Half-title: The makers of Canada, v.11)
Series title also at head of t.-p.
1. Mackenzie, William Lyon, 1795–1861. 2. Canada – Hist. – Rebellion, 1837–1838. I. Lindsey, George Goldwin Smith, 1860–   ed.
Series (contents)

MB NN
NL 0384900   TxU OCl PU PBa NcD NBuU MiU OClWHi OU

VOLUME 334

Lindsey, Charles, 1820–1908.
.... William Lyon Mackenzie, by Charles Lindsey. Edited with numerous additions by G. G. S. Lindsey. Toronto, Morang & Co., 1910.
[4], ix–xviii, 542 p. front. (port.) 22ᶜᵐ. (*In* The makers of Canada, [vol. x].)

NL 0384901   ICJ CSmH PSt Wa MiD

Lindsey, Charles, 1820–1908.
...William Lyon Mackenzie, by ... ed., with numerous additions, by G. G. S. Lindsey. [University edition] Toronto, Morang & co., limited, 1911.
2 p. l., ix–xviii, 542 p. front. (port.) plates facsim.
(The makers of Canada. [vVI])
On cover: The struggle for responsible government.
First edition Philadelphia and Toronto, 1862, published under title: The life & time of William Lyon Mackenzie ...

NL 0384902   OCU

Lindsey, Charles, 1820–1908.
... William Lyon Mackenzie, by Charles Lindsey; ed., with numerous additions, by G. G. S. Lindsey. Toronto, Morang & co., limited, 1912.
2 p. l., ix–xviii, 542 p. front. (port.) 2 pl., facsim. 21 cm. (The makers of Canada. v. 6)
University ed.
First ed., Philadelphia and Toronto, 1862, pub. under title: The life and times of William Lyon Mackenzie ...

NL 0384903   CtY CaBVa WaS

Lindsey, Charles A
A comparison of silent reading and listening as instructional media in the teaching of certain aspects of language (field study no. 1) Ann Arbor, University Microfilms, 1951.
([University Microfilms, Ann Arbor, Mich.] Publication no. 3185)
Microfilm copy of typescript. Positive.
Collation of the original, as determined from the film: x, 165 l.
Thesis—Colorado State College of Education.
Vita.
Bibliography: leaves 51–55.
1. Language and languages—Study and teaching.
Microfilm AC-1 no. 3185   Mic 52–529

NL 0384904   DLC

Lindsey, Claude, comp.

UA24
.A1
Index

U. S. *Army. Corps of engineers.*
... Index to the reports of the chief of engineers, U. S. Army (including the reports of the Isthmian canal commissions, (1899–1914) 1866–1912 ... Completed under the direction of Brig. Gen. Dan C. Kingman, chief of engineers, U. S. Army, by Colonel George A. Zinn, Corps of engineers. John McClure, compiler ... Washington, Govt. print. off., 1915–16.

Lindsey, Coleman, 1892–
The courts of Louisiana, by Coleman Lindsey. [Baton Rouge, La., Thos. J. Moran's sons, *1939]
79 p. diagrs. 23½ᵐ.

1. Courts—Louisiana.   I. Title.
39–14671

NL 0384906   DLC

Lindsey, Coleman, 1892–
Elections in Louisiana, by Coleman Lindsey. Baton Rouge, Louisiana state Dept. of education, 1940.
vi, 125 p. 23½ᵐ.

1. Election law—Louisiana.   I. Title.
Library of Congress   JK1963.L8L55   40–5799
———— Copy 2.
Copyright A 139023   [2]   324.763

NL 0384907   DLC

Lindsey, Coleman, 1892–
The government of Louisiana, by Coleman Lindsey. [Baton Rouge, La., *1937]
78 p. 24ᵐ.

1. Louisiana—Pol. & govt.   I. Title.
Library of Congress   JK4725.1937.L5   37–9659 Revised
———— Copy 2.
Copyright A 105917   [r39d2]   342.763

NL 0384908   DLC

Law   Lindsey, Coleman, 1892–   comp.

Louisiana. *Laws, statutes, etc.*
Laws of the state of Louisiana relating to banks, savings banks, safe deposit and trust banks, credit unions and small loan companies. Issued by Wilfred J. Begnaud, state bank commissioner. Comp., annotated and indexed by Coleman Lindsey, John H. Cassidy, Jr. [and] Wallace W. Rheams. [Baton Rouge] 1946.

HG2133
.L8A5
1947

Lindsey, Coleman, 1892–   comp.

Louisiana. *Laws, statutes, etc.*
Laws of the State of Louisiana relating to building and loan and homestead associations. Issued by Wilfred J. Begnaud, state bank commissioner. Comp., annotated and indexed by Coleman Lindsey, John H. Cassidy, Jr. [and] Wallace W. Rheams. [Baton Rouge] 1947.

Lindsey, Coleman, 1892–
The legislature of Louisiana, by Coleman Lindsey. [Baton Rouge, La., *1938]
58 p. 24ᵐ.

1. Louisiana. General assembly.   I. Title.
Library of Congress   JK4767.1938.L5   38–14790 Revised
———— Copy 2.
Copyright A 118089   [r39d2]   328.763

NL 0384911   DLC

YA
15183

Lindsey, Daniel Weisiger, 1835–
Papers and evidence in regard to purchase of the Adjutant General' report also report from Senate finance committee and protest of Gen. D. W. Lindsey
Frankfort Ky., 1868   55p

NL 0384912   DLC

Lindsey, Daniel Weisiger, 1835–

Kentucky. *Adjutant-general's office.*
Report of the adjutant general of the state of Kentucky. Printed by authority of the Legislature of Kentucky ... 1861–1866. Frankfort, Ky., Printed at the Kentucky yeoman office, 1866–67.

Lindsey, David, 1566?–1627.
   see   Lindsay, David, 1566?–1627.

Lindsey, David, 1914–
Ohio's Western Reserve, the story of its place names. Cleveland, Press of Western Reserve University and the Western Reserve Historical Society, 1955.
vii, 111 p. illus., maps. 24 cm.

1. Names, Geographical—Ohio—Western Reserve.   I. Title.
F497.W5L5   *917.71 929.4   55–9668

OC1GC OU TxU NN OOxM ODW PPT PP
NL 0384915   DLC OO OC1WHi Or ICN MoU C ICU OC1W OC1

Lindsey, David, 1914–
An outline history of Ohio. [Ann Arbor? 1953]
67 p. 22 cm.

1. Ohio—Hist.
F491.L5   977.1   53–36022

ODW
NL 0384916   DLC OO OC1WHi OU OOxM OO OC1W OC1U OC1

F9999   Lindsey, David, 1914–
Samuel Sullivan Cox, 1824–1889. 1950.
391 l.
Typewritten.
Thesis—Univ. of Chicago.

1. Cox, Samuel Sullivan, 1824–1889.

NL 0384917   ICU

Lindsey, D[avid] P[hilip].
The compend of takigrafy the new fonetic short-hand, containing a summary of the principles of the simple style. New York, D. Kimball, 1879.
34 p., 1 l. 12°.

NL 0384918   NN

Lindsey, Douglas.
Alaska. A complete book of reference and guide to Alaska, with three maps, the latest mining laws and all necessary information in regard to outfits, distances, rates of fare, etc. By Douglas Lindsey. Stockton, Cal., T. W. Hummel, 1897.
24 p. front. (fold. map) illus. 12½ᵐ.
Date of copyright on p. 2 and "Table of distances" on p. 3 of cover.

1. Alaska—Descr. & trav.   2. Gold mines and mining—Alaska. 3. Mining law—U. S.
Library of Congress   F909.L75   1–15762

NL 0384919   DLC ICN WaU

W 4A   LINDSEY, Douglas, 1919–
qL752c   Cancer in the army. [New Haven]
1950   1950.
259 l.
Thesis (Doctor of Public Health) – Yale Univ.
Typewritten copy.
1. Cancer

NL 0384920   DNLM

VOLUME 334

W 4A   LINDSEY, Douglas, 1919–
L752h   Housing standards of the Army.
1948   ₍New Haven, Conn.₎ 1948.
     81 ℓ.   illus.
     Thesis (Master of Public Health) –
Yale Univ.
     Contains author's signature.
     1. Autographs - Lindsey, Douglas,
1919–   2. Housing

NL   0384921   DNLM

₍Lindsey, E   D ₎
   French flats. ₍New York, Sutton, 18--₎
6, ₍2₎ p. 23ᵐ.

   E. D. Lindsey and Douglas Smyth, architects.

   1. Apartment houses - New York (City)
I. Smyth, Douglas   Joint author
II. Title.

NL   0384922   NNC

Lindsey, E   G.
   A history of the events which transpired during the Navy
Island campaign: to which is added the correspondence of dif-
ferent public officers, with the affidavits of individuals in the
United States and Canada. By E. G. Lindsey. Lewiston
₍N. Y.₎ J. A. Harrison, printer, 1838.
   40 p. 23½ᵐ.
   Imperfect: p. 11-14, 19-22, 25-32 wanting. Mutilated and discolored.

   1. Navy Island campaign, 1837-1838.

                         2—10624
Library of Congress   F1032.L75

NL   0384923   DLC PPL

Lindsey, E   G   novelist.
   Marie; or, Fort Beauharnois; an historic tale of early
days in the Northwest, by E. G. L. Minneapolis, Minn.,
A. C. Bausman ₍1893₎
   4 p. l., ₍7₎-176 p., 1 l., iv p. pl. 20½ᵐ.

                         7–19013†
Library of Congress   PZ3.L6535M

NL   0384924   DLC CU

Lindsey, Edward, 1872–
   Appeals in homicide cases in Pennsylvania 1905-
1910. 1910.
   Pamphlet vol 286, no 1.

NL   0384925   PPB

Lindsey, Edward, 1872–
   Indeterminate sentence
       see under   American Institute of
Criminal Law and Criminology.

Lindsey, Edward, 1872–
   The International court, by Edward Lindsey. New York,
Thomas Y. Crowell company ₍1931₎
   xix, 347 p. 22½ᵐ.

   1. Hague. Permanent court of international justice. 2. International
law—Hist. 3. Arbitration, International—Hist.   I. Title.
            ₍Full name: Edward Sherman Lindsey₎
Library of Congress   JX1971.5.L55   31–21228
             ₍a45g1₎   341.1

Or CaBVa
NN OC1 OO OU MiHM ViU-L ViU OrP OrPR WaS OrSaW OrU
NL   0384927   DLC PJB MH-L MB OKentU NjN PPT PPGi NcD

Lindsey, Edward, 1872–
   The juvenile court movement from a lawyer's standpoint. By Edward Lindsey.
   From Annals of the American academy of standpoint
(political and social science), Philadelphia, v. 52.
1914.

NL   0384928   DL

Lindsey, Edward Delano
   Class ode.
   (In Harvard university--Class of 1862. The
Baccalaureate sermon ... Cambridge, 1862.
p [51])

NL   0384929   RPB

Lindsey, Edward Sherman.
     see   Lindsey, Edward, 1872–

Lindsey, Edwin Samuel, 1897–
   Centennial history of St. Paul's Episcopal Church, Chattanooga, Tennessee, 1853–1953. ₍Chattanooga₎ Vestry of St.
Paul's Parish, 1953.
   190 p. illus. 25 cm.

   1. Chattanooga, Tenn. St. Paul's Episcopal Church.   I. Title.

   BX5980.C33S3   283.768   53–19894 ‡

NL   0384931   DLC AU

Lindsey, Edwin Samuel, 1897–
   The music of the songs in Fletcher's plays, by Edwin S.
Lindsey ... ₍Chapel Hill, N. C., The University press, 1924₎
   cover-title, 325–355 p. 23 cm.
   Music: p. 331, 353.
   "Reprinted from Studies in philology, XXI, 2, April, 1924."

   1. Fletcher, John, 1579–1625. 2. Music—Hist. & crit.—17th cent.
3. Songs, English—Hist. & crit.   I. Title.

   ML80.F5L45   24–20755 rev

NL   0384932   DLC OU NN

Lindsey, Edwin Samuel, 1897– Chapel Hill, 1923.
Music of the songs in the Elizabethan drama.

NL   0384933   NcU

Lindsey, Edwin Samuel, 1897–
   The original music for Beaumont's play
The knight of the burning pestle, by ...
(In studies in philology. 1929. v. 27,
p. 425–443)

NL   0384934   OU

Lindsey, Edwin Samuel, 1897– Chapel Hill, 1921.
Relation of Spenser to Sidney.

NL   0384935   NcU

₍Lindsey, Edwin Thomas₎ 1876–
   Our presidents. ₍Memphis, S. C. Toof & company, ᶜ1941₎
   ₍40₎ p. col. illus. (ports.) 28 x 22ᵐ.

   1. Presidents—U. S.—Biog. 2. Presidents—U. S.—Portraits.
I. Title.

                       42–5014
Library of Congress   E176.1.L53
             ..   923.173

NL   0384936   DLC

Lindsey, Forrest R   1903–
   Pipefitters handbook. New York, Industrial Press ₍1953₎
   282 p. illus. 17 cm.

   1. Pipe-fitting.   I. Title.

   TH6711.L5   696.102   53–3296 ‡

   MB WaT Wa WaS OrP ICJ Or OrCS WaE
NL   0384937   DLC NN ViU ICJ NcC PP TxU NcD PSt OC1

Lindsey, Frank E   G

   The secret of making $8640.00 per year or
$30.00 per day! Great secret of alchemy re-
vealed! Gold and silver. ₍Dated₎ Ravens
Nest, Washington Co., Va., 1862. ₍n.p., 1862
broadside ₍3 p.₎ 25 x 39ᶜᵐ. fold. to 25 x 10ᶜᵐ

   1. Alchemy. 2. Gold. 3. Silver. I. Title.
II. Title:Great secret of alchemy revealed.

NL   0384938   ViU

Lindsey, Frederick Brooks.
   The spirit Prospero, and other poems, by Frederick
Brooks Lindsey. Boston, Sherman, French & company,
1912.
   3 p. l., 99 p. 19¼ᶜᵐ. $1.00

   I. Title.

                      13–1594
Library of Congress   PS3523.I6S7 1912

NL   0384939   DLC OO MB NN

Lindsey, George
   Pens and papier mache, ...

   (In Bevan, G. P., ed. British manufacturing
industries. London, 1876-77. 17 cm. [v.3] p.
TS57   151-180)
.B8

NL   0384940   DLC

Lindsey, George.
   Pens and papier mâché, ammunition, percussion caps and cartridges,
anchors and chain cables.
   (In British manufacturing industries. 2d edition. Vol. 3, pp.
151-208. London. 1878.)
   Two copies.

   F6557 — Pens. — Papier mâché. -- ... ors. — Ammunition. — Chain cables.
   — Cartridges.

NL   0384941   MB

VOLUME 334

D
919
C3
Lindsey, George Goldwin Smith, 1860–
Cricket across the sea; or, The wanderings and matches of the gentlemen of Canada, 1887, by two of the vagrants ¿George Goldwin Smith Lindsey and Dyce W. Saunders¿ Toronto, J. Murray, 1887.
223 p.

Bound with Callan, Hugh. Wanderings on wheel and on foot through Europe. London, 1887.

NL 0384942   CaOTU

TA1c
.P35
no. 30
Lindsey, Glen Aven, 1902–

Walker, Elton David.
Studies at the sewage treatment plant, the Pennsylvania state college, by Elton D. Walker, Glen A. Lindsey ¿and¿ Philip M. Jones ... State College, Pa., 1930.

Lindsey, Glen Aven, 1902–
Variation in bacteria, by Glen Aven Lindsey ... Urbana, Ill., 1928.
7 p. 23ᶜᵐ.
Abstract of thesis (PH. D.)—University of Illinois, 1928.
Vita.
"References": p. ¿8¿

1. Bacteria. 2. Variation (Biology)

Library of Congress   QR84.L5 1928   28-19486

NL 0384944   DLC OU

Lindsey, Hargrove.
Random, rambling rippling rhymes and rosy reflections. n.p., 1927.
[49] p. front. (port) 25 cm.
Cover title.

NL 0384945   RPB

Lindsey, Helen Bradley
Early days in Campbell County, Kentucky, 1790–1850. [Frankfort, 1928]
8p. 8°

(Reprint from Reg. of Ky. Hist. Soc., 1928)

NL 0384946   MWA

Lindsey, Helen Bradley.
Early settlers in Campbell County, Ky. Lindsey—McPike—Noble. By Helen Bradley Lindsey, Newport, Ky. ¿n. p., 1927?¿
p. 9–22. 25½ᶜᵐ.

1. Lindsay family.

CA 29-28 Unrev'd

Library of Congress   CS71.L753 1927

NL 0384947   DLC ICN Or MWA NN OClWHi

976.902
3829
No. 3
Lindsey, Helen Bradley
Leitch Station in Campbell county, Kentucky. ¿Frankfort, Ky., 1938¿

8p. Map. 25.5cm.

Reprinted from Kentucky State Historical Register, v.36 (Oct.,1938) p. 359–364.

1. Ky.–Campbell county. I Title.

NL 0384948   KyHi KyU

Lindsey, Helen B[radley]
Thomas Noble Lindsey and descendants. [Frankfort, 1928]
8p. 8°

(Reprint from Reg. of Ky. Hist. Soc., 1928)

NL 0384949   MWA

Lindsey, Henry C
Call me Penny, a comedy in three acts.
New York, S. French ¿c1952¿
58,¿1¿ p. diagr. 19 cm.

NL 0384950   RPB OrCS

Lindsey, Henry C.
Forever Judy; a comedy in one act.
New York, French ¿c1953¿
23 p. diagr. 19 cm.

NL 0384951   N RPB NN OrCS

Lindsey, Henry C.
Mr. Sweeney's conversion, a domestic comedy in one act. New York, French [c1955]
22, [1] p. diag. 19 cm.

NL 0384952   RPB NN

LINDSEY,J.S.
A brief Tudor-Stuart book-list; being alphabetical and classified lists of English works of general interest,bearing on British history,1485–1714,with particulars of dates and prices and various editions and schemes of study,prepared for the use of teachers and elementary students of history. Cambridge, [Eng.],W.Heffer and sons,ltd.,etc.,etc.,1914.

4°. pp.(4),28.
(LINDSEY historical series.) Br 55.64

NL 0384953   MH

Lindsey, J S.
Certificate note-book of European history, 1814–1848; a course of study containing thirty-two typical questions arranged in the form of eight one-hour test papers with full answers, hints, and references, also, brief survey of the period, hints on answering questions in history, suggestive notes and queries on teaching history, select list of books useful to the teacher and learner, notable topics and sayings of the period, short biographies and a vocabulary; by J. S. Lindsey ... Cambridge, Heffer & sons, 1902.
viii, 48 p. 26½ᶜᵐ.
Subject entries: Europe   —Hist.—Outlines, syllabi, etc.

2-21897

NL 0384954   DLC CtY

Lindsey, J S
... London matriculation test-papers in English history, being all the questions on this subject for matriculation at London university June 1888–January 1902. Arranged ... by J.S. Lindsey.   Cambridge, W. Heffer & sons, 1902.
Pamphlet. (The Lindsey historical series)

NL 0384955   CtY

LINDSEY,J.   S.
The student's guide to British history. Pts. I–IV. A class-book containing a scheme of study based on the best books,outline sketch,chronological synopses,[etc.].   Cambridge,Heffer and Sons,etc.,etc.,1905.

26 cm.
"Extracted for pupils' use from the second volume of Problems and exercises in British history."
Contnets:–1–1v.Mediaeval British history from the earliest times to   the accession of Henry VIII.

NL 0384956   MH

Lindsey, J S
A student's note-book of European history, 1789–1848. A course of study containing sixty-four typical questions arranged in the form of sixteen one-hour test-papers with full answers, hints, and references, also brief survey of the period, geographico-chronological synopsis ... pt [1–2]   Cambridge, Heffer & Sons, 1904.
2 pts. in 1 v.   4°.

NL 0384957   NN

Lindsey, J W of Delaware, O.
... The financial key to prosperity, by J. W. Lindsey ... Delaware, O., Social science bureau, 1897.
cover-title, 64 p. 18ᶜᵐ.

1. Currency question—U. S.

Library of Congress   HG529.L75   6-20799†

NL 0384958   DLC

Lindsey, Jessie M   (Higbee)
Hawaiian pedigree chart, compiled by Corporal Jessie M. (Higbee) Lindsey ... ¿n. p., 1943.
geneal. tab. 36½ x 50½ᶜᵐ.
Photostat reproduction (positive)
The Hawaiian ancestry of the Lindsey family, descended from James Fay and Kaipukai Laula Kahahana.
Includes a bibliography.

1. Lindsay family.   I. Title.

Library of Congress   CS2209.L5   44-31797

NL 0384959   DLC

Pam
68-1911
Lindsey, Jim T.
THE TEXAS LEGISLATIVE COUNCIL. [n.p., 1950?]
[15] p.

Cover title.
Reprint from the Baylor Law Review, Spring 1950.

NL 0384960   WHi

Lindsey, John, *pseud.*
see
Muriel, John St. Clair, 1909–

VOLUME 334

Lindsey, John, 1788-1858.
A discourse,delivered before the honorable
legislature of Vermont,on the anniversary
election,October 10,1822. By John Lindsey ...
Montpelier,Vt., Printed by E.P.Walton, 1822.

27 p.   21.3cm.

No.16 in calf vol.labeled "Sermons."

1.Election sermons-Vermont.

NL 0384962   MiU-C NN

LD
2668
R4
1955
L752

Lindsey, John Albert.
Review of research pertaining to
dairy cattle management.
71 l.   (K.S.U. Master's Report, 1955)

NL 0384963   KMK

Lindsey, John Berrien.

Mitchell, S[amuel] Augustus.
... A system of modern geography ... By S. Augustus Mitchell ... Rev. ed. ... Philadelphia, J. H. Butler & co., 1879.

Lindsey, John Clark, 1875-   joint author.
Hunkins, Ralph Valentine, 1890-
South Dakota, its past, present, and future, by Ralph V. Hunkins ... and John Clark Lindsey ... New York, The Macmillan company, 1932.

Lindsey, John Hathaway, 1870-
English-French glossary of x-ray terms
see under title

Lindsey, John Hathaway, 1870-   comp.
Medical quotations from English prose [by] John H. Lindsey ... Boston, R. G. Badger [1924]
298 p. front., ports., facsim. 21½cm.

CONTENTS.— Sir John Mandeville.— Sir Thomas More.— Francis Bacon.—Robert Burton.—Sir Thomas Browne.—Samuel Pepys.—Jonathan Swift.—George Berkeley.—Laurence Sterne.

1. Medicine—Anecdotes, facetiae, satire, etc. 2. Quotations, English. I. Title.

Library of Congress   R705.L6   24—20663

NL 0384967   DLC DNLM OC1 OU MBCo KU-M ViU ICJ OrCS

Lindsey, Joseph Bridgeo, 1862-
Balanced rations for business cows. n. t.-p. n. p. [190-?]
2 l. 12°. (Massachusetts. Agricultural Experiment Station.)

NL 0384968   NN

Lindsey, Joseph Bridgeo, 1862-
... Balanced rations for dairy stock. By J. B. Lindsey. [Amherst, Mass.] 1911.
7 p. 25cm. (Massachusetts. Agricultural experiment station, Amherst, 1888- Circular no. 30)

"In co-operation with the State board of agriculture."

1. Feeding and feeding stuffs. II. Title.   I. Massachusetts.   State board of agriculture.

Title from Mass. Agr   College. Printed by L. C.

NL 0384969   MU

Lindsey, J[oseph] B[ridgeo], 1862-
Balanced rations for dairy stock.   Boston: Wright & Potter Prtg. Co., 1914. 11 p. 8°. (Massachusetts. Agriculture Board. Circular 3.)

Supplanting Nature leaflet no. 42.

1. Cow.—Feeding, U. S.: Mass.
N. Y. P. L.   November 3, 1916.

NL 0384970   NN MB

Lindsey, Joseph Bridgeo, 1862-
The calcium requirements of dairy heifers. By J. B. Lindsey ... J. G. Archibald ... and P. R. Nelson ...
(In U. S. Dept. of agriculture. Journal of agricultural research. v. 42, no. 12, June 15, 1931, p. 883-896. illus., diagrs. 23½cm. Washington, 1931)
Contribution from Massachusetts agricultural experiment station (Mass.—29)
Contribution no. 112 of the Massachusetts agricultural experiment station.
Published July 11, 1931.

1. Calcium [in animal nutrition] 2. Cows. 3. Feeding and feeding stuffs. [2. 3. Cows, Dairy—Feeding] I. Archibald, John Geddie, 1894- joint author. II. Nelson, Paul Redfield, 1903- joint author. III. [Title]

Library, U. S. Dept. of   Agr 31-973
Library of Congress   Agriculture 1Ag84J vol. 42, no. 12
                           [S21.A75 vol. 42, no. 12]
                                    [5*]

NL 0384971   DNAL

Lindsey, Joseph Bridgeo, 1862-

Beals, Carlos Loring, 1889-
Chemical composition, digestibility, and feeding value of vegetable-ivory meal. By C. L. Beals and J. B. Lindsey ...
(In U. S. Dept. of agriculture. Journal of agricultural research. vol. VII, no. 7, p. 301-320 incl. tables. 26cm. Washington, 1916)

1587   Lindsey, Joseph Bridgeo, 1862-
25   ...Compilations of analyses, by J. B. Lindsey, H. D. Haskins, P. H. Smith, and C. L. Beals ... Amherst, Mass., Agricultural experiment station, 1919.
101 p. tables. 23cm. (Massachusetts. Agricultural experiment station, Amherst. Special bulletin, November, 1919)

Exchange?   Est. 30¢; binding 20¢.

NL 0384973   OrCS

Lindsey, Joseph Bridgeo, 1862-
I. The composition, digestibility and feeding value of alfalfa. II. The value of corn bran for milk production, by J. B. Lindsey and C. L. Beals ... Amherst, Mass., 1918.
p. [105]-153. 23cm. (Massachusetts. Agricultural experiment station, 1888- Bulletin no. 186)

1. Alfalfa. 2. [Bran]   I. Beals, Carlos Loring, 1889- joint author.
                                    A 19-1011
Title from Mass. Agr.   College. Printed by L. C.

NL 0384974   MU

Lindsey, Joseph Bridgeo, 1862-
... The composition, digestibility and feeding value of molassine meal, cottonseed meal and hulls, cocoa shells, grain screenings, flax shives, Mellen's food refuse, and Postum cereal residue (CXX feed) by J. B. Lindsey and P. H. Smith ... Amherst, Mass., 1914.
2 p. l., p. [53]-71. 24cm. (Massachusetts. Agricultural experiment station, 1888- Bulletin no. 158)

1. Feeding and feeding stuffs.   I. Smith, Philip Henry, 1876- joint author.
                                    A 15-1592
Title from Mass. Agr.   College. Printed by L. C.

NL 0384975   MU PP NN

Lindsey, Joseph Bridgeo, 1862-
... The composition, digestibility and feeding value of pumpkins ... Amherst, Mass., 1917.
2 p. l., p. [55]-71 incl. tables. 23cm. (Massachusetts. Agricultural experiment station, Amherst, 1888- Bulletin no. 174)

1. Feeding and feeding stuffs.   I. Title.
                                    A 18-245
Title from Mass. Agr.   College. Printed by L. C.

NL 0384976   MU

Lindsey, Joseph Bridgeo, 1862-
Concentrated feeds.   Amherst: Press of Carpenter & Moorehouse, 1903. 51(1) p. 8°. (Massachusetts. Hatch Experiment Station. Bulletin 93.)

1. Fodder.—Analysis, U. S.: Mass.
N. Y. P. L.   September 4, 1912.

NL 0384977   NN

[Lindsey, Joseph Bridgeo] 1862-
... Condimental stock and poultry foods. [By Joseph B. Lindsey] ... Amherst, Mass., Press of Carpenter & Morehouse, 1905.
24 p. 24cm. (Massachusetts. Agricultural experiment station, Amherst, 1888- Bulletin no. 106)

At head of title: Hatch experiment station of the Massachusetts agricultural college.
"The examination of the various condimental foods ... was largely under the supervision of Mr. E. B. Holland ... assisted by Mr. P. H. Smith and Mr. W. E. Tottingham. The microscopic work was executed by Mr. A. V. Osmun."

1. [Poultry—Feeding]   I. Holland, Edward Bertram, 1876-
                                    A 15-1491
Title from Mass. Agr.   College. Printed by L. C.

NL 0384978   MU NN

[Lindsey, Joseph Bridgeo] 1862-
... The cost of testing pure bred cows. (Supplementary to Circular no. 7) [By J. B. Lindsey] [Amherst, Mass.] 1908.
[2] p. 25cm. (Massachusetts. Agricultural experiment station, Amherst, 1888- Circular no. 15)
Caption title.

1. Milk—Analysis and examination.   I. Title.
                                    A 15-1398
Title from Mass. Agr.   College. Printed by L. C.

NL 0384979   MU

Lindsey, Joseph Bridgeo, 1862-
... Cottonseed meal. [By] J. B. Lindsey and P. H. Smith. [Amherst, Mass.] 1907.
8 numb. l. 25cm. (Massachusetts. Agricultural experiment station, Amherst, 1888- Circular no. 1)
Caption title.

1. [Cotton seed meal]   I. Smith, Philip Henry, joint author.
                                    A 15-1384
Title from Mass. Agr.   College. Printed by L. C.

NL 0384980   MU

VOLUME 334

Lindsey, Joseph Bridgeo, 1862–
... Cottonseed meal. By J. B. Lindsey. ₁Amherst, Mass.₎ 1909.

7 p. illus. 25ᶜᵐ. (Massachusetts. Agricultural experiment station, Amherst, 1888–   Circular no. 25 (rev. of no. 1))
Caption title.

1. ₁Cotton-seed meal₎   A 15–1407

Title from Mass. Agr.   College. Printed by L. C.

NL 0384981   MU NN

₁**Lindsey, Joseph Bridgeo**₎ 1862–
... The dairy law and its results ₁by Joseph B. Lindsey₎ Amherst, Mass., Press of Carpenter & Morehouse, 1903.

14 p. illus. 23ᶜᵐ. (Massachusetts. Agricultural experiment station, Amherst, 1888–   Special bulletin, July, 1903)
At head of title: Hatch experiment station of the Massachusetts agricultural college.
CONTENTS.—A. Dairy law.—B. Inspection of glassware, by Joseph B. Lindsey.—C. Inspection of Babcock machines, by Nathan J. Hunting.—D. Babcock test by Edward B. Holland.—E. Creameries and milk deposits in Massachusetts.

1. Dairy laws.   I. Massachusetts. Laws, statutes, etc. II. Hunting, Nathan J. III. Holland, Edward Bertram.   A 15–1359

Title from Mass. Agr.   College. Printed by L. C.

NL 0384982   MU

Lindsey, Joseph Bridges, 1862–
The dairy problem.
= Amherst. 1917. ₍2₎ pp. [Massachusetts Agricultural College. Extension service. Extension circular no. 33.] 23 cm.
Deals with the feeding of cows.

L2184 — Feeding of animals. — Cows. — S.r.c.

NL 0384983   MB

Lindsey, Joseph Bridgeo, 1862–
The digestibility and energy values of feeds for horses. By J. B. Lindsey, C. L. Beals, and J. G. Archibald.

(*In* U. S. Dept. of agriculture. Journal of agricultural research. vol. XXXII, no. 6, March 15, 1926, p. 569–604. illus. 23ᶜᵐ. Washington, 1926)
Contribution from Massachusetts agricultural experiment station (Mass.—14)
Published March 13, 1926.
"Literature cited": p. 603–604.

1. ₁Feeding stuffs—Digestibility₎ 2. ₁Feeding stuffs—Energy value₎ 3. Feeding and feeding stuffs. ₍3. Horses—Feeding₎ I. Archibald, John Geddie, 1894–   joint author. II. Beals, Carlos Loring, 1889–   joint author.   Agr 26–903

Library, U. S. Dept. of   Agriculture 1Ag84J vol. 32

NL 0384984   DNAL

Lindsey, Joseph Bridgeo, 1862–
... The digestibility of cattle foods, by J. B. Lindsey and P. H. Smith ... Amherst, Mass., 1914.

2 p. l., p. ₁79₎–120. 24ᶜᵐ. (Massachusetts. Agricultural experiment station, Amherst, 1888–   Bulletin no. 152)

1. Cattle. 2. Feeding and feeding stuffs. ₍1, 2. Cattle — Feeding₎ I. Smith, Philip Henry, 1876–   joint author. II. Title.   A 15–1586

Title from Mass. Agr.   College. Printed by L. C.

NL 0384985   MU NN

Lindsey, Joseph Bridgeo, 1862–
... Digestion experiments with cattle feeds, by J. B. Lindsey, C. L. Beals, P. B. Smith and J. G. Archibald. Amherst, Mass., 1923.

2, ₍54₎–62 p. tables. 23ᶜᵐ. (Massachusetts. Agricultural experiment station, 1888–   Bulletin no. 216)

1. Cattle. 2. Feeding and feeding stuffs. I. Beals, Carlos Loring, 1889–   joint author. II. Smith, Philip Henry, 1876–   joint author. III. Archibald, John Geddes, 1894–   joint author. IV. Title.
     A 23–2242

Title from Mass. Agr.   College. Printed by L. C.

₍4₎

NL 0384986   MU

Lindsey, Joseph Bridgeo, 1862–
... Digestion experiments with sheep, by J. B. Lindsey, C. L. Beals and P. H. Smith ... Amherst, Mass., 1917.

2 p. l., p. ₁241₎–335 incl. tables. 23ᶜᵐ. (Massachusetts. Agricultura experiment station, Amherst, 1888–   Bulletin no. 181)

1. Feeding and feeding stuffs. 2. Sheep. I. Beals, Carlos Loring, 1889–   II. Smith, Philip Henry, 1876–   III. Title.
     A 18–549

Title from Mass. Agr.   College. Printed by L. C.

NL 0384987   MU

₁**Lindsey, Joseph Bridgeo**₎ 1862–
... Distillery and brewery by-products. ₁By Joseph B. Lindsey, with the cooperation of E. B. Holland and P. H. Smith₎ ... Amherst, Mass., Press of Carpenter & Morehouse, 1904.

28 p. illus. 24ᶜᵐ. (Massachusetts. Agricultural experiment station, Amherst, 1888–   Bulletin no. 94)
At head of title: Hatch experiment station of the Massachusetts agricultural college.

1. ₁Brewing industries — By-products₎ 2. ₁Distilling industries — By-products₎ I. Holland, Edward Bertram, 1872–   II. Smith, Philip Henry, 1876–   III. Title.
     A 15–1486

Title from Mass. Agr.   College. Printed by L. C.

NL 0384988   MU

₁**Lindsey, Joseph Bridgeo**₎ 1862–
... I. Dried molasses-beet-pulp. ₁By Joseph B. Lindsey, with E. B. Holland, P. H. Smith and J. G. Cook₎ II. The nutrition of horses. ₁By J. B. Lindsey and P. H. Smith₎ ... Amherst, Mass., Press of Carpenter & Morehouse, 1904.

16 p. illus. 24ᶜᵐ. (Massachusetts. Agricultural experiment station, Amherst, 1888–   Bulletin, no. 99)
At head of title: Hatch experiment station of the Massachusetts agricultural college.

1. ₁Horse—Feeding₎ I. Holland, Edward Bertram, 1872–   II. Smith, Philip Henry, 1876–   III. Cook, J. G.
     A 15–1489

Title from Mass. Agr.   College. Printed by L. C

NL 0384989   MU NN

₁**Lindsey, Joseph Bridgeo**₎ 1862–
... Economic feeding of milch cows. ₁By Joseph B. Lindsey₎ ... Amherst, Mass., Press of Carpenter & Morehouse, 1896.

21, ₍1₎ p., 1 l. 24ᶜᵐ. (Massachusetts. Agricultural experiment station, Amherst, 1888–   Bulletin no. 39)
At head of title: Hatch experiment station of the Massachusetts agricultural college.

1. ₁Cattle—Feeding₎ I. Title.
     A 15–1461

Title from Mass. Agr.   College. Printed by L. C.

NL 0384990   MU

₁**Lindsey, Joseph Bridgeo**₎ 1862–
... The examination of cattle and poultry foods. ₁By Joseph B. Lindsey with the cooperation of E. B. Holland, P. H. Smith and L. S. Walker₎ ... Amherst, Mass., Press of Carpenter & Morehouse, 1907.

58, ₍2₎ p. 24ᶜᵐ. (Massachusetts. Agricultural experiment station, Amherst, 1888–   Bulletin no. 112)
At head of title: Hatch experiment station of the Massachusetts agricultural college.

1. Feeding and feeding-stuffs. I. Holland, Edward Bertram, 1872–   II. Smith, Philip Henry, 1876–   III. Walker, Lewell Seth.
     A 15–1493

Title from Mass. Agr.   College. Printed by L. C.

NL 0384991   MU NN

Lindsey, Joseph Bridgeo, 1862–
... The feeding value of apple pomace. ₁By J. B. Lindsey. ₁Amherst, Mass.₎ 1914.

4 p. 23ᶜᵐ. (Massachusetts. Agricultural experiment station, Amherst, 1888–   Circular no. 47)
Caption title.

1. Feeding and feeding stuffs. I. Title: Apple pomace, The feeding value of.   A 15–1429

Title from Mass. Agr.   College. Printed by L. C.

NL 0384992   MU

Lindsey, Joseph Bridgeo, 1862–
The feeding value of corn stover.

(*In* U. S. Dept. of agriculture. Yearbook, 1896, p. 353–360. 23ᶜᵐ. Washington, 1897)

1. Corn stover.   Agr 7—759

U. S. Dept. of agr. Library
for Library of Congress   ₍a43c1₎

NL 0384993   DNAL

₁**Lindsey, Joseph Bridgeo**₎ 1862–
... The feeding value of salt marsh hay. ₁By J. B. Lindsey and B. K. Jones₎ ... Amherst, Mass., Press of Carpenter & Morehouse, 1898.

48 p. illus. 24ᶜᵐ. (Massachusetts. Agricultural experiment station, Amherst, 1888–   Bulletin no. 50)
At head of title: Hatch experiment station of the Massachusetts agricultural college.
"The laboratory work ... was performed ... by E. B. Holland and F. W. Mossman."

1. Feeding and feeding stuffs. 2. Hay. I. Jones, Benjamin Kent, joint author. II. Title: Salt marsh hay.
     A 15–1468

Title from Mass. Agr.   College. Printed by L. C.

NL 0384994   MU

Lindsey, Joseph Bridgeo, 1862–
... Green crops for summer soiling, by J. B. Lindsey ... ₁Amherst, Mass.₎ 1910.

20 p. 24ᶜᵐ. (Massachusetts. Agricultural experiment station, Amherst, 1888–   Bulletin no. 133)

1. Feeding and feeding stuffs. I. Title.
     A 15–1508

Title from Mass. Agr.   College. Printed by L. C.

NL 0384995   MU NN

Lindsey, Joseph Bridgeo, 1862–
How the agricultural college and experiment station benefit the farmer. By Dr. J. B. Lindsey ... Amherst₎ Mass., 1896₎₎

22 p. 22½ᶜᵐ.
Caption title.

1. Massachusetts. Agricultural college, Amherst. 2. Massachusetts. Agricultural experiment station, Amherst. I. Title.
     E 15–2896 Revised

Library, U. S. Bur. of   Education S537.M4L6
     ₍r23c2₎

NL 0384996   DHEW

Lindsey, Joseph Bridgeo, 1862–

Massachusetts. Agricultural experiment station, *Amherst,* 1888–
... Inspection of concentrates ... Amherst, Mass., Press of Carpenter & Morehouse, 1904–06.

VOLUME 334

[Lindsey, Joseph Bridgeo] 1862–
... Market milk. [By J. B. Lindsey and P. H. Smith] ... Amherst, Mass., Press of Carpenter & Morehouse, 1906.
48 p. illus. 24ᶜᵐ. (Massachusetts. Agricultural experiment station, Amherst, 1888– Bulletin no. 110)
At head of title: Hatch experiment station of the Massachusetts agricultural college.

1. Milk. I. Smith, Philip Henry, 1876– joint author. II. Title.
A 15–1492

NL 0384998 MU NN

Lindsey, Joseph Bridgeo, 1862–
... Milk substitutes for calves. By J. B. Lindsey and J. G Archibald ... Amherst, Mass., 1929.
p. [115]–122. tables. 22ᶜᵐ. (Massachusetts. Agricultural experiment station, 1888– Bulletin no. 253)

1. Calves. 2. Feeding and feeding stuffs. I. Archibald, John Geddes, 1894– joint author. II. Title.
[873.E4 no. 253] A 30–58

Title from Mass. Agr. College. Printed by L. C.
[3]

NL 0384999 MU

Lindsey, Joseph Bridgeo, 1862–
Milk substitutes in the rearing of young calves, by J. B. Lindsey and J. G. Archibald ... Amherst, Mass., 1925.
p. [41]–51. tables. 23½ᶜᵐ. (Massachusetts. Agricultural experiment station, 1888– Bulletin no. 223)

1. Calves. 2. Feeding and feeding stuffs. I. Archibald, John Geddie, 1894– joint author. II. Title.
Mass. State coll. Library A 25–629
for Library of Congress [873.E4 no. 223]
[a38e1] (630.72)

NL 0385000 MU DLC

Lindsey, Joseph Bridgeo, 1862–
... Molasses and molasses feeds for farm stock, by J. B. Lindsey, E. B. Holland and P. H. Smith ... [Amherst, Mass.] 1907.
31, [1] p. 24ᶜᵐ. (Massachusetts. Agricultural experiment station, 1888– Bulletin no. 118)

1. Molasses. 2. Feeding and feeding stuffs. I. Holland, Edward Bertram, 1872– II. Smith, Philip Henry, 1876–
A 15–1498

Title from Mass. Agr. College. Printed by L. C.

NL 0385001 MU NN

Lindsey, Joseph Bridgeo, 1862–
Haskins, Henri D 1870–
... New fertilizer materials and by-products, by H. D. Haskins; and Cocoanut meal, by J. B. Lindsey ... Amherst, Mass., 1914.

Lindsey, Joseph Bridgeo.
Massachusetts. Agricultural experiment station, Amherst, 1882–1895.
Notes on feeding experiments with pigs.
(In Massachusetts. Agricultural experiment station, Amherst, 1882–1895. 23½ᶜᵐ. Bulletin no. 13, p. [1]–11; no. 18, p. 2–18; no. 25, p. [1]–16; no. 30, p. [1]–16; no. 47, p. [2]–14)

Lindsey, Joseph Bridgeo, 1862–
The nutrition of the horse ... Amherst, Mass., 1918.
p. [243]–263. 23ᶜᵐ. (Massachusetts. Agricultural experiment station, 1888– Bulletin no. 188)

1. Feeding and feeding stuffs. I. Title.

Title from Mass. Agr. College. Printed by L. C.
A 19–1013

NL 0385004 MU MB

Lindsey, Joseph Bridgeo, 1862–
The nutritive value of cattle feeds. no. 1– September, 1920– Amherst, Mass., 1920–
v. tables. 23ᶜᵐ. (Massachusetts. Agricultural experiment station, 1888– Bulletin 197, 200, 205)
CONTENTS.—no. 1. Velvet bean feed for farm stock.—no. 2. Oat by-products for farm stock, both by J. B. Lindsey and C. L. Beals.—no. 3. Dried apple pomace for farm stock, by J. B. Lindsey, C. L. Beals and J. G. Archibald.

1. Feeding and feeding stuffs. I. Beals, Carlos Loring, 1889– joint author. II. Archibald, John G., joint author. III. Title.
A 21–289 Revised

Title from Mass. Agr. College. Printed by L. C.
[r22d2]

NL 0385005 MU

Lindsey, Joseph Bridgeo, 1862–
... Record of the station dairy herd and the cost of milk production. By J. B. Lindsey ... [Amherst, Mass.] 1913.
31, [1] p. 24ᶜᵐ. (Massachusetts. Agricultural experiment station, Amherst, 1888– Bulletin no. 145)

1. Milk—[Cost of production] 2. Dairying—Massachusetts.
A 15–1514

Title from Mass. Agr College. Printed by L. C.

NL 0385006 MU NN

Lindsey, Joseph Bridgeo, 1862– joint author.
Massachusetts. Agricultural experiment station, Amherst, 1888–
... Research service to Massachusetts animal industry. Progress reports. Amherst, Mass., 1926.

Lindsey, Joseph Bridgeo, 1862–
... Studies in mineral nutrition. By J. B. Lindsey and J. G. Archibald. Amherst, Mass., 1929.
p. [152]–166. tables. 23ᶜᵐ. (Massachusetts. Agricultural experiment station, 1888– Bulletin no. 255)

1. Nutrition. 2. Feeding and feeding stuffs. I. Archibald, John Geddie, 1894– joint author. II. Title: Mineral nutrition, Studies in.
[873.E4 no. 255] A 30–396

Title from Mass. Agr. College. Printed by L. C.
[3]

NL 0385008 MU PPAmP

Lindsey, Joseph Bridgeo, 1862–
... I. Substitutes for milk in the rearing of dairy calves; II. The cost of rearing a dairy cow. By J. B. Lindsey ... Amherst, Mass., 1915.
2 p. l., p. [49]–71. 23ᶜᵐ. (Massachusetts. Agricultural experiment station, Amherst, 1888– Bulletin no. 164)

1. Feeding and feeding stuffs. 2. Cow. [Dairy—Feeding]
A 16–412

Title from Mass. Agr. College. Printed by L. C.

NL 0385009 MU NN

[Lindsey, Joseph Bridgeo] 1862–
... Summer forage crops. [By Joseph B. Lindsey, assisted by E. B. Holland and P. H. Smith] ... Amherst, Mass., Press of Carpenter & Morehouse, 1901.
16 p. illus., plates. 24ᶜᵐ. (Massachusetts. Agricultural experiment station, Amherst, 1888– Bulletin no. 72)
Plates are printed on both sides of leaf.
At head of title: Hatch experiment station of the Massachusetts agricultural college.

1. Forage plants. I. Holland, Edward Bertram. II. Smith, Philip Henry, 1876– III. Title.
A 15–1478

Title from Mass. Agr. College. Printed by L. C.

NL 0385010 MU

Lindsey, Joseph Bridgeo, 1862–
... Two systems of feeding dairy cows, high roughage and low grain versus low roughage and high grain, by J. B. Lindsey and J. G. Archibald. Amherst, Mass., Massachusetts state college, 1932.
p. [3]–15. tables. 23½ᶜᵐ. (Massachusetts. Agricultural experiment station, 1888– Bulletin no. 291)

1. Feeding and feeding stuffs. I. Archibald, John Geddie, 1894– joint author. II. Title.
Title from Mass. State College A 33–1259
Library of Congress [873.E35 no. 291]
[3]

NL 0385011 MU

Lindsey, Joseph Bridgeo, 1862–
... The value of buttermilk and lactic acid in pig feeding, by J. B. Lindsey and C. L. Beals. Amherst, Mass., 1923.
p. [63]–67. tab. 23ᶜᵐ. (Massachusetts agricultural experiment station, 1888– Bulletin no. 217)

1. Feeding and feeding stuffs. I. Beals, Carlos Loring, 1889– joint author. II. Title.
A 24–697
Title from Mass. Agr. College. Printed by L. C.
[2]

NL 0385012 MU

Lindsey, Joseph Bridgeo, 1862–
The value of calcium phosphate as a supplement to the ration of dairy cows. By J. B. Lindsey ... and J. G. Archibald ...
(In U. S. Dept. of agriculture. Journal of agricultural research. vol. XXXI, no. 8, October 15, 1925, p. 771–791 incl. 4 pl. diagrs. 23ᶜᵐ. Washington, 1926)
Contribution from Massachusetts agricultural experiment station (Mass.—12)
Published January 19, 1926; preprint December 23, 1925.
"Literature cited": p. 790–791.
1. Calcium phosphate. 2. Cow. 3. Dairying. 4. Feeding and feeding stuffs. [2–4. Cows, Dairy—Feeding] I. Archibald, John Geddie, 1894– joint author. II. Title.
Library, U. S. Dept. of Agriculture 1Ag84J vol. 31 Agr 26–322
[4]

NL 0385013 DNAL

TN24
N6L7 Lindsey, Kenneth B
Petroleum, natural gas and asphalt in the Arkansas and Red River Basins of New Mexico. Final report. Arkansas-White-Red Basins Inter-Agency Committee, Minerals and Geology Work Group. [Pittsburgh, Bureau of Mines] 1954.
ii, 47 p. plates, fold. map, diagr., tables (1 fold.) 27 cm.
Cover title.
Prepared in the Fuels Technology Division, Petroleum and Natural Gas Branch, Region IV, Bureau of Mines.

Bibliography: p. 46–47 and bibliographical footnotes.

1. Petroleum – New Mexico. 2. Gas, Natural – New Mexico. 3. Asphalt. I. U.S. Arkansas-White-Red Basins Inter-Agency Committee. II. U.S. Bureau of Mines. III. Title.

NL 0385015 DI

VOLUME 334

342
L642s Lindsey, Lilah D
Study course in citizenship on federal and
Oklahoma laws, pertaining to women and child-
ren. For the Woman's Christian Temperance
Union of the State of Oklahoma.   Muskogee
[Okla.] Bowman Press [c1924]
40 p. 23 cm.

Cover title.

1. Citizenship--Study and teaching.

NL   0385016   OkU

Lindsey, Loyd Putnam
Care and Culture of the African Violet. Loyd
Putnam Lindsey, Ashville, N.C. 1943.

NL   0385017   OC1GC Or

QL291
.S3
L5   Lindsey, Loyd Putnam
1949   Care and culture of the African violet (Saintpaulia) 4th ed. Asheville, N. C., 1949.
28 p. illus. 26 cm.

1. Gesneriaceae. 2. Saintpaulia – Culture.
i. t.

NL   0385018   NNBG

LB1715
.A63   Lindsey, Margaret.

American Association of Teachers Colleges.

Major findings and recommendations in the study of professional laboratory experiences [by] Margaret Lindsey, research associate for the sub-committee. [n. p.] 1948.

Lindsey, Mark McDonald, 1920–
FOR OTHER EDITIONS
SEE MAIN ENTRY
Yale university. Class of 1942.

A history of the class of 1942 ... [New Haven] Published
with the assistance of the Yale banner and the Class secretaries
bureau [1942–

Lindsey, Mary.

Historic homes and landmarks of Alexandria, Virginia, by
Mary Lindsey. Alexandria, Va. [Newell-Cole company, inc.]
1931.

52 p. illus. 24ᵐ.

Map on p. [3] of cover.

1. Alexandria, Va.—Historic houses, etc. 2. Alexandria, Va.—Hist.
I. Title.
32–5355
Library of Congress   F234.A3L5
———— Copy 2.
Copyright A 48667   [3]   917.55296

NL   0385021   DLC PHi DI Vi NIC OU OC1

Lindsey, Mary.
Historic homes and landmarks of Alexandria, Virginia. Alexandria, Va. [Newell-
Cole Co.] 1949.
56 p. illus. 24ᶜᵐ.

1. Alexandria, Va.—Historic houses, etc.
2. Alexandria, Va.—Hist. I. Title.

NL   0385022   ViU NNC MB ViN

Lindsey, Mary, *pseud.*
see
Terry, *Mrs.* **Adolphine (Fletcher)** 1882–

QE
532
.L75   Lindsey, Mary Elizabeth,
History of earthquake registration at the
University of Michigan Observatory, Ann Arbor,
Michigan, 1922-1942 inclusive, by Mary E. Lindsey.
[Ann Arbor, Mich., 1943]
2 p.l., 68 numb.l. 28ᶜᵐ.
Type-written.

1. Michigan. University. Observatory. 2. Earthquakes--
Observations.

NL   0385024   MiU

---

*EC65
L6454   Lindsey, Montague Bertie, 2d earl of, 1608?–
643d   1666.
A declaration and iustification, of the Earle
of Lindsey, now prisoner in Warwicke-castle,
wherein hee makes apparent the iustice of His
Maiestyes cause in taking armes for the preservation of his royall person and prerogative.
As it was sent in a letter to the Right
honourable Henry, earle of Newarke, now resident
with His Maiesty at Oxford Ianuary. 26. 1643.
It being a true character of loyalty and
myrrour of odedience[!] for all His Maiestyes
louing subiects.

Oxford printed by Leonard Leychfield, printer
to the Vniversitie of Oxford[i.e.London.1643].
8p. 19.5cm.
Madan 1218.
False imprint.
Title vignette.
Dated by Thomason 3 February 1643.
Page 7 misnumbered 5.
Also published with title: The Earle of Lind-
sey his declara-   tion and iustification,
who is now pri-   soner ...

NL   0385026   MH CSmH CtY

Lindsey, Montagu Peregrine Bertie, 11th earl of,
1815–1899.
Gt. Brit. *Historical manuscripts commission.*
... The manuscripts of the Earl of Buckinghamshire, the
Earl of Lindsey, the Earl of Onslow, Lord Emly, Theodore J.
Hare, esq., and James Round, esq. ... London, Printed for
H. M. Stationery off., by Eyre and Spottiswoode, 1895.

DA25
.M2L55   Lindsey, Montagu Peregrine Albemarle Bertie,
12th earl of, 1861–1938.
Gt. Brit. *Historical manuscripts commission.*
... Supplementary report on the manuscripts of the late
Montagu Bertie, twelfth earl of Lindsey, formerly preserved
at Uffington house, Stamford, Lincolnshire, A. D., 1660–1702.
Edited by the late C. G. O. Bridgeman, M. A., and J. C. Walker,
M. A. London, H. M. Stationery off., 1942.

Lindsey, Morton C.
A study of bus transportation in consolidated schools with
specific recommendations for the established consolidated school
at Monsey, New York, [by] Morton C. Lindsey... [New York?]
1929. 127 p. incl. tables. 8°.

Bibliography, p. 125–127.

456557A. 1. Schools—Transportation   of pupils. 2. Schools, Country—
U. S.—N. Y.—Monsey.   February 17, 1930
N. Y. P. L.

NL   0385030   NN CU NNU-W MiU PPT ODW OCU MH NcU

F
2171
L5   Lindsey, N   Allen.
Cruising in the Madiana; the record of a
winter trip to the tropics. By N. Allen
Lindsey.   Boston, N.A. Lindsey Co., 1901.
182 p. illus. 18 cm.

"Printed for private circulation. Edition
limited to 300 copies."

1. Caribbean area--Descr. & trav. I.
Title.

NL   0385031   LU MH

Lindsey, Neffie Palmer, editor.
The young speakers' library for home, school, church, and
clubs, containing stories, recitations, dramas, and games. Edited
by Neffie Palmer Lindsey... [New York?] Youth Pub. Co.,
1893. 352 p. front., illus. 4°.

32604A. 1. Recitations. 2. Title.
N. Y. P. L.   January 23, 1922.

NL   0385032   NN IU

Lindsey, Philip.
Baccalaureate address, 7th anniversary commence-
ment of University of Nashville. Nashville,
Hunt, Tardiff, co., 1832.

NL   0385033   MdU

Lindsey, Richard Vernon, 1916–
I. Bromostilbendiols. II. Stereochemistry of the monoenol,
1, 2-dimesityl-1-propen-1-ol. By Richard Vernon Lindsey, jr.
... Urbana, Ill., 1941.
6 p. 23ᵐ.
Abstract of thesis (PH. D.)—University of Illinois, 1941.
Vita.
Bibliography : p. 5.

1. Enediols. 2. Stereochemistry.
41–22529
Library of Congress   QD473.L5
[2]   547.8

NL   0385034   DLC IU

Lindsey, Robert, 1801–1863.
Travels of Robert and Sarah Lindsey. Illustrated by Robert
Lindsey Clark, after original sketches by Frederic Mackie. Edited
by one of their daughters.   London: S. Harris and Co., 1886.
189 p. front., plates. 12°.

Preface signed: E. L. G.

145301A. 1. Voyages and travels,   1850–1875. 2. Lindsey, Sarah
(Crosland), 1804–1876. 3. G., E. L   editor. 4. Clark, Robert Lindsey,
illustrator.   illustrator.
N. Y. P. L.   January 14, 1925.

NL   0385035   NN NjR CSmH ICU PHC PSC PSC-Hi

Lindsey, Robert Bertie, 1st Earl of, 1721–1782
see   Bertie, Lord Robert, 1721–1782.

VOLUME 334

Lindsey, Robert Emery.
Survey of general metalworking facilities in industrial arts programs of the larger Indiana high schools with recommendations for improving the Richmond, Indiana general metalworking shop. A thesis ... for the degree of Master of Arts. Oxford, Ohio, Miami University, 1950.
113 p., typed. tables. 28 cm.

NL 0385037   OOxM

Mic 564

Lindsey, Robert Lisle.
The philosophy of a Christian approach to the Jews. Louisville, Ky.,1954.

Louisville Microfilms, Louisville, Ky.
Microfilm copy of typescript. Positive.
Collation of the original: 325 p.
Thesis - Southern Baptist Theological Seminary.

1. Judaism and Christianity. I.ti.

NL 0385038   OCH

Lindsey, Mrs. S.   A.

see

Lindsey, Mrs. Therese (Kayser) 1870-

Lindsey, Samuel A.
... Our rural life and farm problems. Addresses on our rural life and farm problems, the building of a state, and the cooperative agricultural plan, by S. A. Lindsey, chairman, Texas farm life commission ... Washington [Govt. print. off.] 1913.
30 p. 23½ᶜᵐ. ([U. S.] 63d Cong., 2d sess. Senate. Doc. 334)
Presented by Mr. Sheppard. Ordered printed December 18, 1913.

1. Agriculture—U. S. 2. Agriculture, Cooperative—U. S. 3. Texas farm life commission.   I. Title.

Library of Congress   HD1765 1913   14-30023

NL 0385040   DLC OO MiU

T630.973
L6450

LINDSEY, SAMUEL A
Our rural life and farm problems; an address by S.A. Lindsey, Chairman Texas Farm Life Commission, delivered before the Third Annual Farmers' Short Winter Course, A.&M. College, Jan. 8, 1913. [Fort Worth, Texas Commercial Secretaries and Business Men's Ass'n, 1913]
23p. port. 20cm.
Caption title.
1. Agriculture - U.S. 2. Agriculture, Co-operative - U.S. 3. Texas Farm Life Commission.   I. Title.

NL 0385041   TxU IU DNAL

Lindsey, Sandra.
Grandad meets a pal, a farce-comedy in three acts, by Sandra Lindsey ... Cedar Rapids, Ia., The Heuer publishing co., ᶜ1946.
100 p. diagr. 19ᶜᵐ.

I. Title.

PN6120.A5L4817   812.5   47-24413

NL 0385042   DLC ViU

Lindsey, Stephen Marcus.
Bible baptism; a study of the institution, significance, mode and subject of the ordinance, by Stephen Marcus Lindsey ... with an introduction by the Reverend Geo. H. Gilmer, D. D. [Sylvatus, Va.] The author, 1923.
107 p. 20ᶜᵐ.

1. Baptism.   I. Title.

Library of Congress   BV811.L63   24-3092

NL 0385043   DLC

Lindsey, Stephen Marcus.
Bible baptism. (2d and enl. ed.) By Stephen Marcus Lindsey ... Boston, The Christopher publishing house [ᶜ1925]
143 p. 20½ᶜᵐ.

1. Baptism.   I. Title.

Library of Congress   BV811.L63 1925   25-11443

NL 0385044   DLC

Lindsey, Theophilus, 1723-1808, ed.

Priestley, Joseph, 1733-1804.
An answer to Mr. Paine's Age of reason, being a continuation of Letters to the philosophers and politicians of France, on the subject of religion; and of the Letters to a philosophical unbeliever. By Joseph Priestley, LL. D., F. R. S. With a preface by Theophilus Lindsey, A. M. Northumberland town, America, Printed in 1794; London, Reprinted for J. Johnson, M.DCC.XCV.

200
L644

Lindsey, Theophilus, 1723-1808.
The apology of Theophilus Lindsey on resigning the vicarage of Catterick, Yorkshire. London, Printed for J. Johnson, 1774.
236p.

No.1 in a volume lettered: Lindsey's tracts.

1. Unitarianism.

NL 0385046   IU CtY MH PHi MeB OCU

C
56
.506

LINDSEY, THEOPHILUS, 1723-1808.
The apology of Theophilus Lindsey on resigning the vicarage of Catterick, Yorkshire. The 3d ed. London,J.Johnson,1774.
vi,236p. 21cm.

"John Fox's letter [in Latin] to Queen Elizabeth, to dissuade her from burning two Dutch Anabaptists for heresy in Smithfield, 1575": p.226-230; "A confession of faith of the Waldenses": p.231-236.

NL 0385047   ICN MH-AH NNG MH

609.5
L752.4ap
1782

LINDSEY, Theophilus, 1723-1808.
The apology of Theophilus Lindsey, on resigning the vicarage of Catterick, Yorkshire. 4th ed. With some additional illustrations. London, J. Johnson, 1782.
xvi,246p. 22cm.

1p. advertising matter at end.
With this is bound His A sequel to the apology, 1776.

NL 0385048   MH-AH IU CtY

686
Unit
B862tr
1836
v.5
no.1

LINDSEY, Theophilus, 1723-1808.
The apology of Theophilus Lindsey, on resigning the vicarage of Catterick, Yorkshire. The fifth ed. London, printed by George Smallfield for the Unitarian Society; and sold by R. Hunter, 1818.
xii,202p. 19cm. (British and Foreign Unitarian Association. Unitarian tracts, 1836, v.5 [no.1])

No.1 in a   volume of works of and by the author

NL 0385049   MH-AH NNUT NBuG CtY OO

Mnm39
1
1789ℓ

[Lindsey, Theophilus] 1723-1808
An attempt to explain some of the Thirty-nine articles on scriptural principles; by a minister of the Church of England. London,J.Johnson, 1789.
23p. 21cm.

NL 0385050   CtY MH

[Lindsey, Theophilus]
The book of common prayer...

See

Church of England. Book of common prayer.

Mhc9
L645
C28

Lindsey, Theophilus, 1723-1808.
The catechist: or, An inquiry into the doctrine of the Scriptures, concerning the only true God and object of religious worship. In two parts. By Theophilus Lindsey ... London,J.Johnson,1781.
2p.ℓ.,xxiii,[1],132p. 17cm.
No more published?

NL 0385052   CtY MH M

BX
9842
L5
1792

Lindsey, Theophilus, 1723-1808.
The catechist; or, An inquiry into the doctrine of the Scriptures, concerning the only true God, and object of religious worship. London, 1792.
xvii,106 p. 20cm.
First published 1781.
Bound with Melmoth, William. The great importance of a religious life considered. New and rev. ed. London, 1812. Carpenter, Lant. Proof from Scripture that God, even the Father, is the only true God, and the only proper object of religious worship. 2d ed. London, 1818. Browne, Theophilus. Religious liberty and the rights of conscience and private judgment grossly violated. Gloucester, 1819. Elton, Charles A. A word at parting, in a letter to the Reverend Edward Manley. London, 1824.

Newton, John. An answer to the question, Is the doctrine of the Trinity contained in the Bible, or is it of human invention? [Liverpool, 181-?]

1. Unitarianism--Doctrinal and controversial works. 2. Jesus Christ--Divinity. 3. Unitarian Churches--Doctrinal and controversial works. I. Melmoth, William, 1666-1743. The great importance of a religious life considered. II. Carpenter, Lant, 1780-1840. Proof from Scripture that God ... is the only true God. III. Browne, Theophilus, 1763-1835. Religious

liberty and the rights of conscience and private judgment grossly violated. IV. Elton, Charles Abraham, 1778-1853. A word at parting, in a letter to the Reverend Edward Manley. V. Manley, Edward. VI. Newton, John, 1725-1807. An answer to the question, Is the doctrine of the Trinity contained in the Bible, or is it of human invention? VII. Title.

NL 0385055   MWA

686
Unit
B862tr
1836
v.5

LINDSEY, Theophilus, 1723-1808.
The catechist: or, An inquiry into the doctrine of the scriptures, concerning the only true God, and object of religious worship. London, printed by George Smallfield, for the Unitarian Society; and sold by R. Hunter, and D. Eaton, 1818.
xxiv,106p. 19cm. (British and Foreign Unitarian Association. Unitarian tracts, 1836, v.5 [no.2])

No. 2 in a volume of works of and by the author.

NL 0385057   MH-AH NBuG OO CtY

VOLUME 334

[Lindsey, Theophilus] 1723-1808.
    Collection of hymns and psalms for public
worship. 3d ed. improved. London, 1793.
    149 plus 5 pp.   16°.

NL 0385058   MSaE

BX9840 Lindsey, Theophilus, 1723-1808.
.L75   Conversations on Christian idolatry, in the
Rare   year 1791. London, J. Johnson, 1792.
Bk   xiv, 169 p.

        1. Unitarianism--Doctrinal and controversial
works. I. Title.

NL 0385059   ICU OO MeB MH PMA

---

686   LINDSEY, Theophilus, 1723-1808.
Unit   Conversations on Christian idolatry,
U58tr   in the year 1791. Second ed. London,
v.8   Stover, 1805.
no.2   ix,140,4p. 19.5cm. (Unitarian Society
        for Promoting Christian Knowledge and the
        Practice of Virtue. London. Tracts, 2d.
        ser., v.8 [no.2])

        No. 2 in a volume of works by the author.

NL 0385060   MH-AH PPL MeB

Lindsey, Rev. Theophilus, 1723-1808
Conversations on the divine governments;...
2d ed. London, 1803.
12°

NL 0385061   MeB

BX 9841 Lindsey, Theophilus, 1723-1808.
.L 75   Conversations on the divine government;
1805   shewing that every thing is from God, and
        for good, to all ... By Theophilus Lindsey,
        M.A. 2d. ed. London, Printed by R. Taylor
        and co., and sold by J. Johnson and W. Vidler,
        1805.
        viii, 158 p.   17½cm.

NL 0385062   MdBJ CtY RPB MeB MH

Lindsey, Theophilus, 1723-1808.
    A discourse addressed to the congregation at the chapel in Essex
street, Strand, on resigning the pastoral office among them. By
Theophilus Lindsey...   London: Printed for J. Johnson, 1793.
52 p.   22cm.

NL 0385063   NN MWA MH CtY PMA TxDaM

WA   Lindsey, Theophilus, 1723-1808.
12138   Divisione della Polonia, in sette dialoghi
        a guisa di dramma. Conversazione tra potenze
        distinte, in cui si fanno parlare gli interlo-
        cutori secondo i loro principi, e le loro condo
        ta. Opera di G. Pansmouser [pseud.] Tradotta
        dall'inglese. Haja, 1775.
        94p.

NL 0385064   CtY ICU

Lindsey,Theophilus,1723-1808.
    An examination of Mr.Robinson of Cam-
bridge's Plea for the divinity of our Lord
Jesus Christ. Lond.,Johnson,1789. 405p
28cm.

NL 0385065   CBPac MWA MH PMA CtY

BX   LINDSEY, Theophilus, 1723-1808.
9869   A farewell address to the parishioners of
.L5   Catterick. By Theophilus Lindsey, M.A.
A3   London, printed for J. Johnson, No.72, St.
        Paul's Church-yard, 1774.
        23p. 21cm.

        Bound with his The Apology ... London,
1774.

        I. Title.
    [BX9869.L5A3]

NL 0385066   MH-AH NNG CtY MH-AH NN MH

---

686   LINDSEY, Theophilus, 1723-1808.
Unit   A farevel address to the parishioners
U58tr   of Catterick. ... London, C. Stower, 1805.
v.8   12p. 19.5cm. (Unitarian Society for
no.1   Promoting Christian Knowledge and the
        Practice of Virtue. London. Tracts, 2d.
        ser, 1805 v.8, [no.1])

        No.1 in a volume of works by the author.
        Last 4p. are advertisements.

NL 0385067   MH-AH NN NNUT

BX9831 Lindsey, Theophilus, 1723-1808.
.L7   An historical view of the state of the Uni-
        tarian doctrine and worship, from the Reforma-
        tion to our own times. With some account of
        the obstructions which it has met with at dif-
        ferent periods. London, J. Johnson, 1783.
        xxx, 563 p.

        1. Unitarianism--Hist.

NL 0385068   ICU CSt MH-AH CtY MeB NjNbS

BX   Lindsey, Theophilus, 1723-1808.
9853   Hymns for public worship, selected for use
L5   of the congregation in Essex street chapel.
        London, J. Green, 1842.
        216 p. 19 cm.
        Without music.
        Bound with Lindsey, Theophilus. Book of
common prayer reformed. London, 1839.

        1. Hymns, English.

NL 0385069   NRCR

Lindsey, Theophilus, 1723-1808, comp.
    Hymns for public worship; selected for the
use of the congregation in Essex street chapel ...
London, John Chapman, 1849.
    2 p.l., 216 p. 17 cm.
    275 hymns.
    The original compilation of Theophilus Lindsey
was reedited in 1835 and 1849 by T. Madge becoming
practically a new collection.
    Manuscript annotations by Prof. Bird.
    Bound with is: Book of common prayer.
Adaptation. The book of common prayer,
reformed ...   1849.

NL 0385070   NNUT

Lindsey, Theophilus, 1723-1808.
    Letters of Theophilus Lindsey, by H. McLachlan ...
Manchester, The University press; London, New York
[etc.] Longmans, Green, & co., 1920.
    xii, 148 p. incl. front. (port.) 19ᶜᵐ. (Half-title: Publications of the
University of Manchester. Historical series. no. xxxvii)
    On verso of t.-p.: Publications of the University of Manchester. no.
cxxxiv.

    i. McLachlan, Herbert, 1876-   ed.

Library of Congress   BX9869.L5A3 1920   21-468

NL 0385071   DLC MiU NcD NIC PPAmP PU

BS455 Lindsey, Theophilus, 1723-1808.
.G25   A list of the false readings of the Scriptures, and the mis-
        translations of the English Bible which contribute to support
        the great errors concerning Jesus Christ. By Theophilus
        Lindsey ... London, Printed for J. Johnson, 1790.
        [1, vi, 91 p. 23ᶜᵐ. [With [Garnham, R. E.] A letter to the Right Rev. Lewis ...
        bishop of Norwich. London, 1780]

        1. Jesus Christ--Divinity.

NL 0385072   ICU NjR MH NN PU

609.5 LINDSEY, Theophilus, 1723-1808.
L752.4vi   On prayer; and forms of prayer, their
1788   defects, and remedy; a sermon preached
cop.1   at the chapel in Essex Street, Strand;
        on Sunday, April XIV, MDCCXCIII. London,
        J. Johnson, 1793.
        30p. 21cm.

        No.3 in a bound vol. of works by Lindsey
        and William Frend.

NL 0385073   MH-AH PMA CtY MH

4PQ   Lindsey, Theophilus, 1723-1808
Fr.   Le partage de la Pologne en sept
2097   dialogues en forme de drame; ou, Con-
        versation entre des personnages dis-
        tingués, dans laquelle on fait parler
        les interlocuteurs conformément à
        leurs principes et à leur conduite,
        par Gotlieb Pansmouser [pseud.]
        Traduit de l'anglois par miladi***
        duchesse de***. Londres, Impr. de
        P. Elmsy [17]
        68 p

NL 0385074   DLC-P4

943.8 Lindsey, Theophilus, 1723-1808.
L753pXF   Le partage de la Pologne, en sept dialogues
        en forme de drame, ou conversation entre des
        personnages distingués, dans laquelle on fait
        parler les interlocuteurs conformément à
        leurs principes & à leur conduite, par Got-
        lieb Pansmouser [pseud.] Traduit de l'an-
        glois par Miladi*** Duchesse de*** [i.e.
        J.M. Gérard de Rayneval] Londres, P. Elm-
        sly [1775]
        82p. 19cm.

        Translation of The Polish partition.

        1. Poland. Hist. First partition, 1772.
        I. Title.

NL 0385076   IEN CtY MnU

J   [LINDSEY, THEOPHILUS] 1723-1808.
93   Le partage de la Pologne en sept dialogues
.564   en forme de drame, ou Conversation entre des
        personnages distingués, dans laquelle on fait
        parler les interlocuteurs conformément à leurs
        principes & à leur conduite. Par Gotlieb
        Pansmouzer [pseud.] Suivi de la Réfutation
        littéraire et politique du même ouvrage... A
        Londres, P. Elmsly, 1776.
        156p. 17cm.

        Binder's title: Melanges politiques.

NL 0385077   ICN

VOLUME 334

[Lindsey, Theophilus] 1723–1808.
The Polish partition, illustrated; in seven dramatick dialogues, or, Conversation pieces, between remarkable personages, published from the mouths and actions of the interlocutors. By Gotlieb Pansmouzer [pseud.] the baron's nephew ... London, Printed for P. Elmsly [1773]
2 p. l., 89 p. 22ᶜᵐ.

1. Poland—Hist.—First partition, 1772. I. Title.

Library of Congress   DK434.L4   8—18526

NL 0385078   DLC InU CtY CSmH MnU OO

And. Rm.
BT200
L5
Lindsey, Theophilus, 1723–1808.
A second address to the students of Oxford and Cambridge, relating to Jesus Christ, and the origin of the great errors concerning him; with a list of the false readings of the Scriptures, and the mistranslations of the English Bible which contribute to support those errors. By Theophilus Lindsey...London, Printed for J. Johnson, 1790.
xxi [1] 320 p. 21 cm.

NL 0385079   PPiPT PMA CU MH-AH CtY NNUT CBPac

BX
9869
.L52
A3
LINDSEY, Theophilus, 1723–1808.
A sequel to the Apology on resigning the vicarage of Catterick, Yorkshire. By Theophilus Lindsey, M.A. London, Printed for J. Johnson, No. 72, St. Paul's Church Yard, 1776.
xxiv,508p. 22cm.

I. Title.

[BX9869.L52A3]

NjNbS
NL 0385080   MH-AH IU CBPac MiHM MeB CtY PPL IEG

---

v.2015
Lindsey, Theophilus, 1723–1808.
A sermon preached at the opening of the chapel in Essex-House, Essex-street, in the Strand, on Sunday, April 17, 1774 ... To which is added, A summary account of the reformed liturgy, on the plan of the late Dr. Samuel Clarke, made use of in the said chapel ... The 3d ed. London, J. Johnson [1774]
32p. 21½cm.

NL 0385081   CtY RPB MH

---

v.2015
Lindsey, Theophilus, 1723–1808.
A sermon preached at the opening of the new chapel at Essex-street, Strand, on Sunday, March 29, 1778 ... London, Printed for J. Johnson [1778]
36p. 23½cm.

NL 0385082   CtY MH

252
L64s
Lindsey, Theophilus, 1723–1808.
Sermons with appropriate prayers annexed, by the late Rev. Theophilus Lindsey ... London, Printed for J. Johnson and co., 1810.
2v.

Vol.2 imperfect: t.-p. wanting.
Edited by Thomas Belsham.
Book-plate of George Duffield.

1. Sermons. I. Belsham, Thomas, 1750–1829, ed.

NL 0385083   IU MH MH-AH

[Lindsey, Theophilus, 1723–1808.]
Die theilung von Pohlen in sieben gesprächen, oder Unterredung zwischen hohen personen. Verfasset von Gottlieb Pansmouser [pseud.]. Aus dem englischen übersetzt von Miladi *** herzogin von ***. Hanau, 1775.
pp. 80.

NL 0385084   MH

232
L996
Lindsey, Theophilus, 1723–1808.
Two dissertations. I. On the preface to St. John's Gospel. II. On praying to Jesus Christ. With a short postcript by Dr. Jebb. London, J. Johnson, 1779.
[2] l., 152 p. 21 cm.

Bound with Lyttelton, G. L., 1st baron. Observations on the conversion... of St. Paul. London, 1749.

1. Trinity. 2. Jesus Christ.

NL 0385085   N CtY PPL CBPac OO MH

[Lindsey, Theophilus] 1723–1808.
De verdeeling van Polen, in VII samenspraken, tusscnen hooge standspersonen, tooneelswijze voorgedragen; door den Heer Gotlieb Pansmouser [pseud.], uit het Engelsch vertaeld, door eene Kleefsche mevrouw. Keulen, J. Kreitzer, 1775. 112 p. 20cm.

684632. 1. Poland—Hist.—Partition   period, 1763–1796

NL 0385086   NN

Lindsey, Theophilus, 1723–1808.
Vindiciae Priestleianae: an address to the students of Oxford and Cambridge; occasioned by a letter to Dr. Priestley from a person calling himself an undergraduate, but publicly and uncontradictedly ascribed to Dr. Horne, Dean of Canterbury ... By Theophilus Lindsey ... London, Printed for J. Johnson, 1788.
xix, [1], 320 p. 21ᶜᵐ.

1. Priestley, Joseph, 1733–1804. 2. Horne, George, bp. of Norwich, 1730–1792. I. Title.

BX5200.P9SL7

MB MH NN PMA MeB WU CaBVaU
NL 0385087   MiU PSt CU PPL-R PPAmP MH-AH CtY CBPac

Lindsey, *Mrs.* Therese (Kayser) 1870–
Blue norther, Texas poems by Therese Lindsey. New York, H. Vinal, 1925.
5 p. l., 54 p. 23ᶜᵐ.

I. Title.
Library of Congress   PS3523.I 616B5 1925   25–15783

NL 0385088   DLC PP MsU TxU FU NN

Lindsey, *Mrs.* Therese (Kayser) 1870–
The cardinal flower, by Therese Lindsey ... Dallas, Tex., The Kaleidograph press [*1934]
xiii p., 1 l., 17–76 p. 20ᶜᵐ.
Poems.

I. Title.

Library of Congress   PS3523.I 616C3 1934   35–883
Copyright A 77988   [3]   811.5

NL 0385089   DLC

Lindsey, Therese (Kayser), 1870–
Collected poems, by Therese Lindsey.   San Antonio, Tex.
[c1947] viii, 88 p. front. 21cm.
With autograph of author.

POETRY SOCIETY OF AMERICA COLL.

447488B.
N. Y. P. L.   April 20, 1949

NL 0385090   NN RPB

Lindsey, *Mrs.* Therese (Kayser) 1870–
A tale of the Galveston storm [by] Therese Lindsey. Dallas, Tex., The Kaleidograph press [*1936]
40, [1] p. 1 illus. 20ᶜᵐ.
"In a contest sponsored by the Poetry society of Texas in 1925 this poem received first prize in the narrative-poem class."

1. Galveston—Storm, 1900—Poetry.   I. Title.
Library of Congress   PS3523.I 616T3 1936   36–22203
——— Copy 2.
Copyright A 98815   [3]   811.5

NL 0385091   DLC OU

Lindsey, Thomas H.
Lindsey's guide book to western North Carolina ... T. H. Lindsey, author ... Asheville, The Randolph-Kerr printing co., 1890.
2 p. l., [3]–92, [A–G] p. double front. (map) illus., plates. 15½ᶜᵐ.

1. North Carolina—Descr. & trav.—Guide-books. 2. Asheville, N. C.—Descr.—Guide-books. 3. Mountains—North Carolina. I. Title.
Library of Congress   F259.L75   1–6830

NL 0385092   DLC NcD NcU

Lindsey, Thomas Jefferson, 1845–
Ohio. *Shiloh battlefield commission.*
Ohio at Shiloh; report of the commission, by T. J. Lindsey ... [Cincinnati, Printed by C. J. Krehbiel & co., 1903]

Lindsey, Thomas N
The new criminal code of Kentucky
see under   Kentucky. Laws, statutes, etc.

Lindsey, Walter Frank, 1906–   joint author.

TL521
.A33
no. 922
Stack, John, 1906–
Characteristics of low-aspect-ratio wings at supercritical mach numbers, by John Stack and W. F. Lindsey. [Washington, U. S. Govt. Print. Off., 1949]

Lindsey, Walter Frank, 1910–   joint author.

Stack, John, 1906–
... The compressibility burble and the effect of compressibility on pressures and forces acting on an airfoil, by John Stack, W. F. Lindsey and Robert E. Littell. 1938. [Washington, U. S. Govt. print. off., 1939]

Lindsey, Walter Frank, 1910–
... Drag of cylinders of simple shapes, by W. F. Lindsey, 1938 ... [Washington, U. S. Govt. print. off., 1938]
cover-title, 1, [1], 8 p. diagrs. 28½ᶜᵐ. (U. S. National advisory committee for aeronautics. Report no. 619)
"References": p. 8.

1. Air resistance. 2. Cylinders.   I. Title.
Library of Congress   TL521.A33 no. 619   38–26252
——— Copy 2.   TL574.D7L5
[3]   (629.1306173) 629.13234

NL 0385097   DLC OCU OU

VOLUME 334

Lindsey, William, 1858–1922.
   Apples of Istakhar, by William Lindsey. Boston, Copeland and Day, 1895.

   5 p. l., 100 p., 1 l. 20ᶜᵐ.

   Poems.
   "The first edition of this book consists of five hundred copies with fifty additional copies on hand-made paper printed ... by The Everett press, Boston."
   Copy on hand-made paper.

   ɪ. Title.

                                 33–31334

   Library of Congress   PS3523.I62A6 1895   811.5

NL 0385098   DLC PBm NBuG MH OO

Lindsey, William, 1858–
   At start and finish ₍by₎ William Lindsey. Boston, Small, Maynard & company, 1899.

   4 p. l., 256 p. 18ᶜᵐ.

   From Cinder-path tales, with additions.

   CONTENTS.—Old England and New England.—My first for money.—The hollow hammer.—His name is Mud.—How Kitty queered the "mile."—Atherton's last "half."—The charge of the heavy brigade.—A Virginia jumper.—And every one a winner.

                             Mar. 1, 1900–108

   Library of Congress   PZ3.L654A Copyright

NL 0385099   DLC ViU NN MB

FILM
4274
PR
v.3
reel
120

Lindsey, William, 1858–1922.
   At start and finish [by] William Lindsey. Boston, Small, Maynard & company, 1899.
   4 p. l., 256 p. 18 cm.
   (Wright American Fiction, v. III, 1876–1900, no. 3351, Research Publications, Inc. Microfilm, Reel L-20)
   Contents.–Old England and New England.–My first for money.–The hollow hammer.–His name is Mud.–How Kitty queered the "mile."–Atherton's last "half."–The charge of the heavy brigade.–A Virginia jumper.–And every one a winner.

NL 0385100   CU

Lindsey, William, 1858–1922.
   The backsliders, by William Lindsey ... Boston and New York, Houghton Mifflin company, 1922.

   4 p. l., 3–362, ₍1₎ p. 19½ᶜᵐ. $1.90

   ɪ. Title.

                           22–4675

   Library of Congress   PZ3.L654Ba

NL 0385101   DLC PPAmP MB

Lindsey, William, 1858–1922.
   Cinder-path tales, by William Lindsey. Boston, Copeland and Day, 1896.

   3 p. l., 210 p., 1 l. 18ᶜᵐ.

   1,000 copies printed.

   CONTENTS.—My first for money.—The hollow hammer.—How Kitty queered the "mile."—Paddy the leaper's probation.—Atherton's last "half."—A Virginia jumper.—And every one a winner.

   ɪ. Title.

                           7–19011

   Library of Congress   PZ3.L654C

NL 0385102   DLC OKentU TxU MB OCl ViU MB

FILM
4274
PR
v.3
reel
120

Lindsey, William, 1858–1922.
   Cinder-path tales ... Boston, Copeland and Day, 1896.
   210 p. (Wright American Fiction, v. III, 1876–1900, no. 3352, Research Publications, Inc. Microfilm, Reel L-20)

NL 0385103   CU

Lindsey, William, 1858–1922.
   The curtain of forgetfulness, by William Lindsey. Prefatory note by E. M. Tenison; illustrations by Evelyn Paul. Boston & New York, Houghton Mifflin company, 1923.

   6 p. l., 7–31 p. col. mounted front., col. mounted plates. 23ᶜᵐ.

   Poems.
   "Printed in Great Britain."
   "Of this edition of The curtain of forgetfulness have been printed on handmade paper 1,000 copies, of which 500 are for America."

   ɪ. Paul, Evelyn, illus. ɪɪ. Title.

                          A 42–2874

   Vassar college. Library
    for Library of Congress   ₍2₎

NL 0385104   NPV CoU ICU CtY FU OC1 MH

Lindsey, William, 1858 –
   ... Le manteau parti-roman-traduit par Henry D. Davray.   Paris, 1914.
   19 cm.

NL 0385105   RPB

Lindsey, William, 1858–
   Red wine of Roussillon; a play in four acts, by William Lindsey. Boston and New York, Houghton Mifflin company, 1915.

   6 p. l., ₍3₎–174 p., 1 l. 20½ᶜᵐ.

   ɪ. Title.

   Library of Congress   PS3523.I62R4 1915   15–11229

   MiU OCl MB
NL 0385106   DLC OrP MB NcD WaU PCC PU CoU OU NIC NN

Lindsey, William, 1858–
   Red wine of Roussillon; a play in four acts.   London: Constable & Co., Ltd. ₍1915?₎   5 p.l., 174(1) p. 8°.

   1. Title.
   N. Y. P. L.   CENTRAL CIRCULATION.
                                     January 13, 1916

NL 0385107   NN

Lindsey, William, 1858–
   Seremonda. A romantic drama of old France. Originally printed under the title, Red wine of Roussillon.
— [Boston. Houghton Mifflin Co. 1915.] (9), 174, (1) pp. Portrait. 20 cm.
   The title Seremonda, found on the cover, was given to the special edition published on the occasion of Julia Arthur's performance of this play. This edition is otherwise identical with the original.

   L1123 — T.r.

NL 0385108   MB

Lindsey, William, 1858–
   The severed mantle, by William Lindsey ... with seven illustrations in color by Arthur I. Keller. Boston and New York, Houghton Mifflin company, 1909.

   ix, ₍1₎ p., 1 l., 452, ₍2₎ p. col. front., 6 col. pl. 20½ᶜᵐ. $1.35

   ɪ. Title.

                           9–27996

   Library of Congress   PZ3.L654S

NL 0385109   DLC TU ViU OO MiU OC1 MB NN

Lindsey, W₍illiam₎ H₍enry₎ *architect.*
   A season at Harwich, with excursions by land and water: to which is added Researches, historical, natural, and miscellaneous. By W. H. Lindsey ... London, Simpkin, Marshall, & co.; ₍etc., etc.₎ 1851.

   2 pts in 1 v. front., illus., pl., fold. maps. 23ᶜᵐ.

   Added t.-p. engr.
   Illustrated by the author.
   CONTENTS.—pt. 1. A season at Harwich.—pt. 2. Researches in the library of Doctor Bremmer; containing additions historical, natural, and miscellaneous: under heads A. B. C.

   Subject entries: 1. Harwich, Eng. 2. Natural history—England—Essex.

                           2–18153

   Library of Congress, no.   DA690.H34L7.

NL 0385110   DLC

Lindsey, William Thomas, 1845–   joint ed.

Doddridge, Joseph, 1769–1826.
   Notes on the settlement and Indian wars of the western parts of Virginia and Pennsylvania from 1763 to 1783, inclusive, together with a review of the state of society and manners of the first settlers of the western country. By Joseph Doddridge; with a memoir of the author by his daughter, Narcissa Doddridge. Republished with the addition of new and valuable material. By John S. Ritenour and Wm. T. Lindsey. Pittsburgh, Pa., 1912.

WA
303.L7
L75B8

Lindsey, Eng. County Council. Education Committee
   Annual report of the school medical officer. 1st–
   ₍Gainsborough, etc.₎
     v. illus.

   1. School hygiene - Lindsey, Eng.

NL 0385112   DNLM

Lindsey, *Eng. County council. Education committee.*
   ... Practical work in elementary schools. An educational experiment carried out by the Lindsey county council education committee. Report on the first year's work. ₍Lincoln, Morton & sons, ltd., printers, 1911₎

   32, ₍2₎ p., 1 l. illus. 24½ᶜᵐ.

   At head of title: Lindsey (Lincolnshire) county council education committee.
   On cover: By Christopher H. Turnor ... and Walter Birkett.

   1. Industrial education—Elementary schools—Lindsey, Eng. ɪ. Turnor, Christopher Hatton, 1873– ɪɪ. Birkett, Walter. ɪɪɪ. Title.

                          E 13–925

   Library, U. S. Bur. of   Eduction LB1594.L64

NL 0385113   DHEW

W 2
FE5.1
L7C82a

LINDSEY, Eng. County Medical Officer of Health
   Annual report.

   ₍Gainsborough, etc., 1908?₎–
     v. illus.
     Title varies, 190 –1927: Annual report upon the health and sanitary condition of the County.
     1. Public health - England - Lindsey

NL 0385114   DNLM

Lindsey-Hopkins Vocational School, *Miami, Fla.*
   see **Miami, Fla. Lindsey-Hopkins Vocational School.**

Lindsey Local History Society, 1930–1947
   see **Lincolnshire Local History Society.**

L6453

Lindsey Standing Conference of Voluntary Youth Organisations.
   Scunthorpe and its families; a report prepared at the request of the Lindsey Standing Conference of Voluntary Youth Organisations by a Working Party convened by the Scunthorpe Forum and to be presented to the British National Conference on Social Work on the occasion of the second national conference, April 1953. Newland ₍Eng.₎ 1953.
   33p. tables. 34cm.

NL 0385117   OrU

VOLUME 334

200　Lindsey's tracts.　London ɛetc.ɔ 1774-93.
L644　7v. in 1.
　　　Binder's title.

NL 0385118　IU

Lindsiepe, Wilhelm, 1887–
　　Die Essener credit-anstalt, im zusammenhang mit der wirtschaftlichen entwicklung des niederrheinischwestfälischen industriebezirks ... Von Wilhelm Lindsiepe ... Essen, Gebrüder vom Hövel, 1914.
　　118 p., 1 l. 22½ᶜᵐ.
　　Inaug.-diss.—Bonn.
　　Lebenslauf.
　　"Benutzte literatur": p. 8–9.

　　1. Essener credit-anstalt.

　　　　　　　　　　　　　　　　　34–4578
Library of Congress　　HG3060.E74L5 1914　332.31094342

NL 0385119　DLC ICRL CtY PU

Lindsjö, Inga.
　　Det fattas ett par linser, Motståndet; två enaktare. ɛStockholmɔ Wahlström & Widstrand ɛ1951ɔ
　　81 p. 20 cm.

　　ɪ. Title. ɪɪ. Title: Motståndet.

　　　　　　　　　　　　　　　　　A 52–4714
Minnesota. Univ. Libr.
for Library of Congress　　ɛ3ɔ

NL 0385120　MnU

Lindsjö, Inga.
　　Har någon sett Kornelius? Stockholm, Bonnier ɛ1952ɔ
　　150 p. illus. 16 cm. (Bonniers barnbibliotek, 103)

　　ɪ. Title.

　　PZ59.L5H3　　　　　　　　　53–18416 ‡

NL 0385121　DLC

Lindsjö, Inga.
　　Jag vill röra vid ljuskronan. Stockholm, Wahlström & Widstrand ɛ1953ɔ
　　232 p. 22 cm.

　　　　　　　　　　　　　　　　　A 53–8316
Minnesota. Univ. Libr.
for Library of Congress　　ɛ3ɔ

NL 0385122　MnU

Lindsjö, Inga.
　　Som i havets mussla. Stockholm, Wahlström & Widstrand ɛ1949ɔ
　　90 p. 22 cm.

　　ɪ. Title.

　　　　　　　　　　　　　　　　　A 50–3430
Minnesota. Univ. Libr.
for Library of Congress　　ɛ3ɔ

NL 0385123　MnU NN

Lindskog, Birger.
　　African leopard men. ɛUppsala?ɔ 1954.
　　xii, 219 p. plates, maps. 32 cm. (Studia ethnographica Upsaliensia, 7)
　　Label mounted on t. p.: ɛDistributed byɔ W. S. Heinman, New York.
　　Bibliography: p. 207–215.

　　1. Leopard Men.　ɪ. Title.　(Series)

　　GN495.2.L5　　　*572.7　　　　54—13023

　　　　　TxU NcD PU OCl PP NSyU KU CU-S FU GU
NL 0385124　DLC OrU CaBVaU NIC OCU IEN NN CU MH-P

Lindskog, Björn, 1906–
　　Fallskärmar och fallskärmstrupper, fallskärmens historia och användning i krig och fred. Malmö, Allhems forlag, 1947.
　　56, ɛ82ɔ p. (chiefly illus.) 25 cm. (Allhems flygböcker, 5)
　　"Källor": p. ɛ81ɔ

　　1. Parachute troops. 2. Parachutes.　ɪ. Title.

　　UG632.L5　　　　　　　　49–13422*

NL 0385125　DLC

UD480　**Lindskog, Björn,** 1906–　joint author.
.B4
　　Bergman, Bill, 1904–
　　Luftinvasion, av Bill Bergman och Björn Lindskog. Bildred.: Stig. Arne Öström. Stockholm, Bonnier ɛ1942ɔ

Lindskog, Claes, 1870–
　　... Adversaria ad Plutarchi Vitas ... scripsit Claes Lindskog. Lundae, Typis expressit H. Ohlsson, 1907.
　　13 p. 25ᶜᵐ. (Lunds universitets årsskrift. n. f., afd. 1, bd. 1, nr. 4)

　　1. Plutarchus. Vitae parallelae.　ɪ. Title.

Title from John Crerar　　Libr. 058　　　　　A 32–1711
Library of Congress　　[AS284.L8　n. f., afd. 1, bd. 1]

NL 0385127　ICJ NN

Lindskog, Claes, 1870–
　　Beiträge zur Geschichte der Satzstellung im Latein, von Claes Lindskog. Lund: E. Malmström, 1896. 60 p. incl. tables. 4°. (Lund. Universitet. Acta Universitatis Lundensis. Lunds universitets års-skrift. Tomus 32, afdelning 1. ɛno. 5.ɔ)

　　1. Latin language—Word order.
N. Y. P. L.　　　　　　　　　March 27, 1925

NL 0385128　NN MH NIC CtY

Lindskog, Claes, 1870–
　　Bokslut; hågkomster och människor. Stockholm, Bonnier ɛ1949ɔ
　　152 p. ports. 20 cm.

　　ɪ. Title.

　　DL865.L52A3　　　　　　　50–21144

NL 0385129　DLC NN MnU

Lindskog, Claes, 1870–
　　Bonniers illustrerade litteratur historia ...
　　see under title

Lindskog, Claes, 1870–
　　De correcturis secundae manus in codice vetere Plautino. Lundæ: E. Malmström, 1900.　1 p.l., xxx, 28 p.　4°. (Lund. Universitet. Acta universitatis Lundensis. Lunds universitets årsskrift. Bd. 36, afdeln. 1. nr. 4. 1900.)

　　1. Plautus.
N. Y. P. L.　　　　　　　　　December 15, 1911.

NL 0385131　NN PU MH

Lindskog, Claës, 1870–
　　De enuntiatis apud Plautum et Terentium condicionalibus. Lundae, apud H. Möller, [1895].
　　pp. (4), 140 +.

　　Plautus-Lang.|Terentius–ɪ/o.|ɔ

NL 0385132　MH NjP IU ICU MiU OO CtY NcD ICRL CU NIC

Lindskog, Claes, 1870–
　　Euripides; moderna ideer i antik dräkt, av Claes Lindskog. Stockholm: H. Gebers förlagɛ, 1928ɔ.　vi, 280 p.　front.　8°.

　　1. Drama, Greek—Hist. and crit.　　2. Euripides.
N. Y. P. L.　　　　　　　　　　May 9, 1929

NL 0385133　NN

PA3016　**Lindskog, Claes,** 1870–
W7L5　　Graeske kvindeskikkelser. Autoriseret oversaettelse af H. P. Hoff-Hansen.　København, G. E. C. Gad, 1923.
　　vi, 256 p.

　　Contains studies of women characters in Greek literature, and also studies of contemporary women, namely: Sappho, Aspasia, Arsinoë, Berenike, Cleopatra and Hypatia.

　　1. Women in literature.　2. Women in Greece.　3. Greek literature - Hist. & crit.　4. Women in Greece - Biog.

NL 0385134　CU

Lindskog, Claes, 1870–
　　Grekiska hjältar och ideal, av Claes Lindskog. Stockholm, H. Geber ɛ1925ɔ
　　5 p. l. ɛ3ɔ–285, ɛ1ɔ p. 24ᶜᵐ.

　　1. Greece—Biog.　ɪ. Title.
　　　　　　　　　　　　　　　　　33–21433
Library of Congress　　DF208.L5　　　920.088

NL 0385135　DLC

Lindskog, Claës, 1870–
　　Quaestiones de parataxi et hypotaxi apud priscos Latinos. Lundae, H. Möller, [1896].
　　pp. (4), 95 +.

　　Latin lang.-Syntax|

NL 0385136　MH CU PBm NIC

Lindskog, Claës, 1870–
　　Studien zum antiken drama; mit zwei miscellen. Lund, H. Möller, 1897.
　　2 pt.
　　Contents: — ɪ. Über die komposition in den dramen des Euripides. — 2. Zu den tragödien des Seneca.

　　Euripides|Seneca,　　　　Lucius Annaeus–Trag

NL 0385137　MH IU NjP CtY PBm NIC CU IaU MiU

VOLUME 334

Lindskog, Eric,
In tropos scriptorum latinorum studia. ... Upsaliae, typis descripserunt Almqvist et Wiksell, 1903.
iv, 64 p., 1 l. 28cm.
Akademisk afhandling—Upsala.

1. Latin language—Figures of speech.

NL 0385138   MiU IU CU ICRL CtY PU

Lindskog, Erik.
On the geographical distribution of fog in Sweden, by Erik Lindskog ... Stockholm, Centraltryckeriet. 1931.
1 p. l., 94 p., 1 l. illus. (charts) diagrs. 24½ x 19cm.
Thesis—Stockholms högskola.
From Geografiska annaler 1931.
"Literature": p. 93–94.

1. Fog. 2. Sweden—Climate.

34–23688
Library of Congress   QC929.F7L5 1931   551.57

NL 0385139   DLC CtY DAS

JN7995
.H6L5
Lindskog, Gösta.
Med Högern för Sveriges framtid. Bok utg. till Höger-partiets 50-årsjubileum 1954. Stockholm, Högerns riks-organisation, 1954.
589 p. illus., ports. 29 cm.

1. Högerns riksorganisation. i. Title.

A 55–3113
Minnesota. Univ. Libr.
for Library of Congress   (1)

NL 0385140   MnU DLC-P4 NN

Lindskog, Gustaf E
Thoracic surgery and related pathology, by Gustaf E. Lindskog and Averill A. Liebow. New York, Appleton-Century-Crofts (1953)
644 p. illus. 26 cm.

1. Chest—Surgery. i. Liebow, Averill A., joint author. ii. Title.

RD536.L55   617.54   53–6359 ‡

PPPH DNLM
PPC PPWM   PU-UH PPJ PPT-M NcD   ICJ ViU AU
NL 0385141   DLC CaBVaU OrU-M OClW OU PPHa OClW-H

Lindskog, Hans Jonas, 1869–   ed.
Beiträge zur religionswissenschaft hrsg. von der Religionswissenschaftlichen gesellschaft in Stockholm ...
Stockholm, A. Bonnier; Leipzig, J. C. Hinrichs (1913–

Lindskog, Inga
see Arwin-Lindskog, Inga.

Div.S. **Lindskog, J**
230
B745A   Auktoritetsprincipen i kristen religion och teologi ... Lund, Gleerupska univ.-bokhandeln [1914]
183 p. 22cm. [With Bosson, Trued. Albrecht Ritschls teologi ... Lund [1895]]

NL 0385144   NcD

Lindskog, J
Krig och försvar i Kristen belysning; populär-vetenskaplig undersökning. Stockholm, Sveriges kristliga studentrörelses bokförlag [1931]

NL 0385145   MH

4DP   **Lindskog , J**
Span.   Spanien blöder. Stockholm, Tidens
232   förlag (1937)
115 p.

NL 0385146   DLC-P4

Lindskog, Joh. Chr. , respondent.
De imperio trapezuntino dissertatio...
see under Afzelius, Petrus Wilhelm, praeses.

Lindskog, Nat(anael) 1858–
En rings rörelse i en vätska ... Upsala, Akademiska boktryckeriet E. Berling, 1885.
2 p. l., 44 p. 26cm.
Inaug.-dis.—Upsala.

1. Toroidal harmonics.

4–27278†
Library of Congress   QA411.L75

NL 0385148   DLC MH ICRL

Lindskog, Petrus E. , respondent.
Fant, Erik Mikael, 1754–1817, praeses.
Specimen academicum de testamento r. Caroli Gustavi ... Upsaliæ, litteris J. Edman (1789)

Lindskog, Petrus Er. , respondent.
Dissertatio philosophica, an sola benevolentia virtutem constituat...
see under Christiernin, Peter Nikolai, praeses.

(Lindskold, Swan) 1878–
... Outline of the science of social relations. Detroit, University town publishers, 1937.
64 p. illus. 19cm.
At head of title: Academy of advanced social science.
Swan Lindskold, author.

NL 0385151   MiU-L

Lindskold, Swan, 1878–
... The story of gold. Ann Arbor, Mich., University town publishers, 1934.
39 p. 19cm.

1. Gold. 2. Money. i. Title.

39–11145
Library of Congress   HG289.L55

NL 0385152   DLC

Lindskold, Swan, 1878 –
Success in the business of living, by Swan Lindskold. Chicago, Ill., State law printing company (1932)
3 p. l., v, 271, (1) p. 19½cm.
Bibliography: (1) p. at end.

1. Conduct of life. i. Title.
32–35599
Library of Congress   BJ1581.L54
——— Copy 2.
Copyright A 58344   (3)   170

NL 0385153   DLC MiU

(**Lindskold, Swan,** 1878–
Whither millions? By Swaine Oakey (pseud.) Boston, The Christopher publishing house (°1934)
170 p. 21cm.

i. Title.

Library of Congress   PZ3.L65402Wh   34–2560

NL 0385154   DLC

LINDSKOUG, Ossian.
Lunkentus och andra gamla sagor å nyo berättade. Illustrerade i silhuett och akvarell av Eric O.Nilsson. Malmö,Forlag Maiander,1917.
Plates and other illustr.   25293.59

NL 0385155   MH

Lindskoug, Ossian   comp.
Skeppet som gick över vatten och land. Lund, Folkminnen och Folktankar, 1915.
95p. illus.

NL 0385156   ICRL

Lindskov Hansen, Johannes, 1907–
Gensyn med Grønland. Tegninger af Ernst Hansen. København, Munksgaard (195–)
27 p. illus. 20 cm.

1. Greenland—Descr. & trav. i. Title.

G743.L56   *919.82   53–35564 rev ‡

NL 0385157   DLC NhD

DL   **Lindskov Hansen, Johannes, 1907–**
118   Øerne i Nordhavet, Færøerne og Grønland.
D39   Redaktion Johannes Lindskov Hansen og
v.10+   Niels Th. Mortensen. (Odense) Forlaget Irnkrone, 1949.
245 p. illus. 26cm. (On spine: Danmark; Landet mellem Hav og Bælt. v. 10)

1. Faroe Islands—Descr. & trav.
2. Greenland—Descr. & trav. I. Title.
II. Series.

NL 0385158   NIC MH NN

839.8136
L64rl **Lindskov Hansen, Johannes, 1907–**
En roman kommer til verden... København, E. Munksgaard, 1946.
32p. illus. 20cm.

NL 0385159   KU NN

VOLUME 334

Lindskov Hansen, Johannes, 1907–
... Vandene aabner sig. København, Gyldendal, 1945.
153 p. 21½ᶜᵐ.
Novel.

I. Title.
PT8175.L535V3

47-20312

NL 0385160 DLC

608.2   LINDSKROG, Christian
L97.9   Den kristne tro; en gennemgang af
Box 3   Luthers Lille katekismus. Koebenhavn,
         Gyldendalske Boghandel-Nordisk Forlag,
         1936.
           174p. 22cm.

NL 0385161 MH-AH

Lindsley, A   B.
   Love and friendship; or, Yankee notions: a comedy, in three
acts. By A. B. Lindsley. New-York: Published by D. Longworth, at the Dramatic repository. Shakspeare-gallery. 1809.
   58 p. 16½ᶜᵐ.

I. Title. II. Title: Yankee notions.

Library of Congress   PS2246.L58L6   1-3466

MH MoU
NL 0385162 DLC MsU NIC IU PU NNC KyU MiU-C MB MnU

Lindsley, Aaron Ladner, 1817-1891.
   Exposure of children to the practice of vice
and the commission of crime
      see his   The right thing first.

Lindsley, Aaron Ladner, 1817-1891.
   Farewell sermon of Rev. A. L. Lindsley, D. D., delivered
upon closing his ministry in the First Presbyterian church,
Portland, Oregon, together with his letter of resignation, the
action of the Presbytery, and of the congregation, and the
address of the Rev. E. W. Garner, D. D., in declaring the pulpit
vacant. Portland, Or., 1886.
   4, ₅, ₇₇-43 p. 18ᶜᵐ.

I. Portland, Or. First Presbyterian church. II. Title.

                                                    28-3266
Library of Congress   BX9225.L5A4

NL 0385164 DLC WaWW OrHi OrP OrU PPPrHi

Lindsley, Aaron Ladner, 1817-1891.
   Harmony and co-operation in the church; a
sermon preached to the First Presbyterian
congregation, September 6, 1885 ... Himes,
1885.
   15 p.

NL 0385165 OrP

---

041   Lindsley, Aaron Ladner, 1817-1891.
F144   National righteousness and national sin: the
v.36   substance of a discourse delivered in the Pres-
no.25   byterian church of South Salem, Westchester co.,
        N.Y., November 20, 1856 ...   New York, Printed by
        E. O. Jenkins, 1857.
           34p.

        ₜFahnestock pamphlets, v.36, no.25₁

           1. U.S.--Pol. & govt.--1857-1861. 2. Thanks
        giving day addresses. I. Title.

NL 0385166 IU NNC MWA N MiU

Lindsley, Aaron Ladner, 1817-1891.
   The natural method of correction and reform.
By A. L. Lindsley, D.D. ... Read before Pacific
Coast conference of charities, Dec. 1886.
   4 p.   23 cm.   [Pamphlets on crime. v. 9]
Caption title.
   1. Social problems.

NL 0385167 CU

Lindsley, Aaron Ladner, 1817-1891.
   Plea for state boards of charities and
corrections on the Pacific coast; delivered at
the conference, San Francisco, December 16, 1887.
Author, 1887.
   18 p.

NL 0385168 OrP CU

Lindsley, Aaron Ladner, 1817-1891.
   The right thing first. The family the sure
foundation of the state. Exposure of children
to the practice of vice and the commission of
crime. A discourse ... April 12, [1885]
[Portland? Oregon? 1885]
   8 p.   8°.
   n. t.-p.
   Repr.: "Morning Oregonian", Apr. 16, 1885.

NL 0385169 NN CU

Lindsley, Aaron Ladner, 1817-1891.
   Sketches of an excursion to southern Alaska.
₍n.p., 1881?₎

   Cover-title.
   Contents.--I. Voyage to Sitka, historical and
descriptive.--II. Geographical. Climatic. Population.--III. Southern Alaska, plans for improving the natives.--IV. Suggestions concerning
schools and buildings, ways and means.--V. Relations of the people of the United States to the
civilization of the native Alaskans, a letter
addressed to President Hayes.--VI. Report to the

Synod of the Columbia, 1880.--VII. Present
condition of the work, May 1881, by S.H. Young.

CtY NjP CSmH AkU
NL 0385171   NN CaBViPA NjR WaU OrHi OrU OrPR ICN MH

19th   LINDSLEY, Charles Augustus, 1826-1906.
cent   Facts in sanitation of practical
RA436   value, by C.A. Lindsley. [n.p., 1890]
L55   29p.   24cm.
1890   At head of caption title: Reprinted
        from Conn. Board of Agriculture Report
        1890.

           1. Hygiene, Public - Addresses, essays,
        lectures I. Title

NL 0385172 CtY-M

Lindsley, C₍harles₎ A₍ugustus₎, 1826-1906.
   The prescription of proprietary medicines for the sick — its
demoralizing effects on the medical profession. An essay read
before the Connecticut Medical Society, at the annual meeting
held at New Haven on May 24th and 25th, 1882. ₍New Haven,
Conn.:₎ Connecticut Medical Society ₍1882₎.   16 p.   8°.

   ₍Toner₎

I. Medicine (Proprietary).
N.Y.P.L.   July 16, 1912.

NL 0385173 NN DNLM PPHa DLC MH

        Lindsley, Charles Augustus, 1826-1906.
T₍p51   Puerperal convulsions ... Hartford, 1858.
1
           "Read before the New Haven county medical
        society, April, 1858."
           "Published by order of the Connecticut
        medical society, May 27, 1858."

           I. Connecticut state medical society.

NL 0385174 CtY

        Lindsley, Charles Augustus, 1826-1906.
Toner   Vaccination; by Prof. C. A. Lindsley ... Hartford, Conn.,
        The Case, Lockwood & Brainard co., printers, 1882.
           29 p. 1 illus. 23ᶜᵐ.
        "From the report of the secretary of state Board of health."

           1. Vaccination. 2. Vaccine lymph.
                                                    34-39771
        Library of Congress   RM787.L5

NL 0385175 DLC DNLM CtY-M

        Lindsley, Charles Bradley.
           Educational philosophy of Thomas Davidson
        ...₍Cin.,₎ 1926.
           110 p.

        Thesis, Univ. of Cincinnati, Ph.D. 1926.

NL 0385176 OCU

        ₍Lindsley, Charles E   ₎
           The English regicides in America.
           (*In* The Magazine of history with notes and queries. Tarrytown,
        N. Y., 1931. 26½ᶜᵐ. Extra number. no. 175 (v. 44, no. 3) p. ₍37₎-58
        incl. map)
           Caption title.
           Signed: Charles E. Lindsley.
           "This story ... was the subject of an address before the Westchester
        county historical society, in 1893 ... and has never before been pub-
        lished in this form."--Editor's pref.

           1. Regicides. 2. Goffe, William, 1605?-1679? 3. Whalley, Edward,
        d. 1675? 4. Dixwell, John, d. 1689. I. Title.
                                                    32-3342
        Library of Congress   E173.M24 no. 175

NL 0385177 DLC MiU OCl

        Lindsley, Charles Frederick, 1894–
           Radio and television communication. 1st ed. New York,
        McGraw-Hill, 1952.
           492 p. illus. 24 cm.
           Includes bibliography.

           1. Radio broadcasting. 2. Television broadcasting. I. Title.

        PN1991.5.L5   *792.94 791.4   52-6543 ‡

        CaBVa MtU MtBC
        ViU PU-Penn OClW FU CaBVaU OrU Or WaSp WaS OrP OrCS
NL 0385178   DLC OrPS OrMonO OrAshS NcD NN TU TxU MB

        Lindsley, Charles H., joint author.

        Douglass, Edward Lewis, *jr.*
           The poet's song; a collection of poems by Edward L.
        Douglass, jr., and Charles H. Lindsley, with introduction
        by Miss G. M. Dennison ... ₍Cincinnati₎ 1926.

VOLUME 334

Lindsley, Charles Halsey, 1908–
The cryoscopic study of certain aliphatic alcohols ... by Charles Halsey Lindsley ... Easton, Pa., Mack printing company, 1934.

cover-title, 5 p. diagrs. 26½ x 20ᶜᵐ.

Thesis (PH. D.)—Princeton university, 1933.
"By T. J. Webb and C. H. Lindsley."
"Reprinted from the Journal of the American chemical society, 56 ... (1934)."

1. Alcohols. 2. Cryoscopy. I. Webb, Thomas Jefferson, 1900– joint author.

34–42156

Library of Congress   QD305.A4L6 1933
Princeton Univ. Libr.

———— Copy 2.   (2)   547.3

NL   0385180   NjP OCU OU DLC

LINDSLEY, David Philip, 1834–1897.
The alphabet of Tachygraphy, on Lindsley's phonetic short hand. n.p., [1864].

pp. pp.(8).   B 4353.67

NL   0385181   MH

[Lindsley, David Philip] 1834–1897.
The alphabet of tachygraphy, with directions for its use, and reading lesson with key. To which is added specimen pages of the "Elements", [by D. P. Lindsley] and table of contents of the Rapid Writer Quarterly ... Boston, O. Clapp & Son [1873?]
6 l. 12°.
Paging various.

NL   0385182   NN

Lindsley, D[avid] P[hilip], 1834–1897.
The compend of takigrafy; the new fonetic short-hand, containing a summary of the principles of the simple style. New York: D. Kimball, 1879.   v, 7–34 p.   12°.

1. Shorthand.—Systems (American).   BEALE SHORTHAND COLL.
N. Y. P. L.   1879.   December 11, 1912.

NL   0385183   NN ICN

Lindsley, D[avid] P[hilip], 1834–1897.
The compendium of tachygraphy; or, Lindsley's *Phonetic* shorthand, explaining and illustrating the common style of the art. Hartford: Brown & Gross, 1864.   32 p.   8°.

———— Boston: O. Clapp, 1865.   34 p., 9 l.   2. ed. 8°.

1. Shorthand.—Systems (American),   BEALE SHORTHAND COLL.
N. Y. P. L.   1865.   November 20, 1912.

NL   0385184   NN MH CtY ICN CU

Lindsley, David Philip, 1834–1897.
The compendium of tachygraphy: or, Lindsley's phonetic shorthand ... By D. P. Lindsley ... 3d ed. Boston, O. Clapp; New York, Schermerhorn, Bancroft, & co.; [etc., etc.] 1866.
38 p., 1 l. 20 pl. on 12 l. 24ᵐ.

1. Shorthand. I. Title: Tachygraphy.

11—6595

Library of Congress   Z56.L75C3

NL   0385185   DLC NN

Lindsley, David Philip, 1834–1897.
The compendium of tachygraphy; or, Lindsley's Phonetic short-hand, explaining and illustrating the common style of the art. By D. P. Lindsley. .... Fourth edition. Boston, O. Clapp, 1867.
58 p. 22ᶜᵐ.
With The Rapid writer, vol. 1.

NL   0385186   ICJ MH CtY

Lindsley, David Philip, 1834–1897.
Dime short-hand writer. By D. P. Lindsley. New York, E. L. Kellogg & co., 1882.
30 p. 15ᶜᵐ.
Also issued under title: Popular short-hand in a nutshell.

1. Shorthand.

11–6604

Library of Congress   Z56.L75D

NL   0385187   DLC

Lindsley, David Philip, 1834–1897.
The elements of tachygraphy ... By David Philip Lindsley. Boston, O. Clapp, 1869.
102, 20 p. 19½ᶜᵐ.
"Reading lessons" (20 p. at end) are engraved.

1. Shorthand.

11–6594

Library of Congress   Z56.L75E '69

NL   0385188   DLC PPM PCC NN ICN OO MB NN

Lindsley, David Philip, 1834–1897.
The elements of tachygraphy, illustrating the first principles of the art ... Boston, O. Clapp & Son, 1873.
128 p. 12°.
3 ed.

NL   0385189   NN DLC CtY MB

Lindsley, David Philip, 1834–1897.
The elements of tachygraphy ... By David Philip Lindsley. 4th ed. Boston, O. Clapp & son, 1874.
116, [113]–128 p. 18½ᵐ.
"Reading lessons" (16 p. at end) are engraved.

1. Shorthand. I. Title: Tachygraphy.

11—6597

Library of Congress   Z56.L75E4

NL   0385190   DLC

Lindsley, David Philip, 1834–1897.
The elements of tachygraphy ... By David Philip Lindsley. 5th ed. Boston, O. Clapp & son, 1876.
143 p. 19ᶜᵐ.
"Reading lessons" (16 p. at end) are engraved.

1. Shorthand.

17–26985

Library of Congress   Z56.L75E5

NL   0385191   DLC NN

Lindsley, David Philip, 1834–1897.
The elements of tachygraphy ... By David Philip Lindsley. 6th ed. Boston, O. Clapp & son, 1878.

42
L641
1878
copy 1
Shorthand
Collection

134, 137–143p. 18½cm.
"Reading lessons": p.[117]–134 are engraved.

42
L641
1878
copy 2

—— ——— Binding variant.

NL   0385192   CtY

Lindsley, David Philip, 1834–1897.
The elements of tachygraphy. Illustrating the first principles of the art, with their adaptation to the wants of literary, professional and business men. Designed as a text-book for classes and for private instruction by David Philip Lindsley. Boston: O. Clapp & Son, 1880.   134 p.   7. ed.   12°.

Differs from another issue only in binding.

1. Shorthand.—Systems (Ameri-   BEALE SHORTHAND COLL.
N. Y. P. L.   can), 1880.   April 19, 1919.

NL   0385193   NN CtY MH

Lindsley, David Philip, 1834–1897.
The elements of tachygraphy ... By David Philip Lindsley. 8th ed. Boston, O. Clapp & son, 1881.
134 p. 18½ᶜᵐ.
"Reading lessons" (p. 119–134) are engraved.

1. Shorthand.

11—6598

Library of Congress   Z56.L75E8

NL   0385194   DLC NN

Z56
L75
1884

Lindsley, David Philip, 1834–1897.
The elements of tachygraphy, illustrating the first principles of the art. 10th ed. Boston, Otis Clapp & Son, 1884.

140p. 19cm.

NL   0385195   NBuG CtY NN

Lindsley, David Philip, 1834–1897.
The elements of tachygraphy, illustrating the first principles of the art, with their adaptation to the wants of literary, professional, and business men. Designed as a text-book for classes and for private instruction. 11th ed. Boston, O. Clapp & son, 1885.

NL   0385196   MH CtY PPL

Lindsley, David Philip, 1834–97
The elements of tachygraphy, illustrating the first principles of the art, with their adaptation to the wants of literary, professional, and business men. 12th ed. Boston, Clapp, 1886
140 p.

NL   0385197   MH NN

Lindsley, David Philip, 1834–1897.
The elements of tachygraphy ... Rewritten and re-engraved. By David Philip Lindsley. 13th ed. Boston, D. Clapp & son, 1889.
115 p. 19ᶜᵐ.

1. Shorthand.

17–26984

Library of Congress   Z56.L75E8 1889

NL   0385198   DLC

VOLUME 334

Lindsley, David Philip, 1834-1897.
The elements of tachygraphy ... Rewritten
and re-engraved. By ... 14th ed. Boston,
D. Clapp & son, 1890.
119 p.

NL 0385199   OC MiU CtY

Lindsley, David Philip.
The elements of tachygraphy. Illustrating the first principles of
the art, with their adaptation to the wants of literary, professional,
and business men. Rewritten and re-engraved. By David Philip
Lindsley. Fifteenth edition. New York, The University Book
Co., 1893. [ᶜ1889].
117 p. 18½ᶜᵐ.

NL 0385200   ICJ NN CtY

Lindsley, David Philip, 1834-1897.
The hand book of takigrafy. Giving briefly the principles of
the contracted style; and designed for the use of amanuenses
and verbatim reporters; with an introductory chapter on the
simple style. By David Philip Lindsley ... New York city,
D. P. Lindsley, 1882.
2 p. l., 168 p. 19½ᶜᵐ.

1. Shorthand.   I. Title: Takigrafy.

Library of Congress   Z56.L75H

11—6600

NL 0385201   DLC ICN CtY NN OC1

Lindsley, David Philip, 1834-1897.
The hand-book of takigrafy. Giving briefly the principles of the contracted style, and designed for the use of
amanuenses and verbatim reporters. With an introductory chapter on the simple style. By David Philip Lindsley ... 2d ed. Chicago, D. Kimball, 1884.
2 p. l., 168 p. 19½ᶜᵐ.
Title edition; literal reprint of the 1882 edition.

1. Shorthand.

Library of Congress   Z56.L75H2

11—6601

NL 0385202   DLC NN ICRL

Lindsley, David Philip, 1834-1897.
The hand-book of takigrafy. Giving briefly the principles of the contracted style, and designed for the use of
amanuenses and verbatim reporters. With an introductory chapter on the simple style. By David Philip Lindsley ... 3d ed. Chicago, D. Kimball, 1888.
2 p. l., 168 p. 19½ᶜᵐ.
Title edition; literal reprint of the 1882 edition.

1. Shorthand.

Library of Congress   Z56.L75H3
1882: 4241

11—6602

NL 0385203   DLC NN ICJ

Lindsley, David Philip, 1834-1897.
Hand-book of takigrafy giving the principles
of the contracted style, & designed for the use
of amanuensis and verbatims reporters. 4th ed.
Chic., Kimball, 1891.
168 p.   D.

NL 0385204   OC CtY

Lindsley, David Philip, 1834-1897.
Key to the Shorthand exercise book. Part 1 ...
Chicago, D. Kimball; Philadelphia, The author,
1887.
31 p.   19 cm.

NL 0385205   CtY

Lindsley, David Philip, 1834-1897.
The manual of fonetic analysis for use in public and
private schools. Designed to accompany a chart of the
new fonetic shorthand alfabet ... By D. P. Lindsley ...
Chicago, D. Kimball, 1888.
31 p. 18½ᶜᵐ.

1. Shorthand.

Library of Congress   Z56.L75M

10-3240

NL 0385206   DLC NN

Lindsley, David Philip, 1834-1897.
The manual of takigrafy, adapted for use in high schools
and academies, with some exercises suitable for children. By
D. P. Lindsley ... Chicago, D. Kimball; Boston, O. Clapp &
son, 1876.
119 p. 20½ᶜᵐ.

1. Shorthand.   I. Title: Takigrafy.

Library of Congress   Z56.L75M2

16—2539

NL 0385207   DLC Wa OO ICJ NN MB

Z
201
.5065c
LINDSLEY, DAVID PHILIP, 1834-1897.
The manual of takigrafy, adapted for use in
high schools and academies, with some exercises
suitable for children. 2d edition.   Chicago,
D. Kimball, 1878.
119p.   illus.   20cm.

Bookplate of James W. Beers.

NL 0385208   ICN NN ICJ MH

Lindsley, David Philip, 1834-1897.
The manual of takigrafy, adapted for use in high schools and
academies, with some exercises suitable for children. By D. P.
Lindsley, ... Third edition. New York, D. P. Lindsley, 1882.
123 p. illus. 20ᶜᵐ.

NL 0385209   ICJ NN CtY

Z
201
.5065
LINDSLEY, DAVID PHILIP, 1834-1897.
The manual of takigrafy, adapted for the
use of high schools and academies, with some
exercises suitable for children. 4th edition.
Plainfield, N.J., 1885[c1876]
123p.   illus.   20cm.
Bookplate of James W. Beers.

Z
201
.5065a
---- ---- 5th edition.   Chicago, D. Kimball,
1887[c1876]
123p.   illus.   20cm.

NL 0385210   ICN CtY NN OC1

Lindsley, D[avid] P[hilip], 1834-1897.
The manual of takigrafy, adapted for use in high schools and
academies, with some exercises suitable for children.   Chicago:
D. Kimball, 1887. 123 p.   5. ed.   12°.

1. Shorthand.—Systems (American).   1887.
N.Y.P.L.

BEALE SHORTHAND COLL.

December 11, 1912.

NL 0385211   NN CtY

[Lindsley, David Philip,] 1834-1897.
The note-taker; or, Elements of tachygraphy, part II. A
treatise on the second style of Lindsley's brief writing... no. 1- 2
Boston: O. Clapp, 1872.   12°.
"To be complete in 8 monthly numbers."

1. Shorthand.—Systems (American),   NAT. SHORTHAND REP. ASSOC.
N.Y.P.L.   1872. 2. Title.
                                                April 23, 1919.

NL 0385212   NN CtY

Lindsley, David Philip.
The note-taker; or, Elements of tachygraphy. Part 2. A
treatise on the second style of Lindsley's brief writing... Boston: O. Clapp & Son, 1873. 233 p. 12°.
Interleaved, with ms. notes. Bookplate of C. C. Beale.

1. Shorthand.—Systems (Ameri-   BEALE SHORTHAND COLL.
N.Y.P.L.   can), 1873.
                                        October 28, 1912.

NL 0385213   NN CtY DLC MH PP ICN

Lindsley, David Philip, 1834-1897.
The note-taker; or, Elements of tachygraphy,
part II. A treatise on the second style of Lindsley's
brief writing ... 2d ed.   Boston, O. Clapp & son;
Chicago, D. Kimball, 1877.
2 p. l., 204 p., 1 l., 16, 223-233 p.   19 cm.
"Reading lessons" (1 l., 16 p. following p. 204)
are engraved.

NL 0385214   CtY NN

Lindsley, David Philip, 1834-1897.
The note-taker; or, Elements of tachygraphy, part II. A treatise
on the second style of Lindsley's Brief writing for the use of lawyers, editors, reporters, students, ... By David Philip Lindsley. Third edition. Boston, O. Clapp & Son, 1881.
[4], 204, 16 p. 19ᶜᵐ.

NL 0385215   ICJ NN ICRL

[Lindsley, David Philip] 1834-1897.
... Popular short-hand in a nutshell. New York, D.
Kimball, 1880.
30 p. 15 x 8½ᶜᵐ.
Also issued under title: Dime short-hand writer.

1. Shorthand.

Library of Congress   Z56.L75P

11—6606

NL 0385216   DLC

[Lindsley, David Philip] 1834-1897.
Popular short-hand in a nutshell. Chicago, D. Kimball,
1883.
30 p. 15½ x 8½ᶜᵐ.
First issued 1880.
Also issued under title: Dime short-hand writer.

1. Shorthand.   I. Title.

Library of Congress   Z56.L75P3

11—6608

NL 0385217   DLC

VOLUME 334

Lindsley, David Philip, 1834-1897.
... Popular short-hand in a nutshell. [4th ed.] Chicago D. Kimball, 1883.
30 p. 15 x 9ᶜᵐ.
Also issued under title: Dime short-hand writer.

1. Shorthand. 11-6607

Library of Congress Z56.L75P4

NL 0385218 DLC

Lindsley, David Philip, 1834-1897,
Prospectus of phonografied phonography.
N. p. [1862.] (4) pp. 19 cm.

M8035 — Shorthand. Works about. — Phonographied phonography.

NL 0385219 MB

Lindsley, David Philip, 1834-1897, ed.
The **Rapid** writer, quarterly, devoted to language, short-hand writing, and kindred topics. v. 1–
Jan. 15, 1869–
[Mendon. Mass., etc.] Rapid writer association [1869–

Lindsley, David Philip, 1834-1897.
[Reading exercises. Boston? 1869.] 20 p. 16°.

O'KEEFE COLLECTION.
1. Shorthand—Exercises, 1869. June 30, 1925
N. Y. P. L.

NL 0385221 NN

Lindsley, David Philip, 1834-1897.
A short course in business shorthand ... By David Philip Lindsley ... Chicago, D. Kimball; Boston, O. Clapp & son, 1888.
95 p. 20½ᶜᵐ.

1. Shorthand. 11-6599

Library of Congress Z56.L75S

NL 0385222 DLC NIC ICN ICJ NN

Lindsley, David Philip, 1834-1897.
Shorthand as a science. [n.p.,n.d.] 32 f.
28 cm.

Caption-title.

1. Shorthand.

NL 0385223 NN

Lindsley, David Philip.
The shorthand exercise book; embodying a new and improved style for the use of intelligent and cultivated people, and for all writing purposes... In five parts. With key. Part 1-2, and key. Chicago: D. Kimball [cop. 1887-88]. 3 v. 12°.

BEALE SHORTHAND COLL.
1. Shorthand.—Exercises. December 27, 1912.
N. Y. P. L.

NL 0385224 NN ICN DLC

Lindsley, D[avid] P[hilip], 1834-1897.
Suggestions for improvement, presented to the short hand revision committe of 1895. In six parts. Part 1. New York: University Book Co., 1895. 1 part. 8°.

1. Shorthand—Systems (American). BEALE SHORTHAND COLL.
N. Y. P. L. 1895. January 31, 1913.

NL 0385225 NN

Lindsley, [David Philip], 1834-1897.
Swift fonetic script for the use of literary, professional, and business men...in accordance with the principles of Lindsley's takigrafy. Arranged and published by D. Kimball. Chicago, 1898. 64 p. ob. 32°.

1. Shorthand.—Systems (American). BEALE SHORTHAND COLL.
N. Y. P. L. 1898. 2. Kimball, Duran, editor. January 11, 1913.

NL 0385226 NN

Lindsley, David Philip, 1834-1897.
... Tachygraphy, or Lindsley's phonetic short-hand.
[Boston, 186-?]
[4] p. 20½ᶜᵐ.
Caption title.
Circular, with terms of instruction.

CA 11-1357 Unrev'd

Library of Congress Z56.L75T

NL 0385227 DLC

Lindsley, David Philip, 1834-1897, ed.
The **Takigrafer**. v. 1–2 (whole no. [1]–9) [Jan.] 1874–Jan. 1876. [Andover, Mass., etc., Rapid writer association] 1874–76.

Lindsley, David Philip, 1834-1897.
The young writer's primer. An introduction to brief and rapid writing, in an available system of phonetic short-hand... New York City: D. P. Lindsley, 1882. 15(1) p. 12°.

1. Shorthand.—Systems (American). BEALE SHORTHAND COLL.
N. Y. P. L. 1882. December 10, 1912.

NL 0385229 NN ICN CtY

Lindsley, Donald Benjamin, 1907–
... Bilateral differences in brain potentials from the two cerebral hemispheres in relation to laterality and stuttering ... [n.p., 1940]
211-225 p. tables, diagrs. 25 cm.
(Brown university--Dept. of psychology. Publications, v. 4)
Caption title.
"Reprinted from the Journal of experimental psychology, vol. 26, no. 2, February 1940."
"References.": p. 225.

NL 0385230 RPB

Lindsley, Donald Benjamin, 1907–
Clinical and electroencephalographic changes in a child during recovery from encephalitis [by] Donald B. Lindsley ... and Katherine Knox Cutts ... Chicago, American medical association 1941.
cover-title, 6 p. table, diagr. (Brown university-- Dept. of psychology Publications, v. 4.)
"Reprinted with additions, from the Archives of neurology and psychiatry. Jan. 1941, vol. 45, p. 156-161."
Bibliographical foot-notes.

NL 0385231 RPB

Lindsley, Donald Benjamin, 1907–
LB1103 .S6 vol. 9, no. 3 Henry, Charles Eric, 1915–
Electroencephalograms of normal children, by Charles E. Henry ... Washington, D. C., Society for research in child development, National research council, 1944.

Lindsley, Henry A.
The municipal code of the city and county of Denver
see under Denver. Ordinances, etc.

HD 211 T4 L52 TXC-Z
Lindsley, Henry D
The Ringgold country and its development [by] Henry D. Lindsley. Ringgold, Tex. [1905?]
16 p. 24 cm.

Cover title.

1. Land - Texas - Montague Co. I. Title.

NL 0385234 TxU

Lindsley, Henry D., & co.
The oil industry in restrospect and prospect (an analysis). Issued by Henry D. Lindsley & co. New York. 1924?
20 p. incl. illus. pl. (fold. diagr.) 23ᶜᵐ.

1. Petroleum. I. Title.

G S 28-116
Library. U. S. Geological Survey 467 L64o

NL 0385235 DI-GS

Lindsley, Irma Y., comp.
Colorado. University. *College of engineering.*
... Alumni directory, 1897-1917, College of engineering. Boulder, Col., 1917.

Lindsley, Ivy.
This is a promise, by Ivy Lindsley ... Cover design by the author. Dallas, Tex., The Kaleidograph press [1944]
xi p., 1 l., 15-96 p. 19½ᶜᵐ.
Poems.

I. Title. 44-6983

Library of Congress PS3523.I624T45
[3] 811.5

NL 0385237 DLC

Lindsley, Ivy.
What matter time or tide, by Ivy Lindsley. Dallas, Tex., The Kaleidograph press [*1936]
92 p. 19½ᶜᵐ.
Poems.

I. Title. 37-4644

Library of Congress PS3523.I624W5 1936
———— Copy 2.
Copyright A 104341 [2] 811.5

NL 0385238 DLC

VOLUME 334

Lindsley, J. V. comp.
    Southern universal catalog and universal price
list
      see under   Columbus Iron Works Co.,
Columbus, Ga.

Lindsley, Jack N
    The effect of temperature cycling on the physical prop-
erties of FS–1 magnesium alloy sheet metal. Pasadena,
1953.
  iv, 41 l. illus. 29 cm. (Guggenheim Aeronautical Laboratory,
California Institute of Technology. GALCIT report)

  Photocopy of typescript (positive)
  Thesis (aeronautical engineer)—California Institute of Technology.
  Bibliography : at 17.

  1. Magnesium alloys—Testing. 2. Metals at high temperatures.
I. Title.   (Series : California Institute of Technology, Pasadena.
Daniel Guggenheim Aeronautical Laboratory. GALCIT report)

  TA480.M3L5   64–47047

  NL 0385240   DLC

Lindsley, James Elliott.
    A history of Saint Peter's Church, Morristown, New
Jersey. ₍Morristown?₎ 1952₎
  102 p. illus. 21 cm.

  1. Morristown, N. J. St. Peter's Church. I. Title.

  BX5980.M67S3   283.749   52–31358 rev ‡

  NL 0385241   DLC

Lindsley, John Berrien, 1822–1897.
    Address before the Alumni Soc. of the University
of Nashville, Oct. 3, 1854. Nashville, 1855.
  8°

  NL 0385242   NN

Lindsley, John Berrien, 1822–1897.
    Address delivered before the Alumni society of the
University of Nashville, by John Berrien Lindsley ... on
the 3d of October, 1854 ... Nashville, Cameron & Fall,
book and job printers, 1854.
  25 p. 21ᶜᵐ.
  Pub. at the request of the Board of trustees.

  I. Nashville, Tenn. University.

                       E 12–737
  Library, U. S. Bur. of   Education LD3605.8.L63

  NL 0385243   DHEW

Lindsley, John Berrien, 1822–1897.
    An address on the life and character of Robert M.
Porter, M. D., late professor of anatomy in the University
of Nashville. By John Berrien Lindsley, M. D., chancellor
of the university. Delivered at Nashville, Nov. 8, 1856.
Pub. by the class. Nashville, Tenn., Printed by E. Val-
lette, 1856.
  47 p. 23¼ᶜᵐ.

  1. Porter, Robert Massengill, 1818–1856.
                        15–2249
  Library of Congress   R154.P75L7

  NL 0385244   DLC DNLM PU PPCP CtY DLC CtHT–W

Lindsley, John Berrien, 1822–1897.
    African colonization and Christian missions. By J. Ber-
rien Lindsley ... ₍Nashville, Tenn, 1873?₎
  24 p. 22½ᶜᵐ.
  Caption title.
  "From the Theological medium. for October, 1873, a Cumberland
Presbyterian quarterly, Nashville, Tenn."

  1. Negroes—Colonization—Africa. I. Title.

                      CA 30–366 Unrev'd
  Library of Congress   E448.L74

  NL 0385245   DLC CtY PHi NIC NjP

Lindsley, John Berrien, 1822–1897.
    Appeal to the citizens of Davidson County, in behalf of
their university, by John Berrien Lindsley ... June 12th,
1856. Nashville, Cameron & Fall, printers, 1856.
  8 p. 23ᶜᵐ.

  1. Nashville, Tenn. University.

                      7–27086†
  Library of Congress   LD3603.L5

  NL 0385246   DLC TNJ NN MB MnHi

Lindsley, John Berrien, 1822–1897.
    Law school of Cumberland university, Lebanon, Ten-
nessee ... Nashville, Tenn., Cumberland Presbyterian
publishing house, 1876.
  cover-title, 25 p. 21½ᶜᵐ.
  Extract from "The educational history of the Cumberland Presbyterian
church by J. Berrien Lindsley."

  1. Cumberland university, Lebanon, Tenn. Law school.

                      E 14–1630
  Library. U. S. Bur. of   Education LC1161.C9L6

  NL 0385247   DHEW

Lindsley, John Berrien, 1822–1897, *ed.*
    The military annals of Tennessee. Confederate. First series:
embracing a review of military operations, with regimental
histories and memorial rolls, compiled from original and official sources, and edited by John Berrien Lindsley ... Printed
for subscribers. Nashville, J. M. Lindsley & co., 1886.
  910 p. front. port. 25ᶜᵐ.
  Cover-title: The civil war; Tennessee roll of honor.
  No more published.

  1. U. S.—Hist.—Civil war.—Regimental histories—Tenn. 2. Tennessee—Militia. 3. Tennessee—Hist.—Civil war. I. Title.

                      2–23124
  Library of Congress   E579.4.L75

      NcD DNW MH NjP ViU MWA
  NL 0385248   DLC MB PHi PPL OClWHi KyHi IU C–S MU

Lindsley, John Berrien, 1822–
  ——. Nashville and the university; an address
delivered Nov. 6, 1865. 16 pp. 8°. *Nashville,
W. H. F. Ligon, 1865.*

  NL 0385249   DNLM

Lindsley, John Berrien, 1822–1897.
    On medical colleges. An introductory lecture, to the course
of 1858–59, in the medical department of the University of
Nashville, by J. Berrien Lindsley ... Pub. by the class. Nashville, Printed by J. T. Bell & co., 1858.
  32 p. 20¾ᶜᵐ.

  1. Medical colleges—U. S. I. Nashville university.

                     E 12–739
  Library, U. S. Office of   Education R745.L64

  NL 0385250   DHEW DNLM DLC NN MB CSmH CtY–M CtHT–W

Lindsley, John Berrien, 1822–1897.
    ... On prison discipline and penal legislation; with special
reference to the state of Tennessee ... By J. Berrien Lindsley
... Nashville, Tenn., Printed for the Robertson association,
1874.
  cover-title, 64 p. 22½ᶜᵐ.

  "Written for the July number of the Theological medium. In substance, preached in the First Cumberland Presbyterian church, of Nashville, August 9 and 16, 1874."
  "Charter of the Robertson association ₍officers—1874; reminiscences,
etc.₎": p. ₍59₎–64.

  1. Prisons. 2. Prisons—Tennessee. I. Robertson association, Nashville, Tenn

  Library of Congress   HV9475.T2L7   10–34615

      MiU OO OCl NN MB MH
  NL 0385251   DLC CtHT–W MnHi GEU–L TxU PPL NcD OFH

Lindsley, John Berrian, *M. D.* 1822——. Report on the yellow fever in Nashville, Tenn., Sept. and
Oct. 1878. 7 pp. ₍Am. Pub. Health Assoc. *Reports,* v. 4,
n. 341.₎

  NL 0385252   MdBP

E   Lindsley, John Berrien, 1822–1897.
464   Specimen pages from The military annals
R29   of Tennessee. Confederate. First series.
v.15   Nashville ₍Tenn.₎ J. M. Lindsley, 1886.
no.9   ₍16₎ p. 25cm.   4

    Editorial review of book reprinted from
Nashville Daily American, May 13, 1886,
inserted.

  NL 0385253   NIC

Lindsley, Mrs. Julia (West) 1827–1905.
    Brief biography of Aaron Ladner Lindsley, D. D.
LL. D., by his wife.   1921?
  37 p.
  Typewritten copy.

  NL 0385254   OrP

Lindsley, Lorna (Stimson)
    War is people ₍by₎ Lorna Lindsley. Boston, Houghton
Mifflin company, 1943.
  xi, ₍1₎, 272, ₍1₎ p. front., illus. 21½ cm.

  1. Spain—Hist.—Civil war, 1936–1939—Personal narratives. 2.
Palestine—Pol. & govt. 3. World war, 1939–1945—France. I. Title.

  D413.L56A3   940.52   43–4215

    WU WaS Or OrP IdB CaBVa WaSp
  NL 0385255   DLC PPL PPPCity OCH OU OCl NcC NcD CoU

Lindsley, Luther Campbell, 1888–
    Industrial microscopy, by L. C. Lindsley ... Richmond, Va.,
The William Byrd press, inc., 1929.
  2 p. l., ₍vii₎–xv, 286 p. illus. 23½ᶜᵐ.
  Contains bibliographies.

  1. Microscope and microscopy. 2. Microchemistry. I. Title.

  Library of Congress   QH207.L5   29–23862

    PPPCPh TU OCU MiU OCl OO OU ICJ MB MH MH–M NcD
  NL 0385256   DLC OrCS MtU MtBuM WaTC MeB CU MsU PHC

Lindsley, Luther Campbell, 1888–
  Some new double selenates. ₍1922.₎

  Thesis(Ph.D.) – Cornell university.
  Abstract of thesis.

  NL 0385257   OU

VOLUME 334

Lindsley, Luther Campbell, 1888–
    Some new double selenates, by L. C. Lindsley ... ₍Ithaca↑ N. Y., 1923↑₎
    2 p. l. 3–17 p. 23ᶜᵐ.
    "Based on a thesis presented to the Graduate school of Cornell university for the degree of doctor of philosophy by Luther Campbell Lindsley, March, 1922."

    1. Selenates.

    Library of Congress   QD181.S5L5   25–2284

NL 0385258   DLC CU

Lindsley, Mary Flora.
    Grand tour and other poems. New York, Philosophical Library ₍1952₎
    128 p. 21 cm.

    I. Title.

    PS3523.I 626G7   811.5   52–11764

NL 0385259   DLC NcD NN ICU

Lindsley, Mary Flora.
    The uncensored letter, and other poems. With an introd. by Joseph J. Reilly. New York, Island Press Cooperative, 1949.
    84 p. 21 cm.

    I. Title.

    PS3523.I 626U6   811.5   50–3905

NL 0385260   DLC NN NcD

LD3617.2
1859   Lindsley, Philip, 1786–1855.
    The works of Philip Lindsley, D. D., late President of the University of Nashville. Philadelphia: J. B. Lippincott & Co.; Nashville: W. T. Berry Co., 1859.
    3 v. front.(incl.port.,fold.facsim.) 24 cm.

    Contents.–I. Educational discourses.–II. Sermons and religious discourses.–III. Miscellaneous discourses and essays.

NL 0385261   T OO PHi PU–S CSaT

Lindsley, Philip, 1786–1855.
    The works of Philip Lindsley ... Edited by Le Roy J. Halsey ... With introductory notices of his life and labours. By the editor ... Philadelphia, J. B. Lippincott & co. ₍1864₎
    3 v. fronts. (incl. 2 port., fold. facsim.) 23ᶜᵐ.
    Contents.—I. Educational discourses.—II. Sermons and religious discourses.—III. Miscellaneous discourses and essays.

NL 0385262   TU

Lindsley, Philip, 1786–1855.
    The works of Philip Lindsley ... Edited by Le Roy J. Halsey ... With introductory notices of his life and labours. ... Philadelphia, J. B. Lippincott & co., 1866.
    3 v. fronts. (incl. 2 port., fold. facsim.) 23ᶜᵐ.
    Contents.—I. Educational discourses.—II. Sermons and religious discourses.—III. Miscellaneous discourses and essays.

    I. Halsey, Leroy Jones, 1812–1896, ed.
                                E15–2667 Revised
    U. S. Off of educ. Library
    for Library of Congress   AC8.L65 1866
                    ₍r45b2₎↑

        OO DLC
NL 0385263   DHEW NIC LU NjP CtY–D PU PP PPPrHi MiU

Lindsley, Philip, 1786–1855.
    An address delivered at Nashville, Ten., Feb. 22, 1832, at the request of the citizens of Nashville and its vicinity, on the occasion of the centennial birth day of George Washington. By Philip Lindsley ... Nashville, Hunt, Tardiff & co., printers, 1832.
    36 p. 22½ᶜᵐ.
    ₍Markoe pamphlets, v. 48, no. 2₎

    1. Washington, George, pres. U. S.—Addresses, sermons, etc.

    Library of Congress   AC901.M2 vol. 48   17–22831

        NjP RPB MdHi
NL 0385264   DLC TU T ViN ViU OOxM CtY CSmH MBAt MBC

Z
378.73
N178   Lindsley, Philip, 1786–1855.
Kℓ.b   Baccalaureate address, delivered on the fourth
1832   anniversary commencement of the University of Nashville, October 7, 1829. 2d ed. Nashville, Printed by Hunt, Tardiff, 1832.
    ₍23₎–67p. 21cm.

    I. Nashville. University. Sp.: Littlefield Fund.

NL 0385265   TxU MdU–M NcD MdBP TxU TNL MHi MH ICP

Lindsley, Philip, 1786–1855.
    An address delivered in Nashville, January 12, 1825, at the inauguration of the president of Cumberland college. By Philip Lindsley ... Nashville, Printed by J. Norvell, 1825.
    48 p. 22½ᶜᵐ.
    On education.

    1. Education—Addresses, essays, lectures.
                                7–26580†
    Library of Congress   LD3617.5 1825
    —— Copy 2.   ₍Bailey pamphlets, v. 46, no. 4₎

        PPL RPB NcU CtY TU PPiPT
NL 0385266   DLC NIC PPAmP ICN ICP MB MHi PPiW CSmH

Lindsley, Philip, 1786–1855.
    Baccalaureate address, pronounced on the evening of the anniversary commencement of the University of Nashville, October 3, 1827. By Philip Lindsley ... Nashville, Printed by J. S. Simpson, 1827.
    30 p. 22½ᶜᵐ.

                                7–26584†
    Library of Congress   LD3617.2 1827

NL 0385267   DLC NcU MH NjP TNP TNL PPAmP

Lindsley, Philip, 1786–1855.
    Baccalaureate address, pronounced on the sixth anniversary commencement of the University of Nashville, Oct. 5, 1831. By Philip Lindsley. Nashville, Printed at the Herald office, 1831.
    36 p., 2 l. 21ᶜᵐ.

                                16–18970
    Library of Congress   LD3617.2 1831

        MH MBC PPL PHi PPPrHi TxU ViU
NL 0385268   DLC CtY MWA PHi PPL NN TNL MdBP MWA MHi

4
370.9768
L645c   Lindsley, Philip, 1786–1855.
    The cause of education in Tennessee; an address delivered to the young gentlemen admitted to the degree of bachelor of arts in Cumberland College, at the anniversary commencement, October 4, 1826. Nashville, Banner Press, 1826.
    36p. 21cm.

    1. Education – Tennessee. I. Nashville. University. II. Title.

NL 0385269   TxU DLC MBC MH–And PPPrHi PPAmP MHi TK.

Lindsley, Philip, 1786–1855
    The cause of education in Tennessee. An address. New Edition. Nashville, Hunt, Tardiff and co., 1832.
    ₍v₎ 39, ₍1₎ p.

NL 0385270   NN P TNL

Lindsley, Philip, 1786–1855.
    The cause of education in Tennessee. An address delivered to the young gentlemen admitted to the degree of bachelor of arts, at the first commencement of the University of Nashville, October 4, 1826. By Philip Lindsley. New ed. Nashville, Hunt, Tardiff and co., printers, 1833.
    39, ₍1₎ p. 22½ᶜᵐ.

    1. Education—Tennessee.
                                7–26581†
    Library of Congress   LD3617.2 1826
        Copy 2.   ₍Waterman pamphlets, v. 163, no. 8₎

        ScCC PPPrHi OKentU THi
NL 0385271   DLC MiU–C NcU OOxM PPL TKL MBAt MH NjP

Lindsley, Philip, 1786–1855.
    The cause of farmers and the University in Tennessee. Two discourses, by Philip Lindsley ... Nashville, Printed by Hunt, Tardiff and co., 1832.
    cover-title, 67 p. 21ᶜᵐ.
    Contents.—Baccalaureate address, pronounced on the seventh anniversary commencement of the University of Nashville, October 3, 1832.—Baccalaureate address, delivered on the fourth anniversary commencement of the University of Nashville, October 7, 1829. 2d ed.

    1. Nashville. University. 2. Universities and colleges—U. S.
                                7–26582
    Library of Congress   LD3617.2 1832

NL 0385272   DLC PHi TxU

BX9178
L52D5   Lindsley, Philip, 1786–1855.
    A discourse, delivered at the installation of Rev. John T. Edgar as pastor of the presbyterian church in Nashville, Tenn., Dec 25th, 1833. Nashville, Tenn., W.H.Hunt & co., 1834.

        NAuT ICP ICN NcD MiU–C ICN T NcD
NL 0385273   DLC PPPrHi RPB TxU TNL OCHP NjP NjR NN

LINDSLEY,Philip,1786–1855.
    The duty of observing the Sabbath, explained and enforced in a sermon addressed more particularly to the young. Trenton, G. Sherman, 1821.
    23 cm. pp.25.

NL 0385274   MH DLC NN RPB NNUT PPL CtY

VOLUME 334

BV4647
.P5L56
Lindsley, Philip, 1786–1855.
Early piety recommended in a sermon, delivered in the college-chapel, Princeton, N. J. May 27, 1821, by Philip Lindsly. Trenton, Printed by G. Shermon.
23 p.   24 cm.

Cover-title.

1. Piety.   I. Title.

NL 0385275   NjR NcD CtY T NN

Lindsley, Philip, 1786–1855.
... Educational discourses. Philadelphia, J. B. Lippincott & co.; Nashville, W. T. Berry & co., 1859.
588 p. incl. front. fold. facsim. 24ᵐ. (*In his* Works. v. 1)
Edited by L. J. Halsey.

1. Education—Addresses, lectures, etc.   I. Halsey, Leroy Jones, 1812–1896, ed.

U. S. Off. of educ. Library   LB41.L65   E 11—306
for Library of Congress   ₍a40b1₎

NL 0385276   DHEW

Lindsley, Philip, 1786–1855.
Improvement of time. Two discourses, delivered in the chapel of the College of New-Jersey; December, 1822. By Philip Lindsly ₍!₎ Trenton, Printed by G.Sherman, 1823.
53 p.   23½ᶜᵐ.

"The preceding discourse ... was delivered on the first, as the present was on the last, sabbath of December."—Footnote to Discourse II, p.29.

1.Conduct of life. I.Title.
                    LB41.L75

NL 0385277   MiU CtY PPiPT ICN MiU-C

*AC8
L6457
821pb
Lindsley, Philip, 1786–1855.
A learned and honest clergy essential to the political and moral welfare of the community: no less than to the spiritual and eternal welfare of individuals. A plea for the theological seminary at Princeton, N.J. A discourse delivered before the presbytery of New-Brunswick at their meeting in Trenton, October 6, 1818. By Philip Lindsly. The second edition.
Trenton[N.J.]Printed by George Sherman.1821.
32p. 22cm.
Also published   with title: A plea for the
theological   seminary.

NL 0385278   MH PPPrHi

Lindsley, Philip, 1786–1855.
A lecture on popular education. By Philip Lindsley ... Nashville, S. Nye & co., printers, 1837.
38 p., 1 l. 18 cm.

"The substance of the following lecture was published in a series of numbers, under the caption of 'Public schools,' in the Nashville republican of 1831 ... It is now re-printed from the 'American Presbyterian' of 1835."

1. Education and state—Tennessee.
LC90.T2L5   E 12—738
U. S. Office of Education.   Library
for Library of Congress   ₍a61b½₎†

NL 0385279   DHEW DLC MH PPPrHi ViW T

BX9178
G77
1821
Lindsly, Philip, 1786–1855.
A plea for the theological seminary at Princeton, N.J. ... Trenton, Printed by George Sherman, 1821.
34 p. 21.5 cm.
Bound with Gray, James. Concio ad clerum. Baltimore, 1821.

1. Princeton Theological Seminary.
I. Title.   Shoemaker 5829

NL 0385280   PPiPT MH NcD NN MiU-C

Lindsley, Philip, 1786–1855.
...A plea for the Theological seminary at Princeton, N. J. A discourse delivered before the Presbytery of New-Brunswick at their meeting in Trenton, October 6, 1818, by Philip Lindsly ₍sic₎ The second edition.   Trenton: Printed by G. Sherman, 1821. 32 p.   23½cm.

At head of title: A learned and honest clergy essential to the political and moral welfare of the community: no less than to the spiritual and eternal welfare of individuals.

1. Princeton theological
N. Y. P. L.   seminary.
                              July 29, 1938

NL 0385281   NN CtY NcD ViU MH PPPrHi MH T

Lindsley, Philip, 1786–1855.
A plea for the Theological seminary at Princeton, N. J. By Philip Lindsly ₍!₎ ... The 3d ed. Trenton, Printed by G. Sherman, 1821.
31 p. 21½ᶜᵐ.

1. Princeton theological seminary.
                                       E 10—811
U. S. Off. of educ. Library
for Library of Congress   ₍a37b1₎

          ViW MH MoSW ICN PPiPT
NL 0385282   DHEW NN DLC MWA PHi ViU CtY NcD MeB

Lindsley, Philip. 1786–1855.
Plea for universities. . .
Columbus, O. Nichols. 1838. 119–128 pp. 8°.
Cut from The Hesperian, or Western Monthly Magazine for June, 1838 [*5387.4.1.1838].

F6354 — Universities.

NL 0385283   MB

Lindsley, Philip, 1786–1855.
A sermon, delivered in the chapel of the College of New-Jersey, August 15, 1824. By Philip Lindsly ₍sic₎ Princeton, N. J., Printed and published by D. A. Borrenstein; also for sale by A. Finley, Philadelphia; Edward J. Coale, Baltimore; John P. Haven, New-York; and by D. Fenton, Trenton, N. J. 1824.

52 p.   21.5cm.

Bound with *his* A plea for the theological seminary at Princeton, N. J. Trenton, 1821.

CtY NcD
NL 0385284   MiU-C T NjNbS PHi PPPrHi NjP NNC OC MH

Lindsley, Philip, 1786–1855.
Speech about colleges, delivered in Nashville, on commencement day. October 4, 1848. By Philip Lindsley. Nashville, J. T. S. Fall, pr., 1848.
32 p. 21ᶜᵐ.

"Appendix. ... Paragraphs ... reprinted from a Baccalaureate address by the author, delivered and published in 1829": p. ₍17₎–32.

I. Education—Tennessee.

Library of Congress   LD3017.2 1848   7-26583

NL 0385285   DLC NcD PHi PPPrHi NN MnHi MdBP

Lindsley, Philip, 1786–1855.
Speech in behalf of the University of Nashville, delivered on the day of the anniversary commencement, October 4, 1837. By Philip Lindsley. Nashville, S. Nye and co., printers, 1837.
38 p. 22ᵐ.

1. Nashville, Tenn. University.
                                       7-26585†
Library of Congress   LD3605.8.L5

    PPPrHi NcD OKentU
NL 0385286   DLC NCH MHi NNC NN CtY MH TKL TNL PHi

Lindsley, Philip, 1786–1855.
Speech in behalf of the University of Nashville, delivered on the day of the anniversary commencement, October 4, 1837. Nashville, S. Nye and Co., printers, 1837.
(American culture series, 64 : 12)
Microfilm copy (positive) made in 1956 by University Microfilms, Ann Arbor, Mich.
Collation of the original : 38 p.

1. Nashville. University.
Microfilm 01291 reel 64, no. 12 E   Mic 59-7928

NL 0385287   DLC ICRL KEmT MiU

Lindsley, Philip, 1842–
A history of greater Dallas and vicinity, by Philip Lindsley ... Chicago, The Lewis publishing company, 1909.
2 v. front., illus., ports. 27½ᶜᵐ. $20.00
Author's name does not appear on t.-p. of v. 2, which has subtitle: Selected biography and memoirs. Mr. L. B. Hill, editor.

1. Dallas, Tex.—Hist. 2. Dallas, Tex.—Biog.   I. Hill, Luther B., ed.
                                       9-28219 Revised
Library of Congress   F394.D2L7

NL 0385288   DLC NcD NN

Lindsley, Philip, 1842–
The humor of the court room; or, Jones vs. Johnson, a lawful comedy, by Philip Lindsley ... With illustrations by Prescott Toomey. Dallas, Tex., J. F. Worley & co., 1899.
2 p. l., 9–70 p. front. (port.) plates. 18½ᵐ.

1. Law—Anecdotes, facetiae, satire, etc.   I. Title.
                                       90-3973 Revised
Library of Congress   PN6231.L4L6
                          ₍r42c2₎   -817.49

NL 0385289   DLC PPYH TxU NcD NcU MH

DO28.53
AL64
Lindsley, Ruth
Bibliography of children's books from the library of Clarence Lown, now in the collection of the Vassar college library, Poughkeepsie, N. Y., 1939. Compiled by Ruth Lindsley ... ₍1939₎
26 l. 27½ᶜᵐ.

Type-written.

1. Children's literature – Bibliography.
I. Lown, Clarence, d. 1931. II. Vassar college. Library.

NL 0385290   NNC

Lindsley, Stephen.
A sermon, delivered in the First Presbyterian Church in Maysville, Kentucky...before a large assembly of free and accepted masons...Maysville, Ky., printed at the Eagle office, 1823.
16 p. 14 x 22.5 cm.

NL 0385291   MBFM

VOLUME 334

Lindsley, Thales.
The classification of society & the classification of universities; the orders of grades of bith and the places of the latter in the former. N.Y., Coby, 1863.
20 p.

NL 0385292   PU

[Lindsley, Thales]
Scheme for defraying federal expenses and extinguishing the national debt, by issuing $25,000,000 bonds annually, and redeeming them biennially in gold. Washington, McGill & Witherow, printers, 1868.
40 p., 1 l., 26 p. 23½ᶜᵐ.
Signed: Thales Lindsley.
"An act authorizing the establishment of a bureau for mining the precious metals, and providing for its inauguration and support": p. [3]-26.

1. Mines and mineral resources—Government ownership. 2. Finance—U. S.

CA 9-4538 Unrev'd

Library of Congress   HD3879.M61L5

NL 0385293   DLC

[Lindsley, Thales.]
Suggestions upon the purchase and sale of lode mining property in Colorado, and the tunnel claim. 24 p. O. [New York 1864.]

NL 0385294   ICJ

Lindsley, Van Sinderen.
Rate regulation of gas and electric lighting, by Van Sinderen Lindsley ... New York, The Banks law publishing company, 1906.
v, 165 p. 21½ cm.

1. Gas companies—U. S.—Rates. 2. Electric utilities—U. S.—Rates. I. Title.

6—5453

NL 0385295   DLC WaU-L IdU PU PPB ViU-L NN ICJ NjP

LINDSLEY, Van Sinderen.
Rate Regulation of Gas, etc., New York, 1907.
v-165 p. 8 vo.

NL 0385296   MH-L

Lindsley, W. D.
Vermillion, Huron, and Sandusky. Speech ... on the public works. Delivered in the House of Representatives, July 12, 1854. [Washington, 1854.] 8 pp. 8°.
There is no title-page.
On the improvement of certain harbors on Lake Erie.

G6750 — Erie, Lake. Harbors. — T.r.

NL 0385297   MB

Lindsley & Drummond, *Chicago.*
Lindsley & Drummond ... manufacturers of portable and ready-made houses ... [Catalogue] [Chicago, 1885]
10 p. illus. 27½ᶜᵐ.

1. Buildings, Prefabricated.

CA 9-3655 Unrev'd

Library of Congress   NA8480.L5

NL 0385298   DLC

CS71
L76L6

Lindsley line.   No imprint.   [1925?]
22p.   24cm.

Manuscript.

NL 0385299   NBuG

Lindsly, Ben Edwin, 1882–
... Effect of vacuum on oil wells, by Ben E. Lindsly and W. B. Berwald. Washington, U. S. Govt. print. off., 1930.
vi, 133 p. incl. illus., tables, diagrs. plates (1 fold.) 25ᶜᵐ. (U. S. Bureau of mines. Bulletin 322)
At head of title: U. S. Department of commerce. R. P. Lamont, secretary. Bureau of mines. Scott Turner, director ...

1. Petroleum—Well-boring.   I. Berwald, W. B., joint author. II. Title. III. Title: Vacuum on oil wells, Effect of.

30-26860

Library of Congress   TN23.U4 no. 322
———— Copy 2.   TN871.L5
[8]   665.5

NL 0385300   DLC MiU OU OCU OCl MB OrU OrCS WaWW

Lindsly, Ben Edwin, 1882–
... Solubility and liberation of gas from natural oil-gas solutions, by Ben E. Lindsly. Washington, U. S. Govt. print. off., 1933.
ii, 65 p. incl. illus., tables, diagrs. 23½ᶜᵐ. (U. S. Bureau of mines. Technical paper 554)
At head of title: U. S. Department of commerce. Daniel C Roper, secretary. Bureau of mines. Scott Turner, director ...
Running title: Liberation of gas from natural oil-gas solutions.

1. Petroleum. 2. Gas. 3. Solubility.   I. Title: Liberation of gas from natural oil-gas solutions.

33-26778

Library of Congress   TN1.U6 no. 554
———— Copy 2.   TN871.L53
[6]   (622.061) 665.5

NL 0385301   DLC OCl OU MB MiU WaWW CaBVaU

Lindsly, Ben Edwin, 1882–
... Unit operation of oil pools, statement to the congressional committee on petroleum investigation, as authorized by H. R. 290, 76th Congress, 1st session, by Ben E. Lindsly and E. C. Dahlgren. [Washington, 1939?]
iii, 48 numb. l.   27ᶜᵐ.
Caption title.
Reproduced from type-written copy.

1. Petroleum industry and trade.   I. Dahlgren, E. C., joint author. II. U. S. Congress. House. Committee on interstate and foreign commerce. III. Title.

44-30216

Library of Congress   TN870.L54
[2]   665.5

NL 0385302   DLC

Toner

Lindsly, Harvey, 1804–1889.
Address of Harvey Lindsly, president of the association ... Philadelphia, Collins, printer, 1859.
12 p. 23½ᶜᵐ.
"From the minutes of the twelfth annual meeting of the American medical association, held in the city of Louisville, May 3, 1859."

1. Medicine—Addresses, essays, lectures.   I. American medical association.

34-37204

Library of Congress   R708.L73

NL 0385303   DLC CtY-M DNLM

Toner

Lindsly, Harvey, 1804–1889.
A brief sketch of some of the principal universities of Europe and of the United States. By Harvey Lindsly ... Washington, J. Gideon, jr., printer, 1836.
27, [1] p. 24½ᶜᵐ.

1. Universities and colleges—Europe.

6—23967

Library of Congress   LA185.L6
———— Copy 2.   [Markoe pamphlets, v. 18, no. 15]
AC901.M2

NL 0385304   DLC PPL NjP MdBP

Lindsly (Harvey) [1804–]. An essay on the origin and introduction into medical practice, etc., of ardent spirits. 130 pp. 12°. Washington, D. Green, 1835.
———— The same.
In: Temperance prize essays. 12°. Washington, 1835, 67-195.

NL 0385305   DNLM

Lindsly, Harvey, 1804–
Medical science and the medical profession in Europe and the United States. An introductory lecture, by Harvey Lindsly ... November, 1840. Washington, P. Force, 1840.
35 p. 23ᶜᵐ.

1. Medicine—Europe. 2. Medicine—U. S.

(Toner)

Library of Congress   R708.L74   5-161†

NL 0385306   DLC PU IEN DNLM MiU ICJ MB

Lindsly, Harvey, 1804–1889.
Temperance prize essays. By Drs. Mussey and Lindsly. Washington [D. C.] D. Green, 1835.

Lindsström, Claes.
Sjöfartens historia. Stockholm, Lindfors [1951]
508 p. illus., ports., maps (part fold.) fold. charts. 28 cm.
Bibliography: p. 597-508.

1. Merchant marine—Hist.   I. Title.

VK15.L5   52-34356

NL 0385308   DLC NN MnU

Lindståhl, Sigvard.
A survey of the geographical distribution of industry in Finland in 1952. Helsinki, 1955.
43 p. maps, tables. 26 cm. (Fennia 79, n:o 1)
Bibliography: p. 42-43.

1. Industries, Location of—Finland.   (Series)

[G23.G4 vol. 79, n:o 1]   A 58-4053

Chicago. Univ. Libr.
for Library of Congress   [1]

NL 0385309   ICU MH NN

TK6550
.7
.L5

Lindstad, B. O., joint author.

Lindstad, Olai, 1893–
ABC i radio, av O. Lindstad og B. O. Lindstad. Oslo, Aschehoug, 1950.

TK6563
.L54

Lindstad, B. O., joint author.

Lindstad, Olai, 1893–
Radiomottageren; det teoretiske grunnlaget [av] O. Lindstad og B. O. Lindstad. Oslo, Aschehoug, 1951.

VOLUME 334

Lindstad, Olai, 1893–
ABC i radio, av O. Lindstad og B. O. Lindstad. Oslo, Aschehoug, 1950.
40 p. 19 cm.

1. Radio.   I. Lindstad, B. O., joint author.   II. Title.

TK6550.7.L5   51–33886

NL 0385312   DLC

Lindstad, Olai, 1893–
Radiomottageren; det teoretiske grunnlaget ₍av₎ O. Lindstad og B. O. Lindstad. Oslo, Aschehoug, 1951.
118 p. diagrs. 21 cm.

1. Radio—Receivers and reception.   I. Lindstad, B. O., joint author.

TK6563.L54   A 52–5042
Mass. Inst. of Technology.   Library
for Library of Congress   ₍3₎†

NL 0385313   MCM NN DLC

Lindstädt (C.) Neuere Forschungen über die Verrichtung der Schilddrüse, ihre Beziehungen zum Kropf, Kretinismus, Epilepsie, etc. Studien auf dem Gebiete der Nervenphysiologie und Pathologie sowie des Blutlebens. Bearbeitet für Aerzte, Tierärzte und gebildete Stände. 2. ed., 40 pp. 8°. Berlin, H. Kornfeld. 1904.

NL 0385314   DNLM

Lindstädt (C.) Die Verrichtungen der Schilddrüse (Glandula thyreoidea). Die Ursachen des Kropfes, der Epilepsie, etc., und ihre Heilung; die Nahrungsmittelfrage (Vegetarianus und Fleischnahrung); die Tuberkulose des Rindviehes als Studien auf dem Gebiete der Nervenphysiologie und Pathologie und des Blutlebens. Bearbeitet für Aerzte, Thierärzte und gebildete Stände. 12 pp. 8°. Perleberg, W. Düwert, 1902.

NL 0385315   DNLM

Lindstaedt, Carl Wilhelm Franz
see **Lindstaedt, Franz,** 1890–

146
V1922
Lindstaedt, Franz, 1890–
Grundwissenschaftliche Kritik der Hauptbegriffe in Vaihingers Philosophie des Als-ob. Königsberg, Steinbacher, 1917.
50 p.

Thesis, Greifswald.

NL 0385317   NNC PU CtY MiU

Lindstädt, Heinz.
Trichomonas vaginalis. Seine klinische bedeutung, morphologie u. therapie.
Inaugural-dissertation, Universität zu München, 1933.

NL 0385318   PPWI CtY

Lindstaedt, Paul, 1872–
Schwangerschaft, geburt und wochenbett...
Inaug. Diss. Marburg, 1899

NL 0385319   ICRL DNLM CtY

W 4
M96
1940
Lindstaedt, Rudolf Heinrich, 1912–
Der gegenwärtige Stand der Strahlenbehandlung bei Myomen (mit Ergebnissen der 1925–1934 an der Universitäts-Frauenklinik zu München vorgenommenen Myombestrahlungen) Bottrop, Postberg, 1940.
41 p.

Inaug.-Diss. – Munich.
Bibliography: p. 40–41.

NL 0385320   DNLM

Lindstaedt, Ruth, 1902–
Die epidemische kinderlaehmung in Ostpreussen. Unter besonderer beruecksichtigung der in der Koenigsberger kinderklinik während der letzten zwei jahre beobachteten faelle.
Inaug. diss. Keonigsberg, 1928.
Bibl.

NL 0385321   ICRL CtY

Lindstaedt, Willi.
... Experimentelle untersuchungen über das Küchenmeisterphänomen. Göttingen, Akademische buchhandlung von Calvör, 1935.
cover-title, 1 p. l., 61 p. diagrs. 23ᶜᵐ. (Untersuchungen zur psychologie, philosophie und pädagogik ... n. f., 9. bd. (3. hft.))

Reproduced from type-written copy.
"Aus dem Psychologischen Institut der Universität Göttingen, leitung: prof. dr. N. Ach."
"Literatur-verzeichnis, alphabetisch geordnet": p. 61.

1. Sound.   I. Title.   II. Title: Küchenmeister-phänomen.

                                              A C 35–1873
Title from Columbia   Univ. Printed by L. C.
                                              ₍2₎

NL 0385322   NNC

AS284
.G7
föl. 5,
ser. A,
bd. 7,
no. 1
Lindstam, Carl Sigfrid, ed.

Digenes Acritas (*Epic poem*)
... Det bysantinska eposet om Digenis basileios Akritas, översättning jämte en inledning, av S. Lindstam ... Göteborg, Elanders boktryckeri aktiebolag, 1940.

Lindstam, Carl Sigfrid.
Göteborgs gatunamn. ₍Göteborg₎ Drätselkammarens gatunamnsberedning ₍1945₎
279 p. 20 cm.

1. Gothenburg, Sweden — Streets.   2. Swedish language — Etymology—Names.   I. Title.

DL991.G6L57   57–39577 ‡

NL 0385324   DLC TxU MH CtY CU

Lindstam, Carl Sigfrid.
Nordisk rättstavning; en utredning och ett program. Stockholm, Norstedt ₍1946₎
106 p. 21 cm. (Skrifter utg. av Nämnden för svensk språkvård, 1)
"Litteratur": p. 102–106.

1. Scandinavian languages—Orthography and spelling.   I. Title.
(Series: Nämnden för svensk språkvård, Stockholm. Skrifter, 1)

                                              A 48–4514*
Harvard Univ.   Library
for Library of Congress   ₍3₎

NL 0385325   MH ICU MnU NN

PT
9552
L75
Lindstam, Ragnar, ed.
Fragment av fornnordiska handskrifter: legenderna om Sita Kristina och Elisabeth i hittills okänd version samt en Lucidarius. Ett bidrag till vår 1300-talslitteratur. Utg. av R. Lindstam.   Huskvarna, M. Rydheim 1922.
46 p. illus. 17cm.

NL 0385326   NIC

DL
991
.H8
L5
Lindstam, Ragnar
Huskvarna krönika; en historik över Huskvarnabygden och dess äldre släkter. Huskvarna, Huskvarna kyrkliga ungdomskrets ₍1923₎
607 p. illus. 25cm.

Includes bibliography.

1. Huskvarna, Sweden - Hist.   I. Title.

NL 0385327   WU MH

4DL
Swed.
493
Lindstam, Ragnar
Om kyrkor som försvunnit och klockor som ha sjungit i Ostbo, Västbo och Sunnerbo. Stockholm, Svenska Kyrkans Diakonistyrelses bokförlag [1935]
177 p.

NL 0385328   DLC-P4 DNLM

B
L75511
Lindstam, Ragnar.
Per Henrik Ling; en släkthistorisk undersökning och en kort levnadsteckning, av Ragnar Lindstam. ₍Nässjö, Tryckeriaktiebolaget Grafia, 1939₎
151p. incl.front.(port.) illus., geneal.tab.

"Använd litteratur": p.149–150.

1. Ling, Per Henrik. 1776–1839.

NL 0385329   IU

AS284
.G7
föl. 5,
ser. A,
bd. 7,
no. 1
Lindstam, Sigfrid Assaf Esaias, 1879–1939, tr.

Digenes Acritas (*Epic poem*)
... Det bysantinska eposet om Digenis basileios Akritas, översättning jämte en inledning, av S. Lindstam ... Göteborg, Elanders boktryckeri aktiebolag, 1940.

Lindstam, Sigfrid Assaf Esaias, 1879–1939.

Lacapenus, Georgius.
Georgii Lacapeni Epistulae X priores cum epimerismis editae; commentatio academica, scripsit Sigfrid Lindstam. Upsaliae, typis descripsit E. Berling, 1910.

Lindstedt, Alf.
Die flora der marinen Cyanophyceen der schwedischen westküste... Lund, Ohlsson, 1943.
119 p. illus. 24½ ᶜᵐ.

Akademisk avhandling - Lund.
"Literaturverzeichnis": p.₍111₎–116.

1. Marine flora of Sweden.   2. Cyanophyceae.

NL 0385332   NjP CtY CU WaU IaU NcD NNBG MiU ICU

VOLUME 334

Lindstedt, Alf

Marine Cyanophyceae from Tristan de Cunha. Oslo, Norske videnskaps-akademi, 1962.
30 p. illus. (Norwegian Scientific Expedition to Tristan da Cunha, 1937-1938. Results, no.50)

Bibliography: p.23-25.

1. Cyanophyceae. I. Title.

NL 0385333   HU

Lindstedt, Anders, 1854-*1939*.
Ålderdomsförsäkringskommitténs förslag till lag om allmän pensionsförsäkring. Kortfattad framställning af förslagets hufvudsakliga innehåll och syfte, af And. Lindstedt, kommitténs ordförande. Stockholm, K. L. Beckmans boktryckeri, 1912.
2 p. l., 70 p. 21½ᶜᵐ.

1. Old age pensions—Sweden. 2. Insurance, Industrial—Sweden. I. Sweden. Ålderdomsförsäkringskommittén. II. Sweden. Laws, statutes, etc. III. Title.

          3+-25227

Library of Congress   HD7106.S8L5   331.25443⒪9485

NL 0385334   DLC NN

A42   **Lindstedt, Anders,** 1854-
+Akl36M   Beitrag zur Integration der Differential-
31   gleichungen der Störungstheorie. St.-Péters-
       bourg, Eggers, 1883.
       20.p. 32cm. (Mémoires de l'Académie
       Impériale des Sciences de St.-Pétersbourg,
       VII sér., t. 31, no. 4)

       1. Differential ations. 2. Perturbations.

NL 0385335   CtY MdBP

Lindstedt, And⟨ers⟩ 1854-
Beobachtungen des Mars während seiner opposition 1877 angestellt auf der sternwarte zu Lund. Von Dr. And. Lindstedt. Lund, F. Berlings buchdruckerei, 1878.
1 p. l., 15 p. 26½ x 21ᶜᵐ.
"Lunds Univ. Årsskr. tom. xiv."

1. Mars—Opposition 1877.

          6-12316†

Library of Congress   QB516.L7

NL 0385336   DLC

Lindstedt, Anders, 1854-

Sweden. *Försäkringskommittén,* 1903.
Betänkande och förslag afgifvet af Kommitterade som i nåder förordnats att i Kungl. civildepartementet biträda vid af Riksdagen begärd utredning angående vissa försäkringsanstalter och utarbetande af lagförslag i ämnet ... Stockholm, K. L. Beckmans boktryckeri, 1905.

Lindstedt, Anders. 1854-

Sweden. *Ålderdomsförsäkringskommittén.*
... Betänkande och förslag angående allmän pensionsförsäkring. Stockholm, K. L. Beckmans boktryckeri, 1912.

Lindstedt, Anders, 1854- *1939*.

Sweden. *Socialförsäkringskommittén.*
... Betänkande och förslag angående allmän sjukförsäkring. Stockholm, K. L. Beckmans boktryckeri, 1919-

---

Lindstedt, Anders, 1854-
... Förslag till lag om allmän sjukförsäkring. Kortfattad redogörelse af And. Lindstedt, kommitténs ordförande. Stockholm, K. L. Beckmans boktryckeri, 1919.
98 p. 21½ᶜᵐ.
At head of title: Socialförsäkringskommittén.

1. Insurance, Health—Sweden. 2. Insurance, Industrial—Sweden. I. Sweden. Socialförsäkringskommittén.

Library of Congress   HD7102.S8L5   20—13666

NL 0385340   DLC ICJ

Lindstedt, Anders, 1854-

Sweden. *Socialdepartementet.*
Förslag till lag om sjukförsäkring. Inom Socialdepartementet verkställd överarbetning av Socialförsäkringskommitténs förslag till lag om allmän sjukförsäkring ... Stockholm, K. L. Beckmans boktryckeri, 1920.

Lindstedt, Anders, 1854-

Sweden. *Arbetareförsäkringskomitén,* 1891.
Nya arbetareförsäkringskomiténs betänkande ... Stockholm, Tryckt hos K. L. Beckman, 1892-93.

⟨**Lindstedt, Anders**⟩ 1854- *1939*
Revideradt förslag till utvidgning och omorganisation af Kungl. tekniska högskolan. Stockholm, K. L. Beckmans boktryckeri, 1904.
cover-title, 1 p. l., 105 p., 1 l., 59, ⟨1⟩ p. fold. plans. 23ᶜᵐ.
Signed: And. Lindstedt.

1. Stockholm. Tekniska högskolan. I. Title. II. Title: Tekniska högskolan. Utvidgning och omorganisation af.

          34–31483

Library of Congress   T173.S889L5   607.487

NL 0385343   DLC

Lindstedt, Anders, 1854-1939.
Ueber die Integration einer für die Störungstheorie wichtigen Differentialgleichung. Kiel, 1882.
7 p. 29 cm.
Astr. Nachr., 103, 1882, col. 211-220. 104, 1882-83, col. 145-150.

NL 0385344   DN-Ob

Lindstedt, Anders, 1854- *1939*.
Ueber die allgemeine form der Integrale des dreikörperproblems. Kiel, 1883.
8 p. 30cm.

Astr. Nachr., 105, 1883, col. 97-112.

NL 0385345   DNC DN-Ob

Lindstedt, Anders, 1854,-1939
Ueber die integration einer gewissen Differentialgleichung. Kiel, 1882.
3 p. 29cm

Astr. Nachr., 104, 1882-83, col. 145-150.

NL 0385346   DN-Ob

Lindstedt, Anders, 1854-
Undersökning af meridiancirkeln på Lunds observatorium, jemte bestämning af densammas polhöjd, af And. Lindstedt. Lund, F. Berlings boktryckeri och stilgjuteri, 1877.
1 p. l., 54 p., 1 l. fold. pl., tables. 26 x 21½ᶜᵐ.

1. Transit circle.

Library of Congress   QB101.L7   5-37126†

NL 0385347   DLC

Lindstedt, Birgit (Key-Åberg).

See

Key-Åberg, Birgit, 1904-

Lindstedt, Emma Maria Pauline

see

Brunius, Pauline, 1881-

LINDSTEDT, Folke, 1884-
Om mätning af främre ogonkammerens djup med ett nytt, for kliniskt bruk afsedt instrument. Akad. Efh. af Folke Lindstedt. Uppsala 1913.

8:o. 86 s. 3 pl. (Ur. Upsala Lakarefor Forhandl. N.H. Bd. 18).
Diss. Uppsal. med.

NL 0385350   MBCo DNLM

Lindstedt, Folke, 1884-
Über die natur der muskelrheumatischen (myalgischen) schmerzsymptome, von dozent dr. Folke Lindstedt ... Stockholm, P. A. Norstedt & söner, 1929.
180 p. illus. 23½ᶜᵐ. (On cover: Acta medica scandinavica. Supplementum xxx)
"Literatur": p. 179-180.

1. Rheumatism. 2. Muscles—Diseases. 3. Pain.
⟨Full name: Ernst Folke Lindstedt⟩
          A C 33-2173
Title from John Crerar   Libr. Printed by L. C.
       ⟨2⟩

NL 0385351   ICJ ViU CtY MiU PPC

Lindstedt, Greta
A study of inherited asymmetry. 1945.

NL 0385352   OrU

Lindstedt, Gustaf, 1883-

Sweden. *Fattigvårdslagstiftningskommittén.*
... Fattigvårdslagstiftningen ... Stockholm, Tryckt hos P. Palmquists aktiebolag, 1915.

VOLUME 334

Lindstedt, Gustaf, 1883–
Högbroforssaken; en granskning. Stockholm, Natur och kultur ₁1953–54₎
3 v. diagrs., facsims., plans. 25 cm.

1. Kreuger, Torsten, 1884– 2. Högbroforsens industriaktiebolag. I. Title.
Full name: Gustaf Ferdinand Lindstedt.

57–23695 rev

NL 0385354   DLC MH-L

Lindstedt, Hilda Sofia, 1881–
Biblioteksstudier i U. S. A. jämte riktlinjer för ett svenskt tekniskt centralbibliotek; föredrag hållet vid Svenska teknologföreningens avdelning för teknisk undervisning årsmöte den 8 oktober 1921 samt å Ingeniörsvetenskapsakademien den 15 mars 1922, av bibliotekarien Hilda S. Lindstedt. ₁Stockholm, Tryckeriet progress A.-B., 1922₎
50 p. 20½ᶜᵐ. (*On cover:* Ingeniörsvetenskaps akademien. Meddelande nr. 18)
1. Libraries, Special. 2. Technical libraries. 3. Classification—Books—Technology.

Library of Congress   Z675.T3L7   23–5283

NL 0385355   DLC ICJ

Lindstedt, Hilda Sofia, 1881–
Stockholm. Tekniska högskolan. *Bibliotek.*
Katalog öfver Kongl. teknologiska institutets bibliothek, år 1848. Stockholm, P. A. Norstedt & söner, 1849.

Lindstedt, Hilda Sofia, 1881–
Katalog över periodiska publikationer tillgängliga i bibliotek i Stockholm och Uppsala och berörande matematik, geodesi, meteorologi, hydrografi, jordmagnetism, fysik, kemi, geologi och mineralogi samt de tekniska vetenskaperna och arkitektur, utarbetad av Hilda S. Lindstedt ... Utgiven av Ingeniörsvetenskapsakademien. Stockholm ₁Centraltryckeriet₎ 1927–31.
xvi, 300 p., 1 l. 27ᶜᵐ.
"Biblioteksförteckning": p. x–xiv.
"Konsulterad bibliografisk litteratur": p. xv.
1. Science—Period.—Bibl. 2. Technology—Period.—Bibl. 3. Architecture—Period.—Bibl. 4. Periodicals—Bibl.—Union lists. 5. Libraries—Stockholm. 6. Libraries—Uppsala. I. Ingeniörsvetenskapsakademien, Stockholm

Library of Congress   Z7403.L73   33–3979
₃₎   [016.51] 016.05

NL 0385357   DLC FTaSU CtY

LINDSTEDT, Hilda S[ofia], 1881–
Några nyare Amerikanska biblioteksbyggnader med hänsyn särskilt till ekonomisering av utrymmet. n.p., [1923]
f°. pp.6. Diagrs. and illustr.
Without title-page. Caption title.
Utvidgat sartryck ur Byggmästaren, haft 22, och 23 1923.

NL 0385358   MH

Lindstedt, Hilda Sofia, 1881–
Tekniska högskolans nya bibliotek, av bibliotekarien Hilda S. Lindstedt. Norrköping, Norrköpings tidningars aktiebolag, 1931.
cover-title, 15 p. illus. (incl. plans) 31ᶜᵐ.
"Särtryck ur Teknisk tidskrift 1931, häfte 7 och 9."

1. Stockholm. Tekniska högskolan. Bibliotek.

32–20776

Library of Congress   Z828.892L   026.6

NL 0385359   DLC NNC CtY OU MiU

Lindstedt, Hilda Sofia, 1881–
Tekniska litteratursällskapet, 1936–1946; en historisk återblick. Norrköping, Norrköpings tidningars aktiebolag, 1946.
₁₄₎ (Tekniska litteratursällskapets skriftserie, 19)

NL 0385360   MH

WZ
260
T262m
1725
LINDSTEDT, Joachim Dietrich
Die wohlerforschte Natur des Feuers, zu mercklicher Ersparung des Brenn-Holtzes...mit beygefügten Figuren...zu Anlegung allerhand gar nützlicher Oefen, Camiene, Brau-Pfannen, Brandtewein- und Distillir-Blasen...beschrieben; zum andern mahl verbessert... Magdeburg, 1720.
56 p. front., 20 plates. 16.6 cm.
Bound with Tentzel, Andreas. Medicinisch-philosophisch- und sympathetische Schrifften. Leipzig und Hof, 1725.
1. Distillation   2. Stoves I. Title

NL 0385361   CLU-M

Lindstedt, Karl, 1846–
Synopsis der saprolegniaceen und beobachtungen über einige arten. Von Karl Lindstedt ... Berlin, R. Friedländer & sohn, 1872.
3 p. l., ₁5₎–69, ₁1₎ p. IV pl. 24ᶜᵐ.

1. Saprolegniaceae.

Agr 26–155

Library, U. S. Dept. of   Agriculture 462L645

NL 0385362   DNAL ICJ MBH MiU MH

Lindstedt, Karl, 1846–
Ueber einige arten aus der familie der *Saprolegniaceae* Berlin, Buchdruckerei von G. Lange (O. Lange) ₁1872₎
32 p. 21½ᶜᵐ.
Inaug.-diss.—Berlin.
Lebenslauf.

1. Saprolegniineae.

Library of Congress   QK621.S24L   5–24947†

NL 0385363   DLC

Lindstedt, Pauline
see
Brunius, Pauline, 1881–

Lindstedt, Ph., publishers
see Aktiebolaget Ph. Lindstedts universitetsbokhandel, Lund, Sweden.

Lindstedt, Philip, 1885–
Untersuchungen über Respiration und Stoffwechsel von Kaltblütern ... [n.p., 1913]
Inaug.-Diss. - Jena.
Lebenslauf.

NL 0385366   CtY MiU

Lindstedts (Ph) universitetsbokhandel Aktiebolaget, Lund, Sweden
see Aktiebolaget Ph. Lindstedts universitetsbokhandel, Lund, Sweden.

Lindsteen (Henric)
*Om möjeligheten och nyttan af krydd-och trägårdars anläggande i Finland... Åbo, 1754. 2 p.l., 12 pp. 4°.

NL 0385368   NN

SB608
.S8
L5
pam
OrU
Lindsten, A
Report on the 1949 western Oregon spruce budworm control project, by A. Lindsten and K.H. Wright. Portland, Ore., 1951.
71 p. illus., graphs, maps, plates, tables. 27½cm.

Issued by Oregon State Board of Forestry and Bureau of Entomology and Plant Quarantine.

1. Spruce bud-worm. 2. Forest insects - Northwest, Pacicif. I. Oregon, State Board of Forestry. II. U.S.D.A. Bureau of Entomology and Plant Quarantine.

NL 0385369   OrCS OrU

SB608
.S8
L51
pam
Lindsten, A
Spruce budworm situation in Oregon and Washington, 1949 season, by A. Lindsten, W.J. Buckhorn, J.F. Wear ₁and others₎ Portland, Ore., 1949.
20, 9 ₁2₎ l. 10 tables, map (fold.) 27cm.

Prepared by Oregon State Board of Forestry and Bureau of Entomology and Plant Quarantine.
Superseded by Report of forest insect surveys in Oregon and Washington, 1950-

1. Spruce bud-insects,   worm. 2. Forest Northwest, Pacific.

NL 0385370   OrCS

VM505
.S6
Lindsten, Don C., joint author.

Spaulding, Charles H
Water treatment, prevention of scale in sea water distillation. Project 8–75–05–002. Prepared by Charles H. Spaulding ₁and₎ Don C. Lindsten. Fort Belvoir, Va., Sanitary Engineering Branch, Engineer Research and Development Laboratories, Corps of Engineers, U. S. Army, 1953.

Lindstøl, Tallak Olsen, 1857–1925.
Mandtallet i Norge samt oplysninger om folkemængdens bevægelse i Norge i det 16de of 17de aarhundrede, bearb. og udg. af Tallak Lindstøl. Kristiania, I kommission hos A. Cammermeyer, 1887.
3 p. l., 48 p. 25ᶜᵐ.

1. Norway—Population.

16–9347

Library of Congress   HB3615.L5

NL 0385372   DLC

DL
596
R59
L75
Lindstøl, Tallak Olsen, 1857-1925.
Risør gjennem 200 aar, 1723-1923. Jubilaeumsskrift ved Tallak Lindstøl. Utgit av Risør kommune. Risør, I hovedkommission hos E. Gunleikson, 1923.
502 p. illus., maps. 25cm.

1. Risør, Norway--Hist.

NL 0385373   NIC WU

VOLUME 334

Lindstøl, Tallak Olsen, 1857–
Stamtavler, væsentlig fra østre Nedenæs. Samlet, redigeret og udgivet af Tallak Lindstøl. Kristiania, J. C. Gundersens bogtrykkeri, 1882.
5 p. l., ₍3₎–606, ₍2₎ p. 25ᶜᵐ.

1. Norway—Geneal. 2. Nedenes—Geneal.

13–14338

Library of Congress   CS919.A2L6

NL 0385374   DLC

Lindstøl, Tallak Olsen, 1857–
Statistik vedkommende kommunevalgene i 1901 og delvis valgene i 1898. Udarb. af Tallak Lindstøl. Udg. af Justits- og politi-departementet. (Bilag nr. 9 til Formandskabslovkomiteens indstilling.) Kristiania, W. C. Fabritius & sønner a/s, 1903.
113 p. 27½ᶜᵐ.

1. Elections—Norway. 2. Local government—Norway.   I. Norway. Justits- og politi-departementet.

16–9350

Library of Congress   JN7653.L7

NL 0385375   DLC

Lindstøl, Tallak Olsen, 1857–1925.
Storthingsrepræsentanter og suppleanter 1814–1891. Biografisk og kronologisk fortegnelse, samlet og bearbeidet af Tallak Lindstøl ... Kristiania, H. Tønsbergs bogtrykkeri, 1892.
viii, 255, ₍1₎ p. 27½ᶜᵐ.
"Bilag til 5te del af Storthingsforhandl. 1892."
Contents.—Alfabetisk fortegnelse.—De enkelte storthing.—Rigsretter.—Valgdistrikter m. v.—Tabeller.

1. Norway—Storthing—Biog.

4–34166

Library of Congress   JN7543.L5

NL 0385376   DLC NN

Lindstøl, Tallak Olsen, 1857–
Stortinget og Statsraadet 1814–1914, efter offentlig foranstaltning utgit av Tallak Lindstøl ... Kristiania, Steenske bogtrykkeri, 1914–15.
2 v. in 4. 25½ᶜᵐ.
Vol. 2 has added general t.-p.
"Grundlaget for nærværende arbeide er 'Storthingsrepræsentanter og suppleanter 1814–1891,' der utkom 1892."—Forord.
Contents.—1. bd. Biografier. 1. del. A–K. 2. del. L–Ø samt tillæg.—2. bd. De enkelte storting og statsraader. 1. del. 1814–1885. 2. del. 1886–1914.

1. Norway. Storting. 2. Norway. Statsraad. 3. Norway—Biog.

16–19104

Library of Congress   JN7543.L5 1914

NL 0385377   DLC NN NdU WU

JN7543
.L5
1945
   Lindstøl, Tallak Olsen, 1857–1925. Stortinget og Statsraadet 1814–1914.
   Haffner, Vilhelm, 1864–
     Stortinget og Statsrådet 1915–1945. Med tillegg til Tallak Lindstøl. Stortinget og Statsraadet 1814–1914. Oslo, Aschehoug, 1949.

Lindstrand, Frans A   1847–
   Pennteckningar och reseskildringar, af onkel Ola. Chicago, Ill., På Svenska Amerikanarens förlag, 1898.
   376 p. port.

   1. U. S. – Description and travel. I. Title.

NL 0385379   WaU PPAmSwM MnU

Lindstrand, Folke.
...Über die Reduktion von sechswertigem Molybdän und deren Anwendung, von Folke Lindstrand. Göteborg, 1945. 12 p. 25cm. (Chalmers tekniska högskola, Gothenburg. Handlingar. nr. 41.)
"Litteraturnachweise," p. 12.

1. Molybdenum—Determination.   I. Ser.
N. Y. P. L.   April 23, 1948

NL 0385380   NN NNC

Lindstrand, Folke.
Über Eisenperchlorate, von Folke Lindstrand.   Lund: C. Bloms boktryckeri, 1939. 102 p. 24cm.
Author's dissertation.

1. Iron chlorate.   September 27, 1943
N. Y. P. L.

NL 0385381   NN CtY MH

Lindstrand, Frans Albin, 1847–
I Öster- och Västerland; illustrorade reseskildringar fran Egypten, det heliga landet, Italien, Schweiz, Tyskland, Danmark och Sverige Chicago, Svenska Amerikanaren, 1899.
387 p. illus. 23 cm.

1. Voyages and travels. I. Title.

NL 0385382   MoKU WaU ICJ MnHi

PT9995
.L56P4
   Lindstrand, Frans Albin, 1847–1913.
   Pennteckningar och reseskildringar, af Onkel Ola. Chicago, Svenska Amerikanarens förlag, 1898.
   376 p. port. 20 cm.

NL 0385383   MnHi

Lindstrand, Kristina, 1898–
Pinbänken. ₍Stockholm₎ Geber ₍1955₎
185 p. 19 cm.

I. Title.   *Full name:* Svea Kristina Lindstrand.
                        A 56–3869

Minnesota. Univ. Libr.
for Library of Congress   ₍8₎

NL 0385384   MnU KyU

Lindstrand, Styrbjörn.
A futura evolução da ortografia portuguesa. Lisboa, 1944.
17 p. 24.5 cm.
"Separata de 'O gráfico,' n.° 22, março, 1944."

NL 0385385   MH

G469.62
L645r
   Lindstrand, Styrbjörn.
   O ritmo no verso português; sobre três critérios não correctos dos tratados de metrificação. Lisboa, 1946.
   15p. 25cm.
   Cover title.

   1. Portuguese language – Versification. I. Tit]

NL 0385386   TxU ICU MH

Lindstrand, Svea Kristina
   see
   Lindstrand, Kristina, 1898–

Lindström, Åke.
Stackars Alexandra, av Åke Lindström.   Stockholm: P. A. Norstedt & söners förlag ₍, 1931₎. 197 p. 12°.
Contents: En stygg kameleont. Mr. Hills gud. Pamela Gordon. En orden. Safari. Mot torktidens slut. Tropisk sol. Musungo. "Stackars Alexandra." "Stjärnornas vän."

553940A. 1. Fiction, Swedish.   I. Title.
N. Y. P. L.   November 19, 1931

NL 0385388   NN

Lindström, Adolphus Udalricus, respondent.
De religionis ad rempublicam habitu apud romanos dissertatio...
     see under   Dahlström, Johannes Albertus, praeses.

LINDSTRÖM, AKSEL.
   Grå grannar. Med teckningar och fotografier av författaren. Stockholm, Medén [1946] 260 p. illus. 24cm.

1. Alaska--Descr. and trav.,   1900–

NL 0385390   NN DLC-P4

Lindström, Aksel.
Kanuks kvinna. Stockholm, LT:s förlag ₍1950₎
240 p. 22 cm.

                        A 51–3366

Minnesota. Univ. Libr.
for Library of Congress   ₍8₎

NL 0385391   MnU

Lindström, Aksel.
Den leende guden; roman. Stockholm, LTs förlag ₍1951₎
319 p. 20 cm.

                        A 52–7122

Minnesota. Univ. Libr.
for Library of Congress   ₍8₎

NL 0385392   MnU OCl

Lindström, Aksel.
Den röda elden; roman. ₍Stockholm₎ LTs förlag ₍1955₎
236 p. 20 cm.

I. Title.

                        A 56–2423

Minnesota. Univ. Libr.
for Library of Congress   ₍8₎

NL 0385393   MnU

VOLUME 334

Lindström, Aksel.
Österhus brinner; roman. ₍Stockholm₎ LTs förlag ₍1952₎
383 p. 20 cm.

A 53–358

Minnesota. Univ. Libr
for Library of Congress   ₍2₎

NL 0385394   MnU

Lindström, Aksel.
Santa-Lo. Stockholm, L. Hökerberg ₍1948₎
338 p. 22 cm.

A 49–5419*

Minnesota. Univ. Libr
for Library of Congress   ₍1₎

NL 0385395   MnU NN

Lindström, Aksel.
Sjung, Debora. ₍Stockholm₎ LT:s förlag ₍1954₎
237 p. 21 cm.

A 55–2666

Minnesota. Univ. Libr.
for Library of Congress   ₍2₎

NL 0385396   MnU

Lindström, Aksel.
Vilddjuret; roman. Stockholm, LT:s förlag ₍1949₎
299 p. 20 cm.

A 50–5916

Minnesota. Univ. Libr.
for Library of Congress   ₍2₎

NL 0385397   MnU

Lindstroem (Albert). *Bidrag till Läran om
Emboli. 60 pp. 8°. Lund, Berlingska Boktryckeriet. 1866.

NL 0385398   DNLM

Lindstroem, Albert
——. Om Meningitis cerebro-spinalis epidemica
och dess uppträdande inom Sverige åren 1854-7.
Akademisk afhandling. 89 pp., 1 pl. 8°. Lund,
Berlingska Boktryckeriet. 1857
——C.

NL 0385399   DNLM

VLD
+

LINDSTRÖM, ALF.
Trikåvarans teknologi. [Borås, Borås tidnings tr.,
1947-48] 2 v. illus. 31cm.

Del 1-2.
Cover title.
CONTENTS.—Del 1. Flatstickmaskinen.—Del 2. Rundstickmaskinen.

1. Knitting-machines.   t. 1947.

NL 0385400   NN

Lindström (Andreas₎
De lege per se imperante. Upsaliae, 1797. 2 p.l., 8
pp. 4°.

NL 0385401   NN

Lindström, Andreas, respondent.
Dissertatio philosophica, de praecipuis...
see under Högmark, Petrus, praeses.

Lindstroem, Andreas.
Vaticinium de eversione Babylonis.
Inaug. diss. Upsala, 1869.

NL 0385403   ICRL

PA2681 **Lindström, Anton.**
.L75   L'analogie dans la déclinaison des substantifs latins en
Gaule ... Upsala, Almqvist & Wiksells boktr., 1897–98.
2 v. in 1. 25ᶜᵐ.
Vol. 1 submitted as thesis, Univ. of Upsala.

1. Latin language, Vulgar—Declension.   2. French language—Old French—
Declension.   3. Provençal language—Declension.

NL 0385404   ICU MH PU CtY CU NjP IU

Lindström, Arne.
Besvärjelse, dikter. Stockholm, Bonnier ₍1947₎
75 p. 20 cm.

I. Title.

PT9875.L633B4   53–27296 ‡

NL 0385405   DLC

Lindström, Arne.
Flykten och havet; dikter. Stockholm, LTs förlag ₍1952₎
67 p. 20 cm.

A 53–3954

Minnesota. Univ. Libr.
for Library of Congress   ₍2₎

NL 0385406   MnU

Lindström, Arne.
Romantiskt landskap; dikter. Stockholm,
A. Bonnier [1931]
53+ p. sm. 4°.

NL 0385407   MH

Lindström, Aron, 1907-
... Untersuchungen über die Eigenschaften
und die Verwendbarkeit des Gussporzellanes Neo-
Eldentog ... [Zeulenroda i. Thür., 1930] ²⁷/₁₀
Inaug.-Diss. - Leipzig.
Lebenslauf.
"Literatur-Verzeichnis": p. 26–27.

NL 0385408   DNLM CtY

Lindström, Aune, 1901-
...Aukusti Uotila. Porvoo, Helsinki, W. Söderström ₍1948₎
130 p. illus. (part col.) 26cm.

"Aukusti Uotilan teokset," p. 104-₍131₎

478539B. 1. Uotila, Aukust, 1858-   1886.
N.Y.P.L.   April 24, 1950

NL 0385409   NN DLC-P4 MnU

Lindström, Aune, 1901-
Fanny Churberg; elämä ja teokset.
Porvoo, W. Söderström ₍1938₎

181 p.   illus.(part col.) ports.
23cm.

"Fanny Churbergin teokset": p.₍137₎-
179.
Bibliography: p.₍180₎-181.

1. Churberg, Fanny Maria, 1845-1902.

NL 0385410   MnU OCl

Lindström, Aune, 1901-
Taiteilijaveljekset von Wright, kirjoittanut
Aune Lindström ... Helsinki, 1932.
242 p.   illus.   21½ cm.

Thesis, Helsingfors.

1. Wright, Ferdinand von, 1822-1906. 2. Wright,
Magnus von, 1805-1868. 3. Wright, Wilhelm von,
1810-1887.

NL 0385411   NNC OU NIC MnU CtY ICRL PU

Lindström, Axel Fredrik, 1839-
... Beskrifning till de agronomiskt geologiska kartorna
öfver Skottorp och Dömmestorp i Hallands län af Axel
Lindström. Stockholm, Kongl. boktryckeriet, P. A. Norstedt & söner, 1881.
29 p. 23½ᶜᵐ. and 2 maps. 28 x 39ᶜᵐ and 50 x 70ᶜᵐ. (Sveriges geologiska undersökning. Ser. Bb. Specialkartor med beskrifningar. n:is 1
& 2)
Map mo. 1: pub. in 1873? Scale 1: 20000.
Map mo. 2: pub. in 1873. Scale 1: 4000.

1. Geology—Sweden—Halland.   2. Geology, Agricultural.

G S 7–1334

NL 0385412   DI-GS NIC

Lindström, Axel Fredrik, 1839-
... Beskrifning till kartbladen Kullen och Höganäs af
Axel Lindström. Stockholm, Kongl. boktryckeriet, P. A.
Norstedt & söner, 1880.
30 p. diagrs. 23½ᶜᵐ. and map. 45 x 59ᶜᵐ. (Sveriges geologiska undersökning. Ser. Aa. Kartblad i skalan 1: 50000 med beskrifningar. n:o
77 & 78)

1. Geology—Sweden.

G S 7–1253

NL 0385413   DI-GS

Lindström, Axel Fredrik, 1839-
... Beskrifning till kartbladet Borås af Axel Lindström
... Stockholm, Kongl. boktryckeriet, P. A. Norstedt &
söner, 1883.
64 p. fold. map. 23½ᶜᵐ. and map. 22½ x 30ᶜᵐ. (Sveriges geologiska
undersökning. Ser. Ab. Kartblad i skalan 1: 200,000 med beskrifningar.
n:o 7)

1. Geology—Sweden.

G S 7–1308

NL 0385414   DI-GS

Lindström, Axel Fredrik, 1839-
... Beskrifning till kartbladet Engelholm af Axel Lindström ... Stockholm, Kongl. boktryckeriet, P. A. Norstedt & söner, 1880.
45 p. pl. (2 maps) 23½ᶜᵐ. and map. 45 x 59½ᶜᵐ. (Sveriges geologiska undersökning. Ser. Aa. Kartblad i skalan 1: 50000 med beskrifningar. n:o 76)

1. Geology—Sweden.

G S 7–1252

NL 0385415   DI-GS

VOLUME 334

Lindström, Axel Fredrik, 1839–
... Beskrifning till kartbladet "Herrevadskloster" (no. 67) af Axel Lindström. Stockholm, P. A. Norstedt & söner, kongl. boktryckare, 1878.

1 p. l., 38 p. 23½ᶜᵐ. *and* map. 44½ x 59½ᶜᵐ. (*On cover:* Sveriges geologiska undersökning. Ser. Aa. Kartblad i skalan 1 : 50000 med beskrifningar. n:o 67 ...)

1. Geology—Sweden.

           G S 7–1243

NL 0385416   DI-GS

Lindström, Axel Fredrik, 1839–
... Beskrifning till kartbladet "Hessleholm" (no. 61) af Axel Lindström. Stockholm, P. A. Norstedt & söner, kongl. boktryckare, 1877.

59 p. 23½ᶜᵐ. *and* map. 45 x 59½ᶜᵐ. (Sveriges geologiska undersökning. ₍Ser. Aa. Kartblad i skalan 1 : 50000 med beskrifningar. no. 61₁)

Map is dated 1876.

1. Geology—Sweden.

           G S 7–1238

NL 0385417   DI-GS

Lindström, Axel Fredrik, 1839–
... Beskrifning till kartbladet Örkelljunga af Axel Lindström. Stockholm, Kungl. boktryckeriet, P. A. Norstedt & söner, 1898.

1 p. l., 39 p. pl. (maps) 23½ᶜᵐ. *and* map. 44½ x 59½ᶜᵐ. (Sveriges geologiska undersökning. Ser. Aa. Kartblad i skalan 1 : 50000 med beskrifningar. no:o 114)

1. Geology—Sweden.

           G S 7–1284

NL 0385418   DI-GS

Lindström, Axel Fredrik, 1839–
... Beskrifning till kartbladet Uddevalla af Axel Lindström. Stockholm, Kungl. boktryckeriet, P. A. Norstedt & söner, 1902.

2 p. l., 115, ₍1₎ p., 1 l. illus. 24ᶜᵐ. *and* map. 44½ x 59ᶜᵐ. (Sveriges geologiska undersökning. Ser. Ac. Kartblad i skalan 1 : 100000 med beskrifningar. n:o 3)

Map is dated 1901.

1. Geology—Sweden.

           G S 7–1321

NL 0385419   DI-GS

Lindström, Axel Fredrik, 1839–
... Beskrifning till kartbladet Venersborg af Axel Lindström. Stockholm, Kungl. boktryckeriet, P. A. Norstedt & söner, 1887.

77 p. 2 maps on fold. pl. 24ᶜᵐ. *and* map. 22½ x 29½ᶜᵐ. (Sveriges geologiska undersökning. Ser. Ab. Kartblad i skalan 1 : 200,000 med beskrifningar. n:o 11)

1. Geology—Sweden.

           G S 7–1312

NL 0385420   DI-GS

Lindström, Axel Fredrik, 1839–
... Några allmänna upplysningar till öfversigtskarta angifvande de kvartära hafsaflagringarnas område samt kalkstens- och mergelförekomsters utbredning i Sverige, på grund af material insamladt genom Sveriges geologiska undersökning sammanställda af A. Lindström. Stockholm, Kungl. boktryckeriet, P. A. Norstedt & söner, 1898.

80 p. 24ᶜᵐ. *and* map. 79½ x 40½ᶜᵐ. (Sveriges geologiska undersökning. Ser. Ba. Öfversigtskartor. no. 5)

Map is dated 1897-98.
Scale of map 1 : 2000000.

1. Geology—Sweden.

           G S 7–1332

NL 0385421   DI-GS

Lindström, Axel Fredrik, 1839–
... Praktiskt geologiska iakttagelser under resor på Gotland 1876–1878 af Axel Lindström ... Stockholm, Kongl. boktryckeriet, P. A. Norstedt & söner, 1879.

2 p. l., 43 p. pl., fold. map. 22½ᶜᵐ. (Sveriges geologiska undersökning. Ser. C. Afhandlingar och uppsatser. n:o 34)

1. Geology—Sweden—Gothland.

           G S 7–1370

NL 0385422   DI-GS

QE282
.A3
Ser. C,
no. 32

Lindström, Axel Fredrik, 1839–
Blomberg, Albert, 1844– *1922.*
... Praktiskt geologiska undersökningar inom Herjedalen och Jemtland, utförda sommaren 1876 af Albert Blomberg och Axel Lindström ... Stockholm, Kongl. boktryckeriet, P. A. Norstedt & söner, 1879.

Lindström, Axel Fredrik, 1839–*1911.*

'**Sweden.** *Sveriges geologiska undersökning.*
... Praktiskt geologiska undersökningar inom norra delen af Kalmar län, utförda på bekostnad af länets norra hushållnings-sällskap genom Sveriges geologiska undersökning åren 1876–1881 ... Stockholm, Kongl. boktryckeriet, P. A. Norstedt & söner, 1884.

QE282
.A3
ser. C,
no. 92;

Lindström, Axel Fredrik, 1839–1911.
Sweden. *Geologiska undersökningen.*
... Praktiskt geologiska undersökningar inom Vesternorrlands län med bidrag af länets hushållningssällskap utförda genom Sveriges geologiska undersökning åren 1881–1887 ... Stockholm, Kongl. boktryckeriet, P. A. Norstedt & söner, 1888–

Lindström, Bernt Martin

see

Lindström, Martin, 1904–

Lindström, Bert, ed.
Svensk grosshandel, under redaktion av Bert Lindström ₍och₁ Ulf af Trolle. ₍Stockholm₁ Sveriges grossistförbund, Seelig i distribution ₍1947₁

422 p. maps, diagrs. 25 cm.

"Sveriges grossistförbund uppdrog åt oss i maj 1946 att til dess 25-årsjubileum i november 1947 'skriva en på insamlade fakta grundad bok om den svenska grosshandeln.'"

1. Wholesale trade—Sweden.   I. Trolle, Ulf af, 1919–   joint ed. II. Title.

HF5349.S87L5   49–14625*

NL 0385427   DLC NN

Lindström, Bo, 1925–
Roentgen absorption spectrophotometry in quantitative cytochemistry. Stockholm, 1955.

206 p. illus. 25 cm. (Acta radiologica. Supplementum 125)

At head of title: From the Institute for Cell Research, Medical Nobel Institute, Karolinska Institutet, Stockholm, Sweden.
Bibliography: p. 197-206.

1. Spectrophotometer. 2. Histochemistry.   I. Title. II. Series.

           A 55–6603

Wisconsin. Univ. Libr.   rev
for Library of Congress   ₍r73c2₁

NL 0385428   WU DSI MoU PPT DNLM ViU

Lindström, Carl, A.-G., Berlin.
Kultur und Schallplatte. Mitteilungen der Carl Lindström A. G., Kultur Abteilung.
Jahrg. 1–

Berlin, 1929–   21½cm.
v. illus. (incl. music, ports.)

Monthly.
Suspended publication

1. Music—Per. and soc. publ.   2. Phonograph—Per. and soc. publ
3. House organs. I. Title.
N. Y. P. L.   June 5, 1934

NL 0385429   NN

Lindström, Carl, A.-G., Berlin.
Odeon-Electric; deutsches Hauptverzeichnis...
19

₍Berlin, 19   21½cm.
v.

————— Odeon Gesamt-Nachtrag. 19

1. Phonograph records—Catalogues.   I. Title.
N. Y. P. L.   November 23, 1934

NL 0385430   NN

Lindström, Carl, A.-G., Berlin.
Parlophon-Beka Electric; deutsches Hauptverzeichnis.
19

₍Berlin, 19   17 – 21½cm.
v.

Title varies: 19   Hauptverzeichnis der Parlophon-, Beka-, Lindström American record, Lindex-Musikplatten; ₍192   Parlophon Electric Hauptkatalog; 1930/31   Parlophon-Beka Electric; deutsches Hauptverzeichnis.

————— Parlophon Gesamt-Nachtrag. 19

1. Phonograph records—Catalogues.   I. Title.
N. Y. P. L.   November 23, 1934

NL 0385431   NN

Lindström, Carl, A.G., Berlin,
2000 Jahre musik auf der schallplatte. Berlin, C. Lindström a.g., Kultur-abteilung ₍n.d.₁
26 p. 26½x30½cm.

Notes to accompany records B-37022 - B-37033.

1. Music - History and criticism. I. Title.

NL 0385432   NPV

₍**Lindström, Carl Ferdinand₁** 1811–1861.
Svensk bokhandels-katalog utgifven år 1845. ₍Stockholm₁ P. A. Norstedt & söner ₍1845–47₁   455 p.   20½cm.

Issued in 3 parts.
"Tillägg ₍1847, och register₁," p. 325-455.

————— Tillægg til Svensk bokhandels-katalog, 1848. ₍Stockholm: P. A. Norstedt & söner, 1848₁   48 p.   20½cm.

Bound with the above.

753488A.   1. Bibliography, Swedish.   I. Title.
N. Y. P. L.   November 8, 1935

NL 0385433   NN MB CtY ICU

Lindström, Carl Ferdinand, 1811–1861, ed.
Wadstena kloster-reglor...
see under Vadstena, Sweden (Birgittine monastery)

VOLUME 334

DRAMATIC LIBRARY
D809.2808
L64
Lindström, Carl Jacob, b 1800
Costumi e vestiture napolitani, disegnati
ed incisi da Carlo Lindström. Napoli, 1836.
40 col. plates.

1. Costume - Naples. 2. Costume - Italy.

NL 0385435   NNC NjP NN

Lindström (C[arl] O[scar]) [1854-]. *Men-
niskokroppens synovialsenskidor och burser.
I. Synovialsenskidor. [Synovial membranes in
human body. I. Synovial tendon sheaths.] 101
pp., 4 pl. 8°. *Stockholm, I. Marcus, 1886.

NL 0385436   DNLM

Lindström, Carlo
see   Lindström, Carl Jacob, b. 1800.

823.8
K54Yfi
Lindström, Erik Lechard, 1891-
Charles Dickens.   Stockholm, H. Gerbers
Förlag [1930]
207p. plates,ports. 21cm.

Bibliography: p. [202]-203.

1. Dickens, Charles, 1812-1870.

NL 0385438   IEN InU

Lindström, Erik Lechard, 1891-
Nordisk folklivsskildring, av Erik Lindström. Stockholm,
P. A. Norstedt & söner [1932]
250 p. illus. (incl. ports.) 17¾cm. [Norstedts lilla bibliotek]
"Rättelse": slip attached to p. 250.
CONTENTS.—Nordisk folklivsskildring.—Från den isländska ättsagan
till Nordlands trompet.—Sjuttonhundratalet.—Romantik och realism.—
Björnson och hans samtida.—Åttiotalets folklivsskildring.—Nittiotalets
folklivsskildring.—Efter nittonhundra.

1. Scandinavian literature—Hist. & crit. 2. Country life—Scandinavia. 3. Scandinavia—Soc. life & cust.   I. Title.
Library of Congress   PT7062.L5   34–34355 Revised
                [r46d2]   839.509

NL 0385439   DLC WU ICU TxU

Lindström, Erik Lechard, 1891-
Strindbergs "Mäster Olof" - dramer.
Lund, Gleerup [1921]
48 p. (Skrifter utgivna av Moders-
målslärarnas förening [nr.14])

NL 0385440   CU

Lindström, Erik Lechard, 1891-
Walter Scott och den historiska romanen och novellen in
Sverige intill 1850, av Erik Lindström. Göteborg, Elanders
boktryckeri aktiebolag, 1925.
1 p. l., [7]-viii, 332 p. 25cm. [Göteborgs högskolas årsskrift. XXXI,
1925: 4]

1. Scott, Sir Walter, bart., 1771-1832. 2. Swedish fiction—Hist. & crit.
3. Historical fiction. 4. Literature, Comparative—English and Swedish.
5. Literature, Comparative—Swedish and English.
                A 46–2020
Michigan. Univ. Library
for Library of Congress   AS284.G6   vol. 31, no. 4
                [3,†

NL 0385441   DLC IU   MiU DSI TxU NcU NN CSmH GU MnU ViU NcD

Lindström, Erik Valter, 1907-
... Stadiernas teologi en Kierkegaard-
studie.   Lund, C.W.K. Gleerup [1943]
370 p., 22½cm.
At head of title: Valter Lindström.
"Källor och litteratur": p. [357]-363.

NL 0385442   NjPT

Lindström, Erika.
Frigjord; en prästmans väg. [Åbo] Bro [1945]
205 p. 22 cm.

I. Title.
                A 48–7369*
New York. Public Libr.
for Library of Congress   [1]

NL 0385443   NN

Lindstroem, Fredr J
Alfred Kordelin; elämäkerrallinen kuvaus.
Helsingissä, Alfred Kordelinin kuolinpesä
[1923]
266 p. illus.

NL 0385444   MH DLC-P4

J14
261p
Lindström, Fredr. J
Taiteen tarkoitus ja moraali; historiallis-
kriitillinen tutkimus [Helsingissä,1914]
346p. 23cm.
Thesis - Helsinki.
"Kirjallisuusluettelo": n.[335]-346.

NL 0385445   CtY ICRL

PT9581
.N9
Lindström, Göran.
Ny lyrik 1946 [redigerat av Johannes Edfelt] Stockholm,
A. Bonnier [1946]

Lindström, Göran, jt. auth.
Nynorsk-svensk ordlista

see under

Dahl, Herleiv.

382.471
L645
Lindström, Gunnar
Suomen kaupasta Aleksanteri I-sen aikana. I.
Järjestymisvuodet 1808-1812. Helsinki, Weilin
& Göös, 1905.
243, 86 p. tables.

Thesis, Helsinki.
Imperfect: p. 87 lacking. Cf. Suomalainen
kirjallisuus, 1901-1905.
Bibliographical footnotes.

NL 0385448   NNC ICRL

Lindström, Gunnar.
...Ur bondebrev och riksdagsvers; ett bidrag till Lantmanna-
partiets krönika, utgivet med understöd från Karl Staaffs fond
för frisinnade ändamål... Malmö: Aktiebolaget Framtidens
bokförlag [1932]. 58 p. ports. 19½cm.

Reprinted from various newspapers.

703011A. 1. Lantmannapartiet.
N. Y. P. L.   May 4, 1934

NL 0385449   NN

Lindström, Gunnar, physicist.
Nuclear resonance absorption applied to precise measurements
of nuclear magnetic moments, and the establishment of an abso-
lute energy scale in β-spectroscopy. Stockholm, Almqvist &
Wiksell, 1951. 80 p. illus., tables. 25cm. (Kungliga
tekniska högskolan, Stockholm. Avhandling. no. 70)
Cover-title.
"Arkiv för fysik...band 4, nr. 1."
Avhandling — Kungl. tekniska högskolan, Stockholm.
Extra t.-p. with thesis note, inserted.
Bibliography, p. 78-80.

.1. Nuclear moments. 2. Nuclear   moments. 1951. I. Series.

NL 0385450   NN

Lindström, Gustaf, 1829-1901.
Anteckningar om Gotlands medeltid, af G. Lindström.
Stockholm, Kungl. boktryckeriet, P. A. Norstedt & söner, 1892-
v. 23¼cm.

1. Gotland—Hist. 2. Wisby, Sweden—Hist.
                28-3115
Library of Congress   DL971.G7L5

NL 0385451   DLC MH CtY

Lindström, Gustaf, 1829-1901.
Anmälanden och kritiker. Die koral-
lenfaunen der etage 5 des norwegischen
silursystems von Johan Kiär. Separat-
abdruck aus Palaeontographica, Bd. XLVI,
Stuttgart 1899. [Stuttgart, 1899]
5 p. (Geol. Fören. Förhandl. N:o 193.
Bd 21. Häft. 4)

NL 0385452   IU

Lindström, Gustaf, 1829-1901.
... The *Ascoceratidæ* and the *Lituitidæ* of the Upper Silurian formation of Gotland, described by G. Lindström. With
seven plates ... Stockholm, P. A. Norstedt & söner, 1890.
54 p. VII pl. 31cm. (Kongl. svenska vetenskaps-akademiens handlingar. [Ny följd] bd. 23, n:o 12)

1. Ascoceratidae. 2. Lituitidae. 3. Paleontology—Sweden—Gotland.
4. Paleontology—Silurian.
                A 43–172
Chicago. Univ. Library
for Library of Congress   Q64.S85 bd. 23, no. 12
                [3,†

NL 0385453   ICU   NN DLC

563.6
L64b
Lindström, Gustaf, 1829-1901.
Beschreibung einiger obersilurischer
korallen aus der insel Gotland ... der
Königl. academie der wissenschaften vorgelegt den 11 Dezember 1895.   Stockholm, 1896.
50p. plates.   (Bihang till K. Svenska
vet. akad. handlingar b.21, afd.4, N:o.7)

NL 0385454   IU

Lindström, Gustaf, 1829-1901.
Bidrag till historien om Gotland såsom hörande till drott-
ning Christinas underhållsländer ... Upsala, C. A. Leffler,
Kongl. akad. boktryckare, 1854.
2 p. l., 20 p. 21¼cm.

Akademisk afhandling—Upsala.

1. Gotland—Hist.
                28-3114
Library of Congress   DL971.G7L52

NL 0385455   DLC MH CtY

VOLUME 334

Lindström, Gustaf, 1829–1901.

Richthofen, Ferdinand Paul Wilhelm, *freiherr von,* 1833–1905.
China. Ergebnisse eigener reisen und darauf gegründeter studien, von Ferdinand freiherrn von Richthofen ... Berlin, D. Reimer, 1877–1912.

Lindström, Gustaf, 1829–1901.
... Contributions to the actinology of the Atlantic ocean, by G. Lindström. With three plates ... Stockholm, P. A. Norstedt & söner, 1877.
26 p. illus. iii pl. 31ᶜᵐ. (Kongl. svenska vetenskaps-akademiens handlingar. ₍Ny följd₎ bd. 14, n:o 6)

1. Corals—Atlantic ocean.   i. Title.
Chicago. Univ. Library   Q64.S85   bd. 14, no. 6   A 43–130
for Library of Congress
₍2₎†

NL   0385457   ICU DLC NN OU

Lindström, Gustaf, 1829–1901.
A description of the anthozoa perforata of Gotland. Stockholm: P. A. Norstedt & Söner, 1870. 12 p., 1 pl. f°. (Kongliga Svenska Vetenskaps-Akademien. Handlingar. Ny följd. Bd. 9, no. 6.)
With bibliographical foot-notes.

1. Anthozoa, Sweden.
N. Y. P. L.   January 4, 1912.

NL   0385458   NN MiU

LINDSTRÖM, Gustaf.   1829–1901.
Forteckning pa Gotlands siluriska crustaceer. [Stockholm], [1885].
1 pam.

NL   0385459   MH-Z

Lindström, Gustaf, 1829–1901.

Angelin, Nils Peter, 1805–1876.
Fragmenta silurica e dono Caroli Henrici Wegelin. Opus studio Nicolai Petri Angelin inchoatum jussu et impensis Academiae regiae scientiarum suecicae edendum curavit G. Lindström ... Holmiae, Samson & Wallin, 1880.

Lindström, Gustaf, 1829–1901.
Iconographia crinoideorum in stratis Sueciae siluricis fossilium...
     see under   Angelin, Nils Peter, 1805–1876.

Lindström, Gustaf, 1829–1901.
...Index to the generic names applied to the corals of the palaeozoic formations by Gustaf Lindström ... Stockholm, K. Boktryckeriet, P. A. Norstedt & söner, 1883.
14 p.

(Bihand till K. svenska vet.-akad. handlingar. bd. 8, no. 9)

NL   0385462   00

₍**Lindström, Gustaf**₎ 1829–1901.
List of the fossils of the upper silurian formation of Gotland. Stockholm, Kongl. boktryckeriet, P. A. Norstedt & söner, 1885.
20 p. 22ᶜᵐ.
Signed: G. Lindström.

1. Paleontology—Silurian.   2. Paleontology—Sweden—Gotland.
i. Title.
                                     28–10693

Library of Congress   QE727.L5

NL   0385463   DLC MH

Lindström, Gustaf, 1829–1902.
Obersilurische Korallen von Tshau-Tiën. Plates.
(In Richthofen, F. v. China. Band 4, pp. 50–74. Berlin. 1883.)

114684 — Coral. Fossil. — Silurian fossils.

NL   0385464   MB

Lindström, Gustaf, 1829–1901.
Om de palaeozoiska formationernas operkelbärande koraller. Stockholm, 1882.
111 p. 9 plates. 8°.
Bihang till K. Svensk. Vetensk. Akademie Handlingar. VII.

NL   0385465   MH-Z

Lindström, Gustaf, 1829–1901.
Om Gotlands Höjning. [Stockholm, 1852]
14 p. 8°.

NL   0385466   CtY

Lindström, G₍ustaf₎ 1829–1901.
Om Gotlands nutida mollusker; af G. Lindström .. Wisby, Tryckt hos T. Norrby, 1868.
1 p. l., 48 p. iii pl. 21½ᶜᵐ.

1. Mollusks—Gotland.

Library of Congress   QL425.S8L7   6–24410†

NL   0385467   DLC

Lindström, Gustaf, 1829–1901.
... Om postglaciala sänkningar af Gotland. Af G. Lindström. ₍Stockholm, 1886₎
p. ₍261₎–281. illus. 21½ᶜᵐ.
Caption title.
"Aftryck ur Geol. föreningens i Stockholm förhandl., n:o 102, bd. VIII, h. 4."

1. Earth movements.   2. Geology—Sweden—Gotland.
                                     27–13059

Library of Congress   GB488.6.L5

NL   0385468   DLC

Lindström, Gustaf, 1829–1901.
... Om trias- och juraförsteningar från Spetsbergen. Af G. Lindström. Med tre taflor ... ₍Stockholm, P. A. Norstedt & söner, 1866†₎
20 p. iii pl. 31ᶜᵐ. (Kongl. svenska vetenskaps-akademiens handlingar. ₍Ny följd₎ bd. 6, n:o 6)
Till Kongl. vet. akad. inlemnad den 11 november 1865.

1. Paleontology — Spitzbergen.   2. Paleontology — Triassic.   3. Paleontology—Jurassic.
                             G S 12–858
Library, U. S. Geol.   survey

NL   0385469   DI-GS NN

Lindström, Gustaf, 1829–1901, joint author.

Thorell, Tord Tamerlan Teodor, 1830–1901.
... On a Silurian scorpion from Gotland, by T. Thorell and G. Lindström. With one plate ... Stockholm, P. A. Norstedt & söner, 1885.

Lindström, Gustaf, 1829–1901.
...On the "Corallia baltica" of Linnaeus, by ... ₍Stockholm? 1895?₎
p. 615–642.

NL   0385471   00

Lindström, G₍ustaf₎ 1829–1901.
On the silurian gastropoda and pteropoda of Gotland. Stockholm: P. A. Norstedt & Söner, 1884. 250 p., 21 pl. f°. (Kongliga Svenska Vetenskaps-Akademien. Handlingar. Ny följd. Bd. 19, no. 6.)
With bibliographical foot-notes.

1. Gasteropoda (Fossil), Sweden: Gotland. 2. Pteropoda (Fossil),
Sweden : Gotland.   January 6, 1912.
N. Y. P. L.

NL   0385472   NN NIC DI-GS CtY MH CSt

Lindström, Gustaf, 1829–1901.
Die rathslinie von Wisby. Von prof. G. Lindström in Stockholm. ₍Lübeck, 1893₎
22 p. 21½ᶜᵐ.
Caption title.
From "Zeitschr. d. Vereins f. lübeckische gesch. u. alterthumskunde, b. 7, 1893".

1. Wisby, Sweden—Hist.   2. Wisby, Sweden—Biog.
                                     28–3113

Library of Congress   DL991.W8L5

NL   0385473   DLC

Lindström, G₍ustaf₎ 1829–1901.
Remarks on the Heliolitidæ.   Stockholm: P. A. Norstedt & Söner, 1899. 140 p., 12 pl. f°. (Kongliga Svenska Vetenskaps-Akademien. Handlingar. Ny följd. Bd. 32, no. 1.)
With bibliographical foot-notes.

1. Corals (Fossil), Sweden.
N. Y. P. L.   December 29, 1911.

NL   0385474   NN CU IU

Lindström, G₍ustaf₎ 1829–1901.
Researches on the visual organs of the trilobites. Stockholm: P. A. Norstedt & Söner, 1901. 86 p., 6 pl. illus. f°. (Kongliga Svenska Vetenskaps-Akademien. Handlingar. Ny följd. Bd. 34, no. 8.)
With bibliographical foot-notes.

1. Trilobita.   2. Palæontology
N. Y. P. L.   (Zoological). December 13, 1911.

NL   0385475   NN

Lindström, Gustaf, 1829–1901.
... Silurische Korallen aus Nord-Russland und Sibirien ... Stockholm, 1882.
Pamphlet (Bihang till K.Svenska vet. akad. Handlingar. Bd. 6. N:o 18)

Sg15
1

NL   0385476   CtY

VOLUME 334

Lindström, Gustaf, 1829–1901.
... Ueber die schichtenfolge des silur auf der insel Gotland.
Von professor G. Lindström ... ₁Stuttgart, 1888₎
p. ₁147₁–164. map. 22½ᶜᵐ.
Caption title.
"Separat-abdruck aus dem Neuen jahrbuch für mineralogie etc., 1888.
bd. I."

1. Geology, Stratigraphic—Silurian. 2. Geology—Sweden—Gotland.

28–10694

Library of Congress   QE661.L5

NL 0385477   DLC

Lindström, Gustaf Axel, 1882–
... An experimental study of myelotoxic sera; therapeutic
attemps ₁ ₁ in myeloid leukaemia, by Gustaf A. Lindström.
Stockholm, P. A. Norstedt & söner, 1927.
vii, 169 p. incl. tables. fold. diagrs. 24½ᶜᵐ. (On cover: Acta medica
scandinavica. Supplementum XXII)
At head of title: From the Medical clinic II of the Serafimerlasarettet,
Stockholm.

1. Leucemia. 2. Serumtherapy.
A C 33–2166
Title from John Crerar   Libr. Printed by L. C.

NL 0385478   ICJ MiU DNLM CtY PPC OC1W-H

Lindström, Gustaf Hilding Sigfrid
see **Lindström, Sigfrid,** 1892–

Lindström, Gustaf Rune
see **Lindström, Rune,** 1916–

Lindström, Hans.
Att samla Strindberg. Stockholm, Sällskapet Bokvännerna ₁1949₎
57, ₁2₁ p. 19 cm. (Bokvännens småskrifter)
"Litteraturen om Strindberg": p. 51–₁58₎

1. Strindberg, August, 1849–1912—Bibl.   (Series)

Z8850.2.L55   53–16594

NL 0385481   DLC

Lindström, Hans.
Hjärnornas kamp; psykologiska idéer och motiv i Strind-
bergs åttiotalsdiktning. Uppsala, Appelbergs boktr., 1952.
329 p. 23 cm.
Akademisk avhandling—Uppsala.
Extra t. p., with thesis statement, inserted.
Bibliography: p. 307–₁317₎

1. Strindberg, August, 1849–1912.   I. Title.

PT9817.P8L5   54–27471

NL 0385482   DLC NcU CtY NNC MH MnU

4BX
835   Lindström, Harald Gustaf Åke,
1905–
John Wesleys budskap och nutids-
människan. Stockholm, Nya bokför-
lag₎[1953]
22 p.

NL 0385483   DLC-P4 MH

BX8495
W5L46 **Lindström, Harald Gustaf Åke,** 1905–
Wesley and sanctification; a study in the doctrine of salva-
tion. Stockholm, Nya bokförlags aktiebolaget ₁1946₎
xvi, 228 p. 24 cm.
Inaug. diss.—Uppsala.
Extra t. p., with thesis statement and imprint (Uppsala, Almqvist
& Wiksells boktr., 1946) inserted.
Tr. by H. S. Harvey.
Corrigenda leaf inserted.
Bibliography: p. 219–226.

1. Wesley, John, 1703–1791. 2. Sanctification—History of doctrines. 3. Salvation—History of doctrines.   I. Harvey, Henry
Stanley, 1911–   tr.   II. Title.

BX8495.W5L46   234.8   49–2298*

KyU KyLxCB PPT IdU OrU
NL 0385484   DLC CtY TxDaM MH PPWe NjP NNUT ICU NIC

Lindström, Henning.
Om människovärdet; bidrag till en kristen antropologi.
Stockholm, Svenska kyrkans diakonistyrelses bokförlag
₁1951₎
210 p. 23 cm.
"Anförd litteratur": p. 200–206.

1. Man (Theology)   I. Title.

A 52–10556

Harvard Univ. Library
for Library of Congress   ₁1₎

NL 0385485   MH MH–AH

Lindström, Henning.
Skapelse och frälsning i Melanchthons teologi. Stock-
holm, Svenska kyrkans diakonistyrelses bokförlag ₁1944₎
415 p. 24 cm.
Akademisk avhandling—Lund.
Extra t. p., with thesis statement, inserted.
Bibliography: p. ₁407₁–413.

1. Melanchthon, Philipp, 1497–1560. 2. Theology, Doctrinal—
Hist.—16th cent. 3. Lutheran Church—Doctrinal and controversial
works.   I. Title.

BR335.L5   52–57357

NL 0385486   DLC ICMcC IEG ICU NjPT NNC NNUT NjP

Lindström, Henry.
Näringsfrihetens utveckling i Sverige 1809–36, av Henry
Lindström.   Göteborg: Elanders boktryckeri aktiebolag, 1923.
xviii, 355 p.   8°.   (Göteborgs högskola. Årsskrift. bd. 29,
nr. 5.)
Bibliography, p. ix–xviii.

1. Economic history—Sweden.   2. Industries and mechanic arts
—Sweden.   October 29, 1926
N. Y. P. L.

NL 0385487   NN WU ICRL MH RPB

HC
375
.L52   Lindström, Henry
Näringsfrihetsfrågan i Sverige 1837–1864.
Göteborg ₁Wettergren & Kerber₎ ₁1929₎.
171 p.   25cm.   (Göteborgs Högskolas
Årsskrift. Bd. 35, nr. 3)

1. Sweden - Indus. - Hist. 2. Sweden -
Commerce - Hist.   I. Title.

NL 0385488   WU RPB

QH9
.T6
no. 171–   **Lindström, Jacob Niclas,** 1801–1834, *respondent.*
175   **Thunberg, Karl Peter,** 1743–1828, *praeses.*
Rare Bk.   Flora runsteniensis ... Upsaliæ, excudebant Zeipel et
Palumblad ₁1815–17₎

LINDSTRÖM, JOHAN.
Bland skogsafverkare och sägverksarbetare;en nu-
tidsberättelse med framtidsperspektiv,af Johan Lindström... Stockholm,A.Bonnier[1898]
151 p. 18cm.

NL 0385490   ICU

PT9875
.L6J8   LINDSTRÖM, JOHAN.
1902   Jungfru Jämtland. En samling berättelser af Johan
Lindström... Illustrerad af Elis Bergh. Stockholm,
A.Bonnier[1902]
120,[1]p. illus. 22cm.

NL 0385491   ICU

Lindstrøm, Johan, 1893–
...Lærdal. Oslo, Mittet & co., 1946. 71 p. illus. (part
col.) 28cm.

355566B. 1. Lærdal, Norway.   October 29, 1946
N. Y. P. L.

NL 0385492   NN WU

Lindstrøm, Johan, 1893–
...Lærdalsøren; et centrum for gammel bygningsskik paa vest-
landet. Kristiania: Grøndahl & søns boktrykkeri, 1921. 40 p.
illus. (incl. plans.) 24cm. (Fortidsminner. ₁nr.₎ 7.)

1. Architecture, Domestic—   Norway—Lærdal. I. Ser.
N. Y. P. L.   July 12, 1937

NL 0385493   NN

Lindström, Johan Henrik, 1893–
... Untersuchung des kohärerwiderstandes als abhängend von
der entfernung des oszillators, von J. H. Lindström und Rolf
Nevanlinna ... ₁Helsingfors, 1922₎
10 p. incl. tables, diagrs. 24ᶜᵐ. (Societas scientiarum fennica. Com-
mentationes physico-mathematicae. I, 25)
Caption title.
"Mitteilungen aus dem physikalischen laboratorium der Universität
Helsingfors. n:o 55."

1. Coherer.   I. Nevanlinna, Rolf Herman, 1895–   joint author.
Title from John Crerar   Libr.   A C 33–1041
Library of Congress   ₁Q60.F555 vol. 1, no. 25₎

NL 0385494   ICJ NcU OU ViU

Hz24
L64   Lindström, Johan Adolf, 1819–1874.
Försök att visa grammatikaliska formers
uppkomst i finska språken, samt förvandt-
skap i andra språk ... Åbo,J.C.Frenckell &
son,1847.
71,[1]p. 20cm.

1. Finnish languages - Grammar, Comparative

NL 0385495   CtY ICN

Lindström, Johan Adolf, 1819–1874.
Om finska folkvandringar enligt grekiska,
romerska och andra källor. Åbo, 1848.
72 p. 20 cm.

NL 0385496   CtY ICN

Lindström, Johan (Saxon)
Bönnera där hemma; viser på Narkesmål.
Stockholm, Nutidens Förlag ₁1922₎
127 p.

NL 0385497   WaU

VOLUME 334

Lindström, Johan (Saxon)
Bondfolk; skisser. Stockholm, Bonnier
〈1887〉
135 p.

NL 0385498   WaU

Lindström, Johan (Saxon)
Där hemma i socknen; folkmotive. Östersund,
Vilhelm Skölds förlag 〈1893〉
78 p.

NL 0385499   WaU

Lindström, Johan (Saxon)
Förtrampad, och andra berättelser.
Östersund, V. Sköld 〈1893〉
112 p.

NL 0385500   WaU

DL   Lindström, Johan (Saxon)
971   Gällersta; en sockenbeskrivning, af J. L.
N3   Saxon. Stockholm, Bokförlaget Nutiden [1915]
L5   62 p. illus.

1. Närke, Sweden - Description and travel.

NL 0385501   WaU

Lindström, Johan (Saxon)
Genom Harjedalen, färder och studier.
Stockholm, Bonnier 〈1894〉
98 p. illus.

1. Sweden - Description and travel. I. Title.

NL 0385502   WaU

Lindström, Johan (Saxon)
I hanegället; dikter av J. L. Saxon 〈pseud.〉
2. tillökade uppl. Stockholm, G. W. Wilhelmsson
〈1909〉
110 p.

NL 0385503   WaU

DL   Lindström, Johan (Saxon),
971   Jämtlands läns kyrkor i ord och bild. Stock-
J3   holm, Bonnier [1904]
L56   82 p. illus.

1. Churches, Jämtland. I. Title.

NL 0385504   WaU

DL   Lindström, Johan (Saxon)
971   Skomakarn, skräddarn och smen;
N3   sockenhantverkare i gamla tiders
L56   Närke. Stockholm Saxon & Lindström
〈1934〉
218 p. illus., ports.

1. Närke Sweden - Civilization.
2. Apprentices - Sweden. I. Title.

NL 0385505   WaU

Lindström, Johannes P., respondent.
Ode prima Pythiorum Pindari...
see under Hesselgren, Brynolph, praeses.

Lindström, Johannes Petr.   respondent.
De idea historiae philosophiae rite formanda...
see under Boëthius, Daniel, 1751-1810,
praeses.

Lindström, Josephus, respondent.
Diss. academica de legibus...
see under Ihre, Johann, 1707-1780.

Lindström, Karl Alfred Rickard
see Lindström, Rickard.

Lindström, Karl J
see Lindström, Carl Jacob, b. 1800.

Lindström, Köesi
see
Kaatra, Köesi, 1882-1928.

DK459   Lindström, Ludvig.
L76?   Skärgårdens frikår. Minnen upptecknade
av Ludvig Lindström. Åbo, E.Wallenius 〈1918〉
3 p.l., 9-199 p. incl.illus.,ports. 20ᵐ.

1.Finland - History - Revolution, 1917-1918.-
- Personal narra   tives. 2.Germany - Army
Infantry - Preu   ssisches jäger-bataillon
no.14. I.Title.

NL 0385512   CSt-H

Lindström (Ludvig J.). *Studien über maligne Nierentumoren. (Pathologische Anatomie und Klinik.) [Helsingfors.] 136 pp. 2 pl. 8°. Jena, G. Fischer, 1921.

NL 0385513   DNLM

Lindstroem, Margit
Kvinnornas problem. [Stockholm, 1946]
23 p. illus. (Dagspolitik, 26)

NL 0385514   MH

HD   Lindström, Margit
6061   Lika lön. Stockholm, Arbetarkulturs förlag,
L5   1947.
23p. illus. 19cm. (Dagspolitik, 34)

1. Equal pay for equal work 2. Woman -
Employment 3. Wages - Women I. Title

NL 0385515   WU MH

Lindström, Martha (Rydell)
see Rydell-Lindström, Martha, 1878-

Lindström, Martin, 1904-
Nordisk kristendom
see under Lindroth, Hjalmar, 1893-   ed.

609.2   LINDSTROEM, Martin, 1904-
N638.9   Philipp Nicolais kristendomstolkning.
L753ph   Stockholm, Svenska Kyrkans Diakonistyrel-
sens Bokfoerlag [1937]
329p. front. (port.) 23cm.

NL 0385518   MH-AH CtY MH CtY-D NNC MiU ICRL

Lindström, Martin, 1904-
Philipp Nicolais verständnis des christentums, von Martin
Lindström ... Gütersloh, C. Bertelsmann, 1939.
vi p., 1 l., 299 p. 25ᶜᵐ. (*Added t.-p.:* Beiträge zur förderung christlicher theologie ... hrsg. von d. Paul Althaus. 2. reihe. Sammlung wissenschaftlicher monographien, 40. bd.)
Issued in part as author's thesis, Lund.
"Verzeichnis von Nicolais theologischen schriften": p. 〈294〉-296.
Bibliographical foot-notes.

1. Nicolai, Philipp, 1556-1608. 2. Reformation—Germany.
〈Full name: Bernt Martin Lindström〉
A 41-2516
General theol. sem. Libr.
for Library of Congress   〈2〉

NL 0385519   NNG CBPac MH-AH

---

230   Lindström, Martin, 1904-
L645   Svensk teologi av i dag. Lund,
Gleerup 〈1953〉
69 p. 21cm. (Skrifter i
teologiska och kyrkliga ämnen. 11)

1. Theology. Doctrinal. History in
Sweden. I. Title.

NL 0385520   MnU NjPT MH-AH

AS284   Lindström, Maurits.
.L82   Structural geology of a small area in the Caledonides of
bd.51,   arctic Sweden. Lund, Gleerup 〈1955〉
nr.15   31 p. illus., fold. col. map. 26 cm. (Lunds universitets årsskrift,
n. f., avd. 2, bd. 51, nr. 15)
Kungl. Fysiografiska sällskapets handlingar, n. f., bd. 66, nr. 15.
Bibliography: p. 30-31.

1. Geology, Structural.   (Series: Lund. Universitet. Acta Universitatis Lundensis, n. s. Lunds universitets årsskrift, n. f., avd. 2, bd. 51, nr. 15. Series: Fysiografiska sällskapet i Lund. Acta. Handlingar, n. f., bd. 66, nr. 15)
[AS284.L82 bd. 51, nr. 15]   A 57-166
Chicago. Univ. Libr.
for Library of Congress   〈2〉

NL 0385521   ICU MoU TxU DLC-P4

Lindström, Nils Johan Olof Herman, bp.,
1842-1916.
Sweden. *Kommittén angående undervisningsväsendet inom
teologiska fakulteterna, 1897.*
Förslag till stadga angående undervisnings-, studie- och examensväsendet inom de teologiska fakulteterna vid universiteten i Upsala och Lund, jämte vissa i samband därmed stående förslag; afgifna af den utaf Kongl. Maj:t den 21 maj 1897 i nåder förordnade kommitté. Stockholm, I. Haeggströms boktryckeri, 1898.

VOLUME 334

Lindström, Nils Johan Olof Herman, 1842-1916.

Sweden. *Folkskolelärarevikariekommittén.*
Underdånigt betänkande och förslag afgifvet den 20 februari 1893 af den af Kungl. Maj : t den 10 augusti 1892 tillsatta kommitté för afgifvande af betänkande och förslag, om och på hvilka vilkor statsbidrag må kunna lämnas till aflönande af vikarie för sådan ordinarie lärare eller lärarinna, som af sjukdom urståndsättes att fullgöra sin tjänst. Stockholm, Kungl. boktryckeriet. P. A. Norstedt & söner, 1893.

Lindström, P. Fredericus.
De Normannis, Italiam occupantibus
   see under
Palmquist, L. G. , praeses.

Lindström, Per.
På en främmande planet. ₁Dikter. Stockholm? Erpo tryckeriaktiebolag, 1952₁
₁40₁ p. 18 cm.

₁ Title₁

Minnesota. Univ. Libr   A 53-3953
for Library of Congress   ₁₂₁

NL   0385525   MnU

Lindstroem, Per Elof, 1863-1924
Anmaerkningar till de obetonade vokalernas bortfall inaagra nordfranska ortnamn.
Inaug. diss. Upsala, 1892.

NL   0385526   ICRL CU

Lindström, Per Elof, 1863-1924.

Sweden. *Lärarelönenämnden,* 1912.
Lärarelönenämndens betänkande ... ₁Stockholm, Kungl. boktryckeriet, P. A. Norstedt & söner, 1914-18₁

L LINDSTRÖM, Per Elof, 1863-1924
Die palatale der lateinischen lehnwörter im althochdeutschen. Lektorabhandlung, Upsala. Stockholm, 1895.
                                                   8257

NL   0385528   MH CtY ICRL

Lindström, Per Elof, 1863-

Sweden. *Gymnastikkommittén.*
Underdånigt utlåtande och förslag angående omorganisation av Gymnastiska centralinstitutet och av gymnastiklärarutbildningen genom upprättandet av en högskola för fysisk fostran samt angående anskaffande av lokaler för en sådan högskola. Stockholm, Kungl. boktryckeriet, P. A. Norstedt & söner, 1918.

Lindström, Per Elof, 1863-1924.
Unetymologische Auflösung Französischer Ortsnamen. Stockholm, Central-Druckerei, 1898.
   41 p. 4°.

NL   0385530   NN CtY

Lindström, Petrus, respondent.
Dissertatio gradualis de usu philosophiae in convertendis gentilibus ...
   see under Asp, Matthias, 1696-1763, praeses.

DL859
.D3L5
Lindström, Rickard.
   Axel Danielsson. Stockholm, Folket i bilds förlag, 1950.
   95 p. ports. 20 cm. (Banerförare, 5)

   1. Danielsson, Axel Ferdinand, 1863-1899.   (Series)
                                                      A 51-2887
Minnesota. Univ. Libr.
for Library of Congress   ₁₂₁

NL   0385532   MnU WU

HX336
.L56
Lindström, Rickard.
   Bolsjevism och fascism; två själar och en tanke. Eskilstuna, Frihet ₁n.d.₁
   16p. 21cm.

   Cover title.

   1. Communism - Addresses, essays, lectures.
   2. Fascism - Addresses, essays, lectures.
   I. Title.
   R 68-1-3DIkj6

NL   0385533   NcU

Lindström, Rickard.
   Försvarets högsta ledning. Stockholm, Forsner, 1947.
   101 p. 23 cm. (Forsners militärbibliotek, n:o 2)

   1. Military administration. 2. Sweden—Defenses.   I. Title.
                                    Full name: Karl Alfred Rickard Lindström.

   UB145.L5   53-28158 ‡

NL   0385534   DLC NN

Lindström, Rickard.
   Karl Marx och fackföreningarna, några historiska anteckningar. Stockholm, Tiden, 1931.

   50 p. (Landsorganisationens skriftserie, 28)

NL   0385535   MH

Lindström, Rickard.
   Den kommunistiska politiken; en vidräkning, av Richard Lindström. Stockholm: Tidens förlag, 1924. 32 p. 12°.

I. Bolshevism.
N. Y. P. L.   July 14, 1925

NL   0385536   NN

HD6759
.S3O4
Lindström, Rickard, joint author.

Olsson, Reinhold.
   En krönika om sågverksarbetare; Svenska sågverksindustriarbetareforbundets minnesskrift ₁av₁ Reinhold Olsson och Richard Lindström. ₁Sundsvall, 1953₁

Lindstroem, Rickard
På Helgeandsholmen, den svenska riksdagen och dess arbete. Stockholm, Natur och kultur [1933]

   152 p. illus.

NL   0385538   MH

Lindström, Rickard.
   Per Albin Hansson. Stockholm, Folket i bilds förlag, 1952.
   95 p. illus., ports. 20 cm. (Banerförare)

   1. Hansson, Per Albin, 1885-1946.
                                    Full name: Karl Alfred Rickard Lindström.

Minnesota. Univ. Libr.   A 52-7838
for Library of Congress   ₁₂₁

NL   0385539   MnU MH

Lindström, Rickard,
   En socialist; fragment ur en självbiografi, av Rickard Lindström. Stockholm: A. Bonniers förlag₁, 1930₁. 208 p. 8°.

523166A. 1. Socialism—Hist.—   Sweden.
N. Y. P. L.   May 11, 1931

NL   0385540   NN WaU WU MH

HX
339
L5
Lindstoöm, Rickard
   Socialistik vardag; uppsatser om arbetarklassens nutidsproblem. Stockholm, A. Bonnier ₁c1928₁
   207p. 22cm.

   1. Socialism 2. Socialism in Sweden
   I. Title

NL   0385541   WU CSt-H MH

HC
335.2
L5
Lindström, Rickard
   En upptäcktsfärd till Sovjetryssland; bör man tro vad herr Kilboms pilgrimer berätta? ₁esEskilstuna, Frihets förlag, 1925₁
   32p. illus. 21cm.

   1. Russia - Economic policy - 1917-1928
   2. Russia - Econ. condit. - 1918-1945
   I. Title

NL   0385542   WU

JX1952
.V28
Lindström, Rickard, ed.
   Vad kan socialdemokratin göra för världsfreden; en rundfråga bland världens ledande socialdemokrater. Med förord av Rickard Lindström. ₁Redaktör: Rickard Lindström₁ Uppsala, Universitas, 1949.

Lindström, Rikard Magnus, 1882-
   Landkänning... Stockholm, A. Bonnier ₁1941₁
   219 p. illus. 20cm.

   Contents.- Skärgårdsskisser.- Lofotenbilder.- Åland.- Från staden.

NL   0385544   MnU

Lindström, Rune, 1916-
   Dalahistorier, samlade och med teckningar av Rune Lindström. Stockholm, Wahlström & Widstrand ₁1948₁
   117 p. illus. 23 cm.

                                    Full name: Gustaf Rune Lindström.
                                                      A 49-7827*
Minnesota. Univ. Libr.
for Library of Congress   ₁₂₁

NL   0385545   MnU NN

VOLUME 334

Lindström, Rune, 1916–
Döden tar studenten. Stockholm, Wahlström & Widstrand [1948]
224 p. 20 cm.

Full name: Gustaf Rune Lindström.
A 49–5400*

Minnesota. Univ. Libr.
for Library of Congress [1]

NL 0385546 MnU

Lindström, Rune, 1916–
Johannesnatten; dansspel i fyra tavlor. [Stockholm] Wahlström & Widstrand [1948]
125 p. col. plates. 24 cm.

Full name: Gustaf Rune Lindström.
A 49–5401*

Minnesota. Univ. Libr.
for Library of Congress [1]

NL 0385547 MnU

Lindström, Rune, 1916–
Ljuslågan, en dramatisering av Selma Lagerlöfs legend. Stockholm, Svenska kyrkans diakonistyrelses bokförlag [1948]
48 p. illus. 21 cm.
"Författad till och uppförd vid Sveriges K. F. U. K:s Scoutförbunds 25-årsjubileum 1946."

I. Lagerlöf, Selma Ottiliana Lovisa, 1858–1940. Ljuslågan.
II. Title.
Full name: Gustaf Rune Lindström.
A 49–5402*

Minnesota. Univ. Libr.
for Library of Congress [1]

NL 0385548 MnU

LINDSTRÖM, RUNE, 1916-
A play which tells of a road that leads to heaven; "sit Dalecarlian wall-paintings." [Translated into English by Elspeth Harley Schubert] Stockholm, Svenska kyrkans diakonistyrelses bokförlag, c1941.
99 p. illus. 23cm.

"Original Swedish title: Ett spel om en väg som til himla bär."

NL 0385549 NN

Lindström, Rune, 1916–
A play which tells of a road that leads to heaven. [Translated by Elspeth Harley Schubert] Stockholm, Svenska kyrkans diakonistyrelses bokförlag [1955] ©1941
99 p. col. illus. 23 cm.
Half title: The play of heaven.

I. Title. II. Title: The play of heaven.
Full name: Gustaf Rune Lindström.
A 57–3382

Minnesota. Univ. Libr.
for Library of Congress [3]

NL 0385550 MnU MU ICU CU C

839.72 **Lindström, Rune,** 1916–
L645s Ett spel om en väg som till Himla bär. 6
1943 dalmalningar. [8 uppl.] Stockholm, Svenska Kyrkans Diakonistyrelse [1943]
97p. col.plates. 24cm.

NL 0385551 IU MnU

PT9555 **Lindström, Rune,** 1916–
.S3 Scripta amicorum. Sewed Sjöholm på femtioårsdagen, MCMLIV. [Texter: Rune Lindström et al. Leksand, Collegium Musicum Leksandense, 1954]

Lindström, Sigfrid, 1892–
De besegrade; dikter, av Sigfrid Lindström. Stockholm: H. Gebers förlag [, 1927]. 85 p. 8°.

428733A. 1. Poetry, Swedish. 2. Title.
N.Y.P.L. September 27, 1929

NL 0385553 NN MH

Lindström, Sigfrid, 1892–
Leksaksballonger, av Sigfrid Lindström. Stockholm: H. Gebers förlag [, 1931]. 209 p. 19cm.

604212A. 1. Fiction, Swedish. I. Title.
N.Y.P.L. September 12, 1932

NL 0385554 NN

Lindström, Sigfrid, 1892–
Sagor på vers och prosa. Stockholm, H. Geber [1948]
387 p. 20 cm.
"Denna bok innehåller, med en del retuscheringar, modifikationer och tillägg, de förut utgivna Leksaksballonger (1931), Vindsröjning (1939), Sagor och meditationer (1922), De besegrade (1927) och I de onda ögonens stad."

I. Title.
Full name: Gustaf Hilding Sigfrid Lindström.
A 49–5403*

Minnesota. Univ. Libr.
for Library of Congress [1]

NL 0385555 MnU MH PU

PT **Lindström, Sigfrid,** 1892–
9875 Sagor pa vers och prosa. 2. uppl. Stockholm, H. Geber [1952]
L54 387p. 20cm.
S2 "Denna bok innehaller, med en del retuscheringar, modifikationer och tillagg, de förut utgivna backerna Leksaksballonger (1931), Vindsrojning (1939), Sagor och meditationer (1922) och De besegrade (1927)"
1952
MAIN

NL 0385556 TxU DLC WaU

Lindström, Sigfrid, 1892–
Vindsröjning. Stockholm, H. Geber, 1939.
133 p. 19cm.

NL 0385557 MnU

Lindström, Sigrid.
Något om bygdedräktens spetsar i Ö. Göinge och Villands härad. [Kristianstad, 1955]
23 p. illus. 21 cm.
Includes bibliographies.

1. Lace and lace making—Sweden—Östra Göinge härad. 2. Lace and lace making—Sweden—Villands härad. I. Title.

NK9461.L5 57–16458 ‡

NL 0385558 DLC

Lindström, Sven Josephus, respondent.
... De capitulationibus Caesareis specimen academicum...
see under Colliander, Samuel, praeses.

Lindström, Thorolf.
On the cranial nerves of the cyclostomes with special reference to n. trigeminus. Stockholm, 1949.
316–458 p. illus. 26 cm.
Akademisk avhandling—Stockholms högskola.
Reprinted from Acta zoologica, 1949. Bd. 30.
Bibliography: p. 450–455.

1. Nerves, Cranial. 2. Trigim. 3. Nervous system—Fishes. 4. Cyclostomi.

QL939.L5 591.48 50–35841

NL 0385560 DLC CtY NIC

Lindström, Ulla.
Den nya skolan. Stockholm, Norstedt [1950]
47 p. (Bra att veta, 1)

NL 0385561 MH

Lindström, Valter.
Stadiernas teologi, en Kierkegaard-studie. Lund, C. W. K. Gleerup [1943]
370 p. 22 cm.
Akademisk avhandling—Lund.
Extra t. p., with thesis statement, inserted.
Bibliography: p. [357]–368.

1. Kierkegaard, Søren Aabye, 1813–1855.

BX4827.K5L47 54–51301

MoSCS MiU CtY
NL 0385562 DLC ICMcC ICU NNC NjP MH MnU CtY-D NjPT

Lindström, Victor Carlsson, 1873–
Commentarii Plautini in fabulas legendas et explicandas studia; disputatio academica scripsit Viktor C:n Lindström. Holmiae, typis descripsit O. L. Svanbäck, 1907.
vi, 140, [2] p., 1 l., [2] p. 24½ᶜᵐ. [Upsala universitets årsskrift, 1907]

1. Plautus, Titus Maccius.

Library of Congress AS284.U7 8—15342

NL 0385563 DLC PU PBm NjP NN CU MiU OCU OClW

---

921 **Lindström, Viggo Oluf Eugen,** 1859–1926.
L6453Li Fra den gamle vinkaelder til det kongelige teater; ungdoms erindringer. København, H. Hagerups Forlag, 1924.
128 p. port.

1. Theater - Norway. I. Title.

NL 0385564 WaU NN NBuG

Drama **Lindström, Viggo Oluf Eugen,** 1859–
PN2748 ... Teatererindringer og oplevelser. København, H. Hagerups forlag, 1925.
L5T3 144p. 20cm.
At head of title: Viggo Lindström.

1. Lindström, Viggo Oluf Eugen, 1859– 2. Theater.-Denmark. I. Title.

NL 0385565 NBuG NN

Lindström, Viktor Carlsson
see **Lindström, Victor Carlsson,** 1873–

VOLUME 334

Lindstrom, C B
    Boiler furnaces and chimneys. Scranton,
Pa., International textbook company ₁1937.
60, 52p. illus. (International textbook
company. Bluebooks; 230B)

    Contents: Boiler furnaces, settings and
chimneys, Parts 1 and 2.

NL 0385567   OC1

Lindstrom, C. B.
    Boiler management, inspection and furnaces, by
C. B. Lindstrom, C. J. Mason ₁and₁ R. T. Strohm.
Scranton, Pa. International textbook co., °1926.
46, 36, 51 p. illus. tables, diagrs. (part fold
(International textbook co. ₁Blue-books₁ 456)

    I. Mason, Charles James. II. Strohm, Rufus
Tracy.

NL 0385568   MiD

Lindstrom, C B.
    Boiler repairs and inspection, by C. B. Lindstrom, under
supervision of A. B. Clemens ... Scranton, Pa., International
textbook company ₁°1925₁

    iv, 45, 37, 36 p. illus., fold. diagr., forms (1 fold.) 19½ᵐ. (₁International textbook company. Bluebooks; 468)

    1. Boilers.   I. Clemens, A. B.
                                           40-26100
    Library of Congress   TJ288.L5
                               ₁3₁   621.184

NL 0385569   DLC

Lindstrom, C. B.
    Boiler repairs and inspection. By C. B. Lindstrom, under super-
vision of A. B. Clemens.
— Scranton, Pa. International Textbook Co. [1929.] 2 parts in
    I v. Illus. Plans. Tables. [International library of tech-
    nology. Blue book series. 468.] 19 cm.

N7386 — S.r. — Steam boilers. — Clemens. A. B., ed.

NL 0385570   MB

Lindstrom, C. B.
    Boilermaking. By C. B. Lindstrom.
— Scranton, Pa. International Textbook Co. [1926.] 5 parts in
    2 v. Illus. Tables. [International library of technology. Blue
    book series. 466, 467.] 19 cm.

N7386 — S.r. — Steam boilers.

NL 0385571   MB MiD WaS

Lindstrom, C. B.
    Steam boilers and boiler mountings.
— Scranton, Pa. International Textbook Co. [1925.] 2 parts in
    I v. Illus. Plans. [International library of technology. Blue
    book series. 228.] 19 cm.

N7391 — S.r. — Steam boilers.

NL 0385572   MB

621.181 Lindstrom, C   B   L
L64s   ... Steam boilers and equipment ...
        Prepared under supervision of A. B.
        Clemens ...   Scranton, Pa., 1926.
        [390]p. illus., diagrs.(1 fold.)
        (International library of technology,
        459)

             Various paging.

NL 0385573   IU MiD

Lindstrom, C. B.

International correspondence schools, *Scranton, Pa.*
    Strength of materials. Steam boiler design. By I. C. S. staff
and C. B. Lindstrom ... Scranton, Pa., International textbook
company ₁1939₁

Lindstrom, David Edgar, 1899–
    American farmers' and rural organizations; edited by Her-
bert McNee Hamlin. Champaign, Ill., Garrard Press ₁1948₁
    xii, 457 p. 22 cm.
    Includes bibliographies.

    1. Agricultural societies—U. S.   I. Hamlin, Herbert McNee, 1894-
ed. II. Title.

    HD1484.L5   630.6273   48—16947*

          TU OU Mi KEmT
NL 0385575   DLC WaTC OrCS Or DNAL WaU PPEB PPT ViU

Lindstrom, David Edgar, 1899–
    American foundations of religious liberty. Champaign,
Ill., Garrard Press, 1950.
    xii, 107 p. 20 cm. (Rauschenbusch lectures, 1950)
    Bibliographical footnotes.

    1. Religious liberty—U. S. 2. Rural churches—U. S.   I. Title.
(Series: Rauschenbusch lectures, Colgate-Rochester Divinity School,
Rochester, N. Y., 1950)

    BR516.L6   261.7   51–1464

NL 0385576   DLC IU CtY TNJ-R KyLxCB KyU

Lindstrom, David Edgar, 1899–
    American rural life, a textbook in sociology; with an
introd. by O. E. Baker. New York, Ronald Press Co. ₁1948₁
    xv, 385 p. illus., maps. 24 cm.
    Includes bibliographies.

    1. Country life—U. S. 2. Sociology, Rural.   I. Title.

    HT421.J5   323.354   48–3407*

        OrCS Or OrP OrStbM WaTC IdU CaBVaU
NL 0385577   DLC MiEM Mi TU PIm RPB TxU CU PSt PLF

Lindstrom, David Edgar, 1899–
    The church in rural life, by David Edgar Lindstrom ...
1st ed. Champaign, Ill., The Garrard press, 1939.
    xiv, 145 p. 19ᵐ.
    "First edition."
    "Readings" at end of each chapter.

    1. Rural churches—U. S. 2. Sociology, Rural.   I. Title.
                                                        39–31173
    Library of Congress   BV638.L5
    ———— Copy 2.
    Copyright A 132753   ₁2₁   261

NL 0385578   DLC NcD ViU OU PCC TU

Lindstrom, David Edgar, 1899–
    Conducting group discussion, by David E. Lindstrom ...
Springfield, Illinois state library, 1943.
    16 p. illus. 23ᵐ.
    "A selected bibliography on techniques of discussion groups": p. 13–16.

    1. Forums (Discussion and debate)   I. Illinois.   State library,
Springfield. II. Title.
    Library of Congress   LC6515.L5   44–42032
                               ₁3₁   374.24

NL 0385579   DLC MiHM NN NNC TxU PP PPD Or

₁Lindstrom, David Edgar₁ 1899–
    Dramatics for farm folks ... ₁Urbana, Ill.₁ University of
Illinois ₁1931₁
    cover-title, 16 p. incl. illus., diagrs. 23ᵐ. (University of Illinois.
College of agriculture and Agricultural experiment station. Circular
373)
    Caption title: By D. E. Lindstrom.
    Bibliographical aids given on back cover.

    1. Amateur theatricals. I. Illinois. University. College of agricul-
ture. II. Illinois. Agricultural experiment station, Urbana. III. Title.
    Title from Illinois Univ.   A 31–332
    Library of Congress   [855.E3 no. 373]

NL 0385580   IU

HD1484
.L48   Lindstrom, David Edgar, 1899–
        Farmers' and rural organizations.
        ₁Champaign, Ill.₁ The author, 1942?₁
        cover-title, 6 p. ., 428 numb. .
        tables, charts. 28 cm.

        Mimeographed
        "Readings" at end of each chapter.

        1. Agricultural societies—History.
        I. Title.

NL 0385581   TU CU

338.1   Lindstrom, David Edgar, 1899–
L643f   Farmers and social policy in Sweden; a report
        of a study.   Urbana, University of Illinois
        Agricultural Experiment Station, 1951.
        29ℓ. tables. 28cm.

        Cover title.
        "RSM, 25."

        1. Agriculture and state—Sweden. 2. Agri-
        culture—Sweden. I. Title.

NL 0385582   IU

Lindstrom, David Edgar, 1899–
    Forces affecting participation of farm people in rural organ-
ization; a study made in four townships in Illinois, by D. E.
Lindstrom ... ₁Urbana, Ill.₁ University of Illinois ₁1936₁
    1 p. l., p. 79–127 incl. illus., tables, diagrs. 23ᵐ. (University of Illi-
nois. Agricultural experiment station. Bulletin 423)

    1. Farm life. 2. Country life—Illinois.   I. Title.
                                                        A 36–691
    Title from Illinois Univ.
    Library of Congress   [S55.E2 no. 423]

NL 0385583   IU

Lindstrom, David Edgar, 1899–
    4-H club work: effect on capability and personal quality, by
D. E. Lindstrom and W. M. Dawson ... ₁Urbana, Ill.₁ 1939₁
    1 p. l., p. 275–343 incl. tables, diagrs. 23ᵐ. (University of Illinois.
Agricultural experiment station. Bulletin 451)

    1. 4-H clubs. I. Dawson, Walker Myrick, 1902–   joint author.
                                                        A 39–455
    Illinois. Univ. Library
        for Library of Congress   [S55.E2 no. 451]
                               ₁2₁   (630.72)

NL 0385584   IU DLC

VOLUME 334

379.773 Lindstrom, David Edgar, 1899
L641   Illinois school district boundaries as
recommended by county school survey committees and as voted by the people; and
farmer participation on survey committees.
Urbana, Research in Rural Sociology, Dept.
of Agricultural Economics, University of
Illinois, Agricultural Experiment Station,
1950.
8ℓ. maps. 28cm. (Illinois. University.
College of Agriculture. Dept. of Agricultural Economics. RSM-24)
Cover title.

NL 0385585   IU

309.1   Lindstrom, David Edgar, 1899–
L643k   Knowing your community; experimental fact-
finding forms designed especially for rural communities. Prepared for Extension Work in Rural
Sociology, Dept. of Agricultural Economics, Extension Service in Agriculture and Home Economics, College of Agriculture, University of Illinois. ₍Urbana, 1941₎
24ℓ. illus. 28cm. (RSE-83)

Cover title.
Bibliography: leaf 24.

NL 0385586   IU

Lindstrom, David Edgar, 1899–   joint author.

HD211   Fielder, V   B
.I32P63   Land use and family welfare in Pope County, by V. B.
Fielder and D. E. Lindstrom. ₍Urbana₎ Dept. of Agricultural Economics, Research in Rural Sociology, Agricultural
Experiment Station, University of Illinois, in cooperation
with the Division of Land Economics, Bureau of Agricultural Economics, U. S. Dept. of Agriculture, 1939.

D374.2
L643

Lindstrom, David Edgar, 1899–
Let's talk it over; a brief manual for discussion groups, by D. E. Linstrom ... ₍Urbana,
Ill.₎ 1944₎
11 p. illus., diagrs. (Circular 581, University of Illinois, College of agriculture, Extension service in agriculture and home economics)

1. Forums (Discussion and debate) I. Title.

NL 0385588   NNC

Lindstrom, David Edgar.
Local group organization among farm people, by D. E.
Lindstrom ... ₍Urbana, Ill.₎ University of Illinois ₍1933₎
1 p. l., p. 127–176 incl. illus., map, tables, diagrs. 23ᶜᵐ. (University of
Illinois. Agricultural experiment station. Bulletin 392)

1. Agricultural societies. 2. Farm life. I. Title.

Title from Illinois Univ.   A 33–2280
Library of Congress   [S55.E2 no. 392]

NL 0385589   IU ICRL

Lindstrom, David Edgar, 1899–
The need for and possibility of rural school
reorganization in McDonough County, Illinois ...
see under Illinois. University. Dept. of
Agricultural Economics.

Lindstrom, David Edgar, 1899–
Needs and opportunities for rural school district reorganization in Fayette County, Illinois,
by D. E. Lindstrom and R. F. Eshleman. Urbana,
Ill., Agricultural Experiment Station, Univ. of
Illinois, College of Agriculture, 1944.
9ℓ. maps, tables. 28cm.

Cover title.
"RSM-14."

NL 0385591   IU

630   Lindstrom, David Edgar, 1899–
L640   The organization of local groups among farm
people of Illinois ... Madison, Wis. ₍1934₎
294 numb.l. incl.tables.
Thesis (Ph.D.)--University of Wisconsin, 1934.
Published also as University of Illinois.
Agricultural experiment station. Bulletin no.
392, under title: Local group organization among
Illinois farm people.
Typewritten (carbon copy)
Bibliography: leaves 282-287.
1. Agricultural societies. 2. Farm life.

NL 0385592   IU

₍Lindstrom, David Edgar₎ 1899 –
Organizing for rural home-talent tournaments ... ₍Urbana,
Ill.₎ University of Illinois ₍1931₎
15 p. incl. illus., tables. 23ᶜᵐ. (University of Illinois. College of
agriculture and Agricultural experiment station. Circular 376)

Caption title: By D. E. Lindstrom.

1. Tournaments. 2. Amateur theatricals. I. Illinois. University.
College of agriculture. II. Illinois. Agricultural experiment station, Urbana. III. Title.

Title from Illinois Univ.   A 31–1354
Library of Congress   [S55.E3 no. 376]
                                                      ₍4₎

NL 0385593   IU

309.77366 Lindstrom, David Edgar, 1899–
L64p   Preferred and actual service centers for
rural people in Champaign County; a study made
by the Champaign-Urbana Junior Chamber of Commerce in cooperation with the Division of Rural
Sociology, Department of Agricultural Economics
University of Illinois Agricultural Experiment
Station.   ₍Urbana₎ 1948.
10ℓ. maps. 28cm.

"RSM-21."

NL 0385594   IU

281.173 Lindstrom, David Edgar, 1899–
L643   A report of a study on farmers and social
policy in Sweden. Urbana, University of
Illinois, Agricultural Experiment Station,
1951.
29 l.

NL 0385595   DNAL

₍Lindstrom, David Edgar₎ 1899 –
Rural community buildings ... ₍Urbana, Ill.₎ 1937₎
cover-title, 3–58 p. incl. illus., plans. 23ᶜᵐ. (University of Illinois.
College of agriculture. Agricultural experiment station and Extension
service in agriculture and home economics. Circular 470)
Caption title: By D. E. Lindstrom, W. A. Foster, and Max G. Fuller.
Contents on p. ₍2₎ of cover.
"References": p. 46.

1. Community centers. I. Foster, William Arthur, 1884–   joint
author. II. Fuller, Max Golden, joint author. III. Title. IV. Title:
Community buildings, Rural.

Illinois. Univ. Library   A 37–266
for Library of Congress   [S55.E3 no. 470]
                                    ₍3₎   (630.72)

NL 0385596   IU Or

309.133 Lindstrom, David Edgar, 1899–
L64r   The rural community unit at the heart of the
1941   community; a manual for community organization
leaders ... Prepared for extension work in rural
sociology ... Revised September, 1941.   Urbana,
Ill. ₍1941₎
34 numb.l. incl.forms, diagr. (Department
of agricultural economics, Extension service in
agriculture and home economics, College of agriculture, University of Illinois. RSE – 10)
Mimeographed.
1. Community life. 2. Sociology, Rural. I.
Title.

NL 0385597   IU

Lindstrom, David Edgar, 1899–
Rural leaders want modern rural schools. Urbana, Re-
search in Rural Sociology, Dept. of Agricultural Economics,
Univ. of Illinois, Agricultural Experiment Station, 1949.
11 l. maps, diagrs. 28 cm.
Cover title.

1. Rural schools—Illinois. I. Illinois. University. College of
Agriculture. Dept. of Agricultural Economics. II. Title.
                                                      A 49–2695*
Illinois. Univ. Library
for Library of Congress   ₍1₎

NL 0385598   IU

Lindstrom, David Edgar, 1899–
Rural life and the church, by David Edgar Lindstrom ... A
revision of The church in rural life. Champaign, Ill., The
Garrard press, 1946.
xiv, 205 p. 20ᶜᵐ.
Errata slip inserted.
"Readings" at end of each chapter.

1. Rural churches—U. S. 2. Sociology, Rural. I. Title.
                                                      46–21429
Library of Congress   BV638.L5 1946
                                    ₍2₎   261

MB TU ViU DNAL
NL 0385599   DLC OrCS Or OrP Wa KEmT   PPEB NcD TxU

Lindstrom, David Edgar.
Rural relief in Illinois, a study of home assistance in thir-
teen counties, by D. E. Lindstrom and Ida D. Johns ...
₍Urbana, Ill.₎ 1941.
1 p. L., p. 395–440 incl. map, tables, diagrs. 23ᶜᵐ. (University of
Illinois. Agricultural experiment station. Bulletin 480)

1. Charities—Illinois. 2. Sociology, Rural. I. Johns, Ida D., joint
author. II. Title.
                                                      A 41–4846
Illinois. Univ. Library
for Library of Congress   [S55.E2 no. 480]
                                    ₍3₎   (630.72)

NL 0385600   IU

Lindstrom, David Edgar, 1899–
Selectivity of 4-H club work; an analysis of factors influenc-
ing membership, by D. E. Lindstrom and W. M. Dawson ...
₍Urbana, Ill.₎ University of Illinois ₍1936₎
1 p. L., p. 247–278 incl. tables, diagrs. 23ᶜᵐ. (University of Illinois.
Agricultural experiment station. Bulletin 426)

1. 4-H clubs. I. Dawson, Walker Myrick, 1902–   joint author.
                                                      A 36–1177
Illinois. Univ. Library
for Library of Congress   [S55.E2 no. 426]
                                    ₍2₎   (630.72)

NL 0385601   IU

VOLUME 334

Lindstrom, David Edgar, 1899–
Some factors affecting social welfare in rural areas of Alexander county, Illinois, 1934, by D. E. Lindstrom. ₍Urbana, University of Illinois Agricultural experiment station in cooperation with Illinois Emergency relief commission ₍1934?₎

cover-title, 1 p. l., 45 numb. l. incl. plates, maps, diagrs. 27½ x 21½ᶜᵐ.

1. Alexander co., Ill.—Soc. condit. 2. Public welfare—Alexander co., Ill. ɪ. Illinois. Agricultural experiment station, Urbana. ɪɪ. Illinois. Emergency relief commission.

HN80.A35L5   309.1773   47–34405

NL 0385602   DLC

309.133
L64s   Lindstrom, David Edgar, 1899–
Some factors affecting social welfare in rural areas of Alexander county, Illinois, 1934, by D. E. Lindstrom. ₍Urbana₎ University of Illinois Agricultural experiment station in cooperation with Illinois Emergency relief commission, 1937.
cover-title, 45 numb. l. incl. plates, maps, tables, diagrs.

Mimeographed.

NL 0385603   IU

BX8042
.I 6G5   **Lindstrom, David Edgar,** 1899–   joint author.
Gilmer, Max.
A study of the Lutheran Church in rural Illinois, 1946, by Max Gilmer and David E. Lindstrom. Urbana, Agricultural Experiment Station, Univ. of Illinois, College of Agriculture, 1948.

NL 0385605

HQ796
.I 375   **Lindstrom, David Edgar,** 1899–   ed.
Illinois. University. *Dept. of Agricultural Economics.*
A study of youth centers in Illinois, made under the direction of David E. Lindstrom and reports on teen towns, State of Illinois, 1946. A joint publication by research in Rural sociology, Dept. of Agricultural Economics, University of Illinois, Agricultural Experiment Station, Urbana, Illinois, in cooperation with the Division for Delinquency Prevention, Dept. of Public Welfare, Springfield, Illinois. ₍Urbana, 1947₎

NL 0385604

1.913
A2Su68   Lindstrom, David Edgar, 1899–
A summary of selected local, state, and national projects on community organization and development. Washington, 1949.
13 p.

Issued Mar. 1949.

1. Community associations. 2. Community life. U.S. I. U.S. Extension Service. II. II. Title: Community organization and development.

NL 0385606   DNAL

Lindstrom, E   George, 1879–
Demon of the sky. Authorized edition. Cleveland, O., High twelve pub. co., ₍c1932₎
19 p.

NL 0385607   OC1

Lindstrom, E   George, 1879–
Oil creek tales, by E. George Lindstrom. Cleveland, O., High twelve publishing company ₍ᶜ1935₎
7 p. l., 13–130 p. 1 illus. 18½ᶜᵐ.

"First edition."

ᴄᴏɴᴛᴇɴᴛꜱ.—The bull wheel turned.—The demon of the sky.—Indian god rock.—The circle completed.—As youth wills.

ɪ. Title.

Library of Congress   PZ3.L65403Oi   38–38720

NL 0385608   DLC NN OC1

Lindstrom, E   George, 1879–
Out of the sand, by E. George Lindstrom. Cleveland, O., High twelve publishing company ₍1943₎
3 p. l., ₍13₎–264 p. pl., map. 19½ᶜᵐ.

ɪ. Title.

Library of Congress   PZ3.L65403Ou   43–11745

NL 0385609   DLC PHC OU OLak

LINDSTROM, E. GEORGE, 1879–
Story of Lakewood, Ohio, edited by Lawrence J. Hawkins. Lakewood, O., The author.[1936?]
156 p.   illus., ports.   24cm.

1. Lakewood, O.—Hist. I. Hawkins, Lawrence J., ed. II. Hawkins, Lawrence J.

NL 0385610   NN OLak

Lindstrom, E   George, 1879–
The temples, before and after destruction. ₍Cleveland, Lindstrom type-setting service, n.d.₎
14 p., il., port., plan.

NL 0385611   OC1

Lindstrom, E   George, 1879–
Unpublished material of Lakewood's history, taken from the private file of E. George Lindstrom, March 20, 1940. ₍Lakewood, Ohio, n.p.₎ 1940.
2 v.

Typewritten.
First volume has date, 1940, on cover.
Carbon copy of second volume is numbered III.

NL 0385612   OLak

Lindstrom, Edwin.
Penmanship and Alphabets. N.Y., Irving Zucher, 1940.
55 pl. folio.

NL 0385613   PPPM-I

LINDSTROM, EDWIN, comp.
Penmanship and alphabets; reproduction of plates engraved and printed in the 18th and 19th century; compiled by Edwin Lindstrom.   New York: I. Zucker [1941?]
1 p.l., 54 pl.   43½cm.

1. Handwriting—Specimens. 2. Alphabet—Specimens.

NL 0385614   NN OC1 ICN NNC

Lindstrom, Eleanor Inga.
Saturday night in town; a study of humanism in American painting. ₍Boulder, University of Colorado Libraries, Dept. of Microphotography, 1945₎

Microfilm copy of typewritten ms. Positive.
Collation of the original, as determined from the film : 88 l. illus. Thesis (ᴍ. ꜰ. ᴀ.)—University of Colorado.
Bibliography : leaves 85–88.

1. Painting, American. ɪ. Title.

Microfilm AC–47   Mic 51–295

NL 0385615   DLC

Z733
.C721
J63
1948   **Lindstrom, Eloise,** 1903–   joint ed.
Johnson, Byron Lamar, 1904–   ed.
The librarian and the teacher in general education: a report of library-instructional activities at Stephens College. Editorial committee: B. Lamar Johnson ₍and₎ Eloise Lindstrom. Chicago, American Library Assn., 1948.

NL 0385616

Lindstrom, Ernest Walter, 1891–
Chlorophyll inheritance in maize ... by E. W. Lindstrom ... ₍Ithaca, 1918₎
68 p. v col. pl. 23ᶜᵐ.

Thesis (ᴘʜ. ᴅ.)—Cornell university, 1918.
"Reprint from the Cornell university experiment station Memoir 13, August 1918."
"Paper no. 65, Department of plant breeding, Cornell university, Ithaca, New York."
"Literature cited": p. 63.

1. Chlorophyl. 2. Maize. 3. Heredity.

Library of Congress   QK981.L5 1918a   19–16518
Cornell Univ. Libr.   ₍2₎

NL 0385617   NIC NjP PU OU DLC

Lindstrom, Ernest Walter, 1891–
The inheritance of ovate and related shapes of tomato fruits.
(*In* U. S. Dept. of agriculture. Journal of agricultural research. v. 34, no. 10, May 15, 1927, p. 961–985. diagrs. 23½ᶜᵐ. Washington, 1927)

Contribution from Iowa agricultural experiment station (Ia.—13)
Published July 9, 1927.
"Literature cited": p. 985.
Paper no. 15 from the Dept. of genetics, Iowa state college, Ames, Iowa.

1. Heredity. 2. Tomatoes.

                                            Agr 27–515
Library, U. S. Dept. of   Agriculture 1Ag84J vol. 34

NL 0385618   DNAL

Lindstrom, Ernest Walter, 1891–   joint author

Cole, Leon Jacob, 1877–
Selection for quality of oil in soy beans. By L. J. Cole, E. W. Lindstrom, and C. M. Woodworth ...
(*In* U. S. Dept. of agriculture. Journal of agricultural research. v. 35, no. 1, July 1, 1927, p. 75–95. illus., diagrs. 23½ᶜᵐ. Washington, 1927)

NL 0385619

HN999   Lindstrom, Frederick Burgess, 1915–
The military mind and the soldier press. 1950.
248 l.

Thesis—Univ. of Chicago.

1. Liberty of the press—U.S. 2. World War, 1939–1945—Periodicals.

NL 0385620   ICU

Lindstrom, Gustaf Thorsten, 1893–
joint author.
Carver, Leland M.
The Ninetieth aero squadron, American expeditionary forces; a history of its activities during the world war, from its formation to its return to the United States, comp. and written by Leland M. Carver, Gustaf A. Lindstrom ₍and₎ A. T. Foster; ed. and pub. by E. Harold Greist. ₍Hinsdale, Ill., ᶜ1920₎

VOLUME 334

Lindstrom, Harold Vernon, 1911–
Qualitative studies in the alkaline decomposition of cystine ... by Harold Vernon Lindstrom ... ₍Baltimore, 1941₎

cover-title, 445–450 p. 22½ᶜᵐ.
Condensed from thesis (PH. D.)—University of Minnesota, 1940.
"By Harold V. Lindstrom and W. M. Sandstrom."
"Published as Paper no. 1839, Journal series, Minnesota Agricultural experiment station."
A reprint from the Journal of biological chemistry, v. 138, no. 2, Apr. 1941, with cover having thesis note and Vita on p. ₍3₎
Bibliography : p. 450.
1. Cystin.   I. Sandstrom, William Martin, 1806–   joint author.

Library of Congress   QD305.A8L55
                                                    42–23292

NL 0385622   DLC

Lindstrom, Harold Vernon, 1911–

Nelson, John Wesley, 1904–
A study of the nutritive value of fresh-water plants ... by John Wesley Nelson ... ₍St. Paul, 1939₎

Lindstrom, Herbert Martin.
An analysis of the organization of the junior high schools in Illinois (field study no. 1) Ann Arbor, University Microfilms, 1950.

(₍University Microfilms, Ann Arbor, Mich.₎ Publication no. 2159)
Microfilm copy of typescript. Positive.
Collation of the original, as determined from the film : xiv, 97 l.
Thesis—Colorado State College of Education.
Vita.
Bibliography : leaves 82–89.
1. Junior high schools.
Microfilm AC–1 no. 2159
                                                    Mic 52–497

NL 0385624   DLC

378.795 **Lindstrom, J   Orville.**
OSℓ   Notes on Oriental basketball tour taken during August and September, 1954. ₍Eugene, Ore., 1954₎
          117ℓ. 30cm.

Caption title.

NL 0385625   OrU

Lindstrom, Johan Daniel
Om cholera-farsoten; academisk afhandling, ... under inseende af Israel Hwasser...Upsala, 1837.
8°

NL 0385626   NN

Lindstrom, John W.
Bungalows. Minneapolis, Minn., J. W. Lindstrom ₍1922₎

1 p. l., 64 p. illus. (part col., incl. plans) 26¼ᶜᵐ.
Illustrated t.-p.

1. Bungalows.

Library of Congress   NA7571.L45
                                                    22–7522

NL 0385627   DLC MB MnHi PP NIC

Lindstrom, John W.
Cottages and semi-bungalows. Minneapolis, Minn., J. W. Lindstrom ₍1922₎

63, ₍1₎ p. col. illus., plans. 26¼ᶜᵐ.
Illustrated t.-p. in colors.

1. Architecture, Domestic—Designs and plans.

Library of Congress   NA7127.L64
                                                    22–7523

NL 0385628   DLC WaS PP MnHi MB NIC

Lindstrom, John W.
Duplex and apartment houses, copyright by J. W. Lindstrom ... Minneapolis, Minn., J. W. Lindstrom ₍1923₎

64 p. illus. (incl. plans) 26ᶜᵐ.

1. Apartment houses. 2. Architecture, Domestic—Designs and plans. I. Title.

Library of Congress   26–4910

NL 0385629   DLC MnHi WaS

LINDSTROM, John W
Duplex and apartment houses.
Minneapolis. Author. 1948? 56p.

This edition contains an entirely new set of designs.

NL 0385630   WaS

Lindstrom, John W.
Summer cottages, log cabins and garages. Minneapolis, Minn., J. W. Lindstrom, ᶜ1931.

64 p. illus. (part col.; incl. plans) 27ᶜᵐ.
On cover: By J. W. Lindstrom.

1. Architecture, Domestic—Designs and plans. 2. Log cabins. 3. Garages. I. Title.
Library of Congress   NA7127.L645
                                                    31–24902
———— Copy 2.
Copyright A 42273   ₍3₎   728

NL 0385631   DLC WaS MB

Lindstrom, John W.
Two story homes. Minneapolis, Minn., J. W. Lindstrom ₍1922₎

63, ₍1₎ p. col. illus., plans. 26¼ᶜᵐ.
Illustrated t.-p. in colors.

1. Architecture, Domestic—Designs and plans.

Library of Congress   NA7127.L65
                                                    22–7524

NL 0385632   DLC MB MnHi

Lindstrom, John W.
see also Lindstrom and Almars, Minneapolis.

Lindstrom, Julius
The culture of adiantum farleyense, by J. Lindstrom. ₍n.p.₎ c1902.
15p. illus. 23½ cm.

NL 0385634   PSt

Lindstrom, Lilla, 1900–
Poems on the Bible. Kansas City, Mo., Brown-White-Lowell Press ₍1952₎

196 p. illus. 23 cm.

1. Bible—History of Biblical events—Poetry. I. Title.
PS3523.I 627A17 1952   811.5   52–37158 ‡

NL 0385635   DLC

Lindstrom, Marjorie Eloise
see Lindstrom, Eloise, 1903–

---

q973.7L63 Lindstrom, Ralph Godfrey, 1891–
GL64a   Address "Abraham Lincoln." Extension of remarks of Hon. Clyde Doyle, of California, in the House of Representatives, Tuesday, March 28, 1950. ₍Washington, U.S. Govt. Print. Off., 1950₎
          4p. 29cm.

Caption title.
At head of title: Congressional record; proceedings and debates of the 81st Congress, second session.

NL 0385638   IU

Lindstrom, Ralph Godfrey, 1891–
A Californian's collection of Lincolniana, by Ralph G. Lindstrom ... Harrogate, Tenn., Dept. of Lincolniana, Lincoln memorial university, 1944.

11 p. illus. (incl. port., facsims.) 25½ᶜᵐ.
On cover: Presenting F. Ray Risdon, esq. and his Lincoln collection. "Limited to 100 copies ... No. 76."
"Reprinted from Lincoln herald, vol. XLV, December, 1943, no. 4."

1. Lincoln, Abraham, pres. U. S.—Bibl. 2. Risdon, F. Ray, 1888– I. Lincoln memorial university, Harrogate, Tenn. Dept. of Lincolniana. II. Title.

Library of Congress   Z8505.L55
                                                    44–53485
                                                    012

NL 0385639   DLC IU

Lindstrom, Ralph Godfrey, 1891–
Lincoln and dynamic civics, a Lincoln day address, by Ralph G. Lindstrom. ₍n. p., 1943₎

28 p. 23 x 10ᶜᵐ.
"The address was delivered to the student body of the Principia upper school in Saint Louis, Missouri and repeated at the Principia college at Elsah, Illinois on February 12, 1943."—p. ₍3₎

1. Lincoln, Abraham, pres. U. S.—Addresses, sermons, etc. 2. Citizenship.
Library of Congress   E457.8.L75
                                                    43–14011
                              ₍3₎   923.173

NL 0385640   DLC

Lindstrom, Ralph Godfrey, 1891–
Lincoln and prevention of war. Which 'blundering generation'? What 'irrepressible conflict'? An interpretation of the Lincolnian view. Harrogate, Tenn., Lincoln Memorial University, 1953.

25 p. 24 cm.

1. Lincoln, Abraham, Pres. U. S., 1809–1865. 2. U. S.—Hist.—Civil War—Causes. 3. War. I. Title.

E458.L74   973.711   54–8394 ‡

NL 0385641   DLC NIC PHC IEN OCl NN NNC IU N MH

Lindstrom, Ralph Godfrey, 1891–
Lincoln, descendant of first family Americans, by Ralph G. Lindstrom, with foreword by F. Ray Risdon. ₍n. p.₎ Lincoln fellowship of Southern California, 1943.

14 p., 1 l. incl. mounted front. (port.) 24ᶜᵐ.
Reprinted from the Los Angeles times' Home of February 7, 1943. *cf.* Foreword.
"One hundred two copies ... printed by the Institute press ... at Los Angeles."

1. Lincoln, Abraham, pres. U. S.—Family. 2. Lincoln family. I. Lincoln fellowship of Southern California.

                                                    43–10571
Library of Congress   E457.32.L43
                              ₍3₎   923.173

NL 0385642   DLC IU

Lindstrom, Ralph Godfrey, 1891–
... Lincoln—the political statesman. By Ralph G. Lindstrom ... ₍Denver, 1930₎

₍6₎ p. 26¼ᶜᵐ.
Caption title.
"Reprinted ₍1₎ from Western medical times, Denver, April, 1930."

1. Lincoln, Abraham, pres. U. S.—Personality.

Library of Congress   E457.L77   33–33154
                              ₍2₎   923.173

NL 0385643   DLC CSmH

VOLUME 334

Lindstrom, Ralph Godfrey, 1891–
Lincoln the religionist. With a foreword
by F. Ray Risdon. [Los Angeles] Lincoln
Fellowship of Southern California, 1944.
17 p. front. (port.) 23cm.
"One hundred copies printed."
Originally appeared in The Christian
Science Monitor, February 5, 1944. Cf.
Foreword.
1. Lincoln, Abraham, Pres. U. S., 1809–
1865—Religion.   I. Title.

NL 0385644   NIC MiDW WHi RPB

Lindstrom, Ralph Godfrey, 1891–
Lincoln's views on government.
[Clayton, Mo., Robert F. Stone & co.,
1953? (c.1953)]
cover-title, [8]p. 19cm.

"Reprinted with permission from the
Christian Science Monitor..."

NL 0385645   IHi

Lindstrom, Thaïs S
Tolstoï en France, 1886–1910. Préf. par J.-M. Carré.
Paris, Institut d'études slaves de l'Université de Paris, 1952.
172 p. 25 cm. (Bibliothèque de l'Institut français de Léningrad
continuée par la Bibliothèque russe de l'Institut d'études slaves, t.
25)

Bibliography: p. [155]–166.

1. Tolstoï, Leo Nikolaevich, graf., 1828–1910. 2. French literature—19th cent.—Hist. & crit.   I. Title.   (Series: Bibliothèque
russe de l'Institut d'études slaves, t. 25)

PG3409.7.F7L5   891.73   53–22574

NBuU OO OU OCl PSt CSt IaU
NL 0385646   DLC ICU CaBVaU MtU NN MH CU-S TxU GU

Lindstrom, Walfred.
Laboratory studies in personality, by Walfred Lindstrom ...
[Angola, Ind.,] 1931.
1 v. diagrs. 24⁰.
Loose-leaf.

1. Personality.   I. Title.
Library of Congress   BF698.L5   CA 31–358 Unrev'd
Copyright A 35602   .2,   137

NL 0385647   DLC

Lindstrom & Almars, *Minneapolis.*
Attractive homes, by Lindstrom & Almars ... [Minne-
apolis, Jensen printing co., 1915]
[96] p. illus. (incl. plans) 25¼⁰. $1.00

1. Architecture, Domestic—Designs and plans.
Library of Congress   NA7127.L67   15–8068

NL 0385648   DLC

Lindstrom & Almars, *Minneapolis.*
Bungalows, by Lindstrom & Almars ... [Minneapolis,
Jensen printing co., 1915]
[97] p. illus. (incl. plans) 25¼⁰. $1.00

1. Bungalows.
Library of Congress   NA7571.L5   15–8067

NL 0385649   DLC

Lindstrom & Almars, *Minneapolis.*
100 plans, by Lindstrom & Almars, architects, Minneapolis, Minn ... [Evansville, Ind., Speed printing & publishing co., *1913]
[104] p. illus. (incl. plans) 25¼⁰. $1.00

1. Architecture, Domestic—Designs and plans.   I. Title.
Library of Congress   NA7127.L7   13–8170

NL 0385650   DLC OCl

Lindstrom & Almars, Minneapolis
see also   Lindstrom, John W.

Lindstrum, Andrew Oliver, 1914–
Functions of a complex variable determined by their values
on non dense sets, by Andrew Oliver Lindstrum, jr. ... Ur-
bana, Ill., 1939.
1 p. l., 8 p., 1 l. 21⁰.
Abstract of thesis (PH. D.)—University of Illinois, 1939.
Vita.
Photoprinted.

1. Functions of a complex variable.
Library of Congress   QA331.L63 1939   40–6274
Univ. of Illinois Libr.
——— Copy 2.   (2)   517.5

NL 0385652   IU NIC DLC

Lindt, August Rodolphe, 1905–
... Im sattel durch Mandschukuo; als sonderberichterstatter
bei generälen und räubern; mit 74 abbildungen nach aufnahmen des verfassers und 3 karten. Leipzig, F. A. Brockhaus,
1934.
272 p. incl. front. (port.) illus., maps. 23½⁰.
At head of title: A. R. Lindt.
Published also in English, 1933, under title: Special correspondent;
with bandit and general in Manchuria.

1. Manchuria—Descr. & trav. 2. Japanese in Manchuria.   I. Title.
Library of Congress   D8782.3.L48   35–4783
Copyright A—Foreign   26968
        (2)   915.18

NL 0385653   DLC PPG CSt NNC OCl

Lindt, August Rodolphe, 1905–
... Das sowjetrussische aktienrecht. Bern und Leipzig, P.
Haupt, 1929.
ix, [1], 92 p. 25⁰.
At head of title: Dr. jur. A. Lindt.
"Berner dissertation."
"Literaturverzeichnis": p. [vi]–ix.

1. Corporation law—Russia.
        46–41902

NL 0385654   DLC CtY CLL NNU-W

Lindt, August Rodolphe, 1905–
Special correspondent; with bandit and general in Manchuria [by] A. R. Lindt. London, Cobden-Sanderson [1933]
292 p. front., plates, map. 22½⁰.

1. Manchuria—Descr. & trav. 2. Japanese in Manchuria.   I. Title.
Library of Congress   DS782.3.L5 1933   33–37238
Copyright A ad int. 18347   (2)   915.18

NL 0385655   DLC CaBVaU NN MB NIC CU

Lindt, Henriette, tr.
Nyirő, József, 1889–
... Het boek van de eenzame bergen. Uit het hongaarsch
vertaald door Henriette Lindt. Antwerpen, N. v. Het
Kompas [1943]

Lindt, Henriette, tr.
Wendt, Herbert, 1914–
... Het dal der zeven heuvelen, vertaald door Henriette
Lindt. 2. druk. Amsterdam, N. v. De Arbeiderspers, 1943.

Lindt, Henriette, tr.
Nyirő, József, 1889–
Uz Bence, uit het Hongaarsch vertaald door Henriette
Lindt. Antwerpen, Het Kompas [1944]

Lindt, Henriette, tr.
Harsányi, Zsolt, 1887–1943.
... Whisky soda. Uit het hongaarsch vertaald door Hen-
riette Lindt ... Antwerpen, Het Kompas, 1944.

Lindt, J   K   respondent.
... Dissertatio juris publici ecclesiastici
see under   Flörcke, Johann Ernst von,
1695–1762, praeses.

Lindt, J   W
Australian aboriginals, 8 photographs. On
the tramp, 3 photos. Sheep-shearing. 1 photo.
Melbourne International Exhibition building 1 photo.,
by N. J. Caire.   Melbourne, [1880?]
13 photographs, mounted 7 3/8 x 5 3/8. ob. 8.

NL 0385661   NN

Lindt, J   W
Picturesque New Guinea. With an historical introduction
and supplementary chapters on the manners and customs of
the Papuans; accompanied with fifty full-page autotype illustrations from negatives of portraits from life and groups and
landscapes from nature. By J. W. Lindt ... London, Longmans, Green, and co., 1887.
xviii, 194 p. illus., L pl. (incl. front., ports.) 26 x 20⁰.
Each plate accompanied by leaf with descriptive letterpress not included in paging.

1. Papua—Descr. & trav. 2. Papuans.
Library of Congress   DU740.L55   44–33150

CLU CtY OO OCU OClW
NL 0385662   DLC MdBP ICJ I ICN MH NN RP MoU PPFr

[Lindt, J   W   ]
Views of New Guinea. [n.p.,
Presentation, 1888]
32 photos. 24 x 31 cm.

Presentation copy to Mr. & Mrs.
Guinness with signature Mr. & Mrs. Shaun.
Two photos. signed J.W. Lindt.

NL 0385663   CaBVaU

Lindt (Joannes Ludovicus). *De aluminis vir-
tate medica. 81 pp., 1 l. 4⁰. *Gottingæ, J. C.
*Dieterich, [1784].

NL 0385664   DNAL

Lindt (Joannes Rudolphus). *De epilepsia, præ-
sertim puerorum umbilicali. 46 pp., 1 l. 8⁰.
*Tubingæ, lit. Fuesianis, 1814.
Also, in: WERKE. Samml. med.-prakt. Diss [etc.] 8⁰
*Tübingen, 1829, I. 44–117.

NL 0385665   DNAL

VOLUME 334

Lindt, Karl.
Beiträge zur Geschichte des deutschen Kriegswesens in der staufischen Zeit im Anschluss an die Kämpfe zwischen Philipp von Schwaben und Otto IV. Freiburg i. B., Mohr, 1881.
71 p. 22 cm.
Inaug.-Diss. - Tübingen.
1. Germany - History, Military. 2. Germany - History - Otto IV, 1208-1214. I. T.

NL 0385666 NjP CU MH

Lindt, Karl Ludwig, joint author.
Nève, Hans de, pseud.
Parole: heiraten! Schwank in drei akten, von Hans de Nève u. Karl-Ludwig Lindt ... Berlin, Vertriebsstelle und verlag deutscher bühnenschriftsteller u. bühnenkomponisten, °1934.

QD3
.A2L64 **Lindt, Ludwig.**
Ueber die einwirkung von alkalipersulfat auf kohlehydrate und sechswertige alkohole. Ueber die einwirkung von alkalipersulfat auf die harnsäuregruppe... ¡Lausanne? 1898¡
57 p. incl. pl. 21cm.
Inaug.diss. - Lausanne.
Placed with other foreign theses in chemistry in a non-serial collection with title: ¡Dissertations and other mono- graphs in chemistry¡

NL 0385668 OCU

W 4
B29 **LINDT, Martin**
1955 Die Scheuermannsche Krankheit der Lendenwirbelsäule. Luzern, 1955.
48 p. illus.
Inaug.-Diss. - Basel.
1. Spine - Abnormalities

NL 0385669 DNLM

Lindt, Peter M
Schriftsteller im exil; zwei jahre deutsche literarische sendung am rundfunk in New York, von Peter M. Lindt. Mit einem vorwort von George N. Shuster ... New York, N. Y., Willard publishing company ¡1944¡
5 p. l., 13-192 p. 19½ᶜᵐ.

1. German literature—20th cent.—Hist. & crit. 2. Authors, German. 3. Refugees, Political. I. Title.

Chicago. Univ. Library for Library of Congress ° ¡6¡

A45-2681

NNC ODW OCU
NL 0385670 ICU OrP OrPR NIC NcD PU PP PSt NBC OCl

Lindt, Richard.
Missstände im unterricht und im prüfungswesen der hochschulen und ihre beseitigung. Von Richard Lindt ... Charlottenburg, G. Heydenreich, 1911.
31, ¡1¡ p. 22½ᶜᵐ.

1. Higher education—Germany. 2. Examinations—Germany.

E 12-93

Library, U. S. Bur. of Education LA728.L64

NL 0385671 DHEW ICJ

Lindt, Richard ¡August¡ 1876–
Das prinzip der virtuellen geschwindigkeiten ... ¡Leipzig, B. G. Teubner, 1904¡
3 p. l., ¡147¡–195, ¡1¡ p. diagrs. 22½ᶜᵐ.
Inaug.-diss.—Berlin.
Lebenslauf.
"Literatur" on last p.
Reprint from the "Abhandlungen zur geschichte der mathematischen wissenschaften, XVIII hft."

1. Mechanics.

Library of Congress QA802.L75 5-26640†

NL 0385672 DLC CU ICJ MB MiU NN

Lindt, Richard August, 1876–
Übungsaufgaben aus der baustatik; 542 zahlenbeispiele und ihre ergebnisse, mit 574 abbildungen, von baurat dr. Richard Lindt ... Leipzig, Dr. M. Jänecke, 1930.
2 v. diagrs. 21ᶜᵐ.
CONTENTS.—1. t. Aufgaben.—2. t. Ergebnisse.

1. Strains and stresses. I. Title.
Library of Congress TG265.L5 31-9656
Copyright A—Foreign 10706
¡2¡ 624.17

NL 0385673 DLC MiU

Lindt, Richard August, 1876–
Übungsaufgaben aus der Baustatik; 584 Zahlenbeispiele und ihre Ergebnisse, mit 620 Abbildungen. 2. Aufl. Leipzig, Fachbuchverlag, 1950 ¡°1930¡
140 p. diagrs. 21 cm.

1. Strains and stresses. I. Title.
TG265.L5 1950 624.17 50-56018

NL 0385674 DLC

Lindt, Richard August, 1876–
Übungsaufgaben aus der Baustatik; 647 Zahlenbeispiele und ihre Ergebnisse, mit 661 Abbildungen. 3. Aufl. Leipzig, Fachbuchverlag, 1951 ¡°1952¡
148 p. illus. 21 cm.

1. Strains and stresses. I. Title.
TG265.L5 1952 52-25567 ‡

NL 0385675 DLC

Lindt (Rolf). * Ueber Paget's Krankheit. 33 pp. 8°. ¡Bern¡, 1895.
——. The same. 40 pp., 1 pl. 8°. Basel & Leipzig, 1895.
Forms Hft. 10, 2. R., of: Mitth. a. Klin. u. med. Inst. d Schweiz.

NL 0385676 DNLM

W 4
B52 **LINDT, Walter**
1949 Arthrorisis des schlaff gelähmten Fusses im obern Sprunggelenk. Biel, Schüler, 1949.
18 p.
Inaug.-Diss. - Bern.
1. Joints - Surgery

NL 0385677 DNLM CtY-M

Lindt, Walter.
R10 Zur Erinnerung an das Jubiläum des hundert-
S9M sten Jahrestages der Gründung der medizinisch-
909ℓ chirurgischen Gesellschaft des Kantons Bern. ... Bern, Stämpfli, 1909.
154p. plates, ports. 23cm.

1. Medizinisch-chirurgische Gesellschaft des Kantons Bern. 2. Medicine - Societies.

NL 0385678 CtY-M

Lindt (Wilhelm). * Mittheilungen über einige neue pathogene Schimmelpilze. ¡Bern.¡ 1 p. l., 30 pp., 1 pl. 8°. Leipzig, J. B. Hirschfeld, 1886

NL 0385679 DNLM

*KB
1568 **Lindt, Willem van der,** 1525-1588.
Apologeticvm Ad Germanos, Pro Religionis Catholicæ Pace, Atqve Solida Ecclesiarvm In Vero Christi Iesv Evangelio Concordia: Cvi Inserta Est Responsio Ad Codicem D. Ferdinando A. pro Confessione Augustana... Auctore Reuerendiss. D. Wilhel. Damasi Lindano... Antverpiæ: Ex officina Christophori Plantini, 1568-70. 2 parts in 1 v. 4°.
Colophon of part 1: Excvdebat Christophorvs Plantinvs Antverpiæ XV. Febrvarii, Anno D. CIƆ IƆ LXIX.
Bound in contemporary stamped vellum.

366478A. 1. Catholic Church, Roman—Pro.
N. Y. P. L. July 31, 1928

NL 0385680 NN NNUT NRU

STC
15653 **Lindt, Willem van der,** 1525-1588.
Certaine tables ... wherein is detected ... the doting dangerous doctrine, and haynous heresyes, of the rashe rablement of heretikes: translated into Englishe by Lewys Euans, and by hym intituled The betraing of the beastlines of heretykes ... Imprinted at Antwerpe by Aegidius Diest, 1565.
A-E⁸. 8vo.
Allison and Rogers, v. 1, p. 86, no. 461.
Harmsworth copy.

NL 0385681 DFo

Lindt, Willem van der, bp., 1525-1588.
Certaine tables sett furth by ... William bushopp of Rurimunde, in Ghelderland: wherein is detected and made manifeste the doting dangerous doctrine, and haynous heresyes, of the rashe rablement of heretikes: translated into Englishe by Lewys Euans, and by hym intituled, The betraing of the beastlines of heretykes ... Imprinted at Antwerpe by Aegidius Diest ... 1565.
University microfilms no.16334 (case 79,carton 474)
Short-title catalogue no.15653.
1.Catholic church—Doctrinal and controversial works —Catholic authors. I. Evans, Lewis, fl.1574, tr. II.Title: The be- traing of the beastlines of heretykes.

NL 0385682 MiU

Case
3A **LINDT, WILLEM VAN DER, Bp., 1525-1588.**
356 Christomachia Calvinistica, et sacramenta-riorvm omnivm vere sathanica: qua inuidus diabolus nunc antichristo suo indies aduenturienti certum præparat iter. Hic est insertus Anti-Sadelivs...Auctore Vvilhelmo Damasi Lindano... Coloniae, Apud M.Cholinum, 1584.
356p. 16cm.
Signatures: A-Y⁸,Z⁴.
Errors in paging: pages 75,114,156 numbered 77, 104, & 166.
Signatures Z₃₋₄ blank.
Library stamps on t.-p.: Dom. Colon and Dom. Script. Prov. Germ. S. J.

NL 0385684 ICN

BX
8063 **Lindt, Willem van der, 1525-1588.**
N4 Cort onderwys teghen de Confessie der ministers
C5 (soo sy hen beromen) Iesu Christi in de Kercke
L5 van Andtwerpen: die haer onwaerachtelijck seyt
1567 met de Confessie van Ausborch t'accorderen ...
Cage Tot Louē, Ghedruct bij Jan Boogaerts, 1567.
*⁸, A⁶, B-H⁸, I² (*2 signed A2) 8vo.
Written against the Confessio ministrorum Jesu Christi, in Ecclesia Antuerpiensi.

NL 0385685 DFo

VOLUME 334

BV4390 Lindt, Willem van der, *bp.*, 1525-1588.
.L75 De apostolico virginitatis voto, atqve evangelico sacerdo-
Rare bk tvm coelibatv, pro defensione s. Concilij tridentini, libri v.
room Contra Martini Chemnitij ... calumnias: quas tertio suo
Examinis tomo non erubuit euomere, & effutire. Auctore
Reverendiss. d. VVilhel. Damasi Lindano ... Coloniae,
apud M. Cholinum, 1577.
[23], 259 p. 19ᶜᵐ.
Initials.
1. Celibacy. 2. Chemnitz, Martin, 1522-1586. Examen Concilii tridentini.
3. Trent, Council of, 1545-1563. 4. Catholic church—Doctrinal and controversial works—Catholic authors.

NL 0385686   ICU NNUT MBtS MH-AH

605.7 Lindt, Willem van der, 1525-1588.
L74.4dev De fvgiendis nostri secvli idolis,
1572 novisqve ad vnvm omnibvs istorvm Euãgelicorum
dogmatibus, nefarijsque irreligiosorum
quorundã moribus, religiosa, piaque ad
omnes vbique Christianos, piosque inprimis
concionatores admonitio ... Coloniae apud
Maternum Cholinum. M.D.LXXX...
16p.ℓ., 227, [16]p. 17.5cm.
Bound with his De vera Christi Iesv
ecclesia ...   1572.

NL 0385687   MH-AH

Lindt, Willem van der, 1525-1588.
De optimo Scriptvras interpretandi genere libri
III.; siue, Vndéna solida Scripturarum Sacrarum
veritas, sensúsq; germanus ac verus nunc temporis
sit petendus: an ex Hebraica, quam dicunt, veritate:
num fontibus Graecis hauriendus: an vulgata potiùs
editione Latina quaerendus, vti in Concilio
Tridentino dudum definiebatur? Avthore Reveren:
D. Vuilhelmo Lindano ...   Coloniae, apud
Maternum Cholinum, 1558.
151 leaves.   15.5 cm.
Defence of Vulgate against the criticism of
Valla, Erasmus, Calvin, and Stephanus.

NL 0385688   NNUT

BT Lindt, Willem van der, 1525-1588.
106 De vera Christi Iesv ecclesia, vbinam locorvm
.L74 nvnc tempestatis certo iuxta ac infallibiliter
1572 invenienda... diatriba analytica, ad egregios
viros Georgium Maiorem, caeterosque Academiae
Wittenbergicae theologos quae novae ipsorum con-
fessioni CXXX. propositionibus anno LXX. aedite,
vanissimisque Germanici sui istius schismatis
causis respondet. Coloniae, apud Maternum
Cholinum, 1572.
310 p. 17cm.
1. Church – History of doctrines – 16th cent.
2. Apologetics –   16th cent.

NL 0385689   DCU MH-AH

Z879L64 Lindt, Willem van der, 1525-1588.
OD 1525-1588.
Dvbitantivs de vera certaqve per Christi
Iesv Euangelium, salutis aeterniae via, libris
III. instructus... Authore VVilhelmo Damasi
Lindano.   Coloniae, apud Maternum Cholinum,
1565.
[30], 327 p.   17 cm.

NL 0385690   MnU

BR904 Lindt, Willem, van der, 1525-1588.
.L94 In hoc libello contenta: Tabvlae grassantivm passim haereseõn anascouasticae,
atque analyticae authore D. Wilhelmo
Lindano Dordraceno, doct. theologo atque
palatij Haghen. decano. Qvibus svbtexitvr sectae Lvtheranae trimembris epitome
per Fridericum Staphylum regis Rom.
consiliarum. Antverpiae, Apud Ioannem
Withagium, 1562.
[73] [18] 26 ℓ. [32] p.   15cm.

Continued in next column

Continued from preceding column

Title vignette.

Bound with this are Staphylus: Theologiae Lutheranae trimembris epitome, 1562
and Scalcus: Oratio lugubris, de sedi-
tione Antiochena..., 1572.

NL 0385692   MnHi

Lindt, Willem van der, 1525-1588.
Missa apostolica ...
see under   Catholic Church. Liturgy
and ritual. Liturgy of Saint Peter. Latin & Greek.

48 Lindt, Willem van der, Bp., 1525-1588.
L753 [Oratio synodica de instauranda Dei Domo
or si sacerdotes suam induantur iustitiam
Law sacerdotalem, habita ad clerum in Synodo
Lib. altera Ruraemunden, anno 70, die 6 Septembris ... Additae sunt Constitutiones syno-
dales in hoc diocesano conventu ... publica-
tae.   Coloniae, M. Cholinum, 1571]
1 v. (unpaged)
Imperfect copy: t.p. wanting. Title supplied from Catalogue général des livres imprimés de la Bibliothèque nationale.
Signatures: A2-H4.

NL 0385694   CU

GS1 Lindt, Willem van der, bp., 1525-1588.
L75 Panoplia evangelica, sive De verbo Dei evange-
Q lico libri qvinqve ... VVilhelmvs Lindanvs ...
1560 faciebat ... Coloniae Agrippinae, Excudebat
Maternus Cholinus, 1560.
2v. in 1. double tables. 32.5cm.
Vol.2 has title: Panopliae evangelicae pars
altera, de sacrosanctae evcharistiae sacramento
...

NL 0385695   NNUT MoU

Tr.R. Lindt, Willem van der, bp., 1525-1588.
Panoplia evangelica, sive De verbo Dei
evangelico libri qvinqve, qvibvs ex scriptura
prophetica et apostolica illius eruitur, & de-
claratur indoles atq natura ... verbum Dei non
scriptum, sed traditum, aduersus infesta Catho-
licae ... ecclesiae hostium tela defenditur.
Altera editio. Coloniae Agrippinae, Maternus
Cholinus, 1563.
14 p.l., 720, [23] p. 31cm.
Colophon: Typis Iacobi Soteris ...

NL 0385696   NcD DCU

Z879L64 Lindt, Willem van der, 1525-1588.
OP Panoplia evangelica, sive De verbo Dei
evangelico libri quinque... Vvilhelmo
Lindano authore. Postrema editio.
Parisiis, apud Guilielmum Iulian, 1564.
[Colophon: Excvdebat Ioannes Le Bland,
impensis Guilielmi & Michaelis Iulian]
[39], 499, [57] ℓ. 18 cm.
I.Title.

NL 0385697   MnU

Micro.F. Lindt, Willem van der, 1525-1588
526n Pro vero atque vivo Christi Domini Nostri
Corpore in Sancta Eucharistia presente
contra execranda Johannis Campani...
Responsio. Coloniae, apud Maternum Cholinum,
M.D.LXXV.
79p.
Microfilm copy(negative) of original in
Bayerische Staatsbibliothek.

NL 0385698   MH-AH

Lindt, Willem van der, Bp., 1525-1588.
Recveil d'avcvnes mensonges de Calvin,
Melancthon, Bucere...
see under   Hervet, Gentian, 1499-1584.

Lindt, Willem van der, 1525-1588.
Rvevvardvs; ein nutzlichs/ wahr evangelisch
Buch/ Ruwardus genant/ das ist/ von wahrer rhu
der Seelen/ wo dieselbig jetziger Zeit zusuchen
und sufinden sey. In lateinischer Sprach be-
schriben/ unnd jetzund in die teutsche Sprach
gebracht durch Herman Baumgartner von Gelnhausen.
[Dilingen, Sebaldus Mayer] 1569.
256 gumb. leaves, 15cm.
Bound in pigskin.

NL 0385700   MnCS MH-AH

Tr.R. Lindt, Willem van der, 1525-1588
... Tabvlae grassantivm passim haereseõn
anasceuasticae, atque analyticae ... qvibvs
svbtexitvr Sectae Lvtheranae trimembris epitome, per Fridericum Staphylum ... item Defen-
sio eivsdem trimembris diuisionis aduersus
quosdam aedificatores turris Babylonicae, eo-
dem Staphylo auctore. Parisiis, Apud Gulielmum Guillard & Almaricum Werancore, 1561.
[37], 47, 71 l. 17cm.
The two works   by Staphylus have special
title pages.
1. Heresies and heretics. 2. Theology,
Doctrinal. 3. Lutheran Church. Doctrinal and
controversial works. I. Staphylus, Friedrich,
512-1564.

NL 0385702   NcD

Lindt, Willem van der, 1525-1588.
Tabulae grassantium passium haereseon
anasceuasticae, etc. Antwerp, 1562.
16°

NL 0385703   MnHi NRCR

Lindt, Willem van der, 1525-1588.
Tabvlae vigentivm nvnc atqve grassantivm passim haereseon anasceuasticae
atque analyticae, ex variis reuerendi
D.VVilhelmi Lindani ... scriptis concinnatae ... Antverpiae, apud Ioannem
VVithagium, an M. D. LVIII.
[88]p. 15½cm.
"Chronologia sanctissimorvm ecclesiae
Christianae patrum scriptorumque ..." p.[78-86]
Contains also Theologiae Lvtheranae trimembris
epitome ... per Frid. Staphylum. 1558.
1.Heresy. 2.   Luther, Martin.

NL 0385704   NRU

Lindtner, *Frau Th*
Reform-Kochbuch enthaltend Recepte für Fleischgerichte, vegeta-
rische Speisen, Mehlspeisen, Gebäcke, etc. Zusammengestellt
von Frau Th. Lindtner. Neu herausgegeben von Dr. med. Lindtner, ... 2. Auflage. Frankfurt (Oder), M. Richter, [1909].
xix, 163 p. 20⁴ᵐ.
Advertisements, p. 147-163.

NL 0385705   ICJ NN

Lindtorp, Olaf, 1877-
Finnskogens folk [av] Olaf Lindtorp. Forssa [Forssan kirja-
paino] 1940. 117 p. illus. 25cm. (Suomen muinais-
muistoyhdistys, Helsingfors. Kansatieteellinen arkisto. 4)
Later editions have title: Fra Finnskogene i Solør og Vermland.
"Litteratur," p. 117.

Finnskogene.

NL 0385706   NN NIC

VOLUME 334

Lindtorp, Olaf, 1877–
Fra Finnskogene i solør og Vermland, beretninger og folkeminne fra grensebygdene. Kongsvinger, Indlandspostens bok- og aksidenstr., 1946–

v. illus., ports., fold. maps. 24 cm.

Vol. 1: 3. oppl.
Includes bibliography.

1. Solør Norway—Hist. 2 Finns in Solør, Norway. 3. Finns in Värmland.

DL576.S63L5   54–29811

NL 0385707   DLC NN MnU InU

Lindtrop, Norbert Teodorovich.
Исследование уровней в скважинах методом упругих волн. Москва, Гос. научно-техн. изд-во нефтяной и горно-топливной лит-ры, 1946.

62, ₂2₎ p. diagrs. 22 cm. (Современная нефтяная техника)

At head of title: Курсы усовершенствования инженерно-технических кадров нефтяной промышленности.
Bibliography: p. ₍63₎

1. Oil wells—Measurement.   I. Series: Sovremennaía neftíanaía tekhnika.
                            Title transliterated: Issledovanie
                            urovneĭ v skvazhinakh.

TN871.L535   49–56710

NL 0385708   DLC

SK361
L287W
no. 9
Linduska, Joseph Paul, 1913–
Chronic toxicity of some new insecticides to bob-white quail ₍by J. P. Linduska and P. F. Springer... Washington, n.d.₎
11 p. tables. 27 cm. (U.S. Fish and Wildlife Service. Special scientific report: Wildlife no. 9)
Cover title.
"Literature cited": p. 6.

1. Insecticides. 2. Toxins and antitoxins.
3. Quails - Ecology   I. Springer, P. F., jt.
auth. II. Title.   (Series)

NL 0385709   DI

Linduska, Joseph Paul, 1913–
Ecology and land-use relationship of small mammals on a Michigan farm. Ann Arbor, University Microfilms, 1949.

(₍University Microfilms, Ann Arbor, Mich.₎ Publication no. 1228)
Microfilm copy of typewritten ms. Positive.
Collation of the original: 272 l. illus., maps, diagrs.
Thesis—Michigan State College of Agriculture and Applied Science.
Abstracted in Microfilm abstracts, v. 9 (1949) no. 2, p. 51–52.
"Literature cited": leaves 248–260.

1. Zoology—Ecology. 2. Rodentia. 3. Mammals — Michigan—Clinton Co.
Microfilm AC-1   no. 1228   Mic A 49-28*
Michigan. Univ. Libr.
for Library of Congress   ₍1₎†

NL 0385710   MiU DLC

Linduska, Joseph Paul, 1913–
Ecology and land-use: relationships of small mammals on a Michigan farm, including results of investigations under Federal aid in wildlife restoration project Michigan 2-R. Lansing, Game Division, Dept. of Conservation, 1950.

ix, 144 p. illus. 23 cm.

Issued also as thesis, Michigan State College of Agriculture and Applied Science, in microfilm form.
Bibliography: p. ₍123₎–130.

1. Zoology—Ecology. 2. Rodentia. 3. Mammals—Clinton Co.   I. Title.

QL751.L47 1950   599   51—61830

NL 0385711   DLC WaS Or OrCS CU DI NIC

Linduska, Jozef
... Priprava francúzskych ovocných zaváranín, výroba kompótov, lekvárov a marmelád, jarov, huspenín a príprava pocukreného ovocia ... Bratislva, Academia, n.d.
47 p. illus., 4 fold. plates.

Slovak.

NL 0385712   OCl

Linduska, Noreen, 1919–
My polio past ... Chicago, Pellegrini & Cudahy ₍1947₎
205 p. 21 cm.

I. Title.
RJ496.P2L63   616.83   Med 47–2432
© Noreen Linduska (Mrs. Edward F. Zahour) Cicero, Ill.;
18Aug47; A15588.

U. S. Army Medical Library   ₍W1045L753m 1947₎
for Library of Congress   ₍4₎†

        NcU-H CaBVa Or WaOB WaT WaE Wa OrU
NL 0385713   DNAL DLC TxU NcC Mi MiU OU TU OrPS WaS

Lindvall, Anshelm Fredrik Wilhelm

see

Lindvall, Fredrik Wilhelm, 1859-1931.

Lindvall, Axel Edvard, 1852–1931.
Minnen från en färd genom Amerika. Af Axel E. Lindvall. Med 72 illustrationer. ₍Nettraby?₎ Författerens förlag; ₍Karlskrona, Länsboktryckeriet, 1890₎

6 p. l., 215 p. incl. illus. (incl. ports.) plates. 21¼ᶜᵐ.

"Förord" dated: Nettraby, Hafgården 1 mars 1890.

1. U. S.—Descr. & trav. 2. Swedes in the U. S.   I. Title.
                                        37–34677
Library of Congress   E168.L764
                          ₍3₎   917.3

NL 0385715   DLC NN ICJ WaU

Lindvall, C.A., ed.
Korsbaneret. Kristlig Kalender. Rock Island, Illinois.
see under title

Z
531.8
L64
Thesis
Lindvall, C. E.
A physiological analysis of fertilizers for available nitrogen. 1914.

NL 0385717   WaPS

FILM
371.3
L645o
Lindvall, Carl Mauritz, 1919–
Observable differences in classroom practices; an analysis of a method for measuring differences in classroom learning situations and an investigation of certain factors related to these differences. Ann Arbor, University Microfilms, 1953.

(₍University Microfilms, Ann Arbor, Mich.₎ Publication no. 5240)

Microfilm copy of typescript. Positive.

Collation of the original: 163 l. diagrs., tables.
Thesis—University of Illinois.
Vita.
Bibliography: leaves 117–121.

1. Teaching. I. Title.

NL 0385719   IU OrU MiDW

Hp20
L64
Lindvall, Fredrik Wilhelm, 1859-1931.
Svensk läsebok för realskolans sjätte klass. 2.upplagan. Stockholm, P.A.Norstedt[1910]
472p. 21cm.

NL 0385720   CtY

---

*Lindvall, Fredrik Wilhelm, 1859-1931, ed.

Tegnér, Esaias, 1782–1846.
Fritiofs saga, av Esaias Tegnér. 28. uppl., till skolornas tjänst översedd och utgiven av F. W. Lindvall ... Stockholm, P. A. Norstedt & söner ₍1923₎

---

arX
2936
Lindvall, Ivar.
De vi et usu coniunctivi futuri periphrastici apud Ciceronem. Gothoburgi, 1888.
iv, 61 p. 27cm.

Diss.--Gothenburg, Sweden.

1. Cicero, Marcus Tullius--Language--Grammar.

NL 0385722   NIC NjP ICRL

Lindvall, Margareta.
... Kärlekens ansikte, av Margareta Lindvall.   Stockholm: Induns redaktion, 1929. 303 p. 12°. (Iduns Romanbibliothek. ₍bd.₎ 86.)

576331A. 1. Fiction, Swedish.   I. Title.   April 4, 1932
N. Y. P. L.

NL 0385723   NN

QC1
.U52
vol. 36,
no. 6
Lindvall, Phoebe W., joint author.

Manov, George Gregory, 1909–
... Effect of sodium chloride on the apparent ionization constant of boric acid and the pH values of borate solutions, by George G. Manov, Nicholas J. De Lollis, Phoebe W. Lindvall, and S. F. Acree ...
(R P 1721, *in* U. S. National bureau of standards. Journal of research of the National bureau of standards. Washington, U. S. Govt. print. off., 1946. 23¼ᶜᵐ. June 1946, v. 36, no. 6, p. 543–558 incl. tables, diagrs.)

Lindvall, Robert Marcus, 1916–
Geology of the Eagleton quadrangle, Montana. Washington, U. S. Geological Survey, 1953.

₍4₎ p. col. map. 76 cm. (U. S. Geological Survey. Geologic quadrangle maps of the United States. GQ29)

"Prepared as part of a program of the Department of the Interior for development of the Missouri River Basin."
"Geologic map" on p. ₍3₎; Scale 1 : 62,500.

1. Geology—Montana—Maps.   I. Title: Eagleton quadrangle, Montana.   (Series)

G3701s.C5 var.U5   Map 55–191

NL 0385725   DLC

Lindvall, Robert W
Handy pocket-sized menu guide for English-speaking tourists in Norway; Norwegian-English, English-Norway... Oslo, Brøggers boktr. forlag ₍1952?₎

39 p. 15cm.

I. Title: Menu guide.

NL 0385726   MnU

Lindvall, Vilhelm

see

Lindvall, Fredrik Wilhelm, 1859-1931.

VOLUME 334

Lindvig, Philip Ervin.
Cholinesterase activity and permeability or the human erythrocyte. ₍n. p.₎, 1951₎
241–250 p. diagrs. 23 cm.
Summary of P. E. Lindvig's thesis—Vanderbilt University.
Reprint of an article, by P. E. Lindvig, M. E. Greig and S. W. Peterson, published in the Archives of biochemistry, v. 30, no. 2, Feb., 1951, under title: Studies on permeability. v. The effects of acetylcholine and physostigmine on the permeability of human erythrocytes to sodium and potassium.
"References": p. 250.

1. Blood—Corpuscles and platelets.   ɪ. Title.

QP91.L72   612.11117   A 51–9990
Joint University   Libraries, Nashville
for Library of Congress   ₍1₎†

NL   0385728   TNJ DLC

Lindvik, Adolf Fridtjof, 1886-   ed.
Platou, Oscar Ludvig Stoud, 1845–1929.
Forelæsninger over norsk selskapsret, av dr. Oscar Platou ... 2. utg. ved dr. Adolf Lindvik ... Oslo, H. Aschehoug & co., 1927–33.

Lindvik, Adolf Fridtjof, 1886-
Juridisk ordbok, av Adolf Lindvik ... Kristiania, C. W. Leisner, 1922.
2 p. l., 245 p. 22½ x 18ᶜᵐ.
Lithographed.

1. Law—Norway—Dictionaries. 2. Norwegian language—Terms and phrases. 3. Norwegian language—Foreign words and phrases. ɪ. Title.
                                                              36–16443
Library of Congress   ₍2₎   [439.823] 347.03

NL   0385730   DLC

Lindvik, Adolf Fridtjof, 1886-   ed.
Platou, Oscar Ludvig Stoud, 1845–1929.
Om aktieselskaper, kommanditselskaper paa aktier og foreninger, av dr. Oscar Platou. 2. utg. ved dr. Adolf Lindvik ... Oslo, H. Aschehoug & co., 1933.

Lindvik, Adolf Fridtjof, 1886-
Prætors rettsskapende virksomhet, av Adolf Lindvik. Kristiania, Nye nordiske forlag, 1924.
2 p. l., 270 p. 20ᶜᵐ.
Label mounted on p. ₍2₎ of cover: På grunnlag av nærværende avhandling er forfatteren kreert til doctor juris ved ... Universitet₍et₎ i Kristiania.

1. Pretors. 2. Roman law.   ɪ. Title.
                                                              28–9807

NL   0385732   DLC

Lindwall, Bengt Anders Gabriel, 1888-
Jordans teori över primitiva metacykliska ekvationer ... Uppsala, Almqvist & Wiksells boktryckeri-a.-b., 1918.
1 p. l., 97, ₍1₎ p. 22½ᶜᵐ.
Akademisk avhandling—Upsala.

1. *Jordan, Camille, 1838-   2. Groups, Theory of.
                                                              24–3821
Library of Congress   QA171.J835

NL   0385733   DLC ICRL CtY ICU MH IU

Lindwall, Bengt Anders Gabriel, 1888-
Q171
.G4518
Gebser, Hans.
Vårt nya tänkande; den moderna forskningens senaste rön i fysik, biologi och psykologi; deras betydelse för samtid och framtid. Förord av Alf Ahlberg. ₍Stockholm₎ Natur och kultur ₍1947₎

Lindvik, Bernhard.
Island idag. Oslo, Aschehoug, 1950.
190 p. illus., fold. map. 22 cm.
Bibliography : p. 198–199.

1. Iceland—Descr. & trav. 2. Iceland—Indus.   ɪ. Title.

DL305.L5   51–32963

NL   0385735   DLC CU NN MnU

Lindwall, Bo, 1915-
Impressionismen ...
see under title

Lindwall, Bo, 1915-   joint author.
ND701
.A7
1950
Arvidsson, Karl Axel.
Det nya måleriet; Radions konsthandbok, av Karl Axel Arvidsson och Bo Lindwall. ₍4. uppl. Stockholm₎ Radiotjänst; ₍Ehlins förlag i distribution, 1950₎

Lindwall, Bo, 1915-   joint author.
N7087
.A7
Alfons, Sven Gunnar, 1918-
Svensk konstkrönika under 100 år ₍1843–1943₎ Utvald och sammanställd av Sven Alfons och Bo Lindwall. Redaktion och inledning: Ragnar Josephson. Stockholm, Natur och kultur ₍1944₎

LINDWALL, Folke
W 4
S86
1950
Om etsskador i oesophagus; en experimentell undersökning på kanin. Göteborg, 1950.
96 p. illus.
Akademisk avhandling - Karolinska institutet, Stockholm.
Added title page, with thesis note, inserted.
Summary in Swedish, German and English.
1. Esophagus - Burns

NL   0385739   DNLM

Lindwall, Gustaf, 1885-
Bland urskogsindianer; Anders Malms resor och äventyr, av Gustav Lindwall; med illustrationer, av David Ljungdahl. Uppsala: J. A. Lindblad ₍1918₎ 125₍1₎ p. illus. 12°. (Pojkarnas äventyrsböcker.)

1. Indians (S. A.)—Fiction. 2. Fiction (Swedish). 3. Ljungdahl, David, illustrator.
N. Y. P. L.   October 28, 1919.

NL   0385740   NN

Lindwall, Gustaf, 1885-
ML410
.C54L58
Chopin; konstnären och människan. Stockholm, Natur och kultur ₍1949₎
181 p. illus., ports., facsims. 23 cm.

1. Chopin, Fryderyk Franciszek, 1810–1849.
                                                              A 50–3537
Oregon. Univ. Libr.
for Library of Congress   ₍1₎

NL   0385741   OrU DLC

Lindwall, Gustaf, 1885-
Guds spelmän; en modern legend av Gustaf Lindwall. Stockholm: P. A. Norstedt & Söner₍, 1924₎. 291 p. 8°.

1. Fiction, Swedish. 2. Title.
N. Y. P. L.   June 18, 1925

NL   0385742   NN WaE

Lindwall, Gustaf, 1885-
...Ingeniören vid Beach street; John Ericssons liv i ny belysning. Stockholm: Ahlén & söner ₍1937₎ 374 p. incl. diagrs., port. illus. (incl. facsims.) 24cm.
Bibliography included in preface.

₍26883A. 1. Ericsson, John, 1803-   1889.   February 23, 1938
N. Y. P. L.

NL   0385743   NN MiU OCl

Lindwall, Gustaf, 1885-
839.73
L645n
Nog klarar jag mig alltid; en berättelse för pojkar, av Gustaf Lindwall. Stockholm, Albert Bonniers förlag ₍c1936₎
171p., 1 l. 20cm.   (On cover: Önskeböckerna; bibliotek för ungdom)

NL   0385744   IU

Lindwall, Gustaf, 1885-
Trömannen, en släkthistoria från färöarna. Stockholm, Norstedt & Soners, 1923.
207 p.

NL   0385745   WaE

Lindwall, Gustaf, 1885-
4PZ
Ger
5097
Wo ist Doktor Gill? Roman. [Übertragung ins Deutsche: Hedwig Kuntschik] Wien, Donau Verlag [c1950]
230 p.

NL   0385746   DLC-P4

Lindwall, Harry Gustave, 1902-
... Condensation reactions of cyclic ketones. ɪɪɪ. Oxindolemalonic acid derivatives, by H. G. Lindwall and Arthur J. Hill. ₍Easton, Pa.₎ 1935₎
cover-title, ₍735₎–737 p. 26½ x 20ᶜᵐ.
Thesis (PH. D.)—Yale university, 1928.
Without thesis note.
"Reprint from the Journal of the American chemical society, 57 ... ₍1935₎."

1. Ketones. 2. Malonic acid. 3. Oxindols.   ɪ. Hill, Arthur Joseph, 1888-   joint author. ɪɪ. Title.
                                                              42–1178
Library of Congress   QD341.A6L73

NL   0385747   DLC

Lindwall, Harry Gustave, 1902-   joint author.
QD401
B228
Barrows, Robert Shepardson, 1915-
Condensation reactions of isoquinaldaldehyde ... by Robert S. Barrows ... ₍n. p., 1942₎

VOLUME 334

Lindwall, Harry Gustave, 1902–   joint author.

Crawford, Raymond Bartlett, 1911–
Ethanolamines of the oxindole series ...   By Raymond B.
Crawford ...   ₍Easton, Pa.₎ 1940₎

QD401
.D54

Lindwall, Harry Gustave, 1902–   joint author.

Di Carlo, Frederick Joseph, 1918–
... Further studies of oxindole compounds ₍by₎ Frederick J.
Di Carlo ...   ₍n. p., 1945₎

QD401
.V25

Lindwall, Harry Gustave, 1902–   joint author.

Van Order, Robert Bruce, 1915–
... Indole-3-aldehyde and certain of its condensation products ₍by₎ Robert Bruce Van Order ...   ₍n. p., 1945₎

Lindwall, Harry Gustave, 1902–   joint author.

Myers, Frederick John, 1912–
Isatin as a reagent in the synthesis of certain oxindoles ...
by Frederick J. Myers ...   ₍Easton, Pa., 1938₎

QD401
.K996
1937

Lindwall, Harry Gustave, 1902–   joint author.

Kwartler, Charles Edward, 1911–
Oxidations and condensations in the quinoline series ... by
Charles E. Kwartler ...   ₍Easton, Pa., 1937₎

Lindwall, Harry Gustave, 1902–   joint author.

DuPuis, Robert Newell.
Phenacyl- and phenacylideneoxindoles ... by Robert N. Du
Puis ...   ₍Easton, Pa., 1934₎

QD401
.D545

Lindwall, Harry Gustave, 1902–   joint author.

Dickerman, Stuart Carlton, 1918–
Studies in piperidone chemistry. I. A synthesis of 5-homopiperazinones.   ₍n. p., 1949₎

QD341
.A9R87

Lindwall, Harry Gustave, 1902–   joint author.

Rousseau, Viateur, 1914–
Studies in the indazole series ₍by₎ Viateur Rousseau ₍and
H. G. Lindwall. n. p., 1950₎

Lindwall, Harry Gustave, 1902–   joint author.

Scudi, John Vincent.
A study of alpha keto amide condensation products ... by
John Vincent Scudi ...   ₍Easton, Pa.₎ 1935₎

Lindwall, Harry Gustave, 1902–   joint author

Bashour, Joseph Tamir.
A study of certain condensation reactions of benzoylformanilide ... by Joseph T. Bashour ...   ₍Easton, Pa., 1935₎

Lindwall, Harry Gustave, 1902–   joint author.

Surrey, Alexander Robert, 1914–
Sulfides and sulfones of pyridine and quinoline and The
reaction of 2-chloro-5-nitropyridine and thiourea. By Alexander R. Surrey ...   ₍Easton, Pa., 1940₎

QD341
.K2P15

Lindwall, Harry Gustave, 1902–   joint author.

Padbury, John James, 1916–
... Syntheses and certain reactions of 1-isoquinolyl and 4-isoquinolyl methyl ketones ₍by₎ John J. Padbury, jr. ...   ₍n. p., 1945₎

QD403
.H3

Lindwall, Harry Gustave, 1902–   joint author.

Hansch, Corwin H   1918–
... Syntheses of 3-substituted thianaphthenes ₍by₎ Corwin
Hansch ...   ₍n. p., 1945₎

QD401
.B43

Lindwall, Harry Gustave, 1902–   joint author.

Bell, John Barr, 1919–
The synthesis and reactions of methoxyindole compounds.
₍n. p., 1948₎

QD401
.S438

Lindwall, Harry Gustave, 1902–   joint author.

Searles, Arthur Langley, 1920–
... The synthesis of 3-alkyl-4-methylquinolines ₍by₎ A. Langley Searles ...   ₍n. p., 1946₎

QD401
.B65

Lindwall, Harry Gustave, 1902–   joint author.

Blume, Roe Calvin, 1916–
2-phenylindole-3-aldehyde and certain of its derivatives ₍by₎
Roe C. Blume ...   ₍n. p., 1946₎

QD401
.K173

Lindwall, Harry Gustave, 1902–

Kaplan, Harry, 1913–
The use of selenium dioxide in the preparation of quinoline
aldehydes, and Condensation reactions of cinchoninaldehyde
and quinaldaldehyde ... by Harry Kaplan ...   ₍n. p., 1943₎

Lindwall, Johan, 1743–1796, respondent.

Linné, Carl von, 1707–1778, *praeses.*
... Observationes in materiam medicam ... Upsaliæ, typis
Edmannianis ₍1772₎

Lindwall, Johan, respondent.
Utkast til en blomstergård af inhemska
wäxter ...
        see under   Kalm, Pehr, 1716–1779, praeses.

Lindwall, Lilly (Lindman).
Desideria, Bernadotternas stammoder, av Lilly Lindwall...
Stockholm: Åhlen & Åkerlund ₍1919₎.   244 p.   plates, ports.
(incl. front.) 8°.

1. Desideria, queen consort   of Charles XIV John, king of
Sweden and Norway, 1781–1860.
N. Y. P. L.   July 7, 1920.

NL 0385768   NN DLC-P4

Lindwall, Robert Edward.
The Greek lives again; a manual on physical and health education that will be used by the junior and senior high school
student. By Robert E. Lindwall and Gordon C. Winder ...
₍Manitowoc, Wis., Printed by Color craft printers, inc., ʿ1934₎
90 p., 1 l. diagrs. 21½ᶜᵐ.

1. Physical education and training. 2. Athletics. I. Winder, Gordon C., joint author. II. Title.
                                                        35–1353
Library of Congress   GV341.L58
——— Copy 2.
Copyright A 78084   ₍3₎   371.7323

NL 0385769   DLC OU OrCS

Lindwall, Robert Edward.
Intramural activities, their organization and administration
in the junior and senior high school, by Robert Edward Lindwall ... Manitowoc, Wis. ₍ʿ1933₎
cover-title, 88 p. 1 illus., diagrs. 23ᶜᵐ.
Bibliography: p. 87–88.

1. School sports. 2. Physical education and training. 3. Student activities. 4. High schools. I. Title.
                                                        33–21764
Library of Congress   GV361.L52
Copyright A 63906   ₍3₎   371.74

OC1W OO OU ODW ViU
NL 0385770   DLC OrCS WaS WU TU PU–Penn OCU PPTU

Lindwart, Egon, 1889–
Ueber eine Methode von Laguerre zur Bestimmung des Geschlechts einer ganzen Funktion...von Egon Lindwart...
Göttingen: Druck der Dieterichschen Universitäts-Buchdruckerei,
1914. 37 p. 8°.
Dissertation, Göttingen.
Lebenslauf.

1. Functions.
N. Y. P. L.   September 27, 1928

NL 0385771   NN NcU MiU MH CtY ICRL IU

Lindway, C. A.
    Annual rainfall and temperature of
the U. S. 1911.
    Reprint.

NL 0385772   DAS

Lindwood, William
        see
Lyndwood, William, bp. of St. David's, 1375?–1446

VOLUME 334

Lindworsky, Johannes,   1875–
Experimentelle Psychologie. 2. Aufl.
München, J. Kösel, 1922.
xi, 306 p. 23 cm. (Philosophische Handbibliothek, Bd. 5)

NL 0385774   PLatS PSt IU

Lindworsky, Johannes, 1875–
Experimentelle psychologie, von
Johannes Lindworsky, S.J. 3.durch-
gesehene aufl. München,Kösel u.
Pustet,1923.
1v. (Philosophische handbibliothek,
hrsg. von Clemens Baeumker ... bd.4)

NL 0385775   PSt CaBVaU PSC PU

Lindworsky, Johannes, 1875–
Experimentelle psychologie, von Johannes Lindworsky,
s. J. 4. mehrfach veränderte aufl. ... München, Kösel &
Pustet, 1927.
xiii, ₁1₁, 275 p. diagrs. 21½ cm. (*Added t.-p.:* Philosophische
handbibliothek, hrsg. von Clemens Baeumker, Ludwig Baur, Max
Ettlinger. ₁Bd. v₁)
Series title also in part on t.-p.
"Literatur" at end of each section.

1. Psychology, Physiological.   I. Title.

[BF183.L   ]   A 41—2472
Catholic Univ. of   America. Library
for Library of Congress   ₁a55c1₁

NL 0385776   DCU CtY NN NNU-W NIC CU

Lindworsky, Johannes, 1875–
Experimental psychology, by Johannes Lindworsky ...
translated from the German (1930) by Harry R. De Silva ..
New York, The Macmillan company, 1931.
xix, 406 p. illus., diagrs. 22½ᶜᵐ.
Includes "Literature".

1. Psychology, Physiological.   I. De Silva, Harry Reginald, 1898–
.II.

                                                 31—12841
Library of Congress   BF183.L5
Copyright A 38116   ₁5₁   150

OCX OCU MH NN ViU OrP MtU OrPR WaSpG
NL 0385777   DLC DNLM PRosC NcD PU PBm OO OC1W MiU OU

BF   LINDWORSKY, Johannes, 1875–
181   Manuale di psicologia sperimentale.
L754e   Traduzione italiana a cura di Arcangelo
1944   Galli e Alessandro Gatti. 3. ed. Milano,
              Società editrice Vita e pensiero, 1944.
              xiv, 307 p.   illus.
              Translation of Experimentelle
              Psychologie.
              1. Psychology - Physiological

NL 0385778   DNLM

Lindworsky, Johannes, 1875–
Methoden der denkforschung, von J. Lindworsky ...
(*In* Abderhalden, Emil, ed. Handbuch der biologischen arbeits-
methoden ... Berlin, 1920–   25ᶜᵐ. abt. vi. Methoden der
experimentellen psychologie. t. ₂, 1. hälfte (1925) p. ₁157₁–184. diagr.)
Bibliographical foot-notes.

1. Thought and thinking.

                                                 A C 36–3268
Title from Ohio State   Univ.
Library of Congress   [QH324.A3 1920 abt.6, t. ₂]
                             ₁2₁   (574.072)

NL 0385779   OU

Lindworsky, Johannes, 1875–
Methoden der phantasieforschung, von J. Lindworsky ...
(*In* Abderhalden, Emil, ed. Handbuch der biologischen arbeits-
methoden ... Berlin, 1920–   25ᶜᵐ. abt. vi. Methoden der
experimentellen psychologie. t. ₂, 1. hälfte (1925) p. ₁131₁–156)
Bibliographical foot-notes.

1. Imagination.

                                                 A C 36–3267
Title from Ohio State   Univ.
Library of Congress   [QH324.A3 1920 abt. 6, t. ₂]
                             ₁2₁   (574.072)

NL 0385780   OU NN

BV   Lindworsky, Johannes, 1875–
5034   Psicología de la ascética. Traducción de A. del Valle G.
L517   Buenos Aires, Editorial Excelsa [1946]
            127 p. 18cm. (Divino maestro, 5)

            Translation of Psychologie de l'ascèse.

            1. Asceticism—Catholic Church.   I. Title.   (Series)

NL 0385781   CLgA

Lindworsky, Johannes, 1875–
The psychology of asceticism, by Johannes Lindworsky,
s. J.; translated by Emil A. Heiring. London, H. W. Edwards ₁1936₁
4 p. l., 95 p. 19ᶜᵐ.
"Translated from the German original ... Psychologie des ₁1₁ ascese,
published 1935 ... English version first published in 1936."

1. Asceticism—Catholic church.   I. Heiring, Emil A., tr. II. Title.

                                                 37—3814
Library of Congress   BV5083.L52
                             ₁3₁   248

NL 0385782   DLC PSt IU OWorP OrStbM OCX OC1JC CtY NN

Lindworsky, Johannes, 1875–
Das schlussfolgernde Denken. Experimentell-psychologische
Untersuchungen. Von Johannes Lindworsky. Freiburg im
Breisgau: Herder, 1916. xvi, 454 p.   8°.   (Stimmen der
Zeit. Ergänzungsheft. Reihe 2: Forschungen. Heft 1.)

1. Thought.—Psychology. 2. In-   ference. 3. Psychology (Experimental).   mental).
N. Y. P. L.   January 3, 1921.

NL 0385783   NN OC1JC IaU CLSU NIC KStMC

Lindworsky, Johannes, 1875–
Das seelenleben des menschen, eine einführung in die psychologie, von dr. Johannes Lindworsky ... Bonn, P. Hanstein,
1934.
vi, 68 p. 26½ᶜᵐ. (*Added t.-p.:* Die philosophie, ihre geschichte und
ihre systematik ... hrsg. von d. dr. Theodor Steinbüchel ... abt. ix)
"Literatur": p. 4.

1. Psychology.   I. Title.

                                                 35—6682
Library of Congress   BF123.L45
Copyright A—Foreign   26989
                             ₁2₁   [159.9] 150

NL 0385784   DLC PV CtY

Lindworsky, Johannes, 1875–
Theoretical psychology, by Johannes Lindworsky ... translated from the German (1932) by Harry R. De Silva ... St.
Louis, Mo. and London, B. Herder book co., 1932.
xi, 145 p. 19½ᶜᵐ.

1. Psychology.   I. De Silva, Harry Reginald, 1898–   tr. II. Title.
                                                 32—19929
Library of Congress   BF133.L63
——— Copy 2.
Copyright A 54262   ₁3₁   150

OrMonO OrStbM
NL 0385785   DLC CtY-M NcD OC1W OO OCU MB WaSpG

Lindworsky, Johannes, 1875–
Theoretische psychologie im umriss; anstelle einer 3. aufl.
der "Umrisskizze zu einer theoretischen psychologie"; von J.
Lindworsky (s. J.) ... Leipzig, J. A. Barth, 1926.
vi, 103 p. 24ᶜᵐ.

1. Psychology.   I. Title.

Library of Congress   BF133.L6   27–14873

NL 0385786   DLC

Lindworsky, Johannes, 1875–
Theoretische psychologie im umriss. 4. durchgesehene aufl.,
von J. Lindworsky ... Leipzig, J. A. Barth, 1932.
vii, ₁1₁, 110 p. 23½ᶜᵐ.
"Das buch erschien in 1. (1922) und 2. aufl. (1923) unter dem titel
'Umrisskizze zu einer theoretischen psychologie'."

1. Psychology.   I. Title.
Library of Congress   BF133.L6 1932   32—28036
Copyright A—Foreign   17956
                             ₁2₁   150

NL 0385787   DLC OC1ND CtY

Lindworsky, Johannes, 1875–
The training of the will, by Johann Lindworsky, s. J.; translated by Arpad Steiner and Edward A. Fitzpatrick; introduction by Edward A. Fitzpatrick ... Milwaukee, Wis., New
York ₁etc.₁ The Bruce publishing company ₁1929₁
226 p. 18½ᶜᵐ. (*Half-title:* The Marquette monographs on education.
no. 4)

1. Will. 2. Educational psychology.   I. Steiner, Arpad, tr.
II. Fitzpatrick, Edward Augustus, 1884–   joint tr. III. Title.
Library of Congress   LB1071.L5   29–21566

CtY PIm
NL 0385788   DLC OrStbM DCU OWorP PU PV OC1 OCX OCU

Lindworsky, Johannes, 1875–
The training of the will by ...,S.J.; a translation by Steiner and A. Fitzpatrick;...Milwaukee,
The Bruce publishing company. ₁1932₁
173 p.
"Carefully revised according to the fourth
edition."

NL 0385789   PHC

LB1071   Lindworsky, Johannes, 1875–
.L5   The training of the will: Translated
1955   by A. Steiner and E. A. Fitzpatrick.
          [4th ed.] Milwaukee, Bruce Pub. Co.
          [1955]
          186 p.   20cm.

          1. Will. 2. Educational psychology.
          I. Steiner, Arpad, tr. II. Fitzpatrick,
          Edward Augustus, 1884–   joint tr.
          III. Title.

NL 0385790   MB

Lindworsky, Johannes, 1875–
Umriszskizze zu einer theoretischen psychologie, von
J. Lindworsky ... 2. unveränderte aufl. ... Leipzig, J.
A. Barth, 1923.
47 p. 21ᶜᵐ.
"Sonderabdruck aus der Zeitschrift für psychologie ... bd. 89."

1. Psychology.

NL 0385791   MiU

VOLUME 334

BF632 Lindworsky, Johannes, 1875-
.L7 Der wille, seine erscheinung und seine beherrschung nach
(Ps) den ergebnissen der experimentellen forschung. Von dr. J.
Lindworsky ... Leipzig, J. A. Barth, 1919.
viii, 208 p. 23½ᶜᵐ.
"Literaturverzeichnis": p. 201-203.

1. Will.

NL 0385792 ICU MH PPC NIC

Lindworsky, Johannes, 1875-
Der Wille, seine Erscheinung und seine Beherrschung nach den
Ergebnissen der experimentellen Forschung, von Dr. J. Lind-
worsky, ... Zweite unveränderte, mit einem Anhang versehene
Auflage. Leipzig, J. A. Barth, 1921.
viii, 222 p. 25ᶜᵐ.
"Literaturverzeichnis," p. 201-203; bibliographical foot-notes.

NL 0385793 ICJ MH ICRL CU CaBVaU

Lindworsky, Johannes, 1875-
Der Wille, seine Erscheinung und seine
Beherrschung nach den Engebnissen der
experimentellen Forschung, von J. Lindworsky.
... 3. erweiterte Auflage. Leipzig, J. A.
Barth. 1923.
3 p.l., 282 p.

NL 0385794 MiU NcD

Lindwurm, Arnold.
Die ausbildung zum handelsstande.
Gedanken eines kaufmannes. ... Bremen,
H. Strack, 1861.
106 p.

NL 0385795 MiU

Lindwurm, Arnold.
Das eigenthumsrecht und die menschheits-idee im staate.
Eine kritik und lösung der socialen frage. Von dr. Arnold
Lindwurm. Leipzig, O. Wigand, 1878.
xxvi p., 1 1., 531, ₁1₎ p. 21ᶜᵐ.
"Das vorliegende werk stellt sich die aufgabe, das in der socialdemo-
kratischen bewegung wissenschaftlich zu rechtfertigen nachzuwei-
sen."—Vorrede.

1. Socialism. 2. Sociology. 3. Political science. I. Title.

34-22686

Library of Congress HX276.L74 335

NL 0385796 DLC KU ICJ

Lindwurm, Arnold.
Die handelsbetriebslehre und die entwickelung des welthan-
dels. Von dr. Arnold Lindwurm ... Stuttgart & Leipzig,
W. Nübling, 1869.
xii, 407 p. 21½ᶜᵐ. (Added t.-p.: Der handel. Sammlung handelswis-
senschaftlicher werke. 1. bd.)

1. Business. 2. Commerce. I. Title.

34-6672

Library of Congress HF1007.L74 650

NL 0385797 DLC

Lindwurm, Arnold.
Die metaphysische wurzel der christlichen ethik, more geo-
metrico aus exacter philosophie, von Arnold Lindwurm ...
Berlin, O. Loewenstein, 1872.
xv, 74 p. 20ᶜᵐ. ₁With Chlebik, Franz. Kraft und stoff. Berlin, 1878₎

1. Knowledge, Theory of. 2. Christian ethics. I. Title.

44-49933

Library of Congress B3216.C453K7

NL 0385798 DLC MH

Lindwurm, Arnold.
Praktische philosophie. Ein nachweis, dass die
philosophie, anstatt der glaubenslehren, die grundlage unseres socialen lebens sein musz. Von Arnold Lindwurm ... Braunschweig, C.A.Schwetschke
und sohn (M. Bruhn) 1874.
xv, 338 p. incl. front. 22½ᶜᵐ.

1. Metaphysics.

BD23.L75

NL 0385799 MiU

4HF Lindwurm, Arnold
695 Reformansprüche der Landwirth-
schaft an die Steuer- und Zoll-gesetz-
gebung im Deutschen Reich; eine neue
Begründung der Freihandelspolitik.
Berlin, Wiegandt, Hempel & Parey,
1875.
114 p.

NL 0385800 DLC-P4

330.81 Lindwurm, Arnold.
L645s Sieben Capitel Wirthschafts-Lehre in
1875 Vorträgen. Braunschweig, M. Bruhn,
1875.
128p. illus. 23cm.

1. Economics. Addresses, essays, lectures. I. Title.

NL 0385801 KU

HQ Lindwurm, Arnold.
31 Ueber die Geschlechtsliebe in social-
L75 ethischer Beziehung; ein Beitrag zur
Bevölkerungslehre. Leipzig, O. Wiegand,
1879.
iv, 290 p. 21cm.

1. Sexual ethics. 2. Love.

NL 0385802 NIC ICJ CU

Lindwurm, Joseph, 1824-1874.
Der Typhus abdominalis auf der Abtheilung von
Dr. Jos. von Lindwurm ...
see under Koerber, J.M.

Lindwurm, Joseph, 1824-1874.
Der Typhus in Irland, beobachtet im Sommer 1852 von Dr.
Joseph Lindwurm ... Erlangen, F. Enke, 1853.
99 p. 24ᶜᵐ.
Habilitationsschrift—München.
Bibliographical foot-notes.

NL 0385804 ICJ DNLM

Lindy Lou. A farce comedy in three acts
see under Neal, Gene, pseud.

Lindzey, Gardner, ed.
Handbook of social psychology. Cambridge, Mass., Addi-
son-Wesley Pub. Co., 1954.
2 v. (x, 1226 p.) illus. 28 cm.
Includes bibliographies.
CONTENTS.—v. 1. Theory and method.—v. 2. Special fields and applications.

1. Social psychology. I. Title.

HM251.L485 301.15 54-5970 rev

OrSaW OrMonO OrPS OrP OrU OrU-M WaS WaSp WaT WaSpG
MtBC CaBVa ICJ IdU MtU Or OrAshS OrCS OrLgE OrPR
PP PHC MiU MH PU PSt PPLas PPD AU OU WaTC WaWW IdPI
CtY-M ViU-M WU CaBVaU OC1W PPT NN MB MiU FU-HC OC1
TxU ViU TU IU OkU-M NcD MeB MsU KyWAT NBuT KEmT MoU
NL 0385806 DLC OOxM ODW NcD NcRS OCU PBm PSC NIC

Lindzey, Gardner, joint author.
Study of values... Rev. ed.
see under Allport, Gordon Willard,
1879-

Lindzey, James Shotwell.
A study of the Columbian black-tailed deer
Odocoileus hemionus columbianus (Richardson)
and its habitat in Oregon, by James Shotwell
Lindzey ... (Corvallis, Ore.) 1943.
10pp. l., 67 numb. l. incl. tables. plates,
diagrs. 28cm.

NL 0385809 OrCS

Lindzey, James Shotwell.
The white-tailed deer in Oklahoma; management
and production. Oklahoma City, Oklahoma Game
and Fish Department, Division of Federal Aid in
Wildlife Restoration ₁195-₎
105 p. illus., maps. 25 cm.
References cited: p. 104-105.

1. Deer. I. Oklahoma. State Game and Fish
Dept. II. Title.

NL 0385810 AkU

Line (Charles). *Contribution à l'étude du
pneumothorax chirurgical. 127 pp. 8°. Paris,
1907. No. 55.

NL 0385811 DNLM

Liné (Charles). *Études sur la narcéine et son
emploi thérapeutique. 71 pp. 4°. Paris, 1865.
No. 227.

NL 0385812 DNLM PPC

Line, Denis.
Contribution à l'étude de méthodes nouvelles en radioto-
moscopie et radiotomographie. Bruxelles, Impr. médicale et
scientifique, 1948.
189 p. illus., facsims. 25 cm.
Diss. (grade d'agrégé de l'enseignement supérieur)—Univ. catholique de Louvain.
"Bibliographie": p. 169-181.

1. Radiography.

RC78.L55 49-3718*

NL 0385813 DLC ICU NIC DNLM

VOLUME 334

Line, Eric Charles, 1897–
The science of meat and biology of food animals, by E. C. Line ... London, The meat trades' journal co. ltd., 1931.

2 v. in 1. front (v. 1) illus., diagrs. 20½ᶜᵐ.

Bibliography at end of some chapters, vol. I; vol. II, p. ₍272₎–274.

1. Veterinary anatomy. ₍1. Domestic animals—Anatomy and physiology; 2. Meat. 3. Meat inspection. ₍3. Meat—Inspection₎ I. Title.

Library, U. S. Dept. of   Agriculture   50L643   Agr 33–146
₍2₎

NL 0385814   DNAL OU PPD

Line, Francis, 1595–1675.
An appendix to Clavis horologiae: or, An explication of the pyramidical dyal set up in His Majesties garden at White-hall, anno 1669. In which very many sorts of dyals are contained; by which besides the hours of all kinds diversly expressed, many things also belonging to geography, astrology, and astronomy, are by the suns shadow made visible to the eye. Amongst which, very many dyals, especially the most curious, are new inventions, hitherto divulged by none. All these particulars are shortly, yet clearly

set forth for the common good, by the reverend Father Francis Hall, otherwise Line, of the Society of Jesus ... Printed at Liege, by Guillaume Street ₍!₎, 1673. Reprinted at London, 1685.

3 p.l., 38 p. plates (1 double, 1 fold.) 21ᶜᵐ.

Preface signed: John Holwell.

Same text as the Liege ed., which has title: An explication of the diall sett up in the kings garden ...

1. Sundials. 2. Mathematical instruments.

NL 0385817   NNC ICN CtY DP MB CSdS MH

Line, Francis, 1595–1675.
An explication of the diall sett up in the Kings garden at London, an. 1669. In which very many sorts of dyalls are contained; by which, besides the houres of all kinds diversly expressed, many things also belonging to geography, astrology, and astronomy, are by the sunnes shadow made visible to the eye. Amongst which, very many dialls, especially the most curious, are new inventions, hitherto divulged be ₍!₎ none. All these parti-

culars are shortly, yet clearly sett forth for the common good, by the Reverend Father Francis Hall, otherwise Line, of the Society of Jesus, professor of mathematicks. Printed at Liege, By Guillaume Henry Streel, in the yeare of Our Lord 1673.

1 p.l.,59,₍1₎ p. fold.front.,illus. 20½ᶜᵐ.

Signatures: 1 leaf unsigned, A–G⁴, H².
Bound in old   calf, rebacked.

NL 0385819   DFo CLU-C

Line, Francis, 1595–1675.
A letter of the learn'd Franc. Linus, to a friend of his in London, animadverting upon Mr. Isaac Newton's theory of light and colors, formerly printed in these tracts.

(In ₍Royal society of London₎ Philosophical transactions. London, 1674. 23ᶜᵐ. ₍v.9₎ numb. 110, Januar. 25. 16 74/75, p.217–219)

First edition.

NL 0385820   CLU-C

Line, Francis, 1595–1675.
Tractatus de corporum inseparabilitate; in quo experimenta de vacuo, tam Torricelliana, quàm magdeburgica, & Boyliana, examinantur, veráque eorum causâ detectâ, ostenditur, vacuum naturaliter dari non posse; unde & Aristotelica de rarefactione sententia, tam contra assertores vacuitatum, quàm corpusculorum, demonstratur. Accessit solutio difficillimi illius problematis Aristotelici de duabus rotis; quáe, licèt valde inaequales, aequales tamen orbitas describunt. Autore   Francisco Lino.

Londini,typis Thomae Roycroft,impensis Joan. Martin,Ja.Allestry,& Tho.Dicas,ad insigne Campanae,in caemeterio divi Pauli,CIↃ IↃ C LXI.

8p.l.,189p. 4 fold.pl. 16.5cm.
"Errata": 8th prelim. leaf.
Imperfect: 1st plate slightly cropped and bound upside down.

Another copy. 17cm.
Bound with Robert Boyle's Nova experimenta physico-mechanica de vi aeris elastica ... Oxoniae, 1661. The 4 fold. plates are bound between the two works, along with the plate to Boyle's work.
Another copy. 16cm.
Imperfect: plates wanting.
With this is bound Gilbert Clark's Tractatus de restitutione   corporum ... Londini. 1662.

NL 0385823   MH PPAmP MnCS DFo CoCA WU

Line, Hagbard.
Aktiv språkopplæring; språkmetodikk for den fyrste opplæring i engelsk. Oslo, Gyldendal, 1955.

125 p. illus. 23 cm. (Arbeidsmåten i den høgre skolen)

1. English language—Study and teaching—Norwegian students. I. Title.

PE1068.N6L5   57–18797 ‡

NL 0385824   DLC NNC-T

BT198 **Line,** *Rev.* **John.**
.L78   ... The doctrine of Christ in history, by Rev. John Line ... Toronto, United church publishing house, 1926.

62 p. 19ᶜᵐ. (Ryerson essay, no. 30)

1. Jesus Christ.

NL 0386001   ICU

Line, John, 1885–
Inspiration and modern criticism; a reconsideration of the inspiration of the New Testament in the light of modern criticism... ₍1st ed.₎ London, Epworth press ₍1925₎
144 p. 20ᶜᵐ.

NL 0386002   NjPT

TF662 **Line, Lemuel B.,** illus.
.B83

Bunce, William Harvey, 1903–
Freight train. Drawings by Lemuel B. Line. New York, Putnam ₍1954₎

VM391 **Line, Lemuel B.,** illus.
.G7

Growden, Gordon A
Freighters and tankers of the U. S. merchant marine. Drawings by Lemuel B. Line. New York, Putnam ₍1954₎

TL147 **Line, Lemuel B.,** illus.
.T6

Todd, Ruthven, 1914–
Trucks, tractors, and trailers. Drawings by Lemuel B. Line. New York, Putnam ₍1954₎

Line, Robert C
Production problems of Western Europe, with a report on the Ninth International Management Congress at Brussels, July 1951; address at the annual dinner of the Northwestern Universities Business Administration Conference at Missoula, October 20, 1951. Missoula, Bureau of Business & Economic Research, School of Business Administration, Montana State University, 1951.

8 p. 23 cm. (₍Montana. State University, Missoula. Bureau of Business and Economic Research₎ Occasional paper no. 1)

1. Europe—Indus. I. Title. (Series)

HC240.L53   338   52–62330

NL 0386006   DLC FTaSU N ViU WaU

Line, Robert C.
... A survey of country stores in ten Minnesota towns, by Robert C. Line ... in collaboration with E. B. Moon ... Minneapolis, Minn., The University of Minnesota, 1919.
14 p. 19 cm.

At head of title: The University of Minnesota. General extension division.

NL 0386007   DHEW

Line, Willard Riggs, 1888–
The ammines of magnesium perchlorate and A new method for the determination of ammonia ... by Willard R. Line. New York city, 1928.

38 p. diagrs. 23½ᶜᵐ.

Thesis (PH. D.)—Columbia university, 1928.
Vita.
Bibliography: p. 37.

1. Metal-ammonia compounds. 2. Magnesium perchlorate. 3. Ammonia.
    29–92
Library of Congress   QD181.N15L5 1928
Columbia Univ. Libr.   ₍3₎

NL 0386008   NNC CU NIC OU DLC

Line, Willard Riggs, 1888–   joint author.
QD98
.F57 **Flagg, John Ferard,** 1914–
Semimicro qualitative analysis; a course in applied chemical equilibrium, by John F. Flagg ... and Willard R. Line ... New York, D. Van Nostrand company, inc., 1943.

Line, William.
The growth of visual perception in children, by W. Line ... Cambridge ₍Eng.₎ The University press, 1931.

x, 148 p. illus., diagrs. 25½ᶜᵐ. (On cover: The British journal of psychology. Monograph supplements. xv)

"Abbreviated form of a thesis approved for the degree of doctor of philosophy in the University of London."
Bibliography: p. ₍147₎–148.

1. Perception. 2. Sight. 3. Gestalt (Psychology) 4. Mental tests. I. Title. II. Title: Visual perception in children, The growth of.

Library of Congress   BF241.L5   32–12306
    ₍5₎   152.1

    CaBVaU
NL 0386010   DLC NBC PU PBm NcD MiU OO OCU MH MB NN OrU

Psych **Line, William,** 1897–
L75452me   Mental health and John Doe. ₍Toronto, 1950₎
5 leaves.

Address to Canadian Conference on Social Work, Vancouver, June 16, 1950.
Reproduced from typewritten copy.

NL 0386011   CaOTU

VOLUME 334

Line, William, [19] joint author.

Griffin, John Douglas Morecroft, 1906–
Mental hygiene; a manual for teachers, by J. D. M. Griffin ...
S. R. Laycock ... and W. Line ... New York, Cincinnati [etc.]
American book company [*1940]

Line. v. 1; Apr./May 1948–1949. [Los Angeles]
1 v. illus. 22 cm.
No more published. Cf. Union list of serials.

AP2.Z8L5   051   59–40434

NL 0386013   DLC DNLM

335.8
L64   The Line.
          Milwaukee Line material company.

          1. Electric lines. Periodicals. 2. Electric
          engineering. Periodicals. I. Line material
          company.

NL 0386014   DNAL

Line and track.
[Scranton. 1905.] 2 parts in 1 v. Illus. Plates. Plans. Diagrams. [International library of technology. Vol. 62, §37, 38.]
8°.
For electric railways.

G185 — Electric railways. — Railroads. Construction.

NL 0386015   MB

The line book by R. H. L.
       see under   [Little, Richard Henry]

Line calculations.
[Scranton. 1905.] 51 pp. Illus. Plans. Diagrams. [Interna-
tional library of technology. Vol. 62, §39.] 8°.
For electric railways.

G185 — Electric railways. — Transmission of electricity.

NL 0386017   MB

Line drives at the Pittsburg Pirates...
       [Pittsburg] , c1910

GV875
.P6L6

NL 0386018   DLC

S147
L5   Line Elevators Farm Service, Winnipeg,
          Manitoba.
          Bulletin, no.2-6;

          Winnipeg, Manitoba, 1944 47.
          no. in v. illus. 23cm.

          No.3 is a revision of no. 1.

          1. Agriculture - Societies. 2. Agricul-
          ture - Canada.
          Contents.

NL 0386019   OrCS ICJ

Line Elevators Farm Service.
   A guide in the use of 2, 4–D and other agricultural chemicals.   Winnipeg [1950]
   24 p.
   1. Dichlorophenoxyacetic acid, 2, 4-
2. Chemicals, Agricultural. I. Title.

NL 0386020   DNAL

280.3
L642   Line Elevators Farm Service.
1950   Producers grading guide.   [Rev.
          Winnipeg] North-West Line Elevators Asso-
          ciation [1950]
            80 p.

            1. Farm produce. Grading and standardi-
          zation. I. North-West Line Elevators
          Association. II. Title.

NL 0386021   DNAL

464.4
L64   Line Elevators Farm Service.
            Seed treatment chart, for treating
          wheat, oats, barley, flax.   [Winnipeg,
          194-]
            [2] p.

            1. Seeds. Disinfection. I. Title.

NL 0386022   DNAL

... Line index to the philosophy of William
   Shakespeare ...
       see under   [Fruit, Henry Dyer] 1855–1941.

Line-Lexington Insurance Company,
   By-laws. Doylestown, Frizer and Darlington,
1863.

NL 0386024   PPeSchw

537.24   Line material company, Milwaukee, Wis.
L64a   ABC of capacitors; an elementary treatise on
          distribution capacitors, their application and
          advantages. By A. R. Waehner ...   [Milwaukee]
          Line material company [194-?]
            cover-title, 23p. diagrs.   (Bulletin 47048)

            1. Condensers (Electricity) I. Waehner, A. R.
          II. Title.

NL 0386025   IU

Line Material Company
   Catalog; street lighting & distribution equipment, pole line hardware, high tension equipment,
potheads, underground equipment, oil switches.
South Milwaukee, Wis.

   Library has
no.28   1927

NL 0386026   MiD

TK3511
.L5   [Line Material Company, Milwaukee, Wis.]
            Fuse coordination with L-M fuse links;
          or, How to confine outages to smallest
          areas...   [Milwaukee, 1942?]
            24 p. illus. 28 cm. [Bulletin no.
          LMB 42101]

            Folded tables in pocket inside back
          cover.

            1. Electric fuses. I. Title.

NL 0386027   TU NNC

Line material company, Milwaukee, Wis.
   The Line. Milwaukee
       see under title

[Line material company]
   When Christmas comes ... [n.p., n.d.]
   [3] 19 p.

NL 0386029   OU

Line Material Industries
   see also
McGraw-Edison Company. *Power Systems Division.*

The line of beauty: or The fair
Quakers of Bristol. A poem...Bath,
Printed by F. Farley, 1732.

NL 0386031   DFo

Line of descent of Elias W. Van Voorhis, of 129 East
36th street, New York city. [New York? n. d.]
broadside. 42½ x 45½.
Latest date mentioned: 1877.

Subject entries: 1. Van Voorhis, Elias William, 1844–   2. Van Voorhis
family.
                                                                2-8908

NL 0386032   DLC

---

hr W
7149   A line of French actresses. [London,
          R. Bently, 1873]
            369-382 p. 22cm.

            Caption title.
            Detached from Temple bar, vol. 39,
          Nov. 1873.
            No. 10 in vol. lettered: Theatrical essays
          and comments.

            1. Actresses, French.

NL 0386033   NIC

The line of liberalitie dulie directing the wel
bestowing of benefites
       see under   [Haward, Nicholas] fl. 1564.

A line of life. Pointing at the immortalitie of
a vertuous name
       see under   [Ford, John] 1586–ca. 1640.

VOLUME 334

Line of Louise Davidson Jenks through Voorhees family of New York. n.p., n.d.
7 p.

NL 0386036   OC1WHi

Line of position book
   see under   [Weems, Philip Van Horn] 1889-

The line of righteousness and justice stretched forth over all merchants, &c
      see under   [Fox, George] 1624-1691.

A Line officer.
   The campaign of Fredericksburg...
      see under title

A line on the life line
      see under   Grocery Manufacturers of America, inc.

TF
64
.R77
L75
The line that Jack built; a souvenir of the Romney,Hythe & Dymchurch Railway. London, I.Allan [1950]
29 p.   illus.,map (on lining paper)
19 cm.

1.Romney,Hythe and Dymchurch Light Railway Company. I.Allan (Ian) ltd.,London.

NL 0386041   MiU

The line up; which side are you on? Decide this question in the light of the facts.   No place, no pub. n.d.
15 p.   O.

NL 0386042   NcU

Line upon line; or, A second series of the earliest religious instruction the infant mind is capable of receiving
      see under   [Mortimer, Mrs. Favell Lee (Bevan)] 1802-1878.

Line-writing exercises
      see under   [Bell, Alexander Melville] 1819-1905.

LINEA; i tessili nuovi. Anno [17]-31 (n.55,58-111); inverno [1952], autunno, 1953-nov. 1966. Milano, Aracne.   v.   illus., (part col.)   33cm.

Quarterly.
Subtitle also in English, French, German and Spanish (beginning with 1964, lacks subtitle).
Ceased publication   with v. 31. 1966.

NL 0386045   NN InU

Chi
HE
9913
.L52
Línea aérea nacional (Chile)
   Guía aérea (Línea aérea nacional) Santiago, Francisco Briones [1938?]
   160 p.   incl. illus., ports., tables.   26.5 cm.
   Paging includes advertisements.

NL 0386046   DPU

Línea Aérea Nacional (*Chile*)
   Memoria.
   [Santiago de Chile]
      v. diagrs, tables. 25-28 cm.

TL720.9.L45A3   387.7065   44-52893 rev*‡

NL 0386047   DLC DPU

Chi
HE
9913
.L51
1938
Línea aérea nacional (Chile)
   ... Reglamento de organizacion y funcionamiento de la Línea aérea nacional.   Santiago, Raúl y Héctor Benapres, 1938.
   66 p.   18 cm.

NL 0386048   DPU

Línea aeropostal venezolana.
   Ediciones gratuitas.   Caracas.

NL 0386049   NN

Linea da Roma a Napoli. Scala metrica: 1 a 250,000.   Roma, Lib. Ferrini [18-]
   41 1/4 x 13 1/4 in. folded into nar. 8° covers.
   Title on cover: Strada ferrata da Roma a Napoli.

NL 0386050   MH

La línea de Chorrillos
      see under   [Paz Soldan y Unanue, Pedro] 1839-1895.

F2851
.C572
La línea de frontera con la República arjentina entre las latitudes 27° i 31° S.
Chile. *Oficina de límites.*
   ... La línea de frontera con la República arjentina entre las latitudes 27° i 31° S., por Luis Riso Patrón S., director. Según los trabajos de la primera subcomisión chilena de límites con la República arjentina a cargo del injeniero don Cárlos Soza B. Con un gráfico, un mapa i cuatro fotograbados. Santiago de Chile, Imprenta i encuadernación universitaria, 1907.

Linea directa espanola de navegacion mediterraneo-pacifico...

   see under

[Hostench, Francisco.]

Linea dopo linea
      see under   [Mortimer, Favell Lee (Bevan)] 1802-1878.

Linea grafica.
   [Milano, Ufficio moderno]
      v. illus. (part col.) col. plates, ports. 31 cm. bimonthly.
   Began in 1946; suspended 1947-Oct. 1948. Cf. Union list of serials.
   Title varies: -Jan./Feb. 1964, Lineagrafica.
   Italian with some also in English or French.
   Vols. for 19 -64 issued in collaboration with the Centro di studi grafici di Milano.

   1. Printing—Periodicals.   I. Centro di studi grafici di Milano.
   II. Title: Lineagrafica.

Z119.L49   655'.05   73-207363

NL 0386055   DLC NN KyU

La linea italo-indiana e la sistemazione dei servizi postali marittimi
      see under   Genuensis, [pseud.]

Linea maschile e femminile
      see   Linemaglia.

Lineage and family records of Alfred Wyman Hoar and his wife Josephine Jackson
      see under   [Hoar, Alfred Wyman] 1834-

Lineage and tradition of the family of John Springs III
      see under   [Gibson, Mrs. Julia Amanda (Springs)] 1842-1917.

Lineage book, National Society of the Daughters of American Revolution
      see under   Daughters of the American Revolution.

Lineage book of the National Society of Daughters of Colonial Wars
      see under   Daughters of Colonial Wars.

Lineage book of the National Society of Daughters of Founders and Patriots of America
      see under   Daughters of Founders and Patriots of America.

Lineage book of the National Society of the Daughters of the American Colonists
      see under   Daughters of American Colonists

Lineage of Dr. Arthur Byron Snow, D. D. S., Saginaw, Mich., with genealogical data on the Gillet Stevens family.
   4 l. (typewritten, carbon copy)

NL 0386064   MiD-B

Lineage of Eliphalet Strong
      see under   [Strong, Sydney Dix] 1860-   con

VOLUME 334

Lineage of Elisha Whipple McGuire. ₍Windham, Conn., Printed at Hawthorn house, 1938₎

₍20₎ p. 22ᵐ.

Includes bibliography.

1. McGuire family.   40-2258

Library of Congress   CS71.M1482 1938

NL 0386066   DLC

Lineage of John Pascal Sawyer, Cleveland, Ohio. Cleveland, Ohio (1935?)
9 p.

Typescript.

NL 0386067   OC1WHi

[Lineage of Lewis C. Hasell]
n. p. 1895.
4 p.

NL 0386068   MWA

Lineage of Sophia Elizabeth Kavanaugh-Baer...
Madison, Ind., S. E. Baer-Sherlock, 1929.

NL 0386069   KyBgW

Lineage of the family of Hovenden
see under   [Hovenden, Robert] 1829?-
1908, ed.

Lineage of William Fletcher Mulkey
see under   [Carlisle, Fredₑrᵢcₖ]   comp.

Lineal ancestors of Captain James Corey...
Rhoda (Axtell) Cory... Susan (Mulford) Corey...
Susan (Kitchell) Mulford...
see under   [Cory, Charles Henry] 1870-

Lineal ancestors of Rufus Remington Young and
Jane Vosburgh...
see under   [Cory, Charles Henry] 1870-

Lineal descendants of Humphrey Jennens
see under   [Gifford, Elton B.]

Lineall, John.
Itur Mediteranium. A true accompt given of the proceedings of the right Honourable, Lord Glin, The Lord chief Justice of England, and the honourable Barron Hill, one of the Barrons for the Exchequer, in their Summer circuit in the counties of Berks, Oxford Gloucester, Monmouth, Hereford Worcester, Salope and Stafford. ... Printed for the Author John Lineall and are to be sold by John Felton, in Stafford, 1658.
1 p.l., 16 p.   small 4 to.   (A-B, each 4 ll.; C., 2 ll.)

Half Spanish morocco and marbled boards, by Rivière.
The Heber-Britwell copy; Britwell Sale, March 1921, no. 140.

NL 0386076   CSmH

---

*Lineamenta commentationis æstheticæ de turpi.   Parts I-IV. *Upsaliae,* ₍1835₎. 4 pts. 4°.

NL 0386077   NN

Linear operators and their spectra
see under   [Courant, Richard] 1888-

---

qA658.06
L645P   LINEAR programming and inventory management seminar, Pittsburgh, 1955.
Proceedings.
[Pittsburgh. Methods engineering council. 1955] v.p. diagrs. tables.

Sponsored by Methods engineering council.

NL 0386079   WaS

Linear Programming Symposium.
Proceedings ...
see   U.S. Air Force.   Office of Scientific Research.
Proceedings of the symposium in linear programming.

---

*Linearum atque superficierum theoria, analytice exposita. [Parts I-XIX.] By F. P. von Knorring [et al] *Upsaliae,* 1814-21. 19 pts. 4°.
Series incomplete.
Part I.   By Franciscus P. von Knorring.
 "   II.   "   Johannes Christoph[erus] Lundeberg.
 "   III.   "   Elavus Wallquist.
 "   IV.   "   N[icolaus] O[lavus] Alner.
 "   V.   "   Laurentius Widholm.
 "   VI.   "   'Sveno Fant.
 "   VII.   "   Laurentius Hambræus.
 "   VIII. "   Enoch von Mellen.
 "   IX.   "   Henricus Frₑₑck.

 "   X   "   Engelbertus Gother.
 "   XI.   "   Adolph[us] Vilh[elmus] Ahlborg.
 "   XII.   "   Ericus Harfwefelt.
 "   XIII. "   Christianus Gravallius.
 "   XIV.   "   Daniel Betulander.
 "   XV.   "   Fridericus Rudberg.
 "   XVI.   "   Isaacus Norström.
 "   XVII. "   Enev[us] Widebeck.
 "   XVIII. "   Johannes Magnus Malmstedt.
 "   XIX.   "   Carolus Gustavus Indebetou.

In: OLK p. v. 1.

NL 0386082   NN

Líneas Aéreas Mexicanas, s. a.
The evolution of "LAMSA" airlines in Mexico. ₍Mexico, 1946?₎
₍6₎ p. plates, fold. map. 27 cm.
Cover title.

TL720.9.L47A5   387.72   48-27746*

NL 0386083   DLC

Líneas Aéreas Mineras, s. a.
see Líneas Aéreas Mexicanas, s. a.

Líneas del estado; guia horario oficial
see   Argentine Republic. Administración general de los ferrocarriles del estado.
Guía horario oficial.

Líneas férreas de México, s. a. de c. v.
...Informe anual de Líneas férreas de México, s. a. de c. v., correspondiente al año social que terminó el 31 de diciembre de 1936
₍México, D. F., 1937   26½cm.
v.   charts, maps, tables.

1936   1st   report.
Reproduced from typewritten copy.

1. No subject.
N. Y. P. L   January 27, 1941

NL 0386086   NN

Lineaweaver, Charles.
The first book of Canada, by Charles and Marion Lineaweaver. Pictures by W. R. Lohse. New York, F. Watts, ⁰1955.
64 p. illus. 23 cm. (₍First books₎ 65)

1. Canada. 2. Canada—History, Juvenile.   I. Lineaweaver, Marion McLennan, 1911-   joint author. II. Title.

F1026.L56   971   55-9599 ‡

NL 0386087   DLC WaSp WaS OrU OrP Or MB MiU PP PWcT OC1

F1026
L56

Lineaweaver, Marion McLennan, 1911-   joint author.

Lineaweaver, Charles.
The first book of Canada, by Charles and Marion Lineaweaver. Pictures by W. R. Lohse. New York, F. Watts, ⁰1955.

Lineaweaver, Marion McLennan, 1911-
The first book of sailing. Pictures by Jack Coggins. New York, Watts, ⁰1953.
69 p. illus. 23 cm. (₍First books₎ 36)

1. Sailing. I. Title.

VK543.L5   797.124   53-6142 ‡

OC1
NL 0386089   DLC OrLgE OrAshS OrP Or WaSp NcGW WaS PP

VOLUME 334

Lineaweaver, Marion McLennan, 1911–
Jimmy and the spy; illustrated by Bob Meyer. ₁1st ed.₁
Indianapolis, Bobbs-Merrill ₁1951₁
180 p. illus. 21 cm.

ɪ. Title.

PZ7.L662Ji   51–9962 rev

NL 0386090   DLC WaS Or

Lineaweaver, Mrs Marion McLennan, 1911–
Let's ski! a book for beginners.
Toronto, Macmillan, 1946. 66p. illus.,
diagrs.

NL 0386091   CaBVa

Lineaweaver, Marion McLennan, 1911–
The Wildfire. Decorations by Alois Fabry, Jr. New
York, Funk & Wagnalls ₁1953₁
187 p. 22 cm.

ɪ. Title.

PZ7.L662Wi   53–10798 ‡

NL 0386092   DLC WaSp OC1 OEac

[Lineaweaver, William C.]
Slide rule for military sketching and map read-
ing...
[Fort Leavenworth, Kan., c1919]

UG470
L6

NL 0386093   DLC

Lineback, Paul Eugene, 1879–
... Studies on the longitudinal muscle of the human
colon, with special reference to the development of the
taeniae. By Paul E. Lineback ... Eight text-figures.
(*In* Carnegie institution of Washington. Contributions to embryology.
Washington, 1920. 29½ x 24ᶜᵐ. vol. XI, p. 33–44. illus.)
Contributions to embryology, no. 50.
Bibliography: p. 44.

ɪ. Colon (Anatomy)

Library of Congress   QM601.C3 vol. 11   21–10305

NL 0386094   DLC CaBVaU OrU NcD MiU OU OO OC1 MB

Cb631.3
L75t **Lineback & Bros., Salem, N.C.**
Testimonials on the use of the Walker fruit
drier, by Lineback & Bros., Salem, N.C., Levi
Cox, Randolph County, N.C., and Lewis Reynolds,
Centre, N.C. ₁n.p.₁, 1882₁
₁1₁p. 33cm.

1. N.C.--Canning and preserving

NL 0386095   NcU

Linebarger, Carol and others comp.
Sketches of pioneer Montana. State
correspondence school, Missoula, Mont. Dept. of
pub. Instruction. Helena. (1943)
Mimeograph.

NL 0386096   MtHi

Linebarger, Charles Elijah, 1867–
Elementary chemistry, by C. E. Linebarger ... Chicago, London ₁etc.₁ Rand, McNally & company ₁1904₁
xv, 352, xlviii p. illus., diagrs. 19½ᶜᵐ.
"Reference books": p. xl–xlii.

1. Chemistry.

Library of Congress   QD33.L75   4–10959 Revised

NL 0386097   DLC CU ICRL ICJ ODW

Linebarger, Charles Elijah, 1867–
Elementary chemistry; a laboratory manual, by C. E.
Linebarger ... Chicago, London ₁etc.₁ Rand, McNally &
company ₁1904₁
xiii, 130, xxxix p. illus. 19½ᶜᵐ.
"This laboratory manual is intended to accompany the author's Elementary
chemistry."—Pref.

1. Chemistry—Laboratory manuals.

Library of Congress   QD45.L75   5–769 Revised

NL 0386098   DLC CU PP ICRL ICJ

Linebarger, Charles Elijah, 1867–   joint
author.
Young, Jacob William Albert, 1865–
The elements of the differential and integral calculus, based
on Kurzgefasstes lehrbuch der differential- und integralrechnung von W. Nernst ... und A. Schönflies ... by J. W. A.
Young ... and C. E. Linebarger ... New York, D. Appleton
and company, 1900.

Linebarger, Charles Elijah, 1867–
A laboratory manual of physics for use in secondary
schools, by C. E. Linebarger ... Boston, New York ₁etc.₁
D. C. Heath & co. ₁ᶜ1911₁
175 p. illus., diagrs. 25 x 21½ᶜᵐ. $0.80

1. Physics—Laboratory manuals.

Library of Congress   QC35.L6   11–19607 Revised

NL 0386100   DLC CU ICJ

Linebarger, Charles Elijah, 1867–
A manual of experiments to accompany the
improved spiral spring balance. Chicago,
Chicago laboratory supply & scale co., 1903.
45 p. illus.

NL 0386101   MiD

Linebarger, Charles Elijah, 1867–
A manual of experiments to accompany the im-
proved spiral spring balance,...
Chicago, 1912

QC107
.L6

NL 0386102   DLC

Linebarger, Charles Elijah, 1867–
Text-book of physics, by C. E. Linebarger ... Boston, D. C.
Heath & co., 1910.
viii. 471 p. illus. 19ᶜᵐ.

1. Physics.

Library of Congress   QC23.L7   10—18000

NL 0386103   DLC CU PPJ ICRL MH NN OrU OrU-D

Linebarger, C₁harles₁ Elijah, 1867–
Text-book of physics. Boston: D. C. Heath & Co., 1911.
viii, 471 p. illus. 12°.

1. Physics.   CENTRAL CIRCULATION.
N. Y. P. L.   September 25, 1911.

NL 0386104   NN

Linebarger, Genevieve (Collins)
The Federal Government in the American novel, 1900–
1950. ₁College Park, Md.₁ 1953.
501 l. 28 cm.
Typescript (carbon)
Thesis—University of Maryland.
Vita.
Bibliography: leaves 437–459.

1. American fiction—20th cent.—Hist. & crit. 2. Political science
in literature. 3. United States in literature. ɪ. Title.

PS374.P6L5   A 54–3715
Maryland. Univ. Libr.
for Library of Congress   ₁3₁†

NL 0386105   MdU DLC

Linebarger, Genevieve Collins.
Washington sources on international affairs; a guide to
some research facilities in the District of Columbia area, by
Genevieve Collins Linebarger and associates, under the direction of Franklin L. Burdette. A preliminary survey resulting from a seminar in the bibliography of government and
politics. College Park, Bureau of Public Administration,
College of Business and Public Administration, University
of Maryland, 1951.
54 p. 24 cm.
1. International relations—Research.   ɪ. Title.

JX1293.U6L5   341.072   51–62535 ‡

CaBVaU
NL 0386106   DLC TxU MH NcU DI ViU MiU NN DNAL WaU-L

Linebarger, Paul M.
Mining laws of Mexico. Washington, 1929.
14 p.

NL 0386107   PP

₁**Linebarger, Paul Myron Anthony**₁ 1913–
Atomsk, a novel of suspense ₁by₁ Carmichael Smith
₁pseud.₁ New York, Duell, Sloan and Pearce ₁1949₁
224 p. 20 cm.

ɪ. Title.

PZ3.L654038At   49–2999*

NL 0386108   DLC PP CaBVaU OrP Or WaT WaE

₁**Linebarger, Paul Myron Anthony**₁ 1913–
Carola, a novel ₁by₁ Felix C. Forrest ₁pseud.₁ ₁1st ed.₁
New York, Duell, Sloan and Pearce ₁1948₁
vii, 307 p. 21 cm.

ɪ. Title.

PZ3.L654038Car   48–5102*

NL 0386109   DLC OU WU ViU

VOLUME 334

Linebarger, Paul Myron Anthony, 1913–
The China of Chiang K'ai-shek: a political study by Paul
M. A. Linebarger ... Boston, World peace foundation, 1941.
xi, 449 p. front., 2 port. (incl. front.) diagrs. (part fold.) 20½ᵐ.
Bibliographical foot-notes.

1. China—Pol. & govt.—1912– 2. Chiang, Kai-shek, 1886–
I. World peace foundation, Boston. II. Title.

Library of Congress   DS774.L48
                                                41–11374
                                                        951

Or WaS OrCS IdU OrSaW MtU CaBVaU MtBC
OC1 OC1W OCU OOxM PPT PHC CU CoU WaSp WaT OrU WaTC
NL 0386110   DLC WaWW IdPI OrPR NcD NcRS OU ViU WaU OO

Linebarger, Paul Myron Anthony, 1913–
The China of Chiang K'ai-shek: a political study by Paul
M. A. Linebarger ... Boston, World peace foundation, 1943.
xi, 449 p. front., 2 ports. (incl. front.) diagrs. (part fold.) 20½ᵐ.
Bibliographical foot-notes.

NL 0386111   ViU IU

Linebarger, Paul Myron Anthony, 1913–
The China of Chiang K'ai-shek; a political
study by Paul M.A. Linebarger.   Boston,
World Peace Foundation, 1943; [Ann Arbor,
Mich., University Microfilms, 1969]
xi, 449p. 2 ports., diagrs. (part fold.) 20cm.

Biographical foot-notes.

✓1.China - Politics and government - 1912-1949. ✓2.Chiang,
Kai-shek, 1886–   ✓I.World Peace Foundation, Boston. ✓II.
Title

NL 0386112   CLSU

Linebarger, Paul Myron Anthony, 1913–
Far Eastern governments and politics: China and Japan
[by] Paul M. A. Linebarger, Djang Chu [and] Ardath W.
Burks. New York, Von Nostrand [1954]
630 p. illus. 24 cm. (Van Nostrand political science series)

1. China—Pol. & govt. 2. Japan—Pol. & govt.   I. Title.

DS740.L5 1954   951   54–11885 ‡

WaS OrPS MH PU PSt PHC PBL WaT WaWW OrU WaSpG
NcD OkU MnU DSI CaBVa CaBVaU MtU Or OrAshS OrLgE
NL 0386113   DLC ViU NN TxU OOxM OC1 PP PSC PU PPT TU

Linebarger, Paul Myron Anthony, 1913–   ed.

Linebarger, Paul Myron Wentworth, 1871–
The gospel of Chung Shan ... according to Paul Linebarger ... edited with introduction and comment by Paul Myron
Anthony Linebarger ... Paris (France) For sale at Brentano's, 1932.

Linebarger, Paul Myron Anthony, 1913–
Government in republican China, by Paul Myron Anthony
Linebarger ... foreword by Fritz Morstein Marx. 1st ed. New
York and London, McGraw-Hill book company, inc., 1938.
xv, 203 p. 23ᶜᵐ. (*Half-title:* McGraw-Hill studies in political science;
Fritz Morstein Marx, editor)
"Notes" at end of each chapter.

1. China—Pol. & govt.—1912–   I. Title.
Library of Congress   DS775.L48
——— Copy 2.   38–25848
Copyright   A 121498   [10]   951

WaU OrSaW WaS OrU OrCS Or ICJ
PHC PBm PU OrP ICJ OO OCU OC1 OU ScU MtU IdU WaWW
NL 0386115   DLC OrPR CaBVaU MtBC NIC FMU NN CoU NcD

Film
951.04   **Linebarger, Paul Myron Anthony,** 1913–
L754g   Government in republican China. Foreword
by Fritz Morstein Marx. New York and
London, McGraw-Hill, 1938.
xv, 203p. (McGraw-Hill Studies in Political
Science, Fritz Morstein Marx, ed.)

Positive microfilm by University Microfilms, Ann Arbor, Michigan.

1. China - Pol. and govt. - 1912–   I.
Title.

NL 0386116   NcU

DS
775   **Linebarger, Paul Myron Anthony,** 1913–
L48a   Government in republican China, by Paul Myron Anthony
Linebarger ... foreword by Fritz Morstein Marx. 1st ed.
New York and London, McGraw-Hill book company, inc.,
1938. [Ann Arbor, Mich., 1967]
xv, 203 p. 23 cm. (*Half-title:* McGraw-Hill studies in political
science: Fritz Morstein Marx, editor)
"Notes" at end of each chapter.
Photocopy (positive) made by University
Microfilms.
Printed on double leaves.
1. China—Pol. & govt.—1912–   I. Title.

NL 0386117   NBuC MiU

Linebarger, Paul Myron Anthony, 1913–   ed.

Linebarger, Paul Myron Wentworth, 1871–
The ocean men; an allegory of the Sun Yat-Sen revolutions, by Paul Myron Linebarger; edited with an introduction
by P. M. Anthony Linebarger. Washington, D. C., Mid-nation editions, °1937.

Linebarger, Paul Myron Anthony, 1913–
The political doctrines of Sun Yat-sen, an exposition of
the San min chu i ... by Paul Myron Anthony Linebarger.
Baltimore, The Johns Hopkins press, 1937.
xiv, 278 p., 1 l. 21 cm.
Thesis (PH. D.)—Johns Hopkins university, 1936.
Vita.
Published also as Johns Hopkins studies in historical and political
science. Extra volumes. new ser., no. 24.
Bibliography: p. 265–273.

1. Sun, Yat-sen, 1866–1925. Sen min chu i. 2. Nationalism and
nationality. 3. World politics. 4. China—For. rel. 5. China—Pol. &
govt. 6. China—Econ. condit.   I. Title.

DS777.L49 1936   951   37–18375
Johns Hopkins Univ.   Library
for Library of Congress   [t63f1]

NL 0386119   MdBJ PBm PU ViU-L IU OrCS WaWW OrPS WaSpG

Linebarger, Paul Myron Anthony, 1913–
The political doctrines of Sun Yat-sen; an exposition of
the San min chu i, by Paul Myron Anthony Linebarger ...
Baltimore, The Johns Hopkins press, 1937.
xiv, 278 p. 22 cm. (*Half-title:* Johns Hopkins university studies
in historical and political science. Extra volumes. New ser., no. 24)
Issued also as thesis (PH. D.) Johns Hopkins university.
Bibliography: p. 265–273.

1. Sun, Yat-sen, 1866–1925. San min chu i. 2. Nationalism—China.
3. World politics. 4. China—For. rel. 5. China—Pol. & govt. 6.
China—Econ. condit.   I. Title.

H31.J62 new ser., no. 24   951   37–12598
——— Copy 2.   DS777.L49 1937

PSt CoU NBuU-L OO OCU OU WaU ODW OC1JC PHC NcD NcU
NL 0386120   DLC OrPR OrSaW WaS OrU OC1JC Wa MB LU MiU

Linebarger, Paul Myron Anthony, 1913–   The
political doctrines of Sun Yat-sen.

Linebarger, Paul Myron Wentworth, 1871–
Livret-questionnaire pour les étudiants sur les doctrines politiques de Sun Yat-Sen, par Paul Myron Linebarger, d'après
The political doctrines of Sun Yat-Sen—an exposition of the
San min chu i, by Paul Myron Anthony Linebarger ... Washington, D. C., Éditions Mid-nation [1937]

Linebarger, Paul Myron Anthony, 1913–
Psychological warfare. [1st ed.] Washington, Infantry
Journal Press [1948]
xiii, 259 p. illus. 24 cm.
Includes bibliographical references.

1. Psychological warfare.

U22.L5   355.43   48–1799*

IdPI OrPS
PCM NcD CU AU OrPR CaBVaU OrU Or WaS OrP OrSaW MtU
NL 0386122   DLC PHC PU ICU DNLM TxU MB ViU MiEM Mi MiU

Linebarger, Paul Myron Anthony, 1913–
Psychological warfare. [2d ed.] New York, Duell, Sloan
and Pearce [°1954]
318 p. illus. 24 cm.

1. Psychological warfare.

UB275.L5 1954   355.43   60–12852 ‡

NL 0386123   DLC MiU OOxM NB DNLM FU

Linebarger, Paul Myron Anthony, 1913–
Psychological warfare. [2d ed.] Washington, Combat
Forces Press [1955, °1954]
318 p. illus. 24 cm.

1. Psychological warfare.

UB275.L5 1955   355.43   55–9078 ‡

WaWW
IdPI IdU MtBC MtU WaSpG OrCS OrP OrPR OrU WaTC WaT
MtBuM OrU-M OrStbM Or CaBVa CaBVaU IdB WaPS Wa WaE
NL 0386124   DLC PPT MB TxU NNC NcD OC1 IaAS PU ViU LU

[Linebarger, Paul Myron Anthony] 1913–
... Ria. New York, Duell, Sloan and Pearce [1947]
5 p. l., 3–242 p. 21 cm.
Author's pseud., Felix C. Forrest, at head of title.
"First edition."

I. Title.
PZ3.L654038Ri   47–3832 re*

NL 0386125   DLC NcD ViU

HM263
.U5   **Linebarger, Paul Myron Anthony,** 1913–
1946   **U.S. War Dept. General Staff.**
A syllabus of psychological warfare. [Prepared by Major
Paul M. A. Linebarger] Washington, Propaganda Branch,
Intelligence Division, WDGS, 1946.

Linebarger, Paul Myron Wentworth, 1871–
Bugle rhymes from France. 1916.

NL 0386127   PPCiC

[Linebarger, Paul Myron Wentworth] 1871–1939.
Bugle rhymes from France, by Paul Myron [pseud.] w[ith]
illustrations by François Olivier. And the ship play a
comedy by the same author, This side of France. Chic[ago]
Mid-nation publishers, 1918.
2 p. l., 7–150 p. illus., plates. 19½ cm.
Advertising matter: p. [139]–150.

I. Title. II. Title: This side of France.
PS3523.I 63B8 1918   18–1

NL 0386128   DLC WaSp NjP NN MB NIC

VOLUME 334

M
1804
.L74
O5
1935

Linebarger, Paul Myron Wentworth, 1871-1939.
Les chansons anniversaires pour Sun Yat Sen, fondateur de la République de Chine. Paroles et musique de Paul Myron Linebarger. ₍Paris, Imp. Chaffange, 1935₎
23p. port. 28cm.

Cover title.
For voice and piano, with English words.
Three of the songs have Chinese words also.
"La musique de ces chansons a été composée en partie comme musique scènique pour le

livret dramatique révolutionnaire 'Les Hommes d'Outre-Mer...'"

1. Songs, Chinese. 2. Sun Yat-sen, 1866-1925. Songs and music. I. Title.

NL 0386130   OrU CtY

Linebarger, Paul Myron Wentworth, 1871-1939.
Les chansons anniversaires pour Sun Yat Sen, fondateur de la République de Chine. Paroles et musique de Paul Myron Linebarger ... ₍Paris, Imp. Chaffange & cⁱᵉ, 1936₎
cover-title, 3-42 p. 27ᶜᵐ.
Text on p. ₍2₎ and ₍4₎ of cover.
Composer's surname also in Chinese on cover.
Third ed. The 1st ed. was published in Shanghai, 1933. cf. p. ₍2₎
For 1-2 voices 1th piano accompaniment. English words. Three of the songs have Chinese words also.
"La musique de ces chansons a été composée en partie comme musique scènique pour le livret dramatique révolutionnaire 'Les hommes d'outre-mer'."
1. Songs, Chinese.   I. Sun, Yat-sen, 1866-1925. II. Title.
                                                           45-32947
Library of Congress   M1804.L74C5 1936

NL 0386131   DLC CtY

Linebarger, Paul Myron Wentworth, 1871-
La Chine et la Judée, trop vieilles pour mourir; une esquisse des révolutions de Sun Yat-Sen, par Paul Myron Linebarger. Washington, D. C., Éditions Mid-nation ₍1937₎
64 p. 22ᶜᵐ.
Printed in Belgium.
"Cette histoire tient plus ou moins de l'allégorie."—p. 63.

I. Title.
                                                           38-15562
Library of Congress   DS777.L46
——— Copy 2.   951

NL 0386132   DLC OrU IU NN

Linebarger, Paul Myron Wentworth, 1871-
La Chine navrée, par Paul-Myron Linebarger (Lim ba keu) ... ₍Paris, Imprimerie Dubois & Bauer, 1931₎
cover-title, 39 p. port. 21½ᶜᵐ.
Consists mainly of answers to questions asked of the author following his lectures on China broadcast from Mt. Vernon Hills, Va., Nov. 1, 1930 to May 27, 1931.

1. China. 2. China—Pol. & govt.—1912-   I. Title.
                                                           33-18858
Library of Congress   DS774.L5
                                                           951

NL 0386133   DLC NN DS IU PU

Linebarger, Paul Myron Wentworth, 1871-
La Chine navrée, par Paul-Myron Linebarger (Lim Ba Keu) ... Paris: Comité général exécutif du Kuomintang en Europe₍, 1932₎. 39 p. 21cm.
Cover-title.
Title also in Chinese.
Portrait on inside of front cover.

732356A. 1. China—Rel., Gen., with   U. S. 2. United States—Rel., Gen.,
with China. 3. China—Politics, 1923-   1931. I. Title.
N. Y. P. L.   October 10, 1934

NL 0386134   NN

Linebarger, Paul Myron Wentworth, 1871-1939.
Deutschlands gegenwärtige gelegenheiten in China, von Paul Myron Linebarger ... Brüssel (Belgien) ₍Impr. aux Presses Tilbury, s., a., L. Flas & fils₎ 1936.
55 p. 22ᶜᵐ.
Author's surname also in Chinese on t-p.

1. China—Relations (general) with Germany. 2. Germany—Relations ₍general₎ with China. 3. China—Pol. & govt.—1912-   I. Title.

Library of Congress   DS777.47.L5   43-30696

NL 0386135   DLC NcD MH MH-B

Linebarger, Paul Myron Wentworth, 1871-
Es España otra China? Por Paul-Myron Linebarger (Lim ba keu) ... ₍Barcelona. Imprenta Borras, 1931₎
cover-title, 32 p . 17ᶜᵐ.

1. Spain—Relations (general) with China. 2. China—Relations (general) with Spain.   I. Title.

Library of Congress   DP86.C5L5   33-21951
——— Copy 2.   327.460951

NL 0386136   DLC MH NN IU CtY IEN DS MiU

Linebarger, Paul Myron Wentworth, 1871-
A family of five republics; a sketch of the origin of the Leyenberger-Lineberger-Linebarger-Lionberger families. By Paul Myron Linebarger ... and Walter Franklin Lineberger ... Hammond, Ind., W. B. Conkey company, 1925.
43 p. 19½ᶜᵐ.
"Published at the expense of the authors as a contribution to the monument fund of the 'family of five republics'."

1. Leyenberger family. I. Lineberger, Walter Franklin, 1883- joint author. II. Title.

Library of Congress   CS71.L683 1925   25-15879

NL 0386137   DLC ViU MWA NN MB NcU OClWHi

Linebarger, Paul Myron Wentworth, 1871-
Gegensätze und aehnlichkeiten zwischen Sun Yat Sens "San min chu i" und dem deutschen national-sozialismus, mit anekdoten von Sun Yat Sen, von Paul Myron Linebarger. Washington, D. C., Éditions Mid-nation ₍1937₎
39 p. 22ᶜᵐ.
Printed in Belgium.

1. Sun, Yat-sen, 1866-1925. San min chu i. 2. Nationalsozialistische deutsche arbeiter-partei.

Library of Congress   DS777.L47   38-15561
                                                           951

NL 0386138   DLC

DS17
514.L1

Linebarger, Paul Myron Wentworth, 1871-
The gospel of Chung Shan ₍title in Chinese characters₎ according to Paul Linebarger ... Illustrated by photos inscribed to Judge Linebarger by Chinese statesmen and scholars. Ed. with introduction and comment by Paul Myron Anthony Linebarger. Paris[Dubois & Bauer]1932. 19cm.

NL 0386139   CtY MiU OU OO OCl

Linebarger, Paul Myron Wentworth, 1871-
The gospel of Chung Shan ... according to Paul Linebarger ... edited with introduction and comment by Paul Myron Anthony Linebarger ... Paris (France) For sale at Brentano's, 1932.
263, ₍1₎ p. illus. (incl. ports., facsims.) 19ᶜᵐ.
Title in Chinese mounted on t-p.
Imprint lettered on cover: Editions-Mid-nations, 1932.
"Public utterances ... in the cause of the revolution ... delivered between September 28, 1906 and June first 1932."—Introductory remarks.

1. Sun, Yat-sen, 1866-1925. 2. China—Pol. & govt.—1912-   3. Kuo min tang.   I. Linebarger, Paul Myron Anthony, 1913-   ed. II. Title.

Library of Congress   DS777.L48   32-31867
——— Copy 2.   ₍3₎   951

ViU ICU WaU
NL 0386140   DLC DNW OrP IdU NN NBC DAU NNC NcD NcU MB

Linebarger, Paul Myron Wentworth, 1871-
Livret-questionnaire pour les étudiants sur les doctrines politiques de Sun Yat-Sen, par Paul Myron Linebarger, d'après The political doctrines of Sun Yat-Sen—an exposition of the San min chu i, by Paul Myron Anthony Linebarger ... Washington, D. C., Éditions Mid-nation ₍1937₎
30 p. 22ᶜᵐ.
Printed in Belgium.

1. Sun, Yat-sen, 1866-1925.   San min chu i.   I. Linebarger, Paul Myron Anthony, 1913-   The political doctrines of Sun Yat-sen. II. Title.

Library of Congress   DS777.L485   38-15563
                                                           951

NL 0386141   DLC OrU DNAL NN

Linebarger, Paul Myron Wentworth, 1871-1939.
Mes mémoires abrégés sur les révolutions de Sun-Yat-Sen, par Paul Myron Linebarger ... Paris (France) Éditions Mid-nation, 1938.
201, ₍1₎ p., 1 l. port. 28½ᶜᵐ.
Autobiography.

1. Sun, Yat-Sen, 1866-1925.   I. Title.
                                                           40-16074
Library of Congress   DS777.L486
                                                           951

NL 0386142   DLC OClJC OCl NN CtY KU ViU

₍Linebarger, Paul Myron Wentworth₎ 1871-
Miss American Dollars; a romance of travel, by Paul Myron ₍pseud₎ ... with original pictures by François Olivier, and other illustrations. Milwaukee, Wis., Mid-nation publishers, 1916.
301 p. incl. front. plates. 20ᶜᵐ. $1.25

I. Title.

Library of Congress   PZ3.L6541M   16-15594

NL 0386143   DLC

Linebarger, Paul Myron Wentworth, 1871-
The ocean men; an allegory of the Sun Yat-Sen revolutions, by Paul Myron Linebarger; edited with an introduction by P. M. Anthony Linebarger. Washington, D. C., Mid-nation editions, ᶜ1937.
67 p. 23ᶜᵐ.
Title and author's name also in Chinese.
"Chinese introduction": p. 63-67.

1. Sun, Yat-sen, 1866-1925.   I. Linebarger, Paul Myron Anthony, 1913-   ed. II. Title.

Library of Congress   DS777.L487   38-16001
——— Copy 2.
Copyright A 104965   [812.5] 951

NL 0386144   DLC CoU CSt-H NN

₍Linebarger, Paul Myron Wentworth₎ 1871-
Our Chinese chances through Europe's war, by Paul Myron ₍pseud.₎ ... Chicago, Milwaukee, Wis., Linebarger brothers, 1915.
220 p. front, plates, ports. 19½ᶜᵐ. $1.25

1. China. 2. U. S.—Comm.—China. 3. European war, 1914-   —Economic aspects—China.   I. Title.

Library of Congress   DS710.L65   15-16414

FTaSU CSt-H ICJ ICN NjP
NL 0386145   DLC KEmT NBuC NN NcD PCC PU PP FMU KU UU

Linebarger, Paul Myron Wentworth, 1871-
... Our common cause with China against imperialism and communism, by Paul Linebarger ... Los Angeles, Calif., Kuomin-tang (Chinese Nationalist party) ₍1927₎
30, ₍2₎ p. 20ᶜᵐ. ("Chinese politics made easy" series)
At head of title: Chinese Nationalist (Kuo min tang) publication.

1. China—For. rel.   I. Kuo min tang. II. Title.

Library of Congress   DS775.L5   27-18659

NL 0386146   DLC CtY NN

VOLUME 334

Linebarger, Paul Myron Wentworth, 1871-
China.
Report of the legal advisor [!] of the national government of China ... [Nanking, 1932-

---

Lineberger, Paul Myron Wentworth, 1871–1939.
Sun Yat Sen and the Chinese republic, by Paul Lineberger ... New York & London, The Century co. [*1925]
xviii, 371 p. front., plates, ports. 20½[cm].

1. Sun, Yat-sen, 1866–1925. 2. China—Hist.—Republic, 1912–
25–4930

Library of Congress   DS777.L5

MiU
OLak OC1 OU MB NN NcD NjN CU OKentU NSyU GU ODW OO
NL 0386148   DLC WaSp Or WaS WaTC OrSaW CaBVaU PPFr PU

Linebarger, Paul Myron Wentworth, 1871–
This side of France. A comedy. By Paul Myron [pseud.].
(In his Bugle rhymes from France. Pp. 116–138. Chicago. 1918.)

L6379 — T.r. — European War, 1914– . Hist. Fict. United States.

NL 0386149   MB

Linebaugh, J   H.
Education: a discourse, preached by Rev. J. H. Linebaugh ... on the 20th October, A. D. 1850. New Orleans, Printed at the office of the Picayune, 1850.
16 p. 21[cm].

1. Education—Addresses, essays, lectures.
31–8863

Library of Congress   LA25.L5

NL 0386150   DLC MdBP

Linebaugh, N   L
Historical sketch of the Vandalia, Ohio, United Brethren church, 1838–1912. [Dayton, O., Otterbein press, 1912?]
15 p., 20½[cm].

NL 0386151   NjPT

Lineberger, Able C.   Chapel Hill, 1911.
A middle English poem on confession.

NL 0386152   NcU

Lineberger, Janet Hite.
ND205
.S36
Santa Barbara, Calif. Museum of art.
... Painting today and yesterday in the United States. June fifth [to] September first, 1941. Santa Barbara, Calif. [Pacific coast publishing company, 1941]

Lineberger, Lawrence Otto, 1897-
Cardinal characters in the New Testament; a study in transition, by Lawrence Otto Lineberger. Philadelphia, Dorrance & company, inc. [*1930]
233 p. front. 19½[cm].   (*Half-title:* Contemporary religious thought, 10)
Bibliography: p. 232–233.

1. Bible. N. T.—Biog.   I. Title.
Library of Congress   [S2430.L5   30–19285
Copyright A 25573   225.92

NL 0386154   DLC MBrZ ODW

Lineberger, Lawrence Otto, 1897-
The man from Tarsus, his world, personality and religious genius, by Lawrence Otto Lineberger ... New York [etc.] Fleming H. Revell company [*1933]
240 p. 19½[cm].

1. Paul, Saint, apostle.   I. Title.
Library of Congress   BS2505.L57   33–6344
——— Copy 2.
Copyright A 60589   [922.1] 225.92

NL 0386155   DLC OrP NRCR ODW

Lineberger, Lawrence Otto, 1897-
Towering figures among the prophets, by L. O. Lineberger ... Philadelphia, Chicago [etc.] The John C. Winston company [*1928]
ix, 181 p. front., pl. 19[cm].

1. Prophets.   I. Title.
Library of Congress   BS1505.L5   29–9851

NL 0386156   DLC ODW

Lineberger, Walter Franklin, 1883-
The diplomatic and consular service of the United States; the activities and need for reorganization and improvement of the nation's foreign service, by Representative W. F. Lineberger of California ... Compiled from official documents, formal statements and Congressional hearing records. [Washington?] 1924.
30, [1] p. 22[cm].

1. U. S.—Diplomatic and consular service.
28–31055
Library of Congress   JX1705.L5

NL 0386157   DLC PU DNW

Lineberger, Walter Franklin, 1883-   joint author.
Linebarger, Paul Myron Wentworth, 1871-
A family of five republics; a sketch of the origin of the Leyenberger-Lineberger-Linebarger-Lionberger families. By Paul Myron Linebarger ... and Walter Franklin Lineberger ... Hammond, Ind., W. B. Conkey company, 1925.

Lineberger, Walter Franklin, 1883-
Milestones in the war against the narcotic peril. Extension of remarks of Hon. Walter F. Lineberger of California in the House of representatives. Wednesday, February 18, 1925 ... [Washington, Govt. print. off., 1925]
16 p. 24[cm].

1. Narcotics.   I. Title.
Library of Congress   HV5825.L5   26–4525   9

NL 0386159   DLC PCC PHi OO

Lineberger, Walter Franklin, 1883-
Milestones in the war against the narcotic peril. Extension of remarks of Hon. Walter F. Lineberger of California in the House of Representatives. 1927.

NL 0386160   PCC

Lineberger, Walter Franklin, 1883-
U. S. *Congress. House. Select committee of inquiry into operations, policies, and affairs of the United States Shipping board and emergency fleet corporation.*
... Report. Inquiry into operations, policies, and affairs of United States Shipping board and emergency fleet corporation. Report of the Select committee of inquiry into operations, policies and affairs of United States Shipping board and emergency fleet corporation, House of representatives, Sixty-eighth Congress ... Washington, Govt. print. off., 1925.

Lineberger, Walter Franklin, 1883–
Philadelphia world conference on narcotic education. Extracts from statement of ...
YA 5000   Wednesday, December 16, 1925. [Washington,
J 17   Govt. print. off., 1926.]
8 p.

NL 0386162   DLC NRCR

Lineberry, Richard A.   Chapel Hill, 1925.
A manufacturing study of North Carolina brick clays.

NL 0386163   NcU

Lineberry, Richard Arthur, 1896-   joint author.
Skinner, Joshua John, 1882-
... Experiments with nitrogen fertilizers on cotton soils. By J. J. Skinner ... R. A. Lineberry ... and J. E. Adams ... and C. B. Williams ... and H. B. Mann ... Washington [U. S. Govt. print. off.] 1934.

Cp929.2
L754L
Lineberry, Winfield Scott, 1847-
The Lineberry family. Dedicated to my grandchildren [by] W. S. Lineberry, 1918. [n.p., Robert E. Lineberry, n.d.]
22p. 23cm.

1. Lineberry family

NL 0386165   NcU NcGU

The Linebook
see under   Chicago tribune.

Lineburg, Bruce.
Nelson, James Allen, 1875-
... Growth and feeding of honeybee larvae. By James A. Nelson ... Arnold P. Sturtevant ... and Bruce Lineburg ... Washington, Govt. print. off., 1924.

VOLUME 334

Lineburg, Bruce.
A laboratory manual for general biology, by Bruce Lineburg and Elizabeth Teter Smith ... Rev. ed. ... Ann Arbor, Mich., Edwards brothers, inc., °1938–

v. illus. 27ᶜᵐ.
Lithoprinted.

1. Biology—Laboratory manuals. I. Smith, Elizabeth Teter, joint author.

CA 34–1214 Unrev'd

Library of Congress   QH317.L48

Copyright AA 144035   574.072

NL   0386168   DLC

Linecar, Arthur.
Reflections of a quiet mind. Bournemouth, W. Earl ₁1947₎
160 p. 22 cm.

1. Mental discipline. I. Title.

BF145.L5   131.3   48–14772*

NL   0386169   DLC KU NNC

Linecar, Howard W   A
British electric trains. London, I. Allan ₁1947₎
133 p. plates. 19 cm.

1. Electric railroads—Gt. Brit. I. Title.

TF1057.L5   625.4   48–22923*

NL   0386170   DLC MiU MH-BA

Linecar, Howard W   A
British electric trains. ₁2d ed.₎ London, I. Allan ₁1949₎
132 p. illus., maps.
"Glossary of technical terms": p.131-132.

1. Electric railroads. 621.33 656.0942 942(656)

NL   0386171   ICJ

Linecar, Howard W   A
Coins. London, Benn ₁1955₎
191 p. illus. 20 cm. (Practical handbooks for collectors)

1. Numismatics—Collectors and collecting.

CJ89.L5   737.4   55–56807 ‡

NL   0386172   DLC CaBVa IdPI Or Wa CaBViPA PP OCU

Linecke, Johann Georg
see Linike, Johann Georg, *ca.* 1680–*ca.* 1730.

Linedansere...
see under   Omre, Arthur, 1887–

LINÉE, A[uguste]
Le cheque postal. Thèse, Paris, Brive, Imp. Roche,1919.

1.8°.
"Bibliographie", pp.[3]-5.

NL   0386175   MH CtY

LINÉE, Auguste.
L'indemnité de requisition. Brive,1918.

93 p.
Thèse --Univ. de Paris.

NL   0386176   MH-L DS

Linee di completamento della rete ferroviaria del Regno
see under   Genoa. Direzione tecnica governativa.

Linegar, Charles Ramon.
A study of the creatine content of cardiac and voluntary muscle and the difference in creatine content of the left and right ventricular muscle.
124 p.
Thesis - Ph.D. degree - Western Reserve university, May 15, 1934.

NL   0386178   OC1W

---

ar V
7228   **Lineham, Ray S**
The street of human habitations; an account of man's dwelling places, customs, utensils, etc., in prehistoric times and in ancient Egypt, Assyria and Chaldea, Phoenicia, Persia, India and Japan.   London, Chapman & Hall, 1894.
xv,350 p. illus. 19cm.

Cover title: Habitations of man.

1. Civilization, Ancient. I. Title.
II. Title: Habitations of man.

NL   0386179   NIC PPD PPL CtY OC1 MB NN

TJ
145
L75   **Lineham, Wilfrid James.**
A text-book of mechanical engineering.
London, Chapman and Hall, 1894.
xix, 772 p. illus. 21 cm.

1. Mechanical engineering.

NL   0386180   DSI PPFr PP CtY

Lineham, Wilfrid James.
Text book of mechanical engineering
1895.

NL   0386181   DN

WB
47400   **Lineham, Wilfrid James**
A text-book of mechanical engineering.
3d ed., rev. and enl. London, Chapman and Hall, 1898.
947 p. illus.

NL   0386182   CtY MiHM

Lineham, Wilfrid James.
A text-book of mechanical engineering. Part I.—Workshop practice. Part II.—Theory and examples. Fourth edition, revised and enlarged. xxi,[3],979 p. il. 21 pl. I table. O. London: Chapman & Hall, 1900.

NL   0386183   ICJ NcD

Lineham, Wilfrid James.
A text-book of mechanical engineering, by Wilfrid J. Lineham ... 5th ed., rev. and enl. London, Chapman and Hall, limited, 1902.
xxi, ₁1₎ p. 1 l., 999 p. front., XVIII pl., diagr. 21ᶜᵐ.
CONTENTS.—pt. I. Workshop practice.—pt. II. Theory and example.

1. Mechanical engineering.

Library of Congress   TJ145.L75   3–14012/2

NL   0386184   DLC PU-Sc NIC ICRL OC1 OU

Lineham, Wilfrid James
A text-book of mechanical engineering.
6th ed. rev. and enl. Philadelphia, J.B. Lippincott company, 1903.
xxi, ₁1₎ p. 1 l., 1042 p. front. illus. diagrs. 19 plates (part fold.)

NL   0386185   OC1

Lineham, Wilfrid James.
A text-book of mechanical engineering. By Wilfrid J. Lineham, ... Seventh edition, revised and enlarged. London, Chapman and Hall, ltd., 1904.
xxi, [3], 1042 p. front., diagrs., XIX pl. (incl. table, partly fold.) 21ᶜᵐ.

NL   0386186   ICJ DN

Lineham, Wilfrid J₁ames₎.
A text-book of mechanical engineering.   Part 1. Workshop practice. Part 2. Theory and examples.   London: Chapman and Hall, Ltd., 1909.   xxi(ii), 1244 p., 24 pl. (11 folded).   illus. 11. ed.   8°.

1. Mechanical engineering.   CENTRAL CIRCULATION.
N.Y.P.L.   March 24, 1911.

NL   0386187   NN WaS

Lineham, Wilfrid J₁ames₎
A text-book of mechanical engineering, by ... 11th ed., rev. and en. London, Chapman and Hall, limited, 1912.
1244 p.

NL   0386188   MiU

Lineham, Wilfrid James.
A text-book of mechanical engineering, by Wilfrid J. Lineham, ... Part I.—Workshop practice. Part II.—Theory and examples. Eleventh edition, revised. London, Chapman and Hall, 1914.
xxi, [3], 1244 p. front., illus., XIX pl. (table, diagrs., partly fold.) 20ᶜᵐ.

NL   0386189   ICJ

VOLUME 334

Lineham, Wilfrid James.
A text-book of mechanical engineering, by Wilfrid J. Lineham ... 11th ed., rev. London, Chapman and Hall, limited, 1919.

xxi, (1) p., 1 l., 1244 p. front., illus., plates (part fold.) diagrs. 21ᶜᵐ.

CONTENTS.—pt. I. Workshop practice.—pt. II. Theory and examples.

1. Mechanical engineering.

Library of Congress   TJ145.L75 1919

19–10001

NL 0386190 DLC

Lineham, Wilfrid James.
... A treatise on hand lettering for engineers, architects, surveyors, and students of mechanical drawing, by Wilfrid J. Lineham ... New York, E. P. Dutton & company (1915)

xii, 282 p., 1 l. incl. 113 pl., diagrs. 4 fold. pl. 31½ᶜᵐ. (The directly-useful technical series, ed. by W. J. Lineham)

1. Lettering. I. Title: Hand lettering for engineers.

A 15–2711

Title from City Library,   Springfield, Mass. Printed by L. C.

NL 0386191 MS MB PP WaS CU IdU OCl OU ICJ NN

Linehan, D   H
An muiṗ-ċuṗaṙ a ḃein 'Réaɫt-na-Maiṙne' oo ṙċṙiḃ D. H. Lineham. laṙ n-a ċuṙ i nɣaeóilɣ oo Cómáṙ oe Ḃial. Baile Áta Cliaṫ, Oiṗiɣ an tSoláṫaiṙ (1943)

40 p. 19 cm.

1. Réalt-na-Maidne (Ship)   I. De Bhial, Tomás, ed. II. Title.
Title transliterated: An muir-thuras a dhein 'Réalt-na-Maidne.'

PB1399.L⸗M8

57–51027

NL 0386192 DLC

B610.24
E44
1806
v.2

Linehan, Daniel.
De respiratione... Edinburgi, Excudebant A. Neill et Socii, 1807.

(6), 20 p. 21 cm. (In Edinburgh. University. Dissertationes medicae, 1806, v.2)

Inaug. Diss. - Edinburgh.

NL 0386193 MnU-B ICRL

---

*M1
.M6
no.196

Linehan, Edward.
Squaw Point boogie; piano solo. Hillman, Minn. (1952)
(4) p. 31cm.

Cover title; illustrated t.p.

NL 0386194 MnHi

Linehan, James Colman, 1902–
... The rational nature of man, with particular reference to the effects of immorality on intelligence according to Saint Thomas Aquinas; a metaphysical study ... by James Colman Linehan ... Washington, D. C., The Catholic university of America, 1937.

127 p. 23ᶜᵐ. (The Catholic university of America. Philosophical studies. vol. XXXVII)
"Biographical note": p. 127.
Thesis (PH. D.)—Catholic university of America, 1937.
Bibliography: p. 121–124.
1. Intellect. 2. Ethics. 3. Inefficiency, Intellectual. 4. Thomas Aquinas, Saint, 1225?–1274. I. Title.

Library of Congress   B765.T54L45 1937
———— Copy 2.   37–16526
Copyright A 106837   189.4

NL 0386195 DLC MoU PU WaSpG OCU ViU OCl OU

CT808
.L5T3

Linehan, John.

Talbot, Beatrice Wight (Bill)
And that's no lie (by) Beatrice Bill Talbot, illustrated by Robert F. Hallock. Boston, Houghton Mifflin company, 1946.

TC 970
L55
1849

Linehan, John.
The drainage engineer and general land improver; a practical work on land and rivulet drainage, conveying of water, subsoiling, embanking, reclamation, and remodelling of estates, water power ... Dublin, J. McGlashan, 1849.
216 p.
1. Drainage. I. Title.

NL 0386197 CaBVaU

Linehan, John, 1925–   ed.
Human conditioning

see under

Meakin, Thomas Kimball, ed.

Linehan, John Cornelius, 1840–1905.
Irish schoolmasters in the American colonies, 1640–1775, with a continuation of the subject during and after the war of the revolution, by John C. Linehan ... and Thomas Hamilton Murray ... Washington, D. C., The American-Irish historical society, 1898.

1 p. l., 31 p. 22ᶜᵐ.

1. Irish in the U. S. 2. Teachers—U. S. I. Murray, Thomas Hamilton, 1857– joint author. II. Title.

Library of Congress   E184.I6L6
4–23725

MB NjP MeB
NL 0386199 DLC Nh ViU PV PHi PPPrHi MiU OClWHi MWA

Linehan, John Cornelius, 1840–1905.
The Irish Scots and the "Scotch-Irish": an historical and ethnological monograph, with some reference to Scotia Major and Scotia Minor; to which is added a chapter on "How the Irish came as builders of the nation". By Hon. John C. Linehan ... Concord, N. H., The American-Irish historical society, 1902.

138 p. incl. front. (port.) 23ᶜᵐ.
Originally published in the Granite monthly, Concord, N. H. Jan.–Mar. 1888. The chapter on "How the Irish came as builders of the nation", is based upon articles contributed to the Boston pilot, 1890, etc., and the Boston Sunday globe, Mar. 17, 1895.
"Supplementary facts and comment": p. (83)–128.
1. Scotch-Irish in the   U. S. 2. Irish in the U.S. 3. Scotch-Irish. I. American-   Irish historical society. II. Title.

Library of Congress   E184.S4L7
3–5238

NL 0386200 DLC TU PU PP PHC CtY OCl MWA NN MH MB NjP

Linehan, John C(ornelius) 1840–1905.
Penacook in the war for the union. By Hon. John C. Linehan ... Concord, N. H., Republican press association, 1889.

23 p. 24½ᶜᵐ.
"Read before W. I. Brown post, G. A. R., May 30, 1889."

1. Penacook, N. H.—Hist.—Civil war.

Library of Congress   E44.P33L7
6–18868

NL 0386201 DLC Nh

Lineham, John Cornelius, 1840–1905.
Pioneer engine company; a record of fifty years. Penacook, 1899.

NL 0386202 Nh

308
Z
Box 842

(Linehan, John Cornelius) 1840–1905.
Souvenir and history of Penacook, N. H. (Souvenir ed. Penacook, 1899)
26 p. illus., ports. 31cm.

1. Penacook, N. H. - Hist.

NL 0386203 NNC

Linehan, John Cornelius, 1840–1905.
War pictures. Concord, 1895.

NL 0386204 NjP

786.4
L645

Linehan, Kathryne.
Reception waltzes. New York, Portland, Graves Music Co. (c1905)
(8) p. 36cm.

For piano.

1. Piano music. I. Title.

NL 0386205 OrU

Linehan, M   P
Canon Sheehan of Doneraile: priest, novelist, man, letters. Dublin, Talbot Press (1952)
169 p. 19 cm.

1. Sheehan, Patrick Augustine, 1852–1913.

PR6037.H37Z7   823.89   53–126

PU CMenSP
NL 0386206 DLC LU PRosC MB MH NN NIC PU OClJC PV

Linehan, M   P
My heart remembers how, being the story of Muscrai, O'Donegan, by M. P. Linehan ... Dublin, J. Duffy & comp, limited, 1944.

4 p. l., 267 p. front. (pl., map) 18½ᶜᵐ.

1. Muskerry, Ire. 2. Cork, Ire. (County)—Descr. & trav. I.

Harvard univ. Library   A 44–472
for Library of Congress   DA990.C79L5
(2)†   94

NL 0386207 MH NN MB DLC

Linehan, Paul Henry, 1879–
Contributions to equilong geometry, by Paul Henry Linehan ... Lancaster, Pa., Press of the New era printing company, 1915.

vi, 38 p. diagrs. 27ᶜᵐ.
Thesis (PH. D.)—Columbia university, 1916.
Vita.

1. Transformations (Mathematics)

16–6592

Library of Congress   QA601.L75
Columbia Univ. Libr.

NL 0386208 NNC CU NN DLC

Linehan, Paul Henry, 1879–
... Contributions to equilong geometry, by Paul Henry Linehan ... Lancaster, Pa.: New Era Prtg. Co., 1915. vi, 38 p. 2

Film reproduction. Positive.
Vita.
Bibliographical footnotes.
Thesis—Columbia university.

1. Transformations (Mathematics).   t. 1915

NL 0386209 NN

VOLUME 334

G127
.C5

Linehan, Urban Joseph.

Cincinnati. University.
Geography, a manual for the army training programs at University of Cincinnati, by John L. Rich, Daniel R. Bergsmark ₍and₎ Urban J. Linehan ... ₍Cincinnati₎ 1944.

NL 0386211   DLC

Linehan, Urban Joseph.
Tornado deaths in the United States. Ann Arbor, University Microfilms ₍1955₎
₍University Microfilms, Ann Arbor, Mich.₎ Publication no. 13,016₎
Microfilm copy (positive) of typescript.
Collation of the original, as determined from the film: xi, 417 l. fold. maps, diagrs, tables.
Thesis—Clark University.
Abstracted in Dissertation abstracts, v. 15 (1955) no. 10, p. 1880.
Bibliography : leaves 293–302.

1. Tornadoes.   I. Title.

Microfilm AC-1 no. 13,016   Mic 55–515

NL 0386211   DLC

Linehan, William, 1892-
A history of Pahang. ₍6₎,256p. front.(port.) plates,maps (1 fold.) fold.tables. ₍Singapore, 1936₎ (In Royal Asiatic society of Great Britain and Ireland - Malayan branch. Journal, v. 14, pt.2)

NL 0386212   OCl CaOTP

FM
000
NYS
585

Linehan, William, 1892 -
A history of Pahang. ₍Singapore, Printers, ltd., 1936₎
256 p. illus., geneal. tables, maps, ports. (Royal Asiatic Society of Great Britain and Ireland. Malayan Branch, Singapore, Journal, vol. 14, pt. 2)

Micro-
form
edition
1. Pahang. Hist.

NL 0386213   N

Linehan, William Francis, 1889-

Boston. *School committee.*
... The educability of the emotions; a suggested discussion approach. Boston, Printing department, 1927.

NL 0386215   ICRL

Linehard, Fritz,1871-
Der gottesbegriff bei Gustav Theodor Fechner. Inaug. diss.   Bern, 1920.
Bibl.

NL 0386215   ICRL

TK6161
L5
951

Линейный надсмотрщик городской телефонной сети. Москва, Гос. изд-во лит-ры по вопросам связи и радио, 1951.
304 p. illus. 23 cm. (Пособия для связистов массовых профессий)
At head of title: Н. Н. Лужецкий ₍и др.₎
Errata slip inserted.
Bibliography : p. ₍350₎

1. Telephone. 2. Telephone—Russia.   I. Luzhetskiĭ, N. N.
Title transliterated: Lineĭnyĭ nadsmotr-shchik gorodskoĭ telefonnoĭ seti.

TK6161.L5 1951   56–32615

NL 0386216   DLC

TK6161
L5
953

Линейный надсмотрщик городской телефонной сети. 2. изд., испр. и доп. Москва, Гос. изд-во лит-ры по вопросам связи и радио, 1953.
400 p. illus. 23 cm. (Пособия для связистов массовых профессий)
At head of title: Н. Н. Лужецкий ₍и др.₎
Bibliography : p. ₍402₎

1. Telephone. 2. Telephone—Russia.   I. Luzhetskiĭ, N. N.
Title transliterated: Lineĭnyĭ nadsmotrshchik gorodskoĭ telefonnoĭ seti.

TK6161.L5 1953   54–42106

NL 0386217   DLC

TJ1125
.V65

Linek, August, joint author.

Voigt, Paul.
Die Fachkunde der Maschinenschlosser und der verwandten Berufe; Werkzeuge, Werkstoffe, Arbeitsverfahren, Werkzeugmaschinen, Maschinenelemente, Kraftmaschinen. Leipzig, J. Klinkhardt, 1941.

TJ1165
V6
1952

Linek, August, joint author.

Voigt, Paul.
Fachkunde für Maschinenschlosser und die verwandten Berufe; physikalische und chemische Grundbegriffe, Werkstoffe, Werkzeuge, Arbeitsverfahren, Werkzeugmaschinen, Maschinenelemente, Kraftmaschinen. Unter Mitwirkung von E. Kern bearb. und hrsg. von Paul Voigt und August Linek. 7. verb. und erweiterte Aufl. Leipzig, Fachbuchverlag, 1952.

Linek, August.
Handbuch für Dreher. Langensalza, J. Beltz ₍1939₎
209 p. illus., tables. 21 cm.
"Berichtigungen": slip inserted.

1. Turning. 2. Lathes.

TJ1215.L5   49–38689 rev*

NL 0386220   DLC

Linek, August.
Spanabhebende Werkzeugmaschinen für die wirtschaftliche Fertigung. Berlin, Schiele & Schön ₍1950–53₎
8 v. illus. 30 cm.

1. Machine-tools.   I. Title.

TJ1185.L5   51–40835 rev ‡

NL 0386221   DLC NN

TJ1185
.A1T3

Linek, August, comp.

Taschenbuch der Werkzeugmaschinen und Werkzeuge.

Berlin, Schiele & Schön.

TJ1280
L47

Linek, August.
Trommeln. Stuttgart, Deutscher Fachzeitschriften- und Fachbuch-Verlag, "Das Industrieblatt" ₍1954₎
60 p. illus. 21 cm. (Schriftenreihe Feinbearbeitung)
Bibliography: p. 60.

1. Grinding and polishing. 2. Metals—Finishing.   I. Title.
(Series)

Illinois. Univ. Library   A 54–4506
for Library of Congress   ₍3₎

NL 0386223   IU NN DLC

QM
311
.L75

Linek, Henry A
Tooth carving manual. ₍Los Angeles? 1949₎
80 p. illus.

1. Teeth.   I. Title.

NL 0386224   MiU

WU
500
L5t
1951

LINEK, Henry A
Tooth carving manual. Los Angeles [c1951]
80 p. illus.

1. Dental prosthesis - Laboratory
manuals

NL 0386225   MBCo NbU

Linek, István
Elkésett emberek; elbeszélések és levelek, 1917. Cleveland, A "Szabadság" nyomása, 1917. ₍144 p.₎

NL 0386226   OCl

Linek, Johannes: Das Wandern der Zähne. [Maschinenschrift.]
41 S. m. Abb. 4°. — Auszug: Breslau 1925: Bresl. Genossensch.-Buchdr. 2 Bl. 8°
Breslau, Med. Diss. v. 22. Mai 1925.   [U 25. 969

NL 0386227   ICRL

Linek, Mathias, 1722-84
Commentationes theologicae de gratia divina, usui theologorum Pragensium commodatae. Vetero-Pragae, Charactere Collegii Clementini Societatis Jesu, 1770
502 p.

NL 0386228   MH

Linekogel ₍Simon Fridericus₎. *De medicamentorum efficientia generatim determinanda.
23 pp. 4°. Gottingae, typ. J. F. Hageri, [1736].

NL 0386229   DNLM

Linekogel ₍Simon Fridericus₎. De transpiratione foetus innoxie impedita. Respondens Lehmann Isaacus Kohen. 24 pp. sm. 4°. Gottingae, typ. J. F. Hageri, [1737].

NL 0386230   DNLM

Linel, Albert.
Der moderne Staat und die Ziele des alten Glaubens. von Albert Linel, ... Leipzig, P. Frohberg, 1878.
viii, 256 p. 23ᶜᵐ.

NL 0386231   ICJ NN

Linel ₍René₎ [1888-   ]. *Etude de la péristaltine; ses indications en thérapeutique.
88 pp. 8°. Lyon. 1912. No. 104.

NL 0386232   DNLM

VOLUME 334

Linell, Anthony.
The law of names, public, private & corporate, by Anthony Linell ... with a foreword by His Honour Judge Dale ... London, Butterworth & co., ltd.; Toronto, Butterworth & co. (Canada), ltd.; ₍etc., etc.₎ 1938.

xxxvi, 286, 19 p. 22ᶜᵐ.

1. Names, Personal—Gt. Brit.—Law. 2. Business names—Gt. Brit. I. Title.   ₍Full name: John Anthony Thorp Linell₎

38–35502

NL 0386233   DLC IU CaBVaU ViU-L IU

Linell, Anthony, ed.

The New County court practice, 1937–   London, Butterworth & co., ltd.: Toronto, Butterworth & co. (Canada), ltd.; ₍etc., etc.₎ 1937–

Linell, Folke, 1913–
... A contribution to the knowledge of the anthropology of Madagascar, by Folke Linell, with an introduction by fil. dr. Walter Kaudern ... Lund, C. W. K. Gleerup ₍1936₎

35 p. incl. illus. (map) tables. IV pl. 26½ᶜᵐ. (Lunds universitets Årsskrift. n. f., avd. 2, bd. 32, nr. 2)

"(From the Institution for anatomy of Lund. Chief: Prof. Dr. med. Gaston Backman)"
"Kungl. fysiografiska sällskapets handlingar. n. f., bd. 47, nr. 2."
"Anthropological results of Doctor Kaudern's expedition": p. ₍11₎–35.
"References": p. ₍25₎
1. Anthropometry—Madagascar.   I. Kaudern, Walter Alexander, 1881–

A 38–1312

Chicago. Univ. Library   AS284.LD6 n. f., avd. 2, bd. 32
for Library of Congress   [AS284.L8 n. f., avd. 2, bd. 32]
                                 ₍2₎   (378.485)

NL 0386235   ICU MH PU DLC OC1

Linell, Folke, 1913–
Handledning i obduktionsteknik
see under Ahlström, Garl Gustaf, 1905–

Linell, Folke, 1913–
Mycobacterium balnei; a new acid-fast bacillus occurring in swimming pools and capable of producing skin lesions in humans, by Folke Linell and Åke Nordén. Lund, H. Ohlssons boktr., 1954.

84 p. plates, diagrs., tables. 25 cm. (Acta tuberculosea Scandinavica. Supplementum 33)
Imprint on cover: Copenhagen, E. Munksgaard, 1954.
Bibliography: p. 80–84.

1. Mycobacterium balnei.   I. Nordén, Åke, joint author. (Series)

A 55–6767

Rochester. Univ. Libr.   RC306
for Library of Congress   ₍2₎

NL 0386237   NRU ViU CU MoU DNLM

Linell, Folke, 1913–
On the tumourpromoting effect of a single mechanical trauma; an experimental study on skin tumours in tarred rabbits. Lund, H. Ohlsson, 1947.

110 p. plates, tables. 25 cm. (Acta pathologica et microbiologica scandinavica. Supplementum 71)
"From the Pathological Institute, University of Lund, Sweden."
Akademisk avhandling—Lund.
Extra t-p. with thesis note, inserted.
Tr. by Lionel Hewitt.
"List of cited authors": p. ₍105₎–110.
1. Skin—Tumors.   I. Hewitt, Lionel, tr.   II. Series.
RL660.L5 1947   [616.992] 616.5   Med 48–1387*

NL 0386238   DLC DNLM ViU ICJ

Linell, Folke, 1913–
... Verlauf der lungengefässe besonders des lobulus beim menschen und bei einigen säugetieren, von Folke Linell und Olov Löfgren ... Lund, C. W. K. Gleerup; ₍etc., etc., 1940₎

15 p. illus. 26½ᶜᵐ. (Lunds universitets Årsskrift. n. f., avd. 2, bd. 36, nr. 6)

"Aus dem Anatom. inst. Lund. Direktor: Professor Gaston Backman."
"Kungl. fysiografiska sällskapets handlingar. n. f., bd. 51, nr. 6."
"Literatur": p. 15.
1. Lungs. 2. Anatomy, Comparative.   I. Löfgren, Olov, 1917–joint author.

A 41–2173

Chicago. Univ. Library   [AS284.L8 n. f., avd. 2, bd. 36]
for Library of Congress   ₍3₎   (378.485)

NL 0386239   ICU PU

Linell, John Anthony Thorp
see   Linell, Anthony.

Linell, Martin Larsson, 1849–1897.
Description of a new species of golden beetle from Costa Rica. By Martin L. Linell ...

(In U. S. National museum. Proceedings. Washington, 1895. 23½ᶜᵐ. v. 18, p. 77–78)
Caption title.

1. Plusiotis.
Library of Congress   Q11.U55   6–21319†

NL 0386241   DLC MiU OO OU

Linell, Martin Larsson, 1849–1897.
... Descriptions of new species of North American Coleoptera in the families *Cerambycidæ* and *Scarabæidæ.* By Martin L. Linell ... Washington, Gov't print. off., 1896.

cover-title, 393–401 p. 24½ᶜᵐ.
At head of title: Smithsonian institution. United States National museum.
From the Proceedings of the United States National museum, vol. XIX, pages 393–401 ⟨no. 1113⟩

1. Cerambycidae. 2. Scarabaeidae.
                                 6–40891†
Library of Congress   QL596.C4L7

NL 0386242   DLC PPAN

Linell, Martin Larsson, 1849–1897.
Descriptions of new species of North American Coleoptera in the families *Cerambycidæ* and *Scarabæidæ.* By Martin L. Linell.

(In U. S. National museum. Proceedings. Washington, 1897. 23½ᶜᵐ. v. 19, p. 393–401)
Issued February 5, 1897.

1. Cerambycidae. 2. Scarabaeidae.
                                 S 33–511
Library, Smithsonian   Institution
Library of Congress   [Q11.U55 vol. 19]

NL 0386243   DSI OU OC1

Linell, Martin Larsson, 1849–1897.
List of *Coleoptera* collected on the Tana river, and on the Jombene range, East Africa, by Mr. William Astor Chanler and Lieutenant Ludwig von Höhnel, with descriptions of new genera and species. By Martin L. Linell.

(In U. S. National museum. Proceedings. Washington, 1896. 23½ᶜᵐ. v. 18, 1895, p. 687–716)
Issued August 12, 1896.

1. Beetles—Africa.   I. Chanler, William Astor, 1867– II. Höhnel, Ludwig, ritter von, 1857–
                                 S 33–494
Smithsonian inst. Library
for Library of Congress   [Q11.U55 vol. 18]
                                 ₍a41c1₎

NL 0386244   DSI

Linell, Martin Larsson, 1849–1897.
List of Coleoptera collected on the Tana River, and on the Jombene range, East Africa, by Mr. W. A. Chanler and Lieutenar L. von Höhnel, with descriptions of new genera and species. Washington: Gov. Prtg. Off., 1896. 687–716 p. 8°. (Smithsonian Institution.)

Repr.: U. S. National Muséum. Proc. v. 18.
Title from cover.

1. Coleoptera, Africa (East). 2.   Chanler, William Astor. 3. Höhnel, Ludwig von.
N. Y. P. L.   January 16, 1914.

NL 0386245   NN OU OC1

Linell, Martin Larsson, 1849–1897.
... New species of *Coleoptera* of the family *Chrysomelidæ,* with a short review of the tribe *Chlamydini.* By Martin L. Linell ... Washington, Gov't print. off., 1897.

cover-title, 473–485 p. 24½ᶜᵐ.
At head of title: Smithsonian institution. United States National museum.
From the Proceedings of the United States National museum, vol. XX, pages 473–485. ⟨no. 1130⟩

1. Chrysomelidae.
                                 6–21320†
Library of Congress   QL596.C5L7

NL 0386246   DLC PPAN NN

Linell, Martin Larsson, 1849–1897.
New species of *Coleoptera* of the family *Chrysomelida,* with a short review of the tribe *Chlamydini.* By Martin L. Linell.

(In U. S. National museum. Proceedings. Washington, 1898. 23½ᶜᵐ. v. 20, p. 473–485)
Issued January 5, 1898.

1. Chrysomelidae.
                                 S 33–527
Library, Smithsonian   Institution
Library of Congress   [Q11.U55 vol. 20]

NL 0386247   DSI OC1 OU

Linell, Martin Larsson, 1849–1897.
New species of North American *Coleoptera* of the family *Scarabæidæ.* By Martin L. Linell.

(In U. S. National museum. Proceedings. Washington, 1896 23½ᶜᵐ. v. 18, 1895, p. 721–731)
Issued October 7, 1896.

1. Scarabaeidae. 2. Beetles—North America.
                                 S 33–495
Library, Smithsonian   Institution
Library of Congress   [Q11.U55 vol. 18]

NL 0386248   DSI

Linell, Martin Larsson, 1849–1897.
New species of North American *Coleoptera* of family *Scarabæidæ.* By Martin L. Linell ... Washington, Gov't print. off., 1896.

cover-title, 721–731 p. 24½ᶜᵐ.
At head of title: Smithsonian institution. United States National museum.
From the Proceedings of the United States National museum, vol. xviii pages 721–731. ⟨no. 1096⟩

1. Scarabaeidae.
                                 6–21318
Library of Congress   QL596.S3L7

NL 0386249   DLC OU OC1 NN

VOLUME 334

Linell, Martin Larsson, 1849–1897.
On the coleopterous insects of Galapagos islands. By Martin L. Linell ...
(*In* U. S. National museum. Proceedings. Washington, 1899. 23½ᶜᵐ. v. 21, p. 249–268)
Issued October 4, 1898.

1. Beetles—Galapagos islands.

Library, Smithsonian
Library of Congress   Institution
                                   [Q11.U55 vol. 21]
                                                        S 33–540

NL 0386250   DSI PP PPAN OU OC1

Linell, Martin Lasson, 1849–1897.
On the cleopterous insects of Galapagos Islands. Washington, Gov. Ptg. Off., 1898.
1 p.l., p. 249–268. 8°. (Smithsonian Inst.)
From: U.S. Nat. Mus. Proc. v. 21.

NL 0386251   NN

Linell, Martin L[arsson] 1849–1897.
... On the insects collected by Doctor Abbott on the Seychelles, Aldabra, Glorioso, and Providence islands, with descriptions of nine new species of *Coleoptera*. By Martin L. Linell ... Washington, Gov't print. off., 1897.
cover-title, 695–706 p. 24½ᶜᵐ.
At head of title: Smithsonian institution. United States National museum.
"From the Proceedings of the United States National museum, vol. xix, pages 695–706. ⟨no. 1119⟩"

1. Insects—Islands of the Indian Ocean. I. U. S. National museum. II. Abbott, W. L.

Library of Congress   QL489.L75   6–14940†

NL 0386252   DLC MdBP

Linell, Martin Larsson, 1849–1897.
On the insects collected by Doctor Abbott on the Seychelles, Aldabra, Glorioso, and Providence islands, with descriptions of nine species of *Coleoptera*. By Martin L. Linell.
(*In* U. S. National museum. Proceedings. Washington, 1897. 23½ᶜᵐ. v. 19, p. 695–706)
Issued May 13, 1897.

1. Insects—Islands of the Indian ocean. 2. Beetles—Islands of the Indian ocean. I. Abbott, William Louis.

Smithsonian inst. Library
for Library of Congress
                                [Q11.U55 vol. 19]
                                                        S 33–517

NL 0386253   DSI OU OO OC1 DLC

TT
500
L52
Linemaglia. v. 1–   1954?–
    Milan.

    Title varies: v. 1–   Linea maschile e femminile.

NL 0386254   KMK

Lineman, H. M., joint author.
Lovingood, Alvin.
California hotel and apartment house laws; a law book including United States laws, state laws, and city ordinances applying to the hotel and apartment house industries in the state of California, by Alvin Lovingood ... and H. M. Lineman ... [Los Angeles, Apar-tel publishing company, °1931]

347.7
L75b
Lineman, Mrs. Mab (Copland)
Business and protective law.
[3d ed.]   Los Angeles, Calif., H.M. Lineman [cl927]
374p. front.(port.) O.

First pub. under title: Business and protective law for women.

NL 0386256   IaU

Lineman, *Mrs.* **Mab (Copland)**
Business and protective law; also known as "The law of common things in California" by Mab Copland Lineman ... Los Angeles, Calif., H. M. Lineman & M. C. Lineman [1939]
3 p. l., [9]–298 p. 23½ᶜᵐ.
"Fourth edition."

1. Business law—California. 2. Law—California. I. Title.
II. Title: The law of common things in California.

Library of Congress   40–8150

NL 0386257   DLC

Lineman, *Mrs.* **Mab Copland.**
Business and protective law for women, by Mab Copland Lineman ... [Los Angeles, Coast printing company, °1926]
3 p. l., 374 p. front. (port.) 20ᶜᵐ.

1. Business law—California. I. Title.

Library of Congress   HF1275.C2L6   27–1945

NL 0386258   DLC

Lineman, *Mrs.* **Mab Copland.**
The law of common things in California, by Mab Copland Lineman ... Los Angeles, Calif., H. M. Lineman & Mab C. Lineman [°1927]
3 p. l., 339 p. 20ᶜᵐ.

1. Law—California. I. Title.
Library of Congress   27–24081

NL 0386259   DLC

QB
155
L75
Linemann, Albert,   praeses.
Disputatio inauguralis mathematica de refractionibvs uranicis quam, ... pro loco in professione mathematicâ ordinario obtinendo, publicae censurae subijcit M. Albertus Linemannus ... respondente Alberto Kieper ... Ad 8 Septembris ... Regiomonti, Excudebat Lavrentivs Segebade, 1634.
[11] l. 18cm.

Diss.--Königsberg (A. Kieper, respondent)

NL 0386260   NIC

MW23
L645b
Linemann, F   H
Berigt omtrent de toetreding van een buitengewoon aantal heidenen in het Likoepangsche, door den zendeling F.H. Linemann te Menado. [Rotterdam, M. Wyt, 1859?]
[299]–314 p. 19 cm.

Caption title.
Detached from Mededeelingen van wege het Nederlandsche Zendelinggenootschap, Rotterdam, 1859.

1. Celebes - Missions. 2. Nederlandsch Zendelinggenootschap. SA(2)

NL 0386261   CtY-D

Linemann, Theodor, 1872–
Die rechtliche Natur der Aktien-Kommanditgesellschaft ... von Theodor Linemann ... Greifswald, J. Abel, 1898.
47 p. 23cm.

Inaug.-Diss. - Greifswald.
"Lebenslauf": p. 47.
"Litteratur-Verzeichnis": p.[5]–6.

NL 0386262   MH-L ICRL

Linen, Herbert M., joint ed.

The Cyclopædia of American biography. New enl. ed. of Appleton's cyclopædia of American biography, originally edited by General James Grant Wilson and John Fiske; revision to 1914 complete under editorial supervision of Hon. Charles Dick ... and James E. Homans ...
New York, The Press association compilers, inc., 1915–

Linen, James, 1808–1873.
The Golden Gate, by James Linen ... San Francisco, E. Bosqui and company, 1869.
38 p. illus. 21ᶜᵐ.
Poem.

I. Title.
                                             17–7239
Library of Congress   PS2246.L592

NL 0386264   DLC ViU

Linen, James, 1808–1873.
The later poems and songs of James Linen. Written between the years 1865 and 1873 ... New York, W. J. Widdleton; San Francisco, A. Roman & company, 1873.
111 p. 20ᶜᵐ.

                                             28–4763
Library of Congress   PS2246.L59

MWA
NL 0386265   DLC CtY ViU WaU NBuG CLSU MiU IU CSmH NcD

4A
1116
LINEN, JAMES, 1808–1873.
The poetical and prose writings of James Linen. New York, W.J.Widdleton; San Francicco, A.Roman & Company, 1865.
423p. front.(port.) 20cm.

NL 0386266   ICN CLU MH NcU RPB OKentU

Linen, James, 1808–1873.
The poetical and prose writings of James Linen. New York, W. J. Widdleton; San Francisco, A. Roman & company, 1866.
6, [vii]–viii, [9]–416 p. front. (port.) 20ᶜᵐ.

Library of Congress   PS2246.L59 1866   3–7970

NL 0386267   DLC NcD InU PPM ViU

Linen, James, 1808–1873.
Songs of the seasons, and other poems. By James Linen. New-York, Redfield [1852]
vi, [1]–iii, [9]–167 p. 18½ᶜᵐ.

I. Title.
                                             28–11504
Library of Congress   PS2246.L598

NL 0386268   DLC PPM ViU NjP MB CSmH NBuG

VOLUME 334

Linen, James, 1803-1873.
Songs of the Seasons ...   New York, [1853]

NL 0386269   PU

Linen, James Alexander, 1787-1812.
Poems, in the Scots and English dialect, on various occasions; by James Alexander Linen ...   Edinburgh, Printed for the editor, by Oliver & Boyd, 1815.
vi, 152 p. 6 pl., 2 port. (incl. front.) 18ᶜᵐ.

25-25706

Library of Congress   PR4889.L44 1815

NL 0386270   DLC TxU

Linen, William
A narrative of facts, as they occured; pointing out the Corruptions of the State Courts of South Carolina...
Charleston, 1806

[Pol. Pam. v.105no. 3]

44

NL 0386271   DLC

PZ264   Linen A B C book; First steps. New York,
.L72   McLoughlin, c1899.
1899   16 p. illus.

1. Alphabets.

NL 0386272   ICU

Pam.
Coll.
          The linen and cotton broad-ware weavers
21923   apology: humbly addressed to the gentlemen man-
          ufacturers of Manchester, and all others whom
          it may concern. By a well-wisher to trade.
          Liverpool, Printed by Robert Williamson, 1758
          [i.e., 19]
          [21] l. 26 cm.

Typewritten manuscript of originsˀ

1. Weavers. Manchester. 2. Trade-unions.
Manchester. History.

NL 0386274   NcD

Linen and Hempen Manufactures of Ireland.
At a meeting of the Right Honorable and Honorable the Trustees of the Linen Manufac-ture, at their house at the Linen-Hall ... the 24th of January, 1786 [-7th of November, 1786]
... [Dublin, Printed by M. Williamson, 1786]
72 p. 20ᶜᵐ.

Includes meetings of January 24 and 51, February 7, 14, 21 and 28, March 7 and 14, April 4, 11 and 25, May 2 and 9, June 6, July 18 and 25, August 15, October 3 and November 7, 1786.

NL 0386275   NNC

Linen and hempen manufactures of Ireland.
At a meeting of the trustees of the Linen and hempen manufactures of Ireland, at their house at the Linen-hall, on Monday the 25th day of January, 1802. Present, six members. Honourable W. J. Skeffington in the chair. [Belfast? Printed by B. and J. Williamson, 1802?]
14-41 p. 20cm.

NL 0386276   NNC

Linen and hempen manufactures of Ireland.
Minutes of the trustees of the Linen and hempen manufactures of Ireland, containing the reports of their secretary, on a tour of in-spection through the province of Ulster, in October, November, and December, 1816. Dub-lin, Printed by W. Folds and sons, 1817.
1 p. l., 2, [5], 152 p. tables. 24ᶜᵐ.

1. Linen - Ireland. 2. Flax - Ireland.

NL 0386277   NNC

A Linen-draper.
An address to the clergy; write some remarks upon the Dean of Down's late sermon
see under *title* .

A linen draper's letter to the friends of Ireland. Dublin, 1778. [Dublin] Printed in the year 1778.
27 p. 19 cm.

NL 0386279   MH-BA CtY NNC

Linen Flax Corporation of New Zealand.
Report. 1st-   1946-
[Wellington]
v. 25 cm. annual.

HD9155.N44L5   338.4767711   49-54942*

NL 0386280   DLC DNAL

Linen hall library, *Belfast*
see
Belfast library and society for promoting knowledge.

The Linen, hemp, and jute trades directory of the world.
192

Belfast[: H. R. Carter, 192   12°.
v.
    192   cover-title reads: Carter's linen, hemp & jute trades directory
of the world.
    Editor: 192   C. R. Carter.

1. Textile industry—Directories.
N. Y. P. L.   November 23, 1926

NL 0386282   NN MiD

The Linen guildsman.
v. 1-

New York, 1926-   8°, f°.
v. illus.
Monthly.
Issued by the Irish and Scottish Linen Damask Guild.

1. Linen—Per. and soc. publ.   2. House organs. I. Title.
N. Y. P. L.   October 14, 1931

NL 0386283   NN

Linen industry post-war planning committee
see
Northern Ireland. *Ministry of commerce and production. Linen industry post-war planning committee.*

Linen Industry Research Association (Gt. Brit.)
Quality in flax
see under
Turner, Arthur James, 1889-

Linen industry research association, Lambeg, Belfast.
[...Prospectus. (Rev. 1924) [n.p.] 1924.
cover-title, 10 p. fold. form. 21cm.

NL 0386286   OrCS

Linen industry research association
Report of the council
Library has
1929-

NL 0386287   OrP CU

Linen of Tlaxcala
see
Lienzo de Tlaxcala.

Linen thread company.
Gold medal netting news
see under title

Linen trade association of New York.
Annual dinner commemorating the fiftieth anniversary of the Linen trade association, 1891-1941, the Waldorf-Astoria, Friday, the second of May, nineteen hundred and forty-one. [New York, 1941] 62 p. illus. (incl. port.) 23½cm.
Advertising matter interspersed.

194801B. I. No subject.
N. Y. P. L.   January 26, 1943

NL 0386290   NN ICU

HD9930
.I 7L5   Linen trade circular.

Belfast, H. R. Carter.
v. in[29 cm. weekly.
Began publication in 1913. cf. Union list of serials.
Vol. numbers irregular: nos. 1599-3061 omitted.

1. Linen—Period.
HD9930.I 7L5   338.47677111   47-40458*

NL 0386291   DLC TxLT

Linen trade circular. Supplement.

Fibres, fabrics and cordage.

[Belfast, H. R. Carter Publications]

VOLUME 334

Linenberger, G   A
Neutron capture cross sections of Ag[107], Ag[109], In[115], and I[127], by G. A. Linenberger, J. A. Miskel [and] E. G. Sogrè. Oak Ridge, Tenn., Technical Information Branch. Tennessee AEC, 1949.
6 p. diagr. 27[cm].
At head of title: United States Atomic Energy Commission. AECD - 2458.
"Declassified: January 24, 1949."
1. Nuclear fission. I. Miskel, J. A., jt. author.
II. Segrè, Emilio G., 1905-   jt. author. III. Ser.

NL 0386293   ViU

Linenberger, Herbert, 1909-
The false denunciation of an innocent confessor; a commentary with historical notes on the manner of making judicial denunciations. Washington, Catholic Univ. of America Press, 1949.
viii, 205 p. 23 cm. (Catholic University of America. Canon law studies, no. 236)
Thesis—Catholic Univ. of America.
Biographical note.
Bibliography: p. 182–189.
1. Malicious prosecution (Canon law)   2. Solicitation (Canon law)
I. Title.   (Series)

Catholic Univ. of   America. Library
for Library of Congress   [3]†   A 49–3842*

NL 0386294   DCU DLC

Linenberger, Joseph M   1838–1911.
Grandfather's story, by Helen Hall, as translated by Louise Rylko. [Carthagena? Ohio, °1955]
45 p. illus. 23 cm.
A translation from the author's Russland die deutschen am Karman.

I. Hall, Helen L.   II. Title.

CT275.L469A313   55–43796 ‡

NL 0386295   DLC NN C KAS WHi

Linens. New York [etc.] 1928–30
see
Linens & domestics.

Linens & domestics. v. 1–   Aug. 1928–
[East Stroudsburg, Pa.,] Haire publishing company; etc., etc., 1928–
v. illus. 31[cm]. monthly.
Editorial and business offices, New York.
No number issued July 1931?
Title varies: Aug. 1928–Sept. 1930, Linens.
Oct. 1930–June 1931, Linens and handkerchiefs.
Aug. 1931–   Linens & domestics.
Editors: Aug. 1928–June 1931, Sylvan Hoffman.—Aug. 1931–
Julien Elfenbein.
Published by Hoffman publications, inc., Aug. 1928–Jan. 1929 in New York, Feb. 1929–June 1931 in New Brunswick, N. J.; published by Haire publishing company, Aug. 1931–Sept. 1933 in New Brunswick, N. J., Oct. 1933–   in East Stroudsburg, Pa.

Absorbed Handkerchiefs in Sept. 1929, continuing the publication as a special section till Aug. 1930. Both the volume numbering and paging of Handkerchiefs are continued in the issues for Sept. and Nov. 1929, Jan. and Mar. 1930 (v. 1, no. 5–8, p. 98–163) In the issues for May and Aug. 1930 the sections are not separately numbered or paged.
Absorbed the Linen guildsman in Jan. 1932, continuing it as a special section. This section remained the official publication of the Irish and Scottish linen damask guild and the Irish linen guild (from May 1934 on, of the Irish linen guild only)
1. Linen—Period. 2. Textile industry and fabrics—Period. 3. Handkerchiefs—Period.   I. Irish and Scottish linen damask guild. II. Irish linen guild. III. Title: Domestics.

                                        35–17444
Library of Congress   HD9850.1.L5
Copyright   [36b1]   677.11605

NL 0386298   DLC NbU OrCS OrP OrCS ICRL NcRS

Linens and domestics (Periodical)
... Directory number. [New York, Haire
Pub. Co.] 1946

I. Haire Publishing Co.

NL 0386299   MiD

Linens & domestics.
Linens & domestics current market map. New York, Haire Pub. Co., °1952.
col. map 22 x 54 cm. on sheet 87 x 56 cm.
Scale ca. 1 : 17,100,000.
Marginal table: Your $662,000,000 linens and domestics market, 1952.

1. Market surveys—U. S.—Maps.   I. Haire Publishing Company, New York.
G3701.Q4 1952.L5   Map 52–247

NL 0386300   DLC

TS1731   Linens & domestics.
L5   Year book and directory.
             1st(1945)–

             East Stroudsburg, Pa., Haire Pub. Co., 1945–
             vols. 29cm.

NL 0386301   NBuG

Linens and handkerchiefs. New York [etc.] 1930–31
see
Linens & domestics.

Linenthal, Harry, 1876–
The analytic method in psychotherapeutics. illustrative cases. By ... and E.W. Taylor, J.D., Boston. From the Dept. of Neurology, Massachusetts General Hospital. n.p.n.d.
p. 145–158.

NL 0386303   OO

Linenthal, Harry, and Edward Wyllys Taylor.
The analytic method in psychotherapeutics. Illustrative cases.
(In Massachusetts General Hospital. Publications. Vol. 1, no. 3, pp. 29–38. Boston. 1907.)
Published in the Boston Medical and Surgical Journal, vol. 155, Nov. 8, 1906 [*5746.1.155].

G6020 — Psycho-therapeutics. — Jt. auth.

NL 0386304   MB

Linenthal, Harry, 1876–
The prevention of occupational diseases. (In: Internat. Congress on Hygiene and Demography, 15. Washington, 1912. Transac. Washington, 1913. 8°. v. 3, p. 900–907.)

1. Occupations.—Diseases of.
N. Y. P. L   October 22, 1917.

NL 0386305   NN

Lineographic Publishing Company.
Lineography; a practical shorthand (Taylor improved). A complete system of stenography, adapted to professional and private purposes; easily acquired; no thickening nor half-lengthening. Glasgow, 1889. 15 p. 8°.

1. Shorthand.—Systems (English).   BEALE SHORTHAND COLL
N. Y. P. L   1889. 2. Taylor, Samuel.
                                          December 10, 1912.

NL 0386306   NN CtY

Linephty, Maur Guillaume.
ND673
.M5L48   Memling, Hans, 1430?–1494.
folio   La châsse de Sainte-Ursule, par Maur Guillaume-
             Linephty. Paris, Éditions Marion, 1939.

NL 0386308   MB

---

*Q.59   Linephty, Maur Guillaume.
.123   D'un age à l'autre. Bruxelles, Musée du
v.32   Livre, 1933.
             51 p. 30cm.
             On mechanical processes for the reproduction of graphic arts.
             Issued as part of the Musée du Livre's Recueil de planches d'art, 1932/33.
             1. Photomechanical processes. I. Brussels.
             Musée du Livre.

NL 0386308   MB

ND673   Linephty, Maur Guillaume.
.M5L45
folio   Memling, Hans, 1430?–1494.
             ... Hans Memling in the Hospital of St. John at Bruges, by Maur Guillaume/Linephty ... Paris, Brussels, The Marion press, 1939.

Linephty, Maur Guillaume.

Memling, Hans, 1430?–1494.
... The shrine of St. Ursula, by Maur Guillaume-Linephty ... Paris, Brussels, The Marion press, 1939.

Linephty, Maur Gillaume.
Le Tchamossé Batisse; grande nouvelle inédite, par Maur G. Linephty.
(In Les Œuvres libres. Paris, 1938. 18[cm]. v. 205, p. [261]–304)

I. Title.   A C 38–8469 Revised
Northwestern univ. Library
for Library of Congress   [PQ1141.O4 vol. 205]

NL 0386311   IEN OU DLC

The Liner; pub. by the Junior class of Hamline university. 1914–
St. Paul, Minn. [1913–   ]
1 v. illus. (incl. ports.) 28 cm.

NL 0386312   DHEW

Liner bills of lading and the international convention for the unification of certain rules relating to bills of lading
see under [Singer, J   C   ]

VOLUME 334

Liner Roma
see under ₍Bötticher, Hans₎ 1883-1934.

Linera, Antonio Alvarez de
see Alvarez de Linera, Antonio.

Linera Grund, Antonio Alvarez de
see
Alvarez de Linera Grund, Antonio, 1888–

Linerais, Jacques.
Au village de...; comédie en un acte représentée pour la première fois à Paris, au Théâtre de la comédie royale, direction Mme. Aimée Faure, le 26 juillet 1915... Paris: Édition lyrique et dramatique, A. Clémenti, 1915. 34 p. sq. 12°.

Author's name at head of title.

1. European war, 1914– .—Drama. 2. Drama (French). 3. Title.
N. Y. P. L. August 28, 1918.

NL 0386317 NN

Linero, Magdalena.
Historia de la literatura castellana, adaptada al programa de los colegios normales, nacionales, liceos y comerciales, por prof. Magdalena Linero ... ₍Córdoba, Imp. Pereyra₎ 1938.
3 p. l., 448 p., 1 l. 23ᶜᵐ.
Imprint on label mounted on t.-p.: Córdoba, Librería Assandri.

1. Spanish literature—Hist. & crit. 2. Spanish literature (Selections: Extracts, etc.)
Library of Congress PQ6037.L5 44–51657
860.9

NL 0386318 DLC

Linerode, Charles Clyde.
Fireside poems ... Canton, Ohio, c1935.
62 p. illus. 18 cm.

NL 0386319 RPB

Lineros Bravo, Carlos.
... La mensura de pertenencias comunes; memoria de prueba para optar al grado de licenciado en la Facultad de ciencias jurídicas y sociales de la Universidad de Chile. ₍Santiago de Chile, Talleres gráficos "Simiente"₎ 1945.
103 p., 2 l. 27ᶜᵐ.
"Bibliografía": 1st leaf at end.

1. Mining law—Chile. 2. Boundaries (Estates)—Chile. I. Title.
46–13477

NL 0386320 DLC DPU

Lines, Alfred, 1875–
... The estimation of passenger earnings on new projects, by A. Lines ... Calcutta, Government of India central publication branch, 1927.
cover-title, 1 p. l., 18 p. fold. map. 23ᶜᵐ. (₍India. Railway board₎ Technical paper no. 259)
"Books and technical papers published by the Railway board": p. 18.

1. Railroads—India—Passenger traffic.
Library of Congress TF7.I 5 no. 259 46–39674
——— Copy 2. HE2501.I 4L5

NL 0386321 DLC NN

Lines, Alfred, 1875–
...Notes on cast iron sleepers, by A. Lines... Calcutta: Superintendent Gov. Prtg., 1920. 15 p. diagrs. f°. (India. Railway Board. Technical paper. no. 203.)
Cover-title.

1. Track—Sleepers. 2. Series.
N. Y. P. L. September 21, 1923.

NL 0386322 NN

Lines, Charles B.
Connecticut Kansas colony
see under Connecticut Kansas colony.

₍Lines, Charles B ₎ *comp.*
Memorial of Edward C. D. Lines, late captain of Co. C, 2d reg't Kansas cavalry. New Haven, Tuttle, Morehouse & Taylor, printers, 1867.
34 p. front. (port.) 22ᶜᵐ.
Preface signed: C. B. L.

1. Lines, Edward C. D., 1836–1863. 2. Kansas cavalry. 2d regt., 1862–1865. I. Title.
15–4523
Library of Congress E508.6.2d

NL 0386324 DLC CtY OC1WHi NcD MB

Lines, Edna C.
Midst autumn fires. From– Connecticut Magazine, v. 10:3, 1906.
412 p. 25 cm.

NL 0386325 RPB

Lines, Edward C. D., 1836–1863.
Memorial of Edward C. D. Lines, late captain of Co. C, 2d reg't Kansas cavalry
see under ₍Lines, Charles B ₎ comp.

Lines, Edward Wolrych Low, 1894–
... The basal (standard) metabolism of the Australian merino sheep. By E. W. Lines, b. sc., with the assistance of A. W. Peirce, b. sc. Melbourne, H. J. Green, government printer, 1931–34.
2 v. diagrs. 24ᶜᵐ. (Australia. Council for scientific and industrial research. Bulletin no. 55, 84)
Vol. 2 by A. W. Peirce.
"References": v. 1, p. 33–34; v. 2, p. 17.

1. Metabolism. 2. Sheep. ₍1, 2. Metabolism in sheep₎ I. Peirce, Alan Wilfred.
Agr 32–441 Revised 2
U. S. Dept. of agr. Library 514Au72B no. 55, 84
for Library of Congress ₍r41e2₎

NL 0386327 DNAL CaBVaU PU–V OU OCU

Lines, Edward Wolrych Low, 1894– joint author.
Marston, Hedley Ralph, 1900–
... Studies on coast disease of sheep in South Australia. From the Nutrition laboratory, Adelaide, Division of animal health and nutrition, by H. R. Marston, R. G. Thomas, D. Murnane, E. W. L. Lines, I. W. McDonald, H. O. Moore, and L. B. Bull. Melbourne, H. J. Green, government printer, 1938.

Lines, Edwin Fuller, 1875–
Chart of the Indiana coal fields, prepared by E. F. Lines to accompany the supplementary report on the coal of Indiana by G. H. Ashley. Indianapolis: W. Burford ₍1909₎. map (50½ in. × 34¾ in.). (Indiana. Geological and natural resources department.)

1. Coal, U. S.: Indiana. 2. Indiana. Geological and natural resources department.
N. Y. P. L. October 24, 1911.

NL 0386329 NN

Lines, Edwin Fuller, 1875–

Shaw, Eugene Wesley, 1881–
Foxburg-Clarion folio, Pennsylvania, by E. W. Shaw and M. J. Munn. Washington, D. C., U. S. Geological survey, 1911.

Lines, Edwin Fuller, 1875–
Pennsylvania fire clays of Illinois, by Edwin H. ₍!₎ Lines.
(*In* Illinois. State geological survey. Bulletin no. 30. Biennial report for 1913 and 1914, administrative report and economic and geological papers. Urbana, 1917. 22½ᶜᵐ. p. 61–73. illus. (map, diagr.))

1. Clay. 2. Clay—Illinois. I. Title.
G S 17—409
U. S. Geol. survey. Library ₍253₎ I1 5b no. 30
for Library of Congress ₍QE105.A16 no. 30₎
₍a40g1₎

NL 0386331 DI–GS CU MtBuM MiU OO OU OC1 ICJ MB

QE105 Lines, Edwin Fuller, 1875– joint author.
.A16
no. 17 Bleininger, Albert Victor, 1873–
... Portland-cement resources of Illinois, by A. V. Bleininger, E. F. Lines, F. E. Layman ... Urbana, University of Illinois, 1912.

Lines, Edwin Fuller, 1875–
... Record of deep well drilling for 1904
see under Fuller, M₍yron₎ L₍eslie₎ 1873–

Lines, Edwin Fuller, 1875–
Statistics and directory of the clay industries of Illinois
see under Illinois. State Geological Survey.

Lines, Edwin Fuller, 1875–

Ashley, George Hall, 1866–
Supplementary report (to report of 1898) on The coal deposits of Indiana, by George Hall Ashley. Accompanied by a chart of Indiana coal and mining, by Edwin F. Lines, and two appendices: (a) Recent analysis of Indiana coal, (b) Descriptive notes on the stratigraphic chart. In cooperation with the U. S. Geological survey ...
(*In* Indiana. Department of geology and natural resources. Annual report, 1908. Indianapolis, ₍1909₎. 23ᶜᵐ. p. 13–150 incl. tables. pl., 4 fold. charts, fold. tab.)

Lines, Edwin Stevens, 1845–
Christ's church at the town of Rye in the county of Westchester and the state of New York ... The sermon preached by the Rt. Rev. Edwin S. Lines ... on the occasion of the two hundredth anniversary of the ordination of the Reverend James Wetmore, rector of Christ's church, Rye, N. Y., 1732-1764, and the missionary of the Society for the propagation of the gospel. Sunday, July 1st, 1923. ₍Rye, N. Y., Rye chronicle press, 1923₎
₍10₎ p., 1 l. 23½ᶜᵐ.

Portrait of Rev. James Wetmore on title-page.

NL 0386337 NNC

VOLUME 334

Slavery
E
185
.2
F85
v.7
Lines, Edwin Stevens, Bp., 1845-1927.
The future of the Negro in America; paper
read before the Church Congress of 1905, in
Brooklyn, N. Y. ₍n. p., 1905?₎
9 p. 23cm.

Caption title.
No. 13 in a vol. lettered: Freedmen pamphlets 7.

1. Negroes.

NL 0386338 NIC

Lines, Edwin Stevens, bp., 1845-1927.
861 Jared Ingersoll, stamp master, and the
1918 Stamp act ...
(In Papers of the New Haven colony historical
society. New Haven,1918. 24cm. v.9,
p.[174]-200)

NL 0386339 CtY

LINES, EDWIN STEVENS, bp., 1845-1927.
Personal recollections of Naugatuck; a paper read at
the fiftieth anniversary of the consecration of St.
Michael's church, Naugatuck, Connecticut, May 26,
1926. [Naugatuck, 1926] 24 p. 23cm.

Film reproduction. Master negative. Original discarded.
Positive in * ZI-48.

NL 0386340 NN

Lines, Mrs. Eliza Jennette (Marks) 1828–
Bethany and its hills; glimpses of the town of Bethany
as it was before the railroads and the fire fiend robbed
it of its glory, by Mrs. Eliza J. Lines ... New Haven, The
Tuttle, Morehouse and Taylor company, 1905.

viii, 65 p., 2 l. front., illus., plates, ports. 24ᶜᵐ.

Includes genealogical sketches.

1. Bethany, Conn.—Hist. 2. Bethany, Conn.—Geneal. I. Title.
16-23105

Library of Congress F104.B5L75

NL 0386341 DLC MB WaS

Lines, Mrs. Eliza Jennette (Marks) 1828–
Marks - Platt ancestry; comp. by Eliza J. Lines ...
Sound Beach, Conn., Pub. by request of A. A. Marks,
1902.

2 p. l., ₍3₎-98, ₍16₎ p. front., plates, ports., geneal. tables. 24½ᶜᵐ.

16 blank pages at end for "descendants' record."
The ancestral record of Amasa Abraham Marks and Lucy Ann Platt
Marks.

1. Marks family (Mordecai Marks, 1706-1771) 2. Platt family (Richard
Platt, d. 1684) 3. Marks, Amasa Abraham, 1825–
3-9126 Revised
Library of Congress CS71.M346 1902

NL 0386342 DLC MWA NN CSf Or

LINES, Elizabeth Geisendorfer, comp.
Brief biography of Knox Butte pioneers,
1923-1939. [25] p. illus. Albany, Oregon.
n. pub. [1939]

NL 0386343 OrP Or

Lines, Fred G.
Insoluble residues of the lower Mississippian
limestones of the Madison group, by Fred G. Lines
... Butte, Montana school of mines, 1942.

36p. plates, photos, maps, diagrs.

Senior thesis.

NL 0386344 MtBuM

Lines, G. W.
The Ladysmith siege, 2nd Nov., 1899 – 1st March, 1900. Rec-
ord containing: Regiments defending the besieged borough.
Lists giving names of local volunteer defence force. Statistics.
The residents: including women and children. Copies of various
military and municipal notices. And a complete copy of the
"Ladysmith Bombshell" published during the siege. ₍Lady-
smith? 190-?₎ 96 p. illus. 20cm.

1. Ladysmith, Union of South Africa—Siege, 1899-1900. 2. Boer
war, 1899-1902—Registers. lists. etc.

NL 0386345 NN MiU WaU

Lines, George.
Some questions concerning corporation insurance;
paper read before the Association of life insurance counsel, December 8th, 1920, by George Lines, general counsel of the Northwestern mutual life insurance company
of Milwaukee, Wisconsin. ₍Milwaukee, 1920₎

cover-title, 14 p. 23½ᶜᵐ.

1. Insurance, Life. I. Title: Corporation insurance.
22-9120
Library of Congress HG8931.L5

NL 0386346 DLC WaU-L

Lines, H. H. Titterstone camp and others.
26 pp. 5 pl. ₍Shropshire Archaeol. and Nat. Hist. Soc.
Trans. 2 s. v. 3, 1891, p. 1.₎

NL 0386347 MdBP

Lines, Henry
1813 A letter, addressed to the Rev. Samuel
L645 Merwin ... [New Haven, 1813]
6 p. 20 cm.
Caption title.

1. Merwin, Samuel, 1777-1839.
Imprint cd: Connecticut. New Haven. 1813.
Conn. imprint
cdu

NL 0386348 CtY PPABP

F814 Lines, Herbert L.
.3 Mining and milling methods and costs at the Ash Peak mine
A86L5 of the Veta Mines, Inc., Duncan, Ariz. [Washington]
U.S. Dept. of the Interior, Bureau of Mines, 1940.
26 p. illus. 28cm. (U.S. Bureau of Mines. Information
circular 7119)

Cover title.

1. Ash Peak Mine, Ariz. 2. Veta Mines, Inc., Duncan, Ariz.
3. Silver mines and mining - Arizona - Duncan. I. U.S.
Bureau of Mines. II. Title.

NL 0386349 CU-B

DS70 Lines, Joan L
.L75 The al 'Ubaid period in Mesopotamia and its
Persian affinities. Cambridge, 1953.
397 p.
Photocopy of typewritten manuscript. Positive.
Diss.—University of Cambridge.

1. Excavations (Archaeology)—Mesopotamia.
2. Iraq—Antiq. I. Title.

NL 0386350 ICU

Lines, Jorge A 1891–
... Los altares de Toyopán, por Jorge A. Lines; estudio
hecho con motivo de la Exposición de arqueología de octubre
1934, donde fue premiado con medalla de oro por el hon. Club
rotario de San José, y leído en conferencia en los cursillos de
la Casa España, el 20 de noviembre. San José, Costa Rica,
1935.
32 p. incl. illus., plates. 23ᶜᵐ.
At head of title: Extractos de la monografía en preparación: "Huacas
huetares de Toyopán."
"Bibliografía": p. 32.
1. Costa Rica—Antiq. 2. Indians of Central America—Art. I. Title.
II. Title: Toyopán, Los altares de.
35-9819
Library of Congress F1545.L65
913.7286

NL 0386351 DLC CLU LU PU-Mu NN CtY

Lines, Jorge A., 1891–

Costa Rica. Secretaría de educación pública.
... El arte en Costa Rica; exposición celebrada en el Teatro
nacional ... San José, Costa Rica, Imprenta nacional, 1941–

Lines, Jorge A 1891–
Bibliografía antropológica aborigen de Costa Rica; incluye
especialmente: arqueología, cartografía, etnología, geografía,
historia y lingüística, por Jorge A. Lines ... San José, Costa
Rica, 1943.
xiv, 263 p., 3 l. incl. col. front. (coat of arms) 22½ᶜᵐ.
On cover: Universidad de Costa Rica. Facultad de letras y filosofía.

1. Indians of Central America—Costa Rica—Bibl. 2. Costa Rica—
Antiq.—Bibl. I. Costa Rica. Universidad nacional, San José. Facultad de letras y filosofía. II. Title.
44-807
Library of Congress Z5114.L63
₍3₎ 016.9701

CtY PU DPU ViU DLC
NL 0386353 OC1 IaU KU NcGU NIC NcU NcD CU ICU OC1

913.7286 Lines, Jorge A 1891–
L645c Cabezas-retrato de los huetares. ₍Dibujos
1940 de Feron: grabados de cabezas. San
Isidro de Coronado, Costa Rica, Sociedad de
Geografía e Historia de Costa Rica, 1940₎
14p. illus. 24cm.

1. Costa Rica. Antiq. 2. Indians of
Central America. Art. 3. Sculpture,
Primitive. I. Title.

NL 0386354 KU

Lines, Jorge A 1891–
Cabezas-retrato de los huetares; ₍conferencia. San José,
Costa Rica, 1941₎
14 p. illus. 22 cm.

1. Guetar Indians. I. Title.

F1545.2.G8L5 71-389811

NL 0386355 DLC DPU FU LNHT

Lines, Jorge A., 18₎1– comp.

San José, Costa Rica. Exposición de arqueología y arte pre-
colombino, 1934.
... Catálogo descriptivo de los objeios ₍!₎ expuestos en la
primera Exposición de arqueología y arte pre-colombino, inau-
gurada en San José de Costa Rica el 12 de octubre de 1934 en
el Teatro nacional; compilado por Jorge A. Lines. ₍San José₎
Imprenta nacional, 1934.

Lines, Jorge A., 1891–
F1547
.A3

Academia Costarricense de la Historia.
Colección de documentos para la historia de Costa Rica
relativos al cuarto y último viaje de Cristóbal Colón. San
José, Impr. y Librería Atenea, 1952.

VOLUME 334

Lines, Jorge A   1891–
... Crónica de nuestro conquistador, Juan Vázquez de Coronado. San José, Costa Rica, Imprenta nacional, 1940.
cover-title, 21 (*i. e.* 19) p. illus. (incl. ports., coats of arms) 24½ᵐ.

1. Vázquez de Coronado, Juan, 1523–1565.

41–22220

Library of Congress   F1437.V435

923.2728

NL 0386358   DLC ICN

913.7286   **Lines, Jorge A**   1891 –
L645e   Esbozo arqueologico de Costa Rica.
1939   [San Juan, Costa Rica?] 1939]
238–255p. illus., map. 24cm.

"Reimpresión de la Actas de la Primera Sesión celebrada en la Ciudad de México en 1939, del vigésimoséptimo Congreso Internacional de Americanistas."

1. Costa Rica.   Antiq. I. Title.

NL 0386359   KU

913.7286   **Lines, Jorge Agustín**, 1891–
L645h   Una hacha monolítica de Río Cuarto
1941   (Provincia de Alajuela, Costa Rica)
San José, Costa Rica, [Impr. Universal, 1941]
14p. illus. 23cm.

1. Río Cuarto, Costa Rica. Antiquities.

NL 0386360   KU LNHT DPU

Lines, Jorge A   1891–
... Una huaca en Zapandi, por Jorge A. Lines ... Notas preliminares tomadas a propósito de las excavaciones arqueológicas hechas a raíz de la inundación del río Tempisque en 1933, en Filadelfia, provincia de Guanacaste, península de Nicoya, Costa Rica. San José, Costa Rica [Imprenta Lehmann, 1936.
46 p. incl. front. (map) illus., pl. 23½ᵐ.
At head of title: Sobre la cultura chorotega.
"Contenido": p. [2] of cover.
"Bibliografía": p. [3] of cover.
1. Costa Rica—Antiq. 2. Mangue Indians. 3. Indians of Central America—Pottery. I. Title. II. Title: Zapandi, Una huaca en. III. Title: Sobre la cultura chorotega.

37–13464

Library of Congress   F1545.L653

970.4

NL 0386361   DLC CU-B PU-Mu PU TxU CU NN

Lines, Jorge A   1891–
... Libros y folletos publicados en Costa Rica durante los años 1830–1849, por Jorge A. Lines ... San José, C. R., 1944.
4 p. l., [xi]–xxxv, 151 p. illus. (facsims.) 23½ cm.
At head of title: Universidad de Costa Rica. Facultad de letras y filosofía.
Bibliography: p. 149–151.

1. Costa Rica—Bibl. 2. Costa Rican literature—Bibl. 3. Printing—Hist.—Costa Rica. I. Title.

Z1451.L5   015.7286   NcU   47–2315

    TxU ViU MiD NcU
NL 0386362   DLC CU CtY IEdS WU ICU FTaSU IU KU OU NcD

G737   **Lines, Jorge A**   , 1891–
L645m   Las monedas de oro y plata emitidas por el dr. Castro, por Jorge A. Lines. [San José, Costa Rica, Imprenta nacional, 1949]
1p.ℓ.,[505]–513p. illus. 25cm.
"Discurso del autor, con motivo del homenaje al doctor don José María Castro Madriz, tributado por la Academia de geografía e historia de Costa Rica, en el Teatro nacional, el día 1º de setiembre de 1948."
"Tiraje aparte de la Revista de los Archivos nacionales de Costa Rica, año XII, nos.9–10, pági-   nas 505 a 513."

NL 0386363   TxU

G913.7286   **Lines, Jorge A**   1891–
L634noT   Notas sobre la arqueología de Costa Rica. Traducción del inglés de Francisco Pablo Labombarda. Curitiba, Instituto Néo-Pitagórico, 1945.
38p. map. 19cm. (Bibliotéca néo-pitagórica, no.17)
1. Costa Rica – Antiq. 2. Indians of Central America – Costa Rica. 3. Indians of Central America – Art. I. Labombarda, Francisco Pablo, tr. II. Title.   III. Series.

NL 0386364   TxU NN DPU

Lines, Jorge A   1891–
Notes on the archaeology of Costa Rica, by Jorge A. Lines ... San José, Costa Rica [Imp. Lehmann] 1936.
30, [2] p. illus. (incl. map) 23½ᵐ.
"This publication comes ... through the courtesy of the National tourist board of Costa Rica."
Bibliography: p. [31]

1. Costa Rica—Antiq. 2. Indians of Central America—Costa Rica. 3. Indians of Central America—Art.   I. Title.

37–6954

Library of Congress   F1545.L656

——— Copy 2.   [2]   970.4

NL 0386365   DLC DPU NN LNHT KU FMU CU CtY

Lines, Jorge A   1891–
Notes on the archaeology of Costa Rica, by Jorge A. Lines ... (2d ed., rev.) San José, Costa Rica [The National tourist board of Costa Rica] 1938.
30, [2] p. illus. (incl. map) 22ᵐ.
"This brochure is presented ... with the compliments of the National tourist board of Costa Rica."
"Bibliographic note": p. [31]

1. Costa Rica—Antiq. 2. Indians of Central America—Costa Rica. 3. Indians of Central America—Art.   I. Costa Rica. Junta nacional de turismo. II. Title.

42–39545

Library of Congress   F1545.L656 1938

[2]   970.4

NL 0386366   DLC LNHT IU CtY OCl DPU MH

Lines, Jorge A   1891–
Notes on the archaeology of Costa Rica, by Jorge A. Lines ... (3d ed., rev.) San José, Costa Rica [The National tourist board of Costa Rica] 1939.
30, [2] p. illus. (incl. map) 22ᵐ.
"Bibliographic note": p. [31]

1. Costa Rica—Antiq. 2. Indians of Central America—Costa Rica. 3. Indians of Central America—Art.   I. Costa Rica. Junta nacional de turismo. II. Title.

42–13822

Library of Congress   F1545.L656 1939

[2]   970.4

NL 0386367   DLC OrCS LNHT TxU CtY DPU

913.7286   **Lines, Jorge A**   1891–
L754mu   Nuestra herencia aurífera; notas sobre la arqueología de Costa Rica. [San José, Costa Rica, 1951]

14 p. illus. 21cm.

Cover-title.
An offprint from La Nación, April 27, 1951 – p.[2].

1. Costa Rica – Antiquities. I. La Nación, San José,   Costa Rica. II. Title

NL 0386368   FU TxU

Lines, Jorge A., 1891–   ed. and tr.
Reminiscencias de un viaje por los Estados Unidos. [San José? Costa Rica] Servicio de Información de los Estados Unidos [1955]
62 p. illus. 26 cm.

1. Washington, D. C.—Public buildings. 2. U. S.—Descr. & trav.—1940–   I. Title.

F204.A1L5   58–49216 ‡

NL 0386369   DLC DPU TxU IU FU

F1544   **Lines, Jorge A., 1891–**   ed. and tr.
.W137   **Wagner, Moritz**, 1813–1887.
... La república de Costa Rica en Centro América. Traducción del alemán por el profesor Jorge A. Lines, asesorado por el dr. Ernesto J. Wender y el prof. José Dávila Solera. San José, Costa Rica [Imprenta Lehmann] 1944.

C52   **Lines, Jorge A**   1891–
439   Sobre la cultura chorotega. Una huaca en Zapandi ... Notas preliminares tomadas a propósito de las excavaciones arqueológicas hechas a raíz de la inundación del río Tempisque en 1933, en Filadelfia, provincia de Guanacaste, península de Nicoya, Costa Rica. San José, Costa Rica, 1936.
Pamphlet.

1.Indians – Chorotes.

NL 0386371   ICJ

Lines, Jorge A   1891–
Sukia: tsúgür o isogro, por Jorge A. Lines ... [San José, Costa Rica, Imp. Falco hnos. & cía., 1938]
30, [2] p. illus. (incl. map) 26ᵐ.
"Reimpresión del estudio publicado en Anales de la Sociedad de geografía e historia de Guatemala, tomo XIV, nº. 4, junio 1938."
"Referencias bibliográficas de las citas": p. [31]

1. Indians of Central America—Costa Rica. 2. Medicine-man. 3. Smoking. 4. Taboo.   I. Title.

42–39380

Library of Congress   F1545.L66 1938 a

NL 0386372   DLC DPU

G913.7286   **Lines, Jorge A**   1891–
L634t   Taxonomía de la arqueología de Costa Rica.
1954   2. ed. San José, Costa Rica, Librería Universitaria Editorial, 1954.
vii, 87ℓ. illus. 28cm. (Colección "Estudio")
Cover title.

1. Costa Rica – Antiq. 2. Indians of Central America – Costa Rica. 3. Indians of Central America – Art. I. Title. II. Series.

NL 0386373   TxU CU MH-H

Lines, Kathleen.
Four to fourteen, a library of books for children. With decorations by Harold Jones. Introd. by Walter de la Mare. [Cambridge] Cambridge University Press, 1950.
204 p. illus. 20 cm.

1. Children's literature—Bibl.   I. Title.

Z1037.L717   028.5   51–83

    MH NNC CU TxU NcGU PU PP OClU OrPS
NL 0386374   DLC IdPI Or WaSp WaS OOxM OKentU NcU ICU

VOLUME 334

Lines, Kathleen, *comp.*
Lavender's blue, a book of nursery rhymes compiled by Kathleen Lines & pictured by Harold Jones. [New York, F. Watts, 1954.
180 p. illus. 26 cm.
1. Nursery rhymes.   I. Jones, Harold, illus.   II. Title.
[PZ8.3]
Printed for U. S. Q. B. R.   54-9816 ‡

NL 0386375   MB MiU FMU AAP DLC

Lines, Kathleen, *ed.*
Stories for girls, edited by Kathleen Lines. London, Faber and Faber ltd. [1938]
616 p. 21 cm.
"First published in November MCMXXXVIII."
Bibliography: p. 613–616.

    I. Title.
                                                        39–29689
Library of Congress   PZ5.L63St

NL 0386376   DLC

Lines, Kathleen, *comp.*
Ten minute story book, illustrated by Winifred Marks. Oxford univ. [1943]
79 [1] p., illus.

NL 0386377   MiD

Lines, Kathleen, *ed.*
The ten minute story book, illustrated by Winifred Marks. [London] Oxford University Press [1955]
79 p. illus. 25 cm.
First published 1942.

1. Children's stories.   I. Title.

NL 0386378   CaBVaU

Lines, Leslie.
Solid geometry, by L. Lines ... London, Macmillan and co., limited, 1935.
xx, 292 p. diagrs. 19 cm.
"Intended primarily for the use of pupils preparing for one of the higher school certificate examinations." --Pref.
"Answers and hints": p. 259–287.

1. Geometry, Solid.
                            QA457.L75

NL 0386379   MiU PSt MiHM NBuU

Lines, Leverett H.
From fifteen to forty-five: or, Thirty years of female life. A treatise on the diseases of females, incident to this period, with their causes, symptoms and treatment, including the theory of conception, and the symptoms of pregnancy. By L. H. Lines ... New York, Printed by F. Somers, 1863.
336 p. illus. 19 cm.
Published 1862 under title: Thirty years of female life.

1. Woman—Diseases.

Library of Congress   RG121.L75   8-3594†

NL 0386380   DLC

Lines, Leverett H.
Thirty years of female life. A treatise on the diseases of females, incident to this period, with their causes, symptoms and treatment; including the theory of conception, and the symptoms of pregnancy. By L. H. Lines ... New York, Printed by W. E. Hilton, 1862.
336 p. illus. 19 cm.

1. Woman—Diseases.
                                                        8-917†
Library of Congress   RG121.L748

NL 0386381   DLC PU

355   **Lines, María v. de.**
El lector costarricense, editado por María v. de Lines ... 2ª ed.   San José, C. R., 1907.
2 v.

NL 0386382   DPU

Lines, Mrs. Martha (Kimberly)

[Kimberly, Dennis]
Thomas Kimberly, New Haven, Conn. 1638. [New Haven, The Tuttle, Morehouse & Taylor press, 1896]

Lines, Robert B.
... Report on telegraphs and on telegraphic administration. By Robert B. Lines ... Washington, Gov't print. off., 1876.
1 p. l., 88 p. illus. fold. tab. diagrs. 24 cm. (*In* U. S. Commission to the Vienna exhibition, 1873. Reports. 1875–76. v. 2, 1)
At head of title: Vienna international exhibition, 1873.

1. Telegraph.
                                                        5-37074†
Library of Congress   T960.E1U5

NL 0386384   DLC CU MdBP OO OCl MiU MB

Lines, Samuel Gregory
Lessons from the Life and Death of James A. Garfield ... Sermon preached in St. Luke's Church, San Francisco, Cal. on Sunday September 25, 1881 ... [Barry, Baird & co.] n.d.
13 p.

NL 0386385   OClWHi NN

BX5145   **Lines, Samuel Gregory,** *joint author.*
.A62J6   Jones, Charles Alfred.
Stories on the collects for every Sunday and holy day throughout the year; with question and answers, by C. A. Jones and the Rev. S. G. Lines ... London, J. S. Virtue & co., limited, 1886–

Lines, Vincent.
Shaping and making: a picture book of crafts.   Lond., Oxford univ. pr. [1944].
32 p. Illus.

NL 0386387   CaBVa

Lines, W   H
... Tax exempt bonds; the millstone around the neck of industry ... Portland, Oregon Voter, 1925.
Cover-title: 8 p.   24 cm.
"Advance print from the Oregon Voter: weekly magazine of citizenship."

NL 0386388   OrPR

Linés Escardó, Enrique.
... Aplicaciones de la teoría de redes regulares al estudio de las funciones cuasiperiódicas ... Madrid, Consejo superio de investigaciones científicas, Patronato "Alfonso el Sabio," Instituto "Jorge Juan," 1943.
2 p. l., 77 p., 1 l. diagrs. 24 cm. (*On cover:* Publicaciones del Instituto "Jorge Juan" de matemáticas)
"Premio del Consejo superior de investigaciones científicas, 1942."
Bibliographical foot-notes.

1. Harmonic analysis.   2. Fourier series.

QA403.L5   A 45–3409
Illinois. Univ. Library
for Library of Congress   [a57c½]†

NL 0386389   IU MnU MH RPB GU NBuU DLC OU CU FMU

Lines. Edinburgh [quarterly]
see   Lines review.

Lines. n.p. [1901?]
see under   [McArthur, Peter] 1866–1924]

Lines addressed to a noble lord
see under   [Barker, Miss]

Lines addressed to Lady Byron
see under   [Cockle, Mary]

Lines addressed to Mrs. Jordan.
London: Printed for T. Becket, ...
26½ cm., in 2s.

K4873 — Jordan, Dorothy. 1762–1816.

NL 0386394   MB

Lines addressed to Mrs. Pogson Smith after reading her poem on "The power of Christianity" [Signed, C. C. V. Philadelphia]
In- Smith, Mrs. Sarah Pogson. The Arabians-Phil., 1844.   15 cm.   p. 55–56.

NL 0386395   RPB

Lines addressed to the most noble Arthur, duke of Wellington
see under   [Woodhouse, William Herbert]

VOLUME 334

Lines addressed to the patients under inoculation **for the** small pox.

This work is available in this library in the Readex Microprint edition of Early American Imprints published by the American Antiquarian Society.

This collection is arranged according to the numbers in Charles Evans' American Bibliography.

NL 0386397 DLC

LINES addressed to Victory. Parma, 1793. Printed by Bodoni.

Amy Lowell Lib.

NL 0386398 MH

LINES and letters. v. 10, no. 1, v. 11-12, no. 1; Jan. 1948, Feb.-May, 1949, winter, 1950. New York. v. illus. 24cm.

Irregular.

Published by the students of the School of education, New York university.

Ceased publication with v. 12, no. 1. Superseded by Point, spring, 1951. (Point is not in the library)

1. Colleges and universities--New York. I. New York   Student publications--U.S.--university. Education, School of.

NL 0386399 NN

The lines behind the lines-the story of railroads in war
    see under   Association of American Railroads. Publicity Section.

Lines by L.C.S.
    see under   [Starbuck, Lucy Coffin]

Lines, composed by a young man of genius, in a deep consumption.
    In- Homer, J. The way of God vindicated. 1804.

NL 0386402 RPB

Lines composed on the death of General Washington.

This work is available in this library in the Readex Microprint edition of Early American Imprints published by the American Antiquarian Society.

This collection is arranged according to the numbers in Charles Evans' American Bibliography.

NL 0386403 DLC

Lines composed on the death of General Washington. [*n. p. 1800?*] 4to broadside.   *Sabin 101847*
Eleven six-line stanzas of verse, in two columns. First line of first stanza reads:
Your morning throng grief oppos'd the scene,

NL 0386404 MSaE MWA NHi

Lines composed on the Death of General Washington (Broadside, *1800?*)
Photostatic reproduction.

NL 0386405 CSmH

Zc95   Lines composed on the death of James Oscar Covill
L64   of Victor, Ontario county, N.Y., who died at Green River, Oregon territory, August 9th, 1857, aged 27 years, on his way to California. [Victor?N.Y., 1858] broadside. 24x20cm. Five poems.

NL 0386406 CtY

LINES composed on the death of Mrs. Jessy Benson, who departed this life Sept. 18, 1870. [B. 1871].

By R.H.B.L.   AL 412.1**

NL 0386407 MH

Lines... composed on the melancholly state of the family of Mr. Benjamin Sandborn
    see under   [Cate, James] 1728?-1813.

Lines composed upon the death of Miss Frances Baker, late of Dedham... died May 26, aged 20 years (Manuscript poem) Unbd. in portfolio.-No. 2.

NL 0386409 RPB

76-01   **Lines** dedicated to the soldiers in the
LL428   **Philippines.** [n.p., 1900?] **cover-title**, [20] p. 16 cm.

Poems.

1. U. S. History--Philippine Insurrection, 1899-1901--Poetry.

NL 0386410 RPB

Lines delivered at the reunion of the Coffin family at Nantucket, Mass.
    see under   [Coffin, Robert Barry] 1826-1886.

Lines for little lips
    see under   [Davidson, Harriet (Miller)] 1839-1883.

Lines for Macmillans' first Christmas party, by H.S.E.   Toronto [The Hunter-Rose co., ltd.] 1928.
    4 l.   24 cm.
    Limited ed. This copy not numbered.

NL 0386413 RPB

1887.

Lines from Dante.
Signed: J.E.C.

NL 0386414 NIC

Rare   **Lines** in commendation of the art of
PN   **printing, extracted from "The rival
6110   roses"; a poem descriptive of the wars
C7C17   between the houses of York and Lancaster; - the period when printing was first introduced into England. [Cambridge, Eng., Univ. Press, 1831] 7 p. 21cm.

No. 1 in vol. lettered: Poems.

NL 0386415 NIC

Wordsworth   Lines in imitation of Wordsworth [poem]
PR   (In The Cambridge University magazine.
5874   Cambridge. 22cm. v. 1 (1839) p. 197-
C17   198)
              Signed: B. R. J.
              Healey 790.

I. J., B. R. II. B. R. J. III.
The Cambridge University magazine, v.1, no. 3, Nov. 1839.

NL 0386416 NIC

Lines, in memory of Rev. Alexander Young, D.D., Minister of the New South society in Boston, who died March 16, 1854. Written by " A Classmate."

NL 0386417 RPB

LINES in verse about Shakers, not published by authority of the society so called, New York, W. Taylor' & co., 1846.

pp. [3]-456.
Imperfect:-lacks title-page: title taken from the cover.   AL 4323.65

NL 0386418 MH

Lines inscribed to Rev. William Veach Morrison
    see under   [Waldron, D.M.]

Lines left out; or, Some of the histories left out in "Line upon line."
    see under   [Mortimer, Mrs. Favell Lee (Bevan)] 1802-1878.

Lines made after the great earthquake, in 1755.

This work is available in this library in the Readex Microprint edition of Early American Imprints published by the American Antiquarian Society.

This collection is arranged according to the numbers in Charles Evans' American Bibliography.

NL 0386421 DLC

Lines occasioned by the death of Capt. Joshua Gray, of Yarmouth
    see under   [Alden, Timothy] 1736-1828.

VOLUME 334

Lines occasioned by the death of poetical genius; parody off the Tron Church, Glasgow. Glasgow, J. Reid, 1831.
12 p.   12°.

NL   0386423   NN

Lines occasioned by the death of the late Rev. Dr. Henry J. Feltus, with notes, biographical and explanatory. By a friend. New-York, J. A. Burtus, 1829.
viii, ₍9₎–80 p.   21ᶜᵐ.

1. Feltus, Henry James, 1775–1828.   I. Kirk, Thomas, supposed author.

34–12488

Library of Congress   BX5995.F4L5   922.373

MB
NL   0386424   DLC PPULC PHi MWA PPAmP CtY NNC CSmH RPB

Lines occasioned by two elegant prints received from Mrs. Mayhew... n.p., n.d.
[4] p.   23 cm.
Manuscript.

NL   0386425   RPB

Lines of a layman
see under   [Price, James C.]

Lines of communication in Piedmont and Genoa. Leipzig, n.d.
1 p.

NL   0386427   PHi

Lines of descent from honored New England ancestors.
see under   Mynderse, Mrs. Hannah Hoskins (Gould) 1858–

Lines of greeting to Dr. Oliver Wendell Holmes
see under   [Heitland, William Emerton] 1847–1935.

Lines of reflection
see under   [Hoffman, Maude Ann]

Lines of type
see   Linotype and Ludlow faces.

Lines on a late resignation at the Royal academy
see under   [Jerningham, Edward] 1737–1812.

Lines on a dog, formerly an attaché of Conant Hall, Since defunct.
In, The Aegis, v. 19, 1875–1876, Lawrence, Mass., 23 cm.   p. 82.

NL   0386433   RPB

Lines on a withered tree in the Viceregal grounds
see under   [Carlisle, George William Frederick Howard, 7th earl of] 1802–1864.

3600
.001
.589   Lines on attempts to diffuse popery. Oxford, Baxter, 1835.
11 p.   18 cm.

NL   0386435   NjP

Lines on Chapel Island in Morecambe Bay. Ulverston, S. Soulby. 1847.
15 p.   12°.

NL   0386436   NN

Lines [on Disraeli and Gladstone, Signed Fool. *London*, 1876?]. 2l.   12°.
In: BTE. p. v. 4.

NL   0386437   NN

Lines on leaving the Bedford St. Schoolhouse
see under   [Santayana, George] 1863–1952.

Lines on my eighty-third birthday, November 24, 1922
see under   [Given, Albert H   ] 1839–

LINES on slaves killing their masters, and the song of Harmodius and Aristogeiton. Portsmouth. 1841.

pp.22.

NL   0386440   MH

Lines on the back of a Confederate note ...
see under   Jonas, Samuel Alroy.

Lines on the commencement of Term₍Michaelmas,1816₎
see under   [Boone, James Shergold] 1799–1859.

Lines on the death of Alvan Hyde, D.D., of Lee. [Signed] J.L. Otis, Jan., 1834.

NL   0386443   RPB

Lines on the death of Ebenezer Ball
see under   [Fisher, Jonathan] 1768–1847.

Lines on the death of   from the Morning chronicle of Monday August 5, 1816
see under   [Moore, Thomas] 1779–1852.

Lines on the death of Sallie, and other pieces
see under   [Keiningham, Joseph R.]

Lines on the death of Sir Walter Scott
see under   [Baillie, Mrs. Joanna, 1762–1851.]

Lines on the death of the Confederate Gen. Albert Sidney Johnston, of Ky. Who fell at the battle of "Shiloh," Miss. [sic] Sunday, April 6, 1862. [n.p., 1862?]
9 1/4 x 4 inches.
Title and text within type-ornament border.
What is apparently another issue is listed by Ellinger, p. 117.

NL   0386448   CSmH

Lines on the death of the President of the United States, – and on the loss of the steam ship President. President Harrison. The messenger of death has come...Steam ship President. This splendid ship from New York sail'd... ₍n.p., 1841₎
broadside.   21 x 30.2cm. (17.3 x 30cm.) Text in two columns.
Poems on death of President Harrison and on the loss of the steamer President with 136 souls.
Vignettes at top; type ornament border.
1. Shipwrecks. 2. Harrison, William Henry, 1775–1841, pres.U.S. 3. Poet   ry. 4. President, steamship.   5. Broadsides.

NL   0386449   MiU-C

XbH   Lines, on the death of those unfortunate
.822   orphan children who perished at the Asylum on
.A10L   the 24th January, 1822.
[Philadelphia, 1822]

broadside. illus. 26 x 21cm.
Within border of type ornaments.

NL   0386450   MB

Lines on the departure of a great poet from this country.   London, John Booth, 1816.
14 p.   21.5 cm.
First edition.

NL   0386451   NcD

Lines on the departure of a great poet from this country.   The second edition, corrected.   London, John Booth, 1816.
iv, ₍5₎–15 p.   8vo   (Binder's title: Byron tracts, v. 3 ₍no. 14₎)

Bound with C. Gordon, Life and genius of Lord Byron.

NL   0386452   InU NcD DLC

VOLUME 334

Lines on the departure of a great poet [lord Byron]
from his country. [anon.] 3d ed.
London, 1816

40

[Misc. pamphlets, v. 56]

NL 0386453   DLC

Lines on the 50th anniversary of the arrival at
Weimar of Maria Paulowna, Grand Duchess of
Saxony and of Russia. Weimar, published
for the benefit of the Frauen-Verein [Leipzig,
printed by B.G. Teubner] 1855.
[8] p.   27.5 x 22.5 cm.
Poem signed: Weimar 1854. J.P. v. P.

NL 0386454   CtY

Lines on the funeral of John G. Wheeler. [by]
E.H.   n.p., n.d.
[1] p.   19 cm.
Caption title.

NL 0386455   RPB

Lines on the inaugural meeting of the Shelley society
see under   [Lang, Andrew] 1844-1912.

Lines on the late debate at the Union.
Cambridge:Published by W.P.Grant.1838.

*fEC8
C1442
Z838w

8p. 30cm.
Satirizing the Cambridge Union's vote of
censure against Charles Stokes in his quarrel
with Temple Frere.
No.6 in a volume labeled on spine:
Whisker papers.

NL 0386457   MH

Lines on the late distressing fire in Newburyport.
From the Newburyport Herald, June 12.
In, Particular account of the great fire at
Newburyport, May 31, 1811... Newburyport,
1811.   21 cm.   8 p.   p. 7-8.

NL 0386458   RPB

Lines on the late Doctor Joseph R. Drake
see under   [Halleck, Fitz-Greene] 1790-
1867.

Lines on the life and death of Capt. James B. Eads
St. Louis, 1887.
broadside.   4°.
In: AGZ p. v. 83. no. 7.

NL 0386460   NN

Lines on the presentation of a picture to Mrs.
S.L. Sheldon, president of the "Owland Book"
club. 1873 [by C.]   n.p., 1873.
[3] p.   20 cm.
Cover title.

NL 0386461   RPB

"Lines", on the removal of the remains of
Commodore O.H. Perry. [poem] from the
Norfolk Herald December 1826. ("Tis well
'tis right! he should not sleep, Upon a foreign
strand")
In-Inauguration of the Perry statue, Sept.
10, 1885 Newport, R.I., 1885.   24 cm.
p. 59-60 (Appendix C)

NL 0386462   RPB

Lines on the tercentenary of Harvard College in
America
see under   [Masefield, John] 1878-

Lines projected, and partly written on the four
hundred and fiftieth anniversary of the opening
of Winchester college
see under   [Selborne, Roundell Palmer,
1st earl of] 1812-1895.

Lines read at a birthday dinner at Seven Oaks,
Bristol, Rhode Island, October 2, 1911.
n.p., 1911.
[20] l.   13 x 23 cm.
Cover title.

NL 0386465   RPB

Lines read at a farewell dinner given to Longfellow,
before his departure for Europe, May 27, 1868
see under   [Holmes, Oliver Wendell] 1809-
1894.

Lines read at a lunch ... at the University club,
Providence, R.I.
see under   [Bourn, Augustus Osborne]
1834-1925.

Lines read at the centennial celebration of the
Hasty pudding club of Harvard college, 1795-
1895 ...
see under   [Wheelwright, John Tyler]
1856-1925.

Lines read at the Davis gathering, Sept. 12, 1872
see under   [Davis, William S   ]

Lines, read at the fiftieth anniversary of the
marriage of W.G. Warren and Mary Eddy,
see under   [Warren, Jonah Goulding]

Lines read at the reunion of the family of Alvin
Greene, Nov. 29, 1883
see under   [Greene, Benjamin]

Lines read before the Yale alumni association of
Fairfield County
see under   Lewis, Alonzo Norton, 1831-
1907.

LINES review. no. 1-
July 1953-
Edinburgh [etc.] M. Macdonald [etc.]

v.   illus. 21-25 cm. quarterly.

Title varies: no. 1-3, Lines.

NL 0386473   CaBVaU OAKU NN

Cb811
L754

Lines sacred to the memory of Capt. Henry C.
Gorell of Greensboro', N.C., of the Second
North Carolina Regiment, who fell in an attack which he led against the Federal Bat-
teries at the battle of Fair Oaks, June 14,
1862... By a Friend of the Cause. ‹n.p.,
n.d.›
‹1›p. 19cm.

1. N.C.--Poetry 2. Gorrell, Henry Clay, 1839
-1862 3. Confederate imprints - North Carolina

NL 0386474   NcU

Lines sacred to the memory of the Reverend
James Grahame
see under   [Wilson, John] 1785-1854.

Lines sent to Lady Miller's vase, January the
fourth, MDCCLXXXI ...
see under   [Bull, Richard] 1725-1806.

Lines suggested on hearing an extract from
a letter by Capt. Chase, brother-in-law

Zc95
D98
1850b

of Mr. Brown Owen, who died on his passage
to California. [n.p., 18--?]
broadside. 25 x 18 cm.

In verse.
Also Published with title: The Dying
Californian.

NL 0386477   CtY

---

*W.99
.1822

Lines, sung at Haverhill, on the twenty second day of February, 1800: in memory of our
beloved General George Washington; who died at
Mount Vernon, December 14, 1799; aged 68.
[Haverhill, Mass.? 1800?]
broadside. 25 x 20cm.
Printed on silk.
Not in Evans or Ford's Massachusetts broadsides.

1. Washington, George, Pres. U. S.--Poetry.
2. Broadsides--   U. S.

NL 0386478   MB

Lines to a boy pursuing a butterfly
see under   [Cockle, Mary]

VOLUME 334

Lines to follow; a cook book.   Buffalo, N. Y.,
Ladies of the Park Presbyterian church, 1896c.

160p.   20cm.

"Authorities consulted" p. 159-160.
Advertising matter interspersed.

NL   0386480   NBuG

369.17
C748

Lines to General Lee.
Confederate Veteran   Vol.II, p.292
(Prose)

NL   0386481   ViLxW

LINES to Mrs. M.B.M. Toland on reading her
poem "Onti Ora" (Indian name for the Catskill
Mountains), by V.L. F. San Francisco, Payot
Upham & company, printers, 1881.

sq.16°. pp.17.
Printed on one side of the leaf only.
                                    AL 3657.7.04

NL   0386482   MH RPB

Lines to my daughter, on her fourteenth birthday
        see under   [Grigsby, Hugh Blair]
1806-1881.

LINES to our sorrowing queen, and other
poems syggested by the death of Prince Albert.
By C.A.D. Kensington, J.Wakeham, 1862.

sm.4°.pp.12.   Br 2165.2

NL   0386484   MH NjP

Lines to the memory of Shakespeare.
London, Printed by W. S. Fortey [1864?]

NL   0386485   DFo

Lines to the Tories of Oxford...
        see under   [Goschen, George Joachim
Goschen] viscount, 1831-1907.

Lines composed by a factory boy, about
fourteen years of age, in Halifax, October
14th, 1836 ... Halifax, J. Nicholson, printer,
[1836?]
[1] p.   18cm.

Caption title.
Last line reads: "My name it is J. C."
Within decorated border.

NL   0386487   MdBJ

LINES written after reading Mrs. M. B. M. Toland's
three poems, "Stella," "Sir Rae," and "Iris, or The romance
of an opal ring." By V. L. F. March, 1879. Philadelphia:
J. B. Lippincott & co., 1879.   17 p.   front.   16½cm.

1. Poetry, American. 2. Toland, Mary B. M.—Poetry.
I. F., V. L.

NL   0386488   NN

Lines written at Ampthill park in the autumn of 1818
        see under   [Luttrell, Henry] 1771-1851.

Lines written at Jerpoint abbey ...
        see under   [Hall, Samuel Carter] 1800-
1889.

Lines written at Warwick castle ...
London, Printed by J.B.Nichols, 1827.
28 p. illus. 30 cm.

Title vignette.
Poem.
Bound with relation du voyage ... 1814.

NL   0386491   MH-BA

Lines written by his sister [upon the death of
Hiram Buffington Anthony]
        see under   [Anthony, Phebe]

LINES written in commemoration of S.Blood's
75 th birthday, and repeated by his grand-
daughter S.B.Sloss, at a family re-union April,
24, 1870. n.p., [1870].

24°. 1 page.

NL   0386493   MH

Lines written in the Album at Cossey-Hall ... [1788]
        see under   [Jerningham, Edward] 1737-1812.

---

*EC8
B8443
819f

Lines written in the library of T. B.
Brydges Barrett, esq. Lee Priory, Kent.
[Kent,Eng.]Lee Priory press.[1817?]

broadside. 24x18.5cm. (In Miscellaneous
articles printed at Lee Priory [1819?])
Vignette (Lee Priory) & quotation at head.
Signed at foot: A. C.
Also issued separately.
In verse.

NL   0386495   MH

Lines written in the month's mind of Mona Dunn
        see under   [Leslie, Shane] 1885-

Lines, written on hearing of the murder
of Mr. Perceval, and of the exultation of the
mob when his body was removed from the House
of Commons, with reference to late riots and
assassinations. [n.p., n.d.]
1 ℓ.   18.5 cm. x 25 cm.

NL   0386497   InU

Lines written on the barley corn.
Dublin, J. Brereton [1867?]

broadside.   illus.   19 X 11cm.

No.26 in a factice collection Irish
broadside ballads.
First line: There was three farmers
in the north as they were passing by.

NL   0386498   MnU

Lines written on the death of Miss Eliza Higgins ...
[by Miranda]
        (In Higgins, Eliza, 1797-1821. Account of
the religious experience and happy death of Miss
Eliza Higgins. New York, 1822. 14 cm. p. 51-
52)
        1. Higgins, Eliza, 1797-1821. Poetry.
I. Miranda.

NL   0386499   RPB

[Lines written on the death of Sally W. and
Claudia A. E., daughters of Dr. & Mrs.
Octavia W. Levert]   [New York, 1849]
[1] p. sq. Q.   ([Fugitive poetry.])
n.t.p.

NL   0386500   RPB

Lines written on the Death of the late ... Samuel
Whitbread ... By a lady, late of Bedford.
Bedford, 1815.
8 p. 8°.   (In "Poems," 32)

NL   0386501   CtY

Lines written on the illiberation of
the clergy. [Dublin] P. Brereton
[1867?]

broadside.   illus.   29 X 11cm.

No.27 in a factice collection Irish
broadside ballads.
First line: You Catholicks all come
let us rejoice.

I. Title

NL   0386502   MnU

Lines written ... on the Isle of St. Pierre ...
        see under   [James, Edwin John] 1812-1882.

Lines written on the railroad accident between Boston and Lawrence,
Jan. 6, 1853, by which four lives were lost!!!!
— [Boston? 1853.] Border. Broadside.

F4103 — Broadsides. — Railroad accidents.

NL   0386504   MB

VOLUME 334

Lines written upon first observing an elephant
devoured by a roc
see under   [Hughes, Richard Arthur
Warren] 1900–

Lines written upon the interment of Her Royal Highness the
Princess Charlotte...   London: J. Hatcahrd [sic], 1817.   12 p.
8°.

1. Charlotte Augusta, princess of Leopold of Saxe-Coburg-Saalfeld, N. Y. P. L.	Wales, princess consort of prince 1796–1817. 2. Poetry, English. November 28, 1928

NL   0386506   NN

Linesman, *pseud.*
    see
Grant, Maurice Harold, 1872–

M787.9
L75
    Linet, Hank

    Fifty famous favorites for the ukulele.
    Rev.   Robbins [c1954]
    59 p.

    1. Music, Popular (Songs, etc.)   2. Ukulele.

NL   0386508   OrP

Rs10
Pa942
    Linet, Jean
    ... Contribution à l'étude de la
    susceptibilité magnétique du bismuth ...
    Paris, 1942.
    Thèse - Univ. de Paris.

NL   0386509   CtY MnU

Linet, Ph.
    Biographical sketch of [Charles Edwin Taylor].
    (*In* Taylor, Charles Edwin. Leaflets from the Danish West
    Indies ... Pp. vii–xv. London. 1888.)

M6475 — Taylor, Charles Edwin.

NL   0386510   MB MdBP

Z7914
.T3R33
    Linetskaia, M. I.
    Расширение ассортимента и улучшение качества трико-
    тажных изделий. Библиогр. указатель. Москва, 19

TH1461
.M69
    Linetskii, A. É.
    Moscow. Vsesoiuznyi nauchno-issledovatel'skii institut po
    stroitel'stvu.
    Литье перегородок и перекрытий из гипсо-известково-
    шлакового раствора. [Брошюра написана С. И. Идашки-
    ным и А. Э. Линецким] Москва, Гос. научно-техн. изд-во
    нефтяной и горно-топливной лит-ры, 1955.

Linetskii, Efim Iakovlevich.
    Сборник заданий по планированию и анализу хозяй-
    ственной деятельности торговых организаций и пред-
    приятий; учебное пособие для торговых вузов. Москва,
    Гос. изд-во торговой лит-ры, 1955.

    146 p.   23 cm.

    At head of title: Е. Я. Линецкий, Д. Я. Савранский.

    1. Russia—Commerce—Handbooks, manuals, etc.   I. Savranskii,
    David Iakovlevich, joint author.   II. Title.
    Title romanized: Sbornik zadanii po planirova-
    nitu i analizu khoziaistvennoi deiatel'nosti.

    HF3627.L5   56–35305

NL   0386513   DLC

Linetskii, IA. L.
    Akademiia arkhitektury SSSR, *Moscow. Institut stroitel'noi
    tekhniki.*
    Монтаж строительных конструкций из готовых железо-
    бетонных элементов. А. Д. Глуховский, Я. И. Линецкий.
    Москва, Гос. изд-во лит-ры по строительству и архитек-
    туре, 1954.

DR267
.L55
    Linetskii, V   N

    Послевоенная Румыния; стенограмма публичной лек-
    ции, прочитанной 17 февраля 1947 года. Москва [Правда]
    1947.

    21 p.   22 cm.

    At head of title: Всесоюзное лекционное бюро при Министерстве
    высшего образования СССР.

    1. Rumania—Pol. & govt.   2. Communism—Rumania.
    Title transliterated: Poslevoennaia Rumyniia.

    DR267.L55   51–29009

NL   0386515   DLC

DT38
.L5
    Linetskii, V   N

    Проникновение США в Африку; стенограмма публич-
    ной лекции, прочитанной 29 июля 1947 года ... в Москве.
    Москва [Правда] 1947.

    23 p.   22 cm.

    At head of title: Всесоюзное общество по распространению
    политических и научных знаний.

    1. U. S.—Relations (general) with Africa. 2. Africa—Relations
    (general) with U. S.
    Title transliterated: Proniknovenie SShA v Afriku.

    DT38.L5   50–18878 ‡

NL   0386516   DLC

Linets'kyi, IU
    see
    Linetskii, Efim Iakovlevich.

PJ5129
.L537B4
Hebraic
Sect.
    Linetzki, Isaac Joel, 1839–1915.
    דער ביוזער מארשעליק, כאמישע פאלקס לידער. ווארשא.
    בדפוס ח. קעלטער. תרל"ט [Варшава, 1879]
    2 v. in 1.   21 cm.

    I. Title.   *Title transliterated:* Der beyzer marshelik.

    PJ5129.L537B4   55–49480 ‡

NL   0386518   DLC

PJ5129
.L537P6
1900
[Hebraic
Sect.]
    Linetzki, Isaac Joel, 1839–1915.
    דאס חסידישע יונגעל. דיא לעבענס-בעשרייבונג פון א פוילישען
    יודען ... פון עלייקין האטאקואלי [pseud.] דיא 3. פאלקסמען
    איבערגעארבייטע אויפ. פאן מיין פוילישען יונגעל. ווילנא.
    הוצאת האחים בלעמענצקי באדעסמא. תרם"ט [Вильна, 1909]
    230 p.   23 cm.

    I. Title.   *Title transliterated:* Dos hasidishe yungel.

    PJ5129.L537P6 1900   55–47263 ‡

NL   0386519   DLC

Dos poylishe yunge

PJ5129
.L537P6
1939
[Hebr
    Linetzki, Isaac Joel, 1839–1915.
    דאס פוילישע יינגל; נעקירצטע אויפל. קעוו. מעלוכע-פארלאג
    פאר די נאציאנאלע מינדערהייטן אין אוקר. [Kiev] 1939.
    152 p.   20 cm.

    I. Title.   *Title transliterated:* Dos Poylishe yingl.

    PJ5129.L537P6 1939   57–52055 ‡

NL   0386520   DLC

PJ5129
.L537P6
Hebraic
Sect.
    Linetzki, Isaac Joel, 1839–1915.
    דאס פוילישע יונגעל; אדער. א ביאגראפיע פון זיך אליין ...
    Das polnische Jüngel. Lemberg, 1896. לבוב. ש. עדעל.
    144 p.   21 cm.
    In Yiddish.

    I. Title.   *Title transliterated:* Dos poylishe yungel.

    PJ5129.L537P6   OCAT   55–47238 ‡

NL   0386521   DLC

PJ
5129
L537P6
1921
    Linetzki, Isaac Joel, 1839–1915.
    דאס פוילישע יונגעל. מים א פארווארם פון מ. זילבערג.
    ווין. פארלאג "דער קוואל." [Vienna] 1921.
    358 p. illus. 17 cm.

    I. Title.   *Title transliterated:* Dos Poylishe yungel.

    PJ5129.L537P6 1921   57–51957 ‡

NL   0386522   DLC MU

Linetzki, Isaac Joel, 1839–1915, tr.
    Iber a pintele
      see under   Gordon, Judah Loeb, 1830–1892.

PJ5129
.L537N5
Hebraic
Sect.
    Linetzki, Isaac Joel, 1839–1915.
    ניט טוידט ניט לעבעדיג; אדער. דעם פוילישען יונגעלס זוהן.
    א בעשרייבונג פון איבערגאנג פונם חסידישען לעבען אין דער
    השכלה-וועלט. ווילנא. תרנ"ח [Вильна, 1898]
    82 p.   24 cm.

    I. Title.   *Title transliterated:* Nit toydt nit lebedig.

    PJ5129.L537N5   OCAT   55–49484 ‡

NL   0386524   DLC

VOLUME 334

PJ5129
.L537V4
Hebraic
Sect.

Linetzki, Isaac Joel, 1839–1915.
דער וועלט-לױ פֿינ'ס יאהר אין כּסף; אדער, דיא אללנעמינע
פֿאַנאָראמע. פֿין עלי קיצין הצחקיאלי ¡pseud.¿ .2 פֿערב. אויפֿ.
אדעססא, נעדרוקקט בײא פֿ. א. זעליגער, תּרמ'ג. 1883.
86 p. 22 cm.

ɪ. Title.   *Title transliterated:* Der velt-luah.

PJ5129.L537V4   OCAT   55–49495 ‡

NL 0386525   DLC

LINETZKY, Moischa.
Die zusammensetzung vegetabilischer tisch-
fertiger speisen der freigewählten arbeit-
erkost. Inaugural-dissertation. Basel,
Buchdr.-Prin & Cie, 1914.

NL 0386526   MH ICRL

Linetzky (Samuel) [1886–]. *Die Beziehungen der Form des Elektrocardiogramms
zu dem Lebensalter, der Herzgrösse und dem
Blutdruck.* 18 pp., 1 ch. 8°. Berlin, L.
Schumacher, 1912.

NL 0386527   DNLM CtY ICRL

Lineu Jordão, João
   see   Jordão, João Lineu, d. 1854.

Lineus, Thomas, b. 1505.
In qvatvor Institvtionvm ivris principis Ivstiniani libros
explicationes & annotationes doctissimae, ex praelectionibus
Thomae Linii ... collectae ... Francoforti, Apvd C. Egenolphum ¡1553¿.
163 p. 31 cm.
   Bound with Aytta, Wigle van. Commentaria in decem titvlos
Institutionum iuris civilis. Basileae, 1552. and Langenbek, Detlev.
Institvtionvm singvli titvli. Coloniae, 1555.
   1. Roman law—Interpretation and construction. 2. Corpus juris
civilis. Institutiones. ɪ. Title.

76–279455

NL 0386529   DLC

Lineus, Thomas, b. 1505
Oratio ‖ in lavdem belli, habita ‖ ab ipfo marte, in poftremo Ca-
meracenfi ‖ concilio, ad conaliandam pacem cõuo-‖cato, poftridie
calendas græ-‖cas. per Thomam Li-‖neum Bufaum-‖ducis. [*Prin-
ter's mark*] Iperis, ‖ Vaenit Gaspari ‖ à lapide, 1531.
   [112] p. ₄ᵗᵒ. 154ᵐᵐ.
   Unpaged.
   Italic type.
   Colophon: Impreffum Parifiis à Chriftiano Wechelo im-‖penfis Gafparis à lapide ciuis
Iperenfis. ‖ 1531.
   Printer's mark also on last page.

NL 0386530   ICJ ICN

Linev, Dmitriĭ Aleksandrovich, 1853–
   По тюрьмамъ ("Впредь до распоряженія"); Записки
заключеннаго. С.-Петербургъ, Тип. Л. В. Фомина, 1878.
   406 p. 24 cm.
   Continued by the author's Въ пересыльной тюрьмѣ.

   1. Prisons—Russia.   ɪ. Title.   ɪɪ. Title: Vpred' do rasporîazhenîi.
                              Title transliterated: Po tîûr'mam.

HV9713.L48   55–55946

NL 0386531   DLC

Linev, Dmitriĭ Aleksandrovich, 1853–
   Въ пересыльной тюрьмѣ. С.-Петербургъ, 1880.
   xii, 347 p. 24 cm.
   "Продолженіе книги 'Впредь до распоряженія' (По тюрьмамъ)"

   1. Prisons—Russia.   ɪ. Title.
                   Title transliterated: V peresyl'noĭ tîûr'mîê.

HV9713.L5   55–55925

NL 0386532   DLC

Lineva, Evgeniîa Éduardovna (Papritẞ) 1854–
   The peasant songs of Great Russia as they are in the folk's
harmonization. Collected and transcribed from phonograms,
by Eugenie Lineff ... Pub. by the Imperial academy of science ... St. Petersburg ¡Printing office of the Imperial academy of science¿; London, Sold by D. Nutt, 1905–12.
   2 v. illus., fold. col. diagrs. 30 cm.
   English and Russian.

      1. Folk-songs, Russian.   ɪ. Akademiîa nauk SSSR. ɪɪ.
   Title.   *Translation of* Великорусские песни в народной гар-
   монизации (*transliterated:* Velikorusskie pesni v narodnoĭ garmoni-
   zatẞiĭ)

M1756.L74V422   9–2293¡ rev 2

   CaBVaU OrP CtY
NL 0386533   DLC WaS PSt NN OO MH MB CtY OC1 CU NcD

Linevich, N. P.

DS517
9
.R8   Russia (1917–   R. S. F. S. R.) TSentral'noe arkhivnoe
          upravlenie.
   Русско-японская война; из дневников А. Н. Куропат-
кина и Н. П. Линевича. С предисл. М. Н. Покровского.
Ленинград, Гос. изд-во, 1925.

Lineva, Evgeniîa Éduardovna (Papritẞ) 1854–
   Russian folk-songs as sung by the people, and peasant wed-
ding ceremonies customary in northern and central Russia.
From authentic material collected and tr. by Mme. Eugenie
Lineff, with a preface on Russian folk-songs by H. E. Krehbiel.
Chicago, C. F. Summy, ᶜ1893.
   63 p. incl. front., illus. 20½ x 16½ᶜᵐ.

      1. Russian ballads and songs. 2. Marriage customs and rites—Russia.
                                             6–10761 Revised
   Library of Congress   ML3690.L75

NL 0386535   DLC Wa WaS PBm ICJ MH CtY ICJ OO

Lineville college, *Lineville, Ala.*
   Catalogue of the officers and students ... with a statement of the course of study, expenses, etc.

   Talladega, Ala.
      v. 19½ᶜᵐ.
   On cover: ... Annual catalogue ...

                              CA 10–707 Unrev'd
   Library of Congress   LD3071.L92

NL 0386536   DLC

TX871
.L54

Linevskiĭ, A   A
   Борьба с обвалами в бурящихся скважинах. Москва,
1949.
   63 p. diagrs. 20 cm. (Бюро технико-экономической информации
ЦИМТнефти. Обмен отечественным опытом. Вып. ¿)

   ¡On тыл Antirẞ¿
                      ɪ. Title.   (Series: Moscow. TSen-
   tral'nyĭ nauchno-issledovatel'skiĭ institut mekhanizatẞiĭ i organizatẞiĭ
   truda v neftîanoĭ promyshlennosti. Bîuro tekhniko-ékonomicheskoĭ
   informatẞiĭ. Obmen otechestvennym opytom)
                      Title transliterated: Bor'ba s obvalami.

TX871.L54   51–27078

NL 0386537   DLC

Linevskiĭ, Aleksandr Mikhaĭlovich.
   Доктор Подобин. Петрозаводск, Кирья, 1937–
      v. 21 cm.

         ɪ. Title.
                              Title transliterated: Doktor Podobin.

PG3476.L59D6   53–56371 ‡

NL 0386538   DLC

Linevskiĭ, Aleksandr Mikhaĭlovich.
   Как это было (партизаны Беломорья); повесть. ¡Пе-
трозаводск¿ Каргосиздат, 1939.
      170 p. illus. 22 cm.

      1. Russia—History—Revolution, 1917–1921—Fiction. ɪ. Title.
                              Title transliterated: Kak éto bylo.

PG3476.L59K3   54–45506 ‡

NL 0386539   DLC

Linevskiĭ, Aleksandr Mikhaĭlovich.
   Листы каменной книги. Петрозаводск, Карельское гос.
изд-во, 1939.
      77 p. illus. 22 cm.

         ɪ. Title.
                              Title transliterated: Listy kamennoĭ knigi.

PG3476.L59L5   53–56377 ‡

NL 0386540   DLC

Linevskiĭ, Aleksandr Mikhaĭlovich.
   Листы каменной книги. Петрозаводск, Гос. изд-во
Карело-Финской ССР, 1952.
      222 p. illus. 21 cm.

         ɪ. Title.
                              Title transliterated: Listy kamennoĭ knigi.

PG3476.L59L5 1952   55–21350 ‡

NL 0386541   DLC

Linevski, Aleksandr Mikhaĭlovich, 1902–
   ...Rock engravings of Karelia. Part 1–   ¡Petrozavodsk¿
Karelian state pub. house, 1939–   v. diagrs., illus. (incl. map.)
22½cm.
   At head of title: Karelian scientific research institute of culture. A. M. Linevski.
   Added t.-p. in Russian: Петроглифы Карелии. Часть 1–   Петро-
заводск, 1939–
   Text in Russian; summary in English.
   Bibliographical footnotes.

      ɪ. Rock drawings—Russia—
   dovatel'ski institut kul'tury, Petroza-   Karelia. ɪ. Karel'ski nauchno-issle-
   glify Karelii.   vodsk, U. S. S. R. ɪɪ. Title: Petro-
   N. Y. P. L.   April 5, 1943

NL 0386542   NN

Lineweaver, Elsie
   A little leaven; an interracial play by ...
¡and¿ Mary Reed. New York, N.Y., Pub. by
the Department of race relations, The
Federal council of the churches of Christ
in America, n.d.
   Cover-title, 14, ¡1¿ p.

   (Interracial publications. Pamphlet no. 21)
   "Second printing."
   Illus. t.-p.

NL 0386543   OC1 OrU

VOLUME 334

Lineweaver, Elsie
A little leaven; an interracial
play, by Elsie Lineweaver [and] Mary
Reed. New York [1935?]
15 p. 23 cm. (Federal Council of
the Churches of Christ in America.
Race relations department. Interracial publications, no. 24)

NL 0386544 MiD

Lineweaver, G. W.
Virginia. *Commission on sea food industry.*
Report of the Commission to investigate and survey the sea
food industry of Virginia. Majority and minority reports.
Submitted to the General assembly January, 1927 [!] ... Rich-
mond, D. Bottom, superintendent of public printing. 1928.

Lineweaver, Hans, 1907–
Solubility and physical state of nitrogen gas in nitrogen fix-
ing *Azotobacter* cells ... By Hans Lineweaver ... [Balti-
more?] 1938]
1 p. l., p. 549–567, 501–509, 1 l. incl. illus., tables, diagrs. 22ᶜᵐ.
Biography.
Thesis (PH. D.)—Johns Hopkins university. 1936.
"Reprints from the Journal of biological chemistry, 122 ... (1938), and
the Journal of bacteriology, 35 ... (1938)"
Bibliography: p. 567; "References": p. 508–509.
CONTENTS.—The solubility and chemical and physical absorption of
nitrogen gas in Azotobacter cells.—Physical characteristics of cells of
Azotobacter, Rhizobium, and Saccharomyces.
1. Nitrogen—Fixation. 2. Azotobacter. 3. Rhizobium. 4. Yeast.

Library of Congress   QR84.L53 1936   39–18676
Johns Hopkins Univ. Libr.   [2]   581.13353

NL 0386546 MdBJ MH-F DLC

Linfert, Carl, 1900–
... Albrecht Altdorfer, die enthüllung der landschaft.
[Mainz, Werkstatt für buchdruck und verlag, 1938]
2 p. l., 9–36 p., 2 l. 22½ᶜᵐ.
"Ein tausend abzüge."
Printed on gray paper.

1. Altdorfer, Albrecht, 1488–1538.
Library of Congress   ND588.A4L5   41–2797
                                                   759.3

NL 0386547 DLC

Linfert, Carl, 1900–
Alt-Kölner Meister. München, F. Bruckmann [1941]
109 p. plates (part col.) 27 cm.
"Literatur": p. 107.

1. Painting—Cologne—Hist. 2. Painting, Gothic. 3. Paintings—
Cologne. I. Title.
ND586.C7L5   759.3   48–30529*

NL 0386548 DLC ICA OU OCU ICU MH MiU OClMA InU NjP

Avery
AA
2700
L63
Linfert, Carl, 1900–
Die Grundlagen der Architekturzeichnung.
Mit einem Versuch über granzösische Architek-
turzeichnungen des 18. Jahrhunderts. [1931]
133–246 l. plates. 28cm.

Caption-title.
From Kunstwissenschaftliche Forschungen, I,
1931.
Photocopy.
Bibliographical footnotes.

NL 0386549 NNC

NC885
.K8L5
Fou.
Linfert, Carl, 1900–
Kallmann, Hans Jürgen, 1908–
Pastelle u. Zeichnungen. [Dietmannsried, W. Rau, 1948]

ND2751
.B4H4
Linfert, Carl, 1900–
Heuser, Heinrich, 1887–
Ein Wandgemälde in den Kammerspielen des Deutschen
Theaters Berlin. Mit einem Geleitwort von Carl Linfert.
Berlin-Grunewald, F. A. Herbig [1948]

Linfert, Carl, 1900–
Xaver Fuhr, neunundvierzig Bilder
see under Fuhr, Xaver, 1898–

NC1140
Z4
folio
Linfert, Carl, 1900–
Zeichnungen und Graphik lebender deutscher Künstler, ausgewählt von einer Gruppe von Deutschen und Amerikanern
in Berlin. [Berlin] Gebr. Mann, 1947.

Linfert, Harriette Elise.
... A scale for measuring the mental development of infants
during the first year of life, by Harriette-Elise Linfert, M. A.,
and Helen M. Hierholzer, M. A. Baltimore, The Williams &
Wilkins company [1928]
v, 33 p. diagr. 23ᶜᵐ. (Studies in psychology and psychiatry. vol. I,
no. 4)
Bibliography: p. 27–28.

1. Infants. 2. Mental tests. 3. Child study. I. Hierholzer, Helen
M., joint author.
Library of Congress   LB1117.L5   29–15493

NL 0386554 DLC MoU NIC OClW OO OCl OU ICJ

LINFIELD, Ben Zion.
Espace discret parametrique et non parame-
trique. These, Strasbourg. Paris, Gauthier-
Villars et cie, 1925.

NL 0386555 MH CtY RPB

Linfield, Ben Zion.
Integral and matric geometry, Euclidean and non-Eucli-
dean. [Ann Arbor? 1955, °1954–
v. 23 cm.

1. Geometry, Analytic. I. Title.
QA551.L5   516   55–23031 ‡

NL 0386556 DLC

Linfield, Ben-Zion, 1897–
On certain polar curves with their application
to the location of the roots of the derivatives
of a rational function, by B. Z. Linfield. Lancaster, Pa., and New York, 1923.
cover-title, p.239–258. 28ᶜᵐ.
Printed by Lütcke & Wulff, Hamburg, Germany.
"Reprinted from the Transactions of the American mathematical society, vol.25, no.2 ... April, 1923."
Bibliographical foot-notes.

1. Curves.

NL 0386557 ViU

LINFIELD, Ben Zion.
On the theory of discrete varieties.
Thesis, Harvard University ,1923.
Manifold copy, 1.8°. ff.(1). 51.
HU 90.1509

NL 0386558 MH

BF
1999
L35
Linfield, Cornelius S.
The Holy Trinity; a metaphysical drawing...
La Crosse, Wis., °1923.
1pam. obl. 8°

NL 0386559 DLC

Linfield, Cornelius S.
Reward one thousand dollars, and the truth about
Christian science, by Cornelius S. Linfield ... La Crosse,
Wis., C. S. Linfield [°1925]
25 p. 20ᶜᵐ.

1. Christian science. I. Title.
Library of Congress   BX6955.L5   26–12312

NL 0386560 DLC

Linfield, Cornelius S.
Science of the trinity, by Cornelius S. Linfield ... La
Crosse, Wis., C. S. Linfield, 1927.
201 p. 15½ᶜᵐ.

I. Title.
Library of Congress   BR126.L5   27–9195

NL 0386561 DLC

[Linfield, E.]
The Answer of his Excellencie Sir Thomas
Fairfax (in behalf of the whole Army) to the
votes and desires of both houses of Royall person.
Wherein he declares, I. The reasons of his
advance nearer to the city of London. II. The
Armies resolution to secure the Kings person.
III. Their charging of a party within the city, for
raising a new Army (against them, as they suppose)
which should rendevous near the city of Worcester.
IV. And lastly, The Armies Protestation towards
the Citizens of London; with their propositions,
concerning the bringing of His Royall Majestie to
Whitehall. Sent from the Army by the Commissioners, Iune. 23. London, Printed for Robert
Williamson. 1647.
sm. 4 to unpaged. (A, 4 leaves.)
Unbound; uncut & unopened. Title within type-
ornament border. With 30 other pamphlets relating to Fairfax and the army, in a dark maroon levant solander case, lettered on back: Fairfax
Tracts, 1645, &c.

NL 0386563 CSmH

[Linfield, Frederick Bloomfield] 1866–
By-products of the dairy. (a.) Experiments in
pig feeding. (b.) Experiments in calf feeding.
Salt Lake City, The Utah Lith. Co., 1898.
1 p.l., (1) 198–249 p. 8°. (Utah Exp. Sta.
Bull. no. 57)

NL 0386564 NN

VOLUME 334

Linfield, F. B.
1. Dairy herd record for 1894-95. 2. Winter feeding experiments with dairy cows. 3. Some suggestions on the building and equipment of factories. Logan: Smith, Cummings & Co. [1896] 64 p., 2 pl. 8°. (Utah. Agricultural experiment station. Bulletin 43.)

1. Cow.—Feeding. 2. Dairies
N. Y. P. L. and dairying.
March 23, 1911.

NL 0386565 NN

630.15 [Linfield, Frederick Bloomfield and others]
L64d The disk harrow. [I H C service bureau, International harvester company of America] [Chicago, c1913]
61p. illus.

NL 0386566 IU

Linfield, Frederick Bloomfield, and Atkinson, Alfred. Dry farming in Montana. 8°. pp. 32. pl. 9. chart. Boseman, 1907. (Montana. Agricultural experiment station. Bulletin no. 63.)

NL 0386567 MBH

Linfield, F. B.
Experiments in butter-making and cheese-making. Salt Lake City: Press of the Utah Lithographing Co. [1901] 54 p., 1 pl. 8°. (Utah. Agricultural experiment station. Bulletin 73.)

1. Butter-making. 2. Cheese-
N. Y. P. L. making.
March 13, 1911.

NL 0386568 NN

[Linfield, F. B.]
Experiments in fattening lambs. Provo: Skelton Pub. Co. [1902.] 55 p. 8°. (Utah. Agricultural Experiment Station. Bull. 78.)

1. Sheep.—Feeding.
N. Y. P. L.
May 26, 1915.

NL 0386569 NN

Linfield, Frederick Bloomfield, 1866-
Experiments with dairy cows. 1. A study of their records. 2. Winter feeding ... 3. Summer feeding... Logan, Smith, Cummings & Co., 1900.
iv, (1) 168-309 p. 8°. (Utah Experiment Sta. Bull. no. 68)

NL 0386570 NN

Linfield, Frederick Bloomfield, 1866- ed.

The farm home. Helena, Independent publishing co. [n.d.]
cover-title, 191 p. illus.

At head of t.-p.: Montana farmers' institutes.

NL 0386571 MtBC

Linfield, Frederick Bloomfield 1866 –
Summary of pig feeding experiments at the Utah experiment station from 1890 to 1902, with deductions from the same. Provo: The Skelton Pub. Co. [1903] 1 p.l., 27-62 p. 8°. (Utah. Agricultural experiment station. Bulletin 94.)

1. Hog.—Feeding.
N. Y. P. L.
March 11, 1911.

NL 0386572 NN

Linfield, Harry Sebee, 1889-
The communal census of Jews; methods used in recent years, by H. S. Linfield ... New York, Jewish statistical bureau, 1938.
2 p. l., 3-31 p. incl. forms. 27½ᵐ. (Jewish library of facts, no. 2)
Reproduced from type-written copy.
Bibliographical notes: p. 21.

1. Jews in the U. S. 2. Jews—Stat. I. Title.
40-34940
Library of Congress E184.J5L67
——— Copy 2.
Copyright AA 313708 [5] 296.0973

NL 0386573 DLC OrU ICRL MH PPT TxU NN OC1WHi OCH

Linfield, Harry Sebee, 1889 –
The communal organization of the Jews in Soviet Russia, by H. S. Linfield... Address delivered before the National Conference of Jewish Social Service, Toronto, Canada, June 25, 1924... New York, 1925. 14 p. 8°.

"Proceedings of the National Conference of Jewish Social Service, 1925."

1. Jews in Russia—Communal
N. Y. P. L. organization.
February 17, 1927

NL 0386574 NN TxDaM MH

Linfield, Harry Sebee, 1889-
... The communal organization of the Jews in the United States, 1927, by Harry S. Linfield ... New York, The American Jewish committee, 1930.
xiii, 15-191 p. illus. (map) diagrs. 21ᶜᵐ.
At head of title: The American Jewish committee, Statistical department, New York.

1. Jews in the U. S. 2. Jews—Societies—Stat. 3. Jews in the U. S.—Charities. 4. Jews in the U. S.—Education. I. American Jewish committee. Statistical dept. II. Title.
31-14824
Library of Congress E184.J5L68
——— Copy 2.
Copyright A 32951 [3-5] 296

NL 0386575 DLC CBM MtU OrU PBm PPT MB OC1 WaU MH

Z6367 Linfield, Harry Sebee, 1889- ed.
.H45
Hebr Hasid's index to periodicals and booklist; current magazine articles and new books on the vital aspects of Jewish life. v. 1-6, no. 1/2; Apr. 1932-Feb. 1937. New York [etc., 1932-37]

Z6367 Linfield, Harry Sebee, 1889- ed.
.H46
Hasid's weekly bookletter. -v. 4, no. 15/17; -Apr. 29, 1937. New York, Jewish statistical bureau, 193-37.

Linfield, Harry Sebee, 1889-
Jewish migration. Jewish migration as a part of world migration movements, 1920-1930, by Harry S. Linfield ... New York, Priv. print., 1931.
3 p. l., [3]-43 p. 20½ᵐ. [Jewish library of facts. no. 1]
Label mounted on t.-p.: Jewish library of facts. no. 1. Jewish statistical bureau. New York, 1933.
"Parts of this study are published in the Proceedings of the National conference of Jewish social service, 1930."

1. Jews—Migration.
33-37265
Library of Congress JV6348.J4L5
[a44d1] [325] 296

NL 0386578 DLC OrU OrCS MiU OC1

Linfield, Harry Sebee, 1889-
Jewish migration. Jewish migration as a part of world migration movements, 1920-1930.
= New York, Jewish Statistical Bureau, 1933. (3), 43 pp. Tables. [Jewish library of facts. No. 1.] 20½ cm.
The imprint and the series title appear on a cancel on the title-page.

D6286—T.r.—S.r.—Jews. Emig.

NL 0386579 MB ICRL OCH

Linfield, Harry Sebee, 1889-
... The Jews in the United States, 1927; a study of their number and distribution, by Harry S. Linfield ... New York, The American Jewish committee, 1929.
107, [4] p. incl. illus., tables, diagrs. 21ᶜᵐ.
At head of title: The American Jewish committee, Statistical department, New York.
"Reprinted with corrections and additions from the American Jewish year book, volume 30."

1. Jews in the U. S. 2. Jews—Stat. I. American Jewish committee.
29-9119
Library of Congress E184.J5L69

MiU
NL 0386580 DLC ICJS CBM OU IdU OrP NcD OO OC1 OCX

Linfield, Harry Sebee, 1889-
... The relation of Jewish to Babylonian law ... by Harry Sebee Linfield ... [Chicago, 1919]
1 p. l., p. 40-66. 24ᵐ.
Thesis (PH. D.)—University of Chicago, 1919.
"Private edition, distributed by the University of Chicago libraries, Chicago, Illinois."
"Reprinted from the American Journal of Semitic languages and literatures, vol. xxxvi, no. 1, October 1919."

1. Jews—Law. 2. Law—Babylonia.
20-3438
Library of Congress DS111.2.L5
Univ. of Chicago Libr. [a41c1]

NL 0386581 ICU NcU MB DLC

Linfield, Harry Sebee, 1889-
State population census by faiths; meaning, reliability and value, by H. S. Linfield ... New York, Hasid's bibliographic and library service, 1938.
71, [1] p. 23ᵐ.
"Bibliography, communications from government census offices and from church bodies": p. [69]-[72]

1. Church statistics. I. Title.
39-2576
Library of Congress BR148.L5
——— Copy 2.
Copyright A 124641 [3] 280

OCH OO PU NcD
NL 0386582 DLC OrU CU WaTC N NN PU PPD PCC OC1 OCU

Linfield, Harry Sebee, 1889-
Statistics of Jews and Jewish organizations; historical review of ten censuses, 1850-1937, by H. S. Linfield ... New York, The American Jewish committee, 1939.
64 p. incl. tables. 20½ᵐ.
"Pages 5-28 are reprinted from American Jewish year book, volume 40, p. 61-84, with additions and corrections."
Bibliography: p. 64.

1. Jews in the U. S. 2. Jews—Stat. I. Title.
41-8886
Library of Congress E184.J5L71½
296.0973

ICRL PCC NBuG NN
NL 0386583 DLC OrP OrCS OrU WaT NcRS NcD PPDrop CtY

VOLUME 334

Linfield, Harry Sebee, 1889–
Statistics of Jews, 1925. The number of Jews in the United States and in foreign countries and Jewish immigration, by H. S. Linfield ... Philadelphia, American Jewish year book, 1926.
1 p. l., p. 379–428. illus. (maps) 18ᵐ.

1. Jews—Stat. 2. Jews in the U. S.

27–5371

Library of Congress   E184.J5L7

NL 0386584   DLC NN

Linfield, Harry Sebee, 1889–
Statistics of Jews, 1926; the number of Jews in the United States and in foreign countries, and Jewish immigration, with an appendix: the Jews of Hungary—census of 1920, by H. S. Linfield ... Philadelphia, 1927. 227–281 p. incl. tables. 12°.

Cover-title.
Repr.: Amer. Jewish year book. v. 29. 1927–28.

1. Jews—Stat., 1926. 2. Jews in   the United States, 1926.
N. Y. P. L.   July 6, 1928

NL 0386585   NN OCH

Linfield, Harry Sebee, 1889–
Statistics of Jews, 1927; the number of Jews in the United States and in foreign countries, and Jewish immigration, by H. S. Linfield ... Philadelphia ₁Pa.₎, 1928. 245–270 p. incl. tables. 12°.

Cover-title.
Repr.: Amer. Jewish year book, 5689.

529913A. 1. Jews—Stat., 1926.   2. Jews in the United States, 1926.
N. Y. P. L.   September 3, 1931

NL 0386586   NN

Linfield, Harry Sebee, 1889–
... Statistics of Jews, 1931, by Harry S. Linfield ... New York, The American Jewish committee, 1931.
vii, 9–75 p. incl. tables. 21ᶜᵐ.

At head of title: The American Jewish committee, Statistical department, New York.
"Reprinted with corrections and additions from the American Jewish year book, volume 32."

1. Jews—Stat.   I. American Jewish committee. Statistical dept.
Library of Congress   HD3255.L5   31–22354
————— Copy 2.
Copyright A 40963   ₁3₎   296

CaBVa ICJ OO
NL 0386587   DLC MtBC OrP ICJ MB IdU-SB PPDrop WaS OCl

Linfield, Harry Sebee, 1889–
Survey of year 5686. A survey of Jewish conditions in the United States and abroad during April, 1925–March, 1926, by H. S. Linfield ... Philadelphia, American Jewish year book, 1926.
1 p. l., p. 23–153. 18ᵐ.

1. Jews—Political and social conditions. 2. Jews in the U. S.
I. Title.
                                                  27–4686

Library of Congress   E184.J5L73

NL 0386588   DLC NN

Linfield, Harry Sebee, 1889–
Survey of year 5687; a survey of Jewish conditions in the United States and abroad during April, 1926–March, 1927, by H. S. Linfield... Philadelphia: Amer. Jewish Year Book, 5688—1927. 21–119 p. 12°.

Cover-title.
Repr.: Amer. Jewish year book, 1927.

396551A. 1. Jews—Hist., Modern.
N. Y. P. ᵀ   January 28, 1929

NL 0386589   NN OCH

Linfield, John H
Singers of bygone days; a retrospect of the fifty years—1894 to 1944, and some of the sleeping memories it awakens of those who sang and charmed in these far-off yesterdays. ₁2d ed. n. p., 1952 or 3₎
17 p. 19 cm.

1. Music—England—Hist. & crit. 2. Singers, English.   I. Title.

ML286.L5   780.942   55–17306 ‡

NL 0386590   DLC NN

Linfield, Mary Barrow.
Day of victory ₁by₎ Mary Barrow Linfield. Garden City, N. Y., Doubleday, Doran and company, inc., 1936.
4 p. l., 239 p. 20½ᵐ.
"First edition."

I. Title.
                                                  36–7480
Library of Congress   PZ3.L65406Day

NL 0386591   DLC ViU

Linfield, Mary Barrow.
Japonica grove, by Mary Barrow Linfield. Garden City, N. Y., Doubleday, Doran & company, inc., 1935.
3 p. l., 282 p. 20½ᵐ.
"First edition."

I. Title.
                                                  35–4597
Library of Congress   PZ3.L65406Jap

NL 0386592   DLC WaSp OU PP NcD MB OCf

Linfield, Mary Barrow.
Young woman in love, by Mary Barrow Linfield. New York, The Macaulay company ₁°1929₎
3 p. l., 9–322 p. 20ᵐ.

I. Title.
                                                  29–2737
Library of Congress   PZ3.L65406Yo

NL 0386593   DLC ViU MiU

₁**Linfield, Seymour Laporte**₎
Laws relating to birth control in the United States and its territories. New York, N. Y., Birth control clinical research bureau, 1938.
61 p. 20½ᵐ.

"Prepared for Birth control clinical research bureau by Seymour L. Linfield ... under the direction of Professor Walter Gellhorn."—p. ₁2₎

1. Birth control—U. S.   I. Gellhorn, Walter, 1906–   II. Birth control clinical research bureau, New York.   III. Title.
                                                  38–33379

NL 0386594   DLC PPT Mi OClW MiD OCl NN

Linfield, Thomas, 1650–1724.
An answer to a printed letter, said to be written by Mr. Lesley...
see under   Campbell, Archibald, bp. of Aberdeen, d. 1744.

Linfield, William W , 1862, compiler.
The Declaration of Independence, the Constitution of the United States of America, the Farewell Address of George Washington, and the Proclamation of General Jackson to the Nullifiers of South Carolina in 1832. Arranged by William W. Linfield.   Randolph, Mass.: Printed by Samuel P. Brown. 1862.
123 p., front. (port.) sm. 8 vo.   In the orig. 1/2 black pebbled cloth; gray boards.
Lewisson Collection, September 1922.

NL 0386596   CSmH

378.795 **Linfield College,** McMinnville, Ore.
L₸   Alumni directory, Linfield College, 1884–1947. McMinnville, Ore., 1947.
            105p. 23cm.

1. Linfield College, McMinnville, Ore. Alumni. 2. Linfield College, McMinnville, Ore. Registers.

NL 0386597   OrU

Linfield college, *McMinnville, Or.*
... Annual catalogue ... Announcements ...

McMinnville, Or., 18 –₁19
v. plates. 21–23ᶜᵐ.
At head of title, 18
McMinnville college.
On cover: 19   McMinnville college bulletin ...; 19
Linfield college bulletin ... (series note also at head of title)

Library of Congress   LD3071.L96
                           ₁s32b1₎   378.795

NL 0386598   DLC OrP Or OrHi OrU NjP OrCS PU

LINFIELD COLLEGE, *McMinnville, Oregon.*
Exhibition | of | M'Minville ₁sic₎ College. | July Fourth, 1859. | ₁double wavy rule₎ | Programme: ₁169aa₎
Broadside. 17.2 x 31.8 cm. Decorative border. Printed in 2 columns on blue paper.
The name of McMinnville College, a Baptist institution, was changed to Linfield College in 1922. There was no printer in the vicinity in 1859; the broadside, was, perhaps, printed in the Oregon Weekly Union Office in Corvallis, where most of the 1859 and 1860 printing of the Baptist associations was done.

NL 0386599   OrMcL

Linfield College, McMinnville, Oregon.
Exhibition of M'Minville ₁sic₎ College. July Fourth, 1859. [Double wavy rule] Programme: ₁169aa₎
Broadside. 17.2 x 31.8 cm. Photostat.

NL 0386600   OrU

LINFIELD COLLEGE, McMINNVILLE, ORE.
Inauguration of Elam Jonathan Anderson as the tenth president of Linfield college, Sunday, October twenty-third, nineteen hundred thirty-two, three o'clock p.m. ₁Author, 1932₎
₁8₎ p.

NL 0386601   Or

VOLUME 334

PNC
378.795 Linfield college, McMinnville, Ore.
L643*l*   The Linfield bulletin explaining the new plan
adopted by the faculty and board of trustees, 1933.
McMinnville, Ore., Author, 1933.
48p. illus., ports. (Linfield college
bulletin, v.3, no. 3, Ap. 1933)

Cover-title: The new Linfield plan.

NL 0386602   WaPS

LINFIELD COLLEGE, McMINNVILLE, ORE.
Linfield reporter; news-picture story of Linfield development program. ⟨McMinnville, 1949⟩
1 v. illus.

NL 0386603   Or

LINFIELD COLLEGE, McMINNVILLE, ORE.
A note on Linfield college, McMinnville,
Oregon. ⟨Author, 1937?⟩
⟨4⟩ p.

NL 0386604   Or

LD
3071   Linfield College, McMinnville, Ore.
.L9575   Rules and regulations.   McMinnville
⟨189-?⟩
7p. 18cm.

At head of title: McMinnville College.

NL 0386605   OrU

Linfoot, Benjamin.
... Architectural picture making with pen & ink, by
Benjamin Linfoot ... Philadelphia, 1884.
24 p. illus., 32 pl. 30½ x 45ᶜᵐ. ("Old Ebor" folios)
1st edition, no. 1.

1. Architectural drawing.

Library of Congress   NA2700.L5

11-33354

NL 0386606   DLC NIC PP PSt OCl OOxM MB NjP

Linfoot ⟨Benjamin⟩. Miner's Hospital, Hazle-
ton, Pa. Plan. broadside, 14 by 18 inches. Boston, Heliotype Co., 1889

NL 0386607   DNLM

Linfoot, Edward Hubert.
Recent advances in optics. Oxford, Clarendon Press, 1955.
286 p. illus. 25 cm. (The International series of monographs
on physics)

1. Optics. 2. Optical instruments. I. Title.

QC357.L5   55-14708 ‡

OCl NcD IU
NBC OClCS PPLas PBL MsSM PSt PPD OO ICJ ICU TxU OU
ViU IaU CSt MB NN MtBC CoGuW KyLoU MiU OrU ScCleA TU
NL 0386608   DLC CaBVaU CaBVa IEN MiU PPF NNC NcU CU

F191   Linfoot, Frances Carter.
.S68
1923/   **Society of Virginia of the District of Columbia.**
1933   Minutes of the proceedings of the Society of Virginia of
the District of Columbia (from November 8, 1923 to October 31, 1933, the first ten years) Frances Carter Linfoot,
secretary. ⟨Washington, 1933⟩

Linfoot, Sydney.
Dental caries and the intestinal flora
see under Anderson, T S

Linford, Alexander.
Flow measurement & meters. London, E. & F. N. Spon,
1949.
336 p. illus. 23 cm. (Mechanical engineering series)
"References": p. 326-330.

1. Flow meters.   (Series)

TC177.L56   532.5   50-13878

NL 0386611   DLC CU PSt PP TxU NcD ICJ PPF WaS OrCS ICJ

Linford, Alton A
Old age assistance in Massachusetts. Chicago, University
of Chicago Press ⟨1949⟩
viii, 418 p. diagrs. 23 cm. (Social service monographs)
"Selected bibliography": p. 416-418.

1. Old age pensions—Massachusetts. I. Title.   (Series)

HV1468.M4L5   362.6   49-50014*

MtU OrU Wa WaE
TxU MB ICU NN CU OrCS CaBVaU IdB IdPS MtBC OrP OrPR
WaS OrStbM Or WaPS Wa NcD OClW MH OCl TU OClJC OU
NL 0386612   DLC OrU-M WaWW WaTC WaT OrSaW MtBuM WaSpG

Linford, Alton A., ed.

National Conference on Social Welfare.
Social security in 1953: selected papers on social security
presented at the 80th annual meeting of the National Conference of Social Work, May 31–June 5, 1953, Cleveland,
Ohio. Edited by Alton A. Linford. Columbus, Ohio ⟨1953⟩

PZ   Linford, Dee
4   Man without a star. Chicago, Sears Readers
L754   Club ⟨1952⟩
Man   312p. 21cm.

NL 0386614   WU MB IU

Linford, Dee.
Man without a star. New York, W. Morrow ⟨1952⟩
312 p. 21 cm.

I. Title.

PZ4.L754Man   52-9701 ‡

NL 0386615   DLC CaBVa-WaE WaSp Or CLU NcD NN OOxM

PS3562
I 495   Linford, Dee
M3   Man without a star. New York, Bantam
1955   Books ⟨1955⟩
314 p. 18cm.

First published in 1952.

NL 0386616   GU

C929.4
L645wy Linford, Dee
Wyoming stream names.   Cheyenne,
Wyo., Wyoming Game and Fish Dept., 1944.
33p. illus., map. 23cm. (Wyoming
Game and Fish Dept. Bulletin no.3)

"Material reprinted from Wyoming wild
life, official publication of the Wyoming
Game and Fish Commission."

NL 0386617   CoD NjP

TX357   Linford, Edith (Johnson)
.C2522
California. University. *Heller committee for research in
social economics.*
Wartime food for four income levels. Prices for San Francisco, March 1944, by Ruth Okey and Edith J. Linford. Issued
by the Heller committee for research in social economics, University of California ... Berkeley, Calif., University of California press ⟨*1944⟩

D621.323
L643
Linford, Henry Blood, 1911–
Cleaning and preparation of metals for
electroplating, by Henry B. Linford and Ed-
ward B. Saubestre. Jenkintown, Pa., American
Electroplaters' Society ⟨1951?⟩
cover-title, 84 p. diagrs., tables.
(A. E. S. research report serial, no. 18)

A. E. S. research project no. 12.
Reprinted from Plating, published by the
American Electroplaters' Society, 1950 and
1951.
Includes bibliographies.

NL 0386619   NNC WaT

TS
670   Linford, Henry Blood, 1911–
.L64   The effect of pressure on the electrodepo-
sition of metals; final report by Henry B.
Linford ⟨and⟩ Irving Noch, Jr. ⟨New York,
Columbia University⟩ 1954.
143 l. illus., diagrs., tables.

"Contract No. DA-30-069-ORD-750."
"RAD Order No. OOR-12-52; ORDTS-PS2-1095;
RAD Project No. TB2-00001(447); Cu 954 ORT
750 ChE -."

NL 0386620   NNC

546.83 Linford, Henry Blood, 1911–
L645e   The electrolysis of aqueous solutions of sodium and zirconyl sulfates ... ⟨Pullman, Wash.⟩
1936.
⟨5⟩ 54 l. tables, diagrs.

Thesis (Ph. D) - State college of Washington
Typewritten, on one side of page only.
Bibliography: p. 54.
c.2 is Z. Thesis

NL 0386621   WaPS

VOLUME 334

Linford, Henry Blood, 1911-
The electrolysis of aqueous solutions of
sodium and zirconyl sulfates ...

(In State college of Washington. Research
studies, Pullman, Wash. v.4, no.1, Mar., 1936,
p.53)
Abstract of thesis (Ph.D.) - State college
of Washington, 1936.

1. Zirconium. 2. Sodium.   I. Title

NL 0386622 WaPS

Z
547.26   Linford, Hooper
L645o   Orientation in the benzene ring. The bromina
Thesis   tion of 2-amino-resorcinol-dimethyl ether.
1928. 46*l*

NL 0386623 WaPS

Linford, Hooper
The reducing action of sodium on benzyl
chloride in liquid ammonia solution...
[Cinoin., 1931]
48 l.

NL 0386624 OCU

Linford, James Henry, 1836-1925.
An autobiography of James Henry Linford, Sr., patriarch of
the Church of Jesus Christ of Latter-day Saints of Kaysville,
Utah. [Logan, Utah] John Linford Family Organization,
1947.
vi, 104 p. ports. 25 cm.
"For this new printing the genealogy of the Linford family has been
compiled as completely and accurately as possible as of June 30, 1947."

1. Linford family. 2. Linford family (John Linford, 1808-1856)
F826.L55 1947   920   47-7101*

NL 0386625 DLC WHi MB NN

Linford, Leo Hulme, 1907-
The emission of electrons by swiftly moving
mercury ions, by Leo Hulme Linford ... [Berke-
ley, Calif., 1935]
1 p.l., 28 numb. l. mounted diagrs. 29 cm.
Thesis (Ph. D.) - Univ. of California, May
1935.
"References": p. 28.
1. Electrons. 2. Mercury. 3. Electric
discharges.

NL 0386626 CU

Linford, Leon Blood, 1904-
The effect of intense electric fields on the
photo-electric behavior of thin alkali metal films
on tungsten, by Leon Blood Linford ... [Berke-
ley, 1930]
1 p.l., 30 numb. l. mounted diagrs. 29 cm.
1. Photoelectricity. 2. Metals. I. Title:
Photo-electric behavior of thin alkali metal films
on tungsten.

NL 0386627 CU

Linford, Madeline.
Bread and honey, by Madeline Linford. London, W.
Heinemann, ltd. [1928]
3 p. l., 352 p. 19cm.

I. Title.

Library of Congress   PZ3.L65407Bn
                                              28-13488

NL 0386628 DLC

Linford, Madeline.
Broken bridges [by] Madeline Linford. [London] L.
Parsons, 1923.
312, [1] p. 19½cm.

I. Title.

Library of Congress   PZ3.L65407Br
                                              23-16384

NL 0386629 DLC MiU OC1 OC1h

Linford, Madeline.
Broken bridges, by Madeline Linford.   New York: G. H.
Doran & Co. [1924] 310 p. 12°.

153803A. 1. Fiction (English).   2. Title.
N. Y. P. L.   October 15, 1924

NL 0386630 NN PPM PHC

Linford, Madeline.
A home and children [by] Madeline Linford. [London]
L. Parsons, 1926.
350 p. 19½cm.

I. Title.

Library of Congress   PZ3.L65407Ho
                                              26-11211

NL 0386631 DLC

Linford, Madeline.
Mary Wollstonecraft (1759-1797) by Madeline Linford.
London, L. Parsons; Boston, Small, Maynard and company
[1924]
187, [3] p. front. (port.) 19 cm. (The Roadmaker series)
"Books recommended" : 1 p. at end.

1. Wollstonecraft, Mary, 1759-1797.

PR5841.W8Z755   25-7583

FMU
NBuC WaU NcD MiU CU PRosC PPM OO OU OOxM NN IU ICN
NL 0386632 DLC AAP CaBViP CaBVaU WaS WaSp OrP MeB WU

Linford, Madeline.
Out of the window [by] Madeline Linford. London, E.
Benn limited [1930]
286 p. 19cm.

I. Title.

Library of Congress   PZ3.L65407Ou
                                              30-30616

NL 0386633 DLC

LINFORD, Madeline.
The roadside fire. [London], L.Parsons,
1924.

NL 0386634 MH

SB608
P25L5
Linford, Maurice B.
A fusarium wilt of peas in Wisconsin.
Madison, 1928. 1pam. 8°

NL 0386635 DLC

Linford, Thomas
see
Lynford, Thomas, 1650-1724.

Linford, Velma.
Wyoming, frontier state; drawings by Ramona Bowman.
Denver, Old West Pub. Co., 1947.
xii, 428 p. illus., ports., maps. 24 cm.
Includes bibliographies.

1. Wyoming—Hist.
F761.L65   978.7   47-7183*

ICU CU TxU
NL 0386637 DLC Wa CaBVaU MtU Or MtBC WaT OrP CoU OrU

Lindfors, Per.
Musikens mästare. Stockholm, Wahlström & Widstrand
[1946]
314 p. illus., ports., music. 24 cm.
CONTENTS.—Johann Sebastian Bach.—Georg Friedrich Händel.—
Joseph Haydn.—Wolfgang Amadeus Mozart.—Ludwig van Beethoven.—
Robert Schumann.

1. Composers, German.
ML390.L65   927.8   47-29315*

NL 0386638 DLC

Linforth, Ivan Mortimer, 1879-
The arts of Orpheus, by Ivan M. Linforth. Berkeley and Los
Angeles, University of California press, 1941.
xviii p., 1 l., 370 p. 20cm.
Bibliographical foot-notes.

1. Orpheus. 2. Dionysus. 3. Mysteries, Religious. I. Title.
Library of Congress   BL820.O7L5   41-52443
                                                          292

OrPR OrU Wa WaE
WaSpG MtBuM OrU-M MtBC CaBVaU MtU OrCS IdB OrP IdPI
OrSaW CU OrStbM Or TU WaT WaPS WaTC WaS WaWW WaSp
NL 0386639 DLC ViU MH WaU OU OCU PSC PPWe PU MB NcD

Linforth, Ivan Mortimer, 1879-
The Corybantic rites in Plato, by Ivan M. Linforth. Berkeley and Los Angeles, University of California press, 1946.
1 p. l., 121-162 p. 24cm. (On cover: University of California publications in classical philology, v. 13, no. 5)
Bibliographical foot-notes.

1. Rites and ceremonies—Greece. 2. Plato. I. Title.
                                                          A 46-4755
California. Univ. Libr.
    for Library of Congress   [5]

WaT Wa WaE WaTC WaPS WaS WaWW WaSp Or OrStbM CU
GU OrP OrCS MtU MtBC IdU IdPI IdB CaBVaU OrU WaSpG
NL 0386640 CLU MtBuM OrU-M TxU MB ViU PSt MsU OrPR

Linforth, Ivan Mortimer, 1879-
... Epaphos and the Egyptian Apis, by Ivan M. Linforth.
Berkeley, The University press [1910]
cover-title, p. [81]-92. 27cm. (University of California publications
in classical philology, v. 2, no. 5)
Bibliographical foot-notes.

1. Epaphus. 2. Apis.
California. Univ. Libr.   A 10—1123
    for Library of Congress   PA25.C3 vol. 2, no. 5
——— Copy 2.   BL820.E7L5

ViU DLC NN CU
NL 0386641 CLU CaBVaU OrU OrPR PBm GU NcD MiU OCU OU

VOLUME 334

Linforth, Ivan Mortimer, 1879–
　　Greek gods and foreign gods in Herodotus, by Ivan M. Linworth ... Berkeley, Calif., University of California press, 1926.
　　cover-title, 1 p. l., 25 p. 25ᶜᵐ. (University of California publications in classical philology. v. 9, no. 1)

　　1. Herodotus. 2. Greece—Religion. 3. Mythology, Classical. 4. Religions. I. Title.

Title from Univ. of Calif.　　　Library of Congress　　A 26–265

　　MtBC OrP OrPS Wa OrPR WaE OrU WaPS WaS WaSp CU
　　PBm OrU-M OrSaW OrStbM CU CaBVaU MtBuM IdB IdPI IdU
NL　0386642　CLU MB ViU WaWW OCU OC1 MiU WaT OU NcD Or

Linforth, Ivan Mortimer, 1879–
　　Herodotus' avowal of silence in his account of Egypt, by Ivan M. Linforth ... Berkeley, Calif., University of California press ₁1924₎
　　cover-title, 1 p. l., ₁269₎–292 p. 24½ cm. (University of California publications in classical philology. v. 7, no. 9)
　　Bibliographical foot-notes.

　　1. Herodotus.
　　PA25.C3　vol. 7, no. 9　　　　　　　A 24–1027
　　——— Copy 2.　　PA4004.L5

California. Univ. Libr.
for Library of Congress　　₁a61f½₎†

　　CU GU MsU OC1 OCU ViU DLC
NL　0386643　CLU OrU FTaSU OrPR PBm CaBVaU NcD MiU CSt

Linforth, Ivan Mortimer, 1879–
　　Named and unnamed gods in Herodotus, by Ivan M. Linforth ... Berkeley, Calif., University of California press, 1928.
　　cover-title, 1 p. l., p. ₁201₎–243. 25ᶜᵐ. (University of California publications in classical philology. v. 9, no. 7)

　　1. Herodotus. 2. Gods.　I. Title.
California. Univ. Library　　　　　　A 29–68
for Library of Congress　　PA25.C3　vol. 9, no. 7
　　——— Copy 2.　　PA4004.L52
　　　　　　　　　₁a39e1₎　　　　(480.82)

　　WaPS WaS WaSp OrStbM WaWW CU OrSaW WaTC WaT WaSpG
　　PBm PU MtU MtBC IdU IdPI MsU IdB CaBVaU OrU Wa WaE
NL　0386644　CLU MtBuM OrU-M ViU DLC OrPS OrP OrCS NcD

Linforth, Ivan Mortimer, 1879–
　　The pyre on Mount Oeta in Sophocles' "Trachiniae." Berkeley, University of California Press, 1952.
　　255–267 p. 24 cm. (University of California publications in classical philology, v. 14, no. 7)
　　Bibliographical footnotes.

　　1. Sophocles. Trachiniae.　I. Title.　(Series: California. University. University of California publications in classical philology, v. 14, no. 7)
　　PA25.C3　vol. 14, no. 7　　　　　　A 52–0417
　　——— Copy 2.　　PA4417.L547

California. Univ. Libr.
for Library of Congress　　₁5₎†

　　OrCS OrP OrPR OrU WaTC WaWW WaT WaSpG WaS WaPS CU
　　OrU-M OrSaW GU OrStbM FTaSU Or IdPI IdU MtBC Wa
NL　0386645　CLU DLC TxU ViU OCU PSt IdB CaBVaU MtBuM

Linforth, Ivan Mortimer, 1879–
　　Religion and drama in "Oedipus at Colonus." Berkeley, University of California Press, 1951.
　　75–191 p. 24 cm. (University of California publications in classical philology, v. 14, no. 4)
　　Bibliographical footnotes.

　　1. Sophocles. Œdipus Coloneus. 2. Religion in literature.　(Series: California. University. University of California publications in classical philology, v. 14, no. 4)
　　PA25.C3　vol. 14, no. 4　　　882.2　　A 52–9041
　　——— Copy 2.　　PA4417.L55

California. Univ. Libr.
for Library of Congress

　　OrU-M MtBuM OrSaW Or WaTC WaS WaSpG WaE CU DLC
　　IdPI IdB FTaSU CaBVaU Wa WaPS WaSp WaT WaWW OrStbM
NL　0386646　CLU OrU OrPR OrP OrCS ViU TxU MtU MtBC IdU

Linforth, Ivan Mortimer, 1879–
　　Solon the Athenian, by Ivan M. Linforth. Berkeley, University of California press, 1919.
　　1 p. l., vii, 318 p. 24½ᶜᵐ. (University of California publications in classical philology. v. 6)
　　CONTENTS.—Biographical essay.—The fragments of Solon's poems.—Appendices.

　　1. Solon.
　　　　　　　　　　　　　　　　A 20–324
Title from Univ. of　　　　Calif.
Library of Congress　　　　PA25.C3　ₚol. 6
　　　　　　　　　　　　₁34:1₎

　　WaTC WaS WaSpG WaT WaWW CU
　　IdPS IdU MtBC MtU OrCS OrP OrPR OrU Wa WaE WaPS WaSp
NL　0386647　CLU Or OrStbM OrSaW OrU-M MtBuM CaBVaU IdB

Linforth, Ivan Mortimer, 1879–
　　Solon the Athenian, by Ivan M. Linforth. Berkeley, University of California press, 1919.
　　1 p. l., vii, 318 p. 23ᶜᵐ. (Half-title: Semicentennial publications of the University of California, 1868–1918)
　　Issued originally as University of California publications in classical philology. v. 6.
　　CONTENTS.—Biographical essay.—The fragments of Solon's poems.—Appendices.

　　1. Solon.
　　　　　　　　　　　　　　　A 20–1284
California. Univ. Librar
for Library of Congress　　DF224.S7L5　1919

　　GU OC1 OU OCU ViU IdU
NL　0386648　CLU DLC ViU PHC PSC PBm PU TU NcD MsU CU

Linforth, Ivan Mortimer, 1879–
　　Soul and sieve in Plato's Gorgias, by Ivan M. Linforth. Berkeley and Los Angeles, University of California press, 1944.
　　2 p. l., 295–313 p. incl. facsim. 24ᶜᵐ. (On cover: University of California publications in classical philology, v. 12, no. 17)
　　Bibliographical foot-notes.

　　1. Plato. Gorgias. 2. Soul.　I. Title.
　　　　　　　　　　　　　　　A 44–982
California. Univ. Libr.
for Library of Congress　　PA25.C3　vol. 12, no. 17
　　——— Copy 2.　　PA4279.G7L5
　　　　　　　　　　(480.82)　888.4

　　OrP OrPR OrU Wa WaE WaPS WaS WaSp WaSpG WaT WaTC MtU
　　Or ViU MB PSt PBm MsU CaBVaU IdB IdU MtBC OrCS WaWW
NL　0386649　CLU MtBuM IdPI DLC OCU OrU-M OrSaW OrStbM

Linforth, Ivan Mortimer, 1879–
　　Telestic madness in Plato, Phaedrus 244 DE, by Ivan M. Linforth ... Berkeley and Los Angeles, University of California press, 1946.
　　1 p. l., 163–172 p. 24ᶜᵐ. (University of California publications in classical philology, v. 13, no. 6)

　　1. Insanity in literature. 2. Plato. Phaedrus.　I. Title.
　　　　　　　　　　　　　　　A 46–4756
California. Univ. Libr.
for Library of Congress　　₁5₎

　　WaTC WaWW CaBVaU IdB IdU MtBC MtU OrCS OrP OrPR OrU
　　PSt ViU MB MsU GU Wa WaE WaPS WaS WaSp WaSpG WaT
NL　0386650　CLU TxU OrU-M OrSaW OrStbM MtBuM IdPI Or

Linforth, Ivan Mortimer, 1879–
　　Three scenes in Sophocles' "Ajax." Berkeley, University of California Press, 1954.
　　28 p. 24 cm. (University of California publications in classical philology, v. 15, no. 1)
　　Bibliographical footnotes.

　　1. Sophocles. Ajax.　I. Title.　(Series: California. University. University of California publications in classical philology, v. 15, no. 1)
　　[PA25.C3　vol. 15, no. 1]　　　　A 54–8902

California. Univ. Libr.
for Library of Congress　　₁5₎

　　CaBVaU N MsU ViU GU
NL　0386651　CLU DLC PHC PSt OU OCU TxU LU PBm PSC CU

Zc64　Linforth, James, 1827–1899.
851Lax　　The Rev. C.W.Lawrence's "Few words from a pastor to his people on the subject of the Latter-day saints", replied to and refuted ... [Liverpool,Printed by J.Sadler,1851?]
　　8p. 21cm.
　　Caption title.

NL　0386652　CtY MH

E166　Linforth, James, 1827–1899, ed.
.P66
1855　Piercy, Frederick Hawkins, 1830–1891.
Rare Bk　　Route from Liverpool to Great Salt lake valley, illustrated
Coll　with steel engravings and wood cuts from sketches made by Frederick Piercy ... Together with a geographical and historical description of Utah ... also an authentic history of the Latter day saints' emigration from Europe ... 1855 ... Ed. by James Linforth. Liverpool, F. D. Richards, 1855.

[Ling, Adelaide W]
　　Mantua home coming, June 26, 1909. n.p., [1909?]
　　73p. illus., ports.

　　Introduction signed: Adelaide W. Ling.

NL　0386654　OC1 PHi

TP570　Ling, Arthur Robert, 1861–1937.
.S97
1907　Sykes, Walter John, 1842–1906.
Rare bk.　The principles and practice of brewing, by Walter J. Sykes
Coll.　... 3d ed., thoroughly rev. by the author and Arthur R. Ling ... London, C. Griffin and company, limited, 1907.

Ling, Arthur William.
　　... An agricultural and soil survey of the Bronham district of Wiltshire...
　　　see under　Bristol. University.

Ling, Arthur William.
　　Experiments on the manuring of sugar beet on acid soils. ₍1931₎
　　6 p.

NL　0386657　DNAL

Ling, Arthur William.
　　The Longcloat experiments, 1927 – 1931. ₍1934?₎
　　29 p.

NL　0386658　DNAL

Ling, Arthur William.
　　... The spraying of rough herbage with molasses, by A. W. Ling ... for the Bristol provincial agricultural advisory council. ₁Bristol, Berkeley square centre₎ 1939.
　　12 p. illus. 22ᶜᵐ. (Bulletin no. 22. University of Bristol. Department of agriculture and horticulture ₁Berkeley square centre₎)

　　1. Grazing. 2. Molasses.　I. Bristol provincial agricultural advisory council. II. Title.
Library of Congress　　SF85.L5　　　　42–28490
　　　　　　　　　　　　　　　636.08422

NL　0386659　DLC

VOLUME 334

LING, Axel [J].
Saggio su' pronomi personali della lingua
italiana. Upsala,1869.

NL 0386660　MH

LING, Axel J.
Sur les inversions de la langue française.
Dissertation, Upsal, impr. de l'université
1866.

pp.(4). vi,(1). 41.

NL 0386661　MH ICRL OClW

LING, Axel [J.]
Sur les verbes forts des langues romanes;
études sur la grammaire comparée. Årsskrift.
[Progr]. Upsala, Edquist & Berglund,1869.

opp.(1).64.

NL 0386662　MH

Ling, Axel J
Svensk-engelsk prepositions-och kon-
struktionslära, jämte fullständigt register
för skolor samt till själestudium, utgifven
.1.. Stockholm, H. Gebers. förlag [1894]
319p.

NL 0386663　MiU

LING,Barbara.
Fool's gold. Oxford,B.Blackwell,1926.

20 cm.　pp.(2),45.
Poems.

NL 0386664　MH

Ling,Bing-chung.
Form discrimination as a learning cue in infants ... [Ann Arbor,Mich.] 1939.
xviii,285 numb.£. illus.,photos.,tables (part fold.)
diagrs. (part fold.) 28ᶜᴹ

Abstracted in *University Microfilms. Abstracts*,v.II,
no.1,p.39,1939.
Thesis (PH.D.)--University of Michigan,1939.
Typewritten copy.
Bibliography: p.280-285.

1.Child study. 2.Infants. 3.Perception. I.Title.

NL 0386665　MiU

Ling, Bing-chung.
... Form discrimination as a learning cue in infants [by] Bing-
chung Ling ... Baltimore, Md., The Williams & Wilkins company, ʻ1941.

cover-title, 66 p. 1 illus., diagrs. 25ʲᵐ. (Comparative psychology
monographs. v. 17, no. 2, serial no. 86, April 1941)

Thesis (PH. D.)—University of Michigan.
Thesis note in foot-note on p. 1.
Bibliography: p. 63-66.

1. Learning, Psychology of. 2. Infants.　I. Title.

Library of Congress　　　BF723.I 6L5　　41-14185

　　　　　　　　　　　　[159.92272585] 136.7244

NL 0386666　DLC MU NBuU PPT PBm ViU CU OU

Beinecke
Library
Fvb48
L55

Ling, C　　S
Boekoe peladjaran hoeroef kanji (permoe-
laan), memoeat tjara menoelis, tjara mem-
batja & latihan. Soerakarta, 2603 [i.e. 1943]
96 p. 24 cm.

Cover title.
"Soedah diperiksa dan di-izinkan oleh Gun
Ken Etsu Han"

1. Japanese language - Writing. I. Title.

NL 0386667　CtY

Wason
PL537
L75
1942

Ling, C　　S
Leerboek der Nipoonse taal met grammatica
& oefeningen (voor beginners). 2. verbeterde
druk. Soerakarta, 2602 [1942]
64 p. 22 cm.

Cover title.

1. Japanese language--Text-books for
foreigners--Dutch.

NL 0386668　NIC

BV
3280
T6
L5

Ling, Catharine F.
Dawn in Toda land; a narrative of missionary
effort on the Nilgiri hills, South India, by
C. F. Ling. With a foreword by Amy Wilson-
Carmichael.　London, Morgan & Scott, 1910.
90 p.　illus.　19cm.

1. Missions - Todas I. Title

NL 0386669　WU CtY OCl

Asia
DS432
T6L5

Ling, Catharine F
Sunrise on the Nilgiris; the story of the
Todas, by Catharine F. Ling.　London, Zenith
Press [1934?]
xi, 60 p.　illus.

1. Todas.　2. Missions - Ootacamund.　I.
Title.

NL 0386670　HU CtY

Ling, Ch'ên
see
Ch'ên, Ling, 1917-

Ling, Cheng.
Synthesis of time-varying networks with special applica-
tions. Ann Arbor, University Microfilms [1955]
([University Microfilms, Ann Arbor, Mich.] Publication no. 14,531)
Microfilm copy (positive) of typescript.
Collation of the original: 90, [3] l. diagrs.
Thesis—University of Minnesota.
Abstracted in Dissertation abstracts, v. 15 (1955) no. 12, p. 2504.
Bibliography : leaves [91]-[93]

1. Electric networks.

Microfilm AC-1　no. 14,531　　　　Mic 55-1626

Minnesota. Univ. Libr.
for Library of Congress　　　[1]†

NL 0386672　MnU DLC

Ling, Chih-Bing, 1909-
The stresses in a plate containing an overlapped circular
hole. [n. p., 1948]
405-411 p. diagrs. 27 cm.
"Reprinted from Journal of applied physics, vol. 19, no. 4."

1. Plates (Engineering)　I. Title.

TA660.P6L52　　　531.3　　　51-35095 rev

NL 0386673　DLC

Ling-ch'in, *pseud.*
愛戀情趣　靈琴著　[香港], 星榮出版社 1952.
3, 5, 122 p. 15 cm.

1. Courtship—Addresses, essays, lectures.　I. Title.
　　　　　　　　　　Title romanized: Ai lien ch'ing ch'ü.

HQ801.L48　　　　　　　C 67-1858

NL 0386674　DLC

Ling-ch'in, *pseud.*
甜蜜的生活　靈琴著　[香港], 星榮出版社 1952.
146 p. illus. 15 cm.

1. Courtship. 2. Family.　I. Title.
　　　　　　　　　Title romanized: T'ien mi ti shêng huo.

GT2650.L5　　　　　　　C 59-420 †

NL 0386675　DLC

Ling, Ch'ing.
中日實力的對比　凌青著　[上海] 上海雜誌公
司 總經售 1937.
4, 2, 122 p. 18 cm. (當代青年叢書第1輯之8)

1. China—Defenses. 2. Japan—Defenses.　I. Title.
　　　　　　　　Title romanized: Chung Jih shih li ti tui pi.

UA835.L47　　　　　　　C 66-1191

NL 0386676　DLC

PL2264
.K9
Orien
China

Ling, Ching-yen, joint comp.

Kuo, Shao-yü, 1893-　comp.
(Kuo ku kai yao)　國故概要　郭紹虞編　[北平
燕京大學? 193-]

Ling, Chong-yun.
... La position et les droits du Japon en Mandchourie.
Préface de m. Marcel Sibert ... avec une carte hors texte.
Paris, A. Pedone, 1933.
2 p. L, li, 464 p. fold. map. 24½ᵐ. (Publications de la Revue géné-
rale de droit international public, n. 7)

At head of title: ... C. Y. Ling ...
Issued also as thesis, Paris, 1933.
"Bibliographie" : p. [453]-459.

1. Japan — For. rel — Manchuria. 2. Manchuria—For. rel.—Japan.
3. Manchuria—Pol. & govt. 4. Japanese in Manchuria.　I. Title.

　　　　　　　　　　　　　　35-14018

Library of Congress　　　　DS783.7.L53

　　　　　　　　　　　　　　　951.8

NL 0386678　DLC NBC NIC NNC MiU NjP NN NNC

Film
937

Ling, Chong-yun.
... La position et les droits du Japon en Mandchourie.
Préface de m. Marcel Sibert ... avec une carte hors texte.
Paris, A. Pedone, 1933.
(Publications de la Revue générale de droit
international public, n. 7)
Microfilm copy (negative) made by Library of
Congress Photoduplication Service.
Issued also as thesis, Paris, 1933.
Collation of the original: 464p.　map.

NL 0386679　FTaSU

Ling, Chou
see
Chou, Ling, 1915-

VOLUME 334

Ling, Chu-kê.
China's railway rolling stock; a study of postwar purchase, by Chuke Ling ... ₍Seattle, Pub. for the College of economics and business by the University of Washington press, 1946₎
x p., 1 l., 110 p. incl. tables. 23ᶜᵐ.

1. Railroads—China. 2. Railroads—Equipment and supplies. I. Washington (State) University. College of economics and business. II. Title.
A 47–1008

Washington (State) Univ. Library
for Library of Congress ₍3₎

NL 0386681 WaPS WaS ICU CoU

Ling, Ch'un-shêng.
Chung-kuo chin jih chih pien chiang wên t'i
see under title

DS751
.M5L52 **Ling, Ch'un-shêng.**
湘西苗族調查報告 凌純聲 芮逸夫著 上海
商務印書館 1947.

3, 16, 477 p. illus. maps. 21 cm. (中國科學院語言研究所單
刊甲種之18)
Bibliography: p. 468–477.
1. Miao people. 2. Minorities—Hunan, China (Province) I. Jui, I-fu, joint author. II. Title. (Series: Chung-kuo k'o hsüeh yüan. Yü yen yen chiu so, Peking. Chung-kuo k'o hsüeh yüan yü yen yen chiu so tan k'an) Chia chung chih 18)
Title romanized: Hsiang hsi Miao tsu tiao ch'a pao kao.

DS731.M5L52 C 66–2446

NL 0386683 DLC ViU

Ling, Ch'un-sheng.
Pien chiang wên hua lun chi
see under title

Ling, Damaris Victoria Cady, 1840–1914
Verses. Detroit, Michigan, 1939.
9 p.

NL 0386685 MiD-B

Ling, Daniel Seth, 1924–
The theory of the angular correlation of successive gamma and internally converted gamma radiations. ₍Ann Arbor₎ 1948.
Microfilm copy of typewritten ms. Made in 1948 by University Microfilms (Publication no. 1062) Positive.
Collation of the original: 98, ₍1₎ l. diagrs.
Thesis—Univ. of Michigan.
Abstracted in Microfilm abstracts, v. 8 (1948) no. 2, p. 185–186.
Bibliography: leaf at end.
1. Quantum theory. 2. Gamma rays.
Microfilm AC–1 no. 1062 Mic A 48–161*

Michigan. Univ. Libr.
for Library of Congress ₍2₎†

NL 0386686 MiU DLC

Ling, Donald Percy, 1912–
Geodesics on surfaces of revolution, by Donald Percy Ling ... ₍n. p., 1946₎
1 p. l., 415–429, ₍1₎ p. 27½ᶜᵐ.
Thesis (PH. D.)—Columbia university, 1944.
"Reprinted from the Transactions of the American mathematical society, vol. 59, no. 3 ... May, 1946."

1. Geometry, Differential. 2. Curves on surfaces. I. Title.
QA643.L47 A 47–84

Columbia univ. Libraries
for Library of Congress ₍2₎†

NL 0386687 NNC DLC

MT 1
.L755 **LING, DOROTHY**
La musica en la formación de la
Juventud. ₍Santiago, de Chile, 1943₎
23 p.

1. Music—Instruction and study—Juvenile.
I. Title. Music cds.

NL 0386688 InU

Ling (E.) Om gymnastikens nytta, särskildt med afseende å fruntimmersskolor. [Advantages of gymnastics, especially in schools for girls.] 25 pp. 8°. *Helsingfors, T. Söderholm,* 1865.

NL 0386689 DNLM

Ling, Edgar Roberts.
A text book of dairy chemistry, theoretical and practical, for students of agriculture and dairying, by Edgar R. Ling ... ₍London₎ Chapman & Hall, 1930.
vii, 213 p. illus., pl. 19½ᶜᵐ.
"References" at end of chapters.

1. Dairying. ₍1. Dairy₎ I. Title: Dairy chemistry.
Agr 30–1200

Library, U. S. Dept. of Agriculture 44L641

NL 0386690 DNAL NN WaS MtBC CaBVaU

Ling, Edgar Roberts.
A textbook of dairy chemistry, by Edgar R. Ling ... 2d and rev. ed. ... London, Chapman & Hall ltd., 1944–45.
2 v. illus., tables, diagrs. (1 fold.) 22ᶜᵐ.
Bibliographical foot-notes.
CONTENTS.—v. 1. Theoretical.—v. 2. Practical.

1. Agricultural chemistry. 2. Dairy products—Analysis and examination.
45–14515 Revised

Library of Congress SF253.L6 1944
₍r46d2₎ 637.127

NL 0386691 DLC

44
L641 **Ling, Edgar Roberts.**
.Bd.2a A textbook of dairy chemistry. 2d and
rev. ed., reprinted. London, Chapman &
Hall, 1946–

1. Chemistry, Dairy. 2. Dairy products.
Analysis and examination.

NL 0386692 DNAL

Ling, Ernst.
Die ersatzansprueche eines gesellschafters
gegen die offene handelsgesellschaft. 1919.
Dissertation.

NL 0386693 PU

Ling, Ernest E.
Foreign branches of American national banks. (In: International Trade Conference. New York, 1915. Proceedings... New York ₍1916₎. 8°. p. 260–270.)

1. Banks, etc., U. S., 1915.
N. Y. P. L. July 31, 1916.

NL 0386694 NN

Ling, Etlar, pseud.
see
Baltzer, Eduard, 1814–1887

Ling, Eugene.
Assigned to danger...
see under title

Ling, Fongsun
see
Ling, Frederick Fongsun.

Ling, Frederick Fongsun.
An investigation of sliding friction and interface temperature between two dry metallic surfaces. Pittsburgh, 1954.
108 l. illus., diagrs. 29 cm.
Cover title.
Thesis—Carnegie Institute of Technology.
Bibliography: leaves 97–98.

1. Friction. I. Title.
QC197.L5 55–37686

NL 0386698 DLC NN

Ling, G., pseud.
see Leyden–Backer, Johanna Catharina.

DB 215 **LING, G** V
.L68 Europas Schicksalstunde, vom 20. Februar
zum 21. September 1938; Hintergründe des
tschechoslowakisch-deutschen Problems.
₍Prag, Gesellschaft für Internationale Probleme, 1938?₎
124 p.

1. Czechoslovak Republic—Hist.—1918–1938.
2. Czechoslovak Republic—For. rel.—Germany.
3. Germany—For. rel.—Czechoslovak Republic.
I. Title.

NL 0386700 InU MH

Ling, George Herbert, 1874–
... Elements of projective geometry, by George Herbert Ling, George Wentworth and David Eugene Smith. Boston, New York ₍etc.₎ Ginn and company ₍1922₎
vi, 186 p. diagrs. 21½ cm. (Wentworth-Smith mathematical series)

1. Geometry, Projective. I. Wentworth, George, 1868– joint author. II. Smith, David Eugene, 1860–1944, joint author.
22—20362

Library of Congress QA471.L5

NL 0386701 DLC NBuU ViU NBPol OU OClW CU OrPR IdU

Ling, George Herbert, 1874–
On the solution of a certain differential
equation which presents itself in Laplace's
kinetic theory of tides... n.p., h₂d.
31 p.

NL 0386702 PPAmP

VOLUME 334

Ling, George Herbert, 1874–
On the solution of a certain differential equation which presents itself in Laplace's kinetic theory of tides ... ₍New York₎ 1896.
p. ₍95₎-125.   29½ x 23½ᶜᵐ.
Thesis (PH. D.)—Columbia university.
References to literature of the problem: p. 125.
Reprinted from Annals of mathematics, April 1896, vol. x, no. 4.

1. Differential equations.

A 11–1227

Title from Columbia Univ.   Printed by L. C.

NL 0386703   NNC MB

Q512.86   Ling, George Herbert and Miller, G. A.
L64p   Proof that there is no simple group whose order lies between 1092 and 2001. ₍Ithaca, N.Y., 1899₎
p. 13-26.

"Reprinted from American journal of mathematics. v.22, no.1."

NL 0386704   IU

Film   LING, Gilbert, 1919-
493   The membrane potential and
no.1   metabolism of muscle fibers.   Chicago,
          1948.
          16 *l.* illus.
          Film copy.
          Thesis - Univ. of Chicago.
          1. Muscles - Physiology

NL 0386705   DNLM

Ling, Go Dhiam, 1901–
see   Go Dhiam Ling, 1901–

Ling, Gustaf Alfred.
Oefversigt af dackefejden.
Inaug. diss. Upsala, 1869₎

NL 0386707   ICRL

4-8F   Ling, H
337   Huntide ja ilveste hävitamine.
          Tallinn, Eesti Riiklik Kirjastus,
          1954.
          59 p.

(Eesti NSV Teaduste Akadeemia popular-
teaduslik sari)

NL 0386708   DLC-P4

Thesis   Ling, Harry Wilson, 1927-
1954   A study of some physical and chemical properties
H-D   of the binary system dinitrogen tetroxide-1,4-
           dioxane.   1954.
           91 l.

Thesis - Ohio State University.

1. Phase rule and equilibrium.   I. Title: Binary system dinitrogen tetroxide-1,4-dioxane.   II. Title: Dinitrogen tetroxide -1,4-dioxane.

NL 0386709   OU

Ling, Huai-shu.
我國第一個五年計劃淺釋   凌懷樹編著   廣州
華南人民出版社 1955.
46 p. 19 cm.

1. China—Econ. condit.—1949–   I. Title.
                         Title romanized: Wo kuo ti i ko
                         wu nien chi hua ch'ien shih.

HC427.9.L575

C 62–754 ‡

NL 0386710   DLC

Ling, Hung, *ed. and tr.*
簡明症狀診斷學   凌宏編譯   上海   醫學世界出
版社 1952.
117 p. 19 cm.

1. Diagnosis.   I. Title.
                Title romanized: Chien ming chêng
                chuang chên tuan hsüeh.

RC71.L673

C 61–887 ‡

NL 0386711   DLC

Ling, Hung-hsün, 1894–
Canton-Hankow railway; difficult work over middle section in full progress, entire line to be completed by end of 1936. By H. H. Ling ... ₍Hengchow, Hunan, China, 1935₎
28 p. incl. illus., map. 22ᶜᵐ.

1. Canton-Hankow railway.

                                        43–26064
Library of Congress   HE3290.C3L5

NL 0386712   DLC

Ling, Hung-hsün, 1894–
中國鐵路志   凌鴻勛著   臺北   暢流半月刊社經
銷   民國 43 ₍1954₎
458 p. illus. 21 cm.

1. Railroads—China.   I. Title.
                Title romanized: Chung-kuo t'ieh lu chih.

HE3285.L52

C 63–1033 ‡

NL 0386713   DLC NIC

Ling, Hung-hsün, 1894–
中國鐵路概論   凌鴻勛著   ₍臺北₎   國立編譯館
民國 39 ₍1950₎
272 p. illus. 21 cm.

1. Railroads—China.   I. Title.
                Title romanized: Chung-kuo t'ieh lu kai lun.

HE3285.L53

C 63–895 †

NL 0386714   DLC CtY WU

Ling, Hung-hsün, 1894–   *ed.*
現代工程   凌鴻勛主編   臺北   中華文化出版事
業委員會   民國 41-42 ₍1952-53₎
2 v. in 1. illus., 2 maps (1 fold.) 19 cm. (現代國民基本知識
叢書 ₍第1輯₎)

1. Engineering—Addresses, essays, lectures.   I. Title.
                Title romanized: Hsien tai kung ch'êng.

TA155.L74

C 66–2555

NL 0386715   DLC CLU-C CaBVaU

Ling, Hung-hsün, 1894–
Industrial development of Taiwan. Taipei, China Culture Pub. Foundation, 1953.
35 p. 22 cm. (Pamphlets on Chinese affairs)

1. Formosa—Indus.   I. Title.

HC463.F6L5

55–59045 ‡

NL 0386716   DLC IU MH MiU NjN

Ling, Hung-hsün, 1894–
₍Shina tetsudō mondai₎
支那鐵道問題   ₍凌鴻勛著   新京₎   滿鐵經濟調
査會   昭和11₍1936₎
2. 179 l. 26 cm. (東亞國際關係ノ動向 9輯)
Cover title.
前支那政府鐵道部參事官リシ氏カ一九三五年上海テ著作シタ「支那鐵
道・歷史的概觀ノ本文ノ全頁譯テアル
1. Railroads—China—Finance.   2. Debts, External—China.   I.
Minami Manshū Tetsudō Kabushiki Kaisha. Keizai Chōsakai. II. Title.
III. Series: Tōa kokusai kankei no dōkō, dai 9-shū.

HE3287.L55

72–806031

NL 0386717   DLC

Ling, Janet, pseud.
see   Darling, Diana.

Ling, Jap Kie
see
Jap, Kie Ling.

Ling, Johan Peter, respondent.
De veterum Suecorum et Gothorum praecipuis quae rempublicam spectant institutis disquisitio historica.
see under   Bring, Ebbe Samuel, praeses.

Ling, Johann Evangelist, 1813–1887.
Vorlagblätter verschiedener schriftarten, von Johann Evangelist Ling ... 7. aufl.
Ulm, Krick ₍1865₎
cover-title, 14 plates. 17 x 21 cm.

NL 0386721   NNC

FILM
75
Ling, John, fl. 1648.
A short ansvver of Iohn Ling, to the 16. quaeres of Ioseph Heming, about Christmas. Wherein all the care that can be is taken to a-voyd expence of paper, so much having beene spoyled already. ... ₍London₎ 1648.

1 reel.
Film reproduction of item 91, v. 106, of the Sutro collection of tracts.

1. Heming, Joseph. Certain quaeries touching the rise and observation of Christmas. I. Title.

NL 0386722   CSmH

W.C.L.   Ling, John   R
M780.88   5 pretty little polkas for pretty little
A512CD   people, by J. R. Ling. Philadelphia, Lee &
no.10   Walker ₍1850₎
              7 p. 33 cm.
              Imperfect: p. 1-4 wanting.
              Contents₍—The rosebud.—Peeping violet.—
           The fleetest hour of youth.--Lily of the valley.--
           The May flower.
              ₍No. 10 in a vol. of songs and piano music
           collected by Sarah P. B. Eve.
              1. Polkas   (Piano) 2. Piano music,
           Juvenile.

NL 0386723   NcD

VOLUME 334

Ling, J R
The lay of Pestal: Yes! the die is cast, and Rest troubled heart. Boston, O. Ditson [185-] Pl. no. 5057.
5 p. 34 cm.
For voice and piano.

1. Songs (Medium voice) with piano.   I. Title.
M1.A13L   M 55-1793 rev
—————————— Copy 2. No. 48 in a vol. with binder's title: Songs. [v. p.
ca. 1835-65]   M1.A15 vol. 91, no. 48

NL 0386724   DLC ICN

Ling, John R   arr.
Pestal, or, The prison song. Yes, the die is cast
see under [Kalliwoda, Johann Wenzel]
1801-1866.

Ling, John R
Pestal. Yes, the die is cast, by J.R. Ling [arr]
see under [Kalliwoda, Johann Wenzel]
1801-1866.

Ling, Johnson S L 1923–
The pharmacology of some 8-substituted theophylline derivatives. [College Park, Md.] 1953.
62, [5] l. mounted illus., tables. 28 cm.
Typescript (carbon copy)
Thesis—University of Maryland.
Vita.
Bibliography : leaves [63]-[66]

1. Theophylline. 2. Hypertension.
QP921.T4L5   A 57-6901
Maryland. Univ. Sch.   of Medicine, Baltimore. Library
for Library of Congress   [8]†

NL 0386727   MdU-H DLC

Ling-kai-fu, *pseud.*
see
Ciuró, Wenceslao.

Ling, Katherine G d. 1939
"Every alley green". Verses... Detroit, Michigan, 1939.
25 p.

NL 0386729   MiD-B

Ling, Kian
see Chiang, Ling.

Ling, Kwang Chang, pseud.
see Del Mar, Alexander, 1836-1926.

Ling, Kwang-tien.
Facts about the Lolos: a translation from the original Chinese ... by Archie R.Crouch.   June 10, 1947.
v,[2],81 leaves. 29cm.
Research report - University of Southern California, 1947.

NL 0386732   CLSU

Ling, Lee, 1910–
A contribution to the knowledge of the Ustilaginales in China. Kew, Surrey, Imperial Mycological Institute, 1945.
12 p. illus. 25 cm. (Mycological papers, no. 11)
Includes bibliographies.

1. Smuts. 2. Fungi—China.
QK628.A1L5   57-16798 ‡

NL 0386733   DLC NNBG

Ling, Lee, 1910–
Digest of plant quarantine regulations.
1949–
Rome.
.v.
Edition for 1952– issued as no. 23–of FAO development paper: agriculture.
Kept up to date with supplements.

NL 0386734   MiU

Ling, Lee, 1910–
Digest of plant quarantine regulations. New ed. Rome, Food and Agriculture Organization of the United Nations, 1952.
vi, 164 p. 28 cm. (FAO development paper no. 23)

1. Plant quarantine.   I. Title: Plant quarantine regulations.
(Series: Food and Agriculture Organization of the United Nations.
FAO agricultural development paper no. 23)
S401.U6A13 no. 23   632.93   56-43908 rev

NL 0386735   DLC MtBC DI NN CaBViP CtY

S401
U6A33 **Ling, Lee, 1910–**
no.23   Digest of plant quarantine regulations – first
Suppl.1 supplement. Rome, Plant Production Branch, Agriculture Division, Food and Agriculture Organization of the United Nations, 1954.
[3], ii, 100 p. 28 cm. ([Food and Agriculture Organization of the United Nations. FAO Development paper no. 23, Agriculture, Suppl. 1])

1. Plant quarantine. II. Title. (Series)

NL 0386736   DI

Ling, Lee, 1910–
Hormones herbicides. Rome, Organisation des Nations Unies pour l'alimentation et l'agriculture, 1951.
iii, 41 p. illus. 28 cm. (Études agricoles de la FAO, no 13)
Issued also in English.
Bibliography : p. 39-41.

1. Weed control. 2. Growth inhibiting substances. 3. Herbicides.
I. Title.   (Series: Food and Agriculture Organization of the United
Nations. Études agricoles de la FAO, no 13)
SB611.L554   57-49134

NL 0386737   DLC GU

Ling, Lee, 1910–
The physiology and parasitism of *Urocystis occulta* ... by Lee Ling ... [Washington, 1941]
cover-title, [579]-591, [926]-935, 617-633 p. incl. illus., tables, diagrs. 25] .
Thesis (PH. D.)—University of Minnesota, 1937.
Three reprints from Phytopathology, v. 30, nos. 7 and 11, July and Nov. 1940 and v. 31, no. 7, July 1941, with cover having thesis note and Vita on p. [3]
"Literature cited": p. 591, 935, 633.
CONTENTS.—Factors affecting spore germination and growth of *Uro-cystis occulta* in culture.—The histology of infection of susceptible and resistant selfed lines of rye by the rye smut fungus, *Urocystis occulta*.—Factors affecting infection in rye smut and subsequent development of the fungus in the host.
1. Urocystis occulta.   2. Rye—Diseases and pests.
Library of Congress   SB608.R9L5   48-9963

NL 0386738   DLC

Ling, Lee, 1910–
Weed control by growth-regulating substances. Washington, Food and Agriculture Organization of the United Nations, 1951.
iii, 36 p. 23 cm. (FAO agricultural studies, no. 13)
Bibliography: p. 34-36.

1. Weed control. 2. Growth inhibiting substances. 3. Herbicides.
I. Title.   (Series: Food and Agriculture Organization of the United
Nations. FAO agricultural studies, no. 13)
SB611.L55   632.58   51-11653

NL 0386739   DLC MoU ViU MtU CaBVaU

SB614
.L55   **Ling, Lee, 1910–**
1952   Weed control by growth-regulating substances; an FAO study prepared by Lee Ling. Rome, Food and Agriculture Organization of the United Nations [1952]
iii, 35 p. illus. 23 cm. (FAO agricultural studies, no.13)

"Third printing, December 1952."
Bibliography: p.34-35.
1. Weed control, Chemical. 2. Plant regulators. 3. Herbicides. i. Food and Agriculture Organization of   the United Nations. ii.t. iii.s.

NL 0386740   NNBG

Ling, Louis, 1874–
A century of service; the history of Central Methodist Episcopal church written in commemoration of the one hundredth anniversary of the incorporation of the First Methodist Episcopal society of the city of Detroit, Michigan, by Louis Ling, with an introduction by Dr. Lynn Harold Hough. Pub. by order of the official board, May, 1922. [Detroit, Evans-Winter-Hebb, printers] 1922.
77, [1] p. front., illus. 25 cm.
Bibliography : p. 76.
1. Detroit, Mich. Central Methodist Episcopal church.

Library of Congress   BX8481.D6C4
                                        22-13008 Revised

NL 0386741   DLC WaT WaS NcD

Ling, Lun, *pseud.*
中國.世界地理綱要—初級中學學習適用 伶倫維甲聯合編寫 上海 普及出版社 1954.
1 v. 19 cm. (初中自修參考叢書)

1. Physical geography—China. 2. Physical geography.   I. Wei,
Chin, pseud., joint author. II. Title.
                         Title romanized: Chung-kuo, shih chieh ti li kang yao.
GB316.L53   C 60-3141 ‡

NL 0386742   DLC

TX725
L485   **Ling, Mei-Mei**
Agric.   Chop suey; a collection of simple Chinese recipes adapted
Ref.   for the American home. Honolulu, South Sea Sales [1953]
Service   34 p.

1. Cookery, Chinese. I. Title.

NL 0386743   CU N KMK

Ling-nan-jên, *pseud.*
嶺南舊事 嶺南人著 香港 學文書店 1952.
70 p. 18 cm.

1. Canton—Descr. I. Title.
                         Title romanized: Ling nan chiu shih.
DS796.C2L55   C 58-5442 ‡

NL 0386744   DLC CaBVaU HU-EWC WaU-FE NIC

VOLUME 334

Ling, Nicholas, fl. 1600, ed.   FOR OTHER EDITIONS
SEE MAIN ENTRY

PR1907
.E5
1950   Englands Helicon; edited from the edition of 1600 with additional poems from the edition of 1614, by Hugh Macdonald. London. Routledge and K. Paul [1950]

Ling, Nicholas.

[Bodenham, John], fl. 1600.
Politeuphuia, Wits common-wealth: or, A treasury of divine, moral, historical and political admonitions, similies and sentences. For the use of schools ... Newly revised. London, Printed by J. H. for W. Freeman, 1699.

Ling, P'ei-hsing, 1924–
The study of nicotinic acid metabolism using radioactive nicotinic acid, nicotinamide, and methionine, by Pei-hsing Lin. Urbana, 1952.

[7] p. 21 cm.
Abstract of thesis—University of Illinois.
Vita.
Bibliography: p. [6]

1. Nicotinic acid metabolism. 2. Nicotinamide. 3. Methionine.

QP801.N5L5   A 53–3021

Illinois. Univ. Library
for Library of Congress   [3]†

NL 0386747   IU DNAL DLC NIC

LING, Per Henrik, 1776–1839.
Samlade arbeten.
—   Stockholm. Bonnier. 1861–63. 3 v. in 4. 8°.

NL 0386748   MB

Ling, Per Henrik, 1776–1839.
Samlade arbeten [ed. by Bernhard von Beskow] Stockholm, A. Bonnier, 1861–[1866]
3 v. front. (port.) fold. diagr. 21 cm.
On title pages of v. 2 and v. 3: Utgifne under ledning af B. v. Beskow.
Contents. - 1. bd. 1861 Lefnadsteckning. Gylfe. Asarne. - 2. bd. [1866] Agne. Tirfing. Smärre dikter. Eddornas sinnebildslära, för olärde framställd. Bihanget till Eddornas sinnebildslära, Eylif den Göthiske. Blotsven. Den heliga Birgitta. Mellanspelet till   Birgitta.

3. bd. [1866] Ingjald. Illråda och Ivar Vidfadme. Engelbrekt Engelbrektson. Riksdagen 1527. Gymnastikkens allmänna grunder. Soldatundervisning i gymnastik och bajonettfäktning. Skrifvelser, tal, aforismer [etc.] om gymnastik Jagarerorolgar. Forslag om gymnastikens nytta och nödvändighet för soldaten i allmänhet. Om läkares gymnastikbildning. Tal om bajonettfäktning. Aforismer.

NL 0386750   CtY

PT9773
L92
1866   Ling, Per Henrik, 1776–1839.
Samlade arbeten, utg. under ledning af B. v. Beskow. Stockholm, A. Bonnier [1866]
3 v. in 4. illus., port.

Contents.
1. Gylfi. - Asarne. 2 v.
2. Agne. - Tirfing, eller Dödsvärdet. - Kärleken. - Eddornas sinnebildslära. - Eylif den göthiske. - Blot-Sven. - Den heliga Birgitta.
3. Ingjald Illråda och Ivar Vidfadme. - Engelbrekt Engelbrektson - Riksdagen 1527. - Gymnastikens allmänna grunder. - Soldat-undervisning i gymnastik och bajonettfäktning. - Skrifvelser, tal, aforismer och andra efterlemnade papper om gymnastik.

NL 0386751   CU

Ling, Per Henrik, 1776–1839.
Agne, sorgespel.
Lund, 1812.
8vo.

NL 0386752   NN

LING, [Per Henrik] 1776–1839.
Asarne. [Stockholm, tryckt hos Carl Oeleen, 1816.

nar.12°.

NL 0386753   MH

Ling, [Per Henrik]. Asarne. (Stockholm, 1816–1826.) 2 vols. 12°. pp. (12) + 336 + (2); (6) + 50 + (2).   IcP1L755
Of these two vols., the first contains cantos 1–6, the second, canto 13.

NL 0386754   NIC

Ling, Per Henrik, 1776–1839.
— Asarne. Stockholm, L. J. Hjerta, 1833. 8°. pp. (4) + 692.   IcP1L756
Contains all the three sections (30 cantos).

NL 0386755   NIC MH

Ling, Per Henrik. 1776–1839.   *Cab.79.13.1
A collection of gymnastic positions issued by the Royal Gymnastic Central Institute, Stockholm.
— Stockholm. Norstedt. 1893. (5) pp. 120 plates. F°.
"The present collection of pictures, which has been in part published before, is the work of P. H. Ling and of his son, H. Ling."

G6318 — Kongliga gymnastika centralinstitutet, Stockholm. — T.r. — Swedish system of gymnastics. — Ling. Hjalmar Fredrik. jt. auth. 1820—

NL 0386756   MB MWelC ViU OCl NN

Ling, Per Henrik, 1776–1839.
Gylfe.
Stockholm, 1814.
8vo.

NL 0386757   NN

Ling, Per Henrik, 1776–1839.
The gymnastic free exercises of P.H. Ling, arranged by H. Rothstein. Translated with additions, by M. Roth ... A systemized course of gymnastics without apparatus ... Boston, Ticknor, Reed and Fields, 1853.
xvi, 136p. 2 fold. pl. 18cm.

NL 0386758   PSt NN DNLM MWA

Ling, Per Henrik, 1776–1839.
Gymnastic Free exercises. 2nd. edition. Translated by M. Roth. H. Bailliere, 1854.
136 p.

NL 0386759   PPHa

QTA
L755g
1840   LING, Per Henrik, 1776–1839
Gymnastikens allmänna grunder. Dels af Författaren, dels, enligt dess yttersta vilja, efter dess död, redigerade och på trycket utgifna. Upsala, Leffler och Sebell, 1840.
239 p.

NL 0386760   DNLM

Ling, Per Henrik, 1776–1839.
Gymnastikens allmänna grunder, af Ling, dels af författaren, dels, enligt dess yttersta vilja, efter dess död, redigerade och på trycket utgifna. (Fragment.) [Stockholm, E. Vestrell, 1865.]
[10, 443]–786 p. 2 fold. pl. 22cm.
Extracted from his Samlade arbeten, vol. 3.
Contents.—Gymnastik, meddelad i Stockholms Gymn. centr. institut, och enligt Riksens högl. ständers beslut.—Soldat-undervisning i gymnastik och bajonettfäktning.—Skrifvelser, tal, aforismer o. a. efterlemnade papper om gymnastik.

NL 0386761   ICJ

Ling, Per Henrik, 1776–1839.
Den heliga Birgitta. Sorgspel af Ling. [Stockholm, A. Gadelius, 1818]
18.5 cm.
Engraved title page.

NL 0386762   CtY

RM725
836ℓ   [Ling, Per Henrik] 1776–1839.
Reglemente för gymnastik. Stockholm, Elméns och Granbergs, 1836.
2p.ℓ., 119, [1]p. fold. charts. 20cm.

1. Physical medicine - Exercise.

NL 0386763   CtY-M

[LING, Per Henrik] 1776–1839.
Reglemente för gymnastik. Genomsedd med ledni af Lings egenhandiga namärkningar. 2e uppl. Stockholm, P.J. Meyer, [1853].

Plates.

NL 0386764   MH

Ling, Per Henrik, 1776–1839
Schriften über leibesübungen. Aus dem schwedischen übersetzt von H. F. Massmann. Magdeburg, Heinrichshofen, 1847.
pp. (1), xxvi, (5), 188 +. 3 plates.
With reprint of title-page: Allgemeine begründung der gymnastik von Ling. Upsala, 1834; 1840.

NL 0386765   MH MA IU CtY-M

Ling, Per Henrik, 1776–1839.
Styrbjörn Starke. Historiskt skådespel af Ling. [Stockholm, G. Scheutz, 1824]

132 p. 21cm.

I. Title.

NL 0386766   MnU

Ling, Per Henrik, 1776–1839.
Visburs söner. Sorgspel af Ling. [Stockholm, F.B. Nestius, 1824]

132 p. 22cm.

I. Title.

NL 0386767   MnU NN

VOLUME 334

LING, PETER

Voices offstage; an armchair revue.   London, New York, Longmans, Green ₁1947₎
252p. 19cm.

NL 0386768   PU

Ling, Ping, 1894–
兒童學概論 凌冰編 上海 商務印書館 民國
11 ₁1922₎
156p. illus. 19 cm. (世界叢書)

1. Child study.   I. Title.
Title romanized: Êrh t'ung kai lun.

LB1115.L48   C 62–2316 †

NL 0386769   DLC

Ling, Ping, 1894–
Public schools and the war, by Ping Ling ... ₁Worcester?
Mass.₎ 1919.
158 p. 23ᶜᵐ.
Thesis (PH. D.)—Clark university, 1919.
Bibliography: p. 154–158.

1. Public schools. 2. European war, 1914–1918.   I. Title.

Library of Congress   D639.E2L5   19—10366
Clark Univ. Libr.

NL 0386770   MWC NcD NIC DLC

Ling, Pyau, 1888–
Beiträge zur neuesten Geschichte Chinas, von Dr. Pyau Ling
... Berlin: K. Curtius, 1917. 157(1) p. 8°. (Deutsch-
Chinesischer Verband.   Schriften. no. 3.)

I. China.—History, 1900–   2. Series.
                                 August 12, 1920.

NL 0386771   NN NIC CF1S CtY

Ling, Pyau, 1888 –
Die chinesische revolution.
Inaug. diss. Wuerzburg, 1916. (Berlin).

Chinese division.

NL 0386772   DLC MH CtY PU

---

414   **Ling, S   W**
L64   (Culture, tilapia for food and profit)
        [Bangkok?] 1953.
        16 p., 9 l.
        Siamese with an English translation.

        1. Fish-culture. Siam. I. Sidhthimunka,
        Ariya,   joint author. II. Siam.
        Fisheries Dept.

NL 0386773   DNAL

8401   **Ling, S   W**
U6A257   Report to the Government of Burma on inland
no.361   fisheries development. Rome, 1955.
         9 p.   28 cm. ([Food and Agriculture Organ-
         ization of the United Nations. Expanded tech-
         nical assistance program. FAO] report no.361)
         "Code T. 3551.P."

         1. Fisheries – Burma. (Series)

NL 0386774   DI

Ling, Shan.
愛的新禱 ₁九龍 友聯書報發行所 1953₎
2, 51 p. 17 cm. (中國學生叢書)
PARTIAL CONTENTS.—愛的新禱 凌珊—生命的呼喚 王
是一夜歸 古梅

         1. Chinese essays—20th cent.   I. Wang, Shih, 1919 or 20–
         Shêng ming ti hu huan. II. Ku, Mei. III. Title.
                             Title romanized: Ai ti ch'i tao.

PL2623.L5   C 67–3410

NL 0386775   DLC

Ling, Shan-ch'ing.
全國律師民刑訴狀彙編 凌善清編輯 上海 大
東書局 民國 12 ₁1923₎
2 v. 20 cm.

         1. Procedure (Law)—China. 2. Procedure (Law)—China—Cases.
         I. Title. II. Title: Min hsing su chuang hui pien.
                     *Title romanized: Ch'üan kuo lü shih min hsing
                                   su chuang hui pien.*

                                  C 61–1145 †

NL 0386776   DLC

Ling, Shan-ch'ing, ed.
新編戲學彙考 凌善清 許志豪編 徐慕雲 劉
豁公校閱 上海 大東書局 民國23 ₁1934₎
10 v. illus. (part col.), ports. 19 cm.
CONTENTS.—1–2 戲学編—3–10 戲曲編

         1. Chinese drama. 2. Theater—China.   I. Hsü, Chih-hao, joint
         ed. II. Title. III. Title: Hsi hsüeh hui k'ao.
                     Title romanized: Hsin pien hsi hsüeh hui k'ao.

                                  C 63–1132

Harvard Univ. Chinese·   Japanese Library 5715
for Library of Congress   ₁3₎

NL 0386777   MH-HY

Ling, Shan-ch'ing.
太平天國野史 凌善清編輯 上海 文明書局
民國 15 ₁1926₎
1 v. (various pagings) illus., facsims., port. 22 cm.
Colophon title.

         1. Taiping Rebellion, 1850–1864.   I. Title.
                     Title romanized: T'ai p'ing t'ien kuo yeh shih.

DS759.L76   C 64–1389

NL 0386778   DLC

MANN
Thesis
QL   **Ling, Shao-wen,** 1907–
498   The trichoptera or caddice-flies of the western
1933   United States. ₁Ithaca, N. Y.₎ 1933.
L755   vii, 442 l. illus. 28 cm.

         Thesis (Ph. D.) - Cornell Univ., June 1933.
Thesis ------- Archival copy.
1933   1. Caddis-flies. I. Title.
L755

NL 0386779   NIC

Ling, Shata.
Family life reader; a textbook for adult accom-
plishment, by Shata Ling ... Cassie McClain ...
₁and₎ Mary Edward Mitchell ... Atlanta, Ga.,
Allen, James & co. ₁c1938₎
92 p. illus. 28 cm.
In binder, with original paper cover mounted
on cover.
"Suggestions for teaching" ₁ p. ₁3₎ of cover.

         1. Readers and speakers - 1870–   2. Eng-
         lish language - Text-books for foreigners. I.
         McClain, Cassie,   joint author. II. Mitchell,
         Mary Edward, joint   author. III. Title.
                               PE1128.A2.L75

NL 0386780   Vi ViU

Ling, Shih-ch'iu
      see Liang, Shih-chiu.

Ling, Shu-hua
      see Ling, Su-hua, fl. 1928–

Ling, Stuart James, 1918–
      A study of adolescent mental imagery involving written
responses to certain musical compositions. Ann Arbor, University Microfilms ₁1954₎
      (₁University Microfilms, Ann Arbor, Mich.₎ Publication no. 10,080)
      Microfilm copy of typescript. Positive.
      Collation of the original: xiii, 358 l. tables.
      Thesis—Syracuse University.
      Abstracted in Dissertation abstracts, v. 14 (1954) no. 12, p. 2364–
2365.
      Vita.
      Bibliography: leaves 349–358.
      1. Music—Psychology.   I. Title: Adolescent mental imagery in-
volving written responses to certain musical compositions.

Microfilm AC-1   no. 10,080   Mic A 54–3515
Syracuse. Univ. Libr.
for Library of Congress   ₁1₎†

NL 0386783   NSyU InU DLC

B   **Ling, Su-hua,** fl. 1928–
L7565.E1   Ancient melodies, by Su Hua. With an
         introd. by V. Sackville-West.   London,
         Hogarth Press, 1953.
         255p. illus. 21cm.

NL 0386784   IU WU

PL   **Ling, Su-hua,** fl. 1928 –
2876   小兒哥 ₁i.e. 哥兒倆₎ 凌叔華作 ₁香港₎ 良友圖書
.N5   公司 ₁Pref. 1935₎
H75   102 p. 18 cm. (良友文學叢書袖珍本)
         Short stories.

NL 0386785   OrU

Ling, Su-hua, fl. 1928–
小兒哥 ₁i.e. 哥兒倆₎ 凌叔華作 香港 良友圖書
公司 民國34 ₁1945₎
2, 102 p. 18 cm. (良友文學叢書)
Short stories.

         I. Title.
                     Title romanized: Hsiao ko êrh liang.

PL2781.N4H7   C 61–292

NL 0386786   DLC ViU

VOLUME 334

TL
567
I6
L55
Ling, Sung-ching, 1925–
Measurement of flow characteristics by the hot-film technique. [Iowa City] 1955.
ix, 96 L. illus.

Thesis - State University of Iowa.
Xerox copy of the original.
Bibliography: L.62-63.

1. Anemometer. I. Title.

NL 0386787 WaU

Ling, Sung-ching, 1925–
Measurement of flow characteristics by the hot-film technique. Ann Arbor, University Microfilms [1955]
([University Microfilms, Ann Arbor, Mich.] Publication no. 12,905)
Microfilm copy of typescript. Positive.
Collation of the original: ix, 96 l. illus., diagrs.
Thesis—State University of Iowa.
Abstracted in Dissertation abstracts, v. 15 (1955) no. 10, p. 1818-1819.
Bibliography: leaves 62-63.

1. Anemometer. I. Title.

Microfilm AC-1 no. 12,905   Mic 55-495

Iowa. Univ. Library
for Library of Congress   [1]†

NL 0386788 IaU DLC

Ling, Ta-t'ing.
法帝侵華史　凌大挺著　北京　新潮書店 1951.
77 p. illus. 18 cm.

1. China—For. rel.—France. 2. France—For. rel.—China.
Title.   *Title romanized:* Fa ti ch'in Hua shih.

DS740.5.F8L5   C 59-271 ‡

NL 0386789 DLC

Asia
HD6083
C5L5
Ling, T'ao.
Women in Tientsin industries; a study of the working conditions of women and girls, by T'ao Ling and Lydia Johnson. Peking, Peking Leader Press, 1928.
11 p. (Peking Leader reprints, no. 40)

Cover title.

1. Woman – Employment – Tientsin, China. 2. Labor   and laboring classes – Tientsin, China.   I. Johnson, Lydia. II. Title.

NL 0386790 HU NjP

Wason
SD221
L79
Ling, Tao-yang.
Chapters on China and forestry, by Dau-yang Lin. Shanghai, Commercial Press, 1916.
v, 11, ii, 88 p. 16cm.

1. Forests and forestry--China. I. Title.

NL 0386791 NIC NNU-W

Ling, Tao-yang.
中國農業之經濟觀　凌道揚著　上海　商務印書館　民國15 [1926]
1, 1, 2, 89 p. illus. 23 cm.
Added colophon title: The economic aspect of Chinese agriculture.

1. Agriculture—Economic aspects—China.   I. Title.
          Title romanized: Chung-kuo nung
yeh chih ching chi kuan.

HD2067.L56   C 64-1609

NL 0386792 DLC

Ling, Tao-yang.
Forests and Chihli floods.   [Nanking, 1918]
13 p. 8°.
"This article, written for English reading public, contains the substance of a pamphlet written in Chinese by the same author during his recent investigation trip north."
By D.Y. Lin.

NL 0386793 MH-A

Ling, Tao-yang.
The relation of forests to floods.   [Shanghai, etc., 1918]
illustr. 1. 8°.
Far Eastern review, 1918, xiv, 481-485.
By D.Y. Lin.

NL 0386794 MH-A

Ling, Thomas Mortimer, ed.
Mental health and human relations in industry. With a foreword by Lord Horder. London, H. K. Lewis, 1954.
xix, 265 p. illus. 23 cm.
Includes bibliographies.

1. Psychology, Industrial. 2. Industrial relations.   I. Title.

HD4904.L52   54—39120

OrU CtY CaBVaU
NL 0386795   DLC TxU PBL OC1 NcU NN PP ICU DNLM ICJ

Ling, Thomas Mortimer, ed.
Mental health and human relations in industry. Supplementary introd. by Thomas A. C. Rennie. New York, Hoeber, 1955.
265 p. illus. 23 cm.

1. Psychology, Industrial. 2. Industrial relations.   I. Title.

HD4904.L52 1955   331.82   55-3678 ‡

NL 0386796   DLC PSt MBCo OC1W PPJ PPC ICJ

Ling, Thomas Mortimer.
Recent advances in industrial hygiene and medicine, by T. M. Ling ... With 29 illustrations. Philadelphia, P. Blakiston's son & co., inc., 1937.
ix, 212 p. plates, diagrs., tables. 21ᶜᵐ. (*Half-title:* The recent advances series)
"References" at end of each chapter.

1. Occupations, Diseases and hygiene. 2. Occupations, Dangerous. I. Title.

                          S G 38—33

U. S. Surg.-gen. off. Libr.   RC964
for Library of Congress   [a41f1]

NL 0386797   DNLM DL NN OCU PPHa PPC NcD Or CU ICJ

AC
801
C81+
v. 2
no. 8
Ling, Thomas Tien-Gi.
The oxidation of Chinese wood oil.
Easton, Pa., 1925.
12, 11 p. illus. 23cm.

Thesis (Ph. D.)--Cornell University, 1924.
Reprinted from Industrial and engineering chemistry, v. 16-17, no. 10 and 5, pages 1051 & 508. Oct., 1924, and May, 1925.
Submitted as thesis under title: A study of the oxidatio   n of Chinese wood oil.

NL 0386798 NIC MH CtY

Thesis
1924
L755
Ling, Thomas Tien-Gi.
A study of the oxidation of Chinese wood oil. [Ithaca, N. Y.] 1924.
74 l. illus. 28cm.

Thesis (Ph. D.)--Cornell University, June, 1924.

NL 0386799 NIC RPB

Ling, T'i-an.
鄭子尹年譜　凌惕安編著　長沙　商務印書館　民國 30 [1941]
2, 2, 288 p. illus., port. 18 cm. (國立北平圖書館西南文獻叢刊第 2 種)

1. Chêng, Chên, 1806-1864.   (*Series:* Pei-ching t'u shu kuan.
Kuo li Pei-p'ing t'u shu kuan hsi nan wên hsien ts'ung k'an, ti 2 chung)
          Title romanized: Chêng Tzŭ-yin nien p'u.

DS760.9.C53L5   C 63-1635

NL 0386800   DLC WaU-FE

Ling, Ting, pseud.
see Chiang, Ping-chih, 1907–

Ling, Ting Hung.
Bonding butyl rubber to 70-30 brass.   1954.
Ph.D. Chemical Engineering.

NL 0386802 OC1CS

Ling, Tze-lou
see
Ling, Tzŭ-liu.

Ling-tzŭ, *pseud.*
大陸見聞　靈子著　初版　香港　創墾出版社 1954.
2, 194 p. 19 cm.

1. China—Descr. & trav.—1949–   I. Title.
          Title romanized: Ta lu chien wên.

                          C 62-4037
Yale Univ. Library
for Library of Congress   [1]

NL 0386804 CtY MiU

Ling-tzŭ, *pseud.*
大陸三年　靈子著　新加坡　創墾出版社 1959.
66 p. 18 cm. (創墾小叢書之一)

1. China (People's Republic of China, 1949–   ) I. Title.
          Title romanized: Ta lu san nien.

DS777.55.L48   C 65-295 rev

NL 0386805   DLC ICU NIC WU MH

VOLUME 334

Ling, Tzŭ-liu.
常見的錯字 凌子鎏編 九龍 民國 30 ₍1941₎

72 p. 19 cm.

1. Chinese language—Glossaries, vocabularies, etc. 2. Chinese language—Writing. I. Title.
Title romanized: Ch'ang chien ti ts'o tzŭ.

PL1489.L5 1941 C62-2424 ‡

NL 0386806 DLC

Ling, Tzŭ-liu.
常見的錯字 凌子鎏編 九龍 同志書局 民國 43 ₍1954₎

64 p. 19 cm.

Added title: Common errors in Chinese characters.

1. Chinese language—Glossaries, vocabularies, etc. 2. Chinese language—Writing. I. Title.
Title romanized: Ch'ang chien ti ts'o tzŭ.

PL1489.L5 C 59-50 ‡

NL 0386807 DLC

Ling, W. N.
...The northern Highlands, by W. N. Ling... Edinburgh: The Scottish Mountaineering Club, 1932. 87 p. incl. diagrs. front., maps, plates. 22cm.

Plates printed on both sides.
At head of title: The Scottish Mountaineering Club guide.
Bibliography at end of each chapter.

619775A. 1. Scotland—Highlands. I. Scottish Mountaineering
N. Y. P. L. Club, Edinburgh.
January 28, 1933

NL 0386808 NN NjP

Ling, W N , and J. R. Corbett, eds.
...The northern Highlands, and J. R. Corbett, eds. Edited by W. N. Ling and John Rooke Corbett... Edinburgh: Scottish Mountaineering Club, 1936. 106 p. front., illus., maps, plates. 21½ cm.

At head of title: The Scottish Mountaineering Club guide.
Bibliography at end of each chapter.

844837A. 1. Scotland—Highlands. 2. Mountaineering—Gt. Br.—Scotland.
I. Corbett, John Rooke, jt. ed. II. Scottish Mountaineering Club,
Edinburgh. Edinburgh.
N. Y. P. L. September 15, 1936

NL 0386809 NN

Ling, Wei-min.
俄華兩用字典 （基本俄語與工程術語） Русско-китайский словарь, бытовой и технический. 約 24,000 字 凌渭民編 上海 中國科學圖書儀器公司 1955.

770 p. tables. 18 cm.

1. Russian language—Dictionaries—Chinese. I. Title. II. Title: Russko-kitaĭskiĭ slovar', bytovoĭ i tekhnicheskiĭ.
Title romanized: O Hua liang yung tzŭ tien.

PL1459.R8L5 C 63-667

NL 0386810 DLC

Ling, William.
Oh sleep, thou soother of each woe; a favorite ballad. London, Longman and Broderip ₍179-₎

4 p. 33 cm.

Caption title.
For voice and piano.

1. Songs (High voice) with piano—To 1800. I. Title.

M1621.L 76-287455

NL 0386811 DLC

Ling, William.
Ye banks and braes of Bonny Doon; a favorite Scotish air, arr. & varied. Philadelphia, published by A. Bacon, No. 11. S. 4th. St. and sold by Vallotte & Lété, New, York, and at J. Robinsons Circulating Library, Baltimore ₍1817₎ Pl. no. 59.

3 p. 33 cm.

Caption title.
For piano.

1. Piano music. I. Title.

M1.A1L 73-287457
[M25]

NL 0386812 DLC

Ling, Ying, ed.
國防中心論 凌鷹編 桂林 國防書店 民國 30 ₍1941₎

150 p. 18 cm. (國防叢書)

1. China—Defenses. I. Title.
Title romanized: Kuo fang chung hsin lun.

UA835.L5 C 69-877 ‡

NL 0386813 DLC

Ling, Yong
Les Composées chinoises de l'Herbier de l'Académie de Peiping ₍par₎ Ling Yong. Peiping, 1934-35.
2 pt. 12 plates. 27 cm. (Contributions from the Institute of Botany, National Academy of Peiping, v.2, no.1; v.3, no.4)

XC
.0668
v.2
no.1
etc.
Cover title.
1. Compositae - China. i.t. ii. Kuo li Pei-p'ing yen chiu yüan. Chih wu hsüeh yen chiu so. iii.s(v.2, no.1) iv.s:(v.3, no.4)

NL 0386814 NNBG

Ling, Yong
Compositae sinenses novae vel minus cognitae. I. ₍Par₎ Ling Yong. Peiping, 1937.
30 p. illus., 8 plates. 27 cm. (Contributions from the Institute of Botany, National Academy of Peiping, v.5, no.1)

XC
.0668
v.5
no.1
Cover title.
Abstract in Chinese.

1. Compositae - China. i.t. ii.s.

NL 0386815 NNBG

Ling, Yong.
... Étude des phénomènes de la sexualité chez les mucorinées, suivie d'un appendice sur les mucorinées d'Auvergne et spécialement les mucorinées du sol ... Paris, 1929.
Thèse - Univ. de Paris.
"Index bibliographique": p. [189]-199.

NL 0386816 CtY MH

Ling, Yong
Gentianaceae. Peiping, Chine, Académie nationale de Peiping, 1933.
63 p. 25 plates. 36 cm. (Flore illustrée du nord de la Chine, fasc.2)

fQK355
.F5
fasc.2
Added title in Chinese.
French and Chinese.

1. Gentianaceae - China. i.s.

NL 0386817 NNBG CtY

Ling, Yong
Note sur quelques Chrysanthemum de la Chine par Ling Yong.
(In Contributions from the Institute of Botany, National Academy of Peiping. Peiping, 1935. 27 cm. v.3, no.10, p.459-484. illus., 4 plates)

XC
.0668
v.3
no.10
Caption title.
Summary in Chinese.
1. Chrysanthemum - China. 2. Compositae. i.t. ii.s.

NL 0386818 NNBG

Ling, Yong
Un nouveau Swertia de Shensi, par Ling Yong.
(In Contributions from the Institute of Botany, National Academy of Peiping. Peiping, 1936. 27 cm. v.4, no.6, p.337-339. illus.)

XC
.0668
v.4
no.6
Caption title.
Abstract in Chinese.

1. Swertia heterantha - China - Shensi.
2. Gentianaceae. i.t. ii.s: Contributions from the Institute of Botany, National Academy of Peiping, v.4. no.6.

NL 0386819 NNBG

Ling, Yong
Sur quelques Gentiana de la section Aptera, par Ling Yong.
(In Contributions from the Institute of Botany, National Academy of Peiping. Peiping, 1935. 27 cm. v.3, no.7, p.375-382. illus., plate)

XC
.0668
v.3
no.7
Caption title.
1. Gentiana - China. 2. Gentiana tenuicaulis - China. i. Gentianaceae. i.t. ii.s: Contributions from the Institute of Botany, National Academy of Peiping, v.3, no.7.

NL 0386820 NNBG

Ling, Yu-sing.
...Sketches of Confucius...ed. and pub. by Ling Yu Sing. Foochow, 1948. 12 f. 12 col. pl. 22cm.

Title in Chinese at head of title; text in English and Chinese.
Folded accordion-style with wooden covers.

542957B. 1. Confucius.
N. Y. P. L. January 15, 1951

NL 0386821 NN

Ling, Zeng Seng
... Recherches ethnographiques sur les Yao dans la Chine du Sud ... Paris, 1929.
vi,151p.,2l. front.(map) 25½cm.
Thèse - Univ. de Paris.
"Bibliographie": 1l. at end.

Nkd72
C6
929l
1. Ethnology - China. 2. Yao-min. x. Zeng. x. Seng.

NL 0386822 CtY

Ling de Hernando, Dorothy.
Aqueste sumo saber. ₍Tucumán, 1947₎

206 p. illus., diagr. 19 cm. (Universidad Nacional de Tucumán. Instituto de Arte. Educación por el arte, 1)

1. Art—Addresses, essays, lectures. I. Title. (Series: Tucumán, Argentine Republic. Universidad. Instituto de Arte. Educación por el arte, 1)

N7445.L48 54-25078

NL 0386823 DLC

VOLUME 334

Líng-hoô, Tîh-fun
see
Ling-hu, Tê-fên, 583–666.

Líng-hoô, Tîn-fun
see
Ling-hu, Tê-fên, 583–666.

Ling-hou, Te-fun
see
Ling-hu, Tê-fên, 583–666.

Ling-hu, Hui, *pseud.*
see
Shang-kuan, Mu.

Ling-hu, Tê-fên, 583–666.
Biography of Su Ch'o ₍Chou shu, chüan 23₎ Translated and annotated by Chauncey S. Goodrich. Berkeley, University of California Press, 1953.
116 p. 24 cm. (Institute of East Asiatic Studies, University of California. Chinese dynastic histories translations, no. 3)
Based on the editor's thesis (M. A.)—University of California.
Bibliography: p. 112–116.

1. Su, Ch'o, 498–546.   I. Goodrich, Chauncey Shafter, ed. and tr.
(Series: Chinese dynastic histories translations, no. 3)
[DS741.C3 no. 3]	A 53–9763 rev
California. Univ. Libr.
for Library of Congress	₍r59d2₎

**NL 0386828	CU MiU FTaSU NIC TxU NNC**

Ling-Lander, Yngve.
Hemstadens visor; dikter, av Yngve Ling-Lander. ₍Uppsala: A. B. Akademiska Bokhandeln, 1921.₎ 100 p.   24°.

1. Poetry (Swedish). 2. Title.
N. Y. P. L.	November 28, 1924

**NL 0386829	NN MH**

Ling-Mallison, Eric.
The law relating to advertising, by E. Ling-Mallison ... London, New York ₍etc.₎ Sir I. Pitman & sons, ltd., 1931.
xxviii, 206 p. 19ᶜᵐ.

1. Advertising. 2. Press law—Gt. Brit. 3. Bill-posting—Laws and regulations. I. Title.
₍Full name: Eric Mallie Ling-Mallison₎
32–2986

**NL 0386830	DLC CtY OC1 MH-L NN**

Ling-Mallison, Eric.
Law relating to women, by E. Ling-Mallison ... London ₍etc.₎ The Solicitors' law stationery society, ltd., 1930.
xxxii, 184 p. 22½ᶜᵐ.

1. Woman—Legal status, laws, etc.—Gt. Brit. I. Title.
₍Full name: Eric Mallie Ling-Mallison₎
32–4200

**NL 0386831	DLC NcD CtY PU-L MH-L NN**

Ling Roth, Henry
see   Roth, Henry Ling, 1855–1925.

Ling-Sun, Woo, 1896–
Ueber pneumoperitoneum und pneumoradiographie. Inaug. diss. Wuerzburg, 1925.
Bibl.

**NL 0386833	ICRL**

Ling Association of Teachers of Swedish Gymnastics
see
Physical Education Association of Great Britain and Northern Ireland.

**Ling naam; the news bulletin of Canton Christian college. ....
New York, 1924**
LG51
.C528

**NL 0386835	DLC**

Ling naam hok hau
see   Ling-nan ta hsüeh, Canton, China.

PL2878
.N48K3
Orien
China	**Ling-nan shih shih shê.**
改良嶺南卽事 ₍嶺南時事社編₎ n. p. 195–₎
104 p. 19 cm.

I. Title.

Title romanized: Kai liang Ling-nan chi shih.
PL2878.N48K3	C 62–2366 ‡

**NL 0386837	DLC**

Ling-nan ta hsüeh, Canton, China.
Incorporated in 1893 as a school. In 1916, the College of Arts and Sciences was organized and was known as Canton Christian College. In 1921 the Lingnan Agricultural College was added. In 1926, the name of Lingnan University was adopted.

Ling-nan ta hsüeh, Canton, China.	5999a.116
The agricultural work of Canton Christian College. [Canton, China. 1921.] 5 pp. 22 cm.
There is no title-page.

Myºº5 — Agricultural schools.

**NL 0386839	MB**

Ling-nan ta hsüeh, Canton, China.
The beginnings of the Women's department of the Canton Christian coll....N.Y., Trustees of the Canton Christian coll., 1915.
36p. illus. (incl. ports.)

**NL 0386840	OO**

LG51
.C319
1914a	**Ling-nan ta hsüeh, Canton, China.**
A brief review of the present stage of development of the Canton Christian college and its system of schools. January, 1914 [and May, 1914] New York, 1914.
16 p. diagr. 22½ x 10½ cm.

**NL 0386841	DLC**

Wason
Pamphlet
L
China
7	**Ling-nan ta hsüeh, Canton, China.**
A brief review of the present stage of development of the Canton Christian College and its system of schools. New York, Office of the Trustees, 1916.
24 p. 23 x 11cm.

Cover title: The Canton Christian College.

I. Title.

**NL 0386842	NIC OO**

Ling-nan ta hsueh, Canton, China.
... Bulletin ... Canton, China [1910–]
Library has no. 3 to date. illus., plates, ports. 23 cm.
At head of title: Canton Christian College.
Includes its Annual report, Catalogue, agricultural and other special bulletins.
Some numbers in Chinese.
No. 3–7 published in New York.
No. 9, 11, 14, 17, 23, wanting.

**NL 0386843	ICJ OrCS**

Ling-nan ta hsüeh, Canton, China.
Canton Christian College. Ling Naam Hok Hau. Its growth and outlook ... New York, Trustees of the Canton Christian College ₍1919₎
1 p. l., 66 p. illus. (incl. ports., maps, facsim., plans) 23 x 31 cm.

C319 1919	378.51	E 20–164 rev
U. S. Office of Education.	Library
for Library of Congress	₍r68d2₎†

**NL 0386844	DHEW CU NN MiU DLC OO ICJ NIC Or OC1**

Ling-nan ta hsüeh, Canton, China.
Canton Christian College, its field and work in China; Christian, missionary, undenominational. Founded in the interest of the missions of all denominations at work in South China. ₍New York, Willett Press₎ 1908.
cover-title, 23, ₍1₎ p. incl. illus., ports., maps, plans. 21½ x 21½ cm.

378.51	E 9–555 rev
U. S. Office of Education.	Library LG51
for Library of Congress	₍r67b2₎

**NL 0386845	DHEW ICJ**

LG51
C32
no.10	**Ling-nan ta hsüeh, Canton, China.**
Catalogue for 1917 and 1918 of the College of Arts and Sciences. Canton ₍1917₎
52 p. illus. 24cm. (Canton Christian College. Bulletin, no. 10)

**NL 0386846	NIC**

Ling-nan ta hsüeh, Canton, China.
Catalogue for 1919 of the college of Arts and Sciences. Canton, 1919.
1 v. illus. 73 cm. (Canton Christian College. Bulletin, no. 19)

**NL 0386847	MB**

VOLUME 334

LG51
C32
no.26
Ling-nan ta hsüeh, Canton, China.
Catalogue of the College of Arts and
Sciences, academic year 1920-21. Canton,
China, 1920.
90 p. illus. 23cm. (Canton Christian
College. Bulletin, no. 26.)

NL 0386848 NIC PU OC1 MB

LG51
C32
no.30
Ling-nan ta hsüeh, Canton, China.
Catalogue of the College of Arts and
Sciences, academic year 1921-22. Canton,
1921.
106 p. illus. 22cm. (Canton Christian
College. Bulletin, no. 30)

NL 0386849 NIC

LG51
C32
no.36
Ling-nan ta hsüeh, Canton, China.
Catalogue of College of Arts and
Sciences and College of Agriculture, with
announcements for academic year 1924-25.
Canton, 1924.
137 p. illus. 23cm. (Canton
Christian College. Bulletin, no. 36)

NL 0386850 NIC

LG51
C32
no.37
Ling-nan ta hsüeh, Canton, China.
Catalogue of College of Arts and
Sciences and Ling Nan Agricultural College,
with announcements for academic year 1925-
1926. Canton, 1925.
139 p. illus. 23cm. (Canton Christian
College. Bulletin, no. 37)

NL 0386851 NIC

LG51
C32
no.41
Ling-nan ta hsüeh, Canton, China.
Catalogue of College of Arts and Sciences
College of Agriculture, School of Silk
Industry and College of Business Administra-
tion, with announcements for academic year
1928-29. Canton, 1928.
148 p. 24cm. (Canton Christian College.
Bulletin, no. 41)

NL 0386852 NIC

Ling-nan ta hsüeh, Canton, China.   378.51
... Charter, statutes and agreements, 1913. New York, Trus-   LA1
tees Canton Christian College [1913]
35 p. 24cm. (Canton Christian College bulletin. [no. 7])

NL 0386853 ICJ

LG51
.C319
1914b
Ling-nan ta hsüeh, Canton, China.
... The college and its schools. [New York ?,
1914]
5 l. 28 cm.
At head of title: Trustees of the Canton
Christian College.

NL 0386854 DLC

Ling-nan ta hsüeh, Canton, China.
Metcalf, Franklin Post, 1892-
Flora of Fukien and floristic notes on southeastern China,
by Franklin P. Metcalf ... [Canton, China] Lingnan university, 1942-

4997.32
2447.5
Ling-nan ta hsüeh, Canton, China.
Information and curriculum. 1946-1948.
Canton, China [n.d.]
56 p. 27cm.

NL 0386856 CU-E

Ling-nan ta hsüeh, *Canton, China.*
Lingnan ... [Canton? China, 1931?]
cover-title, [16] p. illus. 25 cm.
A catalogue of Lingnan University.

LG51.C319 1931   33-38943 rev

NL 0386857 DLC

Ling-nan ta hsüeh, Canton, China.
Lingnan science journal
see under title

Asia
Ref.
Z5358
.C5L52
Ling-nan ta hsüeh, Canton, China.
A list of plants growing in the
Lingnan University campus and vicinity.
Canton [Lingnan University] 1947.
113 p. 11 x 21 cm.

Text in Chinese and English. (part.)

1. Botany - China - Canton. 2.
Botany - China - Bibl. I. Title.

NL 0386859 HU NcD NIC DNAL

Ling-nan ta hsüeh, Canton, China.
The making of a Christian college in China; concerning the
beginnings, progress and needs of the Christian college, located
at Canton... New York [1902] 24 p. illus. 20cm.

1. Lingnan university, Canton,   China—Hist.
N. Y. P. L.   April 25, 1947

NL 0386860 NN

LG
51
C3
A3
Ling-nan ta hsüeh, Canton, China.
[Miscellaneous publications] Canton,
China, 1919-1924.
v. illus. 24-26 cm.

1. Canton Chr   istian College,
Canton, China.

NL 0386861 NIC

LG51
.C317
1910
Ling-nan ta hsüeh, Canton, China.
Organization, location field, opportunity, char-
acter work...
N.Y., 1910
1 p. 8°   19¼ cm.

NL 0386862 DLC

460.14
L64
Ling-nan ta hsüeh, Canton, China.
Plant hunting in remote China. New York,
1932.
[4] p.

1. Botany. Voyages and travels. [I.] Groff,
George Weidman, 1884-   II. Title.

NL 0386863 DNAL

Ling-nan ta hsüeh, Canton, China.
Prospectus of a Christian college in China. [New York,
Mission house, 1886] 8 p. map. 23cm.

NL 0386864 NN

Ling-nan ta hsüeh, Canton, China.
Radical drill cards
see under Liang, H   N

LG51-
.C31
Ling-nan ta hsüeh, *Canton, China.*
Report of the president
New York, Trustees of the Canton Christian College.
v. illus. (part. fold.) plans, ports. 23-26 cm. (*Its* Bulletin)
Title varies: President's report.
Vols. for 1909/10-   issued by the college under earlier
form of English name: Canton Christian College.

LG51.C31   78-206560

NL 0386866 DLC DHEW NN ICJ MiU NIC Or

Educ 3715.11.30
Ling-nan ta hsüeh, Canton, China.
A romantic achievement of Chinese and American
cooperation; illustrated historical sketch. New York,
Trustees of Lingnan Univ. [1941?]
[34] p. illus.

NL 0386867 MH

Q
72
.L75
Ling-nan ta hsüeh, Canton, China.
Science bulletin. v.1-   1930-
Canton.

NL 0386868 MiU

Ling-nan ta hsüeh, Canton, China.   5995.11
Sericulture at Canton Christian College.
= [New York. 1921.] 12 pp. Illus. 23½ cm.

D6951 — Silkworm.

NL 0386869 MB

Ling-nan ta hsüeh, Canton, China.
Howard, Charles Walter, 1882-1928.
... The sericulture industry of south China [by] C. W. How-
ard. [n. p.] 1923.

VOLUME 334

Ling-nan ta hsüeh, Canton, China.   **370.951**
Some educational problems in China ... Canton, China,   **R800**
Canton Christian College, 1918.
19, [1] p. 24ᶜᵐ.   *(On cover: Bulletin no. 15)*

NL 0386871   ICJ

Wason   Ling-nan ta hsüeh, Canton, China.
LG51   The spirit and purpose of Lingnan. New York
C326   city, Trustees, Lingnan University [1928?]
1928   29 p. map. 23 cm.

I. Title.

NL 0386872   NIC

Ling-nan ta hsüeh, *Canton, China.*
Students campaign for Canton Christian College. [Canton, China, College Press, printed by students, 1915]
[6] p. plates. 23 cm.
Caption title.
Signed: Charles K. Edmunds, president.

ɪ. Edmunds, Charles Keyser, 1876–   ɪɪ. Title.

LG51.C319 1915a   16–8552 rev

NL 0386873   DLC OO

Ling-nan ta hsüeh, Canton, China.
Teaching children in China at the Canton
Christian college ... New York, Canton
Christian college, 1915.
24 p. plates 21 cm.
Plates printed on both sides.
Contents: The college primary school (by)
H.B. Graybill.–Report of the primary school
(by) Sz-to Wad.–Christmas at the C.C.C.(by)
Julia Post Mitchell.–A natural out-growth.

NL 0386874   DHEW DLC

Ling-nan ta hsüeh, *Canton, China.*
Testimonies to the Canton Christian College ... New
York, Trustees of the Canton Christian College [1912]
11 p. illus. 25¼ cm.

ɪ. Title.

LG51.C319 1912   13–7203 rev

NL 0386875   DLC

378.51   Ling-nan ta hsüeh, Canton, China.
L647rt   Treasurer's report....Canton, China, 1912-

Name varies: To 1926 Canton Christian college.

NL 0386876   WaPS

Ling-nan ta hsüeh, Canton, China. *Canton Hospital*
see   Canton, China. Canton Hospital.

Ling-nan ta hsüeh, Canton, China. Dept. of
horticulture. Economic plant receiving station.
First report of the Economic plant receiving
station in cooperation with the Bureau of agriculture and forestry, Kwantung provincial government, Canton, China. Issued August 1934.
2 p.l., 2–43 numb. l. 38.5 cm.
Mimeographed.

NL 0386878   PSt

Ling-nan ta hsüeh, Canton, China. *Dept. of*
Sociology.
Yao society...
Fortune, Reo Franklin, 1903-   ed.

Ling-nan ta hsüeh, Canton, China. Dr. Sun
Yatsen medical college.
see   Canton, China. Canton hospital.

Ling-nan ta hsüeh, *Canton, China. Fei-wên ch'i hou kuan
ch'a so.*
Daily meteorological record.

Canton, China.
v. in   24 cm.
Frequency varies.
Added title, Oct./Dec. 1933–   :嶺南大學斐文氣
候觀察所逐日氣候報告
Vols. for   published by the University and
observatory under English form of Names: Lingnan University.
Freeman Meteorology—   Observatory.
   1. Meteorology—   China—Canton—Observations.
QC990.C5L5   21–11380

NL 0386881   DLC DAS

Ling-nan ta hsüeh, Canton, China.
Freeman Meteorology Observatory
see   Ling-nan ta hsüeh, Canton, China.
Fei-wen ch'i hou kuan ch'a so.

**19
L5
rien
hina**   **Ling-nan ta hsüeh,** *Canton, China. Hsi-nan shê hui ching
chi yen chiu so.*
嶺南大學西南社會經濟研究所概況   The South
West Social and Economics Institute. Lingnan University;
a review of its activities. 廣州 1949.
16, 16 p. 20 cm.
Cover title.

   1. Social sciences—Societies, etc.
     Title romanized: Ling-nan ta hsüeh hsi-nan
     shê hui ching chi yen chiu so.
H19.L5   72–856251

NL 0386883   DLC

**H 19
L5
1949a**   **Ling-nan ta hsüeh,** *Canton, China. Hsi-nan shê hui ching
chi yen chiu so.*
嶺南大學西南社會經濟研究所概況   The South
West Social and Economics Institute. Lingnan University;
a review of its activities. 廣州 1949.
16, 16 p. 20 cm.
Cover title.
Facsimile reproduction.
   1. Social sciences—Societies, etc.   I. Title.
     Title romanized: Ling-nan ta hsüeh hsi-nan
     shê hui ching chi yen chiu so.

NL 0386884   CaBVaU

Ling-nan ta hsüeh, Canton, China. Hsiao yu
tsung hui
see
Ling-nan ta hsüeh hsiao yu tsung hui.

                 Chinese Lib.
Ling-nan ta hsüeh, Canton, China. *Library.*
List of serials, Lingnan University Library.
[Canton, China?], 1936.

23 cm.

NL 0386886   MH

410.9   Ling-nan ta hsüeh, Canton, China. Lingnan
L642   natural history survey and museum.
   Special publication. no. 1- Jan. 1942-
   Canton, 1942-

NL 0386887   DNAL

**WX
2
JC6
C2L7r**   Ling-nan ta hsüeh, Canton, China. *Medical Dept.*
Report of the Medical Department, in-
cluding the hospital and infirmary.
1928/30. Canton.
32 p. illus.
Period covered by report ends June 30.
No more published?

NL 0386888   DNLM ICU

Ling-nan ta hsüeh, Canton, China. *Medical Dept.*
Report of the Medical Department including
the hospital and infirmary for 1928-1930.
Canton, Shameen Printing Press, [1931].

pp. 42. Illustr., tables. 22 1/2 cm.

NL 0386889   MBCo

Ling-nan ta hsüeh hsiao yu tsung hui.
(Ling-nan hsiao yu t'ung hsün lu)
嶺南校友通訊錄   廣州   嶺南大學校友總會編印
民國 38- [1949-
v. 11 x 20 cm.
Cover title.

I. Title.

LH7.L5   72–842738

NL 0386890   DLC

**Ling-nan ta hsüeh yüan shêng kung yu hsieh shang hui i,
Canton, 1950.**
(Ling-nan ta hsüeh yüan shêng kung yu hsieh shang hui
i chuan k'an) 嶺南大學員生工友協商會議專刊 [廣
州] 嶺南大學員生工友協商會議編輯委員會編印
[1950]
44 p. ports. 27 cm.
Cover title.

LG51.C394 1950   70–841507

NL 0386891   DLC

Ling Physical Education Association
see
**Physical Education Association of Great Britain and
Northern Ireland.**

VOLUME 334

鈴瓏 第1- 期 民國21年-
天津 河北省立天津中學校 [1932-
v. illus. 22 cm. annual.

I. Ho-pei shêng li Tien-ching chung hsüeh hsiao.
Title romanized: Ling tang.

C 66–254

Washington. Univ.,　　Seattle. Far Eastern Library
for Library of Congress　　4997.14
　　　　　　　　　　　　[1]

NL 0386893　WaU–FE

658.562
L755d
Ling-Temco electronics, inc.
Discovery sampling.　Dallas, Tex., Temco
aircraft corporation [1953?]
i, 18 l.　diagrs.,tables.　28cm.
Reproduced from typescript.
"By Statistical section, Quality control en-
gineering, Temco aircraft corporation, Dallas
division."

1. Sampling.　2. Aeroplane industry and trade
--Quality control.　I. Title.

NL 0386894　TxDaM

Lingafelter, Edward Clay, 1914–
Complexes of mercury and ammonia, by
Edward Clay Lingafelter ...　[Berkeley, Calif.,
1939]
2 p.l., 21 numb. l., 1 l.　tables, mounted
diagrs.　29 cm.
Thesis (Ph. D.) - Univ. of California, Dec.
1939.
Each section preceded by leaf not included in
paging.
1. Mercury.　2. Ammonia.

NL 0386895　CU

FSI only
PL8055
.L5
Lingala; grammaire, exercices, conver-
sations, lectures, vocabulaire. Buta,
Procure des frè res maristes, école
[1951]
158 p.　(Collection des frères maristes)

1. Bangala language.　I. Title.

Jk-lsg 9-10-　　　62

NL 0386896　DS

Lingam Lakshmaji Pandit
see Pandit, Lingam Lakshmaji.

JQ298
.A1L5
Lingamurty, V
Political parties in present-day politics.
Anakapalle, Lingamurty publications, Sarada
library, 1955.
23p.

1. Political parties-India.　2. H06.3-
Political parties.

NL 0386898　DS

F128
.47
J54
Lingan, McC., joint comp.

Jennings, Napoleon Augustus, 1856–1919, *comp.*
New York in the blizzard; being an authentic and comprehensive recital of the circumstances and conditions which
surrounded the metropolis in the great storm of March 12,
1888. Compiled by N. A. Jennings and McC. Lingan ...
New York, Rogers & Sherwood [°1888]

30.2
L64
E4.3
Lingán Celis, Octavio.
Nociones de agricultura, arboricultura y
horticultura para las escuelas primarias.
3. ed.　　Lima, Gil, 1919.
56 p.

1. Agriculture.　Text-books.

NL 0386900　DNAL

Lingane, David F., ed.

... Colorado mining directory: containing an accurate description of the mines, mining properties and mills, and the mining, milling, smelting, reducing and refining companies and
corporations of Colorado.　Arranged alphabetically by counties ...　[1st-　　ed.] 1883–
Denver, Colo., The Colorado mining directory co. [1883–

Lingane, James Joseph, 1909–
Electroanalytical chemistry.　New York, Interscience
Publishers, 1953.
448 p. illus. 24 cm.

1. Electrochemistry.　2. Chemistry, Analytic.　I. Title.

QD553.L56　　　　545.3　　　　53—10756 †

DNAL MB ODW OU TxU MiHM PPD PRosC OC1L PBm PBL PHC
CaBVaU NcD NN PPF PSC OCU OC1W ICJ NcU ViU PPC PSt
NL 0386902　DLC ICIU WaS OrPS OrP OrPR OrU MtBC TU PV

Lingane, James Joseph, 1909–
Innovations in electroanalytical chemistry. [State College,
Pa., 1953]
61 p. illus. 28 cm.　(Twenty-seventh annual Priestley lectures)
Includes bibliography.

1. Electrochemical analysis.　I. Title.

QD115.L5　　　　544.9　　　　54–384 ‡

NL 0386903　DLC NcD ScU MB PPD PSt OU ICJ PRosC IU NN

Lingane, James Joseph, 1909–　　joint author.

Kolthoff, Izaak Maurits, 1894–
Polarography: polarographic analysis and voltammetry,
amperometric titrations, by I. M. Kolthoff ... [and] J. J. Lingane ... with 141 illustrations.　New York, N. Y., Interscience
publishers, inc., 1941.

Lingane, James Joseph, 1909–
A study of the fundamental principles of electrolysis with
the dropping mercury electrode ... by James Joseph Lingane ...
[Easton, Pa., 1939]
cover-title, p. [825]–884, [1045]–1051.　illus., diagrs. 26cm.
Thesis (PH. D.)—University of Minnesota, 1938.
"Based on a thesis."
Vita.
"By James J. Lingane and I. M. Kolthoff."
"Reprinted from the Journal of the American chemical society, 61 ...
(1989)."
Bibliographical foot-notes.

CONTENTS.—Fundamental studies with the dropping mercury electrode: I. The Ilkovic equation of polarographic diffusion currents. II. The
migration current.

1. Electrolysis.　2. Mercury.　3. Polarograph and polarography.　4.
Ions—Migration and velocity.　I. Kolthoff, Izaak Maurita, 1894–
joint author.　II. Title: Dropping mercury electrode.

Library of Congress　　QD571.L56 1988　　40–32195
Univ. of Minnesota Libr.

———— Copy 2.　　　　[2]　　　　541.87

NL 0386906　MnU DLC

Lingappa, Jeorige Basava

see

Basava Lingappa, Jeorige

Lingarāju, Kandukūri.

246 p.　19 cm.　Rs 5
In Telugu.
A novel.

I. Title.
Title romanized: Gōdāvari navvindi.

PL4780.9.L52G6　　　　S A 67–5404
　　　　　　　　　　PL 480: I–Te–1344

NL 0386908　DLC CU NSyU

Lingard, Alfred.
Different species of trypanosomata observed in bovines in
India, by Prof. A. Lingard ...　Calcutta, Thacker, Spink & co.,
1907.
cover-title, 47 p.　III col. pl., fold. tab.　25cm.
From the Journal of tropical veterinary science.　vol. II, no. 1, 1907.

1. Trypanosoma.

U. S. Dept. of agr.　Library　　41L644D　　Agr 7--2137
for Library of Congress　　　　　　　[a40b1]

NL 0386909　DNAL

Lingard, Alfred.
Further notes bearing on the *T. equiperdum* with special reference to its presence in plaques, measurements
under various conditions and immunity conferred, if any,
against the *T. evansi*.　By Professor A. Lingard ...　Calcutta, Thacker, Spink & co., 1906.
cover-title, 34 p.　III pl. (2 col.)　24½cm.
From the Journal of tropical veterinary science, vol. I, no. 4, October,
1906.

1. Dourine.　2. Trypanosoma.

Agr 7-1723

Library, U. S. Dept. of　　　Agriculture 41L64F

NL 0386910　DNAL

Lingard, Alfred.
Observations on the filarial embryos found in the general circula-
tion of the equidæ and bovidæ, and their probable pathological
significance.　By Alfred Lingard, ... Fasciculus I.— Bursati.
Six charts, nine text illlustrations, and twelve plates.　London,
Adlard and Son, 1905.
iv, 59 p. incl. 9 illus., tables, 6 diagr.　XII pl.　24½cm.
Each plate accompanied by leaf with descriptive letter-press.
No more published.
"Bibliography," p. [57]–59.

NL 0386911　ICJ

Lingard, Alfred.
Report on dourine in different breeds of equines, together with an account of vesicular exanthema and pyro-
plasmosis which occurred as complications.　By Alfred
Lingard ...　Calcutta, Office of the superintendent of
government printing, India, 1905.
1 p. l., v, 84, xcix p.　XVI pl.　25cm.

1. Dourine.

Agr 5–557

Library, U. S. Dept. of　　　Agriculture 41L644.

NL 0386912　DNAL

Lingard, Alfred.
Report on horse surra at the government central
press
see his　Surra report.

VOLUME 334

Lingard, Alfred.
　　Report on the preparation of rinderpest protective serum with fifty tabular statements. By Alfred Lingard ... Calcutta, Office of the superintendent of government printing, India, 1904.
　　1 p. l., 42 p. 33½ᶜᵐ.

　　1. Rinderpest.　　　　　　　　　　　　Agr 5–788

Library, U. S. Dept. of　　　Agriculture　41L644R.

NL　0386914　DNAL

Lingard, Alfred.
　　... Report on the preparation of rinderpest protective serum with fifty tabular statements. By Alfred Lingard ... Calcutta, Office of the superintendent of government printing, India, 1905.
　　1 p. l., ill, 116 p. incl. tables.　23ᶜᵐ.
　　Revised.

　　1. Rinderpest.　　　　　　　　　　　　Agr 6–119

U. S. Dept. of agr. Library　　41L644R
for Library of Congress　　　　ₐ37b1₎

NL　0386915　DNAL ICJ

Lingard, A₍lfred₎.
　　Some flagellate forms found in the intestinal tracts of *Diptera* and other genera. By A. Lingard ... and Major E. Jennings ... London, Adlard and son, 1906.
　　2 p. l., 25 p. v pl.　24ᶜᵐ.
　　Bibliography: p. 24–25.
　　Each plate accompanied by leaf of descriptive text.

　　1. Beri-beri. 2. Diptera. Parasites. 3. Flagellata.　ɪ. Jennings, Edgar, 1864–　joint author.
　　　　　　　　　　　　　　　　　　　Agr 6–1718

Library, U. S. Dept. of　　Agriculture　439L64

NL　0386916　DNAL

Lingard (Alfred). Summary of further report on Surra. 8 pp. roy. 8°. *Bombay*, 1894.

NL　0386917　DNLM

Lingard, Alfred.
　　Surra report ... by Alfred Lingard ... Bombay, Govt. central press, 1893–1898.
　　3 v.　plates, map (v. 1) tables, diagrs.
　　35 cm.
　　Title varies.
　　Contents.–v. 1. Report on horse surra.–v. 2. 1. Report on surra in equines, bovines, buffaloes and canines, together with an account of experiments conducted with the trypanosoma of rats, bandicoots and fish.–v. 2: 2. Surra report.

　　Appendices including records of cases, charts and illustrations.
　　　1. Trypanosomiasis.　I. Title.

NL　0386919　CU DNAL DNW

Lingard, Amos Lister, 1911–
　　A study of mercury-oil emulsions, by Amos L. Lingard ... ₍Lawrence, Kan.₎ 1940.
　　Film copy of type-written manuscript. Made in 1942 by University microfilms (Publication no. 486) Positive.
　　Collation of the original: 3 p. l., 43 numb. l.　pl. (mounted photos.) diagrs.
　　Thesis (PH. D.)—University of Kansas, 1940.
　　Abstracted in Microfilm abstracts, v. 4 (1942) no. 2, p. 37.
　　Bibliography: leaf 43.

　　1. Emulsions. 2. Mercury. 3. Oils and fats.　ɪ. Title: Mercury-oil emulsions.　　　　　　　　A 43–316

Michigan. Univ. Library　　Film AC–1　no. 486
for Library of Congress

NL　0386920　MiU DLC NcD

Lingard, Charles Cecil, 1901–
　　... The autonomy question in the Canadian north-west ... by Charles Cecil Lingard ... ₍Chicago₎ 1942.
　　1 p. l., 340–352 p.　23ᶜᵐ.
　　Part of thesis (PH. D.)—University of Chicago, 1939.
　　Lithoprinted.
　　Bibliographical foot-notes.

　　1. Northwest Territories, Can.—Pol. & govt.　2. Autonomy.
　　　　　　　　　　　　　　　　　　　A 42–3012

Chicago. Univ. Library　　　F1060.9.L55
for Library of Congress

NL　0386921　ICU Wa Or NIC NcD CU MH Vi OCU DLC

F1034
.C24

Lingard, Charles Cecil, 1901–

Canada in world affairs. London, New York, Oxford University Press, 1941–

F1099
.C3

Lingard, Charles Cecil, 1901–

Canada in world affairs. ₍1935/39₎–
Toronto, Oxford University Press.

Lingard, C₍harles₎ Cecil, 1901–
　　The organs of the United nations ...
Tor.Winston₍c1948₎.
　　58p.illus.plates,port.0.

NL　0386924　CaBViP

Lingard, Charles Cecil, 1901–
　　... Peace with progress, reports by C. C. Lingard and R. G. Trotter on the ninth Institute of Pacific relations conference of January 1945, on "Security in the Pacific" and the third British commonwealth relations conference of February, 1945, on "The commonwealth and the world." Toronto ₍1945₎
　　43 p.　22½ᶜᵐ.　(Special series. The Canadian institute of international affairs)

　　1. Institute of Pacific relations. 9th conference, Hot Springs, Va., 1945. 2. British commonwealth relations conference. 3d, London, 1945. ɪ. Trotter, Reginald George, 1888–
　　　　　　　　　　　　　　　　　　　45–7667

Library of Congress　　　　D734.L5
　　　　　　　　　　　₍4₎　　　　　　　950

NL　0386925　DLC

Lingard, Charles Cecil, 1901–
　　Territorial government in Canada; the autonomy question in the old North-west territories, by C. Cecil Lingard ... Toronto, The University of Toronto press, 1946.
　　xl, 260 p. illus. (maps)　23ᶜᵐ.
　　Bibliography: p. ₍261₎–264.

　　1. Northwest territories, Canada—Constitutional history.　ɪ. Title.
JL462.L5　　　　　342.71　　　　A 47–2812
New York. Public library　　　₍4₎†
for Library of Congress

NL　0386926　CaBViPA MtBC AU CSt NcD CaOTU WaU TxU MnU DLC NNC NN WaU-L CaBViP CaBVa CaBVaU WaS LU NBuU

DU180
.N56A5
1947

Lingard, Eric K., ed.

Newcastle, *Australia. Council.*
　　Newcastle, 150 years. ₍Edited by Eric K. Lingard. Newcastle₎ 1947 ?₎

Lingard, Frank.
　　Prison labour in New Zealand. A historical, statistical, and analytical survey ... By F. Lingard ... Wellington, G. H. Loney, government printer, 1936.
　　75 p. illus., diagrs.　24½ᶜᵐ.
　　"Thesis presented for honours in commerce, 1936."
　　Bibliography: p. 75.

　　1. Convict labor—New Zealand.　ɪ. Title.
　　　　　　　　　　　　　　　　　38–24291
Library of Congress　　HV8931.N25L5　1936
　　　　　　　　　　　　₍3₎　　　　　　365

NL　0386928　DLC

Lingard, Harold Thomas, 1909–
　　Farm-mortgage loans and their distribution by lender groups, 1940–48. Washington ₍U. S. Govt. Print. Off.₎ 1949.
　　63 p. maps. 24 cm. (U. S. Dept. of Agriculture. Circular no. 812)
　　Cover title.
　　Contribution from Bureau of Agricultural Economics.
　　"Revises and brings up to date a report entitled Revised annual estimates of farm-mortgage debt by states, 1930–43, by D. C. Horton and H. D. Umstott ... and a report on Distribution by lender groups of farm-mortgage and real estate holdings, Jan. 1, 1930–45, by H. C. Larsen.
　　1. Mortgages—U. S. ₍1. Farm mortgages—U. S.₎ 2. Agricultural credit—U. S. 3. ₍Agricultural indebtedness—U. S.₎　ɪ. Title. (Series)
HG2051.U5L5　　　　332.72　　　　Agr 49–643*
―――― Copy 2.　　　　S21.A48　no. 812
U. S. Dept. of Agr. Libr.　1Ag84C　no. 812
for Library of Congress　　₍5*₎†

NL　0386929　DNAL PP PU-W DLC

Lingard, Harold Thomas, 1909–
　　... Interest charges payable on farm indebtedness in the United States, 1910–40, by Harold T.Lingard ... and Willard O.Brown ... Washington, D.C., 1942.
　　1 p.ℓ., 46 p.incl.tables, charts.

　　At head of title: United States Department of agriculture, Bureau of agricultural economics. Manifold copy, with printed title-page.

NL　0386930　MH-BA ICU

Lingard, J J H
　　Minutes of the proceedings of the court-martial held on Mr. J.J.H. Lingard, master of His Majesty's ship Brazen on July 17. and 18. 1820 at St. Helena ... with the correspondence, affidavits and counsels' opinions relating thereto &c. ...
London, J. Taylor, 1837.
　　VI, 82 p.　8°.
　　Contains ms. letter of J.J.H. Lingard to the editor of the Naval & Military Gazette.
　　In VWE p. v. 7.

NL　0386931　NN

Lingard, John.
　　A philosophic and practical inquiry into the nature and constitution of timber ... By John Lingard.
　　(*In* The Pamphleteer. London, 1820. 22½ᶜᵐ. v. 16, p. ₍355₎–383)

　　1. Timber. 2. Wood—Preservation.
　　　　　　　　　　　　　　　　　cᴀ 6–135 Unrev'd
Library of Congress　　AP4.P2　vol. 16

NL　0386932　DLC ICN ICRL ICJ MdBP MnHi MB

Lingard, John.
　　A philosophic and practical inquiry into the nature and constitution of timber; including an investigation into the causes of dry rot, and a proposal for effectually preserving timber against premature decay ... By John Lingard ... 2d ed. London, Printed for the author, sold by Longman and co. ₍etc.₎ 1827.
　　xii, 68 p.　21½ᶜᵐ.

　　1. Timber. 2. Wood—Preservation.
　　　　　　　　　　　　　　　　　7–40206
Library of Congress　　TA419.L75

NL　0386933　DLC MH-BA ICRL MiU NN

VOLUME 334

Lingard, John, 1771-1851.
Abrégé de l'histoire d'Angleterre...d'après
Lingard, Hume, Smolet, 1838
see under Boyer, Philippe.

Lingard, John, 1771-1851.
Abridgment of the History of England, by John Lingard, D. D. With continuation from 1688 to the reign of Queen Victoria, by James Burke ... To which is added marginal notes and questions, adapted to the use of schools, by M. J. Kerney ... Baltimore, J. Murphy & co., 1855.
10, 15-693 p. 20ᶜᵐ.

1. Gt. Brit.—Hist.—Compends.

Library of Congress   DA32.L755   2—21340

NL 0386935   DLC OC1StM OCX

DA   Lingard, John, 1771-1851.
32   Abridgment of the History of England. With continuation
L77   from 1688 to the reign of Queen Victoria, by James Burke, and
1873   an appendix to 1873 by the editor of the First Class-book of
             history. To which are added marginal notes and questions
             adapted to the use of schools. 41st rev. and enl. ed.   Baltimore, J. Murphy [1873]
                 721 p. 19cm.

             1. Great Brit. --Hist. --Compends.   I. Burke, James,
             1819-1886, ed.

NL 0386936   CMenSP NN MH OKentU OC1ND OC1

274.2
L646hTG
LINGARD, JOHN, 1771-1851.
Alterthümer der angelsächsischen Kirche.
Ins deutsche übersetzt von F.H. in Rom.
Herausgegeben und mit einer Vorrede begleitet
von J.I. Ritter.   Breslau, G.P. Aderholz, 1847.
xviii, 316p. 21cm.

Translation of Antiquities of the Anglo-
Saxon church.

1. England-Church history.   I. Ritter,
Joseph Ignaz, 1787-1857.   II. Title.

NL 0386937   TxU CtY MH ICU

274.2
L75a
Lingard, John, 1771-1851
The antiquities of the Anglo-Saxon church.
Newcastle, Edward Walker, 1800.
v. illus. 23cm.

Bibliographical footnotes.

1. Gt. Britain - Church history - Anglo-
Saxon period. 2. Gt. Britain - Antiquities.
3. Gt. Britain - History - Anglo-Saxon period,
449-1066. I. Title.

NL 0386938   TNJ

274.2
L646a
Lingard, John, 1771-1851.
The antiquities of the Anglo-Saxon church.
Newcastle, Printed by E. Walker; sold by
Keating, Brown and Keating, London, 1806.
2v.

Bibliographical footnotes.

1. Great Britain--Church history.   2.
Anglo-Saxons.   I. Title.

NL 0386939   TxFTC DNC

Lingard, John, 1771-1851
The antiquities of the Anglo)Saxon church.
The 2d. ed. Newcastle, printed by Edward Walker, 1810.
528p. 22x14 cm.

NL 0386940   MiDSH

BV2031 Lingard, John, 1771-1851. ST. JOHN'S SEMINARY LIBRARY
L5   The antiquities of the Anglo-Saxon church b BRIGHTON 35. MASS.
1841   ...John Lingard. The 1st American, from 2d
          London ed. Philadelphia, M. Fithian [1841?]

          324p. front.(map) 23.5cm.

          "Saxon alphabet" p.323.
          "The Lord's Prayer" [in Saxon] p.324.

          1. Great Britain-Church history-Early period
          to 1066. I. Title.

          IaDuC NjNbS ICN ICU CtY-D PU NIC
NL 0386941   MBtS WaSpG PRosC CtY PPL NN ODW OC1JC NNF

274.2
L64
Lingard, John, 1771-1851.
The antiquities of the Anglo-Saxon Church.
The 1st American, from the 2d London, ed.
Philadelphia, M. Fithian, 1848.

324 p. plate, fold. map. 23 cm.

1. Gt. Brit.--Church history--Anglo-Saxon
period, 449-1066. 2. Anglo-Saxons--Church
history. I. Title.

NL 0386942   MoSU-D PV KAS DNC InStme

Lingard, John, 1771-1851.
The antiquities of the Anglo-Saxon church. 2d American, from
the London edition. Baltimore, J. Murphy & Co., etc. etc. 1851.
pp. 322.
The English edition has the title, "History and antiquities of the Anglo-Saxon
church."

NL 0386943   MH PLatS OCX NcU NNiaU NjPT

4BX Lingard, John, 1771-1851.
866   The antiquities of the Anglo-Saxon
        Church.   3d. American from the 2d London ed.   Baltimore, J. Murphy, 1854.
        322 p.

NL 0386944   DLC-P4 OC1StM PRosC

Lingard, John, 1771-1851.

Bagg, Edward Parsons, 1883–
Another Canterbury tale, A. D. 1937, by Edward P. Bagg,
M. D. [Northampton, Mass., Printed by the Kraushar press,
ᶜ1938]

3A   LINGARD, JOHN, 1771-1851.
4373   Catechistical instructions on the
           doctrines and worship of the Catholic
           Church....   London, C. Dolman, 1840.
           139 p.   20 cm.

NL 0386946   ICN

Lingard, John, Father, 1771-1851.
Catechistical instructions on the doctrines
and worship of the Catholic Church. New York,
Patrick S. Casserly & sons, 1840.

139 p. 19 cm.

Copy 2: a new ed., rev. London, Charles
Dolman 1844.

NL 0386947   PLatS WaSpG DGU

Lingard, John, 1771-1851.
Catechetical instructions on the doctrines
and worship of the Catholic Church. 2nd ed.,
rev. & corr.   N.Y., Casserly, 1841.
167p. 16cm.

NL 0386948   PPPrHi MH

BX1961 Lingard, John, 1771-1851.
.A2L7   Catechetical instructions on the doctrines and worship
1842   of the Catholic church ... By John Lingard, D. D. 2d ed.
         New York, Casserly and sons, 1842.
             [3], 139 p. 18¹ᵐ.

NL 0386949   ICU DLC

Lingard, John, 1771-1851, ed.
The charters, granted by different sovereigns,
to the burgesses of Preston
see under Preston, Eng. (Lancashire)
Charters.

BT   Lingard, John, 1771-1851.
217   A collection of tracts on several subjects,
.L75   connected with the civil and religious
         principles of Catholics.   Baltimore, F. Lucas
         [n.d.]
             384 p.   19cm.

             1. Apologetics.   2. Church of England - Doctrinal and controversial works - Catholic
             authors.

NL 0386951   DCU OCX MoSU-D PV IEdS PLatS

Case   LINGARD, JOHN, 1771-1851.
4A   A collection of tracts, on several sub-
3084   jects, connected with the civil and religious
         principles of Catholics.   By the Rev. J.
         Lingard, D.D.   [3d ed.]   London, Keating
         and Brown, 1826.
             xi p.,[2],[4,]479,[1]p. 24cm.

NL 0386952   ICN

Shea   Lingard, John, 1771-1851.
BX   A collection of tracts on several subjects connected with the civil and religious principles of
890   Catholics, by the Rev. L. Lingard. Baltimore, F.
.L5   Lucas [183-?]
             384 p.

         Reprinted from the London 3d ed., 1826.

NL 0386953   DGU

Spec.   Lingard, John, 1771-1851.
Coll.   A collection of tracts on several subjects
Parsons connected with the civil and religious principles of Catholics, by the Rev. J. Lingard.
1065B   [3d ed.] Baltimore, F. Lucas [ca. 1830]
             384 p.

NL 0386954   DGU

BT   Lingard, John, 1771-1851.
225   A collection of tracts, on several subjects,
.L75   connected with the civil and religious principles of Catholics. Baltimore, F. Lucas
1835   [1835?]

             384 p. 21cm.

             1. Apologetics - 19th century.

NL 0386955   DCU

VOLUME 334

Lingard, John, 1771–1851.
Documents to ascertain the sentiments of British Catholics, in former ages, respecting the power of the popes. London, Printed for J. Booker, 1812.

38, 15 p. 20 cm.
Imperfect: cover wanting.

1. Catholics in   Gt. Brit. 2. Popes
Temporal   power.

NL 0386956   FU ICN NN RPB CaBViP

Lingard, John, 1771–1851.
Ward, Thomas, 1652–1708.
Errata of the Protestant Bible; or, The truth of the English translations examined; in a treatise, showing some of the errors that are to be found in the English translations of the Sacred Scriptures, used by Protestants ... in which also, from their mistranslating the twenty-third verse of the fourteenth chapter of the Acts of the Apostles, the consecration of Dr. Mathew Parker ... is occasionally considered. By Thomas Ward, esq. A new ed., carefully rev. and cor. To which are added, the celebrated preface of the Rev. Doctor L............ in answer

"Analysis", and a vindication, by the Right Rev. Doctor Milner, in answer to Grier's "Reply" ... New York, D. & J Sadlier, 1844.

[Lingard, John] 1771–1851.
Examination of certain opinions, advanced by the Right Rev. Dr. Burgess, bishop of St. David's, in two recent publications, entitled Christ, and not Peter, the Rock, and Johannis Sulgeni versus hexametri in laudem Sulgeni patris. Manchester [Eng.] Printed by Wardle and Bentham, 1813.   6–51 p.   21½cm.

732854A. 1. Burgess, Thomas, bp.   of Salisbury, 1756–1837. 2. Catholic
question—Gt. Br. I. Title.
N. Y. P. L.   November 22, 1935

NL 0386959   NN ICN

Lingard, John, 1771–1851.
Faits mémorables de l'histoire d'Angleterre
see under   [Favre, Léopold] 1817–1890.

Lingard, John, 1771–1851.
Geschichte von England seit dem ersten einfalle der Römer. Aus dem englischen übersetzt von C. A. freiherrn von Salis. Frankfurt, W. L. Wesché, 1827–28.
10 vol.

Gt. Brit.–Hist.]

NL 0386961   MH CtY

Lingard, John, 1771–1851.
Histoire d'Angleterre, depuis la première invasion des Romains, par le docteur John Lingard, traduite de l'Anglais sur la deuxième édition, par M. le chevalier de Roujoux... Paris: Carié de la Charie, 1825–31. 16 v. charts. 8°.

Title varies slightly.
v. 13–14, translated by A. Pichot.
v. 12, 15–16 have imprint: Paris: Parent-Desbarres; v. 13–14, Paris: Fantin.
v. 15 contains: Preuves de l'histoire d'Angleterre; v. 16. Justification de l'histoire d'Angleterre; Mélanges de controverses religieuses avec l'Evêque de Durham et quelques ministres anglicans...traduits...par A. Cumberworth, fils...

1. Gt. Br.—History. 2. Roujoux,   Prudence Guillaume, baron de,
1779–1836, translator. 3. Pichot,   Amédée, 1796–1877, translator.
4. Cumberworth, A., translator.
                                               September 27, 1920.

NL 0386962   NN

942
L6402
Lingard, John, 1771–1851.
Histoire d'Angleterre, par le docteur John Lingard. Traduite par m. Léon de Wailly; avec la continuation jusqu'a nos jours ... Paris, Charpentier, 1843–44.
6 v.

I. Wailly, Léon de, 1804–1863, tr.

NL 0386963   NNC

Lingard, John, 1771–1851.
Histoire d'Angleterre depuis la première invasion des Romains jusqu'à nos jours, par ... John Lingard. Traduite de l'anglais sur la 3. éd., par le baron de Roujoux; rev. et cor. par Camille Baxton [pseud.] d'après les indications memes de l'auteur. 4. éd., rev., cor. avec le plus grand soin, et publiée sous la direction du ... John Lingard... Paris, Parent-Desbarres, 1846.
5 v. 26 cm.

Vol. 5 has title: Continuation de l'Histoire d'Angleterre du ... John Lingard, depuis la révolution de 1688 jusqu'a nos jours, par M. de Marlès.
Vol. 1, 3 lack t.–p.

NL 0386965   CU

274.2
L646h
1845
LINGARD, JOHN, 1771–1851.
The history and antiquities of the Anglo-Saxon church; containing an account of its origin, government, doctrines, worship, revenues, and clerical and monastic institutions ... London, C. Dolman, 1845.
2 v. 23cm.
Third edition (recast and greatly enlarged) of the author's Antiquities of the Anglo-Saxon church.—cf. Pref.
Bibliographical foot-notes.
1. Anglo-Saxons. 2. Great Britain – Church history. I.   Title.

MeB NcGW ICN
PPP OC1StM CtY NjR InStme GU NIC WaSpG CConT MdBP
NL 0386966   TxU MiU MH IU NN CU NCH PLatS MCM PU PHC

BR749 Lingard, John, 1771–1851.
.L75   The history and antiquities of the Anglo-Saxon church; containing an account of its origin, government, doctrines, worship, revenues, and clerical and monastic institutions. By John Lingard, D.D. 2d ed. ... London, T. Baker [1858]
2 v. 19ᵐ.

1. England—Church history. 2. Church history, Medieval. 3. Anglo-Saxons.

ICU MBtS OC1JC IEN CaBVaU
NL 0386967   ICU ICN IMunS IU PPSJ NNiaU PPFr MBrZ

BR
749
L5
Lingard, John, 1771–1851.
The history and antiquities of the Anglo-Saxon church; containing an account of its origins, government, doctrines, worship, revenues and clerical and monastic institutions. London, Catholic Publishing & Bookselling Co., 1858.
2 v. 19cm.

1. Gt. Brit. --Church history--Anglo-Saxon period--449-1066. I. Title.

NL 0386968   CMenSP PLatS KAS

D
245
.507
LINGARD, JOHN, 1771–1851.
The history and antiquities of the Anglo-Saxon church; containing an account of its origin, government, doctrines, worship, revenues, and clerical and monastic institutions... London, C.Dolman,1858.
2v.

Bibliographical foot-notes.

NL 0386969   ICN

Lingard, [John] 1771–1851.
Lingard's history of England abridged; with a continuation, from 1688 to 1854. By James Burke... To which is prefixed a memoir of Dr. Lingard, and marginal notes, by M. J. Kerney. 2d ed. Baltimore, J. Murphy & co.; Pittsburg, G. Quigley, 1855.

23, xv, 25–662 p. front. (port.) 23ᵐ.

Subject entries: Gt. Brit.—Hist.—Compends.   2–21339

Library of Congress, no.   DA32.L736.

NL 0386970   DLC MH

Lingard, John, 1771–1851.
Lingard's history of England abridged: with a continuation, from 1688 to 1854. By James Burke ... And an appendix to 1873, by the editor of the First class book of history ... A memoir of Dr. Lingard, and marginal notes by M. J. Kerney ... 3d rev. and enl. ed. Baltimore, J. Murphy & co., 1875.
23, xv, 25–688 p. front. (port.) 23ᵐ.
Author of appendix signs himself "J. S. S. Georgetown, D. C."

1. Gt. Brit.—Hist.—Compends. I. Burke, James, 1819–1886, ed. II. Kerney, Martin Joseph, 1819–1861, ed.
                                                             2–21341
Library of Congress   DA32.L77 1875
                           [a35h1]   942

NL 0386971   DLC OrStbM PV OC1JC OCX

Lingard, John, 1771–1851.   6513.31
Lingard's History of England abridged: with a continuation, from 1688 to 1854. By James Burke. And an Appendix to 1873. By the editor of the First class book of history. The whole preceded by a memoir of Dr. Lingard, and notes. By M. J. Kerney. 4th enlarged edition.
— Baltimore. Murphy & Co. 1883. xv, 688 pp. 8°.

E1628 — Great Britain. Hist. — Burke, James, continuator. — Kerney, M. J., ed.

NL 0386972   MB ViU

Lingard, John, 1771–1851
Lingard's history of England abridged and continued. G. Bell and sons, 1918.

NL 0386973   OCX OC1JC

Lingard, John, [1771–1851]
A history of England, from the first invasion of the Romans... First American from the last London edition. London, 1819.
6v.

NL 0386974   PPL

Lingard, John, 1771–1851.
A history of England from the first invasion by the Romans ... by John Lingard ... London, J. Mawman, 1819–30.
8 v. geneal. tables. 28 x 23ᵐ.
Vols. VII–VIII have imprint: London, Baldwin and Cradock [etc.]
Bibliographical foot-notes.
CONTENTS.—I–III. To the accession of Henry VIII.—IV. To the accession of Mary.—V. To the accession of James I.—VI. To the Commonwealth.—VII. To the twenty-seventh year of the reign of Charles II.—VIII. To the revolution in 1688.

1. Gt. Brit.—Hist.
                                                             35–34683
Library of Congress   DA30.L7 1819

NL 0386975   DLC

Lingard, John, [1771–1851].
History of England from the first invasion by the Romans. Ed.2. London, Mawman, 1823–25.
9v.

NL 0386976   PU

VOLUME 334

Lingard, John, 1771-1851.
A history of England from the first invasion
by the Romans. 2d ed.   London, J.Mawman, 1823-
31.

14 v.

NL 0386977   MH KAS MdBP PPL

Lingard, John, 1771-1851.
History of England; 2d ed. London, 1825.

14v.

NL 0386978   NSchU

Lingard, John, 1771-1851.   Lond. 1825-29.
A history of England.... 12 vols.

NL 0386979   NWM

LINGARD, John,1771-1851.
A History of England from the first invasion by the Romans. 4th ed. Paris, L. Baudry,
1826-31.

14 vol. Port.

NL 0386980   MH DCU-IA MH OC1StM OC1ND NIC PPDrop

Lingard, John, 1771-1851
A history of England, from the first invasion of
the Romans. vol. vi. First American from the last
London edition. Philadelphia, pub. by Eugene
Cummiskey, 1827.
295p. 23x15 cm.

NL 0386981   MiDSH

Lingard, John, 1771-1851.
History of England from the first invasion by
the Romans. 1st American from the last London
ed. Philadelphia, Eugene Cummiskey, 1827.

8 v. in 4. 22 cm.

1. Gt. Britain - History.

NL 0386982   PLatS

DA30
.L7   Lingard, John, 1771-1851.
1827   A history of England, from the first invasion
by the Romans. By John Lingard, D.D. ... 1st
American from the last London ed. Philadelphia,
E. Cummiskey, 1827.
10 v. 21 1/2cm.

1. Gt. Brit.—Hist.

DA30.L7 1827

NL 0386983   MB PKsL PPP PMA MWA KMK Nh MH Vi

LINGARD, REV. JOHN, D.D.
A | History of England, | From the First | Invasion by the
Romans. | By John Lingard, D.D. | First American, from the
last London Edition. | Philadelphia: | Published by Eugene Cum-
miskey. | J. Harding, Printer. | 1827.
14 v. 25 cm.
Vols. 1-10, dated 1827; vols. 11 & 12: 1830; vols. 13 & 14: F. Lucas,
Balt., 1831. First appeared, London, 1819-1830. Lingard was one of the
most learned men of his time, and his *History* marked an epoch in England. (Gillow, 4, 254-278).

PPL PHC NjP
NL 0386984   DGU MoSU MB MH NN NjP MdW PPL MdBS PPA PV

Lingard, John, 1771-1851.
History of England, from the first invasion by the
Romans. 1827-30. 14 vols. in 7.
Accession numbers.

NL 0386985   DN

DA30
L7   Lingard, John, 1771-1851
1827   A history of England, from the first invasion by the Romans. 1st American, from
the last London ed. Philadelphia, E.
Cummiskey, 1827-31.
14 v. 24 cm.

Vols. 13-14 published in Baltimore by F.
Lucas.

1. Gt. Brit. - Hist.

NL 0386986   MeB PV WU DN-Ob

Lingard, John, 1771-1851.
A history of England from the first invasion by
the Romans, by John Lingard, D.D., by ... Second edition. London, Printed for J. Mawman, MDCCCXXIII-
MDCCCXXX.
14 v. 21½cm.
Bibliographical foot-notes; marginal notes.
Title-pages for vols.1 and 8 and pages i-vi
(vol.8) wanting.

1. Gt. Brit.—Hist.

NL 0386987   ViU

Lingard, John, 1771-1851.
A history of England from the first invasion by
the Romans, by John Lingard, D.D. 4th ed., cor.
and considerably enlarged ... London, Baldwin and
Cradock, 1837.
13 v. 17½cm.
Added t.-p., engr. with vignette.
Bibliographical foot-notes.

1. Gt. Brit.—Hist.

NL 0386988   ViU PPWI

WA   Lingard, John, 1771-1851.
26321   A history of England, from the first
invasion by the Romans. 4th ed., corr.
and considerably enl. London, Baldwin
and Cradock, 1837-45.
13 v. illus.

Vol. 13, New ed., has imprint: London,
C. Dolman, 1845.

NL 0386989   CtY

Lingard, John, 1771-1851.
A history of England, from the first invasion by the Romans. By John Lingard, D. D. 5th ed. complete in eight volumes ... Paris, Baudry's European library, 1840.
8 v. front. (port.) 21½cm. (*Half-title:* Collection of ancient and modern British authors. vol. 273-280)
The 5th English edition, the last revised by the author, appeared in
10 vols. London, 1849.

1. Gt. Brit.—Hist.

                                         6-16115 Revised
Library of Congress   DA30.L7 1840

NL 0386990   DLC CtY ScU MdBP MH I NIC NN OC1W NNUT

Lingard, John. 1771-1851.   2429.2
A history of England, from the first invasion by the Romans [B. C.
55] to the commencement of the reign of William the Third. A
new edition [4th] corrected and enlarged.
London. Dolman. 1837-51. 13 v. Portrait. Engraved title-
pages. Sm. 8°.
Vols. 2, 3 and 4 have the imprint Baldwin & Cradock.

F3062 — Great Britain. Hist.

NL 0386991   MB

Lingard, John,   1771-1851.
A history of England, from the first
invasion by the Romans to the commencement of the reign of William the Third,
by John Lingard... A new ed., corr.and
considerably enl. ...   London,C.Dolman,
1844-45.   13v. front.(port.) 16½cm.

Each volume has an added illustrated
title-page, engraved.

1. Gt.Brit.—Hist.

NL 0386992   MWelC IMunS OOxM MiD

Lingard, John, 1771-1851.
The history of England, from the first invasion by the
Romans to the accession of William and Mary in 1688. By
John Lingard, D. D. 5th ed. rev. and considerably enlarged ...
London, C. Dolman, 1849.
10 v. front. 22cm.

1. Gt. Brit.—Hist.
                                         2—6688
Library of Congress   DA30.L7 1849

NL 0386993   DLC OrStbM WaS Wa ViU PCC PV NIC OC1JC NcU

LINGARD, Rev. John. 1771-1851.
A history of England to the reign of William III. New ed.
London: C. Dolman. 1851, 59. 13 v. 16°
Vol. 2-4 are of the 4th ed., with the imprint: London: Baldwin & Cradock. 1837.
The title page of vol. 1 is missing.

NL 0386994   MB

Lingard, John, 1771-1851.
A history of England from the first invasion by
the Romans to the accession of William and Mary in
1688. From the last rev. London ed. in 13 volumes
Boston, Phillips, Sampson and co., 1853-1855.

13 v. 19 cm.
Added engraved title page.
Bound in leather.

1. Gt. Britain - History.

NL 0386995   PLatS NcA-S PPAp MH

VOLUME 334

Lingard, John, 1771-1851.
Hist. of Eng. fr. the 1st invasion by the
Romans to the accession of Wm. & Mary in
1688. 13v. Boston, 1853-56

NL 0386996 ODW

DA
30
L7
1854
Lingard, John 1771-1851.
A history of England, from the first invasion by the Romans to the accession of
William and Mary, in 1688. A new ed., as
enlarged by Dr. Lingard shortly before his
death... Boston, Phillips, Sampson and co.,
1854.
13 v. 20 cm.

1. Gt. Britain - History.

NL 0386997 IMunS PPMoI

Lingard, John, 1771-1851.
The history of England, from the first invasion by the Romans to the accession of William
and Mary in 1688. 6th ed., revised and considerably enlarged. London, C.Dolman, 1855.

10 v.

NL 0386998 MH CU PPFr PP MnHi PU PHi PPWe PV PPSJ IdU

Lingard, John, 1771-1851.
History of England from the invasion by the
Romans to the accession of William and Mary in
1688. New American ed. N. Y., O'Shea & Bost.,
Phillips, 1855-64.
13 v. index. 18 cm.

NL 0386999 ViLxW KAS

DA30
L7
Lingard, John, 1771-1851.
A history of England from the first invasion
by the Romans to the accession of William and
Mary in 1688, by John Lingard ... a new edition
as enlarged by Dr. Lingard shortly before his
death ... New York, P. O'Shea [1855?]

13 vol. 19.5cm.

1.Gt. Brit.-History. I.Title.

NL 0387000 MBtS CtY InRenS

Lingard, John, 1771-1851.

Hume, David, 1711-1776.
The history of England, from the invasion of Julius Cæsar,
to the revolution in 1688. By David Hume, esq. With notes
and references, exhibiting the most important differences between this author and Dr. Lingard ... Philadelphia, J. B.
Lippincott & co., 1859.

Lingard, John, 1771-1851.
History of England to...1688; new ed. N. Y.,
1860.
13 v.

NL 0387002 NjP

Lingard, John, 1771-1851.
History of England, from the invasion by the
Romans to the accession of William & Mary in
1688. Ed. 6, rev. & enl. Manchester, Ains-
worth, 1868.
10 v.

NL 0387003 OO OClUr OClNd

DA30
.L7
1874
Lingard, John, 1771-1851.
A history of England, from the first invasion by the Romans to the accession of William
and Mary in 1688. By John Lingard...6th ed.,
rev. and considerably enl. Dublin [etc.]J.
Duffy & sons, 1874.
v.   fronts.,plates, 19 1/2 cm.

NL 0387004 DLC MH PHC FU MiU NjR

Lingard, John, 1771-1851.
The history of England, from the first invasion
by the Romans to the accession of William and
Mary in 1688. By John Lingard, D.D. 6th ed.
rev. and considerably enlarged. Dublin,[etc.]
1874-1915.
11 v. front. 19.5 cm.
v. 11 "to the accession of King George the Fifth
by John Lingard and Hilaire Belloc"... New
York, 1915. 23 cm.

NL 0387005 CtY

Lingard, John, 1771-1851.
The history of England from the first invasion
by the Romans to the accession of William and Mary
in 1688. 6th ed. rev. and enl. in 10 volumes.
New York, D. & J. Sadlier, 1879.

10 v. in 5. fronts. 19 cm.

1. Gt. Britain - History.

NL 0387006 PLatS

DA30
.L7
1883
Lingard, John, 1771-1851.
The history of England, from the first
invasion by the Romans to the accession of
William and Mary in 1688. Copyright ed.,
with portraits newly etched by Damman.
Boston, Estes and Lauriat, 1883.
10 v. 10 ports. 23cm.
"Memoir of the Rev. Dr. Lingard": v. 1, p. xxxi-
xlvi.
1. Gt. Brit.—Hist.

NL 0387007 ViU

Lingard, John, 1771-1851.
The history of England, from the first invasion by the
Romans to the accession of William and Mary in 1688.
By John Lingard, D. D. Copyright ed., with ten portraits
newly etched by Damman ... London, J. C. Nimmo &
Bain, 1883.
10 v. fronts. (ports.) 23cm.
"Memoir of the Rev. Dr. Lingard": v. 1, p. xxxi-xlvi.

1. Gt. Brit.—Hist.
                                              17-7125
Library of Congress   DA30.L7 1883

NL 0387008 PPLas OCX OO OU
DLC CaBVa OrP CaBVaU TxU MoSU MBr-Z NjP

Lingard, John, 1771-1851
Hist. of Eng., fr. the 1st invasion by
the Romans to the accession of Wm. & Mary
in 1688. New ed.... N.Y., P.O'Shea, 1887.
13v.

NL 0387009 OClNd OC1StM

Lingard, John, D. D. 1771-1851
Hist. of Eng. fr. the 1st invasion by
the Romans to the accession of Wm. & Mary
in 1688. 10 v. O.
Dublin, 1888.

NL 0387010 OCU PP PPD

Lingard, John, 1771-1851.
The history of England, from the first invasion by the
Romans to the accession of William and Mary in 1688, by
John Lingard, D. D. Copyright ed. ... Edinburgh, J. Grant,
1902.
10 v. fronts. (ports.) 23 cm.
"Memoir of the Rev. Dr. Lingard": v. 1, p. [xxxi]-xlvi.

1. Gt. Brit.—Hist.
DA30.L7 1902   942   35—29137

NL 0387011 DLC WaT OrStbM CoU PPSJ CtY OC1 PRosC TU

Lingard, John, 1771-1851.
The history of England, from the first invasion by the Romans to
the accession of King George the Fifth. [Continued by Hilaire
Belloc.] With an introduction by His Eminence, James Cardinal
Gibbons. Vol. 1-10.
— New York. The Catholic Publication Society of America. 1912.
10 v. Portraits. 22½ cm., in 8s.

H9731 — Belloc, Joseph Hilaire Pierre, continuator. 1870-. — Gibbons, James,
Cardinal, pref. 1834-. — Great Britain. Hist.

NL 0387012 MB

Lingard, John, 1771-1851.
The history of England, from the first invasion by the
Romans to the accession of King George the Fifth, by John
Lingard, D. D., and Hilaire Belloc, B. A. With an introduc-
tion by His Eminence James, cardinal Gibbons ... New
York, The Catholic publication society of America. 1912-15.
11 v. fronts. (ports.) 23 cm.
Memoir of the Rev. Dr. Lingard: v. 1, p. xxxi-xlvi.
Reprint of edition in 10 vols., with addition of vol. xi, covering
period from 1688 to 1910, by Hilaire Belloc.
1. Gt. Brit.—Hist. I. *Belloc, Hilaire, [1870-

DA30.L7 1912   16—85

OrU-M MtBuM NN PPL PPStC NBuG TxFTC OC1JC-U MiD
WaT WaTC WaWW PPLas OCX WU CoU Or OrStbM OrSaW
OrP OrPR OrU PPULC Wa WaE WaPS WaS WaSp WaSpG
NL 0387013 DLC CaBVaU IdB IdPI IdU MtBC OrCS MtU

Lingard, John, 1771-1851.
Lingard's History of England, newly abridged and brought
down to the accession of King Edward VII, by Dom Henry
Norbert Birt, O. S. B., with a preface by Abbot Gasquet, D. D.
London, G. Bell & sons, 1903.
x, [2], 645, [1] p. incl. map. 20½cm.

1. Gt. Brit.—Hist.—Compends. I. Birt, Henry Norbert, 1861-1919,
ed.
                                              4—17439
Library of Congress   DA32.L76
                          [a41j1]   -942

NL 0387014 DLC OKentU WaU PPAp PPLas OC1JC MB

DA
32
.L75
1904
Lingard, John, 1771-1851.
Lingard's History of England, newly abridged and
brought down to the accession of King Edward VII,
by Dom Henry Norbert Birt, O.S.B., with a preface
by Abbot Gasquet, D.D. London, G.Bell & sons,
1904-10.
          incl.map. 20½ cm.
2 v. (645 p.)

1.Gt.Brit.—Hist.—Compends. I.Birt,Henry Norbert,1861-1919,ed.
DC/KKU   DA32.L76

NL 0387015 MiU

Lingard, John, 1771-1851.
Lingard's history of England, newly abridged
and brought down to the accession of King
Edward 7th. L. Bell, 1906.
a

NL 0387016 CoD

VOLUME 334

Lingard, [John] 1771-1851.
History of England; newly abridged and brought down to the accession of King Edward VII, by Henry Norbert Birt. London: G. Bell & Sons, Ltd., 1910. x p., 1 l., 645(1) p. maps. 8°.

1. Great Britain.—History.—General.
N. Y. P. L.

CENTRAL CIRCULATION.
2. Birt, Henry Norbert, editor.
April 19, 1911.

NL 0387017   NN

Lingard, John, 1771-1851.
Lingard's History of England, newly abridged and brought down to the accession of King Edward VII, by Dom Henry Norbert Birt, O. S. B., with a preface by Abbot Gasquet, D. D. London, G. Bell & sons, 1911.

x, [2], 645, [1] p. incl. map. 20½ᵐ.

1. Gt. Brit.—Hist.—Compends.   I. Birt, Henry Norbert, 1861–1919, ed.

NL 0387018   WaTC

Lingard, John, 1771-1851.
Lingard's History of England, newly abridged and brought down to the accession of King George V, by Dom Henry Norbert Birt, O. S. B., with a preface by Abbot Gasquet, D. D. Rev. ... ed. London, G. Bell & sons, ltd., 1912.

x, [2], 651, [1] p. illus. (maps) 20½ cm.

1. Gt. Brit.—Hist.   I. Birt, Henry Norbert, 1861–1919, ed.
[DA32.L7   ]   A 15—851
Stanford Univ. Library
for Library of Congress   [a53d½]

NL 0387019   CSt WaS OC1 PRosC

Ex
1426
.589
.1914

Lingard, John, 1771-1851
Lingard's History of England, newly abridged and brought down to the accession of King George V, by Dom Henry Norbert Birt, with a preface by his eminence Cardinal Gasquet. Rev. and cheaper ed. London, G. Bell and sons, ltd., 1914.

651 p. illus., maps. 20 cm.

"First published, July 1903... revised and cheaper edition, 1912; reprinted, 1914."
F. Scott Fitz-   gerald's copy, with ms. annotations.

NL 0387020   NjP MB

Lingard, John, 1771-1851
(Lingard's) Hist. of Eng., newly abridged & brought down to the accession of King Geo. v, by Dom Henry Norbert Birt, O.S.B., with a preface by Abbot Gasquet, D.D. Rev. ed. Lond., G. Bell & sons., ltd., 1919.
651 p.

NL 0387021   OCX

Lingard, John, 1771-1851

History of England, newly abr. and brought down to the accession of King George V, by Dom Henry Norbert Birt, with a preface by His Eminence Cardinal Gasquet. Abr. ed. v.2, maps. Bell, 1930.

NL 0387022   OrP

Lingard, John, 1771-1851.
Introduction to English history. ed. by Townsend Young, Dublin, Duffy, 1867.

NL 0387023   PPCCH

LINGARD, John, 1771-1851.
Justification de l Histoire d'Angleterre trad. de l'anglais par M. le baron de Roujoux. P. 1833.

NL 0387024   MH

[Lingard, John] 1771-1851.
A letter to a clergyman of the diocese of Durham in answer to his Second letter to the author of the Remarks on the Bishop of Durham's charge. Newcastle upon Tyne, Printed by Preston & Heaton and sold by Bell, 1808.
[1] l., 62 p.   16 cm.

NL 0387025   ICN

[LINGARD, John], 1771-1851.
Mélanges de controverses religieuses [avec l'évêque de Durham et quelques ministres angl.icans; trad. de l''angl. par A. Cumberworth fils, P. 1829?]

Title page wanting.

NL 0387026   MH

Lingard, John, 1771-1851, tr.
A new version of the four Gospels; with notes critical and explanatory... (1836) (1851)
        see under Bible. N. T. Gospels. English. 1836. Lingard.   Also 1851.

RARE
BOOKS
DEPT

[Lingard, John] 1771-1851.
Observations on the laws and ordinances which exist in foreign states relative to the religious concerns of their Roman Catholic subjects. By a British Roman Catholic. London, Keating, Brown, 1817.
39 p.

1. Church and state - Catholic Church.   I. A British Roman Catholic.   II. Title.

NL 0387028   CU RPB CtY ICN

3A
1824

[LINGARD, JOHN] 1771-1851.
Remarks on a charge delivered to the clergy of the Diocese of Durham, by Shute, Bishop of Durham, at the ordinary visitation of that diocese in the year 1806 ... London, Printed and published by Keating, Brown, and Co., 1807.
33p. 16cm.

NL 0387029   ICN RPB

BX5034
.B27L7
1822

SWTS

Lingard, John, 1771-1851.
Remarks on a charge delivered to the clergy of the Diocese of Durham, by Shute, Bishop of Durham at the ordinary visitation of that diocese in the year 1806. 4th ed., enl. Dublin, Richard Coyne, 1822.
282p. 20cm.

1. Barrington, Shute, Bp. of Durham, 1734-1826. A charge delivered to the clergy of the Diocese of Durham. 2. Reformation--England. I. Title.

NL 0387030   IEG

BR83
.206

[Lingard, John] 1771-1851.
Remarks on the "Saint Cuthbert" of the Rev. James Raine M. A. Newcastle, Heaton, 1828.
68 p. 20 cm.

1. Raine, James, 1791-1858. Saint Cuthbert. II. Title.

NL 0387031   MB

Lingard, John, 1771-1851.
A reply to the observations of the Edinburgh review, on the Anglo-Saxon antiquities. By the Rev. John Lingard ...

(In The Pamphleteer. London, 1816. 22½ᵐ. v. 7, p. [531]-544)

CA 6—479 Unrev'd
Library of Congress   AP4.P2 vol.7

NL 0387032   DLC   MH OC1 MnHi ICN

942.073
L647

Lingard, John, 1771-1851.
A review of certain anti-Catholic publications; viz. A charge delivered to the clergy of the diocese of Gloucester, in 1810, by George Isaac Huntingford; A charge delivered to the clergy of the diocese of Lincoln, in 1812, by George Tomline; and Observations on the Catholic question, by the Right Hon. Lord Kenyon. London, Printed for J. Booker, 1813.

88 p.

1. Catholic emancipation I. Huntingford, George Isaac, bp. of Hereford, 1748-1832. A charge ... II. Kenyon, George, 2d baron, 1776-1855. Observations on the Roman Catholic question. III. Tomline, Sir George Pretyman, bar^t successively bp. of Lincoln and of Winchester,   1750-1827. A charge... IV. Title.

NL 0387034   MnU RPB MH FU

3A
1932

65-
3318

LINGARD, JOHN, 1771-1851.
A review of certain anti-Catholic publications; viz. A charge delivered to the clergy of the diocese of Gloucester, in 1810, by George Isaac Huntingford ... (reprinted in 1812.) A charge delivered to the clergy of the diocese of Lincoln, in 1812, by George Tomline ... and Observations on the Catholic question, by the Right Hon. Lord Kenyon. By the Rev. John Lingard ... London, Printed for J. Booker, by J. F. Dove, 1813.
[1] l., 61p.   19cm.

NL 0387035   ICN

VOLUME 334

Lingard, John, 1771-1851.
   Sadler's abridgment of Lingard's History of England, from the invasion of J. Cæsar to James II; abridged for the first time, and continued from that period to 1835, by P. Sadler. Containing a complete series of retrospective and historical questions at the end of each reign ... Illustrated with a coloured map of England ... Paris, Truchy's French and English library, 1836.
   2 p. l., xxiv, 1028 p. front. (fold. map) 19½ᶜᵐ.

   1. Gt. Brit.—Hist.   I. Sadler, Percy.

                                   30-3508

Library of Congress   DA32.L79

  NL 0387036   DLC NN

Lingard, John, 1771-1851, ed.

                    FOR OTHER EDITIONS
                    SEE MAIN ENTRY
White, Thomas, 1764-1826.
   Sermons for the different Sundays and principal festivals of the year; with a few additional sermons on various important subjects. By the late Rev. Thomas White, of Winchester. Selected and arranged from his mss. by the Rev. John Lingard, D. D. 2d ed. London, C. Dolman; Baltimore, J. Murphy & co., 1852.

  Lingard, John, ed.

  White, Thomas.
    Sermons for the Sundays and some festivals of the year, by the Rev. Thomas White; selected and arranged from his mss. by the Rev. John Lingard, D. D. New York, J. F. Wagner [*1911]

4A
7155   LINGARD, JOHN, 1771-1851.
     Strictures on Dr. Marsh's Comparative view of the Churches of England and Rome. By the Rev. John Lingard ... London, Printed by J. F. Dove, for J. Booker, 1815.
    [1 l.,]88p. 20cm.

  NL 0387039   ICN

LINGARD, [John], 1771-1851.
   A true account of the gunpowder plot; extracted from Dr. Lingard's History of England and Dodd's Church History. With notes and prefatory remarks by Vindicator [pseud.] London, C.Dolman,1851.

  NL 0387040   MH PBL CSmH PV

941.58 Lingard, John, 1771-1851.
C692   A vindication of certain passages in
no.57 the fourth and fifth volumes of the His-
no.4   tory of England ... 2d ed.   London,
     1826.
     112p.

    [Collins pamphlets. v.57, no.4]

  NL 0387041   IU PPL RPB

Lingard, John, 1771-1851.
  Vindication of certain passages. 3d ed. London, 1826.
    112 p. 8°. [In v. 768, College Pamphlets]

  NL 0387042   CtY

Lingard (John) 1771-1851.
  A vindication of certain passages in the fourth and fifth volumes of the History of England ... 4. ed. 120 pp. *London: J. Mawman,* 1827. 8°.
    Bd. with: Lingard (J.) Documents to ascertain the sentiments of British Catholics, in former ages, respecting the power of the popes. London, 1812. 8°.

  NL 0387043   NN

LINGARD, J[ohn] 1771-1851.
  Vindication of certain passages in the fourth and fifth volumes of the History of England. 5th ed. London,1827.

  11 2p.

  NL 0387044   MH-L MH PPFr

Lingard, John, 1771-1851.
  Vollständiger Auszug der Geschichte England's. Wien, Druck und verlag der Mechitaristen Congregations Buchhandlung, 1831.

   v. 20 cm.
   Library has 2 Band and 2 Band, 2 Abth.

   1. Gt. Britain - History.

  NL 0387045   PLatS

Lingard, Richard, 1598?-1670.
  Works by this author printed in America before 1801 are available in this library in the Readex Microprint edition of Early American Imprints published by the American Antiquarian Society. This collection is arranged according to the numbers in Charles Evans' American Bibliography.

  NL 0387046   DLC

[Lingard, Richard] 1598-1670.
  A letter of advice to a young gentleman leaving the University, concerning his behaviour and conversation in the world. By R. L. Dublin, Printed by Benjamin Tooke, Printer, to the Kings most Excellent Majesty, and are to be sold by Mary Crook, in Castle-Street, 1670.
    Sm. 12 mo. extended to sm. 4 to. 5 p. l., 59 p. (5 prelim. leaves without sig.-marks; A-E, in 6s) Unbound.
    At end of "An Advertisement from the Printer": To J.L. Esq; at Oxford.

    Bridgewater Library copy, 6/D9 (1), with ex-libris.
    Formerly bound in 3/4 brown calf, with 2 green labels, lettered: Miscellaneous Tracts 1670-1682.

  NL 0387048   CSmH

   Lingard, Richard, 1598?-1670.
*EC65   A letter of advice to a young gentleman leaving
16472 the vniversity, concerning his behaviour and
670Lc conversation in the world. By R. Lingard D.D. D,L.
    London,Printed for Benjamin Tooke,and are to be sold at the Ship in S.Pauls church-yard,1673.

    4p.l.,61p. 12.5cm.
    According to a contemporary ms. note on the t.-p., the "young gentleman" addressed is James Lane, eldest son of Viscount Lanesborough.

  NL 0387049   MH

Lingard, Richard, 1598?-1670.
  A letter of advice to a young gentleman leaving the university, concerning his behaviour and conversation in the world. By R.L. New York, Printed and sold by W. Bradford, printer to His Majesty, King William, at the Bible, 1696.
    3 p.l., 45 p. 12 cm.
    Signature of William Bradford inserted on fly-leaf.
    On verso of 2d fly-leaf at end: Johannis Robinson.
    Liber 1701 ex dono Domini Clap.

    The earliest book known to have been printed in the Colony of New York.
    1. Bradford, William, 1663-1752.   I. Title.

  NL 0387051   NNC NN CtY

Lingard, Richard, 1598?-1670.
  A letter of advice to a young gentleman leaving the university concerning his behaviour and conversation in the world, by R.L. With introduction and notes, by Frank C. Erb ... New York, [McAuliffe & Booth] 1907.
    1 p. l., x, 45 p. facsim. 15½ x 12ᶜᵐ.

   1. Young men.   I. Erb, Frank C.   II. Title.

Library of Congress   BJ1671.L7   7—7481

    OOxM ICJ NSyU KMK
  NL 0387052   DLC RPJCB OKentU ICRL RPJCB PPL NjP OO NN

Lingard, Richard, 1598?-1670.
  A sermon preached before the King at White Hall, July 26. 1668. In defence of the liturgy of our church ... London, Printed by J. M. for J. Crook, 1668.
    30 p. 21ᶜᵐ. [Collection of miscellaneous English sermons. London [etc.] 1641-1795. v.5, no.4]

    Wing L-2353

  NL 0387053   CLU-C InU NNG CtY NBu

Lingard, William Horace, supposed author.
  Captain Jinks.
  see under title

Lingard, William Horace, supposed author.
  Captain Jinks of the horse-marines.
  see under title

---

q784.3 Lingard, William Horace, 1839-
Sh37   Everybody's friend. Written and composed by Wm
v.13 Lingard. [New York, W. A. Pond & co.; Chicago,
no.43 Root & Cady; etc., etc.] c1868.
    6p. (His serio comic songs. no.2)
    [Sheet music printed in Chicago prior to 1871. v.13,no.43]
    Caption title.
    Port. of William Lingard on t.-p.
    Plate no.: 7014.

    I. Title.

  NL 0387056   IU

Lingard, William Horace, 1839
  "The Great Lingard" songster
  see under title

VOLUME 334

Lingard, William Horace,
Wm. Horace Lingard's "New" songster.
= New York. DeWitt. 1872. 176 pp. 16 cm.

H8687 — Songs. Without music. Colls. — T.r.

NL 0387058   MB RPB DLC

Lingard, William Horace, 1839-1927.
William H. Lingard's On the beach at Long Branch song book.
Containing all his original songs, and a complete collection of the
songs sung by the great and inimitable impersonator, William
Horace Lingard.   New York, Dick & Fitzgerald ₍c1868₎ 124 p.
17cm.

Without music, except for a few tunes.
Biographical sketch of W. H. Lingard, p. ₍5₎

at Long Branch song book.   Collections. I. Title: On the beach
N.Y.P.L.   April 25, 1945

NL 0387059   NN ICN MH RPB

Lingard, William Horace.

On the beach at Long Branch. ₍Written and composed by
William Lingard₎ New York, W. A. Pond ₍c1868₎
6 p. 35 cm. (*His* Serio comic songs, 1)

1. Songs (High voice) with piano. 2. Humorous songs.   I. Title.
M1621.L   52-55121

NL 0387060   DLC

Lingard papers.
n.s., no.

₍London, 19
no.   22cm.

"Read before...the Lingard Society."

1. No subject. I. Lingard Society,
N.Y.P.L.   London.
                                       July 19, 1935

NL 0387061   NN

Lingard Society, London.
                    Lingard papers

Lingat, Robert.
... Conférences, 1936, par Robert Lingat et Denise Paulme.
Paris, Domat-Montchrestien, 1937.
2 p. l., 29, 36 pp. 24ᶜᵐ. (Institut de droit comparé. Études de socio-
logie et d'ethnologie juridiques, pub. sous la direction de René Maunier
... xxv)
At head of title: ... Salle de travail d'ethnologie juridique. Faculté
de droit de Paris.
Contents.—L'influence indoue dans l'ancien droit siamois, par Robert
Lingat.—La communauté taisible chez les Dogon (Soudan français) par
Mlle Denise Paulme.
1. Law—Siam—Hist. & crit. 2. Hindu law. 3. Comparative law.
I. Paulme, Denise. II. Paris. Université. Faculté de droit. Salle de
travail d'ethnologie juridique.

43-48733

NL 0387063   DLC

Lingat, Robert.
... L'esclavage privé dans le vieux droit siamois. Paris, Les éditions Domat-Montchrestien,
1931.
xi, 381 p. 25.5 cm. (Pub. also as de sociologie et d'ethnologie juridiques ... VI)
Thèse – Univ. de Paris.
"Bibliographie": p. [379]-381.
1. Slavery.. Siam. I. Siam. Laws, statutes,
etc. II.

NL 0387064   CtY

Lingat, Robert.
... L'esclavage privé dans le vieux droit siamois (avec une
traduction des anciennes lois siamoises sur l'esclavage) Paris,
Les éditions Domat-Montchrestien, 1931.
xi, 395 p. 25¼ᶜᵐ. (*On cover:* Études de sociologie et d'ethnologie juridiques ... vi)
"Bibliographie": p. ₍393₎-395.

1. Slavery in Siam.   I. Siam. Laws, statutes, etc. II. Title.

33-13719

NL 0387065   DLC NNUN CU InU MH NN NPurMC

Lingat, Robert.
Les régimes matrimoniaux du sud-est de l'Asie; essai de
droit comparé indochinois. Paris, E. de Boccard, 1952-
v. 28 cm. (Publications de l'École française d'Extrême-
Orient, v. 34
Bibliographical footnotes.
Contents.—t. 1. Les régimes traditionnels.

1. Marriage law—Indochina.   I. Title.   (Séries: École française d'Extrême-Orient, Hanoi, Indochina. Publications, v. 34

53-26701

    ICU HU
NL 0387066   DLC CaBVaU OrU CU-I MH-P MoU NSyU MH CtY

Lingau, Otto, pseud.
    see Hellinghaus, Otto, 1853-

Lingau, James M.
Tracing by   Connolly from the original
map by   of the mansion house and land
of James M. Lingau of Washington, D.C. made
by direction of J.M. Toner, m.d.
1 sheet.
No. 7.

NL 0387068   DLC

₍Lingay, Joseph₎ d.1851.
De la monarchie avec la charte,...
Paris, 1816

DC197   ₍Napoleon pamphl₎ ets, v. 27, no. 2₎
.N2

NL 0387069   DLC

₍Lingay, Joseph, d.1851₎
Éloge de l'abbé Millot, de l'Académie française,
couronné par l'Académie des arts, sciences et belles-
lettres de Besançon, dans sa séance publique du 24 août
1814. Paris, Chanson, 1814

70 p.
Introd. signed: J.L.

NL 0387070   MH MB

₍Lingay, Joseph₎ d.1851.
Éloge de M. J. de Chénier ... suivi d'un catalogue raisonné de
tous ses ouvrages. Par J. L. Éloge de l'abbé Millot.
—   Paris. Rosa. 1814. 99 pp. 8°.

Chénier, Marie Joseph de.
    Sheet D 4822   Jan. 9, 1000

NL 0387071   MB NjP

4DT   Lingay, Joseph, d.1851
627   La France en Afrique. Paris, A
        la Direction du Musée des familles,
        1846.
            301 p.

NL 0387072   DLC-P4 MH IEN MiU MBU CU

₍Lingay, Joseph₎ d. 1851, *supposed author.*
Histoire du cabinet des Tuileries, depuis le 20 mars 1815,
et de la conspiration qui a ramené Buonaparte en France ...
2. éd. Paris, Chanson ₍etc.₎ 1815.
viii, 94 p. 21 cm.
Attributed also to Sébastien Guillié.

1. Napoléon I—Elba and the hundred days, 1814-1815.   I. Guillié,
Sébastien, 1780-1865, supposed author. II. Title.

DC239.L5 1815   944.05   31-3647

NL 0387073   DLC FTaSU NN NcU NIC

PZ7   Lingbank cottage: a tale for young women.
.L5   New York, American Tract Society, ₍1873₎
         304 p. illus. 16 cm.

    I. American Tract Society.

NL 0387074   NjR

943   LINGBEEK, C   A
Ref.346   Herinneringen uit den tijd der Doleantie.
L755h   Leiden, Jansen, 1929.
           170p. 20.5cm.

NL 0387075   MH-AH

LL64.4   Lingbeek, C   A
D739   De Synode te Dordrecht in 1618/'19; een
Xl64   lezing. Delft, Drukkerij D. Prooper, 1937.
           24 p. 23 cm.

    1. Dort, Synod of, 1618-1619.

NL 0387076   CtY-D MH-AH

Div.S.   Lingbeek, C   A
284.2492
L755S   De Synode te Dordrecht in 1618/19; een
           lezing door C. A. Lingbeek. 's-Gravenhage
           ₍1938₎
           24 p. 23 cm.

    1. Dort, Synod of, 1618-1619. I. Title.

NL 0387077   NcD

VOLUME 334

Lingbeek (G[oswijn] W[illem] S[anne]). De electriciteit in de geneeskundige praktijk. Overzicht der electriciteitsleer voor praktizerende artsen en studenten. 78 pp. 12°. Arnhem, K. van der Zande, 1888.

NL 0387078 DNLM

Lingbeek, Goswijn Willem Sanne
— Genezing door zeewater (onderhuids inespoten). 22 pp., 21 fig. 8°. Amsterdam. ?, van Rossen. 1909.

NL 0387079 DNLM

Lingbeek (Goswijn Willem Sanne). *Over het klinisch onderzoek der morphologische bestanddeelen van het bloed. 2 p l., 124 pp. 8°. Groningen, J. B. Huber, 1954.

NL 0387080 DNLM

WBJ LINGBEEK, Goswijn Willem Sanne
L755z Zeewater als geneesmiddel;
1908 subcutane injecties, methode Quinton. Amsterdam, Van Rossen, 1908. 124 p. illus.

NL 0387081 DNLM

4HS-34 Lingbeek, M S
Humanisme en ritus; bezinning op inhoud en wezen. Bouwstuk opgeleverd in de vergadering van voorzittend-meesters op 25 November 1934. 32 p.

NL 0387082 DLC-P4

Lingbeek, M S
"In den beginne was de Logos." Uitg. ter gelegenheid van het vijftigjarig jubileum van Br. M. S. Lingbeek. Arnhem, De Loge "De Oude Landmerken" [1938]
84 p. 20 cm.
Bibliography: p. 84.

1. Freemasons.
HS425.L5 50-47723

NL 0387083 DLC

DG Lingby, Helge, 1900-
12 Beiträge zur Topographie des Forum-
S97 Boarium Gebietes in Rom. Testimonien
v.7 nebst Kommentar und kritischem Apparat. Lund, C. W. K. Gleerup, 1954.
xxvi, 167 p. illus. 25cm. (Skrifter utgivna av Svenska Institutet i Rom, 8°, 7)

1. Rome (City) Forum boarium. I. Title II. Series: Sv enska Institutet i Rom. Skrifter. Se ries altera, v. 7.

NL 0387084 NIC

BS [Linge, Albert]
610 Das neue Heim der Loge Minerva zu den
L53M56 drei Palmen in Leipzig. Nachrichten über den Neubau und Berichte über die ersten Festlichkeiten in neuen Hause. Leipzig, Oskar Leiner, 1906. 71 p. illus. 24cm.

NL 0387085 NIC

4K Linge, Alphonse de
3131 Des origines de l'ordre des avocats et des vertus professionnelles; discours prononcé à la séance solennelle de rentrée du 6 novembre 1886. Bruxelles, F. Larcier, 1886. 52 p.

At head of title: Conférence du jeune barreau de Bruxelles, trente-cinquième année.

NL 0387086 DLC-P4

Linge, Arent Roelf van, 1870-
Ueber die einwirkung von kaliumhypobromit in alkalischer loesung auf amide. Groningen, 1896.

Dissert. Basel

QD299
A72

NL 0387087 DLC

Linge, Carl, 1782-1849.
De Asinaria Plauti, insigni corruptae apud Atticos sub novae commoediae aevum puerorum educationis exemplo. [Hirschberg, 1834]
Programm - Gymnasium, Hirschberg. Caption title.

NL 0387088 CtY

Linge, Carl, 1782-1849.
De Plauto properante ad exemplar Epicharmi. Commentatio ad Horat. Lib. II. Epist. 1, v. 58. Ratiboriae... 1827.

[Collection of pamphlets on Plautus, v. 5 & 14]

NL 0387089 ICU CtY

LINGE, Carl, 1782-1849
Quaestionum Plautinarum Liber primus sive de Hiatu in Versibus Plautinis. Vratislaviae, 1817.

pp. xvi, 79.

NL 0387090 MH CU

L Linge, Carl, 1782-1849.
2872.3 Quaestionum Plautinarum, liber primus, sive
P69zt de hiatu in versibus Plautinis, scripsit Carolus Lingius ... Vratislaviae, Joseph Max, 1819. xvi, 79 p.

NL 0387091 WaPS NjP

BV3705
.F7L5 Linge, Karl, 1879-
Fredrik Franson, "en man sänd av Gud." Uppsala, Lindblad [1951]
183 p. illus., ports. 21 cm.
Bibliography: p. 181-183.

1. Franson, Fredrik, 1852-1908.
Full name: Karl Johan Linge.
A 52-4538

Minnesota. Univ. Libr.
for Library of Congress [3]

NL 0387092 MnU DLC

BV3780
.L5 Linge, Karl, 1879-
Gestalter i svensk väckelserörelse. Uppsala, Lindbla [1953]
167 p. illus., ports. 19 cm.
Bibliography: p. 165-167.

1. Clergy—Sweden. 2. Revivals—Sweden. 3. Sweden—Church history. I. Title.
Full name: Karl Johan Linge.
A 54-2640

Minnesota. Univ. Libr.
for Library of Congress [3]

NL 0387093 MnU DLC

Linge, Karl, 1879-
...Hur den svenska folkskolan kom till striderna inom och utom riksdagen. Stockholm, Bonnier [1911]
50p. ports. D. (Studentföreningen Verdandis småskrifter. 62)

NL 0387094 NcD PU

Linge, Karl, 1879-
Ropande röster: Per Brandell [och] Lars Levi Læstadius. Uppsala, J. A. Lindblad [1955]
144 p. illus., ports. 19 cm.
Bibliography: p. 141-144.

1. Brandell, Per, 1781-1841. 2. Læstadius, Lars Levi, 1800-1861. I. Title.
Full name: Karl Johan Linge.
BX8080.B67L5 A 56-2016
Minnesota. Univ. Libr.
for Library of Congress [3]†

NL 0387095 MnU NN DLC

Linge, Karl, 1879-
Stockholms folkskolors organisation och förvaltning åren 1842-1861; studier i den svenska folkskolans historia ... av Karl Linge ... Stockholm, P. A. Norstedt & söner [1914]
xx, 211 p. 22½cm.
Akademisk avhandling—Stockholms högskola.
"Källor och litteratur": p. [xiii]-xx.
Errata slip inserted at end.

1. Stockholm—Public schools.
[Full name: Karl Johan Linge]
35-31483
Library of Congress LA909.S7L53 379.487

NL 0387096 DLC CtY PPAmSwM MH

VOLUME 334

Linge, Karl, 1879–
Tre andliga vägröjare. Uppsala, J. A. Lindblad ₁1954₎
173 p. illus. 19 cm.

1. Svenska Kyrkan—Biog. 2. Schartau, Henric, 1757–1825. 3. Hoof, Jacob Otto, 1768–1839. 4. Nyman, Pehr, 1794–1856. ɪ. Title.
Full name: Karl Johan Linge.

BX8039.L5 57–32403 ‡
₍²₎

NL 0387097 DLC

Linge, Kurt, 1900 —
...Die beherrschung des luftzustandes in gekühlten räumen. (Mitteilung aus dem Kältetechnischen institut der Technischen hochschule Karlsruhe) Berlin, Gesellschaft für kältewesen m.b.h., 1933.
47p. (Beihefte zur Zeitschrift für die gesamte kälte-industrie. reihe 2, Hft. 7)

NL 0387098 OU

Linge, Kurt, 1900–
Ueber periodische Absorptionskältemaschinen ... [Berlin, 1929]
Diss. - Karlsruhe (Technische Hochschule)
"Diese Dissertation ist unter dem gleichen Titel als Beiheft zur 'Zeitschrift für die gesamte Kälte-Industrie,' Reihe 2, Heft 1 ... erschienen."

NL 0387099 CtY OU ICRL

968.91
L7553m
Linge, Mona.
Missionär i Afrika. Stockholm, A.Bonnier [1945]
296p. illus. 24cm.

1. Rhodesia, Southern. Descr. & trav. 2. Missions. Rhodesia. Southern. I. Title.

NL 0387100 IEN MB CtY-D

Linge, Ola.
Ole Bull; livshistoria, mannen, kunstnaren. Oslo, Edition "Gamma," 1953.
414 p. illus., ports., facsims. 25 cm.
Prenta med tilskot av Fondet for norsk kulturgransking.
Includes bibliography.
"Musik-tilleg": p. 367–369.

1. Bull, Ole Bornemann, 1810–1880.

ML418.B9L5 A 53–8144
Oregon. Univ. Libr.
for Library of Congress ₍³₎†

NL 0387101 OrU IaDL DLC

Linge, Sophia.
Only a nail. Translated from the Swedish by Maria Sandahl. Original illustrations by Knut Stangenberg, retouched by Florence Bessom.
= Marblehead, Mass. Sandahl. [1926.] Illus., one colored. Plate. 19 cm.

N5025 — T.r. — Sandahl, Maria, tr.

NL 0387102 MB

Linge, Tore, 1892–
... La conception de l'amour dans le drame de Dumas fils et d'Ibsen ... par Tore Linge ... Paris, H. Champion, 1935.
250, ₁1₎ p. 24ᵒᵐ.
Thèse—Univ. de Paris.
"Bibliographie": p. ₁247₎–259.

1. Love. 2. Dumas, Alexandre, 1824–1895. 3. Ibsen, Henrik, 1828–1906. 4. Literature, Comparative—French and Norwegian. 5. Literature, Comparative—Norwegian and French. ɪ. Title.

Library of Congress PQ2231.Z5L5 1935 a 42–33565
₍2₎ 842.84

NL 0387103 DLC MiU OCU OU CtY

Linge, Tore, 1892–
... La conception de l'amour dans le drame de Dumas fils et d'Ibsen. Paris, H. Champion, 1935.
250, ₁1₎ p. 25 cm. (*Half-title:* Bibliothèque de la Revue de littérature comparée, dirigée par mm. F. Baldensperger et P. Hazard. t. 110)
"Bibliographie": p. ₁247₎–259.

1. Love in literature. 2. Dumas, Alexandre, 1824–1895. 3. Ibsen, Henrik, 1828–1906. 4. Literature, Comparative—French and Norwegian. 5. Literature, Comparative—Norwegian and French. ɪ. Title.

PQ2231.Z5L5 842.84 35—19794

NL 0387104 DLC CU WaU OrU OOxM IaU TU

Linge, Waldemar₎ Die Bologneser Roger-Glosse des Rolando-Capelluti aus Parma. Aus d. Inst. f. Gesch. d. Med. an d. Univ. Leipzig. Borna-Leipzig 1919: Noske. 32 S. 8°
Leipzig, Med. Diss. v. 2. Juli 1919, Ref. Sudhoff
[Geb. 2. Okt. 85 Leipzig; Wohnort: Bernburg; Staatsangeh.: Sachsen; Vorbildung: Thomas-G. Leipzig Reife 06; Studium: München 2, Leipzig 13 S.; Coll. 2. Juli 19; Approb. 12. Aug. 14.] [U 19. 1853

NL 0387105 ICRL CtY CtY-M DNLM DLC

Lingée, A G N , ed.
Code des prud' hommes...
see under France. Laws, statutes, etc.

Lingegård, Ingeborg.
Halmboken; halmarbeten för hemmet ... ₁Stockholm₎ Viking ₁1955₎
61 p. illus. 17 x 19 cm.

1. Rafia work.

Ohio State Univ. Libr. TT875 A 56–3793
for Library of Congress ₍8₎

NL 0387107 OU

Lingel, Aegidius.
Zur Frage nach dem Einfluss der Castration auf die Entwikelung der Milchdrüse. Freiburg, 1900 [i.e. 1901]
19, 38 p.
Inaug.-diss. - Freiburg i. B.

NL 0387108 ICRL DNLM

VK985
-D4
L5
Lingel, Robert
The Atlantic Neptune. [New York, 1936]
571-604 p. illus., facsims. 27 cm.
Caption title.
Extracted from the Bulletin of the New York Public Library, vol. 40, no. 7, July, 1936.
Checked for holdings in John Carter Brown Library, with typed list of items not in JCB inserted.

NL 0387109 RPJCB

Z1007
.A475
Lingel, Robert J. C., ed.
The American collector; a monthly magazine of collectors' lore. v. 1–6; Oct. 1925–Sept. 1928. ₁New York, Collector publishing co.; etc., etc., etc., 1925–28₎

Lingel, Robert J C.
A bibliographical checklist of the writings of Richard Le Gallienne, compiled by R. J. C. Lingel, with an introduction by Temple Scott ... Metuchen, N. J., 1926.
95 p. front. (port.) 24½ᶜᵐ. $2.75
"One hundred and fifty-one copies printed for the American collector." no. 68.

1. Le Gallienne, Richard, 1866- —Bibl. ɪ. Title.

Library of Congress Z8495.7.L75 27–21205

IEN
NL 0387111 DLC TxU MB WaU PSt PP PSC NcD MH OU OC1

Lingel, Robert J C.
Educational broadcasting, a bibliography ₁compiled by₎ Robert Lingel ... Chicago, Ill., The University of Chicago press ₁1932₎
x, 162 p. 23 cm.
Arranged under subjects with author and subject indexes.
This list incorporates bibliographies compiled for the American association for adult education by Levering Tyson and J. M. Russell and by the Radio institute of Ohio state university. cf. Introd.
"Radio law: a bibliography ... a revision of the one which appeared in 1 Journal of radio law 178–89. April, 1931 ... Compiled by Arthur W. Scharfeld": p. 123–147.
1. Radio in education—Bibl. 2. Radio broadcasting—Bibl. 3. Radio—Laws and regulations—Bibl. ɪ. Scharfeld, Arthur William, 1903– ɪɪ. Title.

Library of Congress Z5814.R2L7 33—27007
₁a48q1₎ 016.371333

NL 0387112 DLC ViU OU OC1 PSC PPD WaS Or MtU

Lingelbach, Mrs. Anna Lane, 1873–
Applications of the British navigation acts to intercourse with America, 1783-1815.
Univ. of Penna. Ph.D. thesis, 1916.

NL 0387113 PU

Lingelbach, Anna Lane, 1873–
The inception of the British Board of trade.
₁n.p.₎1925.
p. ₁701₎-27.

NL 0387114 PPTU

Lingelbach, Anna Lane, 1873–
Making the contribution of the social studies effective.
(*In* National education association of the United States. **Addresses and proceedings, 1926.** p. 655–659)

1. Social sciences—₁Study and₎ teaching. ɪ. Title.

E 27—895

U. S. Off. of educ. Library
for Library of Congress ₍a40c1₎

NL 0387115 DHEW

Lingelbach, Anna Lane, 1873–
William Penn as seen in excerpts from his writings, by Anna Lane Lingelbach ... prepared by her as chairman of a sub-committee for the Program committee of the commemoration of the two hundred and fiftieth anniversary of the first arrival of William Penn in America, 1682–1932. Philadelphia, The Religious society of Friends (Quakers) 1932.
cover-title, 20 p. 19ᶜᵐ.
Text on p. ₁3–4₎ of cover.
Illustration on cover.

1. Penn, William, 1644–1718. ɪ. Friends, Society of. Philadelphia.

Library of Congress F152.2.L74 33–18740
₍2₎ 923.273

NL 0387116 DLC RPJCB PPAmSwM PSC-Hi PPFr

VOLUME 334

Lingelbach, Daniel
see
Lingelbach, David, 1641–1688.

₁Lingelbach, David₁ 1641–1688.
De bekeerde alchimist; of Bedroogen bedrieger. Kluchtspél. Nooit op deeze wyze in 't licht gegeven. Amsterdam, Gedrukt voor het kunstgenootschap, én te bekomen by de Erven van J. Lescailje, énz. 1714.

4 p. L., 35, ₁3₁ p., 1 l. incl. front. 16½ᶜᵐ.

No. 1 in v. 30 of a collection lettered "Tooneel-stukken 1669–1760."
Engr. title vignette (device of the kunstgenootschap Nil voléntibus arduum)

I. Title. II. Title: Bedroogen bedrieger.

21–13488

Library of Congress   PT5497.T6 vol. 30, no. 1 ₚᵣₒᵥᵢₛᵢₒₙₐₗ

NL 0387118   DLC NN MH ICU

Lingelbach, D₁avid, 1641–1688₁.
Cleomenes. Treurspel. ₁In five acts and in verse₁ Amsterdam: D'erfgen. van J. Lescailje en D. Rank, 1729. 4 p.l., 64 p. 16°.

1. Drama (Dutch). 2. Title.
N. Y. P. L.   March 2, 1911.

NL 0387119   NN

₁Lingelbach, David₁ 1641–1688.
Het huwelyk van Orondates en Statira. Treurspél. Amsteldam, I. Duim, 1736.

4 p. l., 63 p. incl. front. 16ᶜᵐ.

No. 1 in v. 6 of a collection lettered "Tooneel-stukken 1669–1760."
Engr. title vignette (device of kunstgenootschap Nil volentibus arduum)

I. Title. II. Title: Orondates en Statira.
21–10068 Revised

Library of Congress   PT5497.T6 vol. 6, no. 1 ₁ᵣ22ᵦ₁

NL 0387120   DLC

PT5667
.L76L7
1669
Rare
Bk

₁Lingelbach, David₁ 1641–1688.
De liefde van Diana en Endimion, treurspel met konst- en vlieghwerken. Vertoont op d'Amsterdamsche schouwburgh. Amsterdam, J. Lescailje ₁1669₁
72 p. illus. 20 cm.

NL 0387121   ICU

₁Lingelbach, David,₁ 1641–1688.
Lyk-traanen gestort wegens het droevig en schadelyk afsterven van den edelen manhaften heere den Heer Michiel de Ruyter ... ₁Amsterdam? 1676.₁ 21 l. f°.

Caption-title.
Signed: D. Lingelbach.

PROUDFIT COLLECTION.
1607–76. 2. Poetry (Dutch).

1. Ruyter, Michiel Adriaanszoon, 3. Title.
N. Y. P. L.   October 18, 1922.

NL 0387122   NN

PT5667
.L7686
1687
Rare
Bk

Lingelbach, David, 1641–1688.
De ontdekte schyndeugd, bly-spel. Amsterdam, Erfgen van J. Leskailje, 1687.
55 p. front. 19 cm.

NL 0387123   ICU

Lingelbach, David, 1641–1688.
De ontdekte schyndeugd, blyspel. Door D. Lingelbagh. Amsteldam, Erfzen. van J. Lescailje, 1690.

2 p. l., 5–54 p. 16½ᶜᵐ.

No. 3 in v. 8 of a collection lettered "Tooneel-stukken 1669–1760".
Engr. title vignette.

I. Title. II. Title: Schyndeugd, De ontdekte.

21–10073 Revised

Library of Congress   PT5497.T6 vol. 8, no. 3 ₁ᵣ22ᵦ1₁

NL 0387124   DLC

PT5667
.L7606
1734

LINGELBACH, DAVID, 1641–1688.
De ontdekte schyndeugd; blyspel. Door D. Lingelbagh. t'Amsteldam, By I. Duim, 1734.
56 p. 16cm.
Title vignette.

NL 0387125   ICU MH

Lingelbach, David, 1641–1688.
Sardanapalus, trevrspel. Door D. Lingelbach. Amsteldam, I. Duim, 1737.

4 p. l., 9–71 p. 16ᶜᵐ.

No. 1 in v. 19 of a collection lettered "Tooneel-stukken 1669–1760."
Engr. title vignette.

I. Title.
21–13126

Library of Congress   PT5497.T6 vol. 19, no. 1 ₚᵣₒᵥᵢₛᵢₒₙₐₗ

NL 0387126   DLC

M13.1
L755a

Lingelbach, E
Advection and pressure tendency. Bad Kissingen, 1951.
5 numb. ℓ. illus., diagrs. 27cm.

M(05)
M587
v.4

Caption title.
Translation of author's article, Advektion und Luftdrucktendenz, from Meteorologische Rundschau, vol.4, Heft 11/12, Nov./Dec. 1951, pp.209–210, by C.L. Bristor.
Typewritten.

NL 0387127   DAS

448.2
L642

Lingelbach, Franz Albert, 1923–
Vergleichende Untersuchungen über die Leistungsfähigkeit der nach der amtlichen Vorschrift des Fleischbeschaugesetzes, bzw. nach Preuss, bzw. nach einer amerikanischen Vorschrift hergestellten Tetrathionatbouillo · zur Anreicherung von Salmonellen. Giessen 1951.
20 p.

Inaug. ₋Diss. ₋ Giessen. Auszug.

NL 0387128   DNAL

Lingelbach, Heinrich, 1888–
Ueber fettembolie.
Inaug. diss. Giessen, 1915.
Bibl.

NL 0387129   ICRL DNLM

Lingelbach, Helene.
...Christnacht, ein Laienspiel aus altdeutscher Dichtung, von Helene Lingelbach. München: G. D. W. Callwey₁, 1926₁. 50 p. illus. (music.) 12°. (Schatzgräber-Bühne. Nr. 33.)

1. Christmas—Drama. 2. Drama,   German. 3. Title.
N. Y. P. L.   April 2, 1928

NL 0387130   NN OC1

PT 151
.C4 L7

LINGELBACH, HELENE
Der Enterbte und Verfemte/als tragischer Typus; zur Problemgeschichte neuerer deutscher Dichtung. Jena, Fromman, 1928.
87 p.

1. Geman literature—19th cent.—Hist. & crit.
2. German literature—20th cent.—Hist. & crit.
I. Tc.

NL 0387131   InU MH

Lingelbach, Helene.
...Ein Fruehlingstag, ein Laienspiel aus romantischer Dichtung, von Helene Lingelbach. München: G. D. W. Callwey₁, 1926₁. 37 p. 16°. (Schatzgräber-Bühne. Nr. 23.)

Drama in verse.

1. Drama, German. 2. Title.
N. Y. P. L.   May 7, 1928

NL 0387132   NN

Lingelbach, Helene, 1885–
Deutschkunde als gestaltende lehre.
Inaug. diss. Jena, 1927 (Weimar)
Bibl.

NL 0387133   ICRL PU MH CtY

Lingelbach, William Ezra, 1871–   ed.
... Approaches to American social history, edited by William E. Lingelbach. New York, London, D. Appleton-Century company, incorporated ₁ᶜ1937₁
4 p. l., 101 p. 21ᶜᵐ. (The Appleton-Century historical essays)
"The essays brought together in this volume are the outcome of a general session at the annual meeting of the American historical association at Providence in December, 1936. The discussion at the meeting centered about the treatment of American social history in the History of American life series."—Foreword.
CONTENTS.—Foreword, by W. E. Lingelbach.—Remarks by the chairman, R. H. Gabriel.—A political historian looks at social history, by R. F. Nichols.—Interrelations of history and literature, by Bernard De Voto.—Reflections of a social historian, by J. A. Krout.—An editor's second thoughts, by A. M. Schlesinger.
1. U. S.—Hist.—Histori-   ography. 2. A history of American life.   I. Title.
Library of Congress   E175.L56   37–87145
———— Copy 2
Copyright A 111760   ₁5₁   973.07

NL 0387134   OC1 OO OU NcD PPLas NN ViU
   DLC OrU WaS OrPR MtBC WHi NIC MU PU PSC

Lingelbach, William Ezra, 1871–   ed.
           FOR OTHER EDITION
           SEE MAIN ENTRY
Leger, Louis Paul Marie, 1843–1923.
... Austria-Hungary; based on the work of Paul Louis Leger ... by William E. Lingelbach ... New York, P. F. Collier & son corporation ₁ᶜ1939₁

Lingelbach, William Ezra, 1871–
Berlin and the modern Germany, by William E. Lingelbach, ...
127892   (*In* University of Pennsylvania. University lectures delivered by members of the faculty in the Free public lecture course 1913–1914. Philadelphia, Pa., 1915. 22ᶜᵐ. Vol. 1, p. 408–433.)

NL 0387136   MB ICJ OC1 OO OU

VOLUME 334

Lingelbach, William Ezra, 1871–
    The doctrine and practice of intervention in Europe.
    (*In* The annals of the American academy of political and social science. Philadelphia, 1900. vol. XVI, no. 1, p. 1–32)

1. Intervention.   ɪ. Title.

                            C D 17–41

Library of Congress   Card div. H1.A4 vol. 16, no. 1
                       (a39b1)   (306.273)

  NL 0387137   DLC WaS OrCS OrU CaBVaU MB MiU OCU OU ICJ

Lingelbach, William Ezra, 1871–

    ... **Economic** aspects of the war. Selected source material dealing with the economic aspects of the war, arranged by Professor William E. Lingelbach. Effect of the war on the supply of labor and capital, by Professor Ernest L. Bogart. Philadelphia, McKinley publishing company, 1919.

LINGELBACH, William E[zra], 1871–
    England and neutral trade. [Cambridge, Harvard University Press, 1917]

    pp. (26).
    The military historian & economist, 1917, vol. II, no. 2. pp. 153–178.

  NL 0387139   MH

D525 Lingelbach, William Ezra, 1871–
.L66   Geographic factors in the world war [by] William E. Lingelbach. [Philadelphia, 1918]
    cover-title, p. [20]–33. 25½ cm.

    "Reprinted from the Bulletin of the Geographical society of Philadelphia. Vol. XVI, no. 4, October, 1918".

    1. European war, 1914–

  NL 0387140   ICU

G1037 Lingelbach, William Ezra, 1871–   joint
.H37   author.
1918
Map Div. Harding, Samuel Bannister, 1866–
    ... Geography of the war, by Professor Samuel B. Harding and Professor William E. Lingelbach; containing thirteen pages of maps and charts and eight outline maps. Philadelphia, McKinley publishing company, 1918.

---

arW Lingelbach, William Ezra, 1871–
39641   Henry Charles Lea; an address before the Home and School Association of the Henry C. Lea School, in West Philadelphia, March 15, 1915. [Philadelphia?, 1915?]
    8 p. 24 cm.

    1. Lea, Henry Charles, 1825–1909.

  NL 0387142   NIC PHi

Lingelbach, William Ezra, 1871–
    Historical investigation... and the commercial... history of the Napoleonic era. Lancaster, 1914.

  NL 0387143   NjP

Lingelbach, William Ezra, 1871–
    The history of post-war peace proposals. N.Y., Academy of political science, 1929.
    24 p.

  NL 0387144   PPTU

Lingelbach, William Ezra, 1871–
    The internal organisation of the Merchant adventurers of England, by W. E. Lingelbach ...
    (*In* Royal historical society, London. Transactions. London [1902?] 22 cm. n. s., v. 16, p. [19]–67)
    Issued also as thesis, University of Pennsylvania, 1901.

    1. Merchant adventurers of England.

                           A C 36–594

Title from Newberry   Libr.
Library of Congress   [DA20.R9 n. s., vol. 16]
              [2]   (942.0062)

  NL 0387145   ICN CLSU MB

Lingelbach, William Ezra, 1871–
    The internal organisation of the Merchant adventurers of England ... By William E. Lingelbach ... Philadelphia, 1903.

    3 p. l, [3]–56 p. 22½ cm.

    Thesis (PH. D.)—University of Pennsylvania, 1901.
    Bibliography: p. 53–56.

    1. Merchant adventurers of England.

Library of Congress   HF486.M17L7   5–7584
                          [a21c1]

  NL 0387146   DLC CU PBm PU OCU PPRF PPeSchW NN

Lingelbach, William Ezra, 1871–
    The merchant adventurers at Hamburg, by W. E. Lingelbach. Reprinted from the American historical review, vol. IX, no. 2, January, 1904. [New York? 1904]
    cover-title, [267]–287 p. 27 cm.

    1. Merchant adventurers of England. 2. Hamburg—Comm.

Library of Congress   HF486.M77   CA 5—2441 Unrev'd
                        1904

  NL 0387147   DLC

Lingelbach, William Ezra, 1871–
    The merchant adventures of England, their laws and ordinances with other documents. W. E. Lingelbach ... [Philadelphia, Sold by Longmans, Green & co., New York] 1902.
    xxxix, 260 p. 19½ cm. (*Added t.-p.:* Translations and reprints from the original sources of European history ... pub. by the Department of history of the University of Pennsylvania. 2d ser. vol. II)

    1. Gt. Brit.—Comm.—Hist. 2. Merchant adventurers of England.

Library of Congress   D101.P4   3–17824
————— Copy 2.   HF486.M1547

          NN NcD OCl OO OCU DNW ICJ MB
  NL 0387148   DLC Vi MH MU PSt WaTC IdU MtBC WaS WaU-L

Basque
DP   Lingelbach, William Ezra, 1871–
302   Mussolini's war talk: The defiant Basques.
B53   New York, 1934.
L5   110–112 p. 23 cm.

    Offprint of Current history, Oct., 1934, p. 110–112.

    1. Basque Provinces - Hist. 2. Basque Provinces - Pol. & govt. 3. Mussolini, Benito, 1883–1945. I. Title.

  NL 0387149   IdU

---

*
F158
.3   Lingelbach, William Ezra, 1871–
.L5
1949   Old Philadelphia: redevelopment and conservation. Philadelphia, 1949.
    179–207 p. illus. 21 cm.
    Detached from the American Philosophical Society v. 93, no. 2.
    Inscribed by the author.

    1. Philadelphia—Hist. I. Title.

  NL 0387150   ViU

Lingelbach, William Ezra, 1871–
    Peace conference in the light of history. n.p. n.p. 1919.
    322 p.

  NL 0387151   PU

Lingelbach, William Ezra, 1871–   *ed.*
    Portrait of an historian, Edward Potts Cheyney, edited by William E. Lingelbach. Philadelphia, University of Pennsylvania press, 1935.

    viii, 46 p. 2 port. (incl. front.) 23½ cm.

    Includes addresses made upon the occasion of the presentation of the portrait to the University of Pennsylvania by a group of alumni, February 21, 1934. C. A. Herrick, chairman of the alumni committee. *cf.* Prefatory note.

    CONTENTS.—Introductory remarks, by J. H. Penniman.—Presentation of the portrait, by C. A. Herrick.—Acceptance of the portrait, by T. S. Gates.—Edward Potts Cheyney as a member of the American historical association, by J. F. Jameson.—Edward Potts Cheyney as a writer, by Conyers Read.—Last will and testament (academic) by E. P. Cheyney.—A few excerpts from tributes to the teacher, the scholar, and the man.—Bibliography (p. 37–46)

    1. Cheyney, Edward Potts, 1861–1947. ɪ. Herrick, Cheesman Abiah, 1866– ɪɪ. Title.
                                      35—2651

Library of Congress   DA3.C45L5

  NL 0387153   DLC NcU TU PU PPD PSC OClW OU MiU-C NcD

Lingelbach, William Ezra, 1871–
    Russia and the revolution, by William E. Lingelbach, ...
177429 (*In* University of Pennsylvania. University lectures delivered by members of the faculty in the Free public lecture course 1917–1918. Philadelphia, Pa., 1918. 23 cm. Vol. 5, p. 283–306.)

  NL 0387154   ICJ

Lingelbach, William Ezra, 1871–
    Selected source material dealing with economic aspects of the war. Phil., McKinley pub. co., 1919.
    12 p.

  NL 0387155   PU

Lingelbach, William Ezra. 1871–
    Syllabus of a course of six lectures on six European capitals: studies in national development.
  — Philadelphia. The American Society for the Extension of University Teaching. 1905. 11 pp. [University extension lectures. Series 256.] 12°.
    Contents. — 1. St. Petersburg. 2. Berlin. 3. Vienna. 4. Rome. 5. Berne. 6. Paris.
    Books, p. 2.

    G5503 — S.r. — Cities. — Europe. Polit. hist.

  NL 0387156   MB

VOLUME 334

LINGELBACH, WILLIAM EZRA, 1871-
... The story of "Philosophic hall" ...
[Philadelphia,1950.]
cover-title,p.[185]-213. illus.(incl.ports.,fac-
sims.,plan). 26cm.
At head of title: Franklin medal lecture.
"Reprinted from Proceedings of the American phil-
osophical society, vol. 94, no. 3, 1950."
Two columns to the page.
Orig. printed gray wrapper; bradded.
Inscribed: To Dʳ A. W. S. Rosenbach, with sincere
regards, William E. Lin-   gelbach.

NL 0387157   PPRF

D359   Lingelbach, William Ezra, 1871-
.2
.L66   A syllabus of the history of Europe
in the nineteenth century. 1814-1904.
By William E. Lingelbach... [Philadel-
phia] The University of Pennsylvania,
1907.
51 p.   25cm.

"List of books"; p.7-15.

1. Europe -   Hist. - Outlines,
syllabi, etc.   2. Europe - Hist.
1789-1900. I. Title.

NL 0387158   OCU PHi RPB

NA9127   Lingelbach, William Ezra. 1871-
P4   William Penn and city planning. [Philadelphia,
L5   1944]
398-418 p. illus. 26cm.
"Offprint from The Pennsylvania Magazine of
History and Biography, October, 1944."

1. Cities and Towns--Planning--Philadelphia.
2. Penn, William, 1644-1718 I. Title.

NL 0387159   RPJCB

Lingelsheim, A.   Eine neue Acalypha aus der brasilianischen
flora. [Weimar. 1912.] 8°.
"Sonderabdruck aus Mitteilungen des Thür. bot. v." 1912, N.F. xxix,
48-49.

NL 0387160   MH-A

Lingelsheim, Alexander.
... *Oleaceae-Oleoideae-Fraxineae* und *Oleaceae-Ole-
oideae-Syringeae* ... von A. Lingelsheim ...
(*In* Das pflanzenreich, hrsg. von A. Engler. Leipzig, 1900-
72. hft. (IV. 243. I u. II.) 1 p. l, 125 p. 87 illus. in 22 groups, map)   26ᶜᵐ.
Ausgegeben am 29. juni 1920.

1. Oleaceae.
                                         Agr 21-336
Library, U. S. Dept. of   Agriculture 452En3P no.72

NL 0387161   DNAL CLSU CtY PPAN

Lingelsheim, Alexander.
Oleaceae - Oleoideae - Fraxineae und Oleaceae -
Oleoideae - Syringeae. Mit 87 Einzelbildern in
22 Figuren und einer Verbreitungskarte. Von
A. Lingelsheim. Leipzig, Wilhelm Engelmann, 1920.

125 p., illus. (In: Engler, Adolf. Das Pflanzenreich, 72. H. (IV. 243 I/II)

NL 0387162   MH-A NNBG

Lingelsheim, Alexander von, 1874-1937.
Über ein Koniferenholz aus dem Tertiär der
Niederlausitz.
(In Abhandlungen der Naturforschenden Gesell-
schaft zu Görlitz. Görlitz, 1827-   24 cm.
Bd.30, Heft 3(1929) p.103-116. illus.)

XA
.B43
Bd.30   Caption title.
Heft 3   Incorrectly assembled in binding.
          Bibliography: p. 115.

1. Coniferae, Fossil. 2. Paleobotany - Tertiary. 3. Paleobotany - Lusatia. i. t. ii.s: Abhandlungen der   Naturforschenden Gesellschaft zu Görlitz,   Bd.30. Heft 3.

NL 0387163   NNBG

LINGELSHEIM, Alexander von, 1874-1937.
Vorarbeiten zu einer monographie der gattung
fraxinus. Inaug.-diss., Rostock, Leipzig,
1907.

NL 0387164   MH CtY ICRL

Lingelsheim, Georg Michael, 17th cent.

Reifferscheid, Alexander, 1847-1909, *ed.*
Briefe G. M. Lingelsheims, M. Berneggers und ihrer
freunde. Nach handschriften der Kgl. bibliothek in
Kopenhagen, der Reichsbibliothek in Stockholm, der
stadtbibliotheken in Bremen [etc.] ... hrsg. und erläutert
von dr. Alexander Reifferscheid ... Heilbronn, Gebr.
Henninger, 1889.

NL 0387166

Lingelsheim, Georg Michael
Jacobi Bongarsii et Georgii Michaelis Lingel-
shemii epistolae
see under   Bongars, Jacques, 1554-1612.

Lingelsheim, Georg Michael, 17th cent.

PA8147   Reifferscheid, Alexander, 1847-1909, *ed.*
.R4   Quellen zur Geschichte des geistigen Lebens in Deutsch-
land während des siebzehnten Jahrhunderts ... I. Briefe
G. M. Lingelsheims, M. Berneggers und ihrer Freunde.
Heilbronn, Gebr. Henninger, 1889.

NL 0387167

RM111 Lingelsheim, Hugo August Walter von, 1866–
.B4   ... Ätiologie und therapie der streptokokken-infectionen,
no. 1   von dr. W. von Lingelsheim ... Aus dem Institute für experimentelle therapie ... in Marburg. Berlin [etc.] Urban &
Schwarzenberg, 1899.
cover-title, 48 p. incl. tables. 24½ᶜᵐ. (Beiträge zur experimentellen therapie
hrsg. von ... E. Behring. hft 1)
"Literatur": p. 47-48.

1. Streptococcus. 2. Contagion and contagious diseases.

NL 0387168   ICU DNLM

RM111 Lingelsheim, Hugo August Walter von, 1866–
.B4   ... Ätiologie und therapie der staphylokokken-infectionen,
no. 1a von dr. W. von Lingelsheim ... Aus dem Institute für experimentelle therapie ... in Marburg. Berlin [etc.] Urban
& Schwarzenberg, 1900.
cover-title, [49]-92 p. incl. tables. 24½ᶜᵐ. (Beiträge zur experimentellen therapie hrsg. von ... E. Behring. hft. 1a)
"Literatur": p. 90-92.

1. Staphylococcus. 2. Contagion and contagious diseases.

NL 0387169   ICU

Lingelsheim, Hugo August Walter von, 1866 –
Beiträge zur Aetiologie des Milzbrandes. Ueber die milzbrandfeind-
lichen Wirkungen von Säuren und Alkalien im Blutserum.
(In Behring. Gesammelte Abhandlungen zur ätiologischen Therapie von Ansteckenden Krankheiten. Theil 2, pp. 117-124. Leipzig, 1893.)

F6871 — Anthrax.

NL 0387170   MB

von Lingelsheim (Hugo August Walter)
[1866-   ] Experimentelle Untersuchungen
über kulturelle und pathogene Eigenschaften
verschiedener Streptokokken und deren Verhalten zu chemischen Präparaten. 39 pp. 8°.
Berlin, O. Francke, [1891]
Another copy with pages 351-366. Cutting from: Ztschr. f. Hyg. Berl. 1891. X.

NL 0387171   DNLM

Lingelsheim, Hugo August Walter von, 1866 —
Experimentelle Untersuchungen über morphologische, culturelle
und pathogene Eigenschaften verschiedener Streptokokken. —
Beiträge zur Streptokokkenfrage.
(In Behring. Gesammelte Abhandlungen zur ätiologischen Thera-
pie von ansteckenden Krankheiten. Theil 2, pp. 125-192. Leip-
zig. 1893.)
Litteratur-Verzeichniss, pp. 173-175.

F6888 — Streptococci.

NL 0387172   MB MH

Lingelsheim, Hugo August Walter von, 1866 –
T113   Kritisches und Experimentelles zu der Ätiologie
M3   dem Wesen und der Bekämpfund der Streptokokken-
1899   infectionen ... Marburg, 1899.
Habilitations-Schrift - Marburg.
"Litteratur": p.[75]-79.

NL 0387173   CtY DNLM ICRL

Lingelsheim, Wilhelm von, comp.
Familien-Chronik derer von Lingelsheim. Mengering-
hausen. Druck der Weigel'schen Hof- und Regierungs-
buchdr., 1922

86 p.   illus.

1. Lingelsheim family. I. Title

NL 0387174   MH

Lingeman, Eric Ralph, 1898–
Turkey; economic and commercial conditions in Turkey
London, H. M. Stationery Off., 1948.
228 p. 25 cm. ([Gt. Brit.] Export Promotion Dept. Overseas
economic surveys)

1. Turkey—Econ. condit.—1918-   (Series)

HC405.L5   330.956   48-4016*‡

NL 0387175   DLC OrU ViU OKentU PPDrop PU-W

Lingemann, Anneliese.
Angelsächsisches Einkommensteuerrecht. [Obernkirchen,
1949.
87 p. 21 cm. (Schriftenreihe der Arbeitsgemeinschaft der Indu-
strie- und Handelskammern des Vereinigten Wirtschaftsgebietes,
Frankfurt a. M., Heft 2)
Cover title.

1. Income tax—Gt. Brit.—Law. 2. Income tax—U. S.—Law. I.
Title.   (Series: Arbeitsgemeinschaft der Industrie- und Handelskammern des Vereinigten Wirtschaftsgebietes. Schriftenreihe, Heft
2)
                                                      52-64864

NL 0387176   DLC

VOLUME 334

Lingemann, Emil, 1905–
Grundlagen für wirtschaftliches drehen und
bohren von elektron... 1933.   47 p.
Inaug. Diss. –Techn. Hochsch. Berlin, 1933.
Lebenslauf.

NL   0387177   ICRL

Lingemann, Heinrich, joint ed.
Elster, Alexander Nikolaus, 1877–   ed.
Handwörterbuch der kriminologie und der anderen strafrechtlichen hilfswissenschaften, unter mitberatung von justiz-
rat dr. Drucker ... professor dr. graf Gleispach ¡u. a.¿ ... hrsg.
von Alexander Elster ... und Heinrich Lingemann ... Berlin
und Leipzig, W. Gruyter & co., 1933–

Lingemann, Heinrich, 1880–   ed.
Germany. *Laws, statutes, etc.*
Die Strafprozessordnung für das Deutsche reich vom 22.
märz 1924, nebst dem Gerichtsverfassungsgesetz und den gesetzen vom 24. november und 6. dezember 1933. Kommentar
von senatspräsident am Reichsgericht dr. E. Löwe, fortgesetzt
von reichsgerichtsrat dr. A. Hellweg und von reichsgerichtsrat
dr. W. Rosenberg. 19., völlig umgearb. aufl. von Hans Gün-
del ... Fritz Hartung ... Heinrich Lingemann ... ¡und¿ Emil
Niethammer ... Berlin und Leipzig, W. de Gruyter & co., 1934.

Lingemann, Heinrich, 1880–
Strafverfahrensrecht und Strafvollstreckungsrecht, von
H. Lingemann ¡und¿ O. L. v. Hinüber. 80.–84. neu bearb.
Aufl. Düsseldorf, L. Schwann ¡1950¿

155 p.   23 cm.   (Schaeffers Grundriss des Rechts und der Wirtschaft. Abt. 1: Privat- und Prozessrecht, 10. Bd.)
Earlier editions by O. L. v. Hinüber and other joint authors.

1. Criminal procedure—Germany (Federal Republic, 1949–   )
I. Hinüber, Oskar Leuer von, 1892–   joint author. II. Title.

54–18182

NL   0387180   DLC

Lingemann, Heinz, 1902–
Der Ständige internationale gerichtshof ...
von Heinz Lingemann . .   Göttingen ¡Noske¿
1932.
viii, 54 p.   21 cm.

Thesis, Göttingen.
Bibliography.

NL   0387181   NNC CtY

Lingemann, Karl: Ueber die Wahl des Sanierungsalters. [Maschinen-
schrift.] 20 S. m. Tab. u. Kurv.-Taf. 4°. — Auszug: Bonn 1924:
Trapp.   2 Bl.   8°
Bonn, Med. Diss. v. 18. März 1924   [U 24. 1136

NL   0387182   ICRL

Lingemann, Norbert, 1897–
Zur entstehung des altersstares. (Auszug)
Inaug. diss. Rostock, 1924

NL   0387183   ICRL

Lingemann, Paul.
Pariser Tagebuch 1940, Bilder aus meinem Kriegsaufent-
halt in der Weltstadt Paris. Mit 24 Photos auf Kunstdruck
von der Truppe und 2 Zeichnungen vom Kameraden W.
Funke. Meschede i. W., Heimatverlag Wagener ¡1941¿

168 p.   illus., ports.   20 cm.

1. World War, 1939–1945—Campaigns—Western.   2. World War,
1939–1945—Personal narratives, German.   I. Title.

D811.L466   51–52246

NL   0387184   DLC

---

*8037
.411
Lingen, Alfred W
English-German dictionary of technical words:
paper, printing, official correspondence
(questionaires, reports, applications, etc.)
Paderborn, F. Schöningh, 1947.
193, 208 p.   17cm.
Pt. 2 has t. p. in German (German-English)

1. Paper making and trade—Dictionaries. 2. English language—Dictionaries—German. 3. Paper making and
trade—Dictionaries—German. 4. German
language—Dictionaries—English.
5. Printing—Dictionaries.

NL   0387186   MB CU PBL NN CU N

LF4224   LINGEN, BRUNO VON, 1903–
.L75   Album neobaltorum, 1879–1934.   Hrsg. vom
Verwaltungsrat des Philistervereins der
Neobaltia. ¿Reval, 1934¿
106 p.

1. Neobaltia--Dorpat--Universitet. I. Title.

NL   0387187   InU

LINGEN, C. VAN DER.
De dochters van de baas; blijspel in drie bedrijven.
Alkmaar, Vink [1955?] 106 p. 19cm.

1. DRAMA, DUTCH   I. De dochters van de baas

NL   0387188   NN

---

de Lingen (Carolus) [1817–96]. *De phlebi-
tide uterina. 34 pp., 1 l. 8°. Berolini, typ. frat.
Schlesinger, [1841].

NL   0387189   DNLM

W 4   LINGEN, Carolus van Alsem van
L68   Dissertatio physiologico-medica inauguralis,
1766   de pancreate ... Lugduni Batavorum, Apud
L.i   Henricum Mostert, 1766.
39 p.   23 cm.
Diss. - Leyden.

NL   0387190   DNLM

BT12   Lingen, Christian,
1545   Causae Selectae in S. Congregatione Cardina-
A2L5   lium Concilii Tridentini interpretum propositae
per summaria precum ab anno 1823 usque ad annum
1869. Collegerunt Christianus Lingen...et...
Petrus Alexander Reuss...Ratisbonae, Neo-Ebo-
raci et Cincinnatii, Friderici Pustet, ¿1871¿
xxx, 916p.

1. Councils and Synods, Ecumenical. 2. Trent,
Council of. I. Reuss, Alexander,   jt. ed.
II. Title.

NL   0387191   MBtS CtY DCU PLatS

Lingen, Derk van
Onderzoekingen in den koperboog. ... Utrecht,
1936.   54 p.
Inaug. Diss. – Utrecht, 1936.

NL   0387192   ICRL CtY

Lingen, Ernst, pseud.
see Schilling, Elisabeth, 1832–1907.

Lingen, Ernst v. *physician*. Über Masernprophylaxe mit Rekonvaleszenten-
serum nach R. Degkwitz. [Maschinenschrift.] 72 S. 4°. —
Auszug: Greifswald 1923: Adler.   4 S.   8°
Greifswald, Med. Diss. v. 29. Dez. 1922 [1923]   [U 23. 4697

NL   0387194   ICRL

W 4   LINGEN, Helmut, 1929–
M22   Die Verwendung von Cr2O3 als
1954   Testsubstanz bei Verdaulichkeitsver-
suchen an Ratten: Prüfung und
Verbesserung der Methode, ihre Anwendung auf Versuche über den Einfluss
von Sekt und Alkohol auf die Verdaulich-
keit von Fett u. Eiweiss.   Mainz, 1954.
59, ii ℓ.   illus.
Inaug.-Diss. - Mainz.
1. Chromium 2. Digestion - Experimental studies

NL   0387195   DNLM

Lingen, Hermann Ulrich von, *fl.* 1715.
De origine et inventoribvs pecuniæ et numismatum
schediasma qvo probatur inventum pecuniæ, non ad
Ebræos, Lydos aut Græcos, sed potius ad Phoenices referendum esse. Accedit simul demonstratio Romanos jam
ante Servium regem pecunia usos esse, autore Hermanno
Ulrico a Lingen ... Ienæ, prostat apud Wertherum, 1715.

4 p. l., 88 p. 20½ᵐᵐ.

1. Numismatics. 2. Phenicians.

Library of Congress   CJ73.L5   15–10599

NL   0387196   DLC

AC 33   LINGEN, HERRMANN ULRICH VON, *fl.* 1715.
.L755   Kleine, teutschen Schrifften, in welchen
Allerhand aus der Antiquitaet, Historie, Chronologie, Genealogie, Numismatic und andern
Wissenschafften hergenommene Materien abgehand-
elt werden.   Wittenberg, Gerdes, 1730-32.
2 v.

Publisher varies: v.2, Henning.

NL   0387197   InU MH

Lingen, Jan Stephanus van der

see

Van der Lingen, Jan Stephanus, 1887–

---

de Lingen (Joannes (Henricus). *De quinque
neonatorum morbis notatu dignis. 33 pp., 2 pl.
4°. Berolini, typ. Brüschckianis, [1829?]

NL   0387199   DNLM

VOLUME 334

Lingen, John Taylor, reporter.

New South Wales. *Supreme court.*
The term reports. Reports of cases argued and determined in the Supreme court of New South Wales. Vol 1 ₁no. 1–12, first term, 1881–fourth term, 1883₁ Sydney₁ F. Cunninghame & co. ₁1881–83₁

---

von Lingen (Leo) ₁1864– ₁. *Ueber den Gehalt der Leberzellen des Menschen an Phosphor, Schwefel und Eisen. 44 pp., ₁21. 8°. Dorpat, C. Mattiesen, 1891.

NL 0387201   DNLM CU

Lingen, Pieter Moll van der, ₁1879 –
Afrikaans through English idiom, by P. M. v. d. Lingen, B. A., J. P. Botha, B. A., P. I. Hoogenhout, B. A. ... in collaboration with Dr. S. P. E. Boshoff ... Cape Town, M. Miller, limited ₁1928₁

3 p. l., 342 p. 19ᶜᵐ.

1. Afrikaans language—Idioms, corrections, errors. 2. English language—Idioms, corrections, errors. ɪ. Botha, Jacobus Pieter, joint author. ɪɪ. Hoogenhout, Petrus Imker, 1884–   joint author. ɪɪɪ. Boshoff, Stephanus Petrus Erasmus, 1891–   joint author. ɪᴠ. Title.

44–35458

Library of Congress   PF861.L5

NL 0387202   DLC

₁Lingen, Pieter Moll van der₁ 1879–
Hiervan en daarvan, grepies uit die ervarings van 'n skoolinspekteur. Kaapstad, Maskew Miller, beperk ₁1935?₁

7 p. l., 176 p. 19ᶜᵐ.

1. Children—Anecdotes and sayings. ɪ. Title.

46–29025

Library of Congress   LA2377.L5A3
₁25₁

NL 0387203   DLC

Lingen, Pieter Moll van der, ₁1879 –
Maskew Miller's Say, look and say readers. Book A—By P. M. van der Lingen ... and F. W. Mills ... illustrated by Gladie McKay. 3d ed. Cape Town, M. Miller limited ₁1931–
v. col. front., illus. 20½ᶜᵐ.
Book D: 4th ed.   PE1117.L64 1931
—— —— Hints to teachers (how to use the conversation sheets and readers) Cape Town, M. Miller, limited ₁1931₁
16 p.; 16 p. 13½ᶜᵐ.
English and Afrikaans, the Afrikaans text inverted, with separate t-p.
1. Readers and speakers—1870–   ɪ. Mills, Frederick William, inspector of schools, Johannesburg, joint author. ɪɪ. Title. ɪɪɪ. Title: Say, look and say readers.

44–14314

Library of Congress   PE1117.L64 1931 Handbk.
₁2₁   372.4

NL 0387204   DLC

₁Lingen, Ralph Robert₁Wheeler Lingen, baron,₁ 1819–1905.
Lmd92   Quaenam fuerit certaminum publicorum apud
C55   antiquos vis et utilitas?₁Oratio in Theatro
1843   Sheldoniano habita die junii XXVIII,MDCCCXLIII. Oxonii,F.Macpherson,1843.
24p. 18cm. ₁₁Oxford. University. Chancellor's prize. Latin essay, 1843₁₁
Signed: R.R.Wheeler Lingen.

NL 0387205   CtY

834L646   Lingen, Frau Thekla, 1866–1931₁
Oa   Am scheidewege.   Berlin und Leipzig, Schuster & Loeffler, 1898.
84p.

Poems.

NL 0387206   IU InU

PT 2623   LINGEN, THEKLA, 1866–1931₁
.I54 A9   Aus Dunkel und Dämmerung.   Berlin, Schuster
1902   & Loeffler, 1902.
130 p. port.

NL 0387207   InU

Lingen, Thekla, 1866–1931.
M1617   Marx, Joseph, 1882–
.M3?L50   ₁Lieder-album. Und gestern hat er mir Rosen gebracht, arr.₁

Und gestern hat er mir Rosen gebracht. Yesterday roses he brought. ₁Worte und Übersetzung von₁ Th. Löngen ₁!₁ für eine Singstimme und Orchester. For voice and orchestra. Wien, Universal-Edition, °1921.

MW10   Lingen, W   van
L647p   De protestantsche kerk in Ned. Oost-Indië, door W. van Lingen. Baarn, Hollandia-Drukkerij, 1911.
46 p. 21 cm. (Kerk en secte, ser. 5, no. 4)
Humanitas durat, no. 43b.
Cover title.

1. Indonesia - Missions. 2. Reformed Church - Missions - Indonesia. 3. Protestantsche Kerk in Indonesië. 4. Missions, Dutch. I. Title. II. Series. III. Series: Humanitas durat, no. 43b. EA(2)

NL 0387209   CtY-D NIC

Lingen, Germany.
Das Bürgerbuch der Stadt Lingen, 1602–1809, von H. Schröter. Lingen-Ems, Van Acken, 1953

118 p. illus.

NL 0387210   MH

4K   Lingen, Ger. Ordinances, etc.
Ger   Statutarische Bestimmungen für die
2002   Stadt Lingen. Lingen, Druck von
R. van Acken, 1869.
87, 66 p.

NL 0387211   DLC-P4

LINGENBERG, Eduard, 1863 –
Beitrag zur lehre der Cheyne-Stokes'-schen athmung. Berl. [1892].

Med. Sch.

NL 0387212   MH DNLM

Lingenberg, Eduard, 1863–
Das weltbild der naturwissenschaft im lichte voraussetzungsloser forschung. Eine naturphilosophische studie, von E. Lingenberg. Bad Kissingen, Dr. Lingenberg, 1928.
44 p. 23ᶜᵐ.

1. Cosmology. 2. Science—Philosophy. ɪ. Title.

Library of Congress   BD513.L74
30–2631

NL 0387213   DLC

Lingenberg, Eduard, 1863–
Das weltgebäude; eine voraussetzungslose erkenntnistheorie, von E. Lingenberg. 2. umgearb. ausg. Bad Kissingen, Dr. Lingenberg, 1927.
1 p. l., 73, ₁1₁ p. 22½ᶜᵐ.

1. Cosmology. ɪ. Title.

Library of Congress   BD513.L75
29–10305
38504

NL 0387214   DLC

LINGENBERG, Ernst.
Die aufhebung der ehelichen gemeinschaft nach dem bürgerlichen gesetzbuch. Bonn, 1906.

66 p.
Inaug.-diss.,---Leipzig.

NL 0387215   MH-L ICRL

Lingenberg, Hans, 1903–
Abbau der p-Xylensäure zu p-Xylylen-diamin und zu Imino-di-(ω-p-xylylen-ω-carbonsäure) ... Borna-Leipzig, 1932.
Inaug.-Diss. - Köln, 1931.
Lebenslauf.
Full name: Lingenberg, Karl Ernst Hans.

NL 0387216   CtY ICRL

TS295   Lingenberg, Hans, 1903 –
173   Special analytical methods for the deter-
1954   mination of gases and suspended matter in
no.39   detonation products of shotfiring. Translated from the German by L. Meyer. [Sheffield, 1955]
3 p. 24 cm. (International Conference of Directors of Safety in Mines Research, 8th, Dortmund-Derne, Germany, 1954. Paper no. 39)
Bibliography: p. 3.

1. Gases. I. yer, L., tr. II. Title: Shotfiring. (Series)

NL 0387217   DI

Lingenberg, Joachim, 1910–
Verursachungsbegriff, tatbestandsgedanke und adaequanz im aufbau der strafrechtsordnung. ... Düsseldorf, 1937. 46 p.
Inaug. Diss. - Halle-Wittenberg, 1937.
Lebenslauf
Schrifttums-Verzeichnis.

NL 0387218   ICRL

VOLUME 334

Lingenberg, Johann Wilhelm
Platonische bilder und sprichwörter. 21p.
Köln, Druck von F. Greven, 1872.

Programm - K. Friedrich-Wilhelms-gymnasium &
realschule zu Köln.

NL 0387219   OCl NjP NIC

Lingenberg, Johann Wilhelm.
Quaestiones Nicandreae. Halae, Ploetz, 1865.
24 p.

NL 0387220   PU NjP

Lingenberg, Julius, 1879-
Klinisch-anatomischer beitrag zu den neubildungen
am praeputium und penis des pferdes.
Inaug. Diss. Giessen, 1912
Bibl.

NL 0387221   ICRL DNLM MH PU CtY

Lingenberg, Karl Ernst Hans
see Lingenberg, Hans, 1903-

Lingenberg, Walter.
Über die Anwendung von Lochkartenverfahren in Bibliotheken. Köln, Greven Verlag, 1955.
85 p. illus. 21 cm. (Arbeiten aus dem Bibliothekar-Lehrinsti-
tut des Landes Nordrhein-Westfalen, Heft 9)

1. Punched card systems.

Z695.92.L5   62-26099 ‡

NL 0387223   DLC CtY CU MH NIC NNC MiU MnU TU

Lingenbrink, Edmund, 1868-
Ueber hydrazone der dithiokohlensäureester.
Inaug. diss. Erlangen, 1901.

NL 0387224   ICRL PU

Lingenbrink, William.
Modern art in store fronts... Published by Wm. Lingenbrink. Los Angeles₍, 1929?₎. 1 l. 36 pl. 4°.

1. Shops.
N.Y.P.L.

NL 0387225   NN PP OCl MB MiD

Lingenbrink, Wm.
Modernistic architecture. Ed.2.
48pl. Author, n.d.

NL 0387226   WaS

GS5
L755
K

Lingendes, Claude de, 1591-1660.
Concionvm in qvadragesimam Reverendi Patris
de Lingendes e Societate Iesv tomvs primvs
₍-tertius₎ Editio secunda emendatior et avctior,
ut sequens pagina docebit.   Parisiis, Apud
F.Mvgvet,1664.
3v.   19.5cm.

NL 0387227   NNUT

Lingendes, Claude de, 1591-1660.
Responses aux Lettres provinciales publiées par le Secretaire
du Port-Royal, contre les pp. de la Compagnie de Jesvs.
Sur le sujet de la morale desdits peres.   A Liege, Chez Jean
Mathias Hovius.   M.DC.LVIII.

Lingendes, Claude de, 1591-1660. Sermons
sur tous les Evangiles du carême; Sermons pour le
jour de pâques et jours suivants, sur la prudence
humaine, sur le duel, sur la nécessité, la nature, et les
qualités d'une sage détermination. 277 pp. (Migne,
J. P., Orat. sacrés, v. 2, p. 9.)

NL 0387229   MdBP

Lingendes, Jean de, 1580?-1616.
Les changemens de la bergere Iris.   A la princesse de Conti.
Diuisez en cinq chants.   Et augmentez de nouueau de la Com-
plainte de Leandre.   Par I. Delingendes.   A Roven.   Par
Clavde Le Vilain. M.D.CXIV.
12 p. l., 137 p. 14ᶜᵐ.
Signatures: §¹², A-E¹², F⁵.
Post-card from E. T. Griffiths, Manchester (Gt. Britain) to R. Tolnet
inserted, giving collation of his copy.
"Ex bibliotheca R. Tolnet."

I. Title.   II. Title: Iris.

30-24207

Library of Congress   PQ1628.L65A65

NL 0387230   DLC

FILM
13461
PQ

Lingendes, Jean de, 1580?-1616.
Les changemens de la bergère Iris. Revess, corr. & augm.
par l'autheur.   Paris, Toussaint du Bray, 1623.
96 ℓ.   On film (negative)

Microfilm.   Original in Bibliothèque nationale.

I. Title.   II. Title: Iris.

NL 0387231   CU OU

Lingendes, Jean de, 1580?-1616.
Œuvres poétiques de Jean de Lingendes.   Éd. critique,
avec une introduction et des notes, pub. par E.-T. Griffiths
...   Manchester, Impr. de l'Université, 1916.
xliv, 261, ₍1₎ p. 194ᶜᵐ.   (Half-title: Publications de l'Université de Man-
chester.   Série française, n°. II)
On verso of t.-p.: Publications de l'Université de Manchester.   n° cvII.
Bibliography : p. xvii-xix, xxx-xxxvii.

I. Griffiths, Evan Thomas, ed.

MdBJ   17-27898

Library of Congress   PQ1628.L65 1916 a

NL 0387232   DLC MiU OCU OU NN PU OClW MB ICU MdBJ

Lingendes, Jean de, 1580?-1616.
... Œuvres poétiques.   Éd. critique, avec une introduction et des notes, pub. par E.-T. Griffiths.   Paris, Hachette et cⁱᵉ, 1916.
xliv, 261, ₍1₎ p. 19ᶜᵐ.   (Société des textes français modernes. ₍Publica-
tions. 1. sér₎)
Bibliography: p. xvii-xix, xxx-xxxvii.

I. Griffiths, Evan Thomas, ed.

17-3012⁶

Library of Congress   PQ1628.L65 1916

ViU OrPR IdU CaBVaU OrU
NL 0387233   DLC CU TU RWoU NIC PU PBm InU NcD NjP MdBJ

LINGENDES, JEAN DE, 1580?-1616.
Stances, précédées d'une notice par Jacques Madeleine.
Paris, Sansot, 1911.   101 p.   17cm.   (Petite bibliothèque surannée)

I. Madeleine, Jacques, 1859-1941, ed.

NL 0387234   NN MA NcD

Bo47a
643ℓ

Lingendes, Jean de, 1595-1665
Oraison fvnebre dv roy Lovis XIII, svrnommé
le ivste, prononcée en l'eglise de S. Denis ...
Paris, C. Savrevx, 1643.
2p.ℓ.,75p.   23cm.

NL 0387235   CtY

Die Lingener Heimat.   Lingen-Ems
Heft 1-6 (1948-1958)
No more published

NL 0387236   MH

Lingenfelder, Julius, 1864-
Der arzt als führer der neuzeit! Ein "gesundheits-
katechismus" für das denkende volk, von dr. Julius Lingenfelder ... ₍Grand Island, Neb., Printed by Grand
Island publishing co., ʿ1914₎
128 p. front. (port.) 20ᶜᵐ. $1.00

1. Medicine—Addresses, essays, lectures.   I. Title.

R117.L5   14-16732

NL 0387237   DLC ICRL ICJ

Lingenfelder, Julius, 1864-
Der Arzt als Führer der Neuzeit; Volksgesundheit und
Gesellschaftsfrieden als die Vorbedingung und Voraussetzung des
Völkerfriedens, von Dr. Julius Lingenfelder...   Berlin: B.
Westermann Co., Inc.₍, 1933.₎ 157 p.   19cm.

700049A.   I. Essays, German·   American.   2. Ethics.
N.Y.P.L.   June 6, 1934

IU NcRS NcD MH-M OCU
KE-M FMU WaU NNC-M ViU MeB TNJ-M RPB MBCo ICarbS AU
NL 0387238   NN WaTC LU GU CU-S CtY-M MoU FU-HC ScU IEN

610.4
L755a
1933

Lingenfelder, Julius, 1864-1934.
Der Arzt als Führer der Neuzeit; Volksgesund-
heit und Gesellschaftsfrieden als die Vorbedin-
gung und Voraussetzung des Völkerfriedens.
Berlin, New York, B. Westermann ₍c°1933₎
157p. 19cm.
First published 1914 by Grand Island pub. co.,
Grand Island, Neb.

1. Medicine--Addresses, essays, lectures. I.
Title.

NL 0387239   TxDaM

610.4
L647a

Lingenfelder, Julius, 1864-
Der Arzt als Führer der Neuzeit; Volksgesundheit
und Gesellschaftsfrieden als die Vorbedingung und
Voraussetzung des Völkerfriedens.   Berlin, B.
Westermann Co. [c1943]
157p. 19cm.

1. Medicine - Addresses, essays, lectures. I.
Title.

NL 0387240   TxU

VOLUME 334

LB3999 Lingenfelder, Louise Mable, 1916–
The development of methods for constructing a
diagnostic and placement examination over the
general field in education.   1947.
103 l.

Typewritten.
Thesis--Univ. of Chicago.

1. Education--Examinations.

NL 0387241   ICU

Lingenfelder, Wilhelm.
Die Tragfähigkeits-Berechnungen von Balken, Säulen u. dergl.
Praktisches Handbuch zum Selbstunterricht und Gebrauch für
jeden Bauhandwerksmeister und Techniker.   Leichtfasslich bearbeitet von Wilhelm Lingenfelder, ...   Emmendingen, Druck-
und Verlags-Gesellschaft vorm. Dölter, 1902.
61 p. diagrs. 22ᶜᵐ.

NL 0387242   ICJ

Lingenfelser, Franz, 1909–
Die Kartelle und die Organisation der gewerblichen Wirtschaft. Philippsburg (Baden) Buchdr. H. Kruse, 1939.
77 p. 21 cm.

Inaug.-Diss.—Heidelberg.
Lebenslauf.
"Schrifttum": p. 75–77.

1. Trusts, Industrial—Germany. 2. Germany—Indus.   I. Title.
HD2859.L5   A F 47–6681*
Harvard Univ. Library
for Library of Congress

NL 0387243   MH DLC CtY

Thesis Lingenfelter, John Flaig, 1920–
1945   Studies on the autoxidation of pork fat. [Ithaca,
L755   N. Y.] 1945.
68 l. illus. 27 cm.

Thesis (Ph. D.) - Cornell Univ., Feb. 1945.

1. Fat metabolism. 2. Catalysis. 3. Iron.
I. Title: Autoxidation of pork fat. [II. Title]

NL 0387244   NIC

Lingenfelter, Littlebury.
History of Fremont county, Iowa . . .   A correct history of the early settlement of the county, its organization,
growth and development . . .   Scenes and incidents of
early life. Sidney, Iowa : July 4th, A. D. 1876. Hamburg,
Ia., Democrat print [1876] 62 pp. 24°. S.

F627.F8L7   1–Re–955

NL 0387245   MnHi DLC

Lingenfelter, L[ittlebury]
History of Freemont [!] County, Iowa. This work is
intended to give a correct history of the early settlement
of the county, its organization—growth and development—its educational and social advantages ...   Scenes
and incidents of early life. By L. Lingenfelter. Sidney,
Iowa, July 4th, 1876. St. Joseph, Mo., Steam printing
company, printers, 1877.
28 p. 24ᶜᵐ.
Another edition issued, Hamburg, Ia., 1876.

Subject entries: Fremont Co., Ia.—Hist.

Library of Congress, no.   F627.F8L71.
                                          3–21694

NL 0387246   DLC ICN

[Lingenfelter, Littlebury]
History of Fremont county, Iowa; a reprint.   Hamburg, Ia.,
The Hamburg Reporter, 1935.   63 p.   14cm.

With reproduction of t.-p. of 2. ed.: History of Fremont county, Iowa...by L.
Lingenfelter...St. Joseph, Mo., 1877.

1. Fremont county, Ia.—Hist.   I. The Hamburg Reporter, Hamburg,
Ia.
N. Y. P. L.   October 30, 1945

NL 0387247   NN NNC ICU ICN

FILM   Lingenfelter, Lynwood S
016.823   A bibliography of pedagogy in English fiction,
L64b   1750–1825.   Ann Arbor, University Microfilms
[1941]

([University Microfilms, Ann Arbor, Mich.]
Publication no. 343)
Microfilm copy (positive) of typescript.
Collation of the original: 2 pts. in 1v. (xxvi
759 l.)

Thesis—Pennsylvania State College.
Vita.
Bibliography: leaves 744–759.

1. English literature—Bibl. 2. Teaching—
Bibl. I. Title.

NL 0387249   IU

Lingenfelter, Mary Rebecca, 1893–
... Books on wheels, by Mary Rebecca Lingenfelter ...
New York and London, Funk & Wagnalls company, 1938.
viii, [2]–147 p. 19½ cm.   (Kitson career series; ed. by H. D. Kitson)

"First edition."
"Training for library work, reprinted ... from a leaflet issued by
the A L A Board of education for librarianship": p. 135–140; "Ac-
credited library schools": p. 141–145; "Suggested titles for further
reading": p. 146–147.

1. Librarians. 2. Libraries, Traveling. 3. Library schools and
training.   I. Title.
Library of Congress   Z682.L75   38—24149
                                [a50n⁵5]   020.69

MtU OrU OClh CaBVa MtBC Or Wa
NL 0387250   DLC NN ViU OClW OCl PPT PP Or WaSp WaT IdB

Z5811   Lingenfelter, Mary Rebecca, 1893–
.L54   Educational books of 1933, prepared by Mary
Rebecca Lingenfelter and Rea J. Steele. (Re-
printed from school and society, v. 39, no. 1004,
March 24, 1934)
19p. 26cm.

1. Education - Bibl.   I. Steele, Jessica Rea,
1900–   II. Title.

NL 0387251   PSt

Lingenfelter, Mary Rebecca, 1893–

Ohio. State university, *Columbus. Bureau of educational
research and service.*
List of titles in the textbook exhibit, Bureau of educational research. [Columbus] Ohio state university, College
of education, 1930.

Lingenfelter, Mary Rebecca, 1893–   joint
author.
Van Arsdale, May Belle.
Manners now and then, by May B. Van Arsdale and **Mary
Rebecca Lingenfelter**, illustrated by Fred Cooper. New York,
Harcourt, Brace and company [1940]

Lingenfelter, Mary Rebecca, 1893–
Sixty educational books of 1933.
Chicago, American library association,
1934.
4p.

Reprinted from the Journal of the
National education association, April
1934.

NL 0387254   PSt

Lingenfelter, Mary Rebecca, joint comp.
Welch, Lila Merle, *comp.*
Studies of the home economics curriculum; an annotated
bibliography, comp. by Lila Merle Welch and Mary Rebecca
Lingenfelter. [Columbus] Bureau of educational research,
Ohio state university [1930]

Z7164   Lingenfelter, Mary Rebecca, 1893–   joint
.C81K6   author.
1936   Kitson, Harry Dexter, 1886–
Vocational guidance through the library; a guide, showing how the librarian can serve individuals who are trying to
solve vocational problems, by Harry Dexter Kitson ... and
Mary Rebecca Lingenfelter ... 3d ed. Chicago, American
library association, 1936.

Lingenfelter, Mary Rebecca, 1893–   joint
author.
Kitson, Harry Dexter, 1886–
Vocations for boys, by Harry Dexter Kitson and Mary
Rebecca Lingenfelter. New York, Harcourt, Brace and com-
pany [1942]

Lingenfelter, Mary Rebecca, 1893–
Vocations for girls, by Mary Rebecca Lingenfelter and
Harry Dexter Kitson. New York, Harcourt, Brace and com-
pany [1939]
2 p. l., vii–x p., 2 l., 3–358 p. 23½ᵐ.
"Reading lists": p. 325–351.

1. Woman—Employment. 2. Profession, Choice of. 3. Occupations.
I. Kitson, Harry Dexter, 1886–   joint author. II. Title.
Library of Congress   HD6058.L47   39–22231
———— Copy 2.
Copyright A 131909   [15]   396.5

KEmT IdU–SB OrU KyU–A CU PPD PP OCl ODW OU TU
NL 0387258   DLC ICRL OrCS IdB Or OrU WaT CaBVa Or KyU

Lingenfelter, Mary Rebecca, 1893–
Vocations for girls [by] Mary Rebecca Lingenfelter [and]
Harry Dexter Kitson. Rev. ed. New York, Harcourt,
Brace [1951]
xi, 364 p. 21 cm.
Bibliography: p. 337–359.

1. Woman—Employment. 2. Vocational guidance. 3. Occupations.
I. Kitson, Harry Dexter, 1886–   joint author. II. Title.

HD6058.L47 1951   396.5   51—10837

Library of Congress   [58v⁵5]

TU OrAshS NN OrMonO OrU Wa WaE WaS ScU
NL 0387259   DLC WaWW IEN WaT WaSp CaBViP CaBVa Or CU

Lingenfelter, Mary Rebecca, 1893–   comp.
Vocations in fiction; an annotated bibliography, compiled by
Mary Rebecca Lingenfelter ... and Marie Alice Hanson ...
Chicago, American library association, 1932.
100 p. 24½ᵐ.

Autographic reproduction of type-written copy.
"Originally compiled as a study for a course in vocational guidance ...
at the University of Pennsylvania. It has been expanded and completed
as a project of the Bureau of educational research, Ohio state university."

1. Profession, Choice of—Bibl. 2. Fiction—Bibl.   I. Hanson, Marie
Alice, joint comp. II. American library association. III. Title.

Library of Congress   Z7164.C81L7   32—5288
                                [a39m2]   016.371425

PPG PSt MiU OLak OCl PPCCH ICU
NL 0387260   DLC OrU OrCS WaS MB IU MtU WaSp CU Or PSC

VOLUME 334

Lingenfelter, Mary Rebecca, 1893–   *comp.*
Vocations in fiction; an annotated bibliography, compiled by Mary Rebecca Lingenfelter ... 2d ed. Chicago, American library association, 1938.
99 p. 22ᵐ.
First edition, published 1932, compiled by Mary Rebecca Lingenfelter and Marie Alice Hanson.

1. Profession, Choice of—Bibl. 2. Fiction—Bibl. I. Hanson, Marie Alice. II. American library association. III. Title.

Library of Congress   Z7164.C81L7 1938   38–27546
———— Copy 2.
Copyright A 118877   [15–5]   016.371425

OC1 OC1h OC1W OU CU
MtU OrU OrP WaS CoU IdB Or KEmT Wa NBuC PSt PSC PP
NL 0387261   DLC PWcS PCM CaBVa OrAshS OrLgE WaT OrCS

016.37142
L646v
1938r   LINGENFELTER, MARY REBECCA, 1893–   comp.
Library   Vocations in fiction; an annotated bibliog-
School   raphy, compiled by Mary Rebecca Lingenfelter ...
2d ed. Chicago, American library association,
1938 [i.e. 1941]
99p. 22cm.

"Second printing April 1941 [c1938]"

1. Profession, Choice of - Bibl. 2. Fiction - Bibl. I. American library association. II. Title.

NL 0387262   TxU

Lingenfelter, Mary Rebecca, 1893–
Wartime jobs for girls, by Mary Rebecca Lingenfelter. New York, Harcourt, Brace and company [1943]
x, 228 p. 21ᵐ.
"Sources for additional information": p. 224–226.

1. Woman—Employment—U. S.   I. Title.
43–5791
Library of Congress   HD6095.L53
[18]   371.425

NL 0387263   DLC KEmT MtU Or PPD PP NcC OC1 OO OU

SPECIAL
CCLL.
A
L646   Lingenfelter, Williams Evans, 1830–1916.
Correspondence and documents, 1852–1902.
2 folders, incl. 38 letters.

Most of the letters relate to the family, and are written from Missouri to Oregon. Typed copies filed with originals.

NL 0387264   OrU

Lingenhoel (J. Nep.) *Die Nachgeburts-Zö-gerungen, ihre Ursachen und Folgen, sowie das dabei zu beobachtende Heilverfahren. 39 pp 8°. München. C. Wolf, 1838.*

NL 0387265   DNLM

Lingens, Ella.
Prisoners of fear, by Ella Lingens-Reiner. With an introd. by Arturo Barea. London, Gollancz, 1948.
xiii, 195 p. 19 cm.

1. World War, 1939–1945—Prisoners and prisons, German. I. Title.

D805.P7L47   68–126277

NL 0387266   DLC CaBVaU NcU NIC KU NNC NN CU

Lingens, Emil.
Die innere schönheit des christenthums. Von Emil Lingens, s. J. ... Freiburg im Breisgau, St. Louis, Mo. [etc.] Herder, 1895.
ix, 154 p. 22ᵐᵐ. (Ergänzungshefte zu den "Stimmen aus Maria-Laach." 64)

1. Christianity.
A 14–442

Title from Harvard Univ.   Printed by L. C.

NL 0387267   MH PLatS

BO
187   Lingens, Emil
L75   Die innere Schönheit des Christentums...
1902   2. verb. Aufl.   Freiburg im Breisgau,
Herder, 1902.
xii, 207 p.   20 cm.
First publ. as Ergänzungsheft zu den "Stimmen aus Maria-Laach".

1. Christianity.

NL 0387268   IMunS

Lingens, Franz, 1925–
Zum Mechanismus der Kondensationen von tertiären Mannich-Basen und quartären Ammoniumsalzen. [Tübingen, [1954?]

Abstract of Inaug.-Diss. - Tübingen

NL 0387269   MH-C

Lingens, Paul, 1908–
... Zur Frage der Verwendbarkeit von Lumines-zenzlicht bei Untersuchungen der Mundhöhlensch-leimhaut ... [Htls-Krefeld] 1932.
Inaug.-Diss. - Rostock.
Lebenslauf.
"Literatur-Verzeichnis": p. 35–37.
Full name: Paul Michael Everhard Lingens.

NL 0387270   CtY

Lingens, Theodor, 1901–
Aufbau und entwicklung der deutschen teer-derivate-industrie ... Heidelberg, [1928]
'18 p
Inaug.-diss - jena
bibliography

NL 0387271   MiU ICRL PU MH CtY

HD2734
L755   **Lingenselser, Franz,** 1909–
Die Kartelle und die Organisation der ge-werblichen Wirtschaft _ Philippsburg (Baden) 1939.
77 p.
Inaug.-Diss. - Heidelberg.
"Schrifttum": p. 75–77.

1. Trusts, Indu   strial. 2. Industry - Organization,   control, etc. I. Title.

NL 0387272   CSt-H

Lingenslanger, Chris., *pseud.*
see
Crossley, William J.

Lingenthal, Karl Eduard Zachariae von
see   Zachariae von Lingenthal, Karl Eduard, 1812–1894.

Lingenthal, Karl Salomo Zachariä von
see
Zachariä von Lingenthal, Karl Salomo, 1769–1843.

Linger, Carl, 1810–1862.
The song of Australia. Words by C. J. Carleton. Music by Carl Linger. Harmonised and arranged for choral use or for unison singing by E. Harold Davies   Melbourne: Allan & co. prop. ltd., c1934.   Publ. pl. no. B. 2640.   3 p.   25½cm (Allan's part-songs.   no. 244.)
Score: S. A. T. B. and piano.
First line: There is a land where summer skies.
Caption-title.

1. Songs, National—Australia.   I. Carleton, Caroline (Baines),
d 1874. II. Davies, Edward Harold,
N. Y. P. L.

NL 0387276   NN

Linger, Karl Friedrich, ed.
Denkwürdigkeiten aus dem leben des k. k. hofrathes Heinrich Gottfried von Bretschneider
see under   Bretschneider, Heinrich Gott-fried von, 1739–1810.

Linger, Lisbet.
Midsommarfesten på ängen; text och musik [av] Lisbet Linger. Arrangemang [av] Hildur Zetterberg; illus. [av] Olle Norberg. Stockholm, New York, Ljus [1947]
51 p. illus. 25 cm. (Ljus barnböcker, 10)
Children's stories and poems, the latter set for piano with inter linear words.

I. Title.

PZ59.L53M5   54–23570

NL 0387278   DLC

4PT
Ger.   **Linger, Maria.**
386   Rübezahl; ein deutsches Waldmärchen in 8 Bildern. Berlin, Deutscher Bühnenvertrieb des Zentralverlages der NSDAP.
83 p.

NL 0387279   DLC-P4

891.86   **Linger-Amboise,** K   V
L646   O cudném Josefu a choti pana Putifara,
Oo   komořího faraonského a knížete vojska.
[Praha] 1932.
13p. illus. 22cm. (Edice Lotos, sv. 3)
"Vytiskl jí písmem Staro-mediaeval Vladislav Burda ve Vršovicích, v 250 výtiscích; čís. 1-50 na Zandersku, čís. 51-250 na českém ručním papíře s puv. dřevorytem." No.4.

NL 0387280   IU

VOLUME 334

LINGER awhile, ye genial hours; an old English
melody, as a duet for two voices, with an accompaniment
for the piano forte. London, Printed & sold at
Chappell's [183-?] Pl. no. 5253. score(5 p.) 33cm

Music based on Drink to me only with thine eyes.

1. Vocal duos, Secular (Women)--Keyboard acc.

NL 0387281　NN

---

*

The Linger-nots series
　　see under　Miller, Agnes.

PS536
.L5
　　The Lingerer;
　　　Vermilion, S.D. 19-

NL 0387283　DLC

Lingerie and corset fashions.
　　[New York, Fashion House]
　　v. illus. 31 cm. monthly.

1. Lingerie—Period. 2. Corset—Period.

TT670.L56　　　687.2　　　52-22759

NL 0387284　DLC

LINGERIE MANUFACTURERS ASSOCIATION OF
NEW YORK
　　Agreement with Undergarment and negligee workers'
union, Local 62, and the Amalgamated ladies garment
cutters' union, Local 10.
New York.　　　　　　　　　　16cm.

1. Labor contracts, Garment workers'--U.S.--New York. I. International
ladies garment workers union, New York (City) Local 62,
Undergarment and negligee workers union. II. International
ladies garment workers union, New York (City). Local 10,
Amalgamated ladies' garment cutters union.

NL 0387285　NN

Lingerie merchandising. v. 1-
July 1945-
[East Stroudsburg, Pa., Carwil Pub. Corp.]
　　v. in illus. 29-31 cm. monthly.
　　Formerly issued as a section of the Underwear & hosiery review.

1. Underwear—Period.

HD9969.U5L5　　　658.94642　　　48-12650*

NL 0387286　DLC NN NcRS DP

Lingerie merchandising
　　see also　Hosiery and underwear review.

La LINGERIE parisienne.
no.

Vienne: Le grand chic[, 19　　　　　32½cm.
　　no.　illus., plates (part col'd).
　　Annual.
　　no.　　, cover-title.

1. Underwear—Per. and　　　　soc. publ.

NL 0387288　NN

The Lingerie review...
　　v. 1

New York: Style studios of W. Friedman, 1936-　　28cm.
　　v.　illus.

Monthly (slightly irregular).
Reproduced in part from typewritten copy.
Editor : Oct., 1936-　　　　Werther Friedman.

1. Underwear—Per. and soc. publ.　I. Friedman, Werther, ed.
N.Y.P.L.　　　　　　　　　　　　　　March 9, 1939

NL 0387289　NN

Lingerlong, Reuben, *pseud.*
　　see
Carpenter, James M.

Lingesa Vidyabhushana Vedantavachaspati
afterwards Vidyasankara Bharati Svami.
　　see
Vidyasankara Bharati Svami, 1879-

Law
　　　Lingesan, P. M., joint author.
Bhaskaran, S
　　Our Indian constitution; its form and functions, by S.
Bhaskaran and P. M. Lingesan. With an introd. by C. R.
Srinivasan. Madras, Nava India Publications [1950]

Lingesh Mahabhagavat
　　see
Vidyasankara Bharati Svami, 1879-

Linget (G.) [1874-　].　*Contribution à l'étude
du diagnostic clinique des tubercules de la couche
optique. 64 pp. 8°.　Paris, 1900. No. 175.

NL 0387294　DNLM

Lingförbundet.
　　Lingförbundet 1912-1937.　[Göteborg,
1937]
　　63 p.　illus.

NL 0387295　KyU

Lingford (Joseph) and Son, ltd., *Bishop Auckland, Eng.*
　　High Level Tyneside song book, published on the occasion
of the centenary of the opening of the High Level Bridge,
Newcastle upon Tyne, England. [Bishop Auckland, Eng.,
1949]
　　22 p. illus. 22 cm.
　　Without the music.

1. Songs, English.　I. Title.

M1740.L6H5　　　　　　　　M 57-1195 ‡

NL 0387296　DLC

Lingford, S. A., joint author.
　　Thoughts on the Ackworth centennial...
　　see under　[Baker, Guli.]

Lingg, Ann M
　　John Philip Sousa. [1st ed.] New York, Holt [1954]
　　250 p. 22 cm. ([Holt musical biography series])

1. Sousa, John Philip, 1854-1932.

ML410.S688L5　　　927.8　　　54-5451 ‡

OU Or OrP WaE
NL 0387298　DLC WaS KEmT MB NN OC1 PP TxU PRosC PWcT

Lingg, Ann M
　　Mephisto waltz, the story of Franz Liszt. [1st ed.] New
York, Holt [1951]
　　307 p. 22 cm.

1. Liszt, Franz, 1811-1886. 2. Liszt, Franz, 1811-1886—Discography.　I. Title.

ML410.L7L47　　　927.8　　　51-14005 ‡

OWorP PSt MH MB
NL 0387299　DLC WaT WaS WaSp WaE Or CaBViP IU NIC ViU

Lingg, Ann M
　　Mozart, genius of harmony, by Ann M. Lingg; illustrations
by Helen Frank. New York, H. Holt and company [1946]
　　viii p., 2 l., 331 p. illus. 24ᶜᵐ.
　　"First printing."
　　"Mozart works and recordings" : p. 287-315.

1. Mozart, Johann Chrysostom Wolfgang Amadeus, 1756-1791. 2.
Music—Juvenile literature. 3. Mozart, Johann Chrysostom Wolfgang
Amadeus—Discography.

ML3930.M9L5　　　927.8　　　47-92

OrAshS WU PP PPT CaBViP Or OrStbM OrSaW OrU-M MtU-M
IdB WaWW CaBVaU OrPR OrU OrCS OrP ViU Wa WaE WaPS
NL 0387300　DLC WaS WaSp WaSpG MtU MtBC WaT IdU WaTC

Lingg, Anton, 1902-
　　Die Verwaltung der Nationalsozialistischen Deutschen
Arbeiterpartei. München, F. Eher Nachf. [1939]
　　xiv, 328 p. 19 cm.
　　Inaug.-Diss.—Heidelberg.
　　Published also without thesis statement.
　　Lebenslauf.
　　"Literatur-Verzeichnis" : p. 322-327.

1. Nationalsozialistische Deutsche Arbeiter-Partei.　I. Title.

DD253.L554 1939a　　　　　A F 48-1256

Louisiana. State Univ.　Library
for Library of Congress　　[1]†

NL 0387301　LU MH DLC

VOLUME 334

Lingg, Anton, 1902–
Die verwaltung der Nationalsozialistischen deutschen arbeiterpartei, von dr. Anton Lingg ... München, Zentralverlag der NSDAP, Franz Eher nachf., 1939.
xv, [1], 327 p. 19 cm.
Issued also as dissertation, Heidelberg.
"Literatur-verzeichnis": p. 322–327.

1. Nationalsozialistische deutsche arbeiter-partei.   I. Title.
DD253.L554 1939   329.943   A C 40–211
New York. Public Libr.
for Library of Congress   [a56r42e½]†

NL 0387302   NN MU IaU MH MiU IEN CU CtY NcU DLC

Lingg, Anton.
Die verwaltung der Nationalsozialistischen deutschen arbeiterpartei, von dr. Anton Lingg ... 2., erweiterte aufl. München, F. Eher nachf., 1940.
xix, 361, [1] p., 1 l. 19ᶜᵐ.
"Literatur-verzeichnis": p. 322–327, [363].

1. Nationalsozialistische deutsche arbeiter-partei.   I. Title.
                                        46–33689
Library of Congress   JN3070.N3L52
                              [2]   329.943

NL 0387303   DLC CaBVaU CSt MnU TxU IU

329.943
L617v
1940   LINGG, ANTON, 1902–
Die verwaltung der Nationalsozialistischen deutschen arbeiterpartei. [3. aufl.] München, F. Eher nachf., 1940.
xix, 363p. 19cm.
"Literatur-verzeichnis": p.322–327, [363]

1. Nationalsozialistische deutsche arbeiterpartei. I. Title.

NL 0387304   TxU DLC-P4 NNC NcD

943.086
L647
Lingg, Anton, [1902–
Die verwaltung der Nationalsozialistischen deutschen arbeiterpartei, von dr. Anton Lingg ... Mit einem geleitwort von Reichsschatzmeister Schwarz .. München, Zentralverlag der NSDAP, Franz Eher nachf., 1941.
xix, 363 p. 19ᶜᵐ.
"Vierte auflage."
"Literatur-verzeichnis": p. 363.

1. Nationalsozialistische deutsche arbeiterpartei.
2. National socialism.

NL 0387305   NNC

Lingg (Carl). * Beiträge zur Naturkunde Oberschwabens. 32 pp. 12°. *Tübingen, Hopfer de l'Orme,* [1832]. [P., v. 1507.]

NL 0387306   DNLM

Lingg, Claire, 1890–   joint author.
RA407
.3
.C57   **Cohn, Alfred Einstein,** 1879–
The burden of diseases in the United States [by] Alfred E. Cohn and Claire Lingg. New York, Oxford University Press, 1950.

Lingg, Emil,
Baurecht und Staatsrecht. Beiträge zur Lehre von der Staatsauflösung. Von ... Emil Lingg ... Prag, F. Haerpfer, 1899.
38 p. 23½cm.
Bibliographical footnotes.

NL 0387308   MH-L

Lingg, Emil.
Empirische untersuchungen zur allgemeinen staatslehre, von dr. jur. et phil. Emil Lingg ... Wien, A. Hölder, 1890.
xiv, [2], 235, [1] p. 22½ᵐ.
"Schriftsteller-verzeichnis": p. [236]

1. State, The. 2. Political science.   I. Title.
                                        36–25912
Library of Congress   JC234.L5
                              [2]   320.1

NL 0387309   DLC MH PU

LINGG, Emil.
Neue studien zur reform des administrativverfahrens. Wien, Leipzig, n. d.

NL 0387310   MH-L

LINGG, Emil.
Staatsrecht und steuerrecht. Wien, Leipzig, n. d.

NL 0387311   MH-L

Lingg, Emil.
Die staatsrechtliche stellung der im Reichsrathe vertretenen königreiche und länder der Österreichisch-ungarischen monarchie. Beiträge zur lehre von der autonomie und selbstverwaltung. Von dr. jur. et phil. Emil Lingg ... [Wien, Druck von G. Gistel & comp., 189–]
64 p. 22½ᵐ.
Caption title.

1. Austria—Pol. & govt.
                                        42–51807
Library of Congress   JN1637.L5

NL 0387312   DLC

Lingg, Emil.
Ueber den Entwurf einer neuen Bau-Ordnung für die Städte Prag, Pilsen und Budweis und deren Umgebungen. Vortrag gehalten in der General-Versammlung des „Deutschen Vereines" in Prag am 11. April 1899 vom Vereinsmitgliede ... Emil Lingg. Prag, Verlag des „Deutschen Vereines", 1899.
22 p. 23cm.

NL 0387313   MH-L

Lingg, Emil.
Zur Geschäfts-Ordnung des österreichischen Reichsrathes. Fragmente zum österreichischen Staatsrecht. Prag, F. Haerpfer, 1897.
27 p. 23 cm.

1. Austria. Reichsrat. Abgeordnetenhaus. Rules and Regulations. I. Title.

NL 0387314   MnU MH-L

Lingg, Emil.
Zur reform des administrativverfahrens. Bei der ausschreibung des Prager advokatenvereines gekrönte preisschrift, von j. u. et phil. dr. Emil Lingg ... Wien, Manz, 1904.
56 p. 22½ᵐ.

1. Administrative law—Austria.   I. Title.
                                        42–29038

NL 0387315   DLC MiU-L MH-L

QD341   **Lingg, Ferdinand.**
.A2L8   Ueber β-Isophenylessigsaeure... Muenchen, 1898.
24 p. 22½ cm.
Inaug. diss. Tuebingen

NL 0387316   DLC

Lingg, Ferdinand, 1827–1899.
Construction des Meridian-Quadranten auf desse Sehne, nach den Bessel'schen Erddimensionen durch Bestimmung der Lage der Grad - und Halbgrad - Punkte des Meridians, sowie der Richtung ihrer Halbmesser und Lothlinien. entworfen, berechnet und in der Verjüngung von 1:10 Millionen gezeichnet. München, 1893.
2 pl. 6 f. in portf. 52 x 38 cm.

NL 0387317   DN-Ob

Lingg, Ferdinand, 1827–1899.
Erdprofil der Zone von 31° bis 65° N. Br., im Massverhältniss 1 : 1 Million. München, K. B. Priv. Kunstanstalt Piloty & Loehle, 1886.
8 columns. map, diagr., fold. profile. 51 cm.

1. Physical geography—Charts, diagrams, etc.   I. Title.
GB23.L5   56–55107

NL 0387318   DLC MB

Lingg, Ferdinand, 1827–1899.
Ueber den Einfluss der Alpen auf die Vorgänge in einem darüber hinziehenden Luftdruckmaximum. Von Ferdinand Lingg ... [Wien] 1882. 1 l., p. 215–232 p. 8°.
Caption-title.
Repr.: Zeitschrift der österreichischen Gesellschaft für Meteorologie. Juni 1882.

1. Pressure (Atmospheric).
N. Y. P. L.   November 5. 1917.

NL 0387319   NN

Lingg, Ferdinand, 1827–1899.
Ueber die bei Kimmbeobachtungen am Starnberger See wahrgenommnen Refractionserscheinungen. Halle, 1889.
95 p. 3 plates.

NL 0387320   MH

PT2424   **Lingg, Hermann, Ritter von,** 1820–1905.
L5A17   Ausgewählte Gedichte. Hrsg. von Paul Heyse, mit Porträt
1905   nach F. von Lenbach. Stuttgart, Cotta, 1905.
xviii, 268 p. port.

I. Heyse, Paul Johann Ludwig von, 1830–1914, ed.

NL 0387321   CU PPT NjP IU

VOLUME 334

832.91
L75d Lingg, Hermann, ritter von, 1820-1905.
Berthold Schwarz; dramatische Dichtung.
Mit einem Prolog bei Wiederaufnahme der Vor-
stellungen am K. Hof.- und National-Theater
zu München. Stuttgart, G. J. Goschen, 1874.
vii,93p. 19cm. (Bound with the author's
Der Doge Candiano. [Stuttgart, 1873])

I. Title.

NL 0387322   TNJ NcD OU NjP NN MB

KC 14234
Lingg, Hermann, ritter von, 1820-1905.
Die Besiegung der Cholera; ein Satyrdrama mit Vorspiel.
München, G.Beck [1873?]

NL 0387323   MH

Lingg, Hermann, ritter von, 1820-1905.
Byzantinische novellen, von Herman Lingg.
Berlin, O.Janke, 1881.
304p.

NL 0387324   OCU PPG

Lingg, Hermann, *ritter von*, 1820-1905.
Byzantinische novellen, von Hermann Lingg ... Leipzig,
P. Reclam jun. [1896]
112 p. 15ᶜᵐ. (*On cover:* Universal-bibliothek. 3600)
CONTENTS.—Die beiden wagenlenker.—Der bilderstreit.—Niklas.

I. Title.
[*Full name:* Hermann Ludwig Otto, ritter von Lingg]

30-30761

Library of Congress   PT2424.L5B8   833.89

NL 0387325   DLC IEN

PT 2424 LINGG,HERMANN,Ritter von,1820-1905.
.L5 C3   Catilina; Trauerspiel in fünf Acten. München, J. J. Lentner, 1864.
276 p.

Contains also his Violante and his Högni's
letzte Heerfahrt.

NL 0387326   InU PU

Lingg, Hermann, Ritter von, 1820-1905.
Catilina. Trauerspiel in fünf Acten. München,
Verlag der J. J. Lentner'schen Buchhandlung (E.
Stahl), 1864.
276p.

Microcard edition.

NL 0387327   ICRL

Lingg, Hermann, Ritter von, 1820-1905.
Catilina. Trauerspiel in fünf Aufzügen.
München, Brakl's Rubinverlag [1898]
124 p. 24°.

NL 0387328   NN

Lingg, Hermann, ritter von, 1820-1905.
Clytia. Eine Scene aus Pompeji, von Hermann Lingg...
München: T. Ackermann, 1887. 33 p. 2. ed. 16°.

NL 0387329   NN

Lingg, Hermann, ritter von, 1820-1905.
Corsar und Doge. Trauerspiel in drei
Aufzügen. München, Brakl's Rubinverlag,
[1898]
76 p. 24°.

NL 0387330   NN

832.91
L75d Lingg, Hermann, Ritter von, 1820-1905.
Der Doge Candiano; Drama in fünf Akten.
Stuttgart, G. J. Goschen, 1873.
[4],140p. 19cm.
With this is bound the author's Berthold
Schwarz [Stuttgart, 1874]

NL 0387331   TNJ NjP NN NcD ViU

PT2424
.L5A19
1897   Lingg, Hermann, Ritter von, 1820-1905.
Dramatische Dichtungen. Gesamtausg.
Stuttgart, J.G. Cotta, 1897.
264 p. 19 cm.
Imperfect copy: p. 193-200 wanting.
CONTENTS.—Die Catilinarier.—Korsar und
Doge.—Die Bregenzer Klause.—Die Frauen
Salonas.—Clytia.—Högnis letzte Heerfahrt.

NL 0387332   ViU NjP NIC CU PPT OCU OC1W

3469
.525 Lingg, Hermann, ritter von, 1820-1905.
.331   Dramatische Dichtungen. Gesamtausgabe, neue
.1899 Folge. Stuttgart, J.G. Cotta, 1899.
250 p. 19 cm.

NL 0387333   NjP

838
L755du Lingg,Hermann,Ritter von,1820-1905.
Dunkle Gewalten. Epische Dichtungen, Stut-
gart, G.J.Göschen, 1872.
270 p. 18 cm.

Full name: Hermann Ludwig
Otto,Ritter von Lingg.

NL 0387334   MiU MB OC1W

3469
.525 Lingg, Hermann, ritter von, 1820-1905.
.332   Dunkle Gewalten; epische Dichtungen, neue Ausg.
Lindau i.B., J.T.Stettner, 1898.
270 p. 19 cm.

NL 0387335   NjP

Lingg, Hermann, ritter von, 1820-1905.
Die Frauen Salonas. Tragödie mit Chor
in einem Akte. [In verse] München, T. Ackermann, 1887.
34 p. 16°.

NL 0387336   NN NjP

3469
.525 Lingg, Hermann, ritter von, 1820-1905.
.337   Furchen; neue Novellen. Stuttgart, A.Bonz,
1889.
354 p. 19 cm.

NL 0387337   NjP MH

3469
.525 Lingg, Hermann, ritter von, 1820-1905.
.1854   Gedichte, hrsg. durch E.Geibel. Stuttgart,
J.G.Cotta, 1854.
154 p. 19 cm.

I.Geibel, Emanuel. 1815-1885, ed.

NL 0387338   NjP OCU InU

PT2424 Lingg, Hermann, Ritter von, 1820-1905.
.L5A17   Gedichte. Hrsg. von Emanuel Geibel. 2.
1855 unveränd. Abdruck. Stuttgart, J. G. Cotta,
1855.
154 p. 19 cm.

NL 0387339   ViU DLC-P4

Lingg, Hermann, ritter von, 1820-1905.
Gedichte, von Hermann Lingg. 3.verm.
aufl. Stuttgart und Augsburg, J.G.
Cotta'scher verlag,1857.
v1,226p. 18½cm.

NL 0387340   MWelC TNJ IaU MB

PT 2424
L5
A17   Lingg, Hermann, Ritter von, 1820-1905.
1860   Gedichte. 4. verm. Aufl. Stuttgart,
J. G. Cotta, 1860.
304 p.

NL 0387341   CaBVaU CtY

PT2424 Lingg, Hermann, Ritter von, 1820-1905.
L5A17   Gedichte. Stuttgart, J.G. Cotta, 1864-70.
1864 3 v.

Vol.1, 5. verm. Aufl.

NL 0387342   CU PU MH OCU OC1W NN OO WU

3469
.525 Lingg, Hermann, ritter von, 1820-1905.
.1871   Gedichte. Stuttgart, J.G.Cotta, 1871.
3 v.in 1. illus. 18 cm.

Vol.1: 7th ed.

NL 0387343   NjP PU RPB

LINGG, Hermann, ritter von, 1820-1905.
Grenzen. Eine Erzählung aus vormärzlichen Tagen.
(In Deutsche Roman-Zeitung. Jahrg. 19, Bd. 4. Berlin,
1882)

NL 0387344   MB

VOLUME 334

Lingg, Hermann, ritter von, 1820–1905.
Der Herr des Feuers. Dramatisches Gedicht
in 3 Akten.   München, Brakl's Rubinverlag.
[1898]
95 p.   24°.

NL   0387345   NN

Hkl   Lingg, Hermann, Ritter von, 1820–1905.
y357g   Hochsommer; die schönsten Gedichte und Lieder.
Ausgewählt und eingeleitet von Ferdinand Eckert.
Lindau, Im Verlag der Rathaus-Buchhandlung, 1948.
59p.   illus., port.   15cm.
"Verzeichnis der Werke von Hermann Lingg":
p.58.

NL   0387346   CtY

PT 2424   LINGG, HERMANN, Ritter VON, 1820–1905
.L5 C3   Högni's letzte Heerfahrt; nordische Scene
nach einer Sage der Edda. München, G.D.W.
Callwey, 1884.
43 p.

Bound with his Catilina.

NL   0387347   InU

M1533   Lingg, Hermann, Ritter von, 1820–1905.
.Z86H9   Hymnus an die Tonkunst.

Zoller, Anton.
[Hymnus an die Tonkunst. Piano-vocal score. German]

Hymnus an die Tonkunst; Dichtung von Hermann Lingg.
Für Männerchor, Knabenchor, Mezzosopran und Orchester.
Klavierauszug. Heidelberg, K. Hochstein [19—]   Pl. no.
H. 3092 H.

Lingg, Hermann, Ritter von, 1820–1905.
Jahresringe. Neue Gedichte von Hermann Lingg. Mit dem
Porträt des Dichters nach dem Original von Franz von Lenbach.
Stuttgart: J. G. Cotta, 1889.   xiv, 433 p.   front. (port.)
18½cm.

602391A. 1. Poetry, German.   I. Title.
N. Y. P. L.   December 30, 1932

NL   0387349   NN TNJ NcU MH IU NjP

PT1101   Lingg, Hermann, ritter von, 1820–1905.
.D3
reihe 21, Stemplinger, Eduard, 1870–   *ed.*
bd. 3   Kulturhistorische dichtung. Scheffel, Julius Braun,
Lingg, herausgegeben von oberstudiendirektor dr. Eduard
Stemplinger. Leipzig, P. Reclam jun., 1939.

LINGG, HERMANN, ritter von, 1820–1905. ed.

Liebesblüthen aus Deutschlands Dichter-
hain. Lyrische Anthologie...herausg. von
Hermann Lingg.   Düsseldorf, Budich, 1865

xxvi, 229p. illus. 19½cm.

Two title-pages.

NL   0387351   CtY PPCS

3469   Lingg, Hermann, *ritter von, 1820-1905.*
.525   Lyrisches; neue Gedichte. Wien, Prochasta,
.359   1884.
265 p.   18 cm.   (Salon-Bibliothek)

NL   0387352   NjP WU

832.8
L755m   Lingg, Hermann, ritter von, 1820–1905.
Macalda.   Stuttgart, Göschen, 1877.
184p.   19cm.

NL   0387353   IEN NcD MA NjP OC1W NN

PT2424   Lingg, Hermann, Ritter von, 1820–1905.
L5Z5   Meine Lebensreise. Autobiographie. Berlin,
1899   Schuster & Loeffler, 1899.
190 p.   port.   (Zeitgenössische Selbst-
biographieen. Bd. I)

1. Lingg, Hermann, Ritter von, 1820–1905.
I. Title.

MiU NcU
NL   0387354   CU NcU ICarbS CtY OC1W NjP NNC ICU

Lingg, Hermann, Ritter von, 1820–1905.

M1533   Müller-Hermann, Johanna Fr   1878–1941.
.M945   [Ode, women's voices & orchestra, op. 29; arr.]
O 3
Ode, für Soli, Frauenchor und Orchester. Text von Her-
mann von Lingg. Klavierauszug mit Gesang. Wien, Uni-
versal-Edition [1944]

Hkl   Lingg, Hermann, Ritter von, 1820–1905.
y357e   Schlussrhythmen und neueste Gedichte.
Stuttgart, J.G.Cotta, 1901.
viii,271p.   19cm.

NL   0387356   CtY IU NjP TNJ NIC

Lingg, Hermann, Ritter von, 1820–1905.
Schlusssteine. Neue Gedichte, von Hermann Lingg.   Berlin: G. Grote, 1878.   244 p.   17cm.

608577A. 1. Poetry, German.   I. Title.
N. Y. P. L.   October 20, 1933

NL   0387357   NN NjP MH IaU IU

PT2424   Lingg, Hermann, ritter von, 1820–1905.
.L5   Schlusssteine; neue Gedichte. 2. Aufl.
S3   Berlin, G. Grote, 1879.
1879   239p 17cm.

NL   0387358   NcU

Lingg, Hermann, ritter von, 1820–1905. Trost
der musik.

M1533
.L685C8   Lewis, Leo Rich, 1865–
1941   [The consolation of music. Piano-vocal score. English & German]

... The consolation of music. Trost der musik: H. Lingg.
Short cantata for solo quartet, chorus and orchestra. [Op. 5]
The English translation by Fred. Field Bullard. The music by
Leo Rich Lewis. [Rev. ed.] Medford, Mass., Tufts college
bookstore, °1941.

3469   Lingg, Hermann, *ritter von, 1820-1905*
.525   Vaterländische Balladen und Gesänge. München,
.392   J.J.Kentner, 1869.
189 p.   19 cm.

NL   0387360   NjP NIC TNJ

Lingg, Hermann, *ritter von, 1820-1905.*
Violante. Trauerspiel in fünf Aufzügen.   [In verse]   Stuttgart: J. G. Cotta, 1871.   2 p.l., 127 p.   12°.

1. Drama (German).   2. Title.
N. Y. P. L.   February 23, 1912

NL   0387361   NN NjP

838
L755vn   Lingg, Hermann, Ritter von, 1820–1905.
Die Völkerwanderung. Epische Dichtung.
Stuttgart, J.G.Cotta, 1866–68.
3 v.   18 cm.

Full name: Hermann Ludwig
Otto, Ritter von Lingg.

NL   0387362   MiU PU InU DLC-P4 OO MH PPG

3469   Lingg, Hermann, *ritter von, 1820-1905.*
.525   Die Völkerwanderung; Epos. 2.Aufl. Stuttgart,
.394   J. G. Cotta, 1892.
527 p.   18 cm.

NL   0387363   NjP RPB OC1W MH NcU TNJ NIC

---

ar U   Lingg, Hermann, *ritter von, 1820-1905.*
529   Die Walkyren; dramatisches Gedicht.
München, I. I. Lentner, 1864.
155 p.   14cm.

NL   0387364   NIC PSt InU

---

t PT2424   Lingg, Hermann, Ritter von, 1820–1905.
L5W3   Die Walkyren; dramatisches Gedicht in drei Acten.   2. Ausg.
1865   München, J.J. Lentner, 1865.
155 p.   front. 14cm.

NL   0387365   CU

Lingg, Hermann Ludwig Otto,
ritter von, *1820-1905.*

see

Lingg, Hermann, ritter von, 1820–1905.

W 4   LINGG, Ludwig, 1914–
M96   Untersuchungen über den zeitlichen
1952   Ablauf der Blutbakterizidie. [München]
1952.
51 ℓ.
Inaug. -Diss. - Munich.
1. Blood - Experimental studies

NL   0387367   DNLM

VOLUME 334

GER 913 LIN
Lingg, Maximilian, ritter von, 1842-1930.
Die Civilehe vom Standpunkte des Rechts. Eine historisch-dogmatische Abhandlung von ... Max Lingg ... Augsburg, B. Schmid, 1870.

77, [1] p. 24cm.

Bibliographical footnotes.

NL 0387368   MH-L

BX1534 .L75
Lingg, Maximilian, Ritter von, Bp. of Augsburg, 1842-1930.
Geschichte des Instituts der Pfarrvisitation in Deutschland. Kempten, J. Kösel, 1888.
75 p.

1. Visitations, Ecclesiastical--Germany. 2. Catholic church in Germany.

NL 0387369   ICU

LINGG, Maximilian, ritter von, 1842-1930.
Die ehe und die grundsätze des modernen staatsrechts; (das 3. kapitel aus des verfassers abhandlung "Die civilehe vom standpunkt des rechts". Augsburg, 1869.

23 p.

NL 0387370   MH-L

FL8 S9.9 L755e 1921
Lingg, Otto.
Die Entwicklung der Vermögenssteuern in der Stadt Bern seit Einführung des Gesetzes über die Vermögenssteuer vom 15.März 1856. Eine finanzgeschichtliche und sozialstatistische Untersuchung. Bern, Buchdruckerei G.Grunau, 1921.
68 p. forms. 24cm.
Cover title.
Inaug.-Diss. - Bern.
1.Property tax - Bern. I.Title.

NL 0387371   MiU-L PU CtY ICRL

Wason Pamphlet PL Indonesia 81
Lingga Wisjnu M   S   , raden.
Rahasia hidup R.A. Titin Sumarni.
Djakarta, Analisa, 1955.
72 p. illus. 19cm.

1. Titin Sumarni, R   A
I. Title.

NL 0387372   NIC

Linggadjati; de ontwerp-overeenkomst, de toelichting der Commissie-Generaal, de Regeeringsverklaring
see under   Linggadjat Konperensi, Djakarta, 1946.

Wason D8644 L75
Linggadjat Konperensi, Djakarta, 1946.
Linggadjati, de ontwerp-overeenkomst, de toelichting der commissie-generaal, de regeeringsverklaring.   's-Gravenhage, Rijksuitgeverij, 1946.
40 p. 20cm.

1. Indonesia--Pol. & govt.

NL 0387374   NIC

W 4 Z963 1951
LINGGI, Anton, 1921-
Die Bruchfestigkeit der Knochen des Hundes. Affoltern, Weiss, 1951.
73 p. illus.
Inaug.-Diss. - Zürich.
1. Bones 2. Fractures

NL 0387375   DNLM DNAL

Linghagen, Arthur, 1884-
Overförmyndares skyldigheter en handledning jämte fullständig lagtext och formulär av Arthur Lindhagen. 2. omarbetade upplagan ombesörjd av Gösta Walin. Stockholm, Norstedt [1950]
xi, 216 p. forms.

1. Guardian and ward - Sweden.

NL 0387376   NNC

Lingham, Clarence Hart, 1872-   joint author
FOR OTHER EDITIONS
SEE MAIN ENTRY
Davis, Roy, 1877-
Business English and correspondence, by Roy Davis ... and Clarence H. Lingham. Rev. ed. Boston, New York [etc.] Ginn and company [*1921]

Lingham, Clarence Hart, 1872-   joint author.
Davis, Roy, 1877-
Business English workbook, by Roy Davis ... Clarence H Lingham, and Gertrude I. Payne ... Boston, New York [etc. Ginn and company [*1941]

Lingham, Clarence Hart, 1872-   joint author
Davis, Roy, 1877-
Business letter-writing, by Roy Davis ... and Clarence H. Lingham. Boston, New York [etc.] Ginn and company [*1925]

Lingham, Clarence Hart, 1872-   joint author.
FOR OTHER EDITIONS
SEE MAIN ENTRY
Davis, Roy, 1877-
Modern business English. Rev. ed. By Roy Davis ... Clarence H. Lingham, and William H. Stone ... Boston, New York [etc.] Ginn and company [*1940]

Lingham, Edward James.
Vindiciae Lusitanicae; or, an answer to a pamphlet on the causes and consequences of the late emigration to the Brazils. London, [Cox & Baylis] 1808.
11, 67 p. 22cm.

NL 0387381   NcD DLC-P4

Lingham, Gertrude, joint author.
Rood, Elma.
Taking care of the family's health; a teaching guide for rural classes, by Elma Rood ... and Gertrude Lingham ... One hundred illustrations and charts; photographs by Herbert Clarence White. Madison College, Tenn., The Rural press [*1938]

Lingham, Grace E., ed.
Boston teachers news letter
see under title

Lingham, Henry Charles John.
Juvenal in Melbourne. A satire, social and political. By Henry Charles John Lingham ... Melbourne, H. C. J. Lingham [1892] 57 p. 18cm.

1. Satire, Political—Australia.   I. Title.
N. Y. P. L.   October 17, 1945

NL 0387384   NN

Lingham, Henry Charles John,
The last hours of a lion heart. A threnody. London [etc.] Melville, Mullen & Slade [1899]

103 p. port. 16cm.

I. Title.

NL 0387385   MnU MH CtY

Lingham, Henry Charles John.
The litany of love, with The love-prayer of Giovanna II., queen of Naples, and other poems. Melbourne, The Atlas press, 1900.

63 p. 19cm.

I. Title.   II. Title: The love-prayer of Giovanna II.

NL 0387386   MnU TxU

Iq L647 903
Lingham, Henry Charles John
The living pillars of the Colosseum; a dramatic picture-poem of the Roman persecutions, with lyrics from Catullus. Melbourne Echo Pub.Co.[1903]
35p. 19cm.

NL 0387387   CtY

Lingham, S   V
Pictorial potpourri. Foreword by J. N. Unwalla. Madras, Linghams [1947]
vii, 63 p. illus., ports. 19 cm.

1. Photography—Addresses, essays, lectures.   I. Title.

TR185.L5   58-38658

NL 0387388   DLC

Rare PR 4889 L43L12 1814
Lingham, W
The labyrinth farm; or, The fashionable recluse. A comedy in five acts, as performed at the Theatre Royal, Glasgow, with the most brilliant success for many nights. 2d ed. Glasgow, T. Ogilvie, 1814.
79 p. 23cm.

I. Title.   II. Title: The fashionable recluse.

NL 0387389   NIC InU

VOLUME 334

Lingiaden; gymnastikfrämjandets årsbok
see **Boken** om Lingiaden.

Lingis, I
see
Lingys, Juozas.

Lingis, fŪ
see
Lingys, Juozas.

Lingis, Jouzas
see Lingys, Jouzas.

Lingis, Yu.
See
Lingys, Juozas.

Lingius, Carolus
see Linge, Carl, 1782-1849.

Lingjærde, Ottar, 1895-
... Leberuntersuchungen bei geisteskranken, unter besonderer berücksichtigung des verhältnisses von krankheitsverlauf, leberfunktion und nahrungszufuhr bei schizophrenen, von Ottar Lingjaerde. Kopenhagen, Levin & Munksgaard, 1934.
319 p. incl. tables, diagrs. 24ᶜᵐ. (Acta psychiatrica et neurologica. Supplementum v)
"Literatur": p. ₍312₎-319.

1. Insanity. 2. Dementia. 3. Liver—Diseases.
Library of Congress   RC602.L55   40-5959
                              ₍3₎   616.8982

NL 0387396   DLC ICJ ViU MoU

4DC-   Lingk,   Baron von.
563   Das Etappenwesen im Kriege, speziell bei der III. Armee und bei der Okkupationsarmee in Frankreich, 1870-1873. Breslau, Im Selbstverlage des Herausgebers, 1888.
126 p.

NL 0387397   DLC-P4

Lingk,   Baron von
... Souvenirs d'un commandant d'etapes 1870-1873. Le service des etapes a la IIIe armee et pendant la periode de l'occupation Allemande... Traduit de l' allemand par G. Richert... Paris, R. Chapelot et cie, 1909.
xi, 133 p. 1 l., fold.map. 22 cm.
18293

NL 0387398   DNW

Lingk, Carl Ludwig
see Lingk, Karl Ludwig.

Lingk, Karl Ludwig, respondent.
... De cautione fideicommissorum nomine praestanda ...
see under Siegel, Johann Gottlieb, praeses.

Lingke, Friedrich Philipp, respondent.
... De litis contestatione malam fidem non inferente, qvam ...
see under Brokes, Heinrich, 1706-1773, praeses.

Lingke, Friedrich Wilhelm, respondent.
Ad decis. Saxon. el. XXIII. d. a. 1746 ...
see under Bauer, Heinrich Gottfried, praeses.

Lingke, Georg Friedrich, d. 1779?, supposed author.
Einige zum allgemeinen nutzen deutlicher gemachte musikalische erwegungs- und andere leichter eingerichtete uibungs-wahrheiten, ...
see under title

Lingke, Georg Friedrich, *d.* 1779?
George Friedrich Lingkens ... Kurze musiklehre, in welcher nicht allein die verwandschaft aller tonleitern, sondern auch die jeder zukommenden harmonischen sätze gezeigt, und mit praktischen beyspielen erläutert werden. Leipzig, Bey J. G. I. Breitkopf, 1779.
viii, 86 p. illus. 21½ x 17½ᶜᵐ.
Title vignette.
Preface signed: Johann Adam Hiller.

1. Harmony.   i. Hiller, Johann Adam, 1728-1804, ed.
                                        8-16366
Library of Congress   MT50.A2L4

NL 0387404   DLC ICN MiU CtY

Lingke, Georg Friedrich, *d.* 1779?
Die sitze der musicalischen haupt-sätze in einer harten und weichen tonart und wie man damit fortschreitet und ausweichet in zwo tabellen entworffen, erklärt und mit exempeln erläutert von George Friedrich Lingken. Leipzig, Gedruckt und in commission bey B. C. Breitkopf und sohn, 1766.
4 p. l., 60 p. 2 fold. pl. 22½ x 18½ᶜᵐ.

1. Modulation.
                                        9-11283
Library of Congress   MT52.A2L42

NL 0387405   DLC MiU CtY

                              Ger 11681.36
Lingke, Johann Friedrich August.
Chronik der Familie Lingke, 1470 bis 1909, von Joh.Friedr.August Lingke und Otto Friedrich Joachim Lingke. Cöthen, Druck von P.Schettler 1909.
vi, 285 p. illus.

NL 0387406   MH

LINGKE, Johann Theodor,   ed.
D. Martin Luthers merkwuerdige Reisegeschichte, zu Ergaenzung seiner Lebensumstaende und Erlaeuterung der Reformationsgeschichte aus bewaehrten Schriften und zum Theil ungedruckten Nachrichten beschrieben, und nach dem Jubilaeo des Reformationsfestes in Sachsen herausgegeben von M. Johann Theodor Lingke ... Leipzig, Friedrich Gotthold Jacobaeern, 1769.
354p. 21.5cm. front.(fold.map)

NL 0387407   MH-AH PPLT NNUT CtY WU NcD CtHC

Lingke, Johann Theodor.
... Martin Luthers Geschäfte und Andenken in Torgau, zur Erläuterung seiner Lebensgeschichte; nebst zehen ungedruckten Briefen von ihm aus sichern Urkunden ... Torgau, Rudel, [pref. 1764]
94 p.

NL 0387408   PPLT

Lingke, Wilhelm Friedrich. Erfahrungen und erfordernisse bey der schwarzholzsaat. Dresden. 1795. sm. 8°. pp. [8], xii, [14], 140+. Tables and 4 plates.
"Druckfehler." at end.

NL 0387409   MH-A

PF 3871 LINGL,AGNES RITA,Sister.
.L 75   Über den Gebrauch der Abstrakta im Plural im Ahd. und Mhd. München, 1934.
93 p.
Cover title.
Inaug.-Diss.-München.

1. German language—Old High German—Number.
2. German language—Middle High German—Number. I. Tc.

NL 0387410   InU CtY PU

Lingl (Carolus). *De glandula thyreoidea in cavum usque thoracis sub sterno sese expandente, casus singularis. 28 pp., 2 pl. 8°. Monachii. M. Poessenbacher. 1830.

NL 0387411   DNLM

W 4   LINGL, Friedrich Albert, 1927-
M96   Die Rolle der Leber beim Porphyrin-
1952   und Eisenstoffwechsel. ₍München₎ 1952.
44 ℓ.
Inaug.-Diss. - Munich.
Typewritten copy.
1. Iron - Assimilation & excretion
2. Liver - Physiology 3. Porphyrins

NL 0387412   DNLM

Wing   LINGLE, BERTHA KENDALL, 1886-1940.
ZP   Poems and songs of Bertha Kendall Lingle.
983   Chicago,Privately printed,1941.
.K 6584 ₍9₎,65,₍5₎p. front.(port.) 19cm.

Contains music.
Designed by W.A.Kittredge.
Printed at the Lakeside press, Chicago.
Bookplate of W.A.Kittredge.

NL 0387413   ICN

VOLUME 334

Lingle, Clara S   (Souther) *"Mrs.* **Thomas W.**
Lingle," 1874–
　... A course on Americanization; studies of the peoples
and the movements that are building up the American
nation, by Mrs. Thomas W. Lingle ... Chapel Hill, The
University, 1919.
　61 p. 23½ᶜᵐ. (*On cover:* University of North Carolina extension leaf-
lets, vol. II, no. 8)
　After-the-war information series no. 3.
　"Specific references": p. ₁4₂; "General references": p. 55–61.

　1. Americanization. I. Title. II. Title: Americanization, A course on.

　Library of Congress   JK1758.L3
                                                          19–9945

　NL 0387414   DLC Or WaS OrU NcU DL

Lingle, Clara S   (Souther) *"Mrs.* **Thomas W.**
Lingle," 1874–
　... A-course on the historical background and the liter-
ature of the great war, by Mrs. Thomas W. Lingle ...
Chapel Hill, The University, 1918.
　28 p. 23ᶜᵐ. (*On cover:* University of North Carolina extension leaflets,
vol. I, no. 20 ... Division for women series, no. 2)
　Series title in part also at head of t-p.
　On cover: A study for the North Carolina federation of women's clubs,
1918–19.
　"General references": p. 23–27.
　1. European war, 1914–1918—Outlines, syllabi, etc. 2. Europe—Hist.—
Bibl. 3. European war, 1914–1918—Bibl. I. Title: Historical background
and the literature of the great war.

　Library of Congress   D522.5.L5
                                                          18–20875

　NL 0387415   DLC OU

Lingle, Clara S. (Souther) *"Mrs. Thomas W. Lingle",* 1874–
　Studies in the social and industrial condition of women as
affected by the war. By Mrs. Thomas W. Lingle... Chapel
Hill: the university, 1918. 19 p. 8°. (North Carolina.
University of North Carolina: Extension Bureau. After-the-war
information series. no. 2.)
　Extension leaflets v. 2. no. 7. March, 1919.

　1. European war, 1914– —Women's   work. 2. Series.
N. Y. P. L.   October 9, 1919.

　NL 0387416   NN OrU DL DLC MdBJ

Lingle, Clara S   (Souther) Mrs. Thomas W.
Lingle," 1874–
　　Studies in the social and industrial condition
of women as affected by the war. 1919.
(North Carolina. University. Bureau of extension
University of North Carolina extension leaflets:
After-the-war information series. #2)

　NL 0387417   OrU

q629.1342 **Lingle, David G**   1887–
L64a   Army-navy aeronautical standardization; the
　record so far, by Col. D. G. Lingle _ and Capt.
　G. A. Seitz ... ₁n.p., 1942₂
　16p. ports., facsims.

　　"Reprinted from SAE journal, November, 1942,
issue."

　　1. Aeronautics, Military--U.S. 2. Aero-
planes--Standards. 3. U.S.--Aeronautical board
I. Seitz, G. A., joint author. II. Title.

　NL 0387418   IU

*K
.M48875 **Lingle, Henry,** appellant.
v.4,
no.11   Henry Lingle, & als, appellants, versus
　Cook's adm'r, & als, appellees. Record no.
　239. From the Circuit Court of Rockingham
　County. ₁Staunton, Va.₂ "Staunton Spectator"
　Job Print ₁1876?₂
　　132 p. 22cm. ₁Miscellaneous law briefs₂
　　Cover title.
　　"Supreme Court of Appeals of Virginia at
Staunton, Va."
　　Original paper wrappers.
　　I. Cook's (John) administrator, appellee. II.
Virginia. Supreme   Court of Appeals.

　NL 0387419   Vi

Lingle, Jake.
　　Jake Lingle: or Chicago on the spot
　　　see under Boettiger, John, 1900–

₁**Lingle, James M.**₎
　　₁Lingle's lesson sheets.   Philadelphia: Privately printed,
190–?₂ 12 l. f°.
　Author's name and title in ms.
　Key, abbreviations and exercise, no. 2–12, inserted.

　1. Shorthand—Systems, American, 1900.
N. Y. P. L.   July 30, 1926

　NL 0387421   NN

Lingle, James M.
　　Pitman shorthand; Lingle's adaptation of the Benn
Pitman standard shorthand system in book and budget
form. Philadelphia, Penn., ᶜ1908
　3 p. l., 43 numb. l. 15 x 24ᶜᵐ.

　1. Shorthand.   I. Pitman, Benn, 1822–1910.

　Library of Congress   Z56.P684Li
                                                   19–10256

　NL 0387422   DLC NN MH

Lingle, James M
　　The Lingle teacher of new shorthand ideas
　　　see under title

Lingle, Mrs. Thomas Wilson, 1874–

　　see

Lingle, Clara S. (Souther) "Mrs. Thomas W. Lingle", 1874–

Lingle, Thomas Wilson, 1871–   ed.

Davidson college, *Davidson, N. C.*
　　Alumni catalogue of Davidson college, Davidson, N. C.,
1837–1924. Edited by Thomas Wilson Lingle ... assisted by
William Joseph Martin ... and Frederick William Hengeveld
... Charlotte, N. C., The Presbyterian standard pub. co., 1924.

Lingle, Thomas Wilson, 1871–
　　Die bedeutung der entwickelungsgeschichte für die
ethik, mit besonderer rücksicht auf Huxley. Leipzig,
Druck von Sellmann & Henne, 1899.
　58 p. 22ᵐᵐ.
　Inaug.-diss.—Leipzig.
　"Litteraturangabe": p. ₁5₎–6.
　Lebenslauf.

　1. Huxley, Thomas Henry, 1825–1895. 2. Ethics, Evolutional.

　Library of Congress   BJ1263.L7
                                                   1–G–1995

　NL 0387426   DLC CtY NjP PU

DIv.S. **Lingle, Thomas Wilson,** 1871–
285.1756
L755.H   History of Thyatira Church ₁Rowan County,
　North Carolina₂ 1753 to 1925; including address
　delivered by S. C. Alexander at the centennial
　celebration held on October 17, 1885. States-
　ville, N. C., Brady Print. Co., 1925.
　　61 p. illus., group ports. 23 cm.

　　1. Rowan County, N. C. Thyatira Presbyterian Church. I. Alexander, Samuel Caldwell.

　NL 0387427   NcD

Lingle, Thomas Wilson, 1871–   ed.

Ferreira Ramos, Francisco.
　　Industries and electricity in the state of São Paulo, Brazil,
by Francisco Ferreira Ramos ... S. Paulo, Vanorden & co.,
1904.

Lingle, Walter Lee, 1868–
　　Beginnings and development of Presbyterianism in North Carolina to 1863.

　　(In Presbyterian church in the U.S. Synod
of N.C. Centennial addresses.   1913.)

　NL 0387429   NcU

Lingle, Walter Lee, 1868–
　　... The Bible and social problems, by Walter L. Lingle ...
New York, Chicago ₁etc.₂ Fleming H. Revell company ₁ᶜ1929₎
　182 p. 19½ᶜᵐ. (The James Sprunt lectures, 1929. Union theological
seminary, Richmond, Va.)

　1. Sociology, Christian.   I. Title.

　Library of Congress   BS670.L5
                                                   29–8816

　NL 0387430   DLC LU NcD OCl ViU

BX   **Lingle, Walter Lee,** 1868–
9869   The burning of Servetus. ₁n. p. 1909?₂
S49   14 p. 24cm.
L75
　　　　1. Servetus, Michael, 1509 or 11–1553.

　NL 0387431   NIC NcU GEU

BV6480
.C3L5 **Lingle, Walter Lee,** 1868–
1938
　　Cub Creek Church; its place in history.
　₁Hampden–Sidney, Va., Hampden–Sydney College,
　1938₎
　　23 p. 21cm. (Bulletin of Hampden–Sydney
　College, v. 32, no. 3)

　　1. Cub Creek Church, Charlotte Co., Va.

　NL 0387432   ViU Vi

943   **LINGLE,** Walter Lee, 1868–
Pres   The first General Assembly and the events
Box 1   leading up to it; an address delivered
　before the western section, Alliance of the
　Reformed Churchs Throughout the World Holding
　the Presbyterian System, Princeton, New
　Jersey, February 24, 1938. Philadelphia,
　Publicity Dept. of the General Assembly
　₁1938?₂
　　22p. 20.5cm.

　NL 0387433   MH-AH NjPT

VOLUME 334

Lingle, Walter Lee, 1868–
Memories of Davidson College. Richmond, John Knox Press ₁1947₎
5 l., 9–157 p. illus., ports. 24ᶜᵐ.

1. Davidson College, Davidson, N. C.
LD1461.D82L5   378.756   47–4354*

NL 0387434   DLC GU ViU TxU NcC ICU

Lingle, Walter Lee, 1868 -
Presbyterian — a heritage and a challenge...
Richmond, Pres. Comm. of publ n.d.
pamph.

NL 0387435   PPPrHi

Lingle, Walter Lee, 1868–
Presbyterians, their history and beliefs, by Walter L. Lingle ... Richmond, Va. ₁etc.₎ Presbyterian committee of publication ₁°1928₎
199 p. diagr. 20ᶜᵐ.
"Questions and topics for study" at end of each chapter.

1. Presbyterianism. 2. Presbyterianism—Hist.   I. Title.
30–8494
Library of Congress   BX8931.L5

NL 0387436   DLC TxU NcC PPPrHi ICMcC

Lingle, Walter Lee, 1868–
Presbyterians, their history and beliefs, by Walter L. Lingle ... Richmond, Va., John Knox press ₁1944₎
4 p. l., 11–127 p. 20ᶜᵐ.

1. Presbyterianism. 2. Presbyterianism—Hist.   I. Title.
45–5368
Library of Congress   BX8931.L5 1944
                                                     225

NL 0387437   DLC Or NcD NcGU PPWe

Lingle, Walter Lee, 1868–
285.1756.
L755T   **Thyatira Presbyterian Church, Rowan County, North Carolina, 1753–1948 ... Statesville, N. C., Brady Printing Company ₁1948₎**
4 p.l., ₁7₎–71 p. illus., ports. 23½cm.

1. Rowan county, North Carolina.   Thyatira
Presbyterian   Church.

NL 0387438   NcD ICN

Lingle, Walter Lee, 1868–
Union seminary cemetery at Hampden-Sidney, by Walter L. Lingle. ₁Richmond, Richmond press, inc., printers, 1919?₎
16 p. front., plates. 24ᶜᵐ.
Caption title.
On cover: In memoriam.

1. Hampden-Sidney, Va. Union seminary cemetery.
                                                  28–7120
Library of Congress   BV4070.H1759L5
——— Copy 2.

NL 0387439   DLC Vi

Lingle, Walter Lee, 1868–
Why I believe in the deity of Jesus Christ, by Walter I. Lingle ... A lecture delivered on the Macartney foundation in the Arch street Presbyterian church, Philadelphia, January 28, 1936. Richmond, Va., Presbyterian committee of publication, 1936.
34 p. 16ᶜᵐ.

1. Jesus Christ—Divinity.   I. Presbyterian church in the U. S. Executive committee of publication. II. Title.
37–1472
Library of Congress   BT215.L54
——— Copy 2.   ₁3₎   232.8

NL 0387440   DLC

The **Lingle** teacher of new shorthand ideas.
v. 1
Philadelphia: J. M. Lingle Pub. Co., 1908.   4°.
v. illus.
Monthly.
Text partly in shorthand.

1. Shorthand—Per. and soc. publ.   HOWARD SHORTHAND COLL.
N. Y. P. L.   May 12, 1926

NL 0387441   NN

Linglebach, Helene, 1885–
Deutschkunde als gestaltende lehre; zur unterrichtlichen auswertung problemgeschichtlicher forschung ... Weimar, 1927.
Inaug.-diss. - Jena.

NL 0387442   MiU

Lingle's lesson sheets
see under   Lingle, James M.

E178
.1   **Lingley, Charles Ramsdell,** 1877–1934. joint
.T88   author.   FOR OTHER EDITIONS
1946   **Tryon, Rolla Milton,** 1875–   SEE MAIN ENTRY
... The American nation yesterday and today, by Rolla M. Tryon ... Charles R. Lingley ... and Frances Morehouse ... New ed. Boston. New York ₁etc.₎ Ginn and company ₁1946₎

1877–1934.
Lingley, Charles Ramsdell.ᴬ Bibliography ₁of the transition in Virginia from colony to commonwealth₎
6819
(In his The transition in Virginia from colony to commonwealth. Columbia university. Studies in his-

NL 0387445   Vi

Lingley, Charles Ramsdell, 1877–1934.
Since the civil war, by Charles Ramsdell Lingley ... New York, The Century co., 1920.
ix p., 3 l., 3–635 p. maps (part fold.) diagrs. 20½ᶜᵐ. (On verso of half-title: The United States, M. Farand, editor, III)
"Bibliographical note" at end of each chapter.

1. U. S.—Hist.—1865–   I. Title.
21—574
Library of Congress   E661.L75

OCU Or MB NN CaBVaU
NL 0387446   DLC MtBC WaE CU–I PP ICRL TU MiU OCl

E661
.L75   **Lingloy, Charles Ramsdell,** 1877–1934.
1921   Since the civil war. New York, Century Co., 1921.
ix, 635 p. illus. maps (part fold.) 21cm. (The United States, ₁no.₎ 3)
"Bibliographical note" at end of each chapter.

1. U. S.—Hist.—1865–   I. Title.

NL 0387447   MB IdU ODW OCl ViU OClWHi OrPR

E661
.L75   **Lingley, Charles Ramsdell,** 1877–1934.
1923   Since the civil war. New York, Century Co., 1923.
ix, 635 p. illus. maps (part fold.) 21cm.
"Bibliographical note" at end of each chapter.

1. U. S.—Hist.—1865–   I. Title.

NL 0387448   MB ViU OU

Lingley, Charles Ramsdell, 1877–1934.
Since the civil war, by Charles Ramsdell Lingley ... New York, The Century co.,   1924.
ix p., 3 l., 3–635 p. maps (part fold.) diagrs. 20½ᶜᵐ. (On verso of half-title: The United States, M. Farand, editor, III) $2.65
"Bibliographical note" at end of each chapter.

1. U. S.—Hist.—1865–   I. Title.   I. Ser.

NL 0387449   Vi NcRS

KE 32592
Lingley, Charles Ramsdell, 1877–1934.
Since the Civil War. New York, Century, 1925.
ix, 635 (The United States, 3)

NL 0387450   MH

Lingley, Charles Ramsdell, 1877–1934.
Since the civil war, by Charles Ramsdell Lingley ... Rev. ed. New York, The Century co. ₁°1926₎
x, 730 p. maps (part fold.) diagrs. 21ᶜᵐ.
"Bibliographical note" at end of each chapter.

1. U. S.—Hist.—1865–   I. Title.   26—26062
Library of Congress   E661.L75 1926

ODW ViU NN WaSp OrCS WaS MtU
NL 0387451   DLC CaBVaU MU WHi NcC TU MB PP OCl OCU

Lingley, Charles Ramsdell, 1877–1934.
Since the civil war. 3d ed. By Charles Ramsdell Lingley ... and Allen Richard Foley ... New York, London, D. Appleton-Century company, incorporated ₁°1935₎
x, 838 p. maps (part double) diagrs. 20½ᶜᵐ.
"Bibliographical note" at end of each chapter.

1. U. S.—Hist.—1865–   I. Foley, Allen Richard, 1898–   joint
author. II. Title.
36–431
Library of Congress   E661.L75 1935
——— Copy 2.
Copyright A 90104   ₁5₎   973.8

NL 0387452   DLC OrP WaTC PSC PPT KMK MB OClh ViU MB

VOLUME 334

Lingley, Charles Ramsdell, 1877-1934.
Since the civil war. 3d ed. By Charles Ramsdell Lingley ... and Allen Richard Foley ... New York, London, D. Appleton-Century company, incorporated ₁1936₎

viii, 838 p. maps (part fold.) diagrs. 20½ᵐ.

"Bibliographical note" at end of each chapter.

1. U. S.—Hist.—1865-   ɪ. Foley, Allen Richard, 1898-   joint
author. ɪɪ. Title.
                                                38-34418
Library of Congress   E661.L75 1936
                                ₍2₎   973.8

NL 0387453   DLC

Lingley, Charles Ramsdell, 1877-1934, joint author.
FOR OTHER EDITIONS
Foster, Herbert Darling, 1863-   SEE MAIN ENTRY
A syllabus of modern European history, 1500-1920 ... by Herbert Darling Foster, Frank Maloy Anderson, Charles Ramsdell Lingley, Arthur Herbert Basye, of the Department of history, Dartmouth college. Hanover, N. H., The Department, 1920-

---

Lingley, Charles Ramsdell, 1877-1934.
The transition in Virginia from colony to commonwealth ... · New York, 1910.

219 p. 25½ᵐ.

Thesis (ᴘʜ. ᴅ.)—Columbia university.
Vita.
Bibliography: p. 214-218.
Pub. also as Studies in history, economics and public law, v. 36, no. 2.

1. Virginia—Pol. & govt—Revolution.
                                                A 10-1465

Title from Columbia   Univ. Printed by L. C.

NL 0387455   NNC

Lingley, Charles Ramsdell, 1877-1934.
... The transition in Virginia from colony to commonwealth, by Charles Ramsdell Lingley ... New York, Columbia university, Longmans, Green & co., agents; ₍etc.,
etc.₎ 1910.

218 p. 25½ᵐ. (Studies in history, economics and public law, ed. by the Faculty of political science of Columbia university, vol. xxxvi, no. 2; whole no. 96) $1.50

Bibliography: p. ₍214₎-218.

1. Virginia—Pol. & govt.—Revolution.
                                                10-14656
Library of Congress   H31.C7 vol. 36, no. 2
₋copy 2.   E263.V8L7

            OCU ViU ICJ MB CoU OrP WaS OrU WaSpG WaTC
NL 0387456   DLC ViN Vi PV PU-L PBm PPT NcD MiU OCl

Linglin, Jean.
... Méningite cérébro-spinale & dérivés organiques du soufre ... Saint-Omer, Imprimerie Loïez, 1940.
53 p.
Thèse.

NL 0387457   DNLM CtY

LINGLOIS, Petrus Franciscus.
Quinquaginta decisiones imperatoris Justiniani quae a secundo libro codicis usque ad nonum diffusae sunt, graviter huc redactae & enucleatae paucis literis. Antverpiae, 1622.

Same. f°. Antverpiae, 1661.

NL 0387458   MH-L

Lingnaam agricultural review
    see   Lingnan science journal.

LINGNAN science journal. v. 1-20, no. 2/4, Dec. 1922-1942. Canton, China, Lingnan University.

v. illus. 25 cm.

Publication suspended Jan.-May 1930, June-Dec. 1941.
Title varies: v. 1-4, Lingnaam agricultural review.
Indexes:
    Vols. 1-14,   1922-35, in v. 14.

            FU MBdAF MH-G ICJ DSI PPAN NNCC
NL 0387460   OrU CaBVaU NcRS CoD MtBC OrCS NcD MiD

Lingnan Taai Hok ., Canton, China
    see   Ling-nan ta hsüeh, Canton, China.

Lingnan University, Canton, China
    see   Ling-nan ta hsüeh, Canton, China.

Lingnan University; a letter from William Penn Lodge
    see under   [Cadbury, Catherine Jones]

Lingnau, Adalbert, 1862-
Ueber die bedeutung der muekelkörperchen für die regeneration nach verletzungen ... Königsbert i. Pr., M. Liedtke, 1890.
24 p., 2 l.   23 cm.   [Königsberg.
Universität. Dissertation. v. 9, no. 4]
Inaug.-diss. - Königsberg.
Vita.

NL 0387464   CU DNLM

Lingnau, Aenny, 1902-
Die Bankenliquidität unter dem Einfluss der wirtschaftlichen Entwicklung ... Hamburg, 1936.
Diss. - Hamburg.
Teildruck.

NL 0387465   CtY MiU

Lingnau, August Robert: Der gewerbliche Arbeitsnachweis in Ostpreussen. Danzig 1919: Bäcker. 56 S. 8°
Königsberg, Phil. Diss. v. 28. März 1919, Ref. Hesse
₍Geb. 29. Aug. 90 Allenstein; Wohnort: Danzig; Staatsangeh.: Preußen; Vorbildung: Städt. G. Danzig Reife 12; Studium: Danzig TeH. 3. Phil. Königsberg 3 S.; Rig. 22. Febr. 19.₎   [U 19. 2404

NL 0387466   ICRL PU CtY MH

Lingnau, Helmut: Über die bitemporale Hemianopsie während der Gravidität. [Maschinenschrift] 37 S. m. Taf. 4°. — Auszug: Greifswald 1923: Adler. 1 Bl. 8°
Greifswald, Med. Diss. v. 20. Sept. 1924   [U 24. 8945

NL 0387467   ICRL

Gk11
1
L64
Lingnau, J   F
De origine atque ratione terminationum adjectivorum in alis (aris), ilis, elis et ulis desinentium. Regiomonti, 1829.
Pamphlet
Programm - Gymnasium, Brunsberg (Examen publicum)

NL 0387468   CtY

Gk11
O1
L64
Lingneu, J   F
... De origine et natura terminationis nominum in men et mentum exeuntium. Brunsbergae, 1836.
Pamphlet
Programm - K. Ermländisches Gymnasium, Braunsberg.

NL 0387469   CtY MH

LINGNAU, J. F.
De verbalibus quibusdam dubiae originis nominibus in men et mentum exeuntibus disceptatio altera. [Progr]. BRAUNSBERG, 1845, 4°. pp. 1-11).

NL 0387470   MH NjP

Lingnau [Joh.] A[dalbert] 1862-
    see   Lingnau, Adalbert, 1862-

W 4
B51
1940
Lingner, Emil, 1913-
Trauma und Geschbildung. Charlottenburg, Hoffmann ₍1940?₎
47 p.

Inaug.-Diss. - Berlin.

NL 0387472   DNLM

Lingner (Ernst) [1886-   ]. *Fremdkörper in der Harnblase. 34 pp. 8°. Giessen, O Kindt Wwe. 1919.

NL 0387473   DNLM ICRL

Lingner, Käthe.
Die Mutter der Kinder, vom ewigen Auftrag der deutschen Frau. Leipzig, J. Klinkhardt, 1938.
63

(Frauen am Werk. Heft 2)

NL 0387474   NNC

Lingner, Käthe, ed.
Die Mutter der Kinder, vom ewigen Auftrag der deutschen Frau. 2. Aufl. Leipzig, J. Klinkhardt, 1941.
64 p. illus. 21 cm. (Frauen am Werk, Bildungsstoffe für Schule und Leben, Heft 2)

1. Mothers in literature. 2. German literature (Selections: Extracts, etc.) ɪ. Title. (Series)

PT1110.W6L5 1941   53-517₆

NL 0387475   DLC MH CU

VOLUME 334

Lingner, Karl August, 1861–
... Der mensch als organisations-vorbild; gastvortrag gehalten am 14. dezember 1912 vor dem professoren-kollegium der Universität Bern, von wirkl. geh. rat dr. K. A. Lingner ... Bern, M. Drechsel, 1914.

32 p. 23½ᶜᵐ. (Berner universitätsschriften. hft. 4)

1. Physiology—Addresses, essays, lectures. 2. Man.

15–22957

Library of Congress   QP71.L5

NL 0387476   DLC NIC CtY

Lingner, Max.
Mein Leben und meine Arbeit. Eingeleitet von Marcel Cachin und Paul Wandel. Dresden, Verlag der Kunst ₍1955₎

91 p. illus. (part col.) 27 cm.

I. Title.

ND588.L75A2   57–48380

NL 0387477   DLC CLU MH NN

Lingner, Max, 1888–
Max Lingner; dessins et peintures. Texte par Henri Barbusse ₍et₎ Agnès Humbert. 48 reproductions. Paris: Les Écrivains réunis ₍1939₎   23 l.   front., illus.   29cm.

1. Drawings, German.
N. Y. P. L.   August 29, 1941

NL 0387478   NN

Lingner, Reinhold.
Landschaftsgestaltung. Berlin, Aufbau-Verlag, 1952 ₍ᶜ1951₎

75 p. illus. 19 cm. (Wissenschaft und Technik verständlich dargestellt, 3)

1. Landscape. 2. Regional planning. 3. Soil conservation.
I. Title.
QH77.G3L5   55–28066 rev ‡

NL 0387479   DLC DNAL

Lingner-Werke.
50 [i. e. Fünfzig] Jahre Lingner-Werke
see under title

Lingo, Ada E.
... Murder in Texas, by Ada E. Lingo. Boston and New York, Houghton Mifflin company, 1935.

5 p. l., 294 p. illus. (plan) 19½ᶜᵐ.
At head of title: A black band mystery.

I. Title.

35–18849

Library of Congress   PZ3.L6544Mu

NL 0387481   DLC MiU MB TxU

Lingo, Allie I.
Wild oats irrigated with alcohol. Personal experiences of Allie I. Lingo ... Gatesville, Tex., Press of Starforum, 1900.

1 p. l., 140 p. pl. 17½ᶜᵐ.

1. Temperance. I. Title.

Library of Congress   HV5068.L5   0–4592 Revised

NL 0387482   DLC

Lingo, C.   **L.**
Bases for freight charges ₍by₎ C. L. Lingo ... Chicago, La Salle extension university ₍ᶜ1914₎

2 p. l., 62 p. 1 illus. 23ᶜᵐ.
On cover: One of a series of treatises in an interstate commerce and railway traffic course.

1. Railroads—U. S.—Rates. 2. Railroads—U. S.—Freight.   I. La Salle extension university, Chicago. II. Title.

Library of Congress   HE2123.L5   14–4119

NL 0387483   DLC MiU OU ICJ OCl

Lingo, C. L.

Shipping: Bases for freight charges ₍by₎ C. L. Lingo ... Reducing freight charges to a minimum ₍by₎ J. F. Strombeck ... Routing freight shipments ₍by₎ J. F. Morton ... Freight claims ₍by₎ William A. Trimpe ... The bill of lading ₍by₎ Frank A. Larish ... The industrial traffic department ₍by₎ W. N. Agnew ... Chicago. La Salle extension university ₍ᶜ1914₎

Lingo, C. L.
Shipping: Reducing freight charges ₍by₎ J. F. Strombeck ... Bases for freight charges ₍by₎ C. L. Lingo ... Freight claims, ₍by₎ William A. Trimpe ... Investigation of freight claims ₍by₎ George H. Hunt ... Routing freight shipments ₍by₎ J. F. Morton ... The bill of lading ₍by₎ Frank A. Larish ... The industrial traffic department ₍by₎ W. N. Agnew ... Chicago, La Salle extension university ₍ᶜ1915₎

Lingo, Pauline Wiggins.
The tiny tot circus for children from two to eight years of age, by Pauline Wiggins Lingo. Dayton, O., Paine publishing company ₍ᶜ1939₎

18 p. diagrs. 18ᶜᵐ.

I. Title.

89–25892

Library of Congress   PN6120.A5L482
—— —— Copy 2.
Copyright D pub. 65913   ₍2₎   791.3

NL 0387486   DLC

Lingo, Sedley Martin, 1906–

U. S. *Soil conservation service.*
Land use adjustment in the Spring creek area, Campbell county, Wyoming. By R. L. Spurlock ... and S. M. Lingo ... Soil conservation service. United States Department of agriculture. ₍Washington, U. S. Govt. print. off., 1939₎

Lingo, Turner O.
The Australian comic dictionary of words and phrases. Melbourne, E. W. Cole ₍n. d.₎   64 p.   18cm.

1. Wit and humor, Australian.   2. English language—Australia.

NL 0387488   NN

Lingo, W   **H.**
Your Airedale, by W. H. Lingo & J. Horace Lytle, a reasonably complete treatise on the care, raising, training, and handling of the Airedale terrier from puppyhood to full growth. This is compiled from actual experiences as proven successful in the raising of the famous strain of Oorang Airedales at the Oorang kennels of La Rue, Ohio ... La Rue, O., Oorang kennels ₍ᶜ1917₎

21 p. 20ᶜᵐ. $0.50

1. Airedale terrier.   I. Lytle, John Horace, 1884–   joint author.

Library of Congress   SF429.A6L5   17–14241
Copyright A 459933

NL 0387489   DLC ViW

Lingo, William R.
Outline and reference studies in early world history to 1789 A. D., by William R. Lingo ... Philadelphia, McKinley publishing co., 1924.

52 p. 27ᶜᵐ.
Most of alternate pages blank for "Notes".

1. History—Outlines, syllabi, etc. 2. History—Study and teaching.
I. Title.
Library of Congress   D21.L7   24–25762

NL 0387490   DLC Or

Lingo, William R.
The Pennsylvania career of John Brown, by William R. Lingo. Corry, Penna., The Journal, 1926.

32 p. plates, ports., facsim. 22ᶜᵐ.

1. Brown, John, 1800–1859.
Library of Congress   E451.L75   26–14564

NL 0387491   DLC NN OCl

Lingö, Sven.
Vi bygger en modelljärnväg. 2. rev. uppl. Handledning i modelljärnvägsbygge. Ill. av Holger Norrhage. ₍Redigering: Lennart Sundström₎ Stockholm, Lindqvists förlag ₍1950₎

93 p. illus. 20 cm.

1. Railroads—Models.

A 50–6485

Michigan. Univ. Libr.
for Library of Congress   ₍1₎

NL 0387492   MiU

Lingois, Louis₍Abbé.
Leçons élémentaires de mathématiques pour servir d'introduction à l'étude de la physique. Paris, 1779.
8°.

NL 0387493   NN

Lingois (Suzanne). *Contribution à l'étude de l'étiologie de la paralysie; générale, paralysie générale tuberculeuse. 56 pp. 8°. Paris, 1909. No. 377.

NL 0387494   DNLM

VOLUME 334

Lingomba li Yesu Masiya likoyongan'o Bolobo.
Mibeko na Mateyo.   Baptist Missionary
Society, Congo State, 1903.
p. (2), 12.   13.3 cm.
Verso of title-page:"Hannah Wade" printing
press, Baptist Missionary Society, Bolobo,
Congo Independent State.
In Bangi.
F. Starr: Bibl. 44.

NL 0387495   MH

Lingorow, Stella Favre-
   see Favre-Lingorow, Stella.

Lingo's opinions on men and manners
   see under Edwin, John, 1749-1790,
supposed author.

Lingo's wedding. 1784. (Larpent collec-
tion. Ms. #683) New York, 1954.
(In Three centuries of drama: English,
Larpent collection)

Microprint.

I. Larpent collection. Ms. #683.

NL 0387498   MoU

G338.405
L647   O Lingote. ano 1-   (no.1-   ) 25 março
1953-
Rio de Janeiro.
v. illus. 45cm.
"Editado pelo Serviço de Relações Públicas da
Companhia Siderúrgica Nacional."

1. Steel industry and trade - Brazil - Period.
I. Companhia Siderúgica Nacional, Rio de Janeiro.

NL 0387499   TxU

637.1
L64e   Lingrand, L
Étude générale sur le lait de sa conservation et de sa stèrilisation ...
Beauvais, 1896.
cover-title, 24p.   (Société d'hygiène
de l'enfance. Bulletin mensuel nos. de
mars et avril 1896)

NL 0387500   IU

Lingrand (Victor). *Des pertes de sang phy-
siologiques dans les accouchements; cent cinq
accouchements avec pesées du sang, 84 pp.
4°, Paris, 1872, No. 201.

NL 0387501   DNLM

Lingrée, *de.*
Réflexions et maximes ... Paris, 1814.

NL 0387502   PPL

Lingren, Harry Arthur
   see Lindgren, Harry Arthur, 1888-

Lings, Albert A , d.1915.
The life of the Blessed John B. Marie Vianney,
Curé of Ars. With a novena and litany to this
zealous worker in the vineyard of the Lord. Com-
piled from approved sources. New York, Joseph
Schaefer, c1911.

III, 6-110 p., front., (port.), 15 cm.

1. John Baptist Marie Vianney, Saint, 1786-1859.

NL 0387504   PLatS DHN

BX2170   Lings, Albert A., d. 1915, comp.
.N7L5   Our favorite novenas.   New York, Cincinnati
[etc.] Benziger bros. 1897.
1 p.l., 557 p. 18°.

NL 0387505   DLC MBtS CCamarSJ

Lings, Albert A   d. 1915.
Our monthly devotions. By the Very Rev. Dean A. A.
Lings ... New York, Cincinnati [etc.] Benziger brothers, 1899.
635 p. front. 16ᵐ.

1. Catholic church—Prayer-books and devotions—English.   I. Title.

99-2808 Revised
Library of Congress .   BX2170.M6L5

NL 0387506   DLC

Lings, Albert A. d.1915.

Frassinetti, Raphael.
Sermons for children's masses. According to the Sundays
and principal festivals of the year. With advice to the young
on the last day of the scholastic year, and after a retreat.
Adapted from the original of Rev. Raphael Frassinetti, by
Very Rev. Dean A. A. Lings. New York, Cincinnati [etc.]
Benziger brothers, 1900.

Lings, Albert A. d.1915.
The story of the Divine Child. Told for children in pictures
and in words. By Very Rev. Dean A. A. Lings ... New York,
Cincinnati [etc.] Benziger brothers, 1900.
256 p. front., plates. 17ᵐ.

1. Jesus Christ—Childhood—Juvenile literature.   I. Title.

0-648 Revised
Library of Congress   BT302.L7
Copyright 1899: 81665;   (r38b2;   -232.92

NL 0387508   DLC NN

Lings, Harold C.
Musketry lectures for non-commissioned officers of the
territorial force, by Harold C. Lings, with an introduction
by Major-General W. Douglas. London, Gale & Polden,
ltd., 1914.
3 p. l., 86 p. diagrs. 13ᵐ.

1. Rifle practice.

War 14-32
Library, War College Div.   General Staff

NL 0387509   DNW

Lings, Harold C.   623.5 R500
Musketry lectures for officers & non-commissioned officers, by
Harold C. Lings, ... , with an introduction by Major-General
W. Douglas, ... Second edition. London, [etc.], Gale &
Polden, [1915].
[10], 96 p. 14 x 11ᵐ.

NL 0387510   ICJ

Z7052   Lings, Martin, comp.
.B85
British Museum. *Dept. of Oriental Printed Books and
Manuscripts.*
Catalogue of Arabic books in the British Museum, by
A. G. Ellis. London, British Museum, 1894-1935.

Lingsch, Pál.
Felépítményi kisérleti szakaszok a MÁV vonalain; a
Mérnöki Továbbképző Intézet 1948. évi tanfolyamainak
anyaga. Budapest, Mérnöki Továbbképző Intézet, 1948.
12 p. 24 cm. (A Mérnöki Továbbképző Intézet kiadványai, M.
71. sz.)

1. Railroads—Track. 2. Magyar Allamvasutak.   I. Title.

TF240.L55   77-259948

NL 0387512   DLC

Lingsley, Robert, 1903-
Proceedings

see under

Los Angeles. University of Southern California.
School of Law.

Lingston, Rowe.
Verses of country and town. London, Griffith,
Farran, Okeden & Welsh; N. Y. Dutton, 1886.
76p. 18cm.

NL 0387514   FMU

Lingston, Rowe.
Woodland and dreamland. London, 1888.

NL 0387515   PPL

Lingstrom, Freda.
Axel, by Freda Lingstrom. Boston, Little, Brown and com-
pany, 1939.
5 p. l., [3]-401 p. 21ᵐ.
London edition (J. Cape, ltd.) has title: A flower in his hand.
"First edition."

I. Title.   39-30072
Library of Congress   PZ3.L6545Ax

NL 0387516   DLC WaE Or WaS WaSp PP PPL OCl OClh OEa

Lingstrom, Freda.
Beggar's fiddle. London, A. Wingate [1948]
405 p. 19 cm.

I. Title.   A 49-2643*
New York. Public Libr.
for Library of Congress   [3]

NL 0387517   NN

VOLUME 334

Lingstrom, Freda.
En blomma i hans hand, av Freda Lingstrom. Översättning av Chrissy Sterzel. Stockholm, P. A. Norstedt & söner ₁1941₁
2 p. l., 7–407, ₁1₁ p. 20ᶜᵐ.

ɪ. Sterzel, Chrissy, tr. ɪɪ. Title.

A 46–2548

Harvard univ. Library
for Library of Congress   ₂₁

NL 0387518   MH

Lingstrom, Freda.
A flower in his hand, by Freda Lingstrom. London, J. Cape ₁1939₁
5 p. l., 13–415 p. 20½ᶜᵐ.
"First published 1939."

ɪ. Title.

39–19896

Library of Congress   PZ3.L6545Fl

NL 0387519   DLC Or CaBVa

Lingstrom, Freda, ed.
Junior; for young people with ideas; stories, articles and illustrations
see under title

Lingstrom, Freda, illus.
Leigh, Dell.
On the line, by Dell Leigh. Illustrated by Frank H. Mason ... and Freda Lingstrom. Bungay, Suffolk, Richard Clay & sons, ltd. ₁1928₁

Lingstrom, Freda.
The seventh sister, by Freda Lingstrom. London, J. Cape ₁1938₁
307 p. 20ᶜᵐ.
"First published 1938."

ɪ. Title.

38–8100

Library of Congress   PZ3.L6545Se

NL 0387522   DLC

Lingstrom, Freda.
This is Norway, by Freda Lingstrom; with a preface by Sir Karl F. Knudsen, ᴋ. ʙ. ᴇ. London, G. Howe, ltd. ₁ᶜ1933₁
xiv p., 1 l., 152 p. col. front., illus. (incl. maps) plates (part col.) 21ᶜᵐ.
Maps on lining-papers.
Music: p. 58–59.
"Norwegian novels translated into English": p. 48–50; Bibliography: p. 142.

1. Norway. 2. Norway—Descr. & trav.—Guide-books.   ɪ. Title.

33–21098

Library of Congress   DL411.L5
Copyright A ad int. 17981   ₁3₁   914.81

OLak OO NN MB
NL 0387523   DLC CaBVaU CaBVa WaSp Or PPLas CU OCl

Lingstrom, Freda.
This is Norway; with a preface by Sir K. F. Knudsen. ₁2d ed.₁ Howe ₁1936₁
152 p. illus. maps.
Music: p.58–59.
Norwegian novels translated into English: p.48–50. Bibliography: p.142.

NL 0387524   MiD

Lington, Burr, *pseud.*
see
Naramore, Gay H.

Lington, Peter, *pseud.*
see **Chenevix Trench, Charles Pocklington, 1914–**

Lingua, Angelo.   L629.15 R604
.... L'aeroplano e il suo motore: come è construito e come funziona. Prof. Niccolò Silvestrini [e] Ing. Natale Penazzo illustrazioni. Prefazione del presidente della Società aviazione Torino. Con grandi tavole a colori e figure nel testo. Seconda edizione. Torino, Libreria scientifico-industriale S. Lattes & C., [etc., etc.], 1917.
vii, 106, [2] p. col. front., 82 illus., plates (part col., part fold.) 33ᶜᵐ.
At head of title: Società aviazione Torino. Aero club d'Italia. Ing. Angelo Lingua. Ing. Casimiro Boella.

NL 0387527   ICJ DLC-P4

Lingua de Saint-Blanquat, A. de.
Sous le manteau de la cheminée; pièce en un acte, en prose, par A. de Lingua de Saint-Blanquat... Paris: Éditions Occitania, 1926. 28 p. nar. 8°.

1. Drama, French.   2. Title.
N. Y. P. L.   January 18, 1927

NL 0387528   NN

Lingua.
₁Cape Town₁
v. in   24–34 cm.
"Linguistic journal of the University of Cape Town."
Began with 1942 issue.
Chiefly Afrikaans or English.

1. Philology—Periodicals.   ɪ. Cape Town. University of Cape Town.

P9.L45   70–5113

NL 0387529   DLC TxU

Lingua. International review of general linguistics. Revue internationale de linguistique générale. v. 1–
₁Dec. 1947₁–
Haarlem, J. H. Gottmer.
v. ports, fold. maps. 23 cm. irregular.
Chiefly English or French.
Editors: 1947–   A. W. de Groot, A. J. B. N. Reichling.

1. Language and languages—Period.   ɪ. Groot, Albert Willem de, 1892–   ed.

P9.L47   405   52–36290

NbHi NN ICU ViU OCU NNC AzTeS
DCU CU NB AAP CaBVaU NcU CaOTP AzU DNLM KU OkS DSI
NL 0387530   DLC AAP ICN GU MBU CtU KU NN TxU OU OO

ar W   **La lingua del mistero ossieno caratteri**
15005   steganografici, opuscolo. Roma, Presso Antonio Boulzaler, 1835.
12 p. 23cm.

1. Ciphers.

NL 0387531   NIC

... La lingua del pappagallo
see under   [Masetti, Pirro] 1868–

0469.05   **Língua e linguagem.** ano 1, no.1, jan.–fev. 1947.
L648   Rio de Janeiro, Academia brasileiro de filologia.
1v. 23cm.

No more published?

921053   1. Portuguese philology – Period.   I. Academia brasileira de filologia, Rio de Janeiro.

NL 0387533   TxU

LINGVA KOMITATO, Paris.
Jarlibro de la Lingva komitato kaj de ĝia Akademio.
Paris.   no.   16–24cm.
(1923 [i. e. 1925] issued in series: Esperantista centra oficejo. Esperantista dokumentaro pri la oficialaj, historiaj bibliografiaj kaj statistikaj aferoj. Kajero 34 (Junio, 1923) I. Oficiala parto. Sekcio B. Lingva Komitato. 10)

Publisher varies.   MRS. DAVE H. MORRIS COLLECTION

1. Esperanto--Per. and soc. publ.

NL 0387534   NN

LINGUA KOMITATO, Paris.
Raporto de la Prezidanto de la Lingva komitato kaj Akademio. [Paris, 1921]   6 p.   24cm.

Film reproduction. Positive.
Signed: Parizo, la 10 de Julio 1921. Th. Cart.

Mrs. Dave H. Morris Collection

I. Cart, Théophile.

NL 0387535   NN

Lingua ladina; kunde aus ladinischen landen.
Bümpliz, Benteli a.-g. [19–]
17 p.
Cover-title.
Contains music.

NL 0387536   OCl

Lingua nacional cantada, Congresso da
see   **Congresso da lingua nacional cantada.**

Lingua nostra.
₁Firenze₁ Sansoni.
v. in   27 cm. quarterly (irregular)
Began publication with Feb. 1939 issue. Cf. Union list of serials.
Editors: B. Migliorini, G. Devoto.

1. Italian language—Period.   ɪ. Migliorini, Bruno, 1896–   ed.
ɪɪ. Devoto, Giacomo, ed.

PC1001.L5   55–15109

NN DCU PSt PU OU CaOTU CaQMU
NL 0387538   DLC OrU CSt CaQMM KyU CoU MNS NcD CU

VOLUME 334

Lingva: or, The Combat of the Tongue, and
    the fiue Senses for Superiority. A pleasant
    Comoedie
        see under [Tomkis, Thomas] fl. 1604-1615.

PC
5001
.L55

A Língua portuguesa; revista de filologia.
    v. 1-5.
    1929/30-1937/39.
    Lisboa, José Fernandes Júnior, 1929-39.
    5 v. 25cm.

    Frequency varies.
    Edited by Rodrigo de Sá Noguedira.
    Ceased publication.

NL 0387540   NNC CU WU PU CSt PBm

A Língua portuguesa.
    Homenagem ao Dr. José Leite de Vasconcelos
    see under title

A lingua portugueza é filha da latina
        see under [Villa Nova de Fozcôa,
    Francisco Antonio de Campos, barão de]
    1780-1873.

Lingua Posnaniensis; czasopismo poświęcone językoznaw-
stwu porównawczemu i ogólnemu. Revue de philologie comparée et de linguistique générale. 1-
Poznań, Do nabycia w księg. Czytelnik, 1949-
    v. 25 cm. annual.
    Polish, French, English, and other languages.

    1. Philology—Collections. 2. Grammar, Comparative and general
Collections.
    P25.L55   52-2381

    KyU NcU CaBVaU
NL 0387543   DLC PU CoU NcD WaU MB KU CaOTU RPB CSt

PG6701
.A2

Lingua Posnaniensis. Supplement.

Biuletyn fonograficzny. Bulletin phonographique. 1-
Poznań ₁Państwowe Wydawn. Naukowe, etc.₁ 1953-

Lingua tersancta
    see under [Freke, William] 1662-1744.

La lingua volgare e i siciliani
    see under [Isola, Ippolito Gaetano] 1830-1906

Linguae Belgicae. Idea grammatica, poetica,
    rhetorica; deprompta ex adversariis anonymi
    Batavi
        see under Verwer, Hadrianus.

Linguae Graecae institutiones grammaticae in usum
    studiosae juventutis. Editio quinta. Edin-
    burgi, J. Bell et C. Elliot; et E. Wilson,
    1782.
    3 p.l., 144 p.   fold.front.

NL 0387548   PMA MeB MH ViW

475
L648
1757

Linguae latinae rudimenta: in quibus declinatio-
    num, comparationum, et conjugationum paradigmata
    ad captum puerilem accommodata exhibentur, in usum
    tironum Gymnasii medioburgensis accuratissime de-
    nuo expressa.   Medioburgi, apud A. L. et M. H.
    Callenfels, S. Mandelgreen, P. Gillissen et L.
    Taillefert, d.f., bibliopolas, 1757.
    111, [33]p. 2 fold.tab.

    With this are bound: Schotanus, Joannes. Pueri-
lium colloquiorum formulae. Medioburgi, 1757; and

    Heidelberg catechism. Catechesis religionis
christianae. Middelburg, 1757

    1. Latin language--Grammar. I. Middelburg,
Netherlands. Gymnasium. II. Title.

NL 0387550   IU

---

*4939.122

Linguae Latinae rudimenta, in usum Amstelaedamensis gymnasii con-
    cinnata.
    [Amsterdam? 17—?] 227 pp. 15½ cm., in 8s.
    The lower half of the title-page is missing.

    K2842 — Latin language. Gram.

NL 0387551   MB

---

x473
L647

Lingvae romanae dictionarium luculentum novum.
    new dictionary, in five alphabets: representing
    I. The English words and phrases before the Lat-
    in ... II. The Latin-classic before the English
    ... III. The Latin-proper names of those persons
    people or countries that frequently occur, or
    are any way remarkable in classic authors, with
    explications from their several languages, and
    a short account of them historical and geograph-
    ical. IV. The Latin-barbarous, explaining as
    well such technical words or terms of art, as
    are made necessary to us by the many inventions

    and discoveries not known to the ancients, as
    those which crept into the Latin tongue during
    the ignorance and darkness of the middle ages.
    V. The law-Latin, comprehending those words,
    which are made use of by the common lawyers ...
    The whole completed and improved from the sever-
    al works of Stephens, Cooper, Gouldman, Holyoke.
    Dr. Littleton, a large manuscript, in three
    volumes, of Mr. John Milton, &c. In the use of

    all which, for greater exactness, recourse has
    always been had to the authors themselves ...
    Cambridge, Printed for W. Rawlins in St. Bar-
    tholomew's close, T. Dring at the Harrow near
    the Inner-Temple gate in Fleetstreet, R. Chis-
    well at the Rose and Crown in S. Paul's church-
    yard, C. Harper at the Flower-de-luce over
    against S. Dunstan's church in Fleetstreet, W.
    Crook at the Green Dragon without Temple-bar, J

    Place at Furnival's-inn gate in Holborn, and
    the executors of S. Leigh. 1693.
    [1450]p. 25cm.

    In manuscript on t.-p.: William Stanton; on p.
    1452]: William Daniel, 1730.

        CU CtY NjP MH IaU
NL 0387555   IU MH CLU-C MdBP ICU PPA TxU RPB InU

[Linguae sacrae by H. Opitz and others. Leip-
    zig, etc.] 1682-1696]
    1 v. (various pagings) 21 cm.
    I. Opitz, Heinrich, 1642-1712

NL 0387556   PU

Linguae Syricae Grammatica et Chresto-
    mathiola cum glossario scholis accommodata,
    auctore H.G., S.J.   Bertyi Phoeniciorum,
    Typographia PP. Soc. Jesu, 1890.

    87p., ₂59₂p., 36p. 22cm.

NL 0387557   PLatS

Il linguaggio dei fiori; loro valore simbo-
    lico e loro impiego per l'espressione dei propri
    pensieri. Dedicato al gentil sesso. 7. ed.
    illustrata. Milano, Giovanni Gnocchi, 1896.
    136 p. incl. front., illus. 16cm.

NL 0387558   NcD

Linguagrossa, Italy. Ordinances, etc.
    Consuetudini di Linguagrossa ora per la
    prima volta pubblicate da Francesco La Man-
    tia e Giuseppe La Mantia. Palermo, Libreria
    Alberto Reber, 1897[cover 1898].
    xvi.51 p.   25 cm.

    1.Law-Linguagrossa, Italy. I.La Mantia, Fran-
cesco Giuseppe, d.1930. II.La Mantia, Giuseppe. III.Sicily.Laws, statutes, etc. IV.Title.

NL 0387559   DLC-P4 CtY

Linguaphone institute, London.

Stokvis, Jozef Emanuel, 1875-
    ... Afrikaans in 30 lessons, by J. Stokvis ... 2d ed. London,
The Linguaphone institute; ₁etc., etc.₁ 1926.

Linguaphone institute, *London.*
    ... Annotated vocabulary to the Russian conversational
course. London, The Linguaphone institute ₁19—₁

    2 v. 21¼ᵐ. (Linguaphone conversational courses)

    Paged continuously.
    The conversational text-book for which this course was prepared was
published separately.
    On cover: Annotated vocabulary and explanatory notes.

    1. Russian language—Glossaries, vocabularies, etc. I. Title.

    Library of Congress   PG2121.L5   42-30004
                                    ₁2₁   491.78242

NL 0387561   DLC OrU OCl

Linguaphone institute, London.
    Another language
    see under title

Linguaphone Institute, London.
    Bible readings
        see under Bible. English. Selections.
19--.

VOLUME 334

Linguaphone institute, London.

Bruce, Joseph Percy, 1861–
... Chinese, by J. Percy Bruce ... E. Dora Edwards ... ₍and₎ C. C. Shu ... Spoken by C. C. Shu ... With phonetic transcription in the alphabet of the International phonetic association ... 3d ed. London, Linguaphone institute, ltd. ₍193–?₎

Linguaphone institute, London.
...Collateral & alphabetical vocabularies to the French conversational course. [Lond.: N.Y.] The linguaphone inst., [1943?]
v, 129p. (Linguaphone conversational courses)

NL 0387565 OC1

Distribution
Desk Linguaphone institute, London.
... Collateral & alphabetical vocabularies to the German conversational course. ₍London₎ Linguaphone institute ₍1930?₎

3p.ℓ.,145p. 20½cm. (Linguaphone conversational courses)

NL 0387566 NBuG OC1

Linguaphone institute, London.
...Collateral & alphabetical vocabularies to the Italian conversational course. [Lond.] Linguaphone institute, n.d.
78p. (Linguaphone conversational courses)

NL 0387567 OC1

Linguaphone institute, London.
Collateral & alphabetical vocabularies to the Portuguese conversational course. [Lond.] Linguaphone institute, n.d.
114p. (Linguaphone conversational courses)
Portugese.

NL 0387568 OC1

463
L755c Linguaphone Institute, London.
Collateral & alphabetical vocabularies to the Spanish conversational course. ₍London, 19––?₎
80p. (Linguaphone Conversational Courses)

1. Spanish language--Glossaries, vocabularies, etc. I. Title.

NL 0387569 ICarbS MH OC1

Linguaphone institute, London.
...Commercial supplement to the French conversational course. [Lond.: N.Y.], The linguaphone instit., [1943?]
62p. (Linguaphone conversational courses)

NL 0387570 OC1

Distribution
Desk Linguaphone institute, London.
... Commercial supplement to the German conversational course. ₍London₎ Linguaphone institute ₍1930?₎

63p. 20½cm. (Linguaphone conversational courses)

NL 0387571 NBuG

Linguaphon institute, London.
...Commercial supplement to the Italian conversational course. [Lond.] Linguaphone instit., n.d.
63p. (Linguaphone conversational courses)

NL 0387572 OC1

Linguaphone institute, London.
...Commercial supplement to the Spanish conversational course. [Lond.,N.Y.] linguaphone instit. [1943?]
62p. (Linguaphone conversational courses)

NL 0387573 OC1

Linguaphone institute, London.
Companion to the Linguaphone Polish conversational course, containing: The Polish alphabet, with notes & introduction to Polish grammar with tables of declensions. [Lond?]linguaphone insiti., n.d.
22p.

NL 0387574 OC1

Linguaphone institute, London.

Heyworth-Dunne, James, ed.
... Cours d'arabe égyptien parlé, rédigé par J. Heyworth-Dunne ... en collaboration avec m. M. Goma'a ... enregistré par m. M. Goma'a ... A. K. Sourour ... O. I. El-Dessouky ... ₍etc.₎ ... ₍London₎ Linguaphone institute ₍1938?₎

448.242
L648c
19-- **LINGUAPHONE INSTITUTE,** London.
... Cours de conversation français; rédigé à nouveau et revu par Louis H. Pallier et prof. Pernot ... [London] Linguaphone institute [19--]
127,[1]p. illus. 21cm.

At head of title: Linguaphone.
"Supplementary booklet to the illustrated text-book" inserted in pocket.

1. French language - Conversation and phrase books. I. Pallier, Louis H.

NL 0387576 TxU OC1

Linguaphone institute, London.

PF3121
.M4 **Menzerath, Paul,** 1883–
Linguaphone konversations-kursus, deutsch, ausgearbeitet von prof. dr. Paul Menzerath ... Sprecher: geheimrat dr. Theodor Siebs ... professor dr. Paul Menzerath ... dr. Erich Drach ... ₍u. a.₎ ₍London₎ Linguaphone institute ₍19––₎

Linguaphone institute, London.
...The direct method applied to Latin; a handbook for teachers. Written, illus. & recorded by W.H.D.Rouse... Lond., linguaphone instit., n.d.
70p.

NL 0387578 OC1

Linguaphone institute, London.
Engelsk-svensk ordbok till linguaphone kurs, Engelsk. Stockholm, Linguaphone-institutet [1944]
37 p.
Swedish.

NL 0387579 OC1

Linguaphone institute, London.
Eng. pronunciation through the centuries; selected extracts from Anglo-Saxon, Middle Eng., & later Eng.... [Lond., Linguaphone ltd., n.d. pts. in 1.

NL 0387580 OC1W

TS 239.14.20
Linguaphone Institute, London.
English records by Linguaphone: speech, pronunciation, intonation ... [New York, c1941]

48 p. ports.

1. Phonograph records - Bibl. 2. English literature - Discography. I. Title

NL 0387581 MH

PM8213 **LINGUAPHONE INSTITUTE,** LONDON
.L7 ...Esperanto, The Esperanto text prepared by ₍?₎.C.Butler. ₍London₎ Linguaphone institute ₍1946₎ 13+144p. Illus. (Linguaphons conversational course)

Contains also Student's key to the grammar exercises.

NL 0387582 InU

LINGUAPHONE INSTITUTE.
Esperanto in 30 lessons; edited in collaboration with the British Esperanto association (inc.) 1. ed. London, The Linguaphone institute [etc.] 1925.
xiii, 144 p. illus. 20cm. (Roston's pictorial language series)

Cover title: The Linguaphone Esperanto course.
Students' key to the grammar exercises of the Esperanto course (16 p. 16cm.) inserted.
Mrs. Dave H. Morris Collection.
1 Esperanto--Grammar. I. British Esperanto association.

NL 0387583 NN

Linguaphone institute, London.
...Explanatory notes on the German conversational course. [Lond.] The linguaphone institute, n.d.
154p.

NL 0387584 OC1 NBuG MH

Linguaphone institute, London.
...Explanatory notes on the Italian conversational course, by C.E.Earl...[Lond.] Linguaphone institute, n.d.
142p. (Linguaphone conversational courses)

NL 0387585 OC1

VOLUME 334

Linguaphone institute, London.
... Explanatory notes on the Spanish
conversational course.
see under   Lloyd, E.W.

Linguaphone institute, London.
...Explanatory notes to the French conversational course,.   [Lond.:N.Y.] The linguaphone
instit., [1943?]
132p. (Linguaphone conversational courses)

NL   0387587   OCl

PH279
L55
Linguaphone Institute, London.
Finnish conversational course: Vocabulary, and text of sounds
record. [London, 19--]
93 p.

1. Finnish language - Vocabulary. 2. Finnish language -
Dictionaries - English.

NL   0387588   CU

Linguaphone institute, London.
Linguaphone konversationskurs finska, redigerad
av... E.N. Setälä... Helsinfors, Linguaphone
institutet, n.d.
78p.

NL   0387589   OCl

Linguaphone institute, London.
...French; rewritten & rev. by L.H.
Pallier & Prof. Pernot...Recorded by...Paul
Passy...Daniel Michenot [& others] Lond.,
N.Y., Linguaphone instit., ltd., [19--]
14p. (Linguaphone conversational courses)

NL   0387590   OCl

The Linguaphone institute, London.
Linguaphone conversational course: French.
Rewritten & rev. by Louis H. Pallier &
Prof. Pernot. Recorded by Prof. Berthon, [and
others]. Ed. 7. 165p. [Lond., Linguaphone
institute, 1934.]

NL   0387591   OCl

PD2623
.L5
19—
Linguaphone Institute, London.

Grammar of modern Norwegian. [London,
New York, 19—]
48 p. 21cm.

1. Norwegian language—Grammar—1870-

NL   0387592   ViU OCl

Linguaphone institute, London.
...Grammar to the French conversational
course, by L.H.Pallier. [Lond.: N.Y.],
the Linguaphone instit., [1943?]
152p. (Linguaphone conversational courses)

NL   0387593   OCl

Linguaphone institute, London.
...Grammar to the Italian conversational
course, by C.E.Earl... & J.B.Menighetti...
[Lond.] Linguaphone instit., n.d.
111p. (Linguaphone conversational courses)

NL   0387594   OCl

Linguaphone institute, London.
...Grammar to the Spanish conversational
course, ed. by R. Torres... [Lond, N.Y.]
linguaphone instit. [1943?]
53p. (Linguaphone conversational courses)

NL   0387595   OCl

Linguaphone institute, London.

Bargery, George Percy, 1876–   comp.
... Hausa, a series of conversations and readings in Hausa.
With texts, English translation and explanatory notes on the
pronunciation of Hausa. Recorded by Nagogo and Lamba,
sons of the Emir of Katsina, and two of his grandchildren.
Compiled by G. P. Bargery and B. Honikman ... London,
The Linguaphone institute [19—]

Linguaphone institute, London.

Bailey, Thomas Grahame, 1872–
... Hindustani (Urdu) by T. Grahame Bailey ...   Speakers:—Sundar Narain Haksar ... [and] Mohibul Hasan ... London, The Linguaphone institute [19—]

Linguaphone institute, London.

Bailey, Thomas Grahame, 1872–
... Hindustani (Urdu) grammar and Hindustani–English
vocabulary, by T. Grahame Bailey ... London, The Linguaphone institute [19—]

Linguaphone institute, London.

Page, Walter Sutton, 1873–1938.
... An introduction to colloquial Bengali, by W. Sutton
Page ... Cambridge [Eng.] W. Heffer & sons, ltd., 1934.

KD 61349
Linguaphone Institute, London.
Italian in 30 lessons. Rev.by F.Tavani. 8th ed.
London, 1928

155 p. illus. (Roston's pictorial language series)

NL   0387600   MH OCl

Linguaphone institute, London.
...Corso di conversazione: italiano; redatto
dal dottor A.M.Bassani... [Lond.] linguaphone
instit., n.d.
127p., illus.

Supplementary booklet to the illus. text
book (14p) in pocket at front of book.

NL   0387601   OCl

Linguaphone institute, London.

Yoshitake, Saburo.
... Japanese. A series of conversational sentences in colloquial Japanese. With explanatory notes on the Japanese alphabet and pronunciation, phonetic transcription, romanized
transliteration, English translations and reproduction in Japanese script of the texts. Written and recorded by S. Yoshitake
... [London] The Linguaphone institute [19—]

Linguaphone institute, London.
...Latin course; Eng. tr. of Latin text.
N.Y., Linguaphone institute, n.d.
25 numb. l.
Tr. of text in Linguaphone institute.
Direct method applied to Latin

NL   0387603   OCl

PC
1121
L5
Linguaphone Institute, London.
Linguaphone corso d'Italiano. Collabora-
tori: Rolando Anzilotti [et al.] London, n. d.]
150 p. illus. 21 cm.

Designed to accompany Italian phonodiscs
issued by Linguaphone Institute.

PC
1121
L5
vocab.
——— Linguaphone Italian course; vocabularies
and text of sounds record. [London, New York,
n. d.]
133 p. 21 cm.

PC
1121
L5
expl.
——— Linguaphone Italian course; explanatory
notes. [London, New York, n. d.]
139 p. 21 cm.

CU-S
1. Italian language - Conversation and
phrase books. I. Anzilotti, Rolando.

NL   0387605   CU-S

PC1121
.L5
Linguaphone Institute, London.

Linguaphone corso di conversazione italiano.
Redatto dal A. M. Bassani; registrato da:
Riccardo Picozzi [et al. London, New York]
Linguaphone Institute [19—]
144 p. illus. 21cm.

1. Italian language—Conversation and phrase
books. I. Bassani, A   M   ed.
II. Title.

NL   0387606   ViU

Linguaphone institute, London.
Linguaphone cours de conversation.Néerlandais;
Conversational course, Dutch. [Lond.] linguaphone
institute [1943?]
65p. illus.

NL   0387607   OCl

Linguaphone Institute.

PC5073
.F5
Figueiredo, Fidelino de Sousa, 1888–
Linguaphone curso de conversação português, escrito pelo
Exmo. Snr. Dr. Fidelino de Figueiredo. Discos gravados
por: A. A. Rodrigues [et al.], Londres, Nova York] Lingua-
phone Institute [194–?]

Linguaphone Institute, London
Linguaphone curso de conversación español;
impresionado por los eminents profesores y
conferenciantes universitarios siguientes;
Prof. Antonio Pastor; Prof. Federico de Onís;
[etc.] [New York] Linguaphone Institute [n.d.]
144 p. 21cm.

NL   0387609   OrSaW OrStbM ViU OCl MH

VOLUME 334

Linguaphone institute, London.
Linguaphone, curso de conversación, Español ... ₍London₎Linguaphone institute₍1941?₎
127p. illus. 21cm.

"Supplementary booklet to the illustrated text book" in pocket.

1. Spanish language. Conversation and phrase books.

NL 0387610   MWelC

DE6
A20
Text 1
Linguaphone Institute, London.
Linguaphone curso de conversación español, impresionado por Antonio Pastor ₍et al.₎ ₍London, 1951?₎
129p. 21cm.

1. Spanish language. Conversation and phrase books. I. Pastor, Antonio, 1894-

NL 0387611   OrU

PF
3121
L5
Linguaphone Institute, London.
Linguaphone deutscher Kursus. Mitarbeiter: Günter Bergen ₍et al. London, n. d.₎
167 p. illus. 21 cm.

Designed to accompany German phonodiscs issued by Linguaphone Institute.

PF
3121
L5
vocab.
_____ Linguaphone German course; vocabularies and text of sounds record. ₍London, New York, n. d.₎ 135 p. 21 cm.

PF
3121
L5
expl.
_____ Linguaphone German course; explanatory notes. ₍London, New York, n. d.₎ 143 p. 21 cm.

1. German language - Conversation and phrase books. I. Bergen, Günter.

NL 0387613   CU-S

PF121
.L55
1927
Linguaphone Institute, London.
The linguaphone Dutch conversationsl course. London ₍1927₎
63 p. illus. 22cm.

1. Dutch language—Conversation and phrase books.

NL 0387614   ViU

Linguaphone Institute, London.
Linguaphone Dutch grammar
see under   Kruisinga, Etsko, 1875-

Linguaphone institute, London.
Linguaphone finsk kurs: Finsk-svensk ordförteckning, redigerad av.... E. N. Setälä... Lond.; Linguaphone Institute; Helsingfors, linguaphone8institutet, nd.
41 p.

Finnish

NL 0387616   OC1

407
L640ℓℓ
LINGUAPHONE INSTITUTE, London.
Linguaphone foreign language courses. New York, Linguaphone Institute [c1941]
cover-title, 32A, 48p. 28cm.

1. Language and languages - Study and teaching. I. Title.

NL 0387617   TxU

Linguaphone Institute.
Linguaphone; introduction to Russian grammar. ₍London, New York, 19—₎
23 p. 19 cm.
Cover title.

1. Russian language—Grammar.   I. Title.

PG2118.L5   491.75   50-27940

NL 0387618   DLC OC1

Linguaphone institue, London.
Linguaphone kielikurssien opetussuunnitelma...
Helsinki, Linguaphone opisto, n.d.
23 p.

NL 0387619   OC1

L407
L755ℓ
Linguaphone Institute.
Linguaphone language courses: French, German, Spanish, Italian, Russian, Polish, Swedish, Czech, Dutch, Afrikaans, Irish, Chinese, Japanese, Persian, Bengali, Hindustani, Hausa, Effik, Syriac, Latin, Greek, Esperanto, English. New York [193-]
.40p. illus. 26cm.

"Partial list of institutions of learning using linguaphone record courses": p. 34-36.

NL 0387620   IEN TxU

Linguaphone institute, London.
Linguaphone literary course: French. Series B. Selections from famous French writers: prose, poetry, fables, etc. [London, New York, n. d.]
54 p.   21 cm.
Accompanied by 10 12-inch phonograph records spoken by Daniel Michenot, Paul Passy, and George De Warfas.
"Biographical notices": p. 46-54.

NL 0387621   PPT

Linguaphone Institute.
Linguaphone námsskeid í Íslenzku
see under   Einarsson, Stefán, 1897-

PG2121
.L52
1927
Linguaphone Institute.
The linguaphone Russian conversational course. London ₍Pref. 1927₎
63 p. illus. 22cm.
Published earlier under title: Russian.

1. Russian language—Conversation and phrase books.

NL 0387623   ViU

PC
4121
L49
Linguaphone Institute, London.
Linguaphone Spanish dialogues; text of records and alphabetical vocabulary. ₍London, New York₎ Linguaphone Institute in collaboration with the Hispanic Council ₍n.d.₎
39 p. 21 cm.

Designed to accompany Spanish phonodiscs issued by Linguaphone Institute.

1. Spanish language - Conversation and phrase books.

NL 0387625   CU-S

D854.82
L64
Linguaphone institute, London.
Linguaphone travel course. Italian. London, The Linguaphone institute ₍19--?₎
63 p.

1. Italian language - Conversation and phrase books. 2. Italy - Description and travel.

NL 0387626   NNC

Linguaphone institute, *London.*
הַלִּנְגְּוָפוֹן. שִׂיחוֹן עִבְרִית מוֹדֶרְנִית. הִשְׁתַּתְּפוּ בהכנת שיחון
זה: דר' דוד ילין ... דר' ארנסט סימון ... יצחק וַוארטסקי ...
הדבור בלווית־השמע מאת: דר' דוד ילין, האדון יוסף יהודה,
וְהַגְּבֶרֶת דינה חיקין.
₍London, The Linguaphone institute ₍19—₎
x, 1-8, 1a-8a, 9-88 p. 18¼ᵐ.
Accompanied by 12 10-inch phonograph records (24 sides) in case, to be used in conjunction with the text.
Published also in English, under title: Modern Hebrew.
1. Hebrew language—Conversation and phrase books.
transliterated: ha-Lingwafon.
Library of Congress   PJ5014.L5
42-29071 rev

NL 0387627   DLC

Linguaphone institute, London.

Blagden, Charles Otto, 1864-   ed.
... Malay; a conversation in two parts with explanatory notes, phonetic transcription, romanized Malay transliteration, English translations, and Malay text in Arabic script. Edited and transcribed by C. O. Blagden ... Composed by Syed Sheh Barakbah. Recorded by Syed Sheh Barakbah and Ahmed Ramli. London. The Linguaphone institute ₍19—₎

PJ5014
.L75
SWTS
Linguaphone institute.
Modern Hebrew; linguaphone conversational course prepared in collaboration with David Yellin, Ernest Simon, I. Wartski. Recorded by David Yellin, Joseph Yahuda, Dina Chaikin. ₍London₎ Linguaphone Institute ₍19--?₎
2v. 19cm.
1. Hebrew language--Conversation and phrase books. I. Yellin, David, 1864-1941. II. Simon, Enamuel Ernst, 1898-   III. Wartski, Isidore. IV. Title.

NL 0387629   IEG

Linguaphone institute, *London.*
... Modern Hebrew, prepared in collaboration with Dr. David Yellin ... Dr. Ernst Simon ... ₍and₎ I. Wartski ... recorded by Dr. David Yellin, Joseph Yahuda ₍and₎ Dina Chaikin. ₍London₎ The Linguaphone institute ₍19—₎
xviii, 88 p. 18¼ᵐ. (Linguaphone conversational courses₎)
Accompanied by 12 10-inch phonograph records (24 sides) in case, to be used in conjunction with the text.
Published also in Hebrew, under title: הַלִּנְגְּוָפוֹן שִׂיחוֹן עִבְרִית מוֹדֶרְנִית
1. Hebrew language—Conversation and phrase books.   I. Yellin, David, 1864-   II. Simon, Ernst, 1899-   III. Wartski, Isidore. IV. Title.
42-30007
Library of Congress   PJ5014.L52
₍2₎   492.4824

NL 0387630   DLC OC1

VOLUME 334

Linguaphone institute, London.

Wartski, Isidore.
... Modern Hebrew grammar and explanatory notes, by I. Wartski ... ₍London₎ The Linguaphone institute ₍19—₎

PD2627
.L5
19—   Linguaphone Institute, London.

Norsk, utarbeidet av Oscar Krogh. Inntalt av: Didrik Arup Seip ₍et al.₎ London, New York, 19—₎
135 p. illus. 21cm. (Linguaphone Konversasjons Kursus)

1. Norwegian language—Conversation and phrase books. I. Krogh, Oscar, ed.

NL 0387632   ViU OC1

PD2627
.L51
19—   Linguaphone Institute, London.

Norwegian vocabulary. ₍London, 19—₎
51 p. 21cm. (Linguaphone conversational course)
The conversational text-book for which this course was prepared was published separately.

1. Norwegian language—Glossaries, vocabularies, etc.

NL 0387633   ViU

Linguaphone institute, London.
... ...Passages from the Greek classics, recorded by W.H.D.Rouse... ₍Lond.₎ Linguaphone institute, n.d.
10p.

NL 0387634   OC1

Linguaphone institute, London.

Haig, *Sir* **Wolseley,** 1865–
... Persian, by Sir Wolseley Haig ... Darab Khan ... ₍and Mojtaba Minovi ... 3d ed. London, The Linguaphone institute ₍19—₎

Linguaphone institute, London.

Haig, *Sir* **Wolseley,** 1865–1938.
... Persian grammar, by Sir Wolseley Haig ... London, The Linguaphone institute ₍19—₎

Linguaphone institute, London.
... ...Polish-Eng. vocabulary to the Polish conversational course. ₍Lond?₎ linguaphone instit., n.d.
55p.

NL 0387637   OC1

PG6121
.L5
1931   Linguaphone Institute, London.

Polnisch, bearb. von Tytus Benni. Gesprochen von Tadeusz Bocheński ₍et al.₎ 1. Aufl. London, 1931.
71 p. illus. 21cm. (Linguaphone Konversations-kursus)

1. Polish language—Conversation and phrase books. I. Benni, Tytus, ed.

NL 0387638   ViU

Linguaphone institute, London
...Polnisch; bearbeitet von Prof. Dr. Tytus Benni...Gesprochen von Tadeusz Bochenski... Konrad Górski ₍und andere₎ 2. aufl. Lond. linguaphone institute, n.d.
71p., incl. illus. (linguaphone konversations-kursus)

NL 0387639   OC1

Linguaphone institute, *London.*
... Russian, recorded by Dimitri Svjatopolk-Mirskij ... Basil Timotheieff ... Serge Ivanoff ... ₍and others₎ ... ₍London₎ The Linguaphone institute ₍19—₎
94 p. illus., map. 20½ᵐ. (Linguaphone conversational course₍s₎)
Pages 93–94 blank for "Memoranda."
Accompanied by 16 10-inch phonograph records (32 sides) in case, to be used in conjunction with the text.
The vocabulary prepared for this course was published separately.

1. Russian language—Conversation and phrase books.

Library of Congress   PG2121.L52   42–30006
                              ₍2₎   491.78242

NL 0387640   DLC MH ViU

Linguaphone institute.
... Russian, recorded by Dimitri Svjatopolk-Mirskij ... Basil Timotheieff ... Serge Ivanoff ... ₍and others₎ ₍London, New York₎ Linguaphone institute ₍19—₎
76, ₍1₎ p. illus. 21ᵐ. (Linguaphone conversational course₍s₎)
The vocabulary prepared for this course was published separately.
L. C. copy imperfect? Phonograph records in case accompanying text wanting?

1. Russian language—Conversation and phrase books.

PG2121.L52   47–39501

NL 0387641   DLC ViU MtU

The linguaphone institute, London
Linguaphone conversational course, Russian. Lond., The linguaphone inst. ₍1930₎
88p., illus.

Russian

NL 0387642   OC1

Linguaphone institute, *London.*
... Russian course, Russian-English-French-German vocabulary; Cours de russe, vocabulaire russe-anglais-français-allemand; russischer kursus, russisch-englisch-französisch-deutsches wörterverzeichnis. New and rev. ed. London, The Linguaphone institute ₍19—₎
109, ₍1₎ p. 21ᵐ.
At head of title: Linguaphone.
The conversational text-book for which this vocabulary was prepared, was published separately.
Pages 107–₍110₎ blank for "Memoranda."

1. Russian language—Glossaries, vocabularies, etc.

Library of Congress   PG2121.L53   42–30083
                              ₍2₎   491.78242

NL 0387643   DLC OrU NcD OC1

PG2121
.L53
1928   Linguaphone Institute.

Russian course, Russian-English-French-German vocabulary. Cours de russe, vocabulaire russe-anglais-français-allemand. Russischer Kursus, russisch-englisch-französisch-deutsches Wörterverzeichnis. London, ₍Pref. 1928₎
104 p. 22cm.
The conversational text-book for which this vocabulary was prepared, was published separately.
1. Russian language   —Glossaries, vocabularies, etc.

NL 0387644   ViU

The Linguaphone institute, London.
    Russian course; Russian-Eng.-French-German vocabulary; Cours de russe, vocabulaire russe-anglais-français-allemand; Russischer kursus, russisch-englisch-französisch-deutsches wörterverzeichnis. 2d ed. Lond., The linguaphone institute ₍1930₎
104 p.
At head of title: Linguaphone.

NL 0387645   OC1

Linguaphone institute, London
...The sounds of ancient Greek, with accents & quantity; the alphabet, with specimen words & sentences; arranged & recorded by W.H.D.Rouse ₍Lond.₎ linguaphone instit., n.d.
10p., ₍4₎ l.
Eng. tr. of Greek text, ₍4₎ l. at end.

NL 0387646   OC1

Linguaphone institute, London
...Spanish, Recorded by...Antonio Pastor... Federico de Onis (& others) ₍Lond., N.Y.₎ linguaphone inst. ₍194-₎
18p. (Linguaphone conversational course₍s₎)

NL 0387647   OC1

Linguaphone institute, *London.*
... Students' instructions ... ₍London, New York₎ The Linguaphone institute ₍19—₎
28 p. 18½ᵐ. (Linguaphone conversational course)

1. Language and languages—Study and teaching.   I. Title.

Library of Congress   ₂58.L5   42–36233

NL 0387648   DLC OrU OC1 CU

Linguaphone institute, London.
Swedish. written by Elias Wessen ...
    see under   Wessen, Elias, 1889-

Linguaphone institute, London
...Swedish course, Swedish-Eng.-French-German vocabulary. Course suedois, vocabulaire suedois-anglais-français-allemand. Schwedischer kursus, schwedisch-englisch-französisch-deutsches wörterverzeichnis. ₍Lond., N.Y.₎, Linguaphone inst., ₍19—₎.
3,30 (i.e. 60)p.

NL 0387650   OC1

PG4121
.L5
19—   Linguaphone Institute, London.

Tschechisch, bearb. von Miloš Weingart. Gesprochen von Miloš Weingart, Boruslav Hála ₍et al.₎ 1. Aufl. London ₍19—₎
80 p. illus. 21cm. (Linguaphone Konversations-Kurs)

1. Czech language—Conversation and phrase books. I. Weingart, Miloš, 1890–1939, ed.

NL 0387651   ViU

VOLUME 334

DEc
A20
Text ?

Linguaphone Institute, London.
Vocabularies and text of sounds record,
Spanish conversational course. ₍London₎
₍ᵔ. 1951?₎
103p. 21cm.

1. Spanish language. Glossaries,
vocabularies.

NL 0387652 OrU

Linguaphone institute, Lond.
...Vocabulary, Dutch-Eng. to the Dutch
conversational course. N.Y., Linguaphone
institute ltd., [1943?]
29,[1]p. (Linguaphone conversational courses)

NL 0387653 OC1

Linguaphone institute, *London.*
Vocabulary, Persian-English, for the Linguaphone conversational course. London, The Linguaphone institute ₍19—₎
43 p. 21ᶜᵐ.
The conversational text-book for which this vocabulary was prepared
was published separately.

1. Persian language—Glossaries, vocabularies, etc.
42–30005
Library of Congress PK6239.H33
₍2₎ 491.558242

NL 0387654 DLC

PC5075
.G4L5
1920

Linguaphone Institute, London.
Wörterverzeichnis Portugiesisch-Deutsch
zum Linguaphone Konversations-Kursus
Portugiesisch. Berlin, Linquaphone Klasing
₍192–?₎
1v, 48 p. 21cm.

1. Portuguese language—Conversation and
phrase books—German. ? Title.

NL 0387655 ViU

PG4121
.L51
19—

Linguaphone Institute, London.
Wörterverzeichnis tschechisch-deutsch zum
Linguaphone Konversations-Kurs. Tschechisch.
London ₍19—₎
79 p. 21cm.
The conversational text-book for which this
course was prepared was published separately.

1. Czech language—Glossaries, vocabularies,
etc.

NL 0387656 ViU

Ex
1022
.S89

Lingvarvm orientalivm hebraicae, rabinicae,
samaritanae, syriacae, graecae, arabicae, tvrcicae
armenicae, alphabeta. Parisiis, Apud A. Vitray,
1636.
54 p. 20 cm.

Dedication signed: Antoine Vitray.
Colophon has date 1635.

NL 0387657 NjP

Linguarum totius orbis vocabulari comparativa;
Augustissimae cura collecta
see under [Pallas, Peter Simon]
1741-1811, comp.

405
L648

Le Lingue del mondo; unica rivista italiana
di cultura linguistica.
anno

Firenze, Valmartina, 19
₍ illus., ports. 30cm. monthly.

1. Language and languages - Periodicals.
2. Philology, Comparative.

NL 0387659 NNC CU CaOTU MoU

Un lingue international pro le cultivat nations et tot
mund. Grammatic, dialogs, letters ...
see under International Societa pro le
Propagation del Mundolingue.

Lingueglia, Giovanni Battista, O.M.I.
Piccolo mondo ceylonese; schizzi di vita missionaria.
Torino, Società editrice internazionale ₍1949₎
96 p. illus. 17 cm.

1. Missions—Ceylon. 2. Catholic Church—Missions. 3. Children in
Ceylon. I. Title.

BV3275.L5 50-21266

NL 0387661 DLC

Lingueglia, Giovanni Battista, O.M.I.
La danzatrice Africana. Torino, S.E.I.
1953.

99 p.

NL 0387662 DCU

PQ
4686
L55

Lingueglia, Paolo.
Il nonvalore dell'irreligiosità carducci-
ana; saggio apologetico. Faenza, Ed. "Sale-
siana", 1925.
vi, 177p. 20cm. (Conferenze e discorsi,
Serie terza)
Contents.- Pte.I. Carducci e il suo tiempo.
- Pte.II. Analisi dell'errore dottrinale car-
ducciano.

1. Carducci, Giosuè, 1835-1907. I. T.

NL 0387663 CtU MU MH

855L64
Op1915

Lingueglia, Paolo.
Pagine d'arte e letteratura. Torino
1915.
553p.

NL 0387664 IU

PQ
4827
L454

Lingueglia, Paolo.
Primavera di S. Martino; versi 1898-1902.
[Parma, Fiaccadori, 1906]
82p. 22cm.
Title and text within ornamental border in
red.

NL 0387665 CtU

809.1
L64s

Lingueglia, Paolo.
Saggi critici di poesia religiosa.
Bologna, 1914.
248p.

NL 0387666 IU

Linguerri, Franco.
... Sopra un preteso reato di frode
in commercio. Bologna, Zamorani e
Albertazzi, 1895.
cover-title, 1 p.l., ₍5₎-12 p. 30cm.

NL 0387667 MH-L MH

Linguerri, Franco.
... Sull'esercizio abusivo della professione di medico e chirurgo. Imola,
Lega tip., 1899.
7 p. 29cm.

NL 0387668 MH-L

ML63
.M165

Linguet,
Risposta de Linguet al Signor..... *Apologia della musica*
[Napoli, 1786]
163 po 17½ cm.

NL 0387669 DLC

Linguet, Goyer
see Goyer-Linguet,

Linguet, H
Quaestio medico chirurgica...
see under Andry de Bois-Regard, Nicolas,
1658-1742.

Linguet, Simon Nicolas Henri, 1736-1794.
Œuvres de M. Linguet. Tome premier-[sixième]. [Londres,
1774.]
6 vol. in 5. fold. tables. 17½ᶜᵐ.
Half-title.
Each volume has individual t.-p.
Contents.—t. 1-2. Du plus heureux gouvernement, ou Parallèle des consti-
tutions politiques de l'Asie avec celles de l'Europe; servant d'introduction à la
Théorie des loix civiles. 2 vol. in 1.—t. 3-5. Théorie des loix civiles. Nouvelle
édition. 3 vol.—t. 6. Du pain et du bled. xxix, [7]-310 p. fold. tables.

NL 0387672 ICJ CtY NjP NNR

Linguet, Simon Nicolas Henri, 1736-1794.
Collection complète des Œuvres de
M. Linguet. t.1- [n.p., 1780-
1 v. 19 cm.
Contents. - t.1. Appel a la posterité, ou
Recueil des mémoires et plaidoyers ...
[n.p.] 1780.

NL 0387673 CtY

Linguet, Simon Nicolas Henri, 1736-1794.
Adresse au peuple français, concernant ce
qu'il faut faire & ce qu'il ne faut faire; pour
célébrer la fête mémorable & nationale, du 14.
juillet 1790...[Paris?] 1790.
24 p. 22 cm.
"Extrait du No. 124 des Annales politiques,
civiles, et littéraires".

1. France - History - Revolution, 1789-1791.
I. Annales politiques, civiles et littéraires du dix-
huitième siècle.

NL 0387674 NjP

VOLUME 334

Linguet, Simon Nicolas Henri, 1736-1794, ed.

Annales politiques, civiles et littéraires du dix-huitième
siècle; ouvrage périodique ...
Londres, 1777–

Linguet, Simon Nicolas Henri, 1736-1794.
Appel a la postérité; ou, Recueil des mémoires et plaidoyers de M. Linguet, pour lui-même, contre la communauté des avocats du Parlement de Paris. ₍Londres₎ 1779.
484 p.   port.   22 cm.   (His Collection complette des œuvres, v. 1)

I. Title.

77-28341

NL 0387676   DLC CaBVaU MB

Linguet, Simon Nicolas Henri, 1736-1794.
Appel à la posterité, ou Recueil des mémoires
et plaidoyers de M. Linguet, pour lui-même,
contre la communauté des avocats du Parlement
de Paris ...   [n.p.] 1780.
19 cm.   (His Collection complette des œuvres
de M. Linguet. t.1.)

NL 0387677   CtY

₍Linguet, Simon Nicolas Henri₎ 1736-1794.
L'aveu sincere, ou Lettre a une mere sur les
dangers que court la jeunesse en se livrant à
un goût trop vif pour la littérature. A
Londres, & se trouve a Paris, Chez Louis
Cellot, 1768.
99 p.   17cm.

Bound with Linguet, Simon Nicolas Henri.
La cacomonade. 1766.
I. Title.

NL 0387678   NNC

                                        1736-94
₍770. LINGUET, SIMON-NICOLAS-HENRI. Avis
aux Parisiens et Appel de toutes convocations
d'États-généraux où les députés du troisième
ordre ne seroient pas supérieurs aux deux
autres. n. p. [1788.] 11 p.   DFDT p.v.28, no.18
See Garrett, p. 168-176; see also Part 2, Official
Publications, no. 1703.

NL 0387679   NN

                                        Fr 1277.51
Linguet, Simon Nicolas Henri, 1736-1794.
Avis aux souscripteurs des Annales politiques, civiles
&c. [London? 1783]

24 p.
Without title-page. Caption title.

NL 0387680   MH

France
46
L647   Linguet, Simon Nicolas Henri, 1736-1794.
         Des Herrn Linguets Betrachtungen über die
         Rechte des Schriftstellers und seines Verlegers; aus dem Französischen mit einigen Anmerkungen. [Leipzig?] 1778.
         88p.   17cm.

         A translation of an extract from the author's
         Annales politiques, v.3, 1777.

         1. Copyright - France

NL 0387681   CtY-L

WZ
290
L755c
1756   LINGUET, Simon Nicolas Henri, 1736-1794.
         La cacomonade, histoire politique et
         morale. Tr. de l'allemand du docteur
         Pangloss [pseud.] par le docteur lui-même, depuis son retour de Constantinople. Cologne, 1756.
         116 p.

NL 0387682   DNLM

₍Linguet, Simon Nicolas Henri₎ 1736-1794.
La cacomonade: histoire politique et morale, tr. de l'allemand
du docteur Pangloss, par le docteur lui-même, depuis son retour
de Constantinople. Cologne ₍Paris₎ 1766.
2 p. l., ₍vii₎-xxiii, 120 p.   18½ᶜᵐ.

I. Title.
                                        4-29625
Library of Congress   PQ1999.L48C3

NL 0387683   DLC CaBVaU CtY NjP

RC201
.1
.L7ᶜ   [LINGUET, SIMON NICOLAS HENRI] 1736-1794.
        La cacomonade, ouvrage postume du docteur Pangloss
        [pseud.] servant de supplement au chapitre quatrième
        de l'optimisme. 2. ed. augm. d'une lettre du même auteur. Londres, & se trouve a Paris, Chez Cellot, 1767.
        vii,160 p.   16½cm.

        1. Venereal diseases.

NL 0387684   ICU ICN RPJCB

Linguet, Simon Nicolas Henri, 1736-1794.
Canaux navigables, ou Développement des avantages
qui résulteraient de l'exécution de plusieurs projets en
ce genre pour la Picardie, l'Artois, la Bourgogne, la
Champagne, la Bretagne, & toute la France en général.
Avec l'examen de quelques-unes des raisons qui s'y opposent, &c. Par Simon-Nicolas-Henri Linguet ... A Amsterdam, et se trouve a Paris, chez L. Cellot, 1769.
iv, 474 p., 1 l.   17½ᶜᵐ.

1. Inland navigation—France.
                                        11-5551
Library of Congress   HE443.L4 .

NL 0387685   DLC NIC MiU MoU OkU WU NcD MH-BA NNE

KE 380
L554
1790   Linguet, Simon Nicolas Henri, 1736-1794.
         Code criminel de Joseph Second; ou,
         Instructions expéditives données aux
         Tribunaux des Pays-Bas en octobre 1789,
         publiées et commentées par M. Linguet.
         Bruxelles, 1790.
         48 p.
         1. Criminal law - Holy Roman empire.   2.
         Criminal law - Netherlands. I. Holy
         Roman empire. Law , statutes, etc.,
         1765-1790.   (Joseph II) II.
         Title.   rev.

NL 0387686   CaBVaU CtY

LINGUET, [Simon Nicolas Henri], 1736-1794.
Collection des ouvrages relatifs a
la revolution du Brabant. Paris, Imp. de
L'auteur. 1791.

NL 0387687   MH

[Linguet, Simon Nicolas Henri] 1736-1794.
Considerations politiques et philosophiques,
sur les affaires présentes du nord et particulièrement sur celles de Pologne. A Londres, 1773.
168 p.
I. Title.

NL 0387688   CSmH

Kress
Room   Linguet, Simon Nicolas Henri, 1736-1794.
         Considérations sur l'ouverture de l'Escaut
         ... Londres, P.Elmsly, 1784.
         151 p.   21.5 cm.

         1.Scheldt river. 2.Inland navigation.

NL 0387689   MH-BA PPL NN MtU

DC136
.5
.L75   LINGUET, SIMON NICOLAS HENRI, 1736-1794.
        Consultation de M.Linguet, avocat, en réponse à la
        Consultation sur la discipline des avocats, imprimée
        chez Knapen, en mai 1775. Bruxelles,1776.
        [1],69 p.   20cm. [With his La France plus qu'
        angloise... Bruxelles,1788]

        1.Lawyers--France.

NL 0387690   ICU

                                        Fr 1328.07.20
[Linguet, Simon Nicolas Henri, 1736-1794]
Consultation pour la portion des religieux capucins,
désignés dans leur ordre sous le nom de frères lais ou
laïcs. Au sujet des décrets de l'Assemblée nationale, du
19 & du 20 février 1790, sur le traitement des religieux qui sortiront de leurs maisons. [Paris? Impr.
de Vezard & Le Normant, 1790]

12 p.
Signed: Linguet.

I. Title.

NL 0387691   MH

Linguet, Simon Nicolas Henri, 1736-1794.
A critical analysis and review of all Mr. Voltaire's works;
with occasional disquisitions on epic poetry, the drama, romance, &c. Tr. from the French by James Boardman. London, J. Johnson, 1790.
269 p.   22 cm.

1. Voltaire, François Marie Arouet de, 1694-1778.   I. Boardman,
James, of London, tr.

PQ2122.L52   49-38616*

NL 0387692   DLC ICN MdBP MH

Linguet, Simon Nicolas Henri, 1736-1794.
De la dette nationale et du crédit public
en France. Par M. Linguet. Bruxelles, 1789.
24 p.   23cm.

1. Debts, Public - France.

NL 0387693   NNC NjP NN

DC
141   Linguet, Simon Nicolas Henri, 1736-1794.
        De la dette nationale et du crédit
        public en France. Bruxelles, 1789.
        1 card. (Hayden, French revolutionary
        pamphlets, 772)

        Microcard copy.
        Collation of the original: 56 p.

NL 0387694   MiEM

4X
It
1610   Linguet, Simon Nicolas Henri,
        1736-1794.
        Del divorzio; memoria presentata
        all'Assemblea nazionale di Francia
        divisa in due parti, accresciuta di un
        appendice di Pilati, e di alcune
        annotazioni. Traduzione dal francese.
        Milano, Nella stamperia di F. Pogliani
        [179]
        94 p.
        Bound with the author's Del divorzio
        ossia, Danni... [179]

NL 0387695   DLC-P4

VOLUME 334

4X
It
1610
Linguet, Simon Nicolas Henri,
1736-1794.
Del divorzio; ossia, Danni del di
lui abuso; Risposta all'opera sortita
alla luce tradotta dal francese dal
cittadino avvocato Giuseppe dal Pino
intitolata Memoria, presentata
all'Assemblea nazionale di Francia.
[179]
xxii p.
Bound with the author's Del divorzio.
Milano [179]

NL 0387696   DLC-P4

Wing
fZP
739
.P 615
LINGUET, SIMON NICOLAS HENRI, 1736-1794.
Discours destiné a être prononcé par Mᵉ
Linguet, dans l'Assemblée des avocats, le 3
février 1775. Paris, P.-D.Pierres,1775.
44p. 24cm.

NL 0387697   ICN

Linguet, Simon Nicolas Henri, 1736-1794.
Dissertation sur le bled et le pain, par
M. Linguet; avec la réfutation de M. Tissot
... Neufchatel, 1779.
84 p. 20cm.

NL 0387698   NNC

HD9030 Linguet, Simon Nicolas Henri, 1736-1794.
.L75   Du commerce des grains. Nouv. éd. Augmentée d'une
lettre à M. Tissot sur le vrai mérite politique, & phisique
du pain, & du bled. Par M. Linguet ... Bruxelles, 1788.
x, 11-168 p. 21½ᵐ.

1. Grain trade. 2. Tissot, Samuel Auguste André David, 1728-1797.

NL 0387699   ICU NNC

Linguet, Simon Nicolas Henri, 1736-1794.
Du pain et du bled. Par m. Linguet ... Londres, 1774.
xxix, [7]-810 p. 17ᵐ. (Half-title: Œuvres ... t. 6)

1. Wheat. 2. Grain trade. 3. Cereals as food.   I. Title.

                                          37-9565
Library of Congress   HD9030.5.L5
                            [2]   338.1

NL 0387700   DLC CaBVaU MH-BA CU NcD ICU

[Linguet, Simon Nicolas Henri] 1736-1794.
Du plus heureux gouvernement, ou, Parallele des constitu-
tions politiques de l'Asie avec celles de l'Europe; servant d'introduction à la théorie des loix civiles ... Londres, 1774.
2 v. in 1. 17ᵐ. (Half-title: Œuvres de m. Linguet, t. 1-2)

1. Political science. 2. Asia—Politics. 3. Gt. Brit.—Pol. & govt.
I. Title.
                                          37-9564
Library of Congress   JC179.L5
                            [2]   320

NL 0387701   DLC WU KyLoU NcU CaBVaU

944.035 Linguet, Simon Nicolas Henri, 1736-1794.
L755e   Entretien de Me. Linguet et de Me. Bergasse.
Bruxelles, n.p., 1788.
53 p. 19cm.

I. Bergasse, Nicolas, 1750-1832.

NL 0387702   LNHT NIC

Kress
Room
[Linguet, Simon Nicolas Henri] 1736-1794.
Die eröfnung der schiffahrt auf der Schelde.
Erörterung der ihrentwegen zwischen Ihrer
kaiserl. königlichen Majestat und den vereinigten provinzen der Niederlande entstandenen
streitfrage. Nach den jahrschriften des
herrn Linguet. [n.p., 1784]
111 p. 20.5 cm.

Translation of v.11, no.LXXXVIII (1784)
of Annales politiques, civiles et litteraires

du dix-huitième siècle. The issue consists
of 6 articles, all of which are translated
here.

1.Scheldt river. 2.Inland navigation -
Europe. I.Title.

NL 0387704   MH-BA

B102
.L76
[Linguet, Simon Nicolas Henri] 1736-1794.
Esprit de l'histoire générale de l'Europe. De-
puis l'an 476, jusqu'à la paix de Westphalie.
Londres, T. Spilsbury, 1783.
viii, 487 p. tables.

1. Europe—Hist. I. Title.

NL 0387705   ICU MdBP MeB

---

*FC7
L6474
D780e
Linguet, Simon Nicolas Henri, 1734-1791.
Esprit et génie de m. Linguet ...
A Londres[i.e.France?],M.DCC.LXXX.
12°. 1p.ℓ.,300p. 17cm.
False imprint, probably printed in France.

NL 0387706   MH

271
L755e
Linguet, Simon Nicolas Henri, 1736-1794.
Essai philosophique sur le monachisme. Par
Mr. L. Paris, 1775.
175p. 19cm.

1. Monasticism and religious orders.
I. Title. x. Monachism.

CaBVaU
NL 0387707   LNHT MnU CtY ICN NcD ICU PPL NN MH-AH

BX
2430
.L76
1776
Linguet, Simon Nicolas Henri, 1736-1794.
Essai philosophique sur le monachisme. Par
Mʳ.L. Paris, 1776.
192 p. 19 cm.
"Cet ouvrage n'est autre chose que les vingt-
quatre premiers chapitres de l''Histoire impartia-
le des Jésuites',par le même auteur."--Barbier,
Dict.des ouvrages anon.et pseud.

1.Monasticism and religious orders. I.Title.

NL 0387708   MiU WU CtY MoSU-D

842.56
V93Y
L69
Linguet, Simon Nicolas Henri, 1736-1794.
Examen des ouvrages de M. de Voltaire.
A Bruxelles, Chez Lemaire, 1788.
204p. 23cm.

1. Voltaire, François Marie Arouet de,
1694-1778.

NL 0387709   TNJ IU MnU NNU-H PP MH CtY NNC

Linguet, Simon Nicolas Henri, 1736-1794.
Examen impartial des Oeuvres de Voltaire, considéré
comme poète, comme prosateur, comme philosophe.
Hamburg, 1784.
12mo.

NL 0387710   NN

Linguet, Simon Nicolas Henri, 1736-1794.
Examen raisonné des ouvrages de M. de Voltaire, con-
sidéré comme poëte, prosateur et philosophe; par S. N.
H. Linguet. Nouv. éd., avec des notes et des additions ...
Paris, A. Egron, imprimeur, 1817.
2 p. l., xx, 288 p. 20½ᵐᵐ.
First published Brussels, 1788.

1. Voltaire, François Marie Arouet de, 1694-1778.

                                          12-9065
Library of Congress   PQ2122.L5

NL 0387711   DLC OU

PQ1222
C6
v.9
[Linguet, Simon Nicolas Henri] 1736-1794.
Les femmes filles, ou Les maris battus,
parodie d'Hipermnestre [sic] Paris, N.B.
Duchesne, 1759.
26 p. (In Collection of French plays and
librettos [v.9])

Parody of Hypermnestre, by Le Mierre.

I. Le Mierre, Antoine Marin, 1723-1793./
Hypermnestre. II. Title.

NL 0387712   CU CtY MiU

DC136
.5
.L75
LINGUET, SIMON NICOLAS HENRI,1736-1794.
La France plus qu'angloise,ou,Comparaison entre la
procédure entamée à Paris le 25 septembre 1788 contre
les ministres du roi de France, et le procès intenté à
Londres en 1640, au comte de Strafford, principal ministre de Charles Premier,roi d'Angleterre. Avec des
réflexions sur le danger imminent dont les entreprises
de la robe menacent la nation,& les particuliers. Par
M.Linguet... Bruxelles,1788.
147,[2]p. 20cm.
1.France--Pol.&   govt.--1774-1789.

NL 0387713   ICU NNC NIC LNHT MnU MH

Microfilm
R3396/3 Linguet, Simon Nicolas Henri, 1736-1794.
La France plus qu'angloise, ou, Comparaison entre la procédure entamée à Paris
le 25 Septembre 1788, contre les ministres
du Roi de France, et le procès intenté à
Londres en 1640, au Comte de Strafford,
principal ministre de Charles Ier... Avec
des réflexions sur le danger imminent dont
les entreprises de la robe menacent la
nation & les particuliers. 2. éd. Bruxelles,   1788.
175 p.

Microfilm (negative) 1 reel. 35 mm.

1. Charles I, King of Great Britain,
1600-1649. 2. France - Hist. - Louis XVI,
1774-1793. I. Title.

NL 0387715   CaBVaU

VOLUME 334

French
Rev.
DC
138
M42
v.10
no.3

Linguet, Simon Nicolas Henri, 1736-1794.
La France plus qu'angloise; ou, Comparaison entre la procédure entamée à Paris le 25 septembre 1788 contre les ministres du roi de France, et le procès intenté à Londres en 1640, au Comte de Strafford, principal ministre de Charles premier, roi d'Angleterre. Avec des réflexions sur le danger imminent dont les entreprises de la robe menacent la nation, & les particuliers. 2. éd.   Bruxelles, 1789.
149 p.   21cm.

No. 3 in vol. lettered: Masson collection; pamphlets on the immediate antecedents of the French Revolution. Vol. 10.

1. France. Parlement (Paris) 2. Gt. Brit.--Hist.--- Charles I, 1625-1649.

NL 0387717   NIC NjP CtY

Linguet, Simon Nicolas Henri, 1736-1794.
Histoire des révolutions de l'Empire Romain pour servir de suite à celle des revolutions de la République.   1766.
2 v.
In French.

NL 0387718   RP CtW

₍Linguet, Simon Nicolas Henri₎ 1736-1794.
Histoire du siècle d'Alexandre, avec quelques réflexions sur ceux qui l'ont précédé. Amsterdam ₍Paris, Cellot₎ 1762.
xvi, 341 p. 18ᶜᵐ.

1. Alexander, the Great, B. c. 356-323. 2. Greece--Hist.   I. Title.

Library of Congress   DF234.L75
4—34900

NL 0387719   DLC

Rare
DF
234
L75
1769

Linguet, Simon Nicolas Henri, 1736-1794.
Histoire du siecle d'Alexandre. 2. ed., corrigée & augmentée.   A Amsterdam. Et se trouve a Paris, Chez Cellot, 1769.
viij, 466 p. 17cm.

Errors in paging: 455-456 repeated between 458 and ₍461₎; after 456bis: ₍461₎-462, 459-460, 465-466, 463-464.

1. Alexander, the Great, B.C. 356-323. 2. Greece--Hist.

NL 0387720   NIC CtY MiU

Linguet, Simon Nicolas Henri, 1736-1794.
Histoire impartiale des Jésuites. Depuis leur établissement jusqu'à leur première expulsion ... ₍Paris₎ 1768.
2 v. 17½ᶜᵐ.

1.Jesuits--Hist. I.Title.

BX3706.L75

DLC
NL 0387721   MiU WU CtY-D NjP NIC ICN ICU NNUT MH

Linguet, Simon Nicolas Henri, 1736-1794.
Histoire Impartiale des Jesuites. ...
Paris, 1824.

NL 0387722   DLC

French Rev.
DC
138
M42
v.2
no.48

Linguet, Simon Nicolas Henri, 1736-1794.
L'impôt territorial; ou, La dixme royale avec tous ses avantages. Londres, 1787.
88 p. 21cm.

No. 48 in vol. lettered: Masson collection; pamphlets on the immediate antecedents of the French Revolution. Vol. 2.

1. Finance, Public--France--To 1789. 2. Taxation--France--Hist.   I. Title.

NL 0387723   NIC

HJ
2650
.L76

Linguet, Simon Nicolas Henri, 1736-1794.
L'impot territorial; ou, La dixme roiale avec tous ses avantages. Londres, 1787.
99 p.

1.Taxation--France. 2.Tithes--France. I.Title.

NL 0387724   MiU NNC MH-BA NIC CtY MH ICJ MnU

DC
141

Linguet, Simon Nicolas Henri, 1736-1794.
L'impôt territorial, ou la Dixme roiale avec ses avantages. Londres, 1787.
2 cards.   (Hayden, French revolutionary pamphlets, 773)

Microcard copy.
Collation of the original: 104 p.

I. Title.   (Series)

NL 0387725   MiEM

Linguet, Simon Nicolas Henri, 1736-1794.

Justification de l'Assemblée nationale- ₍n.p., n.d.₎
7 p.

NL 0387726   NjP

Soc 5423.51

Linguet, Simon Nicolas Henri, 1736-94.
Légitimité du divorce, justifiée par les Saintes Ecritures, par les Pères, par les Conciles, etc. aux Etats-Généraux. Bruxelles, 1789.

40 p.

NL 0387727   MH

₍Linguet, Simon Nicolas Henri₎ 1736-1794.
Lettre à l'auteur des Observations sur le commerce des grains ... A Amsterdam, 1775.
32 p. 17cm.

Attributed also to L. J. Bourdon des Planches. Cf. Bibl. Natl.
Volume of pamphlets.

NL 0387728   NNC MH-BA

French Rev.
DC
141
F87+
v.585

Linguet, Simon Nicolas Henri, 1736-1794.
Lettre...à un membre de la prétendue Société patriotique de Bruxelles sur la question: Faut-il à la Belgique une Assemblée nationale ou non? Bruxelles, Paris, Maradan, 1790.
48 p. front. 22cm.

1. Belgium--History--Revolution, 1789-1790.

NL 0387729   NIC NjP DLC

Linguet, Simon Nicolas Henri, 1736-1794.
Lettre d'un apothicaire ... pour servir de supplément au no. 97 des annales politiques dans lequel M. Linguet annonce sa traduction d'un discourse, où M. Brambilla, premier chirurgien de l'empereur, s'est proposé de montrer la prééminence de la chirurgie sur la médecine ... Londres, 1788.
35 p. 19.5 cm.
No. 3 of a volume of pamphlets.

NL 0387730   NjP

₍Linguet, Simon Nicolas Henri₎ 1736-1794.
Lettre de Mr. de**a Mr. R** en réponse à la sienne sur la liberté de L'Escaut. Amsterdam, 1781.
I. Title.

NL 0387731   WU MnU

DC137
L5A4

Linguet, Simon Nicolas Henri, 1736-1794.
Lettre de M.Linguet à M.le C.de Vergennes, Ministre des Affaires Étrangères en France...   Londres, 1777.
83p. 17cm.

1. France — Foreign relations. I. Vergennes, Charles Gravier, comte de, 1719-1787.

NL 0387732   IaU NIC DLC-P4 NN MiU MnU

Linguet, Simon Nicolas Henri, 1736-1794.
Lettre de Mr. Linguet à Mr. le comte de Vergennes ... Londres, 1778.
40, 33-40 p. 20 cm.

NL 0387733   CtY

DH
617
L554
1789

Linguet, Simon Nicolas Henri, 1736-1794.
Lettre de M. Linguet au Comité patriotique de Bruxelles. ₍Bruxelles₎ Imprimerie patriotique, 1789.
18 p. 23 cm.

1. Belgium - Hist. - Revolution, 1789-1790 - Sources. I. Title.

NL 0387734   CaBVaU DLC

944.035
L755Lt

Linguet, Simon Nicolas Henri, 1736-1794.
Lettre de M. Linguet au ministre, le comte de Trauttmansdorff. ₍Paris, Chez Maradan₎ 1789.
8p. 19cm.

Caption title.

I. Trauttmansdorff, Ferdinand, 1749-1827.

NL 0387735   LNHT CtY

xDH801
B76L55

Linguet, Simon Nicolas Henri, 1736-1794.
Lettre de M.Linguet, auteur des Annales politiques, civiles & littéraires, à celui ou ceux des Annales patriotiques & littéraires, dirigées par M.Mercier; au sujet du Brabant. ₍Bruxelles₎ 1790.
17p. 20cm.

Caption title.
Imperfect: cover wanting.

1. Brabant - History.

NL 0387736   IaU

VOLUME 334

DH
617
L556
1790

Linguet, Simon Nicolas Henri, 1736-1794.
Lettres de M. Linguet au comte de Trautt-mansdorff, ministre plenipotentiaire pour l'empereur aux pays-bas en 1788, et 1789. Bruxelles, Lemaire, 1790.
xl, 134 p.

1. Belgium - Hist. - Revolution, 1789-1790 - Sour-ces. I. Title.
[1]

NL 0387737   CaBVaU CtY NjP

S878.6
AN84
L121Y
L7

Linguet, Simon Nicolas Henri, 1736-1794.
Lettres sur la nouvelle traduction de Tacite, par M.L.D.L.B. avec un petit recueil de phrases élégantes, tirées de la même traduction, pour l'usage de ses écoliers. Amsterdam, Archstée & Merkus, 1768.
iv,163p. 17cm.

Bound with the author's La pierre philosophale. Haie, 1768., La Cacomonade. Cologne, 1767., and L'aveu sincere. Londres, 1768.

NL 0387738   TNJ NNC

SELIGMAN

[Linguet, Simon Nicolas Henri] 1736-1794.
Lettres sur La théorie des loix civiles, &c. Où l'on examine entr'autres choses s'il est bien vrai que les Anglois soient libres, & que les François doivent, ou imiter leurs opérations, ou porter envie à leur gouverne-ment ... A Amsterdam, 1770.
272 p. 18cm.

Author defends his Théorie des loix civiles. I. Title.

NL 0387739   NNC CtY-L MH-L PP ICN

Kress
Room

Linguet, Simon Nicolas Henri, 1736-1794.
Linguet und Tissot, über das getreid und brod. Aus dem französischen. Nebst der geschichte einer giftigen art erbsen. Von dem uebersetzer [Hans Kaspar Hirzel]. Zürich, J.K.Füssly sohn, 1780.
3 p.l., 150, [1] p. fold. pl. 17.5 cm.

Contents.- Von dem erdapfel-brod, p.1-33, by S.N.H. Linguet; Schreiben an herrn Hirzel, vom getreid und brod, p.34-90, by S.A.A.D. Tissot; Schreiben an herrn doktor Tissot,

über seinen brief an herrn doktor Hirzel ... über das getreid und brod, p.91-119, by Linguet; Geschichte der würkungen einer giftigen art erbsen, p.120-150, by Hirzel.

1.Grain. 2.Bread. 3.Potatoes. I.Hirzel, Hans Kasper, 1725-1803. II.Tissot, Samuel Auguste André David, 1728-1797.

NL 0387741   MH-BA

Linguet, Simon Nicolas Henri, 1736-1794.

[Cousin d'Avallon, Charles Yves Cousin, called] 1769-1840, comp.
Linguetiana; ou, Recueil des principes, maximes, pen-sées diverses, paradoxes et aventures de Linguet: suivi de l'Éloge de l'art d'un coëffeur de femmes, par le même auteur ... par C..... d'Aval. Paris, Impr. de Vatar-Jouannet, an IX—1801.

Linguet, Simon Nicolas Henri, 1736-1794.
Mélanges de politique et de littérature, extraits des annales de M. Linguet, pour servir a l'histoire du XVIIIe. siecle. Bouillon, 1778.

NL 0387743   DLC RPJCB

944.035
L755M

Linguet, Simon Nicolas Henri, 1736-1794.
Mélanges de politique et de littérature, extraits des annales de m. Linguet. Pour servir à l'histoire du XVIIIe siecle. Année 1779. Bouillon, Aus dépens de la Société typograph-ique, 1780.
446, [2] p. 23½cm.

NL 0387744   NcD

Linguet, Simon Nicolas Henri, 1736-1794.
Mémoire au roi, par m. Linguet, concernant ses réclamations, actuellement pendantes au Parlement de Paris. Londres, T. Spilsbury, 1786.
242, [2] p. 20cm.
Concerning the author's controversy with the Duc d'Aiguillon.

1. Aiguillon, Emmanuel Armand Vignerot du Plessis de Richelieu, duc d', 1720-1788.
43-30167

NL 0387745   DLC CaBVaU MnU

944.035
A135

Linguet, Simon Nicolas Henri, 1736-1794.
Mémoire au roi, concernant ses réclamations, actuellement pendantes au Parlement de Paris. Londres, T. Spilsbury, 1787.
198 p. 20cm.

Concerning the author's controversy with the Duc d'Aiguillon.

NL 0387746   NNC NIC CtY

DC
611
.B91
L76

Linguet, Simon Nicolas Henri, 1736-1794.
Mémoire pour M.le duc d'Aiguillon. Paris, Impr.de Quillau, 1770.
199 p.

1.Aiguillon, Armand Emmanuel de Vignerot-Duplessis-Richelieu, duc de, 1720-1782. 2.Brittany--Hist. I.Title.

NL 0387747   MiU MB NNC

[Linguet, Simon Nicholas Henri] 1736-1794.
Mémoire signifié pour le sieur Luneau de Boisjermain, défen-deur. Contre les Syndic & adjoints des libraires & imprimeurs de Paris, demandeurs. [Paris: De l'Imprimerie de Grangé, 1769?]
16 p. 23½cm.

Caption-title.
Text signed: Me Linguet...

1. Publishers and publishing—trade—France. I. Luneau de Bois-1732-1804. II. Paris. Syndic et III. Title.
N.Y.P.L.
France. 2. Booksellers and book jermain, Pierre Joseph François, adjoints des libraires et imprimeurs.
January 9, 1942

NL 0387748   NN

Linguet, Simon Nicolas Henry
Memoires de Linguet et de Latude. Paris, 1866.

NL 0387749   NjP

Linguet, Simon Nicolas Henri, 1736-1794.
Mémoires de Linguet et de Latude, suivis de documents divers sur la Bastille et de fragments concernant la captivité du baron de Trenck. Avec avant-propos et notes par m. Fs. Barrière. Paris, Firmin-Didot et c[ie], 1884.
2 p. l., 383 p., 1 l. 18¼cm. (Half-title: Bibliothèque des mémoires rela-tifs à l'histoire de France pendant le 18e siècle ... t. 28)
Contains: Mémoires, par Linguet.—De l'insurrection parisienne et de la prise de la Bastille, par Dusaulx.—Le despotisme dévoilé, ou Mémoires de Henri Masers de Latude, rédigés par M. Thiéry.—Éclaircissements et notes. (Récit extrait des Mémoires de baron de Trenck, tr. en français par Le Tourneur; pub. à Paris, 1788)
1. Bastille, Paris. 2. France—Hist.—Revolution—Sources. I. Du-saulx, Jean, 1728-1799. II. Latude, Jean Henri Masers de, 1725-1805. III. Thiéry, avocat. IV. Trenck, Friedrich, freiherr von der, 1726-1794.

Library of Congress   DC131.A2B6
F—1989

NL 0387750   DLC NIC OC1W OCU

98139

DC
145
B55
v.39

Linguet, Simon Nicolas Henri, 1736-1794.
Mémoires de Linguet sur la Bastille; et de Dusaulx, sur le 14 juillet. Paris, Baudouin, 1821.
470p. 20cm. (Collection des mémoires relatifs a la révolution française [par Berville et Barrière, v.39])

1. Bastille, Paris. 2. France - Hist. - Revolution, 1789. I. Dusaulx, Jean, 1728-1799. /De l'insurrection parisienne. (Series)

NL 0387751   MU MdBP NcU RPB IaU

DC145
B55L5

Linguet, Simon Nicolas Henri, 1736-1794.
Mémoires de Linguet sur la Bastille, et de Dusaulx, sur le 14 juillet, avec des notices, des notes et des eclaircissemens historiques, par MM Berville et Barrière. 2. éd. Paris, Baudouin frères, 1822.
470, 38 p. illus. 22cm. (Collection des mémoires relatifs à la révolution française)

CONTENTS. - Mémoires sur la Bastille, et sur la détention de l'auteur, par Linguet.-

De l'insurrection parisienne, et de la prise de la Bastille, discours historique, par Dusaulx.- Récit fidèle, non publié jusqu'à ce jour, de la prise de la Bastille, le 14 juillet, 1789, par un ancien officier au régiment des gardes-françaises.

I. Bastille, Paris. I. Dusaulx, Jean, 1728-1799. II. Dusaulx Jean, 1728-1799. De l'insurrection l'insurrection parisienne. III. Title. IV. Title: Récit fidèle de la prise de la Bastille. RMo

NL 0387753   GU FTaSU

K72
L6A35

Linguet, Simon Nicolas Henri, 1736-1794.
Mémoires et plaidoyers. Amsterdam, S. Joly, 1773.
7 v.

NL 0387754   CU CtY ICU MiU MeB

J
4039
.505

LINGUET, SIMON NICOLAS HENRI, 1736-1794.
Mémoires et plaidoyers. Liege, Bassom-pierre, 1776.
11v. 17cm.

Vol.11 has title: Requête au Conseil du roi, contre les arrêts du Parlement de Paris, des 29 mars & 4 février 1775. Amsterdam, 1776.

NL 0387755   ICN NjP

Linguet, Simon Nicolas Henri. 1736-1794.   *3708.1.6
[Mémoires. Plaidoyers. Discours.]
Paris. Warée. 1823. (3), xliii, 551, (1) pp. [Annales du bar-reau français. Barreau ancien. Tome 6.] 20½ cm., in 8s.

K5517 - S.r.

NL 0387756   MB

VOLUME 334

DC
155
.A5
L5   Linguet, Simon Nicolas Henri, 1736-1794
　　　Mémoires pour M. le duc d'Aiguillon.
　　　Paris, A. Boudet, 1770.
　　　x, iv, 354 p.   19 cm.

　　　"Mémoire a consulter, et consultation pour
M. le duc d'Aiguillon...signé Gillet ьet alэ":
p. i-x.

　　　1. Aiguillon, Emmanuel Armand Vignerot du
Plessis de Riche-　　　lieu, duc d', 1720-
1788 I. Title

NL 0387757   WU

DC
167.5
.L75
1783   Linguet,Simon Nicolas Henri,1736-1794.
　　　Mémoires sur la Bastille,et la détention de
l'auteur dans ce Château Royal,depuis le 27
septembre 1780 jusqu'au 19 mai 1782. Londres;
Hambourg, J.G.Virchaux, 1783.
　　　168 p. plate. 20 cm.

　　　1.Bastille,Paris. 2.France--Hist.--

NL 0387758   MiU

Spec.
DC 131 Linguet, Simon Nicolas Henri, 1736-1794.
.9　　　Memoires sur la Bastille, par M. Linguet.
L 5   Londres, T. Spilsbury, 1783.
M 4　　　iv, 160 p. front. 23 cm.
1783
　　　Paper wrappers.
　　　First edition.

　　　1. Bastille, Paris.

NL 0387759   MoSW

---

xDC167.5 Linguet, Simon Nicolas Henri, 1736-1794.
L5　　　Mémoires sur la Bastille, et sur la
détention de M.Linguet, écrits par lui-
même. Londres, Spilsbury, 1783.
　　　157p. front. 19cm.

　　　On t.-p. in manuscript: M.L.Favre &
soeurs.

　　　1. Bastille, Paris.

　　　PPT CtY NN
NL 0387760   IaU ICJ MH CU DLC-P4 NIC NcD OCU NjP

Linguet, ьSimon Nicolas Henriэ 1736-1794.
　　　Mémoires sur la Bastille, et sur la détention de l'auteur
dans ce château royal, depuis le 27 septembre, 1780, jusqu'-
au 19 mai, 1782. Par Linguet ... (*In* Collection des
mémoires relatifs à la révolution française ьpar Berville et
Barrièreэ Paris, 1820-27. 20ᶜᵐ. v. 39 (1821) p. ьxxiэ-xl,
1-249)

　　　1. Bastille, Paris.   4-27550†

NL 0387761   DLC CaBVaU NcD N NN MH MdBP

Linguet, Simon Nicolas Henri, 1736-1794
　　　Mémoires sur la Bastille. Paris, 1872.
　　　24°

NL 0387762   NN

Linguet, Simon Nicolas Henri, 1736-1794.
　　　... Mémoires sur la Bastille, par Linguet ... Paris,
Librairie de la Bibliothèque nationale, 1886.

　　　192 p. 13¹ᶜᵐ. (Bibliothèque nationale; collection des meilleurs auteurs
anciens et modernes. (34))
　　　"Notice sur Linguet" (p. ьзэ-29) signed: N. David.
　　　"Ouvrages de Linguet": p. 17-29.

　　　1. Bastille, Paris. I. David, Nestor, d. 1873.

NL 0387763   DLC

944
B296ℓ1 LINGUET, Simon Nicolas Henry, 1736-
　　　1794.
　　　Mémoires sur la Bastille ьparэ
Linguet - Dusaulx, publiés avec
préface, notes et tables par H.
Monin. Paris, Librairie des
bibliophiles, 1889.

　　　11, 297 p. 18cm. (On cover:
Nouvelle bibliothèque classique
des éditions Jouaust)

　　　1. Bastille, Paris. I. Dusaulx, Jean,
1728-1799. II. Monin, Hippolyte, 1854-
1915, ed.

NL 0387765   MnU RPB NNF PU

Linguet, ьSimon Nicolas Henriэ 1736-1794.
　　　Memoirs of the Bastille. Containing a full exposition
of the mysterious policy and despotic oppression of the
French government, in the interior administration of that
state-prison. Interspersed with a variety of curious anecdotes ... Tr. from the French of the celebrated Mr. Linguet, who was imprisoned there from September 1780,
to May 1782. London, G. Kearsly, 1783.

　　　2 pts. in 1 v. 16ᵐᵒ.

　　　1. Bastille, Paris.   4-12498

NL 0387766   DLC MB OC1 MdBP CtY ICU MiD NcD MH

DC16.
.5
.L752   Linguet, Simon Nicolas Henri, 1736-1794.
Rare Bk.　　　Memoirs of the Bastille, tr. from the French of the cele-
Coll.　　brated Mr. Linguet. Ed. by Edmund Goldsmid. Edin-
　　　burgh, Priv. print., 1884-87.
　　　4 v. 18 cm. (Collectanea adamantæa, 4)
　　　"Of this edition only 75 large-paper copies and 275 small-paper
copies are printed for subscribers."
　　　Reprint of the Dublin ed. of 1783, with reproduction of t. p.

　　　1. Bastille, Paris.   (Series)

　　　DC167.5.L752   49-43958*

NL 0387767   DLC

Linguet, Simon Nicolas Henri, 1736-1794.

Latude, Jean Henri Masers de, 1725-1805.
　　　... Memoirs of the Bastille, by Latude and Linguet, trans-
lated with an introduction by J. and S. F. Mills Whitham.
London, G. Routledge & sons, ltd. ь1927э

NL 0387769   NSchU NN

Linguet, Simon Nicolas Henri, 1736-1794.
　　　Nouvelle dissertation et considérations sur
l'ouverture de l'Escaut. Par M. Linguet.   Edition
généralement refondue & augmentée par l'auteur
même ...   A Bruxelles, Chez B. Le Francq, 1785.
　　　82 p. 20 cm.

　　　"Tiré des Annales politiques, civiles, &c. du
dix-huitième siecle ... nos LXXXVIII & LXXXIX."
　　　No. ь2э in a volume of pamphlets with binder's
title: Recueil.

　　　1. Scheldt river.

DH
617
L558
1790   Linguet, Simon Nicolas Henri, 1736-1794.
　　　Observations d'un républicain, sur un
mémoire publié sous le nom de Son A. R. le
grand duc de Toscane, comme rédigé du viv-
ant de feu Joseph Second, pour n'être re-
mis qu'après sa mort, aux États des Pays-
Bas, ci-devant autrichiens. Bruxelles,
Lemaire, 1790.
　　　32 p. 23 cm.

　　　1. Belgium - Hist. - Revolution, 1789-
1790 -   Sources. I. Title.

NL 0387770   CaBVaU

Linguet, Simon Nicolas Henri, 1736-1794.
　　　Observations sur un imprimé intitulé, Réponse
des États de Bretagne au Mémoire du Duc d'Aiguillon, par Simon-Nicolas-Henri Linguet. A
Paris, Chez Le Jay, 1771.
　　　2 p. l., viii, 262 p. 27cm.

　　　1. Réponse des États de Bretagne. 2. Aiguillon, Emmanuel Armand de Vignerot du Plessis de
Richelieu, duc d', 1720-1788.

NL 0387771   NNC

944.035 Linguet, Simon Nicolas Henri, 1736-1794.
L755o　　　Observations sur le nouvel arrêté du Parlement de Paris, en date du 5 décembre 1788 ...
Bruxelles, Chez Lemaire, 1789.
　　　2p.ℓ., 28p. 19cm.

　　　1. France - Hist. - Louis XVI, 1774-1792.
2. France. Parlement (Paris) I. Title.

NL 0387772   LNHT NN

DC
141   Linguet, Simon Nicolas Henri, 1736-1794.
　　　Observations sur le nouvel Arrêté du
parlement de Paris, en date du 5 décembre
1788. Bruxelles: Lemaire, 1789.
　　　1 card.   (Hayden, French revolutionary
pamphlets, 775)

　　　Microcard copy.
　　　Collation of the original: 28 p.

NL 0387773   MiEM

Wing
fZP
739   ьLINGUET, SIMON NICOLAS HENRIэ 1736-1744.
P 615   Observations sur un imprimé ayant pour titre:
Mémoire pour Mᵉ Gerbier, ancien avocat_.   Paris,
P.D.Pierres,1775.
　　　36p. 25cm.

　　　Signed: Mᵉ Linguet, avocat.

NL 0387774   ICN MH CU

JN
2428
L5   Linguet, Simon Nicolas Henri, 1736-1794.
　　　Onguent pour la brûlure, ou Observations sur
ur réquisitoire imprimé en tête de l'arrêt du
Parlement de Paris, du 27 septembre 1788, rendu
contre les annales de M. Linguet. Avec des
réflexions sur l'usage de faire brûler des
livres par la main du bourreau. Londres, ь1788э
　　　32 p. 19 cm.

　　　Addresses to: Me. Antoine Seguier.

　　　1. Paris. Parlement - Hist. 2. France -
Pol. & govt. - 1774-1793 - Sources. I. Seguier,
Louis Antoine,   1726-1792. II. Title.
　　　　　　　　　　　　　　　　　　　　　x

NL 0387776   CU-S NIC NN NjP

VOLUME 334

944.035
L755on2
[Linguet, Simon Nicolas Henri] 1736-1794.
Onguent pour la brulure, ou, Observations sur un réquisitoire imprimé en tête de l'arrêt du parlement de Paris du 27 september 1788, rendu contre les annales de M. Linguet, avec des reflexions sur l'usage de faire brûler des livres par la main du bourreau. Seconde édition ... Bruxelles, 1788.
40p. 19cm.

NL 0387777   LNHT CtY NNC

J
93946
.51
Linguet, Simon Nicolas Henri,   1736-1794.
Ouverture de la navigation sur l'Escaut. État de la question agitée entre sa majesté impériale, et les Provinces Unies, a ce sujet. D'après les annales de M.Linguet.   n.p.1784.

NL 0387778   ICN

[Linguet, Simon Nicolas Henri] 1736-1794.
Plaidoyer pour le comte de Morangiés.   Paris: Impr. de L. Cellot, 1772.   104 p.   25cm.

In answer to the charges of having swindled the widow Veron.
Signed: Monsieur de Vergès, avocat général. M* Linguet, avocat. M* Moynat, avocat du Parlement.
"Observations sur l'imprimé intitulé: Dénonciation du comte de Morangiés, avec des notes," p. 97-104.

1. Morangiés, Jean François   Charles de Molette, comte de.
2. Veron, Marie Anne (Regnault).
N. Y. P. L.   August 4, 1938

NL 0387779   NN

Wing
fZP
739
.P 615
LINGUET, SIMON NICOLAS HENRI, 1736-1794.
Plaidoyer pour M° Linguet, avocat au Parlement, prononcé par lui-même en la Grand' chambre, les 4 & 11 janvier 1775: avec l'arrêt intervenu en sa faveur.   Paris, P.-D.Pierres,1775.
[21]-90,[3]p.   24cm.

Inserted at end: Arrest de la cour du Parlement, dated July 2, 1773, and Extrait des registres du Parlement, dated Feb.4, 1775, both dealing with Linguet.

NL 0387780   ICN

French
Rev.
DC
138
M42
v.14
no.13
Linguet, Simon Nicolas Henri, 1736-1794.
Point de banqueroute, plus d'emprunts, et si l'on veut, bientôt plus de dettes en réduisant les impôts a un seul. Avec un moyen facile de supprimer la mendicité, en assurant a toutes les classes du peuple, une existence aisée dans la vieillesse. Plan proposé à tous les peuples libres & notamment à l'Assemblée nationale de France. [Paris?] 1789.
79 p. 21cm.

No. 13 in vol. lettered: Masson collection; pamphlets on the immediate antecedents of the French Revolution. Vol. 14.

NL 0387782   NIC ICU NNC

Linguet, Simon Nicolas Henri, 1736-1794.
Political and philosophical speculations on the distinguishing characteristics of the present century; and on the state of legislation, military establishments, finances, and commerce, in Europe: with occasional reflections on the probable effects of American independency. By Mr. Linguet...   London: Printed for Fielding and Walker, 1778.   152 p.   8°.
Sabin 41332.

                                        FORD COLLECTION.
1. Eighteenth century. 2. Europe—   Govt., 18th cent. 3. Europe—
Social conditions. 4. United States—   Hist.—Revolution.
N. Y. P. L.   August 28, 1928

NL 0387783   NN ICU ViU MH CtY DLC RPJCB

Microfiche
s424
Linguet, Simon Nicolas Henri, 1736-1794.
Political and philosophical speculations on the distinguishing characteristics of the present century; and on the state of legislation, military establishments, finances, and commerce, in Europe: with occasional reflections on the probable effects of American independency. London: Printed for Fielding and Walker, MDCCLXXVIII.
Microcard edition (4 cards).
First English edition.
Translated from his "Annales politiques, civiles et littéraires du 18ieme siècle".—cf. Advertisement.
Sabin 41332.
1. Europe—Hist.—18th cent. 2. U. S.—Hist.—Revolution.

NL 0387784   ViU PSt ICRL CaBVaU TxU

Linguet, Simon Nicolas Henri, 1736-1794, supposed author.
Het proces der drie koningen ...
see under   [Goudar, Ange] 1720-1791, supposed author.

D289
.G6
1780
Rare bk.
Coll.
Linguet, Simon Nicolas Henri, 1736-1794, supposed author.
[Goudar, Ange] 1720-1791, *supposed author.*
Le procès des trois rois, Louis xvi. de France-Bourbon, Charles iii. d'Espagne-Bourbon, et George iii, d'Hanovre, fabricant de boutons, plaidé au tribunal des puissances-européénes [!]. Par appendix, L'appel au pape. Traduit de l'anglois. Londres, Chez Georges Carenaught [Paris?] 1780.

[Linguet, Simon Nicolas Henri] 1736-1794.
Prospectus pour le projet d'une nouvelle académie de musique
see under title

JN
2471
.L76
Linguet,Simon Nicolas Henri,1736-1794.
Protestations contre les arrêts du Parlement de Paris des 25,& 27 septembre 1788. [n.p.,] 1788.
12 p.

1.France—Constitutional history. 2.France—Pol.& govt.--1774-   1793. I.France. Parlement (Paris)   II.Title.

NL 0387788   MiU LNHT

Linguet, Simon Nicolas Henri, 1736-1794.
328.4409
L755Q
Quelle est l'origine des états-généraux? ... [n.p.] 1788.
65 p. 21½cm.

NL 0387789   NcD

Linguet, Simon Nicolas Henri, 1736-1794, supposed author.
Rechtshandel der drey Könige
see under   [Goudar, Ange] 1720-1791, supposed author.

Linguet, Simon Nicolas Henri, 1736-1794.
Réflexions sur la lumière, ou Conjectures sur la part qu'elle a au mouvement des corps célestes. Londres, T. Spilsbury, 1784.
134 p. 22cm.

1. Light. 2. Mechanics, Celestial.

NL 0387791   CSt

QC353
L5
Linguet, Simon Nicolas Henri, 1736-1794.
Réflexions sur la lumière, ou Conjectures sur la part qu'elle a au mouvement des corps célestes.   Londres, T. Spilsbury, 1787.
156 p.

Has bound in:
[1] Grégoire. Mémoire sur les couleurs des bulles de savon. 1789.
[2] David. Dissertation sur la cause de la pesanteur et de l'uniformité des phénomènes qu'elle nous présente.   1767.

1. Optics - To 1800.   2. Mechanics, Celestial.

NL 0387792   CU CtY MH

MICROFORMS
CENTER
Film
2919
Linguet, Simon Nicolas Henri, 1736-1794
Réponse aux docteurs modernes; ou, Apologie pour l'auteur de la Théorie des loix, et des lettres sur cette théorie. Avec la réfutation du système des philosophes économistes. [Paris?] 1771.
3v. in 2.
Bibliographical footnotes.
Microfilm (negative) Paris, Bibliothèque nationale. 1968. 1 reel.
1. Libel and slander - France 2. Linguet, Simon Nicolas   Henri, 1736-1794. Théo-

rie des loix civiles 3. Linguet, Simon Nicolas Henri, 1736-1794. Lettres sur la théorie des loix civiles I. Title II. Title: Apologie pour l'auteur

NL 0387794   WU

[Linguet, Simon Nicholas Henri] 1736-1794.
Réponse signifiée. Pour le sieur Luneau de Boisjermain, au précis signifié par les Syndic & adjoints des libraires de Paris. [Paris: De l'Imprimerie de L. Cellot, 1769] 54 p.   23½cm.

Caption-title.
Text signed: M* Linguet...

1. Publishers and publishing—   France. 2. Booksellers and book
trade—France. I. Luneau de   Boisjermain, Pierre Joseph François,
1732-1804. II. Paris. Syndic   adjoints des libraires et imprimeurs.
III. Title.
N. Y. P. L.   January 14, 1942

NL 0387795   NN MH

KV 1179
L554
1776
Linguet, Simon Nicolas Henri, 1736-1794.
Requête au Conseil du Roi contre les arrêts du Parlement de Paris des 29 mars & 4 février 1775. Amsterdam, M.M. Rey, 1776.
260 p.

I. France. Parlement (Paris)   II. Title.

NL 0387796   CaBVaU CtY

XG
.3656
.8
no.2
Linguet, Simon Nicolas Henri, 1736-1794.
Seroit-il trop tard? Aux trois ordres. Par m. Linguet ...   [Paris?] 1789.

43p. 18.5cm.(8vo);bd.to 21.5cm.
Title vignette.
Opposes voting by the three Orders.

NL 0387797   MB NcD NNC NIC NjP

PQ1222
C6
v.116
[Linguet, Simon Nicolas Henri] 1736-1794.
Socrate, tragédie en cinq actes.   Amsterdam, M.M. Rey, 1764.
xxiii,75 p.   (In Collection of French plays and librettos [v.116])

I. Title.

NL 0387798   CU

VOLUME 334

Wing
ZP
739
.P 615

[LINGUET, SIMON NICOLAS HENRI] 1736–1794.
Supplément aux Réflexions pour M⁰ Linguet,
avocat de la comtesse de Bethune.   Paris,P.D.
Pierres,1775.
40p.   24cm.

Signed: M⁰ Linguet, avocat.

I. Title.

NL 0387799   ICN

XG
.3656
.19
no.23

Linguet, Simon Nicolas Henri, 1736–1794.
Tableaux de commande, par les députés, pour
servir de suite à ceux du Salon.
A Paris, Chez Lallemande,au Palais-Royal,N°.
203;& chez les marchands de nouveautés. [1791]

23p.   20cm.(8vo);bd.to 21.5cm.
Floral vignette on t.p.
An attack on the Assemblée nationale.

NL 0387800   MB

943.057
L755tY

Linguet, Simon Nicolas Henri, 1736–1794, tr.
Testament de Joseph II, empereur et roi
des romains, traduit de l'allemand, par M.
Linguet ...   Bruxelles, De l'imprimerie des
etats; 1790.
31 p.   19cm.

1. Joseph II, 1741–1790, emp. of Germany —
Will. I. Title.

NL 0387801   LNHT PPAmP

[Linguet, Simon Nicolas Henri] 1736–1794, comp. and tr.
Théâtre espagnol ... Paris, De Hansy, le jeune, 1770.

4 v. 17 cm.

CONTENTS.—t. 1. Lopes de Vega Carpio, La constance à l'épreuve,
en espagnol, La esclava de su galan; Le précepteur supposé, en
espagnol, El domine Lucas; Les vapeurs ou La fille délicate, en
espagnol, La dama melindrosa. Calderon de la Barca, Il y a du
mieux, en espagnol, Mejor esta que estava.—t. 2. Calderon de la
Barca, Le viol puni, en espagnol, L'alcalde de Zalamea; La cloison, en
espagnol, El escondido y la tapada; Se défier des apparences, en
espagnol, Nunca lo peor es cierto; La journée difficile, en espagnol,
Los empeños de seis horas.—t. 3. Calderon de la Barca, On ne badine
point avec l'amour, en espagnol, No al burlas con el amor. Augustin

Moreto, La chose impossible, en espagnol, Non puede ser; La ressem-
blance, en espagnol, El parecido; L'occasion fait le larron, en espagnol,
La occasion haze al ladron.—t. 4. Juan de Mathos Fragoso, Le sage
dans sa retraite, en espagnol, El Sabio en su retiro. Francisco
Bandes [!] y Candamo, La fidélité difficile, en espagnol, El duelo contra
su dama. Antonio de Solis, Le fou incommode, en espagnol, Un bobo
haze ciento. Intermede des melons et de la femme têtue, en espagnol,
Entremes del melonar y la respondona. Intermede des beignets, en
espagnol, Intermes de los buñuelos. Intermede du malade imaginaire,
en espagnol, Don Juan Rana comilon. Intermede de la relique, en
espagnol, Entremes de la reliquia. Intermede de l'ecolier magicien, en
espagnol, Entremes de la cueva de Salamanca.

1. Spanish drama—Translations into French. 2. French drama—
Translations from Spanish. I. Vega Carpio, Lope Félix de, 1562–
1635. II. Calderón de la Barca, Pedro, 1600–1681. III. Moreto y
Cavana, Augustin, 1618–1669. IV. Matos Fragoso, Juan de, 1608–1688.
V. Bances Candamo, Francisco Antonio de, 1661?–1704. VI. Solis y
Rivadeneyra, Antonio de, 1610–1686. VII. Title.

PQ6267.F6L5   20—15651

NL 0387804   DLC PSt OO NcD OU WaU IEN

[Linguet, Simon Nicolas Henri] 1736–1794.
Théorie des loix civiles. Nouv. éd., rev. cor. & augm. ... A
Londres, M.DCC.LXXIV.

3 v. 17ᵐ. (Half-title: Œuvres de monsieur Linguet, t. 3–5)

1. Civil law. I. Title.

32–28242

NL 0387805   DLC NcD

[Linguet, Simon Nicolas Henri] 1736–1794.
Théorie des loix civiles, ou Principes fondamentaux de la société
... Londres, 1767.   2 v.   18cm.

455564–5B. 1. Law—Philosophy.   2. Marriage—Jurisp. 3. Slavery—
Jurisp.
N.Y.P.L.   September 17, 1951

CaBVaU OC1W CLU ICN NNC MWiW-C NIC
NL 0387806   NN MiU MiU-L CtY ICU CU NNF MH-L MH-BA

[Linguet, Simon Nicolas Henri] 1736–1794.
Théorie du libelle; ou, L'art de calomnier avec fruit,
dialogue philosophique, pour servir de supplément a la
Théorie du paradoxe ...   Amsterdam [i. e. Paris] 1775.

228 p.   17ᵐ. [With Morellet, André. Théorie du paradoxe. Amsterdam [i. e. Paris] 1775]
A reply to Morellet's Théorie du paradoxe.

1. Morellet, André, 1727–1819. I. Title. II. Title: Libelle, Théorie du.

17–8514

Library of Congress   PN228.P2M6

NL 0387807   DLC ICU MiU IU CU NjP PP MH-BA NcD

Liguet, Simon Nicolas Henri, 1736–1794.
Véto d'un citoyen; ou, Dénonciation à la
nation du rapport fait à l'Assemblée nationale, au
nom du Comité de l'imposition sur la
contribution personnelle, le octobre 1790.
Extrait des Annales politiques civiles et littéraires
du dixhuitieme siecle. Par M. Linguet.   Paris,
Chez l'auteur [1790]
25 p.   19.5 cm.
[Bound with Le Nouvelliste de France. Paris
[1790–91]]

NL 0387808   CtY

Linguetiana; ou, Recueil des principes, maximes,
pensées diverses, paradoxes et aventures de
Linguet
see under [Cousin d'Avallon, Charles Yves
Cousin, called] 1769–1840, comp.

LINGUIN, René.
De la responsabilité des agents de change
notamment en matiere des transferts de rentes
sur l'etat. Paris,1914.

Thèse ——Univ. de Paris.

NL 0387810   MH-L CtY

The LINGUIST. v. 2, no. 3–v. 16, no. 7; June, 1939–July, 1954.
London.   v.   illus.   21–31cm.

Monthly (slightly irregular).
Text chiefly in English with articles, lessons, etc., in French,
German, Spanish, Italian or Esperanto.
Published by the Linguists' club, London.

1. Philology—Per. and soc. publ. I. Linguists' club, London.

NL 0387811   NN CoU HU AzU InU CaOTU GU

The Linguist; or, Weekly instructions in the French &
German languages, calculated to enable the student to
acquire or to improve the knowledge of these two most
useful languages, without the assistance of a master.
London, Printed for T. Boosey & sons [etc.] 1825–26.
2 v.   21ᵐ. weekly.
Paged continuously.

1. French language—Composition and exercises. 2. German language—
Composition and exercises.

10–28712†

Library of Congress   PC2109.L83

NL 0387812   DLC IU

Linguist. Unabhängige zeitung für alle freunde der
weltspracheidee. Gazette indépendante pour tous les
amis d'une lange universelle. Independent gazette
for all friends of a universal language. Gased nedes-
lopik plo flens valik vapükadöla ... 1.–2. jahrg.; 1896–
97. Hannover, Hofbuchdruckerei gebr. Jänecke [etc.]
1896–97]

2 v. in 1. 23ᵐ. monthly.

Max Wahren, editor.
No more published.

I. Wahren, Max, ed.

6–34896

Library of Congress

NL 0387813   DLC

Linguistic bibliography
see under   Permanent International Committee
of Linguists.

Linguistic Circle, *Prague*
see
Pražský linguistický kroužek.

LINGUISTIC CIRCLE OF CANBERRA.
Papers in Australian linguistics. no. 1–
Canberra, Australian national university.
no.   26cm.
(Pacific linguistics. Series A: Occasional papers.)

1. Australian languages.

NL 0387816   NN

LINGUISTIC CIRCLE OF CANBERRA.
Papers in Borneo linguistics. no. 1–
Canberra, Australian national university.
26cm. (Pacific linguistics. Series A: Occasional papers)

1. Malay language--Dialects   Borneo.

NL 0387817   NN

LINGUISTIC CIRCLE OF CANBERRA.
Papers in linguistics of Melanesia. no. 1–
Canberra, Australian national university.   no.
26cm. (Pacific linguistics. Series A: Occasional papers.)

1. Oceanic languages--   Melanesian.

NL 0387818   NN

LINGUISTIC CIRCLE OF CANBERRA.
Papers in New Guinea linguistics. no. 1–
Canberra, Australian national university.
no.   26cm.
(Pacific linguistics. Series A: Occasional papers.)

1. Oceanic languages--   Papuan.

NL 0387819   NN

LINGUISTIC CIRCLE OF CANBERRA.
Papers in Philippine linguistics. no. 1–
Canberra, Australian national university.
no.   26cm.
(Pacific linguistics. Series A: Occasional papers.)

1. Philippine   languages.

NL 0387820   NN

VOLUME 334

LINGUISTIC CIRCLE OF CANBERRA.
Papers in South East Asian linguistics. no. 1-
Canberra, Australian national university.
no.   26cm.
(Pacific linguistics. Series A: Occasional papers.)

1. Asiatic languages.

NL 0387821   NN

PK
1501 **Linguistic Circle of Delhi.**
.L76   Transactions. 1955-
₍New Delhi₎,
v. 25 cm. annual.

1. Indo-Aryan philology—Societies, etc.

PK1501.L5   58-18854

NL 0387822   DLC MiU

Linguistic circle of New York
Bulletin. v. 1, no. 1-3/4; Oct./Nov.
1943-Mar./May 1944.   New York, The
Circle, 1943-44.
1 v.   28 cm.   mimeographed.

NL 0387823   NcU PP

---

806   Linguistic Circle of New York.
L64p   Publications. no.1-
New York, 1953-
v. 23 cm.

Called Special publications on various lists.
No.2 is reprint of Word, v.10, no.2-3. No. 4
is reprint of Word, v.18, no.1-2.
No.5 issued as Supplement to Word, v.20, no.3.

1.Language and languages--Collections. I.
Linguistic Circle of New York. Special publications.

NL 0387824   LU NN

P1
.W65   **Linguistic Circle of New York,**

Word. v. 1-   Apr. 1945-
New York.

LINGUISTIC CIRCLE OF SAIGON.
Publication.
Saigon.

Issued in cooperation with the Summer institute
of linguistics.

x Summer institute of   linguistics.

NL 0387826   NN

Linguistic guide in thirty foreign languages
see under   [International linguistic institute
of Chicago]

Baltimore.
LINGUISTIC INSTITUTE, Announcement. 2d session, July 8/Aug. 16,
1929. Baltimore. Md. [1929]

NL 0387828   CtY

Linguistic map of Graubünden, showing subdivisions
of the Romansh language
see under   [Schorta, Andrea]

Linguistic notes on some obscure prefixes in Greek
and Latin
see under   Crawford, Francis.

Linguistic particularism
see under   [Wells, Rulon Seymour]

P 1   **Linguistic Society of America.**
.L32   Bulletin. no.1- Dec. 1926- Baltimore,
Md., Waverly Press, inc.
No. 2- issued as supplement to
Language, journal of the Linguistic
society of America.
▪Holdings under main entry in
▪serial record.

1. Language and languages--Societies,
etc. 2. Philology, Comparative--
Societies, etc.

IdU
NL 0387832   ICU CU DSI IU FTaSU NN NbHi CStbS CaBVaU

PF121   Linguistic society of America.
.B53
Bloomfield, Leonard, 1887-
Colloquial Dutch ₍by₎ Leonard Bloomfield. ₍Baltimore,
Linguistic society of America, 1944₎

PC13   Linguistic Society of America.
.C6
Cornell University.
Cornell romance studies. v. 1-
Ithaca, Cornell Univ. Press and Linguistic Society of Amer-
ica ₍etc.₎ 1925-

PL1125   Linguistic society of America.
.E6H67
1945   **Hockett, Charles Francis.**
Guide's manual for Spoken Chinese, by Charles F. Hockett
... and Chaoying Fang ... ₍New York₎ H. Holt and company
₍1945₎

GN4   Linguistic Society of America.
.I5
Indiana. University.
Indiana University publications in anthropology and
linguistics. Memoir 1-
Baltimore, Waverly Press, 1948-

PM101   Linguistic Society of America.
.I5
International journal of American linguistics. v. 1-
July 1917-
Baltimore ₍etc.₎ Indiana University ₍etc.₎

P1   **Linguistic Society of America.**
.L3
Language. v. 1-
Mar. 1925-
Baltimore ₍etc.₎ Waverly Press ₍etc.₎

Linguistic Society of America.
Language dissertations
see under title

Linguistic society of America.

Hall, Robert Anderson.
... Melanesian pidgin English; grammar, texts, vocabulary,
by Robert A. Hall, jr. ... With the collaboration of Gregory
Bateson, Phyllis M. Kaberry ₍and others₎ ... Baltimore, Md.,
Pub. by the Linguistic society of America at the Waverly press,
inc., 1943.

Linguistic society of America.

Hall, Robert Anderson.
... Melanesian pidgin English, short grammar and vocabu-
lary, with grammatical introduction, by Robert A. Hall, jr.
With the collaboration of Gregory Bateson ₍and₎ John M. ₍!₎
W. ₍!₎ Whiting. Baltimore, Md., Pub. by Linguistic society of
America at the Waverly press, inc., 1943.

Linguistic society of America.

Sapir, Edward, 1884-1939, *ed.*
Navaho texts, by Edward Sapir, with supplementary texts
by Harry Hoijer, edited by Harry Hoijer ... Iowa City, Ia.,
Linguistic society of America. University of Iowa. 1942.

Linguistic society of America.
... The recently published Old Persian inscriptions
see under   Kent, Roland Brubb, 1877-

Linguistic society of America.
Special publications of the Linguistic
society of America, edited by B. Bloch, H.
Kurath, M. B. Emeneau, U. T. Holmes, jr.
Baltimore, Md., Linguistic society of America,
1941-
v. 25 1/2cm.

1. Philology—Collections. 2. Language and
languages—Collected works. I. Bloch, Bernard,
ed. II. Kurath, Hans, 1891-   ed. III.
Emeneau, Murray   Barnson, ed. IV. Holmes,
Urban Tigner, jr.,   ed.

NL 0387844   MB ICN PBL KyU MiD

PL3933   Linguistic society of America.
.C7   FOR OTHER EDITIONS
SEE MAIN ENTRY
Cornyn, William Stewart.
... Spoken Burmese, basic course ... by William S. Cornyn.
₍Madison, Wis.₎ Pub. for the United States armed forces by
the Linguistic society of America and the Intensive language
program, American council of learned societies ₍1945-46₎

Linguistic society of America.

PL1125   **Hockett, Charles Francis.**   FOR OTHER EDITIONS
.E6H65   SEE MAIN ENTRY
Spoken Chinese; basic course, units 1-12, by Charles F.
Hockett ... and Chaoying Fang. Published for the United
States Armed forces institute by the Linguistic society of Amer-
ica and the Intensive language program, American council of
learned societies. ₍Baltimore, Waverly press, 1944₎

VOLUME 334

Linguistic society of America.

PD3121
.D4

FOR OTHER EDITIONS
SEE MAIN ENTRY

Dearden, Jeannette.
Spoken Danish, basic course ... by Jeannette Dearden and Karin Stig-Nielsen. Identical with the edition published for the United States armed forces by the Linguistic society of America and the Intensive language program, American council of learned societies. ₍Washington, 1945₎

Linguistic society of America.

PF121

FOR OTHER EDITIONS
SEE MAIN ENTRY

Bloomfield, Leonard, 1887–
Spoken Dutch, basic course ... by Leonard Bloomfield. ₍Silver Spring, Md., Linguistic society of America, 1944–45₎

Linguistic society of America.

PF3121
.M62

FOR OTHER EDITIONS
SEE MAIN ENTRY

Moulton, William Gamwell, 1914–
... Spoken German, basic course ... By William G. and Jenni Karding Moulton. ₍Madison, Wis.₎ Pub. for the United States armed forces by the Linguistic society of America and the Intensive language program, American council of learned societies ₍1945, '44₎

Linguistic society of America.

PA1059
.K16

FOR OTHER EDITIONS
SEE MAIN ENTRY

Kahane, Henry Romanos, 1902–
... Spoken Greek, basic course ... by Henry & Renée Kahane and Ralph L. Ward. ₍Silver Spring, Md.₎ Pub. for the United States armed forces by the Linguistic society of America and the Intensive language program, American council of learned societies ₍1945–46₎

Linguistic society of America.

PK1985
.H6

FOR OTHER EDITIONS
SEE MAIN ENTRY

Hoenigswald, Heinrich Max Franz, 1915–
Spoken Hindustani, basic course ... by Heinrich Hoenigswald ... ₍Silver Spring, Md., Linguistic society of America, 1945–

Linguistic society of America.

PH2121
.S42

FOR OTHER EDITIONS
SEE MAIN ENTRY

Sebeok, Thomas Albert, 1920–
... Spoken Hungarian, basic course ... By Thomas A. Sebeok. ₍Madison, Wis.₎ Pub. for the United States Armed forces institute by the Linguistic society of America and the Intensive language program, American council of learned societies ₍1944–45₎

Linguistic society of America.

PL539
.B6

FOR OTHER EDITIONS
SEE MAIN ENTRY

Bloch, Bernard, 1907–
Spoken Japanese, basic course ... by Bernard Bloch and Eleanor Harz Jorden ... ₍Silver Spring, Md., Linguistic society of America, 1945–

Linguistic Society of America.

PL913
.L82

FOR OTHER EDITIONS
SEE MAIN ENTRY

₍**Lukoff, Fred**₎
Spoken Korean, basic course. ₍Ithaca, N. Y.₎ Pub. for the United States armed forces by the Linguistic Society of America and the Intensive Language Program, American Council of Learned Societies ₍19

Linguistic society of America.

PL5108
.D9
1945 a

FOR OTHER EDITIONS
SEE MAIN ENTRY

Dyen, Isidore, 1913–
... Spoken Malay, basic course ... by Isidore Dyen. ₍Madison, Wis.₎ Pub. for the United States Armed forces institute by the Linguistic society of America and the Intensive language program, American council of learned societies ₍1945₎

Linguistic society of America.

PD2627
.H32

FOR OTHER EDITIONS
SEE MAIN ENTRY

Haugen, Einar Ingvald, 1906–
... Spoken Norwegian, basic course ... by Einar Haugen. ₍Madison, Wis.₎ Pub. for the United States Armed forces institute by the Linguistic society of America and the Intensive language program, American council of learned societies ₍1944–

Linguistic society of America.

PG2121
.L42

FOR OTHER EDITIONS
SEE MAIN ENTRY

Lesnin, I   M
... Spoken Russian, basic course ... by I. M. Lesnin and Luba Petrova. ₍Madison, Wis.₎ Pub. for the United States Armed forces institute by the Linguistic society of America and the Intensive language program, American council of learned societies ₍1945–

Linguistic society of America.

PG1238
.H58

FOR OTHER EDITIONS
SEE MAIN ENTRY

Hodge, Carleton Taylor, 1917–
... Spoken Serbo-Croatian, basic course ... by Carleton Hodge. ₍Madison, Wis.₎ Pub. for the United States armed forces by the Linguistic society of America and the Intensive language program, American council of learned societies ₍1945₎

Linguistic society of America.

PL4163
.H3165

FOR OTHER EDITIONS
SEE MAIN ENTRY

Haas, Mary Rosamond, 1910–
Spoken Thai, basic course ... by Mary R. Haas and Heng R. Subhanka ... ₍Silver Spring, Md., Linguistic society of America, 1946–48₎

Linguistic society of America.

PL127
.M25

FOR OTHER EDITIONS
SEE MAIN ENTRY

₍**McQuown, Norman A**   ₎
... Spoken Turkish, basic course ... ₍Madison₎ Pub. for the United States Armed forces institute by the Linguistic society of America and the Intensive language program, American council of learned societies ₍1944–45₎

Linguistic Society of America.

PB13
.S77

Structural sketches. 1–
Baltimore, Linguistic Society of America ₍1948–

Linguistic society of India.
Historical syntax of Middle Indo-Aryan

see under

Sen, Sukumar.

Linguistic Society of India.

PK1501
.L52

Indian linguistics.

₍Calcutta₎

Linguistic Society of India.
Suniti Kumar Chatterfi jubilee volume

see under

Deccan college post-graduate and research institute, Poona, India.

Linguistic Society of Japan.
Gengo kenkyu. no. 1–   1939–
Tokyo.
semi-annual

Linguistics - Societies, etc.

no. 55–

NL 0387864   GU

Linguistic states in India; miscellaneous publications. [Madras, etc., 1948–56]
1 v. of pamphlets.
Title supplied by CU
Table of contents. in volume.
1. India - Administrative and political divisions. 2. State governments - India. 3. Federal government - India.

NL 0387865   CU

... **Linguistic structures of native America**
see under   Osgood, Cornelius, 1905– ed.

830.6   **Linguistic studies in Germanic.** no.1–5; 1915–20.
L753a   Chicago, University of Chicago Press. ₍i.e. New York, AMS Press₎

A reissue of the original edition.

NL 0387867   MiU OCU ICU

Linguistic studies in some Elizabethan writings. København, Munksgaard, 1951– v.

NL 0387868   OC1W

Linguistic survey of India
see under   India. Linguistic survey.

A **Linguistic** survey of the Gaelic dialects of Scotland. Oslo, Aschehoug, 1940–

v. map. 26 cm. (Norsk tidsskrift for sprogvidenskap. Suppl. bind 1, 2,   4

"Abbreviations and references": v. 1, p. 279–280.

CONTENTS.—1. The dialects of the outer Hebrides, by C. H. Borgstrøm.—2. The dialects of Skye and Ross-shire, by C. H. Borgstrøm.—3. The Gaelic of Leurbost, Isle of Lewis, by M. Oftedal.

1. Gaelic language—Dialects.   I. Borgstrøm, Carl Hjalmar. II. Oftedal, Magne.   (Series: Norsk tidsskrift for sprogvidenskap. Supplement bind 1–2 ₍etc.₎)

PB1596.L5   491.637   58–44122

NN ViU MH NN ICarbS CLSU GU TxU MnU MiEM WU
NL 0387870   DLC KMK KU RPB MdBJ LU MU CaBVaU PU IaU

VOLUME 334

Linguistica. leto 1–
1955–
[Ljubljana]

v. 25 cm. semiannual.

Vols. 1– issued as a supplement to and bound with Slavistična
revija (v. 8–
Slovenian, with summaries in French; French, with summaries
in Slovenian.

1. Language and languages—Period.

PG1801.S4 vol. 8–9   58–21757

NL 0387871   DLC NSyU MiU

Linguistica slovaca.

Bratislava.

v. port. 27 cm.

Issued by Slovenská akadémia vied a umeni.

1. Language and languages—Yearbooks. 2. Slovak language—
Yearbooks. I. Slovenská akadémia vied a umeni, Bratislava.

P10.L56   50–27119

NL 0387872   DLC CaBVaU NN CSt OU TxU

Linguistický kroužek, *Prague*
  see Pražský linguistický kroužek.

Linguistics today, edited by André Martinet and Uriel Weinreich. New York, 1954.

v. 280 p. 26 cm. (Publications of the Linguistic Circle of New
York, no. 2)
"Published on the occasion of the Columbia University bicenten-
nial."
Issued also as v. 10, no. 2–3 of Word.
Bibliographical footnotes.
CONTENTS.—The unity of linguistics, by A. Martinet.—The choice
of criteria in structural linguistics, by C. E. Bazell.—Critères de deli-
mitation, by H. Frei.—Distributional structure, by Z. S. Harris.—La
stratification du langage, by L. Hjelmslev.—Les problèmes des lois
internes de développement du langage et la linguistique soviétique,
by R. L'Hermitte.—The strategy of phonemics, by M. Halle.—Two
models of grammatical description, by C. F. Hockett.—Meaning and
use, by R. Wells.—Problèmes sémantiques de la reconstruction, by E.
Benveniste.—Etymology and the structure of word families, by Y.
Malkiel.—Internal reconstruction of pre-Indo-European word-forms,
by C. H. Borgström.—Le Französisches Etymologisches Wörterbuch:
évolution et problèmes actuels, by W. von Wartburg.—Perspectives
and problems of Amerindian comparative linguistics, by M. Swa-
desh.—Linguistics and prehistory, by A. Tovar.—Comment recon-
struire le chinois archaïque, by A. G. Haudricourt.—Contact of languages, by H. Vogt.—Linguistic geography: achievements, methods
and orientations, by G. Bottiglioni.—Is a structural dialectology possible? By U. Weinreich.
1. Linguistics—Addresses, essays, lectures. I. Martinet, André,
ed. II. Weinreich, Uriel, ed. III. Columbia University. (Series:
Linguistic Circle of New York. Publications, no. 2)

P121.L57   68–50164

NL 0387875   DLC ICU WaU NBuC IU

P
25
.L55

Linguistische Studien.
[1]– 19 –
Halle, Saale, M. Niemeyer.

1. Linguistics—Collections.

NL 0387876   DAU

Linguists' club, London.
The Linguist
  see under title

The LINGUISTS' review. v. 4–6 (no. 17–22, 24–25);
1928–Apr./June, Oct./Dec. 1929–Jan./Mar. 1930.
Nottingham, Eng.   v.   27 cm.
Quarterly.
Organ of the Institute of linguists.
Chiefly in English with articles, lessons, etc. in
French, German, Spanish and other languages.
Superseded by the Incorporated linguist.
1. Philology—Per. and soc. publ. I. Institute of
linguists.

NL 0387878   NN OU

Linguiti (A.) medicina operatoria svolta secondo il programma della R. Università. 96 pp.
16°. *Napoli, D. Cesareo,* 1883.

NL 0387879   DNLM

851.89
L755A

Linguiti, Alfonso, fl. 1863–1874.
Armonie; versi. Salerno, Stab. tip.
nazionale, 1874.
xx, 291 p. 20 cm.

NL 0387880   NcD

Linguiti, Alfonso, fl. 1863–1874.
Lucrezio Caro, carme di Alfonso Linguiti ...
Salerno, Stab. tipografico Migliaccio, 1874.
12 p. 24 cm.
1. Lucretius Carus, Titus.

NL 0387881   CU

LINGUITI, Alfonso, fl. 1863–1874.
Pel sesto secolare anniversario della
nascita di Dante Alighieri Carme. Salerno, 1865.

pp. 18.   On 562.3

NL 0387882   MH NIC

LINGUITI, Alfonso, fl. 1863–1874.
Per la solenne commemorazione di Torquato
Tasso nel R. Liceo di Salerno. Salerno, 1866.

Pamphlet.

NL 0387883   MH

Linguiti, Francesco.
Elogic funebre di Vittorio Emanuele II, re
d'Italia detto ne' solenni funerali celebrati
dalla provincia e dal municipio di Salerno nella
chiesa della SS. Annunziata il 9 marzo 1878.
Salerno, Stab. tip. nazionale, 1878.
70, (1) p. 1.8°.
Title-page and text bordered in black.

NL 0387884   MH

PQ4007
L5

Linguiti, Francesco.
Le lettere italiane considerate nella storia, ovvero nelle loro
attenenze colle condizioni morali e civili degl'italiani, ad uso
dei licei.
204 p.
Salerno, R. Migliaccio, 1865.

1. Italian literature – Hist. & crit. 2. Literature – Philosophy.

NL 0387885   CU

Linguiti, Francesco.
Le lettere italiane considerate nella storia,
... 1875.

NL 0387886   NIC

LINGUITI, Francesco.
Per la festa commemorative di Torquato
Tasso e per la solenne distribuzionne de'
premii agli alunni del Liceo di Salerno
il dì XVII marzo 1866. Salerno, 1866.

Pamphlet.

NL 0387887   MH

LINGUITI, Francesco.
Sul nuovo indirizzo degli studi letterari,
storici e critici riguardato nelle sue cause e
nei suoi effetti. [Progr]. Salerno, stabilimento
tip. nazionale, 1878].

1.8°. pp. v–xxxiii.

NL 0387888   MH

PG1201
.N3

Lingvističko društvo, Belgrad.

Наш језик. г. 1– ; 1933– ; нова сер., књ. 1–
1949–
Београд.

Lingvističko društvo, *Belgrad*
  see also
Srpska akademija nauka i umetnosti, *Belgrad. Institut
za srpskohrvatski jezik.*

Lingvistkredsen, *Copenhagen.*
Bulletin.
Copenhague, E. Munksgaard.
no. diagrs. 24 cm. annual.
Began publication in 1934. Cf. Union list of serials.

1. Language and languages—Period.

P1.A1L52   59–58170

       CU-I NNC LU TxU
NL 0387891   DLC OrU ICU MH IU NIC PPiU CU NN CaBVaU

P25
.L77
v. 1

LINGVISTKREDSEN, Copenhagen.
Études linguistiques 1944. Copenhague, E.
Munksgaard, 1945.
96 p. (Travaux du Cercle linguistique de
Copenhague, v. 1)
Bibliographical footnotes.
Contents.—On the Spenserian style, by N. Bøg-
holm.– Zu den sylterfriesischen Diphthongen ia
und ua, von Peter Jørgensen.—On the preservation
of the word-identity, by Aage Hansen.—Uhlenbeck's
Eskimo-Indoeuropean hypothesis; a critical revi-
sion, by William   Thalbitzer.

NL 0387892   ICU OU ViU NcD GU RPB OCU NNC CU MH

Lingvistkredsen, Copenhagen.

Trubetskoĭ, Nikolaĭ Sergĕevich, knîazʹ, 1890–1938.
... Grundzüge der phonologie. Publié avec l'appui du Cercle linguistique de Copenhague et du Ministère de l'instruction
publique de la République tchéco-slovaque. Prague, 1939.

Lingvistkredsen, *Copenhagen.*
Rapport sur l'activité du Cercle linguistique de Copenhague, 1931–1951. Copenhague, Nordisk sprog- og kulturforlag, 1951.
67 p. 25 cm.
"Publié à l'occasion du 20mes anniversaire de la fondation du Cercle."
"Publications" : p. [47]–51.

1. Philology—Societies.

Chicago. Univ. Libr.   A 52–10251
for Library of Congress   [3]

NL 0387894   ICU CU-I OrPR MCM NN MdBJ WaU TxU CtY

VOLUME 334

P25
.L77
v.5
LINGVISTKREDSEN, Copenhagen.
Recherches structurales 1949; interventions dans
le debat glossematique. Publiées à l'occasion du
cinquantenaire de Louis Hjelmslev. Copenhague,
Nordisk sprog- og kulturforlag, 1949.
307 p. (Travaux du Cercle Linguistique de
Copenhague, v.5)
"Bibliographie" (works of Hjelmslev of interest
for the glossematic method): p.₍305₎-307. Bibliographical footnotes.

1. Hjelmslev, Louis, 1899-   2. Philology,
Comparative--   Addresses, essays,
lectures.

NL 0387895   ICU CtY NIC MH

Lingvistkredsen, *Copenhagen.*
Travaux du Cercle linguistique de Copenhague. ₍no.₎ 1-

Copenhague, E. Munksgaard, 1944-
no. 25 cm. irregular.
English, French or German.

1. Philology—Collections.

P25.L56   52-25026

TU PBm NcD ICU OU TxU NN
NL 0387896   DLC KU OrU CaBVaU MiU CLSU TxHR WaU CU

Lingvo internacia; monata gazeto por la lingvo esperanto ...
₍1₎-   jaro; jan. 1896-
Upsala, Klubo esperantista ₍1896-
v. illus. 23ᶜᵐ. monthly (irregular)
Caption title.
Includes "Prova numero" dated Dec. 1895.

1. Esperanto—Period.   I. Klubo esperantista, Upsala.

Library of Congress   PM8201.L45   34-13892
                       ₍2₎   406.92

NL 0387897   DLC

Lingvo internacia. Literatura aldono. 1905-1907.   *2959a.259
— Paris, Presa Esperantista Societo. 1905-07. 3 v. Illus. 19½
cm.
Contents.—1905. Guy de Maupassant: La horlo (trad. Stellano). — V.
Korolenko: Paska nokto (trad. A. Vejtcler. — E. Boirac: Perdita kaj
retrovita. — Bernardin de Saint-Pierre: Paŭlo kaj Virginio (trad. H.
Hodler). — V. Garŝin: Ruĝa floro (trad. K. Boguŝeviĉ. — J. Słowacki:
La patro de pestuloj en El-Arish, poemo (trad. A. Grabowski).—Neniam
estas pli bone ol malfrue (trad. H. I. Bulthuis kaj L. Touchebeuf). —
Grasa lignajisto (trad. Gabriel Chavet). — I. Malfeliĉulo: Dum atendo
de l'pramo. 1906. La benkoj de la promenejo, de J. Jouy (trad. P. Corret). — La luphomo, de L. Frechette (trad. A. B. Beauchemin). — Mal-

                                            *2959a.259
vento, de M. Reboul (trad. L. Touchebeuf) — Ruĝa rido, de L. An-
drejev (trad. F. Avilov). 1907. A. Kofman: Kristino, pretigu la liton.—
Florian, —— trad. H. J. Bulthuis kaj L. Touchebeuf: Du biletoj. — L.
Biart, —— trad. Lotus: Akvo dormanta. — J. Renard, —— trad. H. Muf-
fang: Karotharulo. — P. Corret kaj D-ro Era: La tria Universala Kon-
greso de Esperanto.

M2456

NL 0387899   MB CU

Lingvo internacia.
...Malnovaj pagoj el Lingvo internacia.
1st-   ser. 1896-
Paris, Press Esperantista societo, 1908-

NL 0387900   OC1

Lingvo internacia. Supplement.

Saint-Pierre, Jacques Henri Bernardin de, 1737-1814.
... Paŭlo kaj Virginio, tradukis H. Hodler. Paris, Press
Esperantista societo, 1905.

Linguo Internaciona di la Delegitaro
Lektolibro.   Paris, Ch. Delagrave, 1909-
v. 19cm.

1. Ido.   I. Title.

NL 0387902   IEN ICN

Lingwood, F. Houchen.
The State control of education.   Tor., Crocker
Printing Co., n.d.
135 p.   table.

NL 0387903   CaOTU

V
1845
.506
LINGWOOD, H   n.
Ipswich playhouses: chapters of local
theatrical history. Ipswich,"East Anglian
daily times",1936.
40p. illus.,plate,ports. 21cm.

NL 0387904   ICN

NC
242
.R11
1894
L64
Lingwood, Lemmon.
The illustrated guide to Wells-next-the-Sea,
including Hokham, Walsingham, Fakenham and
district... London, Jarrold ₍1894₎
164 p. illus., plates. 17cm.

On spine: Jarrold's Wells-next-the-sea.
Illustrated by Arthur Rackham.
Paperbound edition; covers lacking.

NL 0387905   NNC

GR 47
.S8 L7
LINGYS, JUOZAS.
Hembygdrörelsen i Blekinge, Halland och
Skåne ₍en oversikt av₎ Juozas Lingis och Sig-
urd Erixon.   Stockholm, Gothia, 1948.
247-268 p.   illus.

Reprinted from Svensk bygd och folkkultur.

1. Folk-lore—Sweden—Study and teaching. 2.
Ethnology—Sweden. I. Erixon, Sigurd Emanuel,
1888-   II. Te.   Folk-lore cds.

NL 0387906   InU

Lingys, Juozas.
Lietuvių liaudies šokiai. ₍Kaunas₎ Valstybinė grožinės
literatūros leidykla, 1948.
148 p. illus. 22 cm.
"Šokių muzika" (for piano) edited by J. Švedas: p. ₍181₎-148.
Errata slip inserted.
CONTENTS.—Pratarmė.—Sutartiniai ženklai ir terminai.—Bendrieji
žingsniai. — Kalvelis. — Kublias. — BuguČiai. — Kepurinė. — Oše-
lis. — Sukčius. — Lenciūgėlis. — Sadutė. — Mikita. — Malūnėlis.—
Šokių nuotraukos.—Šokių muzika.

1. Dancing—Lithuania.   I. Title.

GV1688.L5L5 1948   54-40524

NL 0387907   DLC

Lingys, Juozas.
Lietuvių liaudies šokiai. ₍Vilniuje₎ Valstybinė grožinės
literatūros leidykla, 1952.
126 p. illus. 22 cm.
"Šokių muzika" (principally for piano) edited by J. Švedas and
E. Pilypaitis: p. ₍105₎-₍127₎
CONTENTS.—Pratarmė.—Kolūkio pirmininkas.—Blezdingėlė.—Žio
geliai. — Gyvataras. — Linelis. — Rugeliai. — Gaidys. — Polka su
ragučiais.—Bendrieji žingsniai.

1. Dancing—Lithuania.   I. Title.

GV1688.L5L5 195?   54-40520

NL 0387908   DLC

GV1688
.L5L5
1954
Lingys, Juozas.
Lietuvių liaudies sokiai. Chicago, 1954.
148 p. diagrs. 22 cm.
Includes music.

1. Dancing--Lithuania.   I. Title.

NL 0387909   MB

Lingys, Juozas.
Lietuvių liaudies žaidimai. ₍Kaune₎ Valstybinė grožinės
literatūros leidykla ₍1955₎
197 p. diagrs. 22 cm.
Includes music.

1. Dancing—Lithuania.   I. Title.

GV1688.L5L52   57-44550

NL 0387910   DLC PU MH

GV1688
.L5L53
1955
Lingys, Juozas.
Литовские народные танцы. 2., доп. и перер. изд. Под
ред. З. Славюнаса. Вильнюс, Гос. изд-во полит. и науч.
лит-ры Литовской ССР, 1955.
308 p. illus. 23 cm.
At head of title: Ю. Лингис, З. Славюнас, В. Якелайтис.
Includes music.
Folk.   2. Folk dance music, Lithuanian.
Dancing—Lithuania.   I. Title.
              Title transliterated: Litovskie narodnye tancy.

GV1688.L5L53 1955   56-28321

NL 0387911   DLC

Linham, Helen Loomis.
I hear earth sing ₍by₎ Helen Loomis Linham. Dallas, Tex.,
The Kaleidograph press ₍1936₎
82 p. 20ᶜᵐ.

I. Title.

Library of Congress   PS3523.I 637 I 2 1936   37-4648
—— Copy 2.
Copyright A 104351   ₍2₎   811.5

NL 0387912   DLC NcD NN

Linham, Helen Loomis.
Lovingly, Helen. [Poems]   Dallas, Story
book press [c1954]   68 p.   20cm.

NL 0387913   NN

DB879
I456L5
f
Linhard, František.
Kniha o Místku. Obrazovou část zhotovil,
sebral a uspořádal Ant.Přecechtěl. Perokres-
bové obrázky, barevný akvarel a iniciálky
vytvořil Josef Müller.   V Místku,
Nákladem Národní záložny, 1929.
358 p. illus. 31cm.
Includes bibliographical references.

1.Místek, Czechoslovak Republic. I.Title.

NL 0387914   CSt

W
4
B72
1936/37
Linhard, Jacques Charles Michel, 1910-
Étiologie, diagnostic de la mort du
foetus in utero et de sa macération.
Bordeaux, Bière, 1936.
93 p. (Bordeaux. Université. Faculté
de médecine et de pharmacie. Thèse.
1936/37. no. 52)

NL 0387915   DNLM CtY NNC

VOLUME 334

Linhard, M   A
₍Reiter galop, piano₎

Reiter-gallopp, for piano-forte. ₍n. p., 18—₎
₍3₎ p. 30 cm.
Copyist's ms.

1. Galops (Piano)   I. Title.

M31.L   M 54–1266

NL 0387916   DLC

Linhard, M   A
₍Reiter galop, piano₎

Reiter galop; for the piano. Baltimore, W. C. Miller,
ᵉ1869.
5 p. 36 cm.

1. Galops (Piano)   I. Title.

M31.L   52–55738

NL 0387917   DLC

Linhardt, Adolf, 1881–
...Dichter und Vagabund; Leben und Sterben des Paul Verlaine. Wien, J. L. Bondi & Sohn ₍c1949₎ 98 p. 17cm.

483396B. 1. Verlaine, Paul Marie,   1844–1896.
N. Y. P. L.   May 6, 1949

NL 0387918   NN MiU MH NcD IEN

Linhardt, Adolf, 1881–
Der Fünfziger, Roman. Wien, A. Swoboda ₍1947, ᵉ1946₎
71 p. 19 cm. [With, as issued, his Hochzeitsnacht. Wien ₍1947,
ᵉ1946₎]

I. Title.

PT2623.I 614H6   833.91   48–22213*

NL 0387919   DLC

Linhardt, Adolf, 1881–
Hochzeitsnacht, Roman. Wien, A. Swoboda ₍1947, ᵉ1946₎
53 p. 19 cm.
With this is bound, as issued, the author's Der Fünfziger. Wien
₍1947, ᵉ1946₎

I. Title.

PT2623.I 614H6   833.91   48–22212*

NL 0387920   DLC

Linhardt, Adolf, 1881–
...Papierkunde. Kurze Darstellung der Geschichte und
Fabrikation von Papier, sowie der Erzeugnisse der Papierin-
dustrie. Verfasst von Adolf Linhardt... B. Leipa: J. Künstner₍,
1932₎. 75 p. illus. 15cm. (Künstners Hilfsbüchlein.
Heft Nr. 150.)

Samples of paper, at end.

681358A. 1. Paper.
N. Y. P. L.   November 17, 1933

NL 0387921   NN

Linhardt, Ernst.
Ueber fluorescenz erster art.
Inaug. Diss. Erlangen, 1882

NL 0387922   ICRL DNLM

Linhardt, Ernst, 1913–
Das Britische Weltreich in der Weltlederwirtschaft... von
Ernst Linhardt... Erlangen: Gutenberg-Druckerei (Reinhold
& Limmert), 1936. x, 117 p. incl. tables. 22cm.

Inaugural-Dissertation — Erlangen, 1936.
Lebenslauf.
"Literaturverzeichnis," p. ₍115₎–117.

1. Leather—Trade and stat.—   Gt. Br.
N. Y. P. L.   December 10, 1937

NL 0387923   NN CtY ICRL

Linhardt, Hanns, 1901–
... Die britischen investment trusts, von diplom-kaufmann
dr. rer. pol. Hanns Linhardt ... Berlin, Wien, Industrierver-
lag Spaeth & Linde, 1935.
522 p. tables (part fold.) diagrs. 23ᶜᵐ. (Betriebs- und finanzwirt-
schaftliche forschungen ... II. ser., hft. 62)

1. Investment trusts. 2. Trust companies—Gt. Brit. 3. Investments—
Gt. Brit.   I. Title.
                                                36–6519
Library of Congress   HG4497.L5
                            ₍2₎   332.140942

NL 0387924   DLC

Linhardt, Hanns, 1901–

Jacobi, Ernst, 1867–
... Derecho cambiario (la letra de cambio y el cheque) con
un estudio sobre la importancia económica de los instrumentos
cambiarios por Hanns Linhardt. Traducción del alemán con
prólogo, notas y concordancias de derecho español, por W.
Roces ... 1. ed. Madrid, Editorial Logos ltda., 1930.

Linhardt, Hanns, 1901–
Grundlagen der Betriebsorganisation. Essen, W. Girardet
₍1954₎
180 p. illus. 21 cm. (Betriebswirtschaftliche Bibliothek, Reihe
A/6)

1. Business enterprises.   I. Title.

HD21.L5   57–26466 ‡

NL 0387926   DLC

LINHARDT, Hanns, 1901–
Die kontrolle im bankbetrieb... Stuttgart,
C.E.Poeschel, 1926.

pp.332. Tables.
(Betriebswirtschaftliche abhandlungen...bd.2.
"Literaturverzeichnis": p.309–311.

NL 0387927   MH–BA

Linhardt, Hanns, 1901–
Kreditkontrolle. Essen, W. Girardet ₍1954₎
322 p. 21 cm. (Betriebswirtschaftliche Bibliothek, Reihe A/5)
Includes bibliography.

1. Credit—Germany (Federal Republic, 1949–   ) 2. Credit.
I. Title.
HG3729.G3L5   55–15309 ‡

NL 0387928   DLC MH–BA

Linhardt, Hans.
Wacht am Böhmerwald; Bilder aus dem
Oberpfälzerwald un aus Weiden
see under   Linhardt, Josef.

LD   Linhardt, Brother John, F.S.C.
3907   The effect of group discussion
.E3   on personal and social attitudes
1968   of high school seniors.
.L56   178p.
also   Thesis (Ph.D.) – N.Y.U., School
Film   of Education.
T7428

            1. Dissertations, Academic –
         N.Y.U. – 1968. I. Title.

NL 0387930   NNU

Linhardt, Josef.
Wacht am Böhmerwald; Bilder aus dem
Oberpfälzerwald und aus Weiden, von Josef
Linhardt; Text von Hans Linhardt. Weiden,
Oberpfals, F. Nickl (Verlag: Oberpfälzischer
Kurier), 1931.
71 p. illus. 32 cm.
Dedication by the Oberbürgermeister of
Weiden.

NL 0387931   DLC

Linhardt, Kurt: Beitrag zur Kenntnis der Pyrvliumverbindungen.
                                                        Auszug ₍Ma-
schinenschrift₎ 1 Bl. 4°
Erlangen, Phil. Diss. v. 23. April 1923   [U 23. 1913

NL 0387932   ICRL

Linhardt, Robert.
Bernhard von Clairvaux, 1090–1153
see under   Bernard de Clairvaux, Saint,
1091–1153.

Linhardt, Robert.
Brennender Dornbusch, Vorträge zur Lebensge-
staltung im Geiste des Evangeliums ... Freiburg,
Herder, 1926.
2 v. 21 cm.

NL 0387934   OrStbM

Linhardt, Robert.
Feurige Wolke, Kanzelvorträge für die Sonn-
und Festtage des Kirchenjahres....2und 3. auflage.
Freiburg, Herder ₍1927₎

2 v., 21 cm.

NL 0387935   OrStbM PPG

Linhardt, Robert.
Die mystik des hl. Bernhard von Clairvaux, von dr. theol.
Robert Linhardt ... München, Verlag Natur u. kultur, a. g.
₍1923₎
1 p. l., ₍1₎, vii, 247 p. 21¼ᶜᵐ.
"Literaturverzeichnis": p. v–vii.

1. Bernard de Clairvaux, Saint, 1091–1153. 2. Mysticism.   I. Title.

                                                        32–104
Library of Congress   BX4700.B5L5   922.244

NL 0387936   DLC NcD OO

VOLUME 334

Linhardt, Robert.
Die sozialprinzipien des heiligen Thomas von Aquin; versuch einer grundlegung der speziellen soziallehren des Aquinaten, aus den quellen erarbeitet von dr. Robert Linhardt ... Freiburg im Breisgau, Herder & co. g. m. b. h., 1932.
xiv, 239 p. 24ᶜᵐ.
"Literaturverzeichnis": p. 226–231.

1. Thomas Aquinas, Saint, 1225?–1274. 2. Social ethics. 3. Social sciences. 4. Sociology, Christian—Middle ages. I. Title.

Title from Yale Univ.   Printed by L. C.
                                            A C 34–232

NL 0387937   CtY MH InStme

Linhardt, Robert.
... Unser glaube; einführung in die geisteswelt des katholischen dogmas für gebildete laien. Freiburg im Breisgau, Herder & co., g. m. b. h., 1931.
vii, ₁1₎, 349, ₁1₎ p. 19ᶜᵐ.

1. Catholic church—Doctrinal and controversial works. 2. Theology, Doctrinal. I. Title.
                                            32–9772
Library of Congress   BX1754.L5
Copyright A—Foreign   16009
                              ₁2₎   230.2

NL 0387938   DLC

241.01
L648u   **Linhardt, Robert.**
Unsere Ideale; lebenswichtige Kapitel aus der katholischen Ethik. 1. bis 5. tausend. Freiburg im Breisgau, Herder & co. G. m. b. H., 1930.
xi, ₁1₎ p., 1 ℓ., 3–348, ₁1₎ p. 19 cm.

1. Moral theology. I. Title.

NL 0387939   MoSU

Linhardt, Stuart Ritter v.: Einfluß der Röntgenstrahlen auf die Blutgerinnung und das Blutbild. (Vergl. Verwendung d. Methoden Bürker u. Wintz-Fingerhut.) [Maschinenschrift.] 28 S. 4° [Lag nicht vor.] — Auszug [Maschinenschrift]: 2 Bl. 4° ¶Ersch. auch in: **Strahlentherapie.**
Erlangen, Med. Diss. v. 9. Juli 1923   [U 23. 1759]

NL 0387940   ICRL

Linhares, Alberto Carlos Hermínio
see   **Linhares, Hermínio.**

Linhares, Augusto, *comp.*
Coletânea de poetas cearenses. Rio de Janeiro, Editora Minerva, 1952.
296 p. 24 cm. (Coletânea de poetas do Brasil)

1. Brazilian poetry—Ceará (State)   I. Title.
PQ9691.C42L5   58–16255 ‡

NL 0387942   DLC WU OU MH

Linhares, Augusto.
Raimundo Corrêa. ₁Carta de guia de letrados indispensável à leitura e melhor compreensão da novíssima edição "Virgulina" das "Poesias completas"₎ Rio de Janeiro, 1949.
33 p. 22 cm.

1. Correia, Raymundo, 1860–1911.
PQ9697.C55Z8   A 51–10548
New York. Public Libr.
for Library of Congress   ₁1₎†

NL 0387943   NN NcU DCU-IA DLC MoU

Linhares, Herminio.
Contribuição à história das lutas operárias no Brasil. Rio de Janeiro, 1955.
130 p. 19 cm.

1. Labor and laboring classes — Brazil. 2. Trade-unions — Brazil. 3. Socialism in Brazil.   I. Title.

HD8284.L5   64–39367

NL 0387944   DLC

RC206
L64   **Linhares, Hermínio.**
... Pesquisas sobre a febre amarela. Rio de Janeiro, Imprensa nacional, 1941.
78 p. diagrs.

At head of title: Dr. Hermínio Linhares Alberto Carlos ...
Tese, Brasil.
Contains summaries in English.
Contains bibliographies.
Date on cover: 1942.

1. Yellow fever.

NL 0387945   NNC MH NRU DNLM

Linhares, Josaphat de Lima.
... A moeda e as finanças publicas. Ceará, Estabelecimento graphico Urania, 1936.
4 p. l., 100 p., 2 l. 18½ cm.
Errata slip inserted.
"Bibliographia": 1st leaf at end.

1. Currency question. 2. Finance, Public. I. Title.
HG221.L548   45–33046 rev

NL 0387946   DLC

Linhares, Josaphat de Lima.
O processo inflacionário no Brasil; suas repercussões na elevação do custo de vida ₁por₎ Josaphat Linhares. Fortaleza, Centro de Divulgação Universitária, 1953.
145 p. 23 cm. ₁Biblioteca de divulgação e cultura: série 1.: estudos e ensaios, publicação no. 1₎

1. Inflation (Finance)—Brazil. 2. Cost and standard of living—Brazil. 3. Brazil—Economic conditions—1918–   I. Title.
HG832.L55   75–204367

NL 0387947   DLC OU NcU

Linhares, José.
... O Codigo de águas e a taxa de aproveitamento de energia hidroeletrica
        see under   **Brazil. Procuradoria geral da republica.**

Linhares, José.
São Paulo, Brazil. (City) *Departamento juridico.*
... Recurso extraordinario n.° 3.712 do estado de São Paulo. Recorrente: Sociedade anônima Frigorifico anglo. Recorrida: Prefeitura do municipio de São Paulo. Relator: exmo. sr. ministro José Linhares. Razões da recorrida pelo diretor do Departamento juridico da Prefeitura de São Paulo Oswaldo Aranha Bandeira de Mello. ₁São Paulo₎ Prefeitura do municipio de São Paulo ₁1940?₎

Gz
364.13
L631n   **Linhares, Marcelo J.**
Natureza, fins e efeitos da prisão administrativa ₁por₎ Marcelo J. Linhares. Belo Horizonte, 1953.
109p. 23cm.

Author's autograph presentation copy.
Bibliography: p. 103–109.

1. Administrative responsibility - Brazil.
2. Misconduct in office - Brazil. I. Title.

NL 0387950   TxU

G962.4
L646r   **Linhares, Maria Yedda Leite.**
As relações anglo-egípcias e o Sudão, março 1950-novembro 1951. Rio de Janeiro, 1953.
xi, 158p. map. 23cm.
"Tese de concurso à livre docência da cadeira no. XXV—História Moderna e Contemporânea—na Faculdade Nacional de Filosofia da Universidade do Brasil."
Includes bibliography.
1. Sudan. 2. Egypt - For. rel. - Gt. Brit.
3. Gt. Brit. - For. rel. - Egypt.

NL 0387951   TxU

Linhares, Mario, 1886–
História literária do Ceará. Rio de Janeiro ₁Federação das Academias de Letras do Brasil₎ 1948.
208 p. ports. 23 cm. (História da literatura brasileira, t. 1)

1. Brazilian literature—Ceará, Brazil (State)—Hist. & crit.
(Series)
PQ9511.H58 t.1   869.09   52–64313

NL 0387952   DLC MH IU TxU NN MnU

Linhares, Mario, 1886–
Os Linhares, retrospecto genealógico, 1690–1954. ₁2. ed.₎ Rio de Janeiro, Irmãos Pongetti, 1954.
228 p. illus. 22 cm.

1. Linhares family.
CS309.L54 1954   56–34509 ‡

NL 0387953   DLC NNC

Linhares, Mario, 1886 –
Novo orientacao da pintura brasileira.
Rio de Janeiro, 1926.
43p.

NL 0387954   DCU-IA

Linhares, Mario, 1886–
... Poetas esquecidos. Rio de Janeiro, Irmãos Pongetti, 1938.
308 p., 2 l. port. 18½ᶜᵐ.
Criticism of the author's Poesias: p. ₁295₎–308.

1. Poets, Brazilian. I. Title.
                                           40–31487
Library of Congress   PQ9571.L5
                              ₁2₎   869.109

NL 0387955   DLC

869.8
L75s   **Linhares, Mario,** 1886 –
... Semeadores. Rio ₁de Janeiro₎ Mendonça, Machado & ca. 1926.
193 p., 2 l. 18½ᶜᵐ.

Contains poetry.

1. Authors, Brazilian. 2. Brazilian literature - History and   criticism. I. Title.

NL 0387956   CSt

Linhares, Miguel de Noronha, *conde de*
see
Noronha, Miguel de, *conde de Linhares,* d. 1649.

VOLUME 334

Linhares, Rodrigo de Sousa Coutinho, *conde de*
see
Sousa Coutinho, Rodrigo de, *conde de Linhares, 1745–1812.*

Linhares, Temistocles.
Introdução ao mundo do romance. Rio de Janeiro, J. Olympio, 1953.
499 p. 22 cm.

1. Fiction—Hist. & crit.   I. Title.

PN3458.L52   56–34853

NL 0387959   DLC CU NN MiU DPU TxU

Linhares, Temistocles.
Paraná vivo; um retrato sem retoques. Com ilustrações de Poty. Rio de Janeiro, J. Olympio, 1953.
360 p. illus. 23 cm. (Coleção Documentos brasileiros, 78)
Includes bibliography.

1. Paraná, Brazil (State)   I. Title.

F2596.L57   54–31958 ‡

NcD TxU
NL 0387960   DLC CaBVaU IaU LNHT CaOTP CU CtY FU NN

Linhares Beuttenmüller, Leonila.
... O orfeão na escola nova; aprovado pela Superintendencia de educação musical e artistica e adotado pelo Departamento de educação do Distrito federal. Contendo gráficos e ilustrações da autora. Rio ¡de Janeiro¿ Irmãos Pongetti, 1937.
8 p. l., ¡9¿–80 p., 2 l. illus. (incl. music) plates, diagrs. 19ᶜᵐ.
"Bibliografia": 1st leaf at end.

1. Choirs (Music) 2. Music—Instruction and study—Brazil.   I. Title.

Library of Congress   MT915.L56   44–51955
                         ¡3¿   784.96

NL 0387961   DLC

Linhares Uruguay, Alice
see Uruguay, Alice Linhares.

Linhares, Counts of. *Library.*
... Catalogo da importante livraria dos ex.ᵐᵒˢ srs. condes de Linhares que sera vendida em leilão no dia 1 de novembro e seguintes ... Lisboa, Impr. de L. da Silva, 1895.
iv, 267 p. 21ᶜᵐ.
2443 entries.
Issued also with a new title-page announcing the auction for December 1 and days following, by the Empreza editora de Francisco Arthur da Silva, as "Catalogo n.º 44."

1. History—Bibl.—Catalogs. 2. Manuscripts, Portuguese—Catalogs.

                                            43–42896
Library of Congress   Z997.L76 1895

NL 0387963   DLC

Linhares, Counts of. *Library.*
... Catalogo da importante livraria dos ex.ᵐᵒˢ srs. condes de Linhares que será vendida em leilão no dia 1 de dezembro e seguintes ... sob a direcção de Francisco Arthur da Silva ... Lisboa, F. A. da Silva, 1895.
iv, 267 p. 21ᶜᵐ.
"Catalogo 44. Leilão 23."
2443 entries.
Previously issued with a title-page announcing the auction for November 1 and days following, and having imprint: Lisboa, Impr. de L. da Silva, 1895.

1. History—Bibl.—Catalogs. 2. Manuscripts, Portuguese—Catalogs.

                                            43–41075
Library of Congress   Z997.L76 1895 a

NL 0387964   DLC

PG   Linhart, Anton Tomaž, *1756–1795.*
1918   Izbrano delo. Priredil Alfonz Gspan. V
L5A6   Celju, Fran Milavec, 1938.
1938   238 p.   facsim.   18cm.   (Cvetje iz
         domačih in tujih logov, 14)

NL 0387965   CoU

Linhart, Anton Tomaž, 1756–1795.
Versuch einer Geschichte von Krain und der übrigen südlichen Slaven Oesterreichs. Laibach, Mit Egerschen Schriften, 1788–
v. col. map. 21 cm.
Includes bibliographical references.
CONTENTS: 1. Bd. Von den ersten Spuren einer Bevölkerung im Lande bis zur ersten Anpflanzung der krainischen Slaven.

1. Carniola—History. 2. Slavs, Southern—History.   I. Title.

DB314.L5   77–289349

NL 0387966   DLC PSt NNC CU WU NSyU CtY MH NN

Linhart, Anton Tomaž, 1756–1795.
Veseli dan; ali, Matiček se ženi; komedija v pet aktih. ¡Priredil Alfonz Gspan. V Ljubljani¿ Ljudska prosveta Slovenije, 1951.
119 p. illus. 20 cm. (Knjižnica ljudskih iger, 2)
An adaptation of Le mariage de Figaro, by P. A. de Beaumarchais.

I. Beaumarchais, Pierre Augustin Caron de, 1732–1799. Le mariage de Figaro. II. Title. III. Title: Matiček se ženi.

PG1918.L5V4   56–36051 ‡

NL 0387967   DLC

PG1918   Linhart, Anton Tomaž, 1756–1795.
L55   Zbrano delo. [Uredil Alfonz Gspan.   V Ljubljani,
1950   Državna založba Slovenije 1950–
           v. (Zbrana dela slovenskih pesnikov in pisateljev)

         Contents. – 1. knj. Županova Micka. Ta veseli dan ali
         Matiček se ženi. Miss Jenny Love. Blumen aus Krain. Pisma.
         Dostavek.

         CoU MH ICU
NL 0387968   CU NN NNC FTaSU CLU MiU DLC-P4 CLSU IU

Linhart, Anton Tomaž, 1756–1795.
Županova Micika. Veseloigra spetjem v dveh dejanjih. Po nemškem priredil [Richter.] [Predigra, poigra po osnovi dr. Josipa Vošnjaka spisal Anonimus] V Gorici, A Gabršček, 1905.
xvi, 27, 49, 19 (1) p. 24°. (Talija [no.] 20.)

NL 0387969   NN

Linhart, Anton Tomaž, 1756–1795.
Županova Micka. Veseli dan, ali Matiček se ženi. Nova Izd. Ljubljana, Tiskovna Zadruga, 1923.
140p. (Oder zbirka gledaliških iger, 5 zvezek.)
Slovenian.

NL 0387970   OCl

DB215   Linhart, Bedřich, 1858–
L756   Smlouva za mír s Německem a náš stát. Napsal
        judr. Bedřich Linhart.   Praha, F.Topič ¡1919¿
          5 p.l., 9–155,¡1¿ p.   18ᶜᵐ. (Added t.-p.: Duch
        a svět ... 47)

        1.Czechoslovak Republic- History. 2.Versailles, Treaty of, June 28, 1919 (Germany) 3.European war, 1914–1918- Czechoslovak Republic. I.Title. II.Ser.

NL 0387971   CSt-H OCl

Linhart, Christopher Philip, 1861–
A handbook of gymnastics, by C. P. Linhart ... ¡Columbus? O., 1900¿
75 p. illus., fold. chart. 17ᶜᵐ.

1. Gymnastics. 2. Physical education and training.

Library of Congress   GV461.L75   1–30605 Revised

NL 0387972   DLC IU OU

Linhart, Elisabeth.
Das kartellwesen im rahmen der berufsständischen ordnung. ... München, 1938. 79 p.
Inaug. Diss. – München, 1938.
Literaturverzeichnis.

NL 0387973   ICRL CtY

Linhart, Emil.
Noční boj pěchoty. V Praze, Vědecký ústav vojenský, 1934.
99 p. illus. 25 cm.

1. Night fighting (Military science)   I. Title.

U167.5.N5L5   59–56945 ‡

NL 0387974   DLC

DB   Linhart, František.
217   Masaryk a budoucnost náboženství. Praha
M3   ¡Blahoslav¿ 1946.
L5   21p. 22cm. (Český zápas, sv.7)

         1. Masaryk, Tomáš Garrigue, Pres.
         Czechoslovak Republic, 1850–1937 I. Title

NL 0387975   WU

Linhart, František.
Náboženství a světový názor. ¡1. vyd.¿ Praha, Orbis, 1949.
30 p. 22 cm. (Přednášky a diskuse, sv. 14)
Includes bibliography.

1. Christian life.   I. Title.

BV4510.L5   62–33393 ‡

NL 0387976   DLC

BQV364   Linhart, Franz Seraph., ed.
L755   Sammlung der für das Königreich Böhmen im
1833   Jahre 1820 (–1832) in publico ecclesiasticis
         und in Studiensachen ergangenen k.k. Verord-
         nungen. Hrsg. von Franz Seraph. Linhart.
         Budweis, Martin Zdarsfa, 1833–1838.
Robbins   13 v.
Coll.

         1. Ecclesiastical law - Bohemia. 2. Church and state - Bohemia. 3. Education - Bohemia. I. Title.

NL 0387977   CU-L

Linhart, George Augustus, 1884–
The entropy of physical growth. Riverside, Calif., Junior College, 1929.
21 p. illus. 26 cm. (Occasional papers of Riverside Junior College, v. 4, no. 2)

1. Growth. 2. Biomathematics.   I. Title.

QH511.L5   52–57211 ‡

NL 0387978   DLC MnU CU ICU

VOLUME 334

Linhart, George Augustus, 1884–
... A new and simplified method for the statistical interpretation of biometrical data, by George A. Linhart. Berkeley, University of California press, 1920.

cover-title, p. [159]–181. diagrs. 27½ᶜᵐ. (University of California publications in agricultural sciences. v. 4, no. 7)

"From the Division of soil chemistry and bacteriology, College of agriculture, University of California, Berkeley."
"Literature cited": p. 169.

1. Graphic methods.   I. Title.
                                              A 20–1270
California. Univ. Library
for Library of Congress   S405.C3 vol. 4, no. 7
——— Copy 2.   QA90.L5
                                 [a39f1]   (630.82)

NL 0387979   CU CaBVaU OrU OrCS PPAmP DLC MB

Linhart, George Augustus, 1884–
Out of the melting pot, by George A. Linhart. [Riverside, Calif.] 1923.

3 p. l., 213 p. port. 20ᶜᵐ.
"A few copies of the rough notes of the contents of this book were printed in 1921–22, in sections, under the copyright title: 'Lessons in Americanization. A crystal from the melting pot'."

I. Title.

Library of Congress   E170.5.L75
                                              23—12185

NL 0387980   DLC PP PU ICU OCl

QC318   **Linhart, George Augustus,** 1884–
L5   The relation between chronodynamic entropy
            and time. Riverside, Calif., The Junior
            College, 1929.
            8 p. (Occasional papers of Riverside
            Junior College. v.4, no.3)

            Cover title.

            1. Entropy.

NL 0387981   CU

Linhart, György, 1844–
... Legfontosabb mezőgazdasági kultúrnövényeinken előforduló élősdi gombák, illetve bacteriumok és az ellenök való védekésmódok. [2. kiadás] Linhart Györgytől. Magyar-Óvár [Győr, Nitsmann J. könyvnyomdája] 1904.

cover-title, 44 p. 25½ᶜᵐ.
At head of title: M. Kir. növényélet- és kórtani állomás, Magyar-Óvár.

1. Vegetable pathology.
                                              Agr 12—631
U. S. Dept. of agr. Library
for Library of Congress   464L64L
                                 [a41b1]

NL 0387982   DNAL

Linhart, György, 1844–
A magyarországi felsőbb gazdasági tanügy újjászervezésének kérdése. Irta Linhart György... Jelentés Dr. Darányi Ignácz, val. belső t. tanácsos, földmivelésügyi m. kir. minister úr ö nagyméltóságához, Franacziaország, Németország, Svájcz és Ausztriában az 1897. év nyarán tett tanulmányútról. Magyar-Óvár: S. Czéh, 1900. 99 p. incl. tables. 2. ed. 8°.

1. Agriculture—Education—Hun[
N. Y. P. L.   December 27, 1926

NL 0387983   NN

4UG   **Linhart, Heinz.**
12   Gasschutz-Leitfaden, von Heinz Linhart
            und Josef Lenz. [München, 1935]
            136 p.

NL 0387984   DLC-P4

QL639   **Linhart, Horst,** 1922–
L5   Spektroskopische blutuntersuchungen an fischen
            nach vergiftung mit blut- und abwassergiften.
            München, 1951.
            96 p. illus., fold. diagr. 20 cm.
            Inaug.-Diss.-Ludwig-Maximilians-Universität
            in München.
            Lebenslauf.
            At head of title: Aus dem Zoologisch-Parasitologischen Institut der Tierärztlichen Fakultät der
            Universität München...
            Bibliography: p. 94–96.

            1. Fishes. 2.   Blood. 3. Poisons –
            Physiological   effect. I. Title.

NL 0387985   DI

Linhart, J. A.
Grundzüge der crystallographie, von J. A.
Linhart. Prag[1825.

NL 0387986   PPAN

4PG   **Linhart, Jan.**
Czech.-   Jan houslista Josefa Hory. [Vyd. 1. V
48   Praze] J. Vilímek, 1947.
            46 p. (Hlasy, sv. 11)

NL 0387987   DLC-P4

Linhart, Jan.
L'udovít Štúr. [Vyd. 1.] Praha, Československý spisovatel, 1952.
82 p. 22 cm. (Postavy a dílo. Malá řada, sv. 3)
Bibliography: p. 80–81.

1. Štúr, L'udovít, 1815–1856.

DB678.L5   58–20160

NL 0387988   DLC InU CLU IU MH NNC

Linhart, Josef.
Americký pragmatismus; rozbor krise buržoasního myšlení. [1. vyd. V Praze, Melantrich [1949]
235 p. 20 cm.
Bibliography: p. 232–234.
Summary in English and Russian.

1. Pragmatism. 2. Philosophy, American.   I. Title.

B832.L5   52–64556

NL 0387989   DLC CaBVaU

WZ   **LINHART, Josef.**
100   Učení I. P. Pavlova a psychologie.
P338LI   [1. vyd.] Praha, Osvěta, 1951.
1951   32 p. (Knihovna Socialistické akademie, sv. 24)
            1. Pavlov, Ivan Petrovich, 1849–1936
            2. Psychology

NL 0387990   DNLM

WL   **LINHART, Josef.**
102   Vyšší nervová činnost dítěte. [1. vyd.]
qL755v   Praha, Státní pedagogické nakl., [1953]
            v. illus. (Učební texty vysokých
            škol)
            Contents. – díl 1. Obecné zákonitosti
            vyšší nervové činnosti dětí
            1. Nervous system – Physiology

NL 0387991   DNLM

Linhart, Josef, *ed.*
Vývoj osobnosti a její rozvoj v socialismu. [Kolektivní práce za redakčního vedení Josefa Linharta a redakční spolupráce Vl. Tardyho a Miloše Machače. Vyd. 1] Praha, Státní pedagogické nakl., 19

v. 21 cm. (Pedagogická přítomnost, sv.
542 kn. edice Dědictví Komenského.

1. Socialism. 2. Personality.   I. Title.

HX260.C8L5   56–17457 ‡

NL 0387992   DLC NN PPiU

Linhart, Karel.
Krmelínský sborníček. [V Krmelíně] Obec Krmelín,
1948.
51 p. illus., port. 21 cm.

1. Krmelín, Czechoslovak Republic. 2. World War, 1939–1945—
Czechoslovak Republic—Krmelín.

DB879.K92L5   50–29451

NL 0387993   DLC

PN 1994   LINHART, LUBOMÍR.
.L75   Malá abeceda filmu. V Praze, Pokrok, 1930.
            85 p. (Dobrá četba, sv. 66)

            1. Moving-pictures.   I. Title.

NL 0387994   InU

Linhart, Magda Maria.
... Gesicht im spiegel; ein buch von sehnsucht
und erfüllung. Reichenberg, Sudetendeutscher
verlag Franz Kraus, 1922.
77 p. illus. 22ᶜᵐ.
Poems.

NL 0387995   ViU

Linhart, Roy Dalzell.
At the cross; three groups of Lenten sermons and addresses, by James W. Schillinger, Roy D. Linhart [and] Harold L. Yochum. Columbus, O., The Lutheran book concern [*1932]

W   **Linhart, Rubin Aron,** 1909–
4   Étude clinique de la gynécomastie.
N17 –   Champigneulles, Impr. alsacienne, 1936.
1935/36   48 p. (Nancy. Université. Faculté
            de médecine. Thèse. 1935/36. no. 24)

            Bibliography: p. [43]–48.

NL 0387997   DNLM CtY

WO   **LINHART, Wenzel von,** 1821–1877.
L755c   Compendium der chirurgischen Operationslehre. Wien, Braumüller, 1856.
1856   xii, 748, viii p. illus.

NL 0388001   DNLM NIC NNC OClW-H PPC

WO   **LINHART, Wenzel von,** 1821–1877.
L755c   Compendium der chirurgischen Operationslehre. 2. durchaus umgearb. und
1862   verm. Aufl. Wien, Braumüller, 1862.
            xviii, xviii, 918 p. illus.

NL 0388002   DNLM NNC

VOLUME 334

RD32
L64
1867

Linhart, Wenzel von, 1821-1877.
Compendium der chirurgischen operationslehre, von dr. Wenzel von Linhart ... 3.
durchaus umgearb. und verm. aufl. ... Wien,
Braumüller, 1867.
xvi, xix, 982, ₍2₎ p. illus. 23ᶜᵐ.

Binder's title: ... Operationslehre.

1. Surgery, Operative.   I. Title.

NL 0388003   NNC CtY DNLM

Linhart, Wenzel von, 1821-1877.
Compendium der chirurgischen operationslehre,
von dr. Wenzel von Linhart ... 4. durchaus umgearb. und verm. aufl. Mit 518 holzschnitten ...
Wien, W. Braumüller, 1874.
2 v. in 1. illus.   23½ᶜᵐ.
Paged continuously.

1. Surgery, Operative.

NL 0388004   ViU CtY PPC NN DNLM

Linhart, Wenzel von, 1821-1877.
Ueber die Schenkelhernie. Mit 7 lithographirten Tafeln. Erlangen, Ferdinand Enke, 1852.
vi, 70p. illus., 7 plates. 23cm.

NL 0388005   KU-M ICJ MH

WI
L755v
1866

LINHART, Wenzel von, 1821-1877
Vorlesungen über Unterleibs-
Hernien, gehalten im Sommer-Semester
1864. Würzburg, Stuber, 1866.
viii, 272 p. illus.

NL 0388006   DNLM KU-M CtY-M ICJ MH ViU

Linhart, Wenzel von, 1821-1877.
----. Vorlesung über Unterleibs-Hernien gehalten in Sommer-Semester 1864. Neue Ausg.
viii, 272 pp., 1 l. 8º. Würzburg, A. Stuber,
1866.

NL 0388007   DNLM

Linhart, Willy.
Führer durch Gmunden und das Traunsee-Gebiet. Gmunden, Mader, 1953.
71 p. illus. 17 cm.

1. Gmunden, Austria—Descr.—Guide-books.   I. Title.

DB879.G57L5   55-34901 ‡

NL 0388008   DLC

ML410
.M382
S33
1946

Linhartová, Božena, tr

Šafránek, Miloš, 1894-
Bohuslav Martinů, the man and his music ₍tr. from the
Czech by Božena Linhartová; English text rev. by Rebecca
Clarke₎ London, D. Dobson, 1946.

Linhof, Adelbert, pseud.
see Heuwekemeyer, Antonius Johannus, 1899-

Linhof, R. A.
Die Kultur der Münchener Friedhofs-Anlagen Hans Grässels.
Von Dipl.-Ing. Architekt R. A. Linhof.   München, 1918.   67 p.
illus., plans, plates.   f°.
Repr.: Wasmuth's Monatshefte für Baukunst. Jahrg. 3, Heft 6-7.

1. Cemeteries, Germany: Munich.   2. Graessel, Hans, 1860-
                                              June 20, 1921.

NL 0388011   NN

Linhof guide (Kling-version)
see under   Crøy, Otto R   1902-

Linhoff, Albrecht.
Indirekte steuern oder nicht ... Cöslin, Gedruckt bei
C. G. Hendess, 1875.
35 p. 19ᵐ.
Inaug.-diss.—Jena.

1. Taxation.
                                              8-6199†
Library of Congress   HJ5001.L8

NL 0388013   DLC

Linhorst, Erwin Frederick, 1903-
The thermal decomposition of nitrogen pentoxide at low
pressures ... by Erwin Frederick Linhorst ... Easton, Pa.,
Mack printing company, 1934.
8 p. 1 illus., diagrs. 26½ x 20ᶜᵐ.
Thesis (PH. D.)—University of Michigan, 1931.
"Reprinted from the Journal of the American chemical society, 56 ...
(1934)."

1. Nitrogen pentoxide. 2. Dissociation.

Library of Congress   QD181.N1L5 1931   35-1902
Univ. of Michigan Libr.   546.17

NL 0388014   MiU DLC

W 4
M961
1951

LINHUBER, Hans, 1919-
Beitrag zur Aktivierung und
Vergiftung von Papain.   München, 1951.
25 ℓ.
Inaug.-Diss. - Munich.
1. Proteinases

NL 0388015   DNLM

WZ
240
L756t
1576

LINI, Giovanni Antonio, fl. 1575.
Trattato contra peste novamente ... composto ... Diviso
in cinque parti secondo l'ordine naturale ... Aggiuntovi il
retto giudicio del sequent'anno. 1576. Col Lunario, & altro
calculato pur dal detto al meridiano della città di Correggio.
Bologna, Alessandro Benacci, 1576.
₍19₎ p. 20 cm.

NL 0388016   DNLM

... Linia z dnia 8 grudnia 1919 i "Linia Curzona"
z dnia 11 lipca 1920
see under ₍Piszczkowski, Tadeusz₎

Linian, Tomás Cuber y
see   Cuber y Linian, Tomás.

Linick, Art.
Schlagenhauer's boom-booms, by Art Linick and illustrated
by Pedro Llanuza. Chicago, Shrewesbury publishing co.
₍ᶜ1926₎
112 p. incl. front., illus. 23¼ᶜᵐ.

I. Title.

Library of Congress   PN6231.D6L5   27-980

NL 0388019   DLC

Linick, Leroy Marion, 1907-
Der Subjektivismus im Werke Georg Kaisers...von Leroy
Marion Linick...   Strassburg: Heitz & Co., 1937.   166 p.
24cm.

Abhandlung—Zürich, 1936.
Lebenslauf.
"Diese Arbeit erscheint zugleich als Band 4 der Sammlung Heitz (Akademische
Abhandlungen zur Kulturgeschichte, II. Reihe)."
"Bibliographie," p. ₍157₎-163.

990492A. 1. Kaiser, Georg, 1878-
                                              August 16, 1939

NL 0388020   NN ICU CtY MH NNC ICRL

838
K130
L76

Linick, Leroy Marion, 1907-
Der Subjektivismus im Werke Georg Kaisers.
Strassburg, Heitz, 1938.
163 p.   (Sammlung Heitz, Reihe 2, Bd. 4)
Includes bibliography.

1. Kaiser, Georg, 1878-1945. I. Title.

NL 0388021   MiU OCU RPB

Linick, Leslie Lloyd, 1890-
Jewelers' workshop practices; processes, shop-kinks, short-
cuts and trade-secrets in jewelry manufacture and precious
metal finishing in non-technical language. ₍1st ed.₎ Chicago, H. Paulson ₍1948₎
516 p. illus. 22 cm.

1. Jewelry.   I. Title.

TS725.L55   739.27   49-6140*

NL 0388022   DLC CU OU MB MiD OCISA TU

Linicke, Johann Georg
see Linike, Johann Georg, ca. 1680-ca. 1730.

LINICUS, Werner, 1903-
Versuche über die eigenschaften gezogener
drähte und den kraftbedarf beim drahtziehen.
Diss.   Berlin, J. Springer, 1931.
f°. pp. (31). Illustr.
"Lebenslauf", at end.
Pp. [38]-64 of a larger work.

NL 0388024   MH ICRL

De Linie. jaarg. 1-   (nr. 1-   );
29 Maart 1946-
₍Amsterdam₎
v. illus., ports. 60-63 cm. weekly.

AP15.L58   59-27241

NL 0388025   DLC

VOLUME 334

Linieff, Eugenie.

See

Lineva, Evgeniia Eduardovna (Paprits) 1854-1919.

Linien.
Julefluen; moderne kunst & litteratur. [København, E. Bille; expedition Kommissionsanstalten] 1935.
31p. illus. 31cm.

"Ssernummer af 'Linien'."
"En foraarsaften; drama af Jens August Schade": 15p. laid in.

I. Title.

NL 0388027   IEN

8010a.85.2.Abschnitt 1-3
Linienführung und Bahngestaltung, Oberbau und Bahnhofs-Anlagen. Wiesbaden. Kreidel. 1899. 3 sections in 2 v. Illus. Plans. Maps. Charts. Tables. Diagrams. Profiles. [Die Eisenbahn-Technik der Gegenwart. Band 2, Abschnitt 1-3.] 26 cm., in 8s.
Contents.—Abschnitt 1, 2. Bahngattungen, Grundlagen für deren Gestaltung und Wahl. Paul.—Aufsuchen und Entwerfen einer Bahnlinie. Paul.—Anforderung des Betriebes an die Gestaltung und Eintheilung der Bahn. Paul.—Lage der Bahn zum Hochwasser, Schutzmassregeln gegen Wasserschäden, Rutschungen, Frostwirkungen, Felsstürze, Feuersgefahr und Schnee. Schubert.—Lage der Bahn im Verhältnisse zu

kreuzende Verkehrswegen, Ausrustung der Bahn auf freier Strecke mit Nebenanlagen. Blum.—Linienführung elektrischer Bahnen. Zehme.—Allgemeine Grundlagen für die Anordnung des Oberbaues und den Bau des Gleises. Blum.—Ergebnisse der theoretischen Untersuchungen über Berechnung der Oberbaues. Blum.—Herstellung und Entwässerung des Planums, der Bettung und der Bahnkrone auf der freien Strecke und auf den Bahnhöfen. Schubert.—Der Bau des Gleises. Blum.—Besondere Gestaltung des Oberbaues für elektrische Bahnen. Zehme.

Abschnitt 3. Weichen und Kreuzungen. Himbeck.—Drehscheiben für Wagen und Lokomotiven. Fraenkel.—Schiebebühnen für Lokomotiven und Wagen. Fraenkel.—Bahnhöfe: Einleitung. Anordnung der Stationen im Allgemeinen. Haltepunkte und Haltestellen. Kleinere und mittlere zwischenbahnhöfe mit vereinigtem Personen-, Güter- und Verschiebedienste. Grössere Bahnhofsanlagen. Güterbahnhöfe. Laistner.—Verschiebebahnhöfe. Jäger.—Bahnhofshochbauten. Groeschel.—Bahnsteigbedachungen und Bahnhofshallen. Ebert und Groeschel.—Abort- und Nebengebaude. Groeschel.—Hochbauten für den Güter-

verkehr. Groeschel.—Hochbauten für Betriebszwecke. Groeschel.—Ausrüstung der Lokomotivschuppen; Betriebswerkstätten. Fraenkel.—Wasser-Stationen und Krähne. Lehners.—Reinigung des Speisewassers. Wehrenfennig. Wagenschuppen. Aufenthalts- und Übernachtungs-Gebäude. Groeschel.—Bahnsteige, Bahnsteig-Tunnel und Brücken. Bahnsteigabsperrung. Rampen. von Beyer.—Kohlenladevorrichtungen. Hebevorrichtungen. Brücken- und Gepäckwaagen. Berndt.—Beleuchtungs-Anlagen. Sommerguth.—Entseuchungs-Anstalten. Leissner.—Bahnhofsanlagen elektrischer Bahnen. Zehme.

L4526

NL 0388031   MB

Linière, Bartholomew de.
True Account of the Horrid Conspiracy against the Life of William III. King of England, Scotland, France and Ireland, &c., setting forth by whom it was contrived, how it was to be carried on, and the manner of its discovery. Published by Authority. [London]. 1692.
8 p. f°.

NL 0388032   MH-L

Linière, Marc Ferdinand de Groubentall de
see **Groubentall de Linière, Marc Ferdinand de, 1739-1815?**

Linière, Raoul de.
Armorial de la Sarthe (2e série) Notices généalogiques sur les familles résidantes ou possessionnées dans la région sarthoise au cours des XVII° et XVIII° siècles. Le Mans, Impr. M. Vilaire, 1948.
2 v. (vi, 726 p.) 25 cm.
"Bibliographie héraldique": v. 2, p. 725.

1. Sarthe, France (Dept.)—Geneal. 2. Sarthe, France (Dept.)—Nobility. 3. Heraldry—France—Sarthe (Dept.) I. Title.

CS597.S3L56   929   49-5517*

NL 0388034   DLC

Microcard
57-11
ser.2
no.792

Linières, comte de.
Le connoisseur; ou, À quelque chose malheur est bon, comédie en vers & en trois actes. Bordeaux, Labottière, 1779. [Louisville, Ky., Falls City Press, 1959]
1 card. [Three centuries of French drama. ser.2: 17th, 18th and 19th centuries, no.792]

Microcard edition.
Collation of original: 46 p.

NL 0388035   AU ICRL NNC

Linières,   comte de.
Corisandre, comédie opera
see under   **Langlé, Honoré François Marie, 1741-1807.**

Linieres, Eduardo Enrique Teodoro Turreau de
see   **Turreau de Linieres, Eduardo Enrique Teodoro.**

Linières, Louis Marie Turreau de, baron.
See
Turreau de Linières, Louis Marie, baron, 1756-1816.

[LINIERS, Amaury de]
Notice sur la famille Du chesne de Vauvert. [1502-1862]. Niort, impr. de L. Favre et cie, [1863].

1.8°. Geneal. table.

I. Title.

NL 0388039   MH

Liniers, Jacques Antoine Marie de
see   **Liniers y Bremond, Santiago Antonio Maria de, conde de Buenos Aires, 1753-1810.**

Liniers, Santiago.
see   **Liniers y Bremond, Santiago Antonio Maria de, conde de Buenos Aires, 1753-1810.**

TN36
L7
Liniers de Estrada,
Notas históricas alrededor de un yacimiento minero. Buenos Aires, Editorial P.Y.M.A., 1950.
26 p.   23 cm.

1. Mines and mineral resources - Argentine Republic.

NL 0388042   DI

F2841
.S35
Liniers de Estrada, ——, ed.

Sánchez de Mendeville, María, 1786-1868.
Recuerdos del Buenos Aires virreynal [por] Mariquita Sánchez. Prólogo y notas por Liniers de Estrada. Buenos Aires, ENE Editorial [1953]

Liniers y Bremond, Santiago Antonio Maria de, conde de Buenos Aires, 1753-1810.
... Hommage à Jacques de Liniers, comte de Buenos-Aires
see under title

Liniers y de Bremond, Santiago Antonio Maria de, 1753-1810.
Proclama del Excmo. Sr. Virey de estas provincias D. Santiago Liniers y Bremond, etc. A la Ciudad de Montevideo, su guarnicion, vecinos y habitantes de ella, y sus campañas.   Buenos Aires, 1808.
6 p.
Dated: [3] Nov., 1808.
Caption title: imprint at end.

NL 0388045   RPJCB

Liniers y de Bremond, Santiago Antonio Maria de, 1753-1810.
Dn Santiago Liniers [sic] y Bremond, Caballero del Orden de San Juan ... Valerosos y fidelisimos habitantes de Buenos Ayres ... Buenos Aires, 1808.
Title from caption and beginning of text; imprint at end.
Dated at end: 15 Aug. 1808.

NL 0388046   RPJCB

Liniers y de Bremond, Santiago Antonio Maria de, 1753-1810.
Don Santiago Liniers y Bremond, Caballero de la Orden de San Juan, Comendador de Ares del Maestre en la Montesa ... Por quanto el dia de ayer vi con el mayor dolor ... [Buenos Aires, 1809]
3 p.
Dated 2 Jan. 1809.

NL 0388047   RPJCB

Liniers y de Bremond, Santiago Antonio Maria de 1753-1810.
Dn Santiago Liniers y Bremond ... Por quanto se ha dirigido á este Superior Gobierno la Carta Acordada del Real ...   Buenos Aires, 1809.
4 p.
Caption title; imprint at end.
Dated 21 April, 1809.

NL 0388048   RPJCB

Liniers y de Bremond, Santiago Antonio Maria de, 1753-1810.
Don Santiago Liniers y Bremond, ... Proclama. Nobles y generosos habitantes de Buenos-Ayres ...   Buenos Aires, 1809.
12 p.
Dated: 20, Feb. 1809.
Caption title; imprint at end.

NL 0388049   RPJCB

VOLUME 334

*Liniers y Gallo Alcántara, Santiago, conde de, 1842-1908.
Discursos leídos ante la Real acade-
mia española en la recepción pública de
Sr. D. Santiago de Liniers, el día 2 de
febrero de 1894. ¡Florecimiento del estilo
epistolar en España¡ Madrid, Fortanet
1894. 104p. 26cm.
Contestación del D. Francisco Silvela.

NL 0388050 CU MH

PQ
6534
.L38
N6
Liniers y Gallo Alcántara, Santiago, conde de,
1842-1908
Novísimo espejo y doctrinal de caballeros,
en doce romances, por el br. d. Diego de
Bringas ¡pseud.¡ Madrid, Impr. de A. Pérez
Dubrull, 1887.
227 p. 18 cm.

NL 0388051 WU

Linificio e canapificio nazionale.
Linifico & canapificio nazionale, società anonima, Milano,
1873-1923. ¡Milano, 1923¡
512 p. illus. (part col.) ports., col. maps. 26 x 34 cm.
Text in Italian, English, and French.

1. Linen—Italy.
HD9930.I 84L528 1923   53-50471

NL 0388052 DLC

Linificio e canapificio nazionale.
Linificio e canapificio nazionale, Milano, 1873-1948.
¡Milano, 1949¡
1 v. illus. (part col.) ports., plans. 33 cm.
Text in Italian and English in parallel columns.

1. Linen—Italy.

New York Univ. Wash.   A 53-2448
for Library of Congress   Sq. Library

NL 0388053 NNU-W NN

Wason
DS619
L75
Liniger, Hans
Saja, Tuan. Zürich, Büchergilde Guten-
berg, 1943.
300p. illus., map. 24cm.

1. Dutch East Indies -- Descr. & trav.
I. Title.

NL 0388054 NIC CtY

Liniger, Hans, 1894-
... Geologie des Delsberger Beckens und der umgebung von
Movelier ... von Hans Liniger. (Ausgegeben im dezember
1925) Bern, In kommission bei A. Francke a.-g., 1925.
viii, 71 p. illus., ii fold. pl., fold. tab. 32cm. (Beiträge zur geologischen karte der Schweiz; hrsg. von der Geologischen kommission der
Schweiz. naturforschenden gesellschaft, subventioniert von der Eidge-
nossenschaft, n. f., 55. lief., iv. abt., des ganzen werkes 85. lief.)
"Literaturverzeichnis": p. v–vii.

1. Geology—Switzerland. I. Title.
                                        G S 26-351
Library, U. S. Geological   Survey (535) qB2 vol. 55, pt. 4

NL 0388055 DI-GS CoU GU NIC CU ICJ NN

Liniger, Hans, 1894-
Die Tertiärbildungen des Delsberger beckens und seiner
nördlichen umgebung ... von Hans Liniger ... Bern, Gedruckt
bei Stämpfli & cie., 1925.
viii, ¡3¡, 54 p. illus., ¡2¡ fold. pl. (profile, tab.) 31cm.
Inaug.-diss.—Univ. Basel.
Separatabdruck aus: "Beiträge zur geologischen karte der Schweiz,
n. f., 55. lief, iv. abt."
Curriculum vitae: p. 54.
Literaturverzeichnis: p. v–vii.

1. Geology, Stratigraphic—Tertiary. 2. Geology—Alps. I. Title.
                                          G S 28-117
U. S. Geol. survey. Library   351 qL64t
for Library of Congress   ¡a40c1¡

NL 0388056 DI-GS CtY ICRL MiU NN

Liniger, Hans, 1894-   ed.
Schweizerische Auswanderung in Vergangenheit und Zu-
kunft; Berichte aus fünf Erdteilen. Luzern, Der Schweizer
Pionier im Ausland ¡1948-
v. illus. 23 cm.
CONTENTS—Bd. 1. Das Grundsätzliche.

1. Switzerland—Emig. & immig. I. Title.
JV8281.L5   325.2494   49-20209*

NL 0388057 DLC ICU MH CaBVa NNUN

W
600
L756be
1910
LINIGER, Hans, d. 1933.
Begutachtung der Finger-, Arm-, und
Beinverletzungen, mit Zusammenstellung
der neuesten Entscheidungen des Reichs-
Versicherungsamtes. Düsseldorf,
Schwann ¡1910¡
viii, 338 p.
I. Germany. Reichsversicherungsamt

NL 0388058 DNLM ICJ

W
600
L756b
1909
LINIGER, Hans, d. 1933.
Begutachtung der Finger- und Hand-
verletzungen, mit Zusammenstellung der
neuesten Entscheidungen des Reichs-
Versicherungsamtes. Düsseldorf,
Schwann ¡1909¡
161 p.
I. Germany. Reichsversicherungsamt
Title

NL 0388059 DNLM

Liniger, Hans, d. 1933.   ed.
Handbuch der ärztlichen begutachtung, bearbeitet von A.
de Bary ... M. J. Bauer ... ¡u. a.¡ ... herausgegeben von H.
Liniger, R. Weichbrodt, A. W. Fischer ... Leipzig, J. A
Barth, 1931.
2 v. illus. 24½cm.
Contains bibliographies.

1. Medical jurisprudence. 2. Insurance, Accident—Medical examinations. 3. Insurance, Life—Medical examinations. 4. Accidents—Adjustment of claims. 5. Insurance law—Germany. I. Weichbrodt, Raphael,
1886-   joint ed. II. Fischer, Albert Wilhelm. 1892-   joint ed
III. Title.
Library of Congress   RA1121.L5   31-12741
Copyright A—Foreig   11834
                                                 340.6

NL 0388060 DLC DNLM ICJ PPC ICRL

Liniger, Hans, d. 1933.
Die Rechtsprechung des Reichs-Versicherungs-
amtes bei dauernden Unfallschäden. 3te auf.
Düsseldorf. [Pref. 1912]

NL 0388061 MH-L

W
925
L756r
Liniger, Hans, d. 1933
Der Rentenmann. ¡1.¡-   Aufl.
Leipzig, Barth, 1917-
v. illus.

Pam
3460
no.5
7th- editions edited by G. Molineus.
9th edition. 1942, classed in pamphlet
collection.

1. Disability 2. Employer's liability -
Germany

NL 0388062 DNLM PU-W

Liniger, Hans, d. 1933.
Der rentenmann, von H. Liniger. 8., verb. und ergänzte aufl.
Herausgegeben von prof. dr. G. Molineus ... Mit 86 abbildun-
gen auf 9 tafeln. Leipzig, J. A. Barth, 1940.
38 p., 1 l. ix pl. (1 fold.) on 5 l. 25cm.
First published in 1917.

1. Insurance, Accident—Medical examinations. I. Molineus, Gustav, 1880-   ed. II. Title.
                                        45-33967
Library of Congress   HG8886.L5 1940
                                        331.25441

NL 0388063 DLC DNLM

Liniger, Hans, d. 1933.
Der Rentenmann. 9. ergänzte Aufl.
hrsg. von Prof. Dr. G. Molineus. Leipzig,
J. A. Barth, 1942.
38

NL 0388064 DNLM MnU

W
925
L756r
1949
LINIGER, Hans, d. 1933.
Der Rentenmann. 11. ergänzte Aufl.,
hrsg. von G. Molineus. München,
Barth, 1949.
38 p. illus.
1. Accident insurance - Germany
I. Molineus, Gustav, 1880-   Title

NL 0388065 DNLM

Liniger, Hans, d. 1933.
Der Rentenmann. 12., verb. und ergänzte Aufl. hrsg. von
G. Molineus. München, J. A. Barth, 1951.
37 p. illus. (1 fold.) 24 cm.
At head of title: Liniger-Molineus.
First published in 1917.

1. Insurance, Accident—Medical examinations. I. Molineus, Gustav, 1880-   ed. II. Title.
[HG8886.L   ]   A 52-7350
Illinois. Univ. Library
for Library of Congress

NL 0388066 IU DNLM

W
925
L756r
1954
LINIGER, Hans, d. 1933.
Der Rentenmann. 13. Aufl. hrsg. von
G. Molineus. Neubearb. von Werner
Jantke und Helmut Beckmann. München,
Barth, 1954.
45 p. illus.
1. Accident insurance - Germany
I. Molineus, Gustav, 1880-   ed.
Title

NL 0388067 DNLM MH

VOLUME 334

Liniger, Hans, d. 1933.
Der unfallmann; ein vademekum für begutachtende ärzte, berufsgenossenschaften und spruchbehörden in medizinischen fragen, von prof. dr. H. Liniger ... und prof. dr. G. Molineus ... Leipzig, J. A. Barth, 1928.

3 p. l., 156 p. incl. tables. 24½ᵐ.

1. Accidents. 2. Fractures. 3. Insurance, Accident—Germany. ɪ. Molineus, Gustav, joint author. ɪɪ. Title.

Library of Congress   RD131.L5   29–12293 Revised

NL 0388068   DLC

W
160
L176u
1930
Liniger, Hans, d. 1933.
Der Unfallmann, ein Vademekum für begutachtende Ärzte Berufsgenossenschaften und Spruchbehörden in medizinischen Fragen, von H. Liniger und G. Molineus. 2., durchgesehene und ergänzte Aufl. Leipzig, Barth, 1930.
vi, 159 p.

1. Accident insurance - Germany 2. Health insurance - Germany I. Molineus, Gustav, 1880- Title

NL 0388069   DNLM

Liniger, Hans, d. 1933.
Der unfallmann; ein vademekum für begutachtende ärzte, berufsgenossenschaften und spruchbehörden in medizinischen fragen, von H. Liniger† und G. Molineus. 3., durchgesehene und ergänzte aufl. bearbeitet von prof. dr. G. Molineus ... Leipzig, J. A. Barth, 1934.

vii, 167 p. 25ᵐᵐ.

1. Accidents. 2. Fractures. 3. Insurance, Accident—Germany. ɪ. Molineus, Gustav, 1880- joint author. ɪɪ. Title.

Library of Congress   RD131.L5 1934   35–12810
Copyright A—Foreign   26143
    617.1

NL 0388070   DLC

Liniger, Hans, d. 1933.
... Der unfallmann; ein vademekum für begutachtende ärzte, berufsgenossenschaften und spruchbehörden in medizinischen fragen. 4., umgearb. und ergänzte aufl., hrsg. von prof. dr. Gustav Molineus ... Leipzig, J. A. Barth, 1940.

vii, 172 p. 25ᵐ.

At head of title: Liniger-Molineus.
"1. auflage 1928."

1. Accidents. 2. Fractures. 3. Insurance, Accident—Germany. ɪ. Molineus, Gustav, 1880- joint author. ɪɪ. Title.

Library of Congress   RD131.L5 1940   41–13598
    617.1

NL 0388071   DLC DNLM MnU

W
925
L756u
1950
LINIGER, Hans, d. 1933.
Der Unfallmann. 6., ergänzte Aufl., hrsg. von G. Molineus. München, Barth, 1950.
200 p.
1. Accident insurance - Germany
2. Health insurance - Germany
I. Molineus, Gustav, 1880- Title

NL 0388072   DNLM

Liniger, Hans, d. 1933.
Der Unfallmann. 7. verb. Aufl., hrsg. von Gustav Molineus. München, J. A. Barth, 1951.

194 p. 24 cm.

1. Accidents. 2. Fractures. 3. Insurance, Employers' liability—Germany. ɪ. Title.

RD131.L5 1951   *614.88 617.1   53–21304 ‡

NL 0388073   DLC IU

LINIGER, Hermann, 1880-
Gelenkmaus und unfall. Inaug.-diss., Bonn, 1907.
37 p.

NL 0388074   MBCo ICRL MH DNLM

Liniger, Jean.
Le monde et Dieu selon Philippe de Commynes. Neuchâtel, 1943.

xxiii, 97 p. port. 24 cm.

Thèse—Neuchâtel.
"Bibliographie": p. ₍x₎–xii.

1. Comines, Philippe de, sieur d'Argenton, 1445?–1511. ɪ. Title.

DC106.9.C78L⁵   923.244   48–39631*

NL 0388075   DLC LU CtY PU NNC MH

LINIGER, W
Les marques postales de la Suisse romande, 1690-1850, par W. Liniger, J.-L. Nagel ₍et₎ L. Vuille. ₍Yverdon₎ Impr. du Journal d'Yverdon, 1955. 92 p. illus. 25cm.

"10 exemplaires hors commerce sur papier couché, numérotés de I à X et 300 exemplaires sur papier satiné, numérotés de 1 à 300." no. 220.
Bibliography, p. 88–89.
1. POSTMARKS--SWITZERLAND ɪ. Nagel, J. L ɪɪ. Vuille, L

NL 0388076   NN

M317
L7569
Linike, Johann George, ca.1680–ca.1730.
₍Overture, 2 recorders & continuo, C major₎
Ouverture in C-dur, für zwei Alt-Blockfloten in F oder andere Melodie-Instrumente und Continuo. Hrsg. und bearb. von Hans Fischer. Berlin-Lichterfelde, C.F. Vieweg ₍c1938₎
Pl. no. V. 2151.
score (7 p.) & 3 pts. 31cm. (Musikschätze der Vergangenheit; Vokal- und Instrumentalmusik des 16. bis 18. Jahrhunderts)
Edited from a ms. in the Landesbibliothek, Schwerin.
1.Suites (Harpsichord, 2 recorders)
I.Fischer, Hans,

NL 0388077   CSt

Linike, Johann Georg, ca. 1680–ca. 1730.
₍Suite, 2 recorders & continuo, G minor₎
Suite für zwei Blockflöten und Generalbass, hrsg. von Hans Fischer. Partitur zugleich Cembalo- (Klavier-) Stimme. Berlin-Lichterfelde, C. F. Vieweg ₍c1939₎
score (12 p.) and parts. 31 cm. (Musikschätze der Vergangenheit, Vokal- und Instrumentalmusik des 16. bis 18. Jahrhunderts)
Edited from a manuscript in the Landesbibliothek, Schwerin.
Unfigured bass realized for harpsichord; violoncello part included.
1. Suites (Harpsichord, 2 recorders)—To 1800. ɪ. Fischer, Hans, 1899- ed. (Series)

M317.L68S8   M A 53–4 rev
Southern Methodist   Univ. Library
for Library of Congress   ₍r53b1₎†

NL 0388078   TxDaM NBuG CtY NN TxU CoU IU OCl DLC

M 317
.L73S9
Linike, Johann Georg, 1680ca.–1730ca.
₍Suites, 2 flutes & continuo₎
Zwei Suiten für zwei Flöten und Klavier (Basso continuo) Bearb. und hrsg. von Curt Rücker. Halle (Saale) Mitteldeutscher Verlag ₍1952?₎
score (10 p.) and 2 parts. (Alte Meister)
"Bestell-Nr. V 1224."

1. Suites (Harpsichord, 2 flutes)

NL 0388079   ICU

Linin, Anatoliĭ Mikhaĭlovich, 1901–1938.
... А. С. Пушкин на Дону; историко-литературные очерки. Ростов на Дону, Ростовское областное книгоиздательство, 1941.
173, ₍3₎ p. 17ᵐ.
At head of title: А. Линин.
"Под общей редакцией ... М. А. Полторацкой."
Bibliographical references included in "Примечания" (p. 88–93, 152–173)
Bibliographical foot-notes.
Contents.— А. С. Пушкин на Дону и Кубани.— История войска донского В. Д. Сухорукова и А. С. Пушкин.
1. Pushkin, Aleksandr Sergeevich, 1799–1837. 2. Sukhorukov, Vasiliĭ Dmitrievich, 1794 or 5–1841. ɪ. Poltoratskaia, Marianna A., 1906– *Title transliterated: A. S. Pushkin na Donu.*

    43–27382

NL 0388080   DLC

PG3458
.A1A2
Linin, Anatoliĭ Mikhaĭlovich, 1901–1938, ed.
А. П. Чехов и наш край; к 75-летию со дня рождения. Сборник под общей ред. А. М. Линина. Ростов н-Д., Азово-Черноморское краевое кн-во, 1935.

NL 0388082   DLC MH

Linin, Anatoliĭ Mikhaĭlovich, 1901–1938.
К истории буржуазного стиля в русской литературе; творчество П. Д. Боборыкина. Ростов-Дон, 1935.

135 p. 25 cm.

Bibliography: p. 130–135.

1. Boborykin, Petr Dmitrievich, 1836–1921. ɪ. Title. *Title transliterated: K istorii burzhuaznogo stilia v russkoi literature.*

PG3453.B62Z7   55–53379

NL 0388083   DLC

Linin, Anatoliĭ Mikhaĭlovich, 1901–1938.
К вопросу о влиянии Гоголя на Островского. Ростов н-Д., 1935.

21–34 p. 25 cm.

"Отдельный оттиск из 6 тома 'Известий РПИ.'"

1. Ostrovskiĭ, Aleksandr Nikolaevich, 1823–1886. 2. Gogol', Nikolaĭ Vasil'evich, 1809–1852. *Title transliterated: K voprosu o vliianii Gogolia na Ostrovskogo.*

PG3337.O8Z675   54–48162 ‡

NL 0388084   DLC

₍Linin, Anatoliĭ Mikhaĭlovich₎ 1901–1938.
... Критика о Горьком. (С. Балухатый, Критика о М. Горьком.' Библиография статей и книг, 1893–1932 г. Огиз, ГИХЛ, 1934. Стр. 594). ₍Ростов н-Д., Гостипография им. Калинина, 1935₎
179–183, ₍1₎ p. 24½ᵐ.
Caption title.
"Отдельный оттиск из VI тома 'Известий РПИ.'"
On cover: А. М. Линин.
"Пропуски библиографических указаний в книге Балухатого": p. 186–₍189₎.
1. Balukhatyĭ, Sergeĭ Dmitrievich, 1893–1945. Критика о Горьком. ɪ. Title. *Title transliterated: Kritika o Gor'kom.*

Library of Congress   Z8357.8.B33L5   42–41423

NL 0388084   DLC

Linin, Anatoliĭ Mikhaĭlovich, 1901–1938.
Творчество А. Н. Островского. К 50-летию со дня смерти. Ростов на Дону, Азово-Черноморское краевое изд-во, 1937.

246 p. illus. 17 cm.

1. Ostrovskiĭ, Aleksandr Nikolaevich, 1823–1886. *Title transliterated: Tvorchestvo A. N. Ostrovskogo.*

PG3337.O8Z68   54–47186 ‡

NL 0388085   DLC

VOLUME 334

Lining, Charles.
The cruise of the Confederate steamship "Shenandoah".

(In Tennessee historical magazine.   July, 1924.   v.8, no.2.)

NL 0388086   NcU

Lining, Mrs. Ida Marshall, ed.
The Keystone; a monthly journal devoted to women's work. v. 1–14; June 1899–June 1913. Charleston, S. C., 1899–1913.

Lining, John, 1708–1760.
Works by this author printed in America before 1801 are available in this library in the Readex Microprint edition of Early American Imprints published by the American Antiquarian Society.
This collection is arranged according to the numbers in Charles Evans' American Bibliography.

NL 0388088   DLC

WZ
270
L756d
1799
LINING, John, 1708–1760.
A description of the American yellow fever, which prevailed at Charleston, in South Carolina, in the year 1748 ... Philadelphia, Thomas Dobson, 1799.
30 p.   24 cm.
Evans 35733.
A letter, dated 1753, addressed to Dr. Robert Whytt of Edinburgh.
I. Whytt, Robert, 1714–1766

NL 0388089   DNLM NNNAM

Lining, John, 1708–1760.
Chisholm, Colin, 1755–1825.
An essay on the malignant pestilential fever introduced into the West Indian islands from Boullam, on the coast of Guinea, as it appeared in 1793 and 1794. By C. Chisholm ... To which is annexed, A description of the American yellow fever, which prevailed at Charleston in 1748, in a letter from Dr. John Lining. Philadelphia: Printed for Thomas Dobson, at the Stone house, n° 41, South Second street, 1799.

Lining, Thomas.
British Tracts 1691 L64
An account of the methods and motives of the late union and submission to the Assembly; offered and subscribed by Mr. Thomas Lining, Mr. Alexander Sheilds, Mr. William Boyd... [Edinburgh]1691.
46p.   19cm.

NL 0388091   CtY ICN PPPrHi

Lininger, Fred Fouse, 1892–
... Dairy products under the Agricultural adjustment act; developments up to April 1934, by F. F. Lininger. Washington, The Brookings institution, 1934.
viii, 99 p.   diagrs.   22½ᵐ.   (The Brookings institution. Pamphlet series, no. 13)
Half-title: The Institute of economics of the Brookings institution.

1. Agriculture and state—U. S.   2. U. S. Agricultural adjustment administration.   3. Agriculture—Economic aspects—U. S.   4. Dairy products—Marketing.   I. Brookings institution, Washington, D. C. Institute of economics.   II. Title.

Library of Congress   HD9275.U6L5
                                         ₍44k1₎   338.1

AAP ViU CU
NL 0388092   DLC OrCS WaS Or OrP OKentU PSC PHC NbU

Lininger, Fred Fouse, 1892–   joint author.
Swinson, Carl Robert, 1891–
... Marketing apples grown in the Cumberland-Shenandoah region of Pennsylvania, Virginia, and West Virginia. By Carl R. Swinson ... J. J. Vernon ... F. F. Lininger ... and F. P. Weaver ... and A. J. Dadisman ... Washington ₍U. S. Govt. print. off.₎ 1931]

Lininger, Fred Fouse, 1892–
Potato marketing in Pennsylvania.   State College, 1932.
39 p.

NL 0388094   PP

Lininger, Fred Fouse, 1892–
The relation of production and foreign trade of agricultural products to the agricultural depression. ₍n.p.,n.d.₎ 12p.,7ℓ.   tables.

Mimeographed.

NL 0388095   PSt

Lininger, Fred Fouse, 1892–
The relation of the basic-surplus marketing plan to milk production in the Philadelphia milk shed ... by Fred Fouse Lininger. Ithaca, N. Y., 1928.
cover-title, 63 p.   illus. (map) diagrs.   22ᵐ.
Thesis (PH. D.)—Cornell university, 1926.
Bulletin 281, August, 1928, of the Pennsylvania state college School of agriculture and experiment station, with cover containing thesis note.

1. Milk supply—Philadelphia.   2. Marketing.

Library of Congress   SF261.L5 1926   31–10273
                                                                   338.1

NL 0388096   DLC PBm NIC PP MH

Lininger, George W.
Catalogue of the art collection of Geo. W. Lininger, Omaha. ₍3d ed.₎ Omaha, Neb., F. B. Festner, printer, 1896.
56 p.   illus. (incl. port., plates) 24ᵐ.

1. Lininger art gallery, Omaha, Neb.   2. Art—Omaha, Neb.—Catalogs.

                                                             CA 9–6093 Unrev'd
Library of Congress   N660.A6 1896

NL 0388097   DLC

Lininger, Hattie.
Wind swept thoughts; poems by Hattie Lininger. New York, The Paebar company, 1939.
5 p. l., 9–47 p.   21ᵐ.

I. Title.
                                                             41–2387
Library of Congress   PS3523.I 639W5 1939
——— Copy 2.
Copyright   811.5

NL 0388098   DLC

Lininger, Peter.
Rollumbus, Entdeckungsfahrten im Burgenland; ein kleiner Reiseführer. Unter Mitarbeit von Rudolf A. Hrandek, Johann Mayer ₍und₎ Margit Pflagner. Bebildert von Ernst Schrom. ₍Wien₎ Burgenland-Verlag ₍ᶜ1952–
v.   illus. 18 cm.

1. Burgenland—Descr. & trav.   I. Title.

DB785.B8L5   57–57379 ‡

NL 0388099   DLC NN

Lininger, William Harding, 1862–
The Liningers, genealogical register of the descendants of Henry Lininger, compiled and published by William H. Lininger. Chicago, Ill., 1930.
23, ₍1₎ p. illus. (incl. ports., map, double facsim.) 24ᵐ.

1. Lininger family (Henry Lininger, 1797–1866)
                                                             32–30555
Library of Congress   CS71.L756 1930

NL 0388100   DLC ViU OClWHi MB NN

Linington, Ann.
Other doors, by Ann Linington. Poughkeepsie, N. Y., Vassar co-operative bookshop, 1927.
30 p. 20ᵐ.
"The first printing of poems by Ann Linington is limited to 200 copies."

I. Title.

Library of Congress   PS3523.I 6408 1927   27–17955

NL 0388101   DLC

Linington, Elizabeth.
The proud man; a novel. New York, Viking Press, 1955.
405 p. illus. 22 cm.

1. O'Neill, Shane, of Tyrone, 1530?–1567—Fiction.   I. Title.

PZ4.L756P   55—9641

                    OrU WaT Or WaS CaBVa
                    OC1 TxU ViU IU AU MsU UU FTaSU PP OrP PPAN OrP WaE
NL 0388102   DLC MoU NcD FMU CoU FU CLSU MsSM OU CU

Liniņš, V
Lopkopība. Rediģējis V. Liniņš. Mācības grāmata lauksaimniecības skolām. Rīgā, Lauksaimniecības pārvaldes izdevums, 1938.
455 p. illus. 23 cm.
At head of title: V. Liniņš ₍et al.₎

1. Stock and stock-breeding—Latvia.   2. Poultry—Latvia.   I. Title.

SF55.L3L5   59–57749 ‡

NL 0388103   DLC

Linitskiĭ, A   M.
... Нотариат советских республик ... Под редакцией проф. Ал. Малицкого. Харьков, Юридическое издательство НКЮ УССР, 1927–
\ v. 22ᵐ.
At head of title: А. М. Линицкий ...
Errata slip inserted in v. 1.
Bibliography: v. 1, p. 4.

1. Notaries—Russia. 2. Notaries—Ukraine.   I. Malitskiĭ, Aleksandr Leonidovich, 1874–   ed. II. Russia (1917–   R. S. F. S. R.) Laws, statutes, etc. III. Ukraine. Laws, statutes, etc.   IV. Title.

                                                             41–34167

NL 0388104   DLC

Linitskiĭ, Petr Ivanovich, 1839–1906.
Пособіе къ изученію вопросовъ философіи; элементы философскаго міросозерцанія. Харьковъ, Тип. Губ. правленія, 1892.
425 p. 26 cm.

1. Philosophy—Study and teaching.   I. Title.
                                                    Title romanized: Posobie k izuchenīîu voprosov filosofii.

B52.L55   72–226471

NL 0388105   DLC

VOLUME 334

Liniťskiĭ, Petr Ivanovich, 1839–1906.
Славянофильство и либерализмъ; опытъ систематическаго обозрѣнія того и другаго П. Линицкаго. Кіевъ, Тип. Г. Т. Корчакъ-Новицкаго, 1882.
iv, 255 p. 24 cm.
"Изъ журнала 'Труды Кіевской дух. академіи' за 1882 г."
Bibliographical footnotes.

1. Slavophilism. 2. Liberalism. I. Title.
Title transliterated: Slavíànofíl'stvo i liberalizm.

DK32.7.L55   66–52128

NL 0388106   DLC CaBVaU

Linius
see Martin von Cochem, Father, 1634?–1712.

Linius, Thomas.
In quatuor Institutionum iuris principis Iustiniani libros, explicationes & annotationes doctissimae, ex praelectionibus Dn. Thomae Linii... Francoforti, apud Christianum Egenolphum ₍1553₎
₍4₎, 163 ℓ. 34cm.

Bound with Francisci Hotomani... Commentarius in quatuor libros Institutionum Juris Civilis. 1560.
1. Corpus   Juris Civilis. Institutionum.

NL 0388108   MnU

[Link, ——]
Jellachich vor Wien. Was der Jellachich für Augen macht, wie er an der Spitze seiner Horden den Heldensitz Wien anglotzt.
[Wien]Gedruckt bei Franz Edlen von Schmid. [1848]
[2]p. 1 illus. 40.5x24.5cm.
Caption title; imprint on p.[2]; dated & signed: Wien im Oktober 1848. Link.
I.Title.

*pGB8
V6755R
10.10.48

NL 0388109   MH

Link, Mrs. Adeline Mae (De Sale) 1892–
joint author.
Schlesinger, Hermann Irving, 1889–
Laboratory manual of general chemistry, by H. I. Schlesinger ... and Adeline De Sale Link ... New ed. to conform to the third edition of Schlesinger's General chemistry. New York, London ₍etc.₎ Longmans, Green and co., 1937.

Link, Adeline Mae (De Sale) 1892–
Chicago. University.
Syllabus for Chemistry 104, 105, prepared by Adeline De Sale Link. The University of Chicago, college course in general inorganic chemistry ... 3d ed., September, 1937. Chicago, Ill., Distributed by the University of Chicago bookstore, ₍1937.

Link,Mrs.Adeline Mae(De Sale) 1892 –
...The velocity of rearrangement of benzoyl azide...by Adeline M.DeSale. Chicago,1917.
1 1.,57,5 numb.1.incl.tables. diagrs.(1 fold.)
29ᵐ.
Typewritten.
Thesis(Ph.D.)–University of Chicago,1917.
Bibliographical foot-notes.
"Abstract":5 1.at end.

QD1099
.L75

1.Benzoyl azide.

NL 0388112   ICU

232
L756c

Theol.

Link, Adolf, 1860–
Christi Person und Werk im Hirten des Hermas. Marburg, N.G. Elwert, 1886.
61p. 23cm.

1. Jesus Christ--Person and offices. 2. Hermas. I. Title.

NL 0388113   TxDaM MH-AH OCH ICRL

Link, Adolf, 1860–
Die einheit des Pastor Hermae. Von lic. Adolf Link ... Marburg, N. G. Elwert, 1888.
2 p. l., 47, ₍1₎ p. 23ᵐ.

1. Hermas. I. Title.
                         39–18376
Library of Congress   BS2900.H5L5

NL 0388114   DLC NcD MH-AH NNUT MiU OCU

LINK, Adolf , 1887–
Die deutsche lederindustrie; eine standortsstudie. Inaug.-diss., Heidelberg, Tübingen, H.Laupp, 1913.
"Curriculum vitae, " p.53
                    Econ 7723.1

NL 0388115   MH NNU-W CtY ICRL

QD412
.A7L4

Link, Albert.
Ueber aromatische arsen- und phosphor-verbindungen.
Freiburg, 1880.
37p.
Inaug.-diss.– Freiburg.

NL 0388116   DLC

Link, Alfred G. W.
Die einschraenkung des grundsatzes der veraeusserungsfreiheit des eigentuemers in den rechtsformen der neueren bodenpolitik. Auszug. Inaug. diss. Marburg, 1924.

NL 0388117   ICRL

Link, Anton.
Das Dorfbuch als Mittelpunkt des dörflichen Lebens, unter Mitwirkung von Wilhelm Philipp bearb. von Anton Link. Berlin, Verlag der Deutschen Arbeitsfront ₍1941₎
60 p. illus. 21 cm. (Politische Heimatkunde, Schriften zur Volksbildungsarbeit auf dem Lande, 3. Heft)
"Unser Dorfbuch, von Wilhelm Philipp": p. 53–60.

1. Villages — Germany. 2. Germany — Hist. — Historiography. 3. Germany—History, Local. I. Philipp, Wilhelm. II. Title. (Series)
DD86.L55   943.007   A F 49–645*
California. Univ. Libr.
for Library of Congress   †

NL 0388118   CU MH CoFS NN IU DLC

Link, Anton, 1773–1833.
Homilien der ersten Art. das ist: Predigten auf alle Festtage im Jahre, in welchen die gewöhnlichen festtäglichen Evangelien erklärt und angewandt werden. Linz, Cajetan Haslinger, 1829.
246p 19cm

NL 0388119   MnCS

LINK, Anton,1889–
Über ringbildung bei einigen tropenhölzern. Inaug.-diss., Heidelberg, C.Winter,1915.

Diagrs. and other illustr.
"Lebenslauf", p.41.

NL 0388120   MH ICRL CtY

Link, Arthur Stanley, 1920–
American epoch; a history of the United States since the 1890's. ₍1st ed.₎ New York, Knopf, 1955.
xxii, 724, xxxvii p. illus., ports. maps. 24 cm.
Bibliography: p. ₍705₎–724.

1. U. S.—Hist.—20th cent. I. Title.

E741.L55   973.91   54–13244

OrP KU OCl NN PPFr CaBVaU WaT OrCS OrU WaSp WaS OrP
TU IU PJA PSt PP PPD PBL MB ViU NcD OCU NcC ScCleU PW
NL 0388121   DLC TxU CoU MoU Wa OrMonO IdPI KyLx DSI

Link, Arthur Stanley, 1920–
The South and the Democratic campaign of 1912. Chapel Hill [University of North Carolina] 1945.
iv, 542 l. maps.
Thesis - University of North Carolina.
Bibliography: l. [489]–542.
Microfilm (negative) Gainesville, University of Florida Library, 1969. 1 reel. 35mm.
1. Presidents - U.S. - Election - 1912.
2. Wilson, Woodrow, Pres. U.S., 1856–1924.
3. Southern States - Pol. & govt. - 1865–
I. Title.

NL 0388122   FU

Link, Arthur Stanley, 1920–
Wilson. Princeton, Princeton University Press, 1947–
v. illus., plates. 24 cm.
Includes bibliographies.
Contents.—₍1₎ The road to the White House.—₍2₎ The new freedom. — ₍3₎ The struggle for neutrality.

1. Wilson, Woodrow, Pres. U. S., 1856–1924.

E767.L65   923.173   47–3554 rev*

PPL PPT PWcS PPAmP PPD MB NcRS NcGU NcD
PJA C KU WHi IEN OU DSI ICU TxU MH ViU PHi PP PPA
OC1U PBL PSC OO PHi PJB OC1W PPT PLF OOxM DI PCM WaU
OKentU NN MU FU DSI PIm NcD CU AU OC1W PSt ScC1eU PV
DS AU MiU OU ViU CtY-L IU TU LU MeB KyWA NIC MoU NNC
OrU Wa WaS WaSp KEmT TNJ NIC CU MsSM ScU GU KyLx TxU
IdPI IdU MtU Or OrAshS OrCS OrMonO OrP OrPR OrSaW
NL 0388123   DLC WaSpG WaT WaTC WaU WaWW CaBVa CaBVaU

Z8976
.9
.T8

Link, Arthur Stanley, 1920 –
Turnbull, Laura Shearer, 1887–
Woodrow Wilson, a selected bibliography of his published writings, addresses and public papers. Princeton, Princeton Univ. Press, 1948.

973
C734n
v.17

Link, Arthur Stanley, 1920–
Woodrow Wilson and the progressive era, 1910–1917, by ... N.Y., Harper & Row, 1943.
xviii,331p. illus. 22cm. (The New American Nation Series)

I.Title. 1.WILSON, WOODROW, PRES. U.S., 1856–1924 2.U.S. – POLITICS & GOVERNMENT – 1898–1919

NL 0388126   OWorP

VOLUME 334

Link, Arthur Stanley, 1920–
Woodrow Wilson and the progressive era, 1910–1917. [1st ed.] New York, Harper [*1954]
xvii, 331 p. illus., ports., maps. 22 cm. (The New American nation series)
Bibliographical footnotes. "Essay on sources": p. 283–313.

1. U. S.—Pol. & govt.—1913–1921. 2. Wilson, Woodrow, Pres. U. S., 1856–1924.

E766.L5   973.913   53–11849

WaSpG WaT WaWW WaTC
IdU CaBVaU IdPI CaBVaU CaBViP IdPI Wa WaE WaSp WaS NNC FMU DNAL DSI OrP OrLgE OrPR OrMonO OrAshS OrSaW OrCS UU ScCleU KyU-A Ky-LEKyLxT MoU MeB KyWnS MB
NL 0388127   DLC WU DSI TxU DCU MBtS NjR Or MtBC OrU

W 4
W95
1948
LINK, August, 1921–
Ueber Beobachtungen der Pericarditis in den letzten zehn Jahren. [Miltenberg, Volkhardt] 1948.
35 p.
Inaug.-Diss. - Würzburg.
1. Pericarditis

NL 0388129   DNLM CtY

W 4
E69
1939
LINK, Auguste, 1915–
Kaffee-Kohle. Erlangen, Döres, 1939.
9 p.
Inaug.-Diss. - Erlangen.
Reprinted from Hippokrates, Heft 1, 1939.
1. Charcoal   Title

NL 0388130   DNLM

Link, C. F.
see Link, Heinrich Friedrich, 1767–1851.

TS
377
120F
Link, Carl, 1887–
Passionstypen Oberammergau 1922 [von] Carl Link New=York.
D. & R. Bischoff Verlagsanstalt, München N.W. [1922]
1p.l., 14 col.pl., [2]p. 38cm.
Publishers' device on t.-p.
Colored drawings of players at the Oberammergau passion play; 11 of them are autographed by the players depicted.
Unbound plates as issued in decorated blue board portfolio.

NL 0388132   MH

[Link, Carl G]
Shorthand elucidated. A complete and simple textbook of phonography. [New York] 1894.
59, [1], A1–A24, [4] p. 21cm.
Ms. note on t.-p.: By Carl G. Link.

1. Shorthand. I. Title.
                                        11–6603
Library of Congress   Z56.L757

NL 0388133   DLC

Link, Carolyn Crosby (Wilson)
Fir trees and fireflies, by Carolyn Crosby Wilson. New York and London, G. P. Putnam's sons, 1920.
ix p., 1 l., 69 p. 20¼cm.
Poems.

I. Title.
                                        21–3253 Revised
Library of Congress   PS3523.I 646F5

NL 0388134   DLC NcD ViU NN TxU

Link, Carolyn Crosby (Wilson)
There is still time [by] Carolyn Wilson Link. New York, The League to support poetry, 1944.
6 p. l., 15–60 p. 20cm.

I. League to support poetry, New York. II. Title.
                                        44–51318
Library of Congress   PS3523.I 646T5
                                        811.5

NL 0388135   DLC WaS WU TNJ UU NcGU OrU OrP

Link, Charles.
Le beseda, danse de salon bohème. Arrangée par Charles Link ... Prague: Édition de la Librairie slave [1863] 16 p. 4 pl. 15½ x 12½cm.

1. Dancing—Instruction. I. Title.   CARNEGIE CORP. OF NEW YORK.
                                        August 28, 1940

NL 0388136   NN

GV1767
.L75
Link, Charles, pub.
Unique dancing call book ... Rochester, N. Y., C. Link, *1893.
cover-title, [82] p. 9 x 15¼cm.
Printed parallel with back.

1. Dancing.

Library of Congress   CA 5–1755 Unrev'd

NL 0388137   DLC

LINK, Christian.
[Chemistry. Buffalo, N.Y. 185–?]
pp.1–224.
Title-page wanting.
                                        Chem 3016.2

NL 0388138   MH-C

Link, Conrad Barnett, 1912–
An anatomical study of the seedling of chrysanthemum morifolium Bailey... [Columbus] The O. state univ., 1940.
4p. l., 2–43, [1] numb. l.
Thesis (Ph.D.) - O. state univ.

NL 0388139   OU

Link, Eberhard, 1914–
Untersuchungen zur Symmorienrede (xiv) des Demosthenes. Limburg an der Lahn, 1940.
66 p. 21 cm.
Inaug.-Diss.—Frankfurt.
Vita.
Bibliography: p. 65–66.

1. Demosthenes. De classibus. I. Title: Symmorienrede.

PA3950.S9L5   51–48207

NL 0388140   DLC CU

Link, Edith (Murr) 1923–
The emancipation of the Austrian peasant, 1740–1798. New York, Columbia Univ. Press, 1949.
204 p. 23 cm. (Columbia University. Faculty of Political Science. Studies in history, economics and public law, no. 544)
Bibliography: p. 191–199.
Issued also as thesis, Columbia Univ.

1. Peasantry—Austria. 2. Land tenure—Austria. 3. Serfdom—Austria. I. Title. (Series)

H31.C7   no. 544   323.33   49–8621*
——— Copy 2.   HD634.L5 1949

MB OO OU
NL 0388141   DLC NBuC PSC PPT PSt PP PBm ViU TxU

Link, Edith (Murr) 1923–
The emancipation of the Austrian peasant, 1740–1798. New York, 1949.
204 p. 23 cm.
Thesis—Columbia University.
Published also as Studies in history, economics, and public law, edited by the Faculty of Political Science of Columbia University, no. 544.
Vita.
Bibliography: p. 191–199.

1. Peasantry—Austria. 2. Land tenure—Austria. 3. Serfdom—Austria. I. Title.

HD634.L5 1949a   323.33   A 49–3434*
Columbia Univ.   Libraries
for Library of Congress   [a50b½]†

NL 0388142   NNC CaBVaU OrCS DNAL IdPI WaS WaSpG DL

Link, Eduard.
Statistika obchodu. [Vyd. 1.] Praha, Státní pedagogické nakl., 1953.
228 p. illus. 21 cm. (Učební texty vysokých škol)
At head of title: Vysoká škola ekonomická v Praze. Fakulta statistiky.

1. Statistics. I. Title.

HA40.E3L5   58–29372 ‡

NL 0388143   DLC

Link, Edwin Albert, 1904–   joint author.

Weems, Philip Van Horn, 1889–
Simplified celestial navigation, by P. V. H. Weems and E. A. Link, jr. Annapolis, Md., Weems system of navigation, *1940.

[19..–]
LINK, Erich. Untersuchung[e]n über die Kräfte intermaxillärer Gummizüge und orthodontischer Fingerfedern [Tübingen] 48p. 8° Metzingen, 1935.

NL 0388145   DNLM

Link, Ernst, 1873–   627.8 S500
Ein Beitrag zur Querschnittbestimmung der Staumauern. Dissertation zur Erlangung der Würde eines Doktoringenieurs. Von E. Link, ... Mit 38 Abbildungen. Essen, [Druck von C. W. Haarfeld], 1925.
85, [1] p. diagrs. 22½cm.
A continuation of the author's work, published 1910, under the title: Die Bestimmung der Querschnitte von Staumauern und Wehren aus dreieckigen Grundformen.

NL 0388146   ICJ

Link, Erwin.   627.8 R002
Die Bestimmung der Querschnitte von Staumauern und Wehren aus dreieckigen Grundformen. Von E. Link, ... Mit 33 Abbildungen. Berlin, J. Springer, 1910.
61, [1] p. 33 illus. (diagrs.) 24cm.

NL 0388147   ICJ NN

VOLUME 334

Link, Erwin.
... Erdbau, von Erwin Link ... mit 72 abbildungen. Berlin und Leipzig, G. J. Göschen, 1912.
135 p. illus., diagrs. 16ᶜᵐ. (Sammlung Göschen. ₍630₎)
"Literatur": p. 6.

1. Earthwork. 2. Excavating machinery.

13-14998

Library of Congress   TA715.L5

NL 0388148   DLC MiD

Link, Erwin.
...Erdbau... 2. Aufl. Berlin, Gruyter & co., 1920.
135 p. illus. diagrs. (Sammlung Göschen. ₍630₎)
"Literatur": p.6.

NL 0388149   MiD MtBC

1885–
Link, Eugen; Aus d. Zool. Inst. d. Univ. Tübingen. Über die Stirnaugen der Neuropteren und Lepidopteren. Naumburg a. S. 1909: Lippert. 30 S. 8° ¶(Aus: Zool. Jahrbücher. Bd 27. Abt. f. Anat.)
Tübingen, Naturw. Diss. v. 31. Juli 1908, Ref. Blochmann
[Geb. 15. Juni 85 Trölleshof, O.-A. Nagold; Wohnort: Tübingen; Staatsangeh.: Württemberg; Vorbildung: Gymn. Reutlingen Reife Juli 03; Studium: Tübingen 10 S.; Coll. 31. Juli 08.]   [U 09. 4009

NL 0388150   ICRL MH-Z

Link, Eugene Perry, 1908–
... Democratic-Republican societies, 1790–1800 ... New York, Columbia university press, 1942.
xii p., 2 l., ₍3₎–256 p., 1 l. incl. front. (map) 23ᶜᵐ. (*Half-title:* Columbia studies in American culture, no. 9)
Thesis (PH. D.)—Columbia university, 1941.
Published also without thesis note.
Vita.
Bibliography: p. ₍213₎–242.

1. U. S.—Hist.—Constitutional period, 1789–1800. 2. Political clubs. I. Title.

Columbia univ. Libraries   A 42–837
for Library of Congress   E310.L6 1942
†   973.4

MdBE
NL 0388151   NNC FMU DAU OCU OO OU WaU ViU PPD DLC

Link, Eugene Perry, 1908–
... Democratic-Republican societies, 1790–1800. New York, Columbia university press, 1942.
xii p., 2 l., ₍3₎–256 p. incl. front. (map) 23½ᶜᵐ. (*Half-title:* Columbia studies in American culture, no. 9)
Issued also as thesis (PH. D.) Columbia university.
Bibliography: p. ₍213₎–242.

1. U. S.—Hist.—Constitutional period, 1789–1800. 2. Political clubs. I. Title.

Library of Congress   E310.L6 1942 a   42–5015
973.4

PPD ViU MB OrPR
NL 0388152   DLC WaTC OrCS OrU NIC PBm NcU PPT PU

Undergraduate
Library
E   **Link, Eugene Perry,** 1908–
31C   ... Democratic-Republican societies, 1790–1800. New York,
L75   Columbia university press, 1942. ₍Ann Arbor, Mich., 1959₎
1942a   xii p., 2 l., ₍3₎–256 p. incl. front. (map) 23½ᶜᵐ. (*Half-title:* Columbia studies in American culture, no. 9)
Issued also as thesis (PH. D.) Columbia university.
Bibliography: p. ₍213₎–242.
Photocopy (positive) made by University Microfilms.
Printed on double pages.

NL 0388153   MiU

---

s.g.
p369.1
L64d   **Link, Eugene Perry,** 1908–
The democratic societies of the Carolinas. (In: The North Carolina Historical Review, vol. XVIII, no. 3, July, 1941. p. 259–277.)

Detached copy in pamphlet binder.

1. Patriotic societies. I. Title.

NL 0388154   ScU

Link, Ewald.
Das Subsidiaritätsprinzip; sein Wesen und seine Bedeutung für die Sozialethik. Freiburg, Herder, 1955.
viii, 121 ₍1₎ p. 22 cm.

Prepared as dissertation, Johannes-Gutenberg-Universität, Mainz, 1949.
"Literaturverzeichnis": p. 120–₍122₎

1. Solidarity. 2. Social ethics. I. Title.

NL 0388155   DCU NjP NN WU

QB14   **Link, F.,** joint author.
.S75
1949   **Šternberk, Bohumil,** 1897–
Jen bychom radi věděli ... Astronomický slovníček. Redigovali B. Šternberk a F. Link. 2. vyd. V Praze, Čs. společnost astronomická, 1949.

Wason   **Link, Francis L**
PL6042   ₍Abstract of a portion of the Sulu grammar
L75   contained in a typewritten draft entitled "The Sulu dialect," by Charles R. Cameron. Jolo, Sulu, P.I.? 1924?₎
1 v. (unpaged) 25 cm.

1. Sulu language--Grammar. I. Cameron, Charles Raymond, 1875–

NL 0388157   NIC

Link, Frank J., 1869–

Chicago. *City council. Committee on efficiency, economy and rehabilitation.*
Operation, maintenance and construction of the municipal reduction plant of the city of Chicago. Report of the subcommittee on waste disposal of the Committee on efficiency, economy and rehabilitation of the City council of the city of Chicago, together with a Report of Irwin S. Osborn, consulting engineer. Printed by order of the City council. James T. Igoe, city clerk. ₍Chicago, 1921₎

PS2246   [LINK, FRANK M   ]
f.L68M2   "Madge," the orphan;or,The mountain rose. A sensational drama in five acts. [1884]
1884   cover-title,76,37 numb.l. 32½cm.
Rare bk   Manuscript.
room

NL 0388159   ICU

Link, František.
Co víme o hvězdách? ₍Vyd. 1. V Praze₎ Jednota československých mathematiků a fysiků ₍1947₎
143 p. illus. 18 cm. (Cesta k vědění, sv. 82)

1. Astronomy. I. Title.

QB43.L46 1947   57–48696 ‡

NL 0388160   DLC

Link, František.
Dioptrische Tafeln der Erdatmosphäre. Tables dioptriques de l'atmosphère terrestre. ₍P₎raha, Tiskárna "Prometheus," 1940.

28 p.

Publikace Pražské Hvězdárny – C. 14.)
At head of title: František Link – Zdeněk Sakera.

NL 0388161   MCM

522.19
F8842   **Link, František,** ed.
10.18   ... Extension des tables dioptriques de l'atmosphère terrestre; réd. d'après les calculs de A. Čížek, E. Fluss, V. Chmelařová ₍et d'autres₎ ... par F. Link. Exploration météorique de la haute atmosphère ₍par₎ F. Link. Praha, 1947.
15, 12 p. diagrs., tables. 28ᶜᵐ. (Publikace Pražské státní hvězdarny, č. 18 ...)

1. Atmosphere. 2. Atmosphere, Upper. 3. Refraction – Tables, etc.

NL 0388162   NNC

Link, František.
Jak poznává astrofysika vesmír? ₍Vyd. 2.₎ V Praze, Přírodovědecké nakladatelství ₍1949₎
106 p. illus. 17 cm. (Cesta k vědění, sv. 6)

1. Astrophysics. I. Title.

QB461.L55 1949   59–24342

NL 0388163   DLC

Link, František.
Lety do stratosféry a výzkum vysoké atmosféry. ₍2. vyd.₎ Praha, Vědecké vydavatelství ₍1951₎
145 p. illus. 17 cm. (Cesta k vědění, 11)
At head of title: František Link, Luděk Neužil.
Third ed. published in 1957 under title: Raketové lety a výzkum vysoké atmosféry.
Bibliography: p. 145.

1. Atmosphere. I. Neužil, Luděk, joint author. II. Title.

QC879.L53 1951   68–33838

NL 0388164   DLC

Link, František.
...Potulky vesmírem. ₍Praha₎ F. Borový, 1947.   257 p. illus. 24cm. (Objevy bez konce. sv. 5.)

475125B. 1. Astronomy—Elementary   and popular works, 1947. I. Title.
August 9, 1949

NL 0388165   NN

Link, František.
Slunce a jeho vlivy na zemi. ₍Vyd. 1.₎ Praha, Nakl. Československé akademie věd, 1953.
166 p. illus., port. 21 cm. (Československá akademie věd. Sekce matematicko-fysikální. Věda všem, sv. 5)
At head of title: František Link, Zdeněk Švestka.
Bibliography: p. 163.

1. Sun. 2. Solar radiation. I. Švestka, Zdeněk, joint author. II. Title.

QB521.L72   59–25461

NL 0388166   DLC

VOLUME 334

LINK, FRANTIŠEK.
Tables d'apex solaire, rédigées d'après les calculs de El. Chvojková [et al.] Praha, Printed by "Prometheus," 1948.
51 p. (p. 8-51 tables) 28cm. (Česká společnost astronomická. Prague. Memoirs and observations, no. 9)

1. Sun—Tables. 2. Sun—Tables 1948. I. Series.

NL 0388167   NN ViU

Link, František.
Tafeln zur Berechnung der galaktischen Bewegungskomponenten der Sterne. Mit einer Vorrede von J. H. Oort. Zusammengestellt nach den Berechnungen der Mitglieder der Rechnungsgruppe der Tschechischen Astronomischen Gesellschaft in Prag: Jos. Bartek [et al.] Hrsg. mit der Subvention des Tschechischen Nationalforschungsrates. Praha, Tiskárna "Melantrich," 1941.
48 p. 30 cm. (Veröffentlichungen der Prager Sternwarte, Nr. 17)
1. Stars—Motion in line of sight. 2. Stars—Tables. I. Title: Berechnung der galaktischen Bewegungskomponenten der Sterne.

QB901.L54   '59–59054 ‡

NL 0388168   DLC MH ICU

Link, Franz H.
Diagnostische Bedeutung indirekter Herdsymptome bei Gehirnerkrankungen. [Fulda, 1898]
37 p.
Inaug.-diss. - Jena.
Bibl.

NL 0388169   ICRL

Link, Friedrich.
Merkbuch zur berufs- und handelskunde, von Fr. Link ... dr. H. Stollreither ... [und] B. Wolf ... 4. aufl. München, M. Beckstein, 1936.
80 p.   21.5 cm.
1. Business education - Germany. I. Wolf, Bruno, joint author. II. Title.

NL 0388170   MiU

Link, Georg.
Klosterbuch der Diöcese Würzburg...von George Link... Würzburg: J. Standinger, 1873-1876.   2 v.   8°.
Bd. 1. Geschichte der Benediktinerklöster.
Bd. 2. Geschichte der übrigen Klöster und klösterlichen Institute.

1. Monasteries—Germany—Würzburg.   2. Nunneries—Germany—Würzburg. 3. Title.
February 27, 1929

NL 0388171   NN KAS NIC MH

Link (Georg) [1889-   ]. *Ueber Hydrops congenitus bei fetaler Thrombose. [Freiburg.]
21 pp. 8°. Jena. G. Fischer. 1914.

NL 0388172   DNLM ICRL CtY

Link, George Konrad Karl, 1888-
Anthracnose of muskmelons. [By] George K. K. Link and F. C. Meier ... Washington, Govt. print. off., 1922.
1 p. L, 4 p.   pl. 23cm. (U. S. Dept. of agriculture. Department circular 217)
Contribution from the Bureau of plant industry (Office of cotton, truck and forage crop disease investigations)

1. Anthracnose. 2. Melons—Diseases and pests. [2. Muskmelons—Diseases] I. Meier, Fred Campbell, 1893- joint author.
Agr 22–1000
Library, U. S. Dept.   Agriculture 1Ag84D no.217

NL 0388173   DNAL WaWW

Link, George Konrad Karl, 1888-   joint author.
Meier, Fred Campbell, 1893-
Bacterial spot of cucumbers. [By] F. C. Meier and G. K. K. Link ... Washington, Govt. print. off., 1922.

Link, George Konrad Karl, 1888-
Botrytis rot of the globe artichoke. By George K. K. Link ... Glen B. Ramsey ... and Alice A. Bailey ...
(In U. S. Dept. of agriculture. Journal of agricultural research. vol. XXIX, no. 2, July 15, 1924, p. 85-92. col. pl. 25cm. Washington, 1925)
Contribution from Bureau of plant industry (G-403)
"Paper from the Cooperative laboratory for the investigation of market and transit diseases of vegetables and fruits, the U. S. Dept. of agriculture and the University of Chicago cooperating."
Published January 24, 1925.

1. Artichokes—Diseases [and pests] I. Bailey, Mrs. Alice Linna (Allen) 1896- joint author. II. Ramsey, Glen Blaine, joint author. III. Title.
Agr 25–248
Library, U. S. Dept.   Agriculture 1Ag84J vol. 29

NL 0388175   DNAL

Link, George Konrad Karl, 1888-   joint author.
Shapovalov, Michael, 1880-
... Control of potato-tuber diseases. [By Michael Shapovalov and George K. K. Link] [Washington, Govt. print. off., 1924]

Link, George Konrad Karl, 1888-
Fusaria causing bulb rot of onions. By George K. K. Link ... and Alice A. Bailey ...
(In U. S. Dept. of agriculture. Journal of agricultural research. v. 33, no. 10, November 15, 1926, p. 929-952. Illus., diagr. 23½cm. Washington, 1926)
Contribution from ... Bureau of plant industry and the Botany dept. of the University of Chicago, cooperating.
Published December 28, 1926.
"Literature cited" : p. 951-952.

1. Onions—Diseases [and pests] I. Bailey, Mrs. Alice Linna (Allen) 1896- joint author. II. Title.
Agr 27–96
Library, U. S. Dept.   Agriculture 1Ag84J vol. 33

NL 0388177   DNAL

Link, George Konrad Karl, 1888-
Fusarium tuber rot of potatoes. [By] George K. K. Link and F. C. Meier ... Washington, Govt. print. off., 1922.
8 p.   II pl. on 1 l. 23cm. (U. S. Dept. of agriculture. Department circular 214)
Contribution from the Bureau of plant industry (Office of cotton, truck, and forage crop disease investigations)

1. Fusarium. 2. Potatoes—Diseases [and pests] I. Meier, Fred Campbell, 1893- joint author. II. Title.
Agr 22–625
Library, U. S. Dept.   Agriculture 1Ag84D no. 214

NL 0388178   DNAL WaWW

Link, George Konrad Karl, 1888-
A handbook of Nebraska grasses
see under   Wilcox, E. Mead.

Link, George Konrad Karl, 1888-
Late-blight tuber rot of the potato. [By] George K. K. Link and F. C. Meier ... Washington, Govt. print. off., 1922.
cover-title, 5, [1] p.   II pl. on 1 l. 23cm. (U. S. Dept. of agriculture. Department circular 220)
Contribution from the Bureau of plant industry (Office of cotton, truck, and forage crop disease investigations)

1. Potatoes—Diseases [and pests] 2. Phytophthora infestans. I. Meier, Fred Campbell, 1893- joint author. II. Title.
Agr 22–576
Library, U. S. Dept.   Agriculture 1Ag84D no. 220

NL 0388180   DNAL WaWW CaBViP

Link, George Konrad Karl, 1888-
... Late-blight tuber rot of the potato. [By] George K. K. Link and F. C. Meier ... Issued May 1922; rev. Feb. 1924. Washington [Govt. print. off.] 1924.
5, [1] p.   II pl. on 1 l. 23cm. (U. S. Dept. of agriculture. Department circular 220)
Contribution from Bureau of plant industry.

1. Potatoes—Diseases [and pests] 2. Phytophthora infestans. I. Meier, Fred Campbell, 1893- joint author. II. Title.
Agr 24–457
Library, U. S. Dept. of   Agriculture 1Ag84D no. 220

NL 0388181   DNAL

Link, George Konrad Karl, 1888-   joint author
SB601 .R3
Ramsey, Glen Blaine, 1889-
... Market diseases of fruits and vegetables: crucifers and cucurbits. By Glen B. Ramsey ... James S. Wiant ... and George K. K. Link ... Washington [U. S. Govt. print. off.] 1938]

Link, George Konrad Karl, 1888-
... Market diseases of fruits and vegetables: potatoes. By George K. K. Link ... and Glen B. Ramsey ... Washington [U. S. Govt. print. off.] 1932.
cover-title, 63 p.   15 pl. (13 col.) on 14 l. 23½cm. (U. S. Dept. of agriculture. Miscellaneous publication no. 98)
Contribution from Bureau of plant industry.
"Literature cited" : p. 53–62.

1. Potatoes—Diseases [and pests] 2. Farm produce—Marketing. [2. Potatoes—Marketing] I. Ramsey, Glen Blaine, 1889- joint author. II. [Title]
Agr 32–353
Library, U. S. Dept. of   Agriculture 1Ag84M no. 98
Library of Congress   [S21.A46 no. 98]

NL 0388183   DNAL WaWW MB

Link, George Konrad Karl, 1888- joint author.
Ramsey, Glen Blaine, 1889-
... Market diseases of fruits and vegetables: tomatoes, peppers, eggplants. By Glen B. Ramsey ... and George K. K. Link ... Washington [U. S. Govt. print. off.] 1932.

Link, George Konrad Karl, 1888-
Phoma rot of tomatoes. [By] George K. K. Link and F. C. Meier ... Washington, Govt. print. off., 1922.
cover-title, 5 p.   pl. 23cm. (U. S. Dept. of agriculture. Department circular 219)
Contribution from the Bureau of plant industry (Office of cotton, truck, and forage crop investigations)

1. Phoma destructiva. 2. Tomatoes—Diseases [and pests] I. Meier, Fred Campbell, 1893- joint author. II. Title.
Agr 22–627
Library, U. S. Dept. of   Agriculture 1Ag84D no. 219

NL 0388185   DNAL WaWW

Link, George Konrad Karl, 1888-
... A physiological study of two strains of *Fusarium* in their causal relation to tuber rot and wilt of potato ... by George Konrad Karl Link ... Chicago, Ill., The University of Chicago press [1916]
1 p. l., 169-209. illus. 24cm.
Thesis (PH. D.)—University of Chicago, 1916.
"A private edition distributed by the University of Chicago libraries."
"Reprinted from the Botanical gazette, vol. LXII, no. 3."
"Contributions from the Hull botanical laboratory 219."
"Literature cited" : p. 207-209.

1. Fusarium. 2. Potatoes—Diseases and pests.
17–1826
Library of Congress   SB608.P8L5
Univ. of Chicago Libr.

NL 0388186   ICU PPAN NIC ViU NjP DLC

Link, George Konrad Karl, 1888- joint aut.
Meier, Fred Campbell, 1893-
... Potato brown-rot. [By] F. C. Meier and G. K. K. Link ... Washington [Govt. print. off.] 1923.

VOLUME 334

Link, George Konrad Karl, 1888–

Chicago. University.
Readings in phytopathology. Ancient Greek phytopathology, by George K. K. Link ... 1st ed., October, 1941. Chicago, Ill., The University of Chicago bookstore, ᶜ1941.

Link, George Konrad Karl, 1888–

Chicago. University.
Syllabus for Botany 240, introduction to phytopathology, prepared by George K. K. Link ... 1st ed. September, 1940. Chicago, Ill., Distributed by the University of Chicago bookstore, ᶜ1940.

Link, George Konrad Karl, 1888–

Chicago. University.
Syllabus for Introduction to phytopathology: Botany 240 (general phytopathology) Botany 340 (anatomic phytopathology) Botany 341 (infectious diseases) by George K. K. Link. The University of Chicago ... Chicago, Ill., Distributed by the University of Chicago bookstore, 1937.

Link, George Matthew, 1896–

Illinois. *Dept. of conservation. Division of forestry.*
... Forest trees of Illinois; how to know them. A pocket manual describing their most important characteristics. Revised by Dr. George D. Fuller ... in cooperation with Reverend George M. Link ... and Anton J. Tomasek ... Springfield, Dept. of conservation, Division of forestry ₁1941₎

QH11
.G37

Link, George Matthew, 1896–   ed.

Getting at nature; its mystery and its message. v. 1 ₁no. 1₎–2; summer 1939–winter/spring 1940. ₁Springfield? Ill., 1939–40₎

Link, Gerhard, 1911–
... "Wie wird das Tiranal bisher beurteilt?" (Eine Literaturumschau) ... [Tübingen, n.d.] Inaug.-Diss. - Tübingen.
Lebenslauf.
"Literaturverzeichnis": p. 25–26.

NL 0388193   CtY OU

Link, Gerhard Adolf, 1915–
Die verfassungsrechtliche und machtpolitische stellung des englischen Oberhauses ... von Gerhard Adolf Link ... München, Hansa-druckerei, inh. H. Schneider jun., 1940.

122 p. 21ᶜᵐ.
Diss.—Munich.
Lebenslauf: slip mounted on p. 122.
"Literaturverzeichnis": p. 118–122.

1. Gt. Brit. Parliament. House of lords.
43–40549

Library of Congress   JN627.L5

NL 0388194   DLC

Q
11
C44m
no.92

Link, Goethe.
Records of the coral snake, Micrurus fulvius, in Indiana and Ohio. Chicago, Chicago Academy of Sciences, 1951.

5 p. 25 cm. (Natural history miscellanea, no. 92)

Dated December 14, 1951.
Bibliography: p. 4–5.

1. Micrurus fulvius. 2. Elapidae.

NL 0388195   ICF

Link, Goethe
see also Indiana. University. *Goethe Link Observatory.*

811
L648a

Link, Gordden.
Apocalypse. An excerpt for the thoughtful in this troubled season from the atomic age section of the Congressional anthology, poems selected by senators and representatives. ₁Washington₎ University Press of Washington D.C. ₁1955₎

₁4₎p. 22cm.

"No. 1 in 'The Excerpts from current literature series.'"

NL 0388197   IU

Link, Gordden.
Three poems for now. Washington, University Press of Washington, D.C. ₁1953₎

29 p. 19 cm. (The Pocket poets)

I. Title.

PS3523.I 648T4   811.5   53–12585 ‡

OrU
NL 0388198   DLC MiU IU OClJC PU PSt ViU PP NN Or

Link, Gottlieb Christian Karl, 1757–1798, tr.

Filangieri, Gaetano, 1752–1788.
System der gesetzgebung ... Aus dem italienischen des ritters Caietan Filangieri ... 2. verb. aufl. Anspach, B. F. Haueisen, 1788–93.

W 4
M96
1953

LINK, Günter, 1928–
Ein Beitrag zu strahlenbedingten Veränderungen epithelialer Elemente im weiblichen Genitaltrakt mit hilfe der Cytodiagnostik. ₁München₎ 1953.
58 ℓ. illus.
Inaug.-Diss. - Munich.
1. Genitals - Female
2. Radium - Effects 3. Roentgen rays - Effects

NL 0388200   DNLM

Link, Guilelmus, 1886–
see Link, Wilhelm, 1886–

Link, Gustav A   sr.
... List of the Coleoptera
see under Holland, William Jacob, 1848–1932.

Link, Gustav A   sr.
... List of the Hymenoptera ...
see under Holland, William Jacob, 1848–1932.

TN23
.U4
no. 532

Link, H. B., joint author.
Ash, Simon Harry, 1889–
Surface-water seepage into anthracite mines in the western middle field, anthracite region of Pennsylvania, by S. H. Ash and H. B. Link. Washington, U. S. Govt. Print. Off., 1953.

Link, Hans
Die lage der wurzelkanaleingaenge bei den oberen und unteren molaren,...₎Auszug₎
Inaug. diss. Erlangen, 1924

NL 0388205   ICRL

Link, Hans, 1905–
Hilaire Bellocs Weltanschauung dargestellt auf Grunde einer wichtigsten Romane und Essays... von Hans Link... ₍allmünz: M. Lassleben, 1929. 61 p. 8°.

Dissertation, Erlangen, 1929.
Lebenslauf.
Bibliography, p. 60–61.

494156A. 1. Belloc, Hilaire, 1870–   September 16, 1930

NL 0388206   ICRL MiU CtY PU MH IU

Link, Harriet Jane.
An experimental inquiry into the use of suggesters in the teaching of American history ... ₁by₎ Harriet Jane Link. Philadelphia, 1927.

126 p. 23ᶜᵐ.

Thesis (PH. D.)—University of Pennsylvania, 1927.

1. U. S.—Hist.—Study and teaching.   I. Title: Suggesters, The use of.
27–22185
Library of Congress   E175.8.L75
Univ. of Pennsylvania   Libr.

MB DLC
NL 0388207   PU IdU MtU NIC NcD NcU MiU OCl OCU IU

Link, Harry, 1896–
I was introduced to heaven when I was introduced to you. Lyric by Sammy Mysels and Dorothy Dick. Music by Harry Link... New York, Santly bros., inc. ₁c1932₎

First line: When I used to dream of heaven.
Introduced by Larry Funk and his orchestra.
Portrait of Larry Funk on t.-p.

Printed for the Music Division
1. Heaven. 2. Funk, Larry—   Port. I. Mysels, Sammy. II. Dick, Dorothy. III. Song index (2).
March 15, 1948

NL 0388208   NN

Link, Harry, 1896–
In a boat out to sea. Lyric by Dorothy Dick. Music by Harry Link... New York, Santly bros. inc. ₁c1931₎

First line: Sweetheart let me whisper to you.
Introduced and featured by Will Osborne.
Portrait of Will Osborne on t.-p.

Printed for the Music Division
1. Osborne, Will—Port. I. Dick, Dorothy, 1900– . II. Song index (2).
August 25, 1950

NL 0388209   NN

VOLUME 334

Link, Harry, 1896–

The kiss that you've forgotten is the kiss I can't forget. Words by Dorothy Dick. Music by Harry Link... New York, Santly bros., inc. [c1931]

First line: Our romance is over.
Chorus: For the kiss that you've forgotten.
Featured by Ben Alley.
Portrait of Ben Alley on t.-p.

1. Kissing. 2. Alley, Ben—Port. I. Dick, Dorothy, 1900– . II. Song index (3).

Printed for the Music Division
November 13, 1950

NL 0388210   NN

LINK, HARRY, 1896–

A toast to Troast. Lyric by Lou Cunningham. Music by Harry Link. New York, E. B. Marks music corp. [c1953]

First line: The butcher, the baker.
Chorus: Here's a toast to Troast.
Portrait of Paul Troast on   t.-p.
1. Songs, Popular—1890–   2. Politics. 3. Troast, Paul.
I. Cunningham, Lou.

NL 0388211   NN

Link, Harry, 1896–

Tell me while we're dancing. Lyric by Nick Kenny. Music by Harry Link. New York, Santly bros. inc., c1932.

First line: Here we are together once again.

1. Dancing. I. Kenny, Nick.

Printed for the Music Division
II. Song index (2).
February 13, 1948

NL 0388212   NN

Link, Heinrich, 1906–

... Zur Histopathologie der Pseudowut ... Osterwarngau am Taubenberg (Obby.) 1933. Inaug.-Diss. - München.

NL 0388213   CtY

Link, Heinrich Friedrich, 1767–1851.
Abbildungen auserlesener gewächse des Königlichen botanischen gartens zu Berlin, nebst beschreibungen und anleitung sie zu ziehen, von H. F. Link ... und F. Otto ... Berlin, 1820. v. col. plates. 26 cm.

Added t.-p.: Icones plantarum selectarum Horti regii botanici berolinensis cum descriptionibus et colendi ratione ...

1. Berlin, Universität. Botanischer garten. I. Otto, Friedrich, 1782–1856, jt. au.

NL 0388214   NNC

QK73
B4L53
1828
Biology
Library

Link, Heinrich Friedrich, 1767–1851.
Abbildungen auserlesener Gewächse des Königlichen Botanischen Gartens zu Berlin, nebst Beschreibungen und Anleitung sie zu ziehen von H.F. Link und F. Otto. Zehn Hefte. Berlin, 1828.
128 p. 60 col. plates.

Added t.p. in Latin: Icones plantarum selectarum Horti Regii Botanici Berolinensis ...

1. Berlin, Ger. Universität. Botanischer Garten. 2. Botany - 1753–1900. 3. Botany - Pictorial works. I. Otto, Friedrich, 1783–1856, joint author.

NL 0388215   CU

1767-1851
Link, Heinrich Friedrich. ^ Abietinae Horti regii botanici berolinensis cultae. [Halle a. d. S. 1841.] 8°.
Linnaea, 1841, XV, 481–545.

NL 0388216   MH-A

Link, Heinrich Friedrich, 1767–1851.
Das alterthum und der übergang zur neuern zeit. Eine fortsetzung des buches über Die urwelt und das alterthum. Von Dr. H. F. Link ... Berlin, F. Dümmler, 1842.
vi, 369 p. 20 cm.

1. Civilization, Ancient. 2. Civilization—Hist.

CB311.L7   4—7388

NL 0388217   DLC PU IEN NIC

Link, H[einrich] F[riedrich] 1767–1851.
Anatomia plantarum, iconibus illustrata; auctore H. F. Link ... Anatomie der pflanzen in abbildungen; von H. F. Link ... Berlin, C. G. Lüderitz, 1843–47.
3 pts. in 1 v. XXXVI pl. (partly col.) 27½ᶜᵐ.
Latin and German in parallel columns.

1. Botany—Anatomy.

Library of Congress   QK671.L75   5-30940†

NL 0388218   DLC MB

1767-1851.
Link, Heinrich Friedrich. Annual report on researches in physiological botany during the years 1844 and 1845. (*In* HENFREY, Arthur, *editor.* Reports and papers on botany, v. 2, 1849, pp. 191–313.)

NL 0388219   MBH MdBP MH-A

Link, Heinrich Friedrich, 1767–1851.
Bemerkungen auf einer reise durch Frankreich, Spanien, und vorzüglich Portugal, von d. Heinrich Friedrich Link ... Kiel, In der Neuen academischen buchhandlung; Helmstädt und Braunschweig, In commission bey C. G. Fleckeisen, 1801–04.
3 v. in 1. fold. map. 20ᶜᵐ.
"Ueber die portugiesische litteratur und sprache": v. 2, p. 229–263.

1. Portugal—Descr. & trav. 2. Spain—Descr. & trav.

Library of Congress   DP524.L7   36-2446

914.69

NL 0388220   DLC DCU-IA

AS
182
B51
A31+
1849
no.4

Link, Heinrich Friedrich, 1767–1851.
Bemerkungen über den Bau der Orchideen.

(In Akademie der Wissenschaften, Berlin. Abhandlungen. Berlin. 27cm. [v.34](1849) Physikalische Abhandlungen. p. [103]–127. illus.)

NL 0388221   NIC DLC

Link, Heinrich Friedrich. 1767–1851.   *3322.2.1820/1821, 1822/1823
Bemerkungen über die natürlichen Ordnungen der Gewächse. Abhandlung 1, 2. Mit einem Nachtrag von Ph. Buttmann.
(In Koeniglich-preussische Akademie der Wissenschaften. Physikalische Klasse. Abhandlungen. 1820/1821, pp. 121–144. 1822/1823, pp. 157–186. Berlin. 1822, 1825.)

G9004 — Botany. Structural.

NL 0388222   MB DLC

Link, Heinrich Friedrich, 1767–1851.
Beschreibung der naturalien-sammlung der Universität zu Rostock, von Heinrich Friedrich Link, 1806–1808. Facsimile reproduction of the pages relating to *Mollusca.* [Hertford, S. Austin and sons, ltd., printers] 1931.
3 p. l., 83–160, [2], 7–23 p., 1 l., 33–37, [3] p. 20½ᶜᵐ.
Preface signed: J. R. Le B. Tomlin. R. Winckworth. London, 1ª July 1931.
With reproduction of original title-pages.

1. Mollusks. 2. Rostock. Universität. I. Tomlin, John Read Le Brockton. ed. II. Winckworth, Ronald, joint ed.

Library of Congr.   QL406.L55   32-25071
594.074

NL 0388223   DLC DSI PPAN VtU WaU LU FTaSU MiU CU

Link, Heinrich Friedrich, 1767–1851.
Beyträge zur naturgeschichte, von Heinr. Friedr. Link ... Rostock und Leipzig, K. C. Stiller, 1797–1801.
2 v. in 1. 18ᶜᵐ.
CONTENTS.—bd. 1, stück 1. Ueber die leiter der natur, das natürliche und künstliche system. 1794.—bd. 1, stück 2. Ueber die lebenskräfte in natur-historischer rücksicht, und die classification der säugethiere. 1795.—bd. 1, stück 3. Beyträge zur philosophie der naturgeschichte. 1797.—th. 2. Geologische und mineralogische bemerkungen auf einer reise durch das südwestliche Europe, besonders Portugal. 1801.

1. Natural history.

Agr 10-1671

Library, U. S. Dept. of   Agriculture 409L64

NL 0388224   DNAL

QC
19
L75

Link, Heinrich Friedrich, 1767–1851.
Beyträge zur Physik und Chemie. Rostock, C. Stiller, 1795–97.
3 v. 25 cm.
Added t.p. for Stück 1 cites author: C. F. Link.

1. Physics - Early works to 1800.
2. Chemistry - Early works to 1800.
I. Title.

NL 0388225   DSI

Link, Heinrich Friedrich, 1767–1851.

Berg, Otto Karl, 1815–1866.
Characteristik der für die arzneikunde und technik wichtigsten pflanzen-genera in illustrationen nebst erläuterndem texte nach seinem Handbuche der pharmaceutischen botanik, geordnet von dr. Otto Berg ... mit einem vorworte von H. F. Link. 2. abdruck. Berlin, L. Nitze, 1851.

Hist.
18th c.

WZ
260
L756C
1788

Link, Heinrich Friedrich, 1767–1851.
... Commentatio de analysi urinae et origine calculi... Gottingae, Typis Jo. Christ. Dieterich [1788?]
72 p. 23 cm.
"In concertatione civium Academiae Georgia Augustae IV. Junii cIɔIɔccLXXXVIII. praemio a Rege M. Britanniae Aug. constituto ab medicorum ordine ornata."

1. Urinary Calculi. I. Title.

NL 0388229   WU-M DNLM

Link, Heinrich Friedrich. 1767–1851.   *3322.2.1832.1
De structura caulis plantarum monocotylearum. Plates.
(In Koeniglich-preussische Akademie der Wissenschaften. Physikalische Klasse. Abhandlungen. 1832, pp. 85–89. Berlin. 1834.)
: AS 182. B 33

G9082 — Monocotyledoneæ.

NL 0388230   MB DLC

VOLUME 334

Link, Heinrich Friedrich, 1767–1851.
  Elementa philosophiae botanicae. Auctore Henr.
Frid. Link ... Berolini, Haude et Spener, 1824.
  2 p. 1., 486 p. iv pl. 21½ᶜᵐ.

  1. Botany.   Agr 5–820

  Library, U. S. Dept. of   Agriculture 452L642E

NL 0388231   DNAL NIC CtY MiU MH–A

Link, Heinrich Friedrich, 1767–1851.
  Elementa philosophiae botanicae. Auctore Henr. Frid.
Link ... Editio altera. Berolini, sumtibus Haude et Spener,
1837.
  2 v. 21 cm.
  Added title in German.
  Text in Latin and German on opposite pages.

  1. Botany.   Agr 25—98

  U. S. Dept. of Agr. Libr.   452.04L639E
  for Library of Congress   ₍a58c₎₎

NL 0388232   DNAL NNBG

Link, Heinrich Friedrich. 1767–1851.   *3322.2.1824, 1848
  Entwurf eines phytologischen Pflanzensystems nebst einer Anordnung der Kryptophyten. [1. Abhandlung.]
  (In Koeniglich-preussische Akademie der Wissenschaften. Physikalische Klasse. Abhandlungen. 1824, pp. 145–194. Berlin.
1826.)
  Same. 2. Abhandlung. (In Same. Berichte. Aus dem Jahre 1848,
pp. 101–104. Berlin. [1848].)

  H606 — Botany. Structural.

NL 0388233   MB MH DLC

Link, Heinrich Friedrich, 1767–1851.
  Enumeratio plantarum Horti regii botanici berolinensis
altera. Auctore dr. H. F. Link ... Berolini, apud G. Reimer, 1821–22.
  2 v. 20½ᶜᵐ.

  1. Botany. 2. Berlin. Königlich botanischer garten.
                                               Agr 11–694

  Library, U. S. Dept. of   Agriculture 452L642

MH–A
NL 0388234   DNAL InU MnU CU PPAN MsSM NIC MiU NN

Link, Heinrich Friedrich, 1767–1851.
  Enumeratio plantarum Horti regii botanici berolinensis.
₍Hoffmannsegg, Johann Centurius von Hoffmann, graf
von₎ 1766–1849.
  Verzeichniss der pflanzenkulturen in den Gräfl. Hoff-
mannseggischen gärten zu Dresden und Rammenau, nebst
einigen kritischen bemerkungen, einer verbessernden an-
zeige der hauptsächlichsten druckfehler in Herrn Prof.
Links Enumeratio etc. und einem steindruck. Dresden,
In commission der Arnoldischen buchhandlung, 1824.

Link, Heinrich Friedrich, 1767–1851.
  Filicum species in Horto regio botanico berolinensi cultae recensitae a Henr. Frid. Link ... Berolini, Veitii et
socii sumptibus, 1841.
  2 p. 1., 179, ₍1₎ p. 21ᶜᵐ. ₍With Fenzl, Eduard. Pugillus plantarum nova-
rum Syriae et Tauri occidentalis primus. Vindobonae, 1842₎

  1. Berlin. Universität. Botanischer garten. 2. Ferns.
                                               Agr 11–695 Revised
  Library, U. S. Dept. of   Agriculture 460.17F36

NL 0388236   DNAL CtY IaU CLSU CU

QK390 Link, Heinrich Friedrich, 1767–1851.
.G4   Florae Goettingensis specimen, sistens vegeta-
L5   bilia saxo calcareo propria. ₍Goettingae₎ Typis
       H. M. Grape, 1789.
         43 p. 21 cm.

         Diss. inaug. – Göttingen.
         Copy 2: Barnhart library. Inscribed: G. Egeling
       Annotated.
         5377 Pritzel.

         1. Lichenes – Germany – Göttingen. i.t.
       a. Barnhart, John Hendley, 1871–1949. b. Egel-
       ing, G.

NL 0388237   NNBG

Microfiche
QK   LINK, HEINRICH FRIEDRICH, 1767–1851.
69   Florae Goettingensis. Specimen sistens
       vegetabilia saxo calcareo propria. ₍Göttingen₎
       1789.
         43 p.

         Dissertation inauguratis botanica—Academia
       Georgia Augusta.
           1 card.
         Microfiche. Zug, Switzerland, Inter-Docu-
       mentation Comp. ₍196?₎
         1. Botany—Hanover. I. Title.   Bot.cds.
       Microf. cd.

NL 0388238   InU

QK830 Link, Heinrich Friedrich, 1767–1851, joint
.H7   author.
Rare Bk Hoffmannsegg, Johann Centurius von Hoffmann, graf von,
Coll   1766–1849.
         Flore portugaise; ou Déscription de toutes les plantes qui
       croissent naturellement en Portugal ... par J. C. comte de Hoff-
       mannsegg ... et H. F. Link ... Berlin, De l'impr. de C. F.
       Amelang ₍etc.₎ 1809–20.

QK671 Link, Heinrich Friedrich, 1767–1851.
.L75   Grundlehren der anatomie und physiologie der pflanzen.
       Von d. H. F. Link ... Göttingen, J. F. Danckwerts, 1807.
         ₍4₎, 305, ₍1₎ p. vi pl. 20½ᶜᵐ.

         ——— ——— Nachträge ... ₍1–2. hft ... ₎ Göttingen,
       J. F. Danckwerts, 1809–12.
         2 v. in 1. 20½ᶜᵐ. ₍With the preceding₎

         1. Botany—Anatomy. 2. Botany—Physiology.

NL 0388240   ICU ICJ CU CSt OU MH

QK45 Link, Heinrich Friedrich, 1767–1851.
.L72   Grundlehren der kräuterkunde, von Heinr. Friedr. Link ...
       Mit vier lithographirten tafeln. 2. ausg. Berlin, Haude
       und Spener, 1837.
         2 v. iv pl. 20ᶜᵐ.
         Added t.-p. in Latin; text in German and Latin on opposite pages.

         1. Botany.

NL 0388241   ICU MH–G CU MH

Link, Heinrich Friedrich, 1767–1851.
  Willdenow, Karl Ludwig, 1765–1812.
  Grundriss der kräuterkunde zu vorlesungen entworfen
von d. Carl Ludwig Willdenow ... Nach dessen tode
neu hrsg. mit zusätzen von d. H. F. Link ... Berlin, In
der Haude und Spenerschen buchhandlung, 1829–33.

Link, H₍einrich₎ F₍riedrich₎, 1767–1851.   PhG 358.26
  Handbuch der physikalischen erdbeschreibung. Theil i; ii. 1.
Berlin, F. Dümmler, 1826–30.
  Plate.
  No more published.

NL 0388243   MH DI–GS NN

QK   Link, Heinrich Friedrich, 1767–1851.
93   Handbuch zur Erkennung der nutzbarsten und
L75   am häufigsten vorkommenden Gewächse. Berlin,
Vault In der Haude und Spenerschen Buchhandlung,
       1829–1833.
         3 v. 18 cm.

         Added t. -p.: Grundriss der Kräuterkunde zu
       Vorlesungen entworfen von Carl Ludwig Willdenow.
       Nach dessen Tode neu hrsg. mit Zusätzen von
       D. H. F. Link. Zweiter (Praktischer) Theil.

         1. Botany - Classification. 2. Botany.
       ₍I. Title₎ II. Willdenow, Karl Ludwig, 1765–
       1812. Grundriss der Kräuterkunde. 2. Theil.

NL 0388245   NIC NNBG MH–A IU MH NcD

Link, Heinrich Friedrich, 1767–1851.
  Hortus regius botanicus berolinensis, descriptus ab
Henrico Friderico Link ... Berolini, apud G. Reimer,
1827–33.
  2 v. 22½ᶜᵐ.

  1. Berlin, Königlich botanischer garten zu.
                                               Agr 4–869

  Library, U. S. Dept. of   Agriculture 89L64

NL 0388246   DNAL CU MH–A NIC TNJ InU

QK711 Link, Heinrich Friedrich, 1767–1851.
f.L77   Icones anatomico-botanicae ad illustranda elementa philo-
       sophiae botanicae Henr. Frid. Linkii. Ed. 2 ... Anatomisch-
       botanische abbildungen zur erläuterung der grundlehren der
       kräuterkunde ... Berlin, Haude und Spener, 1837–38.
         3 v. in 1. xxiv pl. (part col.) 43ᶜᵐ.
         Latin and German text in parallel columns.
         Paged continuously.

         1. Botany—Physiology. 2. Botany—Anatomy.

NL 0388247   ICU MWelC IU MH–A NN

Link, Heinrich Friedrich, 1767–1851.
  Icones plantarum rariorum Horti regii botanici berolinensis. Abbildungen seltener pflanzen des Königl. botanischen gartens zu Berlin, hrsg. von H. F. Link ... Fr.
Klotzsch ... F. Otto ... Berlin, Veit und comp., 1841–44.
  2 v. in 1. 48 col. pl. 27½ᶜᵐ.

  Paged continuously.
  Vol. 2, Verlag der Nicolaischen buchhandlung.

  1. Berlin. Königlich botanischer garten. 2. Botany. i. Klotzsch, Johann Friedrich, 1805–1860, joint author. ii. Otto, Friedrich i. e. Christoph
Friedrich, 1783–1856, joint author.
                                               Agr 11–696

  Library, U. S. Dept. of   Agriculture 452L642 I

NL 0388248   DNAL PPAN MBH CU MH NN

Link, Heinrich Friedrich, 1767–1851.
  Icones plantarum rariorum Horti regii botanici berolinensis cum descriptionibus et colendi ratione. Auctoribus, H. F. Link et F. Otto. Pars prima. Berolini,
sumptibus L. Oehmigke, 1828.
  96 p. 48 pl. 22ᶜᵐ.

  Added t. -p. in German.
  Issued in 8 fasc. 1828–1831. No more published.
  Dept. of agriculture copy is photostat.

  1. Berlin. Universität. Botanischer garten. 2. Botany. i. *Otto,
Friedrich, 1783–1856, joint author.
                                               Agr 25–494

  Library, U. S. Dept. of   Agriculture 452L6421

NL 0388249   DNAL MH

VOLUME 334

Link, Heinrich Friedrich, 1767–1851.
Icones selectae anatomico-botanicae, auctore Henr.
Frid. Link ... Ausgewählte anatomisch-botanische abbildungen, von Heinr. Friedr. Link ... Berlin, Haude
und Spenersche buchhandlung, 1839–42.
4 v. in 1. 32 pl. (part col.) 44ᶜᵐ.
Latin and German in parallel columns.

1. Botany—Physiology. 2. Botany—Anatomy. ₍1, 2. Botany, Physiological and structural₎

Agr 17–1200

Library, U. S. Dept. of   Agriculture 463.4L63

NL 0388250   DNAL MH-G NIC MH-A

Q
175
L55

Link, Heinrich Friedrich, 1767–1851.
Ideen zu einer philosophischen Naturkunde.
Breslau, J. F. Korn, 1814.
203p. 18cm.

1. Philosophy of nature 2. Science –
Philosophy I. Title

NL 0388251   WU IU

Link, Heinrich Friedrich, 1767–1851.
Jahresbericht über die arbeiten für physiologische botanik
... 1834–46. (*In* Archiv für naturgeschichte. Berlin, 1835–47.) 21ᶜᵐ. 1.–8., 10., 12.–13. jahrg.)

Zeta
819
812S

Link, Heinrich Friedrich, 1767–1851.
Kritische Bemerkungen und Zusätze zu
Kurt Sprengel's Werk über den Bau und die
Natur der Gewächse. Halle, C. A. Kümmel,
1812.
59 p. 21 cm. [Bound with Sprengel, K.P.J.
Von dem Bau und der Natur der Gewächse.
Halle, 1812]

NL 0388253   CtY

Link, Heinrich Friedrich, 1767–1851.
—— [Lectures on botany. MS. notes taken
by H. C. L. Barkow, Berlin, 1817.] 1 v. 4°.
[s. p., s. d.]
German script.

NL 0388254   DNLM

Link, Heinrich Friedrich, 1767–1851.
—— [Lectures on pharmacology. MS. notes
taken by H. C. L. Barkow.] 1 v. 4°. [s. p., s. d.]
German script.

NL 0388255   DNLM

Link, Heinrich Friedrich, 1767–1851.
Nachträge zu den Grundlehren der Anatomie
and Physiologie der Pflanzen.
see his Grundlehren der anatomie und
physiologie der pflanzen.

501
L648n

Link, Heinrich Friedrich, 1767–1851.
Natur und Philosophie. Ein Versuch.
Leipzig, Im Verlage der Stillerschen Buchhandlung, 1811.
x, 342p. 15cm.

Continued in next column

Continued from preceding column

1. Science—Philosophy. I. Title.

NL 0388257   IU

Link, Heinrich Friedrich, 1767–1851.
—— Oratio solemnibus gratulatoriis Christo-
phoro Guilelmo Hufeland habita. 8 pp. 4°
Berolini, typ. Academiae, [1833].

NL 0388258   DNLM

Link, Heinrich Friedrich, 1767–1851.
Philosophiae botanicae novae sev Institvtionvm phyto-
graphicarvm prodromvs. Auctore Henr. Frid. Link ...
Gottingae, typis I. C. Dieterich, 1798.
192 p. 17ᶜᵐ.

1. Botany.

Agr 5–1081

Library, U. S. Dept. of   Agriculture 452L642P

NL 0388259   DNAL NIC

6006
.589

Link, Heinrich Friedrich, 1767–1851.
Die philosophie der gesunden vernunft.
Berlin, Nicolai, 1850.
6,190 p. 21½ ᶜᵐ.

1. Reason.

NL 0388260   NjP

Link, Heinrich Friedrich, 1767–1851.
A picture of Lisbon; taken on the spot by
a gentleman many years resident there... London,
1809.

NL 0388261   PPL

Q158
.L73

LINK, HEINRICH FRIEDRICH, 1767–1851.
Propyläen der naturkunde, von dr. H. F. Link... Berlin, F. Dümmler, 1836–39.
2 v. fold. pl. 20cm.

1. Science.

NL 0388262   ICU MB MA

W
L756r
1834

LINK, Heinrich Friedrich, 1767–1851
Rede zur Feier des vierzigsten Stif-
tungs-Tages des Königlichen Medicinisch-
Chirurgischen Friedrich-Wilhelms-
Instituts, am 2ten August 1834. Berlin,
Unger ₍1834?₎
15 p.
1. Berlin. Medizinisch-Chirurgisches
Friedrich Wilhelms Institut

NL 0388263   DNLM

W
L756re
1826

LINK, Heinrich Friedrich, 1767–1851.
Rede zur Feier des zwei und dreis-
sigsten Stiftungs-Tages des Königlichen
Medicinisch-Chirurgischen Friedrich-
Wilhelms-Instituts, am 2ten August 1826.
Berlin, Spener, 1826.
16 p.

NL 0388264   DNLM

Link, Heinrich Friedrich, 1767–1851.
—— Report on the progress of physiological botany during
the year 1841. pp. 104. (*In* RAY SOCIETY. Reports on
the progress of zoology and botany, 1845.)

NL 0388265   MBH ICJ MA DNLM

Link, Heinrich Friedrich, 1767–1851.
—— Report on the progress of physiological botany during
the years 1842 and 1843. (*In* HENFREY, Arthur, *editor*.
Reports and papers on botany, v. 1, 1846, pp. 293–440.)

NL 0388266   MBH MH-A CaBVaU ICJ

Link, Heinrich Friedrich, 1767–1851.
Ray society.
Reports and papers on botany ... London, Printed for the
Ray society, 1846–49.

Link, Heinrich Friedrich, 1767–1851.
Ray society, *London.*
Reports on the progress of zoology and botany, 1841, 1842.
Edinburgh, Printed for the Ray society, 1845.

Link, Heinrich Friedrich, 1767–1851.   3849.29
Revisio abietinarum Horti regii botanici Berolinensis.
[Halle a. S. Braunschweig, Schwetschke & Sohn. 1847.] 283–
298 pp. 8°.
Cut from Linnaea, vol. 20, 1847.
This is a supplement to Link's Abietinae Horti regii botanici Berolinensis
cultae, in Linnaea, vol. 15, 1841.
Contents. — Pinus. — Picea.

F5298 — Pines. — Koeniglich-botanischer Garten, Berlin.

NL 0388269   MB MH-A

Link, Heinrich Friedrich, 1767–1851.
—— Some materials for the illustration of the botanical
geography of the southwestern parts of Europe. Translated from the German. (*In* KONIG, Charles. Tracts
relative to botany, 1805, pp. 27–74.)

NL 0388270   MH-A

Link, Heinrich Friedrich, 1767–1851.
Species plantarum
see under Linné, Carl von, 1770–1778.

Link, Heinrich Friedrich, 1767–1851.
₍König, Carl Dietrich Eberhard₎ 1774–1851.
Tracts relative to botany, tr. from different languages.
Illustrated by nine copper plates, and occasional remarks.
London, Printed by Phillips and Fardon ₍etc.₎ 1805.

VOLUME 334

Link, Heinrich Friedrich, 1767–1851.
Travels in Portugal, by Henry Frederick Link ...
(*In* Pelham, Cavendish, comp. The world: or, The present state of the universe ... London, 1806-08. 27½ᶜᵐ. vol. ii, p. [345]-400)

1. Portugal—Descr. & trav.

Library of Congress   [36b1]   CA 8-1350 Unrev'd
                             G161.P38

NL 0388273   DLC CaBViPA

Link, Heinrich Friedrich, 1767–1851.
Travels in Portugal, and through France and Spain. With a dissertation on the literature of Portugal, and the Spanish and Portugueze languages. By Henry Frederick Link ... Tr. from the German by John Hinckley, esq. With notes by the translator. London, T. N. Longman and O. Rees, 1801.
viii, 504 p. 21½ᶜᵐ.

1. Portugal—Descr. & trav. 2. Spain—Descr. & trav. I. Hinckley, John, tr., d. 1814.

Library of Congress   DP524.L74   4-32120

NL 0388274   MnU NN OCU CtY NcD CLU KyLx DLC

AS   Link, Heinrich Friedrich, 1767–1851.
182   Über das Anwachsen von Theile in den
B51A31+   Pflanzen.
1836   (In Akademie der Wissenschaften, Berlin.
no.5   Abhandlungen. Berlin. 27cm. Physikalische
1845   Klasse. 1836, p. [179]-186; 1845, p. [393]-
no.5   403)

NL 0388275   NIC DLC MB

Link, Heinrich Friedrich, *1767–1851.*   *3322.2.1829
Über das cyrenäische Silphium der Alten.
(*In* Koeniglich-preussische Akademie der Wissenschaften. Physikalische Klasse. Abhandlungen. 1829, pp. 115-125. Berlin. 1832.)

M9857 — Cyrenaica. Botany. — Silphium.

NL 0388276   MB DLC MH

Link, Heinrich Friedrich. 1767–1851.   *3322.2.1834.1835.1840.1841
Über den Bau der Farrnkräuter. Abhandlung 1-4. Plates.
(*In* Koeniglich-preussische Akademie der Wissenschaften. Physikalisch-mathematische Klasse. 1834, pp. 375-387; 1835, pp. 83-91; 1840, pp. 175-186; 1841, pp. 283-290. Berlin. 1836-1843.)

H3538 — Ferns.

NL 0388277   MB NIC DLC

Link, Heinrich Friedrich. 1767–1851.   *3322.2.1833.1
Über den innern Bau und die Früchte der Tangarten (*Fucoideae*). Plates.
(*In* Koeniglich-preussische Akademie der Wissenschaften. Physikalische Klasse. Abhandlungen. 1833, pp. 457-467. Berlin. 1835.)

G9083 — Fucoides.

NL 0388278   MB DLC

AS   Link, Heinrich Friedrich, 1767–1851.
182   Über den Ursprung der Steinkohlen und Braun-
551A31+   kohlen nach mikroskopischen Untersuchungen.
1838   (In Akademie der Wissenschaften, Berlin.
no.2   Abhandlungen. Berlin. 27cm. [v. 23] (1838)
             Physikalische Abhandlungen, p. [33]-44)

NL 0388279   NIC DLC

3842   Link, Heinrich Friedrich, 1767–1851.
.1   Über die Aechtheit der Ossianischen
.791   Gedichte. Berlin, Buchhandlung des Berliner
             Lesekabinets, 1843.
             16 p. 22 cm.

1. Ossian. 2. Macpherson, James, 1736-1796.

NL 0388280   NjP MH

Link, Heinrich Friedrich. 1767–1851.   *3322.2.1816/1817, 1826
Ueber die ältere Geschichte der Getreidearten, Erste und Zweite Abhandlung.
(In Koeniglich-preussische Akademie der Wissenschaften. Physikalische Klasse. Abhandlungen. 1816/1817, pp. 123-142; 1826, pp. 67-82. Berlin. 1819, 29.)

G8937 — Paleobotany. — Grain.

NL 0388281   MB DLC

Link, Heinrich Friedrich. 1767–1851.   *3322.2.1827
Über die Familie *Pinus* und die europäischen Arten derselben.
(In Koeniglich-preussische Akademie der Wissenschaften. Physikalische Klasse. Abhandlungen. 1827, pp. 157-191. Berlin. 1830.)

G9023 — Conifers.

NL 0388282   MB MH-A DLC

Link, Heinrich Friedrich, *1767- 1851.*

—— **and Otto, Friedrich.** Ueber die gattungen Melocactus und Echinocactus, nebst beschreibung und abbildung der im Königl. botanischen garten bei Berlin befindlichen arten. 4°. pp. [22]. pl. 17. [Berlin, 1827].
Verhandlungen des Vereins zur beförderung des gartenbaues in den königl. preuss. staaten, 3. bd., pp. 412-432.

NL 0388283   MBH

Link, Heinrich Friedrich. 1767–1851.   *3322.2.1825
Über die natürliche Ordnung der Gräser.
(In Koeniglich-preussische Akademie der Wissenschaften. Physikalische Klasse. Abhandlungen. 1825, pp. 17-44. Berlin. 1828.)

G9018 — Grasses.

NL 0388284   MB DLC

Link, Heinrich Friedrich, 1767–1851.
Ueber die natur des lichts. Zwey von der Kaiserl. akademie der wissenschaften zu St. Petersburg gekrönte preisschriften von Heinrich Friedrich Link ... und Placidus Heinrich ... St. Petersburg, Gedruckt bey der Kaiserl. akademie der wissenschaften, 1808.
8, 92, xx, 287 p. 24½ᶜᵐ.
CONTENTS.—Ueber die chemischen eigenschaften des lichts [von Heinrich Friedrich Link]—Von der natur und den eigenschaften des lichtes [von Placidus Heinrich]
1. Optics.   I. Heinrich, Placidus, 1758-1825. II. I. Akademīīā nauk, Petrograd.
                              11-23593
Library of Congress   QC361.L75

NL 0388285   DLC NjP NcD

Link, Heinrich Friedrich. 1767–1851.   *3322.2.1830
Über die Pflanzenthiere überhaupt und die dazu gerechneten Gewächse besonders. Plate.
(In Koeniglich-preussische Akademie der Wissenschaften. Physikalische Klasse. Abhandlungen. 1830, pp. 109-13. Berlin. 1832.)

G9042 — Zoophytes.

NL 0388286   MB DLC

Link, Heinrich Friedrich. 1767–1851.   *3322.2.1843, 1846.1
Über die Stellung der Cycadeen im natürlichen System. Abhandlung 1, 2.
(In Koeniglich-preussische Akademie der Wissenschaften. Physikalische Klasse. Abhandlungen. 1843, pp. 99-108; 1846, pp. 313-323. Berlin. 1845, 1848.)

H3254 — Cycadeae.

NL 0388287   MB DLC NIC

          Link, Heinrich Friedrich, 1767–1851.
          Ueber Naturphilosophie. Leipzig und Rostock, in der Stillerschen Buchhandlung, 1806.
          viii, 202 p. 18cm.

          1. Physics.

NL 0388288   NNC NjP

Link, Heinrich Friedrich, 1767–1851.
Die urwelt und das alterthum, erläutert durch die naturkunde, von H. F. Link ... Berlin, F. Dümmler, 1821-22.
          2 v. 19½ᶜᵐ.
          "Dieses buch ist aus kleinen abhandlungen entstanden, welche ich ... in den gesellschaften vorgelesen habe."—Vorrede.

          1. Cosmogony. 2. Paleontology.

NL 0388289   ICU WU OkU NjP

Link, H[einrich] F[riedrich], 1767–1851.   NH 3558.34
Die urwelt und das alterthum, erläutert durch die naturkunde.
Berlin, F. Dümmler, 1834, '22.
2 pt.
Pt. 1 is "2ᵉ umgearbeitete ausg."

NL 0388290   MH ICU NN DI-GS

Link, Heinrich Friedrich, 1767–1851.
Versuch einer Anleitung zur geologischen Kenntniss der Mineralien ... Göttingen, bey J.C. Dieterich, 1790.
8 p.l., 239 p. 17.5 cm.
1. Mineralogy.

NL 0388291   CtY

Link, Heinrich Friedrich, 1767–1851.
Verzeichniss der von dem herrn dr. Heinrich Friedrich Link ... hinterlassenen bibliothek, welche am 24. november 1851 ... im T. O. Weigel'schen auctions-locale versteigert werden soll. Leipzig, T. O. Weigel, 1851.
2 pt. in 1 v. 22ᶜᵐ. [*With* Varnhagen von Ense, Karl A. L. P. Verzeichniss der hinterlassenen bibliotheken. [1859]]
T. O. Weigel's bücherauction. 1851. III.

1. Botany—Bibl.—Catalogs.

                              14-4619

Library of Congress   Z997.V32

NL 0388292   DLC MB

Link, Heinrich Friedrich, 1767–1851.
Voyage en Portugal, depuis 1797 jusqu'en 1799. Par m. Link ... Suivi d'un essai sur le commerce du Portugal, traduit de l'allemand ... Paris, Levrault, Schoell et cᵒⁱᵉ, an XII-1803.
2 v. 20ᶜᵐ.

1. Portugal—Descr. & trav.   *Translation of* Bemerkungen auf einer reise durch Frankreich, Spanien und vorzüglich Portugal.

                              35-30341
Library of Congress   DP524.L75 1803   914.60

NL 0388293   DLC FTaSU CU

VOLUME 334

Link, Heinrich Friedrich, 1767-1851.
Voyage en Portugal, depuis 1797 jusqu'en 1799. Suivi d'un essai sur le commerce du Portugal, traduit de l'allemand. Paris, Levrault, Schoell., 1803-05.

3 v. 21 cm.

Vol. 3 has title: Voyage en Portugal par M. le comte de Hoffmansegg, rédigé par M. Link, et faisant suite à son voyage dans le même pays.
Translation of Bemerkungen auf einer Reise durch Frankreich, Spanien und vorzüglich Portugal.
"Essai politique sur le commerce du Portugal et celui de ses colonies par Jose Joaquim da Cunha de Azeredo Coutinho ... Traduit du portugais": v. 2, p. [223]-395.

1. Portugal—Descr. & trav. 2. Spain—Descr. & trav. I. Hoffmannsegg, Johann Centurius von Hoffmann, Graf von, 1766-1849.
Voyage en Portugal. II. Coutinho, José Joaquim da Cunha de Azeredo. Bp., 1742-1818. Essai politique sur le commerce du Portugal et celui de ses colonies. III. Title.

DP524.L752   68-37530

NL 0388295   DLC DCU-IA MH ICN

Link, [**Heinrich Friedrich**] 1767-1851.
Voyage en Portugal, fait depuis 1797 jusqu'en 1799, par M. Link et le comte de Hoffmansegg ... Tr. de l'allemand ... Paris, Dentu, 1808.

3 v. 20ᶜᵐ.

1. Portugal—Descr. & trav. 2. Spain—Descr. & trav. I. Hoffmannsegg, Johann Centurius von Hoffmann, graf von, 1766-1849.

Library of Congress   DP524.L75   4-30318†

NL 0388296   DLC

Link, Heinrich Friedrich, 1767-1851.
Zwei Gedächtnissreden gehalten bei der Trauerfeier ...
see under Klöden, Karl Friedrich von, 1786-1856.

Link, Helen Kendall, 1911-
Our Father; thoughts and prayers for children. Illus. by Harold Minton. Philadelphia, Christian Education Press [1952].

96 p. illus. 23 cm.

1. Children—Religious life. I. Title.

BV4571.L52   248   52-29137 ‡

NL 0388298   DLC

Link, Helen Kendall, 1911-
Sunday school is fun! Illus. by Charlotte Rehfeld. Philadelphia, Christian Education Press [1948].

[31] p. illus. 20 x 26 cm.

1. Sunday-schools. I. Rehfeld, Charlotte, illus.

BV1525.L55   268   48-11077*

NL 0388299   DLC Or PPEB IEG

Link, Henry Charles, 1889-
Education and industry, by Henry C. Link ... New York, The Macmillan company, 1923.

xv p., 1 l., 265 p. illus., diagrs. 21ᶜᵐ.

1. Technical education. I. Title.

Library of Congress   LC1081.L5   23-7554

DL ViU ICJ NN MB WaS IdU-SB Or
NL 0388300   DLC WaSp NcRS PSC PU PHC MiU OC1 OCU

Link, Henry Charles, 1889-
Employment psychology; the application of scientific methods to the selection, training and grading of employees, by Henry C. Link, PH. D. New York, The Macmillan company, 1919.

xii, 440 p. incl. tables, diagrs. 21 cm.

1. Personnel management. I. Title. II. Title: Psychology, Employment.

HF5549.L5   19—12404

NcRS OKentU OrPR MtU Wa NjP CoU MU TU CaBViP
NL 0388301   DLC NIC CU CtY-M NN MB ICJ ODW OO OC1

Link, Henry Charles
Employment psychology; the application of scientific methods to the selection, training and rating of employees; with an introduction by Edward L. Thorndike.   New York: The Macmillan Co., 1920. 440 p.   8°.

1. Employment systems. 2. Ability   CENTRAL CIRCULATION.
tests.   February 28, 1921.

NL 0388302   NN ViU

LINK, Henry Charles
Employment psychology; the application of scientific methods of the selection, training and rating of employees. New York, The Macmillan Co., 1921[cop. 1919].
Econ 7409.21.55

NL 0388303   MH ICRL TU

LINK, Henry C[harles]
Employment psychology; the application of scientific methods to the selection, training and rating of employees. With an introduction by Edward L. Thorndike. New York, The Macmillan co., 1922.

NL 0388304   MH PSC PU-Penn ViU OU

Link, Henry Charles, 1889-
Employment psychology; the application of scientific methods to the selection, training and grading of employees, by Henry C. Link, PH. D.* New York, The Macmillan company, 1924.

xii, 440 p. incl. tables, diagrs. 21ᶜᵐ.
With an introduction by Edward L. Thorndike, PH.D.

NL 0388305   ViU NcD NcRS TU MH

331
L75

Link, Henry Charles.
Employment psychology; the application of scientific methods to the selection, training and grading of employees, by Henry C. Link, PH. D. New York, The Macmillan company, 1928.

xii, 440 p. incl. tables, diagrs. 21ᶜᵐ. $2.50

NL 0388306   TU WaTC

Link, Henry Charles, 1889-   joint author.
Kleppner, Otto, 1899-
Fundamentals of advertising, by Otto Kleppner ... and Henry C. Link ... Scranton, Pa., International textbook company [*1937]

Link, Henry Charles.
... Instinct and value, by Henry C. Link ... Ithaca, N. Y., The American journal of psychology [1922]

cover-title, 18 p. 23ᶜᵐ.

Abstract of author's doctoral dissertation, Yale university, 1916.
"Offprinted from the American journal of psychology ... January, 1922, vol. xxxiii."

Continued in next column

Continued from preceding column

1. Instinct.

Library of Congress   BF685.L5   22-16987

NL 0388308   DLC

Link, Henry Charles, 1889-
The new psychology of selling and advertising, by Henry C. Link ... foreword by John Broadus Watson ... New York, The Macmillan company, 1932.

xxiii, 293 p. illus., diagrs. 22ᶜᵐ.

1. Advertising. 2. Psychology, Applied. 3. Salesmen and salesmanship. 4. Market surveys. I. Title. II. Title: Psychology of selling and advertising.

Library of Congress   HF5822.L5   32-10405

Copyright A 50727   658.801

OO OU CoU ScU MB NN
NL 0388309   DLC ViU KMK OKentU CU PPD PPCuP MiU OC1

658.801
L756n

Link, Henry Charles, 1889-
The new psychology of selling and advertising, by Henry C. Link ... foreword by John Broadus Watson ... New York, The Macmillan company, 1938.

xxiii, 293 p. illus., diagrs. 22ᶜᵐ.

NL 0388310   TU NcD NcRS PPT

Link, Henry Charles, 1889-
People and books, a study of reading and book-buying habits, by Henry C. Link ... and Harry Arthur Hopf ... New York, Book industry committee, Book manufacturers' institute, 1946.

166 p., 1 l. incl. forms. map, diagrs. 23½ᶜᵐ.

1. Books and reading. 2. Booksellers and bookselling—U. S. I. Hopf, Harry Arthur, 1882-   joint author. II. Book manufacturers' institute. III. Title.

Library of Congress   Z1003.L6   46-3470

                                            028.9

OC1W Or NcC OrPS IdPI Wa WaS WaT CaBVaU
NL 0388311   DLC IdU KEmT CU NBuU CU-I PP PPD PSt MB

Link, Henry Charles, 1889-
... Practical test of employees by Henry C. Link. The Society of industrial engineers. [n. p., 1922]

14 p., 1 l. 23ᶜᵐ. (Society of industrial engineers. Department of publications. Vol. v, no. 4. October, 1922)
"Reprint. Report of Proceedings, eighth national convention, Detroit, April, 1922."

1. Employment management. I. Title.

NL 0388312   MiU DLC

Link, Henry Charles, 1889-
... Psychology of advertising, prepared especially for home study ... [Scranton, 1937]

cover-title, 42 p. illus. 19ᶜᵐ.
At head of title: International correspondence schools, Scranton, Pa.
"Serial 3353, edition 1."

1. Advertising. 2. Psychology, Applied. I. International correspondence schools, Scranton, Pa.

                                            43-30060
                                            Brief cataloging
Library of Congress   HF5822.L52
                                            659.15

NL 0388313   DLC NcRS

VOLUME 334

Link, Henry Charles, 1889–
    The rediscovery of man, by Henry C. Link, PH. D.   New York, The Macmillan company, 1938.
    ix p., 2 l., 3–257 p.   20½ᶜᵐ.
    Bibliography: p. 255–257.

    1. Personality.   2. Psychology, Applied.   I. Title.
    Library of Congress   BF698.L53   38–30988

    Copyright A 122050   ₍10–10₎   [159.923] 137

WaS WaSp KyWAT KyLxT Or OrPS MtU WaTC OrP Wa WaT
ViU NN KyLxC KyMdC CaBVaU OrMonO OrCS OrSaW WaWW IdB
NL 0388314   DLC KyLx KEmT NIC IU PPEB NcC OCl OU NcD

Link, Henry Charles, 1889–
    The rediscovery of man.   Toronto, Macmillan, 1938.
    257 p.
    Bibliography: p. 255–57.
    Contents: 1. Personality.   2. Psychology, Applied.   3. Success.

NL 0388315   CaBVaU

Phil 5251.44.7
Link, Henry Charles, 1889–
    The rediscovery of man.   New York, Macmillan co., 1939.

    ix, 257 p.   20.5 cm.

NL 0388316   MH TU

BF698
944£   LINK, Henry Charles, 1889–
        The rediscovery of man.   New York, Macmillan, 1944.
        257p.   21cm.
        1. Personality.   2. Psychology, Applied.
        I. Title.

NL 0388317   CtY-M

Link, Henry Charles, 1889–
    The rediscovery of morals, with special reference to race and class conflict, by Henry C. Link ...   New York, E. P. Dutton & company, inc., 1947.
    223 p.   21ᶜᵐ.
    "An American mercury book."
    "First edition."
    Bibliography: p. 219–223.

    1. Social ethics.   2. Race problems.   3. Class struggle.   I. Title.
    HM216.L55   301.1532   47–1803

WaT
KyU CaBVa IdPI OrPS IdU MtBC Or OrCS WaSp Wa WaS
PPRETS ViU TU OClW MSohG CoU NIC KyLxT KyLxCB MiU
NL 0388318   DLC NcRS NcD CU OO PSt PPFr PP PPL TxU

HM
216   Link, Henry Charles, 1889–
.L55   The rediscovery of morals, with special reference to race and class conflict, by Henry C. Link ...   New York, E. P. Dutton & company, inc., 1947.
        223 p.   21 cm.
        "An American mercury book."
        "First edition."
        Bibliography: p. 219–223.

        Xerox reprint, Ann Arbor, Mich., 1966.

NL 0388320   NBuU

301.153
L756r   Link, Henry Charles, 1889–
1949   The rediscovery of morals, with special reference to race and class conflict, by Henry C. Link.   New York, Garden City Pub. Co. [1949]
        223p.   21cm.

        Bibliography: p. 219–223.

        1. Social ethics.   2. Race problems.   3. Class struggle.   I. Title.

NL 0388321   IEN CaBVaU PPT

Link, Henry Charles, 1889–
    The return to religion, by Henry C. Link ...   New York, The Macmillan company, 1936.
    5. p. l., 3–181 p.   20½ cm.

    1. Psychology, Religious.   2. Personality.   3. Psychology, Applied.   4. Apologetics.   I. Title.
    BL53.L5   201   36—8628

CaBVaU CaBVa
WaWW OrSaW OrU WaS OrCS OrAshS OrU IdU MtBuM WaOB
AU NN OU MB KEmT WaE IdU WaTC OrP Wa MtBC WaSp Or
OCU PPL PPLT PPC NcC NcRS NcD KyU-A KyLx KyU NIC
NL 0388322   DLC KyWAT KyLxCB OKentU MiHM ViU ODW

Link, Henry Charles, 1889–
    The return to religion, by Henry C. Link, PH. D.   New York, The Macmillan company, 1937.
    5 p. l., 3–181 p.   20½ cm.
    "Published March, 1936 ... eighteenth printing, February, 1937."

    1. Psychology, Religious.   2. Personality.   3. Psychology, Applied.   4. Apologetics—20th cent.   I. Title.
    BL53.L5   1937a   201   37—3813

OClW MH OCl
NL 0388324   DLC WaT Wa WaSpG MtU IdU-SB ViU OClU

Link, Henry Charles, 1889–
    The Return to Religion.
    New York, Macmillan, 1938.   ...
    181 p.   8°.

NL 0388325   PPDrop

Link, Henry Charles.
    The return to religion.   New York, The Macmillan company, 1939, ₍c1936₎
    5 p. l., 3–181 p.   21 cm.

NL 0388326   TU

A–17653
Link, Henry Charles, 1889–
    The return to religion.   New York, Macmillan, 1945.
    181p.

NL 0388327   ICRL

Link, Henry Charles, 1889–
American management association.   Committee on training methods.
    Tendencies in training methods; report by the Committee on training methods (with discussion); chairman, Henry C. Link ...   New York, N. Y., American management association, °1924.

Link, Henry Charles, 1889–
    The way to security.   ₍1st ed.₎   Garden City, N. Y., Doubleday, 1951.
    224 p.   21 cm.

    1. Security (Psychology)   I. Title.
    BF67.L5   137.32   51–9963

TU
Or OrU Wa WaE MeB OKentU CaOTP FMU CoU PSt NN TxU
NL 0388329   DLC IdU CaBVaU WaT WaSp WaS CaBVa OrP

Link, Henry Frederick
    see   Link, Heinrich Friedrich, 1767–

Link, Hermann.
    Die stellung des einzelhaft im heutigen deutschen strafvollzuge ... von Hermann Link ...   Mannheim, Druck der hofbuchdruckerei M. Hahn & comp., 1902.
    90 p.   20½ᶜᵐ.
    Inaug.-diss.—Göttingen.

    1. Punishment—Germany.   2. Prisons—Germany—Laws and regulations.   I. Title.
    Library of Congress   HV8728.L55 1902

                                    37–23175
                                    343.2

NL 0388331   DLC MH-L

HV85
.A36   Link, Irene, joint author.
no. 13   Farnham, Rebecca Tufts, 1903–
        ... Effects of the works program on rural relief.   A survey of rural relief cases closed in seven states, July through November 1935, by Rebecca Farnham and Irene Link ...   Washington, U. S. Govt. print. off., 1938.

LINK, Jakob, 1904–
    Beiträge zur kenntnis der benziloxime.
    Inaug.-diss., Tübingen, E. Göbel, 1927.

    pp. 47.
    "Lebenslauf", p. 47.

NL 0388333   MH-C CtY

788.485   Link, Joachim Dietrich, 1925–
L64s   ₍Sonatina, tuba & piano₎

        Sonatine für Tuba und Klavier (1951)   Leipzig, F. Hofmeister ₍195–₎   Pl. no. 7102.
        score (11 p.) and part.   31 cm.

        1. Sonatas (Tuba and piano)

        M265.L   M 59–1114

NL 0388334   DLC IU OO KEmT

Link, Joachim Dietrich, 1925–
    ₍Sonata, piano, no. 2₎

    Zweite Sonate für Klavier.   Leipzig, Breitkopf & Härtel ₍1950₎
    13 p.   31 cm.   (Edition Breitkopf, Nr. 5774)

    1. Sonatas (Piano)
    M23.L763   no. 2   51–16545

NL 0388335   DLC

VOLUME 334

Link, Johann, 1908–
... Zur Aetiologie, Klinik und Therapie der
Duodenalstenose ... Erlangen, 1938.
Inaug.-Diss. - Erlangen.
Lebenslauf.
"Literatur": p. 24-26.

NL 0388336   CtY PPJ

Link, Johann George, respondent.
De angelis malis
see under   Ohm, Gottfried, praeses.

Ts
234
L648p
Link, John Bodkin, b. 1825.
A practical inquiry into the New Testament doc-
trine of faith, justification and good works.
Introd. by O.C. Pope.   Houston, Tex., Office of
Texas Baptist herald, 1878.
53p. 13cm.

1. Faith. 2. Justification. 3. Good works
(Theology)

NL 0388338   TxU

Link, John Bodkin, b. 1825, ed.
Texas historical and biographical magazine
see under title

Link, John Joseph, 1863–
Propositions and discussions for world peace.   Submitted to
the American Peace Award, November 1923, by Dr. J. J. Link...
[St. Louis, 1923.]   2 p.   12°.

1. Federation, Universal.

August 9, 1928

NL 0388340   NN DLC MH

Link, John Joseph, 1863–
Two coeval evils, by Dr. J. J. Link.   Boston, Meador publishing company, 1941.
123 p. 20ᶜᵐ.

I. Title.

41-23084

Library of Congress   PZ3.L65457Tw

NL 0388341   DLC

QE135
.A4
no.7
Link, John Thomas, 1873–1936.
... The origin of the place names of Nebraska (The topon-
omy of Nebraska) by J. T. Link.   [Lincoln] Printed by au-
thority of the state of Nebraska, 1933.
186 p. 25ᶜᵐ. (Nebraska. Geological survey. Bulletin 7, 2d ser.)
At head of title: University of Nebraska.
Issued also as the author's thesis, PH. D., University of Nebraska,
1932, under title: The toponomy of Nebraska.
Bibliography: p. [161]-170.

1. Names, Geographical—Nebraska.   I. Title: The toponomy of
Nebraska.

U. S. Geol. survey. Library   G S 33-87
for Library of Congress

[38-1]   KGL4

NL 0388342   DI-GS OrP MtBuM WaS CU UU MoU DLC SdSpeT

Link, John Thomas, 1873-1936
The toponomy of Nebraska, by John Thomas Link ...
Lincoln, Neb., Department of industry and survey, 1932.
186 p. 25ᶜᵐ.
Thesis (PH. D.)—University of Nebraska, 1932.
Bibliography: p. [161]-170.

1. Names, Geographical—Nebraska.   I. Title.

Library of Congress   F664.L56   33-18909

929.4

NL 0388343   DLC OrU PU NcU MiU OU NIC MB

F666
.C736L7
Link, John Thomas, 1873-1936.
A workbook by J.T. Link for use with
Condra's Geography, agriculture, industries of Nebraska.   [Lincoln] The University publishing company [c1936]
cover-title, 72 p.   illus.(incl.maps)
28cm.

NL 0388344   MnHi

49
F81
Link, Josef, 1881–
Das Schulwesen in der ehemaligen deutsch-
ordens-ballei Franken. ... Kallmünz, 1935.
111 p.
Inaug. Diss. - Erlangen, 1935.
Vitae
Quellenverzeichnis.

NL 0388345   ICRL CtY MiU

Link (Karl). * Statistisch casuistischer Bericht
über die Irrenabtheilung des kgl. Juliusbospi-
tals zu Würzburg für die Jahre 1873-1882 incl
[Würzburg.] 57 pp. 8°. Berlin, 1884.

NL 0388346   DNLM

Link, Josef.
* Die Geschichte der Schauspieler nach einem
syrischen Manuscript der Königlichen Bibliothek in Berlin. ... Bern. ...   Berlin, H.
Itzkowski, 1904.
44 p., 1 l.
Text also in Syriac.

NL 0388347   NN

Link, Karl, 1863–
Über berberin und hydroberberin ...   Marburg,
1892.
40 p., 1 l.   23 cm.   [Marburg. Universität.
Dissertationen. v. 19, no. 4]
Inaug.-diss. - Marburg.
Lebenslauf.

NL 0388348   CU MH ICRL

W
4
H46
1937
Link, Karl, 1914–
Über das Schicksal von Vitamin C in
Silagen. Kaiserslautern, Pfeiffer
[1937?]
28 p.
Inaug.-Diss. - Heidelberg.
Bibliography: p. 25-26.

NL 0388349   DNLM

W 1
VE783
Bd. 12
Heft 4
1945
LINK, Karl H
Traumatische sub- und intradurale
Blutung: Pachymeningitis haemorrhagica.
Jena, Fischer, 1945.
120 p. illus. (Veröffentlichungen
aus der Konstitutions- und
Wehrpathologie, 55. Heft, 12. Bd.,
Heft 4)
1. Meninges - Hemorrhage   Series

NL 0388350   DNLM ICU

Link, Karl H   1903–
... Die unfallbegutachtung in der zahn-, mund- und kiefer-
heilkunde, von dr. med. habil. K. H. Link ... Mit 7 abbildungen im text. Leipzig, H. Meusser, 1936.
viii, 179 p. illus. 23½ᶜᵐ. (Sammlung Meusser; abhandlungen aus
dem gebiete der klinischen zahnheilkunde, hft. 26)
"Schrifttum": p. [174]-176.

1. Mouth—Wounds and injuries. 2. Occupations—Diseases and hygiene. 3. Insurance, Employers' liability—Germany.   I. Title.

Library of Congress   RD131.L55   37-12672 Revised

[r43c2]   [613.6] 617.1

NL 0388351   DLC DNLM

1889–
Link, Karl Heinrich, Referendar: Die Rechte der Gläubiger
bei dem Untergange eines rechtsfähigen Vereins. Borna-
Leipzig 1912: Noske.   x, 66 S. 8°
Marburg, Jur. Diss. v. 25. Nov. 1912, Ref. Leonhard
[Geb. 31. Jan. 89 Frankfurt a. M.; Wohnort: Frankfurt; Staatsangeh.: Preußen;
Vorbildung: Kaiser-Friedrich-Gymn. Frankfurt Reife O. 07; Studium: Lau-
sanne 1, Freiburg i. B. 2, Berlin 1, München 1, Berlin 1, Marburg 2 S.;
Rig. 30. Sept. 12.]   [U 12. 6270]

NL 0388352   ICRL MH-L

Link, Karl Paul, 1901–
... The chemical composition of corn (Zea mays) seedlings
... [Easton, Pa., 1929]
2 pt. 23½ᶜᵐ.
Cover title.
Thesis (PH. D.)—University of Wisconsin, 1925.
Thesis note stamped on cover of pt. 1.
"Reprint from the Journal of the American chemical society, 51 ...
(1929)."
CONTENTS.—I. The isolation of xylan and cellulose from the cell
walls.—II. The isolation of a dextrin similar to the trihexosan obtained
by the thermal depolymerization of potato starch.
1. Maize. 2. Seedlings. 3. Plants—Chemical analysis.

Library of Congress   QK866.M3L5 1925   30-12804
Univ. of Wisconsin Libr.

NL 0388353   WU DLC

Link, Karl Paul, joint author

Tottingham, William Edward, 1881–
Climatic effects in the metabolism of the sugar beet.   By
W. E. Tottingham and S. Lepkovsky ... and E. R. Schulz and
K. P. Link ...
(In U. S. Dept. of agriculture. Journal of agricultural research.
v. 33, no. 1, July 1, 1926, p. 59-76. diagrs. 23½ᶜᵐ. Washington, 1926)

Link, Karl Paul, 1901–   joint author.

Baur, Lorenz.
The methylglycosides of the naturally occurring hexuronic
acids. IV. Polygalacturonic acid-methylglycosides derived
from Ehrlich's "pektolsäure" and "pektolactonsäure", by
Lorenz Baur and Karl Paul Link ... [Baltimore, Waverly
press, inc., 1935]

Link, L.
(Die) einheitliche Aussprache in
Deutschen: theoretisch und praktisch darges-
tellt. 49p. Paderborn, Schöningh, 1898.

NL 0388356   OC1

VOLUME 334

Link, L   Mabel.
    Chalmers, the peace scout. Story outlines
for leaders and teachers of juniors ...   London
[n. d.]
    cover-title, 44 p.   incl. illus., map.
21.5 cm.

NL 0388357   CtY

Link, L   Mabel.
    Histoires missionnaires sur l'Afrique
à l'usage des élèves des ecoles du dimanche
et du jeudi et des cadets et cadettes des unions
chrétiennes; traduction libre de l'anglais (Story
lessons on Africa) par N. Poivre, pasteur.
Paris, 1929.
    64 p. incl. illus., port. map.   22.5 cm.
    Maps inside covers.

NL 0388358   CtY

Link, L   Mabel.
    Story lessons on Africa; deeds of missionary
adventure on the Niger, the Cameroons, and the
Congo. For teachers of boys and girls (aged 8
to 11) ...   London, 1921.
    64 p.   illus.   19.5 cm.

NL 0388359   CtY

Link, L   Mabel.
    Williams the seafarer; story outlines for
leaders and teachers of juniors ... by Mabel
Link and Vera Walker.   London [1915]
    44 p.   illus.   22 cm.

NL 0388360   CtY

Link, Ludwig, *1885-*
    Über die Kondensation von Alloxan mit in
ω-Stellung alkylierten Acetophenonen. (Berlin 1910:
G. Schade)   55 S. 8°
    Berlin, Phil. Diss. v. 9. März 1910, Ref. Gabriel
    [Geb. 13. April 85 Heilbronn; Wohnort: Heilbronn; Staatsangeh.: Württem-
berg; Vorbildung: Gymn. Heilbronn Reife M. 03; Studium: Heidelberg 6,
München 2, Berlin 3 S.; Rig. 24. Febr. 10.]   [U 10. 208]

NL 0388361   ICRL CtY

Link, Mabel
        see Link, L   Mabel.

Link, Mae Mills.

D807
.U6A515
    U.S. *Air Force. Medical Service.*
        Medical support of the Army Air Forces in World War II,
by Mae Mills Link [and] Hubert A. Coleman. Washington,
Office of the Surgeon General, USAF, 1955.

Link, Margaret Schevill.
    Beautiful on the earth. With 5 illus. reproduced from
the author's drawings in serigraph by Louie Ewing. Santa
Fe, N. M., H. Dreis Editions [1947]
    xv, 155 p. col. plates. 27 cm.
    "Five hundred copies ... printed."

Continued in next column

Continued from preceding column

    1. Navaho Indians—Religion and mythology. 2. Navaho Indians—
    Rites and ceremonies.   I. Title.

E99.N3L65   [299.7] 970.62   47–19962 rev*

NL 0388362   DLC OrPR CaBVaU NN PU-Mu OU

F819
.2
L5
    Link, Margaret Schevill
        Desert sheaf [by] Margaret Erwin Schevill. Tucson, Ariz.,
    Desert Press [1942]
        [31] p. 24cm.
        Cover title.
        Poems.

NL 0388363   CU-B ViU RPB NN

Link, Margaret Schevill.
    In the garden of the home god, a retelling of a Navajo
tale. Santa Fe, N. M., H. Dreis Editions, 1943.
    25 p. col. illus. 26 cm.

    I. Title.

PZ8.1.L5 In   44–20548 rev*

NL 0388364   DLC Or CU-B PP TxU

Link, Martin, 1890-
    Ein Beitrag zur Kasuistik der Kleinhirnbrücken-
winkeltumoren.
    Inaug. diss. Kiel, 1915.   *21 p.*
    Bibl.

NL 0388365   ICRL DNLM CtY

Link, Martin Wilhelm Carl, 1890-
        see Link, Martin, 1890-

LINK, Mathias, *1864-*
    Ein fall von Gangraen der Trachea. Kiel.
1891.

NL 0388367   MBCo CtY DNLM

W 4
M96
1952
    LINK, Max Rüdiger, 1915-
        Über einen Fall von Polycythaemia vera
    mit früher Milzexstirpation und Quer-
    schnittslähmung; zugleich ein Beitrag zur
    Frage der Beteiligung der Milz an diesem
    Krankheitsbild. [München] 1952.
        50 p.
        Inaug.-Diss. - Munich.
        Typewritten copy.
        1. Polycythemia vera 2. Spleen

NL 0388368   DNLM

Link, Nelle Weymouth, 1889-
    Precision draping; a simple method for developing de-
signing talent. New York, Funk & Wagnalls Co. [1948]
    x, 166 p. illus. 28 cm.

    1. Garment cutting. 2. Costume design.   I. Title.

TT520.L74   646.4   48–5306*

        IdB Or OrSaW OrU Wa WaE WaS
NL 0388369   DLC WaT MB OU Mi PPMI MU TU CaBVa CaBVaU

Link, Nelle Weymouth, 1889-
    Stitching for style; fabric manipulation for self trim.
New York, Liveright Pub. Corp. [1948]
    111 p. illus. 28 cm.

    1. Dressmaking. 2. Needlework.   I. Title.

TT751.L5   746.42   48–6104*

NL 0388370   DLC CaBViP CaBVa Or OrP Wa WaE WaT NN Mi

W 4
M96
1951
    LINK, Ottmar, 1908-
        Die Entwicklung der Abszesstonsillek-
    tomie und ihre Indikation.   München,
    1951.
        62 *l.*
        Inaug.-Diss. -+Munich.
        1. Tonsillectomy

NL 0388371   DNLM

BT192
R2L66
    Link, Otto
        Mess-Stipendien. Regensburg, G. J. Manz,
    1901.*
        xv, 339 p. 22cm.

        I. Mass stipends. I. Title.

NL 0388372   MBtS

Link, Otto, 1866-
    Anleitung zum Lösen von Schachproblemen, von Otto Link.
Ansbach: C. Brügel & Sohn, 1898.   248 p.   illus.   16½cm.

                        FRANK J. MARSHALL CHESS COLL.
                            1898.
634205A. 1. Chess—Problems,   June 27, 1933

NL 0388373   NN PP MH OC1

LINK, Otto, *1866-*
    Anleitung zum lösen von schachproblemen.
Ansbach, C. Brügel & sohn, 1898.

    17 cm. Diagrs.   SG 3655.280.2*
    Another copy in the Treasure Room.
    This copy annotated. Bound at the end are 20
leaves containing blank diagrams on recto with
some filled in manuscript.

NL 0388374   MH

LINK, Otto.
    Anleitung zum Lösen von Schachproblemen.
II.Aufl. Ansbach, C. Brügel & Sohn, 1911.

    17 cm. Illustr.

NL 0388375   MH OC1

Link, Otto, 1866-
    Vidi vici auf dem Schachbrett, von Otto Link.   Berlin: B.
Kagan[, pref. 1921].   84 p.   illus.   22cm.

                        FRANK J. MARSHALL CHESS COLL.
                            1921.
634300A. 1. Chess—Problems,   June 27, 1933

NL 0388376   NN OC1

VOLUME 334

Link, Otto, 1905–
Die kältewellen in Nordamerika und ihr
einbruch in das amerikanische mittelmeergebiet.
... Lohr a. Main, 1934.   146 p.
Inaug. Diss. – Würzburg, 1934.
Lebenslauf.
Bibliography.

NL 0388377   ICRL DAS MH

Link, Pablo, 1903–
All about wool; a new comprensive [!] dictionary
see his   Diccionario de términos laneros.

45
L642Pre   Link, Pablo, 1903–
All American wool production.   Buenos
Aires, Nilssen, Olsen ₍1949₎
100 p.

Translation of his Producción lanera de
las Americas (45 L642Pr)

1. Wool trade and industry. America.
2. America. Sheep.

NL 0388379   DNAL

Link, Pablo, 1903–
Alpaca, llama, vicuña, guanaco. Buenos Aires ₍Ferrari
Hermanos, 1949₎
45, ₍2₎ p. 23 cm.
Bibliography: p. ₍46₎

1. Llamas. 2. Huanaco.

New York. Public Libr.   A 52-2451
for Library of Congress

NL 0388380   NN LU DNAL CU IU TxCsA PPPTe PSt

Link, Pablo   Jud 600.948
Bases del judaismo. Buenos Aires [c1948]

225 p. illus.

NL 0388381   MH

BM560
.L5   Link, Pablo, 1903–
Bases del Judaismo. Buenos Aires
₍Imp. Ferrari Hermanos, 1949₎
225p. tables. 20cm.

NL 0388382   NNU-W NN CtY MH

636.32   Link, Pablo.
L64c   El Corriedale. 2.ed. rev. y ampliada.
1947   Premiada por la Asociación Argentina Criado-
res de Corriedale. Buenos Aires ₍Ferrari,
1947₎
237p. illus., map. 21cm.

Bibliography: p. ₍235₎-237.

1. Corriedale sheep.

NL 0388383   IU NN

Link, Pablo, 1903–
La cría del karakul...   Buenos Aires, J. Peuser, 1938.   81 p.
illus., map. 24cm.

596539B. 1. Sheep, Karakul.
                                                       •
                                            October 16, 1951

NL 0388384   NN IU DNAL

Link, Pablo, 1903–
40 años de precios de lanas argentinas en pesos moneda nacional, curso legal. Cotizaciones.   Buenos Aires, Nilssen, Olsen
& cía., 1949.   chart.   64 x 40cm.   folded 23cm.

"Copyright by Professor Paul Link."

1. Prices, Wool—Argentine   Republic, 1910–1949.
                                            February 19, 1952

NL 0388385   NN

Link, Pablo, 1903–
El desarrollo de la cría del merino australiano...   Buenos
Aires, Ferrari hnos., 1942.   74 p.   illus., maps.   24cm.

596541B. 1. Sheep, Merino.
                                                       •
                                            October 16, 1951

NL 0388386   NN

Link, Pablo, 1903–
Diccionario de términos laneros, por Pablo Link ..
Buenos Aires ₍Imprenta Ferrari hnos.₎ 1940.
135, ₍17₎ p. 20 cm.
Added t.-p.: All about wool, a new comprensive ₍!₎ dictionary, b₍
Paul Link.
English and Spanish in parallel columns.

1. Wool trade and industry—Dictionaries. 2. Wool trade and in
dustry—Dictionaries—Spanish. 3. English language—Dictionaries—
Spanish.   I. Title.   II. Title: All about wool.

TS1309.L68 1940   677.303   41—24022

NL 0388387   DLC DFT PPD MH OC1 OU

Link, Pablo, 1903–
Diccionario lanero, por Pablo Link ... 2. ed. ampliada.
Buenos Aires ₍Imprenta Ferrari hermanos₎ 1944.
13 p. l., ₍29₎–230, ₍1₎ p., 11 l. 16 cm.
Added t.-p.: Wool glossary by Paul Link.
English and Spanish in parallel columns.
First edition published 1940 under title: Diccionario de términos
laneros.

1. Wool. 2. Sheep. 3. Textile industry and fabrics—Dictionaries.
4. Textile industry and fabrics—Dictionaries—Spanish. 5. English
language—Dictionaries—Spanish. 6. Spanish language—Dictionaries—English.   I. Title.   II. Title: Wool glossary.

TS1309.L68 1944   677.303   46–23425

NL 0388388   DLC DNAL NcRS PSt

Link, Pablo, 1903–
Diccionario lanero
see also his   Wool glossary.

Link, Pablo, 1903–
Enciclopedia textil. ₍Buenos Aires, 1954₎
630 p. (p. 600–630 advertisements) 23 cm.
Added t. p., in English.
English and Spanish.

1. Textile industry and fabrics — Dictionaries. 2. English language—Dictionaries—Spanish. 3. Textile industry and trade— Dictionaries—Spanish. 4. Spanish language — Dictionaries — English.
I. Title.

TS1309.L72   59–31911

NL 0388390   DLC DNAL PPPTe MBU N NN MB

Link, Pablo.
Evolución del judaísmo ₍por₎ Pablo Link. Buenos Aires,
Abolsky hnos. ₍1984?₎
115 p., 2 l. incl. plates, map, tab. 17½ᶜᵐ.
CONTENTS.—Influencias extrañas sobre la Palestina preisraelita.—La
evolución racial del judaismo.—La evolución cultural del judaismo.

1. Jews—Hist.   I. Title.   36–29207

Library of Congress   DS118.L65

                                                       953

NL 0388391   DLC CtY OCH NNJ IaU

Link, Pablo, 1903–
Fibras textiles...   Buenos Aires ₍1949₎   183 p.   illus.,
maps. 21cm.

596185B. 1. Textile fibers.
                                                       •
                                            November 13, 1951

NL 0388392   NN DNAL

Link, Pablo, 1903–
El futuro de la lana, por el profesor Pablo Link ... Buenos
Aires ₍Imprenta Ferrari hermanos₎ 1943.
71, ₍1₎ p. incl. maps, tables, diagrs. 23ᶜᵐ.
Added t.-p.: The future of wool, by Professor Paul Link.
Spanish and English.
"Bibliografía": p. 69.

1. Wool trade and industry—Argentine republic.   I. Title.   II. Title:
The future of wool.

Library of Congress   HD9904.A72L5   45–13144

                                            338.476773

NL 0388393   DLC PPPTe

Link, Pablo, 1903–
El futuro de la lana, por el profesor Pablo
Link ... Buenos Aires [Imprenta Ferrari
hermanos] 1944.
71 [1] p. incl. maps, tables, diagrs. 23 cm.
Added t. -p. : The future of wool, by Professor
Paul Link.
Spanish and English.
"Bibliografía": p. 69.

NL 0388394   NN PSt CtY

Link, Pablo, 1903–
...Habla la oveja.   Buenos Aires ₍1946₎   125 p.   illus.
22cm.

596022B. 1. Sheep—Legends and   stories. 2. Fiction, Argentine.
I. Title.
                                                       •
                                            September 25, 1951

NL 0388395   NN IU

                   Link, Pablo, 1903–   ed.
BM675
.P4L5
Hebraic   Jews. *Liturgy and ritual. Hagadah. 1949.*
Sect.   הגדה של פסח ₍Editado por₎ Pablo Link. Buenos
Aires ₍1949₎

Link, Pablo.
Lanares y lanas de la República Argentina...
1933.
144 p.

NL 0388397   DNAL

VOLUME 334

Link, Pablo.
Lanares y lanas de la republica Argentina, por el profesor Pablo Link ... Segunda edicion ampliada. Buenos Aires, Imprenta Ferrari hnos., 1938.

255, ₍3₎ p., 2 l. illus., maps, diagrs. 24ᶜᵐ.

Dept. of agriculture copy numbered 162.
"Bibliografía": p. ₍253₎-255.
Advertising matter included in paging.

1. Sheep—Argentine republic. ₍1. Argentine republic—Sheep₎ 2. Wool.

U. S. Dept. of agr. Library   45L642   Ed. 2   Agr 38-896
for Library of Congress   [SF375]

NL 0388398   DNAL

Link, Pablo, 1903–
Lavadero de lanas...   Buenos Aires ₍1948₎   105 p.   illus. 20cm.

596055B. 1. Wool—Manufacture.

October 19, 1951

NL 0388399   NN DNAL

Link, Pablo, 1903–
Manual enciclopédico judío. Buenos Aires, Editorial Israel, 1950.

415 p. illus., maps, ports. 26 cm. (Biblioteca Israel. Ediciones judías en castellano)

1. Jews—Dict. & encyc.   I. Title.

DS102.8.L5   68-53495

NL 0388400   DLC CtY MH NN OCH

Link, Pablo, 1903–
...La oveja y la lana lincoln. Buenos Aires, 1942.   130 p. illus., maps.   24cm.

596549B. 1. Sheep.

October 16, 1951

NL 0388401   NN DNAL

Link, Pablo.
Patagonia y Tierra del Fuego ₍por₎ Pablo Link ... Buenos Aires, Talleres Sociedad anónima casa Jacobo Peuser, ltda., 1936.

29, ₍3₎ p. incl. illus., plates. 26ᶜᵐ.

1. Patagonia—Descr. & trav. 2. Tierra del Fuego—Descr. & trav. 3. Agriculture—Patagonia. 4. Agriculture—Tierra del Fuego.

Library of Congress   F2936.L66   37-8411
                                      918.2

NL 0388402   DLC

Link, Pablo, 1903–
Pelos y pieles. Buenos Aires ₍1952₎

53 p. illus. 22 cm.

1. Animal fibers.   I. Title.

TS1545.L5   57-47756 ‡

NL 0388403   DLC DNAL NN

Link, Pablo, 1903–
La posición de la lana.   Buenos Aires ₍1952₎

60 p. illus. 22 cm.

1. Wool.   I. Title.

TS1547.L52   59-40715 ‡

NL 0388404   DLC DNAL NN

LINK, PABLO, 1903–
Producción lanera de la República Argentina, 1936-1938. Wool production in the Argentine Republic. [1. ed.] Buenos Aires, Tall. gráf. J. Hays Bell, 1938 [i.e. 1937] 44 p. illus., map. 24cm.

Title and text in Spanish and English.
Colophon dated₎ 1937.

1. WOOL—TRADE AND STAT.—ARGENTINE REPUBLIC,1937-1938

NL 0388405   NN DNAL

△
HD9895
.A2L5
Link, Pablo, 1903–
Producción lanera de las Américas. All American wool production. Buenos Aires ₍Imprenta Ferrari Hnos., 1948₎
176 p. illus., maps, tables. 24 cm.
Bibliography: p. ₍175₎-176.

1. Wool trade and industry—America. I. Title. II. Title: All American wool production.

NL 0388406   MB ScC1eU TxCsA PPPTe NNU-W DNAL

Link, Pablo.
Razas ovinas ₍por₎ profesor Pablo Link ... Buenos Aires, S. a. Casa J. Peuser, lda., 1937.

2 p. l., ₍7₎-305 p., 2 l. incl. illus., plates, diagrs. 24ᶜᵐ.

"Bibliografía": p. ₍303₎-305.

1. Sheep—₍Breeds₎

U. S. Dept. of agr. Library   45L642R   Agr 38-226
for Library of Congress   [SF375]

NL 0388407   DNAL OU

Link, Pablo.
Sheep breeding and wool production in the Argentine republic ₍by₎ Paul Link ... Buenos Aires, Argentina, 1934.

48 p. illus., maps, tables, diagrs. 26½ᶜᵐ.

Advertisements: p. 43-48.

1. Sheep—Argentine republic. ₍1. Argentine republic—Sheep₎ 2. Wool.

U. S. Dept. of agr. Library   45L642S   Agr 37-705
for Library of Congress   [SF375]

NL 0388408   DNAL

Ecbn 7866.57
LINK,Pablo.
Sheep breeding and wool production in the Argentine Republic. [By] Paul Link. Buenos Aires,1934.

26 cm. pp.42. Charts and other illustr.

NL 0388409   MH

Link, Pablo, 1903–
Textile encyclopedia
see his   Enciclopedia textil.

Link, Pablo, 1903–
Wool glossary. Diccionario lanero. English, Spanish, French, German. Inglés, español, francés, alemán. ₍3d ed.₎ Buenos Aires ₍1954₎

199 p. 19 cm.

First ed. published 1940 under title: Diccionario de términos laneros.

1. Wool trade and industry—Dictionaries. 2. Wool trade and industry—Dictionaries—Spanish. 3. English language—Dictionaries—Spanish. 4. Dictionaries, Polyglot. I. Title. II. Title: Diccionario lanero.

TS1309.L68 1954   677.303   59-2078

NL 0388411   DLC DNAL NN LU N

TS1309
L68
1954
Agric.
Ref.
Service
Link, Pablo, 1903–
Wool glossary. Diccionario lanero. 3d ed. Buenos Aires ₍c1954₎
161 p. (p. 161 advertisement)
First ed. published 1940 under title: Diccionario de términos laneros.

1. Wool trade and industry - Dictionaries. 2. Wool trade and industry - Dictionaries - Spanish. 3. English language - Dictionaries - Spanish. I. Title. II. Title: Diccionario lanero.

NL 0388412   CU

Link, Pablo, 1903–
Wool glossary
see also his   Diccionario lanero.

Link, Paul
see

Link, Pablo, 1903–

Link, Paxson Rude, 1897–
The Link family; antecedents and descendants of John Jacob Link, 1417-1951, with much history about the Stoner, Crowell, Demory, Remsberg, Thraves, Ropp, Boyer, Fuchs (Fox), Beard (Bart), Miller, Filler, Hanger, Wayland, Osbourn, Hendricks, Reinhart, Stone, Burrier, Root, Houff, Stover, Turner, La Grange, Smith, Kneiple, Shank, Grove, Cale, Palmer, Lewis, Allen, Woodward, Burnett, McChesney, Baylor, Freer, Garrett, Girdner, Creager, Burckhardt, and Eisenhower families. ₍Paris?₎ Ill.₎ 1951.
xiv, 872 p. illus., ports., maps. 24 cm.
1. Link family.

CS71.L7563 1951   53-22402

NL 0388415   DLC OFH MiD-B IU IHi NN ICN NBuG Vi ViU

Link (Peter). *De tumore cranii sanguineo recens natorum.* 16 pp. 8°. *Monachii, J. A. Giesser,* 1836.

NL 0388416   DNLM

Link (Richard). *Ueber den Vereinigungswahn.* 44 pp. 8°. *Freiburg i. B., C. A. Wagner,* 1895.

NL 0388417   DNLM

Link, Richard.
... Wird bei kaninchen und meerschweinchen experimentell hervorgerufene tuberkulose durch injektionen von hundeblutserum beeinflusst? Habilitationsschrift ... von dr. Richard Link ... Naumburg a. S., Lippert & co., 1904.
1 p.l., 40 p.   2 col. pl., diagrs. 20 cm.
Bibliographical foot-notes.
1. Tuberculosis in animals. 2. Serumtherapy.

NL 0388418   CU

VOLUME 334

W 4
W951
1954
LINK, Robert, 1922-
Die Glucuronidbildung nach peroraler
Salicylamidapplikation in Beziehung zum
Leberstoffwechsel. Würzburg, 1954.
24 p. illus.
Inaug.-Diss. - Würzburg.
1. Glucuronic acid 2. Liver -
Function tests 3. Salicylates

NL 0388419 DNLM

SK601
L47x
Link, Robert E 1915-
Camping for counselors. [Brooklyn.?]
Brooklyn College c1952.
45 p. 28 cm.

1. Camping. I. Brooklyn College. School of
General Studies. Division of Adult Education.
II. Title.

NL 0388420 CaQMM

Link, Robert E 1915-
Counselors' manual on camping; a manual used in camping courses given at the School of General Studies, Division
of Adult Education at Brooklyn College. [Brooklyn?] °1953.
62 l. 28 cm.

1. Camping. I. Brooklyn College. School of General Studies.
Division of Adult Education. II. Title.

SK601.L48 371.393 53-28363 ‡

NL 0388421 DLC MB

Link, Robert Grant. 1918-
Studies in English theories of economic
fluctuations, 1815-1848. [New York, c1953]
341 l. diagrs. 29cm.

Thesis, Columbia university.
Typescript.
Bibliography: l. 327-341.

NL 0388422 NNC

Link, Robert Grant, 1918-
Studies in English theories of economic fluctuations, 1815-
1848. Ann Arbor, University Microfilms [1954]
([University Microfilms, Ann Arbor, Mich.] Publication 6663)
Microfilm copy of typescript. Positive.
Collation of the original: 341 l.
Thesis—Columbia University.
Bibliography : leaves 327-341.

1. Business cycles. I. Title.

Microfilm AC-1 no. 6663 Mic 54-837

NL 0388423 DLC

619.4
L648s
Link, Roger Paul, 1910-
A study of the effect of repeated intra-
peritoneal injections of glucose in pigs.
Urbana [1951]
78 l. illus., tables. 28cm.

Thesis--University of Illinois.
Typewritten (carbon copy)
Vita.
Bibliography: leaves 72-76.
---- ---- Thesis copy.

NL 0388424 IU

Link (Rudolf.) * Ueber Anästhesie durch künst-
liches Oedem. 43 pp. 8°. *Würzburg, P. Schei-
ner. 1896.*

NL 0388425 DNLM

1888-
Link, Rudolf. Beitrag zur Kenntnis der Cystinurie und der
Cystinsteine. Leipzig 1912: Sturm & Koppe. 48 S. 8°
Leipzig, Med. Diss. v. 3. Aug. 1912, Ref. Payr
[Geb. 28. Jan. 88 Leipzig; Wohnort: Leipzig; Staatsangeh.: Preußen; Vor-
bildung: Thomasch. Leipzig Reife O. 07; Studium: Freiburg i. B. 1, Leipzig 4,
München 1, Leipzig 5 S.; Coll. 3. Aug. 12.] [U 12.3102

NL 0388426 ICRL CtY DNLM

Link, Rudolf, 1899-
*Der Ersatz einzelner Zähne bei
nicht vorhandener Wurzel. 27p. 8° Erlangen,
1932.

NL 0388427 DNLM

Link, Rudolf Emil Albert, 1888-
see Link, Rudolf, 1888-

Link, Rüdiger, 1919-
Die besteuerung von schweizerischen hotelbetrieben, nach
rapporten der Schweizerischen hotel-treuhand-gesellschaft ...
von Rüdiger Link ... Weinfelden, Neuenschwander' sche verlagsbuchhandlung ag., 1943.
5 p. l., 71, 24, [2] p., 1 l. tables. 23°°.
Diss.—Basel.
"Die vorliegende dissertation erscheint gleichzeitig als band 13 der ...
sammlung 'Staatswissenschaftliche studien.' Neuenschwander'sche
verlagsbuchhandlung ag. in Weinfelden."
Lebenslauf.
"Quellen und literatur": p. [25]-[26] at end.
1. Hotels, taverns, etc.—Switzerland. I. Schweizerische hotel-
treuhand-gesellschaft, Zürich.

Library of Congress TX917.S03L5 1943 46-18437
647.94

NL 0388429 DLC CtY MH NN NcD

LINK, Samuel Albert, 1848-
Dr. Frank O. Ticknor, the southern lyric poet,
and Henry Timord, the unfortunate singer.
Nashville, Barbee & Smith, [cop. 1896].

pp.(60). (In his Pioneers of southern literature, no.3).
Catalogued from the cover.

NL 0388430 MH

B
P745Li
Link, Samuel Albert, 1848-
Edgar Allan Poe; a genius in story and
song. Nashville, Tenn., Barbee & Smith
[1898]
285-334p. 17cm. (His Pioneers of Southern literature. no.6)

Cover title.

1. Poe, Edgar Allan, 1809-1849.

NL 0388431 IU DLC RPB

LINK, Samuel Albert.
A glance at the field: here a tale; there a song. 4409a.168.1
⌐ Nashville. Barbee & Smith. [1898?] 42 pp. [Pioneers o
↓outhern literature. I.] 16°.

NL 0388432 MB MH

Link, Samuel Albert, 1848-
Judge Longstreet, J. G. Baldwin, J. J. Hooper,
W. T. Thompson, Davy Crockett, and other
Southern humorists. Nashville, Tenn., Barbee and
Smith, Agents [1896]
[84] p. (Pioneers of Southern Literature, no. 9]]

1. American literature - Southern States.
I. Title.

NL 0388433 MsSM

Link, Samuel Albert, 1848-
Paul H. Hayne. By S. A. Link. Nashville,
Bell, 1901.
40 p. D. (Biographies of great American
authors. V. 3)

NL 0388434 NcD

Link, S[amuel] A[lbert] 1848-
Pioneers of southern literature ...
From- New England Mag. March 1894.
n.p., 1894. 24 cm. p. 14-19. port.

NL 0388435 RPB

928.11
H423
L75
Link, Samuel Albert, 1848-
Paul Hamilton Hayne. n.p.,n.p.,n.d.
cover title, 73-85p. 24cm.

Reprinted from The Quarterly review of the
M.E. Church, South, Apr. 1889.

1. Hayne, Paul Hamilton, 1830-

NL 0388436 LNHT NRU

810.9
L756p
Link, Samuel Albert, 1848-
Pioneers of southern literature. Nashville, Tenn., Dallas, Tex., Barbee & Smith,
agents, 1895[?]-1896.
10 nos.
Contents.—1. A glance at the field; here a tale, there
a song.—2. Paul Hamilton Hayne, poet laureate of the South.
—3. Dr. Frank O. Ticknor, the southern lyric poet; and Henry
Timord/ the unfortunate singer.—4. William Gilmore Simms:
the novelist, the poet.—5. John P. Kennedy, John Esten Cooke
and other southern novelists.—6. Edgar Allan Poe: a genius i
story and song.—7. War poets of the South: singers on fire.—

8. Singers in various keys: John R. Thompson, James Barron
Hope, Henry Lynden Flash, and others.—9. Southern humorists:
Longstreet, Baldwin, Hooper, W. T. Thompson, Davy Crockett,
and others.—10. Political writers and historians.

1. American literature—Southern states. I. Title.
II. Title: Political writers and historians.

NL 0388438 ICarbS GU

Link, Samuel Albert.
Pioneers of Southern literature. no. 4-7. Nashville,
Tenn.: Barbee & Smith [cop. 1898]. 4 parts. 16°.

no. 4. William Gilmore Simms, the novelist, the poet.
no. 5. John Pendleton Kennedy, John Esten Cooke, and other Southern novelists.
no. 6. Edgar Allan Poe, a genius in story and song.
no. 7. War poets of the South, singers on fire.

1. American literature.—History.

March 6, 1911.

NL 0388439 NN

VOLUME 334

Link, Samuel Albert
  Pioneers of Southern literature.   Barbee &
Smith, agents., c1898.
  284p. (Paperbound)

NL 0388440   GColu

PS
261   Link, Samuel Albert, 1848-
.L6   Pioneers of southern literature. By Samuel
    Albert Link... Nashville, Tenn., Dallas,
    Tex., Publishing House, M. E. Church, South,
    Barbee & Smith, agents, 1899-1900.
      2 v. 16 cm.
      Paged continuously.
      Contents.- v.1. A glance at the field; here a
    tale, there a song. Paul Hamilton Hayne,
    poet laureate of the South. Dr. Frank O.
    Tichnor, the southern lyric poet; and Henry
    Timrod, the   unfortunate singer.

    William Gilmore Simms: the novelist, the poet.
    John Pendleton Kennedy, John Esten Cooke, and
    other southern novelists.- v.2. Edgar Allan
    Poe: a genius in story and song. War poets of
    the South; singers on fire. Singers in var-
    ious keys: John R. Thompson, James Barron
    Hope, Henry Lynden Flash, and others. South-
    ern humorists: Longstreet, Baldwin, Hooper,
    W. T. Thompson   Davy Crockett, and

    others. Political writers and historians.

      1. American literature - Southern states.
    I. Title.

      NRU PPD CoU OU MB
NL 0388443   NBuU NcRS TxU TU PV NcC DLC CU PBa NcD

Link, Samuel Albert, 1848-
  Pioneers of southern literature...
Nashville, Tenn., Dallas, Tex., [c1896-1901]

PS261
.L5

NL 0388444   DLC OC1

Link, Samuel Albert, 1848-
  Pioneers of southern literature. By Samuel
Albert Link ... Nashville, Tennessee, Dallas,
Texas, Publishing house, M. E. church, South,
Bigham & Smith, agents, 1900-03 [c1899-1900]
  2 v. 16 cm.

NL 0388445   KEmT

Link, Samuel Albert, *b.* 1848.
  Pioneers of southern literature. By Samuel Albert Link ...
Nashville, Tenn., Dallas, Tex., Publishing house, M. E.
church, South, Bigham & Smith, agents, 1903.
  2 v. 16 cm.
  Paged continuously.
  CONTENTS.—v. 1. A glance at the field; here a tale, there a song.
  Paul Hamilton Hayne, poet laureate of the South. Dr. Frank O.
  Tichnor, the southern lyric poet; and Henry Timrod, the unfortunate
  singer. William Gilmore Simms: the novelist, the poet. John Pendle-
  ton Kennedy, John Esten Cooke, and other southern novelists.—v. 2.
  Edgar Allan Poe: a genius in story and song. War poets of the South;
  singers on fire. Singers in various keys: John R. Thompson, James
  Barron Hope, Henry Lynden Flash, and others. Southern humorists:
  Longstreet, Baldwin,   Hooper, W. T. Thompson, Davy
  Crockett, and others.   Political writers and historians.
    1. American litera-   I. Title.
  ture—Southern states.   PS261.L6
  Library of Congress   5—7889
                                        [a48k1]

NL 0388446   DLC ViU OC1 NcD

Link, Samuel Albert, 1848-
PS261   Pioneers of southern literature. By Samuel
L55   Albert Link ... Nashville, Tenn. [etc.] Pub-
    lishing house, M. E. church, South, Smith &
    Lamar, agents, 1911-1913.
      2 v. 16 cm. Red cloth.
      Paged continuously.
      V. 1 has only Nashville in imprint.
      Contents.--v. 1. A glance at the field; here a
    tale, there a song.-Paul Hamilton Hayne, poet
    laureate of the South.-Dr. Frank O. Tichnor, the
    southern lyric poet.-William Gilmore Simms: the

    novelist, the poet. John Pendleton Kennedy, John
    Esten Cooke, and other southern novelists.--v.2.
    Edgar Allan Poe: a genius in story and song.-War
    poets of the South; singers on fire.-Singers in
    various keys: John R. Thompson, James Barron
    Hope, Henry Lynden Flash, and others.-Southern
    humorists: Longstreet, Baldwin, Hooper, W. T.
    Thompson, Davy Crockett, and others.--Political
    writers and historians.

      1. American literature--Southern states. 2.
    Authors, American-- Southern states. I.
    Title.

NL 0388448   CSmH

Link, Samuel Albert, 1848-   AL 3414.065
  William Gilmore Simms, the novelist, the poet. Nashville,
Tenn., Barbee & Smith, [cop. 1896.]
  pp. (75). (Pioneers of southern literature, 4.)
  Cover serves as title-page.

  Simms||.

NL 0388449   MH MB

Link, Samuel Wolf
  Die geschichte Josefs, angeblich verfasst von
Basilius dem grossen auf Cäsarea ... Berlin, 1895.
  Inaug. Diss. - Bern, 1895.

NL 0388450   ICRL OCH PPDrop

Link, Seymour Gordden

  Christ in the breadline; a book of poems for Christmas and
Lent, by Kenneth W. Porter, Seymour Gordden Link [and]
Harry Elmore Hurd; with an introduction by John Haynes
Holmes. North Montpelier, Vt., The Driftwind press, 1932.

LINK, SEYMOUR GORDDEN.
  A dozen years after (November 11, 1930), by Seymour
Gordden Link... Nashville, Tenn.: The Peabody press,
1935. 3 l. 22½cm.

  With autograph of author.
  Poems.
  "Reprint from Contemporary vision, spring 1931, for the
Honorable Ruby Laffoon, governor of Kentucky."

  1. Poetry, American. I. Title.

NL 0388452   NN

Link, Seymour Gordden.
  ... Matthew Arnold's "sweetness and light" in America, 1848-
1938, by Seymour Gordden Link ... Nashville, Tenn., George
Peabody college for teachers, 1938.
    1 p. l., 12 p. 23½ᶜᵐ. ([George Peabody college for teachers, Nashville]
  Abstract of Contribution to education no. 209)
    Abstract of thesis (PH. D.)—George Peabody college for teachers.

  1. Arnold, Matthew, 1822-1888. 2. U. S.—Civilization.

  Library of Congress   LA2377.A7L5 1936   38—37876
                                [a41d1]   370.81

NL 0388453   DLC LU MoU ViU PU OU

Link, Seymour Gordden.
  One small unwilling captain, by Seymour Gordden Link...
[Utica, N. Y.: H. Coggeshall, 1937] 6 l. 14½cm.
  "Printed by Howard Coggeshall, Utica, New York <title page by Frederic W.
Goudy>, for friends of Sarah and Bill Lewis. December 25, 1937."
  "From Globe. October 1937."
  Letter from Capt. Mitsui [pseud.] formerly a Japanese student at Columbia
university, written to his friend S. G. Link, on the present relations between China
and Japan, l. 3-5.
  With autograph of author.

933300A. 1. Japan—For. rel.—   China, 1931- . 2. China—For.
rel.—Japan, 1931-   3. Japanese   literature—Letters. I. Title.
                                          October 24, 1938

NL 0388454   NN

PZ7   Link, Stanley.
.L76A4   The adventures of tiny Tim, by Stanley
    Link. Racine, Wis., Whitman publishing
    company [1935]
      378p. front., illus. 11cm.

NL 0388455   NNU-W

Link, Theodor, ed.

  Goebel, Max, 1811-1857.
    Geschichte des christlichen lebens in der rheinisch-west-
  phälischen Evangelischen kirche, von Max Goebel ... Co-
  blenz, In commission bei K. Bädeker, 1849-60.

942.39   LINK, Theodor
L756k   Kirchliche Skizzen aus dem evangelischen
    Frankreich. Herausgegeben von der Dorner-
    Bach=Stiftung in Bonn. Goettingen, Vanden-
    hoeck und Ruprecht, 1855.
      100p. 22.5cm.

NL 0388457   MH-AH

LINK, Theodor, of Amorbach.
  Eine sprachliche studie über die anglomor-
mannische version der Amissage.   München,
M. Kellerer's h. C. hofbuch-& Kunsthandlung,
1885.

  pp. (2). 42.

NL 0388458   MH OC1

Link, Theodor, of Amorbach.
  Ueber die sprache der chronique rimée von
Philippe Mousket.   Erlangen, 1882.
  Inaug-Diss. - Wuerzburg.

NL 0388459   ICRL

PQ1496   Link, Theodor., of Amorbach.
M84C68L7   Über die sprache der Chronique rimée von Philippe
    Mousket. Von dr. Theodor Link ... Erlangen, A.
    Deichert, 1882.
      [1], 37 p. 22½ᶜᵐ.
    Published also as author's inaug.-diss., Würzburg, 1882.

      1. Mousket, Philippe, 13th cent. Chronique rimée. 2. French language
    —Dialects—Picardy.

NL 0388460   ICU PHC MeB IU MH

VOLUME 334

M873
21.7 **Link,** Theodore August, 1897–
Oil in Alberta and western Canada. An address to the Toronto Branch of the Canadian Institute of Mining and Metallurgical Engineers. [Calgary, Pacific Petroleums] 1949.
35 p. illus., maps, diagrs. 23 cm.

1. Petroleum – Canada. I. Title.

NL 0388461 DI

Link, Theodore August, 1897– ed.
Alberta society of petroleum geologists.
Stratigraphy of plains of southern Alberta; Donaldson Bogart Dowling memorial symposium; fourteen papers by members of the Alberta society of petroleum geologists and the American association of petroleum geologists ... Tulsa, Okl., The American association of petroleum geologists; London, T. Murby & co., 1931.

QE999 Link, Theodore August, 1897–
.L75 ... Three-dimensional experiments in earth deformation ... by Theodore August Link. Chicago, 1927.
v, 227, 6 numb. l. mounted photos., maps (1 fold.) diagrs. (part fold.) 29ᶜᵐ.
Typewritten.
Thesis (PH. D.)—University of Chicago, 1927.
"Previous work": l. 3–19.
"Abstract": 6 l. at end.

1. Geology, Structural.

NL 0388463 ICU

378.763 Link, Theodore Carl, 1850–
L93pl General plan of the Louisiana State University and A. & M. College, Baton Rouge, La. Theo C. Link, Architect.
[n.p., 192–?]
blueprint. 140 x 107 cm.

Legend gives names of buildings.
Scale: 5 inches equal 500 ft.
One corner of blueprint torn.

1. Louisiana State University and Agricultural and Mechanical College.

NL 0388464 LU

Link, Thomas, 1869–
Die pädagogik des philosophen Christian Wolff (Halle) ... Bamberg, Gedruckt in der Handels-druckerei, 1906.
107 p., 2 l. 22ᶜᵐ.
Inaug.-diss.—Erlangen.
Lebenslauf.
"Verzeichnis der benützten literatur": 1 leaf following p. 107.

1. Wolff, Christian, freiherr von, 1679–1754.
7—16544

Library of Congress LB575.W8L5

NL 0388465 DLC NjP PU CtY ICRL ICJ NN

Link, Ulrich, joint author.
Wirsing, Giselher, 1906–
La Guerra 1939/40 en mapas, editado por Giselher Wirsing; en colaboración con Albrecht Haushofer, Wolfgang Höpker, Horst Michael, Ulrich Link. [n. p., 1940?]

Link, Ulrich, joint author.
Wirsing, Giselher, 1906–
Der krieg 1939/40 in karten. In verbindung mit Albrecht Haushofer, Wolfgang Höpker, Horst Michael [und] Ulrich Link, herausgegeben von Giselher Wirsing. München, Knorr & Hirth [1940]

Link, Ulrich, joint author.
Wirsing, Giselher, 1906–
The war in maps, 1939/40, edited by Giselher Wirsing, in collaboration with Albrecht Haushofer, Wolfgang Höpker, Horst Michael [and] Ulrich Link. New York, German library of information, 1941.

Link, Ulrich.
Mount Everest; der Kampf um den Gipfel der Erde. [1. Aufl.] München, R. Rother [1953]
40 p. 20 plates, maps. 24 cm.

1. Everest, Mount.
A 54–1818

Harvard Univ. Library
for Library of Congress

NL 0388469 MH

Link, Ulrich.
Nanga Parbat, Berg des Schicksals im Himalaya. München, R. Rother [1953]
52 p. 24 plates, maps. 24 cm.

1. Nanga Parbat.
A 54–1819

Harvard Univ. Library
for Library of Congress

NL 0388470 MH NN

Link, Vernon B
A history of plague in the United States of America. [Washington, U. S. Govt. Print. Off., 1955]
viii, 120 p. illus., maps, diagrs., tables. 27 cm. (U. S. Public Health Service. Publication no. 392. Public health monograph no. 26)
Includes bibliographies.

1. Plague—U. S.—Hist. (Series: U. S. Public Health Service. Publication no. 392. Series: U. S. Public Health Service. Public health monograph no. 26)
RC176.A2L5 614.4973 55—60013

OkU-M FU-HC CU-M AAP MU
NL 0388471 DLC CaBVa WaS WaSp PPWM PPT ViU DNLM

TD1954
L648 **Link,** Virginia Lee (Eubank) 1890–
Determining the desirable music experiences that should be included in the training of elementary teachers for Texas schools. Austin, Tex., 1954.
239 l. tables. 28cm.
Thesis (Ph.D.) - University of Texas, 1954.
Vita.
Bibliography: l.162–178.
1. Teachers, Training of. 2. Education, Elementary. 3. Music - Instruction and study. 4. Education - Texas. Dept.: Education.

unacc.,
cop.1
unacc.,
cop.2

NL 0388472 TxU

Link, Walter, 1905–
Ueber multiple sklerose. Inaug. Diss. Kiel, 1929.
Bibl.

NL 0388473 ICRL CtY

Link, Walter, 1906–
Die mai – verordnung vom jahre 1927 und die krisenerscheinungen in der deutschen zigarettenindustrie. ... Berlin, 1933. 83 p.
Inaug. Diss. –Leipzig, 1933.
Lebenslauf.
Bibliography.

NL 0388474 ICRL PU CtY

Link, Waltraut, 1919–
Das Verhältnis von Mensch und Schicksal in Chr. D. Grabbes Dramen. [Heidelberg] 1945.
224 l. 30 cm.
Typewritten (carbon copy)
Inaug.-Diss.—Heidelberg.
Vita.
Bibliography : leaves 4–7.

1. Grabbe, Christian Dietrich, 1801–1836. I. Title.

PT2253.G3L5 50–29017

NL 0388475 DLC

PA **Link,** Wilhelm, 1886–
2350 De vocis 'sanctus' usu pagano quaestiones
.L65 selectae... Regimonti, ex officina Hartungiana, 1910.
90 p., 1 l. 22cm.
Inaug.-diss.–Königsberg.
Vita.

1. Latin language - Semantics. I. Title: 'Sanctus'.

NL 0388476 DCU ICRL MH NN NjP CtY OClW

Link, Wilhelm, 1908–1938.
Das ringen Luthers um die freiheit der theologie von der philosophie, von Wilhelm Link (†); hrsg. von E. Wolf und M. Mezger. München, C. Kaiser, 1940.
ix, [1], 391, [1] p. 23½ᶜᵐ. (Added t.-p.: Forschungen zur geschichte und lehre des protestantismus, hrsg. von Ernst Wolf. 9. reihe, bd. III)
"Literaturverzeichnis": p. 386–[392]

1. Luther, Martin, 1483–1546. 2. Philosophy and religion. I. Wolf, Ernst, 1902– ed. II. Mezger, Manfred, joint ed. III. Title.
A 41–2517

General theol. sem. Libr.
for Library of Congress

NL 0388477 DI-GS PPLT NN G

BR **Link,** Wilhelm, 1908–1938.
333 Das Ringen Luthers um die Freiheit der
L55 Theologie von der Philosophie; hrsg. von Ernst Wolf und Manfred Mezger. Berlin, Evangelische Verlagsanstalt [1954]
391p. 24cm.

Includes bibliography.

1. Luther, Martin, 1483–1546. 2. Philosophy and religion. I. Wolf, Ernst, 1902– ed. II. Mezger, Manfred, ed.

NL 0388478 MU TNJ-R CLSU

BR333 **Link,** Wilhelm, 1908–1938.
L55 Das Ringen Luthers um die Freiheit der Theologie von der
1955 Philosophie; hrsg. von Ernst Wolf und Manfred Mezger. 2. unveränderte Aufl. München, C. Kaiser, 1955.
ix, 391, [1] p.

"Literaturverzeichnis": p. 386–[392]

1. Luther, Martin, 1483–1546. 2. Philosophy and religion. I. Wolf, Ernst, 1902– ed. II. Mezger, Manfred, joint ed.

ICN IU IaU PU MoSCS OU
NL 0388479 CU MnU RPB CU TxDaM KU CtY-D InU NcD

VOLUME 334

Link, Wilhelm Friedrich
  see
Linck, Wilhelm Friedrich, 1725-1788.

Link (William) company, *Newark, N. J.*
  Officers' insignia, gold, silver, bronze ... Newark,
N. J., William Link company
  v. illus. 20½ᶜᵐ.
  Cover-title.
  Catalog.

  1. U. S.—Army—Insignia.

Library of Congress   UC533.L5   18-10706

NL 0388481   DLC

[Link, William F]
  .ː The Hudson by daylight map, showing the prominent residences, historic landmarks, old reaches of the Hudson, Indian
names, &c. With descriptive pages. New York, W. F. Link
[1878]
  1 p l., 15 l. illus., fold. map. 16°.
  Illustrated cover.
  Cover-title: By W. F. Link.

  1. Hudson River—Descr. & trav—Maps. ɪ. Title.

Library of Congress   F127.H8L7   1—14123

NL 0388482   DLC PP MWA MnHi OO MH NN Nh

[Link, William F.]
  The Hudson by daylight. Map, showing the prominent residences, historic landmarks, old reaches of the Hudson, Indian
names, &c., with descriptive pages... New York: W. F. Link[,
1880]. 16 l. illus., 1 map. 16°.
  Text and advertisements on opposite pages.
  Map wanting.

586675. 1. Hudson river—Maps.   2. Title.   September 25, 1929

NL 0388483   NN

Link, Wm. F.
  The Hudson by Daylight.
  12°
  N.Y., 1883. 12°

NL 0388484   MWA

[Link, William F.]
  The Hudson by daylight. Map showing the prominent residences, historic landmarks, old reaches of the Hudson, Indian
names, &c., with descriptive pages... New York: W. F. Link[,
1884]. 16 l. illus., 1 map. 16°.
  Text and advertisements on opposite pages.
  Illustrated cover, with title: The Hudson by daylight, by William F. Link.

1. Hudson river—Maps. 2. Title.   September 21, 1929

NL 0388485   NN

[Link, William F.]
  The Hudson by daylight. Map showing the prominent residences, historic landmarks, old reaches of the Hudson, Indian
names, &c., with descriptive pages... New York: Bryant Literary Union[, 1892]. 16 l. illus., 1 map. 16°.
  Text and advertisements on opposite pages.
  Illustrated cover, with title: The Hudson by daylight, by William F. Link.

1. Hudson river—Maps. 2. Title.   September 21, 1929

NL 0388486   NN

F127   [Link, William F   ]
H8L75   The Hudson river map via the New York Central
          and Hudson river r.r. What the traveller wishes
          to see and know... New York, Bryant literary
          union [1885?]

Transportation 8 numb. l. illus., fold. map. 15cm.
          Title on map: The Hudson river map from New
        York bay to the head of tide water...[Wm.F.Link.
          Lettered on cover: Albany.
          Book-label: Cuyler Reynolds' collection.
        1.Hudson river- Guide-books. I.Title.

NL 0388487   CSt

F127   Link, William F
H8L68   The old reaches of the Hudson and old
          Indian names [map] New York, 1878.

          map.(fold.) 14cm.

NL 0388488   NBuG

Link, William F., osteopath, ed.
  The Popular osteopath, a monthly magazine devoted to
the interests of osteopathy. v. 1–
Jan. 1899–
Kirksville, Mo. [etc.] Popular osteopath publishing co.,
1899–

Link (W[illiam] H.) Object lessons in gynae-
cology. III. 4 pp. 8°. [*Philadelphia*, 1892.]
Repr. from: Med. & Surg. Reporter, Phila., 1892, lxvii.

NL 0388490   DNLM

Link
    see also
  Linck
  Lincke
  Linke

020.6   Link.
LIN
          Bristol, Eng.
          no. 21cm.
          "Journal of the Bristol & District Division of
        the Association of Assistant Librarians."

NL 0388492   IU

The Link. 1800–
  Hoboken, N. J. [etc.] 1890–
    v. illus., plates (part col.) 23-27½ᶜᵐ. annual.
    Published by the Junior class, Stevens institute of technology.
    Formed by the union of the Bolt and the Eccentric.
  Title varies: 1890, The Link.
    1891, The Stevens link.
    1892–   The Link.

  ɪ. Stevens institute of technology, Hoboken, N. J.

Library of Congress   T171.S86L5   46-32490

NL 0388493   DLC NN DHEW CU OC1 NNC

The Link. v. 1–   July 1948–
  [Kurseong, Assam Rail Link Project]
    v. illus. 34 cm. monthly.

  1. Railroads—Assam—Employees—Period. 2. Employees' maga-
zines, handbooks, etc.—Assam. ɪ. Assam Rail Link Project.

        HD8039.R12 I 45   S A 67-6769

NL 0388494   DLC

Link. London, 1939
    see Newcomen bulletin.

The LINK. [Toronto] v. 1-4: 1936-38
  Toronto.   v.

Film reproduction. Positive.

1. Labor--Education--Canada. 2. Labor--Per. and soc. publ.--Canada.

NL 0388496   NN

The Link. v. 1–
    Jan./Feb. 1943–
  [Washington, etc.]
    v. illus. 20 cm. monthly.
    Published by the Service Men's Christian League and, Sept. 1946–
        the General Commission on Chaplains (called Sept.
    1946–Nov. 1947, General Commission on Army and Navy Chaplains)

  1. Soldiers—Religious life. ɪ. Service Men's Christian League.
  ɪɪ. General Commission on Chaplains.

BV4588.L56   355.34   51-20226

NL 0388497   DLC MoU PPPrHi

The link. (Federal Land Bank of New Orleans
    see under   Federal Land Bank of New
  Orleans.

The Link (Newcomen quarterly bulletin)
      see
The N. Q. B. (Newcomen quarterly bulletin)

The Link; a review of mediaeval and modern Greek. no. 1–
      June 1938–
  Oxford, B. Blackwell [1938–
    v. 22ᶜᵐ.

  1. Greek philology—Period. 2. Greek language, Medieval and late—
Period. 3. Greek language, Modern—Period.
                                          44-49002
Library of Congress   PA1001.L5
                                          489

NL 0388500   DLC

The Link; an intermediary for literary men,
  correspondents, collectors & students
    see   The Linkman; a literary and artistic
  quarterly review of congenial interests.

The Link; the Journal of the Beta Phi Fraternity
    see   The Link of Beta Phi.

The LINK; Wagner college alumni news.

Staten Island, N. Y.   v.   illus.   29cm.

Quarterly (slightly irregular).
Published by the Wagner college alumni association.
With the Wagner college bulletin (not in the library) superseded by
Wagner.
  ɪ. Wagner memorial Lutheran college, Staten Island, N. Y. Alumni
association. ɪɪ. Wagner college   bulletin.

NL 0388503   NN

VOLUME 334

Mason
XL83.8
C5W87
Link. Woochefee bulletin for cultural
cooperation. v.1-   Oct. 1946-
New York, Woochefee Institue
of New York.
v. illus. 22cm.

NL 0388504   NIC ICRL NN

The LINK audit of the public's attitude toward leading
industrial companies.
New York.   no.   diagrs., tables.   29cm.
(Psychological barometer report)

Semiannual.
Issued by the Marketing and social research division of the Psychological corporation.

1. Market surveys--U.S.   2. Corporations--U.S.   I. Psychological
corporation, New York. Marketing and social research division.

NL 0388506   NN

629.1307 Link Aviation Devices, inc., Binghamton, N.Y.
L64a   Aviation education, teacher's guide.   Binghamton, N.Y., 1947.
vii, 75p. 28cm.

Includes bibliographies.

1. Aeronautics--Study and teaching.   I. Title

NL 0388507   IU

TL546
.P6
Link aviation devices, inc., Binghamton,
N.Y.
Potter, Norman.
Fundamentals of aviation, by Norman Potter [and] William
J. Konicek ... [Binghamton, N. Y., Link aviation devices, inc.,
1946]

Link-belt company, Chicago, Ill.
Incorporated Nov. 13, 1880, in Illinois, as the
Link-belt machinery company; name changed to
Link-belt company May 28, 1906, upon purchase
of associated companies. Business is the manufacture of chains of practically every character
which can be applied to the transmission of power.
Company's products also include materials-handling
equipment.

Link-Belt [Company.
Annual report.
[Chicago][,]
v. illus. 24-28 cm.

HD9705.U64L543   49-25620*‡

NL 0388510   DLC

Link-belt company.
Approved appliances for reducing the
cost of handling raw and manufactured
products. Philadelphia,1905.
264p.,illus.,diagrs 24cm. (Catalog
no.40)

NL 0388511   PSt NN RPB

Link-belt company .

Link-belt engineering company, *Philadelphia.*
... Approved elevating and conveying appliances. The
Link-belt engineering company ... Philadelphia, Pa.,
New York, The Link-belt enginering company, 1892.

Link-Belt company.   621.8 x
Booklet [catalogues].   Chicago, 1904-1905.
7 nos. in 1 vol. illus. 23½cm.
Contents.—no. 35. Machinery for handling freight and packages horizontally or vertically for transfer or storage. Complete installation for railroad freight houses, steamship
docks and warehouses, industrial plants. 48 p.—no. 39. The Renold silent chain gear.
1904. 34 p.—no. 42. Washing bituminous coal for coke or fuel. *1905. 40 p.—
no. 45. Link-Belt car hauls. 8 p.—no. 47. Wholesale and retail coal pockets. 1905.
48 p.—no. 51. Carriers for press rooms and binderies. 1905. 16 p.—[no. 63.]
The automobile washstand-turntable. 4 p.

NL 0388513   ICJ

Link-Belt Company.
Caldwell helicoid and sectional flight
conveyor. Chicago, 1933.
128 p.

NL 0388514   PPF

Link-belt company
[Catalogue] Chicago, 1889.
il. D.

NL 0388515   RPB

Link-Belt Company.
Coal pockets and machinery for retail coal
yards. Catalogue no. 72. Phila., 1909.
52 p.

NL 0388516   PPF

Link-Belt Company.
Data book, silent chain drive.   [Philadelphia,
Chicago, etc, c1939-41]
6 v. in 1. illus., tables, diagrs. 28 cm.
Binder's title.
1. Link-belting.

NL 0388517   CU

Link-Belt company.
Elevating and conveying machinery. Illustrated
circular. Chicago, n.d.
unp.

NL 0388518   PPF

Link-Belt company
Link-Belt aircraft precision built silent and
roller chains. Indianapolis, Chicago [etc. The
Author,] *1943.
1 v. illus. (Engineering data book 1825)

NL 0388519   MiD

Link-Belt Company.
Link-Belt belt conveyors...   Chicago: Link-Belt Co.[, cop.
1928.]   148 p. incl. tables.   illus. (incl. plans.)   2. ed.   8°.
"Data book 615."

358947A. 1. Link-belting—Cata-   logues.
N. Y. P. L.   June 23, 1928

NL 0388520   NN

Link-belt company.
Link-belt conveyors in American industry...   [Philadelphia,
etc., Link-belt co., 1940]   45 p. illus. 28cm.
"Book no. 1700."

1. Link-belting. 2. Hoisting and   conveying machinery.
N. Y. P. L.   November 27, 1941

NL 0388521   NN

Link-belt company.
Link-belt general catalog ... Philadelphia, Chicago, [etc.]
v. illus., diagrs. 23cm.

1. Conveying machinery—Catalogs. 2. Link-belting.
    5-7906 Revised
Library of Congress   TJ1353.L75

NL 0388522   DLC NjP Or WaE NN ICJ

621.8   **Link-belt** company.
L64g   **General catalog no. 300. Elevating
machinery and accessories, power transmission machinery, engineering installa-
tions.   [Chicago, 192-]
587p. illus.**

NL 0388523   IU

---

q621.8   Link-Belt Company.
L756   Link-Belt general catalog, 900. [Chicago?]
c1950.
1295 p. illus., diagrs., tables. 29cm.

1. Link-belting. 2. Power transmission.
3. Gearing. 4. Conveying machinery.

NL 0388524   KyLx IaDM MB PU

Link-Belt Company.
Link-Belt news
see under title

Link-Belt Company.
Link-Belt positive drives. Binder 2100.
Phila., 1937-38.
10 pts.

NL 0388526   PPF

Link-belt company
Link-belt roller chain, "RC" class, for
power transmission & conveying applications
...data book 1257. 96p. incl. illus., tables.
Chicago, Link-belt co.,c1929.

NL 0388527   OC1 PPF

Link-Belt Company.
Link-Belt shovel news
see under title

VOLUME 334

C-18202
Cat. A

Link-Belt Co.
    Link-Belt silent chain drive for power trans-
mission. Chicago, Indianapolis ₍etc.₎ c1929.
170p. illus.

NL 0388529   ICRL PPF

Link-belt company.
    Link-belt silverlink roller chains and sprockets...   ₍New
York, 1938₎ 174 p. incl. diagrs., tables. illus. (incl. charts.)
28½cm.   (Its: Data book. 1757.)

Cover-title.

958326A. 1. Link-belting.
                                                    January 24, 1939

NL 0388530   NN

Link-Belt Company.
                        Link Belt stone and lime
handling machinery. Chicago, Ill. Co., 1921.
80 p.

Catalogue no. 416.

NL 0388531   PPF

Link-Belt Company
    Modern methods applied to the coaling of locomotives, dis-
posing of cinders, and to the handling of freight in railroad depots,
steamship docks and warehouses. New York, 1903.   2 p.l.,
95(1) p., 1 l., 1 pl.   illus.   f°.   (Book no. 36.)

—— Supplement no. 1 to book no. 36.

Binder's title : Coal cinders and freight.

1. Hoisting and conveying machinery.——   Dealers' catalogues.
                                                    March 27, 1912.

NL 0388532   NN

    Link-belt *company.*
    Modern methods as exemplified in the handling of raw
and manufactured products and the transmission of
power ... ₍Catalogue no. 24₎ Philadelphia and New
York, The Link-belt engineering co., 1898.
300 p. illus. 8°.

Library of Congress   Copyright   Aug. 17, 98-26

NL 0388533   DLC

Link-Belt Company.
    The original Ewart Link-Belt, how to use it and
why. no. 78. Phila., 1908.
32 p.

NL 0388534   PPF

Link-Belt. Company.
    Peck carrier, Book no. 81. Phila., The
Co., 1910
90 p.

NL 0388535   PPF

15   Link-belt company.
            Special catalogue mining machinery. 1892.
₍Chicago, 1894₎
    48 p.   12°.

NL 0388536   DLC

    Link-belt company.
    The story of Link-belt, 1875-1925.   Chicago
₍etc.₎ Link-belt co. ₍c1925₎
    47, ₍4₎ p. illus.

    Link-belt news, Feb., 1945 in pocket.

NL 0388537   MH-BA

Link-Belt Company,
                Link-Belt traceling water
screens for condenser intakes. Phila. Company,
1920.
    23 p.

Book no. 352

NL 0388538   PPF

Link-Belt Company
    see also
Ewart Manufacturing Company.
Link-Belt Engineering Company, *Philadelphia.*

Link-belt engineering company, *Philadelphia.*
    ... Approved elevating and conveying appliances. The
Link-belt engineering company ... Philadelphia, Pa.,
New York, The Link-belt engineering company, 1892.
    156 p. incl. illus., plates. front. 20ᶜᵐ.

    Another issue by the Link-belt machinery company, **Chicago.**

1. Conveying machinery—Catalogs. 2. Link belting.   1. Link-belt
machinery company, Chicago.

Library of Congress   TJ1353.L723   ᶜᴬ 7—1552 Unrev'd

NL 0388540   DLC NN

Link-belt engineering company, *Philadelphia.*
    Carriers for press rooms and binderies, booklet no. 51, 1905.
Philadelphia, New York ₍etc.₎ The Link-belt engineering company ₍1905₎
    16 p. illus. 23ᶜᵐ.

1. Conveying machinery—Catalogs.

Library of Congress   TJ1353.L726   ᶜᴬ 6—893 Unrev'd
                            ₍33b1₎

NL 0388541   DLC

15   The Link-Belt engineering co, Philadelphia.
9427a   Catalogue 1893.   [New York, Peerless press,
            1893]
                12°.

NL 0388542   DLC

15   The Link-Belt engineering company, Philadelphia.
9427a   Catalogue of elevating and conveying machinery
            for sugar plantations and refiners. [New York,
            G. M. Allen & co., 1891]
                2 p.l., 34 p.   12°.

NL 0388543   DLC

Link-Belt Engineering Co., *Philadelphia.*
    Illustrated circular. Nicetown, Phila., n.d.
35 p.

NL 0388544   PPF

Link-belt engineering company, *Philadelphia.*
    ... The Link-belt engineering co. ... manufacturers of
machinery for sugar estates and refineries employing
Ewart detachable link-belting ... ₍Catalogue 1892, 1893₎
New York, 1891-93
    2 v. illus. 20ᶜᵐ.

1. Conveying machinery—Catalogs. 2. Link belting.

                                            ᶜᴬ 7–5591 Unrev'd

Library of Congress   TJ1353.L727

NL 0388545   DLC

621.836 Link-belt engineering company, Phila-
L641   delphia.
            Link-belt silent chain for the effi-
        cient transmission of power.   Phila-
        delphia, c1914.
            111p. illus., tables, diagrs.   (Book
        no. 125)

NL 0388546   IU NIC

    Link-Belt Engineering Company, Philadelphia.
    Métodos modernos destinados al manejo de
la caña de azúcar y sus productos. [New York,
Nicoll & Roy Co., 1899]
    1 p.l., 49 (1) p. illus. 8°.

NL 0388547   NN

ar V   Link-Belt Engineering Company; Philadelphia.
21065   Modern methods applied to power transmission
        The Renold silent chain gear. Philadelphia,
        1907.
            34 p. illus. 19cm.

        "Booklet no. 39."

NL 0388548   NIC

Link-Belt Engineering Co., Philadelphia.
621.867   Modern methods applied to the elevating
L756M   and conveying of materials and the transmission
        of power ... Philadelphia, 1902.
            319 p. illus. 23½cm.

            1. Conveying machinery. Catalogs I. Link
        belting

NL 0388549   NcD

The Link-belt engineering company, *Philadelphia.*
    Modern methods applied to the elevating and convey-
ing of materials and the transmission of power. Book
no. 37. 1904 ... Philadelphia, Pa., New York ₍etc.₎ The
Link-belt engineering company, 1904–
    v. illus. 23½ᶜᵐ.

                                                4-18751†

Library of Congress   TA431.L75 Copyright

NL 0388550   DLC PPF

VOLUME 334

Link-Belt Engineering Company, *Philadelphia.*
Modern methods as exemplified in the handling of raw and manufactured products ...
see under Link-belt company.

The Link-belt engineering company, *Philadelphia.*
The trump measuring and mixing machine for sand-brick and artificial stone manufacture. Booklet no. 56, 1905. Philadelphia, The Link-belt engineering company; New York, Chicago [etc.] The Link-belt machinery company [°1905]
16 p. illus. 23ᶜᵐ.

1. Stone, Artificial. 2. Sand-lime brick. CA 10-2192 Unrev'd

Library of Congress   TP871.L75

NL 0388552   DLC

Link-Belt Engineering Company, *Philadelphia*
see also
Link-Belt Company.

Link-Belt Machinery Company
see
Link-Belt Company.

Link-Belt news. Dec. 1929-May, 1931; [new ser.] v. 1-34, no. 3; Aug. 1934-June/July, 1967. **Chicago**
8 v. illus. 23-41cm.

Lacking v. 2, no. 12; Dec. 1935.
Irregular Dec. 1929-May, 1931; monthly (irregular) Aug. 1934-1952; bimonthly (irregular) 1953- July, 1967.
None published June, 1931-July, 1934.--cf. ULS.

1. Link-belting--Per. and soc. publ. 2. House organs. I. Title.

NL 0388556   NN AAP

Link-belt news.
Selected editorials from Link-belt news ... [Chicago, Ill.: Link-belt co., c1940] 64 p. illus., pl. 19½cm.

Cover-title.

1. No subject.   January 20, 1942

NL 0388557   NN

Link-belt shovel news.
1929-

Chicago, 1929-   8°.
v. illus. (incl. diagrs.)
Irregular.

TA 735. L5

1. House organs. I. Title.

February 16, 1932

NL 0388558   NN DLC

A link in the chain; a ship canal between Lake St. Clair and Lake Erie. 1897.
70p. fold.illus. 23cm.

1. St. Clair and Erie Ship Canal.

NL 0388559   IEN MiD DLC-P4

A link in the chain. A ship canal between Lake St. Calire & Lake Erie. Detroit, W. Graham printing co. [1899]
69p.

NL 0388560   MiU

The Link of Beta Phi.
v. 1-

[Chicago, 1914-   8°.
v. in illus., plates, ports.
Irregular.
Published by Beta Phi.
Title varies: Sept., 1914- The Link; the journal of the Beta Phi fraternity; The Link of Beta Phi.

1. College societies (Greek letter): BAIRD FRATERNITY COLL.
Beta Phi.   May 9, 1923.

NL 0388561   NN

... **The link of the golden horse-shoe**
see under [Colver, Rachel]

Link radio corporation.

U. S. *War dept.*
... Instruction book. Radio transmitter-receiver, type 1498 (50 watts) and associated equipment. February 19, 1943.
[Washington, 1943]

[**Link radio corporation**]
Tom tom to electron. [New York, 1944]
cover-title, [44] p. illus. (incl. ports.) 30 x 23ᶜᵐ.
Presented by Link radio corporation. cf. p. [3]

1. Radio--Hist. 2. Signals and signaling--Hist. I. Title.
45-3054
Library of Congress   TK6547.L5
621.384

NL 0388564   DLC IU NN Or

A link with Magellan; being a chart of the East Indies, c. 1522, in the possession of Boies Penrose. [Philadelphia, Wm. F. Fell co., printers] Priv. print., 1929.
[18] p., 1 l. double map. 36½ x 28½ cm.

1. Magalhães, Fernão de, d. 1521. 2. East Indies--Disc. & explor. 3. Maps, Early. I. Penrose, Boies, 1902-

GA1081.L5   29-20368

MH NjP NN MB MWA MiU-C
NL 0388565   DLC NcD GU DSI ViW PHC PU PP RPJCB

Linka, Giovanni.
La fisica del domani o della micromeccanica. [1. ed.] Trieste, F. Zigiotti, 1944.
62 p. 22 cm.

1. Physics.

QC25.L5   50-53367

NL 0388566   DLC

Linkan, Guggi, pseud.
see Lindgren, Gösta, 1896-
[Supplement]

Linke, A., joint author.
Patzig, R.
Tätiger geist und geschickte hand. Ein beitrag zur schulreform. Im anschluss an den lehrplan für alle 8 schuljahre bearb. von R. Patzig ... und A. Linke ... Leipzig, E. Wunderlich, 1912.

Linke, Abraham Adolphe, 1889-
A study in mental hygiene, by A. Adolphe Linke ... Los Angeles, Calif., The Olive leaf press [°1935]
6 p. l., 15-208 p. 20½ᶜᵐ.
"First edition."
"Acknowledgment": 4th prelim. leaf.

1. Mental physiology and hygiene. 2. Hygiene.

Library of Congress   RA790.L55   35-18796
———— Copy 2.
Copyright A 86408   613

NL 0388569   DLC OrCS DNLM

Linke, Abraham Adolphe, 1889-
A study in reconstructive mental hygiene, by A. Adolphe Linke ... Boston, Meador publishing company [1945]
249 p. 20½ᶜᵐ.
"Revised and expanded edition of A study in mental hygiene (1935)"
Bibliography: p. 5-6.

1. Mental physiology and hygiene. 2. Hygiene.

U. S. Surg.-gen. off. Libr.   S G 46-152
for Library of Congress   RA790.L55 1945
†   613

NL 0388570   DI-GS CaBVaU UU NcD DLC TxU DNLM

W   **Linke, Adolf,** 1919-
4   Zur Physiologie der Bürger'schen Press-
L53   druckprobe; der Ekg-Typ unter der Einwirkung
1944   intrapulmonaler Drucksteigerung. Leipzig, Dittert, 1943.
         32 p.

Inaug.-Diss. - Leipzig.
Bibliography: p. 30-32.

NL 0388571   DNLM

W 4   **Linke, Alfons,** 1914-
351   Das sogenannte traumatische Ödem des
1941   Handrückens. Zittau, Zittauer Morgen,
         Zeitung [1941?]
         29 p.

Inaug.-Diss. - Berlin.
Bibliography: p. 29.

NL 0388572   DNLM NlC

VOLUME 334

Linke (Alfred) [1868–]. *Zur Chirurgie der Gallenwege. [Marburg.] 41 pp., 1 l. 8°. Breslau. W. Friedrich. [1892].

NL 0388573   DNLM

423
L642   Linke, Antoni.
    Klucz do określania uszkodzeń zwierzęcych
    na roślinach warzywnych. ₍Poznan₎ 1934.
    31 l.

    1. Vegetables. Pests. 2. Poland.
Entomology. I. Poznan. Państwowa Szkoła
Ogrodnictwa.

NL 0388574   DNAL

PF
5997   Linke, August
L2L6   ₍Deutsches handwerksburschen-lexikon.
    Ein unentbehrlicher ratngeber für jeden
    wandernden handwerksburschen. Hrsg. von
    August Linke. Mit neuester eisenbahn-.
    post- und weg-karte von Deutschland ...
    Dresden, R. H. Dietrich [n.d.]
    32 p. fold. map.

    Sub-title on cover: Mit einer neuesten
post-, eisenbahn- und wege-karte von
Deutschland und Oesterreich.

    1. German language - Slang. 2. Labor
and laboring classes - Germany.
I. Title.

NL 0388576   CLU

    Linke, Bernhard.
AC831   Tibullus quantum in poesi profecerit comparato
L8   Catullo. Luckau, 1877.
1877   19 p.
    "1877. Progr. No. 62 ₍i.e. 66₎"
Stack   Programmschrift - Gymnasium, Luckau.
    Accompanies Schulnachrichten.

    1.Tibullus, Albius. 2.Catullus, Gaius
Valerius.

NL 0388577   CSt MH CtY CU

    Linke, Bernhard.
    Wie lässt ... Goethes Iphigenie für die
religionsstunde nutzbar machen? Luckau, 1907.

NL 0388578   NjP

4B   Linke, Bernhard, 1926–
1742   Eros und Liebe und das Wesen der
    Erziehung unter besonderer Berücksichti-
    gung der Werke von Max Scheler und
    Martin Buber. ₍München₎ 1954.
    212 l.

NL 0388579   DLC-P4

    Linke, Bernhard Erich Ernst, 1906–
      see Linke, Erich, 1906–

Linke, Carl.
    Die Brikettierkunst, von C. Linke... Halle (Saale): W.
Knapp, 1923. 33 p. 8°. (Abhandlungen aus der Braun-
kohlen- und Kali-Industrie. Heft 4.)

1. Briquets ₍Fuel₎. 2. Ser.   January 12, 1925

NL 0388581   NN

Linke (C[arl]). *Erkraakungen der Leber
während der Gravidität und des Puerperiums.
66 pp., 1 l. 8°. Jena, G. Neuenhahn. 1888. c.

NL 0388582   MBCo CU

Linke, Carl Friedrich
    see Linke, Karl Friedrich.

Linke, Carola
    see Linke, Karola, 1904–

Linke, Caroline Glocksin.
    The trend of life (the key to the bottomless pit) or.
The old creed revised. Part I. A rehearsal by the soul.
By Caroline Glocksin Linke. Chicago ₍Printed by R. R.
Donnelley and sons company₎ 1901.

    154 p., 1 l. front. 12°.

    Copyright by Caroline Glocksin Linke, Chicago, Ill. Class A, XXc,
no. 10382, May 31, 1901; 2 copies rec'd Aug. 13, 1901.

           1-24975–M 4 Nov. 7

NL 0388585   DLC

Film
679   Linke, Charles Eugene.
    A study of pitch characteristics of
    female voices and their relationship to
    vocal effectiveness. Ann Arbor, University
    Microfilms ₍1953₎
    (₍University Microfilms₎ Publication no.
    6531)

    Microfilm copy of typescript. Positive.
Collation of the original as determined
from the film: vi, 78 l. tables.

    Thesis - State University of Iowa.
    Abstracted in Dissertation abstracts, v.
14 (1954) p. 183.
    Bibliographic footnotes.

    1. Voice. 2. Voice culture. I. Title:
Pitch characteris   tics of female voices
and their relatio   nship to vocal effect-
iveness.

NL 0388587   LU OKentU

Linke, Edmund.
    Die Anfechtung des Versailler Vertrages; die Lösung des
Zeitproblems der Selbsterhaltung der Völker Europas, ₍von₎
Edmund Linke. Leipzig: Pädag-Verlag₎ 1927₎. 16 p. 4°.

    Declaration of a German film war as a reprisal against the alleged American anti-
German film propaganda.

421826A. 1. Moving pictures—U. S.   July 30, 1929

NL 0388588   NN

D
539   Linke, Eduard.
.L76   Regiments-Geschichte des Infanterie-Regi-
    mentes Nr.42,1674-1918. ₍Leitmeritz₎
    Herausgeber und Verleger: Unterstützungs-
    verband Gedienter Infanteristen des Ergän-
    zungsbezirkes Leitmeritz und Böhm.-Leipa,
    1933.
    1030 p. illus.
    "Kartenheft zur Regiments-Geschichte I.R.
42" (55 p.) lain in.
    ₍1.Austro-Hungarian Monarchy. Heer. Infan-
terie-Regiment Nr.42. 2.Austria. Armee. In-
fanterie-Regiment ment Nr.42. I.Unterstüt-
zungsverband Gedienter Infanteristen
des Ergänzung- sbezirkes Leitmeritz und
Böhm.-Leipa. II.Title. MiU

NL 0388589   MiU NN

Linke (Eduard) ₍1900– ₎. *Beitrag zur Statistik und Aetiologie des Carcinoma cervicis
uteri. 36 pp., 1 l. 8°. Halle a. S. 1895.

NL 0388590   DNLM

4GV   Linke, Erich
677   Sport im Dorf, von Erich Linke
    und Hans Kruse. Leipzig, B.G. Teub-
    ner, 1936.
    64 p.

    (Teubners Sportbücher)

NL 0388591   DLC-P4

Linke, Erich, 1906–
    ... Die Behandlung des Magencarcinoms
durch Resektion und seine Ergebnisse ...
Borna-Leipzig, 1935.
    Inaug.-Diss. - Griefswald.
    Lebenslauf.
    "Literaturverzeichnis": p. 33-35.

NL 0388592   CtY

Linke, Ernst Oscar
    see Linke, Oscar, 1854-1928.

Linke, Eva Hoffmann
    see Hoffmann-Linke, Eva Elizabeth, 1845–

Linke (F.). Säuglingspflege, Vortrag. 16 pp.,
2 l. 3 pl. 8°. Berlin, A. Tetzlaff, 1908.

NL 0388595   DNLM

Linke, Felix, ed.
    Reichswahlgesetz vom 27. April 1920 nebst
Reichswahlordnung vom 1. Mai 1920; mit Einleitung
und Erläutrungen [sic] in Form eines Stichwort-
registers hrsg. von Felix Linke
      see under Germany. Laws, statutes, etc.

LINKE, FELIX, 1879–
    Der ewige Kreislauf des Werdens; Betrachtungen über das
Schicksal der Erde und des Lebens... Leipzig, Thomas,
1922. 152 p. illus. (incl. charts, ports.) 22cm.

751158A 1. Cosmology.

NL 0388597   DNLM PPAN

VOLUME 334

Linke, Felix, 1879–

Ist die welt bewohnt? Eine darstellung der frage nach der bewohnbarkeit anderer weltkörper auf grund unseres jetzigen wissens von der natur derselben und vom leben... Stuttgart, Dietz, 1910.
110 p. illus. (Kleine bibliothek. nr.9)

1.Plurality of worlds.

NL 0388598   NjP DLC-P4

Linke, Felix, 1879–
Kann die Erde untergehen? Betrachtungen über die kosmische Stabilität unseres Erdenlebens, von Felix Linke... Stuttgart: J. H. W. Dietz Nachf., G.m.b.H., 1911.   134 p. incl. diagrs., tables. illus. (incl. port.) 12°. (Kleine Bibliothek. Nr. 14.)
"Vereinsausgabe."

587667A. 1. Cosmology. I. Ser.

June 21, 1932

NL 0388599   NN MH

Linke, Felix, 1879–
Raketenflug ins Weltall. Die Eroberung des Universums durch den Menschen. München, Franzis-Verlag ₁1952₎
278 p. illus. 21 cm.

1. Space flight. 2. Rockets (Aeronautics)   I. Title.
Full name: Felix Georg Hugo Linke.

TL790.L49   57–35501 ‡

NL 0388600   DLC CU MCM

Linke, Felix, 1879–
... Das raketenweltraumschiff; wanderung zum monde und zu andern planeten ... Hamburg, Auer & co., 1928.
100 p. illus. (incl. ports.) 19ᶜᵐ.

1. Interplanetary voyages. 2. Rockets (Aeronautics)   I. Title.
Full name: Felix Georg Hugo Linke₎

Library of Congress   ·TL790.L5   32–203

629.13

NL 0388601   DLC NN

Linke, Felix, 1879–
... Die verwandtschaft der welten und die bewohnbarkeit der himmelskörper, von Felix Linke. Leipzig, Quelle & Meyer ₁pref. 1925₎
viii, 165 p. illus. 20½ᶜᵐ. (Naturwissenschaftliche bibliothek für jugend und volk)
Colored illustration mounted on cover.

1. Plurality of worlds.   I. Title.
Full name: Felix Georg Hugo Linke₎

Library of Congress   QB54.L5   33–37041

523.18

NL 0388602   DLC

Linke, Felix, 1879–
Das Werden im Weltall; eine moderne Weltentwicklungslehre, von Felix Linke. Leipzig: T. Thomas, 1910. 77 p. incl. diagrs. illus. 21cm.

624682A. 1. Cosmology.
N.Y.P.L.   July 13, 1933

NL 0388603   NN

Linke, Felix Georg · Hugo
see Linke, Felix, 1879–

Linke, Franz, 1878–1944.
Die Abhängigkeit der Luftdichte von der Meereshöhe (pyknometrische Höhenformeln). (Frankfurt a.M. 1924.)

8p. 28cm.

NL 0388605   DAS

Linke, Franz, 1878–1944.
Aeronautische meteorologie, von dr. Franz Linke ... Frankfurt a. M., F. B. Auffarth, 1911.
2 v. illus., tables, diagrs. 22½ cm. (Added t.-p.: Luftfahrzeugbau und- führung, hand- und lehrbücher des gesamtgebietes ... hrsg. von P. Neumann. I.–II. bd.)

1. Meteorology in aeronautics.   I. Title.
₁Full name: Karl Wilhelm Franz Linke₎

TL556.L45   1911   [551.5] · 629.13   11–13122 rev

NL 0388606   DLC NN DNW ICJ

Linke, Franz, 1878–1944.
Aeronautische meteorologie, von dr. Franz Linke ... München und Berlin, R. Oldenbourg, 1911.
2 v. illus. (incl. charts) diagrs. 22½ᶜᵐ. (Added t.-p.: Luftfahrzeugbau und -führung ... I.–II. bd.)

1. Meteorology in aeronautics.   I. Title.
₁Full name: Karl Wilhelm Franz Linke₎
Library of Congress   TL556.L45 1911a   31–24192
₁a47b1₎   [551.5] 629.13

NL 0388607   DLC MiU

Linke, Franz
Die Bedeutung des Öffnungsverhältnisses eines Aktinometers für messungen der Sonnen-und Himmelsstrahlung. 1931.
p. 351-357   figs.   24 1/2 cm

NL 0388608   DAS

HT107
.F7
1940

Linke, Franz, 1878–   joint ed.

Frankfurter konferenz für medizinisch-naturwissenschaftliche zusammenarbeit. *4th,* 1940.
...₁Biologie der grossstadt. Dresden und Leipzig, T. Steinkopff, 1940.

Linke, Franz, 1878–   L063.36
                                    11   v.7
... Die Brandungsbewegungen des Erdbodens und ein Versuch ihrer Verwendung in der praktischen Meteorologie. (Nach den Registrierungen und Beobachtungen des Samoa-Observatoriums) Von Franz Linke. Mit 3 Tafeln. Berlin, Weidmannsche Buchhandlung, 1909.
₂, 58 p. incl. tables. III pl. (part fold.; 2 maps, 1 diagr.) 27½ᶜᵐ. (Abhandlungen der Königlichen Gesellschaft der Wissenschaften zu Göttingen. Mathematisch-physikalische Klasse. Neue Folge, Bd. VII, Nro. 3)
Ergebnisse der Arbeiten des Samoa-Observatoriums der Königlichen Gesellschaft der Wissenschaften zu Göttingen. III.
Bibliographical foot-notes.

NL 0388610   ICJ

Linke, Franz, 1878–   L063.36
                                    11   v.9
... Die erdmagnetischen Registrierungen der Jahre 1905 bis 1908, von F. Linke und G. Angenheister. Mit 9 Tafeln und 4 in den Text gedruckten Figuren. Berlin, Weidmannsche Buchhandlung, 1911.
₄, 52, cxxxix p. incl. illus., tables. IX fold. diagrs. 28½ᶜᵐ. (Abhandlungen der Königlichen Gesellschaft der Wissenschaften zu Göttingen. Mathematisch-physikalische Klasse. Neue Folge, Bd. IX, Nro. 1)
Ergebnisse der Arbeiten des Samoa-Observatoriums der Königlichen Gesellschaft der Wissenschaften zu Göttingen. V.

NL 0388611   ICJ

Linke, Franz.
Kritik der Cadmiumzelle. 1930.
p. 62-71. 24½cm.

NL 0388612   DAS

Linke, Franz, 1878–
... Luftelektrische messungen bei zwölf ballonfahrten, von F. Linke. Berlin, Weidmannsche buchhandlung, 1904.
90 p. incl. tables. IV pl. (part double) diagrs. 27½ᶜᵐ. (Abhandlungen der Königlichen gesellschaft der wissenschaften zu Göttingen. Mathematisch-physikalische klasse. n. f., bd. III, nr. 5)
Bibliographical foot-notes.

1. Atmospheric electricity.   ₁Full name: Karl Wilhelm Franz Linke₎
Title from John Crerar   Libr.   A C 33–3906
Library of Congress   [AS182.G811 n. f., bd. 3, nr. 5]

NL 0388613   ICJ DLC MiU OCU OU NN

Linke, Franz i.e. Karl Wilhelm Franz, 1878– 1944.   629.19 Q921
Die Luftschiffahrt von Montgolfier bis Graf Zeppelin. Von Dr. Franz Linke, ... Mit einem Beitrage über Militärluftschiffahrt von Hauptmann a. D. A. Hildebrandt, ... Mit zahlreichen Bildern. Berlin, A. Schall, [1909]
378 p. front. (port.), 34 pl. (1 fold.) 25ᶜᵐ.

NL 0388614   ICJ WU DLC-P4 CU NN

Linke, Franz, 1878–1944.
Die luftschiffahrt von Montgolfier bis graf Zeppelin, von dr. Franz Linke ... Mit einem beitrag über militärluftschiffahrt, von hauptmann a. d. A. Hildebrandt ... Mit zahlreichen bildern ... Berlin, Verlag des Vereins der bücherfreunde ₁1910₎
379 p. front. (port.) plates. 19 cm.
"Am 17. oktober 1900 auf der Internat. luftschiffahrt-ausstellung zu Frankfurt a. M. als bestes populär-wissenschaftliches werk über die luftschiffahrt preisgekrönt."
1. Aeronautics. 2. Aeronautics, Military.   I. Hildebrandt, Alfred, 1870–   II. Title.

TL605.L5   629.1332   33—6880

NL 0388615   DLC DSI

Linke, Franz, 1878–   ed.
Medizinisch-meteorologische Statistik
see under   Frankfurter Konferenz für Medizinisch-Naturwissenschaftliche Zusammenarbeit, 1st, 1936.

Linke, Franz, 1878–
Messungen des Ionengehaltes und der Radioaktivität der Luft auf dem Grossen Ozean. Von F. Linke. ₁Göttingen, 1906.₎
3 p.   8°.
Cover-title.
"Aus den Nachrichten der K. Gesellschaft der Wissenschaften zu Göttingen. Mathematisch-physikalische Klasse. 1906."

1. Radioactivity (Atmospheric).

June 16, 1916.

NL 0388617   NN

VOLUME 334

Linke, Franz, 1878–
Die meteorologische ausbildung des fliegers; im auftrage
und mit unterstützung des Kuratoriums der national-flug-
spende herausgegeben von dr. Franz Linke ... mit 30 textabbildungen, 3 wolkenbildern, 5 farbigen wetterkarten und 3
tabellen. München und Berlin, R. Oldenbourg, 1913.
2 p. l., 70 p. illus. (incl. charts) 22^{cm}.

1. Meteorology in aeronautics.   I. Title.
⟨Full name: Karl Wilhelm Franz Linke⟩
31–8446

Library of Congress   TL556.L5 1913   629.13

NL 0388618   DLC DAS ICJ MiU NN CtY

Linke, Franz, 1878–
Die meteorologische ausbildung des fliegers, von dr. Franz
Linke ... mit 37 textabbildungen, 4 wolkenbildern, 5 farbigen
wetterkarten und 4 tabellen. 2. umgearb. und verm. aufl.
München und Berlin, R. Oldenbourg, 1917.
3 p. l., 92 p. illus. (incl. charts) 2 diagr. on fold. l. 22^{cm}.

1. Meteorology in aeronautics.   I. Title.
⟨Full name: Karl Wilhelm Franz Linke⟩
31–8445

Library of Congress   TL556.L5 1917   629.13

NL 0388619   DLC DNW CtY ICJ DAL

Linke, Franz.
Die meteorologischen Institute und Organisa-
tionen in Deutschen Reich. Frankfurt a. M.
1929.
15p. map. tables (in pocket.) 20½cm.

NL 0388620   DAS

551.5   Linke, Franz, 1878–   ed.
L755   \ Meteorologisches taschenbuch. 1.–   ausg....
Herausgegeben von F.Linke ... Leipzig,Akade-
mische verlagsgesellschaft m.b.h., 1931–
v. illus., tables,diagrs. 21^{cm}.
Supplementary material to some of the chapters appears in each succeeding "ausgabe "
Contents.–1.ausg. I.Meteorologische geschichtstabellen. Von C.Kassner. II.Die meteorologischen
institute. Von F.Linke.III.Die wichtigsten meteorologischen zeitschriften. Von F.Linke. IV.Ver-
zeichnis der funkstellen,die regelmässig wettertelegramme   aussenden.Von K.Keil.

V.Schlüssel für wettertelegramme.Von K.Keil.VI.
Grundlagen der theoretischen meteorologie. Von
G.Stüve. VII.Meteorologische apparate und be-
obachtungsmethoden. Von E.Kleinschmidt. VIII.
Monats– und jahresmittel für luftdruck,tempera-
tur und niederschläge. Von K.Knoch. IX.Konstan-
ten und tabellen. Von F.Linke.– 2.ausg.X.Grund-
lagen,einheiten und formeln der atmosphärischen
strahlungsforschung. Von F.Linke.XI.Apparate

und messmethoden der atmosphärischen strahlungsforschung. Von F.Albrecht. XII.Luftelektrizität
grundlagen und messmethoden. Von H.Israël.XIII.
Bearbeitung aerologischer messungen. Von G.
Stüve. XIV. Rechnerische und mathematisch-
statistische hilfsmittel des meteorologen. Von
F.Baur. XV. Meteorologisches worterbuch. Von C.
Kassner...
1.Meteorology.   2.Meteorology – Dictionaries.

NL 0388623   CSt DAS DNAL PPF

Linke, Franz, 1878–   , editor.
Meteorologisches Taschenbuch; erste Ausgabe unter Mitarbeit von C. Kassner, K. Keil, E. Kleinschmidt...herausgegeben
von F. Linke...   Leipzig: Akademische Verlagsgesellschaft
m.b.H., 1931.   xi, 316 p. incl. diagrs., tables.   illus.   8°.

581727A. 1. Meteorology.   September 29, 1932

NL 0388624   NN DAS MiU

Linke, Franz, 1878–1944, ed.
Meteorologisches Taschenbuch.   Leipzig,
Akademische Verlagsgesellschaft, 1931–39.
5 v. illus. 21 cm.
1. Meteorology. I. Title.

NL 0388625   PSt

QC864   Linke, Franz, 1878–1944, ed.
.L5   Meteorologisches Taschenbuch. 2. Ausg. Unter
1933   Mitarbeit von F. Albrecht ⟨und anderen⟩
Leipzig, Akademische Verlagsgesellschaft, 1933.
336p. illus. 22cm.

Contents.– II. (Fortsetzung) Die meteorologi-
schen Institute.– IV. (Nachtrag) Verzeichnis der
Funkstellen, von K. Keil.– V. (Nachtrag)
Schlüssel für Wettertelegramme, von K. Keil.– X.
Grundlagen, Einheiten und Formeln der atmosphä-
rischen Strahlungsforschung, von F. Linke.– XI.
Apparate und   Messmethoden der atmosphä-

rischen Strahlungsforschung, von F. Albrecht.–
XII. Luftelektrizität, Grundlagen und Mess-
methoden, von H. Israël.– XIII. Bearbeitung
aerologischer Messungen, von G. Stüve.– XIV.
Rechnerische und mathematisch-statistische
Hilfsmittel des Meteorologen, von Franz Baur.–
XV. Meteorologisches Wörterbuch, von C. Kassner
⟨und anderen⟩.– XI. Konstanten und Tabellen
(Fortsetzung von Ausgabe I) – Sachverzeichnis.
Errata slip tipped in.
⟨Full name: Karl Wilhelm
Franz Linke⟩

NL 0388627   FMU

Linke, Franz, 1878–   ed.
Meteorologisches taschenbuch. 3. ausg. Unter mitarbeit
von T. Bergeron, C. Kassner, K. Keil und K. Knoch herausgegeben von F. Linke ... Leipzig, Akademische verlagsgesellschaft m. b. h., 1939.
viii, 268 p. incl. tables, diagrs. 21^{cm}.
"Schrifttum über wetterfunkdienst": p. 91.
Contents.—Meteorologische geschichtstabellen. Von C. Kassner. Internationale meteorologische organisation.—Einige wichtige internationale vereinbarungen.—Funkwettermeldungen. Von K. Keil.—Monats-
und jahresmittelwerte der temperatur und des niederschlags für Nord-
west- und Mitteleuropa. Von K. Knoch.—Sechssprachiges meteorologisches wörterbuch. Von Tor Bergeron.

1. Meteorology. 2. Meteorology—Dictionaries. 3. Meteorology—Societies, etc.   I. *Bergeron, Tor, 1891–   II. *Kassner, Carl, 1864–
III. *Keil, Karl, 1898–   IV. Knoch, Karl, 1883–   V. Title.
⟨Full name: Karl Wilhelm Franz Linke⟩
40–124

Library of Congress   QC864.L5 1939
Copyright A—Foreign   44227
551.502

NL 0388629   DLC PPF MCM DAS

Linke, Franz, 1878–   ed.
Meteorologisches taschenbuch, 4. ausg. unter mitarbeit von
F. Baur und H. Philipps herausgegeben von F. Linke ... Mit
10 abbildungen im text. Leipzig, Akademische verlagsgesellschaft m. b. h., 1939.
xii, 286 p. incl. tables, diagrs. 21^{cm}.
"Partes proportionales": table laid in.
Contents.—Meteorologische formelzeichen. — Mathematische formel-
sammlung für den meteorologen. Von K. Keil.—Monats- unter mitarbeit von H. Philipps.
Zeichen und formeln der vektorrechnung. Von F. Baur.—Rechnerische
und mathematisch-statistische hilfsmittel des meteorologen. Von F.
Baur.—Konstanten und tabellen.
1. Meteorology—Tables, etc. 2. Physics—Tables, etc. 3. Mathemat-
ics—Tables, etc. 4. Mathematics—Formulae.   I. Baur, Franz, 1887–
II. Philipps, Horst. III. Title.
⟨Full name: Karl Wilhelm Franz Linke⟩
Library of Congress   QC864.L5 1939 a   40–36168
Copyright A—Foreign   44880
⟨2⟩   551.50835

NL 0388630   DLC DAS

Linke, Frantisek
Meteorologisches Taschenbuch. Vierte
Ausgabe. Unter Mitarbeit von F. Baur und
H. Philipps. Herausgegeben von F. Linke ...
Mit 10 Abbildungen im text. Unveränderter
Nachdruck. Leipzig, Akademische Verlags-
gesellschaft, 1943.

286 p.

v. IV.

NL 0388631   MCM

Linke, Franz, 1878–   ed.
Meteorologisches taschenbuch. 5. ausg. unter mitarbeit von
F. Albrecht, H. Ertel, H. Israël ⟨u. a.⟩ ... herausgegeben von
F. Linke ... Mit 108 abbildungen im text. Unveränderter
nachdruck. Leipzig, Akademische verlagsgesellschaft m. b. h.,
1939.
xi, 354 p. illus., diagrs. 21^{cm}.
Includes bibliographies.
Contents.—Die theoretischen grundlagen der dynamischen meteorologie, von H. Ertel.—Meteorologische apparate und beobachtungs-
methoden, von E. Kleinschmidt.—Die drahtlosen aerologischen messmethoden, von G. Loeser.—Bearbeitung aerologischer messungen, von
G. Stüve und K. Schneider-Carius.—Grundlagen, einheiten und formeln

der atmosphärischen strahlungsforschung, von F. Linke.—Apparate und
messmethoden der atmosphärischen strahlungsforschung, von F. Albrecht.—Luftelektrizität, grundlagen und messmethoden, von H. Israël.

1. Meteorology.   I. *Albrecht, Fritz, 1896–   II. *Ertel, Hans,
1904–   III. Israël, Hans. IV. Title.
⟨Full name: Karl Wilhelm Franz Linke⟩
45–45218

Library of Congress   QC864.L525
551.5

NL 0388633   DLC MH MCM

QC864   Linke, Franz, 1878–1944, ed.
L5   Meteorologisches Taschenbuch. Neue Ausg.
Hrsg. von Franz Baur. Leipzig, Akademische
Verlagsgesellschaft Geest & Portig ⟨c1950–
v. illus. (part fold.) 22cm.

v.1: 2. Aufl.

1.Meteorology   Handbooks, manuals, etc.
2.Meteorology –   Dictionaries – Polyglot.
I.Baur, Franz,   1887– ed. II.Title.

NL 0388634   OrCS ICU CU

Linke, Franz, 1878–1944, ed.
Linkes Meteorologisches Taschenbuch, unter Mitarbeit von
Tor Bergeron ⟨et al.⟩ Neue Ausg., hrsg. von Franz Baur.
Leipzig, Geest & Portig, 1951–
v. 22 cm.

1. Meteorology.   I. Title: Meteorologisches Taschenbuch.

QC864.L53   551.5   52–41222 ‡

NL 0388635   DLC ICU MH-GM MoSU NN PSt TxU NN

Linke, Franz, 1878–1944, ed.
Linkes meteorologisches Taschenbuch. Neue
Ausgabe. Hrsg. vom Franz Baur unter Mitarbeit
von Tor Bergeron [et al.] Leipzig, Geest &
Portig, 1951–1957.
3 v. illus.

I. Baur, Franz, ed. II. Title: Meteorologisches
Taschenbuch. 551.5

NL 0388636   ICJ

VOLUME 334

Sch.F. **Linke, Franz,** 1878–1944, *ed.*
551.5 Linkes Meteorologisches Taschenbuch, unter Mitarbeit von
L756M Tor Bergeron ⟨et al.⟩ Neue Ausg., hrsg. von Franz Baur.
Leipzig, Geest & Portig, 1953–
3 v. illus. 21 cm.

NL 0388637 NcD

Linke, Franz, 1878–
Moderne luftschiffahrt, von dr. Franz Linke ... Mit 37
abbildungen auf 24 tafeln. Berlin, A. Schall, 1903.
296 p. front., plates (1 double) diagrs. 23ᶜᵐ.
CONTENTS.—Die entwicklung der luftschiffahrt.—Technik der luft-
schiffahrt.—Fahrtbeschreibungen.—Wissenschaftliche luftschiffahrt.—
Registrier- und fesselballon; drachen.—Militärische luftschiffahrt.—
Lenkbare luftschiffahrt.

1. Aeronautics. 2. Balloons. 3. Aeronautics in meteorology. I. Title.
⟨Full name: Karl Wilhelm Franz Linke⟩

33–34307

Library of Congress   TL545.L5 1903   629.13

NL 0388638 DLC DSI MiU NN DP

Linke, Franz, 1878–
Moderne luftschiffahrt, von dr. Franz Linke ... Berlin. A.
Schall ⟨1903?⟩
1 p. l., ⟨5⟩–359, ⟨1⟩ p. front., illus., plates, diagrs. 18½ᶜᵐ.
CONTENTS. — Die entwicklung der luftschiffahrt. — Technik der luft-
schiffahrt. — Fahrtbeschreibungen. — Wissenschaftliche luftschiffahrt.—
Registrier- und fesselballon; drachen.—Militärische luftschiffahrt.—
Lenkbare luftschiffahrt.

1. Aeronautics. 2. Balloons. 3. Aeronautics in meteorology.
I. Title.
⟨Full name: Karl Wilhelm Franz Linke⟩

33–31808

Library of Congress   TL545.L5 1903 a   629.13

NL 0388639 DLC ICJ DAL OrCS CtY

Linke, Franz, 1878–
Numerische Uebersicht der am Samoa-Observatorium im
Jahre 1905 registrierten Fern- und Naherdbeben. Von F. Linke.
⟨Göttingen, 1906.⟩ 4 p. Tables. 8°.
Cover-title.
"Aus den Nachrichten der K. Gesellschaft der Wissenschaften zu Göttingen.
Mathematisch-physikalische Klasse. 1906."

1. Earthquakes, Samoa, 1905.
June 20, 1916.

NL 0388640 NN

Linke, Franz, 1878–
Numerische Uebersicht der am Samoa-Observatorium im
Jahre 1906 registrierten Fern- und Naherdbeben. Von F. Linke.
⟨Göttingen, 1907.⟩ 3 p. Tables. 8°.
Cover-title.
"Aus den Nachrichten der K. Gesellschaft der Wissenschaften zu Göttingen.
Mathematisch-physikalische Klasse. 1907."

1. Earthquakes, Samoa, 1906.
June 20, 1916.

NL 0388641 NN

Linke, Franz, 1878–   joint ed.

Otto, Richard, 1872–   *ed.*
... Organismen und umwelt, 20 vorträge, gehalten von H.
Cauer ... ⟨u. a.⟩ Herausgegeben von dr. R. Otto ... in gemeinschaft mit dr. K. Felix ... und dr. F. Linke ... Mit 67 abbildungen. Dresden und Leipzig, T. Steinkopff, 1939.

Sch.F. **Linke, Franz,** 1878–1944, *ed.*
551.508 Physik der Atmosphäre I; atmosphärische
L756P Strahlungsforschung. Unter Mitwirkung zahl-
reicher Fachgelehrter hrsg. von Franz Linke
und Fritz Möller. Berlin, G. Borntraeger,
1942–61.
xvi, 1102 p. illus. (part col.) diagrs.
(part col.) 26 cm. (Handbuch der Geophysik,
Bd. 8)
Issued in parts.
Includes bibliographies.

1. Atmosphere. Collected works. I.
Möller, Fritz   jt. ed. II. Title.

NL 0388644 NcD MU MoKL FMU CoU OrCS ICJ

Linke, Franz, 1878–   , *ed.*
Probleme der Bioklimatologie, hrsg. von F. Linke...B. de
Rudder... ⟨und⟩ F. Ruttner... Bd. 1–   Leipzig, Becker
& Erler, 1943–   v. illus. 23cm.
Each volume has also special t.-p.
"Benützte Literatur," v. 1, p. 105–109.
CONTENTS.—Bd. 1. Föhn und Föhnwirkungen; der gegenwärtige Stand der Frage,
von H. v. Ficker und B. de Rudder.

1. Föhn. 2. Weather—Physio-   logical effects. I. Rudder, Bernhard
de, 1894–   , jt. ed. II. Ruttner,   Franz, 1882–   , jt. ed. III. Ficker,
Heinrich von, 1881–
June 23, 1948

NL 0388645 NN

Linke, Franz, 1878–
Ueber die Bedeutung auf- und absteigender Luftströme für
die atmosphärische Elektricität. Von F. Linke.   Leipzig: J. A.
Barth ⟨1902⟩.   231–235 p.   8°.
Cover-title.
Repr.: Annalen der Physik. Vierte Folge. Bd. 7. 1902.

1. Electricity (Atmospheric).
June 16, 1916.

NL 0388646 NN

Linke, Franz, 1878–
Ueber luftelektrische Messungen im Freiballon. n. p. ⟨190–?⟩
1 p.l., 140–142 p. diagr. 8°.
Caption-title.

1. Electricity (Atmospheric).—   Measurement.
June 16, 1916.

NL 0388647 NN

Linke, Franz, 1878–
Über messungen elektrischer potentialdifferenzen vermittels
collektoren im ballon und auf der erde ... Potsdam, Druck
von E. Stein, 1901.
2 p.l., 50 p., 1 l. illus., tables, diagrs. 21ᶜᵐ.
Inaug.-diss.—Berlin.
Lebenslauf.

1. Atmospheric electricity.
⟨Full name: Karl Wilhelm Franz Linke⟩
Library of Congress   QC962.L75   5–21762

NL 0388648 DLC CU CtY NN

Linke, Franz
Ein Universalaktinometer. Leipzig. 1924.
p. 59–62. illus. 27cm.

NL 0388649 DAS

Linke, Franz, 1878–
Vergleich der Messung der Horizontalintensität des Erd-
magnetismus in Potsdam und Cheltenham im Jahre 1904. Von
F. Linke.   ⟨Göttingen, 1907.⟩ 7 p. illus. 8°.
Cover-title.
"Aus den Nachrichten der K. Gesellschaft der Wissenschaften zu Göttingen.
Mathematisch-physikalische Klasse. 1907."

1. Magnetism (Terrestrial), Ger-   many: Potsdam, 1904. 2. Magnetism (Terrestrial), Gt. Br.: Chelten-   ham, 1904.
June 19, 1916.

NL 0388650 NN

Linke, Franz, and J. Cloessner.
Der wetterkundliche Unterricht; ein systematischer Lehrgang bearbeitet von Dr. F. Linke in Gemeinschaft mit J. Clössner.
Frankfurt am Main: F. B. Auffarth, 1911.   viii, 177 p., 2 tables.
illus. 8°.

1. Meteorology.—Compends and   textbooks, 1911. 2. Weather.
3. Cloessner, Jacob, jt. au.
January 2, 1912.

NL 0388651 NN

QC869 Linke, Franz, 1878–
L5   Der wetterkundliche Unterricht, ein systematischer Lehrgang,
1912   bearb. von Franz Linke in Gemeinschaft mit Jacob Clössner.
2. und 3. durchgesehene Aufl.   Frankfurt am Main, F. B.
Auffarth, 1912.
viii, 176 p. illus., maps, tables.

1. Meteorology - Study and teaching.   I. Clössner, Jacob,
joint author.

NL 0388652 CU ICJ

Linke, Franz.
Der wetterkundliche Unterricht. 1921

NL 0388653 DAS

Linke, Franz, 1878–1944.
Die zehntägigen Witterungsvoraussagen im Sommer 1933.
Berlin 1933.
p. 953. 31 cm.
(Mitteilungen der Deutschen Landwirtschafts-Gesell-
schaft. 48. Jahrg. 28. Okt. 1933. Stück 43.)
n. a.

NL 0388654 DAS

Linke, Franz Josef, 1904–
... Pathologisch-anatomische Untersuchungen
über das harte traumatische Oedem ...   Breslau,
1933.
Inaug.-Diss. - Breslau.
Lebenslauf.
"Literatur-Verzeichnis": p. 14–15.

NL 0388655 CtY MiU DNLM

Linke, Friedrich.   L667.6 Q406
Die Malerfarben, Mal- und Bindemittel und ihre Verwendung in
der Maltechnik. Zur Belehrung über die chemisch-technischen
Grundlagen der Malerei für Kunstschulen, Kunst- und Dekora-
tionsmaler. Von Dr. Friedrich Linke. ... Stuttgart, P. Neff
Verlag (C. Büchle), 1904.
xii, 122 p. 25½ᶜᵐ.

NL 0388656 ICJ

VOLUME 334

Linke, Friedrich, 1908-
... Über die Raumbeständigkeit der Füllungsze-
mente ...　Leipzig, 1936.
Inaug.-Diss. - Leipzig.
Lebenslauf.

NL 0388657　　CtY

Linke, Fritz, 1889-
19 faelle von tubargraviditaet.
Inaug. diss. Berlin, 1898.

NL 0388658　　ICRL CtY

Linke, Georg, 1901-
Die entstehung mittelbaren besitzes(§868 BGB)
Inaug. diss. Breslau, 1928.
Bibl.

NL 0388659　　DLC

Linke, Georg-Linus.
Über die Einwirkung von Phosphortrichlorid,
Phosphoroxychlorid und Phosphorsulfochlorid auf
Thiophenol.　Rostock, 1902.
44 p.
Inaug.-Diss. - Rostock.

NL 0388660　　MH-C ICRL

Linke, Gerhard, 1910-
Der Wortschatz des mittelengl. Epos Genesis
und Exodus mit grammatischer Einleitung ...
Saalfeld Ostpr. [1935]
4 p.l., 165 p., 1 l.　23.5 cm.
Inaug.-Diss. - Berlin.
Published also in series: Palaestra 197.
Lebenslauf.
"Benutzte Literatur": p. 163-165.
1. Genesis and Exodus (Middle English poem)
2. Middle English language - Glossaries, vocabu-
laries, etc.

NL 0388661　　CtY ICRL MiU OCU OU

Linke, Gerhard.
... Der wortschatz des mittelengl. epos Genesis und Exodus,
mit grammatischer einleitung, von Gerhard Linke. Leipzig,
Mayer & Müller, g. m. b. h., 1935.
4 p. l., 165 p. 24ᶜᵐ. (Palaestra 197)
"Benutzte literatur": p. 163-165.

1. Genesis and Exodus (Middle English poem) 2. English language—
Middle English (1100-1500)—Glossaries, vocabularies, etc.

Library of Congress　　PD25.P3 no. 197

35-10610

(808)　$21.19

NL 0388662　　DLC CU CtY MoU PU PBm ViU

Linke, Grete, 1910-
Spätinfektion nach Elliot-Trepanation ...
Beerfelden i.o., 1937.
Inaug.-Diss. - Heidelberg.
Lebenslauf.
"Literatur": p. 26.

NL 0388663　　CtY

Linke, Günther, 1908-
Der händler-verband für gummi- asbest- und
technische bedarfsartikel und seine bedeutung
für den technischen handel. ... Bleicherode am
Harz, 1937.　120 p.
Inaug. Diss. - Leipzig, 1937.
Lebenslauf.
Schrifttum.

NL 0388664　　ICRL CtY NNC

[Linke, Guilherme Augusto]
... A causa paulistas contra brasileiros perante o superior
tribunal divino. [São Paulo?] 1932.
54 p.　23ᶜᵐ.
At head of title: En nome e pela gloria de Deus!
Signed: São Paulo, dia da independencia de 1932. Guilherme Augusto
Linke.

1. São Paulo (State)—Hist.—Revolution, 1932.　I. Title.

Library of Congress　　F2631.L66

33-2920

981

NL 0388665　　DLC

TH
2451
L5
Linke, Gustav
Der Bau der Dorn'schen Lehmdächer nach
eigenen Erfahrungen mit Rücksicht auf die
dabei vorkommenden Holzconstructionen und
Kostenberechnungen.　Braunschweig, F.
Vieweg, 1837.
79 p.　fold. plate.　20 cm.

1. Roofing.　I. Title.

NL 0388666　　DS

TH145　Linke, Gustav.
.L7　Vorträge über baukonstruktionslehre am Königl.
gewerbe-institut und der Königl. allgemeinen-bau-
schule, von G.Linke...　Berlin,1850.
[1],298 p.　illus.,plates,diagrs.　28x23½ᶜᵐ.

Autographed.
Most of the plates printed on both sides.

1. Building.

NL 0388667　　ICU

Linke, Gustav.
Vortraege ueber kameralbau.　n.p.,n.p.,n.d.
2v.

NL 0388668　　PU

Linke, H.
Hand-gestures as an instructional aid
see under　Downs, Sophie W

Linke, H.
Handzeichen im ersten Leseunterricht
see also　Downs, Sophie W
Hand-gestures as an instructional aid.

W 4
B51
1940
Linke, Hans Joachim, 1915-
Über die Beziehungen der perniziösen
Anämie zur Physiologie und Pathologie des
Magens; Mitteilung von vier Krankheitsfällen.
Lengerich i. W., Lengericher Handelsdruckerei
[1940]
35 p.

Inaug.-Diss. - Friedrich Wilhelms Univ.,
Berlin.
Bibliography: p. 29-34.

NL 0388671　　DNLM

W 4
M96
1950
LINKE, Harald Karl, 1923-
Über psychische Infektionen; Beiträge
zur Kasuistik und zur Darstellung des
Übertragungsmodus von induzierter
Reaktion und konformem Wahn.　[München]
1950.
63 l.
Inaug.-Diss. - Munich.
1. Mental disorders

NL 0388672　　DNLM

[LINKE, Heinrich Moritz].
Ansichten, erfahrungen und urtheile über geistliche beredtsamkeit und geistliche rednerbil-
dung mit besonderer rucksicht auf Sachsen.
Mitgetheilt in driefen von Einem sachsischen
prediger.　Leipz. 1836.

11 x 19.

NL 0388673　　MH-AH

Linke, Heinrich Moritz.
D. Martin Luther. Das Wichtigste aus seinem
Leben und Wirken grossentheils nach Mathesius
erzählt von H. M. Linke ...　Zwickau, Eigen-
thum des Vereins zur Verbreitung guter und
wohlfeiler Volksschriften, 1846.
80 p.　19 cm.

NL 0388674　　CtHC

W 6
P3
LINKE, Heinz
Wunder und Aberglauben in der Heil-
kunde; kulturgeschichtliche Studie zur
Charakterisierung der Gegenwart.
Oranienburg, Orania-Verlag [190-?]
29 p.　　W6 P3

NL 0388675　　DNLM

Linke, Helene, 1903-
Blutzuckerbestimmungen bei ekzem, psoriasis,
lichen vidal und ulcus cruris.
Inaug. diss. Breslau, 1929.
Bibl.

NL 0388676　　ICRL CtY DNLM

294n
L756
na
Law
Library
Linke, Helmut.
Nationalwirtschaft und internationale Kartelle.　Würzburg,
K. Triltsch, 1938.
69 p.
Inaug.-Diss. — Frankfurt am Main.
Bibliography: p. 67-69.

NL 0388677　　CU

VOLUME 334

Linke, Helmut, 1913-
Die anfechtung wegen eigenschafts-
irrtums nach § 119 Abs. II BGB im
kunst- und antiquitätenhandel ... von
Helmut Linke ... Würzburg, R. Mayr,
1936.
2 p.l., 37 p., 1 l. 22cm.
Inaug.-Diss. - Köln.
"Lebenslauf": 1 l. at end.
"Literaturverzeichnis": p. [36]-37.

NL 0388678   MH-L ICRL

Linke, Hendrik, 1909-
... Ein Fall von Selbstkastration ...   Weida
i. Thür, 1937.
Inaug-Diss. - Jena.
Lebenslauf.
"Literaturangaben": p. 3-4.

NL 0388679   CtY

WU   Linke, Henry A
201   Tooth carving manual. [Los Angeles? c1948]
L756t   1 v. (unpaged) illus.
1948

1. Teeth

NL 0388680   DNLM

1889-
Linke, Hermann: Über die Einflüsse des Krieges auf die
Geschlechtsbildung, die Gewichte der Neugeborenen und
die Stillfähigkeit der Mütter. Aus d. Frauenkl. d. Akad.
f. prakt. Med. in Düsseldorf (Pankow). Heidelberg 1919:
Rößler & Herbert. 42 S. 8°
Heidelberg, Med. Diss. v. 13. April 1921, Ref. Menge
[Geb. 26. März 89 Glauchau; Wohnort: Heidelberg; Staatsangeh.: Sachsen;
Vorbildung: RG. Chemnitz Reife 09; Studium: Heidelberg 3, Rostock 2,
München 2, Breslau 1, Würzburg 2 S.; Coll. 11. Juli 19; Approb. 11. Dez. 14.]
[U 21. 4059]

NL 0388681   ICRL DNLM CtY

1894-
Linke, Hermann: Die Virunga-Vulkane. Leipzig 1917: Sturm
& Koppe. 90 S, 6 Taf. 8°
Leipzig, Phil. Diss. v. 4. Mai 1917, Ref. Meyer, Partsch
[Geb. 29. April 94 Wanne; Wohnort: Leipzig; Staatsangeh.: Sachsen; Vor-
bildung: OR. Leipzig Reife 13; Studium: Leipzig 7 S.; Rig. 16. Nov. 16.]
[U 17. 1690]

NL 0388682   ICRL CtY MH OCU

Linke, Herbert
Zur theorie und messung des auflösungsvermögens
photographischer Schichten. ... Borna-Leipzig,
1937. 34 p.
Inaug. Diss. - Techn. Hochschule Dresden, 1937.
Literatur.

NL 0388683   ICRL

Linke, Hugo, 1859-
Neue Bruchstücke der Freisinger Itala...
Sitzungsberichte ...   München, 1893
see under   Bible. N. T. Latin.
1893. Old Latin.

113   Linke, Hugo, 1859-
W373g   Quaestiones de Macrobii Saturnaliorum
fontibus. Vratislaviae, Apud G.Koeb-
nerum, 1880.
57p. 22cm.
Cover-title.
Diss.Inaug.- Breslau.
Vita.
Bound with Weber, Ferdinand Hugo. Die genetische Ent-
wickelung des Zahl- und Raumbegriffes in der griechischen
Philosophie bis Aristoteles.
Bibliographical footnotes.

1.Macrobius,   Ambrosius Aurelius Theo-
dosius.   Sa-   turnalia lib.VII. LC

NL 0388685   CLSU CU MH MiU NjP NcD PU

Linke, Hugo, 1859-
... Studien zur Itala. Von dr. Hugo Linke ...
Breslau, druck von Grass, Barth und comp. , 1889.
28 p. 27 cm.
At head of title: Städtisches evangelisches gymnasium zu St. Elisabet. Wissenschaftliche beilage
zum Osterprogramm 1889.
1. Bible Latin Versions - Italia. 2. Bible.
Latin - Hist.

NL 0388686   CU MH NjP

Linke, J.M.
Zwei fälle von Erstickungstod durch Bolus.
Inaug.-diss., Basel, Buchdruckerei Brin & co.,
Spalenvorstadt 9, 1915.
21 p. 2 plates.

NL 0388687   MBCo MiU CtY DNLM

Linke, J. R. Atlas der officinellen pflanzen sämmtlicher
pharmacopoeen mit beschreibung in medicinisch-pharma-
ceutischer und botanischer hinsicht. Leipzig. 1850. 1. 8°.
pp. [2], 143. 66 colored plates.

NL 0388688   MH-A

Linke, Johannes, 1847-
Die behandlung der Basedow'schen nach maassgabe
der ergebnisse der gesamtlitteratur des 19.
Jahrhunderts... Halle a. S., C. A. Kaemmerer &
co., 1901.
Cover-title: 45 p.
Inaug.-diss. - Friedrich-Universität Halle-
Wittenberg.
Lebenslauf.

NL 0388689   ICRL DNLM MBCo MiDW-M

Linke, Johannes, 1847-
Die Behandlung der Basedow'schen Krankheit
nach Maassgabe der Ergebnisse der
Gesamtlitteratur des 19. Jahrhunderts.   Halle
a. S., C. A. Kaemmerer & Co., 1902.
43 p. 8°.

NL 0388690   DNLM

Linke, Johannes, 1847-1914, ed.
Te Deum laudamus. Die lateinischen Hymnen
der alten Kirche ... verdeutscht durch Johannes
Linke ...   Bielefeld und Leipzig, Velhagen und
Klassing, 1884-
v. 14 cm.
Latin text of hymns is also given.
Added title-page: Bd. 1. Die Hymnen des Hilar-
ius und Ambrosius.

NL 0388691   NNUT NN

Linke, Johannes, 1847-1914, ed. and tr.
Die Hymnen des Hilarius und Ambrosius
verdeutscht durch Johannes Linke
see under   Hilarius, Saint, bp. of Poitiers,
d. 367?

Linke, Johannes, 1847-1914, ed.
Martin Rinkarts geistliche Lieder
see under   Rinkart, Martin, 1586-1649.

Linke, Johannes, 1847-1914.
M. Martin Rinkarts Leben. M. Martin Rinkarts
Werke und sonstige schriftliche Hinterlassen-
schaften.
(In Rinkart, Martin. Martin Rinkarts Geistliche
Lieder. 1886, p. 1-222)

NL 0388694   NNUT

ar W   Linke, Johannes, 1847-
51408   Specimen hymnologicum de fontibus
hymnorum Latinorum festum dedicationis
ecclesiae celebrantium [in honorem
festi dedicationis novae aedis Petri-
nae Lipsiensis] Lipsiae, B.
Liebischius, 1885.
24 p. 23cm.

NL 0388695   NIC

Linke, Johannes, 1847-1914.
Wann wurde das Lutherlied, Ein feste burg ist unser
Gott, verfasst? Historisch-kritische untersuchung von
d. Johannes Linke. Leipzig, Buchhandlung des Vereins-
hauses, 1886.
3 p. l., 192 p. 22cm.

1. Luther, Martin, 1483-1546. Ein feste burg ist unser Gott.
24-15608
Library of Congress   ML410.L964L4

NL 0388696   DLC PU

Linke, Johannes, 1900-
... Der baum; ein gedichtkreis. Leipzig, L. Staackman
[1934]
175, [4] p. 19½cm.

1. Title.   A C 34-4599
Title from Princeton   .   Univ. Printed by L. C.

NL 0388697   NjP IEN CtY CU NN

Linke, Johannes, 1900-
Der Brunnstock. [2. Aufl. Gütersloh, C. Bertelsmann,
1943]
81 p. 14 cm. (Bertelsmann-Feldposthefte)

1. Title.
PT2623.I 63B7 1943   49-34071*

NL 0388698   DLC CtY

VOLUME 334

3469   Linke, Johannes, 1900–
.54   ...Das festliche jahr. Leipzig, Auf-
.334   stieg, 1928.
      42 p. illus. 24½ ᶜᵐ.

      One of an edition of 300 copies.
      Poems.

NL 0388699   NjP

Linke, Johannes, 1900–
    Ein Jahr rollt übers Gebirg. Berlin, Deutsche
Buch-Gemeinschaft[c1934]
    439p. illus. 19cm.

NL 0388700   CtY

Linke, Johannes, 1900–
    ... Ein jahr rollt übers gebirg. Leipzig, L. Staackmann
[ᶜ1934]
    421. [1] p. incl. front. 19½ᶜᵐ.

      I. Title.
      Library of Congress   PT2623.I 63J3 1934   34–20973
      Copyright A—Foreign   24886
                                       833.9

NL 0388701   DLC PHC PBm NN

Linke, Johannes, 1900–
    ... Ein jahr rollt übers gebirg. Leipzig,
L. Staackmann [1941, c1934]
    421, [1] p. incl. front. 19.5 cm.

NL 0388702   NNC

Linke, Johannes, 1900–
    Ein jahr rollt übers gebirg.
München, Neuner·1954·   367p.

NL 0388703   CaBVa OrP

Linke, Johannes, 1900–
    ... Kurzgefasste lebensbeschreibung des Alfons Haigl; erzäh-
lung. Graz, Steirische verlagsanstalt, 1943.
    81, [1] p. illus. 19ᶜᵐ.

    "Erste auflage."
    "Der erzählung ist ein nachwort von Hanns Arens angefügt."
    "Die holzschnitte stammen von Fritz Mayer-Beck."

      I. Title.
      Yale univ. Library   A F 46–87
      for Library of Congress   PT2623.I 63K8
                        †   833.91

NL 0388704   CtY DLC

Linke, Johannes, 1900–
    Lieder vom Baum und Wald
      see under   Haas, Joseph, 1879–1960.

PT
2623
.I63   Linke, Johannes, 1900–
I6   Lohwasser; eine Erzählung. Leipzig, L.
    Staackmann [1941]
    159 p.

NL 0388706   NNC

Hky   Linke, Johannes, 1900–
L647   Los Nächte. [1.-8. Taus.] Leipzig, L.Staack-
L89   mann[c1941]
      218p. 20cm.
      Stories and poems.

NL 0388707   CtY OCU

Linke, Johannes, 1900–
    Losnächte. Leipzig, L. Staackmann [ᶜ1942]
    218 p. 20 cm.
    Prose and verse.

      I. Title.

      PT2623.I 63L6   56–49117 ‡

NL 0388708   DLC MB MH NNC NN RPB CU PU IEN

Linke, Johannes, 1900–
    ...Das Radl; eine Inflationskomödie...
Kassel [etc., 1951]   85 p.   18cm.
(Bärenreiter-Laienspiele.   Nr. 163)

      1. Drama, German. I. Title.

NL 0388709   NN

Linke, Johannes, 1900–
    ... Das Reich, gesänge. Leipzig, L. Staackmann [1938]
    93 p., 1 l. 24½ᶜᵐ.
    "8. bis 10. tausend."

      I. Title.
                               45–22309
      Library of Congress   PT2623.I 63R4
                                    831.91

NL 0388710   DLC IaU CU MH NjR MoU CtY NjP

Slavic   Linke, Johannes, 1900–
Coll.   Rok se vali přes hory. [Z německé předlohy
420.91   přeložil Miloš Hlávka] Praha, Evropský
G4   literární klub [1936]
L55   374 p. 22 cm. (Evropský literární klub)
      English translation of title: One year
      rolls over the mountain. Translated from
      German by Miloš Hlávka.   rw

NL 0388711   IEdS

Linke, Johannes, 1900–
    De Silvesternacht en andere novellen. [Geautoriseerde
vertaling door R. Adriaensens. Antwerpen] Die Poorte
[1943]
    71 p. 18 cm. (Novellenbibliotheek "Die Poorte," no. 13)

      I. Title.

      PT2623.I 63S52   54–55234 ‡

NL 0388712   DLC

Linke, Johannes, 1900–
    ... Die Silvesternacht; erzählung. Mit 19 zeichnungen von
Wolfgang Felten und einem nachwort von Wilhelm Westecker.
Leipzig, P. Reclam jun. [1943]
    75, [1] p. illus. 15½ᶜᵐ. [Reclams universal-bibliothek, nr. 7555]

      I. Title.
      PT2623.I 63S5   A F 47–1185
      Yale univ. Library
      for Library of Congress   †

NL 0388713   CtY WU PU IU CU DLC

838
L756t   Linke, Johannes, 1900–
    ... Das totenbrünnel; die geschichten
der sonnwendnacht. Leipzig, L.Staack-
mann [ᵒ1940]
    175, [1] p. 19ᶜᵐ.

      1. European war, 1914-1918—Fiction. I.
Title.

NL 0388714   MiU

Linke, Johannes, 1900–
    ... Das Totenbrünnel, die geschichten der
sonnwendnacht. Leipzig, Der Jugend-
Buchring, [c1940].
      201p.

NL 0388715   CU

LINKE, JOHANNES, 1900–
    Das Totenbrünnel; die Geschichten der Sonnwend-
nacht. Leipzig, L. Staackmann [1941, c1940]
    175 p. 20cm.

NL 0388716   NN

Linke, Johannes, 1900–
    Das Totenbrünnel, die geschichten der
sonnwendnacht. Leipzig, L. Staackmann
[1942]
    162 p.

NL 0388717   NNC MB MH

Linke, Johannes, 1900–
    ... Das Totenbrünnel, die geschichten der sonnwendnacht.
Leipzig, L. Staackmann [1943]
    191 p. 15½ᶜᵐ.
    "18.–62. tausend. 1943."

      I. Title.   A F 46–117
      Yale univ. Library
      for Library of Congress   PT2623.I 63T6

NL 0388718   CtY IaU MiD MnU NjP DLC

Linke, Johannes, 1900–
    ... Die wachsende reut, ein erzählbuch. [Leipzig, L. Staack-
mann [1944]
    580, [1] p., 1 l. 19ᶜᵐ.
    "1. auflage 1944."

      I. Title.
                               46–21942
      Library of Congress   PT2623.I 63W3
                                    833.91

NL 0388719   DLC WU CtY

634.90943
L756w
    Linke, Johannes, 1900–
    Wälder und Wäldler, ein Bilderbuch aus
dem Bayerischen Wald. Bamberg, L.
Staackmann [c1936]

      103p. plates. 25cm.

      1. Bavarian Forest. I. Title.

NL 0388720   FU

VOLUME 334

DB
785
.B55L5
1936

Linke, Johannes, 1900–
Wälder und Wäldler; ein Bilderbuch aus dem Bayern- und Böhmerwald, von Johannes und Käte Linke. Leipzig, L. Staackmann 1936.
127 p. illus. 24 cm.

1. Bohemian Forest. 2. Bavarian Forest. I. Linke, Käte, joint author. II. Title

NL 0388721   OKentU NN MH

Linke, Johannes, 1900–
Wälder und Wäldler, ein Bilderbuch aus dem Bayern- und Böhmerwald, von Johannes und Käte Linke. Leipzig, L. Staackmann ₁1940₎
127 p. plates. 24 cm.

1. Bohemian Forest. 2. Bavarian Forest. I. Linke, Käte, joint author. II. Title.

DB785.B55L5   51–46121

NL 0388722   DLC

Linke, Johannes, 1900–
...Der wald und seine kinder. Leipzig, Staackmann ₍c1937₎
80 p.

NL 0388723   PPT

PT2623
.I 63W34
Linke, Johannes, 1900–
Der Wald und seine Kinder. [6.–10. Tsd.] Leipzig, L. Staackmann [1940]
80 p. 19cm. (Dichtung und Deutung; eine Schriftenreihe)
Prose and poetry.
"Nachwort" signed, Eduard Rothemund.
"Bibliographie und Quellenangabe": p. 80.
1. Cooperative acquisitions project (Library of Congress)—German texts, 1938-1945. I. Rothemund, Eduard. II. Title.

NL 0388724   MB

Linke, Johannes, 1900–
... Der wald und seine kinder; eine auswahl. Leipzig, L. Staackmann ₍1944₎
80 p. 18¼˙˙.
"Nachwort" (p. 77-80) biographical notes on the author, signed Eduard Rothemund.
"11.–30. tsd."
Prose and poetry.

I. Rothemund, Eduard. II. Title.

Yale univ. Library
for Library of Congress   PT2623.I 63W34
                                           A F 46–318
                              †   833.91

NL 0388725   CtY MB NjP NN IU CU DLC

Linke, Johannes. Christian.
Veränderung der wirtschaftsgeographischen Beziehungen in Korea unter dem Einfluss der Erschliessung; die Grundlagen und ursprüngliche Ausgestaltung, von Dr. Johannes Linke. Stuttgart: C. E. Poeschel, 1933. 134 p. incl. diagrs., tables. illus. (charts.) 24cm. (Weltwirtschaftliche Abhandlungen. Bd. 10.)

"Erscheint gleichzeitig als Inauguraldissertation... Universität Leipzig."
"Literaturverzeichnis," p. 132–134.

675156A. 1. Economic history—   Korea. I. Ser.
                                        October 11, 1933

NL 0388726   NN ICJ

₍Linke, John Austin₎ 1871–
⸠... Agricultural education; organization and administration ... Revised 1939. United States Department of the interior, Harold L. Ickes, secretary. Office of education, John W. Studebaker, commissioner. Washington, U. S. Govt. print. off., 1940.
vi, 50 p. 23 cm. (U. S. Office of education. Vocational division. Bulletin no. 13. Agricultural series, no. 1)
"The first edition ... was prepared and published by the Federal board for vocational education in 1918 ... The bulletin has been revised several times ... This revision has been made by J. A. Linke."—Foreword.

1. Agricultural education—U. S.   I. Title.

LC1045.A25   no. 13e
                              (371.426082)
U. S. Office of Education.   Library
for Library of Congress   ₍r49g2₎†
                                      E 40–514 rev

NL 0388727   DHEW DLC

₍Linke, John Austin₎ 1871–
... Agricultural evening schools; methods of organizing and conducting evening schools and suggestions for content of courses. November, 1923. Issued by the Federal board for vocational education, Washington, D. C. Washington, Govt. print. off., 1923.
v, 41 p. pl. 23 cm. (₍U. S.₎ Federal board for vocational education. Bulletin no. 89. Agricultural series, no. 17)
"Prepared by Mr. J. A. Linke."—Foreword.

1. Evening ₍and continuation₎ schools. 2. Education of adults. ₍2. Adult education₎ 3. Agricultural education.   I. Title.

LC1045.A25   no. 89   E 24–55 rev 2

U. S. Office of Education.   Library
for Library of Congress   ₍r49g1₎†

NL 0388728   DHEW DLC

₍Linke, John Austin₎ 1871–
⸠... Agricultural evening schools, methods of organizing and conducting evening schools. Revised 1930. Issued by the Federal board for vocational education, Washington, D. C. ₍Washington, U. S. Govt. print. off., 1930₎
vii, 15 p. 23 cm. (₍U. S.₎ Federal board for vocational education. Bulletin no. 89. Agricultural series, no. 17)
"This bulletin ... originally prepared by J. A. Linke ... was revised under the direction of Dr. C. H. Lane ... by James H. Pearson."— p. vii.

1. Evening ₍and continuation₎ schools. 2. Education of adults. 3. Agricultural education.   I. Pearson, James Hurt, 1893–   II. Title.

LC1045.A25   no. 89a   E 30–238 rev 2
U. S. Office of Education.   Library
for Library of Congress   ₍r49h2₎†

NL 0388729   DHEW DLC OrCS OrU

₍Linke, John Austin₎ 1871–
... Agricultural evening schools, methods of organizing and conducting schools for adult farmers. Revised, 1934. United States Department of the interior, Harold L. Ickes, secretary. Office of education, George F. Zook, commissioner. Washington, U. S. Govt. print. off., 1934.
v, 14 p. 23 cm. (₍U. S.₎ Office of education. ₍Vocational division₎ Vocational education bulletin no. 89. Agricultural series, no. 17)
"This bulletin ... originally prepared ... by J. A. Linke ... revised ... by James H. Pearson."—Foreword.

1. Evening ₍and continuation₎ schools. 2. Education of adults. ₍2. Adult education₎ 3. Agricultural education.   I. Pearson, James Hurt, 1893–   II. Title.

LC1045.A25   no. 89b   E 34–477
U. S. Office of Education.   Library
for Library of Congress   ₍67r49j4₎†

NL 0388730   DHEW DLC

₍Linke, John Austin₎ 1871–
⸠... Agricultural part-time schools. Methods of organizing and conducting part-time schools and suggestions for content of courses. Washington, D. C., Federal board for vocational education, 1926.
vii, 29 p. 23 cm. (₍U. S.₎ Federal board for vocational education. Bulletin no. 108. Agricultural series, no. 27)
"Prepared ... by J. A. Linke."—p. vii.
Revised in 1933 by James H. Pearson.

1. Agriculture—Study and teaching.   I. Title.

LC1045.A25   no. 108   E 26–334 rev

U. S. Office of Education.   Library
for Library of Congress   ₍r48l2₎†

NL 0388731   DHEW ICJ DLC

Linke, John Austin, 1871– comp.
Conferences of state supervisors and teacher trainers in agricultural education. *North central region.*
... Report of sectional conferences of state supervisors and teacher trainers in agricultural education, North central region. St. Joseph, Mo., March 29-30, 1934. Ortonville, Minn., April 3-4, 1934 ₍and₎ Indianapolis, Ind., April 12, 13, 14, 1934. ₍Washington, D. C., 1934₎

Linke ₍Josef₎. ⸠Zur Kasuistik der Nævi. ⸡ po. 8°. *München, M. Ernst*, 1887.

NL 0388733   DNLM

RB129
839L

Linke, Joseph
Dissertatio ... sistens historiam febris subcontinuae tortii in clinico medico pragensi anni schol. 1839 tractatae. Pragae, J. Spurny, 1839.
43, ₍1₎p. 19cm.

Inaug. diss. - Prague.

1. Fever.

NL 0388734   CtY-M DNLM

DB785
.B55L5
Linke, Käte, joint author.

Linke, Johannes, 1900–
Wälder und Wäldler, ein Bilderbuch aus dem Bayern- und Böhmerwald, von Johannes und Käte Linke. Leipzig, L. Staackmann ₍1940₎

Linke, Karl.
Arnold Schönberg. Mit beiträgen von Alban Berg, Paris von Gütersloh, K. Horwitz, Heinrich Jalowetz, W. Kandinsky, Paul Königer, Karl Linke, Robert Neumann, Erwin Stein, Ant. v. Webern, Egon Wellesz. München, R. Piper & co., 1912.

Linke, Karl, 1884–
Der erzählende geschichtsunterricht, von Karl Linke. Hamburg, A. Janssen, 1914.
136 p. 20½˙˙. (*Added t.-p.:* Handbücher für modernen unterricht)

1. Story-telling. 2. History—Study and teaching.   I. Title.

Library of Congress   LB1582.G3L5   14–13355

NL 0388737   DLC

Linke, Karl, 1884–
Der freie Aufsatz auf der Unterstufe, Mittelstufe, und Oberstufe; mit Schüleraufsätzen und Schülerzeichnungen. Braunschweig, G. Westermann ₍1928, °1916₎
252 p. illus. 21 cm. (Handbücher für modernen Unterricht)
"Fünfte ergänzte und verbesserte Auflage des Buches 'Der deutsche Aufsatz auf der Unterstufe, Mittelstufe und Oberstufe.'"

1. German language—Rhetoric. 2. German language—Study and teaching.   I. Title. II. Series: Handbücher für modernen Unterricht. Hamburg and Berlin.

PF3420.L5 1928   A F 48–48*
Yale Univ. Library
for Library of Congress   †

NL 0388738   CtY DLC

Linke, Karl, 1884–
Die geschichte des handwerkerstandes mit besonderer berücksichtigung Österreichs. Ein kulturgeschichtlicher längsschnitt, von Karl Linke. Wien ₍etc.₎ Schulwissenschaftlicher verlag A. Haase, ges. m. b. h., 1924.
79 p. 21˙˙. ₍Schulreform-bücherei. Nr. 13₎
"Benützte literatur": p. 77–78.

1. Labor and laboring classes—Hist. 2. Gilds. 3. Artisans—Vienna.

Library of Congress   HD4841.L5   27–21350

NL 0388739   DLC

VOLUME 334

DB5
L55
Linke, Karl, 1884–
Gesellschaft, Staat und Kultur in ihren Wechselbeziehungen; gezeigt an ausgewählten Kapiteln aus der deutschen und österreichischen Geschichte. Wien, Deutscher Verlag für Jugend und Volk, 1929.
238 p.

Includes bibliography.

1. Austria - Hist. - Addresses, essays, lectures. 2. Austria - Constitutional history - Addresses, essays, lectures.

NL 0388740   CU DLC-P4

Linke, Karl, 1884–
Karl Linke den Serbest tahrir. Kültür bakanliği tarafindan ilkokul öğretmenleri için kilavuz olarak negredilmiştir. İstanbul, Devlet basimevi, 1937.
4 p. l., 198 p. 19½ᵐ.

Translated by M. Rauf İnan.

1. German language—Orthography and spelling. I. İnan, M. Rauf, tr. II. Title: Serbest tahrir. *Translation of* Methodik des rechtschreibunterrichts.
Library of Congress   PF3143.L53   41–41581

NL 0388741   DLC

Linke, Karl, 1884–
...Kulturgeschichte der Deutschen des Mittelalters. Von Karl Linke. Prag Annahof: A. Haase, 1920. viii, 256 p. diagrs., illus. (incl. plan.) 8°. (Schriften für Lehrerfortbildung. Nr. 14.)

1. Culture—Hist.—Germany, Middle   Ages. 2. Ser.   September 14, 1925

NL 0388742   NN

Linke, Karl, 1884–
Methodik des Deutschunterrichtes für Volksschulen. Braunschweig, G. Westermann, 1939.
155 p. 21 cm.

1. German language—Study and teaching. I. Title.
PF3065.L47   50–50664

NL 0388743   DLC

Linke, Karl, 1884–
Methodik des rechtschreibunterrichts, von Karl Linke. Vollständig umgearb. 4. aufl. des buches "Der rechtschreibunterricht in der arbeitsschule". Braunschweig und Hamburg, G. Westermann, 1923.
123, (2) p. 20½ᵐ. (*Added t.-p.:* Handbücher für modernen unterricht)

1. German language—Orthography and spelling.
Library of Congress   PF3143.L5 1923   25–17295

NL 0388744   DLC

Linke, Karl, 1884–
Nauczanie łączne i nauczanie języka ojczystego w szkole powszechnej. Warszawa ₁1933₎

NL 0388745   WU

PT875
.L74
LINKE, KARL, 1884–
Neue wege der jugendschriftenbewegung und der klassen-lektüre, von Karl Linke... Wien, Deutscher verlag für jugend und volk[1929]
cover-title, 99 p. 22½cm.
Bibliographical foot-notes.

1. Children's literature.

NL 0388746   ICU

Linke, Karl.
Die österreichische Nordpolfahrt von Payer und Weyprecht in den Jahren 1872 bis 1874, aus den Originalberichten ausgewählt. Wien, Verlag für Jugend und Volk ₁1946₎
121 p. col. illus., fold. map. 19 cm.
Bibliography: p. ₍2₎

1. Payer, Julius, Ritter von, 1842–1915. 2. Weyprecht, Karl, 1838–1881. 3. Tegetthoff Expedition, 1872–1874. 4. Arctic regions. 5. Franz Josef Land. I. Title.
G810.L5   51–26499

NL 0388747   DLC

Linke, Karl, 1884–
Sprachlehre in lebensgebieten; ein handbuch für lehrer, von Karl Linke. Hamburg und Berlin, A. Janssen, 1913.
196 p. 20½ᵐ. (*Added t.-p.:* Handbücher für modernen unterricht. ₍4₎)
"Quellenverzeichnis": p. 196.

1. German language—Grammar—1870–   2. German language—Study and teaching.
Library of Congress   PF3111.L5   14–4736

NL 0388748   DLC

Linke, Karl Friedrich.   2873.144
Poesiestunden. Die deutsche Dichtung von den Sängern der Freiheitskriege bis zur Gegenwart. Zu freudigem Schauen, Geniessen und Vertiefen. Den deutschen Lehrern und Lehrerinnen zur Auswahl und Darbietung fur die deutschen Schulen und zur Selbstbildung.
Hannover. Meyer. 1904. xv, 556 pp. [Erziehung durch die Kunst.] 8°.

F8429 — Germany. Lit. Poetry. — S.r.

NL 0388749   MB

Linke, Karl Hermann Walter, 1886–
  see   Linke, Walter, 1886–

Linke, Karl Robert
  see   Linke, Robert, philologist.

Linke, Karl Wilhelm Franz
  see   Linke, Franz, 1878–1944.

Linke, Karola, 1904–
Beiträge zur Topologie der dreidimensionalen polyedralen Gebilde verschiedener Metrik ... Kirchhain, 1934.
38 p.
Inaug.-Diss. - Rostock.
Teildruck aus der Dissertation: Beiträge zur Geometrie der polyedralen Gebilde verschiedener Metrik ...
Lebenslauf
"Literatur": 1 l. following p. vi.

NL 0388753   CtY ICRL

Linke, Carola, 1904–
Beitrage zur topologie der dreidimensionalen polyedralen gebilde verschiedener metrik ... Kirchhain, M. Schmersow, 1934.
vi p., 1 l., 38, [2] p. diagrs.
Film copy of the original at Harvard. Negative.
Abstract of thesis - Rostock.
Title of original thesis: Beiträge zur geometrie der polyedralen gebilde verschiedener metrik insbesondere zum beweise für den hauptsatz der dreidimensionalen topologie.
Lebenslauf
Errata leaf inserted.

NL 0388754   RPB

Linke, Lilo.
Allah dethroned; a journey through modern Turkey, by Lilo Linke. With 81 illustrations and a map. London, Constable & co., ltd. ₁1937₎
xvi, 341 p. XLVI pl. (incl. front., ports., facsims.) on 32 l., fold. map. 22½ᵐ.
Bibliography: p. 336–337.

1. Turkey—Descr. & trav. I. Title.   37–18238
Library of Congress   DR428.L5   915.6

WaS WaT GS
MoU TxU NcC NcD CtY OU NN MB WaSp WaTC Or OrP Wa WaE
NL 0388755   DLC OCl OCU VtMiM OOxM NIC PPFr PPT ScU

Linke, Lilo.
Andean adventure; a social and political study of Colombia, Ecuador and Bolivia, by Lilo Linke. London, New York ₍etc.₎, Hutchinson & co. ltd. ₁1945₎
5 p. l., 7–288 p. front., plates, ports. 24 cm.

1. South America—Descr. & trav. 2. South America—Politics. I. Title.
F2223.L7   918   45–10200

NL 0388756   DLC CaBVaU IU FU ViU NcU FMU MU IaU MB

Linke, Lilo.
... Cancel all vows. London, Constable and co., ltd. ₁1938₎
3 p. l., 361, ₍1₎ p. 20½ᵐ.
"First published 1938."

I. Title.   39–4663
Library of Congress   PZ3.L6546Can

NL 0388757   DLC CtY

Linke, Lilo.
Ecuador; country of contrasts. London, New York, Royal Institute of International Affairs ₁1954₎
ix, 173 p. maps. 21 cm.
Bibliography: p. 167–170.

1. Ecuador.
F3708.L5   *918.66   A 54–8960
Rochester. Univ. Libr.
for Library of Congress   ₍55k10₎†

CaBViP CaBVa CaBVaU IdU OrP OrAshS OrU Wa WaS WaSpG
NcU DLC PBL PU-W PSt PBm PP NcD OCl CLSU PPC Or WaT
NL 0388758   NRU OOxM OU TxU MiD N ViU MH NNC NN

Linke, Lilo.
Ecuador; country of contrasts. 2d ed. London, New York, Royal Institute of International Affairs ₁1955₎
ix, 174 p. maps, tables. 21 cm.
Bibliography: p. 168–171.

1. Ecuador.
F3708.L5 1955   *918.66   56–1598

PBm PP CU PSt NcD OCl ViU MB NcU CSt-H OCU NIC
NL 0388759   DLC IdPI IdU CaBVa OrP OrSaW ICD FMU Tx*

VOLUME 334

Linke, Lilo.

Fabian society, *London. International research section.*
Hitler's route to Bagdad. Prepared for the International
research section of the Fabian society by Barbara Ward, the
Hon. Barbara Buckmaster, Clare Hollingworth ₍and others₎ ...
Introduction by Leonard Woolf; maps by J. F. Horrabin.
London, G. Allen & Unwin, ltd. ₍1939₎

Linke, Lilo.
Magic Yucatan; a journey remembered. London, New
York, Hutchinson ₍1950₎
160 p. plates. ports. 22 cm.

1. Yucatan—Descr. & trav.   I. Title.

F1376.L76   917.26

                                                        51–3914

NL 0388761   MB NN OCl
              DLC CaBVa CaBViP OrMonO CU CU-B ViU TxU

Linke, Lilo.
Restless days; a German girl's autobiography, by Lilo Linke.
New York, A. A. Knopf, 1935.
xi, 432 p., 1 l. 22ᶜᵐ.
"First American edition."

I. Title.

Library of Congress   CT1098.L5A32 1935
                                          ₍43q1₎   920.1

                                                      35–27197

NL 0388762   PPCCH OCl OClh NcRS KyLx OU CU WaE OrP WaT OrCS OrU
              DLC CoU MeB MiU NN NSyU NIC TU PCC PSC

Linke, Lilo.   CT
Restless flags; a German girl's story.   1098
London Constable, 1935.   L5A32
354p. 19cm.

NL 0388763   MU

Linke, Lilo, tr.   DD253
                    .L32
Langhoff, Wolfgang, 1901–
Rubber truncheon; being an account of thirteen months
spent in a concentration camp, by Wolfgang Langhoff; translated from the German of "Die moorsoldaten" by Lilo Linke;
with a foreword by Lion Feuchtwanger. New York, E. P.
Dutton & co., inc. ₍°1935₎

Linke, Lilo.   CT
Tale without end, by Lilo Linke;   1098
with an introduction by Storm Jameson.   .L5A3
London, Constable, 1934.
xl, 217 p. illus. 20 cm.

1. France—Descr. & trav.—1919–
I. Jameson, Storm, 1897–   II. Title

NL 0388765   OKentU

Linke, Lilo.
Tale without end, by Lilo Linke; with an introduction by
Storm Jameson. New York, A. A. Knopf, 1934.
xxxvii, 220, ₍2₎ p. incl. front. (port.) 19½ᶜᵐ.
"First American edition."

1. France—Descr. & trav.—1919–   I. *Jameson, Storm, 1897–
II. Title.

Library of Congress   CT1098.L5A3 1934
——— Copy 2.
Copyright A 74469   914.4

                                                      34–23434

NL 0388766   OU MB
              DLC CaBVa WaS Or CU NN NcRS MiU OCl OCU

Linke, Max
        see Lincke, Max.

Linke, Oscar, 1854–1928.   PT2623
₍ Das Bild des Eros; neue milesische   L1633B5
Märchen.   Jena, H. Costenoble,
1882–
        v.

NL 0388768   CU

Linke, Oscar, 1854–1928.
Leukothea. Ein Roman aus Alt-Hellas.   *6890.1.(1884) vol.
(In Deutsche Roman-Zeitung. Jahrg. 21, Bd. 1. Berlin, 1884.)

Sheet C 9506   May 6, 1898

NL 0388769   MB CU

[Linke, Oscar] 1854–1928.
... Die madonna von Swidlowice. Bilder und
skizzen. Von Taras Kunowski [pseud.]
Grossenhain, Baumert & Ronge [1896]
182 p.   15 cm.   (Collection Victoria regia)
Title vignette.

NL 0388770   IEN

Linke, Oscar.   KD 40730
Milesische Märchen. 2.Aufl. Dresden, etc.,
C.Reissner, 1901.

NL 0388771   MH

LINKE, OSCAR, 1854–1928.   PN998
Neue milesische märchen, von Oskar Linke... Halle   .M6L7
a. d. S., O. Hendel [1901]
[3],139 p. 18cm.

1. Legends, Greek.

NL 0388772   ICU

Linke, Oscar, 1854–1928.
Triumph der Liebe. Brüderlichkeit! Gleichheit!
Freiheit! Dramatische Trilogie von Oscar
Linke ... Leipzig, W. Friedrich [1890]
3 p. l. [9]–331 p. 19.5 cm.
In "Weltende, Dramatisch-phantastischer Epilog
zum Triumph der Liebe", pp. [315]–331,
Theophilus Faustus and Ahasverus appear as
characters.

NL 0388773   CtY

Linke, Otto.
Austragungen für Karosseriebauer; eine leichtverständliche Einführung in das Zeichnen für Karosserie- und Fahrzeugbauer. Berlin, R. C. Schmidt ₍1939₎
2 v. diagrs. 30 cm. (Das Fachbuch für den Karosserie- und
Fahrzeugbau, Bd. 2)

1. Automobiles—Bodies.   I. Title.   (Series)

TL255.L53   49–32174*

NL 0388774   DLC

Linke, Otto.
Beschlag- und Ansichtszeichnen für den Karosserie- und
Fahrzeugbau; eine leichtverständliche Einführung in das
Zeichnen für Karosserie- und Fahrzeugbauer. Berlin, R. C.
Schmidt ₍1940₎
78 p. illus., tables. 30 cm. (Das Fachbuch für den Karosserie-
und Fahrzeugbau, Bd. 5)

1. Automobiles—Design and construction. 2. Automobiles—Bodies.
3. Mechanical drawing.   (Series)

TL255.L54   48–43420*

NL 0388775   DLC

Linke, Otto.
Festigkeitslehre für den Fahrzeugbau, mit Anhang: Schieberrechnen. 2. Aufl. Braunschweig, R. C. Schmidt ₍1953₎
210 p. illus. 24 cm. (Fachbuchreihe für den Fahrzeugbau)
"Schieberrechnen: der Rechenschieber und seine Anwendung" (40
p.) and "Tabellenbuch" (74 p.) inserted in pocket.

1. Automobiles. 2. Automobiles—Design and construction.
I. Title.

Detroit. Public Library   A 58–6473
for Library of Congress

NL 0388776   MiD

Linke, Otto.
Werkstoffkunde für den Karosserie- und Fahrzeugbau.
Berlin, R. C. Schmidt ₍1940₎
viii, 71 p. illus., tables. 30 cm. (Das Fachbuch für den Karosserie-
und Fahrzeugbau, Bd. 1)

1. Automobiles—Apparatus and supplies. 2. Materials. (Series)

TL159.L55   48–44252*

NL 0388777   DLC

Linke, Otto.   Lawyer.
Vertragsverbindungen und gemischte gegenseitige
schuldrechtliche Verträge unt. bes. Berücks. d. Vermischung
v. Kauf u. Miete. [Maschinenschrift.] 84 S. 4°. — Auszug:
Liegnitz 1924: Krebs. 2 Bl. 8°
Breslau, R.- u. staatswiss. Diss. v. 22. Okt. 1924 [1925]   [U 25. 744]

NL 0388778   ICRL

Linke, Otto, 1846–
Die controverse über Hannibal's Alpenübergang ...
Breslau, A. Neumann ₍1873₎
2 p. l., 40, ₍3₎ p. 21½ᶜᵐ.
Inaug.-dis.—Breslau.
Lebenslauf.

1. Hannibal—Crossing of the Alps, 218 B. C.

Library of Congress   DG247.2.L75   4–35232†

NL 0388779   DLC ICRL MH

LINKE, Paul Ferdinand, 1876–
D. Humes lehre vom wissen; ein beitrag zur
relationstheorie im anschluss an Locke und
Hume. Inaug.-diss., Leipzig, W. Engelmann,
1901.
pp.54.
Cover serves as title-page.
"Vita", at end.
Sonderabdruck aus Wundt, Philosophische
studien, XVII, 4".

NL 0388780   MH ICRL PU RPB CtY OU

VOLUME 334

DD491   Linke, Otto, 1846–
S45D3   Friedrich Theodor von Merckel im Dienste fürs
v.5,10   Vaterland. Breslau, E. Wohlfarth, 1907-1910.
     2v. 25cm. (Darstellungen und Quellen zur
schlesischen Geschichte, 5. und 10. Bände)

Bibliographical footnotes.

1. Merckel, Friedrich Theodor, 1775–

NL 0388781   IaU ICN MH NN

BF   Linke, Paul Ferdinand, 1876–
311   Grundfragen der Wahrnehmungslehre;
L75   Untersuchungen über die Bedeutung der
Gegenstandstheorie und Phänomenologie für
die experimentelle Psychologie. München,
E. Reinhardt, 1918.
     xxvi, 382 p. 24cm.

1. Perception.

NL 0388782   NIC MH

Linke, Paul Ferdinand, 1876–
   Grundfragen der wahrnehmungslehre, von Paul Ferdinand
Linke. 2., durchgesehene und um ein nachwort über gegen-
standsphänomenologie und gestalttheorie verm. aufl. München, E. Reinhardt, 1929.
   xxvi, 430 p. 23½cm.
   Bibliographical foot-notes.

1. Perception. 2. Gestalt (Psychology)
                        A 30-536
Title from Univ. of Chi-   cago BF233.L68 Printed by L. C.

NL 0388783   ICU PBm PU NcD MiU OU TxU MH

Linke, Paul. **Ferdinand,** 1876–   *3604.187.17
Hume's Lehre vom Wissen.
(In Wundt. Philosophische Studien. Band 17, pp. 624-673. Leip-
zig, 1901.)

         Aug. 27,   1903
F576 — Hume, David. — Knowledge.

NL 0388784   MB

---

142   Linke, Paul Ferdinand, 1876–
L756p   Die phänomenale Sphäre und das reale
Bewusstsein; eine Studie zur phänomeno-
logischen Betrachtungsweise. Halle
a.d.S., M. Niemeyer, 1912.
     iv, 50p. 20cm.

1. Phenomenology. I. Title.

NL 0388785   CLSU OU NjP MH

Linke, Paul, Ferdinand, 1876–
   Die stroboskopischen erscheinungen als
täuschungen des identitätsbewusstseins und das
problem des sehens von bewegungen ... Leipzig,
W. Engelmann, 1907.
   159 [1] p. illus. 22.5 cm.
   Pro venia legendi – Jena.
   Abhandlung – Jena.
   "Sonderdruck aus Wundt, 'Psycholog. Studien III.
Bd. 5/6 Heft."

NL 0388786   CtY NN

Linke, Paul, Ferdinand, 1876–
   Die stroboskopischen erscheinungen als täuschungen
des identitätsbewusstseins und das problem des sehens
von bewegungen ... Leipzig, W. Engelmann, 1907.
   159, [1] p. illus. 22½cm.
   Pro venia legendi–Jena.

1. Sight. 2. Hallucinations and illusions.

                       10-3425
Library of Congress   QP481.L7

NL 0388787   DLC NjP CU OU PU FU ICRL ICJ

Linke, Paul Ferdinand, 1876–
   Verstehen, erkennen und geist; zur philosophie der psycho-
logisch-geisteswissenschaftlichen betrachtungsweise, von Paul
F. Linke ... Leipzig, Akademische verlagsgesellschaft m. b. h.,
1936.
   2 p. l., 44 p. 23cm.
   "Diese arbeit ist zugleich im 'Archiv für die gesamte psychologie'
band 97, heft 1/2 (Wirth-festschrift) ... veröffentlicht."

1. Knowledge, Theory of. 2. Methodology. I. Title.

Library of Congress   BD163.L5   40-10264
                                      121

NL 0388788   DLC CU

Linke (Paul Friedrich) [1869–   ]. *Neun-
zehn Fälle von Tubargravidität.   39 pp., 1 l.
8°.   Berlin, E. Ebering, [1898].

NL 0388789   DNLM

Linke, Reinhold Hermann
      see Linke, Hermann, 1894–

Linke, Robert
   ... Wohlfahrtswesen von dr. jur. Robert
Linke ... Wien, Manz, 1942.
   viii, 140 p. 21cm. (Schriftenreihe verwaltung der Alpen- und Donau-reichsgaue,
bd. 4)
   "Schrifttum": p. 126-127.

NL 0388791   MH-L

PA   Linke, Robert, *philologist.*
   De particulae ... significatione affirmativa apud
Sophoclem. Dissertatio...
Halis Saxonum... 1873
   42 p.

NL 0388792   DLC PU NjP

LINKE, Rudolf.
   Anleitung zum bau und zur bewirtschaftung
von teich-anlagen, von Rudolf Linke... und
Ingenieur Friedrich Paul Böhm. ....Mit zahlzeichen abbildungen. [Dresden, C. Engelmann,
n. d.]
   2 p.1, 92 p. Illus. 26 1/2 cm.

NL 0388793   MH

LINKE, Rudolf.
   Anleitung zum bau und zur bewirtschaftung
von teichanlagem, von Rudolf Linke... und Ingenieur Friedrich Paul Böhm.... Mit 81 abbildungen im texte. Neudamm, Verlag von J. Neumann,
1908.
   2 p.1., 92 p. Illus. 26 cm.

NL 0388794   MH

            1890–
Linke, Rudolf, bacc. iur.: Der Aufführungsagenturvertrag.
   Borna-Leipzig 1913: Noske. VIII, 79 S. 8°
Leipzig, Jur. Diss. v. 10. Dez. 1913
   [Geb. 20. Nov. 90 Glauchau i. Sa.; Wohnort: Glauchau; Staatsangeh.:
   Sachsen; Vorbildung: G. Chemnitz Reife 10; Studium: Kiel 1, München 1,
   Heidelberg 1, Leipzig 4 S.; Rig. 8. Juli 13.]   [U 13. 1037]

NL 0388795   ICRL

            1886–
Linke, Walter: Das gotische Markusevangelium. Ein Beitrag
   zur Quellenkritik und Textgeschichte. Kiel 1920: Jebens.
   VII, 209 S. 8°
Kiel, Phil. Diss. v. 1. März 1920, Ref. Kauffmann
   [Geb. 3. Febr. 86 Berlin; Wohnort: Kiel; Staatsangeh.: Preußen; Vorbildung:
   Lessing-G. Berlin Reife 07; Studium: Berlin 3, Kiel 15 S.; Rig. 8. Juli 16.]
                                       [U 20. 3718]

NL 0388796   ICRL MiU MH ICU NRU OCl CtY RPB

Linke, Werner.
   Handbuch des Handwerks; Meisterprüfung und Meisterwissen in Frage und Antwort. 2. Aufl. Schloss Bleckede
a. d. Elbe, O. Meissner, 1949.
   350 p. 21 cm.
   First ed. published in 1947 under title: Die Meisterprüfung in
Frage und Antwort.

1. Artisans—Germany—Handbooks, manuals, etc.   I. Title.
II. Title: Meisterprüfung und Meisterwissen in Frage und Antwort.
   HD2346.G3L5 1949   338.64   50-27299

NL 0388797   DLC

Linke, Werner, 1907–
   Neue messungen zur aerodynamik des
zylinders, insbesondere seines reinen
reibungswiderstandes. Leipzig, A. Pries, 1931
   Inaugural-dissertation – Leipzig.
   "Sonderdruck der Physikalischen zeitschrift.
32. jahrgang, 1931, nr. 22, s. 900-914."
   "Lebenslauf", p. 18.

NL 0388798   MH ICRL CtY

Linke, Wilhelm.
   Anlage und Betrieb eines modernen Emaillierwerkes, von
Ing. Wilh. Linke... Dresden: "Die Glashütte", 1925. viii,
196 p. illus., plans. 2. ed. 8°
   p. 165-196, advertising matter.

262013A. 1. Enamelling.   November 9. 1926

NL 0388799   NN

Linke, Wilhelm,
   Der hopfenbau
      see Linke, Willi.

VOLUME 334

Linke, Wilhelm
　　Hopfenanbaugebiet ...
　　　see　Linke, Willi.

Linke (Wilhelm). *Zwei Fälle von primärem
Carcinom der prolabirten Vagina. 33 pp., 1 pl.
8°. Jena, G. Neuenhahn, 1895.

NL 0388802　　DNLM ICRL

Ref
DD
491
.H235
L5
　　LINKE, Wilhelm, 1874-1929.
　　　Katalog der Leichenpredigten und sonstigen
　　Personalschriften des Staatsarchivs zu
　　Hannover. Nebst Ergaenzungen zu des Ver-
　　fassers Niedersaechsischer Familienkunde,
　　von Wilhelm Linke. Leipzig, Verlag Degener
　　& Co., Inh.: Oswald Spohr, 1931.
　　　276p. 24cm. (Sonderveroeffentlichungen der
　　Ostfaelischen Familienkundlichen Kommission, 7)

　　　1. Funeral sermons - Catalogs. 2. Saxony,

Lower - Genealogy. 3. Saxony, Lower -
Biography. I. Title. II. Hannover, Ger.
Staatsarchiv.

NL 0388804　　MH-AH InU

Linke, Wilhelm, 1874-1929.
　　Niedersächsische familienkunde; ein biographisches
verzeichnis auf grund der leichenpredigten und sonstigen
personalschriften der Königlichen bibliothek zu Hannover und anderer hannoverscher sammlungen, hrsg. von
Wilhelm Linke ... Hannover, E. Geibel, 1912.
　　4 p. l., 420 p., 1 l. 23½ᶜᵐ.

　　1. Saxony, Lower—Biog.—Dictionaries. 2. Saxony, Lower—Geneal.

　　　　　　　　　　　　　　　　　　　　　　　12–15165
　　Library of Congress　　　　DD491.H2L5

NL 0388805　　DLC MH

Linke, Willi.
　　Der hopfenbau, eine anleitung für praxis und unterricht über
anbau, pflege, schädlingsbekämpfung und ernte, von dr.-ing.
Willi Linke ... Mit 43 abbildungen und 10 tafeln. Berlin, P.
Parey, 1942.
　　viii, 239 p. illus. (incl. plans) diagrs. 22ᶜᵐ.

　　1. Hops. 2. Hops—Diseases and pests.
　　　　　　　　　　　　　　　　　　　　　　　45–30172
　　Library of Congress　　　　SB295.H8L53
　　　　　　　　　　　　　　　　　　　　　　　633.89

NL 0388806　　DLC

70
164
Ed.2
　　Linke, Willi.
　　　Der Hopfenbau. [2. erweiterte Aufl.]
　　Nürnberg, Carl [1950]
　　　345 p.

　　　1. Hops. 2. Hops, Germany.

NL 0388807　　DNAL

70
164
　　Linke, Willi.
　　　Hopfenanbaugebiet Hersbrucker Gebirge.
　　Nürnberg, Carl [1949]
　　　16 p.

　　　1. Hops. Hersbruck, Ger. I. Weigand,
　　Karl.

NL 0388808　　DNAL

Linke, Willi, 1910-
　　Untersuchungen über den fettgehalt der leber
bei kastrierten und mit follikel-, gelbkörper-
und hypophysenvorderlappenhormon behandelten
ratten. ... Bonn, 1938. 16 p.
　　Inaug. Diss. - Bonn, 1938.
　　Lebenslauf.
　　Literatur.

NL 0388809　　CtY

QD66
.S4
1940
　　Linke, William F., 1924-

　　　　　　　　　　　FOR OTHER EDITIONS
　　　　　　　　　　　SEE MAIN ENTRY

　　Seidell, Atherton, 1878-
　　　Solubilities of inorganic and metal organic compounds; a
compilation of quantitative solubility data from the periodical literature. 3d ed. New York, Van Nostrand, 1940-41.

NL 0388811　　NNU-W

LD3907
.G7
1948
.L5
　　Linke, William F 1924-
　　　Some aqueous solubility relation-
ships among the molybdates... New
York, 1948.
　　　, 128 typewritten leaves. tables,
diagrs. 29cm.
　　　Thesis (Ph.D.) - New York Universi-
ty, Graduate School, 1948.
　　　Bibliography: p.126-128.

TK 1141
L 56
　　Linke, Willy, 1880-1918.
　　　Technik der Wechselströme u. Mehrphasen-
ströme mit Berücksichtigung der wichtigsten
Messmethoden. Berlin, Buchhandlung der Lit-
terarischen Monatsberichte, 1903.
　　　v. (Studium der Elektrotechnik in
Theorie und Praxis)

　　　1. Electric currents, Alternating.

NL 0388812　　MoSW NNCoCi

4PT
Ger.
-5096
　　Linke, Wolf, 1922-
　　　Wettlauf ins Nichts; Atomforschung am
Scheidewege, ein Roman. Gütersloh, C.
Bertelsmann [1950]
　　　390 p.
　　　Verlag C. Bertelsmann, Gütersloh; 10 Jan 50;
AFO-1070.

NL 0388813　　DLC-P4 IU

1886-
Linke, Wolfgang, Zahnarzt: Ueber Spontanfrakturen des Unter-
kiefers. Aus d. Abt. f. Zahn- u. Kieferersatz d. zahnärztl.
Inst. d. Univ. Berlin. [In Maschinenschrift.] 72 S. 4°(2°). —
Auszug: o. O. (1920). 3 Bl. 8°
Berlin, Med. Diss. v. 28. Okt. 1920, Ref. Schröder
[Geb. 29. Nov. 86 Schweidnitz; Wohnort: Charlottenburg; Staatsangeh.: Preußen;
Vorbildung: G. Schweidnitz Reife 05; Studium: Berlin 8 S.; Coll. 26. Okt. 20;
Zahnärztl. Approb. 16. Febr. 19.]　　　　　　[U 20. 1362

NL 0388814　　ICRL

40.2
164
　　Linke-Crawford, Emmi.
　　　Angora die lohnendste Kaninchenzucht.
　　Wien, 1953.
　　　104 p.

　　　1. Angora rabbits.

NL 0388815　　DNAL

Linke Poot, pseud.
　　See
Doeblin, Alfred, 1878-1957.

Linke-Hofmann-Lauchhammer, Aktiengesellschaft.
　　200 Jahre Lauchhammer, 1725-1925. [1925]
　　105 p. illus., plates, ports., facsims.

NL 0388817　　NNC MH

Linke-Hofmann Werke Aktiengesellschaft.
　　Festschrift zum 50jährigen Jubiläum der
Linke-Hofmannwerke Aktiengesellschaft.
Breslau, Cöln, Ehrenfeld, Warmbrunn.
[Breslau? 1921?]
　　100 p. illus., plates, ports.

　　On cover: Linke-Hofmann Werke, 1871-1921.

NL 0388818　　MH-AH NNC

Linke Kommunisten.
　　Die Aufgaben der linken Kommunisten; Beschlüsse der
Reichskonferenz der Linken Kommunisten zur Vorbereitung der
Gründung des Leninbundes... [Berlin, 1928.] 40 p. 24°.
("Fahne des Kommunismus." Flugschriften.)
　　Cover-title.

584407A. 1. Bolshevism—Germany.
　　　　　　　　　　　　　　　　　　　　　　　June 6, 1932

NL 0388819　　NN

Ger 8105.17
Linkemeyer, Carl
　　Hamburg im Zeichen des Krummstabes; Studien aus dem
Mittelalter. Hamburg, Lettenbauer, 1926
　　604 p. illus.

NL 0388820　　MH

Linkenbach, Carl, 1842-
　　Die aufbereitung der erze. Handbuch für ausübende und
angehende berg-ingenieure, von C. Linkenbach ... Mit 24
lithographirten tafeln. Berlin, J. Springer, 1887.
　　xii, 152 p. xxiv fold. pl., v tab. on fold. l. 27½ᶜᵐ.

　　1. Ore-dressing.　ɪ. Title.
　　　　　　　　　　　　　　　　　　　　　　　37–37883
　　Library of Congress　　　　TN500.L5
　　　　　　　　　　　　　　　　　　　　　　　622.7

NL 0388821　　DLC CU ICJ MiHM

Linkenbach, Baldur
　　Das prinzip des tragischen. ... Würzburg, 1933.
　　110 p.
　　Inaug. Diss. - Bonn, 1933.
　　Lebenslauf.

NL 0388822　　ICRL PU NcU CtY

VOLUME 334

622.7
L64aFc   Linkenbach, Carl, 1842–
    Traité pratique de la préparation des minerais;
    manuel à l'usage des practiciens et des ingéni-
    eurs des mines. Traduit de l'allemand par H.
    Coutrot.   Paris, Baudry, 1893.
    xiv, 158p. 24 plates. 28cm.

    1. Ore-dressing.

NL 0388823   IU

Linkenbach, Hans Ludwig, 1876–1939.
    Johanniswunder, ein festspiel zur Gutenbergfeier in Mainz;
    von Hans Ludwig Linkenbach. Mainz, Verlag der Gutenberg-
    gesellschaft, 1932.
    4 p. l., ₁11₁–24 p., 1 l. 21½ᵐ. ₁Kleiner druck der Gutenberg-gesell-
    schaft. XVIII₁

    1. Gutenberg, Johannes, 1397?–1468—Drama. I. Title.

Library of Cong   Z126.Z7L7   33–11643
                                          832.91

NNC NjP MB NN
NL 0388824   DLC NNC MB NjP CSt NN NNGr MiU NIC CSmH

831.08
L75n   Linkenbach, Hans Ludwig, 1876–1939.
        comp.
        Nassauisches dichterbuch. Leip-
        zig, Kesselringsche hofbuchhandlung,
        1908.
        154p. plates. O.

NL 0388825   IaU

Linkenbach, Hans Ludwig, 1876–1939.
    The miracle of John Gutenberg; a festival
    play for the Gutenberg celebration in Mainz.
    Translated from the German by John Charles
    Tarr. ₁Chiswick₁ Chiswick Polytechnic School
    of Art ₁1932₁
    18 p. 28cm.

    "Originally published by the Gutenberg So-
    ciety under the title "Johanniswunder", as
    Number XVIII of the Kleiner Druck ..."

NL 0388826   NNC

W 4
M22
1952   LINKENBACH, Heinz, 1924–
        Der Blutdruck bei Asthma bronchiale,
        unter Berücksichtigung der Vital-
        Kapazität. ₁Mainz₁ 1952.
        37 ℓ.
        Inaug.-Diss. - Mainz.
        1. Asthma

NL 0388827   DNLM

1891–
Linkenbach, Max, Arzt: Ueber die zerstückelnden geburtshilflichen Operationen unt. Benutzung d. Materials d. Mar-
burger Frauenkl. v. 1911–1919. [In Maschinenschrift.]
70, II S. m. 8 Tab. 4º(2º). — Auszug: Marburg 1920: Hamel.
6 S. 8º
Marburg, Med. Diss. v. 15. Sept. 1920 [1921], Ref. Zange-
meister
₁Geb. 8. Sept. 91 Bad Ems; Wohnort: Marburg; Staatsangeh.: Preußen; Vorbildung: G. Koblenz Reife 11; Studium: Freiburg 4, Kiel 1, Freiburg 2,
Marburg 2 S.; Coll. 24. Sept. 19; Approb. 30. Juli 19.₁   [U 21. 5010

NL 0388828   ICRL

Linkenheimer, Wayne Henry.
    Effects of trauma and stress on tissue sulfhydryl. Ann
Arbor, University Microfilms ₁1954₁
    (₁University Microfilms, Ann Arbor, Mich.₁ Publication no. 8902)
    Microfilm copy of typescript. Positive.
    Collation of the original: 90 l. diagrs., tables.
    Thesis—University of Pittsburgh.
    Abstracted in Dissertation abstracts, v. 14 (1954) no. 9, p. 1443.
    Bibliography: leaves ₁85₁–90.

    1. Mercaptans. 2. Traumatism.   I. Title: Tissue sulfhydryl.

Microfilm AC–1 no. 8902   Mic A 56–

Pittsburgh. Univ. Libr.
for Library of Congress   †

NL 0388829   PiU DLC

Law   Linkenheld, ————, ministerialrat.

Rutz, Karl, ed.
    Die Reichsfürsorgepflicht-verordnung und die dazu gelten-
den ausführungsbestimmungen, mit besonderer berücksichtigung der süd- und mitteldeutschen länder mit mitwirkung
von oberregierungsrat dr. Schühly ... ministerialrat Linkenheld ₁u. a.₁ ... erläutert von Karl Rutz ... München, Beck, 1930.

Linkenheld, Friedrich Philipp Lothar, 1877–
    see Linkenheld, Fritz, 1877–

Linkenheld, Fritz, 1877–
    Zur casuistik der geschwuelste der schaedeldecken.
    Inaug. diss. Giessen, 1902.
    34 p.

NL 0388832   ICRL MBCo DNLM

Linkenheld, Lothar
    ————. Die locale Anwendung des Wiesbadener
    Kochbrunnenwassers in Form von Inhalationen,
    Gargelungen und Nasenspülungen bei den
    Erkrankungen des Halses und der Nase. 1 p. l.,
    24 pp. 12º. *Wiesbaden, H. Lützenkirchen,* 1894.

NL 0388833   DNLM

Linkenheld (Lothar). *Ueber primär von
den Beckenknochen ausgehende Myxome und
Myxo-Sarcome.* [Wurzburg.] 18 pp. 8º.
Köln, A. Seehl, 1895.

NL 0388834   DNLM ICRL

M-Q111
C75
1954   Linker, Alfred, 1919–
        The enzymatic breakdown of hyaluronic acid.
        New York, 1954.
        95 l. tables. (Columbia University.
        Faculty of Pure Science. Dissertations)

        Bibliographical footnotes.

        1. Hyaluronic acid. I. Series.

NL 0388835   NNC

Linker, Alfred, 1919–
    The enzymatic breakdown of hyaluronic acid. Ann
Arbor, University Microfilms ₁1954₁
    (₁University Microfilms, Ann Arbor, Mich.₁ Publication no. 8718)
    Microfilm copy of typescript. Positive.
    Collation of the original: 95 l. diagrs., tables.
    Thesis—Columbia University.
    Abstracted in Dissertation abstracts, v. 14 (1954) no. 9, p. 1301.
    Bibliographical footnotes.

    1. Uronic acids. 2. Hyaluronidase.   I. Title.

Microfilm AC–1 no. 8718   Mic A 55–3365

Columbia Univ.   Libraries
for Library of Congress   †

NL 0388836   NNC DLC

Linker, Arthur
    see
    Linker, Paul Benjamin Arthur, 1874–1949.

W 4
M22
1951   LINKER, Gertrude Auguste, 1923–
        Medikamentöse Geburtseinleitung.
        ₁Mainz₁ 1951.
        41 ℓ. illus.
        Inaug.-Diss. - Mainz.
        1. Hormones 2. Labor

NL 0388838   DNLM

Linker, Gustav
    see Linker, Gustav Wilhelm Reinhard,
    1827–

LINKER, Gustav Wilhelm Reinhard, 1827–
    Die älteste sagengeschichte Roms ein
    vortrag gehalten am 20. märz 1858 im grossen
    ständischen saale zu Wien. Wien, C. Gerold's
    sohn, 1858.

    Cover serves as title-page.

NL 0388840   MH PU OC1

Linker, Gustav Wilhelm Reinhard, 1827–
    Emendationen zu Sallust auf Grund seiner
    Quellen und Nachahmer. Wien, 1854.
    34 p.

NL 0388841   PU

Linker, Gustav. Wilhelm Reinhard, 1827–
    Emendationes Vergilianae. Liegnitz, 1886.

NL 0388842   PU

Linker, Gustav Wilhelm Reinhard, 1927–
    Horatius. Vindobonae, 1858.
    p. 5–14.

NL 0388843   ICU

Linker, Gustav Wilhelm Reinhard, 1827–
    Quaestiones Horatianae. Pragae, 1877.
    (v. 23, pt. 11 of PTT 2865. 73)

NL 0388844   NjP ICU

Linker, Gustav. Wilhelm Reinhard, 1827–   *3340.3.10
    Ueber die Wahl des altrömischen Praefectus urbis feriarum Latina-
    rum.
    (In Kaiserliche Akademie der Wissenschaften, Vienna. Philo-
    sophisch-historische Classe. Sitzungsberichte. Band 10, pp. 7–
    28. Wien. 1853.)

H5678 — Rome, Pol. hist. — Praefectus urbis feriarum Latinarum.

NL 0388845   MB MH

VOLUME 334

ar V
516
Linker, Hans Willi, 1896–
Kleine Welt im Herbst, Junger Zweig im
Schnee. Bremen, Walter Dorn, [c1947]
103 p. 20cm.

NL 0388846 NIC

4PT
Ger.
346
[Linker, Hans Willi] 1896–
Singular in Spielswinkel [von] Hans Willi Linker
Cottbus, A. Heine, 1938.
232 p.

NL 0388847 DLC-P4

Linker, Hans Willi, 1896–
Spiel in Flandern, eine Novelle aus dem grossen Kriege.
Gütersloh, C. Bertelsmann [c1936]
63 p. 16 cm. (Das Kleine Buch, Nr. 33)

1. European War, 1914–1918—Fiction.   I. Title.
Full name: Johannes Wilhelm Heinrich Linker.
PT2623.I 635S6   1936   50–46051

NL 0388848 DLC

Linker, Hans Willi, 1896–
... Spiel in Flandern; eine novelle aus dem grossen kriege.
Gütersloh, C. Bertelsmann [1943]
54, [1] p. illus. 18 cm.
"Mit holzschnitten von Siegfr. Kortemeier."

I. Title.
Full name: Johannes Wilhelm Heinrich Linker.
PT2623.I 636S6 1943   833.91   A 46–3480
Lehigh Univ. Library
for Library of Congress   [a56r50e½]†

OrU RPB TxU IaU DLC
NL 0388849   PBL MB DLC CU CoU GAT CtY MiU UU ScU

Linker, Hans Willi, 1896–
... Spiel in Flandern; eine novelle aus dem grossen kriege.
Gütersloh, C. Bertelsmann [1946?]
66, [1] p. illus. 18ᵐ.
Author's pseud., Hans Willi Linker, at head of title.
"Mit holzschnitten von Siegfr. Kortemeier."
"7. auflage."

NL 0388850 ViU

Linker, Hans Willi, 1896–
Spel in Vlaanderen, novelle uit den grooten oorlog. Met
teekeningen van Nelly Degouy. Brussel, Uitgeverij Steen-
landt [1942]
60 p. illus. 19 cm.

I. Title.
Full name: Johannes Wilhelm Heinrich Linker.
PT2623.I 636S62   A F 50–137 rev
California. Univ. Libr.
for Library of Congress   [r55b½]†

NL 0388851 CU CtY DLC

917.298
L756b
Linker, J   Dutch photograph.
Beautiful souvenirs of joyous days; a
collection of photographs of the visit of Her
Royal Highness Princess Juliana to the
Netherlands West Indies and Venezuela,
February 26th–March 5th, 1944. Photographs
by J. Linker. Text by F. v. Tilburg.
Curaçao, "St. Augustine" Booksellers [1945]
1 v. (chiefly illus.) 22x28cm.
Title page also in Dutch.
Text in Dutch.

NL 0388852 FU

Linker, Johannes Wilhelm Heinrich
see Linker, Hans Willi, 1896–

AC
8..
Linker, Josef, 1910–
Subjektive und objektive tendenzen in der
einkommensbesteuerung. ... 125 p.
Inaug. Diss. – Berlin, [1934]
Lebenslauf.
Bibliography.

NL 0388854 ICRL CtY

Linker, Joseph Burton, 1897–
Archibald Henderson.

(In Charlotte observer.   June 11, 1922.)

NL 0388855 NcU

Linker, Joseph Burton, 1897–   joint author.

Hill, Michael Arendell, 1898–   FOR OTHER EDITIONS
Brief course in analytics [by] M. A. Hill, Jr. [and] J. B.   SEE MAIN ENTRY
Linker. Rev. ed. New York, Holt [1951]

Linker, Joseph Burton.
Calculation of symmetric functions,
Chapel Hill, 1920.

NL 0388857 NcU

Linker, Joseph Burton, 1897–   joint author.

Hill, Michael Arendell, 1898–
First year college mathematics, by M. A. Hill, jr. ... and
J. Burton Linker ... New York, H. Holt and company [c1936]

QA37
.H533
1955
Linker, Joseph Burton, 1897–   joint author.
          FOR OTHER EDITIONS
Hill, Michael Arendell, 1898–   SEE MAIN ENTRY
Introduction to college mathematics [by] M. A. Hill, Jr.
and J. Burton Linker. Rev. ed. New York, Holt [1955]

Linker, Joseph Burton, 1897–
Mathematics of finance [by] J. B. Linker and M. A. Hill,
Jr. New York, H. Holt [1948]
viii, 175, 83 p. tables. 22 cm.

1. Business mathematics.   I. Hill, Michael Arendell, 1898–
joint author.
HF5691.L5   511.8   48—2598*

NL 0388860 DLC OrP CU IU NcU

Linker, Julius, 1907–
Die reichsaufsicht über die finanzen der länder
und gemeinden. ... Marburg, 1933.   65 p.
Inaug. Diss. – Marburg, 1933.
Lebenslauf.
Bibliography.

NL 0388861 ICRL CtY

HF1558
L756
Linker, Ludwig, 1905–
Der Umfang der Exterritorialität mit besondere
Berücksichtigung der sowjetrussischen Handels-
vertretungen. Würzburg, Druck von Gebrüder
Memminger, 1929.
viii, 71 p. 21ᶜᵐ.
Inaug.-Diss.–Würzburg.
Lebenslauf.
"Literatur-Verzeichnis": p.vi-viii.

1.Russia - Commerical policy. 2.Russia -
Commerce - Germa[ny]. 3.Germany - Com-
merce - Russia.   4.Exterritoriality.
I.Title.

NL 0388862 CSt-H CtY

Linker, Paul Benjamin Arthur, 1874–1949.
Elektromaschinenbau; berechnung elektrischer ma-
schinen in theorie und praxis, von dr.-ing. P. B. Arthur
Linker ... Mit 128 textfiguren und 14 anlagen. Berlin,
J. Springer, 1925.
2 p. l., [iii]-viii, 304 p. illus., diagrs. 23½ᶜᵐ.
"Anlagen" in pocket.

1. Electric motors—Design and construction. 2. Dynamos—Design and
construction.   I. Title.
Library of Congress   TK2331.L5   26–7852

NL 0388863 DLC CaBVaU ICJ MiU ICJ

Linker, Paul Benjamin Arthur, 1874–1949.   537.7 Q600
Elektrotechnische Messkunde von Arthur Linker, ... Mit 385
in den Text gedruckten Figuren. Berlin, J. Springer, 1906.
viii, 442 p. 385 illus. incl. diagrs. 21ᶜᵐ.
"Literaturnachweis," p. [438].

NL 0388864 ICJ NjP CU NN DBS

Linker, Paul Benjamin Arthur, 1874–1949.   537.7 R201
Elektrotechnische Messkunde. Von Dr.-Ing. P. B. Arthur Linker. Zweite, völlig umgearbeitete und verbesserte Auflage. Mit
380 in den Text gedruckten Figuren. Berlin, J. Springer, 1912.
xv, 533, [1] p. incl. tables, 380 diagr. 21ᶜᵐ.
Bibliographische "Anmerkungen", p. [xiv]-xv.

NL 0388865 ICJ NN MiU NjR

Linker, Paul Benjamin Arthur, 1874–1949.
Elektrotechnische messkunde, von ... P. B.
Arthur Linker. 3., völlig umgearb. und erweiterte
aufl. Mit 408 textfiguren. Berlin, Springer,
1920.
xii, 571 p. diagrs. 21 cm.

Bibliographical foot-notes.

NL 0388866 NNCoCi DBS

Linker, Paul Benjamin Arthur, 1874–1949.
Elektrotechnische messkunde, von dr.-ing. P. B. Arthur
Linker ... Vierte völlig umgearbeitete und erweiterte auflage,
mit 450 textabbildungen. Berlin, Julius Springer, 1932.
x, 619, [1] p. diagrs. 21ᶜᵐ.
Bibliographical foot-notes.

1. Electric measurements.   I. Title.
N. Y. Public library   A 32–2543
for Library of Congress   QC535.L47 1932
Copyright A—Foreign   18707
          [a37b1]   537.7

NL 0388867 NN

VOLUME 334

621.312　Linker, Paul Benjamin Arthur, 1874-1949.
L64g　　Grundlagen der wechselstromtheorie ...
　　　　Berlin, 1928.
　　　　245p.　tables, diagrs.

NL　0388868　　IU

Linker, Paul Benjamin Arthur, 1874-1949.
　　Die hauptsächlichsten elektrischen Messinstrumente.　Berlin: O. Dreyer (pref. 1904).　2 p.l., 73 p.　8°.

1. Engineering (Electrical).　　　2. Electricity.—Measurement,
1910.　　　　　　　　　　　　　　　　　1910.
　　　　　　N. Y. PUBLIC LIBRARY　January 19, 1911.

NL　0388869　　NN

Linker, Paul Benjamin Arthur, 1874-1949.　537.7 Q50I
Die hauptsächlichsten elektrischen Messinstrumente, von A. Linker, ...　Mit 74 Abbildungen.　Berlin-Steglitz, Buchhandlung der Litterarischen Monatsberichte, 1905.
[6], 73 p.　74 illus.　22½ᶜᵐ.　(Added t.-p.: Das Studium der Elektrotechnik in Theorie und Praxis. ... .)

NL　0388870　　ICJ

Linker, Paul Benjamin Arthur, 1874-1949.
Die historische entwicklung...
Inaug. Diss.　Karlsruhe, 1907　(Berlin)

NL　0388871　　ICRL PPF

4QC
516　　Linker, Paul Benjamin Arthur, 1874-1949.
　　　1874-
　　　Praktische Elektrizitätslehre;
　　　auf der Grundlage der Elektronen-
　　　theorie dargestellt.　Mit 79 Abbil-
　　　dungen.　Hagen (Westf.), Kommissions-
　　　verlag: O. Hammerschmidt, 1921.
　　　199 p.

NL　0388872　　DLC-P4

Linker, Paul Benjamin Arthur, 1874-1949.
Tratado de medidas eléctricas, por el Dr.-Ing. P. B. Arturo Linker.　Traducido de la 3. ed. alemana por Conrado Meisterhans ...　Con 408 figuras.　Barcelona, L. Gili, 1927.
xii, 579 p.　tables, diagrs.　21ᶜᵐ.

1. Electric measurements.　　I. Meisterhans, Conrado, tr.　II. Title.
　　　　　　　　　　　　　　　　　　　　　　　27-22332
Library of Congress　　QC535.L5 1927

NL　0388873　　DLC

Linker, Robert White, ed.

PQ1426
.A3L5　**Aucassin et Nicolette.**
　　　Aucassin et Nicolete, ed. by Robert White Linker.　Chapel Hill, Univ. of North Carolina Press (1948)

Linker, Robert White, joint ed.

Maurois, André, 1885-
　　... Climats; abridged and edited with introduction, notes and vocabulary by W. L. Wiley and R. W. Linker ...　New York, H. Holt and company (1936)

Linker, Robert White.
(Du Bartas' La première sepmaine and Pliny's Naturalis historiae.　Chapel Hill, N. C., 1928.

NL　0388876　　NcU

Linker, Robert White.
M2
.A535F7
Apel, Willi, 1893-　　*ed.*
　　French secular music of the late fourteenth century. Edition of the literary texts by Robert W. Linker and Urban T. Holmes, Jr.; with foreword by Paul Hindemith.　Cambridge, Mass., Mediaeval Academy of America, 1950.

Linker, Robert White, ed.
PQ1573
.A1
1950　**Pathelin.**
　　　Maistre Pierre Pathelin, edited by Robert White Linker. Chapel Hill, N. C., Book Exchange, 1950.

Linker, Robert White.
　　A mediaeval Italian anthology
　　　see under　Barrett, Linton Lomas, ed.

Linker, Robert White, *ed.*
　　A Provençal anthology, by Robert White Linker.　Columbus, O., H. L. Hedrick (1940)
　　104 p.　23ᶜᵐ.
　　Reproduced from type-written copy.

1. Provençal poetry (Collections)　I. Title.
　　　　　　　　　　　　　　　　　　　　41-20236
Library of Congress　　PC3323.L5
　　　　　　　　　　　　　　　　849.10822

NL　0388880　　DLC OU CU-I FU MsSM

Linker, Robert White, tr.
PQ1447
.E5L5
Chrestien de Troyes, *12th cent.*
　　The story of the Grail.　Translated by Robert White Linker.　Chapel Hill (N. C.) Book Exchange, 1952.

Linker, Robert White, joint ed.

Du Bartas, Guillaume de Salluste, *seigneur*, 1544-1590.
　　The works of Guillaume de Salluste, sieur Du Bartas, a critical edition with introduction, commentary, and variants ... by Urban Tigner Holmes, jr., John Coriden Lyons, Robert White Linker, with the assistance of others ...　Chapel Hill. The University of North Carolina press, 1935-

---

Linker, Wilhelm
　　see　Linker, Hans Willi, 1896-

Linker, William M., Jr.　　Chapel Hill, 1925.
Regularity of learning in a multiple unit maze.

NL　0388884　　NcU

LINKERMANN, Gustav, 1901-
　　Vergleichende untersuchungen über die bodenphosphorsäure.　Inaug.-diss., Halle-Wittenberg.　Halle '(Saale), [etc.], G. Reichardt, 1926.
　　pp.54-.　Tables.
　　"Lebenslauf", at end.

NL　0388885　　MH ICRL

Linkert, Lothar.
　　Die verbogene Seelenachse.　(Frankfurt a. M.) G. Ammelburg, 1954 (i. e. 1955)
　　48 p. (chiefly illus.)　15 x 21 cm.

1. German wit and humor, Pictorial.　I. Title.
NC1509.L5A5　　　　　　　　　55-28115 ‡

NL　0388886　　DLC MH

Linkholt, Fritz Schulz-
see
Schulz-Linkholt, Fritz.

Linkholt, Heinrich, 1906-
　　Der nachweis der eutertuberkulose durch die komplementbindungsmethode... 1933.
　　47 p.

NL　0388888　　DNAL

Law　　Linkhorst, Kurt, 1907-　ed.

　　Germany (*Democratic Republic, 1949-*)　*Laws, statutes, etc.*
　　Baurecht; bearb. von Kurt Linkhorst.　Berlin, Deutscher Zentralverlag (1953-

---

Linkhorst, Kurt, 1907-
　　Die rechtsstellung der betriebsvertretungen
　　Inaug. Diss.　Greifswald, 1931.
　　Bibl.

NL　0388890　　ICRL MiU

Linkiewicz, Joh.
　　Case of the eight Nazi saboteurs.　New York, The author, 1942.
　　4 p.

NL　0388891　　NN

Linkin, Larry R　　　arr.
　　Prelude et scherzo pour flute et piano, op. 35
　　　see under　Busser, Henri, 1872-

The Linking ring.　v. 1-
　　(Jan. 1923?)-
　　(Bluffton, Ohio, etc.)
　　v. in　illus., ports.　23-28 cm.　monthly (irregular)
　　Vol. 1, no. 1-2 undated.
　　Official publication of the International Brotherhood of Magicians.

1. Conjuring—Period.　I. International Brotherhood of Magicians.
GV1541.L5　　　　　　　　　57-48103

NL　0388893　　DLC

VOLUME 334

Linking school work with business enterprises.
(*In* National education association of the United States. Journal of proceedings and addresses, 1915. p. 903-925)

1. Business education.

E 16-734

Library, U. S. Bur. of   Education

NL 0388894   DHEW

Linking science and industry. [A collective work]
see under   Metcalf, Henry Clayton, 1867-

Linking the past with the present; Early ship-building and Benedict Arnold, by Observer.
2 *l.* (typewritten)

NL 0388896   MiD-B

Linking up the state
see under   Darling River Railway League.

Linkinwater, Tim, *pseud.*
see
Waldo, James Curtis, 1835-1901.

Linkius, Johannes Georgius
see   Link, Johann George, respondent.

Linklater, ___ **Elizabeth (Young)**
A child under sail, by Elizabeth Linklater; with a fore-word by Eric Linklater. London, J. Cape ₍1938₎
222 p. 20½ᶜᵐ.
"First published, February 1938 ... Third impression, March 1938."

1. Seafaring life. 2. Voyages and travels. I. Title.

Library of Congress   G540.L65 1938 b   38-31268
                 910.4

NL 0388900   DLC CaBVaU WaS TxU

LINKLATER, ELIZABETH (YOUNG)
A child under sail. With a foreword by Eric Linklater. London, J. Cape [1938] 222 p. 21cm.

Film reproduction. Positive.

l. Sea life. 2. Voyages and travels, 1875-1900.

NL 0388901   NN

Linklater, Mrs. Elizabeth (Young)
A child under sail, by Elizabeth Linklater; with a foreword by Eric Linklater. New York, Toronto, Farrar & Rhinehart ₍1938₎
222 p. 20½cm.

1. Seafaring life. 2. Voyages and travels. I. Title.

NL 0388902   AU

Linklater, Elizabeth (Young)
A child under sail. With a foreword by Eric Linklater. London, R. Hart-Davis, 1949.
232 p. front. 20 cm. (The Mariners library, 2)

1. Seafaring life. 2. Voyages and travels. I. Title. (Series)

G540.L65 1949   910.4   50-18361

NL 0388903   DLC CaBViP MB

Linklater, Eric, 1899-
Angelo buon diavolo; romanzo. ₍Traduzione dall'inglese di Elena Gasparini. 1. ed. Milano₎ Mondadori, 1947.
245 p. 20 cm. (Medusa; i grandi narratori d'ogni paese, 190)
Translation of Private Angelo.

I. Title.
                Full name: Eric Robert Russell Lindlater.

PR6023.I 582P76   50-27809

NL 0388904   DLC

Linklater, Eric, 1899-
Angelo, gewoon soldaat. ₍Geautoriseerde vertaling uit het Engels van W. A. Fick-Lugten₎ Amsterdam, Van Holkema & Warendorf ₍1947₎
277 p. 20 cm.
Translation of Private Angelo.

I. Title.
                Full name: Eric Robert Russell Linklater.

PR6023.I 582P73   48-25337*‡

NL 0388905   DLC CaBVaU

Linklater, Eric, 1899-
Angelo; roman picaresque, traduit de l'anglais par Cecile Seresia. Bruxelles, De Visscher, 1947.
336 p. 19 cm. (Collection extra muros)
Translation of Private Angelo.

I. Title.
                Full name: Eric Robert Russell Linklater.

PR6023.I 582P74   50-27808

NL 0388906   DLC

Linklater, Eric, 1899-
The art of adventure. London, Macmillan, 1947.
vii, 292 p. 20 cm.
CONTENTS.—General Alexander.—James Bridie.—Evelyn Waugh.—Trevie Napier.—Richard Hillary.—Mr. Berenson.—Robert Burns.—The married poet.—Jean Armour.—Dr. McGrigor.—The first attack.—The Atlantic garrisons.—The Rock.—H. M. S. Flint Castle.—Primavera.—The art of adventure.

1. Gt. Brit.—Biog. 2. World War, 1939-1945—Personal narratives, English. I. Title.
             Full name: Eric Robert Russell Linklater.
CT774.L5   920.042   A 48-5323*
Harvard Univ. Library
for Library of Congress   †

         FMU Or OrP PSt PPT OOxM NcGU CU NcRS OU TxU CtY DLC
NL 0388907   MH INS AU OrCS WaE Wa CaBVa CaBVaU MtU

PR6023
.I582A7 Linklater, Eric, 1899-
1948
     The art of adventure ₍essays₎ London, Macmillan, 1948.
     vii, 292 p. 20cm.

     CONTENTS.—Some people.—Some older people.—Some episodes.—The art of adventure.

     I. Title.
        Full name: Eric Robert Russell Linklater.

NL 0388908   ViU MB KU IdU WaT WaS CaBViP

Linklater, Eric, 1899-
Ben Jonson and King James; biography and portrait, by Eric Linklater. London, J. Cape ₍1931₎
328 p. front., plates, ports. 21 cm.
"First published 1931."

1. Jonson, Ben, 1573?-1637. 2. James I, king of Great Britain, 1566-1625. 3. Gt. Brit.—Court and courtiers.
            Full name: Eric Robert Russell Linklater.
PR2631.L5 1931   928.2   32—1334

     WaU NN MH NIC MsSM NcRS KEmT CaBVaU CaBViP OrU
NL 0388909   DLC WU TxU NBuU PPT PPL NcD MiU OCl OCU

Linklater, Eric, 1899-
Ben Jonson and King James; biography and portrait, by Eric Linklater. New York, J. Cape &, H. Smith, London, Toronto, J. Cape [1931?]
328 p. front., plates, ports. 21 cm.
First published 1931.
Printed in Great Britain.

NL 0388910   ViU GU TxU

Linklater, Eric.   2545·46
Ben Jonson and King James. Biography and portrait.
— New York. Cape & Smith. [1932.] 328 pp. Portraits. Plate. 20 cm., in 8s.

D256 — Jonson, Ben, 1573?-1637. — James I., of England, 1566-1625.

NL 0388911   MB NcD NN

Linklater, Eric, 1899-
Ben Jonson and King James ... London, J. Cape, 1937.

NL 0388912   MsU

        Linklater, Eric, 1899-
822.34
J81ZL   Ben Jonson and King James ... ₍new ed.₎ London, Jonathan Cape ₍1938₎
     328 p. front., plates. 23 cm.

     First published in 1931.

     1. Jonson, Ben, 1573?-1637. 2. James I, King of Great Britain, 1566-1625. 3. Gt. Brit. Court and Courtiers.

NL 0388913   NcD

Linklater, Eric, 1899-
The campaign in Italy. London, H. M. Stationery Off., 1951.
480 p. illus. 22 cm. (The Second World War, 1939-1945)

1. World War, 1939-1945—Campaigns—Italy.
          Full name: Eric Robert Russell Linklater.
D763.I 8L6   940.542   52-582 ‡

     NN TxU
NL 0388914   DLC CaBVa CaBViP CaBVaU OrU Wa WaT TU

VOLUME 334

Linklater, Eric, 1899–
La 51ᵐᵉ (Highland division) par Eric Linklater ... Londres, H. M. Stationery off., 1943.

96 p. illus. (maps) 19ᵐ. (L'Armée en guerre)

"Publié pour le Ministère de la guerre par le Ministère de l'information."

Text on p. ₍2₎ and ₍3₎ of cover.

1. World war, 1939– —Regimental histories—Gt. Brit.—51st (Highland) division. 2. Gt. Brit.—Army—51st (Highland) division. I. Title.

₍Full name: Eric Robert Russell Linklater₎

43–22567

Library of Congress   D759.5.51st.L52

940.541242

NL 0388915   DLC

Linklater, Eric, 1899–
The cornerstones; a conversation in Elysium, by Eric Linklater. London, Macmillan & co. ltd, 1941.

2 l., 84, ₍1₎ p. 19½ᵐ.

An imaginary conversation between Confucius, Lincoln, Lenin, a British airman and a soldier in which they demand that humanity in the present crisis be given a nobler purpose and more certain aim.

1. Imaginary conversations.   I. Title.

₍Full name: Eric Robert Russell Linklater₎

A 42–1247 Revised

Harvard univ. Libra
for Library of Congress   PR6023.I 582C6

₍r42c2₎†   828.91

NL 0388916   OrU InU   MH TxU LU GU NcD IEN ScU TU MB DLC NN

Linklater, Eric, 1899–
The cornerstones; a conversation in Elysium,
by Eric Linklater.   London, Macmillan & co. ltd.,
1941.
2 p.l., 84, [1] p.   19.5 cm.
"First edition, December 1941. Reprinted
December 1941."

NL 0388917   CtY

822.91 L382.5
Linklater, Eric, 1899–
The cornerstones: a conversation in Elysium,
by Eric Linklater. London, Macmillan & co.
ltd., 1942.
84 p.

NL 0388918   CaOTP OCl PP

AW
2
N55
Linklater, Eric, 1899–
The cornerstones, a conversation
in Elysium. London, MacMillan & Co.,
ltd., 1942.
85p. 19cm.
Micro-opaque.

NL 0388919   CaBVaU CSt

PR6023
.I 582C6 Linklater, Eric, 1899–
1943   The cornerstones; a conversation in Elysium.
London, Macmillan, 1943.
84 p. 20 cm.
An imaginary conversation between Confucius,
Lincoln, Lenin, a British airman and a soldier
in which they demand that humanity in the
present crisis be given a nobler purpose and
more certain aim.
1. Imaginary conversations. I. Title.
Full name: Eric Robert Russell Linklater.

NL 0388920   RPB UU

Linklater, Eric, 1899–
Crisis in heaven, an Elysian comedy by Eric Linklater. London, Macmillan & co., ltd, 1944.

vi, 108 p., 1 l. 19ᵐ.

"Books by Eric Linklater": leaf at end.

I. Title.

₍Full name: Eric Robert Russell Linklater₎

44–7696

Library of Congress   PR6023.I 582C7

822.91

NL 0388921   TxU MtBC Or WaSpG WaU NcD OU CaOTP
DLC NcGU OOxM CtY NcC TU PP IU ScU InU

Linklater, Eric, 1899–
The crusader's key, by Eric Linklater. ₍London₎ The White owl press ₍1933₎

3 p. l., ₍9₎–35 p., 1 l. illus. 22½ᶜᵐ.

"First published, April, 1933; reprinted, May, 1933."

I. Title.

33–20982

Library of Congress   PZ3.L6547Cr

NL 0388922   DLC PP PSC CtY

Linklater, Eric, 1899–
The crusader's key, by Eric Linklater. New York, A. A. Knopf, 1933.

3 p. l., 3–42 p., 1 l. 23½ cm.

Head-piece.
"First American edition."

I. Title.

Full name: Eric Robert Russell Linklater.

33–34788

PZ3.L6547Cr 2

NL 0388923   DLC GU ScU FMU NN

Linklater, Eric, 1899–
The defence of Calais, by Eric Linklater ... London, H. M. Stationery off., 1941.

36 p. illus. (map) 18ᵐ. (The Army at war)

"Issued for the War office by the Ministry of information."—p. ₍2₎ of cover.

1. Calais, Battle of, 1940.   I. Gt. Brit. War office. II. Gt. Brit. Ministry of information. III. Title.

₍Full name: Eric Robert Russell Linklater₎

42–51091

Library of Congress   D756.5.C2L5 1941

940.542

NL 0388924   FTaSU   DLC ScU IEN IU TU PPD PP OCU NIC CtY

Linklater, Eric, 1899–
La défense de Calais, par Eric Linklater ... Londres, H. M. Stationery off., 1942.

36 p. illus. (map) 18ᵐ. (L'Armée en guerre)

"Publié pour le Ministère de la guerre par les soins du Ministère de l'information."—p. ₍2₎ of cover.

1. Calais, Battle of, 1940.   I. Gt. Brit. War office. II. Gt. Brit. Ministry of information. III. Title.

₍Full name: Eric Robert Russell Linklater₎

42–51092

Library of Congress   D756.5.C2L52

940.542

NL 0388925   DLC MH

Linklater, Eric, 1899–
The devil's in the news; a comedy to be played with occasional music, by Eric Linklater. London, J. Cape ₍1934₎

3 p. l., 9–160 p. 20ᵐ.

I. Title.

35–12689

Library of Congress   PR6023.I 582D4 1934

822.91

NL 0388926   MH INS   DLC TxU TU FMU ScU InU OU OCl OOxM NN

Linklater, Eric.
A dragon laughed, and other poems, by Eric Linklater. London, J. Cape ₍1930₎

109, ₍1₎ p., 1 l. 20ᵐ.

I. Title.

31–635

Library of Congress   PR6023.I 582D7 1930

Copyright A ad int. 14527   821.91

NL 0388927   DLC MU WU CLSU CtY

Linklater, Eric, 1899–
The faithful ally. London, J. Cape ₍1954₎

257 p. 20 cm.

I. Title.

Full name: Eric Robert Russell Linklater.

PZ3.L6547Fai   54—40034 ‡

NL 0388928   LU CSt ScU TxU InU NBuU   DLC CaBVa CaBVaU CtY MH NN IEN NcD MiU

Linklater, Eric, 1899–
... God likes them plain; short stories. London, J. Cape ₍1935₎

2 p. l., 7–317 p. 20ᵐ.

I. Title.

36–4466

Library of Congress   PZ3.L6547Go

Copyright A ad int. 21052

NL 0388929   DLC CLSU IEN MiU ScU InU CtY

Linklater, Eric, 1899–
The great ship and Rabelais replies; two conversations, by Eric Linklater. London, Macmillan & co. ltd, 1944.

2 p. l., 64, ₍2₎ p. 19½ᵐ.

"Conversations" broadcast in May and October, 1943, concluding the author's "The cornerstones," broadcast and published in 1941, and "The raft and Socrates asks why," broadcast and published in 1942.

1. Imaginary conversations. 2. World war, 1939– —Miscellanea. I. Title. II. Title: Rabelais replies.

₍Full name: Eric Robert Russell Linklater₎

A 44—1895

Harvard univ. Library
for Library of Congress   PR6023.I 582G7

₍a45d1₎   828.91

NL 0388930   OU OCl MB CtY ScU NcD TU INS NIC WaU CaOTP
MH CaBVaU WaSpG MtBC Or TxU NcGU OOxM

4PR-64   Linklater, Eric, 1899–
A gyáva Ángelo, regény. [Budapest]
Révai [c1947]
287 p.

NL 0388931   DLC-P4

VOLUME 334

Linklater, Eric, 1899–
The Highland division, by Eric Linklater ... London, H. M. Stationery off., 1942.
96 p. illus. (maps) 19ᶜᵐ. (The Army at war)
"Issued for the War office by the Ministry of Information."
"Order of battle, the Fifty-first (Highland) division": p. ₍2₎ of cover and p. ₍1₎

1. World war, 1939– —Regimental histories—Gt. Brit.—51st (Highland) division. 2. Gt. Brit.—Army—51st (Highland) division. I. Title.
₍Full name: Eric Robert Russell Linklater₎
43–1479
Library of Congress   D759.5.51st.L5
940.541242

IEN IU CtY CaOTU NjP MBAt MnU TU CaMW
NL 0388932   DLC CaBViP InU LU ScU KU MH InU NBuG

Linklater, Eric, 1899–
The House of Gair, a novel. London, J. Cape ₍1953₎
224 p. 20 cm.

I. Title.
Full name: Eric Robert Russell Linklater.

PZ3.L6547Ho   53–37535 ‡

TxU CtY NN TU MH MU ScU TxU LU
NL 0388933   DLC TxU LU OrCS CaBVa CtY NcD PU NIC

Linklater, Eric, 1899–
The House of Gair, a novel. ₍1st American ed.₎ New York, Harcourt, Brace ₍1954₎
251 p. 21 cm.

I. Title.
Full name: Eric Robert Russell Linklater.

PZ3.L6547Ho 2   54–5251 ‡

OC1U PP PPL TxU WaS WaT
NL 0388934   DLC OrU MtBC WaE Or OrP OC1 OC1W OOxM

PR6023   **Linklater, Eric,** 1899–
I582I4   The impregnable women. London, J.Cape
1938   ₍1938₎
              348 p. 20ᶜᵐ
              "First published 1938."

ScU ICU
NL 0388935   CSt CU-S CtY TxU IU TU OKentU MU MiU

Linklater, Eric, 1899–
The impregnable women, by Eric Linklater. New York, Farrar & Rinehart, incorporated ₍ᶜ1938₎
5 p. l., 3–312 p. 21ᶜᵐ.

I. Title.
38–19254
Library of Congress   PZ3.L6547 I m

NL 0388936   DLC NBuU TNJ OC1 OLak OOxM

828   **Linklater, Eric,** 1899–
L6481   The impregnable women. The Orkney edition.
London, J. Cape ₍1952₎
286 p. 20 cm.

NL 0388937   LU NcD

Linklater, Eric, 1899–
... Juan en China; versión castellana de León Mirlas. Buenos Aires–México, Espasa–Calpe argentina, s. a. ₍1942₎
5 p. l., 13–312 p., 1 l. 22½ᶜᵐ.

I. Mirlas, León, tr. II. Title.
₍Full name: Eric Robert Russell Linklater₎
43–48373
Library of Congress   PR6023.I 582J85

NL 0388938   DLC

PR6023   **Linklater, Eric,** 1899–
I582J8   Juan in America; a novel. London, J.Cape;
1931a   New York, J.Cape & H.Smith ₍1931₎
              458 p. geneal.table. 21cm.
              "First published 1931."

NL 0388939   CSt NIC OrU INS InU TxU ICarbS

Linklater, Eric.
Juan in America, by Eric Linklater. New York, J. Cape & H. Smith ₍ᶜ1931₎
vii, 466 p. incl. geneal. tab. 21ᶜᵐ.

I. Title.
31–7637
Library of Congress   PZ3.L6547Ju

MiU OC1 OO OLak ViU MB NcU
NL 0388940   DLC MtBC WaT WaS TxU CaBVa IdPI ScU MU

PR   **Linklater, Eric,** 1899–
6023   Juan in America; a novel. [Cheaper ed.]
.I 582   London, J. Cape [1933]
J7   458p. 21cm.
1933

NL 0388941   NNCU-G

PR6023   **Linklater, Eric,** 1899–
I582J8   Juan in America.   London, Jonathan
              Cape [1934, 1933]
              458 p.

NL 0388942   NBuU

Linklater, Eric, 1899–
Juan in America; a novel by Eric Linklater. London, Toronto, J. Cape ₍1937₎
2 p. l., 7–458 p. 20½ᶜᵐ.
"First published, March, 1931 ... nineteenth impression, September, 1937."

I. Title.
39–9942
Library of Congress   PZ3.L6547Ju 5

NL 0388943   DLC CaBVaU OrU WaTC OC1

823.91 L38.6
Linklater, Eric, 1899–
Juan in America; a novel.
London, J. Cape [1943]
458 p.

NL 0388944   CaOTP

Linklater, Eric, 1899–
Juan in America; a novel by Eric Linklater.
London, Jonathan Cape, ₍1949₎
458p. 21cm.

NL 0388945   PU

Linklater, Eric, 1899–
Juan in America. The Orkney ed. London, J. Cape [1953] 458 p. 20cm.

NL 0388946   NN

Linklater, Eric, 1899–
... Juan in Amerika. Stuttgart, Franckh ₍ᶜ1942₎
512 p. 20½ᶜᵐ.
"Berechtigte übertragung ins deutsche von dr. Karl Blanck."
"98.–121. tausend."

I. Blanck, Karl, 1884–   tr. II. Title.
₍Full name: Eric Robert Russell Linklater₎
44–22252
Library of Congress   PR6023.I 582J74
823.91

NL 0388947   DLC CtY CU MB IU ICU

Rare Book   **Linklater, Eric,** 1899–
Room   Juan in China, by Eric Linklater. London,
Iq   J.Cape[1937]
L648   3p.l.,9–383p. 20cm.
937J   "First published 1937."

NL 0388948   CtY TxU IU WU OU MH CaOTP

Linklater, Eric, 1899–
Juan in China, by Eric Linklater. New York, Farrar & Rinehart, inc. ₍ᶜ1937₎
3 p. l., 298 p. 21ᶜᵐ.

I. Title.
37–4265
Library of Congress   PZ3.L6547Jv

NL 0388949   DLC CaBVa TxU IdPI PU PP ScU

820   **Linklater, Eric,** 1899–
L756   Juan in China. Orkney ed. London, J.
tJUA.7   Cape [1950]
             326p. 19cm.

             "First printed 1937 ... First published
             in the Orkney edition 1950."

NL 0388950   CLSU NcD LU

Slavic   **Linklater, Eric,** 1899–
Coll.   Juan v Čině [román. Z anglické předlohy
420.91   přeložila Běla Vrbová–Pavloušková. Studii o
E5   autorovi napsal Zdeněk Vančura] Praha,
L56   Evropský literární klub [1937]

             362 p. 22 cm. (Evropský literární klub)
             English translation of title: Juan in China,
             a novel. Translated from English by Běla
             Vrbová–Pavloušková. The study on the author
             written by Zdeněk Vančura.   rw

NL 0388951   IEdS

Linklater, Eric, 1899–
Judas; a novel, by Eric Linklater. London, J. Cape ₍1939₎
223 p. 20ᶜᵐ.
"First published 1939.

1. Judas Iscariot—Fiction. I. Title.
39–13358
Library of Congress   PZ3.L6547Jw

NL 0388952   DLC TxU FMU CtY ScU WU INS OC1 OC1h NN

VOLUME 334

Linklater, Eric, 1899–
Judas, by Eric Linklater. New York, Farrar & Rinehart,
incorporated [*1939]
4 p. l., 3–243 p. 21ᶜᵐ.

1. Judas Iscariot—Fiction.   I. Title.
[Full name: Eric Robert Russell Linklater]
Library of Congress   PZ3.L6547Jw 2   39–20244

NL 0388953   DLC TxU PPM ViU WU UU NIC

Linklater, Eric, 1899–
Judas; roman traduit de l'anglais par Marie Avoye.
Bruxelles, Éditions de Visscher, 1946.
242 p. illus. 19 cm. (Collection Extra muros)

1. Judas Iscariot—Fiction.
Full name: Eric Robert Russell Linklater.
PR6023.I 582J873   57–58041 ‡

NL 0388954   DLC NPurMC

Linklater, Eric, 1899–
Laxdale Hall, a novel. London, Cape [1951]
301 p. 20 cm.

I. Title.
Full name: Eric Robert Russell Linklater.
PZ3.L6547Lax   52–16445 ‡

CtY WU INS
NL 0388955   DLC CaBVa WaE TxU FMU NjR MH NN RPB ScU

Linklater, Eric, 1899–
Laxdale Hall; a novel. New York, Harcourt, Brace
[1952]
301 p. 20 cm.

I. Title.
PZ3.L6547Lax 2   52—9852 ‡

OOxM TxU TNJ
NL 0388956   DLC OrP WaS WaT OrCS WaSpG ViU PPL NNC

LINKLATER, ERIC, 1899–
The lion & the unicorn; or, What England has meant to
Scotland, by Eric Linklater. London: G.Routledge and Sons,
Ltd., 1935. 191 p. 19¼cm. (The voice of Scotland.)

809586A. 1. Scotland—Rel., Gen., with England. 2. England
—Rel., Gen., with Scotland. 3. Nationalism and nationality
—Scotland. I. Title.

NL 0388957   NN TxU ICU IEN NIC MU WU CtY

Linklater, Eric, 1899–
Love in Albania, a comedy in three acts. London, English
Theatre Guild [1950]
94 p. front. 19 cm. (Guild library)

I. Title.
Full name: Eric Robert Russell Linklater.
PR6023.I 582L6   822.91   51–22758

NL 0388958   DLC

Linklater, Eric, 1899–
... Magnus Merriman, a novel. London & Toronto, J. Cape
[1934]
362 p. 20ᶜᵐ.

I. Title.
Library of Congress   PZ3.L6547Mag 2   34–6204

CSt MsU CtY OrU
NL 0388959   DLC TxU CaBVaU CaBVa OrP OrU PP PPD WU

*
AC8
.A6   Linklater, Eric, 1899–
no.N-26   Magnus Merriman. New York, Editions
1934   for the Armed Services, ᶜ1934.
351 p. 11 x 17cm. (Armed Services
ed. N-26)

NL 0388960   ViU

Linklater, Eric, 1899–
Magnus Merriman, by Eric Linklater. New York, Farrar &
Rinehart, incorporated [*1934]
viii, 376 p. 21¼ᶜᵐ.

I. Title.
Library of Congress   PZ3.L6547Mag   34–5279

OC1h
NL 0388961   DLC NN IdPI WaSp OrSaW ScU ViU OC1 OU

PR
6023   Linklater, Eric, 1899–
.I 582   Magnus Merriman, The Orkney edition.
M3   London, J. Cape [1950]
1950   347 p.

"First printed 1934."

NL 0388962   INS NcD MB TNJ

Linklater, Eric, 1899–
The man on my back, an autobiography, by Eric Linklater.
London, Macmillan & co. ltd., 1941.
vii, 340, [1] p. 22ᶜᵐ.

I. Title.
[Full name: Eric Robert Russell Linklater]
Library of Congress   PR6023.I 582Z5 1941   41—13711

TU OC1 KyLx MiU OU CtY FMU OLak WU MU DLC
NL 0388963   LU WaTC OrU CaBVa WaS OrP Or PPD PU

Lilly
PR 6023   LINKLATER,ERIC,1899–
.I 56 Z5   The man on my back, an autobiography ...
1941   London, Macmillan & Co. Ltd., 1947.
vii,340,[1] p. 21.6 cm.

"First edition, March 1941. Reprinted ...
1947."
Bound in bright red cloth; in printed
jacket.

NL 0388964   InU ScU

Linklater, Eric, 1899–
823.91   The man on my back, an autobiography, by Eric Linklater.
L756M   Loudon, Macmillan & co. ltd., 1950.
vii, 340, [1] p. 22ᶜᵐ.

"First edition ... 1941."

NL 0388965   NcD

Linklater, Eric, 1899–
Mary, queen of Scots. [London] 'Daily
Express' Publications [1933?]
152p. 19cm.

"Bibliographical note": p.147.

1. Mary Stuart, Queen of the Scots, 1542–1587.

NL 0388966   IEN

Linklater, Eric, 1899–
Mary, queen of Scots, by Eric Linklater ... [London, P.
Davies, limited, 1933.
160 p. front. (port.) 20 cm.
"Bibliographical note": p. 156.

1. Mary Stuart, queen of the Scots, 1542–1587.
DA787.A1L65   923.141   33—20858

NL 0388967   DLC CtY IU NN OCX MiU TxU WU CtY NcGU

Linklater, Eric, 1899–
Mary, queen of Scots, by Eric Linklater. New York, D.
Appleton-Century company, incorporated, 1933.
3 p. l., 161, [1] p. front. (port.) 19¼ᶜᵐ. [Appleton biographies]
"Bibliographical note": p. 158.

1. Mary Stuart, queen of the Scots, 1542–1587.   33–27347
Library of Congress   DA787.A1L65 1933 a
Copyright A 65489   923.141

PJB OC1 OU ViU NN
NL 0388968   DLC OrP Or WaS CaBVaU CaBViP IdU KyLx

DA787
.A1L65   Linklater, Eric, 1899–
1934   Mary, queen of Scots. [London] P.
Davies, 1934.
160 p. port. 20cm.
Includes bibliography.

1. Mary Stuart, Queen of the Scots, 1542–1587.

NL 0388969   ViU OCU

Linklater, Eric, 1899–
Mary Queen of Scots.   London, Dobson, 1939
(Twentieth Century Classics)

NL 0388970   IaU

Linklater, Eric, 1899–
Mary, Queen of Scots. London, D. Dobson [1952]
160 p. illus. 20 cm. (Twentieth century classics)

1. Mary Stuart, Queen of the Scots, 1542–1587.
DA787.A1L65 1952   923.141   53–24658

N NNC AU NcU NcD ScU NbU
NL 0388971   DLC CaBViP CaBVa GU TU MB MH FTaSU CL

Linklater, Eric.
The men of Ness; the saga of Thorlief Coalbiter's sons,
Eric Linklater. London, J. Cape [1932]
2 p. l., 7–287 p. illus. (map) 20ᶜᵐ.

I. Title.
Library of Congress   PZ3.L6547Me   33–1965

NL 0388972   DLC ViU IEN CaBVa WU IU OO CtY

VOLUME 334

Linklater, Eric.
The men of Ness (The saga of Thorlief Coalbiter's sons) by Eric Linklater. New York, Farrar & Rinehart, inc. [¹1933]
4 p. l., 3–309 p. 19½ᶜᵐ.

I. Title.
Library of Congress   PZ3.L6547Me 2   33–6710

NL 0388973   DLC TxU Wa IdPI WaS ScU NIC

PR
6023   Linklater, Eric.
I582M38   The men of Ness; the saga of Thorlief
1952   Coalbiter's sons. The Orkney edition.
London, J. Cape, 1952.
254p. 20cm.

NL 0388974   MU MiU MB LU

Linklater, Eric, 1899–
Menig Angelo. Oversatt av Leo Strøm.
Oslo, Aschehoug, 1946. 320p.

NL 0388975   CaBVaU

Linklater, Eric, 1899–
Mr. Byculla, a story. London, R. Hart-Davis, 1950.
167 p. 21 cm.

I. Title.
Full name: Eric Robert Russell Linklater.

PZ3.L6547Mi   50–30390

NL 0388976   DLC TxU CaBVaU MH PU InU ScU CtY TU

Linklater, Eric, 1899–
Mr. Byculla. [1st American ed.] New York, Harcourt, Brace [1951]
160 p. 21 cm.

I. Title.

PZ3.L6547Mi 2   51—9210

ViU TNJ NcD
NL 0388977   DLC WaT CaBVaU Or OrP WaSp WaE CU TxU

Linklater, Eric, 1899–
The Mortimer touch, a farcical comedy. London, French [1952]
83 p. illus. 22 cm. (French's acting edition, no. 508)

I. Title.
Full name: Eric Robert Russell Linklater.

PR6023.I 582M6   822.91   53–23790 ‡

NL 0388978   DLC TxU MiD NN

Linklater, Eric, 1899–
The northern garrisons, by Eric Linklater ... London, H. M. Stationery off., 1941.
72 p. illus. (double map) 19ᶜᵐ. [Half-title: The army at war, issued for the War office by the Ministry of information]
Maps on p. [2] and [3] of cover.
"First published 1941."

1. European war, 1939–   —Iceland. 2. European war, 1939—
Gt. Brit. 3. Islands of the Atlantic. 4. Garrisons—Gt. Brit.   I. Title.
[Full name: Eric Robert Russell Linklater]

Library of Congress   D763.I 2L5 1941   41–27712

940.53491

NL 0388979   DLC TxU CaBVaU NBuG

Linklater, Eric, 1899–
The northern garrisons, the defense of Iceland and the Faeroe, Orkney and Shetland islands, by Eric Linklater. Garden City, N. Y., Garden City publishing co., inc. [¹1941]
vii, [1], 71 p. illus. (maps) plates. 19½ᶜᵐ.
"Issued by arrangement with the British War office and the Ministry of information."

1. European war, 1939–   —Iceland. 2. European war, 1939— —
Gt. Brit. 3. Islands of the Atlantic. 4. Garrisons—Gt. Brit.   I. Title.
[Full name: Eric Robert Russell Linklater]

Library of Congress   D763.I 2L5 1941 a   41–25510

940.53491

OC1 OLak NIC DNAL
NL 0388980   DLC TU Or CLSU WaT OrP InU NcC TxU ViU

Linklater, Eric, 1899–
Our men in Korea [the Commonwealth part in the campaign, first official account. Prepared for the Admiralty, War Office, and Air Ministry by the Central Office of Information] London, H. M. Stationery Off., 1952.
79 p. illus., maps. 21 cm.

1. Korean War, 1950–   I. Gt. Brit. Central Office of Information. II. Title.

DS918.L5   951.9   52—29934
[a53b1]

ViU PP
NL 0388981   DLC CU TU MiU GU CaBVa CaBViP NcD MH NN

Linklater, Eric, 1899–
The pirates in the deep green sea; a story for children.
Illus. by William Reeves. London, Macmillan, 1949.
397 p. illus. 20 cm.

I. Title.

PZ8.L674Pi   49–5189*

NL 0388982   DLC Or WaS WaSp OC1 MU PP

AC–L
L648po   Linklater, Eric, 1899–
1929   Poet's Pub, by Eric Linklater.   London,
J. Cape [1929]
4 p.ℓ., 11–317, [1] p. 20cm.

"First published in MCMXXIX."

NL 0388983   TxU CtY

Linklater, Eric, 1899–
Poet's Pub [by] Eric Linklater. New York, J. Cape & H. Smith [¹1930]
3 p. l., 373 p. 19½ᶜᵐ.

I. Title.
[Full name: Eric Robert Russell Linklater]

Library of Congress   PZ3.L6547Po   30—3073
[a41e1]

NL 0388984   DLC TxU Or MtBC IdPI ViU NN

Linklater, Eric, 1899–
Poet's pub... London, Toronto, J. Cape [1932]
Half-title: Florin books [no.18]

NL 0388985   PU

Linklater, Eric, 1899–
Poet's Pub [by] Eric Linklater. London,
J. Cape [1932]
2d impression, Dec., 1932.

NL 0388986   OU

LINKLATER, ERIC, 1899–
Poet's pub.   London, Penguin Books [1935]
282p. 19cm.   (Penguin Books, no.3)

"First published...1929...Published in Penguin Books...1935. Second impression...1935."

NL 0388987   PU

Linklater, Eric, 1899–   23690.61.2300
Poet's pub. The Orkney ed. L, Cape [1952]
285 p.

NL 0388988   MH CaBVa

Linklater, Eric, 1899–
Poobie, [by] E. R. R. Linklater; designs by Isobel H. Walker
... [Edinburgh: The Porpoise Press, 1925.]   8 p.   illus.
22½ x 18cm.   (The Porpoise Press broadsheets. ser. 2, no. 2.)
Cover-title.
Printed by W. Hodge & Co., Ltd., Glasgow and Edinburgh.
Poems.

675879A. 1. Poetry, Scottish.   J. S. BILLINGS MEM. COLL.
II. Title.   I. Walker, Isobel H., illustrator.
March 29, 1934

NL 0388989   NN KU ICN MH NNC

Linklater, Eric, 1899–
Private Angelo, a novel by Eric Linklater. London, J. Cape [1946]
271, [1] p. 19½ᶜᵐ.
"First published 1946."

I. Title.
[Full name: Eric Robert Russell Linklater]

Library of Congress   PZ3.L6547Pr   46–16631

TxU
NL 0388990   DLC TxU MU OkU PPT PP PSt CtY WU ScU

Linklater, Eric, 1899–
Private Angelo, a novel by Eric Linklater. New York, The Macmillan company [1946]
3 p. l., 267 p. 21½ᶜᵐ.
"First [American] printing."

I. Title.
[Full name: Eric Robert Russell Linklater]

PZ3.L6547Pr 2   46–8554

OU PSt MiU
NL 0388991   DLC WaT WaE OrU TxU OrP Or WU ICU MH MU

Linklater, Eric, 1899–
Private Angelo, a novel. Toronto, Jonathan Cape, [1946].
265p.

NL 0388992   CaOTU CaBVa

PR6023   Linklater, Eric, 1899–
I582P7   Private Angelo; a novel.   London,
J. Cape [1948]
271 p. 20cm.

NL 0388993   CSt

VOLUME 334

*PR6023
.I 582P7
1948
Linklater, Eric, 1899–
Private Angelo, a novel, by Eric Linklater.
London, Reprint Society [1948]
271, [1] p. 19 1/2cm.

     I. Title.
Full name: Eric Robert Russell Linklater.

NL   0388994   MB ViU CaBVaU

Linklater, Eric, 1899–
Private Angelo, a novel by Eric Linklater.
London, J. Cape [1955]
271, [1] p. 19.5 cm.
"First published 1946."
"The Orkney edition."

NL   0388995   NcD PU LU

Linklater, Eric, 1899–
The raft and Socrates asks why; two conversations, by Eric
Linklater. London, Macmillan & co. ltd, 1942.
3 p. l., 121, [1] p. 19¼ᵐ.
"Conversations," broadcast in August and October, 1942, continuing
the author's "The cornerstones," broadcast and published in 1941.

     1. Imaginary conversations. 2. World war, 1939– —Miscellanea.
I. Title. II. Title: Socrates asks why.
              [Full name: Eric Robert Russell Linklater]
                         43–5820
Library of Congress   PR6023.I 582R3
                                828.91

         OC1 CaBVaU CaOTP IU FMU WaS ScU
NL   0388996   DLC WaS TxU InU MU NcD PPT CtY LU TU

AW
2
N55
Linklater, Eric, 1899–
The raft and Socrates asks why,
two conversations. London, MacMillan
& Co., ltd., 1942.
121p. 19cm.

    Micro-opaque.

NL   0388997   CaBVaU CSt

PR 6023
I582 R3
1944
Linklater, Eric, 1899–
The raft and Socrates asks why; two conversations, by Eric
Linklater. London, Macmillan & co. ltd, 1944 [c1942]
3 p. l., 121, [1] p. 19¼ᵐ.
"Conversations," broadcast in August and October, 1942, continuing
the author's "The cornerstones," broadcast and published in 1941.

NL   0388998   OU

Linklater, Eric, 1899–
The revolution, by Eric Linklater. London, The White owl
press [1934]
4 p. l., 11–79, [1] p. 22½ᵐ.
CONTENTS.—The actress Olenina.—The revolution.—Jean Paris.

     I. Title.

                               34–21161
Library of Congress   PZ3.L6547Re
Copyright   A ad int. 19108

NL   0388999   DLC TxU OU CtY

LINKLATER, ERIC, 1899–
...Ripeness is all; a novel... London: J. Cape [1935]
383 p. incl. diagrs., geneal. table. 20cm.

827547A. 1. Fiction, Scottish. I. Title.

NL   0389000   NN ICarbS WU CSt OKentU

Linklater, Eric, 1899–
... Ripeness is all. New York, Farrar & Rinehart, inc.
[1935]
5 p. l., 333 p. 20ᵐ.

     I. Title.
Library of Congress   35–6856
                   PZ3.L6547R1

       ViU ScU
NL   0389001   DLC TxU WaE IdPI PP NcD OC1 OO OU NcU

823.9
L75r
1954
Linklater, Eric, 1899–
Ripeness is all. Orkney ed. London, J.
Cape, [1954]
383p. 20cm.

NL   0389002   TNJ

Linklater, Eric, 1899–
Robert the Bruce, by Eric Linklater; with a frontispiece
and two maps. [London] P. Davies, limited, 1934.
181 p. incl. maps. front. 19¼ᵐ.
Bibliography: p. 177.

     1. Robert I, king of Scotland, 1274–1329. 2. Scotland—Hist.—War of
independence, 1285–1371.
                   34–21506
Library of Congress   DA783.4.L5 1934
Copyright   A ad int. 19125   [3]   923.141

NL   0389003   DLC CLSU MU ScU WU PPD TxU IU CtY NN

Linklater, Eric, 1899–
Robert the Bruce, by Eric Linklater; with a frontispiece
and two maps. New York, London, D. Appleton-Century
company incorporated, 1934.
vii, [1], 183, [1] p. front., illus. (2 maps) 19¼ᵐ. [Appleton biogra-
phies]
     Bibliography: p. [180]

     1. Robert I, king of Scotland, 1274–1329. 2. Scotland—Hist.—War of
independence, 1285–1371.
                   34–25724
Library of Congress   DA783.4.L5 1934 a
——— Copy 2.
Copyright   A 75048   [5]   923.141

       ViU Or WaS CaBViP WaE
NL   0389004   DLC TxU MH MeB TU NcGU OC1 OC1h MB NN

Linklater, Eric, 1899–
The sailor's holiday, by Eric Linklater. London, J. Cape
[1937]
284 p. 20ᵐ.

     I. Title.
                   38–1570
Library of Congress   PZ3.L6547Sai

NL   0389005   DLC CLSU CaBVaU CtY WU INS TxU

Linklater, Eric, 1899–
... The sailor's holiday. New York, Toronto, Farrar &
Rinehart, incorporated [1938]
3 p. l., 3–246 p. 20ᵐ.
Illustrated t-p.

     I. Title.
                   38–2812
Library of Congress   PZ3.L6547Sai 2

NL   0389006   DLC NN PP ScU OC1 OLak OC1h

823.9
L75sa
1954
Linklater, Eric, 1899–
The sailor's holiday. Orkney edition.
London, J. Cape [c1954]
192p. 19cm.

     "First printed 1937"

NL   0389007   TNJ MU LU NcD

Linklater, Eric, 1899–
Sealskin trousers, and other stories, with wood engravings by Joan Hassall. London, R. Hart-Davis [1947]
127 p. illus. 21 cm.

     I. Title.
                    Full name: Eric Robert Russell Linklater.

                   PZ3.L6547Se   48—14923*

       OrU CtY NNC
NL   0389008   DLC CU MU NNC MH IU LU TxU UU ScU OU

Linklater, Eric, 1899–
Soldat Angelo; översättning av Margaretha Odelberg. 3.
uppl. Stockholm, Norstedt [1946]
304 p. 22 cm.

     I. Title.
                    Full name: Eric Robert Russell Linklater.
PR6023.I 582P77   1946   50–25925

NL   0389009   DLC

Linklater, Eric, 1899–
A spell for old bones. London, J. Cape [1949]
223 p. 20 cm.

     I. Title.
                    Full name: Eric Robert Russell Linklater.
                   PZ3.L6547Sp   50–958

       CaBVaU InU PPGi MB
NL   0389010   DLC MU TxU TNJ CtY NjR PPL PP IU WaT

Linklater, Eric, 1899–
A spell for old bones. New York, Macmillan, 1950 [*1949]
223 p. 20 cm.

     I. Title.
                    Full name: Eric Robert Russell Linklater.
                   PZ3.L6547Sp 2   50–6430

       OrPS OrU
NL   0389011   DLC CaBVa WaS TxU Or OC1 OEac WU ScU

Linklater, Eric, 1899–
Det store skib, fem samtaler eller radiospil. Overs. og
indledt af Gudmund Roger Henrichsen. København,
Schønbergske forlag, 1947.
233 p. 22 cm.
"Originalernes titler: 'The cornerstones,' 'The raft,' 'Sokrates asks
why,' 'The great ship' og 'Rabelais replies.'"

     1. Imaginary conversations. 2. World War, 1939–1945—Miscellanea.
I. Title.
                    Full name: Eric Robert Russell Linklater.
PR6023.I 582G72   828.91   50–23256

NL   0389012   DLC

Linklater, Eric, 1899–
The Sultan and the lady; a story of His Highness Zafrul-
lah bin Ismail bin Said, Sultan of Namua, Lord of the Island
Sea who retained also his grandfather's title of honour:
Faithful Ally of Queen Victoria. [1st American ed.] New
York, Harcourt, Brace [*1954]
256 p. 21 cm.

     I. Title.
                    Full name: Eric Robert Russell Linklater.
                   PZ3.L6547Su   55–5317 ‡

       NcD PPL PP
NL   0389013   DLC TxU WaS WaE Or OrU OrP OrCS OC1 NN

VOLUME 334

Linklater, Eric, 1899–
The thistle and the pen; an anthology of modern Scottish writers. London, New York, Nelson ₁1950₎
xv, 319 p. 21 cm.

1. Scottish literature—20th cent. 2. English literature—Scottish authors. I. Title.
Full name: Eric Robert Russell Linklater.

PR8635.L5   820.82   52–539

NL 0389014   DLC WaS TxU MH NIC CU NN DGU ICU NcD MU

Linklater, Eric, 1899–
Two comedies: Love in Albania, and To meet the Mac-Gregors. London, Macmillan, 1950.
vii, 215 p. illus. 20 cm.
Music: p. 202–215.

I. Title: Love in Albania. II. Title: To meet the MacGregors.
Full name: Eric Robert Russell Linklater.

A 51–9024

Yale Univ. Library
for Library of Congress   ₁5₎

ScU CaBVaU WaSpG CaBVa WaU INS
NL 0389015   CtY TxU CU–I PP CU NIC MH MB NN MiEM NBC

Linklater, Eric, 1899–
The ultimate Viking. London, Macmillan, 1955.
295 p. illus. 23 cm.

1. Orkney Islands—Hist. 2. Vikings. I. Title.
Full name: Eric Robert Russell Linklater.

DA880.O6L5 1955   941.12   56–117 ‡

NN IEN CtY TxU MiD NIC WaS NcD ScU
NL 0389016   DLC CaBVaU CaBViPA CaBVa WaS ICU PP OCl

Rare Book **Linklater, Eric,** 1899–
Room   White maa's saga, by Eric Linklater. London,
Iq   J. Cape₁1929₎
L648   4 p. ℓ., 11–283, ₁1₎ p. 19 cm.
929W   "First published in MCMXXIX."

NL 0389017   CtY

Linklater, Eric, 1899–
White-maa's saga, by Eric Linklater ... London ₁etc.₎ J. Cape ₁1937₎
256 p. 18½ᵐ. (Half-title: Florin books)
"First published 1929 ... re-issued in Florin books 1937."

I. Title.
38–31841

Library of Congress   PZ3.L6548Wh
₁4₎

NL 0389018   DLC ScU CaOTP

823.91 **Linklater, Eric,** 1899–
L756W   ... White-maa's saga ... London, Jonathan
Cape ₁1952₎
255 p. 19½ cm.

"The Orkney edition."
"First published 1929 ... first published in the Orkney edition 1952."
I. Title.

NL 0389019   NcD MB MU LU PPT

Linklater, Eric, 1899–
The wind on the moon, a story for children by Eric Linklater; Nicolas Bentley drew the pictures. London, Macmillan & co. ltd, 1944.
3 p. l., 363, ₁1₎ p. illus. 19½ᵐ.

I. *Bentley, Nicolas, 1907–   illus.   II. Title.
₁Full name: Eric Robert Russell Linklater₎
44–47872

Library of Congress   PZ8.L674Wi

NL 0389020   DLC TxU MU OU OCl OO ScU

Linklater, Eric, 1899–
The wind on the moon, by Eric Linklater; Nicolas Bentley drew the pictures. New York, The Macmillan company, 1944.
4 p. l., 323 p. illus. 19½ᵐ.
"First printing."

I. *Bentley, Nicolas, 1907–   illus.   II. Title.
₁Full name: Eric Robert Russell Linklater₎
44–40381

Library of Congress   PZ8.L674Wi 2

NL 0389021   DLC CaBVaU PPGi IU OrP Or ODW

Linklater, Eric.
The wind on the moon: a story for children. Nicolas Bentley drew the pictures. Toronto, Macmillan, 1944.

NL 0389022   CaBVa

Linklater, Eric, 1899–
A year of space; a chapter in autobiography. Toronto, World Books Society ₁n. d.₎
319 p. 19 cm.

NL 0389023   CaBVaU

Linklater, Eric, 1899–
A year of space, a chapter in autobiography. London, Macmillan, 1953.
272 p. 23 cm.

I. Title.
Full name: Eric Robert Russell Linklater.
PR6023.I582Z53 1953   928.2   53—1407 ‡

TxU CtY WaS MH NN
NL 0389024   DLC CaBVa CaBViP TxU FMU ScU OrU OU TU

Linklater, Eric, 1899–
A year of space, a chapter in autobiography. ₁1st American ed.₎ New York, Harcourt, Brace, 1953.
272 p. 22 cm.

I. Title.
Full name: Eric Robert Russell Linklater
PR6023.I582Z53 1953a   928.2   53–7840 ‡

PPL NcC OCl Vi MB TxU ViU CoU
NL 0389025   DLC OrP Or WaS WaE WaT PSt PU NcD PP

PR6023
.I582Z53 **Linklater, Eric,** 1899–
1954
A year of space; a chapter in autobiography. London, Reprint Society ₁1954₎
319 p. 19cm.

I. Title.
Full name: Eric Robert Russell Linklater.

NL 0389026   ViU

Linklater, Eric, 1899–
Žuans Amerikā; romāns. Grāmatu Draugs, 1953.
395p.

NL 0389027   OCl

Linklater, Eric Robert Russell
see
Linklater, Eric, 1899–

Linklater, George James Irvine, joint author.
RT67   **Guy, John.**   FOR OTHER EDITIONS
.G8   SEE MAIN ENTRY
1943   Hygiene for nurses, by John Guy ... and G. J. I. Linklater ... 6th ed. Edinburgh, E. & S. Livingstone, 1943.

Linklater, J. Lane, *pseud.*
see **Watkins, Alex.**

443 **Linklater, Philip.**
L64m   Mon premier dictionnaire français. Illus.
1951   de l'auteur. ₁2d ed.₎   London, University of London Press ₁1951₎
xii, 216 p. illus., col. plates, maps (on lining papers) 20cm.

1. French language—Dictionaries. I. Title.

NL 0389031   IU

Rev.
Linklater, Robert, ed.
The Lord's day and the holy eucharist, treated in a series of essays by various authors, with a preface by Robert Linklater... London, New York, Longmans, Green, and co., 1892.
viii, 228 p. 19 1–2 cm.

Contents: 1. Worship, by Lord Halifax, p. 1–40.—2. Temple worship, by T. Lacey, p. 41–83.—3. Canonical Sunday worship, by E. Wood, p. 69–95.—4. Catholic worship and the Book of common prayer, by E. Sergeant, p. 96–155.—5. The holy eucharist the divinely appointed service of the church, by R. Linklater, p. 156–171.—6. The holy eucharist, by Earl Nelson, p. 172–180.—7. Eucharistic worship, by J. Going, p. 181–220.—8. The musical rendering of the holy eucharist, by J. Powell, p. 221–228.

NL 0389033   NNG PPLT IEG

Rev.
Linklater, Robert.
The making of the body of Christ ... Lond., Skeffington, 1906.
₁126₎ p.

NL 0389034   PPEB

YA **Linklater, Rev. Robert.**
11796   The public worship regulation bill. Abolish the mass; or, The mass in masquerade. London, ₁18– ₎
8p.

NL 0389035   DLC

87 **Linklater, R₁obert₎, ed.**
1844   Sunday and recreation;...
London, 1889

NL 0389036   DLC PPL

VOLUME 334

Linklater, Rev. Robert, ed.
True limits of ritual in the church. Edited
by Rev. Robert Linklater.   London, [etc.]
Longmans, Green, 1899.
xvi, 250 p.   20 cm.
1. Ritualism.   I. Title.

NL 0389037   IEG PPPD NbFC

Rev.
Linklater, Robert.
The Witness of the first four general Councils
as, against Papal Supremacy; considered in a letter
to a friend.   London.
30 p.

NL 0389038   PHi

Linklater, William.
The magic snake, being a group of stories for children concerning the habits, customs, beliefs, ceremonies, corroborees and
legends of the Australian aborigines.   Stories by William Linklater.   Illustrated and edited by Mavis Mallinson.   Sydney, The
Currawong publishing company [1943?]
95, [1] p.   col. front., illus.   24 cm.

1. Folk-lore—Australia.   I. Mallinson, Mavis, ed.   II. Title.

PZ8.1.L6 Mag   47–42359

NL 0389039   DLC CLU IEN

Linklater, William Albert, d. 1937.
... Are dairymen prosperous? ...
(In Western Washington experiment
station. Monthly bulletin, v. 6, no. 7, October,
1918)
1. State college of Washington authors,
Works of. 2. Dairying.

NL 0389040   WaPS

E639.73   Linklater, William Albert, d. 1937
W27bm   ... The best type of sheep for Western
v.6,no.12 Washington ...

(In Western Washington experiment station.
Monthly bulletin, v. 6, no. 12, March, 1919)

1. State college of Washington authors, Works
of. 2. Sheep - Washington (State).

NL 0389041   WaPS

Linklater, William Albert, d. 1937.
... Brown hay ...
(In Western Washington experiment station.
Monthly bulletin, v. 7, no. 3, June, 1919)
1. State college of Washington authors,
Works of. 2. Haying.

NL 0389042   WaPS

E639.73   Linklater, William Albert, d. 1937
W27bm   ... Concerning dairy rations ...
v.8,no.7
(In Western Washington experiment station.
Monthly bulletin, v. 8, no. 7, October, 1920)

1. State college of Washington authors, Works
of. 2. Feeding and feeding stuffs.

NL 0389043   WaPS

E639.73   Linklater, William Albert,   d, 1937.
W27bm   ... Concerning ground limestone ...
V.3,no.7
(In Western Washington experiment station.
Monthly bulletin, V. 3, no. 7, October, 1915)

1. State college of Washington authors, Works
of. 2. Liming of soils. 3. Limestone.

NL 0389044   WaPS

E639.73   Linklater, William Albert,   d. 1937.
W27bm   ... Concerning hog raising ...
V.3,no.1
(In Western Washington experiment station.
Monthly bulletin, V. 3, no. 1, April, 1915)

1. State college of Washington authors, Works
of. 2. Swine - Feeding.

NL 0389045   WaPS

E639.73   Linklater, William Albert, d. 1937
W27bm   ... Concerning land clearing ...
v.8,no.8
(In Western Washington experiment station.
Monthly bulletin, v. 8, no. 8, November, 1920)

1. State college of Washington authors, Works
of. 2. Clearing of land.

NL 0389046   WaPS

E639.73   Linklater, William Albert
W27bp   ... The construction and filling of silos..
no.10   [Pullman, State college] 1908.
[8]p. diagrs. (Washington (State) Agricultural experiment station. Popular bulletin
no. 10)

1. State college of Washington authors, Works
of. 2. Silo. I. Title.

NL 0389047   WaPS NN

E639.73   Linklater, William Albert, d, 1937
W27bm   ... Dairy feed supply ...
v.5,no.12
(In Western Washington experiment station.
Monthly bulletin, v. 5, no. 12, March, 1918)

1. State college of Washington authors, Works
of. 2. Feeding and feeding stuffs. 3. Cattle
Dairy.

NL 0389048   WaPS

Linklater, William Albert, d. 1937
... The dairymen's problem ...

(In Western Washington experiment station.
Monthly bulletin, v. 6, no. 5, August, 1918)

1. State college of Washington authors, Works
of. 2. Dairy products - Cost of production.
3. Dairy products - Marketing.

NL 0389049   WaPS

Linklater, William Albert, d. 1937
... Establishing a farm flock ...

(In Western Washington experiment station.
Monthly bulletin, v. 7, no. 2, May, 1919)

1. State college of Washington authors, Works
of. 2. Sheep.

NL 0389050   WaPS

E639.73   Linklater, William Albert, d. 1937
W27bm   ... Experiences with sheep ...
v. 6,no.11
(In Western Washington experiment station.
Monthly bulletin, v. 6, no. 11, February, 1919)

1. State college of Washington authors, Works
of. 2. Sheep - Washington (State).

NL 0389051   WaPS

E639.73   Linklater, William Albert, d. 1937
W27bm   ... The experiment station and the poultry
v.8,no.9 industry ...

(In Western Washington experiment station.
Monthly bulletin, v. 8, no. 9, December, 1920)

1. State college of Washington authors, Works
of. 2. Washington (State) Agricultural
experiment station. Western Washington experiment station. 3. Poultry industry and trade.

NL 0389052   WaPS

Linklater, William Albert,   d. 1937
... Extension of the work of the Experiment station ...

(In Western Washington experiment station.
Monthly bulletin, v. 7, no. 5, August, 1919)

1. State college of Washington authors, Works
of. 2. Washington (State) Agricultural
experiment station. Western Washington experiment station.

NL 0389053   WaPS

Linklater, William Albert, d. 1937
... Factors influencing the quality of milk
for condensing purposes. The succulent feed-
supply ...

(In Western Washington experiment station.
Monthly bulletin, V. 2, no. 9, November, 1914.

1. State college of Washington authors, Works
of. 2. Milk, Condensed. 3. Feeding and
feeding stuffs.

NL 0389054   WaPS

E639.73   Linklater, William Albert, d. 1937
W27bm   ... Fire and grass seed ...
v.8,no.6
(In Western Washington experiment station.
Monthly bulletin, v. 8, no. 6, September, 1920)

1. State college of Washington authors, Works
of. 2. Grazing. 3. Logged-off lands.

NL 0389055   WaPS

E639.73   Linklater, William Albert, d. 1937
W27bm   ... Feeding straw ...
v.5,no.6
(In Western Washington experiment station.
Monthly bulletin, v. 5, no. 6, September, 1917)

1. State college of Washington authors, Works
of. 2. Straw. 3. Feeding and feeding stuffs.

NL 0389056   WaPS

Linklater, William Albert, d, 1937.
Hog feeding.   Stillwater [1912].   16 p.   8°.   (Oklahoma, state. Agricultural Experiment Station. Bulletin 94.)

1. Hog—Feeding.
N. Y. P. L.   August 2, 1913.

NL 0389057   NN

VOLUME 334

E639.73 Linklater, William Albert, d. 1937
W27bm   ... Hog raising in Western Washington ...
v.8,no.5
(In Western Washington experiment station.
Monthly bulletin, v. 8, no. 5, August, 1920)

1. State college of Washington authors, Works
of. 2. Swine.

NL 0389058   WaPS

E639.73 Linklater, William Albert, d. 1937
W27bm   ... Hog raising on partially cleared land.
V. 2,no.2
(In Western Washington experiment station.
Monthly bulletin, V. 2, no. 2, May, 1914)

1. State college of Washington authors, Works
of. 2. Swine. 3. Hog industry.

NL 0389059   WaPS

Linklater, William Albert, d. 1937
... Important factors in milk production
...
(In Western Washington experiment station.
Monthly bulletin, v. 6, no. 6, September, 1918)

1. State college of Washington authors, Works
of. 2. Dairy products. 3. Farm produce -
Cost of production.

NL 0389060   WaPS

E639.73 Linklater, William Albert, d. 1937
W27bm   ... Market for mole skins ...
v.4,no.5
(In Western Washington experiment station.
Monthly bulletin, v. 4, no. 5, August, 1916)

1. State college of Washington authors, Works
of. 2. Moles (Animals). 3. Hides and skins

NL 0389061   WaPS

E639.73 Linklater, William Albert, d. 1937
W27bm   ... Notes on pig feeding ...
v.9,no.3
(In Western Washington experiment station.
Bi-monthly bulletin, v. 9, no. 3, July, 1921)

1. State college of Washington authors, Works
of. 2. Swine - Feeding.

NL 0389062   WaPS

E639.73 Linklater, William Albert
W27bp   ... Notes on swine management ... Pullman,
no.4   Wash., 1908.
         [4]p. illus. (Washington (State) Agricul-
tural experiment station. Popular bulletin
no. 4)

1. State college of Washington authors, Works
of. 2. Swine. 3. Swine - Feeding and
feeding stuffs.

NL 0389063   WaPS NN

Linklater, William Albert, d. 1937
... Proposed plan for buying and distribut-
ing breeding sheep for Western Washington farm
flocks ...
(In Western Washington experiment station.
Monthly bulletin, v. 7, no. 1, April, 1919)

1. State college of Washington authors, Works
of. 2. Sheep - Breeding. 3. Sheep -
Washington (State).

NL 0389064   WaPS

E639.73 Linklater, William Albert, d. 1937
W27bm   ... Saving the hay crop. Concerning hog
v.6,no.3 raising ...
(In Western Washington experiment station.
Monthly bulletin, v. 6, no. 3, June, 1918)

1. State college of Washington authors, Works
of. 2. Haying. 3. Swine.

NL 0389065   WaPS

Linklater, William Albert, d. 1937
... Sheep for farm flocks. Control of
Canadian thistles ...
(In Western Washington experiment station.
Monthly bulletin, v. 7, no. 4, July, 1919)

1. State college of Washington authors, Works
of. 2. Sheep. 3. Thistle, Canada.

NL 0389066   WaPS

Linklater, William Albert d. 1937.
... Some hog raising experiments ...
(In Western Washington experiment station.
Monthly bulletin, v. 3, no. 12, March, 1916)

1. State college of Washington authors, Work
of. 2. Swine.

NL 0389067   WaPS

Linklater, William Albert, d. 1937
... Warning (Against Carco) ...
(In Western Washington experiment station.
Monthly bulletin, v. 6, no. 4, July, 1918)

1. State college of Washington authors, Works
of. 2. Carco.

NL 0389068   WaPS

E639.73 Linklater, William Albert, d. 1937.
W27bm   ... The winter school ...
v.3,no.9
(In Western Washington experiment station.
Monthly bulletin, v. 3, no. 9, December, 1915)

1. State college of Washington authors, Works
of. 2. Agricultural colleges - Short courses.

NL 0389069   WaPS

E639.73 Linklater, William Albert, d. 1937
W27bm   ... The winter school ...
v.4,no.9
(In Western Washington experiment station.
Monthly bulletin, v. 4, no. 9, December, 1916)

1. State college of Washington authors, Work
of. 2. Agricultural colleges - Short courses

NL 0389070   WaPS

E639.73 Linklater, William Albert, d. 1937.
W27bm   ... Winter school for farmers ...
v.3,no.8
(In Western Washington experiment station.
Monthly bulletin, v. 3, no. 8, November, 1915)

1. State college of Washington authors, Works
of. 2. Agricultural colleges - Short courses.

NL 0389071   WaPS

Linklaters & Paines.
The Companies' act, 1929. Notes on the provisions of the Companies' act, 1929, as affecting the
placing of shares or securities of a company
see under Gt. Brit. Laws, statutes, etc.,
1910-1936 (George V)

HG2051   Linkletter, A. M., joint author.
.C38C7
Croteau, John Tougas, 1910-
The Farmers' creditors arrangement act in Prince Edward
Island [by] J. T. Croteau and A. M. Linkletter. [Halifax,
N. S., 1941]

F869   Linkletter, Arthur Gordon, 1912-
S3   Cavalcade of the Golden West, presented by the Golden Gate
.963   International Exposition, Adolph L. Vollmann, producer and
L5   general director. Written by A. G. Linkletter under supervision
of Samuel G. Blythe. Music composed and arranged by Emil
Gerstenberger. [San Francisco, 1939?]
[13] p. illus. 28cm.

NL 0389074   CU-B

Linkletter, Arthur Gordon, 1912-
People are funny; introd. by Bing Crosby. Illus. by
Reisie Lonette. [1st ed.] Garden City, N. Y., Doubleday,
1947.
x, 273 p. illus. 20 cm.
Story of the two radio shows, People are funny and House party.

1. People are funny (Radio program) 2. House party (Radio
program)

TK6570.B7L53   791.4   47—31232*

NL 0389075   DLC OrStbM Mi NcC OkU WaE WaS Or

TK   Linkletter, Arthur Gordon, 1912-
6570   People are funny; introd. by Bing Crosby. [Illus. by
B7L53   Reisie Lonette. Garden City, N. Y., Doubleday,
1948 [c1947]
x, 273 p. illus. 20 cm.
Story of the two radio shows, People are funny and House party.

NL 0389076   CoU

AP2   The Linkman; a literary and artistic quarterly review of con-
.L693   genial interests. v. 1, no. 1-v. 3, no. 2. Jan. 1916-July
1918. Gloucester [Eng.] J. Bellows [etc.] 1916-18.
3 v. in 1. 25 [?]
Title varies: v. 1-2, The Link; an intermediary for literary men, correspondents, col-
lectors & students.
Editors: 1916-1917, Max Bellows. 1918, W. G. Raffé.
No more published.

NL 0389077   ICU

Linko, Aleksandr K
Hydraires (Hydroidea). St. Petersbourg,
1911-12.
2 v. illus. (Faune de la Russie et des pays
limitrophes [i. e. Fauna SSSR] vol. 1, vol. 2,
livr. 1)

NL 0389078   MH

R96   Linko, Eino.
.A61   The orthostatic circulatory reactions of
v.40   patients with neurocirculatory asthenia, an
electrocardiographic study. Helsinki, Mer-
catorin Kirjapaino, 1951.
132 p. diagrs. (Annales medicinae internae
Fenniae, v.40, supplementum 11)

NL 0389079   ICU ViU

VOLUME 334

WX
2
GS8
L7C3a

LINKÖPING, Sweden. Centrallasarettet
  Årsberättelse.
  Vadstena ₁1886?₁-
    v. ~~WX2GS8 L7C3a~~
  Report for includes report of J. G.
  Westmans BB paviljong and of The
  Tuberkulospaviljong.

NL 0389080 DNLM

Linköping, Sweden. Domkyrkan. Biblioteket.
  Catalog öfver Linköping domkyrkas bibliothek
   see Linköping, Sweden. Stifts- och landsbiblioteket.

Linköping, Sweden. Frökontrollanstalten.
  Verksamhet.
  ₁Linköping₁
   v. 23 cm. annual.
  Report year ends June 30.

   1. Seed adulteration and inspection—Sweden.

  SB114.S8L5   51-20384

NL 0389082 DLC

Linköping, Sweden. Gymnasiet
 see
 Linköping, Sweden. Högre allmänna läroverket.

Linköping. Högre allmänna läroverket.
 Redogörelse för allmänna läroverken i Linköping, Eksjö
 och Vadstena.
 Linköping, 18
  v. 26ᵐ.

  ₁I.₁ Eksjö, Sweden. Lägre allmänna läroverket. II. Vadstena, Sweden.
 Lägre allmänna läroverket.

         CA 9-3259 Unrev'd
 Library of Congress LF4605.L5H6

NL 0389084 DLC

Linköping, Sweden. Östergötlands fornminnesförening
 see Östergötlands fornminnesförening.

Linköping, Sweden. Östergötlands läns hushållningssäll-
 skap
 see Östergötlands läns hushållningssällskap.

Linköping, Sweden. Östergötlands och Linköpings
 stads museum
  see Östergötlands och Linköpings stads
 museum.

Linköping, Sweden. Stifts- och läroverksbibliotek.
 ...₁ Katalog öfver Linköpings stifts- och läroverksbiblio-
 teks inkunabler, upprättad af Isak Collijn ... Uppsala,
 Almqvist & Wiksell; Leipzig, R. Haupt ₁1910₁

  50 p., 1 l. 25½ cm. (*Half-title:* Kataloge der inkunabeln der
 schwedischen öffentlichen bibliotheken von Isak Collijn. III)

  Series title in Swedish at head of t-p.
  On cover: Arbeten utgifna med understöd af Vilhelm Ekmans uni-
 versitetsfond, Uppsala. 7.
  Verso of t-p. dated 1909.

   1. Incunabula—Bibl.—Catalogs. I. Collijn, Isak Gustaf Alfred,

  Z240.L74   10-14494 rev

NL 0389088 DLC PU ICJ MdNWA OC1 ViU NN MoSFRR

Linköping, Sweden. Stifts- och läroverksbibliotek.
 Linköpings bibliotheks handlingar. Första₁-andra₁ delen
 ... Linköping, G. W. Lordicer och Björckegrens enka,
 1793-95.
  2 v. 18½ cm.
  Edited by J. A. Lindblom.

   1. Manuscripts. Sweden—Catalogs. I. Lindblom, Jakob Axelsson, 1746-1819.

  Z6621.L75   7-15802 rev

NL 0389089 DLC

Microfilm
F1880

Linköping, Sweden. Stifts- och läroverksbibliotek.
 Linköpings bibliotheks handlingar. Första₁-andra₁ delen
 ... Linköping, G. W. Lordicer och Björckegrens enka,
 1793-95.
  2 v. 18½ cm. on 1 reel.
  Edited by J. A. Lindblom.
  Microfilm of copy at Smithsonian Institute.
  Negative.

   1. Manuscripts. Sweden—Catalogs. I. Lindblom, Jakob Axelsson, 1746-1819.

NL 0389090 NNC

X327
L64J

Linköping, Sweden. Stifts- och läroverks-
 bibliothek.
 Linköpings bibliotheks handlingar. ny serie,
 bd.1- 1920-
 Linköping₍1934-
    plates. 21-26cm.

NL 0389091 CtY ICJ PBa

Linköping. Stifts- och läroverksbibliotek.
 Repertorium benzelianum
  see under Benzelius, Erik, Abp., 1675-
 1743.

Linköping, Sweden. Stifts- och läroverksbibliotek
 see also
 Linköping, Sweden. Stifts- och landsbiblioteket.

AS285
.G6
vol. 55,
no. 4

Linköping, Sweden. Stifts- och läroverks-
 bibliotek. Mss. (Kh 27)
 Gregorius, *monk of Stockholm, 15th cent.*
  Miracula defixionis Domini; en mirakelsamling från
 Stockholms dominikankloster efter Kh 27 i Linköpings
 stifts- och landsbibliotek utg. med inledning, översättning
 och register av Tryggve Lundén. Göteborg, Elanders
 boktr.. 1960.

Linköping, Sweden. Stifts- och landsbiblioteket.
 Berättelse.
 ₁Linköping₁
  v. 23 cm.
  Report year ends June 30.

  Z828.L54   55-40345 ‡

NL 0389095 DLC

       B 1288.4.5
Linkoeping, Sweden Stifts- och landsbiblioteket
₁Catalog öfver Linköpings domkyrkas bibliothek.
Linköping, 1861₁

 138 p.
 Binder's title
 Imperfect: all before p.1 lacking

 X refs.: Linkoeping, Sweden (City). Domkyrkan.
Biblioteket. Linkoeping, Sweden (Diocese). Domkyrkans
biblioteket (to main entry)

NL 0389096 MH

Linköping, Sweden. Stifts- och landsbiblioteket
 see also
Linköping, Sweden. Stifts- och läroverksbibliotek.

Linköping, *Sweden* (*Diocese*) *Bishop, 1589-1606* (*Petrus Benedicti*)
 Linköpingsbiskopen Petrus Benedicti's visitationsbok.
 Utg. av K. H. Johansson. Kalmar ₁1954₁
  xxviii, 138 p. facsims. 23 cm.

   1. Visitations, Ecclesiastical—Linköping, Sweden (Diocese) 2.
 Linköping, Sweden (Diocese) I. Johansson, Karl Herbert, 1891-
 ed.
             57-6720

  Minnesota. Univ. Libr.
 for Library of Congress ₁8₁

NL 0389098 MnU NN

Linköping, Sweden (Diocese) Domkyrkans
 biblioteket
  see Linköping, Sweden. Stifts- och
 landsbiblioteket.

Linköping, *Sweden* (*Diocese*) *Prästmötet.*
 Handlingar.
 Linköping, Östgöta correspondentens bogtr.
  v. illus. 25 cm.

  BX8040.L5A3   52-16843 rev

NL 0389100 DLC

016.9485
L648

Linköping domkapitel.
 Linköpings domkapitels arkiv;
 arkivstudier af Otto Holmström.
 Stockholm, Iduns kungl. hofboktr.,
 1901.
  x, 364 p. 25cm.
  1. Linköping (Diocese) Bibl.
 2. Sweden. Bibl.

NL 0389101 MnU

Linköpings bibliotheks handlingar
  see under Linköping, Sweden. Stifts- och
 läroverksbibliotek.

Linköpings domkyrkas bibliothek
  see Linköping, Sweden. Stifts- och
 landsbiblioteket.

Linköpings stift
 see Linköping, *Sweden* (*Diocese*)

QK31
.V3
L5

Linkola, Kaarlo, 1888-
 Edvard August Vainio, 1853-1929. Helsingforsiae, 1934.
  26 p. port. 24 cm. (Acta Societatis pro
 Fauna et Flora Fennica 57, no. 3)

XA
.C76
v.57:3

  Bibliography: p. 21-26.

   1. Vainio, Edvard August, 1853-1929.
 2. Vainio, Edvard August, 1853-1929 - Portraits.
 2. Vainio, Edvard August, 1853-1929 - Bibl. i. s.

NL 0389105 NNBG

VOLUME 334

Linkola, Kaarlo.
Lisätietoja Kuopion pitäjän kasvistosta. Helsingissä, 1914.
XA
.C76
v.39:5
52 p. 24 cm. (Acta Societatis pro Fauna et Flora Fennica, 39, no. 5)

1, Botany - Finland. i. t. ii. s.

NL 0389106   NNBG

4LF-48   Linkola, Kaarlo, 1888-
Puheita Helsingin Yliopiston lukuvuoden avajaisissa. Helsinki,   1950.
44 p.

NL 0389107   DLC-P4

Linkola, Kaarlo, 1888-
Studien ueber den einfluss der kultur auf die in den gegenden noerdlich vom Ladogasee. Helsingfors,1916.
Ina.Diss.

NL 0389108   ICRL

QK321.3
.L5   Linkola, Kaarlo, 1888-
Studien über den Einfluss der Kultur auf die Flora in den Gegenden nördlich vom Ladogasee. Helsingfors, 1916-21.
XA
.C76
v.45
2 v. 24 cm. (Acta Societatis pro Fauna et Flora Fennica 45, no. 1-2)

Copy 1 inscribed: Dr. H. A. Gleason hochachtungsvoll vom Verf.

1. Botany - Karelia. 2. Ethnobotany. i. t.
ii. s. a. b. Gleason, Henry Allan, 1882-

NL 0389109   NNBG OU

Linkol'n, Avraam
see
Lincoln, Abraham, *Pres. U. S.*, 1809-1865.

Linkomies, Edwin, Johan Hildegard, 1894-
...Antiikin kulttuuri tutkimuksen kohteena... Helsingissä, Otava [1947] 184 p. illus.,maps. 21cm.

Bibliographies, p. 181-182.

436150B. 1. Civilization, Ancient.

NL 0389111   NN

Q 60   LINKOMIES, EDWIN JOHAN HILDEGARD, 1894-
.H4   Auguralia und Verwandtes, von Edwin Flinck.
ser.B   Helsingfors, 1921.
v.11
pt.10
74 p. (Suomalainen tiedeakatemia, Helsinki. Toimituksia, ser. B, t. 11, 10)

1. Divination. 2. Augur (The word) I. Title.

NL 0389112   InU OCl

Linkomies, Edwin Johan Hildegard, 1894-
De ablativo absoluto quaestiones scripsit Edwin Flinck-Linkomies ... Helsingforsiae, 1929.

5 p.l.,[7]-272 p. 25ᶜᵐ. (Added t.-p.: Suomalaisen tiedeakatemian Toimituksia. Annales Academiae scientiarum fennicae. Sarja ... B,nid. ... XX [nio 1])

1.Latin language--Case.

NL 0389113   MiU InU ICU OCl CU OCU

Linkomies, Edwin Johan Hildegard, 1894-
De Octaviae praetextae auctore...
1919.
Inaug.-diss.-Helsingfors.

NL 0389114   MiU CU ICRL NjP IU

Q 60   LINKOMIES, EDWIN JOHAN HILDEGARD, 1894-
.H4   De Octaviae Praetextas auctore. Scripsit
ser.B   Edwin Flinck. Helsingforsiae, 1919.
v.11
pt.12
101 p. (Suomalainen tiedeakatemia, Helsinki. Toimituksia, ser. B, t. 11, 12)

1. Seneca, Lucius Annaeus, ca. 4 B.C.-65 A.D.--Octavia. I. Title.

NL 0389115   InU CtY OCl ICU

Q 60   LINKOMIES, EDWIN JOHAN HILDEGARD, 1894-
.H4   De singulari quadam epigrammatum antiquorum
ser.B   forma, scripsit Edwin Flinck. Helsingforsiae,
v.16   1922.
pt.2
32 p. (Suomalainen tiedeakatemia, Helsinki. Toimituksia, ser. B, t. 16, 2)

1. Epigrams--Greek--Hist. & crit. 2. Epigrams--Latin--Hist. & crit. I. Title.

NL 0389116   InU OCl PU

Linkomies, Edwin Johan Hildegard, 1894-
F. E. Sillanpää; eräitä peruspiirteitä. Helsingissä, Otava [1948]
42 p. 19 cm.
"Kirjoitettu Satakuntalaisen Osakunnan F. E. Sillanpään 60-vuotispäiväksi toimittamaa juhlajulkaisua varten."

1. Sillanpää, Frans Eemil, 1888-

New York. Public Libr.   A 51-660
for Library of Congress   [1]

NL 0389117   NN

Linkomies, Edwin, Johan Hildegard, 1894-
...Homeros... Helsingissä, Otava [1948] 493 p. illus.,maps. 25cm.

Bibliography, p. 483-487.

476099B. 1. Homer--Commentaries and criticism.

NL 0389118   NN

Johan Hildegard,
Linkomies, Edwin, 1894-
Ihmishengen tie; valikoima puheita. Helsingissä, Otava [1954] 209 p. 20cm.

1. Essays, Finnish.

NL 0389119   NN

Linkomies, Edwin Johan Hildegard, 1894-
Keisari Augustus ja rooman perintö. Helsingissä, Kustannusosakeyhtiö Otava [1946]
255 p. illus. 21 cm.

1. Augustus, Emperor of Rome, 63 B. c.-14 A. D. 2. Rome--Civilization. I. Title.
Name originally: Edwin Johan Hildegard Flinck.

DG279.L47   54-40870 ‡

NL 0389120   DLC NN

[Linkomies, Edwin Johan Hildegard] 1894-
Kutsu kuulemaan sitä julkista esitelmää jonka Helsingin Yliopiston maantieteen professori filosofiantohtori Väinö Tanner pitää virkaanastujaisissaan ... tammikuun 20 p:nä 1932./— inbjudning till åhörande av det offentliga föredrag ... varmed professorn i geografi vid Helsingfors Universitet filosofiedoktorn Väinö Tanner tillträder sitt ämbete den 20 januari 1932. [Einladung zur Professor-Installation.] Helsinki 1932. 12 pg. 8:o.
Progr. Hels.

NL 0389121   ICRL

LINKOMIES, Edwin Johan Hildegard] 1894-
Kutsu kuulemaan sitä julkista esitelmää jonka Helsingin Yliopiston suomalais-ugrilaisen/kansatieteen professori filosofian tohtori Albert Hämäläinen pitää virkaansa astuessaan ... helmikuun 3 p:nä 1932./— inbjudning till åhörande av det offentliga föredrag ... varmed professorn i finsk-ugrisk etnografi vid Helsingfors Universitet filosofiedoktorn Albert Hämäläinen tillträder sitt ämbete den 3 februari 1932. [Einladung zur Professor-Installation.] 7 pg. 8:o.
Progr. Hels.

NL 0389122   ICRL

LINKOMIES, Edwin Johan Hildegard] 1894-
Kutsu kuulemaan sitä julkista esitelmää jonka Helsingin Yliopiston pohjoismaisen filologian professori filosofian tohtori Torsten Evert Karsten pitää virkaansa astuessaan ... tammikuun 20 p:nä 1932./— inbjudning till åhörande av det offentliga föredrag ... varmed professorn i nordisk filologi vid Helsingfors Universitet filosofie doktorn Torsten Evert Karsten tillträder sitt ämbete den 20 januari 1932. [Einladung zur Professor-Installation.] Helsinki 1932. 11 pg. 8:o.
Progr. Hels.

NL 0389123   ICRL

4DE   Linkomies, Edwin Johan Hildegard,
47   1894-
Muinaisuuden näköaloja. Helsingissä, Kustannusosakeyhtiö Otava [1953]
213 p.

NL 0389124   DLC-P4 NN

Linkomies, Edwin Johan Hildegard, 1894-
Eine neue mithrische inschrift aus Ostia. Von Edwin Flinck.
(In Studia orientalia. Helsingforsiae, 1925. v. 1, p. [14]-24)
Caption title.
Bibliographical.

NL 0389125   PU

870.6
Is7
v.12
Linkomies, Edwin Johan Hildegard, 1894-
L'opera di Livio nella cultura finlandese. Roma, Reale Istituto di studi romani, 1943.
14 p. 25cm. (Quaderni liviani; l'opera di Livio nella cultura europea, 2)

[Gli studi romani nel mondo. vol. 12]

1. Livius, Titus. 2. Finland - Intellectual life.

NL 0389126   NNC

Linkomies, Edwin Johan Hildegard, 1894-   tr.
Law
Calonius, Matthias, 1738-1817.
Siviilioikeuden luennot. Wilhelm Chydeniuksen ja Väinö Nordströmin julkaisemasta latinankielisestä painoksesta suomentanut Edwin Linkomies. Helsinki, W. Söderström [1946]

VOLUME 334

Law

Linkomies, Edwin Johan Hildegard, 1894–
   defendant.
Ryti, Risto Heikki, *Pres. Finland, 1889–1956, defendant.*
   Sotasyyllisoikeudenkäynnin asiakirjoja. ₍Helsinki, Suomalaisen Kirjallisuuden Seuran Kirjapaino, 1945–

NL 0389129   CtY NN

Linkomies, Edwin Johan Hildegard, 1894–
   Die Syrerinnen im Kaiserpalast Roms. Helsingforsiae 1945.
   8 p. 25 cm. (Studia orientalia edidit Societas Orientalis Fennica, v. 11, no. 5)
   Bibliographical footnotes.

   1. Women in Rome (City) 2. Roman empresses.   I. Title.
(Series: Suomen Itämainen Seura, Helsingfors. Studia Orientalia, v. 11, no. 5)

   [PJ9.S86   vol. 11, no. 5]   A 53–5038

   Yale Univ. Library
   for Library of Congress   ₍1₎

NL 0389129   CtY NN

Linkous, C. E., joint author.
TN295 .U4 no. 7365   **Miller, Alexander Uriah,** 1880–
   ... Safety record of mine no. 7, Island creek coal co., Holden, Logan county, W. Va., by Alex U. Miller and C. E. Linkous. ₍Washington, 1946₎

TK3351 .L74   **Linkov, A**   **V**
   Производство силовых кабелей с бумажной изоляцией до 10 кв. Москва, Гос. энерг. изд-во, 1952.
   151 p. illus. 20 cm.
   Erratum slip inserted.
   Bibliography: p. ₍150₎

   1. Cables.   I. Title.
        Title transliterated: Proizvodstvo silovykh kabelei

   TK3351.L74   54–35131

NL 0389131   DLC

Lin'kov, G   **I**
   Внеклассная работа по математике. Москва, Гос. учебно-педагог. изд-во, 1954.
   61, ₍3₎ p. port., diagrs. 20 cm. (Опыт передового учителя)
   Bibliography: p. ₍63₎

   1. Mathematics—Study and teaching.   I. Title.
        Title transliterated: Vneklassnaia rabota po matematike.

   QA11.L72   55–36822

NL 0389132   DLC

4PG Rus. 740   **Lin'kov, Grigoriĭ Matveevich**
   Die unsichtbare Front. [1. Aufl.] Berlin, Verlag Volk und Welt, 1955.
   723 p.

NL 0389133   DLC-P4 CSt-H MB

D811 .L468 1947   **Lin'kov, Grigoriĭ Matveevich.**
   Война в тылу врага. Москва, Советский писатель, 1947.
   227 p. 20 cm.

   1. World War, 1939–1945—Personal narratives, Russian. 2. World War, 1939–1945—Underground movements—White Russia.   I. Title.
      Title transliterated: Voina v tylu vraga.

   D811.L468 1947   52–25044

NL 0389134   DLC

D811 .L468 1953   **Lin'kov, Grigoriĭ Matveevich.**
   Война в тылу врага. Москва, Советский писатель, 1953.
   653 p. illus. 21 cm.

   1. World War, 1939–1945—Personal narratives, Russian. 2. World War, 1939–1945—Underground movements—White Russia.   I. Title.
      Title transliterated: Voina v tylu vraga.

   D811.L468 1953   54–30356 ↑

NL 0389135   DLC

D81. .L468 1951   **Lin'kov, Grigoriĭ Matveevich.**
   Война в тылу врага. ₍Изд. 2., испр. и доп.₎ Москва, Гос. изд-во худож. лит-ры, 1951.
   570 p. illus., ports. 21 cm.

   1. World War, 1939–1945—Personal narratives, Russian. 2. World War, 1939–1945—Underground movements—White Russia.   I. Title.
      Title transliterated: Voina v tylu vraga.

   D811.L468 1951   52–25037

NL 0389136   DLC

Lin'kov, Grigoriĭ Matveevich.
   Вынужденные признания самураев. Москва, Гос. воен. изд-во, 1939.
   14 p. 18 cm. (Библиотека красноармейца)

   1. Russia—Bound.—Manchuria. 2. Manchuria—Bound. — Russia.   I. Title.   (Series: Biblioteka krasnoarmeitsa)
        Title transliterated: Vynuzhdennye priznaniia samuraev.

   DS784.L5   51–54133

NL 0389137   DLC

DK507 L7566 ed.2   **Lin'kov, Grigorii Matveevich.**
   Wojna na tyłach wroga. ₍Przełożył z rosyjskiego Adam Galis₎ wyd.2. ₍Wrszawa₎ Wyd. "Prasa wojskowa" ₍1948₎
   305, ₍1₎ p. 22ᶜᵐ.
   At head of title: G. Linkow.
   Translation of Voina v tulu vraga.

   1. World War, 1939–1945 – White Russia. 2. Guerrillas. 3. World War, 1939–1945 – Personal narratives, Russi an. I. Galis, Adam, tr. II. Title.

NL 0389138   CSt-H

Lin'kov, Grigorii Matveevich.
   Записки партизана. ₍Москва₎ Московский рабочий, 1949.
   137 p. 17 cm.

   1. World War, 1939–1945—Personal narratives, Russian. 2. Guerrillas.   I. Title.   *Title transliterated:* Zapiski partizana.

   D811.L47   50–35454 rev

NL 0389139   DLC

Linkov, IA   **I**
   Очерки истории крестьянского движения в России в 1825–1861 гг. Москва, Гос. учебно-педагог. изд-во, 1952.
   276 p. 3 fold. maps. 23 cm.

   1. Peasantry—Russia—Hist. 2. Russia—Pol. & govt.—19th cent.   I. Title(/) NUC SEE   *Title transliterated:* Ocherki istorii krest'ianskogo dvizheniia v Rossii.

   HD715.L55   54–15776

NL 0389140   DLC OrU CSt CtY

TN845 .L5   **Linkov, IA**   **L**
   Обработка графитовых руд; пособие по техминимуму. Москва, Гос. изд-во лит-ры по строит. материалам, 1949.
   47 p. diagrs. 21 cm.
   At head of title: Я. Л. Линков, И. Д. Аренков.

   1. Graphite.   I. Arenkov, I. D., joint author.
        Title transliterated: Obrabotka grafitovykh rud.

   TN845.L5   50–15549

NL 0389141   DLC

Lin'kov, Lev Aleksandrovich, 1908–
   Источник жизни; рассказы. ₍Москва₎ Молодая гвардия, 1949.
   157 p. col. plates. 17 cm.
   Contents.—Источник жизни.—"Пост семи героев."—Свидетель с заставы № 3.—Обыкновенная операция.—Заслон у Большой зарубки.—Женщина на берегу.—Крепыш.—Гость из Америки.—Призвание.—Яблони в цвету.

   I. Title.   *Title transliterated:* Istochnik zhizni.

   PG3476.L595 I 8   51–35452

NL 0389142   DLC

Lin'kov, Lev Aleksandrovich, 1908–
   Капитан "Старой черепахи"; повесть. ₍Москва₎ Молодая гвардия, 1948.
   197 p. plates. 21 cm.

   I. Title.   *Title transliterated:* Kapitan "Staroi cherepakhi."

   PG3476.L595K3 1948   51–35451

NL 0389143   DLC

Lin'kov, Lev Aleksandrovich, 1908–
   Отважные сердца. ₍Москва₎ Молодая гвардия, 1951.
   349 p. plates. 21 cm.
   Contents.—Солдаты Дзержинского.—Источник жизни.—Исполнение желаний.—Обыкновенная операция.—Встреча в поезде.—Женщина на берегу.—Заслон у Большой зарубки.—Самая большая любовь.—Счастье Петра Орлова.—Капитан "Старой черепахи."

   I. Title.   *Title transliterated:* Otvazhnye serdtsa.

   PG3476.L595O8   51–35450

NL 0389144   DLC

Lin'kov, Lev Aleksandrovich, 1908–
   У заставы; рассказы. ₍Москва₎ Молодая гвардия ₍1954₎
   181 p. 21 cm.

   I. Title.   *Title transliterated:* U zastavy.

   PG3476.L595U2   56–20627 ↑

NL 0389145   DLC

Linkovski, Barukh
   see
   Linn, Baruch, 1898–1964.

Linkow, G
   see Linkov, Grigorii Matveevich.

TN815 L7   **Linkowski, L**
   Application of the shaking conveyor to mining, by L. Linkowski, C. R. Claghorn ₍and₎ R. A. Walter. Bochum, Germany, New York, Eickhoff Brothers ₍1927₎.
   111 p. illus., diagrs. 21 cm.
   ₍Print no. 574₎
   A translation of the original German: Die schüttelrutsche und ihre anwendung im bergbau.

   1. Conveying   machinery. 2. Mining machinery.

NL 0389148   DI

VOLUME 334

TW815
L71
1926
Linkowski, L
Die schüttelrutsche und ihre anwendung im bergbau. [2.aufl.] Bochum [Germany], New York, Gebrüder Eickhoff, 1926.
100 [1] p. illus., diagrs. 21 cm.
(Druckschrift nr. 1054)

1. Conveying machinery. 2. Mining machinery.

NL 0389149 DI

Links, Emil, d. 1914, ed.

Austria. *Oberster gerichts- und cassationshof.*
Die rechtsprechung des K. K. Obersten gerichtshofes in civil-, handels-, wechsel-, marken-, musterschutz- und privilegiensachen, einschliesslich der Advocaten- und Notariatsordnung nebst einem anhange: Die entscheidungen des deutschen Reichsgerichtes in handels- und wechselsachen. Herausgeber: d' Emil Links ... 1.- bd.; 1888-19
Wien, Plaut & comp. [etc.] 1889-19

Links, Jan, 1922-
Een hypothese over het mechanisme van de (phobo-) chemotaxis. De carotenoïden, steroïden en vetzuren van *Polytoma uvella.* 's-Gravenhage, Excelsior [1955]
153 p. diagrs., tables. 25 cm.
Proefschrift—Leyden.
Vita.
Summary in English.
"Errata" leaf inserted.
"Stellingen": [3] p. inserted.
Includes bibliographies.

1. Chemotaxis. 2. Polytoma uvella. 3. Carotinoids. 4. Steroids. 5. Acids, Fatty.
QH511.L53   59-42103

NL 0389151 DLC MH-F CtY NIC NN

Sp Col
Underground
L Du
L7565ka
[Links, Karel] illus.
[Kalender voor het jaar 1944. Met tekeningen door K.L. Links. Utrecht, Bezige Bij, 1944]
[6]f. col. illus. 28cm.

Jong. 441.

NL 0389152 IEN

Sp Col
Underground
Du
H675Yt
[Links, Karel] illus.
Moffenspiegel; een boekje over Adolf de Eerste (en de laatste) en zein trawanten. [1. druk. Utrecht] Bezige Bij, 1944.
[40]p. col. illus. 19cm.

Jong. 569.

1. Hitler, Adolf, 1889-1945. Portraits, caricatures, etc. I. Title.

NL 0389153 IEN

Links, Karel.
Moffenspiegel; een boekje over Adolf de Eerste (en de laatste) en zijn trawanten. [Amsterdam] De Bezige Bij, 1945.
[44] p. (p. [5]-[43]; illus. (part col.)) 20 cm.

1. Hitler, Adolf, 1889- —Portraits, caricatures, etc. 2. World War, 1939-1945—Humor, caricatures, etc. 3. Netherlands—Hist.—German occupation, 1940-1945. I. Title.
A 48-2850*
Harvard Univ. Library
for Library of Congress   [1]

NL 0389154 MH CtY IEN

Links, Karl Leendert
see Links, Karel.

Links, Marty, illus.

Weill, Irma.
About Tom, by Irma Weill, illustrated by Marty Links. New York, The Island workshop press, 1941.

Links, Marty.
Bobby sox; the life and times of Emmy Lou. [1st ed.] New York, Hawthorn Books [1954]
unpaged. illus. 24 cm.

1. American wit and humor, Pictorial.   I. Title.

NC1429.L54A43   741.5   54-9887 †

NL 0389157 DLC NN WaT

Links, Rudolf
Die verletzung der anzeigepflicht in der lebensversicherung ... von Rudolf Links. Düsseldorf, G.H. Nolte, 1935.
iv, 35 p. 22cm.
Inaug.-diss.- Köln.
"Literatur-verzeichnis": p. iv.

NL 0389158 MH-L

HX6
.L48
Links.
Offenbach/M [Verlag 2000]
v. illus. 32 cm. monthly.
"Sozialistische Zeitung."
Issued by Sozialistisches Büro.

1. Communism—Periodicals.   I. Sozialistisches Büro.

HX6.L48   75-649919

NL 0389159 DLC

Links. *Portland, 1888*
see under Clark, Mrs. A   O   com

Link's business college, Portland, Ore.
[Announcement]

NL 0389161 OrP

650.7
L648
Link's Business College, Portland, Ore.
Link's Business College (incorporated) a school of efficiency in bookkeeping, accounting, office practice, shorthand, typewriting, secretarial training, and allied business subjects. Portland [Ore., 1920?]
[24]p. illus.,ports. 27cm.

1. Oregon. Business education. x Portland, Ore. Link's Business College.

NL 0389162 OrU

LINKS CLUB, INC., New York.
The Links.
New York.   v.   16°.

Includes its Certificate of incorporation, constitution, by-laws and list of members.

1. Golf--Clubs and assoc.--U.S.--   N.Y.--New York.   I. Title.

NL 0389163 NN

Coll
LI555
1890
Harris
Collection
Links of memory. New York, Holiday publishing co. [1890?]
[16]p. front., col. illus. 17cm.

Title-page illustrated in color.
Includes American poetry.

NL 0389164 RPB

... The links of the Canterbury tales, and the Wife of Bath's prologue
see under Chaucer, Geoffrey, d. 1400. Canterbury tales. Two or more tales.

Links of the Lower house. Or, an alphabetical list of the members of the House of commons, showing the counties, cities, or boroughs for which they sit; and also showing the offices, pensions ... services, and other matters and things, belonging or attached to the ... members and their families. [London] Printed by C. Clement, and sold by J. M. Cobbett [1821]
32 p. 21½cm.
[Queen Caroline pamphlets, v. 1, no. 2]
Caption title.
1. Gt. Brit. Parliament. House of commons.
4-28171†
Library of Congress   DA538.A22Q3
——— Copy 2.   [Miscellaneous pamphlets, v. 972, no. ;

NL 0389166 DLC CtY MnU

Links und rechts der Autobahn. [Herausgeber: Benzin-Benzol-Vertrieb (BV) Essen, W. Witzel, 1951]
5 v. (chiefly col. illus., col. maps) 24 x 25 cm.
Cover title.
CONTENTS.—[1] Lübeck-Bremen, Helmstedt-Herford.—[2] Göttingen-Bruchsal.—[3] Karlsruhe-Salzburg.—[4] Hof-München.—[5] Herford-Frankfurt/M.

1. Germany—Descr. & trav.—1945-   I. Benzin-Benzol-Vertrieb.
DD43.L52 1951   55-35414

NL 0389167 DLC

Links und rechts der Autobahn. [Herausgeber: BV-Aral Aktiengesellschaft. Essen, Witzel, 1952?]
5 v. (chiefly col. illus., col. maps) 24 x 25 cm.
Cover title.
CONTENTS.—[1] Lübeck-Bremen, Helmstedt-Herford.—[2] Northeim-Bruchsal, Mannheim-Kaiserlautern.—[3] Karlsruhe-Salzburg.—[4] Hof-München.—[5] Herford-Frankfurt/M, Aachen-Düren (Köln) "Der BV ... hat dieses Werk geschaffen."

1. Germany—Descr. & trav.—1945-   I. Benzin-Benzol-Vertrieb. II. BV-Aral Aktiengesellschaft.
DD43.L52 1952   55-36562

NL 0389168 DLC

DK511
.2L756
Linksch, Erich.
..Litauen und die Litauer; einführende betrachtungen. Stuttgart, Z.Schrader, 1917.
1 p.l., [5]-57 p. 21½cm.

1.Lithuania - History. 2. Lithuania - Economic conditions. 3. Lithuania - Race question. 4. Lithuanians. I. Title.

NL 0389169 CSt-H DLC-P4 PU

FILM
HX
no.1
Die Linkskurve.
Herausgeber: Johannes R. Becher, Andor Gabor (u.a.) v.1-4; August 1929-December 1932. Berlin, Internationaler Arbeiterverlag, 1929-1932.
v. illus. monthly.

Microfilm (negative) [New York] The New York Public Library. 1 reel. 35mm.

√1.Socialism - Period. √2.Socialism in Germany - Period.

NL 0389170 CLSU

VOLUME 334

GF
L648

Die Linkskurve.
/ Goethe-sonderheft, die Linkskurve ... ¡Berlin, 1932?¡
cover-title, 40 p.

  Contents.--K. A. Wittfogel: Goethe-"feier"?--Marx und Engels über Goethe; eine unbekannte abhandlung aus dem jahre 1847.--Georg Lukacs: Der faschisierte Goethe.

  1. Goethe, Johann Wolfgang von, 1749-1832 - Criticism, interpretation, etc.

NL 0389171   NNC

---

                                    *5061.20**

Linksma Walanda. Nedelinis rasztas, paszwenstas del suraminimo lietuwiu Amerike ... surinktos ir iszduotos per D. T. Boczkauska. Metas 2. Jan. 3–Dec. 26, 1900.
Mahanoy City. 1900. 1 v. 31½ cm.

N1354 <del>↕</del> Boczkauskas, D. T., ed. – Lithuania. Periodicals. — Lithuania. Lang. Works in Lithuanian. — Periodicals. Lithuanian. United States.

NL 0389172   MB

    Ein Linkspolitiker.

JN8971
S6W4

    Der Weg der schweizerischen Sozialdemokratie; Entscheidung des demokratischen Sozialismus, von einem Linkspolitiker. Aarburg, Schlossverlag, 1948.

    Linksz, Arthur, 1900–
Physiology of the eye. Foreword by Walter B. Lancaster. New York, Grune & Stratton, 1950–

    v. diagrs. 26 cm.

    Bibliography: v. 1, p. 325.

    Contents.--v. 1. Optics.

    1. Eye. 2. Optics, Physiological.   I. Title.

    QP475.L7   612.84   50–5797

DNLM TxU OU ViU NbU-M OrU-M OrU CaBVaU
NL 0389174   DLC IdPI CU GU CSt PU PPC PPJ ICU ICJ

    Linksz, Arthur, 1900–
The stereoscope as an orthoptic instrument ¡by¡ A. Linksz, M.D. ... Chicago, Ill., c1941.
cover-title, 19p. illus., diagrs. 25½ cm.

    "Reprinted from the Archives of ophthalmology, September 1941, vol. 26."

NL 0389175   PSt

Linksz, Artur: Versuche zur Narkose der Leberfunktionen. 1. Der Einfluss von Narkotiumlösungen auf den Zuckerstoffwechsel der überlebenden Froschleber. Berlin: J. Springer 1924. S. 572 —586. 8°. — Auszug: o. O. (1925). 1 Bl. 8° ¶ Vollst. in: Pflügers Archiv f. d. ges. Physiol. Bd 204.
Kiel, Med. Diss. v. 27. Juli 1925   [U 25. 5296

NL 0389176   ICRL

    Linküln, Abrakham
      see
    Lincoln, Abraham, *Pres. U. S.,* 1809–1865.

    Linküln, Ibrăhim
      see
    Lincoln, Abraham, *Pres. U. S.,* 1809–1865.

Linkus, Anicetus M   *ed.*
Šv. Kryžiaus lietuvių parapijos 50 metų istoriniai bruožai. ¡Chicago¡ 1954.

    154 p. illus., ports. 28 cm.

    Cover title: Golden Jubilee of Holy Cross Lithuanian Roman Catholic Parish, Chicago, Illinois, 1904–1954.
Lithuanian and English.

    1. Chicago. Holy Cross Church (Lithuanian)   I. Title. II. Title: Golden Jubilee of Holy Cross Lithuanian Roman Catholic Parish.

    BX4603.C5H6   56–18084

NL 0389179   DLC

LINLEY, Arthur.
Der freischütz.   [Boston, cop. 1865].

    Mus 460.15

NL 0389180   MH

Linley, C M.
... Details of typical mechanisms, by C. M. Linley ... with eighty-five illustrations. London, Scott, Greenwood & son, 1923.

    viii, 104 p. illus., diagrs. 19ᶜᵐ. (The Broadway engineering handbooks, vol. xxxiii)

    1. Mechanical movements.   I. Title.

    Library of Congress   ¡J181.L5   24–6175

NL 0389181   DLC MtBC WaS CU MiU OC1 ICJ MB NN

Linley, C M.
... The lathe users' handbook, by C. M. Linley ... with ninety illustrations and diagrams. London, Scott, Greenwood & son, 1923.

    vii, 187 p. illus., diagrs. 19ᶜᵐ. (The Broadway engineering handbooks. vol. xxxiv)

    1. Lathes.

    Library of Congress   TJ1218.L5   24–6024

NL 0389182   DLC ICJ NN

Linley, C M.
Practical advice to inventors and patentees; inventions and how to patent them, by C. M. Linley. London, New York ¡etc.¡ Sir I. Pitman & sons, ltd., 1925.

    vi, 126 p. illus. 18½ᶜᵐ.

    1. Inventions. 2. Patents.

    Library of Congress   T339.L45   25—14062

NL 0389183   DLC NcD NN

Linley, C M.
Recent progress in engineering production, by C. M. Linley ... London, E. Benn limited, 1924.

    xiii p., 1 l., 17–340 p. illus., II fold. pl. 25ᶜᵐ.

    1. Mechanical engineering. 2. Machinery. 3. Machine-tools. 4. Metal-work.   I. Title: Engineering production.

    Library of Congress   TJ145.L77   25—11008

NL 0389184   DLC PPD CtY MiU OC1 NN

Linley, C M   L621.9 8500
Recent progress in engineering production, by C. M. Linley, ... New York, D. Van Nostrand Company, 1925.

    xiii, [2], 17–340 p. illus., II fold. pl. 25½ᶜᵐ.

    "Latest developments and improvements in connection with machine tools, works practice, manufacturing methods, processes and alloys."—Pref.
Printed in Great Britain.

NL 0389185   ICJ PPF CU MH MB

Linley, Dora K
[Anatomical drawings] 72 plates in portfolio.

    Photostat reproductions.
Plates in duplicate, positive & negative.

NL 0389186   OC1

Linley, Florence.
I am coming, papa. Louisville, D. P. Faulds ¡*1869¡
8 p. 36 cm.

    1. Songs (Medium voice) with piano.   I. Title.

    M1621.L   52–55801

NL 0389187   DLC

Linley, Francis, 1774–1800.
    Works by this author printed in America before 1801 are available in this library in the Readex Microprint edition of Early American Imprints published by the American Antiquarian Society.
    This collection is arranged according to the numbers in Charles Evans' American Bibliography.

NL 0389188   DLC

Linley, Francis, 1774–1800.
A lover I'm born; a song. Holborn, Printed for I. Carr ¡17—¡

    ¡2¡ p. 32 cm.

    Caption title.
No. 20 in a vol. with title: ¡Collection of songs. v. p., ca. 1800¡
For piano, with interlinear words; part for guitar at end.

    1. Songs (High voice) with piano—To 1800.   I. Title.

    M1.A1C no. 20   M 54–386

NL 0389189   DLC

Linley, Francis, 1774–1800.
The loyal soldier a favorite song. Sung by Mr. Page at the Public Concerts, composed by F. Linley, organist of Pentonville Chapel. The words by Mr. Romer. London, printed & sold by J. Bland...45 Holborne.
3p. folio.

    First line: Ned oft had brav'd the field of battle.
"German flute?"- 4 lines at end.

NL 0389190   MH

M   Linley, Francis, 1771–1800.
1533   Musical riddles. A selection of enigmas,
L5   arranged as duetts for two voices, with an
cage   accompaniment for the harp and piano forte, for the improvement of juvenile performers.... Op. 10. London, E. Riley, [ca. 1799].

    [2], 16 p. Fol.

NL 0389191   DFo

---

q780.8
8h37
no.12   LINLEY, FRANCIS, 1771–1800.
Rare   My love is the pride of the plain. A ballad.
Books   Sung by Mʳˢ Harlowe of Sadlers Wells. Comᵈ by
Col   F. Linley ...
     London Printed by J. Carr Middle Row Holborn ... [17—] 2l. 34½ cm.

    No. [12] in volume with title [Sheet music]
Caption title.
With piano accompaniment.
Score for the guitar at end.

    I. Title.

NL 0389192   TxU DLC PPiU

VOLUME 334

Linley, Francis, 1774-1800.

A new assistant for the piano-forte or harpsichord, containing the necessary rudiments for beginners, with twelve airs or short lessons, progressively arrang'd: to which is added, six sonatas ... with preludes, rules for thorough bass, a short dictionary of musical terms. &c. ... Compil'd, compos'd, and arrang'd, by F. Linley ... Baltimore Printed & sold by I: Carr at his music store Market street. And by B: Carr at his musical repositorys Market street Philadelphia & William s⁴. New York [179–]

3 p. l., [3]-32 p. 33ᶜᵐ.
Engraved throughout.
1. Pianoforte—Instruc-   tion and study.

Library of Congress   MT222.A2L70   9—4327

NL 0389193   DLC NN MBHM

[Linley, Francis] 1774-1800.
[Practical introduction to the organ, op. 6]
Fifteen preludes for the organ...Eight voluntarys [sic]...[eight "introductions" and fugues, and thirty-six psalm tunes] [London, Printed by the Author c.1797-98]
Title page and description of the organ lacking: Information re-constructed from Dictionary of National Biography; Fetis, v.5, p.312; Humphries, Music publishers in the British Isles, p. 213; and Gentlemen's Magazine, 1800, p. 1006.

NL 0389194   PPi

LINLEY, FRANCIS, 1771-1800.

A practical introduction to the organ; in five parts, viz: necessary observations, preludes, voluntaries, fugues, & full pieces, and a selection of all the psalms in general use, with interludes; ..by F. Linley. Op. 6... 9ᵗʰ edition corrected and enlarged.   [London] Printed for A. Hamilton [ca. 1800]   119 p.   18 x 26cm.
The first two parts have special title pages.
1. Organ.

NL 0389195   NN

M786.41   **Linley, Francis, 1774-1800.**
L757s   [Sonatas, piano]
Music   ... Six sonatas, one of which is adapted
lib.   for two performers ... Baltimore, I. Carr
Also   [179–]
Film   2, 11-21p.   34cm.
M786.4   Xerox copy of original at the New York
P581b   Public Library.
Music   His: A new assistant for the piano-forte
lib.   or harpsichord, p[1]-2, 11-21.

NL 0389196   NcU

Linley, Francis, 1774-1800.

Six solos for the German flute... composed in a familar style for the amusement of juvenile performers... [London, 1815?]
28 p.

NL 0389197   NjP

Spec Collec
Sheet Music
784.3061   **Linley, George, 1798-1865.**
L648a   The angel child: ballad, written by
Charlotte Elizabeth [pseud.]; music by
George Linley. Boston, Oliver Ditson, ca.
1845. Pl. no. 1835.
5p. 26x33cm.
Caption title.

1. Ballads, American. 2. Songs (Medium voice) with piano. I. Tonna, Charlotte Elizabeth (Browne), 1790-1846. II. Title.

NL 0389198   KPT

Linley, George, 1798-1865.

Be but the same; a ballad.   Boston, Parker & Ditson [ca. 1840]

4 p. 34 cm.

Caption title.
For voice and piano.

1. Songs (Medium voice) with piano.   I. Title.

M1.A13L   M 60-1173

NL 0389199   DLC

---

*
M1
S444   **Linley, George, 1798-1865.**
v.67
no.30   Be but the same, a ballad.   Boston,
Parker & Ditson, 135 Washington Street
[before 1842?]
4 p.   32cm.   [Sheet music collection, v. 67,
no. 30]

1. Songs with piano.   I. Title.

NL 0389200   ViU

W.C.L.   **Linley, George, 1798-1865.**
M780.88
A512VT   Bonnie new moon; ballad, composed by
no.10   George Linley.   New York, W. Hall [186-]
Pl. no. 4392.
7 p.   34 cm.

For voice and piano.
[No. 10] in a vol. of songs compiled by
A. L. Newcomer.
1. Songs (Medium voice) with piano.   I.
Title.

NL 0389201   NcD

---

*
M1
.A13N   **Linley, George, 1798-1865.**
.L45B6
1860   Bonnie new moon; ballad.   Figure 2½ in
7 pointed star.   Boston, Oliver Ditson & Co.,
277 Washington St. ...   [1860?]   Pl. no.
19715.
5 p.   34cm.

1. Songs with piano.   I. Title.

NL 0389202   ViU

Linley, George, 1798-1865.
By the waters of Xarama
see under   Loder, Edward James, 1813-
1865.

Linley, George, 1798-1865.
Catherine Grey; a grand opera, in three acts...
see under   Balfe, Michael William 1808-
1870.

---

*
M1
.A13N   **Linley, George, 1798-1865.**
.L45C4
1850   Clara; ballad from David Copperfield.   25¢
nett.   New York, Wm. Hall & Son, 239 Broad-
way; Rochester, A. Grant, 51 State St.
[185-?]   Pl. no. 1190.
5 p.   34cm.
"Inscribed to Mrs. Charles Dickens."
Pearson, Eng'r.
Imperfect: p. 3-4 wanting.
1. Songs with piano.   I. Dickens, Charles.
David Copperfield.   II. Title.

NL 0389205   ViU

---

*
M1
.A13N
.L45C6   **Linley, George, 1798-1865.**
1840   Come to the dance; a favorite song.
Written, composed and arr. for the piano
forte by George Linley.   Philadelphia, A. Fiot, Publisher, Importer of
music, musical instruments &c.   196 Chesnut
St.   [184-?]
5 p.   34cm.
Moland, Sc.
1. Songs with piano.   I. Title.

NL 0389206   ViU

Linley, George, 1798-1865.
Comrades in arms...
see under
Adam, Adolphe Charles, 1803-1856.

Linley, George, 1798-1865.
The Corsair's Farewell! Song, written and com-
posed by G. Linley. [Piano acc.]   London,
D'Almaine & Co. [18-]
5 p.   F.   (Illustrated Songs, Ballads, & Duets,
No. 4)

NL 0389208   NN

Linley, George, 1798-1865.
Der Zigeunerin Warnung...
see under   Benedict, Sir Julius, 1804-1885

---

*
M1
.S444   **Linley, George, 1798-1865.**
v.120
10.14   The dining gentleman.   Most respectfully
dedicated to all lovers of good company.
New York, Firth & Hall, 1 Franklin Sqr [sic]
[183- or 184-]
[5] p.   34cm.   [Sheet music collection, v. 120,
no. 14]
Illustrated cover: Lith. of Endicott.

1. Songs with piano.   I. Title.

NL 0389210   ViU

LINLEY, GEORGE, 1798-1865.

Estelle! Ballad, written and composed by George
Linley.   London, Cramer, Addison & Beale [184-?]
Pl. no. 2636.   4 p.   illus.   34cm.

For voice and piano.
First line: By him forsaken, bereft of home.

1. Songs, English.

NL 0389211   NN

Music
ML   **Linley, George, 1798-1865.**
48
N714   [Francesca Doria. Libretto. English]
v.1
no.2   Francesca Doria: or, The bandit of the
Abruzzi. A new and original opera, in two
acts, the libretto by Val Morris. The poetry, overture, and the whole of the music by
George Linley. First performed at the Princess's Theatre. Oxford Street, on Saturday,
March 3rd, 1849. London, Printed by S. G.
Fairbrother [1849?]
29 p.   24cm.

No. 2 in vol. lettered: Nineteenth century
operas. Librettos. 1.

1. Operas--Librettos. I. Morris, Val.
Francesca Doria. II. Title. III. Title: The
bandit of the Abruzzi.

NL 0389213   NIC

VOLUME 334

Linley, George, 1798-1865.   No. 1 in **M.235.16
God save King William. The new national anthem. [With accompaniment for pianoforte.]
London. Goulding & D'Almaine. [183-?] (1), 5 pp. 33 cm.

M4380 — T.r. — National and patriotic songs. England.

NL 0389214   MB

---

q784.3   Linley, George, 1798-1865.
Sh37   The golden ring, Scotch ballad … as sung by
v.9   Miss Addie S. Ryan, at the concerts of the "Men-
no.1   delssohn quintette club." Arranged by Thos.
          Ryan.   Boston, O. Ditson & co.; Chicago, Lyon
          & Healy; [etc., etc.] c1865.
          5p.
          [Sheet music printed in Chicago prior to 1871.
          v.9, no.1]
          Plate no.: 22548.

          I. Ryan, Thomas, 1827-1903. II. Title.

NL 0389215   IU MB

W.C.L. Linley, George, 1798-1865.
M780.88
A512VJ   Good night sweet mother. Cleveland, S.
no.38   Brainard & Co. [185-]
          6 p. 35 cm.
          For two voices and piano.
          At head of title: Brainard &Co's. edition
          [of] select vocal duetts by various authors.
          [No. 38] in a collection of vocal music
          compiled by Celia B. Mann, v. p., ca. 1845-60.
          1. Vocal duets with piano. I. Title.

NL 0389216   NcD

LINLEY, GEORGE, 1798-1865.

          Grace Darling; ballad written and composed by
          George Linley. Third edition. London, Cramer,
          Addison & Beale [184-?] Pl. no. 2604. 5 p. illus.
          35cm.
          For voice and piano.
          First line: Oh! Father lov'd, the storm is raging.
          1. Songs, English.

NL 0389217   NN

VM   LINLEY, GEORGE, 1798-1865.
1   Grace Darling; or, The wrecker's daughter.
F 91   Ballad. Written and composed by George Linley.
no.153   Philadelphia, G.Willig [18--]
          5p. 33½cm.

          Vocal solo.

—   —— Philadelphia, G.E.Blake [18--]
no.154   [2]p. 33½cm.

NL 0389218   ICN

---

*
M1
.S444   Linley, George, 1798-1865.
v.160
no.48   Grace darling; or, the Wreckers daughter.
          Ballad. Price 50 cents. Philadelphia,
          George Willig, 171 Chesnut [sic] Street
          [after 1819?]
          5 p. 33cm. [Sheet music collection, v. 160,
          no. 48]
          P. S. David, Lith.

          1. Songs with piano. I. Title.

NL 0389219   ViU

Linley, George, 1798-1865.   No. 2 in *8050a.730.23
Hear me but once. Ballad [with pianoforte accompaniment.]
= London. Cramer, Beale & Co. [185-?] 5 pp. 36 cm.

L4969 — T.r. — Songs. With music.

NL 0389220   MB

Linley, George.   8051.641
The heart of thy Norah is breaking for thee. An Irish ballad. [Accomp. for piano.]
= New York. Jaques. [185-?] 5 pp. F°.

G4048 — T.r. — Songs. With music.

NL 0389221   MB

Linley, George.   8053.322
The heart of thy Norah is breaking for thee. [Ballad. Accomp. for pianoforte.]
= Boston. Ditson & Co. [186-?] 5 pp. [The boudoir.] F°.

G3984 — T.r. — Songs. With music.

NL 0389222   MB

---

*
M1
.S444   Linley, George, 1798-1865.
v.78,
no.28   The heart of thy Norah is breaking for
          thee. An Irish ballad, sung by Mr. John
          Templeton. 25¢ nett. New York, Atwill,
          201 Broadway [186-?]
          5 p. 35cm. [Sheet music collection, v. 78,
          no. 28]
          Stamped on cover: G. W. Willig, Baltimore.

          1. Songs with piano. I. Title.

NL 0389223   ViU NN

Linley, George. 1798-1865.   8053.349
I do not ask to offer thee. [Song. A. Accomp. for pianoforte.]
= Boston. Ditson & Co. [184-?] 5 pp. [The boudoir. A collection of favorite songs.] F°.

G3080 — T.r. — Songs. With music.

NL 0389224   MB

---

q784.3   Linley, George, 1798-1865.
Sh37   I hear the wee bird singing, as sung by Miss
v.11   Addie S. Ryan, at the concerts of the Mendelssohn
no.9   quintette club. Music by Geo. Linley, arranged by
          Thos. Ryan.   Boston, O. Ditson & co.; Chicago,
          Lyon & Healy; [etc., etc.] c1865.
          5p.
          [Sheet music printed in Chicago prior to 1871.
          v.11,no.9]
          Plate no.: 22615.

          I. Ryan, Thomas, 1827-1903. II. Title.

NL 0389225   IU MB

VM   LINLEY, GEORGE, 1798-1865.
1   …I heard a wee bird singing…   Philadelphia,
V 71   Lee, n.d.
          5p.   (Lights and shadows)
v.1
          Binder's title: Nineteenth century music.
          v.1.
          Song with piano accompaniment.
          Plate no.: 10287.

NL 0389226   ICN

Linley, George. 1798-1865.   No. 72 in *8053.3
I heard the wee bird singing. [Song, with pianoforte accomp.]
Boston. Cundy. 1869. (3) pp. [Cundy's Five cent series of popular music. No. 72.] 8°.

F5887 — T.r. — Songs. With music.

NL 0389227   MB

Linley, George, 1798-1865.   No. 4 in *8050a.730.23
I mourn thee in silence. [Song, with accompaniment for pianoforte.]
= [Boston? 184-?] 5 pp. 35½ cm.
The title-page is missing.

L4969 — T.r. — Songs. With music.

NL 0389228   MB

---

*
M1
.S444   Linley, George, 1798-1865.
v.79,
no.35   I turn my steps to home; ballad. Arr.
          for the Spanish guitar by Francis Weiland.
          Philadelphia, George Willig, 171 Chesnut St.,
          c1841.
          [2] p. 35cm. [Sheet music collection, v. 79,
          no. 35]
          Caption title.
          Stamped on first page: J. W. Randolph & Co.,
          Booksellers, Richmond, Va.
          1. Songs with guitar. I. Weiland, Francis,
          arr. II. Title.

NL 0389229   ViU

Linley, George, 1798-1865.

          I was happy ere I loved you; ballad. Written and composed by George Linley. Boston Published by Oliver Ditson 115 Washington St. [ca. 1850] Pl. no. 2299.
          5 p. 35 cm.
          Caption title.
          For voice and piano.

          1. Songs (Medium voice) with piano. I. Title.

M1.A13L   52-52949

NL 0389230   DLC

VM   LINLEY, GEORGE, 1798-1865.
1   …I've left my snow clad hills…   Philadel-
F 91   phia, J.C.Smith [ca. 1850]
no.14   5p. 34cm. (Jenny Lind's songs)

          Caption title.

NL 0389231   ICN

---

*
M1
.S444   Linley, George, 1798-1865.
v.95,
no.19   I've left my snow-clad hills. Figure 3
          in six pointed star. Philadelphia, Lee &
          Walker, 722 Chestnut St.; Wm. H. Boner &
          Co., 1102 Chestnut St. [1856?] Pl. no.
          323.4.
          5 p. 35cm. (Gems of our time, a selection of
          choice songs and ballads, from distinguished
          authors, No. 27)
          [Sheet music collection, v. 95, no. 19]

          1. Songs with   piano. I. Title.

NL 0389232   ViU

Linley, George. 1798-1865.   8053.628
I've left the snow-clad hills. [Song. A. Accomp. for pianoforte.]
= Boston. Marsh. [186-?] 6 pp. [Jenny Lind's Swedish melodies.]

G5646 — T.r. — Songs. With music.

NL 0389233   MB

M1   Linley, G
A13S6
no.1   I've left the snow-clad hills. [By] G.
          Linley. [n.p., n.d.]
          6p. 32cm. (In [Songs published in the U.S.
          in the 19th century. v.p., ca.1840-1860] no.1)

          Caption title.

          1. Songs (Medium voice) with piano. I.
          Title.

NL 0389234   IaU

VOLUME 334

Linley, George, 1798–1865.
  I've left the snow-clad hills. Philadel-
phia, E. Ferrett & Co., 40 South Eighth
Street ₍184–?₎
    ₍3₎ p. 35cm. (A set of Jenny Lind's songs
  arranged for the piano, no. 1)
    ₍Sheet music collection, v. 78, no. 21₎
  Portrait of Jenny Lind following no. 2.

    1. Songs with piano. I. Title. II. Title:
  Jenny Lind's songs.

NL 0389235   ViU NN

Linley, George, 1798–1865.   No. 1 in **M.483-465
  I've left the snow-clad hills. [Song by] G. Linley. [With accom-
paniment for the pianoforte.]
  New York. Holt. [184–?] 6 pp. Portrait. 33.5 cm.
  The portrait is of Jenny Lind.

D8719 — T.r. — Songs. With music. — Lind, Jenny, 1820–188?

NL 0389236   MB

Linley, George, 1798–1865.
  I've left the snow-clad hills. [Song with accompaniment for piano-
forte.]
  [Boston. Reed. 185–?] 5 pp. [Jenny Lind's songs. No. 3.]
33 cm.   No. 21 in *8050a.708
  The title-page is missing.

M1932 — T.r. — Songs. With music.

NL 0389237   MB

Linley, George, 1798–1865.
  I've left the snow-clad hills. Boston, Reed
[187–?]
  5 p. [Jenny Lind's Songs, no. 3]

NL 0389238   MB

Linley, George, 1798–1865.
  Jessie; by G. Linley. Eufford & Co.'s
lithograph. Boston. New York, Firth, Hall &
Pond, c1846.
  7 p. 34 cm.
  For voice and piano.
  ₍No. 1₎ in a volume of songs and piano
music, 1822-1855, with binder's title: Music.

    1. Songs (Medium voice) with piano. I. Title

NL 0389239   NcD

Linley, George, 1798–1865.
  Kate O'Shane. Price 25 cts. nett. Philadelphia, Osbourn's Music Saloon, 112 So.
Third St., ₍after 1835?₎ Pl. no. 464.4.
  5 p. 33 cm. ₍Sheet music collection, v. 160,
no. 58₎

    1. Songs with piano. I. Title.

NL 0389240   ViU

Linley, George, 1798–1865.
  Kate O'Shane; ballad. Words and music by G. Linley.
Boston: E. H. Wade 197 Washington St. ₍18—₎
  4 p. 36 cm.
  Caption title.
  For voice and piano.

    1. Songs (Medium voice) with piano. I. Title.

M1.A13L   52-4847

NL 0389241   DLC

Linley, George, 1798–1865.
  Law versus love. A comedietta, in one act.
London, T. H. Lacy ₍n.d.₎
  16p. 18cm.

  "First performed at the Royal Princess's
Theatre ... on Monday, December 6th, 1862."

NL 0389242   IU

Linley, George, 1798–1865.
  The merry tambourine; song of the glee maiden. Written
& composed by G. Linley, Esq. Fiot, Meignen & Cᵒ 217
Chesnut Sᵗ Philadelphia, ₍ca. 1838₎ Pl. no. 441.
  4 p. 33 cm.
  Caption title.
  For voice and piano.

    1. Songs (High voice) with piano. I. Title.

M1.A13L   52-5293.

NL 0389243   DLC

Linley, George, 1798–1865.
  ... The modern Hudibras; a poem, in three cantos;
by George Linley ... London, J. C. Hotten, 1864.
  2 p. l. 80 p. 23ᶜᵐ.

NL 0389244   NIC

Linley, George, 1798–1865.
  ... The modern Hudibras; a poem, in three cantos;
by George Linley ... London, J. C. Hotten, 1864.
  2 p. l, 90 p. 23ᶜᵐ.
  At head of title: Second edition—enlarged.

    I. Title.

                                     25-25707
Library of Congress   PR4889.L46M6 1864

NL 0389245   DLC

Linley, George, 1798–1865.
  Moonlight is sleeping; song. Written and composed by
George Linley, Esq. Boston. Published by Oliver Ditson
115 Washington St. ... ₍ca. 1850₎
  6 p. 35 cm.

    1. Songs (Medium voice) with piano. I. Title.

M1.A13L   52-52957

NL 0389246   DLC

Linley, George, 1798–1865.
  The mountain daisy. As sung by Jetty
Treffz. 25¢ net. Boston, Oliver Ditson,
115 Washington St.; New Orleans, Tyler &
Hewitt ... ₍1851?₎ Pl. no. 2255.
  5 p. 33cm.
  "To Miss M. P. Abrams."
  Greene & Weller, sc.

    1. Songs with piano. I. Title.

NL 0389247   ViU

Linley, George, 1798–1865.
  Musical cynics of London, a satire. (Sketch the first), by
George Linley. London, G. Bubb, 1862. 39 p. 21cm.
  "A savage onslaught upon Chorley the critic." — *Dict. of nat. biog.*

Drexel 2218.12
———— ———— Second copy.
  Author's presentation copy to Dr. Rimbault.

NCI p.v.41
———— ———— Third copy.

    1. Music—Anecdotes, facetiae,   satire, etc. 2. Chorley, Henry Fother-
gill, 1808–1872.   gill, 1808–1872.   Card revised
N.Y.P.L.   July 6, 1945

NL 0389248   NN MH

Linley, George, 1798–1865.   No. 3 in **M.450.135
  My blessing with thee go. New ballad. [With accompaniment for
the pianoforte. Composed by George Linley. [Words by E. H.
Reed.]
— New York. Firth, Pond & Co. [1851.] 5 pp. 34½ cm.

D3611 — Double main card. — Linley, George, 1798–1865. (M1) — Reed, E. H.
(M2) — T.r. Song. (1) — Songs. With music. (1)

NL 0389249   MB

Linley, George, 1798–1865.
  "My dreams are now no more of thee"
    see under Lavenu, Louis Henry, 1818–1859.

Linley, George, 1798–1865.
  My fondest! My fairest! Hummel's celebrated
air à la Tyrolienne... written and arranged [for
voice with piano acc.] by G. Linley. New York,
E. Riley [18]
  5 p. F°.

NL 0389251   NN

Linley, George, 1798–1865.   8053.540
  The night before the bridal. [Song. Accomp. for pianoforte.]
= Boston. Ditson. [184–?] 4 pp. F°.

G5609 — T.r. — Songs. With music.

NL 0389252   MB

Linley, George, 1798–1865.
  No flow'r that blows. [Song for voice & piano
acc.] composed by Linley. New York, J. & M.
Paff [18]
  f°.

NL 0389253   NN

Linley, George, 1798–1865
  Onkel Tom's hütte; lieder und balladen
mit pianofortebegleitung von Georg Linley.
... Leipzig, Weber ₍1853?₎
  cover-title, 16p. illus. 23 cm.
  Adapted from Harriet Beecher Stowe's
novel, Uncle Tom's cabin.
  German text.

    I. Stowe, Mrs. Harriet Elizabeth (Beecher)
  1811–1896—Uncle   Tom's cabin.

NL 0389254   RPB

Linley, George, 1798–1865.
  Only for thee; romance. ₍Words by G.
Linley, the younger₎ Figure 2½ in 7 pointed
star. Boston, Oliver Ditson & Co., 277
Washington St. ... ₍1860?₎ Pl. no. 21392.
  5 p. 34cm.

    1. Songs with piano. I. Title.

NL 0389255   ViU

Linley, George, 1798–   No. 67 in 8050a.232
  Passing away. [Song, the accomp.] arranged for the guitar by
Samuel Keene.
= Boston. Ditson. [184–?] 2 pp. F°.

G3338 — Songs. With music. — T.r. — Keene, Samuel, ed.

NL 0389256   MB MWA

VOLUME 334

Linley, George, 1798–1865.
Passing away; or, Dreams of the heart. Written & composed by George Linley. New York Firth, Pond & Cº 1 Franklin Square. ₁185–₎ Pl. no. 1124.
₁3₎ p. 35 cm.
Caption title.
For voice and piano.

1. Songs (Medium voice) with piano.   ɪ. Title.

M1.A13L   52–52956

NL 0389257   DLC

Linley, George, 1798–1865.
The river sprite
see under   Mori, Frank.

Linley, George, 1798–1865.
Robin Hood, a cantata
see under   Hatton, John Liptrott, 1809–1886.

Linley, George, 1798–1865.
The Rose of my heart
see under   Lavenu, Louis Henry, 1818–1859.

LINLEY, George.
₁Selection of Welsh melodies, the words written and the symphonies and accompaniments composed and arranged by George Linley.
[London. Boosey & co., etc., etc., cir 1890]
pp.40. (Boosey's musical cabinet, 42)

NL 0389261   MH

Linley, George.
Geo. Linley's songs and ballads. [With accompaniment for pianoforte.] No. 2, 3.
= Boston. Reed & Co. [185–?] 2 v. in ɪ. 35½ cm.
Contents.—   Moor'd is my boat. — Why do I
love thee?

L4954 — T.r. (2) — Songs. With music.

NL 0389262   MB

Lilly
PR 4889
.L 54 05   LINLEY, GEORGE, 1798–1865
^Songs, duets, trios, recitatives, choruses, &c. in the new grand romantic opera of The gipsy's warning! ... The poetry by George Linley ... Represented, for the first time at the Theatre Royal, Drury Lane, on Thursday, April 19th, 1838. London,W. Wright, Printer ₁1838₎
24 p. 19 cm.

First edition.
In modern   plain wrappers.

NL 0389263   InU CSmH

LINLEY, GEORGE, 1798–1865.
Songs of fashionable life. The poetry by Thomas Haynes Bayly. London, S. Chappell [183–?]
Pl. no. 4227. illus. 35cm.

No. 3.
For voice and piano.
CONTENTS.--No.3. I'm just eighteen and quite a man.

1. Songs, English. ɪ. Bayly, Thomas Haynes, 1797–1839.
ɪɪ. Title.

NL 0389264   NN

---

*
M1
.S444   Linley, George, 1798–1865.
v.104
no.41   The strangers bride; ballad sung by Mr. Parry, Jr. Pr. 38. New York, Dubois & Stodart, 167 Broadway ₁before 1837?₎
4 p. 33cm. ₁Sheet music collection, v. 104, no. 41₎
Caption title.
Stamped: Sold at Cole's Music Store, Baltimore.

1. Songs with piano. ɪ. Title.

NL 0389265   ViU NN

Linley, George, 1798–1865.
The Stranger's bride. Ballad [with piano acc.] written and composed by George Linley. New York, Dubois & Stodart [18   ]
4 p. f°.

NL 0389266   NN

Linley, George, 1798–1865.   No. 62 in 8050a.230
The Swiss girl. [Song, A., the accomp.] arranged for the guitar by L Meignen.
= Philadelphia. Fiot. 1849. (2) pp. F°.

G3350 — Meignen, Leopold, ed. — Songs. With music. — T.r.

NL 0389267   MB

---

sVM
285
L 757s   LINLEY, GEORGE, 1798–1865.
₁The Swiss girl; arr.₎ The Swiss girl, as sung by Miss Dolby at M. Jullien's concerts, arranged with variations for the concertina, and an accompaniment for the piano forte (ad libitum) by Giulio Regondi.
London, Published by G.Case₁184–?₎
5p. 35cm.

Without the piano part.

NL 0389268   ICN

---

*
M1
.S444   Linley, George, 1798–1865.
v.68
no. 16   The Swiss girl, as sung with rapturous applause by M'lle Lovarney. Boston, Oliver Ditson, 115 Washington Sᵗ ₁before 1857?₎
Pl. no. 1490.
5 p. 31cm. ₁Sheet music collection, v. 68, no. 16₎
Caption title.

1. Songs with piano. ɪ. Title.

NL 0389269   ViU

Linley, George.   8053–543
Take back the gems you gave me. A favorite song. [Accomp. for pianoforte.]
= Boston. Ditson. [185–?] 5 pp. F°.

G5600 — T.r. — Songs. With music.

NL 0389270   MB

Linley, George, 1798–1865.
They say, my love is dead! Song with piano acc. written by G. Linley. Arranged by J. Barnett. London, Goulding & D'Almaine [18   ]
5 p. f°.

NL 0389271   NN

Linley, George, 1798–1865.   No. 5 in *8050a.730.23
Think on me. [Song, with accompaniment for pianoforte.] Written by Thomas Blake, Esq. [Music Composed by George Linley.
= Boston. Reed & Co. [185–?] 7 pp. 35½ cm.

NL 0389272   MB

Linley, George, 1798–1865.
Those happy days are gone
see under   Lavenu, Louis Henry, 1818–1859.

NL 0389273

M1
.A13H   Linley, George, 1798–1865. Thou art gone from my gaze.
Horn, Charles Edward, 1786–1849.
₁I've been roaming₎
I've been roaming; ballad, by C. E. Horn. Thou art gone from my gaze; ballad. ₁Words and music₎ by G. Linley. New-York: Alexander Montgomery, 12 & 17 Spruce St. Boston, F. Parker, 35 Washington Street. Sold by all booksellers. ₁18 ₎

---

*
M1
.A13N   Linley, George, 1798–1865.
.L45T4
1851   Thou art gone from my gaze; a favorite song. Arr. for the Spanish guitar, by P. Ernst. ©1849 by Jaques & Brother, Southern District of New York. New York, Horace Waters, 333 Broadway ₁1851?₎
₁2₎ p. 34cm.
Caption title.
G. W. Ackerman, Eng. & Pr.
1. Songs with guitar. ɪ. Ernst, P   arr.
ɪɪ. Title.

NL 0389275   ViU

Linley, George.   No. 6 in *8050a.730.23
Thou art gone from my gaze, or the spirit of love. [Song, with accompaniment for pianoforte.]
= Boston. Ditson. [185–?] 5 pp. 35½ cm.

L4969 — T.r. — Songs. With music.

NL 0389276   MB

---

*
M1
.S444   Linley, George, 1798–1865.
v.82
no.43   Thou art gone from my gaze, or Thy spirit of love keeps a watch over me, written & composed for the piano forte. 25 cts. net. Baltimore, Henry McCaffrey ₁18— ₎ Pl. no. 131.
5 p. 36cm. ₁Sheet music collection, v.82, no.43₎

1. Songs with piano. ɪ. Title. ɪɪ. Title: Thy spirit of love keeps a watch over me.

NL 0389277   ViU

M1619
S69   Linley, George, 1798–1865.
₁Thou art gone from my gaze; voice, acc. piano₎
v.701   Thou art gone from my gaze; or, The spirit of love keeps a watch over me. Ballad. Words & music by G. Linley. Philadelphia, A. Fiot ₁18--?₎
5 p. 35ᵐ.
Cover title.
No. 3 in a vol. lettered: Songs, v.701.

1.Ballads,   English. I.Title. ɪɪ.
Title:The spirit   of love keeps a watch
over me.

NL 0389278   CSt

---

*
M1
.S444   Linley, George, 1798–1865.
v.62
no.24   Thou art gone from my gaze, or The spirit of love keeps a watch over me; arranged for the guitar by Max Zorer. New York, Firth, Pond & Co., No. 1 Franklin Square, ©1849. Pl. no. 448.
₁2₎ p. 31cm. ₁Sheet music collection, v. 62, no. 24₎
Caption title.

1. Songs with guitar. ɪ. Title. ɪɪ. Title: The spirit of love keeps a watch over me.

NL 0389279   ViU

VOLUME 334

M1
.S444
v.65
no.17

Linley, George, 1798-1865.
Thou art gone from my gaze; or, Thy spirit of love keeps a watch over me. Written & composed for the piano forte. ₍Price₎ 25 cts. net. Baltimore, F. D. Benteen; New Orleans, W. T. Mayo ₍before 1864?₎ Pl. no. 1579.
5 p. 33cm. ₍Sheet music collection, v. 65, no. 17₎
Webb.
Inscribed V. M. Timberlake, Charlottesville.
1. Songs with piano. I. Title. II. Title: Thy spirit of love keeps a watch over me.

NL 0389280   ViU

fM1
A13S6
no.4

Linley, George, 1798-1865.
Thou art gone from my gaze; or The spirit of love keeps a watch over me. Words and music by G.Linley. Boston, Published by W.H.Oakes and for sale by E.H.Wade, 197 Washington St. ₍ca. 185-₎ Pl.no.305-5.
7p. 32cm. (In ₍Songs published in the U.S. in the 19th century. v.p., ca.1840-1860₎ no.4)

Cover title.

NL 0389281   IaU

M1
.A13N
.L45T4
1852

Linley, George, 1798-1865.
Thou art gone from my gaze; song. New York, Firth, Pond & Co., 1 Franklin Sq. ... ₍ca. 1852₎ Pl. no. 1630.
5 p. 33cm.
T. C. Wakelam, sc.; Quidor, Engvr.
Stamped on cover: Skinner & Sperry, 154 Chapel St., New Haven, Ct.

NL 0389282   ViU

M1
.S444
v.150
no.15

Linley, George
To meet again with thee, a favorite ballad. Philadelphia, Fiot, Meignen & Co., 217 Chesnut ₍sic₎ St. ₍after 1837?₎ Pl. no. 212.
3 p. 32cm. ₍Sheet music collection, v. 150, no. 15₎
Caption title.
E. Gillingham.
1. Songs with piano. I. Title.

NL 0389283   ViU NN

Linley, George.
To meet again with thee. A favorite ballad ... arranged for the pianoforte.
= Philadelphia. Fiot, Meignen & Co. ₍184-?₎ 5 pp. 35½ cm.

No. 14 in *8050a.723

L.5572 — T.r. — Songs. With music.

NL 0389284   MB

M1551
.2
.M53Z9

Linley, George, 1798-1865, tr.

Mendelssohn-Bartholdy, Felix, 1809-1847.
₍Zweistimmige lieder, op. 63₎
... Twelve vocal duets, by Mendelssohn, Keller, and Kucken, with English words by George Linley ... New York, Boosey & co. ₍186-?₎

LINLEY, GEORGE, 1798-1865.
Uncle Tom's cabin. [Words and music by G. Linley] London, Chappell [1852] Pl. no. 8767. 1 no. illus. 36cm.

No. 3.
For voice and piano.
CONTENTS. —No. 3. Evangeline.

1. Songs, English. 2. Song cycles. I. Title.

NL 0389286   NN

LINLEY, GEORGE, 1798-1865.
Welcome, my bonnie lad; Scotch song, written composed by George Linley. London, Campbell, Ransford [18--] Pl. no.C.R.& Co. 279. 5[1] p. 35cm.
For voice and piano; orchestra acc. in score printed on p. [6].
1. Songs, English. 2. Songs, with orchestra

NL 0389287   NN

Linley, George, 1798-
Well-a-day! Duet. [S.A., with accompaniment for pianoforte.] Words by W. H. Bellamy. Music by G. Linley.
= Boston. Reed. [185-?] ₍1₎, 7 pp. 33 cm.

No. 18 in *8050a.708

L4955 — Double main card. — Linley, George. (M1) — Bellamy, William Henry. (M2) — T.r. (1) — Duets. Vocal. (1)

NL 0389288   MB

Linley, George.
Why do I love thee yet. Ballad. [Accomp. for pianoforte.]
= Boston. Ditson. [185-?] 5pp. F°.

8053.510

G5617 — T.r. — Songs. With music.

NL 0389289   MB

Linley, George, 1798-1865.
The wild harp of our land is broken; song. The subject from Bellini, written and arranged by George Linley. New York, Published by Wm Hall & Son, 239 Broadway ₍18-₎ Pl. no. 1184.
5 p. 34 cm.
With piano acc.

1. Songs (Medium voice) with piano.   I. Bellini, Vincenzo, 1801-1835.   II. Title.

M1.A13L   52-49058

NL 0389290   DLC

M1
.S444
v.92
no.19

Linley, George, 1798-1865.
Years have roll'd since we did part, or, To meet again with thee; a favorite ballad written, composed and arr. for the piano. Philadelphia, Lee & Walker, 120 Walnut St. ₍184-?₎ Pl. no. 311.
3 p. 35cm. ₍Sheet music collection, v. 92, no. 19₎
Caption title.
1. Songs with piano. I. Title. II. Title: To meet again with thee.

NL 0389291   ViU

₍LINLEY, PHILIP₎.
Discourse. Exodus. XXXV, 21,29. n.p., n. d.

15 x 23.
Imp.:- title-page missing.

NL 0389292   MH-AH

Linley, Thomas, 1732-1795.
Works by this author printed in America before 1801 are available in this library in the Readex Microprint edition of Early American Imprints published by the American Antiquarian Society.
This collection is arranged according to the numbers in Charles Evans' American Bibliography.

NL 0389293   DLC

Linley, Thomas, 1732-1795.
Ah sure a pair &c. A favourite song in the Duenna. ... ₍Dublin₎ Eliah Rhames ₍1780?₎ [1] p. fol.
Excerpts.
At bottom of page, the melody of the song arranged "For the Guitar."
By Thos. Linley and T. Linley Jr.

NL 0389294   DLC

W.C.L.
M780.88
C697B
no.12

Linley, Thomas, 1732-1795.
₍The duenna. Ah sure a pair; arr.₎
Ah sure a pair; a favorite song, as sung by Mr. Philipps. ₍n. p., ca. 181-₎
₍1₎ l. 30 cm.
Caption title.
For voice and piano.
₍No. 12₎ in a collection of early American music, published or manuscript, 1790?-182-.
1. Operas. To 1800. Excerpts. Vocal scores with piano. I. Title.

NL 0389295   NcD

Linley, Thomas, 1732-1795.
₍Monody on the death of Garrick. Libretto. English₎
The airs and choruses in The monody on the death of Mr. Garrick. Set to music by Mr. Linley. ₍London? 1779?₎ 3 p.

Microfilm of issue in the British Museum. Words by Richard B. Sheridan. TOSCANINI MEMORIAL ARCHIVES.

1. Librettos. (1) Sheridan, Richard Brinsley Butler, 1751-1816. Monody on the death of Garrick. (2) TITLE: Monody on the death of Garrick.

NL 0389297   NN

Linley, Thomas, 1732-1795.
Airs, duet, trios, &c. &c. in the revived Persian tale, ₍in two acts,₎ called Selima and Azor. Performed at the Theatre Royal, Covent-Garden. With additions by Bishop, T. Welsh, T. Cooke, &c. London: Printed by E. Macleish, 1813.
19 p. 20cm. ₍Fawcett's collection of 18th and 19th century English drama, v. 49, no. 4₎
Without the music.
Libretto by G. Collier.

NL 0389298   ViU

Linley, Thomas, 1732-1795.
₍Tickell, Richard₎ 1751-1793.
The camp, a musical entertainment, as performed at the Theatre Royal, Drury-Lane. By R. B. Sheridan, esq. London, Printed and sold by J. Roach, 1803.

Linley, Thomas, 1732-1795.
₍Tickell, Richard₎ 1751-1793.
The camp: a musical entertainment, in one act, by Richard Brinsley Sheridan ... Printed from the acting copy, with remarks, biographical and critical, by D.—G. ... As performed at the Theatres Royal ... London, G. H. Davidson ₍n. d.₎

VOLUME 334

M1503
L62
C37
Linley, Thomas, 1732-1795
₍The carnival of Venice. Piano-vocal score.
English₎
The carnival of Venice; a comic opera as
performed at the Theatre Royal in Drury-Lane,
composed by Mᵣ. Linley. For the voice and
harpsichord. London, Printed for S. A. & P.
Thompson ₍1781₎
score (58 p.)

Pages 55-58 wanting, replaced by Xerox
copies.
Libretto by   Tickell; first performed in 1781.   cf. Groves.

NL 0389301   WaU PU

Linley, Thomas, 1732-1795.
[Carnival of Venice. Libretto. English]
Carnival of Venice, Songs, etc. [by]
Richard Tickell. London, 1781.
(In Three centuries of drama: English,
1751-1800)

Microprint.

I Tickell, Richard, 1751-1793. Carnival
of Venice. II. Title.

NL 0389302   MoU

---

sVM
1621
L 75c
LINLEY, THOMAS, 1732-1795.
Cheerly my hearts of courage true, sung at
the Theatres Royal, written by R.B.Sheridan,
esqr. Composed by the late Mr. Linley. London, Preston₍1797?₎
3p.

Caption title.
Imperfect: mutilated.
Includes part for flute.

NL 0389303   ICN

Linley, Thomas. 1725-1795.   No. 6 in **M.384.48
Come, come my jolly lads. A favorite song in the
pantomime of Robinson Crusoe. [T., and chorus, with accomp. for pianoforte.]
= London. Thompson. [178-?] 2-4 pp. F°.

F8126 — T.r. — Songs. With music.

NL 0389304   MB

Linley, Thomas.   No. 210 in **M.215.21
Come, come, my jolly lads. Glee [T. T. B.].
(In Social Harmony. Pp. 254, 255. London. [1818.])

Mar. 21,   1902
E₁₁₀₁ — T.r. — Part songs.

NL 0389305   MB

Linley, Thomas, 1732-1795.
₍The duenna. Could I each fault remember; arr.₎

Could I each fault remember; a favourite song sung in the
opera of The duenna. ₍Dublin₎ A. Lee ₍177-?₎
₍1₎ l. 31cm.

For piano, with interlinear words; originally for voice and orchestra.
Part for guitar printed at end.
Bound with The battle of La Hogue. ₍n. p. n. d.₎

1. Operas—To 1800—Excerpts—Vocal scores with piano. 2. Songs
(High voice) with piano—To 1800. I. Title.

M1508   M 56-113

NL 0389306   DLC

M1621
.A2
Linley, Thomas, 1732-1795.
The Crimson morn, a favorite duett in the
Duenna.
Printed on same sheet with "William:.,"
adaptation to an air by Haydn.

NL 0389307   DLC

Lilly
M 219
.V157
₍LINLEY, THOMAS₎1732-1795

The crimson morn. From the Duenna. London, Printed by the Polyhymnian Company &
sold wholesale by G. Walker ₍n.d.₎
1 l. 34 cm.

Caption title: "No. 31."
Bound with Valentine, Ann. Ten sonatas.

NL 0389308   InU

₍Linley, Thomas₎ 1732-1795.
₍The duenna. Libretto. French₎

La duègne et le Juif portugais; farce en trois actes, pour le
carnaval. Par B. Sheridan, traduite par A. H. Chateauneuf.
Paris, Impr. de A. Coniam, 1827.
24 p. 22 cm.
The music composed by Thomas Linley and his son.
"Tirée à quelques exemplaires, ni publiés, ni vendus."

₍1. Operas—Librettos₎ I. Sheridan, Richard Brinsley Butler,
1751-1816. The duenna. II. Linley, Thomas, 1756-1778, joint composer. III. Title.

ML50.L744D83   1827   54-49968

NL 0389309   DLC

₍Linley, Thomas₎ 1732-1795.
₍The duenna. Libretto. English₎

The duenna: a comic opera, in three acts. By Richard
Brinsley Sheridan ... Printed from the acting copy, with
remarks, biographical and critical, by D.—G. ... As performed at the Theatres Royal ... London, G. H. Davidson
₍n. d.₎
58 p. incl. front. 15 cm. (Cumberland's British theatre. London,
ca. 1825-55. v. 2 ₍no. 2₎)
Remarks by George Daniel, editor of the series.
A reissue of Cumberland's earlier edition ca. 1829.
The music composed by Thomas Linley and his son.

———— Another issue. (Davidson's shilling volume of
Cumberland's plays. London, ca. 1849-55. 15 cm. v. 3
₍no. 3₎)
PR1243.C82   vol. 3, no. 3
₍1. Operas—Librettos₎ I. Sheridan, Richard Brinsley Butler,
1751-1816. The duenna. II. Linley, Thomas, 1756-1778, joint composer. III. Title.
PR1243.C8   vol. 2, no. 2   21-18997 rev

NL 0389311   DLC

₍Linley, Thomas₎ 1732-1795.
₍The duenna. Libretto. English₎

The duenna; a comic opera, in three acts; by Richard Brins-
ley Sheridan, esq. As performed at the Theatres Royal,
Drury Lane and Covent Garden ... With remarks by Mrs.
Inchbald. London, Longman, Hurst, Rees, Orme, and
Brown ₍n.d.₎
74 p. front. 16 cm. (Inchbald, Elizabeth. The British theatre
... London, 1808. v. 19 ₍no. 3₎)
The music composed by Thomas Linley and his son.
₍1. Operas—Librettos₎ I. Sheridan, Richard Brinsley Butler,
1751-1816. The duenna. II. Linley, Thomas, 1756-1778, joint com-
poser. III. Title.
PR1243.I 4   vol. 19   32-22119 rev

NL 0389312   DLC CtY MH CSmH

812.08
F87
v.7
₍Linley, Thomas₎ 1732-1795.
...The duenna. An opera, in three
acts... New-York, French, n.d.
56p. S. (French's standard drama, no.
LIV)
Libretto by R. B. Sheridan.

NL 0389313   IaU

Linley, Thomas, 1732-1795.
The Duenna, a comick opera; as performed at
the Theatre Royal. Covent Garden. Composed by
Mr. Linley. London, Printed for Harrison,
Cluse, & Co. [ca. 1775]
2 p.l., 3-66 p.
This is wholly a musical score. Engraved
throughout. *Libretto by R.B. Sheridan*

NL 0389314   CSmH

[Linley, Thomas] 1732-1795.
The Duenna, or Double elopement, a comic
opera, as performed at the theatre royal in Crow
street, under the title of the Governess, sett for
the voice, harpsichord, violin, G: Flute &
Guitar. [Composed by Thomas Linley, text by
Sheridan. Vocal score.] Dublin, John Lee [1775]
52 p. f°.
Bd. with Comus by Dr. Arne.

NL 0389315   NN

Linley, Thomas.   No. 3 in **M.391.54
The duenna, or double elopement. A comic opera ₍by R. B. Sheri-
dan₎. Composed and selected by T. Linley. [Accomp. for pianoforte.]
= London. Dale. [1775?] 43 pp. F°.

Mar. 21,   1902
E₃₃₉₃ — Sheridan, Richard Brinsley Butler. — Operas.

NL 0389316   MB

-VM
1503
L 75d
₍LINLEY, THOMAS₎ 1732-1795.
The duenna; or, Double elopement, a comic-
opera as performed at the Theatre Royal in Covent Garden, for the voice, harpsichord, or violin. London, C. and S.Thompson₍1775₎
57p.

English words.
Libretto by R.B.Sheridan.
The music was composed and compiled by Thom-
as Linley in conjunction with his son Thomas.

NL 0389317   ICN MH PU

M
1503
.L76
D9
1775
₍Linley,Thomas₎ 1732-1795.
₍The duenna. English₎
The duenna or Double elopement,a comic-opera
as performed at the Theatre Royal in Covent
Garden,for the voice,harpsichord,or violin.
London, Printed for C.and S.Thompson ₍1775₎
2 p.l.,60 p. 24 x 33 cm.
Libretto by Richard Brinsley Sheridan.
Music by Thomas Linley,the elder,and son.

1.Operas--To 1800--Vocal scores with piano.
I.Linley,Thomas,1756-1778,joint composer
II.Sheridan,Richard Brinsley Butler,1751-1816.
The duenna. III.   Title.

NL 0389318   MiU ICU CtY WaU NN ViU DFo NcU MH

₍Linley, Thomas₎ 1732-1795.
₍The duenna. Libretto. English₎

The duenna: a comic opera, in three acts: as it is performed, by His Majesty's servants ... London, E. Johnson,
1776.
1 p. l., ll, 43 p. 21½ cm.
₍Longe, F. Collection of plays. v. 310, no. 2₎
A parody of Sheridan's play, by I. Pottinger; the music composed
by Thomas Linley and his son.
₍1. Operas—Librettos₎ I. Linley, Thomas, 1756-1778, joint composer. II. Pottinger, Israel, fl. 1759-1761. The duenna. III. Sheridan,
Richard Brinsley Butler, 1751-1816. The duenna. IV. Title.
PR1241.L6   vol. 310, no. 2   28-1509 rev

NL 0389319   DLC MiU

₍Linley, Thomas₎ 1732-1795.
₍The duenna. Libretto. English₎

The duenna, a comic opera, in three acts: as it is performed
by His Majesty's servants. New ed. London, Printed for
E. Johnson ₍1776₎
43 p. 21 cm.
A parody on Sheridan's play, by I. Pottinger. The music composed by Thomas Linley and his son; tunes indicated by quotation
of first lines.
₍1. Operas—Librettos₎ I. Linley, Thomas, 1756-1778, joint composer. II. Pottinger, Israel, fl. 1759-1761. The duenna. III. Sheridan,
Richard Brinsley Butler, 1751-1816. The duenna. IV. Title.
ML50.2.D852L5   1776   9-16080 rev*

NL 0389320   DLC NN MiU MB OrU TxU IaU

VOLUME 334

-VM
1500
L 75dP

⌐LINLEY, THOMAS¬ 1732-1795.
The duenna; or, The double elopement, a comic-opera, as performed at the Theatre Royal in Covent Garden, for the German-flute.   London,C.& S.Thompson⌐1777?¬
29p.

Without words; songs indicated by title only.
The music for Sheridan's comedy was composed and compiled by Thomas Linley in conjunction with his son Thomas.

NL   0389321   ICN

⌐Linley, Thomas¬ 1732-1795.
⌐The duenna. Vocal score¬
The duenna; or, Double elopement. A comic-opera as performed at the Theatre Royal in Covent Garden. For the voice, harpsichord, or violin...   London: Printed by Longman and Broderip ⌐178-?¬   60 p.   26 x 36½cm.

Score: 1 to 4 voices and figured bass including instrumental cues. English words.
First performed in 1775.

"In conjunction with his eldest son, Thomas, he ⌐Thomas Linley¬ composed and compiled the music for 'The duenna' by his son-in-law, Sheridan." — *Grove. Dict. of music and musicians.*
Imperfect: t.-p. and p. ⌐1¬-2 mutilated.

I. Operas, Comic—Vocal score.   I. Linley, Thomas, 1756-1778.
II. Sheridan, Richard Brinsley   Butler, 1751-1816. The duenna.
N.Y.P.L.   December 20, 1939

NL   0389323   NN ICN CtY

⌐Linley, Thomas,¬ 1732-1795.
The duenna; or, Double elopement. A comic opera as perform'd at the Theatre Royal in Crow street, under the title of The governess, sett for the voice, harpsichord, violin, G: flute & guittar.   Dublin: J. Lee⌐, ca. 1780¬   52 p.   f°.

Vocal score. English words.
First performed in 1775.
"In conjunction with his eldest son, Thomas, he ⌐Thomas Linley¬ composed and compiled the music for 'The duenna' by his son-in-law, Sheridan." — *Grove's Dict. of music and musicians.*

1. Operas—Piano and voice.   2. Operas, Comic—Piano and voice.
3. Linley, Thomas, 1756-1778.   4. Sheridan, Richard Brinsley Butler,
1751-1816. 5. Title. 6. Title: The governess.
N.Y.P.L.   November 27, 1928

NL   0389324   NN

⌐Linley, Thomas¬ 1732-1795.
The duenna; or, The double elopement. A comic opera. As it is performed at the Theatre-Royal in Covent-Garden.   London, 1783.
40p. 18cm.
By R. B. Sheridan.
With this is bound Sheridan's The school for scandal. Dublin, 1783.

NL   0389325   IEN DFo CtY CSmH MH TxU PPL

Linley, Thomas, 1732-1795.
⌐The duenna. Libretto. English¬
The duenna ⌐or, The double elopement, by¬ Richard Brinsley Sheridan. London, 1783.
(In Three centuries of drama: English, 1751-1800)

Microprint.
Published also under the title The governess.
The music composed by Thomas Linley and his son.

I. Sheridan, Richard Brinsley Butler, 1751-1816. The duenna. II. Linley, Thomas, 1756-1778, joint composer. III. Title. IV. Title: The double elopement. V. Title.

NL   0389327   MoU

Rare Book
Room
Im
Sh53
783Bb

Linley, Thomas¬ 1732-1795.
The duenna: or, The double elopement. A comic opera. As it is performed at the Theatre-Royal in Covent-Garden. London: Printed in the year 1784.
47p. 16cm.
Signatures: A-F⁴.
By R. B. Sheridan.

NL   0389328   CtY MH RPB

Rare Book
Room
Im
Sh53
783Bd

⌐Linley, Thomas¬ 1732-1795.
The duenna; or, The double elopement: a comic-opera: as it is acted at the Theatre, Smoke-alley, Dublin. [Dublin]Printed for the booksellers.1785.
37p. 15cm.
Signatures: A-E⁴(E₄ [blank] wanting)
By R. B. Sheridan

NL   0389329   CtY MH OkU

PR
3682
.D8
1786

⌐Linley, Thomas¬ 1732-1795.
The duenna; or, The double elopement: a comic opera: as it is acted at the Theatre,Smoke-Alley,Dublin. ⌐Dublin¬ Printed for the booksellers, 1786.
37 p.   15 cm.
By R. B. Sheridan.

I.Title.   II.Title: The double elopement.

NL   0389330   MiU MH NNC CtY

Rare Book
Room
Im
Sh53
783Cb

⌐Linley, Thomas¬ 1732-1795.
The duenna: or, The double elopement. A comic opera. As it is performed at the Theatre-Royal in Covent-Garden. Dublin:Printed in the year 1787.
40p. 17cm.
Signatures: A-E⁴.
By R. B. Sheridan.

NL   0389331   CtY

⌐Linley, Thomas¬ 1732-1795.
The Duenna; or The double elopement: a comic opera. London, 1789.
47 p.

NL   0389332   CtY

Rare Book
Room
Im
Sh53
783De

⌐Linley, Thomas¬ 1732-1795.
The duenna: a comic opera. In three acts. As performed at the Theatre Royal, Covent Garden ... By R. B. Sheridan, esq. Dublin: Messrs.G.Burnet,Abbey-street,P.Wogan,P. Byrne,W.Jones,and J.Milliken.1794.
3p.l.,64p. 16cm.
Signatures: [A]³B-F⁶G3(G₃ blank)

NL   0389333   CtY

Linley, Thomas, 1732-1795.
The duenna: a comic opera. In three acts. As performed at the Theatre Royal, Covent Garden: with universal applause. Dublin, G. Burnet, P. Wogan ⌐etc.¬ 1794.
60 + p.   20cm.
By R. B. Sheridan

NL   0389334   ViU PP CSmH

⌐Linley, Thomas¬ 1732-1795.
⌐The duenna. Libretto. English¬
The duenna; a comic opera in three acts. By R. B. Sheridan. London, T. N. Longman, 1794.
78 p.   19 cm.
Music composed and compiled by Thomas Linley and his son. Cf. Loewenberg. Annals of opera.

1. Operas—Librettos.   I. Linley, Thomas, 1756-1778, joint composer. II. Sheridan, Richard Brinsley Butler, 1751-1816. The duenna. III. Title.

ML50.2.D85L5   1794   59-49196

NL   0389335   DLC PSt

Wm
Sh53
783dd

⌐Linley, Thomas¬ 1732-1795.
The duenna: a comic opera. In three acts. As performed at the Theatre Royal, Covent Garden: with universal applause. By R. B. Sheridan, esq.
London:Printed by G.Woodfall,Paternoster-Row,for T.N.Longman,No.39,Paternoster-Row. 1794. 2p.l.,[9]-78p. 21cm.
The first authorized edition.
Another issue has not the printer's name in the imprint on the t.-p.

NL   0389336   TxU CtY ICU NN CSmH MWiW-C OkU MH IaU

---

v.79

⌐Linley, Thomas¬ 1732-1795.
The duenna: a comic opera. In three acts. As performed at the Theatre Royal, Covent Garden: with universal applause. By R.B.Sheridan, esq. London:Printed by G.Woodfall,Paternoster-Row, for T.N.Longman,No.39,Paternoster-Row.1794. 2p.l.,[9]-78p. 22½p.
Signatures: [A]², B-I⁴, K⁴ (K₄ blank and wanting)
First authorized edition, second issue; a pirated edition was published in 1783.
Without the music (by Thomas Linley and his son)

NL   0389337   CtY IaU

Linley, Thomas, 1732-1795.
The Duenna, a comick-opera; as performed at the Theatre Royal, Covent Garden, composed by Mr. Linley.   London, Harrison & Co. [1795?] 66 p.   25 cm.
Vocal score with figured bass. Overture and interludes for instruments, not specified.
Music composed and selected by Thomas Linley and Thomas Linley, junior.
Libretto by Richard Brinley Sheridan.
First performance, October or November, 1775.

NL   0389338   CtY

Mus 404.60 (5)

Linley, Thomas, 1732-95.
The duenna (2) Piano-vocal score
The duenna; a comick opera. L, Harrison, Cluse [1798?] Pl.no.67

Score (66 p.) (Piano-forte magazine, vol.5, no.1)
Bd.with: Giordano, T. 6 sonatas for the piano forte, op.24 [i.e.Sonatas, violin & keyboard, op.24] & 6 sonatas for the piano forte [op.10] – 3 celebrated English overtures [Rush, G. The royal shepherd, et al.] – Giuliani, F. 6 sonatas for the piano forte, op.6. – Dibdin, C. The padlock. – Schobert, J. 2 sonatas for the pianoforte [i.e.Sonatas,   violin & harpsichord. op. 1]

NL   0389339   MH NRU-Mus

18-

⌐Linley, Thomas¬ 1732-1795.
The duenna; a comic opera,in three acts. London,printed for Longman,Hurst,Rees,Orme, and Brown,[18-].

Front.
By R. B. Sheridan.

NL   0389340   MH

⌐Linley, Thomas¬ 1732-1795.
The duenna: a comic opera. In three acts. ....   New York. Longworth. 1806. 75. (3) pp. 14½ cm., in 6s.   **K.38.2
Words only. (In British drama. Vol. 2, pp. 294-311. Philadelphia. 1832.)   6560a.67.2
Same. (In Same. 1853.)   6571.4.2
By R. B. Sheridan

K-480 — T.r. made.

NL   0389341   MB PPL PU

VOLUME 334

⌐Linley, Thomas¬ 1732-1795.
  The duenna; a comic opera, in three acts ... With remarks by
Mrs. Inchbald.
  London. Longman, Hurst, Rees & Orme. [1808.] 74 pp. [The
British theatre. Inchbald. Vol. 19.] 12°.   No. 3 in *6558.6.19
  Same. [A new edition.] Longman, Hurst, Rees, Orme & Brown.
[180-?] Plate. [Vol. 15.]   No. 4 in *6557.54.15
  By R. B. Sheridan

G6132 — S.r.

NL 0389342   MB

⌐Linley, Thomas¬ 1732-1795.
  ⌐The duenna. Libretto. English¬

    The duenna. A comic opera. In three acts. By R. B.
Sheridan, esq. As performed at the theatres Covent-Garden
and New-York. 2d ed. ... New-York: Published by David
Longworth, at the Dramatic repository, Shakspeare gallery.
1808.
  72 p. 15 cm.   ⌐Dramatic pamphlets. v. 32, no. 1¬
  The music composed by Thomas Linley and his son.
  ⌐1. Operas—Librettos¬   I. Sheridan, Richard Brinsley Butler,
1751-1816. The duenna. II. Linley, Thomas, 1756-1778, joint composer. III. Title.
  PR1241.D7 vol.   32, no. 1   34-22977 rev

NL 0389343   DLC PP MB NIC

---

822   ⌐Linley, Thomas¬ 1732-1795.
Sh5d   The duenna; a comic opera, in three acts;
181-   as performed at the Theatres Royal, Drury Lane
and Covent Garden. Printed under the authority
of the managers from the prompt book. With
remarks by Mrs. Inchbald.   London, Printed
for Longman, Hurst, Rees, and Orme ⌐181-?¬
  74p. front. 16cm.
  By R. B. Sheridan.

NL 0389344   IU

⌐Linley, Thomas¬ 1732-1795.
  ⌐The duenna. Libretto. English¬

    ... The duenna, an opera; by the Right Hon. R. B. Sheri-
dan... faithfully marked with the stage business, and stage
directions, as it is performed at the Theatres Royal. London,
Pub. for the Proprietors, by W. Simpkin and R. Marshall
⌐etc.¬ 1818.
  1v. ⌐2¬, 61 p. front. (port.) diagr. 18 cm. (Oxberry, William.
The new English drama. London, 1818-25. v. 2 ⌐no. 2¬)
  At head of title: Oxberry's edition.
  The music composed by Thomas Linley and his son.
  ⌐1. Operas—Librettos¬   I. Sheridan, Richard Brinsley Butler,
1751-1816. The duenna. II. Linley, Thomas, 1756-1778, joint
composer. III. Title.
  PR1243.O8 vol. 2   no. 2   18-21052 rev

NL 0389345   DLC MH MB CtY NIC

⌐Linley, Thomas¬ 1732-1795.
  The duenna; a comic opera in three acts.
  [London. Sherwood & Co. 182-?] 16 pp. Illus. [The Lon-
don stage. Vol. I.] 21 cm., in 8s.
  Words only.
  By R. B. Sheridan.

NL 0389346   MB

ML   Linley, Thomas, 1732-1795.
49   ⌐The duenna. Libretto. English¬
A2
L75   The duenna; an opera by R. B. Sheridan.
no.3   With prefatory remarks. The only edition
existing which is faithfully marked with
the stage business, and stage directions,
as it is performed at the Theatres Royal
by W. Oxberry. London, W. Simpkin, and
R. Marshall, and C. Chapple, 1820.

L75
no.3   65 p. 19cm. (Oxberry's edition)

     1. Operas—To 1800—Librettos.
I. Sheridan, Richard Brinsley Butler, 1751-
1816. The duenna. II. Title.

NL 0389348   NIC ICU

⌐Linky, Thomas¬ 1732-1795.
  ... The duenna, an opera; by R. B. Sheridan.
With prefatory remarks ... faithfully marked with the
stage business, and stage directions, as it
is performed at the Theatres Royal. By W. Oxber-
ry, comedian. Boston, Wells and Lilly; New York,
A. T. Goodrich & co., 1822.
  83 p. diagr. 15cm. (Added t.-p.: Oxberry,
William. The new English drama. Boston, 1824.
v.7 ⌐no.2¬)
  At head of title: Oxberry's edition.
  On cover: Oxberry's British drama.
  I. Title. II.   Ser.

NL 0389349   ViU NNC MH PPL

⌐Linley, Thomas¬ 1732-1795.
  The duenna: a comic opera in three acts. Printed from the acting
copy, with remarks biographical and critical, by D— G. [George
Daniel].
  London. Cumberland. [1823.] 58 pp. Plate. [British theatre.
Cumberland. No. 9.] 12°.
  By R. B. Sheridan.

G6137 — S.r. — Daniel, George, ed. 1789-1864.

NL 0389350   MB

⌐Linley, Thomas¬ 1732-1795.
  ⌐The duenna. Libretto. English¬

    ... The duenna, a comic opera, in three acts. By the Rt.
Hon. R. B. Sheridan, esq. Printed under the authority of the
managers, from the prompt book. With notes, critical and
explanatory. Also, an authentic description of the costume,
and the general stage business, as performed at the Theatres-
Royal, London. Embellished with a wood engraving, from
an original drawing made expressly for this work, by Mr.
I. R. Cruikshank... London, T. Dolby, 1823.
  iv, ⌐2¬, ⌐7¬-60 p. front. 14½ cm. (Dolby's British theatre)

  The music composed by Thomas Linley and his son.
  Vol. 4, no. 9 in a set of volumes lettered: Dolby's British theatre.

  ⌐1. Operas—Librettos¬   I. Sheridan, Richard Brinsley Butler,
1751-1816. The duenna. II. Linley, Thomas, 1756-1778, joint composer. III. Title.

  PR1243.D6   vol. 4, no. 9   37-8331 rev

          (822.0822)   822.66

NL 0389352   DLC OkU PU-F

⌐Linley, Thomas¬ 1732-1795.
  The duenna; a comic opera in three acts.
London, printed for Longman, Hurst, Rees, Orme,
and Brown, [1824].

  pp. 74. Front.
  (In INCHBALD, Mrs. ⌐E. (S.)¬, editor. The
British theatre, 1824, 7.)
  By R. B. Sheridan.

NL 0389353   MH

⌐Linley, Thomas¬ 1732-1795.
  ⌐The duenna. Libretto. English¬

    The duenna; a comic opera, in three acts. By R. B.
Sheridan.
  (In The London stage. London ⌐1824-27¬ 22½ cm. v. 1 ⌐no. 5¬
16 p. 1 illus.)
  Caption title.
  The music composed by Thomas Linley and his son.
  ⌐1. Operas—Librettos¬   I. Sheridan, Richard Brinsley Butler,
1751-1816. The duenna. II. Linley, Thomas, 1756-1778, joint com-
poser. III. Title.
  PR1243.L7   vol. 1, no. 5   17-8689 rev
  ——— Copy 2. (In The London stage. London ⌐1824-27¬ 22½
cm. ⌐2d set¬ v. 4 ⌐no. 2¬)   PR1243.L7   vol. 4, no. 2   2d set

NL 0389354   DLC

⌐Linley, Thomas¬ 1732-1795.
  The duenna, a comic opera...by R. B. Sheridan, esq. Printed
from the acting copy, with remarks. To which are added, a description of the costume, cast of the characters...and the whole
of the stage business... London, T. Dolby, 1825. vi ⌐7¬-58 p.
illus. 15cm. (Dolby's British theatre.)
  Without music.

NL 0389355   NN

⌐Linley, Thomas¬ 1732-1795.
  The duenna: a comic opera, in three acts. By R. B. Sheridan
... (In: The British drama. London, 1826.   v. 2, p. ⌐1102-¬
1119.)
  Caption-title.

  1. No subject. 2. Title.
N.Y.P.L.   December 21, 1927

NL 0389356   NN

⌐Linley, Thomas¬ 1732-1795.
  The Duenna. A comic opera. With remarks.
Edinburgh, Stirling & Kenney, 1828.
  52 p. 1 pl. 16°. (Huie's British Drama.
No. 10)
  By R. B. Sheridan

NL 0389357   NN

812.1   ⌐Linley, Thomas¬ 1732-1795.
S552d
1829   The duenna: a comic opera, in three
acts. Printed from the acting copy,
with remarks, biographical and critical
... Embellished with a wood engraving,
by Mr. White, from a drawing by R.
Cruikshank.   London, Cumberland
⌐1829?¬
  58p. plate. T.
  By R. B. Sheridan
  Without the music (by Thomas Linley and
his son)

     With this are bound his The rivals, The
school for scandal, and The critic; Vanbrugh,
Sir John. A trip to Scarborough; Kotzebue,
A.F.F. von. Pizarro (all pub. 1829?)

NL 0389359   IaU

⌐Linley, Thomas¬ 1732-1795.
  The duenna; a comic opera, in three acts.
London, J. Cumberland, [183-].

  Front.
  This copy is cut for acting.
  By R. B. Sheridan.

NL 0389360   MH

PR   ⌐Linley, Thomas¬ 1733-1795.
1243   ⌐The duenna. Libretto. English¬
P72   The duenna, an opera in three acts by R.
v.9   B. Sheridan... As performed at the London
theatres. Embellished with a fine engraving
by Mr. Findlay... Duncombe's ed. London,
J. Duncombe ⌐183-?¬
  50 p. illus. 15cm.

  The music composed by Thomas Linley and
his son. Cf. Brit. Mus. cat. print. mus.
Vol. 9,   no. 4 in a set
lettered: Plays.

NL 0389361   NIC

⌐Linley, Thomas¬ 1732-1795.
  The duenna; comic opera, in three acts.
London, Sherwood and Bowyer, 1844.

  24°.
  On cover: Dramatic library, 10.
  By R. B. Sheridan.

NL 0389362   MH

---

34   ⌐Linley, Thomas¬ 1732-1795.
     The duenna; an opera... New York, W.
Taylor & Co. [1846]
  56 p. 16°. [Modern standard drama, v. 7]
  By R. B. Sheridan.

NL 0389363   DLC

VOLUME 334

[Linley, Thomas] 1732-1795.
... The duenna; an opera in three acts. By
Richard Brinsley Sheridan. With the stage business
cast of characters, costumes, relative positions
&c. New York, W. Taylor & company [1847?]
v, [1], [7]-56p. 19ᶜᵐ. (Modern standard drama.
[vol. vII] no. LIV)
Editorial introduction signed: H.[i.e.] John
William Stanhope Hows]

NL 0389364   ViU MB MiU

[Linley, Thomas] 1732-1795.
[The duenna. Libretto. English]
... The duenna; an opera in three acts. By Richard
Brinsley Sheridan. With the stage business, cast of characters, costumes, relative positions, &c. New York, J. Douglas, 1848.
v, [1], [7]-56 p. 19 cm. (Modern standard drama. [vol. vII]
no. LIV)
Editorial introduction signed: H. [i. e. John William Stanhope
Hows]
The music composed by Thomas Linley and his son.
[1. Operas—Librettos] I. Sheridan, Richard Brinsley Butler,
1751-1795. The duenna. II. Linley, Thomas, 1756-1778, joint
composer. III. Title.
Rochester. Univ. Libr.   A 34-2268 rev
for Library of Congress   PR1243.M68 no. 54
                              [r53c†]

NL 0389365   NRU CtY NN MH NIC

[Linley, Thomas] 1732-1795.
[The duenna. Libretto. English]
The duenna: a comic opera, in three acts. By R. B.
Sheridan, esq.
(In The British drama. Philadelphia, 1850. 23 cm. v. 2,
p. 294-311)
The music composed by Thomas Linley and his son.
[1. Operas—Librettos] I. Sheridan, Richard Brinsley Butler,
1751-1816. The duenna. II. Linley, Thomas, 1756-1778, joint com-
poser. III. Title.
PR1243.B8 vol. 2   12-3354 rev

NL 0389366   DLC

Am
Sh53
863d   [Linley, Thomas] 1732-1795.
Rare   ... The duenna. By R.B. Sheridan ...
Books   London: J. Dicks, 313, Strand; and all book-
Col   sellers. New York: Samuel French & son, 122,
        Nassau Street-sole agents [1883?] cover
        title, [1055]-1072p. 1 illus. 18cm. in
        envelope in folder 23cm. (Dicks' standard
        plays. no.186)
        Title vignette.
        In double columns.
        Without the music.
        Advertisements: inside front cover, [2]p.
        at end.
        I. Title.

NL 0389367   TxU

[Linley, Thomas] 1732-1795.
The duenna; a comic opera by Richard Brinsley Sheridan.
(In: Stevens, D. H. Types of English drama, 1660-1780. Bos-
ton, [1923]. 8°. p. 774-801.)
In three acts.
96523A. 1. Drama (English).   2. Title.
N. Y. P. L.   September 10, 1923.

NL 0389368   NN OC1W

ML
50.2   Linley, Thomas, 1732-1795
D85   [The duenna. Libretto. English]
L5   The duenna; a comic opera in three acts by
1924   Richard Brinsley Sheridan; with an introd. by
        Nigel Playfair, and illustrated with the designs
        for costumes and scenery used in the production
        at the Lyric Theatre Hammersmith, and other
        drawings by George Sheringham. London,
        Constable [1924?]
        105p. illus. 26cm.
        1. Operas - Librettos I. Sheridan, Richard
        Brinsley Butler, 1751-1816. The duenna
        II. Title

NL 0389369   WU NjP CtY MiD

[Linley, Thomas] 1732-1795.
The duenna; a comic opera in three acts.
London, Martin Secker, 1924.
By R. B. Sheridan,

NL 0389370   MH OU

ML
50
.L6   [Linley, Thomas] 1732-1795.
D85   [The duenna. Libretto. English]
1925   The duenna; a comic opera in three acts by
       Richard Brinsley Sheridan. With an introd. by
       Nigel Playfair, and illustrated with the designs
       for costumes and scenery used in the production
       at the Lyric Theatre, Hammersmith, and other
       drawings by George Sheringham. Boston,
       Houghton Mifflin [1925]
       xxvii, 105 p. illus. (part col.)
       Printed at the Chiswick Press, London.
       The music by Thomas Linley and his son.

       1. Operas—Librettos. I. Sheridan, Richard
       Brinsley Butler, 1751-1816. The duenna. II.
       Linley, Thomas, 1756-1778. III. Chiswick Press,
       London. IV. Sheringham, George, 1884-1937,
       illus. V. Title.

NL 0389372   INS WaU CLU NRU MB OU ViU

Linley, Thomas, 1732-1795.
The duenna by R. B. Sheridan...as performed at the Lyric
Theatre, Hammersmith, the music composed and arranged by
Alfred Reynolds. After Linley...   London: Boosey & Co., Ltd.,
1925.   Publ. pl. no. H. 11489.   v, 111 p.   4°.

Vocal score. English words.
"The music for the original production...in 1775 was composed and compiled
by... Thomas Linley, in conjunction with his son Thomas. In addition to the music
composed by the Linleys it consisted of airs by contemporary Italian composers and

arrangements of popular airs of the period... Many of the tunes have been altered and
partly re-written, and, wherever necessary, new airs have been composed for Sheridan's
verses." — Note.

                              JUILLIARD FOUNDATION FUND.
1. Operas—Piano and voice.   2. Operas, Comic—Piano and voice.
3. Sheridan, Richard Brinsley Butler,   1751-1816. 4. Reynolds, Alfred
5. Title.   December 31, 1925
N. Y. P. L.

NL 0389374   NN CtY MB

LINLEY, THOMAS, 1732-1795.
[THE DUENNA. OVERTURE]
The duenna; or, The double elopement, 1775 [by]
Thomas Linley, Jr. Arranged and edited by Adam Carse.
London, Augener [c1941]   15 p. 32cm. (18th century overtures)

Score: orchestra.
"In conjunction with his eldest son, Thomas, he [Thomas Linley]
composed and compiled the music." — Grove.   Drexel Musical Fund

1. Overtures—To 1800. I. Carse, Adam, 1878- ,ed. II. Linley, Thomas,
1756-1778.   III. 18th century overtures.
IV. Title.

NL 0389375   NN MB MH WaU NBC ICU MiU IU CLSU

Linley, Thomas, 1732-1795.
The duenna
For a parody of Sheridan's libretto for
Linley's opera see under   Pottinger, Israel,
fl. 1759-1761.

4478   Linley, Thomas, 1732-1795.
.589q
        Elegies for three voices, with an
        accompanyment for a harpsichord and
        violoncello... London, Printed by P. Wel-
        cher for the author [1770?]
        56 p. 33 ᶜᵐ.

        Words and music.

        1. Songs, English-Collections. I. Main
        cd. (Music)

NL 0389377   NjP DFo

[Linley, Thomas] 1732-1795.
For tenderness form'd. Printed at B: Carr's Musical Re-
positories Philadelphia & New York & J: Carr's Baltimore
(Price 12 cents) [ca. 1795]
[1] l. 34 cm. ([Collection of early American music, published or
manuscript. v. p., 179-?-182-?] v. 13, no. 42)
For voice and piano.
Adaptation of Saper bramate from Il barbiere di Siviglia by G.
Paisiello.
1. Songs (Medium voice) with piano—To 1800.   I. Paisiello, Gio-
vanni, 1740-1816. Il barbiere di Siviglia. Saper bramate.   II. Title.
M1.A11   vol. 13, no. 42   63-48431/M

NL 0389378   DLC

[Linley, Thomas] 1732-1795.
For tenderness form'd in early day. A
favorite song in the comedy of the Heiress [by
Sir] John Burgoyne. Price 12 cents. Printed at
B. Carr's Musical Repositories.   Philadelphia,
New York, & J. Carr's Baltimore [1794]
12°.
Evans 26720.

NL 0389379   PHi

q780.8   Linley, Thomas, 1732-1795.
En34   A favourite song, in the new comedy of The
v.5   heiress, as performed with universal applause at
         Drury lane theatre. Adapted to an air of Sigʳ.
         Paesiello by Mr. Linley. Sung by Mrs. Crouch.
         London, Printed for S. A. & P. Thompson [1786]
4p.   :M621.L

         [English sheet music. 1765?-1819? v.5,no.26]
         Caption title.
         Text begins: For tenderness form'd.
         Arrangements for guitar and German flute at end.

NL 0389380   IU DLC

Linley, Thomas, 1732-   .B
A favourite song, in the comedy of the Heiress, [For
tenderness form'd in life's early day]. Adapted to an air of Sigʳ. Paesiello
by Mr. Linley. [T. with piano accomp.]
London. Thompson. [179-?] 4 pp. Fᵒ.

F8122 — T.r. — Songs. With music.

NL 0389381   MB

Linley, Thomas.
From blushing morn to ev'ning mild. Elegy [S. A. B.]
(In Collection of Glees and Catches. Pp. 152-156. [London,
181-?])   No. 42 in **M.110.8
Same. (In Webbe, jr. Convito Armonico. Vol. 1, pp. 92-94,
[1828?]   No. 30 in **M.234.3.1
Same. (In Turle and Taylor. The People's Music Book. Vol. 3,
pp. 91-93. 1844.)   No. 37 in **M.111.4-3

                Mar. 21,   1902
E3393 — T.r. — Part songs.

NL 0389382   MB

Linley, Thomas, 1732-1795, an
A general toast
see under title

Linley, Thomas, 1732-1795.
[O'Beirne, Thomas Lewis] bp. of Meath, 1748?-1823.
The generous impostor: a comedy, as it is now per-
forming at the Theatre-Royal, Drury-Lane ... London,
Printed by W. Richardson for J. Robson, 1781.

Linley, Thomas, 1732-1795.
The Gondeliers. An admired ballad for the
piano-forte [and voice] composed by the late T.
Linley. London,[18]
3 p. fᵒ.
no title page.

NL 0389385   NN

VOLUME 334

⌐Linley, Thomas₎ 1732-1795.
　The governess, a comic opera: as it is performed at
the Theatre-Royal in Crow-street. Dublin, 1777.
　3 p. l., 40 p. 16¹ᵐ.
　⌐Longe, F. Collection of plays. v. 148, no. 2₎
　A pirated version of Sheridan's "Duenna". Imperfect: half-title want-
ing.
　Without the music (by Thomas Linley and his son)

　ᵢ. Linley, Thomas, 1732-1795. II. Sheridan, Richard Brinsley
Butler, 1751-1816. The duenna.　　　　　　　　　26-2674
　Library of Congress　　　PR1241.L6 vol. 148
　―――Copy 2. 17¼ᵐ.　　⌐Longe, F. Collection of plays₎
　v. 323, no. 10₎　　　　PR1241.L6 vol. 323

　NL　0389386　　DLC CtY ICU MB CSmH

Music
ML　　　Linley, Thomas, 1732-1795.
49　　　⌐The duenna. Libretto. English₎
A2
L75　　　The governess; a comic opera as it is
no.2　performed at the Theatre-Royal in Crow-
　　　Street.　Newry, Printed by R. Stevenson,
　　　1778.
　　　41 p.　17cm.

　　　Pirated version of The duenna by R. B.
　　　Sheridan. Cf.　　Loewenberg. Annals
　　　of opera.

　　　1. Operas—To 1800—Librettos.
　　I. Sheridan, Richard Brinsley Butler, 1751-
　　1816. The duenna. II. Title. III. Title:
　　The duenna.

　NL　0389388　　NIC

⌐Linley, Thomas₎ 1732-1795.
　The governess: a comic opera. [Anon.]
　　Dublin : pr. in the year 1788.　(3), 40 pp.　Sm. 8°.
　　No. 4 in **K.48.23=**G.3976₎

　NL　0389389　　MB PPL

⌐Linley, Thomas₎ 1732-1795.
　The governess. A comic opera. By R. B. Sheridan, esq.
Adapted for theatrical representation. As performed at the
theatres-royal, Drury-Lane, Covent-Garden, and Smock-Alley.
Regulated from the prompt-books...　Dublin, W. Jones, 1793.
59 p.　17cm.　(In: Jones's British theatre. Dublin, 1795.
v. 6 ₎no. 4₎)

　A pirated version of Sheridan's "Duenna."
　Without the music by Thomas Linley, father and Thomas Linley, son.

　NL　0389390　　NN OC1 PU MH MB

Linley, Thomas, 1732-1795.
　[The governess. Libretto. English]
　The governess [by] Richard Brinsley
Sheridan.　Pirated version of his Duenna
[or, The double elopement] Dublin, 1793.
　(In Three centuries of drama: English,
1751-1800)

　Microprint.
　The music composed by Thomas Linley and
his son.

　I. Sheridan, Richard Brinsley Butler, 1751-
1816. The governess. II. Linley, Thomas,
1756-1778, joint composer. III. Title. IV.
Title: The duenna. V. Title: The double
elopement.

　NL　0389392　　MoU

Linley, Thomas, 1732-1795.
　Had I a heart &c. A favourite song in the
Duenna. ...　[Dublin₎ Elix. Rhames [1780?]
　[1] p.　fol.
　At bottom of page, the melody of the song is
arranged "For the Guitar."

　NL　0389393　　DLC

⌐Closed Shelf
M　　　Linley, Thomas, 1732-
1.A1　　⌐The Duenna₎ Had I a heart.　Irish
L757　　Air of Gramachree ₎voice and piano.
　　　Philadelphia, B. Carr & Co., 179-?₎
　　　₎1₎,33cm. (Elegant Extracts, Book
　　　the 1st, p.26?)
　　　Engraved.
　　　Caption title.

　NL　0389394　　NRU-Mus

M1508　　[Linley, Thomas] 1732-1795.
.L　　　[The duenna. Had I a heart for falsehood
Case　fram'd] sung by Mr. Webster.　n.i. [ca. 1775]
　　　1 l.　33 cm.
　　　Caption-title.
　　　Pfte. 2 hds. with interlinear text.
　　　Melody arr. for guitar at bottom of leaf.
　　　First part of title cut off.

　NL　0389395　　DLC

W.C.L. ⌐Linley, Thomas₎ 1732-1795.
M780.88　⌐The duenna. Had I a heart for falsehood
M987EC　framed₎ arr.₎

no.45　　Had I a heart for falshood ₎sic₎ framed. A fa-
　　　vorite song in the opera of the Duenna. Lon-
　　　don, G. Shade ₎ca. 1820₎
　　　3 p.　34 cm.
　　　Caption title.
　　　For voice and piano. Part for flute at end.
　　　₎No. 45₎ in a collection of American and English songs and piano pieces, ca. 1818-1825.
　　　1. Operas. Excerpts, Arr. Vocal scores
with piano.　2.　Songs (High voice) with
piano.　I. Title.

　NL　0389396　　NcD

M1508　　Linley, Thomas, 1732-1795.
Case　　How oft Louisa hast thou said.　A favourite song,
　　　sung by Mr. Marshall at the Theatre Royal Covent
　　　Gardens in the Duenna.　London, Printed & sold
　　　at A Bland & Wallers [17　]
　　　p. 2-3　(inside pages.　fol.)
　　　By Thomas Linley and Thomas Linley Jr.

　NL　0389397　　DLC

Linley, Thomas, 1732-1795.
　⌐The carnival of Venice. In my pleasant native plains; arr.₎

　In my pleasant native plains; a favourite song in The
carnival of Venice. London, S. A. & P. Thompson ₎1781?₎
　₎3₎ p.　34 cm.
　Caption title.
　Acc. originally for orchestra.
　Melodies for flute and guitar at end.

　　1. Operas—To 1800—Excerpts—Vocal scores with piano.
　ᵢ. Title.
　M1508.L　　　　　　　　　　　M 60-1446

　NL　0389398　　DLC PPiU

Linley, Thomas.　　　　　　No. 31 in **M.235.18.4
　In my pleasant native plains. Roundelay [S. or T.] from The car-
nival of Venice. [Accomp. for pianoforte.]
　(In Musical Library. Vol. 4, pp. 94, 95.　London, 1854.)

　　　　　　　　Mar 21,　1902
　E3393 — T.r. — Songs. With music.

　NL　0389399　　MB

Linley, Thomas.　　　　　　No. 16 in **M.234.3.2
　In thousand thoughts. Elegy [S. A. B.]
　(In Webbe, jr. Convito Armonico. Vol. 2, pp. 160, 161.　London.
[1828?])

　　　　　　　　Mar. 21,　190⸳
　E3393 — T.r. — Part songs.

　NL　0389400　　MB

Linley, Thomas.
　Let me careless. [Madrigal, S. A. T. B. B.]
　(In Clementi.　Vocal Harmony.　Vol. 7, pp. 682-691.　London.
[181-?])　　　　　　　　　　　　No. 3 in **M.235.9.7
Same. (In Same.　2d edition.　Vol. 1, pp. 86-95.　[1832])
　　　　　　　　　　　　　　　　No. 15 in **M.234.2.1
Same. (Cut from Same.)　　　　No. 13 in **M.235.7.1
Same. (In The Apollo.　Vol. 4, pp. 286-296.　[182-?])
　　　　　　　　　　　　　　　　No. 13 in **M.139a.18.2

Same. (In Webbe, Jr. Convito Armonico.　Vol. 3, pp. 280-287.
[1828?])　　　　　　　　　　　　No. 14 in **M.234.3.3
Same. (In Turle and Taylor. The People's Music Book. Vol. 3,
pp. 352-359.　1844.)　　　　　　No. 114 in **M.111.4.3
Same. (In Novello's Glee-Hive. Vol. 1, pp. 107-110.　[1851.])
　　　　　　　　　　No. 16 in 8052.45.1=No. 16 in **M.157.20.1

　NL　0389402　　MB

Linley, Thomas.　　　　　　No. 9 in **M.234.3.4
　Let vanquished nature. Elegy [S. S. B.].
　(In Webbe, Jr. Convito Armonico.　Vol. 4, pp. 392, 393.　London.
[1828?])

　　　　　　　Mar. 21,　1902
　E3394 — T.r. — Part songs.

　NL　0389403　　MB

⌐Linley, Thomas₎ 1732-1795.
　⌐Love in the East. Libretto. English₎

　Love in the East: or, Adventures of twelve hours: a comic
opera, in three acts.　Written by the author of The strangers at
home.　As performed at the Theatre-Royal, Drury-Lane.　Dublin, Printed by W. Porter for Messrs. Wilkinson, Burnet ₎etc.₎
1788.
　8 p. l., 64 p.　17ᵐ.
　No. 2 in a volume lettered : Comedys.
　Libretto, by James Cobb.
　₎1. Operas—Libretto₎　ᵢ. Cobb, James, 1756-1818. Love in the East.
　　　　　　　　　　　　　　　　　　　　　45-40209
　Library of Congress　　　PR1269.C6　no. 2

　NL　0389404　　DLC ICU PP PPL MH PPULC

Linley, Thomas₎ 1732-1795.

　Love in the East; or, adventures of twelve
hours: a comic opera, in three acts.　Written
by the author of The Strangers at home.　As performed at the Theatre-Royal, Drury-Lane.
London: Printed for W. Lowndes, 1788.

　iv₎2₎80p.　20cm.　(Bound with: Bickerstaffe,
Isaac.　Daphne and Amintor.　1766)
　Libretto only.

　NL　0389404-1　　NBu

MICPT　Linley, Thomas, 1732-1795.
822.08　[Love in the East. Libretto. English]
　　　Love in the East [or, Adventures of twelve
　　　hours, by] James Cobb.　London, 1788.
　　　(In Three centuries of drama: English,
　　　1751-1800)

　　　Microprint.

　　　I. Cobb, James, 1756-1818. Love in the east.
　　　II. Title. III. Title: Adventures of twelve
　　　hours.

　NL　0389405　　MoU

⌐Linley, Thomas₎ 1732-1795.
　Love in the East; or, Adventures of twelve hours: a comic
opera, in three acts.　Written by the author of The strangers
at home.　As performed at the Theatre-Royal, Drury-Lane.
London, W. Lowndes, 1788.
　iv, ₎2₎, 81 p.　21ᵐ.
　₎Longe, F. Collection of plays. v. 110, no. 7₎
　Dedication to Thomas Linley signed : J. C.
　Libretto only ; music by Thomas Linley.

　ᵢ. Cobb, James, 1756-1818. Love in the East. ıı. Title.
　　　　　　　　　　　　　　　　25-4134 Revised
　Library of Congress　　　PR1241.L6 vol. 110, no. 7

　　　TxU CtY PPULC　PSt InU NjP MiU OU
　NL　0389406　　DLC NcD NIC ICU ViU CLU-C NN MH CSmH

VOLUME 334

---

*
PN6111
.F37
1731-
1916
v.25,
no.2
⌈Linley, Thomas⌉ 1732-1795.
　　Love in the East; or, Adventures of twelve
hours: a comic opera, in three acts.
Written by the author of the Strangers at
home. As performed at the Theatre-Royal,
Drury-Lane. London: Printed for W. Lowndes,
1788.
　　iv, 81 p.　20cm.　(Fawcett's collection of 18th
and 19th century English drama, v. 25, no. 2)
　　Without the music (by Thomas Linley) Libretto by J. Cobb
　　I. Cobb, James, 1756-1818.　II. Title.

NL 0389407　ViU

LINLEY, THOMAS, 1732-1795.
⌈LOVE IN THE EAST. VOCAL SCORE. ENGLISH⌉
　Love in the east; or, Adventures of twelve hours, a
comic opera as performed at the Theatre royale in
Drury lane. The music composed & compiled by Mr.
Linley. For the harpsichord and voice. London,
Printed for S. A. & P. Thompson [1788] 67 p. 26 X 36cm.

Libretto by James Cobb. --cf. Grove.
1. Operas, Comic--Vocal scores. I. Cobb, James, 1756-1818.
Love in the East. II. Title.

NL 0389408　NN MB

M1578
.C74
case
vol.21
Linley, (Thomas)
　　Madrigal. Tho: Linley. 8p. obl. fol.
　　Ms. (18th cent.)
　　For five voices.
　　First line: Let me careless and unthoughtful
lying

NL 0389409　DLC

⌈LINLEY, THOMAS⌉ 1732-1795.
⌈THE GLORIOUS FIRST OF JUNE. THE MID-WATCH⌉
　The mid-watch. Sung by Mr. Incledon at the
Theatre royal Covent garden. ⌈London? 179-?⌉
⌈2⌉ p.　34cm.

　　Caption title.
　　For voice and piano; part for guitar printed on
p.⌈2⌉
1.Songs, English.　　　　　2.Songs, with guitar.
I.Title. II.Title:The　　glorious first of June.

NL 0389410　NN

Film
10371
⌈Linley, Thomas⌉ 1732-1795.
　⌈Monody. Libretto. English⌉
　Monody ⌈Verses to the memory of Garrick⌉
1779.
　　⌈1⌉,6ℓ.

　　Larpent 471.
　　"Linley set such portions of Sheridan's
Monody on the death of Garrick, 1779, as were
intended to be sung." - Grove, 5th ed.
　　Microfilm copy (negative) of original in MS.
San Marino, Calif., Henry E.Huntington Library,
1966. 1 reel.
　　On reel with ⌈Playford, John⌉ Choice ayres
and songs... second book. London,
1679.

NL 0389411　IaU

⌈Linley, Thomas⌉ 1732-1795
　⌈The duenna. Libretto. English⌉

　A new edition of The duenna, or Double
elopement, a comic-opera, for the voice,
harpsichord or violin. London, R. Birchall
⌈178-?⌉
60 p.　36cm.

　　I. Linley, Thomas, 1756-1778, jt. composer. II.
Sheridan, Richard Brinsley Butler, 1751-1816. The
duenna. III. Title.

NL 0389412　ViU

M
1497
018(6)
Cage
Linley, Thomas, 1732-1795.
　　No flow'r that blows. Sung by Mrs.
Baddeley in Selima & Azor ... ⌈London⌉
S. A. P. T⌈hompson, ca. 1780⌉

　　2 folio leaves.

NL 0389413　DFo

---

q780.8
En34
v.6
Linley, Thomas, 1732-1795.
　　No flower that blows, sung by Miss Howell at the
Theatre Royal, Covent Garden in Selima & Azor.
Composed by T. Linley.　　London, Printed by G.
Walker ⌈179-?⌉
　　2-3p.

　　⌈English sheet music. 1765?-1819? v.6,no.15⌉
　　Caption title.

NL 0389414　IU

Linley, Thomas.
　No flower that blows. Song [S. or T. Accomp. for pianoforte.]
(In Musical Library. Vol. 3, pp. 29-31. London, 1854.)

E3394 — T.r. — Songs. With music.
Mar. 21,　　1902

NL 0389415　MB

Linley, Thomas, 1732-1795.
　Oh! Richard oh! my love
　　see under ⌈Grétry, André Ernest Modeste⌉
1741-1813.

M1740
.S7
⌈Linley, Thomas⌉ 1732-1795
　⌈The duenna⌉ O the days when I was young.
Sung by Mr. Wilson in the Duenna. ⌈London⌉
C. ⌈&⌉ S. T⌈hompson, 1775?⌉
　　⌈1⌉ 1.
　　No.45 in v.4 of a collection with binder's
title: Songs.

NL 0389417　ICU

Linley, Thomas, 1732-
[Robinson Crusoe.] \The\ overture, comic-tunes, & song in the new
pantomime of Robinson Crusoe. [Anon. Pianoforte score.]
London. Thompson. [1790?] (1), 30 pp. L. 8°, obl.
　No. 1 in **M.220.18

E3396 — Pantomimes.
Apr. 1,　　1902

NL 0389418　MB

[Linley, Thomas, 1732-95]
　　The overture, comic tunes, and song, in the new pantomime of Robinson Crusoe, as performed at the Theatre-Royal in Drury-Lane... London, S.A. & P. Thompson [17--]
30 p.

NL 0389419　MH

---

q780.8
En34
v.3
⌈Linley, Thomas⌉ 1732-1795.
　　Overture, in The duenna.　　⌈London, Printed by
R. Falkener, 1775?⌉
　　4p.

　　⌈English sheet music. 1765?-1819? v.3,no.5⌉
　　Caption title.
　　Composed by Thomas Linley and Thomas Linley, jr.
　　Arranged for keyboard instrument.

　　1. Harpsichord music. 2. Pianoforte music. I.
Linley, Thomas, 1756-1778. II. Title: The duenna.

NL 0389420　IU

Linley, Thomas, 1732-　No. 4 in **M.391.54=No. 6 in **M.220.18
[The gentle shepherd.] /The/ overture, songs and duets in the pas-
toral opera of The gentle shepherd [alterd from Ramsay's by
Richard Tickell. The music by T. Linley. Accomp. for piano-
forte.]
= London. Dale. [1781?]. (1), 25 pp. F°.

E3393 — Tickell, Richard. — Operas.
Mar. 21,　　1902

NL 0389421　MB NRU-Mus NN CLU MB DFo ICN

Linley, Thomas, 1732-　. 3 in **M.220.25
[The Spanish rivals.] The overture, songs, duets, &c. in the Spanish
rivals, a musical farce. [By M. Lonsdale.] Composed by Thomas
Linley. [Accomp. for pianoforte.]
London. Thompson. [1784.] 38 pp. F°, obl.

E5583 — Operas. — Lonsdale, M.
Aug. 18,　　1902

NL 0389422　MB

---

sVM
1004
L 75d
LINLEY, THOMAS, 1756-1778.
　⌈The duenna. Overture⌉ Overture to The duenna, or, The double elopement (1775) Full score.
⌈Arr. by Adam Carse⌉　London, Augener ⌈c1941⌉
　　15p.　31cm.　(18th century overtures, arranged and edited by Adam Carse)

　　Scored for oboes, bassoons, horns and trum-
pets in D, timpani in D.A., violins I-II, viola,
violoncello and bass.
　　Plate no.: 17925.

NL 0389423　ICN

FILM
9973
M
Music
Library
Linley, Thomas, 1732-1795.
　　⌈The Spanish rivals. Selections⌉
　　The overtures, songs, duets, &c. in the Spanish rivals, a
musical farce as performed at the Theatre Royal in Drury Lane.
London, Printed for S. A. & P. Thompson [178-?]
score (38 p.) On film (Negative)

　　Microfilm. Original in Bodleian Library, Oxford University.

　　I. Title: The Spanish rivals.

NL 0389424　CU

Cage
M
1497
L648p
1800
Linley, (Thomas), 1732-1795.
　　[Vocal works. Selections]
　　The posthumous vocal works, of Mr. Linley,
and Mr. T. Linley, consisting of songs, duetts,
cantatas, madrigals, and glees. London,
Preston [ca.1800]
　　2 v.

　　1. Vocal music - To 1800. I. Linley,
Thomas, 1756-1778. II. Title.

NL 0389425　CLU ICN

Linley, Thomas, 1732-1795.

　Primroses deck; a favorite rondo. Price 25 cents. Philadelphia Printed & sold at Carr & Co's Musical Repository
⌈1794⌉
　4 p. 33 cm. (⌈Collection of early American music, published or
manuscript. v.p., 179-?-182-?⌉ v. 26, no. 22)
　Caption title.
　For voice and piano; part for flute at end.
　1. Songs (High voice) with piano--To 1800. I. Title.
M1.A11 vol. 26, no. 22　　　64-57770/M

NL 0389426　DLC PU

Linley, Thomas, 1732-1795.

Sedaine, Michel Jean, 1719-1797.
　Richard Cœur de Lion. An historical romance. From
the French of Monsr. Sedaine. As performed at the
Theatre-Royal, Drury-Lane. London, J. Debrett, 1786.

VOLUME 334

Linley, Thomas, 1732-1795.

[Sédaine, Michel Jean] 1719-1797.
Richard Cœur de Lion. An opera. By General Burgoyne. Correctly given, from copies used in the theatres, by Thomas Dibdin ... London, Printed at the Chiswick press for Whittingham and Arliss, 1814.

[Linley, Thomas, 1732-1795.
[The rose. [n.i., actually published by G. Willig, Philadelphia]
8-9pp. 33cm.

First line: No flow'r that blows.

NL 0389429   MWA

W-
1368/C   Linley, Thomas, the Elder
(bk)
A-286   The Rose. A favorite song in the opera of Selima and Azor. Composed by T. Linley. No publisher[engraved by I. Aitken)
[c.1780]

4p. with 2p. of music. Piano, two-hands, with interlinear text.

NL 0389430   ViMtvL

Linley, Thomas, 1732-1795.

Fletcher, John, 1579-1625.
The royal merchant : an opera. Founded on Beaumont and Fletcher. As it is performed at the Theatre Royal, in Covent-Garden. London, W. Griffin, 1768.

FILM
6880   [Linley, Thomas] 1732-1795.
[The gentle shepherd. Libretto. English]
Select songs of The gentle shepherd, as it is performed at the Theatre-Royal, Drury Lane. 1st ed. London, Printed for T.Becker, 1781.
19 p.
Libretto by Richard Tickell based on Allan Ramsay's play. Cf.Grove,5th ed.
Microfilm (negative) of original in Franklin and Marshall College Library,Lancaster,Pa. 1941.
1 reel.
1.Ballad operas   --To 1800--Librettos.
I.Tickell,Richard,   1751-1798. The gentle shepherd. II.Title   The gentle shepherd.

NL 0389432   MiU CSmH

Linley, Thomas, 1732-1795.
The select songs of The gentle shepherd...
London, T. Becket, 1784.
19 p.   19 cm.

NL 0389433   CtY

M1503   Linley, Thomas, 1732-1795.
L5S3   [Selima and Azor, acc.arr.]
Case   Selima and Azor; a Persian tale as performed at the Theatre
X   Royal in Drury Lane.   London, Printed for C. and S. Thompson, No. 75, St. Pauls Church Yard [1776?]
38 p.   24x33cm.

With figured bass. The overture arr. for harpsichord or piano.
The libretto is an adaptation by Sir George Collier of Marmontle's Zémire et Azor, and the music is to some extent an arrangement by Linley of Grétry's music for the French text. Cf. Grove's Dict. of music and musicians, 5th ed.

NL 0389434   CU MB

[Linley, Thomas] 1732-1795.
... Selima and Azor... second edition...
London, 1776.
By George Collier.

NL 0389435   PU

Linley, Thomas, 1732-1795.
[Selima and Azor. Libretto. English]
Selima and Azor [by] George Collier. 1776.
(Larpent collection. Ms. #421) New York, 1954.
(In Three centuries of drama: English, Larpent collection)

Microprint.
Libretto adapted from Marmontel's Zémire et Azor; Linley makes some use of Gretry's music to the same work.

I. Collier, Sir George, 1738-1795. Selima and Azor. II. Gretry, André Ernest Modeste, 1741-1813. Zémire et Azore. III. Marmontel, Jean François, 1723-1789. Zémire et Azore. IV. Title. V. Title: Zémire et Azore. VI. Larpent collection. Ms. #421.

NL 0389437   MoU

[Linley, Thomas] 1732-1795.
[Selima and Azor. Libretto. English]
Selima & Azor, a Persian tale, in three parts: as performed at the Theatre-Royal in Drury-Lane ... London, J. Bell, 1784.
4 p. L. 39 p. 21½ cm.
[Longe, F. Collection of plays. v. 95, no. 8]
Libretto by Sir George Collier, adapted from Marmontel's Zémire et Azor. Cf. Grove's dictionary of music and musicians, 5th ed.
[1. Operas—Librettos]   I. Collier, Sir George, 1738-1795. Selima and Azor. II. Title: Selima and Azor.

PR1241.L6   vol. 95, no. 8   25-4552 rev

TxU MiU NN
NL 0389438   DLC CSmH ViU IEN MB MH CtY DFo NcD NIC

MICPT
822.08   Linley, Thomas, 173-1795.
[Selima and Azor. Libretto. English]
Selima & Azor [by] George Collier.
London, 1784.
(In Three centuries of drama: English, 1751-1800)

Microprint.
Libretto based on Marmontel's Zémire et Azore; Linley makes some use to Gretry's music to the same work.

I. Collier, Sir George, 1738-1795. Selima and Azor. II. Gretry, André Ernest Modeste, 1741-1813. Zémire et Azore. III. Marmontel, Jean François, 1723-1789. Zémire et Azore. IV. Title. V. Title: Zémire et Azore.

NL 0389440   MoU

Linley, Thomas, 1732-1795.   n **G.3966.1.5
Selima & Azor, a Persian tale. Adapted for theatrical representation: as performed at the Theatre Royal, Covent Garden. Regulated from the prompt-book, by permission of the managers ... London. Cawthorn. 1806. 46 pp. Portrait. [Cawthorn's Minor British theatre. Vol. 5.] 14 cm., in 6s.

M6147 — T.r. Play. — S.r.c.

NL 0389441   MB ICN CtY

Linley, Thomas, 1725-1795.
Smiling love to thee belong. Roundelay in the comedy of Dissipation ... London,
S. A. P. T[hompson, c. 1781]
(2) p.   fol.

NL 0389442   PPiU

---

q780.8   Linley, Thomas, 1725-1795.
En34   The song sung by Mr. Gaudry in the new pantomim
v.2   of Robinson Crusoe. Set by Mr. Linley.   [London, 1781?]
[2]p.

[English sheet music. 1765?-1819? v.2,no.28]
Caption title.
Text begins: Come, come, my jolly lads.
Arrangement for German flute at end.

I. Title: Come, come, my jolly lads.

NL 0389443   IU

Linley, Thomas, 1732-1795.
Songs and choruses in the comic opera of Love in the East; or, Adventures of twelve hours. As performed at the Theatre Royal, Drury Lane. London, Printed by J. Jarvis, 1788.
1 p. L., 23 p.   21½ cm.
Words only, by James Cobb; music by Thomas Linley.

I. Cobb, James, 1756-1818. Love in the East. II. Title. III. Title: Love in the East.
Library of Congress   ML50.2.L61L5 1788
43-37066
NL 0389444   DLC CLU-C

Y
134   [Linley, Thomas] 1732-1795.
.26   Songs, duets, &c. in The duenna, as performed at the Theatres Royal, Covent Garden,
v.5   and Drury Lane; including Mrs. Billington's new Bravura song. Written by R.B.Sheridan. London,Printed by G.Woodfall for T.N.Longman,1801.
24p.
Binder's title: English plays. vol.V.
Without the music (by Thomas Linley and his son)
"Bravura song, introduced by Mrs. Billington, composed by   Nasolini; the words adapted (from the   Italian) by T.Dibdin."

NL 0389445   ICN MH

[Linley, Thomas] 1732-1795.
[The duenna. Libretto. English]
Songs, duets, trios, &c. in The duenna; or, The double elopement. As performed at the Theatre-Royal in Covent-Garden. London, Printed for J. Wilkie, 1775.
20 p.   20 cm.
Libretto by Sheridan; the music composed and compiled by Thomas Linley and his son.
[1. Operas—Librettos]   I. Sheridan, Richard Brinsley Butler, 1751-1816. The duenna. II. Linley, Thomas, 1756-1778, joint composer. III. Title: The duenna.
ML50.2.D85L5 1775   9-4322 rev*

NL 0389446   DLC

Bd.in [Linley, Thomas] 1732-1795.
PR   Songs, duets, trios, &c. in The duenna; or,
1240   The double elopement. As performed at the Theatre-
v.67   Royal in Covent-Garden. 13th ed. London, J.
Cage   Wilkie and T. Evans, 1776.
[4] 20 p. [A]², B-C⁴, L². 8vo.
Without the music.
Bound in Plays of the 18th century, v. 67.
Libretti by R. B. Sheridan

NL 0389447   DFo

[Linley, Thomas] 1732-1795.
Songs, duets, trios in The Duenna; or The double elopement, as performed at the Theatre Royal in Covent Garden, 15th ed. London, printed for J.Wilkie, etc., 1776.

4°. pp.24. Front.
Libretto. Words only, by R. B. Sheridan.

NL 0389448   MH ICN

Linley, Thomas, 1732-1795.
Songs, duets, trios, &c. in The duenna, or The double elopement. 16th ed. Dublin, M.Mills, 1777.

pp.24.
Imperfect:- pp.19-20 are torn.
Text by R. B. Sheridan.

NL 0389449   MH

Am
Sh53   [Linley, Thomas] 1732-1795.
775sw   Songs, duets, trios, &c. in The duenna; or, The double elopement. As performed at the Theatre-Royal in Covent-Garden. Written by Richard Brinsley Sheridan, esq. The 23d ed.
London:Printed for J.Wilkie in St.Paul's Church-yard;and T.Evans in the Strand.1777.
24p. 21cm.,in case 25cm.
The words only are given.
The music was composed and compiled by Thomas Linley in conjunction with his son Thomas.

NL 0389450   TxU

VOLUME 334

Linley, Thomas, 1732-1795.
Songs, duets, trios, &c. in The duenna, or The double elopement. Tamworth, printed and sold by B. Shelton, [1780?].

24°. pp. (4), 20.
Words only, by R. B. Sheridan.
Imperfect;- The title-page is defaced.

NL 0389451   MH

Am
C689
776s
Rare
Books
Col

Linley, Thomas, 1732-1795.
Songs, duets, trios, &c. in the dramatic romance of Selima and Azor, as performed at the Theatre-Royal in Drury-Lane.
London: Printed for J. Wilkie, St. Paul's Church-yard. M.DCC.LXXVI. 22p. 21½cm. in envelope in folder 23cm.
Libretto by G. Collier.
Signatures: [A]-C⁴ (C₄ blank)

NL 0389452   TxU NNC CLU-C

ML
49
A2
L75
no.5

Linley, Thomas, 1732-1795.
[Selima and Azor. Libretto. English]

Songs, duets, trios, &c. in the dramatic romance of Selima and Azor, as performed at the Theatre-Royal in Drury-Lane. 2d. ed. London, Printed for J. Wilkie, 1776.
22 p. 22cm.

Libretto by Sir George Collier. Cf. Grove's Dictionary of Music & Musicians.

1. Operas—To 1800—Librettos.
I. Collier, Sir George, 1738-1795.
Selima and Azor.   II. Title: Selima and Azor.

NL 0389454   NIC

PR3349
.C8854
1777

Linley, Thomas, 1732-1795.
Songs, duets, trios, &c. in the dramatic romance of Selima and Azor, as performed at the Theatre-Royal in Drury-Lane. The 3rd ed. London, Printed for J. Wilkie, 1777.
[3]-22p. 19½cm.
Libretto by G. Collier.
Imperfect; Half-title wanting?
Without the music (by Linley)

NL 0389455   ICU CtY DFo

Linley, Thomas, 1732-1795.
The Spanish rivals
For libretti see under   [Lonsdale, Mark]

Linley, Thomas, 1732-1795.
[The Spanish rivals. Still the lark finds repose]

Still the lark finds repose, the favourite rondo sung by Miss Phillips in The Spanish rivals. London, S.A. & P. Thompson [1784?]

4 p.   34 cm.

Includes optional acc. for German flute and guitar.

NL 0389457   CaBVaU DFo

Linley, Thomas, 1732-1795.
[The Spanish rivals. Still the lark finds repose; arr.]

Still the lark finds repose; a favorite rondo. [London] Printed by W. Gawler [179-?]

[2] l. 31 cm.

Caption title.
For piano, with interlinear words; acc. originally for orchestra.
Part for German flute printed at end.

1. Operas—To 1800—Excerpts—Vocal scores with piano.   I. Title.

M1508   M 55-1643

NL 0389458   DLC NcD

M1500
L557S7
Case
X

Linley, Thomas, 1732-1795.
[The strangers at home. English]
The strangers at home; a comic opera performed with universal applause at the Theatre Royal, Drury Lane. Selected & composed by Thos. Linley. London, Printed for Longman & Broderip, No. 26 Cheapside [1786?]
score (65 p.)

Skeleton score.   The overture arranged for piano.
The libretto by J. Cobb.
"New music printed & sold by Longman and Broderip, No. 26 Cheapside, London ...": verso of p. 65.

I. Longman & Broderip,   firm, publishers.

NL 0389459   CU

Linley, Thomas, 1732-1795.
Strangers at home
for libretti see under   Cobb, James, 1756-1818.

W.C.L.
M780.88
A512VL
no.27

Linley, Thomas, 1732-1795.
The Switzer's farewell. Abschied von der Sennerinn [sic]. Philadelphia, Beck & Lawton [185-?]
5 p.   34 cm.   (Home delights, no. 19)
Caption title.
For voice and piano.
[No. 27] in a vol. of songs, ca. 1848-60 collected by Anna Hespeler.
1. Songs (Medium voice) with piano.   I. Title.
II. Title: Abschied von der Sennerin.

NL 0389461   NcD

Linley, Thomas.
This bottle's the sun. Glee [T. T. B.]
(In Social Harmony. Pp. 58, 59. London. [1818.])   No. 48 in **M.215.21
Same. (In The Apollo. Vol. 5, pp. 391, 392. London. [182-?])   No. 22 in **M.139a.18.5

Mar. 21.   1902
E3394 — T.r. — Part songs.

NL 0389462   MB

Linley, Thomas, 1732-1795.
Tom Jones, a comic opera
For libretti see under   Reed, Joseph, 1723-1787.

M780.88
A512VK
no.2

Linley, Thomas, 1732-1795.
[Selima and Azor. Remain we sisters still awake; arr.]

The trio of the sisters, from Selima and Azor [by] W. [sic] Linley. [Philadelphia, published by Carr & Schetky ... 1807?]
score (12-14 p.)   34 cm. [The Ladies collection of glees, rounds & chorusses [sic])
Caption title.
For three voices and piano.
Reissue from original plates, 1804-05. Cf. Wolfe.
[No. 2] in a collection of early American music.

1. Operas. To 1800. Excerpts. Vocal scores with piano. 2. Choruses, Secular (Women's voices, 3 pts.) with piano. I. Title: Remain we sisters still awake.

NL 0389465   NcD

Linley, [Thomas].
The tunes, songs, glee, &c. in the pantomime of The triumph of mirth; or, Harlequin's wedding, as performed at the Theatre Royal in Drury Lane; composed and selected by Mr. Linley. London: S. A. & P. Thompson [1782]. 1 p.l., 49 p. ob. 8°.

1. Operas.—Piano and voice.   2. Melodrama.—Piano and voice.
3. Pantomimes.—Piano and voice.   4. Title.
N. Y. P. L.   June 26. 1913.

NL 0389466   NN

Linley, Thomas, 1732-1795.
[Ballads]
Twelve ballads. London, Printed for A. Portal [1780]
27 p.   24 x 33 cm.
With harpsichord acc.

1. Songs with harpsichord—To 1800.

M1621.L   77-240704

NL 0389467   DLC NjP

M
1621
L75++
Thompson

Linley, Thomas, 1732-1795.
[Ballads]
Twelve ballads.   London, S.A. & P.
Thompson [Dedication 1780]
27 p.   25 x 34cm.

For soprano with harpsichord accompaniment.

1. Songs (High voice) with harpsichord—To 1800.   2. Ballads, English.

NL 0389468   NIC

Linley, Thomas, 1732-1795.   Mus 502.6
Twelve ballads set to music. London, A. Portal, [dedication, 1780].
obl. 8°. pp. (3), 27. Engraved.

NL 0389469   MH NjP

W.C.L.
M780.88
E581
no.19

Linley, Thomas, 1732-1795.
[The duenna. What bard, o time discover; arr.]

What bard, o time discover; a favorite song in the duenna. Adapted for the harp by Ed. Jones. London, Printed for Rt. Birchall [ca. 1800]
3 p.   34 cm.
Caption title.
For voice and harp.
[No. 19] in a collection of harp and piano music with binder's title: Music.
1. Songs (High voice) with harp. 2. Operas. Excerpts. Vocal scores with harp. I. Jones, Edward. II.   Title: The duenna. III. Title.

NL 0389470   NcD

LINLEY, THOMAS, 1732-1795.
[RICHARD COEUR DE LION. WHEN NICHOLAS FIRST TO COURT BEGAN]
When Nicholas first to court began; a celebrated glee from Richard Cour de Lion. Composed by Linley... London, Printed & sold by G. Walker [179-] score (3 p.) 34cm.

Caption title.

Music for Gretry's opera adapted by Linley in 1786. --Cf. Loewenberg. Annals of opera.
For 3 voices.

1. Choral music, Secular (Mixed, 3 pt.)--Unacc. 2. Glees. I. Grétry, André Ernest Modeste, 1741-1813. Richard Coeur de Lion.

NL 0389472   NN

LINLEY, THOMAS, 1732-1795.

When 'tis night, and the mid watch is come. A favorite song, sung by Mr. Bannister; composed by Mr. Linley... [London? ca. 1795] 2 l. 34cm.

Caption title.
For voice and piano; part for guitar printed at end.
Sung in the pasticcio The glorious first of June.

1. Songs, English. 2. Songs, with guitar. I. Sheridan, Richard Brinsley Butler, 1751-1816. II. Title: The glorious first of June.

NL 0389474   NN IU

VOLUME 334

Linley, Thomas.
    While grief and anguish. Elegy [S. S.B.].   No. 53 in **M.235.18.4
    (In Musical Library. Vol. 4, pp. 154, 155. London, 1854.)

            Mar. 21,   190-
    E3394 — T.r. — Part songs.

NL 0389475   MB

Linley, Thomas.
    The woodman. [Song, T. Accomp. for pianoforte.]
    London. Laveau & Mitchell. [179-?] 4 pp. F°.
                                            No. 46 in **M.237.7
    Same. (In Musical Library. Vol. 1, pp. 80, 81. London, 1854.)
                                            No. 36 in **M.235.18.1

            Mar 21.   1902
    E3304 — T.r. — Songs. With music.

NL 0389476   MB

---

q780.8 Linley, Thomas, 1732-1795.
En34   The woodman, written by Wm. Pearce ... Set to
v.5   music by Mr. Linley.   London, Printed by Preston
        & son [1795?]
        2-4p.   DLC: M 1621· L

        [English sheet music. 1765?-1819? v.5,no.9]
        Caption title.
        Arrangement for German flute at end.

        I. Pearce, William. II. Title.

NL 0389477   IU

Linley, Thomas, 1732-1795.
    The woodman, written by Wm.Pearce esqr. Set to
music by Mr.Linley. Price 25 cents. Printed and
sold by R.Shaw at his music store No.13 South
Fourth St.,Philadelphia [1800?]
    [2] p.   30.5cm.

    Caption title.
    Sonneck,O. A bibl.of early secular music in
America,p.477.
    1.Vocal music.2.Evans suppl. I.t.II.Pearce,
William. III.Ptr.

NL 0389478   MiU-C NcD

W-   [Linley, Thomas] 1732-1795.
1368/B   Young Lubin, A favourite Song Sung by Mrs.
(bk)   Cargill in the New Opera The Carnival of Venice.
A-286
        n.i., n.d.

        p.24 from an unidentified collection.
        Piano, two-hands, with interlinear text.

NL 0389479   ViMtvL

M   Linley, Thomas, 1732-1795.
1497   Young Lubin was a shepherd boy, a
018(7) favourite song sung by Mrs. Cargill in
Cage   the Carnival of Venice ... London, Printed
        for S. A. & P. Thompson [1781]

NL 0389480   DFo PPiU

ML50   Linley, Thomas, 1756-1778, joint composer.
.L744D83
1827   [Linley, Thomas] 1732-1795.
        [The duenna. Libretto. French]

        La duègne et le Juif portugais; farce en trois actes, pour le
    carnaval. Par B. Sheridan, traduite par A. H. Chateauneuf.
    Paris, Impr. de A. Coniam, 1827.

ML50   Linley, Thomas, 1756-1778, joint composer.
.2
.D85L5 Linley, Thomas, 1732-1795.   FOR OTHER EDITIONS
1794   SEE MAIN ENTRY
Case   [The duenna. Libretto. English]

        The duenna; a comic opera in three acts. By R. B. Sheri-
    dan. London, T. N. Longman, 1794.

ML50   Linley, Thomas, 1756-1778, joint composer.
.2
.D85L5 Linley, Thomas, 1732-1795.   FOR OTHER EDITIONS
1793   SEE MAIN ENTRY
Case   [The duenna. Libretto. English]

        The governess. A comic opera. By R. B. Sheridan, esq.
    Adapted for theatrical representation. As performed at the
    Theatres-Royal, Drury-Lane, Covent-Garden, and Smock-
    Alley ... Dublin, Printed by Graisberry and Campbell for W.
    Jones, 1793.

        Linley, Thomas, 1756-1778, joint composer.
        Had I a heart
            see under   Linley, Thomas, 1732-1795.

Linley, Thomas, 1756-1778.   No. 24 in **M.220.9.4
    Hark, the birds. Madrigal [S. S. A. T. B.].
    (In Warren. Collection of Catches. Vol. 4, pp. 66-72. London.
    [1787.])

            Mar. 21,   1902
    E3395 — T.r. — Part songs.

NL 0389485   MB

        Linley, Thomas, 1756-1778, joint composer.
        How oft Louisa hast thou said
            see under   Linley, Thomas, 1732-1795.

PR   Linley, Thomas, 1756-1778.
2884   An ode on the spirits of Shakespear, written
.L76   by Dʳ Lawrance, set to musick by Thomas Linley,
        junior, and performed at the theatre in Drury
        Lane March the 20th 1776 ... [n.p., 1776]
        3 pts.   31 x 24½ cm.
        In manuscript.
        Text published anonymously,1776,under title:
    A lyric ode on the fairies,aerial beings,and
    witches of Shakespeare. cf.Jaggard,Shakespeare
    bibl.

        "A list of vocal,and instrumental parts of
    an 'Ode on the spirits of Shakespeare'": one
    leaf inserted after t.p.,pt.1.
        Contents.--[pt.1] Bass. Principale.--[pt.2]
    Soprano. Principale.--[pt.3] Violino primo.
    --   copy 2
        30 x 24 cm.
        Holograph. cf.note on leaf inserted in pt.1,
    copy 1.
        1.Shakespeare in fiction,drama,poetry,etc.
    2.Shakespeare,William--Music. I.Lawrance,Dr.
    II.Title. III.   Title: A lyric ode on
    the fairies ...   of Shakespeare.

NL 0389488   MiU MB

ML50   Linley, Thomas, 1756-1778, joint composer.
.2
.D85L5 [Linley, Thomas] 1732-1795.
1775   [The duenna. Libretto. English]
case
        Songs, duets, trios, &c. in The duenna; or, The double
    elopement. As performed at the Theatre-Royal in Covent-
    Garden. London, Printed for J. Wilkie, 1775.

Linley, William, 1771-1835.   18494.13
    The adventures of Ralph Reybridge, containing sketches of
modern characteristics, manners, and education. London, printed
for R. Phillips, 1809.
    4 vol.

    ||Title|Do.: Ralph Reybridge|AcS 186157

NL 0389490   MH ICU NcU IU

Linley, William, 1771?-1835.
    The airs, choruses, &c., in the new pantomime, called Harle-
quin captive; or, The magick fire. As performed by His Majesty's servants, at the Theatre-royal Drury-Lane. The musick
by Mr. W. Linley. The scenes entirely new, and painted by
Mr. Greenwood. The machinery and decorations by Messrs.
Cabanel, Johnston, and Jacobs. The dresses by Mr. Johnston
and Miss Rein. [London] Printed by C. Lowndes, 1796.
    12 p. 21½ᵐ.
    Without the music; both words and music by Linley.
    1. Title: Harlequin captive.

                                            43-30678
    Library of Congress   ML52.2.H192L5

NL 0389491   DLC CtY CSmH

Linley, William, 1771?-1835.   No. 3 in **G.4060.1
    Ariel's adieu to Prospero. Words by W. L. Bowles. [Composed by
    William Linley. With accompaniment for pianoforte.]
    (In Linley, William. Eight songs for a tenor or soprano voice.
    Pp. 32-38. London. [1800?])

    K3268 — Bowles, William Lisle. 17..-1850. — Shakespeare, William. Music.
    Songs. Interpolated. — Songs. With music. — T.r.

NL 0389492   MB

LINLEY, William.   **M.235.
    Eight glees.
        London. Hawes. [182-?] (4), 4, 81 pp. Portr. F°.
    Contents. — Prolick and free [A. T. T. B.]. — Go, musing traveller [S. A. T. B.].
    — At that dread hour [A. T. T. B.]. — Ye little troops of fairies [A. T. T. B.]. — Hark!
    from yon ruin'd abbey [A. T. T. B.]. — Now the blue-fly's gone [A. T. T. B.]. — On the
    down of a thistle [A. T. T. B.]. — Thou to whom the world unknown [A. T. T. B.].

NL 0389493   MB MH

Linley, William, 1771-1835.
    Eight pastoral canzonets for two soprano voices, with an ac-
compt. for the piano forte, composed...by...W. Linley. London, Printed by Clementi & co. [1816?] 36 p. 33cm.
    Contents.—Must I then say.—Oh solitude!—In vain my Sylvia.—The sighing
breeze.—The chilling gale.—Far in some shady sweet retreat.—Go rose.—A tender
passion.

    284214B. 1. Vocal duos, Secular—   Women—Keyboard acc.
    N. Y. P. L.   September 1, 1944

NL 0389494   NN

Linley, William.   No. 3 in **G.4060.1
    Eight songs for a tenor or soprano voice with accompaniment for the
    pianoforte.
    London. Birchall. [1800?] 38, (1) pp. 35 cm.
    Contents. — [Take back the sigh, . . . — Though Fate, my girl, may bid us
    part . . . — Oh! if your tears, . . . — Does the harp of Rosa slumber
    . . .] The words by Thoˢ Moore. — [Fair Liela . . .] — Oh! why
    should the girl . . .] by Thoˢ Moore. — When lovely woman stoops to
    folly . . .] by Dr. Goldsmith. — Ariel's adieu to Prospero . . . by W.
    L. Bowles.
    Ariel's adieu . . . is catalogued separately.

    K3280 — Songs. With music. Colls.

NL 0389495   MB

Linley, William, 1771-   No. 55 in **M.235.18.4
    Fair Liela. Song [S. or T. Acccmp. for pianoforte].
    (In Musical Library. Vol. 4, pp. 158-160. London, 1834.)

            Mar. 21,   1902
    E3395 — T.r. — Songs. With music.

NL 0389496   MB

---

*EC8   Linley, William, 1771-1835.
16487   Forbidden apartments. A tale. In two volumes.
800f   By William Linley ...
        London:Printed at the Minerva-press,for
    William Lane,Leadenhall-street.1800.
        12°. 2v. 19.5cm.

NL 0389497   MH NcU CtY NjP

VOLUME 334

Linley, William, 1771-1835, supposed author.
Harlequin captive [or, The magic fire]
1796. (Larpent collection. Ms. #1106) New
York, 1954.
(In Three centuries of drama: English,
Larpent collection)

Microprint.

I. Title. II. Title: The magic fire.
III. Larpent collection. Ms. #1106.

NL 0389498   MoU

Linley, William, 1771-1835.
...Honour, riches, marriage, blessing ¡sic¡ (Tempest) ¡for¡ S. &
M. S. ¡by¡ W. Linley.. London: Augener & Co. ¡187-?¡
Publ. pl. no. 5313. 5 p. 34cm.

Duet for soprano and mezzo-soprano with piano acc.
At head of title: Vocal duets, with accompaniment for the pianoforte. Fourth series.
No. ...179.

	CARNEGIE CORPORATION OF NEW YORK.
1. Vocal duos, Secular—Women	—Keyboard acc. I. Shakespeare,
William. Plays. The tempest.	
N.Y.P.L.	January 11, 1937

NL 0389499   NN

¡Linley, William¡ 1771-1835.

...Le melange; the favorite air as danced in the
Honey moon [by W. Linley] Arranged as a rondo for
the piano forte by H. Denman... London. Printed by
Lavenu & Mitchell [180-?] 4 p. 33cm.

Caption title.

1. Piano. I. Linley, William,   1771-1835. The honey moon.

NL 0389500   NN

Linley, William, 1771?-1835.
¡A trip to the Nore. The night was dark; arr.¡

The night was dark; a favorite song. New York Printed
& sold at J. Hewitt's musical repository Nº 131 William
Street. Sold also by B. Carr Philadelphia & J. Carr Baltimore. Price 12½ cᵗˢ ¡1798?¡
¡1¡ 1. 33 cm.
Caption title.
Bound with Hewitt, James. The Federal Constitution & liberty
for ever. New York ¡1798¡
For piano, with interlinear words, acc. originally for orchestra.
1. Operas—To 1800—Excerpts—Vocal scores with piano.
I. Title.

M1.A1H   M 54-668

NL 0389501   DLC

Linley, William, 1771-1835.
The night was dark. A much admired song
sung by Mrs. Bland in A Trip to the Nore ...
London, Longman & Broderip [1796]
4 p. fol.

NL 0389502   PPiU

Linley, William, 1771-1835.
O'er the rude rocks which bound her coasts.
A favorite song sung by Mr. Sedgwick in A Trip
to the Nore. London, Longman and Broderip [1797]
4 p. fol.

NL 0389503   PPiU

Linley, William.   No. 1 in **M.220.29
Requiem II.
(In Fane, John. A requiem to the memory of the late Samuel
Webbe ... Pp. 12-21. London, 1818?)

| | June 20, | 1902 |
| E4872 — Part songs. | | |

NL 0389504   MB

Linley, William. 1771-1835.
Shakespeare's dramatic songs, consisting
of all the songs, duets, trios, and choruses,
in character, as introduced by him in his
various dramas; the music, partly new and
partly selected with new symphonies and accompaniments for the pianoforte . . . to
which are prefixed a general introduction of
the subject and explanatory remarks on each
play. London, n. d. 2 v. in 1, 4°.   —2731

NL 0389505   MdBP

Linley, William, 1771-1835.
... Shakspeare's dramatic songs, consisting of all the songs, duets, trios and
chorusses ... the music, partly new & partly
selected with ... accompaniments for the
piano forte from the works of Purcell,
Fielding ... to which are prefixed a general
introduction ... and explanatory remarks ...
by Wm. Linley ... Together with an appendix
containing a new arrangement of the music of
Macbeth by ... S. Wesley. London, Printed
by Preston [18—?]
2 v. in 1.   35 cm.
Engraved t.-p.

NL 0389506   MdBP

6A
.251   LINLEY, WILLIAM, 1771?-1835, comp.
Shakespeare's dramatic songs, consisting of
all the songs, duets, trios and chorusses, in
character, as introduced by him in his various
dramas; the music, partly new & partly selected
with new symphonies and accompaniments for the
pianoforte, from the works of Purcell, Fielding, Drs Boyce, Nares, Arne, Cooke, Heers.J.
Smith, T. Linley Junr. and R.I.Stevens..
London,printed & sold by Preston¡1815-16¡
1517   2v.in 1.   34cm.

NL 0389507   ICN

M
1516   Linley, William, 1771-1835, ed.
S3   Shakespeare's dramatic songs ... as intro-
L4   duced by him in his various dramas the music,
Copy 1 partly new & partly selected with new symphonies
        and accompaniments for the piano forte from the
        works of Purcell ... And R.I.S. Stevens to which
        are prefixed a general introduction of the subject
        and explanatory remarks on each play ... In
        two volumes.   London, Printed & sold by Preston
        [ca. 1820]
        2 v. Fo.
        "Catalogue of musical works by the most

esteemed classic authors, printed published and
sold by Preston" on single leaf at end of vol. 1.
        Title to vol. 2 reads "... Together with an
appendix containing a new arrangement of the
music of Macbeth by Mr. S. Wesley."
        Initialled by the editor.
        Cummings copy.

--- --- Another issue.
        Vol. 1 has new title-page with note of Appendix.
Catalogue of Preston on verso of p. 89 of vol. 2
"Select classical publications ..."
        Initialled by the editor.

NL 0389510   DFo

Linley, William, 1771?-1835.
The Songs, Chorusses, &c. &c. In the Honey
Moon, A Comick Opera, ... [London] 1797.

NL 0389511   CSmH

PR
4889   Linley,William,1771-1835.
.L35   ¡ Songs,duets,&c.in The pavilion. A musical en-
P31   tertainment,in two acts,performed by their
        Majesties servants,at the Theatre royal,Drury-
        Lane on Saturday,November 16th. 1799. The over-
        ture and musick entirely new composed by Mr.
        Linley. London, Printed by C.Lowndes ¡1799¡
        12 p. 21½cm.
        Without the music.

I.Title. II.Title: The pavilion.

NL 0389512   MiU CSmH

Linley, William, 1771?-1835.
Songs, Duets, &c. In The Ring; or, Love me
for Myself. A Musical Entertainment, ...
London [1800]
Alteration of the Pavilion.

NL 0389513   CSmH

Linley, William, 1771?-1835.
Sonnets, odes, and other poems, by the late
Mr. Charles Leftley
see under Leftley, Charles, 1770-1797.

Linley, William, 1771-1835.
The trio of the sisters, from Selima and Azor
see under Linley, Thomas, 1732-1795.

Linley's assistant for the pianoforte. Containing
the necessary rudiments for beginners and
twenty four lessons progressively arranged with
preludes, rules of thorough bass and a short
dictionary of musical terms, & c. ... A new
edition.   Printed & sold by I. Carr at his
music store, Market street, Baltimore ...
        1 p.l., 32 p. 31.5 cm.
        The sonatas are by Benjamin Carr -
Sonneck-Upton.
        Lessons: Nägeli, Samuel Arnold, anon.

NL 0389516   MdHi MWA

Linlithgow, Marquess of
see Linlithgow, Victor Alexander John
Hope, 2d marquis of, 1887-

Linlithgow, Helen (Hay) Livingston, Countess of.
The confession and conversion of my lady
C. of L.
        see under title [Supplement]

¡Linlithgow, John Adrian Louis Hope¡ 1st marquis of,
1860-1908.
The Hopetoun house library. Catalogue of the library
of the Right Honourable the Earl of Hopetoun. Which
will be sold by auction, by Messrs. Sotheby, Wilkinson &
Hodge, auctioneers ... the 25th of February, 1889, and
three following days ... London, Dryden press, J. Davy
and sons ¡1889¡
v, 82 p. 25½ᶜᵐ.
The 1,263 lots realized £6,117.
1. Bibliography—Rare books.   I. Title.
                                                        13-6488
Library of Congress   Z999.S7
————— Copy 2. Priced.   Z997.11797

NL 0389519   DLC MB MH

¡ Linlithgow, John Adrian Louis Hope, 1st marquis of¡
1860-1908.
LETTER from an heritor to his fellows, the landed
interest of Scotland, to meet in delegation at Edinburgh,
on Monday, July 2, 1792... Edinburgh: Printed for the
author, 1792. 21 p. 26 x 22½cm.

Manuscript note on cover: By Earl of Hopetoun.

892099A. 1. Suffrage—Gt.Br.—Scotland. I. Hopetoun,
James Hope, 3d earl of, 1741-1816, supposed au.

N. Y. P. L.   June 8, 1937

NL 0389520   NN

Linlithgow, Victor Alexander John Hope,2d.
marquis of, 1887-
Gt. Brit. Royal commission on agriculture in India.
... Abridged report ¡and Report¡ Bombay, Printed at the
Government central press, 1928.

VOLUME 334

Linlithgow, Victor Alexander John Hope, 2d
marquis of, 1887–
Gt. Brit. *Ministry of agriculture and fisheries. Committee on distribution and prices of agricultural produce.*
... Final report ... London, H. M. Stationery off.
[printed by Eyre and Spottiswoode, ltd.] 1924.

Linlithgow, Victor Alexander John Hope, *2d marquis of,*
1887–
The Indian peasant, by the Marquess of Linlithgow ... with
a foreword by the Lord Irwin ... London, Faber & Faber
limited [1932]
32 p. 20ᵐᵐ. (*Half-title:* Criterion miscellany, no. 40)

1. Peasantry—India. 2. India—Soc. condit. ɪ. Title.

Library of Congress   DS421.5.L5   34–35144 rev.
     [r36c2]   915.4

NL 0389524   DLC LU NN NSyU PPLT MB NcD

Linlithgow, Victor Alexander John Hope,
2d marquis of, 1887–
... Interim and final reports
     see under   Gt. Brit. Ministry of
agriculture and fisheries.

Linlithgow, Victor John Alexander Hope,
2d marquis of, 1887–1952.
... Interim report on cereals, flour and
bread ...
     see under   Gt. Brit. Ministry of
agriculture and fisheries. Committee on
distribution and prices of agricultural produce.

Linlithgow, Victor Alexander John Hope,
2d marquis of, 1887–1952.
... Interim report on fruit and vegetables ...
     see under   Gt. Brit. Ministry of
agriculture and fisheries. Committee on distribution and prices of agricultural produce.

Linlithgow, Victor Alexander John Hope, 2d
marquis of, 1887–
Gt. Brit. *Ministry of agriculture and fisheries. Committee
on distribution and prices of agricultural produce.*
... Interim report on meat, poultry and eggs ... London,
H. M. Stationery off. [printed by Eyre and Spottiswoode, ltd.]
1923.

Linlithgow, Victor Alexander John Hope
2d marquis of, 1887–
Gt. Brit. *Ministry of agriculture and fisheries. Committee on distribution and prices of agricultural produce.*
... Interim report on milk and milk products ... London, H. M. Stationery off. [printed by Eyre and Spottiswoode, ltd.] 1923.

Linlithgow, Victor Alexander John Hope, 2d.
marquis of, 1887–
Gt. Brit. *Parliament. Joint committee on Indian constitutional reform.*
... Report [Proceedings and Records] London, H. M. Stationery off., 1934.

Linlithgow, Victor Alexander John Hope, 2d
marquis of, 1887–
Gt. Brit. *Parliament. Joint committee on Indian constitutional reform.*
... Report ... together with the Proceedings of the committee ... [Minutes of evidence and Records] London, H. M. Stationery off., 1934.

Linlithgow, Victor Alexander John Hope, *2d marquis of,*
1887–
Speeches. Simla, Printed by the Manager, Govt. of India
Press, 1940–44.

2 v. 22 cm.

Contents.—v. 1. From 17th April 1936 to 23rd April 1938.—v. 2.
From 29th November 1938 to 16th October 1943.

1. India—Pol. & govt.—1919–1947.

DS480.82.L49   52–57343 ‡

NL 0389532   DLC CaBVaU NSyU WU

Linlithgow, Victor Alexander John Hope, *2d marquis of,*
1887–
Speeches and statements by the Marquess of Linlithgow ...
New Delhi, Bureau of public information, government of
India, 1945.
xxii, 467 p. front., ports. 23ᵐᵐ.
On cover: Speeches and statements, 1936–43.

1. India—Pol. & govt.—1919–   —Addresses, essays, lectures.
ɪ. India. Bureau of public information.

DS480.82.L5   954   46–8382

NL 0389533   DLC CaBVaU IU NcD MiU CtY MoU NNC

Linlithgow, Victor Alexander John Hope, *2d marquis of,*
1887–
The transitional provisions of the Government of India
act, 1935. Being the presidential address of the president
of the Holdsworth Club ... [Birmingham, Eng.] Holdsworth Club of the University of Birmingham [1945?]
11 p. 26 cm.

1. India—Constitutional law. 2. India—Pol. & govt.—1919–1947.
3. Veto—India. ɪ. Birmingham, Eng. University. Faculty of
Law. Holdsworth Club. ɪɪ. Title. ɪɪɪ. Title: The Government of
India act, 1935.

                  59–38089 ‡

NL 0389534   DLC CaBVaU

Linlithgow, Victor Alexander John Hope,
2d marquis of, 1887–
     see also   India. Governor-general,
1936–1943 (Marquis of Linlithgow)

LINLITHGOW in pictures... with an introduction by Angus
Macdonald... London: A. & C. Black, Ltd. [, 1932.]
80 p. incl. front. illus. (incl. facsims., ports.), plan.
23½cm.

622793A. 1. Linlithgow, Scotland. 2. Linlithgow, Scotland
—Views. I. Macdonald,   Angus.

NL 0389536   NN

308t   **Linlor,** William Ivan, 1915–
L7577   Variation of neutron total cross section
of bismuth and uranium between 45 and 160
Mev. [Berkeley, 1953]
11,94 *l.* illus., diagrs., tables.

Thesis (Ph.D. in Physics) – Univ. of
California, Sept. 1953.
Also issued as UCRL [i.e. University of
California Radiation Laboratory] 2303.
Bibliography: p.69.

NL 0389537   CU

Linlow, Fritz, 1903–
... Über die isolierten Querfortsatzbrüche der
Wirbelsäule mit besonderer Berücksichtigung
ihrer Entschädigung in der Reichsunfallversich-
erung ... Leipzig, 1929.
Inaug.-Diss. - Leipzig.
Lebenslauf.
"Literatur": p. 77.

NL 0389538   CtY

Linly, George
     see
Linley, George, 1798–1865.

Linmaier, Josef, 1902–
Das Recht der Aktiengesellschaften in den
Vereinigten Staaten von Nordamerika.
Inaug. diss. Erlangen, n.d. (1928)
Bibl.

NL 0389540   ICRL PU

There are no cards for numbers
NL 0389541 to NL 0390000

Linn, Alice.
Buying children's shoes, pre-school and
grade school

see under

U.S. Federal Extension Service.

Linn, Alice.
Buying foundation garments

see under

U.S. Federal Extension Service.

Linn, Alice.
Buying men's suits

see under

U.S. Federal Extension Service.

Linn, Alice.
Buying women's street dresses (man-made
fibers and cotton)

see under

U.S. Federal Extension Service.

Linn, Alice.
Sewing machine conversion kits

see under

U.S. Federal Extension Service.

VOLUME 334

Linn, Alice.
Some references on textiles

see under

U.S. Federal Extension Service.

₁Linn, Allen Dawson₁ 1845–
Instructions in vapor process drying. ₁Grand Rapids?
Mich., ᶜ1910₁
cover-title, 1 p. l., 71, ₁1₁ p. incl. illus., 2 fold. pl. pl., fold. plans. 23ᶜᵐ.

1. Lumber—Drying.
Library of Congress   TS837.L7   10–7465

NL 0390007   DLC

---

ar W
47593   Linn, Alvin Frank, 1864–
no.7   I. Sulphon-fluorescein and related compounds. II. Some experiments on the rate of oxidation of the three toluic acids by
potassium permanganate in alkaline solution ... By A. F.
Linn ... Baltimore, Press of the Friedenwald co. ₁1892?₁
25 p. 2 diagr. 23 ᵐ.
Thesis (PH. D.)—Johns Hopkins university, 1892.
Biographical sketch: p. 25.

1. Sulphonphthaleins. 2. Toluic acid.
Library of Congress   QD441.L52   44–16481

NL 0390008   DLC ICU MB MiU MdBP NIC

Linn, Annie M. E., ed.

Sudduth, Hugh Thomas, 1850–1922.
Poems and prose, by H. T. Sudduth, compiled and edited in
memory of the author by Annie M. E. Linn and Clara Linn
Braden. Washington, D. C., 1936.

AC901
.P 3   Linn, Archibald Ladley, 1802–1857.
v. 30   An oration, delivered in Schenectady, N.Y.,
no. 4   July 4, 1822, by Archibald L. Linn, A.B. Pub-
Office   lished at the request of the Committee of arrangements. Schenectady, I. Riggs, printer, 1822.
15 p.   20 cm.   [Pamphlets, v. 30, no. 4]

NL 0390010   DLC NSyU

Linn, Archibald Ladley, 1802–1857.
Speech...on the revenue b' 11
Delivered in the House of representat-
ives of the United States July 27, 1841

Washington 1841   12p.

YA5000
J 17   (Congressional speeches, by author)

NL 0390011   DLC

Western
Americana   Linn, Archibald Ladley, 1802–1857.
Zc52   Speech ... upon the mission to Mexico,
842Lj   and annexation of Texas. Delivered in the
House of Representatives of the U. S.,
April 13, 1842. Washington, Printed at
the National Intelligencer Office, 1842,
26 p. 24 cm.

Streeter no. 1420.

1. Texas – Hist. – Republic, 1836–1846.

NL 0390012   CtY ViU NNC TxU NIC N DLC

Linn, Arthur, 1867–
Juristische Natur der durch die Social-
gesetzgebung des Deutschen Reiches aufgestellten Versicherungspflichtigkeit ...
von Arthur Linn ... Greifswald, J. Abel,
1893.
4 p. l., 29 p. 23cm.
Inaug.-Diss. - Greifswald.
"Lebenslauf": p. 29.
"Litteratur": 4th prelim. leaf.

NL 0390013   MH-L ICRL

LB2864
.L5   Linn, Avery J
Your school bus program: suggestions for
board members, administrators, drivers and
teachers. Prepared by Avery J. Linn and
LeRoy Ortgiesen. ₁Lincoln₁ State Dept. of
Public Instruction ₁1954₁
50 p.

1. School buses. 2. School children -
Transportation. I. Title.

NL 0390014   NbU

HD7235
.P3L5   Linn, Baruch, 1898– 1964,
Hebr)   במוח סוציאלי. ₁הוצאת, ההסתדרות הכללית של העובדים
העברים בארץ-ישראל. מרכז לתרבות והסברה.
₁Tel-Aviv, 1951₁
32 p. 17 cm.

1. Insurance, Social—Israel. 2. Insurance, Social.
Title transliterated: Bituaḥ sotsiali.
HD7235.P3L5   57–50802 ‡
Library of Congress   ₁8₁

NL 0390015   DLC

Linn, Beth.
One little mustard seed. New York,
E.P. Dutton, 1890.
259p. illus. 17cm.

NL 0390016   IEN DLC

Linn, Bettina.
Flea circus, by Bettina Linn. New York, H. Smith and R.
Haas, 1936.
318 p. 19¼ᶜᵐ.
"First printing."

1. Title.
Library of Congress   PZ3.L6549Fl   36–6667

NL 0390017   DLC NN

WG
27559   Linn, Carl, 1881–
Zur Kenntnis des Cholesterins. [Berlin,
1908?]
30 p.

Inaug.-Diss. - Berlin.

NL 0390018   CtY ICRL

Linn, Carl Barnes, 1907–
... The catalyzed reaction of ethylmagnesium bromide with
ethyl bromide, by C. B. Linn and C. R. Noller ... ₁Easton,
Pa., 1936₁
cover-title, p. ₁810₁–819. diagr. 26¼ x 20ᶜᵐ. (Stanford university.
Contributions from the Department of chemistry. vol. VII, no. 25. 1936)
"This paper embodies a portion of the material presented as a thesis
... for the degree of doctor of philosophy at Stanford university ₁1934₁"—
Slip attached to recto of first leaf.
"Reprinted from the Journal of the American chemical society, vol. 58
... (May, 1936)."

1. Ethylmagnesium bromide. 2. Ethyl bromide. 3. Catalysis.
I. Noller, Carl Robert, 1900– joint author.
Library of Congress   QD412.M4L5 1934   37–10223
Leland Stanford Junior   Univ. Libr.
₁3₁   541.39

NL 0390019   CSt DLC

Linn, Charles Adolphus, 1870–   ed.

Jerusalem Evangelical Lutheran church, *Effingham Co., Ga.*
Ebenezer record book, containing early records of Jerusalem
Evangelical Lutheran church, Effingham, Ga., more commonly known as Ebenezer church; translated by A. G. Voigt ...
edited and published by C. A. Linn ... Savannah, Ga., 1929.

Linn, Charles Adolphus, 1890–
The history of the German friendly society of Savannah,
Georgia, by C. A. Linn. 1837–1937. Savannah,
Ga., The German friendly society, 1937.
5 p. l., ₁19₁–102 p. plates, ports., facsims. 23½ᶜᵐ.

1. German friendly society, Savannah. 2. Germans in Savannah.
Library of Congress   HS1510.G383L5   38–2911

NL 0390021   DLC TxU

Linn, Clement Huntingford, 1886–
Hallelujah Jack, being the story of a sinner saved by
grace, by Rev. Jack Linn, evangelist (Hallelujah Jack)
Louisville, Ky., Pentecostal publishing company ₁ᶜ1917₁
120 p. front. (port.) 19½ᶜᵐ. $0.75

1. Title.
Library of Congress   BV3785.L5A3   17–19829 Revised

NL 0390022   DLC

Linn, Clement Huntingford, 1886–
The letters of a converted boy to his mother, by Rev.
C. H. Linn ... Louisville, Ky., Pentecostal publishing
company ₁ᶜ1918₁
93 p. 19½ᶜᵐ.

1. Title.
Library of Congress   BV3785.L5A4   18–12197

NL 0390023   DLC

Linn, Clement Huntingford Jack

see

Linn, Clement Huntingford, 1886–

Linn, Mrs. Edith (Willis) 1865–   ed.

Willis, Frederick Llewellyn Hovey, 1830–1914.
Alcott memoirs, posthumously comp. from papers, journals
and memoranda of the late Dr. Frederick L. H. Willis, by
E. W. L. & H. B. Boston, R. G. Badger, ₁etc., etc.₁, ᶜ1915₁

VOLUME 334

Linn, *Mrs.* **Edith**   (Willis) 1865–
A cycle of sonnets, by Edith Willis Linn. New York,
J. T. White & co., 1918.
125 p. 18¼ᶜᵐ.

I. Title.

Library of Congress   PS3523.I 66C9   18–3206

NL 0390026   DLC NBuU TxU NjP

Linn, *Mrs.* **Edith**   (Willis) 1865–
From dream to dream; poems by Edith Willis Linn.
New York, J. T. White & co., 1918.
126 p. 18¼ᶜᵐ.

I. Title.

Library of Congress   PS3523.I 66F7 1918   18–13822

NL 0390027   DLC NN NjP

Linn, *Mrs.* **Edith (Willis)** 1865–
Out of the deep; pen pictures in prose and verse, by Edith
Willis Linn. New York, The Metaphysical publishing co.
₁1895₎
30 p. 17¼ᶜᵐ.

I. Title.
                         ₁Full name: Mrs. Edith Lenore (Willis) Linn₎

Library of Congress   PS3523.I 66O8 1895   33–35299
                                                          818.5

NL 0390028   DLC NBuG

Linn, *Mrs.* **Edith (Willis)** 1865–
Poems, by Edith Willis Linn. Buffalo, C. W. Moulton, 1892.
ix p., 1 l., 167 p. front. (port.) 17¼ᶜᵐ.

                         ₁Full name: Mrs. Edith Lenore (Willis) Linn₎

Library of Congress   PS3523.I 66P6 1892   33–35300
                                                          811.5

NL 0390029   DLC NBuG NcD NBuHi ViU MB MH NN

Linn, *Mrs.* **Edith (Willis)** 1865–
Within, above, beyond, by Edith Willis Linn. ₁Washington,
D. C., Beresford, pr., 1899₎
cover-title, 11 p. 17ᶜᵐ.
Poems.

I. Title.
                         ₁Full name: Mrs. Edith Lenore (Willis) Linn₎
                                              0–1464 Revised
Library of Congress   PS3523.I 66W5 1900

NL 0390030   DLC

T1952 **Linn, Edmund Holt**
L758   The rhetorical theory and practice of
          Harry Emerson Fosdick. ₁Iowa City₎ 1952.
          vii,691l. illus. 28cm.

          Thesis (Ph.D.) - University of Iowa.

          1. Fosdick, Harry Emerson, 1878–
          I. Title.

NL 0390031   IaU MNtcA

FILM Linn, Edmund Holt.
251   The rhetorical theory and practice of Harry
L64r   Emerson Fosdick. ₁Iowa City, Iowa₎ 1952.
          vii, 704p.

          Thesis--State University of Iowa.
          Bibliography: leaves 668–691.
          Microfilm copy of typescript. Iowa City,
          Iowa, University of Iowa Microfilm Service,
          1965. 1 reel. 35mm.

NL 0390032   IU PPT

Linn, Edward R
     A forest industries survey of Oklahoma...
Stillwater, Okla. 1948.
     35 p. tables.
(Oklahoma. Agricultural experiment station,
Stillwater. Experiment station bulletin no.
B–325)

     Cover-title.
     Footnotes.

NL 0390033   PP

Linn, *Mrs.* **Elizabeth A**   (Relfe)
     The life and public services of Dr. Lewis F. Linn, for
ten years a senator of the United States from the state of
Missouri. By E. A. Linn and N. Sargent. New York,
D. Appleton and company, 1857.
     441 p. front. (port.) pl. 22¼ᶜᵐ.
     "Public life of Dr. Linn ... By N. Sargent": p. ₁125₎–340.

     1. Linn, Lewis Fields, 1795–1843. I. Sargent, Nathan, 1794–1875.

Library of Congress   E340.L7L7   9—259

                Or CaBViPA OrSaW WaTC
                IaU MiU NcD KyHi ICJ MdBP MWA MB NN WaU OrP OrHi
NL 0390034   DLC WaT WaU MnHi NIC NcU FTaSU PPGi ViU

HB3999 Linn, Erwin Louis, 1918–
     The association of death rates from selected
causes with the business cycle, 1919–1947.
1952.
     163 l.

     Thesis--Univ. of Chicago.

     1. Mortality. 2. Business cycles.

NL 0390036   ICU DNLM

Linn, Eva Emma.
     Ability in the mechanics of written English as
related to general intelligence. ₁Phila.,1927₎
65 p.

NL 0390037   PPT

Linn, Fletcher, 1866–   comp.
     The "gay nineties."   ₁n.p., 1940?₎
     19l.   41½cm.
Scrapbook of pictures and miscellanea concerning
the class of 1890, with some material on classes of
1891 and 1894, University of Oregon.

NL 0390038   OrU

Linn, Frits.
Die staatsrechtliche stellung des präsidenten der Ver
einigten Staaten von Amerika ... Würzburg ₁Darm-
stadt, L. C. Wittich'sche hofbuchdruckerei₎ 1926.
     5 p. l., 3–144 p. 24ᶜᵐ.
     Inaug.-diss.--Würzburg.
     "Literatur-verzeichnis": 2d prelim. leaf.

     1. Presidents--U. S.--Powers and duties.

NL 0390039   MiU ICRL PU CtY OClW MH

JK 516 Linn, Fritz
.L 55   Die staatsrechtliche stellung des Präsidenten
1928   der Vereinigten Staaten von Amerika. Bonn,
          Schroeder, 1928.
          [8], 144 p. 24cm.

          Bibliography: p. [3–4]

          1. Presidents - U. S. I. Title.

NL 0390040   MdBJ CtY MH ICN MiU-L DS NN MH-L

LINN, Fritz, 1877–
Über die wirkung lokaler arsonvalisation
Inaug.-diss., Heidelberg, Leipzig,1908.
24 p.

NL 0390041   MBCo ICRL DNLM MH

LINN, GEORGE DANA.
     How to balance budgets, federal, state, county, mu-
nicipal [by] George Dana Linn. Seattle, Wash. [1938]
15 p. 23cm.

     1. Unearned increment—Taxation. I. Title.

NL 0390042   NN

Linn, George Dana
     Why we should oppose placing the so-called
40-mill tax law into the constitution. Seattle,
Author, 1943?
     [2] p.
     Reproduced from type-written copy.
     With which is bound his Keep the 40-mill out
of the constitution. 5 p.

NL 0390043   WaS

Linn, George Ward.
     Catalogue of patriotic covers of world war II ... compiled
and published by George W. Linn. Sidney, O. ₁1944?₎
     94 p. 21½ᶜᵐ.
     "Includes covers known up to October 1, 1943."

     1. Covers (Philately) I. Title: Patriotic covers of world war II.
                                                          44–14077
Library of Congress   HE6185.U6L5
                                     ₁3₎   383.22

NL 0390044   DLC

Linn, George Ward.
     A check list of the postage stamps of the state of Sonora and
the constitutionalist government of Mexico, by George Ward
Linn. ₁Columbus, O.: G. W. Linn Co., 1913?₎ 4 l. nar. 8°.
     Caption-title.

     1. Postage stamps, Mexico.
N.Y.P.L.   July 19, 1918

NL 0390045   NN

VOLUME 334

Linn, George Ward.
Mexico, the white and green seal issues of Sonora; a study of the stamps, together with a reproduction of the various printings and a complete list of all varieties known to the author, by George Ward Linn. Columbus, O., George W. Linn company, 1916.
106 p. incl. front. (port.) illus. xxv pl. 24ᶜᵐ. $1.00

1. Postage-stamps—Mexico—Sonora.

Library of Congress   HE6185.M6S6   16-10308

NL 0390046   DLC CaOTP CU-B

Linn, George Ward.
The paid markings on the three cent U. S. stamp of 1861. Sidney, Ohio, G. W. Linn Co., 1955.
104 p. illus. 21 cm.

1. Cancellations (Philately)—U. S.   I. Title.

HE6185.U6L52   383.22   57-23053 ‡

NL 0390047   DLC

Linn, George Ward.
... Philatelic handbooks
    see   Linn's philatelic handbooks.

Linn, George Ward, ed.

The Stamp collector. v. 1-2, v. 3, no. 1-10; Nov. 1909–Oct. 1911. Columbus, O., G. W. Linn, 1909-11.

Linn, George Ward.
The war stamps of Mexico; a brief study of the different issues and a specialized check list of all varieties known to the author. Columbus, Ohio, G. W. Linn Co., 1917.
91 p. illus. 24 cm.

1. Postage-stamps—Mexico.   I. Title.

HE6185.M5L5   59-59451 ‡

NL 0390050   DLC NN CaOTP

Linn, George Wilds, 1844–
An echo of the civil war. From Richmond to Appomattox; some account of the evacuation of Richmond and Petersburg and the surrender of General Robert E. Lee, by an eye-witness in the advance column: George Wilds Linn. ₍Lebanon, Pa., Press of Sowers printing company, ᵉ1911₎
25 p. incl. front. 20ᶜᵐ. $0.30

1. U. S.—Hist.—Civil war—Campaigns and battles. 2. Appomattox, Lee's surrender at.
11-25582

Library of Congress   E477.67.L75

NL 0390051   DLC

Linn, George Wilds, 1844–
A history of a fragment of the clan Linn and a genealogy of the Linn and related families, by Dr. George Wilds Linn ... ₍Lebanon, Pa., Report print₎ 1905.
204, ₍13₎ p. 3 port. (incl. front.) 22½ᶜᵐ.
13 blank pages at end, for records of marriages, births, and deaths.
CONTENTS.—pt. 1. Historical.—pt. 2. Genealogy of the Linn and related families.—pt. 3. Biographical sketches.

1. Lynn family (Hugh Linn, 1753–1815)

6-20341

Library of Congress   CS71.L989 1905

NL 0390052   DLC MWA MB OC1 NN

Linn, Harry D
Horse-breaking ₍by₎ Harry D. Linn, Iowa Horse and Mule Breeders' Ass'n, Des Moines, Iowa and The Horse Association of America, Chicago, Illinois. ₍Des Moines, 1929?₎
30, ₍1₎ p. illus. 23ᶜᵐ.

NL 0390053   ICJ OrCS IU

LB3235
.A9
Educ.
Library
Linn, Henry Harold, 1897–
Check list forms for rating school custodial service, by H.H. Linn, L.C. Helm and K.P. Grabarkiewicz. ₍New York, Teachers College, Columbia University, 1940₎
1 v. (unpaged)

Caption title.

1. Janitors. 2. School-houses. I. Helm, Leslie C   joint author.

NL 0390054   CU InU IaU IU

Linn, Henry Harold, 1897–
Insurance practices in school administration, by Henry H. Linn and Schuyler C. Joyner. New York, Ronald Press Co. ₍1952₎
446 p. illus. 21 cm.

1. Insurance—U. S. 2. School management and organization. I. Title.

LB2830.5.L55   371.2   52-10123 ‡

OrSaW
ViU PBL WaU MsSM MB KEmT WaS OrPS IdU MtU OrCS OrP
NL 0390055   DLC IdPI OrLgE ScU NcD PU-Penn TxU

Linn, Henry Harold, 1897–

LB3221
.C9
Cyr, Frank William, 1900–
Planning rural community school buildings; prepared under the supervision of Frank W. Cyr and Henry H. Linn; staff: Kenneth H. Bailey ₍and others₎ New York, Bureau of Publications, Teachers College, Columbia University, 1949.

Linn, Henry Harold, 1897–
Practical school economies, by Henry H. Linn ... New York city, Teachers college, Columbia university, 1934.
xxiv p., 1 l., 461 p. diagrs. 23½ᶜᵐ. (Half-title: School administration series)
Includes bibliographies.

1. Education—Finance. 2. Public schools—U. S.—Finance. 3. School management and organization. I. Title. II. Title: School economies.
34-18134

Library of Congress   LB2829.L5

OrStbM OrSaW OrU-M
Wa WaE WaPS WaS WaSp WaSpG WaT WaTC WaWW Or
OC1 OU NN CaBVaU IdB IdPI IdU MtBC MtU OrCS OrP
NL 0390057   DLC OrPR OrU KEmT PU PP PPPL NcD OCU

Linn, Henry Harold, 1897–
Safeguarding school funds, by Henry H. Linn ... New York city, Teachers college, Columbia university, 1929.
x, 187, ₍1₎ p. 23ᶜᵐ.
Thesis (PH. D.)—Columbia university, 1930.
Vita.
Published also as Teachers college, Columbia university, Contributions to education, no. 387.
Bibliography: p. 182–187.

1. Education—U. S.—Finance. 2. Public schools—U. S.—Finance. 3. Insurance, Surety and fidelity. 4. Banks and banking—U. S. I. Title.
30-5683

Library of Congress   LB2825.L55 1930
Columbia Univ. Libr.   ₍3₎

NL 0390059   NNC DLC Or

Linn, Henry Harold, 1897–
Safeguarding school funds, by Henry H. Linn ... New York city, Teachers college, Columbia university, 1929.
x, 187 p. 23½ᶜᵐ. (Teachers college, Columbia university. Contributions to education, no. 387)
Published also as thesis (PH. D.) Columbia university.
Bibliography: p. 182–187.

1. Education—U. S.—Finance. 2. Public schools—U. S.—Finance. 3. Insurance, Surety and fidelity. 4. Banks and banking—U. S. I. Title.
30-5251

Library of Congress   LB2825.L55 1929

MH MB ViU OrCS KEmT PSt OrU CaBVaU WaTC
NL 0390060   DLC OrP MtU NIC NcD MoU MiU OC1 OCU OU

Linn, Henry Harold, 1897–
The school custodian's housekeeping handbook, by Henry H. Linn, Leslie C. Helm ₍and₎ K. P. Grabarkiewicz. New York, Bureau of Publications, Teachers College, Columbia Univ., 1948.
xviii, 256 p. illus. 24 cm.

1. Janitors. 2. School-houses. I. Helm, Leslie C., joint author. II. Grabarkiewicz, Kazmer P., joint author. III. Title.

LB3235.L5   371.62   48-7731*

OrP OrSaW OrU PPPL PU-Penn Wa WaS WaT
OU IdU WaU IdPI CaBVaU OrPS CaBViP MtBC MtU Or OrCS
NL 0390061   DLC PBL PSt PP Mi IU TxU OC1CC ICU ViU

Linn, Henry Harold, 1897–

Nebraska state education association. *Legislative committee.*
... The status of taxation in Nebraska. State aid for school transportation. Lincoln, Neb., Nebraska state teachers association, 1928.

Linn, Henry Harold, 1897–
Suggestions for the use of check list forms for rating school custodial service. By H.H.Linn, L.C.Helm, and K.P.Grabarkiewicz ... ₍New York, Bureau of publications, Teachers college, c1940₎
₍29₎p. 28½ᶜᵐ.

Caption title.
"Check list for rating school custodial service": p.₍3₎-₍29₎

NL 0390063   MoU

Linn,Henry William,1904–
The satirical element in the letters of Saint Jerome ... ₍St.Louis,Mo.₎ 1934.
1 p.l.,554 numb.l.   28ᶜᵐ. (University Microfilms. Pub.no.178)
Abstracted in University Microfilms. Abstracts,v.II, no.2,p.83,1940.
Thesis (PH.D.)--St.Louis university,1933.
Vita auctoris.
Typewritten copy.
Bibliography: p.546-553.

1.Hieronymous,Saint. Epistolae. 2.Satire,Latin. I.Title.

NL 0390064   MiU

LINN, HERBERT C.
Zur Lösung der Judenfrage.   Wien, W. Frick, 1946.   23 p. 21cm.

Film reproduction. Negative.

1. Jewish question.

NL 0390065   NN ICU MH

VOLUME 334

Linn, Hugh Alexander.
Influences affecting rural pupils' choice of high schools in
northeast Nebraska. ₍Boulder, Colo.₎ 1942.
Microfilm copy of typewritten ms. Positive.
Collation of the original, as determined from the film: 57, ₍2₎, ₁v l.
maps.
Thesis (M. ED.)—University of Colorado.
Bibliography: leaves ₍58₎–₍59₎

1. High schools—Nebraska.

Microfilm AC–21   Mic 50–317

NL 0390066   DLC

1.
LD3907
.G7   **Linn, Irving.**
1942   Widwilt, son of Gawain...   New York,
.L5   1941.
cxlviii,183,177 typewritten leaves.
29cm.
Thesis (Ph.D.) – New York university,
Graduate school, 1942.
"The first romance in Judeo-German
based on a surviving manuscript ever to
be printed in its original character."
Foreword, p.₍iii₎

"The manuscript used as the basis for
the text is ms. Trinity college, Cambridge, F.12.44." - Introd. p.₍ix₎
Text in the original Judeo-German
characters (177p. at end) and in transliterated form, with a synopsis in English.
Bibliography: p.₍180₎–183.

NL 0390068   NNU-W

Linn, Irving, 1912–
Widwilt, son of Gawain ₍by₎ Irving Linn ... New York,
New York university, 1946.
17 p. diagr. 23ᶜᵐ.
Abridgment of thesis (PH. D.)—New York university, 1942.
"The romance in the Judeo-German language which is the subject of
the study, is based on ms. Trinity college, Cambridge, F.12.44."—Introd.
Bibliographical foot-notes.

1. Artus-hof. 2. Cambridge. University. Trinity college. Library.
Ms. (F.12.44)
PT1501.A75Z7   library   A 46–6192
New York univ. Wash. sq.   ₍2₎†
for Library of Congress

NL 0390069   NNU-W NcD ICU DLC OrU

Linn, Jack

see

Linn, Clement Huntingford, 1886–

Linn, James, 1873–1868
Bellefonte, Pa. Presbyterian church.
Ebenezer; a memorial of the semi-centenary of the pastor-
ate of the Rev. James Linn ... containing a narrative by Dr.
Linn, and a semi-centenary sermon, by Rev. D. X. Junkin ...
Philadelphia, W. S. & A. Martien, 1859.

Linn, James Weber, 1876–

National guard association of the United States.
An appeal to the 74th Congress by the National guard association. Washington's lost plan revived. ₍Chicago? 1935₎

Linn, James Weber, 1876–1939.
The blind princess and the dawn; two poems
see under title

Linn, James Weber, 1876–1939
The chameleon, by James Weber Linn ... New York,
McClure, Phillips & co., 1903.
viii, 418 p. 20ᶜᵐ.

I. Title.

Library of Congress   PZ3.L655C   3–5783

NL 0390074   DLC OrU

---

*
PS3511
.A86L506 **Linn, James Weber,** 1876–1939.
1935   Counterpoint: Light in August
(In Linn, James Weber and Taylor, Houghton
Wells. A foreword to fiction. New York, 1935.
24cm. p. 144–157)

1. Faulkner, William, 1897–   . Light in
August. I. Taylor, Houghton Wells, 1898–
joint author. II. Title.

NL 0390075   ViU

Linn, James Weber, 1876–1939
The essentials of English composition, by James Weber
Linn ... New York, C. Scribner's sons, 1912.
xiv, 186 p. 17ᶜᵐ. $1.00

1. English language—Rhetoric.

Library of Congress   PE1408.L57   12–17989

NL 0390076   DLC WaWW Or PV PP NIC MiU OCl OO

Linn, James Weber, 1876–1939.
The essentials of English composition, by James Weber Linn
... New York, Chicago ₍etc.₎ C. Scribner's sons ₍1912₎
xiv, 186 p. 16¼ᶜᵐ.

1. English language—Rhetoric.
                                                   40–28571
Library of Congress   PE1408.L57 1912 a
                                        ₍2₎   808

NL 0390077   DLC OrCS NcRS NN MiU

PE 1408 **LINN, JAMES WEBER,** 1876–1939
.L75   The essentials of English composition.
New York, C. Scribner's ₍1916₎
186 p.

1. English language—Composition and exercises.

NL 0390078   InU

Linn, James Weber, 1876–1939
The essentials of English composition, by James Weber
Linn ... Rev. ed. New York, Chicago ₍etc.₎ C. Scribner's sons
₍1932₎
xii p., 1 l., 242 p. 17ᶜᵐ.

1. English language—Rhetoric.
Library of Congress   PE1408.L57 1932   32–10915

NL 0390079   DLC MtBC OrLgE IdPI OClCC OClW

Linn, James Weber, 1876–1939.
A foreword to fiction, by James Weber Linn ... and Houghton Wells Taylor ... New York, London, D. Appleton-Century company, incorporated ₍*1935₎
vii, 202 p. 23½ᶜᵐ.
"Reading list": p. 191–194. "Note on secondary sources": p. 195–198.

1. Fiction—Technique. 2. Fiction—Hist. & crit. I. Taylor, Houghton Wells, 1898– joint author. II. Title.
                                                   35–4391
Library of Congress   PN3355.L5
                                        ₍a41o1₎   808.3

OrCS ScU
OClND NIC UU MsU FTaSU MsSM FU KU TU WaWW Or OrSaW
NL 0390080   DLC GU MoU NcD CoU PP OClJC OCl OCU ODW

Linn, James Weber,1876–1939
The head marshal of the University of Chicago.
(In Stories of the colleges. Pp. 323–353. Philadelphia, 1901.)

NL 0390081   MB

1939
Linn, James Weber, 1876–   comp.
Illustrative examples of English composition, by
James Weber Linn ... New York, C. Scribner's sons,
1913.
x, 246 p. 17ᶜᵐ. $1.00
"A companion to the compiler's Essentials of English composition, which
it is primarily intended to supplement."—Introd.
CONTENTS.—Examples of exposition.—Examples of argumentation.—Ex-
amples of description.—Examples of narration.

1. English prose literature. 2. English language—Rhetoric. I. Title.
                                                   13–2008
Library of Congress   PE1417.L6

ViU
NL 0390082   DLC Or OrCS OrU MB PBa NcD OCl OO OLak

Linn, James Weber, 1876–1939.
James Keeley, newspaperman, by James Weber Linn ...
Indianapolis, New York, The Bobbs-Merrill company ₍*1937₎
286 p. front., plates, ports., facsims. 24 cm.
"First edition."

1. Keeley, James, 1867–1934. 2. The Chicago tribune.
                                                   37–31931
Library of Congress   PN4874.K4L5
                                        ₍a48k1₎   920.5

WaTC OKentU
NL 0390083   DLC MtU GU NN NcD OCl OU MB ViU N OrU

Linn, James Weber, 1876– 1939
Jane Addams; a biography, by James Weber Linn ... New
York, London, D. Appleton-Century company, incorporated,
1935.
xi p., 1 l., 457 p. front., plates, ports. 23ᶜᵐ.

1. Addams, Jane, 1860–1935.
                                                   35–18354
Library of Congress   HV28.A35L5

WaTC WaWW OrMonO Or MtBuM
OrCS OrP OrPR OrU Wa WaE WaPS WaS WaSp WaSpG WaT
CSt NBuU MeB IdPI IdU OrStbM OrSaW OrU-M MtBC MtU
OO OFH ViU MB NN CaBVa CoU WHi TNJ MiU CaBVaU IdB
NL 0390084   DLC PSC-Hi NcRS NcD PPT CU ODW OCl OLak

Linn, James Weber, 1876–1939.
Jane Addams; a biography by James Weber Linn.
Illustrated. New York; London D. Appleton-
Century Company Inc. 1936.
[vi] vii–xi, 457 p., 1 l. 22.5 cm.

NL 0390085   DLC TU

VOLUME 334

HV28
A222L7 Linn, James Weber, 1876–1939.
Jane Addams; a biography. New York,
Appleton-Century, 1938 [c1935].
xi, 457 p. illus., ports. 23cm.

1. Addams, Jane, 1860–1935.

NL 0390086   GU

Linn, James Weber, 1876–

Chicago. Century of progress international exposition, 1933.
The official pictures of a Century of progress exposition.
Chicago, 1933; introduction by James Weber Linn; photographs by Kaufmann & Fabry co., official photographers. Chicago, The Reuben H. Donnelley corporation [°1933]

Linn, James Weber, 1876–1939.
... "Oh see, can you say?"
(In: The University of Chicago Magazine,
February, 1938. 30.5 cm.   v. 30, no. 4)
Convocation address, December 21, 1937.

NL 0390088   NcD

Linn, James Weber, 1876–1939, ed.
Poems by Wordsworth, Coleridge, Shelley, and Keats, selected and ed. by James Weber Linn ... New York, H. Holt
and company, 1911.
lvii, 215 p. incl. front., ports. 17ᵐ. (Half-title: English readings for
schools. General editor: W. L. Cross)
Mottoes on end-papers.
"This volume includes all the poems by Wordsworth, Shelley, and
Keats contained in the fourth book of Palgrave's Golden treasury, with
the addition of The rime of the ancient mariner, The eve of St. Agnes,
and favorite lyrics by lesser poets."
Descriptive bibliography: p. lv–lvii.
I. Wordsworth, William, 1770–1850. II. Coleridge, Samuel Taylor,
1772–1834. III. Shelley, Percy Bysshe, 1792–1822. IV. Keats, John, 1795–
1821.

Library of Congress   PR1219.L6   11—18272

NL 0390089   DLC OrP Wa OrCS CoU PU NcC

Keats   Linn, James Weber, 1876–1939, ed.
*EC8   Poems by Wordsworth, Coleridge, Shelley, and
K2262   Keats; selected and edited by James Weber Linn
A911l2e   ...
New York, Henry Holt and company[1927]
lvii, 215 p. incl. front., ports. 17.5cm. (Half-
title: English readings. General editor: Wilbur
Lucius Cross)
Publisher's device on t.-p.
Dated on verso of t.-p.: May, 1927.
"Descriptive bibliography": p. lv-lvii.
Original red   cloth; quotations on end
papers.

NL 0390090   MH

Keats   Linn, James Weber, 1876–1939, ed.
*EC8   Poems by Wordsworth, Coleridge, Shelley, and
K2262   Keats; selected and edited by James Weber Linn
A911l2g   ...
New York, Henry Holt and company[1930]
lvii, 215 p. incl. front., ports. 17.5cm. (Half-
title: English readings. General editor: Wilbur
Lucius Cross)
Publisher's device on t.-p.
Dated on verso of t.-p.: August, 1930.
"Descriptive bibliography": p. lv-lvii.
Original red   cloth; quotations on
end papers.

NL 0390091   MH

Linn, James Weber, 1876–1939, ed.
Poems by Wordsworth, Coleridge, Shelley, and Keats, selected and ed. by James Weber Linn ... New York, H. Holt
and company [1933]
lvii, 215 p. incl. front., ports. 17ᵐ. (Half-title: English readings for
schools. General editor: W. L. Cross)
Mottoes on end-papers.
"This volume includes all the poems by Wordsworth, Shelley, and
Keats contained in the fourth book of Palgrave's Golden treasury, with
the addition of The rime of the ancient mariner, The eve of St. Agnes,
and favorite lyrics by lesser poets."
Descriptive bibliography: p. lv–lvii.

NL 0390092   ViU

Linn, James Weber, 1876–1939.
The second generation, by James Weber Linn. New York,
The Macmillan company; London, Macmillan & co., ltd., 1902.
3 p. l., 305 p. 18ᵐ.

I. Title.

Library of Congress   PZ3.L655S   2–2764 Revised

NL 0390093   DLC MNBedf

Linn, James Weber, 1876–   ed.
                                   FOR OTHER EDITIONS
                                   SEE MAIN ENTRY
Ruskin, John, 1819–1900.
... Sesame and lilies, by John Ruskin, ed. for school use,
by J. W. Linn ... Chicago, New York, Scott, Foresman
and company [°1920]

Linn, James Weber, 1876–1939.
A shrine of labor [by] James Weber Linn. Chicago, The
Lakeside press, R. R. Donnelley & sons company, 1944.
11 p. plates. 17½ᵐ.
Reprinted from the author's column in the Chicago daily times.

1. Lakeside press, Chicago.   I. Title.

Harvard univ. Library   A 44–4281
for Library of Congress   [2]

NL 0390095   MH NBu NN

Linn, James Weber, 1876–
Stories of the colleges; being tales of life at the great
American universities told by noted graduates. Phila-
delphia & London, J. B. Lippincott co., 1901.

Linn, James Weber, 1876–   ed.
Dickens, Charles, 1812–1870.
A tale of two cities, by Charles Dickens; ed., with biograph-
ical and literary notes, by James Weber Linn ... Boston, New
York [etc.] Ginn & company [°1906]

Linn, James Weber, 1876–1939
This was life; a novel by James Weber Linn. Indianapolis,
New York, The Bobbs-Merrill company [°1936]
304 p. 20ᵐ.
"First edition."

I. Title.

Library of Congress   PZ3.L655Th   36–3330

NL 0390098   DLC WaS ICN NcD OCl MB

UA661   Linn, James Weber, 1876–1939. Washington's
.M3   lost plan revived.
1745 a   [Martin,   ] colonel.
A plan for establishing and disciplining a national militia
in Great Britain, Ireland, and in all the British dominions of
America. London, A. Millar, 1745 [Chicago? 1936]

Linn, James Weber, 1876–1939
Winds over the campus, by James Weber Linn ... Indianapolis, New York, The Bobbs-Merrill company [°1936]
4 p. l., 11–344 p. 21ᵐ.
"First edition."

I. Title.   36–22178

Library of Congress   PZ3.L655W1

MiHM
NL 0390100   DLC WaE Or NcD PPL MiU OCl OLak IdPl

Linn, James Weber, 1876–
Die zweite generation. Roman von James Weber
Linn; autorisierte übersetzung aus dem englischen
von Alwina Vischer. Stuttgart, Engelhorn, 1905.
160 p. D. (Engelhorns Allgemeine romanbibliothek... Bd. 24)

NL 0390101   NcD

309.161   Linn, Jeanne Marie
C132   Du douar à l'usine; a l'usage des cadres et
no.13   de la maitrise. [Ont collaboré à la redaction
... Madame Linn [et al] 6. èd. [Les illustrations et les clichés ont été fournis par
Messieurs Thiout Arregros et P. Leriche. Paris,
E.S.N.A., 1951]
36 p. illus. 26cm. (Cahiers nord-africains,
no.13, Mars 1951)

1. Africa, North - Social conditions. I.
Title.

NL 0390102   FU

Linn, John, joint ed.
Potts, Stacy Gardner, 1799–1865.
Precedents and notes of practice, in the Court of chancery,
of New Jersey, together with the rules of the Court of chancery, the Prerogative court, and the Court of appeals. Also, a
digest of the rulings of these courts in matters of pleading and
practice. By Stacy G. Potts ... Revised and enlarged by
Potts & Linn ... New York, J. G. Bryant, 1872.

Linn, John, ed.
New Jersey. *Supreme court.*
Reports of cases argued and adjudicated in the Supreme
court of judicature of the state of New Jersey. From Novem-
ber term 1831 to [November term 1836] ... inclusive. By
James S. Green ... 2d ed., with notes by John Linn ... Jersey
City, F. D. Linn, 1876.

Linn, John, ed.
                                   FOR OTHER EDITIONS
                                   SEE MAIN ENTRY
New Jersey. *Court of chancery.*
Reports of cases argued and determined in the Court of
chancery and in the Prerogative court of the state of New
Jersey. [1861–1863] Thomas N. McCarter, reporter ... 2d
ed. With references showing where the cases have been cited,
affirmed, overruled, questioned, limited, etc., down to part I.,
vol. XLI., N. J. law reports (XII. Vroom), and vol. XXX., N. J.
equity reports (III. Stew.), inclusive. By John Linn ...
Jersey City, F. D. Linn & co., 1886.

VOLUME 334

Linn, John, ed.

New Jersey. *Court of chancery.*
Reports of cases argued and determined in the Court of
chancery, the Prerogative court, and, on appeal, in the Court
of errors and appeals, of the state of New Jersey. ₁1863–1876₎
Charles Ewing Green, reporter ... 2d ed. ... Jersey City,
F. D. Linn, 1877–84.

Linn, John, ed.

New Jersey. *Court of chancery.*
Reports of cases determined in the Court of chancery, and
in the Prerogative court, and, on appeal, in the Court of errors
and appeals, of the state of New Jersey. ₁1845–1853₎ George
B. Halsted, reporter ... 2d ed. With references showing
where the cases have been cited, affirmed, overruled, questioned,
limited, etc., down to part I, vol. xxxix, N. J. law reports (x
Vroom), and part I, vol. xxviii, N. J. eq. reports (I Stew.),
inclusive. By John Linn ... Jersey City, F. D. Linn & co.,
1886.

Linn, John, ed.

New Jersey. *Supreme court.*
Reports of cases determined in the Supreme court of jud
cature of the state of New Jersey ... February term, A.
1837₁–May and September terms, 1842₎ By Josiah Harrison ... 2d ed., with notes by John Linn ... Jersey City,
F. D. Linn, 1876–1902.

Linn, John, ed.

New Jersey. *Supreme court.*
Reports of cases determined in the Supreme court of judicature of the state of New Jersey, ₁1842–1846₎ by Robert D.
Spencer, reporter. 2d ed. with notes by John Linn ... Volume I. Jersey City. F. D. Linn, 1877.

Linn, John Blair, 1777–1804.
Works by this author printed in America before 1801 are available
in this library in the Readex Microprint edition of Early American
Imprints published by the American Antiquarian Society.
This collection is arranged according to the numbers in Charles
Evans' American Bibliography.

NL 0390110   DLC

Linn, John Blair, 1777–1804.
The death of Washington. A poem. In imitation of
the manner of Ossian. By Rev. John Blair Linn ... Philadelphia, Printed by John Ormrod, 1800.
iv, ₅5₎–26 p.   21½ᶜᵐ.

1. Washington, George, pres. U. S.—Poetry.

Library of Congress   E312.65.L75   17–4561

  CtY NjP PPL NN RPJCB MiU-C
NL 0390111   DLC MWA MiU-C PU TxU PPPrHi MH ViU

Linn,John Blair,1777–1804.
A discourse occasioned by the death of the Reverend John Ewing,D.D. late senior pastor of the
First Presbyterian congregation,of the city of
Philadelphia,and provost of the University of Pennsylvania. By John Blair Linn,A.M. pastor of the
said congregation. Philadelphia: from the press of
the late R.Aitken,by Jane Aitken,for John Conrad &
co., 1802.

26 p.   20cm.

NL 0390112   MiU-C DLC NN MH PU PPPrHi PPAmP

₁Linn, John Blair₎ 1777–1804.
History of two celebrated Thebans, Pelopidas
and Epaminondas.   (Fairhaven? Vt., Printed
by James Lyon? 1798?)
84 p.   12°
Bound with: Prideaux, H. The true nature
of imposture ... Fairhaven 1798.
  Evans 34412
  I.Title.

NL 0390113   NN VtMiM

  Linn, John Blair, 1777–1804.
  A letter to Joseph Priestley, L.L.D. F.R.S.
*AC7 in answer to his letter, in defence of his
16494 pamphlet, entitled Socrates and Jesus compared.
8032 By John Blair Linn ...
  Published by John Conrad,& co.no.30,Chesnut-
street,Philadelphia;M.& J.Conrad,& co.no.138,
Market-street,Baltimore;Rapin,Conrad,& co.
Washington City;Bonsal & Conrad,Norfolk;and
Somervell,Conrad,& co.Petersburg.H.Maxwell,
printer.1803.
  144p. 24cm.

NL 0390114   MH MeB NIC NjR MdHi PSt PU PHi MiU-C

And.Rm.
BX8955
G54   Linn, John Blair, 1777–1804.
  A letter to Joseph Priestley...in answer to
his performance, entitled Socrates and Jesus
compared. By John Blair Linn...Philadelphia,
John Conrad & Co., Baltimore, M. and J. Conrad
& Co., Washington City, Rapin Conrad & Co.,
1803.
  66 p. 22 cm.
  Bound with Presbyterian Church in the U.S.A.
General Assembly. Glad tidings...Philadelphia,
1804.
  1. Priestly, Joseph, 1733–1804. Socrates
and Jesus compared. I. Title.

DLC PU
NL 0390115   PPiPT MH NIC CtY CU MeB PPPrHi NN NjP

₁Linn, John Blair₎ 1777–1804.
Miscellaneous works, prose and poetical. By a young
gentleman of New-York ... New-York—Printed by
Thomas Greenleaf. 1795.
6 p. l., ₍7₎–353, ₍1₎ p. 17ᶜᵐ.

I. Title.

Library of Congress   PS2246.L7 1795   23–4214

  NjP NN IU MB MWA IaU NBuG WU TxU N ViU TU NIC
NL 0390116   DLC MH OU PU PHC PHi CtY MiU-C RPB OCl

Linn, John Blair. 1777–1805. Poems. 3 pp.
(Kettell, S., *Specimens of Am. poetry*, v. 2, p. 124.)

NL 0390117   MdBP

₁Linn, John Blair₎ 1777–1804.
The poetical wanderer: containing, dissertations on
The early poetry of Greece, On tragic poetry, and On the
power of noble actions on the mind. To which are added,
several poems. By the author of Miscellaneous works ...
New-York, Printed for the author, by G. Forman, 1796.
112 p., 1 l., ₍4₎ p. 17ᶜᵐ.

I. Title.

Library of Congress   PS2246.L7P5 1796   8–24950

  RPB MB NHi
NL 0390118   DLC CtY OOxM NjP ViU PHi MiU-C NN MWA

PS2246   LINN,JOHN BLAIR,1777–1804.
.L7A7   The powers of genius,a poem,in three parts. By John
1801   Blair Linn... Philadelphia,A.Dickins,1801.
  127 p. 17½cm.

  NjP MH ViU NIC OU TU
NL 0390119   ICU KU CtY RPB PU PHi IU MB MH PU MWA

Linn, John Blair, 1777–1804.
The powers of genius, a poem, in three parts. By John
Blair Linn ...   2d ed., cor. and enl. ...   Philadelphia,
J. Conrad & co., 1802.
191 p. plates. 15½ᶜᵐ.

Library of Congress   9–18541

  NBuG MWA MWH
NL 0390120   DLC PLF ViU PP PPL PU MH IaU OCl NjP

Rare
PS   Linn, John Blair, 1777–1804.
2246   The powers of genius, a poem, in three
L7P8   parts. ₍London₎ Albion Press, 1804.
1804   xv(i.e. xiii), 155 p. illus. 17cm.

NL 0390121   NIC RPB CtY

Linn, John Blair, 1777–1804.
Toner   Valerian, a narrative poem: intended, in part, to describe
the early persecutions of Christians, and rapidly tc illustrate
the influence of Christianity on the manners of nations. By
John Blair Linn, D. D. ... With a sketch of the life and character of the author. Philadelphia, Printed by Thomas and
George Palmer, 116, High Street. 1805.
xxvi p., 1 l., 97 p. front. (port.) 24½ᶜᵐ.
A sketch of the life and character of John Blair Linn, p. ₍iii₎–xxiv,
signed C. B. B. ₍i. e. Charles Brockden Brown₎
1. Brown, Charles Brockden, 1771–1810. II. Title.

        23–4215

PS2246.L7V8

  InU NcU PPA PMA ICN TU MiU-C PPPrHi CaBVaU
  LU NjR OCU ICU ViU NjP CU MH NN NNUT WaU OWoC RPB
NL 0390122   DLC NNUT NjNbS IaU NcD RPB PHC PU CU-A

Linn, John Blair, 1831–
Annals of Buffalo Valley, Pennsylvania. 1755–1855.
Collated by John Blair Linn. Harrisburg, Pa., L. S.
Hart, printer, 1877.
1 p. l., 620 p., 1 l. front., pl., double map. 24ᶜᵐ.

1. Buffalo Valley, Pa.—Hist. 2. Buffalo Valley—Geneal.

Library of Congress   F157.B82L7   1–10462

PWb
  ViU PPLT WHi NN PKsL MdBP NjP MH MnHi MWA
NL 0390123   DLC PPG PLF NcD PSC PHi PPL OC OClWHi

Linn, J. B. The Butler family
of the Pennsylvania line. 6 pp. (*Pa. Mag. Hist.* v. 7,
1883, p. l.)

NL 0390124   MdBP MWA

₁Linn, John Blair₎ 1831–1899, *ed.*
Diary of the revolt in the Pennsylvania line. January,
1781.
(*In* Pennsylvania archives. Harrisburg, 1880. 22ᶜᵐ. 2d ser., v. 11,
₍629₎–674. port., double facsim.)
"The daily journal is from the diary of Capt. Joseph McClellan of the
Ninth Penna."

1. U. S.—Hist.—Revolution—Regimental histories—Pa. I. McClellan,
Joseph, 1747–1834. II. Title.   19–7635

Library of Congress   F146.P41 2d ser., vol. 11

NL 0390125   DLC OClWHi

VOLUME 334

Linn, John Blair, 1831–1899.
  History of Centre and Clinton counties, Pennsylvania.
By John Blair Linn ... Philadelphia, L. H. Everts, 1883.
  x, 672 p. illus., plates, port., maps (part fold.) facsims. (1 fold.) 28ᶜᵐ.
  Title-page mutilated; imprint wanting.

  1. Centre Co., Pa.—Hist. 2. Clinton Co., Pa.—Hist.

  Library of Congress   F157.C3L7   1–10464

NL 0390126   DLC NN WHi N PPL PHi MWA

Linn, John Blair, 1831–1899.

Swope, *Mrs.* Belle McKinney (Hays) 1867–
  History of the families of McKinney—Brady—Quigley, by
Belle McKinney Hays Swope ... Newville, Penna., Chambers-
burg, Penn'a., Franklin repository printery, 1905.

ₜLinn, John Blairₜ 1831–1899, ed.
  List of officers of the colonies on the Delaware and the
province of Pennsylvania. 1614–1776. Harrisburg, E. K.
Meyers, state printer, 1890.
  p. ₍621₎–818. 21½ᶜᵐ. (*In* Pennsylvania archives; second series ... vol.
IX pt. 2ₜ)
  CONTENTS.—Officers of the colonies on the Delaware, 1614–1681.—Officers of the province of Pennsylvania, 1681–1776.—Provincial officers of the
three lower counties, New Castle, Kent, and Sussex.—Provincial officers for
the three original counties, Chester, Philadelphia, and Bucks. 1682–1776.—
Provincial officers for the additional counties. 1729–1776 ₍namely: Lancaster, York, Berks, Cumberland, Northampton, Bedford, Northumberland,
and Westmoreland counties₎
  1. Pennsylvania—Registers. 2. New Sweden—Registers. 3. Delaware—
Registers.   I. Egle, William Henry, 1830–1901, joint ed.
                                                    9–16254
  Library of Congress   F146.P51 2d ser., vol. 9

NL 0390128   DLC OClWHi

ₜLinn, John Blairₜ 1831–1899, ed
  Lochry's expedition.
  (*In* Pennsylvania archives. Harrisburg, 1888. 22ᶜᵐ. 2d ser., v. 14, p.
680–689)
  "Journal of Lieut. Anderson": p. 685–689.

  1. Clark's expedition against Detroit, 1781. 2. Loughery, Archibald, d.
1781.   I. Anderson, Isaac, 1758–1839. II. Title.
                                                    19–7638
  Library of Congress   F146.P41 2d ser., vol. 14

NL 0390129   DLC

ₜLinn, John Blairₜ 1831–1899, ed.
  Minutes of the ₍Pennsylvania₎ Board of war ... 1777.
₍Minutes of the Pennsylvania Navy board, 1777; and
other papers relating to the revolutionary war. Harrisburg, B. Singerly, state printer, 1874₎
  809 p. 8 pl. (1 fold.) fold. map. 22ᶜᵐ. (*Added t.-p.*: Pennsylvania
archives; second series ... vol. I)
  CONTENTS.—Minutes of the Board of war, Mar. 14–Aug. 7, 1777.—Minutes of the Navy board, Feb. 18–Sept. 24, 1777.—List of officers and men
of the Pennsylvania navy, 1775–1781.—Papers relating to the Pennsylvania
navy, 1775 – 1781. — Papers relating to the British prisoners in Pennsylvania.—Memorandum book of the Committee and Council of safety, 1776–
1777.—Col. Atlee's journal of the battle of Long Island, Aug. 26, 1776.—
Journal of Col. Samuel Miles, concerning the battle of Long Island.—
List of sick soldiers in Philadelphia, Dec. 1776.—Papers relating to the
war of the revolution, 1775–1777.—Plans for the construction and raising
of the chevaux de frize in the Delaware River, 1775–1784.—Index.
  1. Pennsylvania—Hist.—Revolution—Sources. 2. U. S.—Hist.—Revolution—Naval operations. 3. U. S.—Hist.—Revolution—Prisoners and prisons. 4. Long Island, Battle of, 1776. 5. Delaware River—Hist.—Revolution.
  I. Egle, William Henry, 1830–1901, joint ed.
                                                    8–32220
  Library of Congress   F146.P41 2d ser., vol. 1

NL 0390131   DLC PPAmP OClWHi

ₜLinn, John Blairₜ 1831– ed.
  Papers relating to the colonies on the Delaware, 1614–
1682. ₍Harrisburg, L. S. Hart, state printer, 1877₎
  2 p. l., ₍3₎–875 p. front. (port.) 2 fold. maps. 21½ᶜᵐ. (*Added t.-p.*:
Pennsylvania archives; second series ... vol. v)
  Half-title.
  Ed. by John Blair Linn and William Henry Egle.

  1. New York (State)—Hist.—Colonial period—Sources. 2. New Sweden — Hist. 3. Delaware — Hist. — Colonial period.   4. Delaware River.
  I. Egle, William Henry, 1830–1901, joint ed. II. Title.

  Library of Congress   F146.P41 2d ser., vol. 5   9–12705

NL 0390132   DLC OClWHi PAnL

ₜLinn, John Blairₜ 1831–   ea.
  Papers relating to the colonies on the Delaware, 1614–
1682. Harrisburg, E. K. Meyers, state printer, 1890.
  2 p. l., ₍3₎–912 p. col. front., ports., fold. maps. 21½ᶜᵐ. (*Added t.-p.*:
Pennsylvania archives; second series ... vol. v)
  First edition published 1877.

  1. New York (State)—Hist.—Colonial period—Sources. 2. New Swe-
den—Hist. 3. Delaware — Hist.—Colonial period. 4. Delaware River.
  I. Egle, William Henry, 1830–1901, joint ed.
                                                    9–13986
  Library of Congress   F167.L75

NL 0390133   DLC PPAmP

Linn, John Blair, 1831–1899, ed.
  Pennsylvania archives ... ₍1st ser.₎ v. 1–2; 2d ser., v. 1–19;
3d ser., v. 1–30; 4th ser., v. 1–12; 5th ser., v. 1–8; 6th ser.,
v. 1–15; 7th ser., v. 1–5; 8th ser., v. 1–8; 9th ser., v. 1–10;
                                                    Philadelphia, Printed by J.
Severns & co., 1852–56; Harrisburg, 1874–19

Linn, John Blair, 1831–1899, ed.

Pennsylvania archives, second series. Reprinted under direc-
tion of the secretary of the commonwealth, edited by John
B. Linn and Wm. H. Egle ...
  Harrisburg, C. M. Busch, state printer, 1896–

Linn, John Blair, 1831–1899, ed.
  Pennsylvania in the war of the revolution, battalions
and line. 1775–1783. Ed. by John Blair Linn, William
H. Egle ... Harrisburg, L. S. Hart, state printer, 1880.
  2 v. col. plates, ports., maps, facsims. 22ᶜᵐ. (*Added t.-p.*: Pennsylvania archives; second series ... vol. x–xi)
  Rosters and brief histories of the various regiments, orderly books of
the First and Seventh regiments, and other papers. For detailed list of contents, see Annual report of the Amer. hist. assoc. for 1904, p. 633–635.
  The rosters are reprinted, with corrections and additions, in Pennsylvania
archives, 5th series, v. 2–4, Harrisburg, 1906.

  "Diary of events in the army of the revolution, from Aug. 1, 1780, to Dec.
31, 1780. From the journal of Capt. Joseph McClellan, of Ninth Penn'a":
v. 2, p. ₍571₎–585.
  "Diary of the revolt in the Pennsylvania line. January, 1781 ₍by Capt.
Joseph McClellan; with other papers relating to the affair₎": v. 2, p. ₍629₎–
674.
  "Diary of the Pennsylvania line. May 26, 1781–April 25, 1782 ₍comp.
from the journals of Capt. Joseph McClellan and Lieut. William Feltman₎":
v. 2, p. ₍675₎–727.
  1. Pennsylvania—Hist.—Revolution—Sources. 2. U. S.—Hist.—Revolution—Regimentary histories—Pa. 3. Pennsylvania—Militia.   I. Egle, William Henry, 1830–1901, joint ed. II. McClellan, Joseph, 1747–1834. III. Title.
  Library of Congress   F146.P41 2d ser., v. 10–11   8–32222

**NL 0390137   OClWHi PPLT NN
                 DLC CU KMK PPAmP PP PHi OCl ICN TU PHi**

Linn, John Blair, 1831–1899.
  Pennsylvanians in Pulaski's Legion. 1778–1783.
(In: Pennsylvania Archives. Harrisburg, Lane S.
Hart, State printer, 1880. Second Series, Vol. XI:
Pennsylvania in the War of the Revolution, Battalions
and Line, 1775–1783. Edited by John Blair Linn and
William H. Egle. Vol. II, p. [151]–156)
  [151]–156 p.   8 vo.   Double-page colored
frontispiece.
  Note: Pulaski's Banner is described, p. 153–154;
the double-page plate shows the reverse and obverse
of the Banner, in original colors.

  A separate copy of the plate is described in the
"Maps and Engravings" Section of the Catalogue.

NL 0390139   GU-De

Linn, John Blair, 1831–1899.
  A Retrospect. 1791–1891. By John Blair Linn,
Esq. From the Reformed Quarterly Review,
October, 1891 ... [Philadelphia, Pa., 1891]
  cover-title. 8 vo.   Tan paper covers.
  The Brook Collection, October 1922.

NL 0390140   CSmH

ₜLinn, John Blairₜ 1831–1899, ed.
  The Sandusky expedition.
  (*In* Pennsylvania archives. Harrisburg, 1888. 22ᶜᵐ. 2d ser., v. 14, p.
₍690₎–727. facsim.)
  "Narrative of Dr. Knight": p. 708–717.
  "Narrative of John Slover": p. 717–727.

  1. Crawford's Indian campaign, 1782. 2. Indians of North America—
Captivities.   I. Knight, John, d. 1838. II. Slover, John, fl. 1773–1782.
III. Title.
                                                    19–7639
  Library of Congress   F146.P41 2d ser., vol. 14

NL 0390141   DLC

ₜLinn, John Blairₜ 1831–   ed.
  Record of Pennsylvania marriages, prior to 1810 .
Harrisburg, L. S. Hart, state printer, 1880–90.
  2 v. col. front., 2 pl. 21½ᶜᵐ. (*Added t.-p.*: Pennsylvania archives:
second series ... vol. VIII–IX)
  Imprint varies: v. 2, E. K. Meyers, state printer, 1890.
  Illustration on verso of t.-p.
  Series t.-p., v. 8, dated 1878.
  Marriages recorded by the registrar general, and also, marriage records
of churches of Philadelphia and vicinity.
  Vol. 2 includes: List of officers of the colonies on the Delaware and the
province of Pennsylvania, 1614–1776, p. ₍621₎–818.
  1. Marriage licenses—Pennsylvania. 2. Registers of births, etc.—Penn-
sylvania. 3. Registers of births, etc.—Philadelphia.   I. Egle, William
Henry, 1830–1901, joint ed. II. Title.
                                                    9–14763
  Library of Congress   F146.P41 2d ser., vol. 8–9

NL 0390142   DLC KyHi OClWHi

Linn, John Gaywood, 1917–
  The court masque and Elizabethan
dramatic structure, 1558–1604. ₍Ithaca,
N. Y.₎ 1951.
  248 l. 28cm.

  Thesis (Ph.D.)—Cornell Univ., Feb.,
1951.

  1. English drama—Early modern and
Elizabethan.

NL 0390143   NIC

Linn, John H.
  A funeral discourse on the life and character of the
Hon. Lewis Field ₍!₎ Linn, delivered before the citizens
of St. Louis, at their request, on Sunday, the 19th day of
November, 1843. By Rev. John H. Linn. St. Louis,
Printed at the office of the Missouri reporter, 1844.
  14 p. 22ᶜᵐ.

  1. Linn, Lewis Fields, 1795–1843.
                                                    17–6703
  Library of Congress   E340.L7L73

NL 0390144   DLC OCHP

Linn, John Joseph, 1798–1885.
  Reminiscences of fifty years in Texas. By John J.
Linn. Pub. for the author. New York, D. & J. Sadlier
& co., 1883.
  369 p. plates, 2 port. (incl. front.) 19ᶜᵐ.

  1. Texas—Hist. 2. Texas—Hist.—Revolution, 1835–1836.

                                                    7—9861
  Library of Congress   F386.L75

**NL 0390145   UU MoU ICN OOxM ICRL
                 DLC MdBP TxU TxHU CSt MsU NjP NBu OClJC**

Linn, John Joseph, 1798–1885.
  ... Reminiscences of fifty years in Texas, by John J. Linn
... Austin, Tex., The Steck company, 1935.
  3 p. l., ₍5₎–369 p. plates, ports. 21½ᶜᵐ. (Original narratives of Texas
history and adventure)
  "A facsimile reproduction of the original" edition, New York, 1883,
including t.-p.

  1. Texas—History. 2. Texas—History—Revolution. 1835–1836.
  I. Title
                                                    A 36–840
  Title from Texas Univ.   Printed by L. C.
                             [F386.L   ]

NL 0390146   TxU WaS TxHU NN NcD CSmH

VOLUME 334

Linn, John Kenneth
Film   The Imperial Edicts of the Shoku-nihongi.
D117   An annotated translation of edicts ## 30-62.
no.2   108 ℓ. illus. 29 cm.

Thesis - Yale, 1950.
Microfilm. Ann Arbor, Mich., University
Microfilms, 1966. 1 reel. 35 mm.

I. Japan. Laws, statutes, etc.

NL 0390147   CtY

Linn, Karl, 1901-
Die verantwortlichkeit der staaten.
Inaug. diss. Wuerzburg, 1927.(Leipzig)
Bibl.

NL 0390148   ICRL CtY

₍Linn, Lee₎
Souvenir of Denison, "the gate city of Texas" . . .
₍Denison, News printing house, 1887₎ 1 p. l., 38 pp. 8°.
Cover-title.
F394.D3L7   1-Rc-2504

NL 0390149   DLC

WZ   LINN, Lewis Fields, 1796-1843
100   A collection of miscellaneous bio-
₍L7575 bibliographical material on this person
        may be found on the shelves under the
        above call number.

NL 0390150   DNLM

Linn, Lewis Fields, 1795-1843.
Address... to the people of Missouri. [n.p.,
n.d.]
20p.
                        YA 18663

NL 0390151   DLC

Linn, Lewis Fields, 1796-1843.
Observations on the La Motte mines and domain, in the
state of Missouri, with some account of the advantages
and inducements there promised to capitalists and individuals desirous of engaging in mining, manufacturing, or farming operations. April 10th, 1839. ₍n. p.₎
Royston & Brown, printers ₍1839₎

---

*A
1841-42
.S644   Linn, Lewis Fields, 1796-1843.
no.50
        Remarks of Mr. Linn and Mr. Wright, on
YA5000 the bill to indemnify General Jackson for
J17   the fine imposed on him at New Orleans in
        1815. ₍Delivered in the United States
        Senate, May 14, 1842. Washington, 1842₎
        13 p. 23cm. ₍Speeches in Congress, 1841-42.
        No. 50₎
        Caption title.
        1. Jackson, Andrew, Pres., U. S., 1767-1845.
        I. Wright, Silas,   1795-1847. II. Ser.

NL 0390153   ViU DLC

---

*A
1841-42
.S644   Linn, Lewis Fields, 1796-1843.
no.33
        Remarks on the subject of the public lands.
YA5000 Delivered in the Senate of the United States,
J17   April, 1842. ₍Washington, 1842₎
        4 p. 23cm. ₍Speeches in Congress, 1841-42.
        No. 33₎
        Caption title.

NL 0390154   ViU DLC

Linn, Lewis, Fields, 1796-1843.
        Remarks...on the loan
bill. Delivered in the United States
Senate April 12, 1842

₍Washington? 1842?₎   4p.

YA5000
J 17   ₍Congressional speeches, by author₎

NL 0390155   DLC

Linn, Lewis Fields, 1795-1843.

U. S. *Congress. Senate. Select committee on bill to
authorize the President to occupy the Oregon Territory.*
... Report: ⟨To accompany Senate bill no. 206.⟩ ₍Wash-
ington₎ Blair & Rives, printers ₍1838₎

Linn, Lewis Fields, 1795-1843.

U. S. *Congress. Senate. Committee on agriculture.*
... Report : ⟨to accompany bill S. no. 241⟩ ... ₍Washington,
Blair & Rives, printers, 1838₎

979.5   Linn, Lewis Fields, 1796-1843.
Or4   Speech...in reply to Mr.McDuffie, on the
v.4   Oregon bill: delivered in the Senate of the
no.2   United States, January 26, 1843. Washing-
        ton, Printed at the Globe Office, 1843.
DLC:YA5000 15p. 23cm. (In Original sources of
J17   Oregon history, v.4,no.2)

        1. U.S. Defenses. 2. Indians of North
        America. Wars. 1815-1875. I. Series.

NL 0390158   OrU DLC CaBViPA WaPS CtY OrP

Linn, Lewis Fields, 1795-1843.
        Speech of Hon. Lewis F. Linn, of Missouri, on his amend-
ment to the Land distribution bill, proposing to appropriate
the revenue from the public lands to the national defences.
In Senate, August 11, 1841. Washington, Printed at the
Globe office, 1842.   YA. 5000 J17
        16 p. 23½ cm.

        1. U. S.—Pol. & govt.—1841-1845. 2. U. S.—Defences.
E396.L75   9—21212

NL 0390159   DLC ViU NN

LINN, ₍Lewis Fields₎, 1795-1843.
        Speech of Mr.Linn of Missouri, on
Mr.Crittenden's amendment, to distribute the
proceeds of the sales of the public lands
among the states. Senate U.S.January 29,1841.
Washington, printed at the Globe Office,1841.

        pp. 7.

NL 0390160   MH ICN

Linn, Louis.
        A handbook of hospital psychiatry; a practical guide to
therapy. New York, International Universities Press ₍1955₎
560 p. 24 cm.

        1. Psychotherapy. 2. Psychiatric hospitals. I. Title: Hospital
psychiatry.

RC480.L54   362.2   55—8237 ‡

        IEG DNLM OCIW AAP
        ICJ CU OU NcD PBL PPPH PBm TxU CtY-M IU IEN FU-HC
NL 0390161   DLC CaBVaU ICJ IdPI OrU-M WaT Wa ICU

Thesis Linn, Manson Bruce, 1908-
1940   Studies on the yellows disease of lettuce
L757   and endive. ₍Ithaca, N. Y.₎ 1940.
        52 l. plates, tables. 28 cm.

        Thesis (Ph. D.) - Cornell University, June 1940.

        1. Lettuce - Diseases and pests. 2. Endive -
Diseases and pests. I. Title. II. Title:
Yellows disease of lettuce and endive.

NL 0390162   NIC

[LINN, MARTHA] 1888-
        About Jesus, son of God & son of Mary, by M. M. & Robin.
London [etc.] Longmans, Green and co. [1937] 33 l. incl.
plates (part col'd). illus. (part col'd.) 22cm. (Half-
title: The new method English library. 7.)

        The illustrations are by Robin.

        1. Jesus Christ—Life. I. M., M. II. Title. III. Ser.

NL 0390163   NN

₍Linn, Martha₎ 1888-
        Love speaks, by M. M. Chicago, Priv. print., G. B. Deutsch
inc. ₍ᶜ1936₎
        ₍109₎ p. 19ᶜᵐ.
        "A book of spiritual exercises."—Compiler's note.

        1. New thought. I. Title.
                                            36-20220
        Library of Congress   BF640.L5

NL 0390164   DLC

BF   Linn, Martha, 1888-
640   Love speaks. New York, Privately
L5   printed, 1951.
1951   1v.(unpaged)

        1. New thought. I. Title.

NL 0390165   UU

Linn, Mortimer Palmer, 1862-

Eads, George W.
        ... Problems of advertising; addresses delivered in
journalism week, 1918, by George W. Eads, N. A. Huse
and M. P. Linn. Columbia, Mo., 1918.

Linn, Nellie Meader.
        Aunt Mary's blunder, a one-act sketch, by Nellie M. Linn ...
Franklin, O., Denver, Colo., Eldridge entertainment house, inc.,
₍1931₎
        10 p. 19ᶜᵐ. (On cover: Eldridge popular one act plays)

        I. Title.
                                            39-11182
        Library of Congress   PS3523.I663A8 1931

NL 0390167   DLC RPB

VOLUME 334

PS3534
.I663B5
1932
    Linn, Nellie Meader.
        Bill's rummage sale.
        Chic. [c1932]
        1 pam. 12°

NL 0390168   DLC

PS3523
.I663H4
1930
    Linn, Nellie Meader.
        Henry's "tux"...
        Franklin, O., c1930.
        1 pam. 12°

NL 0390169   DLC OrCS RPB

    Linn, Nellie Meader.
        Nice Bossy, a little play in one act, by Nellie Linn ... Frank-
        lin, O., Denver, Colo., Eldridge entertainment house, incorpo-
        rated, °1937.
        15 p. 19ᶜᵐ. (On cover: Eldridge popular one act plays)

        I. Title.   38-21020
        Library of Congress   PS3523.I 663N5 1937

NL 0390170   DLC

    Linn, Otto Fernand, 1887–
        The Gospel of John, an exposition by Otto F. Linn ... An-
        derson, Ind., Gospel trumpet company, 1942.
        160 p. 18ᶜᵐ. (*His* Studies in the New Testament series)

        1. Bible. N. T. John — Commentaries. 2. Bible — Commentaries —
        N. T. John.   43-3690
        Library of Congress   BS2615.L47
                                        [2]   226.5

NL 0390171   DLC

    Linn, Otto Fernand, 1887–
        The Gospel of Mark, an exposition by Otto F. Linn ...
        Anderson, Ind., Gospel trumpet company, 1944.
        v, 6–175 p. 18ᶜᵐ.

        1. Bible. N. T. Mark — Commentaries. 2. Bible — Commentaries —
        N. T. Mark.   44-18836
        Library of Congress   BS2585.L5
                                        [2]   226.3

NL 0390172   DLC

    Linn, Otto Fernand, 1887–
        Studies in the New Testament ... by Otto F. Linn, PH. D.
        Anderson, Ind., The Warner press [°1941–
        v. 19 cm.
        "Prepared with the chief aim of stressing the religious values of the
        several books of the New Testament."—Pref.
        CONTENTS.—v. 1. The Gospels and Acts.—[v. 2] Romans to Phile-
        mon.—

        1. Bible. N. T.—Theology.   I. Title.
        BS2361.L5   225.7   41—7012

NL 0390173   DLC NNUT KyLxCB NRCR NcD

    Linn, Otto Fernand, 1887–
        ... The Tetragram, Thomas, and Larissa gospels ... by Otto
        Fernand Linn ... [Chicago] 1939.
        1 p. l., 4 p. 24ᶜᵐ.
        Part of thesis (PH. D.)—University of Chicago, 1935.
        Lithoprinted.
        "Private edition, distributed by the University of Chicago libraries,
        Chicago, Illinois."

        1. Bible. Manuscripts, Greek. N. T. Gospels. 2. Manuscripts, Greek.
        3. Manuscripts. U. S.   I. Title.
                                                         40-5728
        Library of Congress   BS2551.A2L55 1935
        Univ. of Chicago Libr.   [20]

NL 0390174   ICU DLC OrU NIC MH OCU NcD

    Linn, Paul Hinkle, 1873–
        How God made the master singer; a Bible
        reading
                see under   Bible. O.T. English.
        Selections. 1917.

    Linn, Peter, pseud.
        ...The value of a vote. 2d ed. [New York,
        c1898]   YA. 21364
        17p.

NL 0390176   DLC

TA459
.B67
1944
    Linn, Philipp. Materialienlehre.

    Brender, Rudolf.
        Werkstoffkunde für metallberufe, mit kurzer einführung in
        die chemischen grundbegriffe von dr.-ing. Rudolf Brender.
        12. aufl. der früheren "Materialienlehre" mit 68 abbildungen.
        Neu bearb. von dipl.-ing. W. Sorg ... Stuttgart, Holland &
        Josenhans, 1944.

    Linn, Pierre, joint tr.

    Haessle, Johannes.
        ... Le travail, traduit de l'allemand par Étienne Borne &
        Pierre Linn. Paris, Desclée, de Brouwer et cⁱᵉ [1933]

    Linn, R   M.
        Lookout landscape photography: a practical manual
        embodying the formulæ, processes and methods of oper-
        ating used and practiced by the late Prof. R. M. Linn ...
        Philadelphia, Benerman & Wilson, 1872.
        iv, [5]–62 p. 16¼ᶜᵐ.

        1. Photography—Landscapes.
        Library of Congress   TR660.I75   9-4404†

NL 0390179   DLC ICJ

    Linn, Richard.
        Early emigrants to the British North American
        colonies from Banbridge, Co. Down [Ireland]
        Christchurch, N. Z. [Henry & Co.] 1906.
        8 p. 8°.

NL 0390180   NN

F
45927
.5
    LINN, RICHARD.
        A History of Banbridge... Edited by W.S.
        Kerr. [Banbridge] The Banbridge Chronicle
        Press, 1935.
        xii, 269p. illus., ports. 23cm.

NL 0390181   ICN

    Linn, Richard, ed.
        Marriage register of the Presbyterian congrega-
        tion of Banbridge, County Down, 1756–1794; ed.
        by Richard Linn...with foreword by Rev. W. T.
        Latimer... [Submitted January 26, 1909] n. imp.
        [10] p.

NL 0390182   MiD-B

    Linn, Richard.
        Pedigree of the Magennis (Guinness) family of New
        Zealand, and of Dublin, Ireland ... Comp. by Richard
        Linn ... Christchurch, New Zealand, Caygill and Mac-
        laren, 1897.
        58, [1] p. incl. front., illus. (coat of arms) pl., ports. 18½ᶜᵐ.
        Half-title: The Guinness family.

        1. Macginnis family. 2. Guinness family.   I. Title.
                                                         18-2164
        Library of Congress   CS499.M18

NL 0390183   DLC NN

    Linn, Richard, of Bern.
        Ueber die bestaendigkeit von amin-complexen
        Inaug. Diss. Bern, 1915

NL 0390184   ICRL

    LINN, ROBERT.
        The devil's game, by Robert Linn... (In: Cloetingh,
        A.C., editor. Prayers for Passel, and other prize plays.
        New York[, cop. 1931]. 19cm. p. 51–72.)
        In one act.

        599305A. 1. Drama,   American. I. Title.

NL 0390185   NN

*
PS3511 Linn, Robert.
.A862734   Robinson Jeffers and William Faulkner
1934   (In The American spectator yearbook. New
             York, 1934. 22cm. p. 304–307)

        1. Faulkner, William, 1897–   I. Title.
        II. Title: American spectator yearbook.

NL 0390186   ViU

M787   Linn, Robert Theodore
L649q   [Quartet, strings]
         String quartet. Los Angeles, Calif.,
        Affiliated Musicians [c1953]
        score (46p.) 28cm. (AMI edition of
        chamber music literature)
        AMI edition.

        1. String quartets—Scores.

NL 0390187   IU CLSU

VOLUME 334

M784
L649m

Linn, Robert *Theodore.*

Three madrigals. Poems from "Chamber music" by James Joyce. Los Angeles, Calif., Affiliated Musicians ₊c1953₊

score (15p.) 26cm. (AMI library of choral literature)

AMI edition, 2314.
Contents.- Winds of May.- Sleep now.- Who goes amid the green wood.

NL 0390188   IU

Linn, S.
Analytical index of parallel reference to cases ... courts of Pa. Phil. ₁1857-73. and sup.

NL 0390189   NjP

Linn, S.
A supplement to Linn's analytical index of parallel reference to the cases adjudged in the several courts of Pennsylvania
see under   Landis, Jesse, 1821-1873.

Linn, S   Pollock, *comp.*
Dictionary of living thoughts of leading thinkers. A cyclopaedia of quotations designed for the use of the senate, the bar, the pulpit and the orator, by S. Pollock Linn ... New York, W. B. Ketcham ₊1896₊

1 p. l., 9-460 p. 20½ᶜᵐ.

1. Quotations, English. 2. Aphorisms and apothegms.   ɪ. Title.

Library of Congress   PN6331.L5 1896   12—21113

NL 0390191   DLC DN

Linn, S   Pollock, *comp.*
Golden gleams of thought, from the words of leading orators, divines, philosophers, statesmen and poets. By Rev. S. P. Linn ... Chicago, Jansen, McClurg & company, 1882.

448 p. 20½ᶜᵐ.

1. Quotations, English.   ɪ. Title.

Library of Congress   PN6331.L48   12—21130

NL 0390192   DLC PPL OLak

Linn, S   Pollock, comp.
Golden gleams of thought, from the words of leading orators, divines, philosophers, statesmen and poets. ... Chicago, 1888.
448 p. 21 cm.

NL 0390193   RPB

Linn, S   Pollock.
Golden gleams of thought, from the words of leading orators, divines, philosophers, statesmen & poets. Chicago, McClurg, 1891.
448 p.

NL 0390194   OC1 ICRL

Linn, S   Pollock, comp.
Golden gleams of thought; from the words of leading orators, divines, philosophers, statesmen and poets. Chicago, McClurg, 1900.
448p.

1. Quotations, English. I. Title.

NL 0390195   ScU

Linn, S   Pollock.
Golden gleams of thought, from the words of leading orators, divines, philosophers, statesmen and poets. 9th ed. Chicago, McClurg, 1906.

NL 0390196   MH

Linn, Rev. S. P₍ollock₎.
Golden gleams of thought from the words of leading orators, divines, philosophers, statesmen, and poets. Chicago: A. C. McClurg & Co., 1912. 2 p.l., 3-448 p. 11. ed. 8°.

1. Quotations. 2. Title.
N. Y. P. L.   June 11, 1914.

NL 0390197   NN

F808
L75

Linn, S   Pollock, *comp.*
Living thoughts of leading thinkers, a thesaurus by S. P. Linn ... Pittsburg, J. R. Foster & company, 1869.

400 p. 2 port. (incl. front.) 19½ᶜᵐ.

1. Quotations. 2. Aphorisms and apothegms.   ɪ. Title.

Library of Congress   PN6331.L5 1869   12—36166

NL 0390198   DLC RPB OC1 OO ICRL NBuHi

Linn, S   Pollock, *comp.*
Living thoughts of leading thinkers, a thesaurus by S. P. Linn ... Pittsburg, J. R. Foster & company, 1871.
466 p. 2 port. (incl. front.) 19½ᶜᵐ.

NL 0390199   OFH

Linn, S   Pollock, *comp.*
Living thoughts of leading thinkers: a thesaurus. By Rev. S. Pollock Linn, A.M. Pittsburg, J. R. Foster & Co., 1873.
466 p. fronts. (ports.) 19½ᶜᵐ.

NL 0390200   ICJ

Linn, S   Pollock, comp.
Living thoughts of leading thinkers. A thesaurus. By Rev. S. Pollock Linn, A.M.   New York: H. J. Johnson ₊c1880₎
466 p. front., ports. 20½cm.

Added engraved t.-p.

12044B. 1. Quotations. I. Title.
N. Y. P. L.   May 24, 1940

NL 0390201   NN CtY ViU OC1 ODW Wa RPB

Linn, S   Pollock, *comp.*
Words that burn; or, Truth and life. A compilation of the brightest thoughts and choicest selections from the world's best authors. Also biographical and critical notes, and an analytical index of subjects, by S. P. Linn ... With an introduction by Prof. E. D. Morris ... Philadelphia, St. Louis ₊etc.₎ J. H. Chambers & co., 1883.

xii, 3-728 p. front., illus., plates, ports. 24½ᶜᵐ.

"Biographical index of authors": p. 619-699.

1. Quotations, English.   ɪ. Title.

Library of Congress   PN6014.L55   17—20142

NL 0390202   DLC

Linn, S   Pollock, *comp.*
Words that burn; or, Truth and life. A compilation of the brightest thoughts and choicest selections from the world's best authors. Also biographical and critical notes, and an analytical index of subjects, by S. P. Linn ... With an introduction by Prof. E. D. Morris ... Philadelphia, St. Louis ₊etc.₎ J. H. Chambers & co., 1884.

xii, 3-728 p. front., illus., plates, ports. 24ᶜᵐ.

Most of the plates accompanied by guard sheets with descriptive letterpress.

"Biographical index of authors": p. 619-699.

1. Quotations, English.   ɪ. Title.

Library of Congress   PN6014.L55 1884   37—11062
                            ₊2₎   808.8

NL 0390203   DLC

Linn, Samuel.
The seven parables of the kingdom, by Rev. Samuel Linn. ₊Osage, Ia., Press of the Woolverton printing & publishing co., 1908₎

108 p. 15 x 11½ᶜᵐ.

1. Jesus Christ—Parables.   ɪ. Title.
                                            8—18055
Library of Congress   BT375.L5
                            ₊a44b1₎   226.8

NL 0390204   DLC

Linn, Samuel H.
——. Hernia (rupture). Its etiology, strangulation, treatment, and radical cure by electrocataphoric, chemical, hypodermic, and surgical methods. 30 pp., 1 pl. 12°. ₊*Rochester*, 1901.₎

NL 0390205   DNLM

Linn, Samuel H
The teeth: how to preserve them and prevent their decay. A popular treatise on the diseases and care of the teeth. By S. H. Linn, ... With plates and diagrams. London, C. Griffin and Co. ₊pref. 1882₎
viii, 74 p. front., illus. 18½ᶜᵐ.

NL 0390206   ICJ PPiU-D DNLM

Linn, Samuel P   , ed.
The New Testament ... together with the Book of Psalms ... Philadelphia, Potter ₊188-?₎ (571 p.)
see under   Bible. N. T. English. 188-? Authorized.

Linn, Talfourd P
A catalogue of the Talfourd P. Linn collection of Cervantes materials on deposit in the Ohio State University Libraries. Compiled by Dorothy Petersen Ackerman. Edited by Paul J. Kann and Rolland E. Stevens. ₊Columbus₎ Ohio State University Press ₊1963₎

ix, ₊x-xiv₎ 90 p. facsim. 23 cm. (The Ohio State University Libraries publications, no. 1)

Bibliography: p. ₊xiii₎-₊xiv₎

1. Cervantes Saavedra, Miguel de—Bibl.   ɪ. Ackerman, Dorothy Petersen. ɪɪ. Ohio. State University, Columbus. Libraries. ɪɪɪ. Title. (Series: Ohio. State University, Columbus. Libraries. Publications, no. 1)

Z664.04 no. 1   016.8683   63—15974

NL 0390208   TNJ DLC

VOLUME 334

Linn, Thomas, 1845–
—— . Aix-les-Bains. (Savoy, France.) 20 pp.
12°. *Nice, France,* [1892?].

NL 0390209 DNLM

Linn (Thomas) [1845–]. *De l'habitude et
de ses rapports avec l'hygiène et la thérapeutique.* 38 pp., 1 l. 4°. *Paris,* 1888, No. 259.

NL 0390210 DNLM CU

Linn, Thomas, 1845–
The health resorts of Europe. A medical guide to the
mineral springs, climatic, mountain, and seaside health
resorts, milk, whey, grape, earth, mud, sand, and air cures
of Europe. By Thomas Linn ... With a preface by A. E.
Sansom ... London, H. Kimpton [etc.] 1893.
xxiii, 330 p. 19^{cm}.

1. Health resorts, watering-places, etc.—Europe.

Library of Congress   RA846.L76   7—42354

NL 0390211 DLC DNLM OC1

Linn, Thomas, 1845–
The health resorts of Europe, a medical guide to the
mineral springs, climatic, mountain, and seaside health
resorts, milk, whey, grape, earth, mud, sand and air cures
of Europe, by Thomas Linn. With an introduction by
Titus Munson Coan, M. D. New York, D. Appleton and
company, 1893.
xxiii, 330 p. 19½^{cm}.

1. Health resorts, watering-places, etc.—Europe.

Library of Congress   RA846.L75   7—42353

NL 0390212 DLC DNLM MH NN MB

Linn, Thomas, *b.* 1845.
The health resorts of Europe. A medical guide to the
mineral springs, climatic, mountain and seaside health resorts, milk, whey, grape, earth, mud, sand and air cures of
Europe. 3d rev. ed. London, H. Kimpton; New York,
Hirschfeld Bros., 1895.
332 p. illus., fold. map (in pocket) 19 cm.

1. Health resorts, watering-places, etc.—Europe.

RA846.L76 1895   48–43414*

NL 0390213 DLC DAS DN

Linn, Thomas, *b.* 1845.
The health resorts of Europe. A medical guide to the
mineral springs, climatic mountain and seaside health resorts, milk, whey, grape, earth, mud, sand and air cures of
Europe. 5th ed. London, H. Kimpton; New York, Hirschfeld Bros., 1897.
323 p. illus. 18 cm.

1. Health resorts, watering-places, etc.—Europe.

RA846.L76 1897   Med 48–916*

NL 0390214 DLC PP MH NN

LINN, THOMAS, *b. 1845.*
The health resorts of Europe, a medical guide
to the mineral springs, climatic mountain and
seaside health resorts, milk, whey, grape, earth,
mud, sand and air cures of Europe. 6th ed.
London, Henry Kimpton, 1898.
332 p. illus.

NL 0390215 Or

---

ar V
18983
Linn, Thomas, 1845–
The health resorts of Europe. A medical guide to the
mineral springs, climatic, mountain, and seaside health
resorts, milk, whey, grape, earth, mud, sand, and air cures
of Europe. 9th ed. London, H. Klimpton, 1901.
261 p. illus. 18cm.

NL 0390216 NIC ICJ

Linn (Thomas) [1845–]. The health resorts of Europe. A medical guide to the
mineral springs, climatic mountains and seaside health resorts, milk, whey, grape, earth,
mud, sand and air cures of Europe. 12. ed.
258 pp. 12°. London, Marshall, Hamilton
& Co., 1904.

NL 0390217 DNLM

Linn, Thomas, *b. 1845.*
The health resorts of Europe. A medical and popular guide to the
mineral springs, climatic mountain and seaside health resorts,
hydropathics and sanatoria of Europe. Edited by A. C. Glynn
Grylls. 15th edition.
= London. The Health Resorts Bureau. 1907. (1), 283 pp. 17 cm.

L4793 — Europe. Health resorts. — Health resorts. — Grylls, Archibald Campbell Glynn, ed.

NL 0390218 MB

Linn, Thomas, *b. 1845.*
Health resorts of Europe... 18th. ed. London,
Reynolds, 1910.
285 p.

NL 0390219 PPC

RA864
R6
891*l*
LINN, Thomas, 1845–
On the necessary precautions to be
taken to obtain the most benefit from
the climate of Nice and the Riviera.
Nice, 1891.
32p. 19cm.

NL 0390220 CtY-M DNLM NN

Linn, Thomas, 1845–
Where to send patients abroad for mineral and other water
cures and climatic treatment. By Dr. Thomas Linn ... Detroit,
Mich., G. S. Davis, 1894.
2 p. l., 76 p. illus. 19½^{cm}. [Physicians' leisure library]

1. Climatology, Medical. 2. Mineral waters. 3. Health resorts, watering-places, etc.   I. Title.

Library of Congress   RA793.L79   7—38484

NL 0390221 DLC PPC CtY KU-M ICJ ICRL DNLM ICJ

Linn, Thomas Gray, joint author.

TS870
.W6
1950
Wood, Andrew Dick.   FOR OTHER EDITION
SEE MAIN ENTRY
Plywoods; their development, manufacture and applica-
tion, by Andrew Dick Wood and Thomas Gray Linn. Rev.
[i. e. 2d] ed. Edinburgh, W. & A. K. Johnston, 1950.

W 6
P3
LINN, Tizdale E
The physician's duty to the consumptive.
Asheville, N. C. [1900?]
12 p.
Reprinted, with additions, from The
Medical visitor.

NL 0390223 DNLM

Linn, W   M.
The common sense natural gas receipt book. Wapa-
koneta, O., Printed by W. M. Linn, 1888.
[23] p., 9 l. 14½^{cm}.
Compiled by W. M. Linn for the Minster gas and fuel company.
Forms for data: p. [18–23]; blank receipts: 9 leaves at end.

1. Gas, Natural.   I. Minster gas and fuel company, Minster, O.

Library of Congress   TP350.L7   CA 10—2620 Unrev'd

NL 0390224 DLC

Linn, Walter, ed.

Atlantic deeper waterways association.
... Annual convention ... Report of the proceedings. Published by the Atlantic deeper waterways association ... Philadelphia, The Book print, 1909–

Linn, Walter.
The science of Mehitabel; a play in four acts ...
[Carlisle, Pa., c1912]
142 p. 23 cm.

NL 0390226 RPB

D 465
.L72
LINN, WALTER, 1908–
Die Internationalisierung der Meerengen von
Konstantinopel; eine völkerrechtliche Studie.
Ansbach, Buchdruckerei M. Schraut, 1930.
52 p.

1. Eastern question (Balkan). 2. Dardanelles.
3. Bosporus.

NL 0390227 InU ICRL CtY

Linn, Walter Armin, 1903–
False prophets of peace, by W. Armin Linn. Harrisburg,
Pa., The Military service publishing company [*1939]
7 p. l., 13–367 p. illus., plates, ports., diagrs. 23½^{cm}.
Bibliography: p. 366–367.

1. U. S.—History, Military. 2. War. 3. Peace.   I. Title.

Library of Congress   E181.L65   39–32113

NL 0390228 DLC WaTC PSt NcRS NcD PU PP OC1

Linn [William] A.M., Chaplain.
A Military Discourse, delivered in Carlisle,
March the 17th, 1776 to Colonel Irvine's Battal-
ion of Regulars, and a very respectable number of
the Inhabitants. Published at the request of the
Officers. ... Philadelphia: Printed in the Year
MDCCLXXVI.
12 mo.   pp. 23.

NL 0390229 PPL

Linn, William, plaintiff.

Law

Semple, James, 1798–1866.
Substance of the argument of James Semple, esq. ... before
the Supreme court of the state of Illinois, at the December term,
1833, in the case of William Linn, *vs.* the State bank of Illinois.
Lower Alton, Printed by M. Greiner, 1834.

VOLUME 334

Linn, William, 1752–1808.

Works by this author printed in America before 1801 are available in this library in the Readex Microprint edition of Early American Imprints published by the American Antiquarian Society. This collection is arranged according to the numbers in Charles Evans' American Bibliography.

NL 0390231 DLC

Linn, William, 1752–1808.

The blessings of America. A sermon, preached in the Middle Dutch church, on the fourth July, 1791, being the anniversary of the independence of America: at the request of the Tammany society, or Columbian order. By William Linn, D. D. New-York—Printed by Thomas Greenleaf.—1791.

39 p. 20cm.

"An ode, composed for the occasion, at the request of the society. By Dr. William Pitt Smith": p. [37]–39.

1. Fourth of July orations. I. Tammany society, or Columbian order. II. Smith, William Pitt, 1764?–1795. III. Title.

3-6359

Library of Congress E286.N6 1791

NHi MB
ViW OClW NNC ViU NHi PPAmP CtY MBAt NN
NL 0390232 DLC ViU CtY InU MH OClWHi ViW NIC CSt

Linn, William, 1752–1808.

The character of Simon the sorcerer: a sermon, designed to prove that baptism is not regeneration. By William Linn, D.D... New-York: Printed by Thomas Greenleaf, 1793. 30, (i)xxxii-xl p. 8°.

The appendix refutes the sermon by Bishop Moore, entitled "The doctrine of regeneration asserted and explained," printed at New York in 1791 and again in 1792. Bishop Moore replied in "An address to the members of the Protestant Episcopal Church in the City of New York..." New York, 1793; and was answered by Linn's "Remarks on Dr. Moore's Address..." printed at New York the same year.

Edges untrimmed.

1. Baptism.—Regeneration in. 2. Moore, Benjamin, bishop, 1748–1816: The doctrine of regeneration...

N. Y. P. L. April 20, 1916.

RPJCB InU NNC ViW CtY
NL 0390233 NN DLC PPL RPB MWA NHi NjP IC MB MH

Linn, William, 1752–1808.

A collection of the essays on the subject of episcopacy, which originally appeared in the Albany centinel, and which are ascribed principally to the Rev. Dr. Linn, the Rev. Mr. Beasley, and Thomas Y. How, esq. With additional notes and remarks. New-York: Printed by T. & J. Swords, no. 160 Pearl-street. 1806.

viii, 210 p. 23½cm.

Edited by J. H. Hobart.

1. Episcopacy. I. Beasley, Frederick, 1777–1845. II. How, Thomas Yardley. III. Hobart, John Henry, bp., 1775–1830, ed.

Library of Congress BV670.L5 31-6647
[2] 262.12

NL 0390234 DLC NBuG NN NHi CSt NcU MiU MeB

Linn, William, 1752-1808.

A discourse, delivered at Hackinsack, June 28, 1796, on the occasion of the meeting of a commission of synod to compose certain differences in the congregations of Hackinsack and Schralenburgh ... New-York, Printed by T. and J. Swords, 1796.

36 p. 21cm.

Evans 30697; Sabin 41343.

1. Hackensack, N.J. First Reformed Church. 2. Schraalenburg, N.J. Reformed Dutch Church.

NL 0390235 NHi NjR CtY

Linn, William, 1752–1808.

A discourse, delivered April 1st, 1800, in the Brick Presbyterian church, before the New-York Missionary Society, at their annual meeting. By William Linn... New-York: Printed by Isaac Collins. 1800. 40 p. 25cm. (8°.)

Sabin 41348.

Running-title: The Christian's zeal for the church.

Printed at the request of the society.

"Report of the directors," dated: March 31st, 1800, p. [34–]39; "Officers and directors," p. 40.

1. Missions. 2. Indians, N. A.—Missions. I. New York Missionary Society.

N. Y. P. L. *Revised* March 27, 1934

NL 0390237 NN CtY NHi NjR RPJCB CSmH N PHi MDeeP

Linn, William, 1752–1808.

A discourse, delivered on the 26th of November, 1795; being the day recommended by the governor of the state of New-York to be observed as a day of thanksgiving and prayer, on account of the removal of an epidemic fever, and for other national blessings. By William Linn ... New-York: Printed by T. and J. Swords, no. 99 Pearl-street. 1795.

iv, [5]–38 p. 20½cm.

Signatures: [A]–E⁴ (E₄ blank)

1. Thanksgiving day addresses. 2. Yellow fever—New York (City) 1795.

Library of Congress 3V4305.L5 32-15914
——— Copy 2. 252.6

MBAt MHi MWA RPJCB NjP
NL 0390238 DLC MH NNNAM DNLM NHi MH CtY NN CtHi NHi

BV4270 **Linn, William,** 1752–1808.
.L75 A discource on national sins: delivered May 9, 1798; being the day recommended by the President of the United States to be observed as a day of general fast. By William Linn ... New York, Printed by T. & J. Swords, 1798.

vi, [7]–37 p. 22cm.

NNUT CSt
MBAt MWA DGU ICN MH RPB CtY NN CtHi MBC MH PHi
NL 0390239 ICU DLC PHi NjNbS CtY PPPrHi NHi NNC

Linn, William, 1752–1808.

Discourses on the signs of the times. New York, Printed by T. Greenleaf, 1794.

200 p. 21 cm.

1. Reformed Church in America—Sermons. 2. Sermons, American. I. Title. II. Title: Signs of the times.

BX9527.L5D5 58-50050

PPL MiU ICU N NjR NjNbS OClWHi NN MoU MiD-B ICN
NL 0390240 DLC NHi CtY MH-AH MiU-C NcD CtY RPJCB

Linn, William, 1752–1808.

A funeral eulogy, occasioned by the death of General Washington. Delivered February 22d, 1800, before the New-York state society of the Cincinnati. By William Linn, D. D. New-York, Printed by Isaac Collins, 1800.

vi, [7]–44 p. 20½cm.

1. Washington, George, pres. U. S.—Addresses, sermons, etc. I. Society of the Cincinnati. New York.

Library of Congress E312.63.L75 17-4569

MWA RPJCB MiD-B PPL MiU-C NN
NL 0390241 DLC MdBJ-G NHi MB NIC PPL NcD MH ICN

Linn, William, 1752–1808.

Remarks on Dr. Moore's Address to the members of the Protestant Episcopal church, in the city of New-York. By William Linn, D. D. New-York—Printed by Thomas Greenleaf. M,DCC,XC,III.

46 p. 20½cm.

1. Moore, Benjamin, 1748–1816. An address to the members of the Protestant Episcopal church in the city of New York. A 33-3324

Title from H. E. Huntington Libr. Printed by L. C.

NNUT
NL 0390242 CSmH NjP PPL CSmH MH MB NHi MWA RHi NN

[**Linn, William**] 1752–1808.

Serious considerations on the election of a president: addressed to the citizens of the United States. New-York, Printed and sold by J. Furman, 1800.

36 p. 20½cm.

Published anonymously.

"Dr. John M. Mason assisted in the performance."—Sabin, Bibl. amer., v. 10, no. 41347.

An argument against the election of Mr. Jefferson, on the ground of "his disbelief in the Holy Scriptures; or, in other words, his rejection of the Christian religion and open profession of Deism."

1. Jefferson, Thomas, pres. U. S., 1743–1826. 2. U. S.—Pol. & govt.—1797–1801. 3. Campaign literature, 1800—Federalist. I. Mason, John Mitchell, 1770–1829.

Library of Congress E330.L75 9-6998
Copy 2.

MiU MWA RPJCB NN MB CtY PPAmP PPL
NL 0390243 DLC MB M MBAt CtY NIC CSt MiU-C MnU ViU

---

503 [Linn, William] 1752-1808.
J36 Serious considerations on the election of a
1800l president: addressed to the citizens of the United States. Trenton: Printed by Sherman, Mershon & Thomas, 1800.

31p. 22½cm.

Published anonymously.

"Dr. John M. Mason assisted in the performance." - Sabin, Bibl. amer., v.10, no.41347.

An argument against the lection of Mr. Jefferson, on the ground of "his disbelief in the Holy Scriptures: or, in other words, his rejection of the Christian religion and open profession of Deism."

NL 0390244 CtY DLC NHi PPAmP ICU

LINN, WILLIAM, 1752–1808.

Sermons historical and characteristical. By William Linn ... New York:—Printed by Childs and Swaine. «With the privilege of copy-right.» [1791.] xxiii, 360 p. 16½cm. (12°.)

Sabin 41348. Evans 23505.

Imperfect: p. vii–viii slightly mutilated.

681783A. 1. Bible. O.T.—Biog.

NjNbS
MWA OClW RPJCB CtY NNC MH-AH InU ICN CU PPL PPiPT
NL 0390245 NN NjP KyU NHi TNJ-R ICN MBAt NHi PHi

Linn, William, 1790–1867.

The legal and commercial commonplace book, containing decisions of the Supreme court of the United States and of the respective state courts on bills of exchange, checks, and promissory notes ... By William Linn ... Ithaca N. Y., Andrus, Gauntlett & co., 1850.

viii, 9–294 p. 23cm.

1. Bills of exchange. 2. Checks. 3. Negotiable instruments.

A 18-56

Title from Yale Law Libr. Printed by L. C.

NL 0390246 CtY NIC

Linn, William, 1790–1867.

The life of Thomas Jefferson, author of the Declaration of independence, and third president of the United States ... By William Linn. Ithaca, Mack & Andrus, 1834.

267 p. front. (port.) 19cm.

1. Jefferson, Thomas, pres. U. S., 1743–1826.

12-1831

Library of Congress E332.L75

NbOC
MiU OClWHi NjP NIC NN MB MWA ViU PMA CtHT-W IEN
NL 0390247 DLC NN WaU KyHi PP NBuU OFH MiU-C TU

Linn, William.

Life of Thomas Jefferson, author of the Declaration of Independence and third president of the United States. Mobile: Kellog. 1835.

267 p.

NL 0390248 NbOC

Linn, William, 1790–1867.

The life of Thomas Jefferson, author of the Declaration of independence, and third president of the United States ... By William Linn. 2d ed. Ithaca [N. Y.] Mack, Andrus & Woodruff, 1839.

267 p. front. (port.) 18½cm.

1. Jefferson, Thomas, pres. U. S., 1743–1826.

16-25375

Library of Congress E332.L753

NL 0390249 DLC ViU KyLx MWA ViN TxU NIC NN MB

VOLUME 334

Linn, William, 1790–1867.
The life of Thomas Jefferson, author of the Declaration of independence, and third president of the United States ... By William Linn. 3d ed. Ithaca, Andrus, Woodruff, & Gauntlett, 1843.
267 p. front. (port.) 18½ᶜᵐ.

1. Jefferson, Thomas, pres. U. S., 1743–1826.

Library of Congress   E332.L754   30-22528

             923.173

NL   0390250   DLC

Linn, William, 1790–1867.
Momus at home
    see under   [Hayward, Abraham] 1801–1884.

Linn, William, *1790–1867.*
An oration delivered in the Presbyterian meeting-house, in the village of Ithaca, at the celebration of the fifty-fourth anniversary of American independence, July 5, 1830. Ithaca: Mack. 1830.
11 p.

NL   0390252   NCH

Linn, William Alexander, 1846–1917.
Baron Steuben's estate at New Bridge, Bergen County, N. J. with some account of his European experience, and his services to the American army. Read before the Bergen County historical society, February 22, 1904 ... Hackensack [1904]

NL   0390253   CtY NN

Linn, William Alexander, 1846–1917.
[Class] poem by William Alexander Linn Deckertown, N. J.
In- Valedictory poem and oration Yale college. Presentation day, July 1st, 1868.   22 cm.
p. [3] –18.   New Haven, 1868.

NL   0390254   RPB

Linn, William Alexander. 1846–
Building and loan associations. Illus.
(In Homes in city and country. Pp. 160–214. New York. 1893.)

H7340 — Building associations.

NL   0390255   NB

Linn, William Alexander, 1846–19.
Horace Greeley, founder and editor of the New York tribune, by William Alexander Linn ... New York, D. Appleton and company, 1903.
xiii, 267 p. front. (port.) plates, facsims. 19½ᶜᵐ. (*Half-title:* Appletons' historic lives series)

1. Greeley, Horace, 1811–1872.

Library of Congress   E415.9.G8L7   3–6577

             -920.5

TU NjPT NIC DN OKentU MB NN
WaE OrP MtU IdB WaWW Or OrSaW DNW MoU NNC NcU MeB
NL   0390256   DLC WaS MWA OFH PWcS MiU OC1 OCU OU NcD

Linn, William Alexander, 1846–1917.
Horace Greeley, founder and editor of the New York tribune, by William Alexander Linn ... New York, D. Appleton and company, 1912.   and London,
xiii, 267 p. front. (port.) plates, facsims. 19½ᶜᵐ. (*Half-title:* Appletons' historic lives series)

NL   0390257   ViU

Linn, William Alexander, 184–
Rob and his gun, by William Alexander Linn ... New York, C. Scribner's sons, 1902.
xi, 211 p. incl. front. plates. 19½ᶜᵐ.

1. Title.

Library of Congress   PZ7.L663R   2–21489

NL   0390258   DLC NcD NN OC1W MB

Linn, William Alexander, 1846–1917.
The story of the Mormons, from the date of their origin to the year 1901, by William Alexander Linn. New York, The Macmillan company; London, Macmillan & co., ltd., 1902.
xxv, 637 p. facsims., diagr. 23½ cm.

1. Mormons and Mormonism.   2. Utah—Hist.

Library of Congress   BX8611.L5   2–4701

            [a51j½]   -298.3

IEG OrP NcD WaT IdB IdU WaSp
OC1WHi CU ICJ NN ICN CLU MsU NIC WHi MeB MnHi MoU
NL   0390259   DLC PPEB CSmH MB NjNbS PPT MiU OC1 ODW

Linn, William Bomberger, 1871–
Address [Athenaeums: past and present] October 17th, 1947.   [Phila], The Athenaeum of Philadelphia [1947]
15 p.   23 cm.

NL   0390260   PHC

Linn-Linsenbarth, Oskar
    see   Linsenbarth, Oskar, 1847–

Linn Parr, Margaret S.
    see   Parr, Margaret Sands (Linn) 1858–

Linn and North Benton Counties farm and agricultural directory.

Albany, Ore.?
/ v. 23cm.

NL   0390263   OrU

Le linn ár n-óige
    see under   [O'Brien, William] 1852–1928.

SPECIAL COLL.
BK
L649   Linn Baseball Club, Albany, Ore.
Corporate records, 1878–1879.
1v.

Organized March 30, 1878, for "the mutual improvement of its members in the practice of Base Ball and general development of the muscles."

1. Albany, Ore.   2. Baseball.

NL   0390265   OrU

Linn co., *Ia.*   *Auditor*
    see
Linn co., *Ia.*   *Office of county auditor.*

Linn co., *Ia.*   *County auditor*
    see
Linn co., *Ia.*   *Office of county auditor.*

Linn Co., *Iowa.*   *Engineering Dept.*
Atlas of Linn County, Iowa, 1930.   Rev. April 1944. Cedar Rapids [1944]
[1] l., 3–22 maps. 38 x 40 cm.
Maps are on the scale of 1 : 31,680 or 2 inches to 1 mile. Blue line print.

1. Linn Co., Iowa—Maps.   2. Real property—Linn Co., Iowa—Maps.

            Map 49–531*

NL   0390268   DLC

Linn co., *Ia.*   *Office of county auditor.*
Financial report.
Cedar Rapids [19
v. in   illus. (incl. double maps) tables (part fold.) 21½–22½ᶜᵐ.
Title varies, 19 –1916: Handbook and financial report.

1. Finance—Linn co., Ia.

Library of Congress   HJ9012.I 8L5   46–30248

NL   0390269   DLC NN

Linn Co., Mo.
Portrait and biographical record of Clay, Ray, Carroll, Chariton and Linn Counties, Missouri
    see under title

Linn Co., Or.

[Pamphlets] v.p.v.d.

Contents.–Linn county, the heart of the far famed Willamette Valley.–Opportunity awaits you in Linn county, Oregon. –Lebanon, Oregon, the strawberry center of the valley

NL   0390271   OrP

VOLUME 334

LINN CO., OR.   ASSESSOR
Summary of tax roll for 1939
assessment of 1938
Linn County, Oregon. ⟨Albany, 1938⟩
v.

NL 0390272   Or

LINN CO., OR.   COUNTY SCHOOL SUPERINTENDENT
Directory of teachers ⟨and school officers⟩
Linn County, Oregon, 1935/36–1951/52. ⟨Author
1935-51.
17 v.

Title varies.

NL 0390273   Or

Linn co., Or. Immigration agent.
Settler's guide, to homes in the
Willamette valley, Oregon. For the use and
information of immigrants. Published by C.G.
Burkhart, Immigration agent for Linn county.
Albany,Or.[1887?]
75p. illus. 24cm.
Advertisements included in pagination.
Original wrappers.

NL 0390274   CtY

Linn co., Or. Public schools.
Revised course of study for the common schools
of Linn county, Oregon. Taylorville, Ill.,
School news print, C. M. Parker, publisher, 1894.
96 p. illus.,diagr. 21½cm.

NL 0390275   OrCS

Or.
Film   Linn County, School District no. 8
14   Accounts, ⟨census⟩ reports and minutes,
Item   Scio, June 1864 April 1873.
21   57 frames. 16mm negative microfilm.
State   Oregon State Archives public records loan
Archives microfilm 21. From original in possession
of Mrs. R. V. Carleson.

NL 0390276   Or-Ar Or

Linn County   Agricultural Association.
Premium List | of the | Linn County | Agricultural Association,
| to be awarded at its | First Annual Fair, | to be held | At their
Fair Grounds, One Mile South of | Albany, | on | Tuesday,
Wednesday, Thursday and Friday, October | 2nd, 3rd, 4th and
5th, 1866. | [Filet] | "Albany Journal Office" Print. | 1866.
16 p. 9 x 14 cm. Printed gray wrappers.
Printed before August 25, 1866, when the Albany *Journal* suspended
publication.

NL 0390277   OrHi

LINN COUNTY AGRICULTURAL ECONOMIC CONFERENCE,
Albany, Or., 1936.
Report of the Linn County agricultural
economic conference conducted in Albany, Oregon,
January 28 and 29, 1936. Albany, Albany Democrat-herald, 1936.
23 p. illus.

In cooperation with O.S.C. extension service
Issued as the second section of the Albany
Democrat-herald, v.69, no.205, March 10, 1936.

NL 0390278   Or DNAL

LINN COUNTY AGRICULTURAL PLANNING CONFERENCE,
Albany, Or., 1946.
Agricultural planning conference for Linn
county, containing reports of committees submitted and adopted January 29, 1946, Albany,
Oregon. ⟨n.p.⟩ ⟨1946⟩
54 p. illus.

NL 0390279   Or OrU

Linn County (Ia.) bar association.

Cousins, Robert Gordon, 1859–1931.
Eulogy delivered by Robert G. Cousins, L. L. D., on the life
of the late Charles E. Wheeler at the bier of Charles E.
Wheeler, December 2nd, 1927. Published ... by the Linn
county bar association of Linn county, Iowa. ⟨Cedar Rapids?
1927?⟩

Linn County (Ia.) bar association.

Clark, Charles A.
Washington, by Charles A. Clark; an address before
the Linn County bar association and its guests at its
annual banquet at the Hotel Montrose, Cedar Rapids,
Iowa, February 22, 1909. Cedar Rapids, Ia., The Torch
press, 1909.

Linn county business directory for 1883,
containing a detailed description of
Linn county and a complete list of
business houses;together with the
character and ordinances of the principal incorporated towns. Watts,1883.

NL 0390282   OrP

S534   Linn County Farm Bureau news.
.07.L66   v.1-3; Jul.1918-Jun.1921. Albany, Ore.,
qA2   1918-21.
3 v. in ⸺. 27½-29½cm. monthly.

Title varies: v.1 no.1-5, Linn County Agricultural Council news.
v.1 no.6-v.3 no.3, Linn County Farm Bureau
news.
Oregon State College Extension Service and
U.S. Dept. of Agriculture cooperating.
Ceased publication.

1 Agricultural   extension work - Ore. -
Linn Co. 2.   Agricultural extension work -   Period. I.Oregon.

NL 0390283   OrCS Or

SPECIAL
COLL.   (Or.)
B   Linn County Fire Patrol Association.
133   Minutes of directors' meetings, 1911-1934.
1 folder.

Xerox copy of original held by the Association, Sweet Home, Ore.
With the minutes are filed, in original, the
published annual reports of the Association,
1913-1953.

1. Oregon.   Forest fires.   Prevention and
control.

NL 0390284   OrU

Linn County (Ia.) Historical society
see   Historical society of Linn County, Iowa,
Cedar Rapids.

Linn County (Ia.) Medical Society
see   Iowa Union Medical Society.

Linn County (Ia.) Old settlers' association
see   Old settlers' association of Linn County,
Marion, Ia.

Linna, Nicolas de
see   Nicholas of Lynne, fl. 1386.

Linna, Roopert
Kyläkertomuksia, kirjoittanut R.Linna.
Lapualla, Jaakko Hissa [1890]
v.1

NL 0390289   MH

4PH   Linna, Väinö
Fin.   Kreuze in Karelien; Roman.
638   ⟨Deutsch von Karl-Heinz Bolay und
Rolf Schroers⟩   Köln, Kiepenheuer &
Witsch ⟨1955⟩
473 p.

NL 0390290   DLC-P4 CaBVa OrCS

Linna, Väinö
...Musta rakkaus; romaani.   Porvoo, Helsinki, W. Söderström ⟨1948⟩ 266 p. 21cm.

560949B. 1. Fiction, Finnish.   I. Title.
N. Y. P. L.   February 23, 1951

NL 0390291   NN OC1

LINNA, VÄINÖ.
Okänd soldat.
Helsingfors. H. Schildt. 1955. 447p.

NL 0390292   WaS

Linna, Väinö.
De onbekende soldaat, roman.
Amsterdam,De Lange⟨°1955⟩   312p.

NL 0390293   CaBVa

Linna, Väinö
Päämäärä; romaani.   Porvoo, W. Söderström
⟨1947⟩
235p.

Finnish.

NL 0390294   OC1

VOLUME 334

Linna, Väinö.
Tuntematon sotilas. Porvoo, Helsinki, W. Söderström [1954] 476 p. 21cm.

1. Fiction, Finnish. 2. Finno-Russian war, 1939-1940—Fiction. 3. World war, 1939-1945—Fiction,

NL 0390295 NN

Linna, Väinö
Tuntematon sotilas. [9.painos] Helsinki, Söderström [1955]

476 p.

NL 0390296 MH

Linna, Väinö.
Tuntematon sotilas. 14. painos. Helsinki, W. Söderström [1955]
443 p. 21 cm.

1. World War, 1939-1945—Fiction. I. Title.

PH355.L5T8 1955

57-47593

NL 0390297 DLC WaS MH PU

Linnaa, Harriet.
... Markedsuken. Oslo, Gyldendal, 1930.
210 p. 20ᵐ.
A novel.

I. Title.
Library of Congress PT8950.L654M3 1930 31-12365

NL 0390298 DLC

Linnaa, Harriet.
... Vanitas. Oslo, Gyldendal, 1934.
194 p. 20ᵐ.
A novel.

I. Title.
Library of Congress PT8950.L654V3 1934 35-2443
Copyright A—Foreign 26337
[2] 839.8236

NL 0390299 DLC

SB
413
N5
L558

Linnaea, Elisabet Christina, 1743-1782.
Om indianska krassens blickande. [Stockholm, 1762]
p. 284-287.
In Kungliga Svenska Vetenskaps-Akademien. Handlingar. v. 23. 1762.

INDIAN CRESS
NASTURTIUMS
Linné, Carl von, 1707-1778
t

NL 0390300 KMK

Microform
32

Linnaea, Elisabet Christina, 1743-1782.
Indianska krassens blickande. [n.p., 1762]
284-287 p.

From Sv. Vet.-ak. Handl. 1762, p. 284-287.
Includes 4 paragraphs by Carl Linnaeus and an addition by Lector Wilcke.
Microfiche. Zug, Switzerland, Inter-Documentation Company. [196-] 1 box, 1 card 10 x 14 cm.
Krok, p. 422.

NL 0390301 NNBG

QK
1
L75

Linnaea.
1.-43. Bd.; 1826-1882.
Berlin, P. Parey [etc.]
43 v. illus. (part fold.) 22 cm.

Bd. 17-43 have alternative title: Beiträge zur Pflanzenkunde, Bd. 1-18; neue Folge, Bd. 1-9.
Bd. 1-34 edited by D.F.L. von Schlechtendal; Bd. 35-43 by August Garcke.
Date on holdings cards is date given on title page. For dates of public   ation of individual Hefte,

see Stafleu, F.A., Taxonomic literature, p. 419-424.
Superseded by Berlin. Universität. Botanischer Garten. Jahrbuch.

1. Botany - Period. I. Schlechtendal, Diedrich Franz Leonhard von, 1794-1886. II. Garcke, Friedrich August, 1819-1904.

NL 0390303 NjP OU NN

Microfiche

Linnaea; ein Journal für die Botanik in ihrem ganzen Umfange. Bd. 1-43; 1826-82. Berlin [etc.] Parey [etc.]
43 v. illus.
Vols. 35-43 called also "Neue Folge", v. 1-9.
Editors: 1826-66, D. F. L. von Schlechtendal.--1867-82, A. Garcke.
Merged with the Jahrbuch of the Botanischer Garten, Berlin Universität.
Vols. for 1826-42 includes supplement: Litteratur-Beri   cht, v. 1-16 (1828-42

with separate title page and pagination)
"Alphabetisches Inhaltsverzeichnis" included in v. 43.
Microfiche (negative) Tumba, Sweden, International Documentation Centre, 1967? 587 sheets in 14 boxes. 9 x 12 cm.

1. Botany. Period. I. Schlechtendal, Diedrich Franz Leonhard von, 1794-1866, ed. II. Garcke, August, 1819-1904, ed.

NIC MBH CtY WvU
NL 0390305 NcD UU MiU MH DSI IU CoU MeB PSt NcU N

AW
2
L55

Linnaea [Bd. 1-43; 1826-1882.
Berlin, F. Dümmler [etc.]
587 cards. 8 1/2 x 11 1/2 cm.
Microprint copy.
Collation of the original: 43 v.
Bd. 35-43 also called n.F., Bd. 1-9.
Edited 1826-66 by D.F.L. von Schlechtendal.
Merged into Berlin. Universität. Botanischer Garten. Jahrbuch.
1. Botany - Period. I. Schlechtendal, Diedrich   Franz Leonhard von, 1794-1866,   ed. [1] /&Micro 3

NL 0390306 CaBVaU

PT
9991
L54

Linnaea; poetiskt album af svensk-amerikanska publicister i Chicago. Chicago, Hemlandets tryckeri, 1887. 224 p. port.

1. Swedish poetry - Collections and selections

NL 0390307 WaU RPB MnHi

Linnaea entomologica. Zeitschrift hrsg. von dem Entomologischen vereine in Stettin. 1.-16. bd. Berlin, Posen [etc.] E. S. Mittler, 1846-58; Leipzig, F. Fleischer, 1859-66.
16 v. in 15. plates. 22ᵐ.
"Alphabetisches register zu den vier ersten bänden": v. 4, p. 428-441.
"Bibliographia librorum entomologicorum in America-Boreali editorum. Auctore Guil. Sharswood": v. 13, p. 333-353; v. 14, p. 256-264.
Preceded by Zeitschrift für die entomologie.
No more published.

1. Insects—Period.

Library of Congress QL461.Z52 3—24172

NL 0390308 DLC NN OU MH CU GU AAP MiU NN CtY

Linnaean Association of Pennsylvania College
see Pennsylvania College, Gettysburg, Pa. Linnaean Association.

QH1
.L52

Linnaean bulletin.
Lancaster, Pa., 1884-

NL 0390310 DLC

The **Linnaean fern bulletin**. *See* The fern bulletin

Linnaean fern chapter of the Agassiz association.
see
American fern society.

QH
43
A3
1966

[Linnaean letters and manuscripts. n.p., n.d.]
10 items.

Bryk, Felix, 1882-
LINNÉ, CARL VON, 1707-1778

NL 0390313 KMK

Linnaean society...
see also Linnean society...

VOLUME 334

Linnaean Society of New England.
Boston, Jan 27 1815 Sir, At a meeting of the Linnaean society of New England holden Jan 21 1815 you were elected a corresponding member. This society is instituted for the collection of interesting facts and useful information in natural history ... By order of the society, J. Bigelow Corresponding secretary, [to] Loammi Baldwin esq. [Boston, 181-]

[3] p. 24.3cm.
"Officers of the Linnaean society": p. [3]
Addressed on p. [4] to Loammi Baldwin esq from Jacob Bigelow.
Underlined porti   ons in ms.

NL 0390315   MiU-C

Linnaean Society of New England.
Conditions and doings of the Boston Society of Natural History
see under title

Linnaean society of New England.
Report of a committee of the Linnæan society of New England, relative to a large marine animal, supposed to be a serpent, seen near Cape Ann, Massachusetts, in August 1817. Boston, Cummings and Hilliard, 1817.

52 p. 2 pl. (1 fold.) 21½ᶜᵐ.
"Account of the *Scoliophis atlanticus*": p. 38–50.
No. 1 of a volume of pamphlets lettered: Botanical theses, &c.

1. Scoliophis atlanticus. 2. Sea serpent.

5–36995

Library of Congress   QK3.B75

       MeB PBL ICJ
NL 0390317   DLC PPL InU CSt MWH MBCo MH MWA MiU-C

Linnæan society of New England.
Report of a committee of the Linnæan society of New England, relative to a large marine animal, supposed to be a serpent, seen near Cape Ann, Massachusetts, in August, 1817. London, J. Souter, 1818.

59 p. fold. front. 22½ᶜᵐ. [With Schleicher, J. C. Catalogus hucusque absolutus omnium plantarum in Helvetia ... nascentium. [Bex] 1815]
1st edition: Boston, 1817.
"Account of the *Scoliophis atlanticus*": p. 41–55.

1. Sea-serpents. 2. Scoliophis atlanticus.

5–40221†* Cancel

Library of Congress   QK331.S34

NL 0390318   DLC

Linnæan society of New England
see also
Boston society of natural history.

Linnæan Society of New York. Abstract of the proceedings
see its Proceedings.

Q11
.N77

Linnæan society of New York.
Scientific alliance of New York.
Annual directory ... Published by the council under the authority of the several societies. [1st,–14th; 1891–1904. Lancaster, Pa., Press of the New era printing company; etc., etc.] 1891–[1904]

Linnæan society of New York.

Cruickshank, Allan D.
Birds around New York city, where and when to find them, by Allan D. Cruickshank, with the cooperation of the Department of ornithology of the American museum of natural history, and the Linnaean society of New York, with photographs by the author ... New York, 1942.

Linnæan society of New York.

Griscom, Ludlow, 1890–
Birds of the New York city region, by Ludlow Griscom, assistant curator of ornithology, with the cooperation of the Linnæan society of New York ... New York, The Museum, 1923.

Linnæan society of New York.

New York academy of sciences.
Directory of the New York academy of sciences and affiliated societies.
New York, The Academy

QL671
.L55

Linnæan Society of New York.
Linnæan news-letter. v. 1–   Mar. 1947–
New York, Linnæan Society of New York.

Linnæan Society of New York.
Proceedings. no. [1]–
1888/89–
[New York]
       v. in   illus. 23 cm. annual.
Report year ends in Mar.
Issues for 1888/89–1891/92 have no numbering but constitute no. 1–4.
Proceedings for some years issued in combined numbers.
Title varies: 1888/89–1930/32, abstract of the proceedings.

1. Natural history—Societies.

QH1.L88   574.062747   20–4613 rev*

NL 0390326   DLC KEmT ICJ MiU IaAS NcU

QH1
.L882

Linnæan society of New York.
Proceedings of the Linnæan society of New York. v. 33, p. 1–8; July 15, 1920. [New York, 1920]

Apply for
volume
desired

7 p. pl. 23ᶜᵐ.
Caption title.
Issued simultaneously with its Abstract of the proceedings, assuming the volume numbering of the latter.
[No more published.

1. Natural history—Societies.

45–42206

Library of Congress   QH1.L882

NL 0390327   DLC

Linnæan society of New York.
Transactions of the Linnæan society of New York ... New York, Press of L. S. Foster [etc.] 1882–

       v. fronts. (2 port.) 28½ cm.

CONTENTS.—v. 1. The vertebrates of the Adirondack region, northeastern New York. (General introduction—*Mammalia; Carnivora*) By Clinton Hart Merriam. Is not the fish crow (*Corvus ossifragus* Wilson) a winter as well as a summer resident at the northern limit of its range? By William Dutcher. A review of the summer birds of a part of the Catskill mountains, with prefatory remarks on the faunal and floral features of the region. By Eugene Pintard Bicknell. 1882.—v. 2. The vertebrates of the Adirondack region, northeastern New York. (*Mammalia*, concluded) By Clinton Hart Merriam.

Continued in next column

Continued from preceding column

Description of a new genus and species of the *Soricidae*. (*Atophyrax bendirii*, with a plate.) By Clinton Hart Merriam. 1884.—v. 3. The birds of Dutchess county, New York, from records compiled by Maunsell S. Crosby. By Ludlow Griscom. 1933.

1. Zoology—Societies, etc.

QH1.L87   Agr 3–679

U. S. Dept of Agr. Libr.   410.9N482T
for Library of Congress   [a57r54d½]†

       AAP DSI DLC CoD ICJ NN IU CaBVaU OrCS KEmT ILS
NL 0390329   DNAL CaOTU TxU LU PBL NStBU FTaSU CaQMM

Linnaean society of Paris. New York branch
see
Société linnéenne de Paris

Linnaeana, in Nederland aanwezig
see under K. Zoölogisch genootschap "Natura artis magistra" te Amsterdam.

Linnæus, Carl
see
Linné, Carl von, 1707–1778.

Linnaeus, Carolus, respondent.
Dissertatio topographica, de paroecia stenbrohult
see under Brandt, Christianus H, praeses. [supplement]

Linnaeus, Carolus, 1707–1778
see
Linné, Carl von, 1707–1778.

Linnaeus, Elisabet Christina
see Linnæa, Elisabet Christina, 1743–1782.

Linnaeus, Karl
see
Linné, Carl von, 1707–1778

Linnaeus, Nils Ingemarsson, 1674–1748.

Linné, Carl von, 1707–1778.
Caroli Linnæi Adonis stenbrohultensis, utgiven av Felix Bryk. Stockholm, Björck & Börjesson, 1920.

QK31
.L5
L62

Linnaeus after two hundred years. [n.p.. 1907] 105–107 p. port. 25 cm.

Caption title.
From American review of reviews, v.36, no.1, July 1907.

1. Linné, Carl von, 1707–1778.

NL 0390338   NNBG

VOLUME 334

Linnæus and Jussieu; or, The rise and progress of systematic botany. A popular biography, with an historical introduction and sequel. London, J. W. Parker, 1844.

viii, ₉₎–112 p. 17ᶜᵐ. ₍With Cuvier and zoology ... London, 1844₎

1. Linné, Carl von, 1707-1778. 2. Jussieu, Antoine Laurent de, 1748-1836. 3. Botany—Classification.

15-10624

Library of Congress   Q141.C85

NL 0390339   DLC MdBP CU NNUT

Linnala, Aarre
Rintaman takana; 3-näytöksinen näytelmä. Helsinki, Kustannusosakeyhtiö Kansanvalta, 1929

84 p. (Kansanvallan näytelmistö, 4)

NL 0390340   MH

Linnala, Eino Mauno Aleksanteri, 1896–
₍Finnish rhapsody, orchestra₎

Suomalainen rapsodia. Finnish rhapsody. Helsinki, Suomen säveltaiteilijain ₍1938₎

score (58 p.) 35 cm.

For orchestra.
Duration : 10 minutes.

1. Orchestral music—Scores.   ɪ. Title.

M1045.L744F5

50-51654

NL 0390341   DLC NN FTaSU

Linnamies, Olavi.
Metsämiehen karttaoppi. Helsinki, Keskusmetsäseura Tapio ₍1948₎

100 p. illus. (part col.) maps. 22 cm. (Yksityismetsänhoitajayhdistyksen oppikirjasarja, n:o 1)

1. Forests and forestry—Maps. 2. Cartography.   ɪ. Title.
(Series: Yksityismetsänhoitajayhdistys. Oppikirjasarja, n:o 1)

SD361.L5

57-18371

NL 0390342   DLC

Linnaniemi, Walter Mikael, 1876–
... Die apterygotenfauna Finlands ... Von Walter M. (Axelson) Linnaniemi ... ₍Helsingforsiæ, ex Officina typographica Societatis litterariæ fennicæ, 1907₎

2 v. plates, fold. map, tables. 29 x 23ᶜᵐ. (₍Finska vetenskaps-societen, Helsingfors₎ Acta Societatis scientiarum fennicæ. t. xxxiv, n° 7; t. xl, n° 5)

Vol. 1 issued also as the author's thesis, Helsingfors, 1907.
"Literaturverzeichnis": v. 1, p. ₍1₎–xii; v. 2, p. ₍333₎–334.

Contents.—ɪ. Allgemeiner teil.—ɪɪ. Spezieller teil.

1. Aptera. 2. Insects—Finland.

New York. Public library   A C 38-1217
for Library of Congress
                    ₍Q60.F5 vol. 34, no. 7; vol. 40, no. 5₎
r₄₎
                                              (508)

NL 0390343   NN AAP CtY ICRL IU DLC

Linnaniemi, Walter Mikael, 1876–
...Collembola, bearbeitet von W. Linnaniemi... Petrograd, 1919. 15 p. incl. tables. illus. f°. (Akad. Nauk, St. Petersburg. Mém. 8. sér., v. 28, 13.)

1. Collembola—Siberia. 2. Series.
N. Y. P. L.
                                        December 17, 1924

NL 0390344   NN

LINNANIEMI, WALTER MIKAEL, 1876–
...Collembola, von Walter M. Linnaniemi... Bergen: A. S. J. Griegs boktrykkeri, 1933. 4 p. 31cm. (Maudekspeditionen. 1918–1925. Scientific results. v. 5, no. 16 b.)

1. Collembola—Arctic regions. I. Ser.

NL 0390345   NN

Linnaniemi, Walter Mikael, 1876–
Kertomus tuhoeläinten esiintymisestä suomessa. Vuosina 1917–1923. Helsinki, 1935.
159,8 p. map. 25cm. (Helsingfors. Valtion Maatalouskoetoiminnan. Julkaisuja nr. 68)

1. Insects, Injurious and beneficial—Finland. I. Series.

NL 0390346   NIC

Linnaniemi, Walter Mikael, 1876–
Korta anvisningar för bestämmandet af våra skadeinsekter. Helsingfors, Kejserliga Senatens tryckeri, 1915.
viii, 38 p. 31 plates. 25 cm. (Agrikultur-ekonomiska försöksanstaltens landtmannaskrifter, n:o 5)

1. Insects, Injurious and beneficial—Finland. ɪ. Title. (Series: Dickursby, Finland. Lantbruksförsöksanstalten. Lantmannaskrifter, n:o 5)

SB895.F5L5

52-59121

NL 0390347   DLC AAP

Linnaniemi, Walter Mikael, 1876–
Putkilokasvio Pielisen ja Höytiäisen välisellä kannaksella. Walter M. Axelson. Helsinki, 1902.
78 p. 24 cm. (Acta Societatis pro Fauna et Flora Fennica, 23, no. 4)

XA
.C76
v.23:4

1. Botany - Finland. i. t. ii. s.

NL 0390348   NNBG MH-A

Linnaniemi, Walter Mikael, 1876–
...Zur Kenntnis der Apterygotenfauna Norwegens. Von Walter M. (Axelson) Linnaniemi... ₍Bergen: A/S J. Grieg, 1912.₎ 28 p. 8°. (Bergens Museum, Bergen, Norway. Bergens Museums aarbok. 1911, no. 1.)

1. Apterygota, Norway. 2. Series.
N. Y. P. L.
                                              April 26, 1923.

NL 0390349   NN

Linnaniemi, Walter Mikael, 1876–
.... Zur Kenntnis der Apterygotenfauna von Tvärminne. Von Walter M. Axelson. Mit einer Tafel. Helsingfors, 1905.
117911
46 p. 1 pl. 26 x 19¼ᶜᵐ. (In Festschrift Herrn Professor Dr. J. A. Palmén gewidmet, Band 2, ₍n:o 13₎.)

At head of title: Festschrift für Palmén.
"Verzeichnis der zitierten Litteratur," p. 44-45.

NL 0390350   ICJ PPAmP PPAN PU PPULC

Linnaniemi, Walter Mikael, 1876–
Zur Kenntnis der Blattminierer, speziell derjenigen Finnlands. Helsingfors, 1913–
v. illus. 24 cm. (Acta Societatis pro Fauna et Flora Fennica, 37, no. 4

XA
.C76
v.37:4

Includes bibliographies.

1. Leaf-miners. 2. Leaf-miners - Finland.
i. t. ii. s.

NL 0390351   NNBG

Linnankoski, Johannes, pseud.
see
Peltonen, Vihtori, 1869–1913.

Linnarsson, A
Vadstena skola; studier i ett litet läroverks historia från förra hälften av 1400-talet till nuvarande tid. Linköping, Östgöta correspondentens boktr., 1931

283 p. illus.

NL 0390353   MH

Linnarsson, Gustav , respondent.
... De nexu conversionis cum regeneratione...
see under Grenander, Elias Christopherus, praeses.

Linnarsson, Jonas Gustaf Oskar, 1841–1881.
... Beskrifning till kartbladet "Latorp" (no. 55) af G. Linnarsson. Stockholm, P. A. Norstedt & söner, kongl. boktryckare, 1875.

41 p. 28¼ᶜᵐ. and map. 45 x 59½ᶜᵐ. (Sveriges geologiska undersökning. ₍Ser. Aa. Kartblad i skalan 1 : 50000 med beskrifningar. No. 55₎)

1. Geology—Sweden.

U. S. Geol. survey. Library   G S 7-1233 Revised
for Library of Congress
                    ₍QE282.A3 ser. Aa, no. 55₎

NL 0390355   DI-GS DLC

Linnarsson, Jonas Gustaf Oskar, 1841–188?
... Beskrifning till kartbladet Vreta Klo och S. A. Tullberg. Stockholm, Tryck 1882.

45 p. pl. (2 maps) diagrs. 28½ᶜᵐ. and geologiska undersökning. Ser. Aa. Kartbl skrifningar. No 83)

Map is dated 1881.

1. Geology—Sweden.   ɪ. Tullbe₎

U. S. Geol. survey. Library
for Library of Congress

NL 0390356   DI-GS

Linnarsson, Jonas G...
Geognostiska och
tonsandstenen i Ve...
Söner, 1871. 19 p...
Akademien. Han...

1. Palæontology,
N. Y. P. L.

NL 039...

VOLUME 334

Linnarsson, Jonas Gustaf Oskar, 1841–1881.
... Graptolitskiffrar med *Monograptus turriculatus* vid Klub-budden nära Motala. Af G. Linnarsson ... Stockholm, Kongl. boktryckeriet, P. A. Norstedt & söner, 1881.

1 p. l., 24 p. II pl. 22½ᶜᵐ. (Sveriges geologiska undersökning. Ser c. Afhandlingar och uppsatser, n:o 46)

Aftryck ur Geol. föreningens i Stockholm förhandl., 1881, n:r 68, bd. v, n:o 12.

1. Graptolites.
G S 7–1382 Revised

U. S. Geol. survey. Library
for Library of Congress   [QE282.A3   ser. c, no. 46]

NL 0390358   DI-GS

Linnarsson, Jonas Gustaf Oskar, 1841–1881.
... Iakttagelser öfver de graptolitförande skiffrarne i Skåne af G. Linnarsson ... Stockholm, P. A. Norstedt & söner, kongl. boktryckare, 1879.

30 p. pl. 22½ᶜᵐ. (*On cover:* Sveriges geologiska undersökning. Ser. C. Afhandlingar och uppsatser, n:o 31)

Aftryck ur Geologiska föreningens i Stockholm förhandl., 1879, bd. IV.

1. Geology—Sweden—Scania.
G S 7–1368 Revised

U. S. Geol. survey. Library
for Library of Congress   [QE282.A3   ser. C, no. 31]

NL 0390359   DI-GS

Linnarsson, Jonas Gustaf Oskar, 1841–1881.
... Öfversigt af Nerikes öfvergångsbildningar. Af G. Linnarsson ... Stockholm, P. A. Norstedt & söner, kongl. boktryckare, 1875.

47 p. double map. 22½ᶜᵐ. (Sveriges geologiska undersökning. [Ser. c. Afhandlingar och uppsatser, n: o 21;]

Aftryck ur Öfvers. af K. Vet-akad. förhandlingar, 1875, n:o 5.

1. Geology—Sweden—Örebro (Province)   2. Paleontology—Sweden—Örebro (Province)   I. Title.
G S 7–1360 Revised

U. S. Geol. survey. Library
for Library of Congress   [QE282.A3   ser. c.   no. 21]
[r42b2;†]

NL 0390360   DI-GS DLC

[Li]nnarsson, Jonas Gustaf Oscar, 1841–1881.
[O]m de siluriska bildningarne i mellersta Westergötland. [I]naug. diss Upsala, 1866.

[0]390361   ICRL

[Li]nnarsson, Jonas Gustaf Oskar, 1841–1881.
... [O]m faunan i kalken med *Conocoryphe exsulans* ("coro-[n]uskalken"] af G. Linnarsson ... Stockholm, Kongl. bok-[tryck]eriet, P. A. Norstedt & söner, 1879.

[. .] III pl. 22½ᶜᵐ. (Sveriges geologiska undersökning. Ser. C. Af-[handlin]gar och uppsatser, n:o 35)

[. . .]ntology—Sweden. 2. Paleontology—Cretaceous.
G S 7–1371 Revised

[. . . . sur]vey. Library
[. . .] of Congress   [QE282.A3   ser. C, no. 35]

[. . .]-GS

[. . .] Gustaf Oskar, 1841–1881.
[. . . la]gren med *Paradoxides ölandicus*. Af G.
[. . . . Stockh]olm, P. A. Norstedt & söner, kongl. bok-

[. . .]ᶜᵐ. (Sveriges geologiska undersökning. [Ser. . . . sat]ser, n:o 22;)

[. . . för]eningens i Stockholm förhandlingar, 1877,

I. Title.
G S 7–1361 Revised

[. . .]   QE282.A3   ser. c   no. 22
[r42b2;†]

Linnarsson, Jonas Gustaf Oskar, 1841–1881.
... Om försteningarne i de svenska lagren med *Peltura* och *Sphærophthalmus*. Af G. Linnarsson ... Stockholm, Kongl. boktryckeriet, P. A. Norstedt & söner, 1880.

31 p. 2 pl. 22½ᶜᵐ. (Sveriges geologiska undersökning. Ser. c. Afhandlingar och uppsatser, n:o 43)

Aftryck ur Geol. föreningens i Stockholm förhandl., 1880, n:o 60, bd. v, n:o 4.

1. Trilobites.
G S 7–1379 Revised

U. S. Geol. survey. Library
for Library of Congress   [QE282.A3   ser. c, no. 43]

NL 0390364   DI-GS

Linnarsson, Jonas Gustaf Oskar, 1841–1881.
... Om Gotlands graptoliter. Af G. Linnarsson ... Stockholm, Kongl. boktryckeriet, P. A. Norstedt & söner, 1879.

11 p. pl. 22½ᶜᵐ. (Sveriges geologiska undersökning. Ser. c. Afhandlingar och uppsatser, n:o 37)

Aftryck ur Öfvers. af Kongl. vet-akad:s förhandl., 1879.

1. Graptolites.
G S 7–1373 Revised

U. S. Geol. survey. Library
for Library of Congress   [QE282.A3   ser. c, no. 37]

NL 0390365   DI-GS

Linnarsson, Jonas Gustaf Oskar, 1841–1881.
... Om några försteningar från Sveriges och Norges "pri-mordialzon." Af J. G. O. Linnarsson. Stockholm, P. A. Norstedt & söner, kongl. boktryckare, 1873.

1 p. l., 789–796 p. pl. 22½ᶜᵐ. (Sveriges geologiska undersökning. [Ser. C. Afhandlingar och uppsatser, n:o 10;]

Öfversigt af Kongl. Vetenskaps-akademiens förhandlingar 1871, n:o 6.

1. Paleontology—Cambrian.   2. Paleontology—Scandinavia.
I. Title.
G S 7–1350 Revised

U. S. Geol. survey. Library
for Library of Congress   QE282.A3   ser. c, no. 10
[r42b2;†]

NL 0390366   DI-GS PPAmP DLC

Linnarsson, Jonas Gustaf Oskar, 1841–1881.
... Om Vestergötlands cambriska och siluriska aflagringar. Af J. G. O. Linnarsson. Med två taflor ... Stockholm, P. A. Norstedt & söner, 1869.

80 p. II pl. 31ᶜᵐ. (Kongl. svenska vetenskaps-akademiens handlingar. [Ny följd; bd. 8, n:o 2)

1. Paleontology—Cambrian.   2. Paleontology—Silurian.   3. Paleontology—Sweden—Västergötland.
A 43–115

Chicago. Univ. Library
for Library of Congress   Q64.S85   bd. 8, no. 2
[2;†]

NL 0390367   ICU MU DLC NN MB

LINNARSSON, Gustaf, 1841–1881.
On some Fossils found in the Eophyton Sands-tone at Lugnas in Sweden. Translated from Ofvessy af Kongl. Vetenskapfs Akademiens forhand[   ]. March 10, 1869. Stockholm, 1869.

pp. 16. 3 plates.

NL 0390368   MH PPAmP

Linnarsson, Jonas Gustaf Oskar, 1841–1881.
... De paleozoiska bildningarna vid Humlenäs i Småland. Af G. Linnarsson ... Stockholm, P. A. Norstedt & söner, kongl. boktryckare, 1878.

9 p. map. 22½ᶜᵐ. (*On cover:* Sveriges geologiska undersökning. Ser. c. Afhandlingar och uppsatser, n:o 28)

Aftryck ur Geologiska föreningens i Stockholm förhandlingar, band IV.

1. Geology—Sweden.   2. Geology, Stratigraphic—Paleozoic.
I. Title.
G S 7–1366 Revised

U. S. Geol. survey. Library
for Library of Congress   QE282.A3   ser. c, no. 28
[r42b2;†]

NL 0390369   DI-GS DLC

Linnarsson, Jonas Gustaf Oskar, 1841–1881.
... De undre paradoxideslagren vid Andrarum af G. Linnarsson ... Stockholm, Kongl. boktryckeriet, P. A. Norstedt & söner, 1882.

47, [5] p. IV pl. 30ᶜᵐ. (Sveriges geologiska undersökning. Ser. c. Afhandlingar och uppsatser, n:o 54)

1. Paradoxides.   2. Geology—Sweden—Andrarum.   I. Title.
G S 7–1390 Revised

U. S. Geol. survey. Library
for Library of Congress   QE282.A3   ser. c, no. 54
[r42b2;†]

NL 0390370   DI-GS DLC

Linnarsson, Linnar.
Bygd, by och gård, gammal bygd och folkkultur i Gäsene, Laske och Skånings härader. Uppsala, Lundequistska bok-handeln [1948–

v. illus., ports. 25 cm. (Skrifter utg. genom Landsmåls- och folkminnesarkivet i Uppsala, ser. B: 4)

Cover title, v. 1: By, bygd och gård i mellersta Västergötland.

1. Gäsene, Sweden—Civilization.   2. Laske, Sweden—Civilization.   3. Skåning, Sweden—Civilization.   I. Title.   (Series: Sweden. Landsmåls- och folkminnesarkivet i Uppsala. Skrifter, ser. B: 4)

DL971.V4L48
50–33176

NL 0390371   DLC CtY ICU MnU NN

DL991
.E27L5

Linnarsson, Linnar.
Edsveden; en häradsallmännings historia. Skara, Bergers bokhandel [1954]

237 p. illus., fold. maps. 23 cm.

Bibliography: p. [233]–[235]

1. Edsmåren, Sweden.
A 55–4973

Minnesota. Univ. Libr.   ~~DLC~~
for Library of Congress   [2]

NL 0390372   MnU DLC-P4 NN

Linnarsson, Linnar.
Gräfsnäs; ett västgötagods och dess öden. Skara, Bergers bokhandel, i distribution [1955]

158 p. illus. 23 cm.

Includes bibliography.

1. Västergötland, Sweden. Gräfsnäs.
DL991.G7L5
56–32396 ‡

NL 0390373   DLC MnU

NK5161
L75

Linnarsson, Linnar, 1884–
Högkomster från glasbruket i Fåglavik, upptecknade av Linnar Linnarsson. Stockholm, Nordisk Rotogravyr [1943] 157 p. 22 cm.

Corning
Museum
Glass
Library

866.   1. Fåglaviks glasbruk.

NL 0390374   NCorniC MnU

Linnarsson, Linnar.
Mäster Hults Värmlandshistorier; minnen och äventyr från västra Värmland. Stockholm, Wahlström & Widstrand [1952]

183 p. 22cm.

NL 0390375   MnU OrP

VOLUME 334

Linnarsson, Linnar.
...Så berättar gamlefar; sägner och folkminnen från gamla västgötabygder. Uppsala: J. A. Lindblad [1938] 216 p. 21½cm.

3081B. 1. Folk lore—Sweden. I. Title.
N.Y.P.
August 24, 1939

NL 0390376 NN

Linnarsson, Lennart.
Riksrådens licentiering, en studie i frihetstidens parlamentarism. Uppsala, Almquist & Wiksell [1943]
xxvi, 360 p. table. 23 cm. (Skrifter utg. av Statsvetenskapliga föreningen i Uppsala, 16)
Adademisk avhandling—Uppsala.
Extra t. p., with thesis statement, inserted.
Bibliography: p. [xiv]–xxvi.

1. Sweden. Riksrådet. I. Title. (Series: Statsvetenskapliga föreningen i Uppsala. Skrifter, 16)
JN7913.L5
55–47621

NL 0390377 DLC MnU CtY NN CU NIC PU ICU MH

Linnarsson, Nils Josef, 1833–
De illo codicis sacri libro qui koheleth inscribitur quaestiones.
Inaug. diss. Upsala, 1860.

NL 0390378 ICRL

Linnarsson, Nils Josef, 1833–
Thomas Aquino såsom moralteolog ... af N. J. Linnarsson ... Upsala, Edquist & Berglund, 1866.
1 p. l., 110 p., 1 l. 25ᶜᵐ.
Akademisk afhandling—Uppsala.
Published also as Upsala universitets årsskrift 1867. Theologi. 1.
Bibliography: p. [111]

1. Thomas Aquinas, Saint, 1225?–1274.
36–31911
Library of Congress B765.T54L5 1866
[2]
189.4

NL 0390379 DLC IEG MH-AH

Linnartz, Carl Josef.
Das Fachzeichnen des Uhrmachers. Ein Leitfaden für den Zeichenunterricht an Fortbildungsschulen sowie zum Selbstunterricht. Von C. Joseph Linnartz, ... Nach eigenen Erfahrungen zusammengestellt. Zweite, verbesserte Auflage. Halle, (Saale), W. Knapp, 1914.
vi, [80] p. incl. diagrs. 22½ᶜᵐ.

NL 0390380 ICJ PLH

Linnartz, Carl Josef.
Das Fachzeichnen des Uhrmachers; ein Leitfaden für den Zeichenunterricht an Fortbildungsschulen sowie zum Selbstunterricht, nach eigenen Erfahrungen zusammengestellt, von C. Jos. Linnartz... Halle (Saale): W. Knapp, 1929. 93 p. incl. diagrs., tables. 5. ed., rev. 8°.

459816A. 1. Clocks and watches— Construction, 1929.
N.Y.P.L. March 18, 1930

NL 0390381 NN

Linnartz, Carl Josef.
Das Fachzeichnen des Uhrmachers, ein Leitfaden für den Zeichenunterricht an Fortbildungsschulen, sowie zum Selbstunterricht. Nach eigenen Erfahrungen zusammengestellt. Neubearb. von O. Böckle und H. Linfert. 10.–11. Aufl. Halle (Saale) W. Knapp [1949]
iv, 100 p. diagrs. 21 cm.

1. Clock and watch making. 2. Mechanical drawing. I. Title.
TS548.L5 1949
51–23087

NL 0390382 DLC PPF

[Linnartz, Frans Jozef] 1907–
Christoffel Columbus, de laatste kruisvaarder [door] Gabriël Gorris [pseud.] 's-Gravenhage, Uitg. Pax, 1946.
299 p. geneal. table. 26 cm.
Bibliography: p. 298–299.

1. Colombo, Cristoforo.
E111.L768
50–23691

NL 0390383 DLC NN

Linnartz, Frans Jozef, 1907–
Dorp aan de Vliet, geschiedenis van Voorburg. Samengesteld door Gabriël Gorris [pseud.] H. Hardenberg [en] N. J. Pabon, met medewerking van D. van der Meide. Scheveningen [Drukkerij Van Leeuwen] 1953.
312 p. plates, ports., maps. 27 cm.
Bibliography: p. 290–296.

1. Voorburg, Netherlands—Hist. I. Title.
DJ411.V66L5
54–42642

NL 0390384 DLC NNC NN

[Linnartz, Frans Jozef] 1907–
Kroniek van den Pappelhof; de geschiedenis van een oud Limburgsch boerengeslacht [door] Gabriël Gorris [pseud.] 's Gravenhage, Pax, 1947.
490 p. 21 cm.
Fiction.

I. Title.
A 48–8973*
Harvard Univ. Library
for Library of Congress [1]

NL 0390385 MH NN

Linnartz, Frans Jozef, 1907–
Muziek van den schemer [door] Gabriël Gorris [pseud.] 's-Gravenhage, Pax, 1946.
46 p. 20 cm.
Poems.

I. Title.
PT5854.L63M8
55–39972 ‡

NL 0390386 DLC NN

[Linnartz, Frans Jozef] 1907–
Oorlogsnovellen [door] Gabriël Goris [pseud.] Met illustraties van Frans Hamer. 's-Gravenhage, Pax, 1945.
100 p. illus. 20 cm.
CONTENTS.—De "blunder."—Mark.—Episode.

1. World War, 1939–1945—Fiction. I. Title.
PT5854.L63O6
A F 48–3877 rev*
California. Univ. Libr.
for Library of Congress [r48b1]†

NL 0390387 CU NN DLC MnU

PT5854
L63P3
Linnartz, Frans Jozef, 1907–
Palabroea, de witte uil van Hato [door] Gabriël Gorris. Tilburg, Nederland's Boekhuis [1947]
77 p. front. (De zonnewijzer)

NL 0390388 CU

[Linnartz, Frans Jozef] 1907–
Petrus, prins der apostelen [door] Gabriël Gorris [pseud.] Met illustraties van Frans Hamer. 's-Gravenhage, Uitgeverij Pax, 1946.
274 p. illus. 26 cm.

1. Peter, Saint, Apostle.
BS2515.L53 [922.1] 225.92
50–15655

NL 0390389 DLC

Linnartz, Frans Jozef, 1907–
Vioolconcert, door Gabriël Gorris [pseud.] 's-Gravenhage, Het Thijmfonds [1950]
288 p. 20 cm.

I. Title.
A 54–588
Harvard Univ. Library
for Library of Congress [1]

NL 0390390 MH NN

CS2375
.G3W3
1942
Linnartz, Kaspar, ed.
Wasserzieher, Ernst, 1860–1927.
Hans und Grete; zweitausend Vornamen erklärt. 11., verb. Aufl., besorgt von K. Linnartz. Bonn, F. Dümmler, 1942.

PT1848
.Z8L75
LINNARTZ, KASPAR
Studien zur sprache der Annette von Droste-Hülshoff... Berlin [1903]
54 p. 22cm.
Inaug.-diss.—Tübingen.
Lebenslauf.

1. Droste-Hülshoff, Annette Elizabeth, freiin von, 1797–1848.

NL 0390392 ICU MH

PT
1848
Z5A6
Linnartz, Kaspar
Studien zur sprache der Annette von Droste-Hülshoff, von dr. Phil. Kaspar Linnartz... Köln, Druck von F. Elsner [1903]
53 p.

Also pub. as the author's inaug.-diss.-Tübingen.

1. Droste-Hülshoff, Annette Elisabeth, freiin von, 1797–1848.

NL 0390393 CLU

Linnartz, Kaspar.
Unsere familiennamen; zehntausend berufsnamen im abc erklärt, von dr. K. Linnartz. Berlin und Bonn, F. Dümmler, 1936.
169 p. 21ᶜᵐ.
"Hilfsmittel": p. [15]–16.

1. Names, Personal—German. 2. German language—Etymology—Names. I. Title.
37–6093
Library of Congress CS2545.L5
[2]
929.4

NL 0390394 DLC NcD CU OCU OO WU

VOLUME 334

Linnartz, Kaspar.
Unsere familiennamen; aus deutschen und fremden vornamen im abc erklärt, von dr. K. Linnartz. Bonn und Berlin, F. Dümmler, 1939.
xxii (i. e. xxiii), [1], 140, 145 p. 20ᶜᵐ.

"Dieses werk bildet den anschlussband zu: Unsere familiennamen: zehntausend berufsnamen im abc erklärt."

1. Names, Personal — German. 2. German language — Etymology — Names. I. Title.

                         41–2551
Library of Congress   CS2545.L52
           [2]   929.4

NL 0390395   DLC NN WU OOxM

929.4
L649u
1944

LINNARTZ, KASPAR
Unsere familiennamen; aus deutschen und fremden vornamen im abc erklärt, von dr. K. Linnartz. 2. aufl. Bonn und Berlin, F. Dümmler, 1944.
xxiii, [1], 140, 145p. 20cm.

"Dieses werk bildet den anschlussband zu: Unsere familiennamen: zehntausend berufsnamen im abc erklärt."

1. Names, Personal - German. 2. German language - Etymology - Names. I. Title.

NL 0390396   TxU MH DLC

Linnartz, Max
Ein fall von sirenenbildung. Inaug. diss. Wuerzburg, 1898. Bibl.

NL 0390397   ICRL DNLM

Linnartz, Peter.
Betriebsraetegesetz und Theate....von Peter Linnartz... Düren-Rhld: A. Dietrich, 1926. 62 p. 8°.

Dissertation, Erlangen.
Bibliography, p. [59]–[62].

1. Employee representation — Jurisp. — Germany. 2. Stage — Jurisp. — Germany.
N.Y.P.L.   February 17, 1928

NL 0390398   NN NIC PU ICRL CtY

Linnarz, Robert.
Kaisergeburtstagslied. [Ausgabe für gemischten Chor und für 3 stimmigen Kinderchor.] Op. 33. Wittenberg. Herrosé. [188–?] 3, (2) pp. L. 8°.

E.3395 — T.r. — Part songs.

NL 0390399   MB

4PH
Est.
246

Linnasaar, M
Lembitu sündimine. Tallinn, K/Ü. 'Kool', 1921.
108 p.

NL 0390400   DLC-P4 CtY

Linnavuori, Jaako Aleksanteri, 1892–
... Bestimmung des spezifischen gewichtes und der spezifischen wärme von antimon-blei-legierungen, von J. A. Linnavuori ... [Helsingfors, 1922]
13 p. incl. tables, diagrs. 24ᶜᵐ. (Societas scientiarum fennica. Commentationes physico-mathematicae. I, 10)

Caption title.
"Mitteilungen aus dem physikalischen laboratorium der Universität Helsingfors. n:o 40."

1. Alloys. 2. Specific heat. 3. Specific gravity.

                      A C 33–1026
Title from John Crerar   Libr.
Library of Congress   [Q60.F555 vol. 1, no. 10]

NL 0390401   ICJ PPAmP NcU ViU

QL1
S86
v.14
no.6

Linnavuori, Rauno
Studies on the ecology and phenology of the leafhoppers (Homoptera) of Raisio (S. W. Finland). Helsinki, 1952.
[2], 32 p. diagrs., tables. 25 cm. (Suomalainen Eläin- ja Kasvitieteellinen Seura; Vanamo. Eläintieteellisiä julkaisuja, Osa 14, N:o 6)
Finnish summary.
Bibliography: p. 31.

1. Leaf-hoppers.   (Series)

NL 0390402   DI

1894–

Linnbach, Horst, Zahnarzt: Ueber die Aetiologie der Prognathie. [In Handschrift] 63 S. 4° [Lag nicht vor.] — Auszug: (Leipzig 1921: Sturm & Koppe). 12 S. 8° Leipzig, Med. Diss. v. 1. März 1921, Ref. Pfaff
[Geb. 18. Juni 94 Chemnitz; Wohnort: Leipzig; Staatsangeh.: Sachsen; Vorbildung: G. Chemnitz Reife 14; Studium: Theol. Marburg 1, Zahnheilk. Leipzig 7 S.; Coll. 1. März 21; Zahnärztl. Approb. 4. Nov. 20.]   [U 21. 4801

NL 0390403   ICRL DNLM

Linné, André.
... Les champs secrets (épisodes de la résistance en France) New York, N. Y., Éditions de la Maison française, inc., °1943
4 p. l., [11]–246 p. 19ᶜᵐ.
At head of title: André Linné et Edmond Nessler.
Dialogue.

1. World war, 1939– —Drama. I. Nessler, Edmond, joint author. II. Title.
                        43–18978
Library of Congress   PQ2623.I 62C5
           [3]   842.91

NL 0390404   DLC NNU-W NIC OC1 OCU CU OU CtY CaBVaU

Linné, André.
... Les champs secrets (épisodes de la résistance en France) Paris, A. Fayard [1945]
4 p. l., [11]–254 p. 19ᶜᵐ.
At head of title: André Linné et Edmond Nessler.
Dialogue.

1. World war, 1939–1945—Drama. I. Nessler, Edmond, joint author. II. Title.
PQ2623.I 62C5 1945   842.91   47–17745

NL 0390405   DLC NN

Linné, André.
Le retour des insolents; roman [par] André Linné [et] Pierre Bonaventure. [Monte-Carlo, R. Solar [1948]
266 p. 22 cm.

I. Bonaventure, Pierre, joint author. II. Title.

PQ2623.I 62R4   50–25130

NL 0390406   DLC IU

VH
1797

Linne, Bruno, 1881–
Hydrolyse von Bi-, Tri- und Polysacchariden. Basel, 1905.
41 p.

Inaug. diss. - Basel.

NL 0390407   CtY ICRL MH PU MiU

Linné, Carl von, 1707–1778.
Caroli Linnaei Opera. Editio prima critica, plena, ad editiones veras exacta, textum nullo rei detrimento contractum locosque editionum discrepantes exhibens. Vol. 2., Systema vegetabilium; libros diagnostico-botanicos continens. Lipsiae, sumptum fecit O. Wigand, 1835 [i. e. 1835–40]
xxxii, 1102, iv, 202 p. 29 cm.

Issued in parts; no more published.
Special t. p.: Caroli Linnaei Systema, Genera, Species plantarum uno volumine ... In usum botanicorum practicum edidit brevique adnotatione explicavit Herrmannus Eberhardus Richter.

Index, by Wilhelm Ludwig Petermann: 202 p. at end.
L. C. copy imperfect: p. i–iv of the Index wanting.
"Enumeratio autorum in textu Linnaeno citatorum": p. [1089]–1100.

1. Botany—Classification. I. Richter, Hermann Eberhard Friedrich, 1808–1876, ed. II. Petermann, Wilhelm Ludwig, 1806–1855. III. Title: Systema, Genera, Species plantarum uno volumine.

QK91.A1 1835   5–42034 rev

NL 0390409   DLC NNBG OkU

Linné, Carl von, 1707–1778.
Skrifter af Carl von Linné. Utgifna af Kungl. svenska vetenskapsakademien ... Upsala, Almqvist & Wiksells boktryckeri-a.-b., 1905–
v. illus., plates (part fold.) fold. maps. 25ᵗ ᶜᵐ.

1. Natural history. 2. Botany. 3. Botany—Lapland. I. K. Svenska vetenskapsakademien, Stockholm.

                        26–3320
Library of Congress   QH43.A3 1905

ICJ
NL 0390410   DLC CtY KMK WaU MH PPL CtY ICRL MH-A

Linné, Carl von, 1707–1778.
Åkerbärs plantering, ingifven af Carl Linnæus ...
([In K. Svenska vetenskapsakademien. Handlingar. 1762. 20ᶜᵐ. v. 23, p. 192–197)

1. Rubus.
Library of Congress   Q64.S8   30–18834

NL 0390411   DLC KMK

QL
666
O6
L56

Linné, Carl von, 1707-1778.
Äsping. [Stockholm, 1749]
246-251 p. illus.
In Stockholm. Kungliga Svenska Vetenskaps-Akademien. Handlingar. v. 10. 1749.

SERPENTS
t

NL 0390412   KMK

[Linné, Carl von] 1707–1778.
Abhandlung von naturalien-cabinetten, oder Anleitung wie naturalien-cabinette eingerichtet, die natürlichen körper gesammlet, aufgehoben und conserviret werden müssen. Aus dem lateinischen übersetzt, und mit anmerkungen, hrsg. von C. v. M. Leipzig, 1771.
72 p. 17 cm.
Translation of Instructio musaei rerum naturalium, issued in Vol. 3 of the Amoeniates academicae of Linnaeus.
Interleaved

Continued in next column

VOLUME 334

Continued from preceding column

1. Natural history – 1735–1800.   I. Title: Abhandlung von naturalien cabinetten. II. Meidinger, Carl von, tr.

NL 0390414   CU

QL
708
L758a
1802

Linné, Carl von, 1707–1778
Abregé du Système de la nature, de Linné, histoire des mammaires ou des quadrupedes et cétacées. Contenant, 1.° la traduction libre du texte de Linné et de Gmelin; 2.° l'extrait des observations de Buffon, Brisson, Pallas, et autres célèbres zoologistes; 3.° l'anatomie comparée des principales espèces: le tout relatif aux quadrupèdes et aux cétacées les plus curieux et les plus utiles, par J. E. Gilibert. Lyon, Matheron, 1802.

xiv, 576 p. illus., port.

Imperfect copy: preliminary pages not in sequence; several plates lacking.

I. Gmelin, Johann Friedrich, 1748–1804. II. Gilibert, Jean Emmanuel, 1741–1814, ed.

NL 0390416   DNLM PPAN KMK WU

Linné, Carl von, 1707–1778.
Abrégé du Système de la nature, de Linné, histoire des mammaires ou des quadrupèdes et cétacées. Contenant, 1.° la traduction libre du texte de Linné et de Gmelin; 2.° l'extrait des observations de Buffon, Brisson, Pallas, et autres célèbres zoologistes; 3.° l'anatomie comparée des principales espèces: le tout relatif aux quadrupèdes et aux cétacées les plus curieux et les plus utiles. Par m. J. E. Gilibert ... Lyon, Chez l'éditeur, 1805.
xiv, 497 p. 28 pl. 22ᶜᵐ.
1. Mammals—Classification. I. Gmelin, Johann Friedrich, 1748–1804. II. Buffon, Georges Louis Leclerc, comte de, 1707–1788. III. Brisson, Mathurin Jacques, 1723–1806. IV. Pallas, Peter Simon, 1741–1811. V. Gilibert, Jean Emmanuel, 1741–1814, ed.

Library of Congress   QL708.L65   31–337
                                  [2]   599

NL 0390417   DLC CLU-M KMK CU MiU PPWa

Linné, Carl von, 1707–1778.
Ad memoriam primi sui praesidis eiusdemque e conditoribus suis unius Caroli Linnaei opus illud quo primum Systema naturae....
    see his   ...Systema naturae sive Regna tria naturae...

Linné, Carl von, 1707–1778.
Caroli Linnæi Adonis stenbrohultensis, utgiven av Felix Bryk. Stockholm, Björck & Börjesson, 1920.
13 p., 3 l., [28] p. incl. front. pl. 18ᶜᵐ.
Three leaves, 28 pages are facsimile of manuscript work, with special t-p.: Caroli Linnæi ... Adonis stenbrohultensis, [!] sive Enumeratio plantarum quas in Horto suo stenbrohultensi intulit venerandus parens clariss. d⁰⁰⁰ Nicolaus Linnaeus ... secundum methodum propriam in Adonide uplandica traditam recensio stirpium facta est. Stenbroh., 1732.
1. Botany. I. Bryk, Felix, ed. II. Linnaeus, Nils Ingemarsson, 1674–1748. III. Title: Adonis stenbrohultensis.

                                              Agr 20–1983
Library, U. S. Dept. of   Agriculture 452.2L64

NL 0390419   DNAL MiU

Linné, Carl von, 1707–1778, praeses.
   ... Aer habitabilis ... Upsaliæ [1759]
25, [1] p. 21½ x 17½ᶜᵐ (p. 17 to end 17½ x 15½ᶜᵐ)
Library of Congress collection: Dissertationes academicae (Linné) no. 106.
Diss.—Upsala (J. V. Sievert, respondent)
Also in Linné's Amoenitates academicae, v. 5, ed. 1, 1760; ed. 2, 1788, p. 442–460.

1. Air. 2. Climatology, Medical. I. Sievert, Johan Victor, respondent.

                                              30–16755
Library of Congress   QH43.A2 no. 106

NL 0390420   DLC MiU WU

Linné, Carl von, 1707–1778, praeses.
   ... Ambrosiaca ... Upsaliæ [1759]
14 p. 19½ᶜᵐ.
Library of Congress collection: Dissertationes academicae (Linné) no. 100.
Diss.—Upsala (J. Hideen, respondent)
Also in Linné's Amoenitates academicae, v. 9, 1785, p. 106–117.

1. Amber. I. Hideen, Jacob, respondent.

Library of Congress   QH43.A2 no. 100   30–16751
——— Copy 2.   21 x 17ᶜᵐ.
                                  [2]

NL 0390421   DLC MiU WU DSI

Linné, Carl von, 1707–1778.
*Ambrosiaca. Upsaliae, 1759.
8°.
In: Linnaeus. Amoenitates acad. [etc.]
8°. Erlangae, 1785, ix, 106–117.

NL 0390422   DNLM

Linné, Carl von, 1707–1778.
   ... Amoenitates academicae, seu dissertationes variae physicae, medicae, botanicae ... v. 1. Lugduni Batavorum, apud Cornelium Haak, 1749.
1 v.   15 pls. (part fold.) 20 cm.

Edited by Petrus Camper and dedicated to Petro Collinson. Published independently before the first edition of Linnaeus. No more publ.

NL 0390423   PPAN KMK WU NNBG NcD-MC

Linné, Carl von, 1707–1778.

Caroli Linnæi ... Amoenitates academicae, seu Dissertationes variæ physicæ, medicæ, botanicæ, antehac seorsim editæ nunc collectæ et auctæ. Cum tabulis Æneis. [Vignette] Holmiæ et Lipsiæ, apud Godofredum Kiesewetter, 1749–1790.
10 v. plates (part fold.) 20ᶜᵐ.
Imprints vary.—cf. Bibl. nat., v. 98, cols. 612–626, no. 52.
Vol. 1 imperfect: p. 555– wanting.
Vols. 7–10 edited by Johann Christian Daniel Schreber.
1. Natural history. I. Schreber, Johann Christian Daniel, 1739–1810, ed.

        MdBP
NL 0390424   ViU KMK PPAN TNJ PPC PU NN CtY-MHi NNBG

RARE BOOKS

Linné, Carl von, 1707–1778
   Amoenitates academicæ; seu, Dissertationes variæ physicæ, medicæ, botanicæ antehac seorsim editæ nunc collectæ et auctæ cum tabulis aenis. Holmiæ et Lipsiæ, 1749–69.
7 v.

   Vol. 1 is ed. [2?] Holmiæ et Lipsiæ, 1749 [LIN 1282]

   Vol. 2 is ed. 2., revisa & aucta. Holmiæ, 1762 [LIN 1287]

   Vol. 3 is ed. [2?] Holmiæ, 1764 [LIN 1293]

   Vol. 4 is ed. [1.a.] Holmiæ. 1759 [LIN 1296]—cf. Hulth. Bibl. Linnaeana.

NL 0390426   WU CU

Linné, Carl von, 1707–1778.

Caroli Linnæi ... Amoenitates academicae; seu, Dissertationes variæ physicæ, medicæ, botanicæ antehac seorsim editæ nunc collectæ et auctæ ... Accedit Hypothesis nova de febrium intermittentium causa ... Lugduni Batavorum, apud Cornelium Haak, 1749–90.
10 v. 57 fold. pl., fold. tab. 21ᶜᵐ.
Vol. 2. Holmiæ, apud Laurentium Salvium, 1751; v. 3–7. Holmiæ, sumtu & literis L. Salvii, 1752–69; v. 8–9. Ed. Jo. Christianus Daniel Schrebervs. Erlangæ, sumtu Jo. Jacobi Palm, 1785; v. 10. Accedunt Caroli a Linné filii dissertationes botanicae collectae, curante Io. C. D. Schrebero. Erlangæ, I. Iacobi Palm, 1790.
1. Natural history—Collected works. I. Schreber, Johann Christian Daniel, 1739–1810, ed. II. Linné, Carl von, 1741–1783.

                                              5—40709
Library of Congress   QH9.L7

NL 0390427   DLC DSI MdBP PPL IU CSt DNLM PPAN ICJ

Linné, Carl von, 1707–1778.
Caroli Linnæi ... Amoenitates academicae, seu Dissertationes variæ physicæ, medicæ, botanicæ, antehac seorsim editæ nunc collectæ et auctæ cum tabulis æneis, accedit Hypothesis nova de febrium intermittentium causa. Lugduni Batavorum, C. Haak, 1749–69.
7 v. plates (partly fold.) fold. tables. 20½ᶜᵐ.
Vol. 2, 5–6 pub. by Wetstenium.
Imprint of v. 3–4, 7: Holmiæ, sumtu & literis direct. L. Salvii.
Vol. 2 is 2d ed.
1. Botany.
                                              Agr 5–786

Library, U. S. Dept. of   Agriculture 452L645A.

NL 0390428   DNAL KMK CSt MH-A KyBgW InU NNBG MA

LINNÉ, Carl von.
   [Amoenitates academicae. Vol. 2–8.] Upsalia etc., 1749–1776.

   Illustr.

NL 0390429   MH-Z

QK91
.A5
1749a

Linné, Carl von, 1707–1778.
   Amoenitates academicae, seu dissertationes variae physicae, medicae, botanicae antehac seorsim editae nunc collectae et auctae cum tabulis aeneis. Lugduni Batavorum, Apud Wetstenium, 1752–69.
   6 v. (v. 2–7) plates. 21 cm.
   Editio secunda revisa & aucta.
   5425 Pritzel. 1286, 1292, 1297, 1301, 1305, 1309 B. M.
   For contents of the various editions see Hulth, p. 66–71.
   1. Natural history – Collected works. 2. Botany – Collected works. i. t.

NL 0390430   NNBG

Linné, Carl von, 1707–1778.
   Amoenitates academicae; seu, Dissertationes variae physicae, medicae, botanicae antehac seorsim editae nunc collectae et auctae ... Holmiae, Sumtu & Literis L. Salvii, 1756.
   Microfilm copy (negative) of original in the Library of the U. S. Dept. of Agriculture, Washington, D. C.
   Collation of the original as determined from the film: v. 3, plates, tables.

NL 0390431   IU

QH
9
L7
1787

Linné, Carl von, 1707–1778.
   ... Amoenitates academicae seu Dissertationes variae physicae, medicae, botanicae antehac seorsim editae nunc collectae et auctae cum tabulis aeneis ... Editio tertia curante D. Jo. Christiano Daniele Schrebero... Erlangae, sumtu Jo. Jacobi Palm, 1759–
   10v. plates (part fold.) 21 1/2cm.

   At head of title: Caroli a Linné.
   This is a made-up set, lacking vols. 7–10.

   Vols. 1–2 are 3d ed., 1787; vols. 3 & 6, 2d ed., 1787–89; vols. 4–5, Holmiae, Sumtu & literis direct. Laurentii Salvii, 1759–60.
   Some plates are either wanting, or misbound, in this rebound set.

   1. Natural history. I. Schreber, Johann Christian Daniel, 1739–1810, ed. II. Title.

NL 0390433   MU

VOLUME 334

Linné, Carl von, 1707–1778.
Caroli a Linné ... Amoenitates aca'demicae; seu, Dissertationes variae physicae, medicae, botanicae antehac seorsim editae nunc collectae et auctae cum tabulis aeneis ... Editio tertia curante d. Jo. Christiano Daniele Schrebero ... Erlangae, sumtu J. J. Palm, 1785–90.
10 v. in 9. plates. 20½ⁿᵈ.
Vols. 1–2 are 3d edition, 1787; v. 3–7, 2d edition, 1787–89; v. 8–10, 1st edition, 1785–90.
The Erlangen edition is reprinted with identical pagination from earlier editions: v. 1–2, from Stockholm edition, 1749–51; v. 3–7, identically paged in all editions.

Vol. 10 is in 2 parts with separate pagination, the 2d consisting of dissertations and papers of Linné the younger.
"Editionis operum auctoris, quae ad manus nostras pervenire": at end of v. 7.

1. Natural history. I. Linné, Carl von, 1741–1783. II. Schreber, Johann Christian Daniel, 1739–1810, ed.
Agr 11—892

U. S. Dept. of agr. Library   452.4L64
for Library of Congress   ₍a40e1₎

OO DLC MB PPC MNS
NL 0390435   DNAL PP WU NNBG CtY CoU CU KMK NIC MiU

Mif   Linné, Carl von, 1707–1778.
43   Caroli a Linné. Amoenitates academicae;
seu, Dissertationes variae physicae, medicae,
botanicae antehac seorsim editae nunc collectae
et auctae cum tabulis aeneis. Editio tertia
curante d. Jo. Christiano Daniele Schrebero.
Erlangae, J.J. Palm, 1785–90.
10v. in 9. plates.

Vols. 1–2 are 3rd edition, 1787; v.3–7,
2nd edition, 1787–89; v.8–10, 1st edition,

1785–90.
The Erlangen edition is reprinted with
identical pagination from earlier editions:
v.1–2, from Stockholm edition, 1749–51;
v.3–7, identically paged in all editions.
Vol. 10 is in 2 parts with separate pagination, the 2d consisting of dissertations
and papers of Linné the younger.

"Editionis operum auctoris, quae ad manus
nostras pervenire": at end of v.7.
Microfiche. Wumba, Sweden, International
Documentation Centre AB, n.d. 2 boxes.
81 cards.

1. Natural history. I. Linné, Carl von,
1741–1783. II. Schreber, Johann Christian
Daniel, 1739-   1810, ed. x: Linné,
Caroli a

NL 0390438   FTaSU

Linne, Carl. Amoenitates academicae seu dissertationes ... Coloniae-Allobrogum, Piestre, 1786. 2 v.   YA 1420

NL 0390439   DLC

Linné, Carl von, 1707–1778, *praeses.*
... Amphibia Gyllenborgiana ... Upsaliæ ₍1745₎
4 p. l., 34, ₍2₎ p. 19 x 15ᶜᵐ.
Library of Congress collection: Dissertationes academicae (Linné) no. 5.
Diss.—Uppsala (B. R. Hast, respondent)
"A detailed description of 24 species of animals ... presented by Count Gyllenborg to the University of Upsala."—Pulteney.
Also in Linné's Amoenitates academicae, v. 1, ₍ed. 1₎ 1749, p. 520–555; ₍ed. 2₎ 1749, and ed. 3, 1787, p. 107–140. cf. Hulth, Bibl. Linn. (1907) p. 46.
1. Batrachia. 2. Reptiles. I. Gyllenborg, Carl, grefve, 1679–1746. II. Hast, Bartholomaeus Rudolphus, respondent. III. Title.
30–14772 Revised
Library of Congress   QH43.A2 no. 5

NL 0390440   DLC WU MiU

Linné, Carl von, 1707–1778.
Anecdotes of Linnæus
see under   Jardine, Sir William,
bart., 1800–1874.

Linné, Carl von, 1707–1778.
The animal kingdom; or, Zoological system of the celebrated Sir Charles Linnæus. Class I. Mammalia ₍and Class II. Birds₎, ... Being a translation of that part of the Systema naturæ, as lately published with great improvements, by Professor Gmelin, together with numerous additions from more recent zoological writers and illustrated with copperplates; by Robert Kerr. ₍Vol. 1₎ London, Printed for J. Murray, 1792.
644 p. illus. 28 cm.
No more published?
1. Mammals. 2. Birds.   I. Title.

QL605.I473   61–57549 ‡

NL 0390442   DLC ViU CtY-MHi CaBViP

Linné, Carl von, 1707–1778, *praeses.*
... Animalia composita ... Upsaliæ ₍1759₎
2 p. l., 9, ₍1₎ p. 21½ x 17¾ᵐ.
Library of Congress collection: Dissertationes academicae (Linné) no. 98.
Diss.—Uppsala (A. Bäck, respondent)
Also in Linné's Amoenitates academicae, v. 5, ed. 1, 1760; ed. 2, 1788, p. 343–352.

1. Coelenterata. 2. Polyzoa.   I. Bäck, Albert, respondent. II. Title.

Library of Congress   QH43.A2 no. 98   30–16749

NL 0390443   DLC PPAN DNLM WU MiU

Linné, Carl von, 1707–1778.
Caroli Linnæi ... Animalium specierum in classes, ordines, genera, species, methodica dispositio ... Lugduni Batavorum, apud Theodorum Haak, 1759.
2 p. l., 253, ₍3₎ p. 21ᵐ.

1. Zoology—Classification.

Library of Congress   QL352.L73   6–43108†

NL 0390444   DLC OU₍CU WU₍CtY PHC MH-A

QL   Linné, Carl von, 1707–1778.
795   Anmärkning öfver de diuren, som sägas kom-
R2   ma neder utur Skyarna i Norrige. ₍Stockholm,
L55   1743₎
320–325 p.
In Stockholm. Kungliga Svenska Vetenskaps-
Akademien. Handlingar. 1740. v. 1. Nyo
upplagde.

RATS--SWEDEN
t

NL 0390445   KMK

Linné, Carl von, 1707–1778.
... Anmärkning öfver jackashapuck.
(*In* K. Svenska vetenskapsakademien. Handlingar. 1743. 20ᵐ. v. 4, p. 292–295)

I. Title: Jackashapuck.
Library of Congress   Q64.88   30–18323

NL 0390446   DLC

Linné, Carl von, 1707–1778.
Anmärkningar öfver *Amaryllis* den sköna ...
(*In* K. Svenska vetenskapsakademien. Handlingar. 1742. 20ᵐ. v. 3, p. 93–102. fold. pl.)

1. Amaryllis.
Library of Congress   Q64.88   30–17907
——— Copy 2. de-   tached.
Library of Congress col-   lection: Botanical contributions ...
(Linné) no. 6.   QK3.L76 no. 6

NL 0390447   DLC KMK

TP   Linné, Carl von, 1707–1778.
599   Anmärkningar om brännwin. Westerås, P. De-
L5   vall ₍1747₎
p. ₍29–38₎
In Hiorter, O. P. Almanach för skott-åhret
... 1748.

BRANDY
t

NL 0390448   KMK

TP   Linné, Carl von, 1707–1778.
599   Anmärkningar om brännwin. Stockholm, H.
L5   Klemming ₍1747, reprinted 1922₎
1922   ₍16₎ p.

BRANDY
t

NL 0390449   KMK

TP   Linné, Carl von, 1707–1778.
577   Anmärkning om öl. ₍Stockholm, 1763₎
L55   52–59 p.
In Stockholm. Kungliga Svenska Vetenskaps-
Akademien. Handlingar för år 1763. v. 24.

BEER
t

NL 0390450   KMK

QL   Linné, Carl von, 1707–1778.
666   Anmärkning om ormarnas skilje-märken.
O6   ₍Stockholm, 1752₎
L55   206–207 p.
In Stockholm. Kungliga Svenska Vetenskaps-
Akademien. Handlingar. v. 13. 1752.

SERPENTS
t

NL 0390451   KMK

Linné, Carl von, 1707–1778.
... Anteckningar öfver Nemesis divina. Inbjudnings-skrift af Elias Fries. Upsala, 1848.
₍14₎ f. Folio.

NL 0390452   CtY

204
L646
Linné, Carl von, 1707–1778.
Carl von Linnés Anteckningar öfver nemesis divina. Utgifne af Elias Fries och Th. M. Fries. Ny, omarbetad och tillökad upplaga. Upsala, Lundequistska bokhandeln [1878]
[4], 72 p. 22½ᵐ.

NL 0390453   ICJ NNBG MnU CtY

VOLUME 334

Linné, Carl von, 1707–1778, *praeses.*
... Anthropomorpha ... Upsaliæ ₁1760₎

3 p. l., 16 p. iv fold. pl. 20 x 16ᶜᵐ.
Library of Congress collection : Dissertationes academicae (Linné)
no. 111.
Diss.—Upsala (C. E. Hopplus, respondent)
Also in Linné's Amoenitates academicae, v. 6, ed. 1, 1763; ed. 2,
1789, p. 63–76. For other reprints and translations *see* J. M. Hulth,
Bibliographia Linnaeana (1907) p. 120.

1. Apes.   i. Hopplus, Christian Emanuel, b. 1736, respondent.

Library of Congress   QH43.A2 no. 111   30–16759

NL 0390454   DLC WU

Linné, Carl von, 1707–1778, praeses.
Anthropomorpha. Upsaliae, 1760.
In: Linnaeus. Amoenitates acad. [etc.]
8°. Lugd. Bat., 1764, vi, 63–76, 1 pl.
        Christian Emanuel Hoppius, respondent.

NL 0390455   DNLM

Linne, Carl von, 1707–1778, praeses.
Anthropomorpha. Upsaliae, 1760.
In: Selectae ex ... Caroli Linnaei diss.
ad nat. hist. pertinentes. 4°. Graeciae, 1769.
iii, 131–145, 1 pl.
        Christian Emanuel Hoppius, respondent.

NL 0390456   DNLM

QK   Linné, Carl von, 1707–1778.
327   Anwisningar till svenska almänheten, genom
L75   Närings och Hushålds Tidningar, för medbor-
1772   gare på landet och i staden ... Uplagde på
        Lars Wennbergs egen bekostnad. Stockholm,
        Wennberg och Nordström, 1772.
        13 p.

        VEGETABLES
        BOTANY—SWEDEN
        Wennberg, Lars, ed.

NL 0390457   KMK

Linné, Carl von, 1707–1778, *praeses.*
... Arboretum-svecicum ... Upsaliæ ₁1759₎

30 p. 22ᶜᵐ.
Library of Congress collection : Dissertationes academicae (Linné)
no. 101.
Diss.—Upsala (D. D. Pontin, respondent)
Also in Linné's Amoenitates academicae, v. 5, ed. 1, 1760; ed. 2,
1788, p. 174–208. For other reprints and translation *see* J. M. Hulth,
Bibliographia Linnaeana (1907) p. 116.

1. Trees—Sweden.   i. Pontin, David D., 1733–1809, respondent.

Library of Congress   QH43.A2 no. 101   30–16752

NL 0390458   DLC NNBG WU MH-A MiU

Linné, Carl von, 1707–1778, *præses.*
... Arboretum svecicum, quod, præside d. d. Car. Linnæo,
proposuit David Davidis Pontin, Ostro-gothus. Vpsaliæ 1759.
junii 30.

(*In his* Amoenitates academicæ. Holmiæ, 1760. 21ᶜᵐ. vol. v, p. 174–
203)

1. Trees—Sweden.   i. Pontin, David, respondent.   ii. Title.

Library of Congress   QH43.A3   5—23492
———— Copy 2, de-   tached. QK327.L73

NL 0390459   DLC DNLM

Linne, Carl von, 1707–1778, praeses.
Arboretum suecicum. Upsaliae, 1759.
In: Selectae ex ... Caroli Linnaei diss. ad
nat. hist. pertinentes. 4°. Graecii, 1769, iii,
38–72.
        David Davidis Pontin, respondent.

NL 0390460   DNLM

Linné, Carl von, 1707–1778, *praeses.*
... Auctores botanici ... Upsaliæ ₁1759₎

1 p. l., 20 p. 20ᶜᵐ.
Diss.—Upsala (Augustinus Loo, respondent)

1. Botany—Bibliography.   i. Loo, Augustinus, respondent.

                                    Agr 26–1376
Library, U. S. Dept. of   Agriculture 452.4L64D

NL 0390461   DNAL NNBG DNLM WU MnU-B MiU DLC

QH   Linné, Carl von, 1707–1778.
43   Des ritters Carl von Linné, Auserlesene abhand-
.A93   lungen aus der naturgeschichte, physik und arz-
        neywissenschaft ... Leipzig, A.F. Böhme, 1776–
        1778.

        5 v. fold. plates. 20½ᶜᵐ.
        Illustrated title-pages.
        Edited by E.J.T. Hüpfner. cf. Paris. Bibliothèque natio-
        nale. Département des imprimés. Catalogue général.
        Essays selected from his Amoenitates academicae, first
        published 1749–69.
        1. Natural history—Addresses, essays, lectures.
I. Hüpfner, Ernst Justus   Theodor, 1749–1785, ed.
II. Title: Auserlesene   abhandlungen aus der natur-
geschichte physik und   arzneywissenschaft.

NL 0390462   MiU MH

Linné, Carl von, 1707–1778.
Auslandsreise
        see his Linnaeus auslandsreise.

Linné, Carl von, 1707–1778.
Ayenia, en sälsam blomma, beskrefven och ingifven af Carl
Linnæus.

(*In* K. Svenska vetenskapsakademien. Handlingar. 1756. 20ᶜᵐ.
v. 17, p. 23–26. fold. pl.)

1. Ayenia.

Library of Congress   Q64.88   30–18332
———— Copy 2, de-   tached.
Library of Congress col-   lection : Botanical contributions ...
(Linné) no. 19.   QK3.L76 no. 19

NL 0390464   DLC

Linné, Carl von, 1707–1778.
Archiaterns och riddarens af Kongl. Nordstjerne orden Carl
Linnæi, Berättelse om de inhemska wäxter, som i brist af säd
kunna anwändas til bröd- och matredning. Efter Hans Kongl.
Maj:ts allernådigste befallning til trycket befordrad af thess
Collegio medico. Stockholm, Kongl. tryckeriet, 1757.
₍8₎ p. 19¼ᶜᵐ.

1. Botany, Economic. 2. Botany—Sweden.

                                    27—8812
Library of Congress   SB108.S8L5

NL 0390465   DLC PPAmP MH-A

34   Linné, Carl von, 1707–1778.
        Berättelse om the inhemska wäxter, som i
        brist af säd kunna användas til bröd- och
        matredning. Efter Hans Kongl. Maj.ts
        allernådigste befallning til trycket beford-
        rad of thess Collegio Medico. Stockholm,
        Tryckt uti Kongl. Tryckeriet, 1757.
        8 p.

        Microfiche. Zug, Switzerland, Inter-Documen-
        tation Company. ₍196–₎ 10 x 14 cm. 1 box, 1 cd.
        548 B. M.   111 Krok.

NL 0390466   NNBG

Linné, Carl von, 1707–1778.
Beskrifning ofwer stenricket, utgifwen
af E.A.F. Benedicks. Upsala, Almqvist, 1907.
91 p.

NL 0390467   PU-B

Linné, Carl von, 1707–1778.
Beskrifning om öl. Stockholm, L. Salvius
[1748]
[8] p.
In Almanach för året ... 1749.
1. Beer.

NL 0390469   KMK

Linné, Carl von, 1707–1778.
Beskrifning på et Americanskt diur, som
Hans Konglige Höghet gifvit til undersökning.
[Stockholm, 1747]
277–289 p.
In Kungliga Svenska Vetenskaps-Akademien.
Handlingar. v. 8. 1747.
1. Bears.

NL 0390470   KMK

Linné, Carl von, 1707–1778.
Beskrifning på et slag ostindiska ärter, som äro tienlige uti
sten-passionen, ingifne af herr ammiral Ankarcrona, ock be-
skrefne af Carol. Linnæus.

(*In* K. Svenska vetenskapsakademien. Handlingar. 1742. 20ᶜᵐ.
v. 3, p. 202–206. fold. pl.)

1. Peas.

Library of Congress   Q64.88   30–18322
———— Copy 2, de-   tached.
Library of Congress col-   lection : Botanical contributions ...
(Linné) no. 9.   QK3.L76 no. 9

NL 0390471   DLC

Linné, Carl von, 1707–1778.
Beskrifning på sältings-gräset, ingifwen af C. Linnaeus ...

(*In* K. Svenska vetenskapsakademien. Handlingar. 1742. 20ᶜᵐ.
v. 3, p. 146–151. fold. pl.)

1. Triglochin.

Library of Congress   Q64.88   30–17906
———— Copy 2, de-   tached.
Library of Congress col-   lection : Botanical contributions ...
(Linné) no. 7.   QK3.L76 no. 7

NL 0390472   DLC

Linné, Carl von, 1707–1778.
Beskrifning på sno-sparfwen. [Stockholm,
1743]
362–368 p.
In Kungliga Svenska Vetenskaps-Akademien.
Handlingar ... 1740. v. 1. Nyo uplagde.
1. Snow Birds. 2. Sparrows.

NL 0390473   KMK

VOLUME 334

Linné, Carl von, 1707-1778.
Beskrifningar af detta hedegräset hafva botanici
gifvit ... [Stockholm, 1744]
179-180 p.
In Kungliga Svenska Vetenskaps-Akademien.
Handlingar. v. 5. 1744.
1. Grasses.

NL 0390474   KMK

Linné, Carl von, 1707-1778, praeses.
Betula nana; proposuit L. M. Klase.   Upsaliae,
1743.
Plate.
From his "Amoenitates academicae," 1787,
i, 1-22.
Lars Magnus Klase, respondent.

NL 0390475   MH-A

Linné, Carl von, 1707-1778.
Carl von Linnés betydelse såsom naturforskare
och läkare
see under   Svenska vetenskapsakademien,
Stockholm.

Linné, Carl von, 1707-1778.
Caroli Linnaei ... Bibliotheca botanica recensens libros
plus mille de plantis hucusque editos, secundum systema
auctorum naturale in classes, ordines, genera & species
dispositos, additis editionis loco, tempore, forma, lingua
&c. cum explicatione Fundamentorum botanicorum pars
1ma. Amstelodami, apud S. Schouten, 1736.
8 p. l., 153, [13] p., 1 l., [4], 35, [1] p. 14cm.

1. Botany. Bibl.

Agr 11-893

Library, U. S. Dept. of   Agriculture 241.75L645B

NL 0390477   PPL PPAmP ICJ OO CSmH DDO MH-A NIC
     DNAL KyBgW MnU WaU WU OkU NN CtY PBL PPC

**Microfiche
35**
Linné, Carl von, 1707-1778.
Bibliotheca botanica, recensens libros plus
mille de plantis huc usque editos, secundum
systema auctorum naturale in classes, ordines,
genera & species dispositos, additis editionis
loco, tempore, forma, lingua &c. cum explicatione Fundamentorum botanicorum pars 1ma.
Amstelodami, Apud S. Schouten, 1736.
[16], 153, [16]; [4] 35, [1] p.

Microfiche. Tumba, Sweden, International
Documentation Centre [196-] 1 box, 4 cards.
10 x 14 cm.

5406, 5405 Pritzel. 250, 253 B. M. 147,
135 Krok.

1. Botany - Bibl. 2. Botany - Pre-Linnean
works - Bibl. i. Linné, Carl von, 1707-1778.
Fundamenta botanica. ii.t. iii.t: Fundamenta
botanica.

NL 0390479   NNBG

Linné, Carl von, 1707-1778.
Caroli Linnaei ... Bibliotheca botanica recensens libros plus
mille de plantis huc usque editos; secundum systema auctorum
naturale in classes, ordines, genera & species dispositos, additis
editionis loco, tempore, forma, lingua caet. cum explicatione
Fundamentorum botanicorum pars 1. Editio nova multo correctior. Halae Salicae, apud I. G. Bierwirth, 1747.
7 p. l., 124, [8] p. 20½cm. [With his Philosophia botanica. Stockholmiae, 1751]

Dept. of agriculture copy lacks the Fundamenta botanica (78 p.)

1. Botany—Bibliography.

U. S. Dept. of agr. Library   452L645P   Agr 11-894
for Library of Congress   [Z5352.L   ]

**NN
NL 0390480**   DNAL FTaSU PSt MnU WU NNBG MiU MH-A OO

Linné, Carl von, 1707-1778.
Caroli Linnaei ... Bibliotheca botanica recensens libros
plus mille de plantis huc usque editos, secundum systema
auctorum naturale in classes, ordines, genera & species
dispositos, additis editionis loco, tempore, forma, lingua,
&c. Editio altera priori longe auctior & emendatior.
Amstelodami, apud S. Schouten & filium, 1751.
8 p., 220, [13] p. 20cm.

1. Botany. Bibl.

Agr 11-895

Library, U. S. Dept. of   Agriculture 241.75L645B

NL 0390481   DNAL KMK WU NcD PPJ NNBG MH-A PPL

Linné, Carl von, 1707-1778.
Caroli Linnaei ... Bibliotheca botanica,
recensens libros plus mille de plantis huc
usque editos, secundum systema auctorum naturale in classes, ordines, genera & species dispositos, additis editionis loco, tempore,
forma, lingua &c. Editio altera, priori
longe auctior & emendatior. Amstelodami,
Apud viduam S. Schouten & filium, 1751.

Microfilm copy, made in 1963, of the original in Vatican. Biblioteca vaticana. Positive.
Negative film in Vatican. Biblioteca vaticana.

Collation of the original, as determined
from the film: 7 p. l., 220, [13] p.

1. Botany--Bibl. I. Title: Bibliotheca
botanica. (Series: [Manuscripta, microfilms
of rare and out-of-print books. List 43, no.
21])

NL 0390484   MoSU UU

**QK3
L76**
Linne, Carl von, 1707-1778.
Botanical contributions detached from the
Proceedings of the Swedish academy. Stock-
holm, 1739-1762.
21 v. in 1 binder. fold., plates. 23.5 cm.
In Swedish.

NL 0390485   DLC

Linné, Carl von, 1707-1778, _praeses._
... Botaniska exkursioner i trakten av Uppsala (Herba-
tiones upsalienses) Akademisk avhandling under Linnés
praesidium, Upsala 1753. Översatt från latinet av C. A.
Brolén. Uppsala & Stockholm, Almqvist & Wiksells boktryckeri-aktiebolag [1921]
39, [1] p. 22½cm. (His Valda avhandlingar ... n:r 1)

A. N. Fornander, respondent.
"75 ex. tryckta å lumppapper, n:r 15."

1. Botany—Sweden—Upsala.   I. Fornander, Andreas Nicolai, 1719-
1794, respondent. II. Brolén, Carl Axel, 1845-   tr.

27-11647 Revised

Library of Congress   QH43.A45 n:r 1

NL 0390486   DLC NNBG

                              *F
                            (Bergens)
Linné, Carl von, 1707-1778.
...Linné's botaniske "Praelectiones privatissimae" paa Ham-
marby 1770. Utgit efter Martin Vahl's referat, ved Jens Holmboe
... [Bergen: A/S. J. Grieg, 1911.]   69 p. incl. facsim.   8°.
(Bergens Museum, Bergen, Norway. Bergens Museums aarbog.
1910, nr. 1.)

1. Botany. 2. Vahl, Martin, 1749-   1804. 3. Holmboe, Jens, 1880-
4. Series.
N. Y. P. L.   May 15, 1923.

NL 0390487   NN NNBG KMK

**QH44
.U8**
Linné, Carl von, 1707-1778.

Uppsala. Universitet.
Bref och skrifvelser af och till Carl von Linné med un-
derstöd af Svenska staten utgifna af Upsala universitet.
Stockholm, Aktiebolaget Ljus, 1907-

Linné, Carl von, 1707-1778.
Carl von Linnés brefwexling
see under   Åhrling, Evald, 1837-1888.

Linné, Carl von, 1707-1778, _praeses._
... _Buxbaumia_ ... Upsaliae, excud. L. M. Höjer [1757]
16 p. 18½ x 16cm.
Library of Congress collection: Dissertationes academicae (Linné)
no. 85.
Diss.—Upsala (A. R. Martin, respondent)
Title vignette (mounted engraving of Buxbaumia)
Also in Linné's Amoenitates academicae, v. 5, ed. 1, 1760; ed. 2, 1788,
p. 78-91. cf. Hulth, Bibl. Linn. (1907) p. 108.

1. Buxbaumia.   I. Martin, Anton Rolandsson, 1729-1786, respondent.
7-1705 Revised

Library of Congress   QH43.A2 no. 85

NL 0390490   DLC NNBG WU

Linné, Carl von, 1707-1778, _praeses._
... _Buxbaumia,_ quam, sub praesidio D. D. Car. Linnaei, proposuit Antonius Roland Martin ... Upsaliae, 1757.
(In his Amoenitates academicae. Holmiae, 1749-1785. 21cm. v. 5
(1760) p. 78-91. fold. pl.)

1. Buxbaumia.   I. Martin, Antonius Rolandsson, 1729-1786, re-
spondent.   ca 7—2349 Unrev'd
Library of Congress   QH9.L7   de-
Copy 2,   tached.
                           QK539.B9TL7

NL 0390491   DLC

Linné, Carl von, 1707-1778.
Calceolaria pinnata, en rar växt. [Stock-
holm, 1770]
286-292 p.
In Kungliga Svenska Vetenskaps-Akademien.
Handlingar. v. 31. 1770.
1. Slipperwort. 2. Scrophulariaceae.
3. Calceolaria.

NL 0390492   KMK

[Linné, Carl von] 1707-1778, praeses.
The calendar of Flora. By A. M. Berger.
Upsal. 1755.
(In Linné, Carl von, 1707-1778. Miscellaneous
tracts relating to natural history, husbandry, and
physick, 1762, p. 249-286)
Also in other editions.

NL 0390493   MH-A

Linné, Carl von, 1707-1778, _praeses._
... _Calendarium florae_ ... Upsaliae, excud. L. M. Höjer, Reg.
Acad. typogr. [1756]
2 p. l., 5, [19] p. 20½ x 16½cm.
Library of Congress collection: Dissertationes academicae (Linné)
no. 71.
Diss.—Upsala (A. M. Berger, respondent)
Also in Linné's Amoenitates academicae, v. 4, ed. 1, 1759 (and 1760);
ed. 2, 1788, p. 387-414. For other reprints and translations _see_ T. O.
B. N. Krok, Bibliotheca botanica suecana (1925): Linné. 117.

1. Phenology.   I. Berger, Alexander Malachias, 1737-1804, respondent.   7-1701 Revised

Library of Congress   QH43.A2 no. 71

NL 0390494   DLC WU NNBG MiU

VOLUME 334

Linné, Carl von, 1707–1778, *praeses.*
... Calendarium floræ, eller Blomster-almanach, med Medicinska facultetens tilstånd under riddarens och archiaterns herr doct. Carl Linnæi inseende utg. på latin wid Kongl. academien i Upsala, i et academiskt snille prof, och sedermera förswånskat af Alexander Mal. Berger ... Stockholm, Kongl. tryckeriet, 1757.

7, ₍8₎–₍24₎ p. 19½ᶜᵐ.

Book-plate of Felix Bryk.

1. Phenology.   I. Berger, Alexander Malachias, 1737–1804, respondent and tr.

27–9729

Library of Congress   QH544.L75 1757

NL 0390495   DLC

Linné, Carl von, 1707–1778, *praeses.*
... Canones medici ... Upsaliæ, apud J. Edman ₍1775₎

1 p. l., 12 p. 18ᶜᵐ.

Library of Congress collection: Dissertationes academicae (Linné) no. 188.
Diss.—Upsala (S. A. Hedin, respondent and author)
Also in Linné's Amoenitates academicae, v. 9, 1785, p. 278–290.

1. Medicine—Aphorisms.   I. Hedin, Sven Anders, 1750–1821, respondent.

30–17897

Library of Congress   QH43.A2 no.182

NL 0390496   DLC WU MiU PPC

Linné, Carl von, 1707–1778.
Cartas de propria mano de C. Linneo, que se conservan en el Jardín Botánico de Madrid. Madrid, Palacio de Biblioteca y Museos Nacionales, 1908.

[58] p.
1. Linné, Carl von, 1707–1778. Letters.
2. Löfling, Per, 1729–1756.

NL 0390497   KMK

Linné, Carl von, ₍1707–1778₎.   L598.2 F30 v.3
A catalogue of the birds, beasts, fishes, insects, plants, &c. contained in Edwards's Natural history, in seven volumes, with their Latin names by Sir C. Linnæus, ... London, Printed for J. Robson, 1776.

15 p. 30ᶜᵐ.
With engravers' Gleanings of natural history. London, 1764. Vol. 3.

NL 0390498   ICJ CU

Linné, Carl von, 1707–1778.
A catalogue of the birds, beasts, fishes, insects, plants, &c. contained in Edwards's Natural history ... with their Latin names by Sir C. Linnæus ...
London: Printed for J. Robson, bookseller, New Bond Street. MDCCLXXVI. [1776]

15 p. 30cm. (4to) (In Edwards, George. A natural history of birds ... [1776])

NL 0390499   MB

Linné, Carl von, 1707–1778.
A catalogue of the birds, etc. with the Latin names by Linnaeus. [London, Jacob Robson, 1776]

5–15 p. 28 cm.
Photostat copy, supplied from copy in John Crerar library. Catalog appeared in Edward's Natural history, in seven volumes. Printed by Robson as a 15-page crown-folio pamphlet in conjunction with "Some memoirs of the life and works of George Edwards."

NL 0390500   PPAN

QK77
.L5
Linné, Carl von, 1707–1778.

Linnean society of London.
A catalogue of the Linnaean herbarium, compiled and annotated by Spencer Savage ... London, Printed for the Linnean society of London by Taylor & Francis, ltd., 1945.

Linné, Carl von, 1707–1778.
A catalogue of the works of Linnaeus
see under   British Museum. Dept. of Printed Books.

Linné, Carl von, 1709–1777.
Celebration at Flushing of the birthday of Linnaeus
see under   Société linnéenne de Paris.

Linné, Carl von, 1707–1778, *praeses.*
... Censura medicamentorum simplicium vegetabilium ... Holmiæ, exc. P. G. Nyström ₍1753₎

2 p. l., 24 p. 19½ᵐ.

Library of Congress collection: Dissertationes academicae (Linné) no. 53.
Diss.—Upsala (G. J. Caribohm, respondent)
Also in Linné's Amoenitates academicae, v. 4, ed. 1, 1759 (and 1760); ed. 2, 1788, p. 26–42. For other reprints see J. M. Hulth, Bibliographia Linnaeana (1907) p. 94.

1. Botany, Medical.   I. Caribohm, Gustaf Jacob, respondent.

24–3811 Revised

Library of Congress   QH43.A2 no. 53

NL 0390504   DLC NNBG DNLM MiU WU

Linné, Carl von, 1707–1778, *praeses.*
... Centuria insectorum rariorum ... Upsaliæ ₍1763₎

3 p. l., 32 p. 21 x 16½ cm.

Library of Congress collection: Dissertationes academicae (Linné) no. 130.
Diss.—Upsala (B. Johansson, respondent)
Also in Linné's Amoenitates academicae, v. 6, ed. 1, 1763; ed. 2, 1789, p. 384–415. cf. Hulth, Bibl. Linn. (1907) p. 128–129.

1. Entomology—Early works to 1800.   I. Johansson, Boas, respondent.

QH43.A2 no. 13⁰   30—16765

NL 0390505   DLC CSt WU MiU DNLM NN

Linné, Carl von, 1707–1778, *praeses.*
... Centuria I.–II. plantarum ... Upsaliæ, exc. L. M. Höjer ₍1755–56₎

2 v. 19½ x 15½ᵐ.

Library of Congress collection: Dissertationes academicae (Linné) no. 65 and 73.
Diss.—Upsala (I: A. D. Juslenius, respondent.— II: E. Torner, respondent)
Also in Linné's Amoenitates academicae, v. 4, ed. 1, 1759 (and 1760); ed. 2, 1788, p. 261–332. cf. Hulth, Bibl. Linn. (1907) p. 100.

1. Botany.   I. Juslenius, Abraham D., respondent.   II. Torner, Erik, respondent.

24–3812 Revised

Library of Congress   QH43.A2 no. 65, 73

                                    DNLM WU
NL 0390506   DLC NNBG WU DSI MnU-B OkU CU MiU MH-A

Linné, Carl von, 1707–1778, *praeses.*
... Cervus rheno ... Upsaliæ, exc. L. M. Höjer ₍1754₎

2 p. l., 24 p. illus. 18½ᵐ.

Library of Congress collection: Dissertationes academicae (Linné) no. 60.
Diss.—Upsala (C. F. Hoffberg, respondent)
Also under title Cervus tarandus in Linné's Amoenitates academicae, v. 4, ed. 1, 1759 (and 1760); ed. 2, 1788, p. 144–168. Translation: On the rhendeer. Brand. Select diss., 1781, p. 167–214. cf. J. M. Hulth, Bibl. Linn. (1907) p. 98.

1. Reindeer.   I. Hoffberg, Carl Fredrik, 1729–1790, respondent.

30–14801

Library of Congress   QH43.A2 no. 60

NL 0390507   DLC WU MiU

Linné, Carl von, 1707–1778, *praeses.*
*Cervus tarandus. Upsaliae, 1754.
In: Linnaeus. Amoenitates acad. [etc.]
8°. Lugd. Bat., 1760, iv, 144–168, 1 pl.
Carl Fredrik Hoffberg, respondent.

NL 0390508   DNLM PPAN

Linné, Carl von, 1707–1778, *praeses.*
Chinensia Lagerstroemiana. Upsaliae, 1754. Diss.
In: Linnaeus. Amoenitates acad. [etc.]
8°. Lugd. Bat., 1760, iv, 230–260, 1 pl.
Johan Lorens Odhelius, respondent.

NL 0390509   DNLM

Linné, Carl von, 1707–1778, *praeses.*
... Circa fervidorum et gelidorum usum parænesis ... Upsaliæ ₍1765₎

23 p. 21ᶜᵐ.

Library of Congress collection: Dissertationes academicae (Linné) no. 139.
Diss.—Upsala (C. Ribe, respondent)
Also in Linné's Amoenitates academicae, v. 7, ed. 1, 1769; ed. 2, 1789, p. 214–235. cf. Hulth, Bibl. Linn. (1907) p. 131.

1. Digestion.   I. Ribben, Carl, 1738–1803, respondent.

30–16773

Library of Congress   QH43.A2 no. 139

NL 0390510   DLC WU MiU PPC

Linné, Carl von, 1707–1778.
The classes and orders of the Linnaean system of botany
see under   [Duppa, Richard] 1770–1831.

Linné, Carl von, 1707–1778.
Caroli Linnaei ... Classes plantarum; seu, Systema plantarum omnia a fructificatione desumta, quorum xvi universalia & xiii partialia, compendiose proposita, secundum classes, ordines et nomina generica cum clave cujusvis methodi et synonymis genericis. Fundamentorum botanicorum pars II. Lugduni Batavorum, apud C. Wishoff, 1738.

5 p. l., 5–606 col., 607–656, ₍1₎ p. 21½ cm.

1. Botany.

Agr 11—896

U. S. Nat'l Agr. Libr.   452.04L64
for Library of Congress   ₍66d½₎

IaAS MiEM CU NcU PPAmP
NL   DNAL KyBgW CtY PPL OO PPC NNBG WU MiU-C

Linné, Carl von, 1707–1778.
Caroli Linnæi ... Classes plantarvm. Sev Systemata plantarvm omnia a frvctificatione desvmta, qvorvm xvi vniversalia et xiii partialia, compendiose proposita secvndvm classes ordines et nomina generica cvm clave evivsvis methodi et synonymis genericis. Fvndamentorvm botanicorvm pars II. Halæ Magdebvrgicæ, apvd I. G. Bierwirth, 1747.

5 p. l., 5–606 col., 607–656, ₍1₎ p. 20ᵐ.

Department of agriculture library copy lacks p. 656, ₍1₎

1. Botany.

Agr 25–1459

Library, U. S. Dept. of   Agriculture 452.04L64

ICJ MH NN MH-A
NL 0390513   DNAL MiU NNBG NIC CU MiEM MiU PBa PPAN

Linné, Carl von, 1707–1778.   L570.4 L542 v.3
Caroli Linnæi opus quod inscribitur Classes plantarum. Impensis Regiæ Academiæ scientiarum Suecicæ denuo editum. Uppsaliæ, typis descripserunt Almqvist & Wiksell Soc., 1907.
[12], 656, [1] p. 26ᵐ. (In Skrifter af Carl von Linné. III.)
With reproduction of the title-page to the first edition: Lugduni Batavorum 1738.

NL 0390514   ICJ MH-A

VOLUME 334

QK91
.C58   Linné, Carl von, 1707–1778.
Clavis medicinae duplex, exterior & interior.
Holmiae, L. Salvii, 1766.
29 p.   21 cm.

QK91   980 B. M. Hulth p. 133.
.M2   Another copy bound with Linné's Mantissa
plantarum. Holmiae, 1767–71.

1. Medicine.   i. t.

NL 0390515   NNBG DNLM MH NNC

Linné, Carl von, 1707–1778.
Caroli a Linné... Clavis medicinæ dvplex, exterior & interior... Iterata editio foras dedit et præfatvs est Ern. Godofr.
Baldinger... Longosalissæ: Apvd I. C. Martini, 1767.   59 p.
21cm.

Bound with: Reuss, C. F. Compendivm botanices systematis Linnæani. Ulmæ,
1774. 21cm.

1. Botany, Medical.   I. Baldinger,   Ernst Gottfried, 1738–1804. *Revised*
N. Y. P. L.   *May 31, 1933*

NL 0390516   NN

Linné, Carl von (1707–1778).

—— Clavis medicinæ duplex, exterior & interior. Holmiæ. 1766. (*In* HULT, O. E. A. Carl von Linné säsom
läkare och medicinak författare, 1907, pp. 159–242.)

NL 0390517   MH-A

Linné, Carl von, 1707–1778.
Collectio epistolarvm quas ad viros illustres et clarissimos scripsit Carolus a Linné. Accedunt opuscula pro et
contra virum immortalem scripta, extra suecinam rarissi-
ma. Edidit Dietericus Henricus Stoever ... Hamburgi,
impensis B. G. Hoffmann, 1792.

xiv, 194 p. 22ᶜᵐ.
Letters are to Albrecht Haller, Thomas Pennant, K. P. Thunberg, P. D.
Giseke.
The Opuscula are: Decades binae thesivm medicarvm qvas ... svbjicivnt
avctar J. G. Wallerivs ... et respondens J. A. Darelivs. 1741; Orbis eru-
diti judicium de C. Linnaei. 1741; Quid Linnaeo patri, debeat medicina,
dissertatione ... quam ... proponit ... S. A. Hedin ... respondente C. Carlander. 1784.

I. Stöver, Dietrich Johann Heinrich. II. Haller, Albrecht *i. e.* Victor
Albrecht von, 1708–1777. III. Pennant, Thomas, 1726–1798. IV. Thunberg,
Karl Peter, 1743–1828. V. Giseke, Paul Dietrich, 1741–1796. VI. Wallerius,
Johann Gottschalk, 1709–1785. VII. Darelius, Joh. Andr. VIII. Hedin, Svens
Anders, 1750–1821. IX. Carlander, Christophus.
                                                              Agr 25–1460

Library, U. S. Dept. of   Agriculture 120L64Lc
                                                              (2)

NL 0390519   DNAL KMK NNBG NN IU MH-A MB MH

Linné, Carl von, 1707–1778, praeses.
... Consectaria electrico-medica ... Upsaliæ, exc. L. M. Höjer
(1754)

8 p. 20½ x 16ᶜᵐ.
Library of Congress collection: Dissertationes academicae (Linné)
no. 59.
Diss.—Upsala (P. Zetzell, respondent)
Also in Linné's Amoenitates academicae, v. 9, 1785, p. 35–42. For
other reprints and translations see J. M. Hulth, Bibliographia Linnaeana
(1907) p. 97–98.

1. Electrotherapeutics.   I. Zetzell, Per, 1724–1802, respondent.
                                                              30–14860

Library of Congress   QH43.A2 no. 59

NL 0390520   DLC WU MiU PU

Linné, Carl von, 1707–1778, praeses.
... Consectaria electrico-medica.
(in Amoen Acad. IX. 1785.)
Petrus Zetzel, respondent.

NL 0390521   PPAN

Linné, Carl von, 1707–1778, praeses.
Corallia Baltica adumbrans
see his   ... Dissertatio, corallia baltica
adumbrans ...

QK91
.G4   Linné, Carl von, 1707–1778.
1742   Corollarium Generum plantarum, exhibens genera
plantarum sexaginta, addenda prioribus charac-
teribus, expositis in Generibus plantarum. Accedit Methodus sexualis. Lugduni Baravorum,
Apud C. Wishoff, 1737.
3 p. ℓ., 25, 23 p. 21 cm.
Bound with the author's Genera plantarum.
Lugduni Batavorum, 1742.
With individual t. p. before last paging:
Methodus sexualis, sistens genera plantarum
secundum mares et feminas in classes et ordines redacta.   Lugduni Batavorum, 1737.
Hulth p. 23.   7?   Junk. 2(b) & (c) Krok

NL 0390523   NNBG DLC PPL MH-A MB WU

Linné, Carl von, 1707–1778.
Corollarium Generum plantarum
see also his   Genera plantarum eorumque
characteres naturales ... 1737.

Linné, Carl von, 1707–1778.
Caroli Linnaei ... Critica botanica in qua nomina plan-
tarum generica, specifica & variantia examini subjiciun-
tur, selectoria confirmantur, indigna rejiciuntur; simulque
doctrina circa denominationem plantarum traditur. Seu
Fundamentorum botanicorum pars IV. Accedit Johannis
Browallii De necessitate historiae naturalis discursus.
Lugduni Batavorum, apud C. Wishoff, 1737.

8 p. l., 270, (44), 24, (8) p. 21ᶜᵐ.

1. Botany.
                                                              Agr 11–1031

Library, U. S. Dept. of   Agriculture 452L64SCr

NL 0390525   PPULC MNS PPAmP PPL PPAN OO ICJ
**   DNAL OkU WU NIC NNBG CaBViP MH-A PPHor**

Linné, Carl von, 1707–1778.
The "Critica botanica" of Linnæus. Translated by the
late Sir Arthur Hort ... revised by Miss M. L. Green ... with
an introduction by Sir Arthur W. Hill ... London, The Ray
society, 1938.

xxvii, 239 p. 22½ cm.   (*Added t.-p.:* The Ray society ... 1937)
"The 'Critica botanica' is an elaboration of the aphorisms 210–324
taken from his 'Fundamenta botanica.'"—p. vii.

1. Botany. 2. Botany—Nomenclature. I. Hort, Sir Arthur Fenton, bart., 1864–1935, tr. II. Green, Mary Letitia. III. Title.

QK91.C73 1938   580.14   38—19046

Library of Congress

NL 0390526   NNBG CoU NcU
**   DLC CaBVaU GU FTaSU NcD MBH NIC ICU**

QK507
L5   Linné, Carl von, 1707–1778.
Cryptogamie complette; ou, Description
des plantes dont les étamines sont peu
apparentes; suivant les ordres ou familles,
les genres, les espèces, avec les caractères
et les différences. 1. éd. française,
calquée sur celle de Gmlin; 2) augm. et
enrichie de notions élémentaires, de notes
diverses, etc. etc. par N. Jolyclerc.
Paris, Levacher, an 7 de la République
(1798/99)
242 p.

NL 0390527   CU MnU NNBG KMK WU

Linné, Carl von, 1707–1778, praeses.
... Culina mutata ... Upsaliæ, excud. L. M. Höjer (1757)
2 p. l., 12 p. 19 x 15¼ᵐ.
Library of Congress collection: Dissertationes academicae (Linné)
no. 88.
Diss.—Upsala (M. G. Österman, respondent)
Also in Linné's Amoenitates academicae, v. 5, ed. 1, 1760; ed. 2,
1788, p. 120–132. cf. Hulth, Bibl. Linn. (1907) p. 109.

1. Food. 2. Cookery. I. Österman, Magnus G., respondent.

Library of Congress   QH43.A2 no. 88   30–16741
                                                              (2)

NL 0390528   DLC WU DNLM MiU

Linné, Carl von (1707–1778).

—— Cycas proposita. [Paris. 1778.] 4°.
Mémoires de l'Académie royale des sciences, 1778, pp. 515–518.

NL 0390529   MH-A

Linné, Carl von, 1707–1778, praeses.
... Cynographia ... Upsaliæ, exc. L. M. Höjer (1753)
3 p. l., 23, (1) p. pl. 22½ x 19ᶜᵐ.
Library of Congress collection: Dissertationes academicae (Linné)
no. 54.
Diss.—Upsala (E. M. Lindecrantz, respondent)
Also under title Canis familiaris in Linné's Amoenitates academicae,
v. 4, ed. 1, 1759 (and 1760); ed. 2, 1788, p. 43–63. cf. J. M. Hulth,
Bibl. Linn. (1907) p. 94–96.

1. Dogs. I. Lindecrantz, Erik Magnus, 1727–1788, respondent.
II. Title.

Library of Congress   QH43.A2 no. 54   30–14798
—— Copy 2.   19 x 15ᶜᵐ.

NL 0390530   DLC WU MiU

Q
64   Linné, Carl von, 1707–1778.
U59   Cyprinus pinnae ani radiis XI, pinnis alben-
tibus. Faun. Svec. 325. Staem Svecis.
(Stockholmiae, L. Salvii, 1751)
p. 35–36. illus.
In Acta Societatis regiae scientiarum Upsaliensis, 1744–50.

CYPRINUS
t

NL 0390531   KMK

Linné, Carl von, 1707–1778, praeses.
D.D. Hypericum ...
see his   ... Hypericum.

Linné, Carl von, 1707–1778, praeses.
D.D. planta Aphyteia ...
see his   ... Planta aphyteia.

Linné, Carl von, 1707–1778, praeses.
D.D. Plantae hybridae.
see his   ... Plantae hybridae ...

Linné, Carl von, 1707–1778.
D.D. plantarum Jamaicen-...
see his   ... Plantarum jamaicensium
pugillus ...

VOLUME 334

Linné, Carl von, 1707-1778.
Linnés Dalaresa, Iter Dalekarlicum, jämte Utlandsresan, Iter ad exteros, och Bergslagsresan, Iter ad fodinas. Med utförlig kommentar. ⌈Redaktör: Arvid Hj. Uggla⌉ Stockholm, Geber ⌈1953⌉
xvi, 482 p. illus., maps (part fold.) 24 cm.
At head of title: Svenska Linné-sällskapet och Nordiska museet.
Bibliography: p. 421-427.
1. Dalecarlia, Sweden—Descr. & trav. 2. Natural history—Sweden—Dalecarlia. 3. Europe—Descr. & trav. 4. Natural history—Europe. I. Uggla, Arvid Hjalmar, 1883– ed. II. Svenska Linné-sällskapet, Uppsala. III. Stockholm. Nordiska museet. IV. Title: Dalaresa. V. Title: Iter Dalekarlicum.

DL971.D2L55   A 53-7229 rev
Minnesota. Univ. Libr.
for Library of Congress   ⌈r56cⅱ⌉†

NL 0390536   MnU CaBVaU CU NN DLC

Linné, Carl von, 1707-1778, praeses.
... De acetariis ...
see his   ... Dissertatio medica, de acetariis ...

Linné, Carl von, 1707-1778, praeses.
De anandria
see his   Dissertatio botanica de anandria.

Linné, Carl von, 1707-1778, praeses.
... De coloniis plantarum ...
see his   ... Dissertatio de coloniis plantarum ...

Linné, Carl von, 1707-1778, praeses.
De crystallorum generatione ⌈1747⌉
see his   ... Specimen academicum de crystallorum generatione ...

Linné, Carl von, 1707-1778, praeses.
De crystallorum generatione. 1749.
see his   Specimen de crystallorum generatione.

Linné, Carl von, 1707-1778, praeses.
De curiositate naturali ⌈1748⌉
see his   Specimen academicum de curiositate naturali.

Linné, Carl von, 1707-1778, praeses.
De curiositate naturali. 1749
see his   Specimen de curiositate naturali.

Linné, Carl von, 1707-1778, praeses.
De erica
see his   ... Dissertationem botanicam, de erica ...

Linné, Carl von, 1707-1778, praeses.
De generatione calculi
see his   Disputatio medica inauguralis, de generatione calculi.

Linné, Carl von, 1707-1778, praeses.
De haemorrhagiis uteri sub statu graviditatis
see his   ... Dissertatio medica de haemorrhagiis uteri.

Linné, Carl von, 1707-1778, praeses.
... De horticultura academica ...
see his   Dissertatio de horticultura academica.

Linné, Carl von, 1707-1778, praeses.
De lavandula
see   Linné, Carl von, 1741-1783, praeses.
... Dissertatio academica de lavandula.

Linné, Carl von, 1707-1778, praeses.
... De maro ...
see his ...   Dissertationem inauguralem, de maro.

Linné, Carl von, 1707-1778, praeses.
De materia medica in regno animali
see his   ... Dissertatio de materia medica in regno animali.

Linné, Carl von, 1707-1778, praeses.
... De menthae usu ...
see his   ... Dissertatio medica de menthae usu.

Linné, Carl von, 1707-1778.
De nuptiis et sexu plantarum ...
see his   Exercitatio botanico - physica de nuptiis et sexu plantarum.

Linné, Carl von, 1707-1778, praeses.
De oeconomia naturae
see his   Specimen academicum de oeconomia naturae.

Linné, Carl von, 1707-1778, praeses.
De pane diaetetico
see his   ... Dissertatio academica, de pane diaetetico ...

Linné, Carl von, 1707-1778, praeses.
De passiflora
see his   Dissertatio botanica de passiflora.

Linné, Carl von, 1707-1778, praeses.
De peloria
see his   ... Dissertatio botanica de peloria.

Linné, Carl von, 1707-1778, praeses.
De perspiratione insensibili
see his   ... Dissertatio physiologica de perspiratione insensibili ...

Linné, Carl von, 1707-1778, praeses.
De pingvedine animali
see his   ... Dissertatio diaetetica, de pingvedine animali ...

Linné, Carl von, 1707-1778.
De planta Sceptrum Carolinum dicta
see his   ... Dissertatio botanica de planta sceptrum carolinum dicta.

Linné, Carl von, 1707-1778, praeses.
De potu chocolatae
see his   ... Dissertatio medica inauguralis de potu chocolatae ...

Linné, Carl von, 1707-1778, *praeses.*
De raphania ... Upsaliæ ⌈1763⌉
2 p. l., 2-21 p. pl. 21 x 17½⌈cm⌉.
Library of Congress collection: Dissertationes academicae (Linné) no. 126.
Diss.—Upsala (G. Rothman, respondent)
Text begins on verso of 2d prelim. leaf.
Also in Linné's Amoenitates academicae, v. 6, ed. 1, 1763; ed. 2, 1789, p. 430-451. cf. Hulth, Bibl. Linn. (1907) p. 128.

1. Ergotism. I. Rothman, Göran, 1739-1778, respondent. II. Title: Raphania.
                            25-17383 Revised
Library of Congress   QH43.A2 no. 126

NL 0390561   DLC DNLM NNBG WU MiU PPC

Linné, Carl von, 1707-1778, praeses.
De spigelia anthelmia
see his   ... Dissertatio medica, de spigelia anthelmia.

Linné, Carl von, 1707-1778, *praeses.*
... De suturis vulnerum in genere ... Upsaliae, typis Edmannianis ⌈1772⌉
21, ⌈1⌉ p. 20⌈cm⌉.
Library of Congress collection: Dissertationes academicae (Linné) no. 172.
Diss.—Upsala (O. E. Boecler, respondent and author)
Also in Linné's Amoenitates academicae, v. 9, 1785, p. 223-244.

1. Sutures. I. Boecler, Christian Ernst, respondent.
                            30-17890
Library of Congress   QH43.A2 no. 172

NL 0390563   DLC KMK WU MiU

VOLUME 335

Linné, Carl von, 1707-1778, praeses.
De taenia
　　see his　... Specimen academicum de
taenia.

Linné, Carl von, 1707-1778, praeses.
... De transmutatione frumentorum ...
　　see his　... Specimen academicum, de
transmutatione frumentorum.

Linné, Carl von, 1707-1778, praeses.
De varia febrium intermittentium curatione
　　see his　Dissertatio medica de varia
febrium intermittentium curatione.

Linne, Carl von, 1707-1778.
De venis resorbibentibus
　　see his　... Dissertationem physiologicam
de venis resorbibentibus.

Linné, Carl von, 1707-1778, praeses.
... De Viola ipecacuanha ...
　　see his　... Dissertatio de Viola
pecacuanha ...

XA
.C763
1741
Linné, Carl von, 1707-1778.
Decem plantarum genera.
(In Acta Societatis Regiae Scientiarum Up-
saliensis. 26 cm. 1741(1746) p. ₍77₎-84)

1. Botany. i.t. ii.s: Acta Societatis Regiae
Scientiarum Upsaliensis, 1741.

NL 0390569　　NNBG KMK

Linné, Carl von, 1707-1778.
Deliciae naturae. Tal, hållit uti Upsala dom-kyrka år 1772
den 14 decemb. vid rectoratets nedläggande, af Carl v. Linné
... Efter de studerandes åstundan, på svenska öfversatt och
utgifvit. Stockholm, Tryckt hos J. G. Lange, 1773.
32 p. 21ᶜᵐ.

1. Natural history.　i. Title.

27-11644

Library of Congress　　　　QH43.D4

NL 0390570　　DLC NNBG MH-A

LINNÉ, Carl von, 1707-1778.
Delineatio plantae. [Upsaliae],Björck &
Borjesson,[1759].

sm.8°.

NL 0390571　　MH MH-A

Linné, Carl von, 1707-1778.
... Delineatio regni animalis, secundum Caroli Linnæi Sys-
tema naturæ. Accedunt vocabula suecica. Denuo edidit Felix
Bryk. Holmiæ, sumptibus editoris, 1919.
cover-title, ₍16₎ p.　19 x 11ᶜᵐ.
At head of title: H. A. Moeller.

1. Zoology.　i. Bryk, Felix, 1882-　ed.　ii. Moeller, Hjalmar
August, 1866-
Agr 30-495
Library, U. S. Dept. of　　Agriculture　411L64D

NL 0390572　　DNAL KMK

Linné, Carl von, 1707-1778, praeses.
... Demonstrationes plantarum in Horto upsaliensi MDCCLIII
... Upsaliæ, excudit L. M. Höjer ₍1753₎
4 p. l., 27, ₍1₎ p.　20 x 15½ᶜᵐ.
Library of Congress collection: Dissertationes academicae (Linné)
no. 49.
Diss.—Upsala (J. C. Höjer, respondent)
Also in Linné's Amoenitates academicae, v. 3, ed. 1, 1756; ed. 2, 1764;
ed. 3, 1787, p. 394-424. cf. J. M. Hulth, Bibl. Linn. (1907) p. 93.

1. Upsala. Universitet. Botaniska trädgården.　i. Höjer, Johan
Christ., respondent.
24-17481 Revised
Library of Congress　　　QH43.A2　no. 49
—— Copy 2.　　　　21 x 17½ᶜᵐ.

NL 0390573　　DLC NNBG DNLM WU MiU

QK91
.S95
1786
Linné, Carl von, 1707-1778.
Des Ritter Carl von Linné Pflanzensystem nach
seinen Klassen, Ordnungen, Gattungen und Arten
mit den Erkennungs- und Unterscheidungszeichen.
14. nach der vorgehenden viel verm. und verb.
Aufl. von Johann Andreas Murray. Aus dem
Lateinischen mit einigen Zusätzen von Xaver
Joseph Lippert. Wien, J. P. Krausischen
Buchhandlung, 1786.
2 v. (xlii, 9689 ₍i.e. 1969₎ p.)　20 cm.

589a B. M.　Hulth p. 146.

NL 0390574　　NNBG PPAN MH KMK

Linné, Carl von, 1707-1778, praeses.
Descriptio horti Upsaliensis.　Upsaliae, 1745.
In: Linnaeus. Amoenitates acad. [etc.]
8°. Lugd. Bat., 1749, i, 20-59, 4 pl.
Samuel Naucler, respondent.

NL 0390575　　DNLM

Z5360
.L53
pt.2
Linne, Carl von, 1707-1778.
Caroli Linnaei Determinationes in hortum
siccum Joachimi Burseri; the text of the
manuscript in the Linnaean collections,
edited by Spencer Savage. London, 1937.
78 p.　25 cm.　(Linnean Society of London.
Library. Catalogue of the manuscripts in the
Library of the Linnean Society, pt.2)

1. Burser, Joachim, 1583-1639.　i. Savage,
Spencer, 1886-　ed.　ii.t: Determinationes
in hortum siccum Joachimi Burseri.　iii.s.

NL 0390576　　NN NNBG

Linné, Carl von, 1707-1778, praeses.
... Diæta acidularis ... Upsaliæ ₍1761₎
2 p. l., 12 p.　19½ x 15ᶜᵐ.
Library of Congress collection: Dissertationes academicae (Linné)
no. 116.
Diss.—Upsala (E. Vigelius, respondent)
Also in Linné's Amoenitates academicae, v. 6, ed. 1, 1763; ed. 2,
1789, p. 148-159. For other reprints and translation see J. M. Hulth,
Bibliographia Linnaeana (1907) p. 122.

1. Mineral waters.　i. Vigelius, Ericus, respondent.
30-16760
Library of Congress　　QH43.A2　no. 116
₍2₎

NL 0390577　　DLC ICJ WU MiU

Linné, Carl von, 1707-1778, praeses.
Diaeta acidularis.　1761.
(in Amoen. Acad. VI. 1763.)
Ericus Vigelius, respondent.

NL 0390578　　PPAN

Linné, Carl von, 1707-1778, praeses.
⚹Diaeta acidularis.　Upsaliae, 1761.
In: Linnaeus. Amoenitates acad. [etc.]
8°. Lugd. Bat., 1764, vi, 148-159.
Ericus Vigelius, respondent.

NL 0390579　　DNLM

Linné, Carl von, 1707-1778
Diary. Tr. from the Swedish.　Ed. by
W. G. Maton.　1885.

NL 0390580　　RP

Linné, Carl von, 1707-1778.
,Linnés dietetik, på grundvalen af dels hans eget origi-
nalutkast till föreläsningar: Lachesis naturalis que tradit diætam naturalem, och dels lärjungeanteckningar
efter dessa hans föreläsningar: Collegium diæteticum;
på uppdrag af Medicinska fakulteten i Uppsala ordnad
och utgifven af A. O. Lindfors.　Uppsala, Akademiska
boktryckeriet, E. Berling, 1907.
1 p. l., viii, 167, 248 p., 1 l. facsim.　25ᶜᵐ.　₍Upsala universitets årsskrift,
1907. Skrifter med anledning af Linnéfesten ... bd. ii₎
"Auctores": p. 158-165 (first paging)
"Uppsatser och akad. afhandlingar af Linné rörande dietetiska ämnen":
p. 245-246.
"Collegium diæteticum"　　has separate paging.
1. Hygiene—Early works　　to 1800. 2. Diet—Early works to 1800.
i. Upsala. Universitet.　　Medicinska fakulteten.　ii. Lindfors,
Axel Otto, 1852-1909, ed.
Library of Congress　　　QH44.I77　　8-14951

NL 0390581　　DLC PPC CU DNLM IU PU PBa MiU OU ICJ

Linné, Carl von, 1707-1778, praeses.
... Disputatio medica, de morsura serpentum ... Upsaliæ
₍1762₎
2 p. l., 19, ₍1₎ p. 1 illus.　19½ x 14½ᶜᵐ.
Library of Congress collection: Dissertationes academicae (Linné)
no. 119.
Diss.—Upsala (J. G. Acrell, respondent)
Illustration mounted on p. 19.
Also in Linné's Amoenitates academicae, v. 6, ed. 1, 1763; ed. 2,
1789, p. 197-216. Translation: On the bite of serpents, Brand, Select.
diss., 1781, p. 265-308.　cf. Hulth, Bibl. Linn. (1907) p. 123-124.

1. Serpents. 2. Venom.　i. Acrel, Johan Gustaf, 1741-1801, respondent.
30-16762
Library of Congress　　　QH43.A2　no. 119
—— Copy 2.

NL 0390582　　DLC PPDrop DNLM ICJ WU MiU

Linné, Carl von, 1707-1778, praeses.
Disputatio medica inauguralis, de generatione calculi ...
Upsaliæ ₍1749₎
2 p. l., 27, ₍1₎ p.　18 x 25ᶜᵐ.
Library of Congress collection: Dissertationes academicae (Linné)
no. 22.
Diss.—Upsala (J. O. Hagström, respondent)
Also in Linné's Amoenitates academicae, v. 2, ed. 1, 1751 (and 1752)
and ed. 3, 1787, p. 154-181; ed. 2, 1762, p. 137-162, under title Genesis
calculi. Translation: Von der erzeugung des steines im thierischen
körper, in his Auserlesene abhandlungen, v. 3, 1778, p. 241-270. cf.
Hulth, Bibl. Linn. (1907) p. 63.

1. Calculi.　i. Hagström, Johan Otto, 1716-1792, respondent.
30-14781
Library of Congress　　　QH43.A2　no. 22

NL 0390583　　DLC MiU WU

Linné, Carl von, 1707-1778, praeses.
... Disputationem botanico-medicam inauguralem quâ *Ficus*,
ejusque historia-naturalis & medica exhibetur ... praeside ...
Carolo Linnæo ... sistit Cornelius Hegardt ... Upsaliae ₍1744₎
2 p. l., 28 p. 18 x 14½ᶜᵐ.
Library of Congress collection: Dissertationes academicae (Linné)
no. 2.
Wants the rare plate. cf. Hulth (1907) p. 43.
Also in Linné's Amoenitates academicae, v. 1 ₍ed. 1₎ 1749, p. 213-243;
ed. 2, 1749 and ed. 3, 1789, p. 23-54. Translation: Vom feigenbaume in
his Auserlesene abhandlungen, v. 2, 1777, p. 333-367.

1. Fig.　i. Hegardt, Cornelius, 1715-1772, respondent.
30-14770
Library of Congress　　　QH43.A2　no. 2

NL 0390584　　DLC MiU WU NNBG DNAL

VOLUME 334

Linné, Carl von, 1707-1778.
Linnés disputationer. En översikt
see under Drake, Gustaf.

Linné, Carl von, 1707-1778, *praeses.*
Disquisitio de prolepsi plantarum ... Upsaliæ [1763]
1 p. l., 18 p. 18½cm.
Library of Congress collection: Dissertationes academicae (Linné) no. 129.
Diss.—Upsala (J. J. Ferber, respondent)
Also in Linné's Amoenitates academicae, v. 6, ed. 1, 1763; ed. 2, 1789, p. 365-383. For other reprints see J. M. Hulth, Bibliographia Linnaeana (1907) p. 128.
1. Botany—Morphology. I. Ferber, Johan Jacob, 1743-1790, respondent.
Library of Congress QH43.A2 no. 129 30-16764

NL 0390586 DLC WU NNBG MiU

Linné, Carl von, 1707-1778.
Caroli Linnaei ... Disqvisitio de qvaestione ab Academia imperiali scientiarivm petropol. in annvm MDCCLIX. pro praemio proposita: Sexum plantarum argumentis et experimentis nouis, praeter adhuc iam cognita, vel corroborare, vel impugnare, praemissa expositione historica et physica omnium plantae partium, quae aliquid ad foecundationem et perfectionem seminis et fructus conferre creduntur, ab eadem Academia die VI. septembris MDCCLX. in conuentu publico praemio ornata. Petropoli, typis Academiae scientiarvm, 1760.
30 p. 28cm.
1. Plants, Sex in.
Library of Congress QK827.L7 5-30228†

NL 0390587 DLC MH-A MB

QK92 .J 59 Rosenwald Coll.
Linné, Carl von, 1707-1778. Disquisitio de quaestione sexum plantarum.
Thornton, Robert John, 1768-1837, *ed.*
New illustration of the sexual system of Carolus von Linnaeus comprehending an elucidation of the several parts of the fructification; a prize dissertation on the sexes of plants [by Carolus Linnaeus] a full explanation of the classes, and orders, of the sexual system; and The temple of Flora, or Garden of nature, being picturesque, botanical, coloured plates of select plants, illustrative of the same, with descriptions. London, 1807 [i. e. 1799-1810]

Linné, Carl von, 1707-1778.
... Disquisitio ... sexum plantarum argumentis & experimentis novis ... [Erlangae,1790]
p.[193]-214. 19 1/2cm.
From the Amoenitates Academicae, 1790, 10: 193-214.
Caption title.

NL 0390589 CtY-M

Linné, Carl von, 1707-1778, *praeses.*
... Dissertatio academica, de mure indico ... Upsaliæ, exc. L. M. Höjer [1754]
1 p. l., 23, [1] p. pl. 17½cm.
Library of Congress collection: Dissertationes academicae (Linné) no. 62.
Diss.—Upsala (J. J. Nauman, respondent)
Imperfect: plate wanting.
Also under title Mus porcellus in Linné's Amoenitates academicae, v. 4, ed. 1, 1759 (and 1760); ed. 2, 1788, p. 190-209. Translation: Vom meerschwein, in his Auserlesene abhandlungen, v. 1, 1776, p. 135-154. cf. Hulth, Bibl. Linn. (1907) p. 98.
1. Guinea-pigs. I. Nauman, Johan Justus, 1735-1778, respondent.
30-14802
Library of Congress QH43.A2 no. 62

NL 0390590 DLC WU DNLM MiU

Linné, Carl von, 1707-1778, *praeses.*
... Dissertatio academica, de pane diætetico ... Upsaliæ, excud. L. M. Höjer [1757]
20 p. 19½ x 15½cm.
Library of Congress collection: Dissertationes academicae (Linné) no. 83.
Diss.—Upsala (I. Svensson, respondent)
Also in Linné's Amoenitates academicae, v. 5, ed. 1, 1760; ed. 2, 1788, p. 50-67. For other reprints and translation see J. M. Hulth, Bibliographia Linnaeana (1907) p. 108.
1. Bread. I. Svensson, Isak, 1726-1795, respondent.
Library of Congress QH43.A2 no. 83 30-16738
[2]

NL 0390591 DLC MiU WU

Linné, Carl von, 1707-1778, *praeses.*
... Dissertatio academica, de phalæna bombyce ... Upsaliæ, excud. L. M. Höjer [1756]
12 p. 21 x 16½cm.
Library of Congress collection: Dissertationes academicae (Linné) no. 78.
Diss.—Upsala (J. Lyman, respondent)
Also in Linne's Amoenitates academicae, v. 4, ed. 1, 1759 (and 1760); ed. 2, 1788, p. 553-564. Translation: On the silk worm, Brand, Select diss., 1781, p. 437-456. cf. Hulth, Bibl. Linn. (1907) p. 105.
1. Silkworms. I. Lyman, Johannes, respondent. II. Title: Phalæna bombyce.
30-14807
Library of Congress QH43.A2 no. 78

NL 0390592 DLC WU MiU

Linné, Carl von, 1707-1778, *praeses.*
... Dissertatio academica de politia naturæ ... Upsaliæ [1760]
1 p. l., 22 p. 22½ x 19cm.
Library of Congress collection: Dissertationes academicae (Linné) no. 109.
Diss.—Upsala (H. C. D. Wilcke, respondent)
Also in Linné's Amoenitates academicae, v. 6, ed. 1, 1763; ed. 2, 1789, p. 17-39. Translation: On the police of nature, Brand, Select diss., 1781, p. 129-166.
1. Nature. 2. Providence and government of God. I. Wilcke, Henrik Christian Daniel, 1739-1788, respondent.
30-16757
Library of Congress QH43.A2 no. 109
——— Copy 2. [2]

NL 0390593 DLC WU MiU

Linné, Carl von, 1707-1778, *praeses.*
Dissertatio academica demonstrans necessitatem promovendæ historiae naturalis in Rossia ... Upsaliæ [1766]
1 p. l., 34, [10] p. fold. pl. 20½cm.
Diss.—Upsala (Alexan. de Karamyschew, respondent)
1. Natural history—Russia. [1. Russia—Natural history] I. Karamyschew, Alexander von, 1744-1791, respondent.
Agr 26-1378
Library, U. S. Dept. of Agriculture 452.4L64D

NL 0390594 DNAL CSt WU MiU

Linné, Carl von, 1707-1778, *praeses.*
... Dissertatio academica demonstrans usum historiæ naturalis in vita communi ... Upsaliæ [1766]
3 p. l., 30, [2] p. fold. pl. 20cm.
Library of Congress collection: Dissertationes academicae (Linné) no. 145.
Diss.—Upsala (M. Aphonin, respondent and author)
Also in Linné's Amoenitates academicae, v. 7, ed. 1, 1769; ed. 2, 1789, p. 409-437. For other reprints and translations see J. M. Hulth, Bibliographia Linnaeana (1907) p. 134.
1. Natural history. I. Afonin, Matvĕĭ Ivanovich, 1740-1810, respondent.
30-17872
Library of Congress QH43.A2 no. 145

NL 0390595 DLC CtY WU MiU

Linné, Carl von, 1707-1778, *praeses.*
... Dissertatio academica, migrationes avium sistens ... Upsaliæ, excud. L. M. Höjer [1757]
38 p. 19 x 15cm.
Library of Congress collection: Dissertationes academicae (Linné) no. 79.
Diss.—Upsala (C. D. Ekmarck, respondent)
Also in Linné's Amoenitates academicae, v. 4, ed. 1, 1759 (and 1760); ed. 2, 1788, p. 565-600. For translations see J. M. Hulth, Bibliographia Linnaeana (1907) p. 107.
1. Birds—Migration. I. Ekmarck, Carl Daniel, 1734-1789, respondent.
30-14806
Library of Congress QH43.A2 no. 79

NL 0390596 DLC WU MiU PPAN

Linné, Carl von, 1707-1778, *praeses.*
... Dissertatio academica, mundum invisibilem, breviter delineatura ... Upsaliæ [1767]
23 p. 18½cm.
Library of Congress collection: Dissertationes academicae (Linné) no. 149.
Diss.—Upsala (J. C. Roos, respondent)
Also in Linné's Amoenitates academicae, v. 7, ed. 1, 1769; ed. 2, 1789, p. 385-408. For translation see J. M. Hulth, Bibliographia Linnaeana (1907) p. 135.
1. Micro-organisms. I. Roos, Johan Carl, 1745-1828, respondent.
30-17875
Library of Congress QH43.A2 no. 149

NL 0390597 DLC NNBG DNAL MiU WU MH PPCP

Linné, Carl von, 1707-1778, *praeses.*
... Dissertatio academica oves breviter adumbrans ... Upsaliæ, exc. L. M. Höjer [1754]
24 p. 18½ x 14½cm.
Library of Congress collection: Dissertationes academicae (Linné) no. 61.
Diss.—Upsala (I. Palmærus, respondent)
Error in paging: p. 12 numbered 13.
Also in Linné's Amoenitates academicae, v. 4, ed. 1, 1759 (and 1760); ed. 2, 1788, p. 169-189.
1. Sheep. I. Palmær, Isak Nilsson, 1734-1787, respondent.
9-1912 Revised
Library of Congress QH43.A2 no. 61
——— Copy 2. [r30d2]

NL 0390598 DLC WU MiU

Linné, Carl von, 1707-1778, *praeses.*
... Dissertatio academica, sistens inebriantia ... Upsaliæ [1761]
26 p. 20½ x 15½cm.
Library of Congress collection: Dissertationes academicae (Linné) no. 117.
Diss.—Upsala (O. R. Alander, respondent)
Also in Linné's Amoenitates academicae, v. 6, ed. 1, 1763; ed. 2, 1789, p. 180-196; and Gilibert's Systema plantarum Europæ, v. 6, 1786, p. 399-414.
1. Narcotics. 2. Stimulants. I. Alander, Olof Reinh., respondent. II. Title: Inebriantia.
30-16761
Library of Congress QH43.A2 no. 117
[2]

NL 0390599 DLC WU MiU

Linné, Carl von, 1707-1778, *praeses.*
... Dissertatio academica sistens iter in Chinam ... Upsaliæ, apud J. Edman [1768]
16 p. 21½ x 17cm.
Library of Congress collection: Dissertationes academicae (Linné) no. 161.
Diss.—Upsala (A. Sparrman, respondent)
Also in Linné's Amoenitates academicae, v. 7, ed. 1, 1769; ed. 2, 1789, p. 497-506. cf. Hulth, Bibl. Linn. (1907) p. 139.
1. Voyages and travels. 2. Natural history. I. Sparrman, Anders, 1748-1820, respondent. II. Title: Iter in Chinam.
30-17882
Library of Congress QH43.A2 no. 161

NL 0390600 DLC IU WU MH NNBG MiU

VOLUME 334

Linné, Carl von, 1707–1778, *praeses.*
... Dissertatio academica, sistens nomenclatorem botanicum ... Holmiæ, literis direct. L. Salvii ₁1759₎

₁3₎–19, ₁1₎ p. 20ᶜᵐ.
Library of Congress collection: Dissertationes academicae (Linné) no. 107.
Diss.—Upsala (B. Berzelius, respondent).
Also in Linné's Amoenitates academicae, v. 5, ed. 1, 1760; ed. 2, 1788, p. 414–441; and in Gilibert's Systema plantarum Europæ, v. 5, 1786, p. 113–139.

1. Botany—Nomenclature.   I. Berzelius, Bengt, 1739–1777, respondent.
24–17480 Revised
Library of Congress   QH43.A2 no. 107
₁r30b2₎

NL 0390601   DLC NNBG MiU WU ICJ

Linné, Carl von, 1707–1778, *praeses.*
... Dissertatio academica, usum muscorum, breviter delineatura ... Upsaliæ ₁1766₎

2 p. l., 14, ₁2₎ p. 21ᶜᵐ.
Library of Congress collection: Dissertationes academicae (Linné) no. 148.
Diss.—Upsala (A. H. Berlin, respondent).
Also in Linné's Amoenitates academicae, v. 7, ed. 1, 1769; ed. 2, 1789, p. 370–384; and Gilibert's Systema plantarum Europæ, v. 5, 1786, p. 493–507.

1. Mosses.   I. Berlin, Anders, 1746–1773, respondent.
24–3814 Revised
Library of Congress   QH43.A2 no. 148
₁r30b2₎

NL 0390602   DLC NNBG WU MiU

Linné, Carl von, 1707–1778, *praeses.*
Dissertatio botanica de anandria ... Upsaliæ ₁1745₎

2 p. l., 15, ₁1₎ p. fold. pl. 19 x 16ᶜᵐ.
Library of Congress collection: Dissertationes academicae (Linné) no. 9.
Also in Linné's Amoenitates academicae, v. 1 ₁ed. 1₎ 1749, p. 161–174; ₁ed. 2₎ 1749 and ed. 3, 1787, p. 243–259. Translation in his Auserlesene abhandlungen, v. 3, 1778, p. 69–88.   *cf.* T. O. B. N. Krok, Bibliotheca botanica suecana (1925): Linné. 54.

1. Anandria.   I. Tursén, Erland Zacharias, 1722–1777, respondent.
7–1702 Revised
Library of Congress   QH43.A2 no. 9
₁r30d2₎

NL 0390603   DLC NNBG DNLM MiU WU ICJ

Linné, Carl von, 1707–1778, praeses.
Dissertatio botanica de Anandria.
(in Amoen. Acad. I. 1749)
Erland Z. Tursén, respondent.

NL 0390604   PPAN

Linné, Carl von, 1707–1778, *praeses.*
... Dissertatio botanica de betula nana ... Stockholmiæ, typis historiographi regni ₁1743₎

2 p. l., 20 p. pl. 19ᶜᵐ.
Library of Congress collection: Dissertationes academicae (Linné) no. 1.
Diss.—Upsala (L. M. Klase, respondent).
Also in Linné's Amoenitates academicae, v. 1 ₁ed. 1₎ 1749, p. 335–351; ₁ed. 2₎ 1749 and ed. 3, 1787, p. 1–22. For translations *see* T. O. B. N. Krok, Bibliotheca botanica suecana (1925): Linné 39.

1. Birch.   I. Klase, Lars Magnus, 1728–1766, respondent.
30–14769
Library of Congress   QH43.A2 no. 1

NL 0390605   DLC WU NNBG MiU

Linné, Carl von, 1707–1778, *praeses.*
... Dissertatio botanica de passiflora ... Holmiæ, typis L. Salvii ₁1745₎

2 p. l., 37, ₁1₎ p. fold. pl. 19½ x 15ᶜᵐ.
Library of Congress collection: Dissertationes academicae (Linné) no. 8.
Diss.—Upsala (J. C. Hallman, respondent).
Also in Linné's Amoenitates academicae, v. 1 ₁ed. 1₎ 1749, p. 244–279; ₁ed. 2₎ 1749 and ed. 3, 1787, p. 211–242.   *cf.* Hulth, Bibl. Linn. (1907) p. 42.

1. Passiflora.   I. Hallman, Johan Gustaf, 1727–1797, respondent.
7–1711 Revised
Library of Congress   QH43.A2 no. 8

NL 0390606   DLC NNBG RPJCB MiU WU

Linné, Carl von, 1707–1778, *praeses.*
... Dissertatio botanica de peloria ... Upsaliæ ₁1744₎

5 p. l., ₁3₎–18, ₁4₎ p. fold. pl. 19 x 16ᶜᵐ.
Library of Congress collection: Dissertationes academicae (Linné) no. 3.
Diss.—Upsala (D. Rudberg, respondent).
Also in Linné's Amoenitates academicae, v. 1 ₁ed. 1₎ 1749, p. 280–298; ₁ed. 2₎ 1749, and ed. 3, 1787, p. 55–73. For translations *see* T. O. B. N. Krok, Bibliotheca botanica suecana (1925): Linné. 40.

1. Peloria.   I. Rudberg, Daniel, d. 1797, respondent.
7–5508 Revised
Library of Congress   QH43.A2 no. 3

NL 0390607   DLC NNBG MiU WU DNLM

Linné, Carl von, 1707–1778, praeses.
    Diss. bot. de peloria.   Upsaliae, 1744.
    8°.
In: Linnaeus. Amoenitates acad. [etc.]
8°. Lugd. Bat., 1749, i, 280–298, 1 pl.
    Daniel Rudberg, respondent.

NL 0390608   DNLM

Linné, Carl von, 1707–1778.
... Dissertatio botanica de planta sceptrum carolinum dicta, quam ... præside Laurentio Robergio ... ventilandam sistit auctor Johannes Olavus Rudbeck ... Upsalis, literis Wernerianis ₁1731₎

4 p. l., 71 (*i. e.* 17), ₁5₎ p. pl. 19ᶜᵐ.
Page 17 erroneously numbered 71.
"Latinska texten + tab. av R.; men svenska utkastet till denna disputation är av Linné."—Krok.

1. Pedicularis.   I. Roberg, Lars, 1664–1742, praeses.   II. Rudbeck, Johan Olof, 1711–1790, respondent.   III. Title: Sceptrum carolinum.
28–6921
Library of Congress   QK495.P4L5

NL 0390609   DLC CtY MoSB

Linné, Carl von, 1707–1778, *praeses.*
... Dissertatio botanica in qua *Acrostichum* ... in Regia academia upsaliensi, præside ... Carolo Linnæo ... subjicit Johann Benjamin Heiligtag ... Upsaliæ ₁1745₎

facsim.: 4 p. l., 17 numb. l. 19 x 16½ᶜᵐ.
Library of Congress collection: Dissertationes academicae (Linné) no. 10.
Collation of original: 2 p. l., 17 p. pl.
Imperfect: plate wanting.
Positive reproduction from negative supplied by Linnean society, London. 1925.
Also in Linné's Amoenitates academicae, v. 1 ₁ed. 1₎ 1749, p. 144–160; ₁ed. 2₎ 1749 and ed. 3, 1787, p. 260–276.   *cf.* Hulth, Bibliogr. Linn. (1907)

1. Acrostichum.   I. Heiligtag, Johann Benjamin, respondent.
31–18800
Library of Congress   QH43.A2 no. 10

NL 0390610   DLC MiU

Linné, Carl von, 1707–1778, *praeses.*
... Dissertatio botanica-medica, sistens lignum qvassiæ ... Upsaliæ, 1763.

1 p. l., 18, ₁1₎ p. fold. pl. 19ᶜᵐ.
Library of Congress collection: Dissertationes academicae (Linné) no. 127.
Diss.—Upsala (C. M. Blom, respondent).
Also appeared in the Amoenitates, v. 6, ed. 1, Holmiae, 1763 (Lugd. Bat., 1764); ed. 2, Erlangae, 1789, p. 416–429, pl. 4.   *cf.* Brit. mus. (Nat. hist.) Library. Catalogue; *also* J. M. Hulth, Bibliographia Linnaeana.

1. Quassia ₁amara₎   I. Blom, Carl Magnus, 1737–1815, respondent.
Agr 25–1463 Revised
Library, U. S. Dept. of   Agriculture 452.8L64L
Library of Congress   QH43.A2 no. 127
₁r30b2₎

NL 0390611   DNAL WU NNBG DSI MiU PPAN PPULC

Linné, Carl von, 1707–1778, *praeses.*
... Dissertatio botanica-medica sistens rariora norvegiæ ... Upsaliæ, litteris J. Edman ₁1768₎

3 p. l., 19. ₁1₎ p. illus. 21½ x 17ᶜᵐ.
Library of Congress collection: Dissertationes academicae (Linné) no. 157.
Diss.—Upsala (H. Tonning, respondent).
Also in Linné's Amoenitates academicae, v. 7, ed. 1, 1769; ed. 2, 1789, p. 466–496.   *cf.* Hulth, Bibl. Linn. (1907) p. 138.
"Corollarium de Gunnera": p. 18–19.
Manuscript leaf inserted between p. 18 and 19.

1. Botany, Medical. ₁1. Medical botany₎ 2. Botany—Norway. ₁2. Norway—Botany₎   I. Tonning, Henrik, 1732–1796, respondent.
Agr 28–1053 Revised 2
Library, U. S. Dept. of   ₁Agriculture 459.1L64R
Library of Congress   QH43.A2 no. 157
₁r31d2₎

NL 0390612   DNAL ICJ WU MH MiU NNBG

Linné, Carl von, 1707–1778, *praeses.*
... Dissertatio botanica metamorphoses plantarum sistens ... Holmiæ, e Typographia regia ₁1755₎

26 p. 19½ x 15½ᶜᵐ.
Library of Congress collection: Dissertationes academicae (Linné) no. 66.
Diss.—Upsala (N. E. Dahlberg, respondent).
Also in Linné's Amoenitates academicae, v. 4, ed. 1, 1759 (and 1760); ed. 2, 1788, p. 368–386. For other reprints *see* J. M. Hulth, Bibliographia Linn. (1907) p. 100.

1. Botany—Morphology.   I. Dalberg, Nils Ericsson, 1736–1820, respondent.
7–1713 Revised
Library of Congress   QH43.A2 no. 66

NL 0390613   DLC WU MiU NNBG

Linné, Carl von, 1707–1778, *praeses.*
... Dissertatio botanica qua nova plantarum genera ... sub præsidio ... Caroli Linnæi ... proponit Leonhard Joh. Chenon ... Upsaliæ ₁1751₎

4 p. l., 47, ₁1₎ p. fold. pl. 18½ x 15½ᶜᵐ.
Library of Congress collection: Dissertationes academicae (Linné) no. 32.
Error in paging: p. 13 numbered 15.
Imperfect: folded plate wanting.
Also in Linné's Amoenitates academicae, v. 3, ed. 1, 1756; ed. 2, 1787 and ed. 3, 1787, p. 1–27.   *cf.* Hulth, Bibl. Linn. (1907) p. 83.
CONTENTS.—Genera Americae septentrionalis.—Genera miscellanea.

1. Botany. 2. Botany—North America.   I. Chenon, Leonhard Johan, 1732–1808, respondent.
30–14787
Library of Congress   QH43.A2 no. 32

NL 0390614   DLC ICJ MiU DNAL NNBG MiU

Linné, Carl von, 1707–1778, *praeses.*
... Dissertatio botanica, qua plantæ Martino-Burserianæ explicantur ... Upsaliæ ₁1745₎

4 p. l., 31, ₁1₎ p. 19½ x 15½ᶜᵐ.
Library of Congress collection: Dissertationes academicae (Linné) no. 6.
Diss.—Upsala (R. Martin, respondent).
Also in Linné's Amoenitates academicae, v. 1 ₁ed. 1₎ 1749, p. 299–332; ₁ed. 2₎ 1749 and ed. 3, 1787, p. 141–171.   *cf.* Hulth, Bibl. Linn. (1907) p. 46.

1. Upsala. Universitet. Herbarium Burserianum. 2. Burser, Joachim, 1583–1639.   I. Martin. Roland, 1726–1788, respondent.   II. Martin, Petrus, 1686–1729.
Agr 26–1390 Revised 2
Library, U. S. Dept. of   Agriculture 452.4L64D
Library of Congress   QH43.A2 no. 6
₁r30d2₎

NL 0390615   DNAL NNBG MiU WU

Linné, Carl von, 1707–1778, *praeses.*
... Dissertatio botanica, sistens nectaria florum ... Upsaliæ ₁1762₎

1 p. l., 16 p. 20ᶜᵐ.
Library of Congress collection: Dissertationes academicae (Linné) no. 122.
Diss.—Upsala (B. M. Hall, respondent).
Also in Linné's Amoenitates academicae, v. 6, ed. 1, 1763; ed. 2, 1789, p. 263–278. For other reprints and translations *see* T. O. B. N. Krok, Bibliotheca botanica suecana (1925): Linné 162.

1. Nectaries.   I. Hall, Birger Martin, 1741–1814, respondent.
24–17485 Revised
Library of Congress   QH43.A2 no. 122

NL 0390616   DLC NNBG WU MiU

Linné, Carl von, 1707–1778, *praeses.*
... Dissertatio botanica sistens splachnum ... Stockholmiæ, typis L. Salvii ₁1750₎

2 p. l., 15, ₁1₎ p. pl. 20 x 16ᶜᵐ.
Library of Congress collection: Dissertationes academicae (Linné) no. 27.
Diss.—Upsala (L. Montin, respondent).
Also in Linné's Amoenitates academicae, v. 2, ed. 1, 1751 (and 1752) and ed. 3, 1787, p. 263–283; ed. 2, 1762, p. 240–260.   *cf.* Hulth, Bibl. Linn. (1907) p. 77.
"Juncus gluma biflora terminali ... descriptio novæ speciei Junci": p. 3–4, note, fig. 3 of the plate.

1. Splachnum. 2. Juncus. 3. Mosses—Lapland.   I. Montin, Lars, 1723–1785, respondent.
30–14784
Library of Congress   QH43.A2 no. 27

NL 0390617   DLC NNBG MiU

Linné, Carl von, 1707–1778, *praeses.*
... Dissertatio botanica, sistens stationes plantarum ... Upsaliæ, exc. L. M. Höjer ₁1754₎

3 p. l., 23, ₁1₎ p. 19½ x 15½ᶜᵐ.
Library of Congress collection: Dissertationes academicae (Linné) no. 55.
Diss.—Upsala (A. Hedenberg, respondent).
Also in Linné's Amoenitates academicae, v. 4, ed. 1, 1759 (and 1760); ed. 2, 1788, p. 64–87. For other reprints and translations *see* J. M. Hulth, Bibliographia Linnaeana (1907) p. 97.

1. Botany—Ecology. 2. Botany—Geographical distribution.   I. Hedenberg, Anders, 1737–1798, respondent.
Agr 26–1379 Revised
Library, U. S. Dept. of   Agriculture 452.4L64D
Library of Congress   QH43.A2 no. 55

NL 0390618   DNAL NNBG WU MiU

VOLUME 334

Linné, Carl von, 1707-1778, praeses.
... Dissertatio botanico-medica de Viola ipecacuanha ...
see his ... Dissertatio de Viola ipecacuanha.

Linné, Carl von, 1707–1778, *praeses.*
... Dissertatio botanico-medica, in qua *Fungus melitensis* ... publice ventilationi proponitur ... Upsaliæ, excud. L. M. Höjer [1755]
2 p. l., 16 p. pl. 20cm.
Library of Congress collection: Dissertationes academicae (Linné) no. 68.
Diss.—Upsala (J. Pfeiffer, respondent)
Also in Linné's Amoenitates academicae, v. 4, ed. 1, 1759 (and 1760); ed. 2, 1788, p. 35[1]-367; Sel. ex Amoenitat. v. 2, 1766, p. 153-171. *cf.* Hulth, Bibl. Linn. (1907) p. 101.
1. Cynomorium coccineum. I. Pfeiffer, Johan, respondent. II. Title: Fungus melitensis.
24-3813 Revised
Library of Congress QH43.A2 no. 68

NL 0390620 DLC NNBG DSI WU MiU

Linné, Carl von, 1707–1778, *praeses.*
... Dissertatio botanico-oeconomica de esca avium domesticarum ... Upsaliæ, typis Edmannianis [1774]
1 p. l., 15 p. 17½ x 14cm.
Library of Congress collection: Dissertationes academicae (Linné) no. 174.
Diss.—Upsala (P. Holmberger, respondent and author)
Error in paging: p. 9 numbered 17.
Also in Linné's Amoenitates academicae, v. 8, 1785, p. 205-220.
1. Insects, Injurious and beneficial. 2. Poultry. I. Holmberger, Per, 1745-1807, respondent.
30-17892
Library of Congress QH43.A2 no. 174

NL 0390621 DLC WU MiU

Linné, Carl von, 1707–1778, *praeses.*
... Dissertatio chemico medica de methodo investigandi vires medicamentorum chemica ... Upsaliæ, exc. L. M. Höjer [1754]
16 p. 18½ x 15cm.
Library of Congress collection: Dissertationes academicae (Linné) no. 58.
Diss.—Upsala (L. Hiortzberg, respondent)
Also in Linné's Amoenitates academicae, v. 9, 1785, p. 23-34.
1. Drugs. I. Hiortzberg, Lars, respondent.
30-14790
Library of Congress QH43.A2 no. 58

NL 0390622 DLC WU DSI PPCP MiU

Linné, Carl von, 1707–1778, *praeses.*
... Dissertatio, corallia baltica adumbrans ... Upsaliæ 1745]
4 p. l., 40 p. fold. pl. 19 x 15cm.
Library of Congress collection: Dissertationes academicae (Linné) no. 4.
Diss.—Upsala (H. Fougt, respondent)
Also in Linné's Amoenitates academicae, v. 1 [ed. 1] 1749, p. 177-212; [ed. 2] 1749 and ed. 3, 1787, p. 74-106. For other reprints and translations *see* J. M. Hulth, Bibliographia Linnaeana (1907) p. 46.
1. Corals—Baltic Sea. I. Fougt, Henrik, respondent.
30-14771
Library of Congress QH43.A2 no. 4

NL 0390623 DLC MiU MnU-B WU

Linné, Carl von, 1707–1778, *praeses.*
... Dissertatio de coloniis plantarum ... Upsaliæ, apud J. Edman [1768]
13 p. 19cm.
Library of Congress collection: Dissertationes academicae (Linné) no. 159.
Diss.—Upsala (J. Flygare, respondent)
Also in Linné's Amoenitates academicae, v. 8, 1785, p. 1-12; and Gilbert's Systema plantarum europa, v. 6, 1786, Suppl. p. 1-12.
1. Plants—Migration. [1. Plant migration] 2. Botany—Sweden. [2. Sweden—Botany] I. Flygare, Jöns, 1746-1806, respondent.
Agr 26-1377 Revised
Library, U. S. Dept. of Agriculture 452.4L64D
Library of Congress QH43.A2 no. 159

NL 0390624 DNAL ICJ WU NNBG MiU

Linné, Carl von, 1707–1778, *praeses.*
... Dissertatio de cortice peruviano ... Upsaliæ, excud. L. M. Höjer [1758]
1 p. l., 38 p. 18½ x 15cm.
Library of Congress collection: Dissertationes academicae (Linné) no. 90.
Diss.—Upsala (J. C. P. Petersen, respondent)
Also in Linné's Amoenitates academicae, v. 9, 1785, p. 64-105.
Part 1 only; pt. II, "Pro gradu doctoris. 1763. Gryphiswald". *cf.* Krok, Bibl. bot. suecana (1925) p. 572.
1. Cinchona. I. Petersen, Johan Christian Peter, 1739-1774, respondent.
30-16743
Library of Congress QH43.A2 no. 90

NL 0390625 DLC RPJCB NNBG MH-A MiU

Linné, Carl von, 1707–1778, *praeses.*
... Dissertatio de horticultura academia ... Upsaliæ, excud. L. M. Höjer [1754]
4 p. l., 21, [3] p. 21 x 18cm.
Library of Congress collection: Dissertationes academicae (Linné) no. 63.
Diss.—Upsala (J. G. Wollrath, respondent)
Also in Linné's Amoenitates academicae, v. 4, ed. 1, 1759 (and 1760); ed. 2, 1788, p. 210-229. For translation *see* T. O. B. N. Krok, Bibliotheca botanica suecana (1925): Linné, 126.
1. Gardening. [1. Horticulture] 2. Botany—Ecology. I. Wollrath, Johan Gustaf, respondent.
Agr 26-1548 Revised
Library, U. S. Dept. of Agriculture 452.4L64D
Library of Congress QH43.A2 no. 62

NL 0390626 DNAL WU NNBG MiU

Linné, Carl von, 1707–1778, *praeses.*
... Dissertatio de materia medica in regno animali ... Upsaliæ [1750]
20 p. 18½ x 14cm.
Library of Congress collection: Dissertationes academicae (Linné) no. 29.
Diss.—Upsala (J. Sidrén, respondent)
Also in Linné's Amoenitates academicae, v. 2, ed. 1, 1751 (and 1752) and ed. 3, 1787, p. 307-331; ed. 2, 1762, p. 281-305. *cf.* Hulth, Bibl. Linn. (1907) p. 77.
"Cette dissertation avec cette autre intitulée: De materia medica in regno lapideo, fut imprimée en 1763, en un seul volume."—Hulth.
1. Materia medica, Animal. I. Sidrén, Jonas, 1723-1799, respondent.
30-14785
Library of Congress QH43.A2 no. 29

NL 0390627 DLC MiU WU DNLM PPC

Linné, Carl von, 1707–1778, *praeses.*
... Dissertatio de materia medica in regno lapideo ... Upsaliæ, excudit L. M. Höjer [1752]
28 p. 18½ x 15cm.
Library of Congress collection: Dissertationes academicae (Linné) no. 37.
Diss.—Upsala (J. Lindhult, respondent)
Also in Linné's Amoenitates academicae, v. 3, ed. 1, 1756; ed. 2, 1762; ed. 3, 1787, p. 132-157. *cf.* Hulth, Bibl. Linn. (1907) p. 85.
1. Materia medica, Mineral. I. Lindhult, Johan, 1718-1770, respondent.
30-17889
Library of Congress QH43.A2 no. 37

NL 0390628 DLC WU MiU PPAN DNLM PPC

Linné, Carl von, 1707–1778, *praeses.*
... Dissertatio de morbis ex hyeme ... Upaliæ [!] excudit L. M. Höjer [1752]
2 p. l., 3-23 p. 20½ x 17cm.
Library of Congress collection: Dissertationes academicae (Linné) no. 38.
Diss.—Upsala (S. Brodd, respondent)
Also in Linné's Amoenitates academicae, v. 3, ed. 1, 1756; ed. 2, 1764; ed. 3, 1787, p. 158-182. *cf.* Hulth, Bibl. Linn. (1907) p. 85.
1. Climatology, Medical. 2. Winter. I. Brodd, Sueno, respondent.
30-14791
Library of Congress QH43.A2 no. 38

NL 0390629 DLC MiU PPC DNLM

Linné, Carl von, 1707–1778, *praeses.*
... Dissertatio de morbis nautarum Indiæ ... Upsaliæ, apud J. Edman [1768]
facsim.: 4 numb. l. 19cm.
Library of Congress collection: Dissertationes academicae (Linné) no. 160.
Diss.—Upsala (C. H. Wånman, respondent and author)
Collation of original: 4 p.
"Cette thèse composée par le respondant en personne ne fut pas admise par la Faculté par cette raison 'que le candidat avait fait preuve de trop de faiblesse tant ce que concernait le latin que la science même'."—Hulth, Bibl. Linn. (1907) p. 138.
Also in Linné's Amoenitates academicae, v. 7, ed. 1, 1769; ed. 2, 1789, p. 497-506.
Positive reproduction from negative supplied by Linnean society, London, 1925.
1. Naval hygiene. I. Wånman, Carolus Henricus, respondent.
30-17881
Library of Congress QH43.A2 no. 160

NL 0390630 DLC MiU PPC

Linné, Carl von, 1707–1778, *praeses.*
... Dissertatio de *Viola ipecacuanha* ... Upsaliæ, typis Edmannianis [1774]
12 p. 18cm.
Library of Congress collection: Dissertationes academicae (Linné) no. 176.
Diss.—Upsala (D. Wickman, respondent and author)
Also in Linné's Amoenitates academicae, v. 8, 1785, p. 238-248.
1. Ipecacuanha. [1. Ionidium ipecacuanha] I. Wickman, Daniel, 1741-1800, respondent. II. [Title: Viola ipecacuanha]
Agr 26-1395 Revised
Library, U. S. Dept. of Agriculture 452.4L64D
Library of Congress QH43.A2 no. 176

NL 0390631 DNAL NNBG WU DNLM MiU

Linné, Carl von, 1707–1778, *praeses.*
... Dissertatio diætetica de diaeta per scalam aetatis humanae observanda ... Upsaliæ [1764]
12 p. 20 x 17 cm.
Library of Congress collection: Dissertationes academicae (Linné) no. 136.
Diss.—Upsala (D. J. Öhrqvist, respondent and author)
Also under title Diaeta aetatum in Linné's Amoenitates academicae, v. 7, ed. 1, 1769; ed. 2, 1789, p. 74-83. *cf.* Hulth, Bibl. Linn. (1907) p. 130.
1. Diet—Early works to 1800. I. Öhrqvist, Daniel Johan, respondent.
QH43.A2 no. 136 30—16770

NL 0390632 DLC ICJ PPC MiU OkU

Linné, Carl von, 1707–1778, *praeses.*
... Dissertatio diætetica, de pingvedine animali ... Upsaliæ [1759]
32 p. 20½cm.
Library of Congress collection: Dissertationes academicae (Linné) no. 108.
Diss.—Upsala (J. Lindh, respondent)
Also under title Sus scrofa in Linné's Amoenitates academicae, v. 5, ed. 1, 1760; ed. 2, 1788, p. 461-483. *cf.* Hulth, Bibl. Linn. (1907) p. 118.
1. Swine. I. Lindh, Jacobus, respondent.
30-16756
Library of Congress QH43.A2 no. 108

NL 0390633 DLC ICJ DNLM MiU WU

Linné, Carl von, 1707–1778, *praeses.*
... Dissertatio diætetica in qua motus polychrestus delineatur ... Upsaliæ [1763]
1 p. l., [1], 20 p. 21 x 17cm.
Library of Congress collection: Dissertationes academicae (Linné) no. 131.
Diss.—Upsala (C. Lado, respondent)
Also in Linné's Amoenitates academicae, v. 7, ed. 1, 1769; ed. 2, 1789, p. 1-17. *cf.* Hulth, Bibl. Linn. (1907) p. 129.
1. Exercise. I. Lado, Christian, respondent.
30-16766
Library of Congress QH43.A2 no. 131
[2]

NL 0390634 DLC WU KMK MiU PPC ICJ

Linné, Carl von, 1707–1778, *praeses.*
... Dissertatio diætetica, in qua spiritus frumenti. proponitur ... Upsaliæ [1764]
20 p. 21½ x 17½cm.
Library of Congress collection: Dissertationes academicae (Linné) no. 135.
Diss.—Upsala (P. Bergius, respondent)
Also in Linné's Amoenitates academicae, v. 7, ed. 1, 1769; ed. 2, 1789, p. 264-281. For other reprints, abstracts, etc. *see* J. M. Hulth, Bibliographia Linnaeana (1907) p. 130.
1. Liquors. I. Bergius, Peter Jonas, 1730-1790, respondent.
30-16769
Library of Congress QH43.A2 no. 135

NL 0390635 DLC MiU WU

Linné, Carl von, 1707–1778, *praeses.*
Dissertatio entomologica, bigas insectorum sistens ... Upsaliæ, typis Edmannianis [1775]
2 p. l., 7, [1] p. fold. pl. 18½cm.
Library of Congress collection: Dissertationes academicae (Linné) no. 184.
Diss.—Upsala (A. Dahl, respondent)
Also in Linné's Amoenitates academicae, v. 8, 1785, p. 303-309.
The two insects described are *Diopsis* and *Paussus*.
1. Diopsis. 2. Paussus. I. Dahl, Anders, 1751-1789, respondent.
30-17898
Library of Congress QH43.A2 no. 184

NL 0390636 DLC PPAN NN WU MiU

VOLUME 334

Linné, Carl von, 1707–1778, *praeses.*
... Dissertatio fundamenta valetudinis sistens ... Upsaliæ, excud. L. M. Höjer ₍1756₎
2 p. l., 13, ₍1₎ p. 22 x 18ᶜᵐ.
Library of Congress collection: Dissertationes academicae (Linné) no. 75.
Diss.—Upsala (P. Engström, respondent)
Also in Linné's Amoenitates academicae, v. 4, ed. 1, 1759 (and 1760); ed. 2, 1788, p. 496–506. *cf.* Hulth, Bibl. Linn. (1907) p. 104.

1. Hygiene.   I. Engström, Peter, 1735–1803, respondent.

30–14805

Library of Congress   QH43.A2 no. 75

NL 0390637   DLC WU MiU DNLM

Linné, Carl von, 1707–1778, *praeses.*
... Dissertatio inauguralis medica, de hæmorrhagiis ex plethora ... Upsaliæ, typis Edmannianis ₍1772₎
2 p. l., 32 p. 19 x 15ᶜᵐ.
Library of Congress collection: Dissertationes academicae (Linné) no. 160.
Diss.—Upsala (E. J. M. ab Heidenstam, respondent and author)
Also in Linné's Amoenitates academicae, v. 9, 1785, p. 195–222.

1. Hemorrhage.   I. Heidenstam, Ernst Joachim Magnus von, 1745–1803, respondent.

30–17889

Library of Congress   QH43.A2 no. 169

NL 0390638   DLC DNLM WU MiU PPC

Linné, Carl von, 1707–1778, *praeses.*
... Dissertatio medica, de acetariis ... Upsaliæ, excud. L. M. Höjer ₍1756₎
2 p. l., 16 p. 18½ x 15ᶜᵐ.
Library of Congress collection: Dissertationes academicae (Linné) no. 77.
Diss.—Upsala (H. von der Burg, respondent)
Also in Linné's Amoenitates academicae, v. 4, ed. 1, 1759 (and 1760); ed. 2, 1788, p. 536–552. For other reprints *see* J. M. Hulth, Bibliographia Linnaeana (1907) p. 105.

1. Botany, Economic. 2. Botany, Medical. 3. Salads.   I. Burg. Hieronymus von der, 1730–1811, respondent.

30–14806

Library of Congress   QH43.A2 no. 77

NL 0390639   DLC WU MiU PPC DNAL

Linné, Carl von, 1707–1778, *praeses.*
... Dissertatio medica, de effectu et cura vitiorum diæteticorum generali ... Upsaliæ ₍1766₎
24 p. 22 x 18ᶜᵐ.
Library of Congress collection: Dissertationes academicae (Linné) no. 147.
Diss.—Upsala (J. G. Bergman, respondent)
Also under title Cura generalis in Linné's Amoenitates academicae, v. 7, ed. 1, 1769; ed. 2, 1789, p. 345–369. *cf.* Hulth, Bibl. Linn. (1907) p. 134.

1. Diet—Early works to 1800.   I. Bergman, Johan Gabriel, 1732–1793, respondent.

30–17874

Library of Congress   QH43.A2 no. 147

NL 0390640   DLC WU MiU PPC

Linné, Carl von, 1707–1778, *praeses.*
... Dissertatio medica de hæmorrhagiis uteri sub statu graviditatis ... Upsaliæ ₍1749₎
23, ₍1₎ p. 18½ x 14½ᶜᵐ.
Library of Congress collection: Dissertationes academicae (Linné) no. 25.
Error in paging: p. 12 numbered 2.
Also in Linné's Amoenitates academicae, v. 9, 1785, p. 1–22.

1. Hemorrhage, Uterine.   I. Elff, Eric, 1718–1761, respondent.

30–14783

Library of Congress   QH43.A2 no. 25

NL 0390641   DLC MiU WU DNLM

Linné, Carl von, 1707–1778, *praeses.*
... Dissertatio medica de ledo palustri ... Upsaliæ, typis Edmannianis ₍1775₎
1 p. l., 18 p. 18½ x 15ᶜᵐ.
Library of Congress collection: Dissertationes academicae (Linné) no. 178.
Diss.—Upsala (J. P. Westring, respondent and author)
Also in Linné's Amoenitates academicae, v. 8, p. 268–288.

1. Ledum palustre.   I. Westring, Johan Peter, 1753–1833, respondent.

7–1714 Revised

Library of Congress   QH43.A2 no. 178

NL 0390642   DLC WU NNBG MiU

Linné, Carl von, 1707–1778, praeses.

Grysselius, Johannes, *respondent and author.*
... Dissertatio medica, De medico sui ipsius. Quam ... submittit stip. reg. Johannes Grysselius ... Upsaliæ, litteris Joh. Edman, 1768.

Linné, Carl von, 1707–1778, *praeses.*
... Dissertatio medica, de meloë vesicatorio ... Upsaliæ ₍1762₎
2 p. l., 15, ₍1₎ p. 19 x 15½ᶜᵐ.
Library of Congress collection: Dissertationes academicae (Linné) no. 125.
Diss.—Upsala (C. A. Lenaeus, respondent)
Also in Linné's Amoenitates academicae, v. 6, ed. 1, 1763; ed. 2, 1789, p. 132–147. *cf.* Hulth, Bibl. Linn. (1907) p. 126.

1. Cantharides.   I. Lenaeus, Knut Aug., 1738–1799, respondent.

30–16763

Library of Congress   QH43.A2 no. 125

NL 0390644   DLC WU MiU

Linné, Carl von, 1707–1778, *praeses.*
... Dissertatio medica de menthæ usu ... Upsaliæ, apud J. Edman ₍1767₎
2 p. l., 11, ₍1₎ p. 21 x 17ᶜᵐ.
Library of Congress collection: Dissertationes academicae (Linné) no. 154.
Diss.—Upsala (C. G. Laurin, respondent)
Also in Linné's Amoenitates academicae, v. 7, ed. 1, 1769; ed. 2, 1789, p. 282–292; and in Gilibert's Systema plantarum Europæ. v. 6, 1786, p. 261–271. *cf.* Hulth, Bibl. Linn. (1907) p. 136.

1. Mentha.   I. Laurin, Carl Gustaf, respondent.

25–17384 Revised

Library of Congress   QH43.A2 no. 154

NL 0390645   DLC NNBG MH WU MiU PPC DNLM DSI

Linné, Carl von, 1707–1778, *praeses.*
... Dissertatio medica, de pulsu intermittente ... Upsaliæ, excud. L. M. Höjer ₍1756₎
2 p. l., 18 p. 23 x 19ᶜᵐ.
Library of Congress collection: Dissertationes academicae (Linné) no. 72.
Diss.—Upsala (A. Wåhlin, respondent)
Also in Linné's Amoenitates academicae, v. 9, 1785, p. 43–63.

1. Pulse.   I. Wåhlin, Anders Magnus, 1731–1797, respondent.

30–14804

Library of Congress   QH43.A2 no. 78

NL 0390646   DLC WU MiU

Linné, Carl von, 1707–1778, *praeses.*
... Dissertatio medica, de spigelia anthelmia ... Upsaliæ, excud. L. M. Höjer ₍1758₎
16 p. fold. pl. 19 x 15ᶜᵐ.
Library of Congress collection: Dissertationes academicae (Linné) no. 89.
Diss.—Upsala (J. G. Colliander, respondent)
Imperfect: folded plate wanting.
Also in Linné's Amoenitates academicae, v. 5, ed. 1, 1760; ed. 2, 1788, p. 133–147. *cf.* Hulth, Bibl. Linn. (1907) p. 112.

1. Spigelia.   I. Colliander, Johan Georg, 1728–1796, respondent.

30–16742

Library of Congress   QH43.A2 no. 89

NL 0390647   DLC NNBG WU MiU

Linné, Carl von, 1707–1778, *praeses.*
Dissertatio medica de varia febrium intermittentium curatione ... Upsaliæ, typis Edmannianis ₍1771₎
56 p., 1 l. 19½ x 16½ᶜᵐ.
Library of Congress collection: Dissertationes academicae (Linné) no. 167.
Diss.—Upsala (P. C. Tillaeus, respondent and author)
Also in Linné's Amoenitates academicae, v. 9, 1785, p. 143–194.
Imperfect: leaf at end wanting.

1. Malarial fever.   I. Tillæus, Pehr Cornelius, b. 1747, respondent.

30–17887

Library of Congress   QH43.A2 no. 167
—————— Copy 2.   Imperfect: p. 49–56 and 1 leaf wanting.

NL 0390648   DLC WU MiU DNLM PPC

Linné, Carl von, 1707–1778, *praeses.*
... Dissertatio medica, in qua potus coffeæ, leviter adumbratur ... Upsaliæ ₍1761₎
1 p. l., 18 p. fold. pl. 19½ x 15½ᶜᵐ.
Library of Congress collection: Dissertationes academicae (Linné) no. 118.
Diss.—Upsala (H. Sparschuch, respondent)
Also in Linné's Amoenitates academicae, v. 6, ed. 1, 1763; ed. 2, 1789, p. 160–179. For other reprints and translations *see* J. M. Hulth, Bibliographia Linnaeana (1907) p. 123.

1. Coffee.   I. Sparschuch, Henrik, 1742–1786, respondent.

7–8930 Revised

Library of Congress   QH43.A2 no. 118

NL 0390649   DLC WU MiU MH-A DNLM NNBG ICJ

Linné, Carl von, 1707–1778, *praeses.*
... Dissertatio medica inauguralis de haemoptysi ... Upsaliæ, litteris J. Edman ₍1767₎
14 p. 22ᶜᵐ.
Library of Congress collection: Dissertationes academicae (Linné) no. 150.
Diss.—Upsala (J. M. Gråberg, respondent)
Also in Linné's Amoenitates academicae, v. 9, 1785, p. 118–130.

1. Hemorrhage.   I. Gråberg, Johan Martin, respondent.

30–17876

Library of Congress   QH43.A2 no. 150

NL 0390650   DLC WU MiU PPC

Linné, Carl von, 1707–1778, *praeses.*
... Dissertatio medica inauguralis de potu chocolatæ ... Holmiæ, literis direct. L. Salvii ₍1765₎
1 p. l., 10 p. 18 x 15ᶜᵐ.
Library of Congress collection: Dissertationes academicae (Linné) no. 142.
Diss.—Upsala (A. Hoffman, respondent)
Also in Linné's Amoenitates academicae, v. 7, ed. 1, 1769; ed. 2, 1789, p. 254–263. For other reprints and translations *see* J. M. Hulth, Bibliographia Linnaeana (1907) p. 132.

1. Chocolate.   I. Hoffman, Anton, 1739–1782, respondent.

7–8931 Revised

Library of Congress   QH43.A2 no. 142

NL 0390651   DLC WU NNBG NN MH-A MiU

Linne, Carl von, 1707–1778, respondent.
Dissertatio medica inauguralis in qua exhibetur hypothesis nova de febrium intermittentium causa...
   see under Gorter, Johannes de, 1689–1762, praeses.

Linné, Carl von, 1707–1778, *praeses.*
Dissertatio medica inauguralis, sistens saporem medicamentorum ... Holmiæ, typis L. Salvii ₍1751₎
20 p. 19½ x 16ᶜᵐ.
Library of Congress collection: Dissertationes academicae (Linné) no. 31.
Diss.—Upsala (J. Rudberg, respondent)
Also in Linné's Amoenitates academicae, v. 2, ed. 1, 1751 (and 1752) and ed. 3, 1787, p. 365–387; ed. 2, 1762, p. 335–355. For other reprints and translation *see* J. M. Hulth, Bibliographia Linnaeana (1907) p. 88.

1. Drugs. 2. Botany, Medical.   I. Rudberg, Jakob, 1725–1778, respondent.

30–14786

Library of Congress   QH43.A2 no. 31

NL 0390653   DLC NNNAM DNLM WU MoSB MiU PPC

VOLUME 334

Linné, Carl von, 1707–1778, *praeses.*
... Dissertatio medica odores medicamentorum **exhibens** ... Stockholmiæ, typis L. Salvii [1752]
2 p. l., 16 p. 19cm.
Library of Congress collection: Dissertationes academicae (Linné) no. 40.
Diss.—Upsala (A. Wåhlin, respondent)
Also in Linné's Amoenitates academicae, v. 3, ed. 1, 1756; ed. 2, 1764; ed. 3, 1787, p. 183–201. For other reprints and translation see J. M. Hulth, Bibliographia Linnaeana (1907) p. 86.

1. Drugs. 2. Odors. I. Wåhlin, Anders Magnus, 1731–1797, respondent.
30-14793
Library of Congress QH43.A2 no. 40

NL 0390654 DLC WU MiU ICJ PPC

Linné, Carl von, 1707–1778, *praeses.*
Dissertatio medica sistens metamorphosin humanam ... Upsaliæ, litteris J. Edman [1767]
2 p. l., 18 p. fold. tab. 20 x 15½cm.
Library of Congress collection: Dissertationes academicae (Linné) no. 155.
Diss.—Upsala (J. A. Wadström, respondent)
Also in Linné's Amoenitates academicae, v. 7, ed. 1, 1769; ed. 2, 1789, p. 326–344. cf. Hulth, Bibl. Linn. (1907) p. 137.

1. Growth. I. Wadström, Johan Adolf, 1748–1809, respondent.
30-17879
Library of Congress QH43.A2 no. 155

NL 0390655 DLC ICJ WU PPL MiU PPC

Linné, Carl von, 1707–1778, *praeses.*
... Dissertatio medica sistens purgantia indigena ... Upsaliæ [1766]
2 p. l., 17, [1] p. 20 x 17cm.
Library of Congress collection: Dissertationes academicae (Linné) no. 144.
Diss.—Upsala (P. Strandman, respondent)
Also in Linné's Amoenitates academicae, v. 7, ed. 1, 1769; ed. 2, 1789, p. 293–310; and Gilibert's Systema plantarum Europæ, v. 6, 1786, p. 245–260. cf. Hulth, Bibl. Linn. (1907) p. 133.

1. Purgatives. 2. Botany, Medical. I. Strandman, Pehr, 1743–1779, respondent.
30-17871
Library of Congress QH43.A2 no. 144

NL 0390656 DLC NN WU MiU PPC

Linné, Carl von, 1707–1778, *praeses.*
... Dissertatio medico-botanica, exhibens plantas officinales ... Upsaliæ, exc. L. M. Höjer [1753]
2 p. l., 31, [1] p. 18½ x 14cm.
Library of Congress collection: Dissertationes academicae (Linné) no. 52.
Diss.—Upsala (N. Gahn, respondent)
Also in Linné's Amoenitates academicae, v. 4, ed. 1, 1759 (and 1760); ed. 2, 1788, p. 1–25; Gilibert's Systema plantarum Europæ, v. 6, 1786, p. 155–180. cf. Hulth, Bibl. Linn. (1907) p. 94.

1. Botany, Medical. I. Gahn, Nils, 1733–1820, respondent.
24-3810 Revised
Library of Congress QH43.A2 no. 52

NL 0390657 DLC NNBG WU MiU PPC

Linné, Carl von, 1707–1778, *praeses.*
... Dissertatio medico botanica, sistens rhabarbarum ... Upsaliæ, excudit L. M. Höjer [1752]
3 p. l., 24 p. fold. pl. 19½ x 17cm.
Library of Congress collection: Dissertationes academicae (Linné) no. 41.
Diss.—Upsala (S. Ziervogel, respondent)
Imperfect: folded plate wanting.
Also in Linné's Amoenitates academicae, v. 3, ed. 1, 1756; ed. 2, 1764; ed. 3, 1787, p. 211–230. cf. Hulth, Bibl. Linn. (1907) p. 86.
"Auctores qui rhabarbari descriptiones tradiderunt": p. 3–4.

1. Rhubarb. I. Ziervogel, Samuel, 1736–1797, respondent.
30-14794
Library of Congress QH43.A2 no. 41

NL 0390658 DLC WU NNBG MiU PPAN DNLM

Linné, Carl von, 1707–1778, *praeses.*
... Dissertatio medico-botanica sistens specifica canadensium ... Scarae [1756]
2 p. l., 28 p. 19 x 15½cm.
Library of Congress collection: Dissertationes academicae (Linné) no. 76.
Diss.—Upsala (J. von Coelln, respondent)
Also in Linné's Amoenitates academicae, v. 4, ed. 1, 1759 (and 1760); ed. 2, 1788, p. 507–535. cf. Hulth, Bibl. Linn. (1907) p. 104.

1. Botany, Medical. 2. Botany—U. S. I. Coelln, Johan von, 1725–1808, respondent.
7-1709 Revised
Library of Congress QH43.A2 no. 76

NL 0390659 DLC MU WU NNBG MiU

Linné, Carl von, 1707–1778, *praeses.*
... Dissertatio medico-chirurgica de hirudine ... Upsaliæ [1764]
2 p. l., 15, [1] p. 21 x 16½cm.
Library of Congress collection: Dissertationes academicae (Linné) no. 132.
Diss.—Upsala (D. Weser, respondent)
The date of the disputation has been changed in ms. on the t.-p. from 1764 to 1765 in agreement with the date given in the Amoenitates.
Also under title Hirudo medicinalis in Linné's Amoenitates academicae, v. 7, ed. 1, 1769; ed. 2, 1789, p. 42–54.

1. Leeches. I. Weser, Daniel, respondent.
30-16767
Library of Congress QH43.A2 no. 132

NL 0390660 DLC WU MiU PPAN

Linné, Carl von, 1707–1778, *praeses.*
Dissertatio physiologica de perspiratione insensibili ... Upsaliæ, apud J. Edman [1775]
11 p. 18½ x 15cm.
Library of Congress collection: Dissertationes academicae (Linné) no. 182.
Diss.—Upsala (N. Avellan, respondent and author)
Also in Linné's Amoenitates academicae, v. 9, 1785, p. 268–277.

1. Perspiration. I. Avellan, Nicolaus, respondent.
30-17896
Library of Congress QH43.A2 no. 182

NL 0390661 DLC DNLM PPAN PPULC WU MiU PPC

Linné, Carl von, 1707–1778, praeses.
Dissertatio topographica, de paroecia stenbrohult
see Brandt, Christianus H., praeses. [Supplement]

Linné, Carl von, 1707–1778.
A dissertation on the sexes of plants. Translated from the Latin of Linnaeus by James Edward Smith. London, Printed for the author, and sold by G. Nicol, 1786.
xv, 62 p. 22 cm.
Translation of Disquisitio de quaestione ...: sexum plantarum.
Bound with the author's Reflections on the study of nature. London, 1785.

1. Plants, Sex in. I. Smith, Sir James Edward, 1759–1828, tr. II. Title.
QH43.M8 1785 574 77-258494
MARC
70 [2]

NNBG
NL 0390663 DLC CtY PPT ICJ PPAmP DNAL PHi NNNAM

Linné, Carl von, 1707–1778, *praeses.*
... Dissertationem botanicam, de erica ... publicae ventilationi offert ... Johan Adolph Dahlgren ... Upsaliæ, typis Edmannianis [1770]
2 p. l., 15, [1] p. pl. 18 x 15cm.
Library of Congress collection: Dissertationes academicae (Linné) no. 163.
Diss.—Upsala (J. A. Dahlgren, respondent)
Also in Linné's Amoenitates academicae, v. 8, 1785, p. 46–62.

1. Erica. I. Dahlgren, Johan Adolph, 1744–1797, respondent.
7-1703 Revised
Library of Congress QH43.A2 no. 163

NL 0390664 DLC NNBG WU MH-A MiU WU

Linné, Carl von, 1707–1778, *praeses.*
... Dissertationem inauguralem, de maro ... praeside ... Carolo V. Linné ... publicae ventilatione offert auctor Joh. Adolph. Dahlgren ... Upsaliæ, typis Edmannianis [1774]
18 p. 21 x 16½cm.
Library of Congress collection: Dissertationes academicae (Linné) no. 175.
Also in Linné's Amoenitates academicae, v. 8, 1785, p. [221]–237.

1. Cat-thyme. I. Dahlgren, Johan Adolph, 1744–1797, respondent.
25-17385 Revised
Library of Congress QH43.A2 no. 175
——— Copy 2. 23 x 19cm.

NL 0390665 DLC NNBG WU PPC MH MiU

Linné, Carl von, 1707–1778, *praeses.*
... Dissertationem medicam de dulcamara ... moderante ... Carolo à Linné ... examinandam sistit ... Georgius Hallenberg ... Upsaliae, ex prelo Edmanniano [1771]
14 p. 21 x 16½cm.
Library of Congress collection: Dissertationes academicae (Linné) no. 164.
Also in Linné's Amoenitates academicae, v. 8, 1785, p. 63–74.

1. Bittersweet. I. Hallenberg, Georg, respondent.
30-17834
Library of Congress QH43.A2 no. 164

NL 0390666 DLC WU NN PPAN MiU

Linné, Carl von, 1707–1778, *praeses.*
... Dissertationem medicam, de varietate ciborum ... moderante ... Carolo à Linné ... publicæ censuræ submittit ... Adolph. Fried. Wedenberg ... Upsaliæ, litteris J. Edman [1767]
19, [1] p. 20½ x 17cm.
Library of Congress collection: Dissertationes academicae (Linné) no. 156.
Also in Linné's Amoenitates academicae, v. 7, ed. 1, 1769; ed. 2, 1789, p. 197–213; and Gilibert's Systema plantarum Europæ, v. 6, 1786, p. 301–316.

1. Food. I. Wedenberg, Adolph Frederik, 1743–1828, respondent.
30-17880
Library of Congress QH43.A2 no. 156

NL 0390667 DLC WU DNLM MiU PPC

Linné, Carl von, 1707–1778, *praeses.*
... Dissertationem medicam, qua morbi artificum leviter adumbrantur ... praeside ... Carolo von Linné ... pro gradu doctoris publico subjicit examini Nicolaus Skragge ... Upsaliæ [1765]
[1], 12 p. 21½ x 18cm.
Library of Congress collection: Dissertationes academicae (Linné) no. 140.
Also in Linné's Amoenitates academicae, v. 7, ed. 1, 1769; ed. 2, 1789, p. 84–93. cf. Hulth, Bibl. Linn. (1907) p. 131–132.

1. Occupations—Diseases and hygiene. I. Skragge, Nicolaus, respondent.
30-16774
Library of Congress QH43.A2 no. 140
[2]

NL 0390668 DLC WU PPL DNLM MiU

Linné, Carl von, 1707–1778, *praeses.*
... Dissertationem physiologicam de venis resorbibentibus ... praeside ... Carolo von Linné ... publicae ventilationi offert ... Carolus Petr. Thunberg ... Upsaliæ, litteris J. Edman [1767]
2 p. l., 10 p. 19 x 15cm.
Library of Congress collection: Dissertationes academicae (Linné) no. 151.
Also in Linné's Amoenitates academicae, v. 9, 1785, p. 131–142.

1. Veins. I. Thunberg, Karl Peter, 1743–1828, respondent.
30-17877
Library of Congress QH43.A2 no. 151

NL 0390669 DLC WU MiU DNLM

QH 43 .A 2
Linné, Carlo von.
[Dissertationes academicae, Upsala, Stockholm, 1743–1778.]
184 v. in 9 binders.

NL 0390670 DLC

VOLUME 334

QH
43
.A2

Linné, Carl von, 1707-1778, praeses.
    Dissertationes academicae, 1743-1776. v.p.,
1743-76.
    186 v. illus. plates. 18½-22 cm.
    A made-up set of the dissertations presented by
students of Uppsala University for which Linné
served as praeses, plus one (v.186) for which his
son Carl was praeses. Arrangement is chronological,
following the numbering in J.H.Lidén Cat.disputa-
tionum in academia... Suecia. The dissertations
are listed, with bibliography, in Brit.Mus.Dept.of
Printed Books. Cat.of the works of Linnaeus,2d ed,
London,1933,p.106-191.
    Laid in most of the dissertationes is the cor-
responding description clipped from Gustaf Drake's
Linnés disputationer,Nässjö,1939.
    I.Uppsala.   Universitet.

NL 0390671   MiU

Linné, Carl von, 1707-1778, *praeses.*
    [Dissertations 1745-1774.]
    25 pamphlets in 1 vol. 20ᶜᵐ.
    Binder's title.

NL 0390672   ICJ

---

x599
L64d

Linné, Carl von, 1707-1778.
    Djur som faller från skyn, Om sjubben, Mar-
kattan Diana: tre djurmonografier av Linnaeus. «Stockholm» Bibliofila klubben
«1951»
    18p. plates. 22cm. (Kuriositeter i lit-
teraturen, 10)

    Cover title.
    Introd. by Arvid Hj. Uggla.
    "Upplagan 475 numrerade exemplar — «Nr. 51»"
    Reprinted from K. Svenska vetenskapsakade-
mien. Handlingar, v.1, 1739-40; v.8,
1747; v.15, 1754.

NL 0390673   IU

Linné, Carl von, 1707-1778.
    Djuret narica. [Stockholm, 1768]
    140-145 p. illus.
    In Kungliga Svenska Vetenskaps-Akademien.
Handlingar. v. 29. 1768.
        Bound with Tvänne anmärkningar uti natu-
ral-historien. 1768.

NL 0390674   KMK

Linné, Carl von, 1707-1778.
    The economy of nature By Isaac J. Biberg.
Upsal, 1749. March 4. Tr. By Benjamin Stelling-
fleet.

    (In: Stillingfleet,Benjamin, ed and tr.
Miscellaneous tracts relating to natural history,
husbandry, and physick, 1762. p. 39-129)

NL 0390675   OU

Linné, Carl von, 1707-1778.
    Egenhändiga anteckningar af Carl Linnæus om sig
sielf, med anmärkningar och tillägg. Stockholm, 1823.
    1 p. l., xxiv, ₍6₎, 248, ₍28₎ p. vi pl. (incl. facsim.) fold. geneal. tab. 25½ᶜᵐ.
    Engr. t.-p.; title vignette (port.)
    "Förord" signed: Adam Afzelius.

    I. Afzelius, Adam, 1750-1837.

Library of Congress   QH44.L75   5-42347†

NL 0390676   DLC ICJ NN KMK WU MH-A DNLM PPAN CtY

Linné, Carl von, 1707-1778.
    Des archiaters und ritters Carl von Linné eigene, anonym
erschienene berichte über die zwölfte lateinische ausgabe seines
Natursystems enthüllt, abermals zum drucke befördert, aus
dem schwedischen übersetzt und mit einer einleitung versehen
von Felix Bryk. Stockholm, Im eigenen verlage, 1922.
    35 p. incl. facsims. 22ᶜᵐ.

    Cover-title: Carl von Linnés eigene referate über sein Systema naturæ.
No. 21 of 50 copies printed.

    1. Linné, Carl von, 1707-1778. Systema naturæ.   I. Bryk, Felix,
1882-

                                         27-9728

Library of Congress   QH43.S8

NL 0390677   DLC

W 1
H132
1955

LINNÉ, Carl von, 1707-1778
    Des Arztes und Naturforschers Carl
Linné eigene Lebensbeschreibung; ausgewählt, mit Anmerkungen und Bildern
versehen von Otto Zekert. ₍Wien, Heil-
mittelwerke Wien, 1954₎
    60 p. illus., ports. (HMW-Jahrbuch,
1955)
    I. Zekert, Otto, 1893-   ed.
Series

NL 0390678   DNLM DSI TxU

Linné, Carl von, 1707-1778.
    Linné's eigenhändige anzeichnungen über sich selbst, mit an-
merkungen und zusätzen von Afzelius. Aus dem schwedischen
übersetzt von Karl Lappe. Mit einer vorrede von dr. K. A.
Rudolphi ... Berlin, G. Reimer, 1826.
    xxiv, ₍2₎, 260, ₍2₎ p. front. (port.) pl. 22ᶜᵐ.

    1. Linné, Carl von, 1707-1778.   I. Afzelius, Adam, 1750-1837.
II. Lappe, Karl, tr. III. Rudolphi, Karl Asmund. 1771-1832.

                                          Agr 11-618

U. S. Dept. of agr. Library   120L64L
for Library of Congress   ₍a37b₎

NL 0390679   DNAL CU NNBG

WZ
290
L758e
1955

LINNÉ, Carl von, 1707-1778, praeses
    Elektriskt-medicinska satser (con-
sectaria electrico-medica) Svensk
översättning av Arvid Hj. Uggla, inledning, noter och efterskrift av Telemak
Fredbärj. ₍Ekenäs, 1955₎
    22 p. (Valda avhandlingar av Carl von
Linné, n:r 19)   WZ290 L758e
    Akademisk avhandling - Uppsala
(Petrus Zetzell, respondent) 1754.

    I. Fredbärj, Telemak, ed. II. Uggla,
Arvid Hjalmar, 1883-   tr. III. Zetzell,
Petrus, 1724-1802, respondent

NL 0390681   DNLM

Linné, Karl von, 1707-1778.

Rose, Hugh.
    The elements of botany ... Being a translation of the
Philosophia botanica, and other treatises of the celebrated
Linnæus, to which is added an appendix, wherein are
described some plants lately found in Norfolk and Suffolk
... By Hugh Rose ... London, T. Cadell ₍etc.₎ 1775.

Linné, Carl von (1707-1778).
    — Elenchus animalium per Sueciam observatorum
(*In his* Oratio de necessitate peregrinationum intra patriam.
1743, pp. 37-94.)

NL 0390683   MH-A

Linné, Carl von, 1707-1778.
    Caroli Linnæi Entomologia, faunæ suecicæ descriptionibus
aucta; DD. Scopoli, Geoffroy, de Geer, Fabricii, Schrank, &c.,
speciebus vel in systemate non enumeratis, vel nuperrime de-
tectis, vel speciebus Galliæ australis locupletata, generum
specierumque rariorum iconibus ornata; curante & augente
Carolo de Villers ... Lugduni, sumptibus Piestre et Dela-
molliere, 1789.
    4 v. xi (i. e. 12) fold. pl., xi fold. tab. 20½ᶜᵐ.
    L. C. copy imperfect: plates and tables wanting.

    1. Insects—Classification.   I. Villers, Charles Joseph de, 1724-
1809, ed.

                                         Agr 4-215 Revised

U. S. Dept. of agr. Library   422L64
for Library of Congress   QL468.L75
                                ₍r44b2₎†

    ICJ MB MnU

NL 0390684   DNAL NcD GU OrCS NcU PPAN OU DLC CtY

Linné, Carl von, 1707-1778.
    Caroli Linnaei epistolae ad Nicolaum Josephum Jacquin; ex
autographis edidit Car. Nic. Jos. eques a Schreibers C. F.;
praefatus est notasque adjecit Stephanus Endlicher. Vindobonae, typis et sumtibus C. Gerold, 1841.
    viii, 167 p. 23ᶜᵐ.

    I. Endlicher, Stephan Friedrich Ladislaus, 1804-1849. II. Jacquin,
Nikolaus Joseph, freiherr von, 1727-1817. III. Schreibers, Karl Nikolaus
Joseph von.

                                        Agr 10—1281

U. S. Dept. of agr. Library   120L64J
for Library of Congress   ₍a41b1₎

NL 0390685   DNAL MiU WU CtY MH-A

Linné, Carl von ₍1707-1778₎.
    Epistolae Caroli a Linne ad Bernardum de Jussieu
ineditae, et mutuae Bernardi ad Linnaeum: curante
Adriano de Jussieu...
    Cantabrigiae Nov. Angl. E.typis Metcalf et soc.,
1854.
    1 p.l.,[179]-234 p.   29cm.
    "Ex Actis Acad. art. et scient. Amer.,ser.Nov.
tom.v."

NL 0390686   DSI

Linné, Carl von, 1707-1778.
    Caroli a Linné ad Bernardum de Jussieu ineditae
et mutuae Bernardi ad Linnaeum epistolae, curante
Adriano de Jussieu. [Cambridge, Mass., etc.,
1855]
    Communicated by Asa Gray.
    In Memoirs of the American Academy of Arts
and Science, 1888, new series, vol. 5, p. 179-234.

NL 0390687   MH-A

Linné, Carl von, 1707-1778.

Hall, Herman Christiaan van, 1801-1874, *comp.*
    Epistolae ineditae Caroli Linnaei; addita parte com-
mercii litterarii inediti, inprimis circa rem botanicam,
J. Burmanni, N. L. Burmanni, Dillenii, Halleri, Schmide-
lii, J. Gesneri, Oederi, Pallasii, Vandellii et Thunbergii;
annis 1736-1793. Ex litteris autographis edidit H. C.
van Hall ... Groningae, apud W. van Boekeren, 1830.

Linné, Carl von, 1707-1778, praeses.
    Euphorbia. 1752.
        (In Amoen. Acad. III, 1764)
    Johan Wiman, respondent.

NL 0390689   PPAN

Linné, Carl von, 1707-1778, praeses.
    Euphorbia. 1752.
        see also hj... Specimen academicum quo
Euphorbia ...

MISSISSIPPI

MsG	William Alexander Percy Memorial Library, Greenville.
MsSC*	Mississippi State University, State College.
MsSM	Mississippi State University, State College.
MsU	University of Mississippi, University.

MONTANA

MtBC	Montana State University, Bozeman.
MtBozC*	Montana State University at Bozeman.
MtU	University of Montana, Missoula.

NEW YORK

N	New York State Library, Albany.
NAlU	State University of New York at Albany.
NAurW	Wells College, Aurora.
NB	Brooklyn Public Library, Brooklyn.
NBB	Brooklyn Museum Libraries, Brooklyn.
NBC	Brooklyn College, Brooklyn.
NBM	Medical Research Library of Brooklyn.
NBPol	Polytechnic Institute of Brooklyn, Brooklyn.
NBSU-M	State University of New York, Downstate Medical Center Library, Brooklyn.
NBiSU-H	State University of New York, Harpur College, Binghamton.
NBronSL	Sarah Lawrence College, Bronxville.
NBu	Buffalo and Erie County Public Library, Buffalo.
NBuC	State University of New York, College at Buffalo.
NBuG	Grosvenor Reference Division, Buffalo and Erie County Public Library, Buffalo.
NBuU	State University of New York at Buffalo.
NCH	Hamilton College, Clinton.
NCaS	St. Lawrence University, Canton.
NCorniC	Corning Glass Works Library, Corning. (Includes Corning Museum of Glass Library)
NCoxHi	Greene County Historical Society, Inc., Coxsackie.
NFQC	Queens College Library, Flushing.
NGrnUN*	United Nations Library.
NHC	Colgate University, Hamilton.
NHi	New York Historical Society, New York.
NIC	Cornell University, Ithaca.
NJQ	Queens Borough Public Library, Jamaica.
NL*	Newberry Library, Chicago.
NLC	Not a library symbol.
NN	New York Public Library.
NNAB	American Bible Society, New York.
NNAHI	Augustinian Historical Institute, New York.
NNAJHi	American Jewish Historical Society, New York.
NNB	Association of the Bar of the City of New York, New York.
NNBG	New York Botanical Garden, Bronx Park, New York.
NNC	Columbia University, New York.
NNC-T	— Teachers College Library.
NNCFR	Council on Foreign Relations, New York.
NNCoCi	City College of New York, New York.
NNE	Engineering Societies Library, New York.
NNF	Fordham University, New York.
NNFI	French Institute in the United States, New York.
NNG	General Theological Seminary of the Protestant Episcopal Church. New York.
NNGr	Grolier Club Library, New York.
NNH	Hispanic Society of America, New York.
NNHeb	Hebrew Union College, Jewish Institute of Religion Library, New York.
NNHi	New York Historical Society.
NNJ	Jewish Theological Seminary of America, New York.
NNJIR*	Jewish Institute of Religion, New York.
NNJef	Jefferson School of Social Science, New York. (Library no longer in existence)
NNM	American Museum of Natural History, New York.
NNMM	Metropolitan Museum of Art Library, New York.
NNMor*	Pierpont Morgan Library.
NNNAM	New York Academy of Medicine, New York.
NNNM	New York Medical College, Flower & Fifth Avenue Hospitals, New York.
NNNPsan	New York Psychoanalytic Institute, New York.
NNPM	Pierpont Morgan Library, New York.
NNQ*	Queens Borough Public Library, New York.
NNQC*	Queens College Library, Flushing.
NNRI	Rockefeller Institute for Medical Research, New York.
NNSU-M*	State University of New York College of Medicine at New York City.

NEW YORK *continued*

NNU	New York University Libraries, New York.
NNU-W	— Washington Square Library.
NNUN	United Nations Library, New York.
NNUN-W	— Woodrow Wilson Memorial Library.
NNUT	Union Theological Seminary, New York.
NNUT-Mc	— McAlpin Collection.
NNWML	Wagner College Library, Staten Island.
NNYI	Yivo Institute for Jewish Research, New York.
NNZI	Zionist Archives and Library of Palestine Foundation, New York.
NNerC	College of New Rochelle, New Rochelle.
NNiaU	Niagara University, Niagara University.
NPV	Vassar College, Poughkeepsie,
NRAB	Samuel Colgate Baptist Historical Library of the American Baptist Historical Society, Rochester.
NRU	University of Rochester, Rochester.
NSchU	Union College, Schenectady.
NSyU	Syracuse University, Syracuse.
NUt	Utica Public Library.
NWM	U.S. Military Academy, West Point.
NYPL*	New York Public Library.
NYhI	International Business Machines Corporation, Thomas J. Watson Research Center, Yorktown Heights.

NEBRASKA

NbOC	Creighton University, Omaha.
NbU	University of Nebraska, Lincoln.

NORTH CAROLINA

Nc	North Carolina State Library, Raleigh.
Nc-Ar	North Carolina State Department of Archives and History, Raleigh.
NcA	Pack Memorial Public Library, Asheville.
NcA-S	— Sondley Reference Library.
NcAS*	Sondley Reference Library, Asheville.
NcC	Public Library of Charlotte & Mecklenburg County, Charlotte.
NcCC	Charlotte College Library, Charlotte.
NcCJ	Johnson C. Smith University, Charlotte.
NcCU	University of North Carolina at Charlotte.
NcD	Duke University, Durham.
NcDurC	North Carolina College at Durham, Durham.
NcGU*	University of North Carolina at Greensboro.
NcGW	University of North Carolina at Greensboro.
NcGuG	Guilford College, Guilford.
NcR	Olivia Raney Public Library, Raleigh.
NcRR	Richard B. Harrison Public Library, Raleigh.
NcRS	North Carolina State University at Raleigh.
NcU	University of North Carolina, Chapel Hill.
NcWfC*	Wake Forest College, Winston-Salem.
NcWfSB	Southeastern Baptist Theological Seminary Library, Wake Forest.
NcWilA	Atlantic Christian College, Wilson.
NcWilC	Carolina Discipliniana Library, Wilson.
NcWsW	Wake Forest College, Winston-Salem.

NORTH DAKOTA

NdFA	North Dakota State University, Fargo. (Formerly North Dakota Agricultural College)
NdHi	State Historical Society of North Dakota, Bismarck.
NdU	University of North Dakota Library, Grand Forks.

NEW HAMPSHIRE

Nh	New Hampshire State Library, Concord.
NhD	Dartmouth College, Hanover.
NhU	University of New Hampshire, Durham.

NEW JERSEY

NjGbS	Glassboro State College, Glassboro.
NjHi	New Jersey Historical Society, Newark.
NjMD	Drew University, Madison.
NjN	Newark Public Library.
NjNBR*	Rutgers–The State University, New Brunswick.
NjNbS	New Brunswick Theological Seminary, New Brunswick.
NjNbT*	New Brunswick Theological Seminary.
NjP	Princeton University, Princeton.
NjPT	Princeton Theological Seminary, Princeton.
NjR	Rutgers–The State University, New Brunswick.
NjT	Trenton Free Library, Trenton.

NEW MEXICO

NmA	Albuquerque Public Library, New Mexico.
NmU	University of New Mexico, Albuquerque.
NmUpU	New Mexico State University, University Park.

NEVADA

NvU	University of Nevada, Reno.

OHIO

O	Ohio State Library, Columbus.
OAU	Ohio University, Athens.
OAkU	University of Akron, Akron.
OBerB	Baldwin-Wallace College, Berea.
OBlC	Bluffton College, Bluffton.
OC	Public Library of Cincinnati and Hamilton County, Cincinnati.
OCH	Hebrew Union College, Cincinnati.
OCHP	Historical and Philosophical Society of Ohio, Cincinnati.
OCLloyd	Lloyd Library and Museum, Cincinnati.
OCU	University of Cincinnati, Cincinnati.
OCX	Xavier University, Cincinnati.
OCl	Cleveland Public Library.
OClCS	Case Institute of Technology, Cleveland.
OClFC	Cleveland State University, Cleveland. (Formerly Fenn College)
OClJC	John Carroll University, Cleveland.
OClMA	Cleveland Museum of Art, Cleveland.
OClSA	Cleveland Institute of Art, Cleveland.
OClW	Case Western Reserve University, Cleveland.
OClWHi	Western Reserve Historical Society, Cleveland.
ODW	Ohio Wesleyan University, Delaware.
ODa	Dayton and Montgomery County Library, Dayton.
ODaStL	St. Leonard College Library, Dayton.
ODaU	University of Dayton, Dayton.
OEac	East Cleveland Public Library.
OFH	Rutherford B. Hayes Library, Fremont.
OGK	Kenyon College, Gambier.
OHi	Ohio State Historical Society, Columbus.
OKentC	Kent State University, Kent.
OO	Oberlin College, Oberlin.
OOxM	Miami University, Oxford.
OSW	Wittenberg University, Springfield.
OTU	University of Toledo, Toledo.
OU	Ohio State University, Columbus.
OWibfU	Wilberforce University, Carnegie Library, Wilberforce.
OWicB	Borromeo Seminary, Wickliffe.
OWoC	College of Wooster, Wooster.
OWorP	Pontifical College Josephinum, Worthington.
OYesA	Antioch College, Yellow Springs.

OKLAHOMA

Ok	Oklahoma State Library, Oklahoma City.
OkEG	Graduate Seminary Library, Enid.
OkS	Oklahoma State University, Stillwater.
OkT	Tulsa Public Library.
OkU	University of Oklahoma, Norman.

OREGON

Or	Oregon State Library, Salem.
OrCS	Oregon State University Library, Corvallis.
OrHi	Oregon Historical Society, Portland.
OrP	Library Association of Portland, Portland.
OrPR	Reed College, Portland.
OrPS	Portland State College, Portland.
OrSaW	Willamette University, Salem.
OrStbM	Mount Angel College, Mount Angel Abbey, Saint Benedict.
OrU	University of Oregon, Eugene.

PENNSYLVANIA

PBL	Lehigh University, Bethlehem.
PBa	Academy of the New Church, Bryn Athyn.
PBm	Bryn Mawr College, Bryn Mawr.
PCA*	Samuel Colgate Baptist Historical Library of the American Baptist Historical Society, Rochester, N. Y.
PCC	Crozer Theological Seminary, Chester.
PCamA	Alliance College, Cambridge Springs.
PCarlD	Dickinson College, Carlisle.
PHC	Haverford College, Haverford.
PHi	Historical Society of Pennsylvania, Philadelphia.
PJA	Abington Library Society, Jenkintown.
PJAlG	Alverthorpe Gallery, Rosenwald Collection, Jenkintown.
PJB	Beaver College, Jenkintown.